3000 800045 82434
St. Louis Community College

D1599663

HANDBOOK FOR SOUND ENGINEERS

THE NEW AUDIO CYCLOPEDIA

HANDBOOK FOR SOUND ENGINEERS

THE NEW AUDIO CYCLOPEDIA

Glen Ballou
Editor

HOWARD W. SAMS & COMPANY
A Division of Macmillan, Inc.
4300 West 62nd Street
Indianapolis, Indiana 46268 USA

FIRST EDITION
SECOND PRINTING—1987

International Standard Book Number: 0-672-21983-2
Library of Congress Catalog Card Number: 85-50023

Acquisitions Editor: *Charlie Dresser*
Editors: *Pryor Associates & Sara Black*
Interior Design: *Don Herrington*
Illustrator: *William D. Basham*
Cover: Design—*Meridian Design Studio, Inc.*
Embossing—*Shirley Engraving Co., Inc.*
Photography—*Visuals Unique*
Composition: *Graphic Typesetting Service, Los Angeles*
Indexer: *James M. Moore*

Printed in the United States of America

CONTENTS

PART 2—ELECTRONIC COMPONENTS FOR SOUND ENGINEERING

PART 3—ELECTROACOUSTIC DEVICES

PART 4—AUDIO ELECTRONIC CIRCUITS AND EQUIPMENT

PART 5—RECORDING AND PLAYBACK

PART 6—DESIGN APPLICATIONS

PART 7—MEASUREMENTS

PREFACE

Our understanding of sound and our methods of producing, reproducing, changing, controlling, reinforcing, and measuring it are improving with the advance of technology. The *Handbook for Sound Engineers: The New Audio Cyclopedia* combines years of technical information and technological development into a comprehensive reference book. To compile this book, the expertise of many people was called upon. The result is a reference volume that covers seven areas: acoustics, electronic components, electroacoustic devices, audio electronic circuits and equipment, recording and playback, design applications, and measurements.

This book begins with the fundamentals of sound and its psychoacoustic effects on humans. With a good foundation of basics, we proceed to voice coloration and how it is affected from room to room depending upon a number of factors, such as the room construction and shape. Rooms for speech are designed for intelligibility, but rooms for music require very different characteristics, because blend is more important than intelligibility. Multipurpose rooms must be designed to satisfy both speech and music. Studios and control rooms are getting more attention recently with the new LEDE® rooms and time-aligned loudspeakers. All of this and more is discussed in detail in Part 1.

Microphones and loudspeakers are discussed in Part 3. The type, pickup pattern, and sensitivity of a microphone determine its use and placement for sound reinforcement and recording; therefore, it is important to understand the basics of microphones, how they work, their various pickup patterns, and the proper method of determining sensitivity and frequency response. Wireless and PZMicrophones, are also discussed in detail.

The chapter on loudspeakers covers building, use, and standard test methods to measure them. The individual components of a loudspeaker and their interrelation are discussed in detail for the engineer. Constant directivity horns, crossover devices, and Thiele enclosures are also included.

With the advent of solid-state devices and digital circuitry, sound system electronics has come of age. Automatic microphone mixers and computerized consoles have changed the way sound is mixed. High-power output devices have produced stable, high-power and versatile amplifiers, and digital circuitry has produced low-noise time delays and special-effect devices. The *Handbook for Sound Engineers: The New Audio Cyclopedia* discusses these new circuits along with the still used standard and special circuits.

Disk and magnetic recording and playback have changed considerably in the past few years, particularly with respect to noise and distortion. Electronics has improved in reliability and headroom. The introduction of digital circuitry, and improved transports and turntables has led to greater stability and less rumble. A knowledge of basics and special circuits is required to properly service this equipment, which is discussed in section 5.

The design of sound systems has changed tremendously with the new electronics, constant directivity loudspeakers, and latest test equipment. Systems can be single source, multiple source, distributed, or time delayed, all with their own particular design problems. These situations are covered, in addition to proper installation techniques and how to design for best articulation, frequency response, coverage, and signal-to-noise ratio through the use of various types of loudspeakers, microphones, and electronics.

The new integrated circuits, digital circuitry, and computers have given us new, sophisticated test gear unthought of ten years ago. The TEF (time-energy-frequency) analyzer developed by Richard Heyser and designed and built by Crown International has changed the way sound is measured. It allows us to measure in real time in a noisy environment and measure with an accuracy never before realized. What to measure, the meaning and relevance of measurements, and the new instrumentation are thoroughly covered.

The understanding of sound, sound reinforcement, and acoustics can be attributed to thousands of people working in the field; however, we must give credit to those who, through their understanding of the problem, their ability to work out the solution, and most importantly their willingness to share it, have truly been modern-day pioneers. Lord Rayleigh, Thomas Edison, Wallace Sabine, Harry Olson, Leo Beranek, Harold Lindsay, Richard Heyser, and the dedicated, knowledgeable authors of *Handbook for Sound Engineers: The New Audio Cyclopedia* who were willing to give of their time to share their forté with the world are foremost on this list and I wish to thank all the authors for their contributions to this book and all the others who supplied these thoughts and comments.

I especially want to give my thanks to Don and Carolyn Davis. Their belief in me and this book and their special attention when things were looking down is a true example of friendship and synergy. Each newsletter they produce under their company, Syn-Aud-Con, starts, "I met a man with a dollar, we exchanged dollars, I still had a dollar. I met a man with an idea, we exchanged ideas, now we each had two ideas." With this thinking, the field of sound will be better understood by all, the result being giant steps forward.

I also wish to thank my wife Debra, who spent as much time at the word processor as I did at the desk and most importantly was constantly there to encourage and drive me.

GLEN BALLOU

CONTRIBUTORS

GEORGE ALEXANDROVICH

George Alexandrovich, born in Yugoslavia, attended schools in Yugoslavia, Hungary, and Germany. After coming to the United States, he studied at the RCA Institute and at Brooklyn Polytech, earning a BSEE.

At Telectro Industries Corp., he was involved in the design and development of the first tape recorders and specialized military electronic test and communications equipment.

After service in the Korean war, he ran Sherman Fairchild's private research lab. While with Fairchild Recording Equipment Corp. he designed and manufactured turntables, tonearms, pickups, mixing consoles and amplifiers, equalizers, reverberation chambers, the first light-activated compander, Autoten, Lumiten compressors, limiters, a line of remote-controlled audio components, and designed the first professional multichannel portable console, a disk-cutting lathe, and stereo cutters.

When Fairchild Recording Equipment Corp. merged with Robins Corp., George also became involved in manufacturing magnetic tape along with a full line of consumer accessories in the hi-fi market. As vice president and general manager his responsibilities included designing and manufacturing the Voice of America recording facilities, NBC TV studio consoles for Johnny Carson, Huntley-Brinkley Newsroom, KNX, KCBS, and other radio stations.

At Stanton Magnetics, Inc., as vice president of field engineering and the professional products manager for phonograph cartridge research, he traveled extensively, holding seminars, giving lectures, and conducting conferences. Presently, George is president and owner of Island Audio Engineering and its subsidiary, Dynamic Sound Devices.

George is the author of the monthly column "Audio Engineer's Handbook" for *dB Magazine* and of over 75 articles and papers in American and foreign trade journals. He has also presented a number of technical papers at the Audio Engineering Society (AES) conventions and is a fellow and a governor of the AES. He holds 17 patents in the field of audio and is chairman of the Electronics Industry Association (EIA) P8.2 Standards Committee.

GLEN BALLOU

Glen graduated from General Motors Institute in 1958 with a bachelor's degree in Engineering and joined the Plant Engineering Department of the Pratt & Whitney Aircraft Division of United Technologies Corp. There he designed special circuits for the newly developed tape control machine tools and was responsible for the design, installation, and operation of the 5-million-square-foot plant public address and two-way radio-paging system.

In 1970, Glen transferred to the Technical Presentations and Orientation section of United Technologies' corporate office where he was responsible for the design and installation of electronics, audio-visual, sound and acoustics for corporate conference rooms and auditoriums. He was also responsible for audio-visual and special effects required for the corporation's exhibit program.

In 1980, Glen transferred to the Sikorsky Aircraft division of United Technologies as manager of marketing communications where his responsibilities included the Sikorsky exhibit and special events program, plus operation and design of all conference rooms.

Glen has attended seminars on tape control equipment and audio seminars by Altec and Syn-Aud-Con including the Syn-Aud-Con TEF seminar and was a Syn-Aud-Con representative. He has been active in the Audio Engineering Society (AES) as governor, three-times papers chairman, and three-times facilities chairman. He is also a member of SMPTE.

ROLLINS BROOK

Rollins (Rolly) Brook has a B.A. in communications from the University of Denver. Since 1948 he has worked in theater, film, television, and recording, dividing his time between the creative and the technical sides of the industry. He has written and produced scores of educational films and television programs and has been responsible for the technical design and operation of several broadcast stations and recording studios.

Currently at Bolt, Beranek, and Newman, he is a senior consultant specializing in electronic systems for the performing arts. With BBN he has been involved in the design of a number of major performing arts facilities—concert halls, theaters, and multipurpose auditoriums—as well as broadcasting and recording studios.

He is an associate editor and a columnist for *Theatre Design and Technology* magazine and has written a number of articles for a variety of magazines on the design and application of electronic systems for the performing arts.

MAHLON D. BURKHARD

Mahlon D. Burkhard, manager of research at Industrial Research Products, Inc., a subsidiary of Knowles Electronics, Inc., has major responsibility for a line of professional audio products. Previously, he was supervisor of acoustics at IIT Research Institute (Armour Research Foundation) and research physicist at the National Bureau of Standards.

He has an A.B. degree from Nebraska Wesleyan University and an M.S. degree from Pennsylvania State University, both in physics. His research has been involved with calibration of microphones, earphones, and other acoustic transducers.

He is a fellow of the Acoustical Society of America (ASA) and of the Audio Engineering Society (AES), a member of the Institute of Electrical and Electronic Engineers (IEEE), a member of Sigma Xi, and a Registered Professional Engineer in the State of Illinois. He is currently serving on the executive council of the Acoustical Society of America. He is a member of the executive committee of the Midwest Acoustics Conference and was its president in 1977. He has published articles in the *Journal of the Acoustical Society of America*, the *Journal of the Audio Engineering Society*, the *Proceedings of the IEEE*, and other periodicals. He has also been active in the writing of acoustic standards, having been chairman of three different writing groups for American National Standards, and a member of two writing groups for the IEC Technical Committee.

DONALD B. DAVIS

Don Davis, with more than 30 years experience in audio, is the founder and co-owner with his wife, Carolyn, of Synergetic Audio Concepts (Syn-Aud-Con), a company engaged in the teaching of sound engineering seminars throughout the United States, Canada, and Europe with over 6,000 graduates to date. He is an international consultant on acoustics and electroacoustic projects.

Don is a fellow of the Audio Engineering Society, a senior member of the Institute of Electrical and Electronic Engineers, and member of the Acoustical Society of America. He is co-inventor of Acousta-Voice equalization and the holder of Patent No. 3629298.

During the past five years, Don and Carolyn Davis have played key roles in the development of the PZM® system of microphony, the Live-End Dead-End™ (LEDE™)

technique of control room design, and the pioneer licensing of the Heyser/Cal Tech TEF® measuring system now manufactured by Crown International, Inc. They are currently engaged in the design and testing of a series of new recording studio projects in the United States as well as participating heavily in their regular consulting activities and sound engineering seminars.

Don is the author of three books: *Acoustical Tests and Measurements, Sound System Engineering* (co-authored with his wife Carolyn), and *How to Build Speaker Enclosures* (co-authored with the late Alexis Badmaieff)—the latter having sold over 225,000 copies. *Sound System Engineering* is the textbook used in teaching electroacoustic design practices at Syn-Aud-Con sound engineering seminars that Don and Carolyn conduct.

Don has also written hundreds of articles dealing with various phases of electroacoustics, audio, and sound engineering, including many papers given at conventions of the Audio Engineering Society, Society of Motion Picture and Television Engineers, and the Acoustical Society of America.

STEVE DOVE

A native of rural Oxfordshire, England, and a product of Henley Grammar School/ King James College, Steve Dove came to the world of professional audio via the rather dubious paths of journalism and pirate radio. A radio amateur since his early teens and largely self-educated in electronics, he built his own gear and even began building for others. Steve then joined Alice Stancoil, Ltd., one of the United Kingdom's leading pro-audio manufacturers as a designer.

He has been significant in the technical development of the British ILR (Independent Local Radio) network since its inception in the early seventies, while also building "even larger and more complicated" mixers and ancillary equipment for recording, video, and film studios. Concurrently, he has acted as technical and acoustic consultant worldwide to studios, theaters, arenas, and a number of major rock acts—"a welcome contrast to sitting behind a desk!" He is also a widely published author in these fields.

F. ALTON EVEREST

A senior thesis project on the measurement of sound absorption coefficients ignited Everest's interest in acoustics. There were bypaths into other areas, but acoustics was never far under the surface at any time. During World War II the late Vern O. Knudsen coaxed him from the chalk dust of a college classroom to serve as a civilian scientist in acoustical research under the University of California contract with the U.S. Navy, where he directed projects on sound and psychoacoustics. At present he is self-employed as an acoustical consultant engaged in designing recording facilities on four continents and church and auditorium acoustics.

Everest taught in the Electrical Engineering Department at Oregon State University and in the Communications Department of Hong Kong Baptist College. He is the author of over 50 papers in professional journals and technical magazines and of the books *Acoustical Techniques for Home and Studio, Handbook of Multichannel Recording, Handbook of Public Address Sound Systems, How to Build a Budget Recording Studio from Scratch*, and *Master Handbook of Acoustics*, all published by TAB Books, Inc. He is also the author and publisher of *Critical Listening*, an audio training course.

He is a life fellow of the Society of Motion Picture and Television Engineers, a senior life member of the Institute of Electrical and Electronic Engineers, a member of the Acoustical Society of America, and a member of the Audio Engineering Society. He is a fellow, co-founder and past president of the American Scientific Affiliation. His academic preparation includes a B.Sc. (Oregon State), E.E. (Stanford), and graduate study in physics at the University of California at Los Angeles (UCLA). Wheaton College bestowed an honorary D.Sc. on him. He was elected to Eta Kappa Nu, national honorary in electrical engineering, and Sigma Xi, national research honorary, and is listed in *American Men and Women of Science*.

DOUGLAS W. FEARN

Douglas W. Fearn began his career in recording and broadcast with the Haverford High School FM broadcast station (WHHS). Later as an engineer for WPEN/WMGK in Philadelphia, he was involved in on-air board operation, studio production, remote broadcasts, maintenance of studio equipment and AM/FM transmitters, and he supervised the construction of their new studios.

As owner of the Veritable Recording Co., a Philadelphia-based 24-track recording studio, his label credits included Atlantic, CBS, Elektra, RCA, and Warner Brothers. He has recorded music from new wave to classical, plus special recordings for audio-visual, multimedia, film scoring, narration, sound effects, radio drama, and electronics.

Currently, he is the president of D. W. Fearn & Associates, an audio and broadcasting consulting firm specializing in optimizing audio for radio stations, and the chief engineer of WKSZ (FM) in Philadelphia, Pennsylvania, and WXDR in Newark, Delaware.

Doug has published articles in *Broadcast Engineering* and *Radio World* and is currently working on a book on practical studio techniques. He holds an FCC first class radiotelephone license and an amateur extra class license.

CHRIS FOREMAN

Chris Foreman is marketing manager of Panasonic Industrial Co., Ramsa Division, in Cypress, California. Previously he directed the marketing and sales of teleconference systems for the Audio Systems Division of Peirce-Phelps in Philadelphia.

Prior to joining Peirce-Phelps, Chris was the commercial products director for Altec-Lansing Corp. and was responsible for the development of new products and for many of Altec's technical papers and seminars.

With Gary Davis (Gary Davis and Associates of Topanga, California), Chris designed and wrote instruction manuals and other technical papers for Yamaha, dbx, White Instruments, and other professional audio companies. His technical articles have appeared in *Recording Engineer/Producer, Sound and Communications, Sound Arts,* and *Sound and Video Contractor.*

Chris has also worked with Community Light and Sound, Inc. of Chester, Pennsylvania, where he directed commercial sound market development, and with Stanal Sound, of Kearney, Nebraska, where he helped design concert touring systems for Neil Diamond, John Denver, and others.

Chris holds a B.S. in electrical engineering from the University of Nebraska and has done graduate work at the California State University at Northridge. He is a member of the Audio Engineering Society, Acoustical Society of America, Institute of Electrical and Electronic Engineers, and the International Teleconferencing Association.

CLIFFORD A. HENRICKSEN

Clifford A. Henricksen has an Associate in Engineering degree from Union College, Cranford, New Jersey, a B.S. degree in mechanical engineering from Union College, Schenectady, New York, and an M.S. degree in mechanical engineering from MIT, Cambridge, Massachusetts.

At Scott Paper's Technology Center in Philadelphia, he was a research project engineer, specializing in process modeling and research with related work in acoustics.

While at Altec Lansing Corp., he formed and supervised the acoustics research group and was author of many U.S. patents in the area of loudspeaker technology, including the Manta-Ray horizontal diffraction horn and the Tangerine radial-slot phase plug for Altec compression drivers. He named the Tangerine phase plug and Altec's Voice of the Highway® auto sound systems components.

As vice president of engineering at Community Light and Sound, Inc. Chester, Pennsylvania, he co-developed and produced the M4 midrange compression driver and many other engineering and design projects. A group leader in loudspeaker engineering at Electro-Voice, Inc., he manages the components group, which develops low frequency drivers, horns, and compression drivers.

He is a contributor of technical papers to the Audio Engineering Society (AES) conventions, and the *Journal of the AES*. He is chairman of the Working Group drafting the first-ever "Recommended Practice for Specifications of Professional Loudspeaker Components" of the AES. He is a recently elected fellow of the AES. Mr. Henricksen is a studio pianist, a composer, a performer, and a member of ASME, Sigma Xi, and ASCAP.

DALE MANQUEN

Dale Manquen is president of Altair Electronics Inc., a design consulting company based in Thousand Oaks, California. Since his graduation from New Mexico State University, he has engaged in the electrical and mechanical design of numerous tape recorders for professional applications while serving as project engineer for the 3M Model 56 recorder, product manager of the Ampex audio recorders for studio use, sales engineer for the Ampex Magnetic Tape Division, and professor of electrical engineering at California State University at Northridge. Recent projects include the design of multitrack continuous playback machines for theme park applications, digital storage of audio messages, and automated tape transport testing systems.

EUGENE T. PATRONIS, JR.

Eugene T. Patronis, Jr. received his B.S. degree in physics from the Georgia Institute of Technology in 1953. He joined the Brookhaven National Laboratory as a research associate in 1957. In 1961 he received a Ph.D. in physics from the Georgia Institute of Technology, and in 1968 became a professor of physics on the faculty of that institute. In addition to teaching and research, Dr. Patronis serves as an independent consultant in both acoustics and electronics. Dr. Patronis has published many scientific papers and is a member of the Society of Motion Picture and Television Engineers, the American Physical Society, Sigma Xi, the American Association for the Advancement of Science, and the Audio Engineering Society.

TED UZZLE

Ted Uzzle has an A.B. degree from Harvard College, where he studied the history of architecture. He has been a consultant in theater design, architectural acoustics, and sound system design in Cambridge, Massachusetts, specializing in motion picture theaters and post-production facilities.

In 1980, Mr. Uzzle joined Altec Lansing Corp., as manager of market development, and assumed responsibility for theater products, application engineering, and Altec-Lansing Sound System Design Seminars for which he developed a technique of solid angle loudspeaker coverage and a series of calculator programs permitting instant verification of the system performance.

Mr. Uzzle is now director, market development, at Altec Lansing, where he is responsible for product and market analysis, technical assistance to Altec's engineering staff and customers, and applications engineering including Altec's seminars.

PART 1

Acoustics

CHAPTER **1**

Fundamentals of Sound

by F. Alton Everest

1.1 DUAL NATURE OF SOUND

Sound has a dual nature: it may be considered a physical disturbance in a medium such as air, or it may be considered a psychophysical perception resulting from nerve impulses stimulating the acoustic cortex of the brain. In audio we are vitally concerned with both. The ear itself determines the quality of sound signals, but the sound is carried to the ear through physical stimuli. The matter of the complex relationship between stimulus and sensation is treated in Chapter 2, dealing with psychoacoustics. In this chapter we are concentrating on the physics of sound.

1.2 TRANSMISSION OF SOUND

For sound to be transmitted from one place to another, a medium is required that has *elasticity* and *inertia*. Air has these vital characteristics, as do steel, water, concrete, and many other substances. When an air particle is booted by a diaphragm, it moves, passing on momentum to adjoining particles as it strikes them. The original air particle is then pulled back toward its equilibrium position by elastic forces residing in the air. Any particular air particle vibrates about its equilibrium position, receives momentum from collisions, and passes on momentum to other particles, which pass it on to others, and so on. The wind sends a wave traveling through a field of grain, but each head of grain merely vibrates back and forth on its stem. Sound is propagated through the air by virtue of elastic and inertial forces acting on the air particles, each of which stays close to home.

1.3 TYPES OF WAVE MOTION

When we think of wave motion, water comes immediately to mind, and water waves have traditionally been associated with demonstrations of acoustical wave concepts. However, we will be spared the throwing of stones into placid pools and get on with the mechanics of wave motion. We have seen that all wave motion is based on the vibration of elemental particles and that these particles stay close to their neutral positions in the process of sending sound waves on their way.

Water waves are produced by particles in circular orbits. Surfboard riders at the crests of waves move toward the shore, but if they get "wiped out," they discover that the water beneath the waves is moving away from the shore. The water particles follow circular orbits, as described in Fig. 1-1A. This circular motion is a form of simple harmonic motion with particle displacement plotted against time, describing a sine wave.

Transverse wave motion is depicted in Fig. 1-1B. In this case the particle vibrates in a plane at right angles to the direction of travel of the wave. Stretched strings used in many musical instruments vibrate transversely as the waves are propagated toward the ends of the strings. It is interesting (but not particularly pertinent) that light, heat, and radio waves in free space travel by transverse vibrations of the electric and magnetic fields.

Our primary interest centers on sound waves that are propagated by longitudinal vibrations of air particles, i.e., by vibrations parallel to the direction of sound travel as in Fig. 1-1C.

All three forms of particle vibration depicted in Fig. 1-1 are simple harmonic motion. The sine wave is a natural outgrowth of all three types of motion. Particles vibrating in transverse and longitudinal orbits are of primary interest in audio, particularly the longitudinal form that applies to the air medium.

1.4 NATURE OF SOUND WAVES

Sounds in air are commonly produced by the vibration of diaphragms (such as loudspeakers or headphones), vocal cords, instrumental strings, jackhammers, or some other solid material. In Fig. 1-2 let us consider as our vibrating body a hypothetical piston, which is driven by a crankshaft and connecting rod. The piston, as shown, is in its extreme position to the right. As it moved to this position, the air particles immediately in front of it are crowded together. As the piston moves back to its opposite extreme (left), a partial vacuum is created as the air particles are spread apart. This disturbance of air particles close to the piston is passed on to adjoining particles, as the momentum imparted to one particle is passed on to another through collision. Each particle vibrates about its neutral position as the wave travels on. Because this piston moves in simple harmonic motion, we expect a sine wave of air pressure to be formed.

The crowding together of air particles constitutes an increase of pressure (compression); their spreading out, a decrease of pressure (rarefaction). Because these air particles are part of the "ocean of air" in which we live, these increases and decreases of pressure are superimposed on the particular prevailing atmospheric pressure, as read off a barometer. These modulations are very small. The weakest sound the human ear can hear [about 20 micropascals (μPa)] will create a pressure ripple only one five-thousandth of a millionth of the atmospheric pressure. Microphones respond to the ripples only, not to the static atmospheric pressure.

1.5 PERIODIC WAVE RELATIONSHIPS

The waves of sound pressure of Fig. 1-1 are called *periodic waves* because they repeat over and over. Periodic waves need not be sine waves—only repetitive waves. A few definitions pertaining to periodic waves are in order as we refer to Fig. 1-3. The peak value is easy to read from

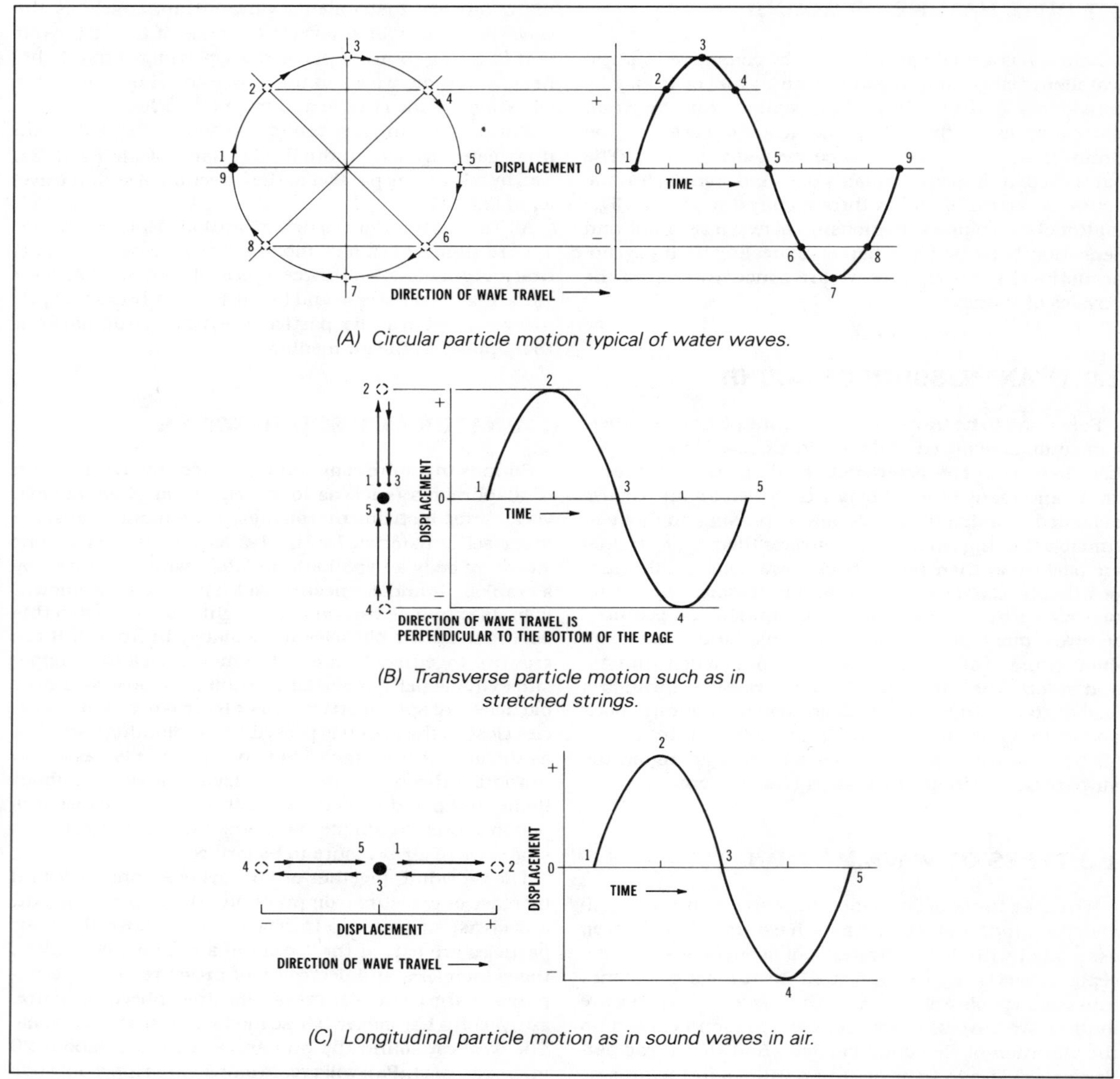

(A) Circular particle motion typical of water waves.

(B) Transverse particle motion such as in stretched strings.

(C) Longitudinal particle motion as in sound waves in air.

Figure 1-1 Orbital motion of particles in the medium differentiates the types of motion.

an oscilloscope trace, but only a few instruments can register it. Peak to peak is, of course, twice the peak value if the waveform is symmetrical.

With an alternating electric current, flowing first in one direction and then in the opposite direction, or an alternating sound-pressure wave, with positive (compression) and negative (rarefaction) loops, how can such constantly changing signals be represented by a single figure? The answer is that the *effective* value must be determined. The effective value is related to producing heat or doing work. It is what is commonly called the *rms* value. To remove some of the mystery, we shall follow through on the meaning of *rms (root mean square)*.

In Fig. 1-4 a definite (but arbitrary) amplitude scale has been introduced. The amplitudes at a, b, c, d, e, and f can be read off for the positive loop and negative amplitudes at a′, b′, c′, d′, e′, and f′ can be read off for the negative loop. The following steps are then taken:

1. Square each amplitude of the positive loop.

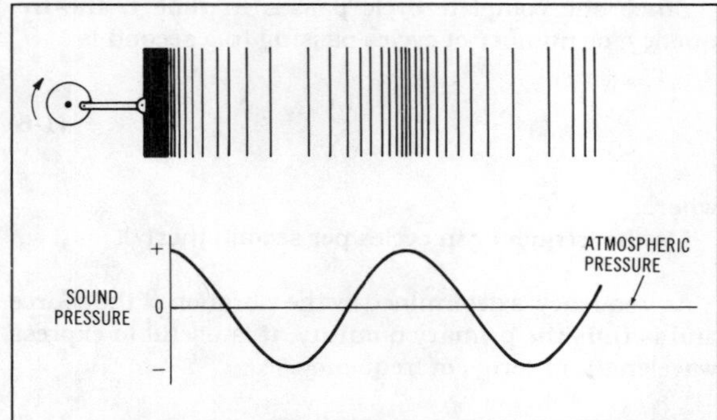

Figure 1-2 A piston as an illustration of wave motion.

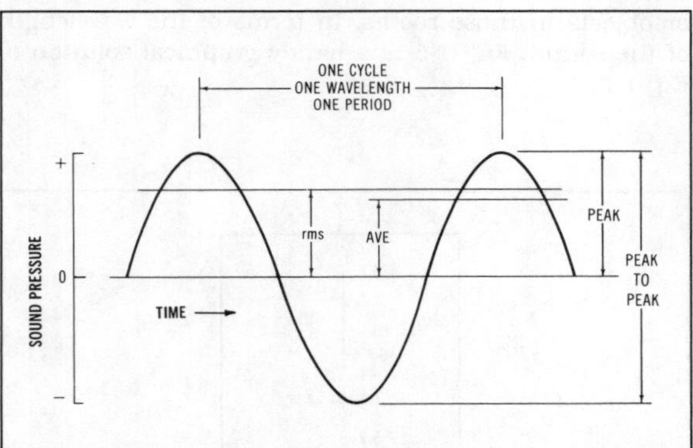

Figure 1-3 A periodic wave. In this case, a sinusoidal wave described in temporal terms by frequency (reciprocal of period).

2. Square each amplitude of the negative loop. Since a minus quantity squared becomes positive, the negative loop values give the same results as though the broken line positive loop were followed, which means that we are duplicating the positive loop.
3. Add all squared values together.
4. Find the average (or mean) of all squared values: divide the result of step 3 by the number of values squared.
5. Take the square root of the mean of step 4.

Following these steps gives us the rms value (the square root of the mean of the sum of the squares = root mean square). This rms value is the effective value of the sine wave of Fig. 1-4. Electrical power is proportional to the square of the rms voltage, and acoustic power is proportional to the square of the rms sound pressure.

Most meters for measuring alternating voltage or sound pressure have dc movements with a full-wave rectifier attached. Thus, they respond to the *average*, not the

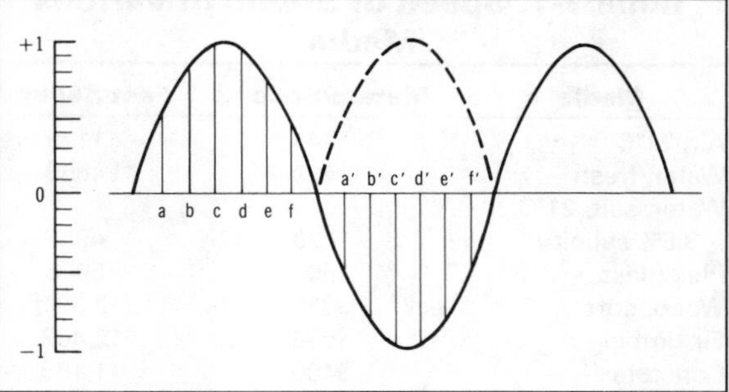

Figure 1-4 Finding the rms (root-mean-square) value of a periodic wave by measuring instantaneous amplitudes.

effective or rms value. However, they are almost universally calibrated in terms of rms, which means that they are accurate only for sine waves. The greater the departure from the sine waveform, the greater the reading error. Thermocouple instruments and those with carefully designed networks read rms directly irrespective of the waveform. The following relationships between rms, peak, and average hold true for sine waves:

$$\begin{aligned} \text{rms} &= \text{peak}/\sqrt{2} \\ &= 0.707 \times \text{peak} \end{aligned} \tag{1-1}$$

or

$$\begin{aligned} \text{rms} &= (\pi/2\sqrt{2}) \times \text{average} \\ &= 1.11 \times \text{average} \end{aligned} \tag{1-2}$$

and

$$\begin{aligned} \text{peak} &= \sqrt{2} \times \text{rms} \\ &= 1.414 \times \text{rms} \end{aligned} \tag{1-3}$$

or

$$\begin{aligned} \text{peak} &= (\pi/2) \times \text{average} \\ &= 1.57 \times \text{average} \end{aligned} \tag{1-4}$$

1.6 SPEED OF SOUND

The words *speed* and *velocity* are often equated, but in the strict technical sense, these terms are not the same. *Speed* means rate of change of position in units such as miles per hour, feet per minute, meters per second, and so on. *Velocity* of a body is a vector quantity, having the same magnitude as its speed but including also the *direction* of motion. If no directional information is at hand, speed is the accepted term. If direction of propagation is involved, velocity is the proper term.

Mersenne (1588–1648) used Galileo's (1564–1640) pendulum to measure the speed of sound in air, obtaining a value of 1038 ft/s.[1] Members of the French Academy

Table 1-1. Speed of Sound in Various Media

Media	Meters/Second	Feet/Second
Air, 21°C	344	1129
Water, fresh	1480	4856
Water, salt, 21°C, 3.5% salinity	1520	4987
Plexiglass	1800	5906
Wood, soft	3350	10,991
Fir timber	3800	12,467
Concrete	3400	11,155
Mild steel	5050	16,568
Aluminum	5150	16,896
Glass	5200	17,060
Gypsum board	6800	22,310

From Bartlett.[4]

in 1738 conducted the first accurate experiments by using cannon fire and measuring the difference between the arrival of the flash and the sound. They came up with a value of 337 m/s (1106 ft/s) for dry air at 0°C.[2] Better control of the measuring process has resulted in an average of 17 determinations[3] as 33,145 ± 5 cm/s or 1087.42 ± 0.16 ft/s for audio frequencies, air temperature of 0°C, one atmosphere pressure, CO_2 of 0.03-mol-percent content, and 0% water content. For practical purposes and under normal conditions, the speed of sound in air and various other media is given in Table 1-1.

The speed of sound in air is commonly rounded off to 1130 ft/s for normal conditions, which is slow compared to light and radio waves (186,000 mi/s) but comparable to the speed of a .22-caliber rifle bullet (about 1000 ft/s). Air speed in air-conditioning ducts in studios is usually held below 500 ft/min (8.33 ft/s), which is less than 1% of the speed of sound. This fact leads us to the conclusion that noise travels equally well upstream or downstream in the ducts. A 20°F change in air temperature results in about 2% change in speed of sound.

1.7 FREQUENCY AND WAVELENGTH

Let us imagine that a sound wave is traveling past us and that we are equipped with "instant replay" and slow-motion facilities. As the wave goes by, we can sense the compression peaks and the rarefaction troughs of air pressure. With a special scale, we measure the distance between successive peaks (wavelength) and the time it takes for 1 wavelength to pass. This time is related to the wavelength and speed of sound according to

$$t = \lambda / c \tag{1-5}$$

where,
t is the period for one cycle in seconds,
λ is the wavelength in feet,
c is the speed of sound, which is 1130 ft/s.

Since one complete cycle passes in time t, the frequency, or number of cycles passing in a second is

$$f = 1/t = c/\lambda \tag{1-6}$$

where,
f is the frequency in cycles per second (hertz).

As frequency is determined by the vibration of the source and is thus the primary quantity, it is useful to express wavelength in terms of frequency:

$$\lambda = 1130/f \tag{1-7}$$

This simple statement will be used many times as we consider the dimensions of our sound-sensitive rooms, or objects in those rooms, in terms of the wavelength of the sound. Fig. 1-5 is a handy graphical solution of Eq. 1-7.

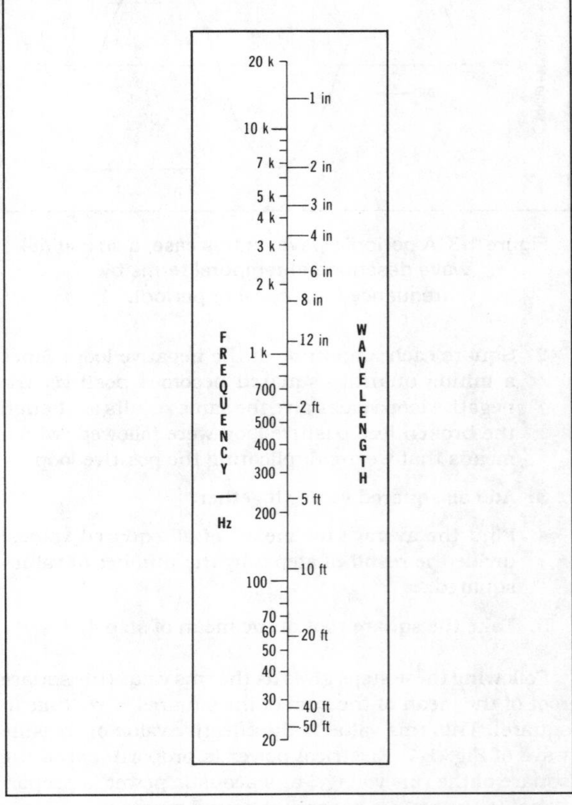

Figure 1-5 A graphic solution of Equation 1-7 showing the relationship of the wavelength of sound in air to frequency (speed of sound taken as 1130 ft/s).

1.8 WAVEFRONTS AND RAYS

A *wavefront* is defined as a line of points in the medium that are at the same part of the vibration cycle (in phase). This definition means all points on the wavefront are equidistant to the source. Waves emitted from a point source have spherical wavefronts, as shown in Fig. 1-6A. At a relatively great distance from the source, a section of a spherical wavefront approximates a plane surface (Fig. 1-6B). Plane and spherical wavefronts are of primary interest and concern in acoustics although other fronts can be produced under certain circumstances.

A ray of sound is the path of an element of the wavefront and, if not deflected in some way, is always perpendicular to the wavefront, as in Fig. 1-6.

We can liken a wavefront to a line of marching people. Each person walks radially away from the source in a spherical wavefront, but in a plane wavefront the people all walk in the same direction.

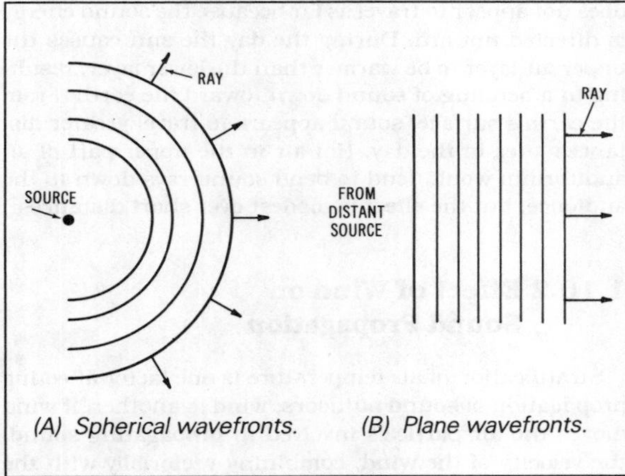

Figure 1-6 A point source in free space sends out spherical wavefronts that tend to become plane wavefronts at great distances.

1.9 REFLECTION OF SOUND

If the wavelength of sound is small compared to the dimensions of a smooth, hard surface, reflection takes place. Like light, the angle of incidence of sound onto a plane surface equals the angle of reflection, as illustrated in Fig. 1-7A. A convex surface, such as Fig. 1-7B, scatters the rays of sound. A good example of this is the so-called "polycylindrical diffuser" sometimes used in acoustical treatment of studios. The concave surface of Fig. 1-7C tends to focus sound. A parabolic surface focuses sound very accurately. Concave architectural shapes in auditoriums can create grave acoustical problems.

No discussion of reflection for those interested in re-

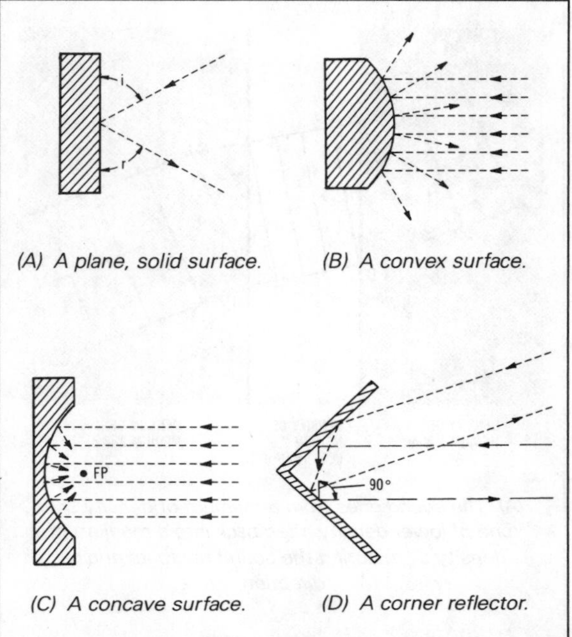

Figure 1-7 Plane wavefronts of sound striking variously shaped surfaces.

cording audio signals is complete without calling attention to the existence of corner reflections in rectangular rooms. Normal (right angle) reflections from the flat walls are almost intuitively sensed; the corner reflections are a bit more obscure. Referring to the long dashed lines of Fig. 1-7D, representing rays of sound, it is seen that the incident ray is sent back toward the source from the reflecting surfaces forming a 90° corner. At any point in the room, this reflection is back toward the source as illustrated by the broken lines of Fig. 1-7D. Not only is this true for the two-wall corner reflectors, it is also true for corners formed by the wall surfaces and ceiling, and the wall surfaces and floor. Fortunately, all these corner reflections include two or more surface reflections which tend to reduce their amplitude. On the other hand, efficient reflections at grazing angles are often involved.

Picture a person in the central part of a recording studio whose voice is being recorded. In treating the room, we must consider the possibility of four "slapback" echoes from the four walls, four from corners at microphone height, four from upper corners, and four from lower corners—sixteen in all.

1.10 REFRACTION OF SOUND

Table 1-1 listed the wide range of sound speeds in different media. As sound waves pass from one medium into

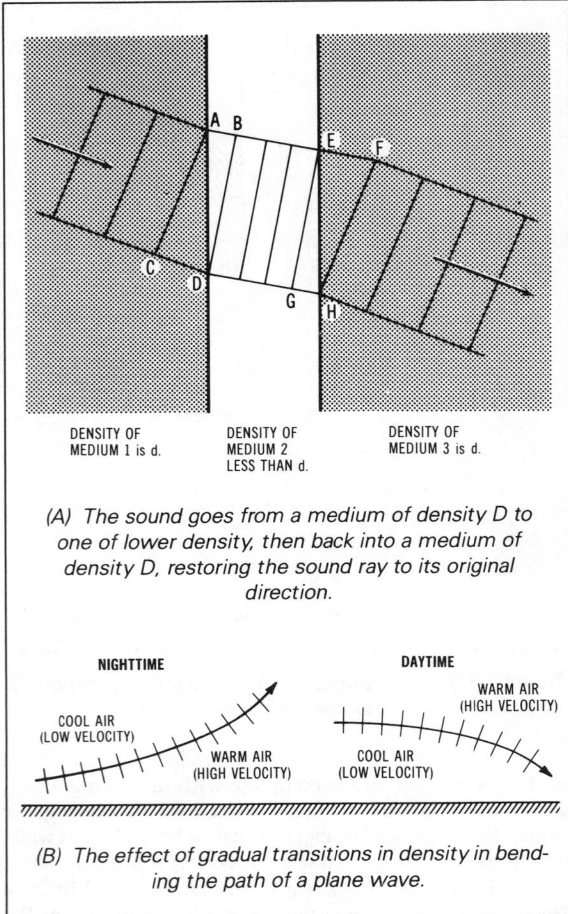

(A) The sound goes from a medium of density D to one of lower density, then back into a medium of density D, restoring the sound ray to its original direction.

(B) The effect of gradual transitions in density in bending the path of a plane wave.

Figure 1-8 The path of a sound is reflected (bent) as it goes through an interface between media of different densities.

another, there will be no refraction or bending of the direction of propagation if the speed of sound is the same in both media. If, however, sound passes from a medium of one density into a medium of greater or lesser density, the direction of propagation will be changed.

In Fig. 1-8A sound travels from dense medium 1 of density d into medium 2 of lower density and then into medium 3, which has the same density d as medium 1. A close examination of what happens at an interface gives us the means of determining which way the ray will be bent. The plane wave incident on the left of Fig. 1-8A is represented by straight lines separated by a wavelength. Line AC begins its sojourn in medium 2 at point A. While the incident ray travels from C to D in medium 1, it travels from A to B in medium 2. In the lower-density medium 2, the sound travels slower because sound speed is proportional to density. The wavelength of the sound is shorter because wavelength is directly proportional to sound speed, Eq. 1-7, which causes the plane waves to go off in a new direction in medium 2. As the sound ray leaves medium 2 and begins to enter medium 3, we see that during the time the wave travels between points G and H and points E and F, propagation is restored to the original direction.

1.10.1 Effect of Air Temperature on Sound Propagation

In Fig. 1-8A the density transitions between media were abrupt, but this is not always true. Fig. 1-8B illustrates a common experience in the propagation of sound outdoors. Sound travels faster in warm air than in cold air. Temperature stratification of air layers near the earth is common. During early morning hours, the warmth of the earth causes the lower layers of air to be warmer than the upper layers. As a result, sound rays bend upward, as in the left sketch of Fig. 1-8B. From the earth's surface, sound does not appear to travel as far because the sound energy is directed upward. During the day the sun causes the upper air layer to be warmer than the lower layer, resulting in a bending of sound down toward the earth. From the earth's surface, sound appears to travel greater distances later in the day. Hot air in the upper part of an auditorium would tend to bend sound rays down to the audience, but the effect is modest over short distances.

1.10.2 Effect of Wind on Sound Propagation

Stratification of air temperature is one factor affecting propagation of sound outdoors; wind is another. If wind moves the air particles involved in propagating sound, the velocity of the wind, combining vectorially with the velocity of sound, affects the direction of travel of sound rays. A 20-mph wind (29.3 ft/s) is only 2.6% of the speed of sound (1130 ft/s), which does not seem like much, but such wind can have a noticeable effect on the propagation of sound near the earth.

Sound from an elevated outdoor loudspeaker traveling with the wind is refracted down toward the earth; thus, the acoustic level is sustained to greater distances. Sound from an elevated outdoor loudspeaker aimed into the wind will not carry as far. In this case the sound is refracted upward over the heads of the audience. Lowering the elevation of the loudspeaker is no solution to wind effects as other effects come into play to limit its range.

Wind of fluctuating velocity creates effects far more devastating on an outdoor sound system. Here the sound from the loudspeakers seems to the distant audience to fluctuate in volume as the beam is bent upward and downward as well as left and right. Rapidly varying effects such as these are more readily perceived than more constant ones, such as temperature effects. The performance of an outdoor sound system on a cold, calm morning may be quite different from its performance on a hot, windy afternoon.

1.11 DIFFRACTION OF SOUND

An ocean wave sweeps past the pilings of a dock almost as though the pilings do not exist. A large island in mid-ocean, however, offers more resistance. Calm seas would be found in its lee, even though waves would spread around each end. The length of a wave is as important for ocean waves as it is for sound waves. For a sound wave that is long compared to the size of an obstacle, the sound wave continues, seemingly unimpeded.

At 50 Hz the wavelength of sound in air is about 23 ft. Will a brick wall 10 ft high shield a house from traffic noise components around 50 Hz? Fig. 1-9A sets up this situation. The source S emits sound that strikes the brick wall. Of course, the brick wall reflects most of the sound energy falling upon it, shielding the house from high-frequency components of the traffic noise. The house is located in a shadow zone behind the wall. This shadow zone exists for high frequencies because the brick wall is large compared to the wavelength of sound; for such conditions rays of sound tend to act like rays of light.

For sound waves in the 50-Hz region and below, however, there is an effect that bends sound into the shadow zone behind the brick wall. Huygen (1629–1695) enunciated a principle that states that every point on a wavefront acts as though it were itself a center of disturbance, sending out little wavelets of its own. These wavefront

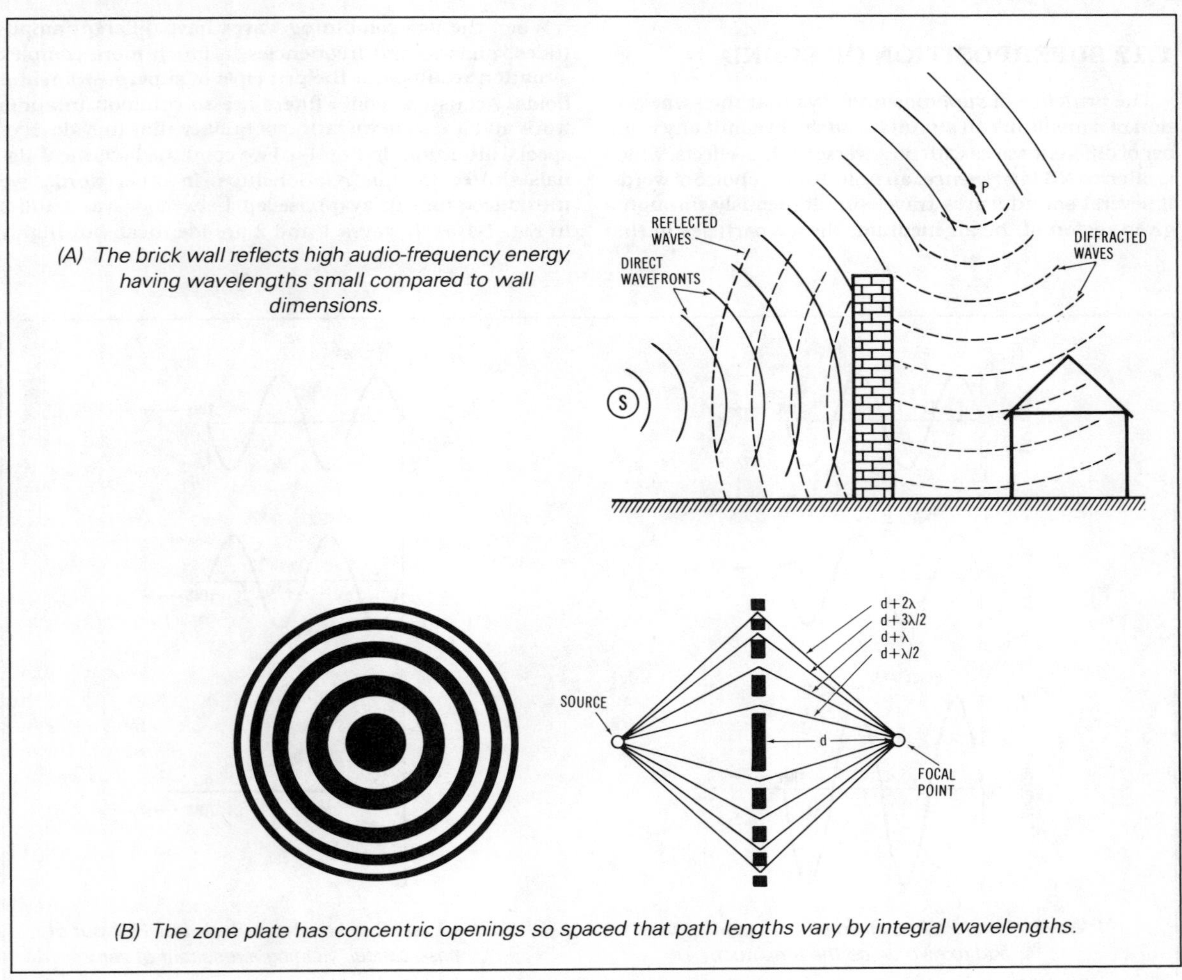

(A) The brick wall reflects high audio-frequency energy having wavelengths small compared to wall dimensions.

(B) The zone plate has concentric openings so spaced that path lengths vary by integral wavelengths.

Figure 1-9 Diffraction of sound.

sources, such as P in Fig. 1-9A, send sound energy into the area behind the wall causing the shadow zone to be something less than "dark." Thus, the brick wall is quite effective in shielding the house from the high-frequency components of traffic noise, but it is less effective for low-frequency components that are "bent" by diffraction into the space behind the wall.

A curious example of diffraction is the zone plate of Fig. 1-9B. A series of concentric openings is placed so that, when the plate is midway between the source and the focal point, the path lengths vary by integral wavelengths that add in phase at the focal point.

Diffraction occurring around our heads affects the way we hear sounds. It affects the directional response of microphones and occurs at loudspeaker cabinet edges, leaving its imprint on performance. Diffraction effects are never very far away in audio systems.

1.12 SUPERPOSITION OF SOUND

The principle of *superposition* says that the same portion of a medium can simultaneously transmit any number of different waves with no adverse mutual effects, which is often called *interference*, an unfortunate choice of words. If several sound waves travel simultaneously through a given region of the air medium, the air particles in that region will respond to the vectorial sum of the displacements of each wave system.

The sketch of Fig. 1-10A is a highly simplified illustration of the principle of superposition. If wave 1 and wave 2 arrive at a given air particle at the same time, how will the particle respond? If these two wave systems have equal amplitudes and are in phase, the air particle must respond to the resultant, which is of the same frequency but twice the amplitude. In Fig. 1-10B wave 2 has the same frequency and amplitude as wave 1 but is displaced in time a half-wavelength (180° phase shift). The resultant of the two is zero as one cancels the other. The air particle serves wave 1 and wave 2 at this spot and at this instant by not moving at all.

1.13 ACOUSTICAL COMB FILTERS

When the two combining waves have different amplitudes, phases, and frequencies, a much more complex situation results, but the principle of superposition still holds. Acoustical comb filters are so common in audio work and are so devastating of quality that they deserve special attention. In Fig. 1-10 we combined identical signals shifted in time relationships. In other words, we introduced time delay (phase lag) between waves 1 and 2 in Fig. 1-10B. If waves 1 and 2 are identical, but highly

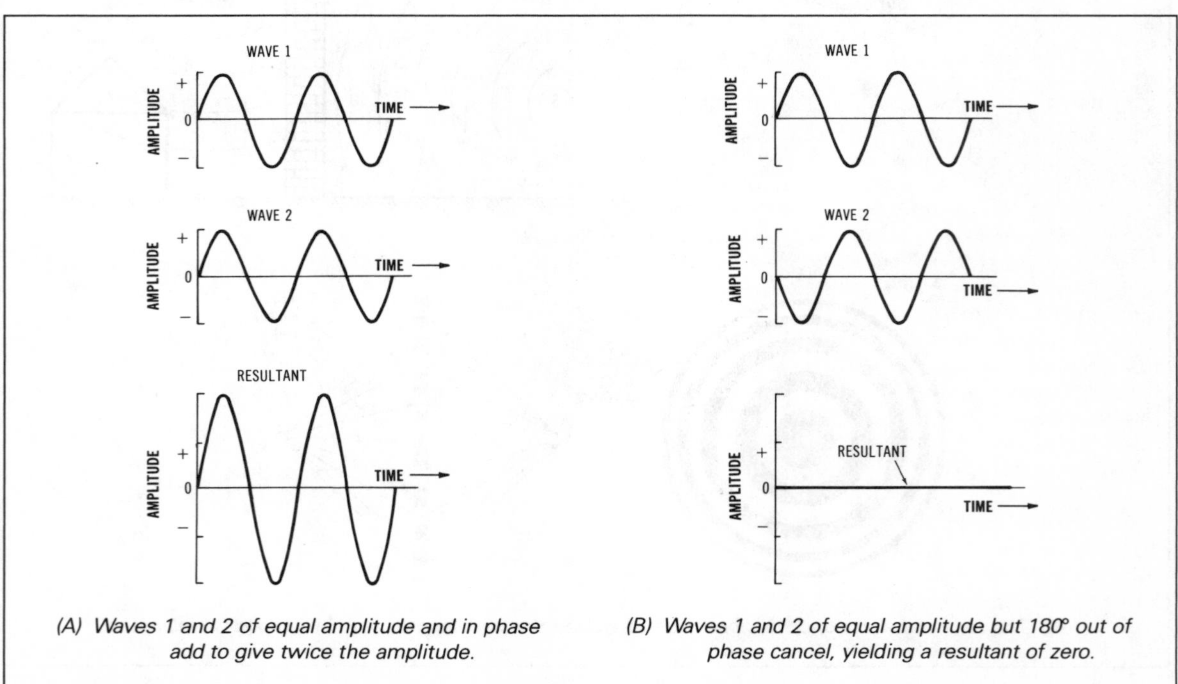

(A) Waves 1 and 2 of equal amplitude and in phase add to give twice the amplitude.

(B) Waves 1 and 2 of equal amplitude but 180° out of phase cancel, yielding a resultant of zero.

Figure 1-10 The extremes of superposition (interference).

complex such as voice or music, we must consider what a time delay does down through the audible spectrum.

The phase lag (ϕ) for any frequency (f) for any given time delay (t) is given by

$$\phi = 2\pi ft \tag{1-8}$$

When two identical signals separated by a phase lag ϕ are added together, the amplitude of the sum depends on the phase lag. If the phase lag $\phi = 0$, the two signals are in phase, as in Fig. 2-10A. Adding two waves, each of amplitude A, gives an amplitude of 2A. If two waves, each having an amplitude A, are added together a half wavelength or 180° (or π radians) out of phase, they cancel each other and the resultant amplitude is zero. A general statement for adding two waves of identical shape and amplitude is given by[4]

$$A_R = |2\cos(\phi/2)|\,A \tag{1-9}$$

where,

A_R is the resultant amplitude,
A is the amplitude of both wave 1 and wave 2,
ϕ is the phase lag between the two waves.

The absolute value of 2 cos (ϕ/2) is taken because the amplitude is always positive.

Combining Eqs. 1-8 and 1-9 gives

$$A_R = |2\cos\pi ft|\,A \tag{1-10}$$

where,

f is the frequency in hertz,
t is the time delay in seconds.

Note that the product πft is in radians, not degrees. Note also the cyclic nature of the cosine term ($\cos 0 = 1$, $\cos \pi/2 = 0$, $\cos \pi = -1$, $\cos 3\pi/2 = 0$, $\cos 2\pi = 1$, and so on). Adding two identical waves with a delay of t seconds between them gives a response that is a series of sine-wave shapes (the same shape as cosine waves) with the negative-going excursion inverted. Response shapes for delays of 0.1, 0.5, and 1.0 ms are shown in Fig. 1-11 plotted on a linear frequency scale. At frequencies that bring the two waves into phase, the amplitude is doubled (+6 dB); when they are 180° out of phase, they cancel giving a deep null. The basis of the term "comb filter" is evident from these responses. The identical responses are plotted to the more familiar logarithmic frequency scale in Fig. 1-12.

Whenever the cosine term of Eq. 1-10 is unity, $A_R = 2A$. Since we are considering amplitudes of voltage or sound pressure and not power, these peaks of amplitude 2A can be expressed in decibel form as

$$\text{amplitude} = 20\log A_R/A$$
$$= 20\log 2$$
$$= +6.02\,\text{dB}$$

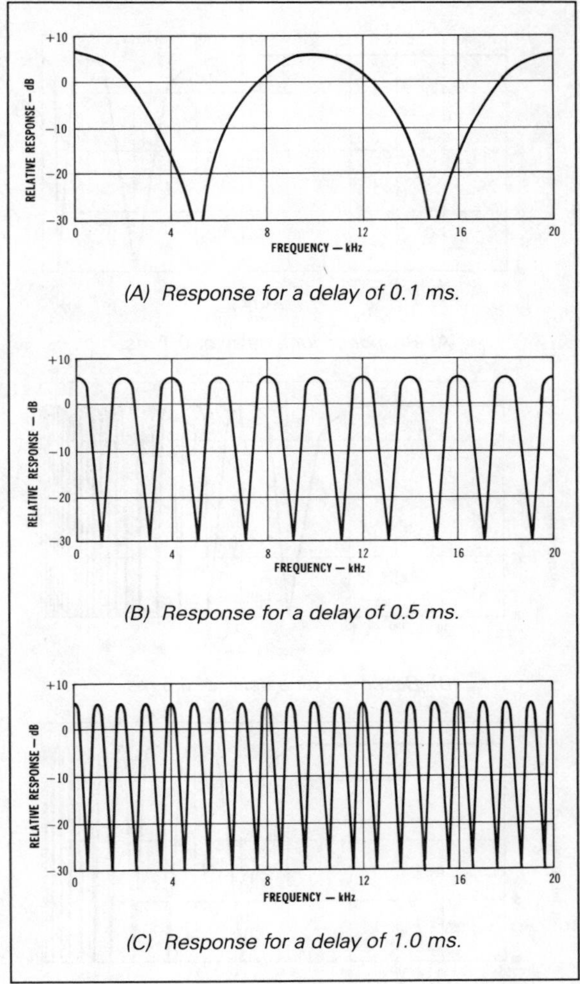

(A) Response for a delay of 0.1 ms.

(B) Response for a delay of 0.5 ms.

(C) Response for a delay of 1.0 ms.

Figure 1-11 Response shape for delays of 0.1, 0.5, and 1.0 ms.

At frequencies at which the cosine term is zero, $A_R = 0$ and cancellation results. The amplitude in decibels becomes

$$\text{amplitude} = 20\log 0/A$$
$$= 20\log 0$$
$$= -\infty\,\text{dB}$$

In practice this cancellation is closer to 20 to 40 dB rather than $-\infty$.

Figs. 1-11 and 1-12 apply to any complex voice or music signal that is combined with itself and delayed by the indicated time. For a delay of 0.1 ms, a deep null at 5 kHz and another at 15 kHz are observed. At these frequencies

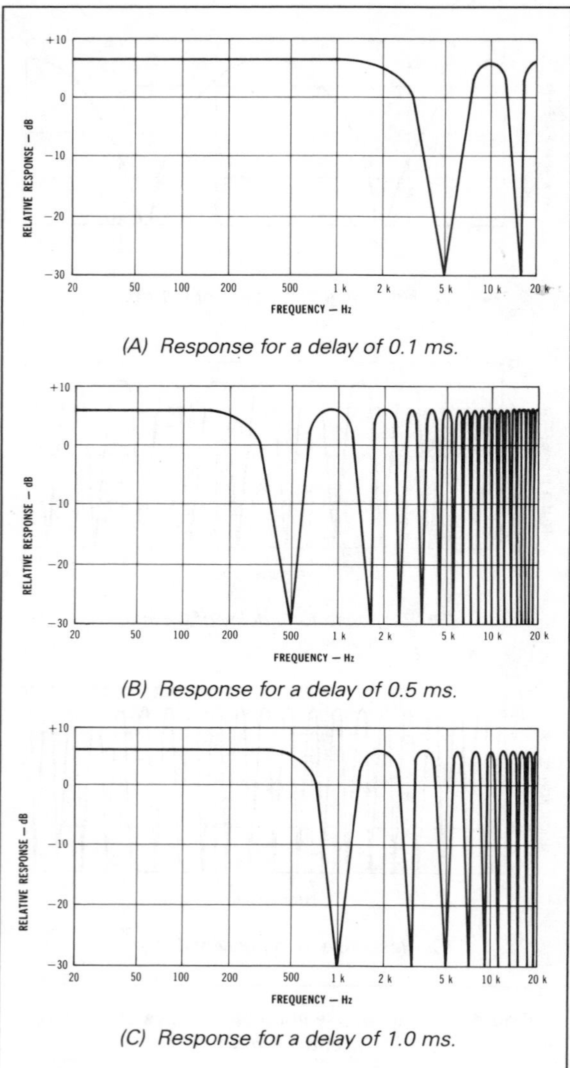

(A) Response for a delay of 0.1 ms.

(B) Response for a delay of 0.5 ms.

(C) Response for a delay of 1.0 ms.

Figure 1-12 Comb filter data from Fig. 1-11 plotted on logarithmic scales.

this 0.1-ms delay places the delayed and undelayed signals in phase opposition, and the null results. Between nulls the signals come into phase, and double amplitude results. Many more nulls occur within the audible band for a delay of 0.5 ms, and still more for 1.0-ms delay.

Certain generalizations can be made

1. The spacing between peaks is always (1/t) Hz.
2. The nulls occur when πft equals $\pi/2$, $3\pi/2$, $5\pi/2$, and so on.
3. For long time delays, the distance between peaks is small.
4. Short time delays give greater peak separation.

The important question is, "How audible are the effects of the response of Fig. 1-12?" Delays of these magnitudes can easily be experienced by recording speech as the talker walks toward a highly reflecting wall holding the microphone at a constant distance from the lips. The reflection of the voice from the wall combines with the direct signal at the microphone diaphragm. The reflection is delayed because of the greater distance traveled. One foot difference of path length gives a delay of 1/1130 ft/s ≈ 0.9 ms, or 1.13 ft corresponds to a 1-ms delay. When the approach to the wall yields delays in the order of 1 ms, significant distortion will be noticed as the recording is played back. For greater delays, the null spacing becomes very small, and the primary effect noticed is the 6-dB increase in level at the peaks.

Bücklein[5] in his study of the audibility of frequency response irregularities found that peaks had considerably greater effect on quality than valleys.

1.14 INVERSE-SQUARE LAW

Those active in audio have many occasions to apply the *inverse-square law*. We know that sound gets weaker as distance from the source is increased. Now all we have to do is find out how much weaker for a given increase in distance. To solve this we assume that a point source is radiating W watts into a free field. The sound energy flows out in all directions on spherical wavefronts. Let us consider the sound flowing outward within a certain solid angle, as shown in Fig. 1-13. Sound intensity is defined as the sound power per square centimeter. In Fig. 1-13 the intensity would be the number of watts divided by the total area of the sphere or

$$I = W/4\pi r^2 \quad (1\text{-}11)$$

where,

I is the sound intensity in watts per centimeter squared,
W is the sound power of source in watts,
r is the distance from the source in centimeters.

At a distance r_1 from the source,

$$W = (I_1) \times (4\pi r_1^2) \quad (1\text{-}12)$$

At a distance r_2 from the source,

$$W = (I_2) \times (4\pi r_2^2) \quad (1\text{-}13)$$

But since the same sound power flows through spheres at both r_1 and r_2, Eqs. 1-12 and 1-13 are equal:

$$(I_1) \times (4\pi r_1^2) = (I_2) \times (4\pi r_2^2) \quad (1\text{-}14)$$

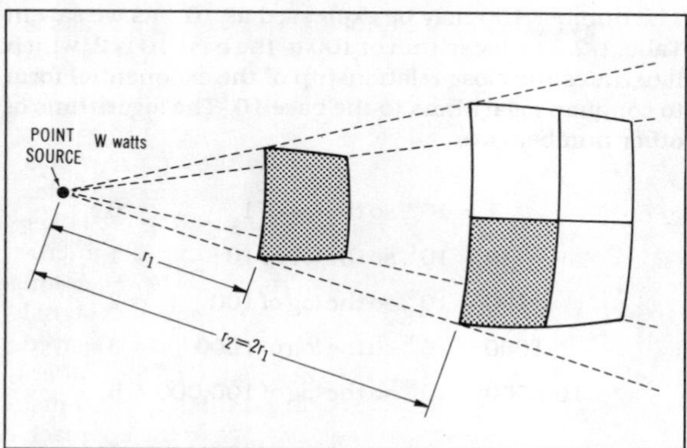

Figure 1-13 Sound flowing outward within a solid angle.

which may be rearranged to

$$I_1/I_2 = (4\pi r_2^2)/(4\pi r_1^2) = r_2^2/r_1^2 \tag{1-15}$$

which is the inverse-square law. It says that the intensity of sound is inversely proportional to the square of the distance from the source. Remember that this law applies only to sound in a free field.

Intensity is a very difficult parameter to measure and requires special techniques. Sound pressure or sound-pressure level, on the other hand, is an easily measured parameter. How is the inverse-square law expressed for sound pressure? In Fig. 1-13 the intensity at r_2 is one-fourth that at r_1. Since sound pressure is proportional to the square root of the intensity, the sound pressure at r_2 is half that at r_1 $(\sqrt{1/4} = 1/2)$, or 6 dB lower, which leads to the familiar and useful statement that sound pressure in a free field falls off "6 dB per distance double."

If the source is outdoors, but near the ground, sound is radiated into a hemisphere rather than a sphere, as in the free-field case. When radiated into a hemisphere, sound pressure falls off something less than 6 dB per distance double. In a confined space such as a studio or listening room, sound falls off even more slowly than in the hemisphere case. In fact, the rate of decay with distance in a room is quite complicated in the near field near the source, whereas greater distances are dominated by reverberation. There *may* be, however, a true 6 dB per distance double (free-field) stretch between the near field and reverberation dominated field, depending on the absorption in the room.

1.15 DIMENSIONAL ANALYSIS

Arithmetic operations can be applied to dimensional labels of numbers as well as to the numbers themselves. The speed of sound is about 1130 ft/s. We know that the number 1130 can be multiplied, added, and divided. It is very convenient to know that the feet per second can also be handled mathematically. The secret is to remember that the "per" is equivalent to a division bar and that in feet per second, the "second" is in the denominator as ft/s. An example will illustrate how dimensional analysis can tell us if our arithmetic is correct. Let us say that our memory tells us the wavelength λ of sound can be found from the speed of sound and its frequency, but we do not remember whether they are multiplied or divided and if divided which is the numerator and which the denominator. Let us try solving for f = 1000 Hz, multiplying:

$$\lambda = (\text{ft/s}) \times (\text{cycles/s}) = \text{ft-cycles/s}^2$$

Absurd! Next, try dividing

$$\lambda = (\text{cycles/s})/(\text{ft/s}) = (\text{cycles/s})(\text{s/ft}) = \text{cycles/ft}$$

It may be interesting sometimes to know how many cycles there are in 1 foot, but we set out to find the wavelength of a 1000-Hz signal:

$$\lambda = (\text{ft/s})/(\text{cycles/s}) = (\text{ft/s})(\text{s/cycles}) = \text{ft/cycle}$$

which is the unit we want for wavelength, the length of a single cycle. Including the dimensional label serves as a check on the correctness of the operation:

$$\lambda = (1130\ \text{ft/s})/(1000\ \text{cycles/s}) = 1.13\ \text{ft/cycle}$$

By including dimensional labels, errors can be avoided and a better understanding of the process can result.

One of the most useful checks on changing to metric units and back again is dimensional analysis. For example, in changing from pounds per cubic foot to kilograms per cubic meter for a variable X when the conversion tables are somewhere else

$$(\text{X lb/ft}^3)\ (1\ \text{kg}/2.2\ \text{lb})\ (3.53\ \text{ft}^3/\text{m}^3) = (16.02 \times \text{X})\ \text{kg/m}^3$$

1.16 DECIBEL NOTATION

In the field of audio, it is necessary to handle a range of numbers from the very small to the very large. There are several number systems available to use as shown in Table 1-2. The decimal, arithmetic, and exponential forms each have their advantages and disadvantages when specific applications are considered. The decimal and arithmetic forms become unwieldy at the large and small extremes. The exponential form is neat and compact, even though it may not be as familiar to some as the decimal and arithmetic forms. With modest application of attention, however, the exponential form can be useful.

The great range of numbers commonly associated with sound stems directly from the tremendous range of the human ear. The average threshold of hearing occurs at a sound pressure of 20 μPa. At the other extreme, the threshold of pain of our ears is over 100 Pa. This represents a ratio of $100/(20 \times 10^{-6}) = 5 \times 10^6$ or 5 million, an awkward number. The human ear-brain mechanism handles such a wide range of stimuli because it, like our other senses, is more or less logarithmic in its response. This suggests that ratios rather than, say, sound pressures are more applicable, and ratios, in turn, suggest decibels. Therefore, we use ratios and decibels because of the amazingly wide response range of our ears.

First, we must consider ratios. Let us say that a riveter produces a sound pressure of 25 Pa at a distance of 10 ft. Our standard reference pressure level for all problems associated with hearing has been agreed upon as 20 μPa, the threshold of hearing. The noise of the riveter is 25 Pa/20 μPa = 1.25×10^6 times higher than the threshold of hearing. This 1.25×10^6 is dimensionless, a pure number, because the pascals in the numerator and the pascals in the denominator cancel. This is important, for our next step involves logarithms, and logarithms can only be taken of pure numbers.

Mentioning logarithms may scare the audio newcomer, but they are the very underpinning of the decibel and, thus, unavoidable in dealing with sound in any depth. The number 100 may be expressed as 10^2, as we saw in Table 1-2. The logarithm of 100 to the base 10 is 2, which illustrates the close relationship of the exponential form to common logarithms to the base 10. The logarithms of other numbers are

$$1 = 10^0, \text{ so the log of } 1 = 0$$
$$10 = 10^1, \text{ so the log of } 10 = 1$$
$$100 = 10^2, \text{ so the log of } 100 = 2$$
$$1000 = 10^3, \text{ so the log of } 1000 = 3$$
$$100{,}000 = 10^5, \text{ so the log of } 100{,}000 = 5$$

These are logarithms to the base 10, the common form of logarithms. When the abbreviation "log" is used, it means logarithms to the base 10. Any base can be used, but there is little reason to complicate an elementary discussion. An exception is the so-called "natural" logarithms to the base ϵ where $\epsilon = 2.7183$. This will be useful when we examine the basic mathematics of wave motion and vibration. Logarithms to the base ϵ are identified by the abbreviation "ln" on the calculator.

Logarithms reduce arithmetic operation one notch in difficulty: division is reduced to subtraction, multiplication is reduced to addition, and exponents are reduced to simple multiplication. For example,

$$\log (A/B) = \log A - \log B$$
$$\log (A \times B) = \log A + \log B$$
$$\log (A^B) = B \log A$$

Table 1-2. Number Systems

Decimal Form	Arithmetic Form	Exponential Form	Decibels (Assuming Sound-Pressure Ratios)
1,000,000	10 × 10 × 10 × 10 × 10 × 10	10^6	120
100,000	10 × 10 × 10 × 10 × 10	10^5	100
10,000	10 × 10 × 10 × 10	10^4	80
1000	10 × 10 × 10	10^3	60
100	10 × 10	10^2	40
10	10 × 1	10^1	20
1	10/10	10^0	0
0.1	1/10	10^{-1}	−20
0.01	1/(10 × 10)	10^{-2}	−40
0.001	1/(10 × 10 × 10)	10^{-3}	−60
0.0001	1/(10 × 10 × 10 × 10)	10^{-4}	−80
100,000	(100 × 1000)	$(10^2)(10^3) = 10^5$	100
100	10,000/100	$10^4 / 10^2 = 10^2$	40
10	100,000/10,000	$10^5 / 10^4 = 10^1$	20
10	$\sqrt{100}$ or $\sqrt[2]{100}$	$100^{1/2}$	20
10	$\sqrt[3]{1000}$	$1000^{1/3}$	20
177.83	$\sqrt[4]{1000^3}$	$1000^{3/4}$	45

Anyone who has ever used a slide rule will recall that this is exactly what it did with logarithmic scales.

Very simple so far, but how about the logarithm of 569? In the old days we would have to go to tables and learn about characteristics and mantissas, but the common hand-held calculator has changed all that. Log of 569? Just punch in 569, push the "log" button, and read 2.755. From this tabulation we note that 569 lies between 100 and 1000, and the log of 569 must lie between 2 and 3, hence 2.755 appears to be reasonable. We can state that 10 to the 2.755 power ($10^{2.755}$) is equal to 569.

The bel (from Alexander Graham Bell) is the basic unit, and it is defined as the logarithm (to base 10) of the ratio of two powers:

$$L_1 \text{ in bels} = \log(W_1/W_2) \qquad (1\text{-}16)$$

The bel is a bit large to serve our purposes so the decibel (one-tenth bel) is adopted, and the level in decibels of a power ratio becomes

$$L_1 \text{ in decibels} = 10\log(W_1/W_2) \qquad (1\text{-}17)$$

A point to be remembered is that the decibel applies basically to powerlike quantities. Acoustic intensity is power per unit area in a specific direction and is, therefore, eligible to be expressed in decibels. Sound pressure is what is normally measured, and the square of sound pressure is proportional to acoustic power. Level in terms of pressure ratio then, from Eq. 1-17, becomes

$$L_P = 10\log(p_1^2/p_2^2)$$

or, (1-18)

$$L_P = 20\log(p_1/p_2)$$

This is a form widely applied in dealing with sound. The 10 log is used for power ratios; the 20 log, for sound pressures as well as electrical voltages and currents.

We are now in a position to refer to Table 1-2 and consider the decibel column. These decibels are calculated from the decimals in the left-hand column, assuming that they are sound pressure ratios (i.e., with respect to 1). For example,

$$20\log 10{,}000 = (20 \times 4)$$

$$= 80\,\text{dB}$$

Note that the decibel column is even simpler than the exponential column.

The term "sound pressure level" suggests that a standard reference level has been used for p_2 in Eq. 1-18. This international reference level for sound in air is 20 μPa, which is close to the threshold of human hearing. Sound level meters are calibrated to read in decibels above this standard pressure. The relationship between the current standard and other reference pressures previously used is graphically presented in Fig. 1-14.

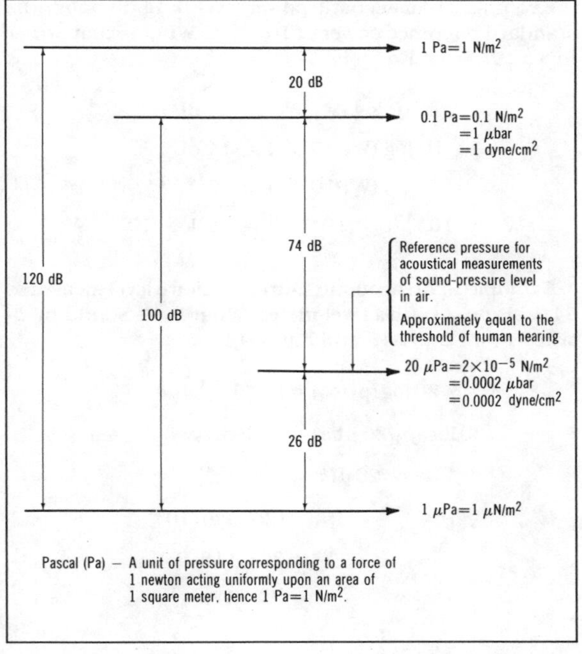

Figure 1-14 Reference pressure in acoustical measurements.

1.17 EQUIVALENCE OF LOGARITHMIC AND EXPONENTIAL FORMS

The ability to convert readily from the logarithmic to the exponential form or vice versa is quite basic in solving audio problems. The expression

$$10\log_{10} 2 = 3.01\,\text{dB}$$

in exponential form is

$$2 = 10^{3.01/10}$$

Thus, the log and y^x keys on the hand-held calculator allow ready transformation from one form to the other. If voltage ratios or ratios of sound pressure are used, the form changes to

$$20\log_{10} 2 = 6.02\,\text{dB}$$

which, in exponential form, is

$$2 = 10^{6.02/20}$$

Example 1: An acoustic power level is 14 dB above the standard reference power of 10^{-12} W. What is that power in watts? From Eq. 1-17

$$10 \log (W_1/W_2) = 14 \text{ dB}$$
$$10 \log (W_1/10^{-12}) = 14 \text{ dB}$$
$$(W_1/10^{-12}) = 10^{14/10}$$
$$W_1 = (10^{-12}) \times (10^{14/10}) = 25.1 \times 10^{-12} \text{ W}$$

Example 2: An acoustic sound pressure level measures 84.3 dB on a sound level meter. What is its sound pressure? From Eq. 1-18 and Fig. 1-14,

$$20 \log (p_1/p_2) = L_p$$
$$20 \log (p_1/20\ \mu\text{Pa}) = 84.3 \text{ dB}$$
$$p_1/20\ \mu\text{Pa} = 10^{84.3/20}$$
$$p_1 = (20\ \mu\text{Pa})(10^{84.3/20})$$
$$= 328{,}118\ \mu\text{Pa}$$
$$= 0.328 \text{ Pa}$$

1.18 INVERSE-DISTANCE LAW AND THE DECIBEL

The inverse-square law pertained to sound intensity, as we saw in Eq. 1-15. Because sound pressures are more accessible to us, the same law can be called the inverse-distance law because

$$(\text{pressure})\ (\text{distance}) = \text{a constant}$$

Therefore, pressure drops off as the first power of distance. As we deal with sound pressure levels, the difference L_D between the sound pressure levels at two points can be expressed as

$$\text{difference} = 20 \log (d_1/d_2) \text{ dB} \qquad (1\text{-}19)$$

For example, if distance d_1 is twice d_2, the difference in sound pressure level is 20 log 2 = 6 dB. Because we know that the sound is weaker twice as far away, we know that the sound pressure level is 6 dB lower. This is the 6-dB-per-distance-double statement. Of course, this is for spherical divergence. In practice the falloff of sound pressure level with distance will almost always be less than this. Here are two examples:

Example 1: The loudspeaker level is 95 dB at 5 ft. What approximate level should we expect at 14 ft?

$$\text{difference} = 20 \log (14/5)$$
$$= 8.9 \text{ dB}$$

and the level at 14 ft is

$$95 - 8.9 = 86.1 \text{ dB}$$

Example 2: A wall reflects a ray of sound from the loudspeaker of Example 1, which travels 10 ft further than the direct path of 14 ft. What is the level of reflected ray compared to the direct ray?

$$\text{difference} = 20 \log [14/(10 + 14)]$$
$$= 4.7 \text{ dB}$$

That is, the reflected ray would be approximately 4.7 dB below the direct ray.

1.19 COMBINING DECIBELS

If a noise source having a level of 80 dB is added to a second source having the same 80-dB level, the combination will yield a level of 83 dB, not 160 dB. Decibels are logarithmic units and cannot be added algebraically. It is necessary to convert each decibel reading to its equivalent power, add or subtract the powers and then convert to a combined decibel level. The combination of two or more levels may be found from

$$\text{combined dB} = 10 \log (10^{dB_1/10} + 10^{dB_2/10} + \ldots + 10^{dB_n/10}) \qquad (1\text{-}20)$$

For example, let us assume that sources measuring 65, 70, and 75 dB are combined. What is the total?

$$\text{combined dB} = 10 \log (10^{65/10} + 10^{70/10} + 10^{75/10})$$
$$= 76.5 \text{ dB}$$

The difference between two levels may be found this way:

$$\text{difference dB} = 10 \log (10^{dB_1/10} - 10^{dB_2/10}) \qquad (1\text{-}21)$$

For example: with both sources combined (dB_1), the level is 88 dB; with one source turned off (dB_2), the level is 84 dB:

$$\text{difference dB} = 10 \log (10^{88/10} - 10^{84/10})$$
$$= +\ 85.8 \text{ dB}$$

In other words one source of 85.8 dB combines with a second source of 84 dB to give the combined total of 88 dB.

All this is a bit messy and, perhaps, more accurate than the circumstances require. For such, the graphical approach of Fig. 1-15 is included. When the levels of two sounds are combined, it must be done on a power basis, not the addition of decibels. This curve may be used to combine two sound levels. For example, the noise of a

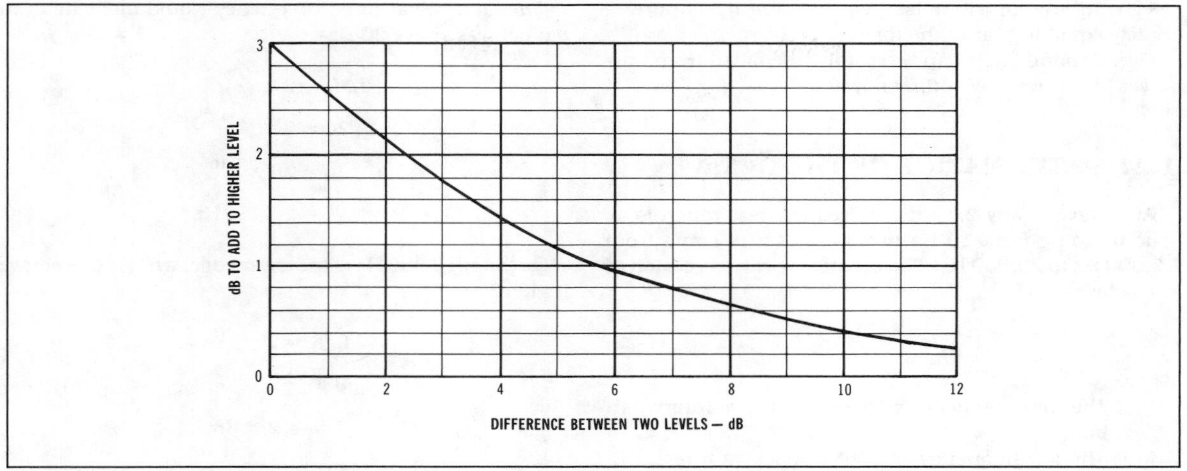

Figure 1-15 Graph used for combining decibels.

ventilating fan A gives a reading of 74 dB at a certain point. Fan B gives a reading of 81 dB at the same point. The difference between the two readings is 7 dB; hence, both fans together would yield a level of 81 + 0.8 = 81.8 dB. Note, as already stated, that when two sources having the same level individually (difference = 0) are combined, the level is 3 dB higher. Also note that if the difference between two levels is 10 dB or more, the combination will be increased 0.5 dB or less. If the noise of a fan being measured is only 10 dB above the background noise, 0.5 dB should be subtracted from the combined reading.

This procedure for combining levels is based on random-type sounds. If two coherent periodic waves are combined, the combined level will be 6 dB higher, not 3 dB.

An example of combining two coherent periodic waves has already been given in Fig. 1-10A and the associated discussion.

1.20 SPECTRUM LEVEL AND THE DECIBEL

Spectrum level is the sound pressure level of a sound with a bandwidth 1 Hz wide. It is a necessary concept in comparing spectra measured with analyzers of different bandwidths. There is no constant bandwidth sound analyzer that measures spectrum level directly, rather we have wave analyzers of finite constant bandwidth such as 1%, 3%, 10%, one-third octave, octave, or other constant percentage bandwidth analyzers. The spectrum level can be obtained from any band level by the following operation:

$$\text{spectrum level} = \text{band level} - 10 \log (f_2 - f_1) \quad (1\text{-}22)$$

where,

$f_2 - f_1$ is the width of the band giving the band level reading. For example, an octave band centered on 1 kHz accepts energy from 707 to 1414 Hz or a bandwidth of 707 Hz. If the sound pressure level of a sound in this band is 76 dB, the spectrum level is

$$76\,\text{dB} - 10 \log 707 = 76 - 28.5 = 47.5\,\text{dB}$$

If the same sound is measured with a one-third octave analyzer centered on 1 kHz, the band sound pressure level would be 71.2 dB for the overall band. To compare this with the octave band spectrum level, 71.2 dB − 10 log 232 = 47.5 dB. The results of measurements by filters of different widths can thus be compared on a spectrum-level basis. Table 1-3 lists correction factors at 1 kHz by which measurements of the same sound by analyzers of five different bandwidths may be compared.

The previous discussion assumes that the sound being measured is continuously distributed throughout the range of interest and that the total level is the result of the addition of powers of components of different frequencies (i.e., that the meter had true rms characteristics).

This 1-Hz bandwidth is also of interest in masking. For example, a tone of a given level is just audible when the

Table 1-3. Spectrum Levels From Filters of Different Bandwidths

Analyzer Type	Bandwidth at 1000 Hz	Correction Factor 10 Log (Bandwidth)
1/1 Octave	707 Hz	28.5 dB
1/3 Octave	232	23.7
10%	100	20.0
3%	30	14.8
1%	10	10.0

spectrum level of the noise just masking it is approximately equal to that of the tone.

Overall band levels can be readily calculated from narrower band levels by adding powers.

1.21 MATHEMATICS OF THE OCTAVE

An octave is any 2:1 ratio of frequencies, which is as true in going from 10 Hz to 20 Hz as it is going from 10,000 Hz to 20,000 Hz. The mathematical expression of the octave is

$$f_H/f_L = 2^N \tag{1-23}$$

where,

f_H is the high-frequency edge of the octave interval in hertz,

f_L is the low-frequency edge of the octave interval in hertz,

N is the number of octaves.

For example, how many octaves are in the 20-Hz to 20-kHz range?

$$2^N = f_H/f_L$$
$$= 20{,}000/20$$
$$= 1000$$

Taking logs of both sides,

$$N \log 2 = \log 1000$$
$$N = \log 1000/\log 2$$
$$= 3/0.3010$$
$$= 9.966$$

Question: What upper frequency would make an even ten octaves above 20 Hz?

$$f_H/f_L = 2^N$$
$$f_H/20 = 2^{10}$$
$$f_H = 20 \times 2^{10}$$
$$= 20{,}480\,\text{Hz}$$

Question: If 880 Hz is the lower edge, what is one octave higher?

$$f_H/f_L = 2^N$$
$$f_H/880 = 2^1$$
$$f_H = 2 \times 880$$
$$= 1760\,\text{Hz}$$

A better question: What is the upper edge of a one-third octave bandwidth centered on 1000 Hz? The f_L = 1000 Hz, but the upper edge would only be one-sixth octave higher (half the one-third octave), so N = ⅙.

$$f_H/1000 = 2^{1/6}$$
$$f_H = 1000 \times 2^{1/6}$$
$$= 1122.5\,\text{Hz}$$

The lower edge of the one-third octave centered on 1000 Hz is

$$1000/f_L = 2^{1/6}$$
$$= 890.9\,\text{Hz}$$

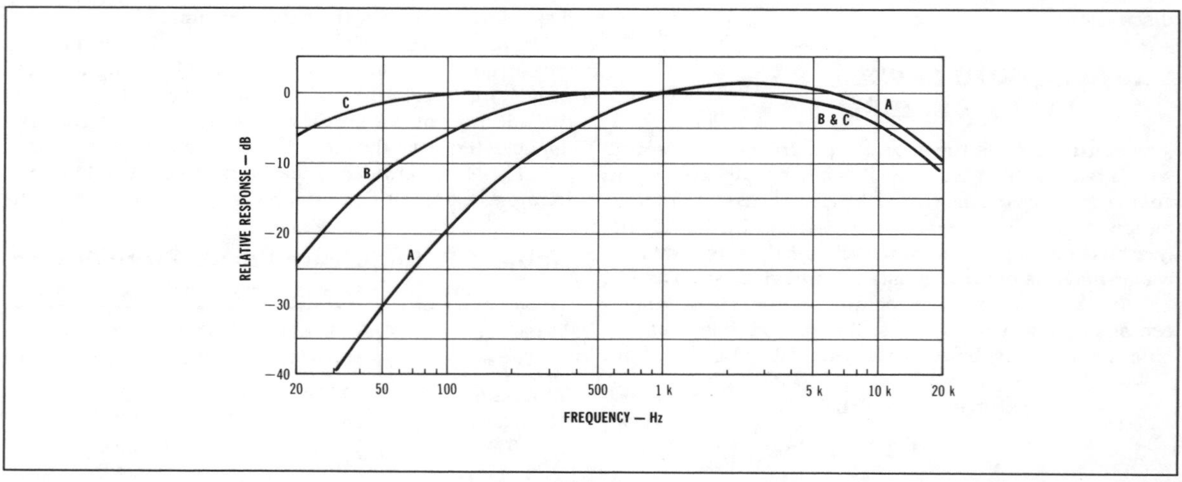

Figure 1-16 The frequency response of three standard networks (A, B, and C).

The percentage bandwidth of the one-third octave centered on 1000 Hz then becomes [(1122.5 − 890.9)/1000] × 100 = 23.16%.

We can conclude that any problem having the word "octave" can be solved by judicious application of the very simple relationship of Eq. 1-23.

1.22 WEIGHTING NETWORKS

Sound level meters come with one or more weighting networks built in. The question confronting the user is, "Which one should I use?" The frequency responses of the three standard networks (A, B, and C) are shown in Fig. 1-16. In simplest terms, these different curves are designed to give readings of sound-pressure level that will correspond, at least roughly, with human response to the sound. As we shall see in Chapter 2 "Psychoacoustics," the Fletcher-Munson curves show that the human ear is less sensitive at lower frequencies than at a frequency of 1 kHz. This effect is greater for lower-level sounds than for louder sounds. Therefore, it makes sense to reduce the sensitivity of the sound level meter (chiefly in the lower frequencies) so that its readings follow the characteristics of the ear more closely.

The A-weighting curve of Fig. 1-16 is based on the 40-phon Fletcher-Munson equal-loudness contour and is to be preferred for measuring lower-level sounds such as background noise. The B-weighting curve is based on the 70-phon equal-loudness contour and is suitable for measuring sounds of intermediate level. Measurements taken with A- and B-weighting are called *weighted sound levels*. The C-weighting is essentially flat and is used for very loud sounds. It is also used when *sound pressure levels* are to be measured and generally when the sound level meter feeds a signal to other instruments for analysis.

Table 1-4. Use of Weighting Networks

Sound Level Range, dB	Recommended Weighting Network
20–55	A
55–85	B
85–140	C

From Berarek.[7]

Table 1-4 gives general suggestions as to which weighting to use for different sound level ranges. When comparing different sound levels, such as in Table 1-5, it may be expedient to use the A-weighting for the entire range rather than to shift weighting in the midst of a series of measurements to be directly compared.

Table 1-5. Typical A-Weighted Sound Levels

Source	Sound Pressure Level, Decibels (A-Weighting)
Jet airplane taking off (200 ft)	120
Subway train (20 ft)	90
Freight train (100 ft)	70
Speech (1 ft)	70
Shopping mall	60
Average residence with TV	50
Quiet residential area at night	40
Soft whisper (5 ft)	30
Recording studio background noise	30
Threshold of hearing	20

REFERENCES

1. L. L. Beranek, *Acoustic Measurements*, New York: John Wiley & Sons, Inc., 1949, p. 4.
2. Lord Rayleigh (John William Strutt), *Theory of Sound*, 1877, New York: Dover Publications, First American Edition, 1945.
3. H. C. Hardy, D. Telfair, and W. H. Pielemeirer, "The Velocity of Sound in Air," *Journal of the ASA*, vol. 13, pp. 226–233, 1942.
4. B. Bartlett, "A Scientific Explanation of Phasing (Flanging)," *Journal of the AES*, vol. 18, no. 6, pp. 674–675, December 1970.
5. R. Bucklein, "The Audibility of Frequency Response Irregularities," *Journal of the AES*, vol. 29, no. 3, pp. 126–131, March 1981.
6. Beranek, *Acoustic Measurement*, Ibid, p. 891.

ADDITIONAL BIBLIOGRAPHY

A. J. Schneider, *Noise and Vibration Pocket Handbook*, Cleveland: Bruel & Kjaer Instruments, Inc.

CHAPTER **2**

Psychoacoustics

by F. Alton Everest

2.1 HUMAN HEARING SYSTEM

It is usually unpopular for us to admit a sense of awe when considering the wonders around and within ourselves. Awe flourishes on mystery, and (viewed superficially) mystery tends to evaporate under the clinical and analytical gaze of science. In considering the human hearing system in any depth, however, it is difficult to escape the conclusion that its intricate functions and structures indicate some beneficient hand in its design. Scientific investigations of how our hearing system really works are continually revealing new marvels, even more awe inspiring than earlier fragmentary knowledge. Surely, those in the field of audio should have every incentive to learn more of this remarkable system, which is at the very heart of all audio activity.

Our hearing mechanism is a system involving many subsystems, and the brain and its handling of auditory data is probably the least understood. Part of the system is metabolic, for our hearing system is a living system. von Bekesy won a Nobel prize for his investigation in auditory research, some of which was on the frequency selectivity of the inner ear. His work showed frequency selectivity far poorer than the ear actually exhibits. William Rhode, in his doctoral research at the University of Wisconsin, found much greater selectivity. The difference is that von Bekesy worked with dead animals and Rhode, with live ones. It is now known that frequency selectivity of the inner ear fades within minutes after metabolism ceases.

2.2 EAR ANATOMY AND FUNCTION

The human ear is commonly considered in three parts: the outer, the middle, and the inner ear. The sound is gathered (and as we shall see later, modified) by the external ear called the *pinna* and directed down the *auditory canal* (meatus). This canal is terminated by the *tympanic membrane* (eardrum). These parts constitute the outer ear, as shown in Figs. 2-1 and 2-2. The other side of the eardrum faces the middle ear. Fastened to it is one of the three ossicles, which are popularly called the hammer, anvil, and stirrup. The foot of the stirrup is affixed to the oval window. As the eardrum vibrates, the vibrations move to the hammer that moves the anvil that in turn activates the stirrup. The middle ear is air filled, and air pressure equalization takes place through the *eustachian* tube opening into the pharynx so that static pressure is the same on both sides of the eardrum. As the stirrup is rocked, it transmits sound to the fluid within the *cochlea*. The clear liquid filling the cochlea is incompressible, like water. The round window is a relatively flexible pressure release allowing sound energy to be transmitted to the fluid of the cochlea via the oval window. In the inner ear the traveling waves set up on the basilar membrane by vibrations of the oval window stimulate hair cells that send nerve impulses to the brain.

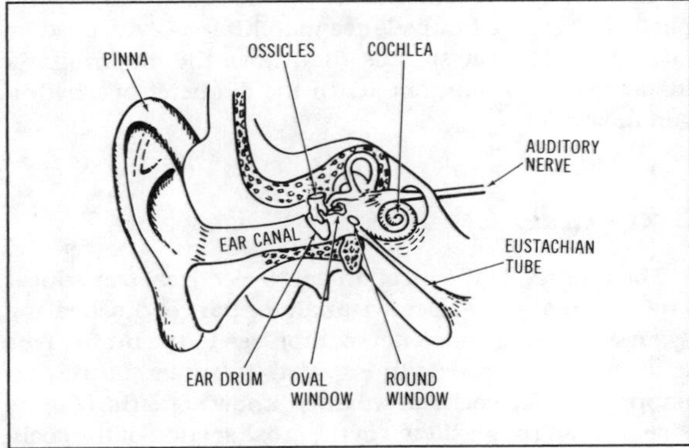

Figure 2-1 A cross section of the human ear showing the arrangement of the various vital parts.

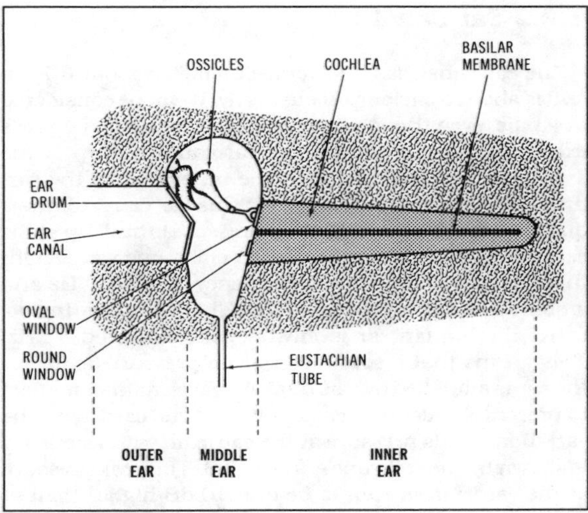

Figure 2-2 Highly idealized portrayal of the outer ear, middle ear, inner ear.

2.2.1 Pinna

These flaps on either side of our head may not be beautiful, but they serve definite acoustical functions. Let us assume for the moment that we have no pinnas, just holes in the head. Cupping our hands around the holes would make sounds louder as sound energy is directed into the opening. Cupping the hand around the pinna increases loudness as well, illustrating their sound-gathering function. The function of the complex convolutions of the pinna has long been a mystery, but we shall see in section 2.13.1 that they indicate the direction from which sound is coming.

2.2.2 Ear Canal

The ear canal has an average diameter about 0.7 cm and is about 3 cm long. Acoustically, it can be considered as a pipe, even though it is somewhat twisted, and pipes exhibit resonance effects. The ear canal is open at the outer end and terminated at the inner end by the eardrum. At the frequency at which this ear canal pipe is a quarter wavelength, maximum pressure is built up at the eardrum. According to Eq. 1-6, 3 cm is one wavelength in air of a sound having a frequency of 11,480 Hz and a quarter wavelength of 2870 Hz. This is interesting because the human ear is most sensitive around 3 kHz. This means that a sound of a given pressure falling on the ear is amplified by this quarter-wavelength pipe effect to present a much higher pressure at the eardrum. The variation of this pressure at the eardrum with frequency is shown by the solid line A in Fig. 2-3. The peak pressure at the eardrum is seen to be over 10 dB higher than at the opening of the ear canal in the region of 2 to 5 kHz. This is not all; a diffraction effect increases the sensitivity of the ear even more. For sound arriving face on, diffraction of sound around the head results in further amplification of sound pressure at the eardrum over and above that resulting from the pipe effect as shown by the dotted line B in Fig. 2-3. The two effects combine to give a 20-dB peak to the sensitivity of the ear at midband frequencies.

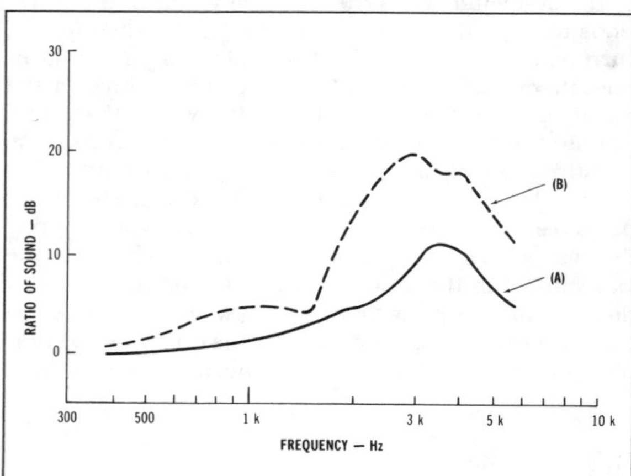

Figure 2-3 Acoustical amplification of eardrum sound pressure by two methods.

2.2.3 Middle Ear

The middle ear is an outstanding example of impedance matching in nature. Sound is brought to the ear canal and the eardrum by an air medium. The efficient transduction of the mechanical movement of the eardrum in air to that of the oval window working against the fluid of the cochlea requires careful design and adjustment of all parameters. Fig. 2-4 indicates how it is done in the middle ear. The eardrum, acting as an acoustic suspension system, works against the compliance of the air trapped in the middle ear. The eustachian tube is open enough to equalize the air pressure on both sides of the diaphragm, but not enough to destroy this compliance. At the other end of the ossicular system is the oval window pushing against the fluid of the inner ear. Specific acoustic impedance is proportional to the density of the medium. The impedance of water is almost 3600 times that of air; the impedance of the cochlear fluid is somewhat lower because the fluid can bulge out the membrane of the round window, yet it is high enough compared to air to require considerable matching. This transformation is accomplished by the ratio of eardrum area to oval window area, $80\ mm^2/3\ mm^2 = 27$, and the lever action of the ossicles, which ranges from 1.3 to 3:1. This gives an increase in mechanical force of from about 35 to 80. The pressure ratio required to match impedance is $\sqrt{3600} = 60$, which falls about midway in the 35 to 80 range. The mechanics of the middle ear accomplish the required impedance matching as evidenced by our ability to hear sounds that move the diaphragm a distance of less than one-tenth the diameter of a hydrogen molecule!

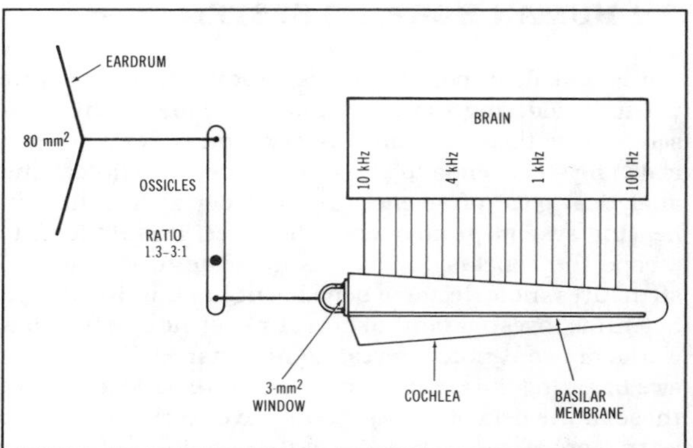

Figure 2-4 The mechanical system of the middle ear.

2.2.4 Inner Ear

The *cochlea* is the mechanical-to-electrical transducer and the frequency-selective analyzer part of our hearing system, sending coded nerve impulses to the brain. This is represented crudely in Fig. 2-4. To understand what happens in the cochlea, we must know something of its structure. A rough sketch of the cross section of the cochlea is shown in Fig. 2-5. The cochlea, throughout its length (some 35 mm if stretched out straight), is divided into three separate compartments by Reissner's membrane

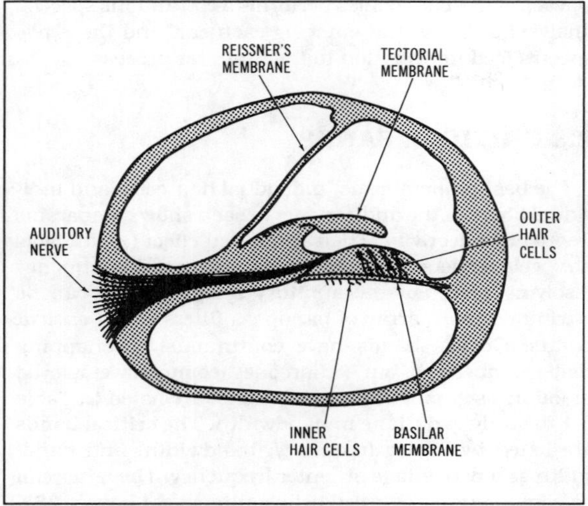

Figure 2-5 Cross-sectional sketch of the cochlea.

and the basilar membrane. The basilar membrane supports the organ of Corti, which contains the hair cells that convert the relative motion between the basilar membrane and the tectorial membrane into nerve pulses to the auditory nerve. There are actually two types of hair cells, but their functions are not yet well understood. There are about 25,000 hair cells on the basilar membrane.

Traveling waves are set up in the fluid of the cochlea by the motion of the oval window. There is a position along the basilar membrane of maximum hair cell excitation for each frequency. The end of the membrane nearest the oval window shows the greatest amplitude (resonates?) at high frequencies; the far end shows the greatest amplitude at low frequencies, as indicated in Fig. 2-4. The fact that the basilar membrane is narrower at the oval window end (0.04 mm) and wider at the apex (0.5 mm) is undoubtedly related to the frequency placement. The traveling-wave phenomenon is illustrated in Fig. 2-6. At A the exaggerated amplitude of the basilar membrane is shown for a 200-Hz wave traveling from left to right. The same wave 1.25 ms later is shown at B. These traveling 200-Hz waves all fall within envelope C of Fig. 2-6. The speed of the waves is indicated by the dis-

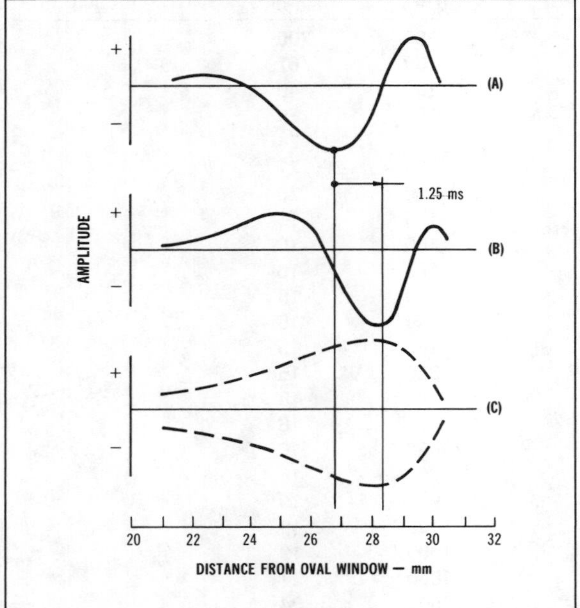

Figure 2-6 A traveling sound wave on the basilar membrane of the inner ear. *(After von Bekesy, Reference 1.)*

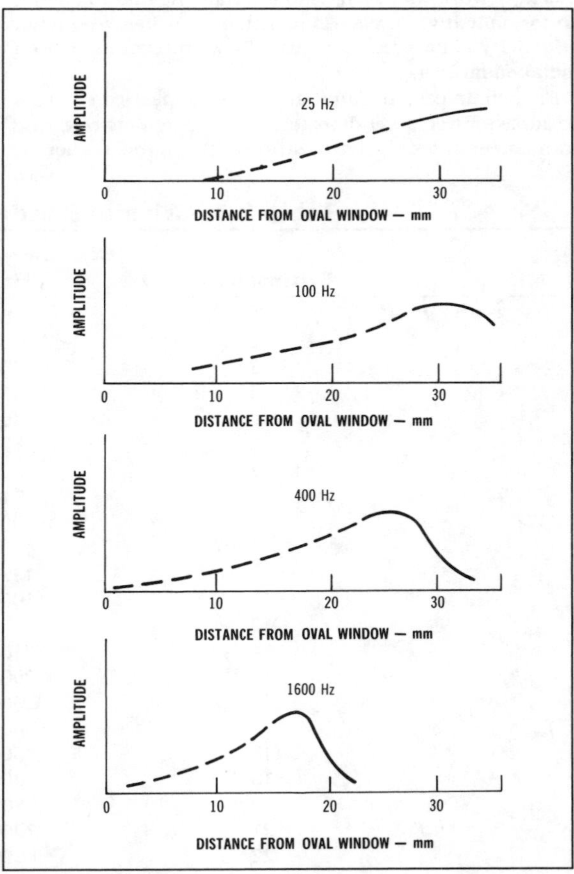

Figure 2-7 An illustration of the "place theory" of human hearing. The hair cells on the basilar membrane "resonate" at different frequencies. *(After von Bekesy, Reference 1.)*

tance the negative peak travels (from 27 to 28.5 mm) in 1.25 ms. This turns out to be 1.5 mm/1.25 ms = 1.2 mm/ms, which is 1.2 m/s or about 1/275 of the speed of sound in air. As sound travels about 331 m/s in air and about 1500 m/s in water, we see that a speed of 1.2 m/s along the basilar membrane is very slow indeed and, to complicate matters, varies with frequency.

Envelopes corresponding to Fig. 2-6 for other frequencies are shown in Fig. 2-7—the higher the frequency the closer to the oval window. This represents the so-called "place theory" of pitch perception, the position of maximum vibration of the basilar membrane corresponding to the perceived pitch of pure tones. The place theory was not well accepted because the low-Q, broad-tuning curves did not agree with sharper human perception found in psychoacoustical experiments. The basilar membrane frequency selectivity has since been demonstrated to be much sharper by Rhode, who was able to work at lower sound levels with live animals.[2] Because Bekesy's work was with dead animals, he had to employ abnormally high levels. As mentioned earlier, frequency selectivity is lowered substantially within minutes after metabolism ceases.[3]

Each hair cell, in familiar terms, appears to have a bandpass filter, level detector, smoothing network, and transducer microminiaturization of the highest order, as Davis put it.[4] The cochlea performs a continuous spectral analysis of the sound entering each ear, and these two spectra feed information to the brain for processing.

2.3 CRITICAL BANDS

The basilar membrane, individual hair cells, and individual fibers of the auditory nerve each show comparable frequency selectivity. Their combined effect (just how is not well understood) results in an overall frequency resolving power of the auditory system which can be attributed to an array of bandpass filters called *critical bands*. Critical bands have continuously overlapping center frequencies, but certain ones (commonly employed in loudness summation calculations) are listed in Table 2-1 to study variations in bandwidth. The critical bands are listed by center frequency, bandwidth, and bandwidth as a percentage of center frequency. The latter can be compared to one-third-octave filters that have a 23% bandwidth. In Fig. 2-8 a plot of the critical bandwidths is compared to common constant percentage filter bandwidths—one-sixth octave (11.6%), one-third octave (23.2%), one-half octave (34.8%), and one octave (70.7%). The fact that the one-third-octave bandwidths follow the critical bandwidth reasonably well explains the popular-

Table 2-1. Critical Bandwidths of the Human Ear*

Critical Band	Center Frequency (Hz)	Bandwidth (Hz)	Bandwidth %
1	50	100	200
2	150	100	67
3	250	100	40
4	350	100	29
5	450	110	24
6	570	120	21
7	700	140	20
8	840	150	18
9	1000	160	16
10	1170	190	16
11	1370	210	15
12	1600	240	15
13	1850	280	15
14	2150	320	15
15	2500	380	15
16	2900	450	16
17	3400	550	16
18	4000	700	18
19	4800	900	19
20	5800	1100	19
21	7000	1300	19
22	8500	1800	21
23	10500	2500	24
24	13500	3500	26

*Source References 1 and 5.

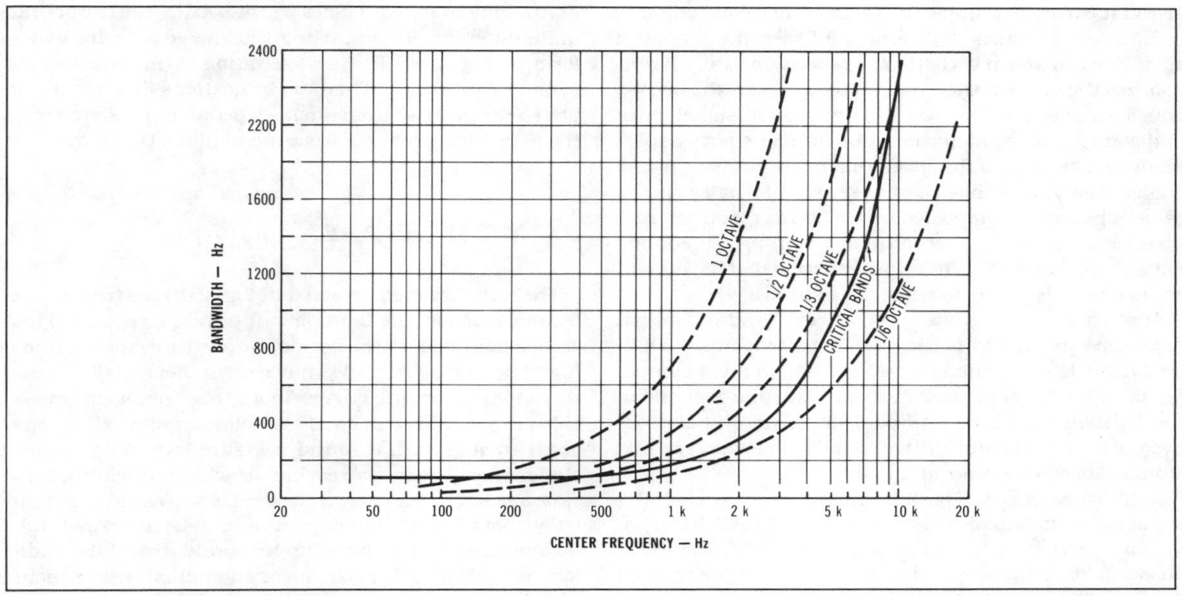

Figure 2-8 A plot of the critical bandwidths of the human ear listed in Table 2-1 compared to constant percentage bandwidth of filter sets commonly used in acoustical measurements. The one-third octave filters follow the critical bands closer than the others.

ity of one-third-octave filters in acoustical measurements, especially those ultimately related to human hearing.

Critical bands are closely related to masking phenomena. Everyone knows that a loud sound can "drown out" a weaker sound. This is one aspect of the complicated field of masking. The critical band can be defined as that range of continuous sound having sound power equal to a just audible tone. Let us enlarge upon that rather opaque statement. In searching for a definition of critical band, let us listen to a wideband noise with a pure tone mixed in. When the tone is just audible in the presence of the noise, the sound power of the tone and the critical bandwidth of noise masking it are equal. The tone is said to have a bandwidth of 1 Hz. The critical bandwidth of noise we wish to evaluate has many 1-Hz bandwidths; the level of sound in each is called the *spectrum level.* A band 100-Hz wide is said to be made up of 100 1-Hz bandwidths. Its overall level would be 10 log 100 = 20 dB higher than the tone it is just masking, but its spectrum level would be equal to that of the tone. By working this line of reasoning backward, the bandwidth of continuous noise to just mask a tone at any desired frequency can be found. This was Fletcher's original procedure, which gives us a critical band by inference. Since then the concept has been confirmed by direct measures of the critical bandwidth by four different approaches.[5]

2.4 NONLINEARITY OF THE EAR

Because of the inherent nonlinearity of the ear, not all the sounds we hear come from the outside. If two tones are presented simultaneously to the ear, new sum and difference "sideband" tones are generated. Such combination tones are evidence of a nonlinearity in the system. The difference tones are much more audible than the sum tones.

The ear is not a highly linear system, even at low intensities. The origin of the nonlinearities is still a mystery but probably is traceable to molecular processes involved with metabolism. If the blood supply to the ear is cut off, the nonlinearities change.

2.5 IS THE EAR PHASE SENSITIVE?

Phase sensitivity is one hearing problem researchers, hi-fi enthusiasts, and audio engineers share, "Is the ear able to detect phase differences?" About the middle of the last century G. S. Ohm wrote, "aural perception depends only on the amplitude spectrum of a sound and is independent of the phase angles of the various components contained in the spectrum." Many apparent confirmations of Ohm's law of acoustics have later been traced to crude measuring techniques and equipment. Schroeder gives an extreme example in which Ohm's conclusion is invalid.[3] He (1) takes 100 seconds of speech, (2) applies a Fourier transform with a 100-s repetition rate, (3) randomizes the phase angles, and (4) then applies the inverse Fourier transform. The resulting processed signal looks and sounds like random noise, but it has a power spectrum equal to that of the speech signal. By shifting phase angles, the speech has been converted to noise. If the same experiment is repeated with a 50-ms repetition rate instead of 100 s, the speech quality coming out sounds natural, not like noise. The message here is that the human ear is phase deaf only to short-time spectra.

Another example given by Schroeder[3] and attributed to Mathes and Miller[6] is the AM-FM experiment. A 2000-Hz carrier is modulated by 100 Hz, which gives components at 1900, 2000, and 2100 Hz. The phase of one of the sidebands is then shifted 180°. Listening alternatively to the signals with and without the phase shift reveals a pronounced difference in quality.

Both waveforms of Fig. 2-9 represent one period of a waveform made up of 31 harmonics (100 to 3100 Hz) of the same amplitude.[3] In Fig. 2-9A all harmonics are in phase. In Fig. 2-9B phase angles from 0 to 180° are selected to control the peak factor. The two are to the same scale. At fundamental frequencies below 200 Hz, the two sound quite different. In fact, using the low peak factor waveform of Fig. 2-9B for the excitation, synthetic speech sounds less "buzzy." There are indications that monaural phase effects arise from phase-dependent interference of the distortion products from the nonlinearity of the ear.

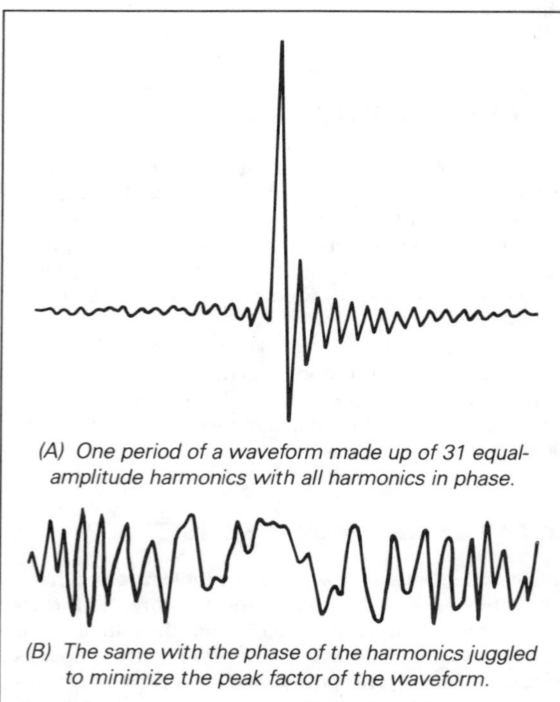

(A) One period of a waveform made up of 31 equal-amplitude harmonics with all harmonics in phase.

(B) The same with the phase of the harmonics juggled to minimize the peak factor of the waveform.

Figure 2-9 Both waveforms represent one period of a waveform made up of 31 harmonics of the same amplitude.

2.6 AUDITORY AREA

The auditory area depicted in Fig. 2-10 describes, in a technical sense, the limits of our aural perception. This area is bounded on the bottom by our threshold of hearing. The softest sounds that can be heard fall on the threshold of hearing curve. Above this line the air molecule movement is sufficient to elicit a response. If, at any given frequency, the sound pressure level is increased sufficiently, a point is reached at which a tickling sensation is felt in the ears. If the level is increased substantially above this threshold of feeling, it becomes painful. So much for the lower and upper boundaries of the auditory area. There are also frequency limitations below about 20 Hz and above about 16 kHz, limitations that (like the two thresholds) vary considerably from individual to individual. We are less concerned here about specific numbers than we are about principles. On the auditory area of Fig. 2-10, all the sounds of life are played out—low frequency or high, very soft or very intense.

Speech does not utilize the entire auditory area, as shown in Fig. 2-11. Its dynamic range and frequency range

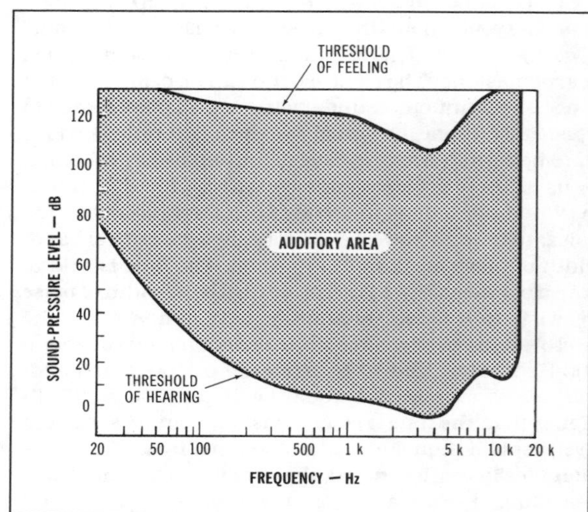

Figure 2-10 All sounds perceived by humans (at least those of average hearing) are technically defined by the auditory area. The low- and high-frequency limits of our hearing define the spectral boundaries.

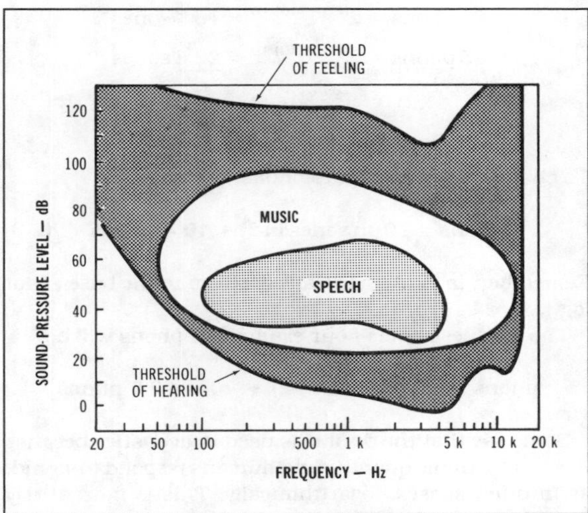

Figure 2-11 Music and speech do not utilize the entire auditory area available, but music uses far more than speech.

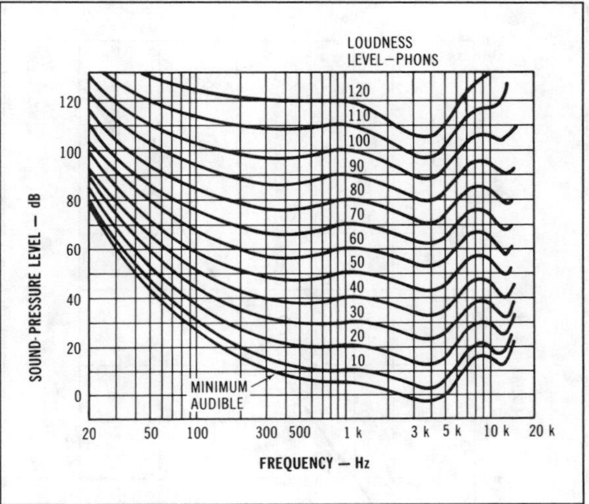

Figure 2-12 Equal loudness contours for pure tones in a frontal sound field applying the average human hearing as determined by Robinson and Dadson. The loudness level in phons corresponds to the sound pressure level at 1 kHz. *(Courtesy ISO Recommendation 226)*

are quite limited. Music has both a greater dynamic range than speech and a greater frequency range. But even music does not utilize the entire auditory area.

2.7 EQUAL LOUDNESS CONTOURS

The lower and upper limiting curves of both Figs. 2-10 and 2-11 are of greater interest to us than the auditory area characteristic of human hearing. Each curve is what is called an *equal loudness contour.* Early work (1933) in this field was done by Fletcher and Munson at Bell Labs, and, even today, these curves are often called the *Fletcher-Munson curves.* Later refinement came through the work of Robinson and Dadson, which has been recognized as an international standard.[7] The end product of Robinson and Dadson's work is shown in Fig. 2-12.

These equal loudness contours can be viewed as inverted frequency response curves of the ear. A 1-kHz tone of a 20-dB sound pressure level has a loudness level of 20 phons by definition. To give the same sensation of loudness at 100 Hz, the sound pressure level must be increased about 17 dB. To give the 20-phon loudness at 20 Hz requires a sound pressure level about 62 dB higher than at 1 kHz. This means that the sensitivity of the ear is much less at lower frequencies than at 1 kHz. From these curves it is evident that the frequency response of our ears is flatter at higher levels, which, unfortunately for their hearing, has encouraged many to listen to reproduced music at abnormally high levels. A study of this family of curves tells us why treble and bass frequencies seem to be missing or down in level when favorite recordings are played back at low levels.[8] The change of the frequency response of the ears with change in level has resulted in the development of the loudness control, which has had its full quota of critics and disappointed users. The impossibility of compensating for all the vagaries of loudspeaker sensitivity, gains of amplifiers and reproducer, and acoustical conditions of the listening room has limited the application of the loudness control to adjust response with change in level.

2.8 LOUDNESS VERSUS LOUDNESS LEVEL

Speaking technically, *loudness* is strictly a subjective term. It has no meaning unless humans are involved somewhere along the way. In Fig. 2-12 the term *loudness level* was defined as the sound pressure level at 1 kHz, but loudness level, in *phons,* has no direct relationship to the subjective term loudness. The only way a subjective term can be defined is by measurements on subjects and that is the way we define loudness in *sones.* By definition, a sone is the loudness of a 1-kHz tone at a loudness level of 40 phons, and this is the only point where phons and sones meet. Therefore, in Fig. 2-13 we have one point on the curve: 1 sone at a 40-dB sound pressure level (SPL), or 40 phons. Tests were made with many subjects, and they agreed fairly consistently when judging whether a 1-kHz tone was either twice as loud or half as loud as another. These points were found to be close to 10 dB up for twice as loud and 10 dB down for half as loud. Twice as loud as 40 phons is called 2 sones and half as loud is called

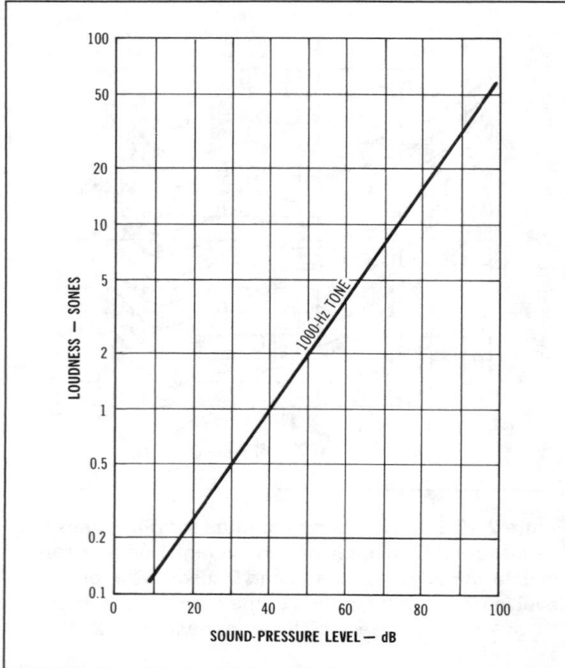

Figure 2-13 Graph showing the relation between sound pressure level and loudness in sones for a 1-kHz tone.

0.5 sone. This gives three points on a line for the 1-kHz tone.

Within the same critical band, two loudness levels in phons may be combined as follows[9]:

$$\text{combined loudness level (phons)} = 10 \log (10^{\text{phons}/10} + 10^{\text{phons}/10}) \qquad (2\text{-}1)$$

This combined level may then be changed to sones by

$$\text{loudness (sones)} = 2^{(\text{phons} - 40)/10} \qquad (2\text{-}2)$$

For example, combine a sound having a loudness level of 80 phons with a second sound of 85 phons:

$$\text{combined loudness level} = 10 \log (10^{80/10} + 10^{85/10}) = 86.2 \text{ phons}$$

Loudness of 86.2 phons $= 2^{(86.2 - 40)/10} = 24.6$ sones, which is a point on the line of Fig. 2-13.

If two sounds are in different critical bands, loudness in sones can be added directly. Let us take the same two loudness levels of 80 and 85 phons and assume they are separated in frequency by more than a critical bandwidth. First, change each to sones:

$$80 \text{ phons} = 2^{(80 - 40)/10} = 16 \text{ sones}$$

$$85 \text{ phons} = 2^{(85 - 40)/10} = \underline{22.6} \text{ sones}$$

$$\text{total} \quad 38.6 \text{ sones}$$

To change sones back into phons:

$$\text{phons} = 10 (\ln \text{sones}/\ln 2) + 40 = \text{phons} \qquad (2\text{-}3)$$

Remember, ln is the natural logarithm to the base ϵ, not $\log_{10}$.

The loudness level of our example in phons will be

$$\text{phons} = 10 (\ln 38.6/\ln 2) + 40 = 92.7 \text{ phons}$$

Some say that the decibel is used in acoustics because it is a logarithmic quantity and humans respond to sound, as in other senses, logarithmically. This is not entirely true. Loudness is approximately proportional to sound pressure raised to the 0.6 power.[10]

For simple tones the previous mathematical manipulations and the equal loudness contours of Fig. 2-12 suffice to obtain loudness level from sound level meter readings and then to sones. For complex sounds there are empirical approaches for determining loudness, notably those of Stevens and Zwicker. Steven's Mark VII method for doing this is described in reference 10.

2.9 LOUDNESS VERSUS BANDWIDTH

Broadband sounds, such as a rocket launching or a jet aircraft taking off, seem to be much louder than pure tones or narrow bands of noise of the same sound pressure level. In fact, increasing bandwidth does not increase loudness until the critical bandwidth is exceeded. Beyond that point multiple critical bands are excited, and the loudness increases markedly with increase in bandwidth. For this reason, the computation of loudness for a wideband sound must be based on spectral distribution of energy. Filters no narrower than critical bands are required and one-third-octave filters are commonly used.

2.10 LOUDNESS OF IMPULSES

Life is filled with impulse-type sounds: snaps, pops, crackles, bangs, bumps, and rattles. For impulses or tone bursts having a duration greater than 100 ms, loudness is independent of pulse width. The effect on loudness for pulses shorter than 200 ms is shown in Fig. 2-14. This curve shows how much higher the level of short pulses of noise and pure tones must be to sound as loud as continuous noise or pure tones. Pulses longer than 200 ms are perceived to be as loud as continuous noise or tones of the same level. For the shorter pulses, the pulse level must be increased to maintain the same loudness as for the longer pulses. Noise and tonal pulses are sim-

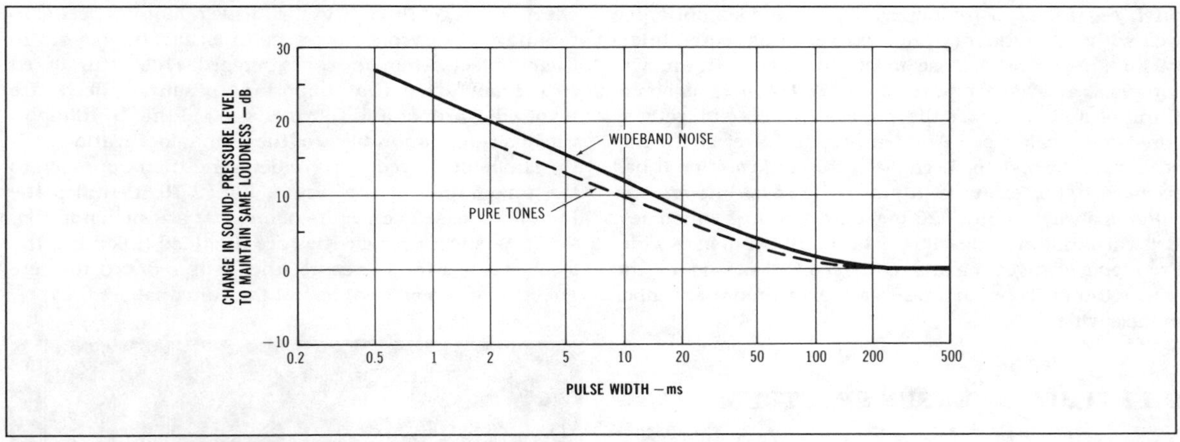

Figure 2-14 Short pulses of sound must be increased in level to sound as loud as longer pulses.

ilar in the level of increase required to maintain the same loudness. Fig. 2-14 is one more indication that the ear has a time constant of about 200 ms. This means that band levels should be measured with rms detectors having integration times of about 200 ms.

2.11 PITCH VERSUS FREQUENCY

Pitch has to do with the human, subjective sensation perceived when a tone of a given frequency is sounded. It would be so convenient if pitch and what a frequency counter indicates would coincide, but we are not put together this way. This requires learning a new term, the *mel*, as a unit of subjective pitch. The relationship between pitch in mels and frequency in hertz is shown in Fig. 2-15.[11] This curve has been obtained by asking subjects whether the pitch of one tone is half as great or twice as great as that of another or whether the pitch of a tone is midway between two other tones or whether two intervals between two pairs of tones are equal.

The broken line of Fig. 2-15 represents what would result if a semitone or octave represented an equal difference in

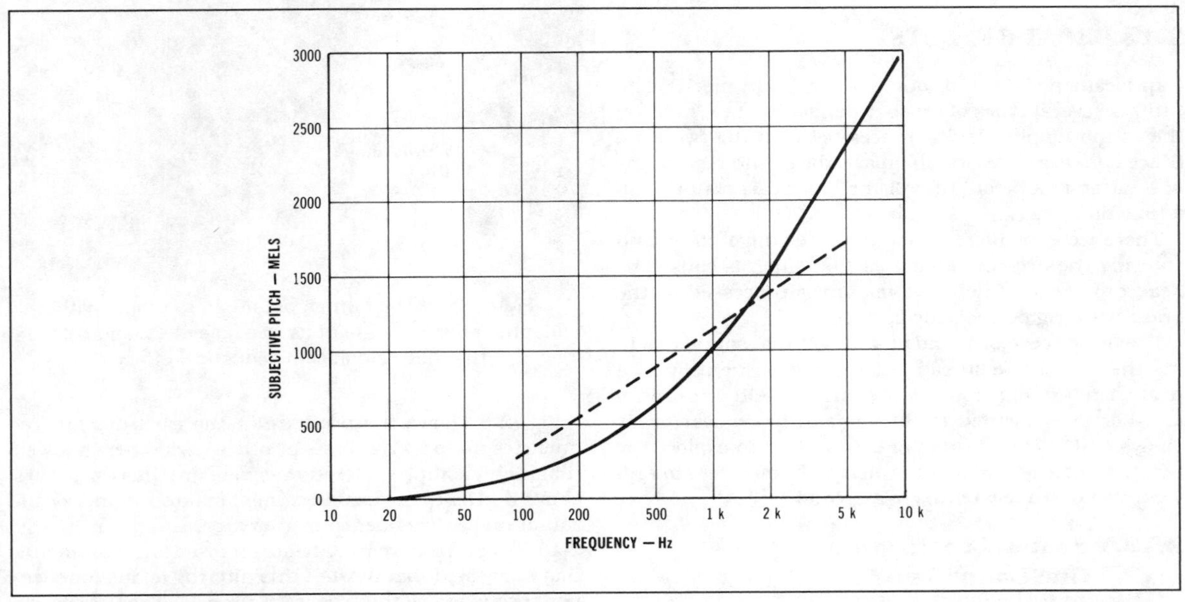

Figure 2-15 The relationship between frequency, a purely physical measurement, and pitch, a subjective reaction to the physical stimulus. *(After Reference 11.)*

pitch regardless of frequency. This line does not agree well with the frequency-pitch curve. Thus, equal intervals of subjective pitch seem not to agree with musical intervals, at least for pure tones. This comes as something of a shock. Isn't the musical scale a subjectively consistent scale also? Any temptation to reject the mel scale must be resisted because of the confirmation it has received.[12] For example, a just noticeable difference in pitch is always about 1/20 mel for different frequencies. Critical bands are a nearly constant number of mels wide. Frequency ranges having equal contributions to the intelligibility of speech are also a nearly constant number of mels wide.

2.12 TIMBRE VERSUS SPECTRUM

Spectra are measured with instruments: analyzers with constant percentage bandwidth (e.g., octave, one-third octave) or constant bandwidth. *Timbre* is another subjective term that must be carefully distinguished from the physical term *spectrum*. Loudness of sounds differs from level and varies with frequency. The perception of pitch of fundamental and harmonics or partials of a musical sound vary also with frequency. The way a signal sounds (its timbre) is related to its spectrum only in a complex manner interrelated by the factors considered in preceding sections. The timbre of a sound in a concert hall even varies with listener position because air absorbs some frequencies differently from others and because of the frequency-dependent absorption characteristics of room surfaces.

2.13 DELAY EFFECTS

In localizing a sound, our ear and brain mechanism utilizes several types of angle-dependent data. There are the sound amplitude differences between the two ears. Since our ears are 8 or 9 in. apart, the sound received by one ear arrives before that of the other ear, resulting in a time difference.

There are also differences in the spectrum of the sound entering the two ear canals, part of which is caused by head diffraction. Such information is processed by the brain, yielding perceptions of direction.

The finite speed of sound guarantees that sound reaching the ear will be spread out in time, principally as a result of reflections from nearby surfaces. All sorts of cues are thereby presented to the ear and brain system for analysis. It is the purpose of this section to explore the response of the ear to time delays from a few microseconds up to a few tenths of a second.

2.13.1 Spatial Localization: One Ear or Two?

Instead of dwelling on the long history of the question of whether localizing sounds is a monaural or binaural effect, let us get directly to the answer. Many experimenters have observed an increase in localization errors in their subjects when one ear is plugged. This naturally led to the suspicion that important binaural effects are involved. Gardner and Gardner showed that by filling in various ridges and valleys of the pinna, localization ability can be destroyed.[13] To understand their approach to the topography of the pinna, Fig. 2-16 identifies the involved areas. The results of one test are shown in Fig. 2-17. As successive cavities are occluded (filled in), the localization error increases until it is reduced to mere guessing when all cavities but the ear canal are filled.

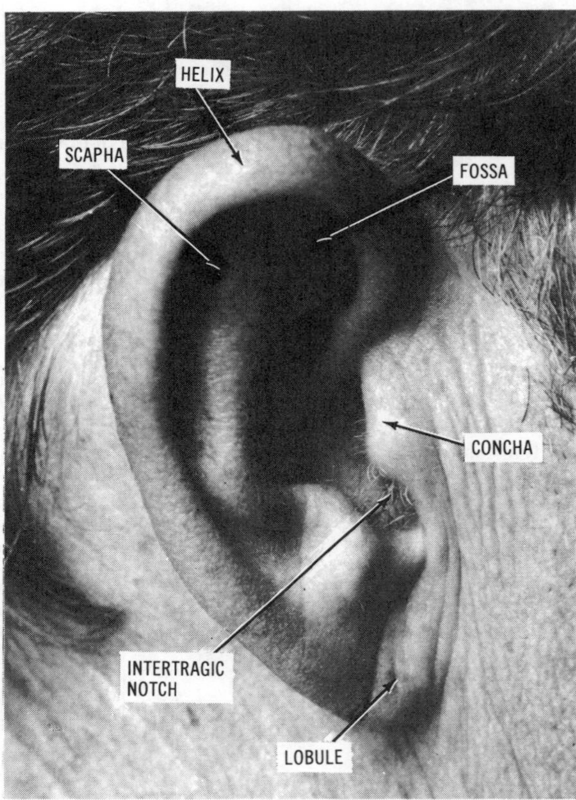

Figure 2-16 The human outer ear, or pinna, with identification of some of its folds, cavities, and ridges that have significant acoustical effect.

Fig. 2-3 shows the pressure at the eardrum for frequencies up to 5 kHz. Tests by other researchers showed that highly complex, direction-dependent filtering occurs above 5 kHz. Shaw explored this area and found localization angle dependence in this area, as shown in Fig. 2-18.[14] The next year Batteau reported measurements that suggested that most of this filtering is due to reflections occurring off the folds of the pinna.[15] The time delays involved range from 10 to 300 μs. These experiments demonstrate that the pinna is probably involved in local-

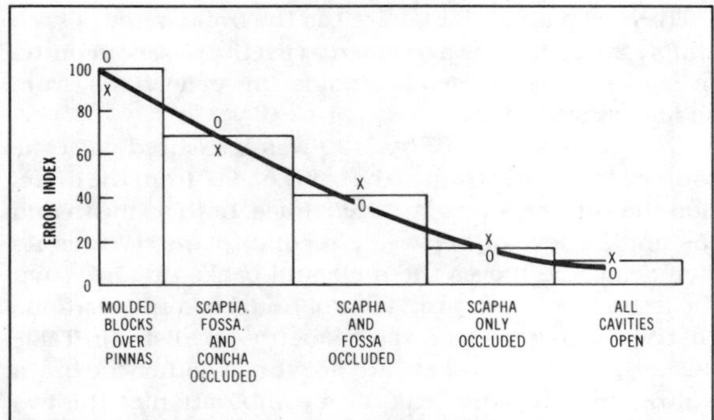

Figure 2-17 When the cavities of the pinna (outer ear) are occluded (filled in, or blocked) the ability of the blindfolded subjects to localize a wideband random noise source in the horizontal planes in front of them is affected. *(After Reference 13.)*

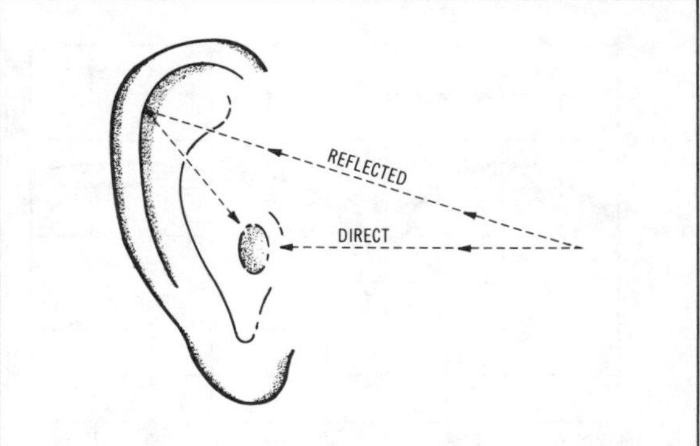

Figure 2-19 The comb-filter effect resulting from acoustical superposition of direct sound and the same sound reflected from the pinna largely determines the response of the sound entering the ear canal.

ization of sounds, that the pinna gives direction-dependent filtering action, and that sounds above 7 kHz are necessary for accurate localization. This leads to the work of Hebrank and Wright, who demonstrated that localizing with one ear was somewhat poorer at first because it was "unnatural."[16] However, subjects were readily trained to localize with one ear as accurately as with two. This is further evidence to support the theory that reflections off the bumps, ridges, and cavities of the pinna provide cues, even to a single ear, that enable the ear system to determine direction to a sound source.

Fig. 2-19 illustrates how a direct wave and the wave reflected from one of the convolutions of the ear combine acoustically at the entrance to the ear canal. This is the classic comb filter situation discussed in Section 1.13. Sound arriving from different azimuth and vertical angles produces widely differing pinna response shapes, giving the ear and brain mechanism cues for determining the location of a sound source. With time delays of 10 to 300 μs and ears with dimensions that are relatively small, the first null occurs at 1/(2t), where t is the delay between direct and reflected components. For a 10-μs delay the frequency of the first null is

$$1/(2 \times 10 \times 10^{-6}) = 50 \text{ kHz}$$

and a 300-μs delay places the first null at

$$1/(2 \times 300 \times 10^{-6}) = 1.67 \text{ kHz}$$

Both are extremes, and 50 kHz is well out of the range of the ear.

In her paper[17] Rodgers gives many actual measurements made with Heyser's time-delay spectrometry techniques.[18] A pinna response measured at the entrance to the ear canal with sound entering the ear directly from the side is shown in Fig. 2-20. A pronounced dip occurs at 8.2 kHz. This means that the delay that gave rise to it had a value of

$$t = 1/(2 \times 8200) = 61 \ \mu\text{s}$$

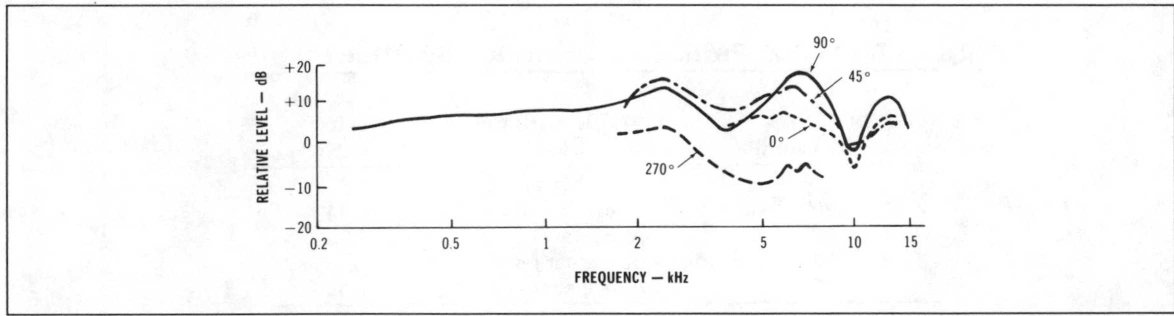

Figure 2-18 Localization-angle dependence of left eardrum sound pressure for 0° (straight ahead of the subject), 45° and 90° to the left of the observer and 90° to the right of the observer. *(After Reference 14.)*

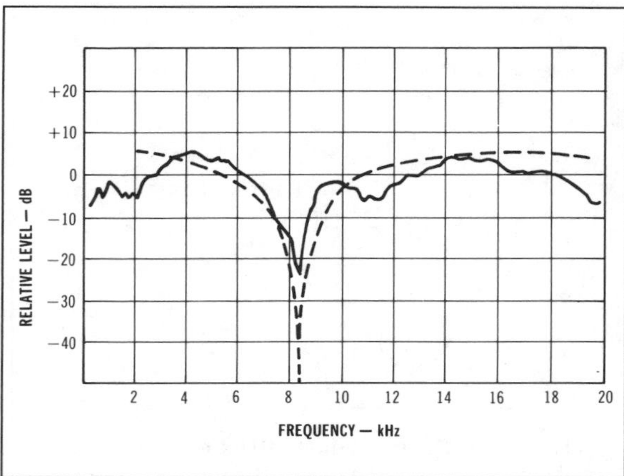

Figure 2-20 The heavy line represents a TDS (time-delay spectrometry) response of sound arriving at the ear canal from a source at ear level and 90° from the direction the subject is facing. The broken line is the calculated comb-filter response for a 61-μs delay. *(After Reference 17.)*

This corresponds to a difference in path length of

$$(1130 \text{ ft/s} \times 61 \times 10^{-6} \text{ s}) = 0.0689 \text{ ft}$$

or 0.83 in., which means the reflection may have come from the helix of the ear or possibly the scapha.

To see how the rest of the observed pinna response fits the usual comb filter shape, the broken line was computed from

$$L_c = \sqrt{(1 + 2\pi ft)^2 + (\sin 2\pi ft)^2}$$

where,

f is the frequency in hertz,
t is the delay in seconds,
L_c is the combined level,
$2\pi ft$ is in radians.

The level plotted in Fig. 2-20 as the broken line is then simply 20 log L_c. The agreement with the observed pinna response is fairly good considering reflections from shoulders and so on.

The 8.2-kHz null of Fig. 2-20 was measured with the source aimed directly into the ear (i.e., 90° from the direction the subject is facing). Each angle, both azimuth and the angle above or below the median plane, creates its own delay and moves the nulls and peaks up and down the frequency spectrum. A few of Rodgers' null positions observed with time-delay spectrometry[17] are listed in Table 2-2, although researchers are not sure whether the brain utilizes the null, the peak, or a combination of the two in its processing.

2.13.2 Fusion Zone

We have seen that delays up to a few hundred microseconds are utilized as localization cues to the ear-brain mechanism. For delays longer than this, we enter another psychoacoustic never-never land that is as amazing as that for very short delays. It is possible to trace seminal work in this area as far back as Joseph Henry, but to Helmut Haas[19] in Germany and Hans Wallach et al.[20] in this country must go credit for developing an understanding of the effect of delayed sound to a level of practical application. The name *Haas effect* has become well established.

Haas considered the simplest sound field—a single echo and its effect on speech. We are interested in determining the conditions under which a reflection is perceived and under what conditions the reflection is masked by the direct sound. In addition, we are interested in learning when a reflection is perceived as a discrete, bothersome echo. Haas's work is summed up in Fig. 2-21. The level of the direct component was decreased until it was the same loudness as the delayed component. This was done for various delays, yielding the curve of Fig. 2-21. Within the range of delays shown, it was found that the reflection must be about 10 dB higher than the direct sound before it was perceived as a reflection! The ear seems to "clamp" onto the first sound arriving so persistently that the "echo"

Table 2-2. Pinna Response Null Positions*

Azimuth Angle†	Angle with Ear Level	First Null Position, kHz
90°	15° above ear level	11
90°	At ear level	8.2
90°	Below ear level	6 to 7
45°	Above ear level	10

*From Rodgers.[17]

†Subject's nose points to 0°.

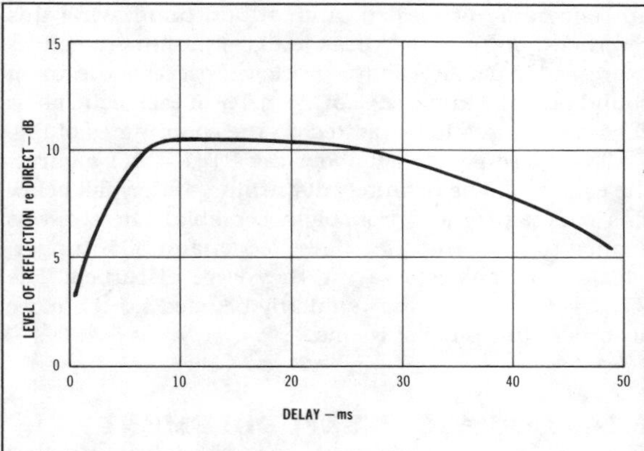

Figure 2-21 The classic Haas effect fusion zone curve.

had to be 20 dB (about fourfold in sound pressure level) higher before it could overpower the "clamping" effect. This effect rises fast in the first 5 ms of delay and persists to about 30 ms, after which it gradually disappears and echoes are perceived. Between 30 and 50 ms is a transition zone. The region below 30 ms is herein called the *fusion zone*. Wallach's term, the *precedence effect*, resulted from his observation that sounds from a different direction following the first (direct) sound gave the impression that the sound came from the direction of the first one. This is Cremer's "law of the first wavefront," which explains how the ear is able to localize sound in a reverberant space. Reflected energy returned to the auditor within the following 30-ms time period is integrated along with the direct energy, giving an impression of a louder, fuller sound. Reflections normally are of lower level than the direct energy because of the greater distance traveled and energy lost at the reflecting surface(s). However, in sound reinforcement situations a purposely delayed and amplified signal is usually much louder than the direct.

2.13.3 Extension of the Fusion Zone

Much of the early experimental work was done with a single echo. What happens if there is a succession of echoes? Fortunately, an additional reflection does not always set up its own new situation; instead, it extends the fusion zone already set up. If all the reflections arrive from the same direction, the situation prevails that is illustrated in Fig. 2-22 for one-, two-, three-, or four-spaced reflections. Fig. 2-22 is based on the work of Seraphim[21] and adapted to the Haas curve of Fig. 2-21. The single reflection R_1 gives us curve 1, which is a repetition of Haas's curve of Fig. 2-21.

If a second reflection R_2 follows R_1, the fusion zone is extended to curve 2. If a third reflection R_3 follows on the heels of R_1 and R_2, the cumulative effect of the three sequential reflections extends the fusion zone to curve 3. Four reflections, adequately spaced, extend the fusion zone to curve 4. It must be emphasized that these results were obtained with speech and that all these reflections are from the front. If the reflections arrive from different directions, the threshold curves tend to jump back to the original curve for a single reflection. In the Live End–Dead End™* control room, reflection management is essential. Some reflections come from the rear; some, from the sides; some, from the adjustments being made to extend the fusion zone to avoid the jump-back tendency.

2.13.4 Echoes

As reflection delays are increased progressively in the 50- to 100-ms region, the reflection is perceived more and more as a discrete echo. Echoes, like reverberation, can be considered a form of noise, acceptable, perhaps, on a Swiss Alp but not in an auditorium or concert hall. Their

*Live End–Dead End is a trademark of Synergetic Audio Concepts.

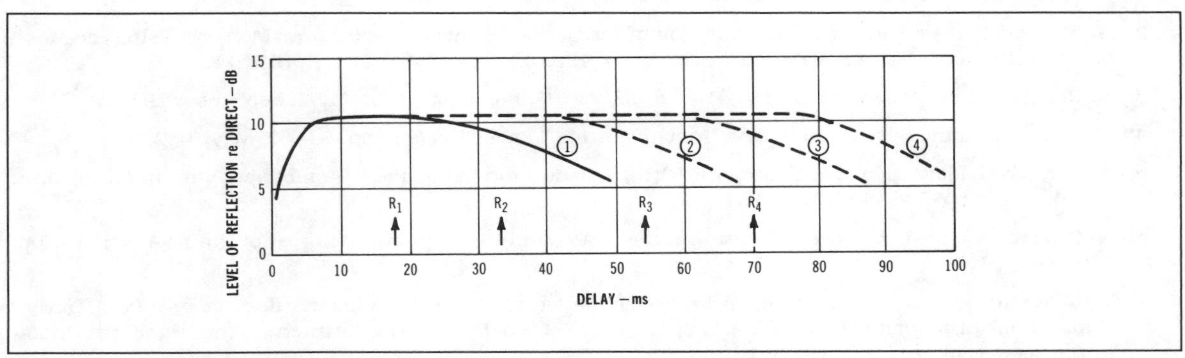

Figure 2-22 Reflections spaced properly can extend the fusion zone materially. *(After Reference 21.)*

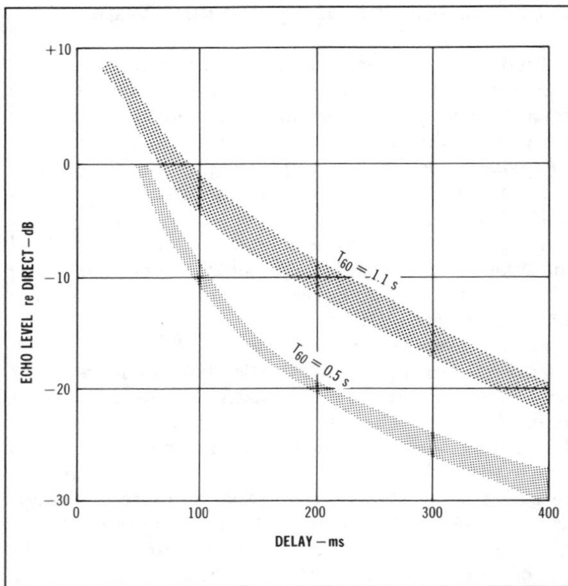

Figure 2-23 The Haas fusion zone of Fig. 2-21 is a detailed picture of the first 50 ms of this graph, which is an extension beyond the fusion zone into the region of discrete echoes. *(After References 22 and 23.)*

interference with speech and music are generally well known.

Some results of important psychoacoustical experiments in Australia are shown in Fig. 2-23[22, 23]. Basically, these are similar to the Haas fusion zone curve of Fig. 2-21 but are carried well into the discrete echo region. Let us first consider the shaded curve of Fig. 2-23 measured under conditions of 1.1-s reverberation time. First, an echogram is recorded in an auditorium having this reverberation time. The peak levels of prominent echoes expressed in decibels above or below the level of the direct sound plus the knowledge of the delay of each echo allow echo-level points to be plotted on the coordinates of Fig. 2-23. If these points fall above the RT_{60} = 1.1-s curve, the echoes will be definitely disturbing. If they fall below this curve, they are probably acceptable. The curve is shaded to represent 20% (lower edge) and 50% (upper-edge) of the subjects saying they were disturbed. The RT_{60} = 0.5-s curve may similarly be used for the more absorbent and smaller rooms.

2.14 ACOUSTICAL BEFUDDLEMENT

In 1957 Leo Beranek wrote an editorial in *Noise Control* magazine in which he succinctly described the dilemma in which audio engineers today find themselves in regard to the subject of acoustics. A whole new vocabulary rains down on our heads: *intensity, decibel, power level, sound pressure level, sound level, sone, loudness, phon, loudness level, mel, pitch, frequency, sabin, mode, microbar, spectrum, octave, dynes per square centimeter, reverberation time, wavefront, Huygen's principle, newtons per square meter.* Much of this proliferation of terms is inherent in the nature of acoustics, which is the need to distinguish carefully between meter readings and subjective reactions. Another reason is that sound is not one dimensional. To describe a sound we must specify its intensity or level, its time pattern, and its frequency composition. Another confusing problem is purely semantic. There are more than 18 different ways to use the decibel, each requiring proper qualification for accurate communication. We can only conclude that each of us should recognize the inherent problem and make our communication to each other and the public as crystal clear as the subject will allow.

REFERENCES

1. G. von Bekesy, *Experiments in Hearing,* New York: McGraw-Hill, 1960.

2. W. S. Rhode, "Observations on the Vibration of the Basilar Membrane in Squirrel Monkeys Using the Mossbauer Technique," *Journal of the ASA,* vol. 49, no. 4, part 2, pp. 1218–1231, April 1971.

3. M. R. Schroeder, "Models of Hearing," *Proc. IEEE,* vol. 63, no. 9, pp. 1332–1352, September 1975.

4. M. F. Davis, "Audio Specifications and Human Hearing," *Stereo Review,* pp. 48–52, May 1982.

5. E. Zwicker, G. Flottorp, and S. S. Stevens, "Critical Bandwidth in Loudness Summation," *Journal of the ASA,* vol. 29, no. 5, pp. 548–557, May 1957.

6. R. C. Mathes and R. L. Miller, "Phase Effects in Monaural Perception," *Journal of the ASA,* vol. 19, pp. 780–797, 1947.

7. D. W. Robinson and R. S. Dadson, "A Re-Determination of the Equal-Loudness Relations for Pure Tones," *British Journal of Applied Physics,* vol. 7, pp. 166–181, 1956. (Adopted by the International Standards Organization as Recommendation R-226.)

8. F. E. Toole, "Loudness—Applications and Implications to Audio," *dB The Sound Engineering Magazine*, Part I, vol. 7, no. 5, pp. 27–30, May 1973; Part II, vol. 7, no. 6, pp. 25–28, June 1973.

9. D. Davis and C. Davis, *Sound System Engineering*, Indianapolis: Howard W. Sams & Co., Inc., 1975.

10. A. P. G. Peterson and E. E. Gross, Jr., *Handbook of Noise Measurement*, Seventh Edition, General Radio, Inc., 1974.

11. S. S. Stevens and J. Volkman, "The Relation of Pitch to Frequency: A Revised Scale," *American Journal of Psychology*, vol. 53, pp. 329–353, 1940.

12. W. A. van Berjeijk, J. R. Pierce, and E. E. David, Jr., *Waves and the Ear*, New York: Anchor Books, Doubleday & Co., Inc., 1960.

13. M. B. Gardner and R. S. Gardner, "Problem of Localization in the Median Plane: Effect of Pinnae Cavity Occlusion," *Journal of the ASA*, vol. 53, no. 2, pp. 400–408, 1973.

14. E. A. G. Shaw, "Earcanal Pressure Generated by a Free Sound Field," *Journal of the ASA*, vol. 39, no. 3, pp. 465–470, 1966.

15. D. W. Batteau, "The Role of the Pinna In Human Localization," *Proceedings Royal Society*, B168 (1011), pp. 158–180.

16. J. Hebrank and D. Wright, "Are Two Ears Necessary for Localization of Sound Sources in the Median Plane?" *Journal of the ASA*, vol. 56, no. 3, pp. 935–938, 1974.

17. C. A. P. Rodgers, "Pinna Transformations and Sound Reproduction," *Journal of the AES*, vol. 29, no. 4, pp. 226–234, April 1981.

18. R. C. Heyser, "Acoustical Measurements by Time Delay Spectrometry," *Journal of the AES*, vol. 15, no. 4, pp. 370–381, April 1967.

19. H. Haas, "The Influence of a Single Echo on the Audibility of Speech," *Acustica*, vol. 1, no. 2, 1951, in German. (An English translation by Dr. Ingr. K. P. R. Ehrenberg appears in the *Journal of the AES*, vol. 20, no. 2, pp. 146–159, March 1972.)

20. H. Wallach, E. B. Newman, and M. R. Rosenzweig, "The Precedence Effect in Sound Localization," *Journal of the AES*, vol. 21, no. 10, pp. 817–826, December 1973.

21. H. P. Seraphim, "Über Die Währnehmbarkeit Mehrerer Ruckwurfe von Sprachschall," *Acustica*, vol. 11, pp. 80–91, 1961.

22. R. W. Muncey, A. F. B. Nickson, and P. Dubout, "The Acceptability of Speech and Music With a Single Artificial Echo," *Acustica*, vol. 3, pp. 168–173, 1953.

23. A. F. B. Nickson, R. W. Muncey, and P. Dubout, "The Acceptability of Artificial Echoes with Reverberent Speech and Music," *Acustica*, vol. 4, pp. 515–518 (original uncorrected pp. 447–450), 1954.

ADDITIONAL BIBLIOGRAPHY

1. J. T. Broch, *Application of B & K Equipment to Acoustic Noise Measurements*, Denmark: Bruel & Kjaer, February 1969.

2. F. M. Weiner, "On the Diffraction of a Progressive Wave by the Human Head," *Journal of the ASA*, vol. 19, no. 1, pp. 143–146, 1947.

3. F. M. Weiner and D. A. Ross, "Pressure Distribution in the Auditory Canal in a Progressive Sound Field," *Journal of the ASA*, vol. 18, no. 2, pp. 401–408, 1946.

CHAPTER **3**

Acoustics of Small Rooms

by F. Alton Everest

No sound system, no sound product, no acoustic environment can be designed by a calculator. Nor a computer, nor a cardboard sliderule, nor a Ouija board. There are no step-by-step instructions a technician can follow; that's like Isaac Newton going to the library and asking for a book on gravity. Design work can only be done by designers, each with his own hierarchy of priorities and criteria. His three most important tools are knowledge, experience, and good judgment.

Ted Uzzle [1]

In this chapter little can be contributed directly to the reader's basic judgment, although information upon which good judgment can be based is presented. Experience is also a very personal thing, but experience is gained only when individuals launch out on a project because they have confidence in their abilities to succeed. Judgment and experience both depend upon the apprehension of knowledge and an understanding of the many complex factors involved in the acoustics of enclosures. Gaining this knowledge and understanding is the primary purpose of this chapter.

Sound in free space with point sources and unimpeded spherical propagation is simple compared to the sound fields in rooms. The acoustics of enclosures is also complicated by the wide range of audible frequencies. The audible spectrum, if taken as the commonly accepted high-fidelity range of 20 Hz to 20 kHz, spans 10 octaves or 3 decades in frequency. Sound wavelength at 20 Hz is 56.5 ft and at 20,000 Hz is 0.0565 ft (about 5/8 in.), where the speed of sound is 1130 ft/s. At low audio frequencies, modal resonance effects dominate room acoustics; at higher audio frequencies, sound acts more or less like rays of light. Throughout the entire audible spectrum, however, room boundaries are effective in containing the sound energy and complicating our analysis. "Divide and conquer" has been a military axiom through the ages. In our desire to conquer the acoustical secrets of enclosures, we find we must divide the audible spectrum and approach the low-frequency portion differently than the high-frequency portion.

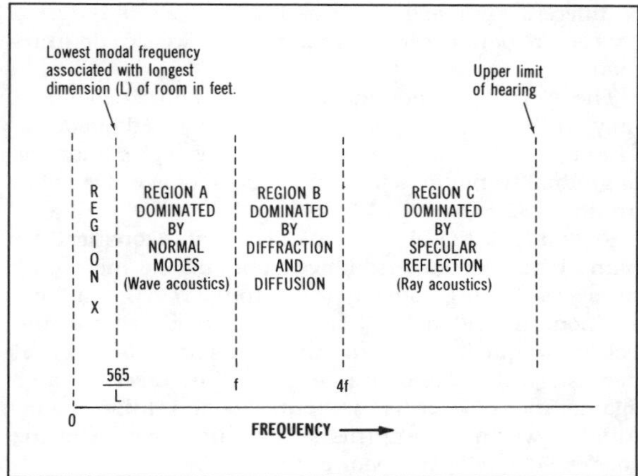

Figure 3-1 The audible frequency spectrum divided into four regions.

3.1 DIVIDING THE AUDIBLE SPECTRUM

It is convenient to consider the audible spectrum in four parts, as illustrated in Fig. 3-1: a low-frequency region A dominated by normal modes, an intermediate region B dominated by diffraction and diffusion, a region C dominated by specular (lightlike) reflection, and a region X where no modal effects can occur. Region A must be approached on the basis of *wave* acoustics, and in Region C *ray* acoustics is more appropriate. Region B in between is a transition region having its own special characteristics.

It is possible for us to compute for a specific room the frequencies bounding these three regions. For example, let us assume a studio 22 ft long, 18 ft wide, and 14 ft high with a reverberation time of 0.5 s. The lowest modal frequency is that associated with the length of the room, which acts like an organ pipe closed at both ends. It will have a pressure maximum at each end and a single null in the center of the room when the frequency is equal to the speed of sound divided by twice the length of the room or 1130/2L or 565/L. For this room the frequency is 565/22 = 26 Hz.

The boundary between region A and region B occurs at a frequency of f Hz, which may be estimated from the following empirical equation:[2]

$$f = 11250\sqrt{\frac{RT}{V}} \tag{3-1}$$

where,

RT is the reverberation time in seconds,

V is the volume of room in cubic feet.

For a reverberation time of RT = 0.5 s and a volume of V = (22 × 18 × 14) = 5544 ft³, the frequency f becomes

$$f = 11250\sqrt{\frac{0.5}{5554}}$$
$$= 107\,\text{Hz}$$

The boundary between region B and region C of Fig. 3-1 is 4f or (4 × 107) = 428 Hz.[2] The four regions of the room of our example are, therefore, bounded as follows:

Region X	0 to 26 Hz
Region A	26 to 107 Hz
Region B	107 to 428 Hz
Region C	428 to 20,000 Hz

A different approach to acoustical analysis is required for each region, except there is nothing we can do in region X.

The 26-Hz lower boundary is a solid figure dependent only on the length of the room and the speed of sound. The values of f and 4f are, however, only approximations of gradual transitions from one type of physical effect to another.

Region X of Fig. 3-1 is, in a sense, an acoustical no-man's-land. Modal resonances abound in increasing numbers in going from region A through B to C, but there are none in region X. This does not mean that sound below a frequency of 565/L cannot exist in a room, but it does suggest that such a sound will be discriminated against because it is without modal reinforcement. Another way of saying this is that the response of the room will be relatively poor in this region.

3.2 EFFECT OF ROOM SIZE

The effect of room size on acoustical quality is revealed in Fig. 3-2. Before discussing details of this figure, however, its shortcomings must be mentioned. The f frequency of Eq. 3-1 and the corresponding 4f frequency are shown in these curves for a reverberation time of 0.5 s, which has been taken for all room volumes even though "optimum" reverberation time normally increases with volume. Also, for the 565/L curve the longest dimension of the room is required. Not knowing the room proportions for the various room volumes, the cube root of the volume has been taken for L. This gives the length of a side of a cubical room, which is an acoustical monstrosity, as we shall see later. The result of these simplifications is that the 565/L curve is slightly higher than it should be, but it is satisfactory for the discussion of the principles.

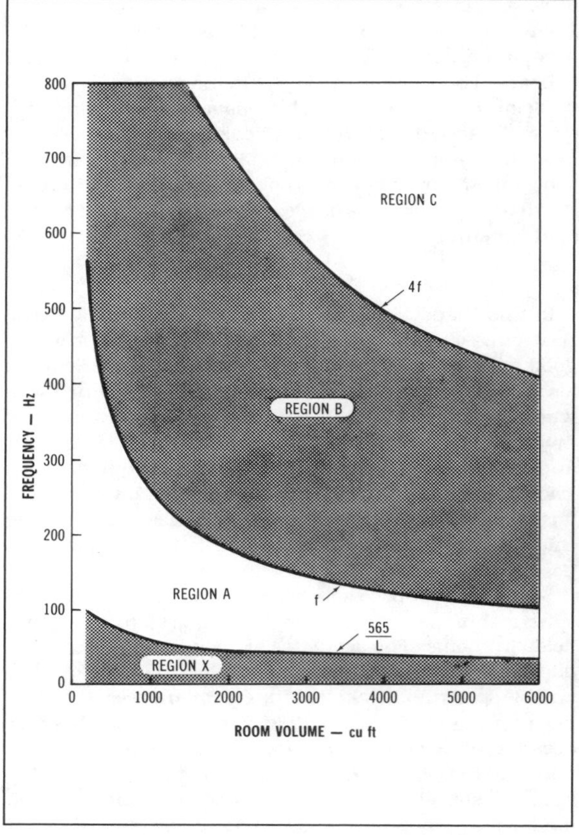

Figure 3-2 The location of the boundaries between the four regions of Fig. 3-1 are dependent upon reverberation time and room volume.

As previously mentioned, the 565/L frequency may be taken as the low-frequency limit of the response of the room. In Fig. 3-2 we note that for small rooms this frequency increases; hence, the smaller the room, the poorer its low-frequency response. For very small rooms intended for speech only, this, in itself, may not be too serious because only 10% of speech power lies below about 200 Hz. Read on for this is only part of the problem.

Region A of Fig. 3-2 increases as room size is reduced. This means that the smaller the room, the greater the portion of the audible spectrum dominated by modal resonances. It also means greater spacing of modal frequencies resulting in irregularity of room response and increasing colorations of sound.

Region B also increases with reduction of room size. Although the problems of diffraction and diffusion are quite different from those of modal resonances on region A, they are nonetheless problems. Region C is the favored area of high modal density and ray acoustics with resulting simplification of acoustical problems. As regions A and B increase, region C is pushed to higher audio frequencies so that more of the spectrum is beset with the difficult acoustical situations characterizing regions A and B.

3.3 REFLECTIONS FROM ROOM SURFACES

In open space (air-filled space, of course) sound travels unimpeded in all directions from a point source. If the source is brought close to a reflecting surface, sound reflected from that surface interacts with unreflected sound affecting the distribution of sound pressure in the field. The reflection can be considered to come from an image of the source on the opposite side of the reflecting surface and equidistant from it. This is the simple case: one source, one surface, and one image. If this reflecting surface considered is one wall of a room, the picture is immediately complicated. The source now has an image in five other surfaces sending energy back. Not only that, images of the images exist and have their effect, and so on. A physicist setting out to derive the mathematical expression for sound intensity from the source in the room at some other point in the room must consider the contributions from images, images of the images, images of the images of the images, and so on. This is a complex and difficult task, but it has been done. We, with heads bowed in gratitude and respect for such ability, humbly accept the end product of such endeavors. First, however, it is helpful to see just how reflecting surfaces can yield what acts like true resonance effects.

3.4 STANDING WAVES WITH TWO ISOLATED SURFACES

Let us consider a sound source S between the two isolated reflecting surfaces of Fig. 3-3 emitting a sinusoidal signal. The oscillator driving the source is slowly increased

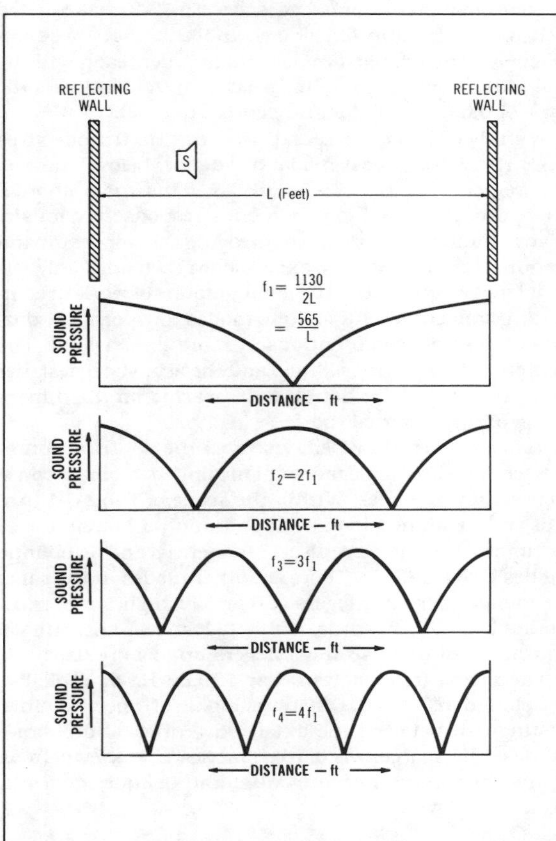

Figure 3-3 The simplest form of "room resonance" can be illustrated by two isolated, parallel, reflecting wall surfaces.

in frequency, starting at a very low frequency. When a frequency of $f_1 = 565/L$ is reached, a so-called *standing-wave* condition is set up as reflected waves traveling to the left and reflected waves traveling to the right come into such a relationship with transit time and the principle of superposition that they cancel each other midway between the reflecting walls. This is a real effect that can be demonstrated by measuring with a sound level meter the maximum pressures near the walls and a distinct null midway between the walls.

As frequency of the source is increased, the initial standing-wave condition is immediately lost, but at a frequency of $2f_1$ another standing wave appears. There are now two nulls and a pressure maximum midway between the walls as well as at the walls. Other standing waves can be set up by exciting the space between the walls at a theoretically infinite string of whole number multiples of f_1. These are called axial modes as they occur along the axis of the two parallel walls.

Notice that pressure maxima always occur at the reflecting surfaces. Particle velocity must be zero at the wall surface since tiny air particles are unable to move the solid wall. Wherever particle velocity is zero, pressure is at maximum level.

3.5 STANDING WAVES WITH SIX SURFACES

The two walls of Fig. 3-3 can be considered the north and south walls of a room. The effect of adding two more pairs of parallel walls to enclose the room is that of adding two more axial standing-wave systems along the east-west and vertical axes. Other resonance systems are also added by fully enclosing the space, but consideration of these must wait.

3.6 WAVE THEORY APPLIED TO ROOM ACOUSTICS

In 1896 Rayleigh showed that the air enclosed in a rectangular room has an infinite number of normal (natural, characteristic) modes of vibration. The frequencies at which these modes occur are given by the following equation:[3]

$$f = (c/2)\sqrt{(p/L)^2 + (q/W)^2 + (r/H)^2} \qquad (3\text{-}2)$$

where,

c is the speed of sound, about 1130 ft/s,
L is the length of the room in feet,
W is the width of the room in feet,
H is the height of the room in feet,
p, q, and r are the integers 0, 1, 2, 3, 4, and so on.

If we consider only the length of the room, q and r are zero, their terms drop out, and we are left with

$$f = (c/2)\sqrt{(1/L)^2}$$
$$= (c/2)(1/L)$$
$$= 1130/2L$$
$$= 565/L$$

which looks familiar because it is the f_1 frequency of Fig. 3-3. In other words, p = 1 gives us f_1, p = 2 gives us f_2, p = 3 gives us f_3, and so on. Eq. 3-2 covers the simple axial mode case, but it also presents us with the opportunity of studying forms of resonances other than the axial modes.

Eq. 3-2 is a three-dimensional statement based on the orientation of our room on the X-, Y-, and Z-axes, as shown in Fig. 3-4. The floor of the room is taken as the XY plane, and the height is along the Z-axis. To apply Eq. 3-2 in an orderly fashion, it is necessary to adhere to standard terminology. As stated, p, q, and r may take on values of zero or any whole number. The values of p, q, and r in the standard order are thus used to describe any mode. Remember that

p is associated with length L,
q is associated with width W,
r is associated with height H.

We can describe the four modes of Fig. 3-3 as 1,0,0; 2,0,0; 3,0,0; and 4,0,0. Any mode can be described by three digits. For example, 0,1,0 is the first-order width mode, and 0,0,2 is the second-order vertical mode of the room. Two zeros in a mode designation mean that it is an *axial* mode. One zero means that the mode involves two pairs of surfaces and is called a *tangential* mode. If there are no zeros in the mode designation, all three pairs of room surfaces are involved, and it is called an *oblique* mode.

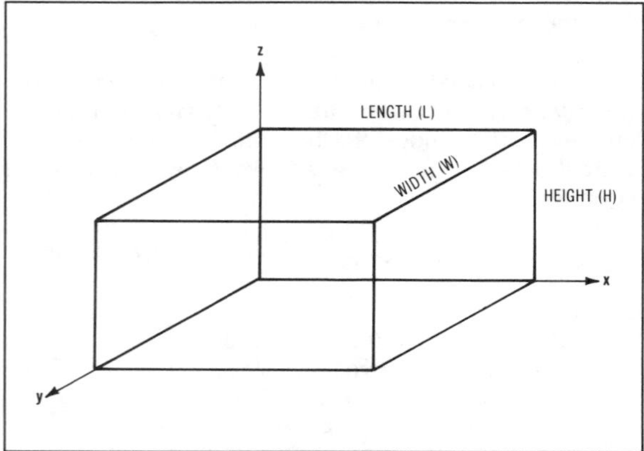

Figure 3-4 The floor of the rectangular room under study is taken to be in the XY plane and the height along the Z axis.

3.7 CALCULATING MODAL FREQUENCIES

It is an excellent exercise in mode appreciation to follow through in calculating the modal frequencies for a typical room. Control rooms of professional recording studios often have a heavy concrete outer shell to handle the low frequencies in a satisfactory manner and a lighter inner shell (essentially transparent to the low frequencies) to give the desired reflection pattern for the higher-frequency components. The room example chosen is a rectangular control room outer shell having the dimensions of 30 × 25 × 19.5 ft. Calling upon information to be considered later, these proportions are favorable for the distribution of modal frequencies for best room response. Feeding these values of L, W, and H and various values of p, q, and r into Eq. 3-2, the modal frequencies listed in Table 3-1 are obtained. To become familiar with these modal frequencies, doing some calculations by hand is good discipline and instruction, but carrying calculations out to values of p, q, and r of 0, 1, 2, 3, 4 employing a computer programmed to solve Eq. 3-2 makes good sense.* In the printout shown in Table 3-1, these frequencies are arranged in ascending order, each with its mode description (p,q,r) and an O, T, or A identifying the type of mode as oblique, tangential, or axial.

A study of Table 3-1 reveals that the 1,0,0 mode gives 18.8 Hz as the lowest modal frequency, below which is the region X of Figs. 3-1 and 3-2. This room should, therefore, give good low-frequency response for music. Many studio designers, acknowledging the important and dominant role played by axial modes, consider only the axial modes because of the great amount of work in computing tangential and oblique modes for, perhaps, dozens of possible combinations of room dimensions. The computer is changing all this, and the acoustical designer of the future will be rich in data bearing on the dimensions of the proposed room.

Table 3-1 certainly demonstrates the contribution of tangential and oblique modes in holding up room response between axial modes. Within the scope of Table 3-1 (p's, q's, and r's limited to 0, 1, 2, 3, 4), only 12 axial modes are found, but there are also 48 tangential and 64 oblique modes below 165 Hz. There are other modes in the same frequency range if integers of 5 or 6 or higher are incorporated. In other words, Table 3-1 shows an artificial thinning out because only integers up to 4 are used.

The modal frequencies below 129.68 Hz of Table 3-1 are plotted in Fig. 3-5. Different heights of "spectral" lines distinguish between the axial, tangential, and oblique modes. The sparceness of axial modes is very evident as is the contribution of tangential and oblique modes in filling in between them.

*I am indebted to David Wright of St. Paul, Minnesota, for the printout that is the basis of Table 3-1. His program computed the speed of sound for 70° (1127.42 ft/s), and this value was used instead of the round figure of 1130 ft/s used elsewhere.

Table 3-1. Computed Modal Frequencies for a Rectangular Room

Mode Number	Freq. (Hz)	Mode Description p, q, r	Type of Mode: Oblique	Tangential	Axial
001	18.79	1 0 0			A
002	22.54	0 1 0			A
003	28.90	0 0 1			A
004	29.35	1 1 0		T	
005	34.47	1 0 1		T	
006	36.66	0 1 1		T	
007	37.58	2 0 0			A
008	41.19	1 1 1	0		
009	43.82	2 1 0		T	
010	45.09	0 2 0			A
011	47.41	2 0 1		T	
012	48.85	1 2 0		T	
013	52.50	2 1 1	0		
014	53.56	0 2 1		T	
015	56.37	3 0 0			A
016	56.76	1 2 1	0		
017	57.81	0 0 2			A
018	58.70	2 2 0		T	
019	60.71	3 1 0		T	
020	60.79	1 0 2		T	
021	62.05	0 1 2		T	
022	63.35	3 0 1		T	
023	64.84	1 1 2	0		
024	65.43	2 2 1	0		
025	67.24	3 1 1	0		
026	67.64	0 3 0			A
027	68.95	2 0 2		T	
028	70.20	1 3 0		T	
029	72.19	3 2 0		T	
030	72.55	2 1 2	0		
031	73.32	0 2 2		T	
032	73.56	0 3 1		T	
033	75.16	4 0 0			A
034	75.69	1 2 2	0		
035	75.92	1 3 1	0		
036	77.38	2 3 0		T	
037	77.76	3 2 1	0		
038	78.47	4 1 0		T	
039	80.52	4 0 1		T	
040	80.74	3 0 2		T	
041	82.39	2 2 2	0		
042	82.60	2 3 1	0		
043	83.62	4 1 1	0		
044	83.83	3 1 2	0		
045	86.72	0 0 3			A
046	87.65	4 2 0		T	
047	88.05	3 3 0		T	
048	88.73	1 0 3		T	
049	88.98	0 3 2		T	
050	89.60	0 1 3		T	
051	90.19	0 4 0			A
052	90.94	1 3 2	0		
053	91.55	1 1 3	0		

(continued on next page)

Table 3-1cont. Computed Modal Frequencies for a Rectangular Room

Mode Number	Freq. (Hz)	Mode Description p, q, r	Type of Mode: Oblique	Tangential	Axial
054	92.13	1 4 0		T	
055	92.29	4 2 1	0		
056	92.48	3 2 2	0		
057	92.67	3 3 1	0		
058	94.51	2 0 3		T	
059	94.71	0 4 1		T	
060	94.82	4 0 2		T	
061	96.55	1 4 1	0		
062	96.59	2 3 2	0		
063	97.16	2 1 3	0		
064	97.47	4 1 2	0		
065	97.71	2 4 0		T	
066	97.74	0 2 3		T	
067	99.53	1 2 3	0		
068	101.11	4 3 0		T	
069	101.89	2 4 1	0		
070	103.43	3 0 3		T	
071	104.72	2 2 3	0		
072	105.00	4 2 2	0		
073	105.17	4 3 1	0		
074	105.33	3 3 2	0		
075	105.86	3 1 3	0		
076	106.36	3 4 0		T	
077	107.13	0 4 2		T	
078	108.76	1 4 2	0		
079	109.98	0 3 3		T	
080	110.21	3 4 1	0		
081	111.58	1 3 3	0		
082	112.83	3 2 3	0		
083	113.53	2 4 2	0		
084	114.76	4 0 3		T	
085	115.63	0 0 4			A
086	116.23	2 3 3	0		
087	116.48	4 3 2	0		
088	116.95	4 1 3	0		
089	117.15	1 0 4		T	
090	117.40	4 4 0		T	
091	117.81	0 1 4		T	
092	119.30	1 1 4	0		
093	120.91	4 4 1	0		
094	121.05	3 4 2	0		
095	121.58	2 0 4		T	
096	123.30	4 2 3	0		
097	123.59	3 3 3	0		
098	123.66	2 1 4	0		
099	124.11	0 2 4		T	
100	125.12	0 4 3		T	
101	125.53	1 2 4	0		
102	126.52	1 4 3	0		
103	128.64	3 0 4		T	
104	129.68	2 2 4	0		
105	130.60	3 1 4	0		
106	130.64	2 4 3	0		

Table 3-1—cont. Computed Modal Frequencies for a Rectangular Room

Mode Number	Freq. (Hz)	Mode Description p, q, r	Type of Mode Oblique	Tangential	Axial
107	130.87	4 4 2	0		
108	133.21	4 3 3	0		
109	133.96	0 3 4		T	
110	135.27	1 3 4	0		
111	136.31	3 2 4	0		
112	137.23	3 4 3	0		
113	137.91	4 0 4		T	
114	139.13	2 3 4	0		
115	139.74	4 1 4	0		
116	145.10	4 2 4	0		
117	145.34	3 3 4	0		
118	145.96	4 4 3	0		
119	146.64	0 4 4		T	
120	147.84	1 4 4	0		
121	151.38	2 4 4	0		
122	153.61	4 3 4	0		
123	157.11	3 4 4	0		
124	164.78	4 4 4	0		

*Length: 30 ft Width: 25 ft Height: 19.5 ft Sound Speed: 1127.42 ft/s

3.8 COMPARISON OF MODAL POTENCY

The relative importance of the three types of modes immediately comes to mind. It is easy to understand that axial modes have the greatest energy because minimum distances and reflections from only two surfaces are involved. Tangential modes, as mentioned previously, involve four surfaces, and oblique modes involve six surfaces of a rectangular room. For this reason, greater reflection losses are sustained and greater distances are traveled, both of which reduce the intensity of the modes. Morse and Bolt state from theoretical considerations that, for a given pressure amplitude, an axial wave has four times the energy of an oblique wave.[4] They also state that the energy factor is one-half for axial modes, one-fourth for tangential waves, and one-eighth for oblique waves. On an energy basis this means that, if we take the axial waves as 0 dB, the tangential waves are −3 dB and the oblique waves are −6 dB.

3.9 MODAL FREQUENCY DENSITY

The combined plot of Fig. 3-5 clearly shows that modes get closer together as frequency is increased. Between 20 and 50 Hz the average spacing is 2.7 Hz. A similar 30-Hz region from 60 to 90 Hz yields an average mode spacing of 0.91 Hz, and this is still in the low-frequency region. As frequency is increased, the number of modal frequencies are packed in so tightly that individual resonances may be neglected and a virtual continuum assumed. The number N of the normal modes below some particular frequency f is given by the following approximate expression (in metric units)[5, 6]:

$$N \approx [(4\pi V/3)(f/c)^3] + [(\pi S/4)(f/c)^2] + [(E/8)(f/c)] \qquad (3\text{-}3)$$

where,

N is the number of modal frequencies below frequency f,
f is the frequency below which the desired number of modes is found in hertz,
c is the speed of sound in meters per second,
V is the volume of the room in cubic meters,
S is the total surface area of the room in square meters,
E is the sum of the lengths of all edges of the room in meters = 4(L+W+H).

For the 30 × 25 × 19.5-ft room of Table 3-1 and Fig. 3-5, the number of modes below 100 Hz calculated from Eq. 3-3 turns out to be 68. Counting the modes in Table 3-1 yields 67, a good agreement. Computing the modes below 80 Hz yields 38, which is the exact count from Table 3-1. From Eq. 3-3 the number of modes below 1000 Hz is 26,900. Carrying p,q,r to 4 instead of stopping at 3 increases the mode count significantly, even to the lower frequencies. From the frequency of the 4,0,0 (33) upward, the integer 4 appears frequently. This tells us that the list of Table 3-1 is not complete and that carrying p,q,r

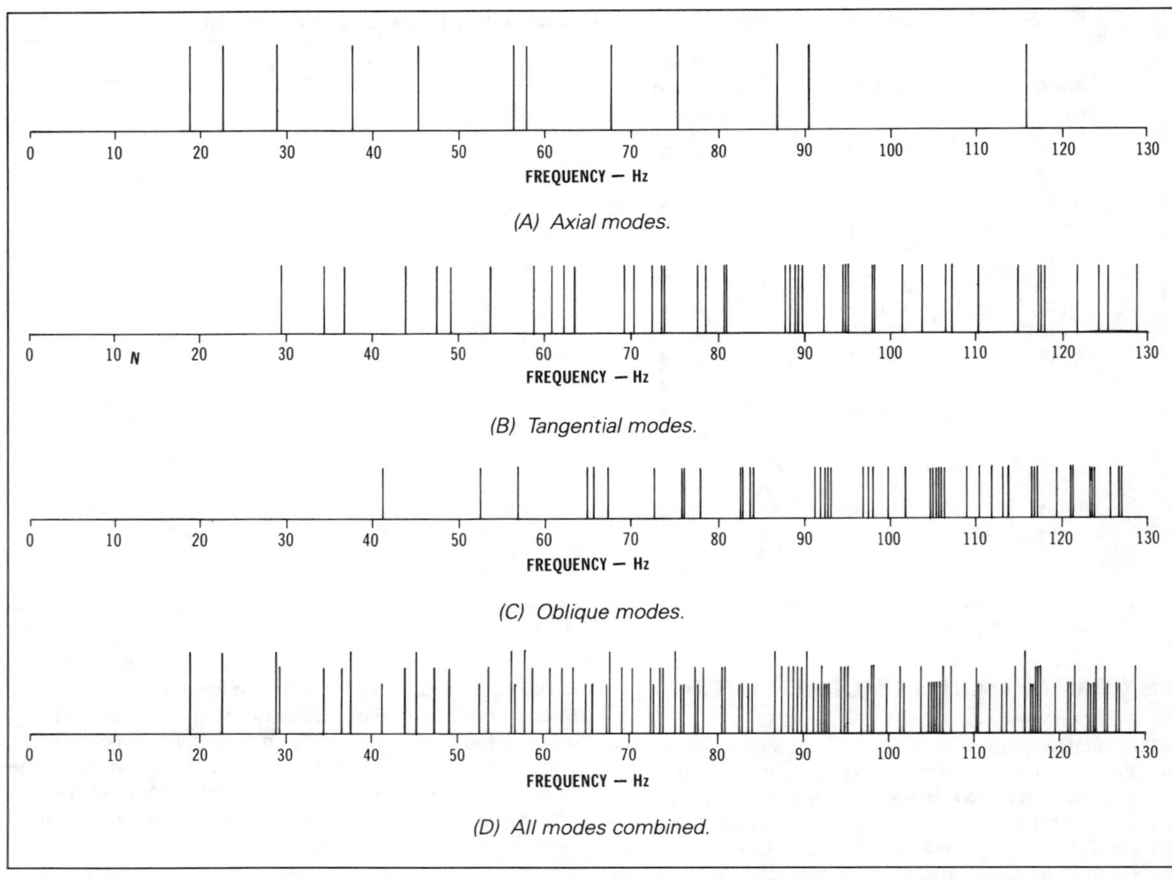

(A) Axial modes.

(B) Tangential modes.

(C) Oblique modes.

(D) All modes combined.

Figure 3-5 The axial, tangential, and oblique modal frequencies for a rectangular control room shell 30 × 25 × 19.5 ft.

to 5 and higher would increase mode density significantly.

It is sometimes of interest to know how many modes, N, occur in a band Δf wide centered on f. The following expression may be used for this purpose (also in metric units)[6]:

$$\Delta N \approx \{[(4\pi V)(f/c)^3] + [(\pi S/2)(f/c)^2] + [(E/8) \times (f/c)]\}(\Delta f/f) \quad (3\text{-}4)$$

There is interest in the number of modes falling within one-third octave bands because bands this wide approximate the critical bands of the human hearing mechanism. For one-third octaves the Δf/f factor is 0.23 in Eq. 3-4; for octaves it is 0.707. Fig. 3-6 is a plot of the number of modes in one-third octave and full octave bands for the 30 × 25 × 19.5-ft room. Above a few hundred hertz, the modal density increases at a phenomenal rate. With modes packed together so tightly, the problems so common at low audio frequencies disappear completely.

We are now in a position to understand the reasons behind dividing the audible frequency spectrum as in Figs. 3-1 and 3-2. The volume of our 30 × 25 × 19.5-ft control room outer shell is 14,625 ft^3. If we assume a reverberation time of 0.4 s, the frequency f of Eq. 3-1 is 58.8 Hz, and 4f is 235 Hz. Referring to Figs. 3-5 and 3-6, we see that the region A frequency range from 18.8 to 58.8 is truly the region with the greatest mode spacing. The region B frequency range from 58.8 to 235 Hz carries to the big up-shoot of Fig. 3-6. Region C is so full of modal resonances as to leave no troublesome spaces between them, thus assuring smooth room response.

3.10 MODAL BANDWIDTH

In Fig. 3-5 the modal frequencies are represented by simple lines. Actually, as in other resonance phenomena, there is a finite bandwidth associated with each modal resonance. If we take the bandwidth as that measured at

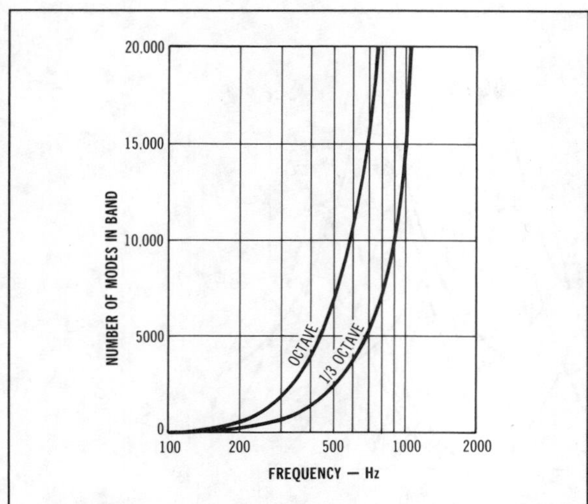

Figure 3-6 The number of modal frequencies in octave and one-third octave bandwidths as calculated from Equation 3-4 for a rectangular 30 × 25 × 19.5-ft control room outer shell.

the half-power points (-3 dB or $1/\sqrt{2}$), the bandwidth is[7]

$$\Delta f = f_2 - f_1$$
$$= k_n/\pi$$

where,

Δf is the bandwidth in hertz,

f_2 is the upper frequency at the -3-dB point,

f_1 is the lower frequency at the -3-dB point,

k_n is the damping factor determined principally by the amount of absorption in the room and by the volume of the room. The more absorbing material in the room, the greater k_n.

If the damping factor k_n is related to the reverberation time of a room, the expression for Δf becomes[8]

$$\Delta f = 6.91/\pi RT_{60} = 2.2/RT_{60} \quad (3\text{-}5)$$

where,

RT_{60} is the reverberation time in seconds.

From Eq. 3-5 a few generalizations may be made. In most well-designed rooms for audio functions, reverberation time is close to being uniform with frequency. Insofar as this is true, modal bandwidth is constant. For reverberation times in the range of 0.3 to 0.5 s, bandwidth is in the range 4.4 to 7.3 Hz. Most audio rooms will have modal bandwidths of the order of 5 Hz.

3.11 SUMMATION OF MODAL EFFECT

The relationship between mode spacing and mode bandwidth is now clear. At low frequencies where only axial modes exist, if two axial modes are separated 20 Hz and each has a bandwidth of 5 Hz, there is a space between with virtually no modal support. This means a dip in the room response. Unattached modes such as these are often contributors to coloration effects in which a single mode, excited whenever voice energy strikes that particular frequency, gives undue emphasis to that frequency in an unnatural and monotonous way.

The room of Table 3-1 and Fig. 3-5 is the 30 × 25 × 19.5-ft control room outer shell. The lines representing the modal frequencies in Fig. 3-5 can each be replaced by, say, a 5-Hz bandwidth resonance curve. Fig. 3-7 does this for the frequency range up to 50 Hz. The five axial modes, six tangential modes, and one oblique mode do a respectable job of filling spaces between modes. The room response is the combined effect of the 12 modes in this illustrative frequency range from 18.8 to 50 Hz. Axial modes dominate below 30 Hz. At 29.4 Hz, tangential modes begin, and the first oblique mode appears at 41.2 Hz.

The room of Fig. 3-7 has a volume of 14,625 ft^3, and the length, width, and height have been adjusted to near-optimum proportions. Therefore, the resonance curves of Fig. 3-7 are numerous and closely spaced to yield excellent room response. A small room of one-tenth the volume would present quite a different situation with fewer modes, greater spacing, more irregular response, and poorer low-frequency response.

3.12 ROOM PROPORTIONS FOR RECTANGULAR ROOMS

To achieve adequate separation of modal frequencies, attention must be given to room proportions. A cubical room is the worst possible selection since the three sets of axial modes coincide with exaggerated spacings. The literature of the past 40 years is replete with different suggestions for the "best" room proportions, and there is little to be gained by dwelling on them. A careful study of actual modal frequencies for a proposed room, as shown in Table 3-1 and Fig. 3-5, is the only method to use. The work involved can be lightened by the use of a computer or programmable calculator. However, it is helpful to have a starting point from which to work. Sepmeyer has suggested several room dimension ratios that offer an excellent starting point in deciding upon room proportions[9]:

Favorable Room Proportions

	Height	Width	Length
A	1.00	1.14	1.39
B	1.00	1.28	1.54
C	1.00	1.60	2.33

Source: Sepmeyer.[9]

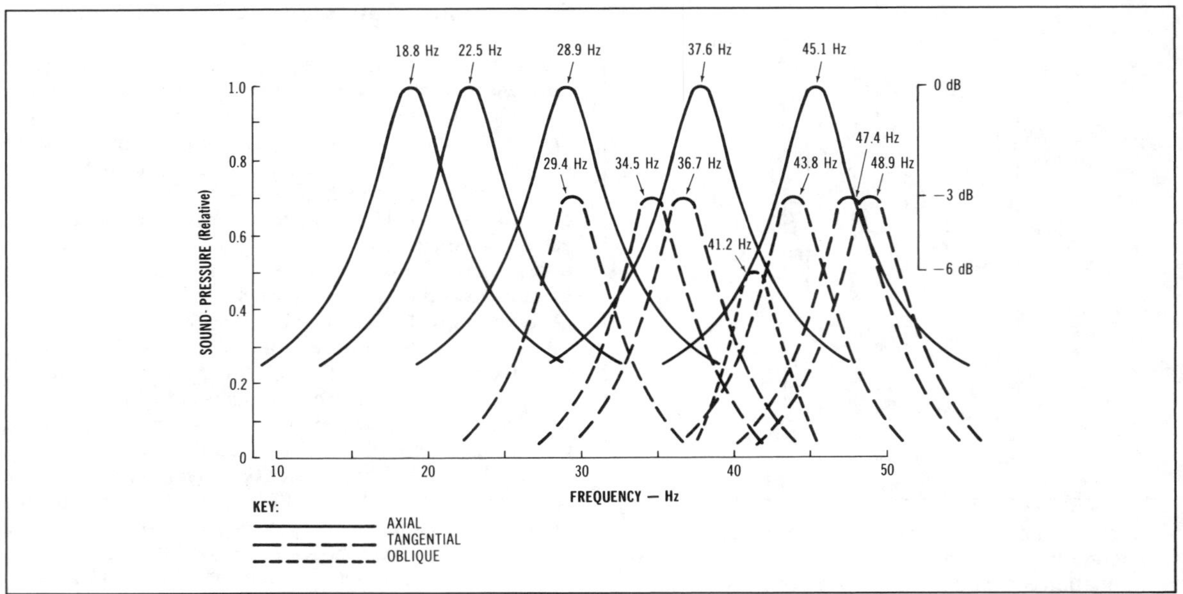

Figure 3-7 The normal modes below 50 Hz of the 30 × 25 × 19.5-ft control room of Fig. 3-5 are shown here with representative bandwidths of 5 Hz at the −3-dB points.

Room proportions A, B, and C are all referenced to ceiling height. For example, for a ceiling height of 10 ft, room C would have a width of 16 ft, a length of 23.3 ft, and a volume of 3728 ft^3.

To decide on room size, referring to Fig. 3-2 reminds us that very small rooms are prone to having too few axial modes with resulting excessive spacings. The experience of the British Broadcasting Corporation (BBC) with their many talk studios is that volumes from 1500 to 4000 ft^3 are generally satisfactory.[10] Difficult voice colorations abound in smaller studios, and economic factors limit those larger than 4000 ft^3. Certainly, the 19.5 × 25 × 30-ft control room of Table 3-1 and Fig. 3-5 (volume 14,625 ft^3) is eminently satisfactory from the modal standpoint. The ratio of height to width to length of this room is 1.00:1.28:1.54, which is the Sepmeyer room B.

When floor space is limited but ceiling height is not, it is sometimes desirable to "stand the room on end" to get adequate volume. In other words, what normally would be considered the length of the room is made the height. Acoustical benefits of the larger volume can be achieved with limited floor space. In such a room, human activity is limited to the smaller "end," which may create other problems (e.g., management of early reflections).

3.13 MODES IN NONRECTANGULAR ROOMS

To achieve diffusion of sound, recourse to nonrectangular rooms is often taken. As this is usually more expensive, it is desirable to see what happens to modal patterns when room surfaces are skewed. At the higher audio frequencies, the density of modal frequencies is so high that sound pressure variations throughout a room are small. At lower audio frequencies, this is not the case. The response of rectangular rooms can be readily calculated from Eq. 3-2. The resonances of a nonrectangular room, however, can be calculated by the more complex finite element method, but this is far beyond the scope of this book. We, therefore, find refuge in the work of van Nieuwland and Weber of the Philips Research Laboratories of Eindhoven, the Netherlands, on reverberation chambers.[11]

When the shape of the room is irregular, the spatial structure of the modal pressure patterns is also irregular. The superposition of different modes will, in general, yield smaller pressure variations in the irregular room. The number of modes per frequency band is determined principally by the volume of the room rather than its shape. The work of van Nieuwland and Weber shows that a nonrectangular room gives a more regular distribution of modal resonance frequencies than a rectangular room with optimum proportions. Instead of axial, tangential, and oblique modes characteristic of the rectangular room, the resonances of the nonrectangular room all have the character of three-dimensional (obliquelike) modes. This has been demonstrated by measuring decay rates and finding less fluctuation from mode to mode.

In Fig. 3-8 the results of finite element calculations are shown for two-dimensional rectangular and nonrectangular rooms of the same area (377 ft^2). The lines are contours of equal sound pressure. The heavy lines represent

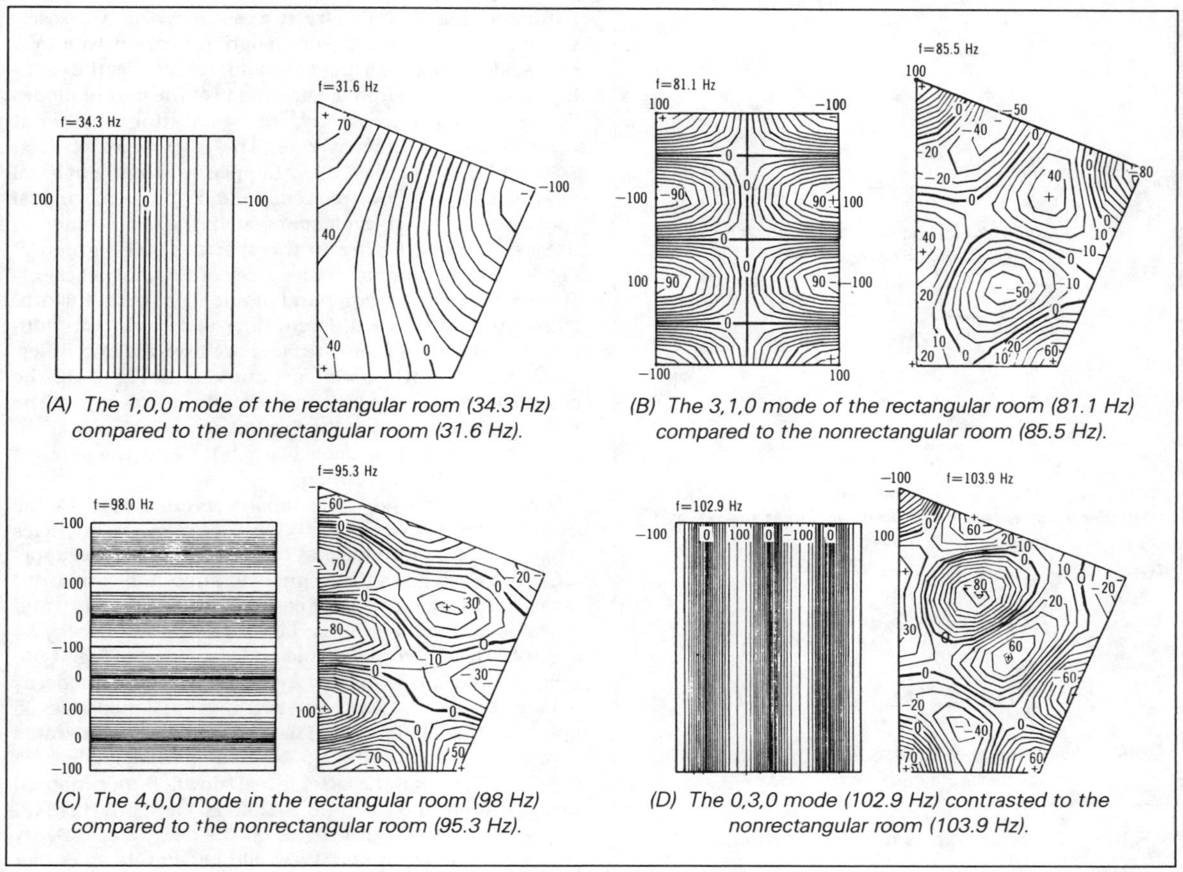

(A) The 1,0,0 mode of the rectangular room (34.3 Hz) compared to the nonrectangular room (31.6 Hz).

(B) The 3,1,0 mode of the rectangular room (81.1 Hz) compared to the nonrectangular room (85.5 Hz).

(C) The 4,0,0 mode in the rectangular room (98 Hz) compared to the nonrectangular room (95.3 Hz).

(D) The 0,3,0 mode (102.9 Hz) contrasted to the nonrectangular room (103.9 Hz).

Figure 3-8 A comparison of calculated two-dimensional sound fields in rectangular and nonrectangular rooms having the same areas. *(After Reference 11.)*

the nodal lines of zero pressure of the standing wave. In Fig. 3-8A the 1,0,0 mode of the rectangular room, resonating at 34.3 Hz, is compared to a 31.6-Hz resonance of the nonrectangular room. The contours of equal pressure are decidedly nonsymmetrical in the latter. In Fig. 3-8B the 3,1,0 mode of the rectangular room (81.1 Hz) is compared to an 85.5-Hz resonance in the nonrectangular room. Increasing frequency in Fig. 3-8C, the 4,0,0 mode at 98 Hz in the rectangular room is compared to a 95.3-Hz mode in the nonrectangular room. Fig. 3-8D shows the 0,3,0 mode at 102.9 Hz of a rectangular room contrasted to a 103.9-Hz resonance in the nonrectangular room. These pressure distribution diagrams of Fig. 3-8 give an excellent appreciation of the distortion of the sound field by extreme skewing of room surfaces. In a room with only walls skewed, a mixture of rectangular- and nonrectangular-type sound fields would result.

3.14 LOW-FREQUENCY REVERBERATION

The whole concept of reverberation time elucidated by Sabine and his followers is based on a sound field that is perfectly diffuse. That is, the sound intensity is uniform throughout the volume of the room, and particle velocities are randomly distributed in direction at any given instant. Such conditions are approached only in rooms that are large compared to the wavelength of sound. In other words, the traditional reverberation equations only strictly apply in a genuine reverberant field. Most recording studios, control rooms, and listening rooms are too small to have a completely diffuse sound field, and the problem is especially aggravated at the lower frequencies.

What happens at low audio frequencies is illustrated in Fig. 3-9. In Fig. 3-9A the room is excited by a sinusoidal signal that coincides in frequency with a mode that is

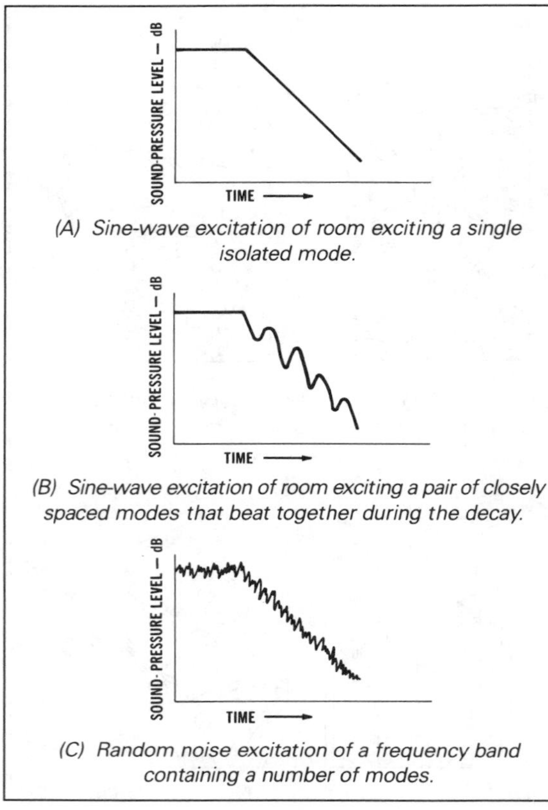

(A) Sine-wave excitation of room exciting a single isolated mode.

(B) Sine-wave excitation of room exciting a pair of closely spaced modes that beat together during the decay.

(C) Random noise excitation of a frequency band containing a number of modes.

Figure 3-9 Reverberatory decay at low frequencies.

well isolated from neighbors. When the source is cut off, the energy stored in that mode decays logarithmically. The rate of decay is determined by the type of mode and the absorbence of whatever surfaces are involved with that mode. Fig. 3-9B illustrates a case in which two closely spaced modes, isolated from neighbors, are driven by a sinusoidal signal exciting the room. As soon as the exciting signal is interrupted, each mode of the pair of modes decays at its own frequency, the two beating together at the difference frequency rate. The pure cases of Figs. 3-9A and B would most likely happen to prominent axial modes at the very low frequency end of the room's modal spectrum, although evidence of such beats is common in decays of sound higher in the spectrum. The graph of Fig. 3-9C shows the composite decay of a number of closely spaced modes in, say, a band of one-third octave width. Different modes have different rates of decay because different numbers of room surfaces are involved and different surface absorption is encountered. In Fig. 3-9C the composite decay is logarithmic because the decays of the individual modes, though of different rates, are logarithmic. Complex beating takes place, but randomness tends to minimize the fluctuations.

What can be said, then, about reverberation in the example control room for Table 3-1 at low frequencies when diffuse conditions may not prevail? To be more specific, Table 3-2 gives the frequency range of the one-third octave bands and the mode count for each. Bands 13 and 14 each embrace a single axial mode, and their decay on a graphic level recorder would approach that of Fig. 3-9A, even though it was excited by random noise. The decay of band 15 with one axial and two tangential modes would approach that of Fig. 3-9C. The axial mode (29.0 Hz) would certainly beat with the 29.4-Hz tangential mode at a 0.4-Hz rate, even if the latter is 3 dB down. Superimposed beats of about 5.6 Hz (34.6 − 29.0 Hz) and 5.2 Hz (34.6 − 29.4 Hz) would put wiggles on the decay trace. Decay traces for bands 16 and 17 would be slightly smoother with a total of 4 or 5 modes. Band 18 with 3 axial, 7 tangential, and 4 oblique modes or a total of 14 would really be the lowest one-third octave band, where decays are smooth enough to establish the slope with some semblance of statistical flavor. Above band 18 the decays would

Table 3-2. Modes in One-Third Octave Bands, Control Room Shell, 30 × 25 × 19.5 ft

	One-Third Octave Bands*			Number of Modes			
Band Number	Center Frequency (Hz)	Lower Cutoff (Hz)	Upper Cutoff (Hz)	Axial	Tangential	Oblique	Total
13	20	17.8	22.4	1	0	0	1
14	25	22.4	28.2	1	0	0	1
15	31.5	28.2	35.5	1	2	0	3
16	40	35.5	44.7	1	2	1	4
17	50	44.7	56.2	1	3	1	5
18	63	56.2	70.8	3	7	4	14
19	80	70.8	89.1	2	11	8	21
20	100	89.1	112.0	1	12	19	32

*ANSI S1.6

get progressively smoother as more modes combine in random fashion in each band.

In this room reverberation measurements below 40 or 50 Hz would record the sort of decay applying to the decay of program signals in the room, even though a far-from-diffuse sound field prevails. One would expect significant variations in reverberation time measured at different positions in the room. Another source of variability in recorded decays is built into random noise, the usual signal for room excitation. By definition, such noise is constantly shifting in amplitude, phase, and frequency. At the instant the switch is opened to initiate a decay, the relative degree of excitation of each mode in the band being measured is indeterminate and variable from decay to decay. Statistical averaging of many decays at each of many microphone positions in the room is the only way to get dependable figures for reverberation time for a given low frequency.

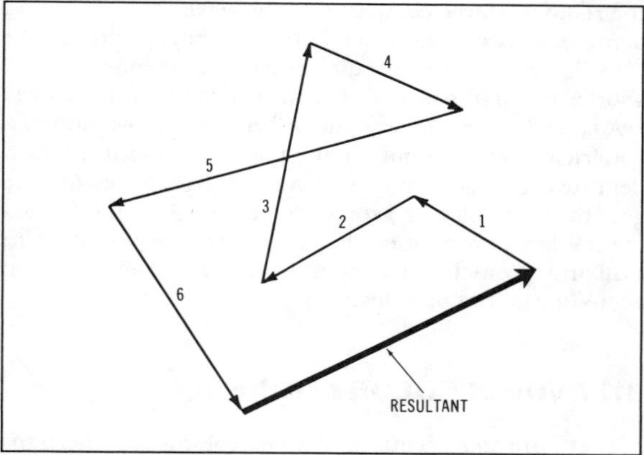

Figure 3-11 Six modes of pressures of varying magnitudes and phases add vectorially to yield the resultant, actuating the microphone at a given frequency in a steady-state room transmission measurement.

3.15 STEADY-STATE ROOM PERFORMANCE

Electronic engineers can get the frequency response of a piece of equipment by introducing a constant-amplitude, variable-frequency signal at the input and measuring the output. Acoustical engineers can perform a similar operation on a room, but the resulting data are not nearly as significant. Fig. 3-10 shows the result of such a test on a recording studio with a 12,000-ft^3 volume. To assure excitation of all room modes, the loudspeaker was placed in a corner of the studio. The microphone was located in the diagonal upper corner. Loudspeaker response has a minor effect above 50 Hz.

The maxima and minima revealed in Fig. 3-10 are astounding to say the least. At any given frequency the resultant pressure activating the microphone is the vector sum of contributions from numerous modes that vary in magnitude and phase in a random manner. When the combination happens to be dominated by in-phase conditions, a maximum appears. If out-of-phase conditions dominate, a null is formed. A glance at Fig. 3-7 at 45 Hz, for example, shows the range of magnitudes for at least six modes, but there is no information here about phase. In Fig. 3-11 six modal pressures of arbitrary phase and magnitude are added vectorially to illustrate how the resultant, which the microphone measures, is formed. The same sort of drastic maxima and minima are observed when frequency is held constant and the microphone is moved.

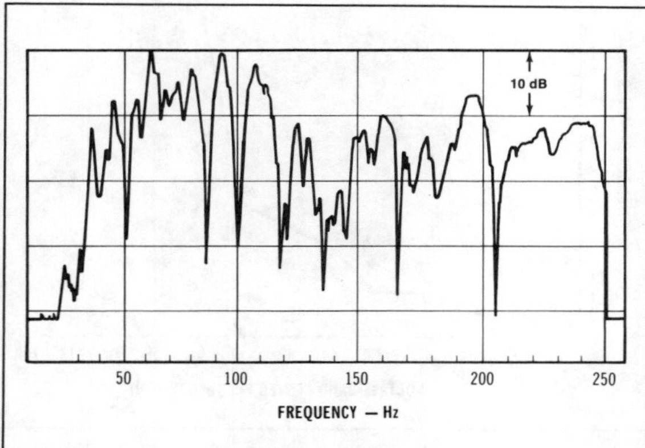

Figure 3-10 Steady-state swept sine response of a recording studio having a volume of 12,000 ft^3.

For many years acoustical researchers have tried to base judgments of room acoustical quality on such transmission tests, but no more. Kuttruff points out that it is impossible to evaluate room acoustical quality from such measurements.[12] The traditional smooth-frequency response, so valued in amplifiers, loudspeakers, and transmission lines, just does not apply in room acoustics. Kuttruff gives several reasons for this. First, speech and music are characterized by such rapid signal fluctuations that a steady-state condition is rarely achieved when excited by such signals. Another reason has to do with psychoacoustics. Our hearing mechanism is unable to perceive small fluctuations in frequency.

3.16 GEOMETRICAL ACOUSTICS

We have referred to the statistical approach (e.g., reverberation) and the wave approach (Section 3.6) to acoustical problems, and now we come to the *geometrical approach.* The one overriding assumption in the application of geometrical acoustics is that the dimensions of the room are large compared to the wavelength of sound being considered. In other words, we must be in region C of Fig. 3-1 where specular reflection prevails and the short wavelengths of sound allow treating sound like rays.

A sound ray is nothing more than a small section of a spherical wave originating at a particular point. It has a definite direction and acts as a ray of light following the general principles of geometric optics. The one fundamental law of acoustics that is of great service to us in utilizing geometrical acoustics in the study of room acoustics is that of reflection.

3.17 VOICE COLORATIONS

There are many causes of voice colorations, perhaps two of the most important being distortions traceable to acoustical comb filters and to modes. Comb filters are discussed in Section 1.13. Here we shall concentrate on colorations resulting from modal problems. Few have dealt with this specific type of voice coloration as thoroughly as Gilford,[10] drawing upon the extensive experience of the research department of the BBC. A most objectionable flaw in speech originating from small studios is coloration in the form of unnatural and monotonously repeated overemphasis of certain frequencies in the voice spectrum. Prominent isolated modes are frequently the cause of such colorations. BBC workers found that subjective detection of such colorations was the most effective, especially if aided by an amplifier that amplified only a narrow band of frequencies. By moving this peak of amplification through the desired portion of the audible spectrum, marginal colorations can be made to stand out dramatically. This method became a part of routine tests of speech studios.

For a male voice most of the colorations were found between 100 and 175 Hz; for a female voice, 200 to 300 Hz. Few male voice colorations were detected outside the 80- to 300-Hz range. Most colorations of this type are directly excited by either the fundamental or first-formant frequency components of the speaker's voice. Gilford's suggestions for discouraging the formation of speech colorations in the design stage include (1) avoiding structural and room lining materials having high Q factors such as plaster on metal lathe, plywood, and plasterboard with an unsupported back surface and (2) paying careful attention to spacing and distribution of room modes as has already been emphasized. Colorations disappear above about 300 Hz because of the greater modal density.

Whether room modes offer coloration potential depends on five factors listed by Gilford[10]:

1. Mode bandwidth,
2. Mode excitation,
3. Isolation of mode from strongly excited neighbors,
4. Location of sound source and microphone in the standing-wave pattern,
5. Spectral content of the source.

3.18 BONELLO CRITERIA

In the design of studios, control rooms, and listening rooms, it is always difficult to know whether a given modal distribution pattern is acceptable. Of course, if two or more modes occupy the same frequency (a degeneracy in the acoustical lexicon) or are bunched up and isolated from neighbors, we are immediately warned of potential coloration problems. It would be nice, however, if there were an objective "go/no-go" type of test to apply to a projected room design. Such a test has emerged from Argentina in the form of an interesting proposal by Bonello.[13, 14, 15]

Bonello's number 1 criterion is to plot the number of modes in one-third octave bands against frequency and to examine the resulting plot to see if the curve increases monotonically (i.e., if each one-third octave has more modes than the preceding one or, at least, an equal number). His number 2 criterion is to examine the modal frequencies to make sure there are no coincident modes, or, at least, if there are coincident modes, there should be five or more modes in that one-third octave band. By applying Bonello's method to our 30 × 25 × 19.5-ft control room shell, we obtained the graph of Fig. 3-12. The data for this plot are taken directly from Table 3-2. The

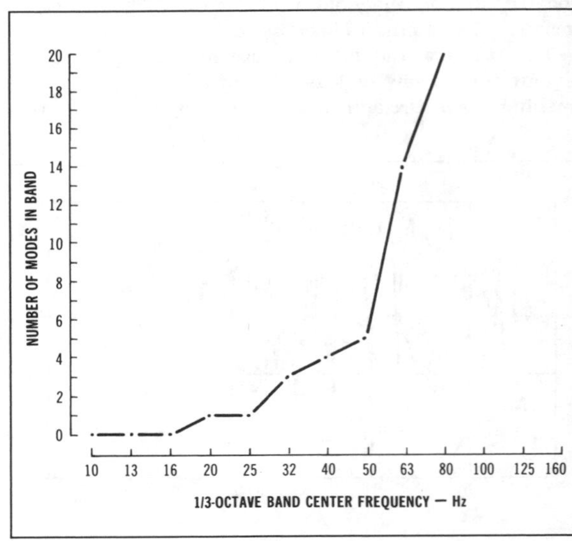

Figure 3-12 The application of Bonello's criterion 1 to the 30 × 25 × 19.5-ft control room outer shell of Table 3-1 and Fig. 3-5.

conditions of both criteria are met. The monotonic increase of successive one-third octave bands confirms that the distribution of modes is favorable.

The graph of Fig. 3-13 is for the first 48 modes of a 2100-ft^3 studio having proportions that fall within Bolt's area, in vogue in the past for specifying favorable dimensional ratios. We see that it fails the Bonello test.

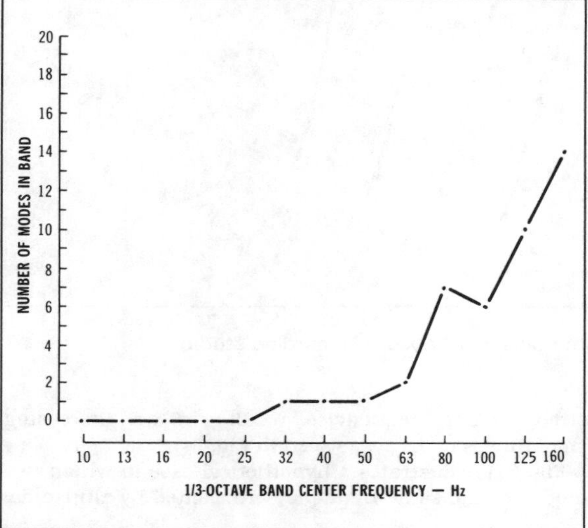

Figure 3-13 Application of Bonello's criterion to a 2100-ft^3 studio. *(Adapted from Reference 8.)*

Knudsen reported data on the old "auditorium studio at CBS in Hollywood," which had dimensions 108 × 48 × 33 ft and an approximate volume of 171,000 ft^3.[16] This large room had the dimensional ratio of 3.27:1.45:1.00. He reported that acoustically it gave highly satisfactory results. A Bonello plot for this large space in Fig. 3-14 shows that it follows criterion 1 beautifully. Also note that for large spaces the plot is shifted to the lower frequencies.

Fig. 3-15 is a plot of the first 48 modes of a 2100-ft^3 room using the same 3.27:1.45:1.00 proportions Knudsen used in the big CBS studio. This smaller studio fails the test miserably. Room volume is an important factor in determining whether a certain set of dimensional ratios will provide good mode distribution. This fact has not received adequate attention in the past.

It is possible that the critical bands of the ear should be used instead of one-third octave bands. The one-third octave bands more or less follow critical bandwidths above 500 Hz, but for the low modal frequencies under discussion, the critical bands tend toward a constant bandwidth of about 100 Hz. Bonello considered critical bands in the early stages of his work but found that one-third octave bands better show subtle effects of small changes in room dimensions.[17] Another question is whether axial, tangential, and oblique modes should be given equal status as Bonello does when their energies are, in fact, quite different. Despite questions, this method is worthy of further application, study, and verification.

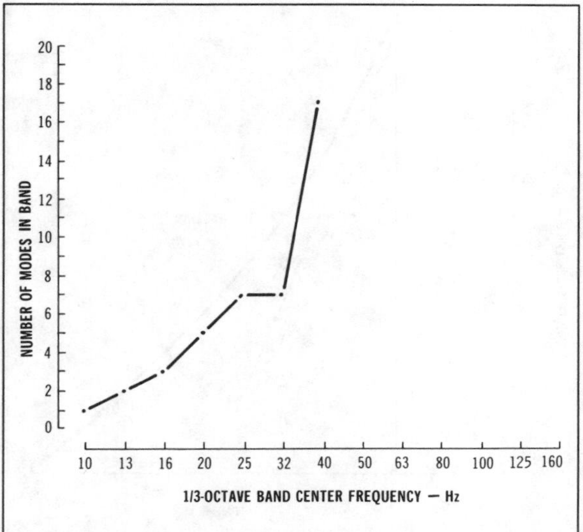

Figure 3-14 Application of Bonello's criterion to a 171,000-ft^3 studio having a dimension ratio or 3.27:1.45:1.00 and reported by Knudsen as having satisfactory acoustical conditions. *(Adapted from Reference 8.)*

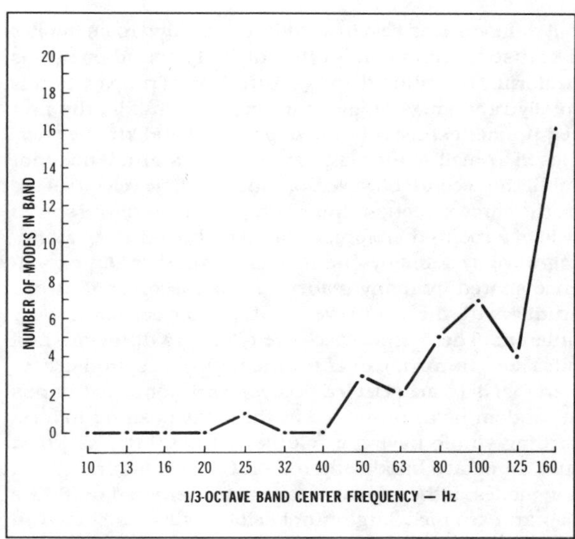

Figure 3-15 This is a Bonello plot of a 2100-ft^3 studio having the same proportions as the 171,000-ft^3 studio of Fig. 3-14. *(Adapted from Reference 8.)*

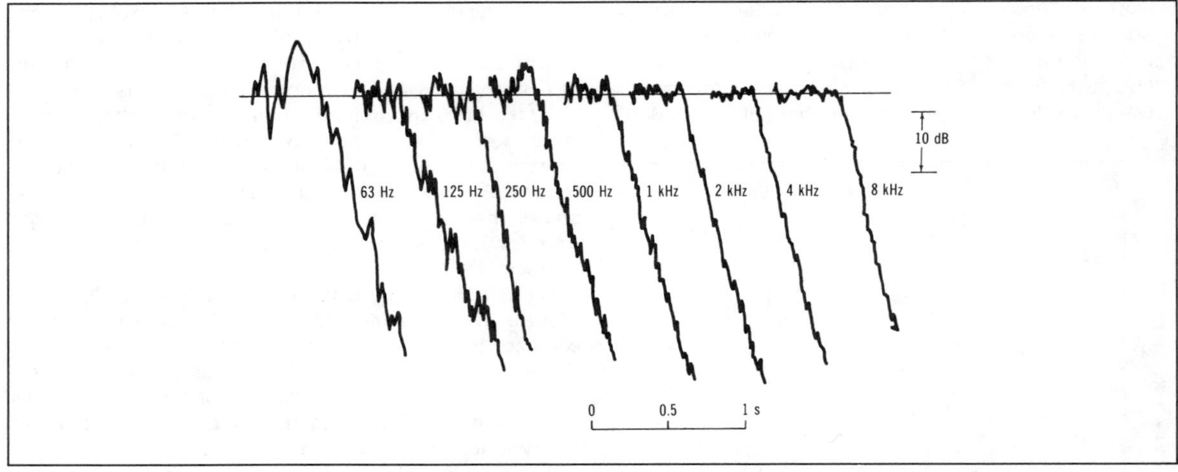

Figure 3-16 Decay of octave bands of random noise in a 12,000-ft^3 recording studio.

Bonello has successfully used this system in the design of 35 broadcasting and recording studios over a four-year period. The adaptability of the method to computer use greatly accelerates the searching for optimum room proportions and frees the designer from the folklore and black magic associated with many dimensional ratios advocated in earlier times from positions of prestige.

3.19 DIFFUSION OF SOUND

A diffuse sound field in a studio or listening room implies a statistical randomness in which (1) sound energy is uniformly distributed and (2) direction of propagation is totally random. A single standing wave fulfills the first requirement since the sum of potential and kinetic energies in a small volume is everywhere constant. It does not fulfill the second, however, because particle velocities are in the same direction. Improving diffusion of the sound field of a room, therefore, is based on breaking up standing-wave systems by one means or another. An experience shared by many readers is the discovery that two studios with the same reverberation time can sound very different. These differences are related to diffusion, and diffusion, in turn, can affect the nature of sound decay.

In Fig. 3-16 are selected decay records for octave bands of random noise measured at the same position in a recording studio having a volume of 12,000 ft^3. We know that an octave band centered on 63 Hz contains only a few modes, although an octave band centered on 8 kHz has an extremely large number of modes, as shown in Fig. 3-6. In the 63-Hz octave the few modes beat with each other as each decays at its own rate and a summation is recorded, albeit a highly fluctuating one. The increasing number of modes contained in octave bands at successively higher frequencies results in an increasing smoothness of decay, as seen in Fig. 3-16.

Fig. 3-17 illustrates a hypothetical case in which two modes of the same frequency are excited by sinusoidal

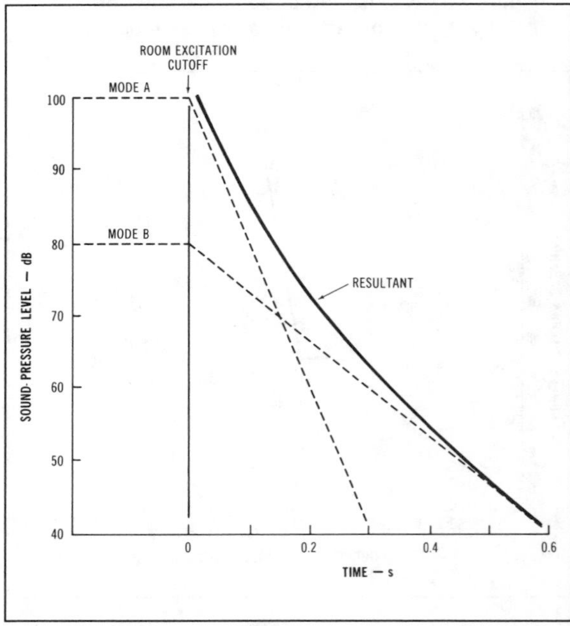

Figure 3-17 If modes A and B are both in the band being measured, a nonlogarithmic resultant is formed. Curvature of the decay is often an indication of lack of diffusion in the room.

sound in the room at that frequency or two modes of different frequency are the only modes in the measurement band and are excited by random noise. Mode A has a reverberation time of 0.3 s and is excited to a level of 100 dB at the instant the excitation is cut off and the decay begins. Mode B decays much more slowly because the surfaces involved are less absorbent and it is excited to a level of 80 dB. As room excitation is removed, each mode decays at its own rate. The resultant is nonlogarithmic. Such double-slope decays result from different damping for modes of different directions; thus, double-slope decays indicate nondiffuse conditions. This is not always true since other things, such as coupled rooms, can also cause double-slope decays. An examination of the decays of Fig. 3-16 indicates good diffusion because all decays are generally straight lines. This is probably the easiest and most effective test for a diffuse condition.

The greatest single step toward grasping the illusory diffuse sound field is that of adjusting of room dimensions, as we have already seen. Radical skewing of walls and ceiling can offer a modest improvement in diffusion over that of a corresponding rectangular room, but it does cost more. As Fig. 3-8 vividly portrays, the asymmetrical room gives a highly asymmetrical sound field for which the modal frequencies can be determined only by sophisticated mathematics and powerful computers. In deciding between an asymmetrical and rectangular outer shell for a control room, for instance, we must decide between easily calculated modal frequencies for the rectangular room and unknown modal frequencies or those calculated with difficulty for the nonrectangular room. It would seem that, at this point in the course of acoustical developments, knowing the low-frequency modal pattern in minute detail before construction is far more valuable than any diffusion advantages the nonrectangular room has to offer. Further, great effort goes into attaining uniform acoustical conditions along the length of the mixing console and, possibly, at positions occupied by producers and other important personnel. Even though we are considering low-frequency sound of long wavelength, the nonsymmetrical sound fields of Fig. 3-8 would seem to be the wrong approach for achieving uniform low-frequency conditions over the critical control room area. A possible exception is the splaying of a couple of walls at about 5° to reduce flutter echo (a higher-frequency phenomenon), although, even here, the gains rarely offset the added cost.

Mounting absorbing material in irregular patches accomplishes two things. It is a significant step toward achieving a diffuse sound field through diffraction of sound at the edges. It also increases the absorbing efficiency of the material. Having patches vary with respect to absorption coefficient also contributes to diffusion.

Another approach to diffusing sound in small rooms (contrasted to large auditoriums and concert halls) is that of employing irregular projections on the walls. Somerville has determined that such diffusing elements must be of the order of one-seventh wavelength in depth to have appreciable effect.[18] The depth of such an element must then be 1.6 ft to be effective at 100 Hz. The space requirements of such protuberances discourage their use. Somerville also found rectangular, boxlike elements to be more effective diffusers than cylindrical or triangular sections.

A new approach to sound diffusion, which involves maximum-length sequences and quadratic residue sequences has been proposed by Schroeder.[19, 20] Their current use in concert halls and control rooms promises future application to studios and listening rooms. This is truly a "groovy" type of diffuser. Reflection coefficients are alternated between +1 and −1 according to a certain mathematical sequence. A reflection coefficient of −1 can be achieved by hard walls with "grooves" a quarter wavelength deep. A sizable body of literature is rapidly building up on this general subject, and it is worth watching.

REFERENCES

1. T. Uzzle, "A Manufacturer's Field Support via the Programmable Scientific Calculator," presented at the 72nd convention of the Audio Engineering Society, Anaheim, California, October, 1982, preprint #1943 (W-4).
2. R. L. McKay, of Bolt, Beranek and Newman, Inc., in a Synergetic Audio Concepts LEDE™ workshop presentation, January 1982, and reported in *Syn-Aud-Con Tech Topics*, vol. 9, no. 5, spring 1982.
3. L. L. Beranek, *Acoustics*, New York: McGraw-Hill, 1954, p. 287.
4. P. M. Morse and R. H. Bolt, "Sound Waves in Rooms," *Reviews of Modern Physics*, vol. 16, no. 2, p. 85, April 1944.
5. Ibid, p. 87.
6. K. B. Ginn, *Architectural Acoustics*, Second Edition, Brüel & Kjaer, 1978, p. 45.
7. L. L. Beranek, *Acoustics*, New York: McGraw-Hill, 154, p. 292
8. O. J. Bonello, "A New Criterion for the Distribution of Normal Room Modes," *Journal of the AES*, vol. 29, no. 9, pp. 597–606, September 1981.

9. L. W. Sepmeyer, "Computed Frequency and Angular Distribution of the Normal Modes of Vibration in Rectangular Rooms," *Journal of the ASA*, vol. 37, no. 3, pp. 413–423, March 1965.

10. C. L. S. Gilford, "The Acoustic Design of Talks Studios and Listening Rooms," *Proc. IEEE*, vol. 106, part B, no. 27, pp. 245–258, May 1959.

11. J. M. van Nieuwland and C. Weber, "Eigenmodes in Nonrectangular Reverberation Rooms," *Noise Control Engineering*, vol. 13, no. 3, pp. 112–121, November-December 1979.

12. H. Kuttruff, *Room Acoustics*, Second Edition, London: Applied Science Publishers Ltd., 1979, p. 61–69.

13. O. J. Bonello, Acoustical Evaluation and Control of Normal Room Modes, Dept. of Research, Solidyne SRL, Tres de Febrero 3254, 1429 Buenos Aires, Argentina.

14. O. J. Bonello, "A New Computer Aided Method for the Complete Acoustical Design of Broadcasting and Recording Studios, *Trans. IEEE*, International Conference on Acoustics, Speech, and Signal Processing, 1979.

15. O. J. Bonello, "A New Criterion for the Distribution of Normal Room Modes," *Journal of the AES*, vol. 29, no. 9, pp. 597–606, September 1981. (See vol. 29, no. 12, p. 905, December 1981 for a correction.)

16. V. O. Knudsen and C. M. Harris, *Acoustical Designing in Architecture*, New York: John Wiley and Sons, Inc., 1950, pp. 402–403. (A 1978 revision of this valuable out-of-print book is now available in paperback from the ASA. In this later edition, see pp. 352–353.)

17. O. J. Bonello, private communication, 1980.

18. T. Somerville, "Investigation of Sound Diffusion in Rooms by Means of a Model," *Acustica*, vol. 1, no. 1, pp. 40–48, 1951.

19. M. R. Schroeder, "Diffuse Sound Reflection by Maximum-Length Sequences," *Journal of the ASA*, vol. 57, no. 1, pp. 149–150, January 1975.

20. M. R. Schroeder, "Binaural Dissimilarity and Optimum Ceilings for Concert Halls: More Lateral Sound Diffusion," *Journal of the ASA*, vol. 65, no. 4, pp. 958–963, April 1979.

CHAPTER **4**

Common Factors in All Audio Rooms

by F. Alton Everest

4.1 SELECTION OF SITES FOR AUDIO ROOMS

It is not wise to choose a site for a suite of audio rooms alongside a busy freeway, an elevated or a ground-level railroad, a busy intersection, an airport, or any other noisy location. When economic or other factors make such a location imperative, due allowance must be made for extra cost of structure to provide the requisite protection from such noise.

A limited amount of outdoor protection can be achieved by erecting earthen embankments or masonry walls between the structure and the noise source. These are effective at high frequencies, but low-frequency components of noise tend to be bent around them by diffraction. Planting dense shrubbery combined with such barriers can yield as much as 10 dB of overall protection. Separation of the proposed structure from the noise source is helpful but limited by the inverse-square law. The 6 dB per distance double applies only to free-field conditions but is useful in rough estimation. Going from 50 to 100 ft (a change of 50 ft) from the source yields the same reduction of noise level as going from 100 to 200 ft (a change of 100 ft); thus, increasing separation counts most when close to the source. At any given location, the position of the sound-sensitive rooms on the side of the building away from a troublesome noise source is a favorable move, especially if no reflective structures are back there to reduce the barrier effect.

Only airborne sound is considered in the preceding paragraph. A highway carrying heavy truck traffic or an overhead or subway railroad, for instance, may literally "shake the earth" to such an extent that large-amplitude, low-frequency vibrations of the ground may be conducted to the foundation of the structure and carried to all points within that structure. Even if such vibrations are in the subsonic range, they have been known to shake microphones with good low-frequency response to such an extent as to overload low-level electronic circuits. Sound, both subsonic and sonic, is carried with amazing efficiency throughout a reinforced concrete structure. A vast masonry wall within that structure, vibrated at high amplitude, can radiate significant levels of sound into the air by diaphragmatic action. It is possible by using a combination of vibration-measuring equipment and calculations (outside the scope of this treatment) to estimate the sound pressure level radiated into a room via such a structure-borne path.

Often the greatest noise to which audio rooms are exposed is that from within the very building in which the rooms are located rather than from the outside. Elevator doors and motors; heating, ventilating, and air-conditioning equipment; heel taps on hard floors; plumbing pipes; and business machines are prolific producers of noise carried to the sound-sensitive area by air- or structure-borne paths. The sections to follow will deal with these types of noises in detail.

4.2 SITE NOISE SURVEY

Audio room surfaces, viewed from the inside, provide the acoustical environment that leaves its imprint on every sound recorded or reproduced within it. This is one way of looking at the six surfaces comprising the room that will be thoroughly explored in later sections. In this section, however, another important function of these walls is under scrutiny. Certain low-noise standards must be adopted as part of the criteria for this inner-room acoustical environment. Background noise levels within are, among other things, a result of environmental noises without, and the only protection from these threatening outer noises is that offered by walls, floor, and ceiling. The transmission loss of these structures determines the degree of attenuation of outer noises actually realized. The question we focus on in the following sections is, "What must be done to attain the desired low-noise level within the audio room?"

Everything depends on the noise level outside. Outdoor ambient noise is a very complex phenomenon composed of a mixture of traffic noises and other noises produced by a variety of human and natural sources. The only satisfactory approach to evaluating outdoor environmental noise is statistical. Subjective approaches are unsatisfactory because others are generally involved who must be convinced by documentation and data, not just nebulous, subjective assurances. Even a modest investment in a studio suite or a listening room justifies the effort and expense of a noise survey of the site that provides the basis for designing walls, floor, and ceiling to achieve the low background noise levels desired inside.

One approach to a noise survey of the immediate vicinity of a proposed audio room is to enter into a contract with an acoustical consultant to do the work and submit a report. If technically oriented persons are available, they may be able to turn in a credible job if supplied with the right equipment and some guidance. The equipment may be rented or purchased, and appropriate guidance will be given here.

The easy way is to use some of the more sophisticated microprocessor-based recording noise meters available today. The measuring microphone may be mounted in a weatherproof housing in the desired location with the microphone cable running to the equipment indoors. The equivalent noise level is designated L_{eq} (equivalent, continuous sound level); the noise level exceeded 10% of the time, L_{10}; 50% of the time, L_{50}; and 90% of the time, L_{90}, or the peak noise level attained can be obtained as desired. A 24-hr observation captures diurnal variations; observations on selected days of the week capture especially noisy events varying from day to day or occurring at certain times during the week.

There is an effective way of getting essentially the same results as the microprocessor noise meter by investing many hours in meticulous and monotonous observations. This method will be described in detail because it is available at little cost. The only equipment needed are proper forms and a sound level meter equipped with an A-weighting network. This weighting network attenuates low-frequency energy to give readings conforming very roughly to loudness (see Section 2.7). The sound level meter itself, or its microphone on an extension cable, should be mounted on a sturdy photographic tripod at a convenient height. Direct and indirect means of calibrating the sound level meter at intervals should be provided.

The form shown in Fig. 4-1 is the basis for this method.[1] A single form is for recording readings over a single hour. Sound level readings are placed in the appropriate 2-dB interval that provides adequate precision for this method. Sound level readings are taken every 15 seconds, which gives a total of 240 readings each hour. Since this method is demanding, alternating observers each hour is desirable. On each 15-s mark, a reading is taken and entered in the lower grid at the proper decibel interval as a simple vertical tally mark. After four marks in one box, the fifth is made diagonally completing that box. The sixth is placed in the next box. This technique facilitates the later counting of marks from the scale at the bottom of the form.

The grid at the top of Fig. 4-1 is reserved for peak-noise readings above 70 dB (A-weighting). Instead of simple tally marks, as used for readings on the 15-s points entered in the lower grid, symbols to identify the source of the noise peak are entered in the upper grid, one to each square. Extra attention to the noise peaks above 70 dB is justified because such changing sounds are far more noticeable inside the sound-sensitive room than the steady sounds. This is why emergency vehicle sirens change pitch to give those in their path maximum warning. The number of airplane or truck or railroad peaks per hour or per day may necessitate selecting a wall with a higher transmission loss than otherwise would be required.

The sample data sheet of typical observations over an hour in Fig. 4-1 shows the tally marks entered every 15 seconds to build a graphical distribution curve. Sound levels below 70 dB (A-weighting) are recorded by tally marks in the closest 2-dB intervals. Above 70 dB, symbols identifying the source are used instead of tally marks in the upper portion. The noise peaks greater than 70 dB during this hour in this sample case were all caused by jet aircraft passing overhead. These peaks are so important that the four peaks were entered even though they did not coincide with the 15-s observation points making a total of 244 observations for the hour, rather than 240. The numbers of tally marks are recorded in the column to the left of the decibel scale, the cumulative number of

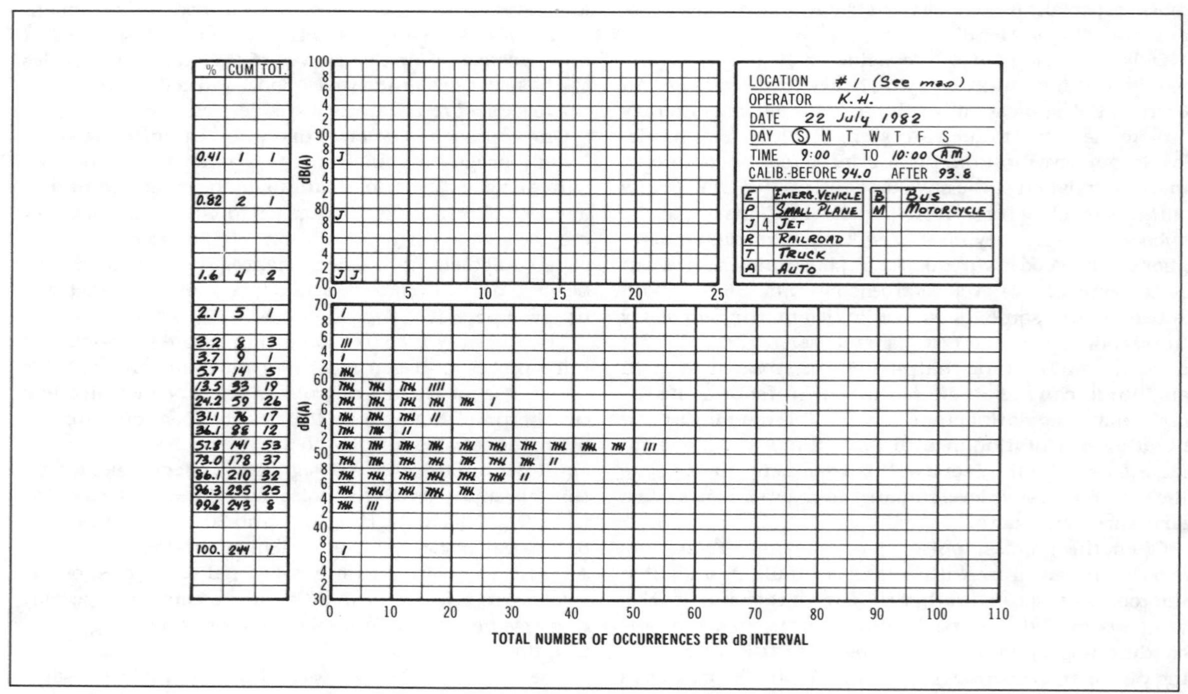

Figure 4-1 An example of the form used for recording site noise levels at 15-second intervals for a period of 1 hr. *(After Reference 1.)*

observations are recorded starting at the top, and the cumulative percentage (% cum) of the total number of observations is entered in the appropriate box.

A typical plot of the cumulative percentage of observations and the midpoint decibel levels of each interval is shown in Fig. 4-2. This amounts to a distribution curve of the levels encountered during that hour. From this curve it is easy to pick off the following significant points:

$$L_{max} = 87\,dB$$

$$L_{10} = 59.5\,dB$$

$$L_{50} = 51\,dB$$

$$L_{90} = 46.5\,dB$$

These four points provide a statistically representative description of noise levels applicable to that hour from 9 to 10 AM. A series of 12 hourly observation sheets covering the 9 AM to 9 PM period provides similar points for plotting, as shown in Fig. 4-3. The four points from Fig. 4-2

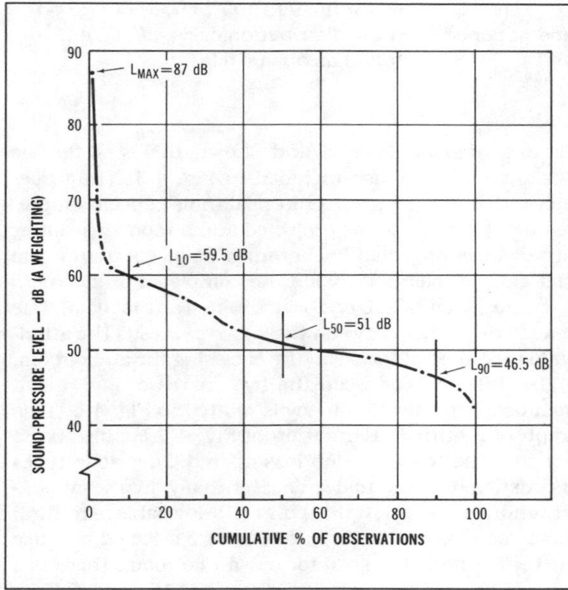

Figure 4-2 Distribution curve of the noise readings obtained during 1 hr tabulated in Fig. 4-1.

are plotted as open circles on a separate graph. Other graphs covering periods of time deemed significant from the outside noise standpoint provide the data necessary for construction specifications for the audio room being planned.

4.3 NOISE CRITERIA (NC)

The background noise that can be tolerated within the audio room must now be considered. The noise criteria (NC) contours of Fig. 4-4 are of help in this.[2] Other families of NC contours have been suggested such as the *PNC* (*preferred noise criteria*)[3] and *NR* (*noise rating*), which is used in Europe. Actually, none of these apply specifically to audio rooms, but the NC family is widely used for this purpose because it approximates the ideal and is convenient.

The beauty of the NC contours is that a spectrum specification is inherent in a single NC number. Considering spectrum shapes of noises is far superior to using a single, wideband noise level. The spectrum of each NC contour can be expressed as an overall decibel level, as shown in Table 4-1. These overall levels apply strictly only to noises where the distributed spectrum matches the corresponding NC contour and without dominant pure tone components.

The question that must be answered for any proposed audio room is, "What NC contour should be selected as a background noise goal?" For the uninitiated it is helpful to see recommended NC ranges for recording studios and other audio rooms compared to criteria applicable to spaces used for other purposes. Table 4-2 is for this purpose. The goals for concert halls and halls for opera, musicals, and plays are low to assure maximum dynamic range for music and greatest intelligibility for speech. This same reasoning applies to high-quality listening rooms such as control rooms. For recording studios, stringent NC goals are required to minimize noise pickup by the microphone. As a rule of thumb, levels below NC-30 are considered by some as "quiet," but there are different degrees of quietness. The NC-25 upper range

Table 4-1. NC (Noise Criteria) Overall Levels*

NC Contour	Equivalent Wideband Level (A-weighting)
15	28
20	33
25	38
30	42
35	46
40	50
45	55
50	60
55	65
60	70
65	75

*Source: Rettinger.[4]

Table 4-2. Noise Criteria Ranges

Use of Space	Noise Criteria Contour Range*
Private urban residence	25–35
Private rural residence	20–30
Hotel rooms	30–40
Hospital, private rooms	25–35
Hospital, lobby, corridors	35–45
Office, executive	30–40
Offices, open	35–45
Restaurant	35–45
Church sanctuary	20–30
Concert, opera halls	15–25
Studios, recording and Sound reproduction	15–25

*Selected from reference 23 for all HVAC systems operating.

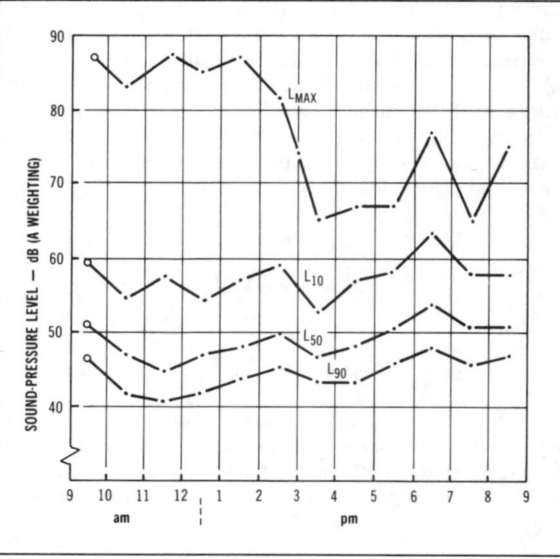

Figure 4-3 The noise levels corresponding to L_{max}, L_{10}, L_{50}, and L_{90} points for the 9 to 10 AM hour of Fig. 4-1 and obtained from the distribution curve of Fig. 4-2 are plotted as open circles.

listed for recording studios is the same as the lower level for an urban residence. Certainly, an NC-25 goal for a high-quality audio room is too high for most situations; a goal of NC-20 or, even better, NC-15 is safer and quite practical with careful design and construction.

4.4 TRANSMISSION-LOSS REQUIREMENT

Studio walls must be constructed heavily enough to solve two problems: (1) protection of the studio space from exterior environmental noise and (2) protection of neighbors from high sound levels produced inside the studio. Fortunately, the transmission loss of walls works both ways, and the methods of determining barrier requirements outlined here are equally applicable to sounds traveling from inside the studio to the outside.

Having determined the outside environmental noise characterizing the site of the proposed audio room by a noise survey and having decided upon a background noise goal for the inside of the space, we are in a position to calculate what is required in the line of walls and other barriers to achieve that goal. From Fig. 4-3 the L_{max} levels, although intermittent, dominate the situation. Jet aircraft created these noise peaks. In a similar way points for other hourly observations are obtained and plotted in this manner, which gives a comprehensive, statistical picture of environmental noise over this period of time.

Noise criteria curves are shown in Fig. 4-4. These curves are useful for establishing background noise goals in audio rooms and in determining compliance to those goals. The shape of the curves reflects the characteristics of the human ear. The noise spectrum of a typical jet aircraft is shown in Fig. 4-5. The level of this spectrum shape has been adjusted to conform to an overall peak reading of 87 dB, recorded at the site and shown in Fig. 4-3. The NC-20 contour is also included in Fig. 4-5. The upper curve, then, is the jet aircraft peak-noise spectrum prevailing at the site of the projected audio room. The lower curve is the projected background noise spectrum goal that can be tolerated inside the completed audio room (assuming that NC-20 has been selected as that goal). The shaded difference between these two curves is the attenuation required of the structure enclosing the audio room.

The difference between the two curves of Fig. 4-5 at each octave center frequency is plotted in Fig. 4-6. This graph of required attenuation of Fig. 4-6 enables us to compare the transmission loss offered by various types of construction and to decide, eventually, just what construction to specify. At this point it is advisable to rethink the noise goal of NC-20. If NC-15 were selected because the best is none too good for our audio room, there is a price to be paid. Lowering NC-20 to NC-15 adds 5 dB to the transmission-loss requirement, which could result in a substantial increase in building costs. On the other hand, four noise peaks produced by jet aircraft occurred between 9 and 10 AM. This frequency would create an everpresent hazard of jet noise intruding into a recorded selection or a critical listening session. The dependence of the barrier transmission-loss requirement on both the noise criterion selected and the observed exterior noise levels is evident. A high-quality (low-noise) interior is reflected in construction costs.

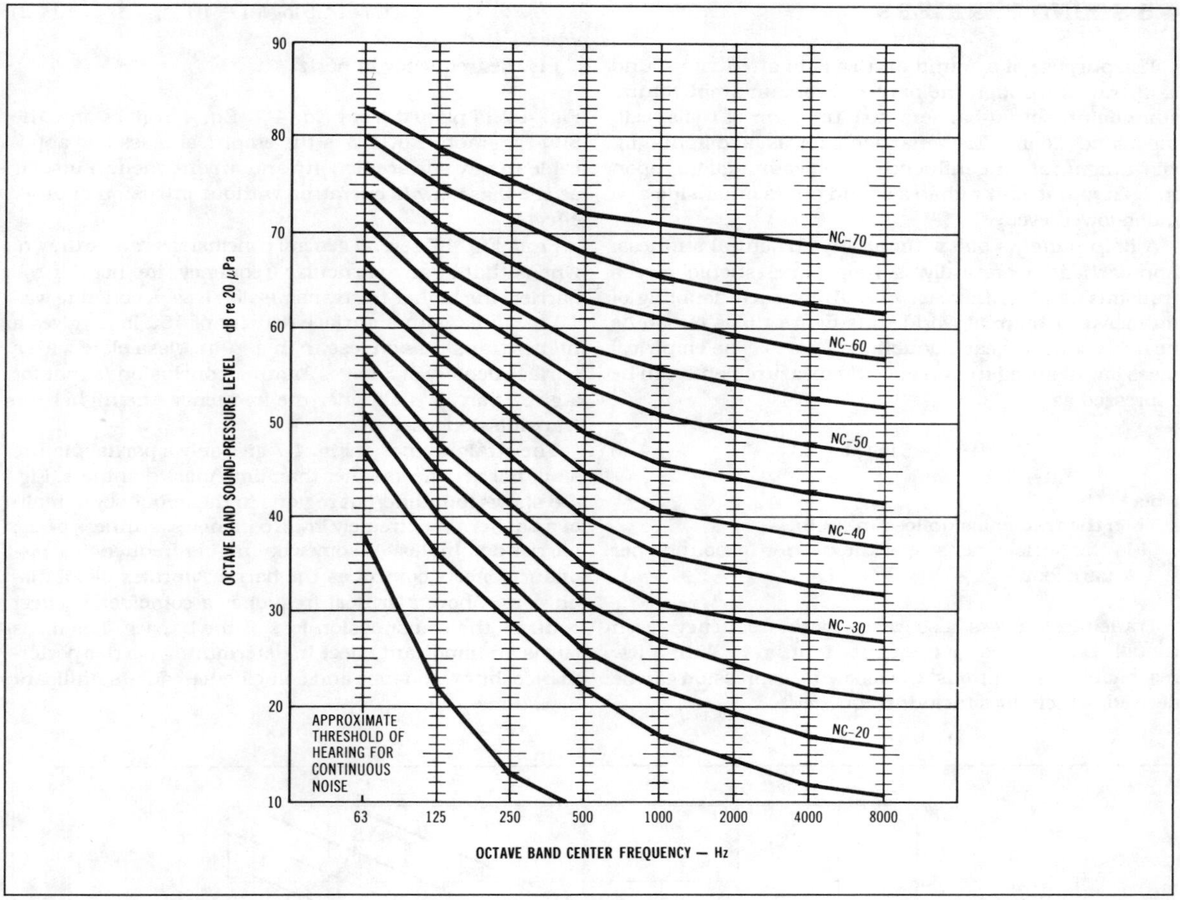

Figure 4-4 Noise criteria (NC) curves.

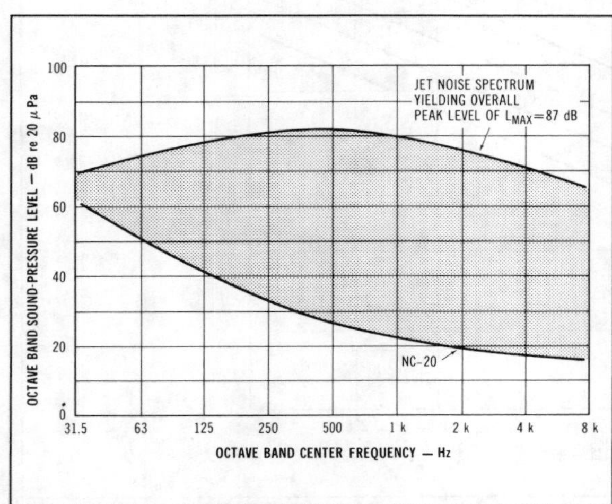

Figure 4-5 Noise spectrum of a typical jet aircraft.

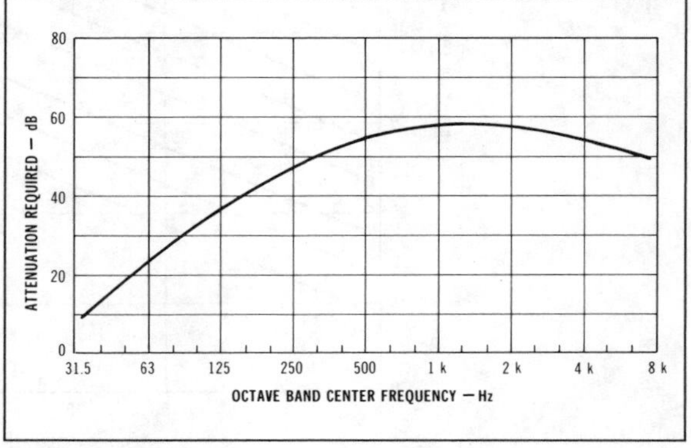

Figure 4-6 The difference between the two curves of Fig. 4-5, i.e., the structural attenuation required, is plotted here.

4.5 SOUND BARRIERS

The purpose of a sound barrier is to attenuate sound as it travels through the barrier. From an architectural standpoint, sound barriers take the form of walls, ceilings, and floors. Each barrier acts as a diaphragm, vibrating under the influence of the sound falling upon it. As it vibrates, it radiates sound on its other side at a much lower level.

A *limp panel* is one without any structural stiffness. Approached theoretically, a limp panel should give a transmission-loss increase of 6 dB for each doubling of its mass. In the real world, this figure turns out to be nearer 4.4 dB for each doubling of mass. The empirical mass law deduced from real-world measurements can be expressed as

$$TL = 14.5 \log M + 23 \qquad (4\text{-}1)$$

where,

TL is the transmission loss in decibels,

M is the surface density of the barrier in pounds per square foot.

Transmission loss also varies with frequency, even though Eq. 4-1 has no frequency term in it. With a few reasonable assumptions, the following expression can be derived, which does include frequency[5]:

$$TL = 14.5 \log Mf - 16 \qquad (4\text{-}2)$$

where,

f is the frequency in hertz.

Fig. 4-7 is plotted from Eq. 4-2. Eq. 4-1 gives only the 500-Hz graph; Eq. 4-2 is the empirical mass law applicable to any surface density and any frequency, insofar as the mass law is operating without intrusion of other effects.

From Fig. 4-7 several general conclusions can be drawn. One is that at any particular frequency, the heavier the barrier, the higher the transmission loss. A concrete wall 12 in. thick with a surface density of 150 lb/ft^2 gives a higher transmission loss than a ¼-in. glass plate with a surface density of 3 lb/ft^2. Another conclusion is that for a given barrier the higher the frequency, the higher the transmission loss.

The straight lines of Fig. 4-7 give only a partial picture since barrier effects other than limp mass dominate. Fig. 4-8 shows four different regions in the frequency domain of a barrier. At extremely low frequencies, stiffness of the barrier dominates. At somewhat higher frequencies, resonance effects control as the barrier vibrates like a diaphragm. Above a critical frequency a coincidence effect controls the transmission loss of the barrier. The mass law is an important effect in determining barrier performance, but resonance and coincidence cause significant deviations.

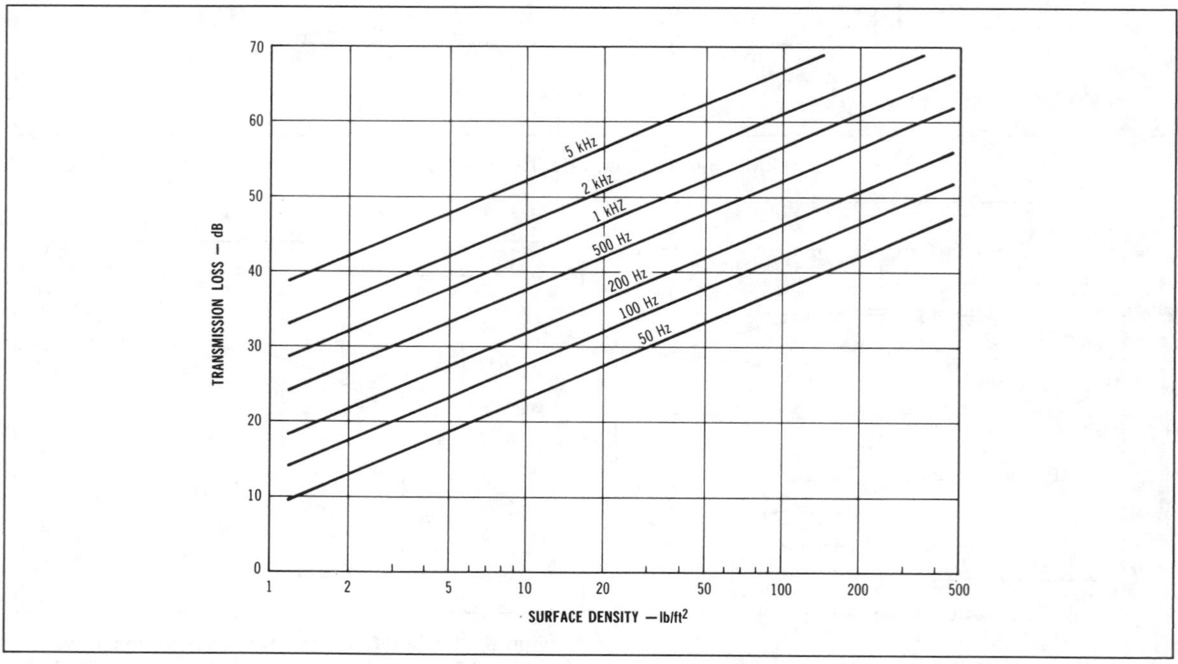

Figure 4-7 The empirical mass law based on real-world measurements of transmission loss. Surface density is the weight of the wall corresponding to a 1-ft^2 wall surface.

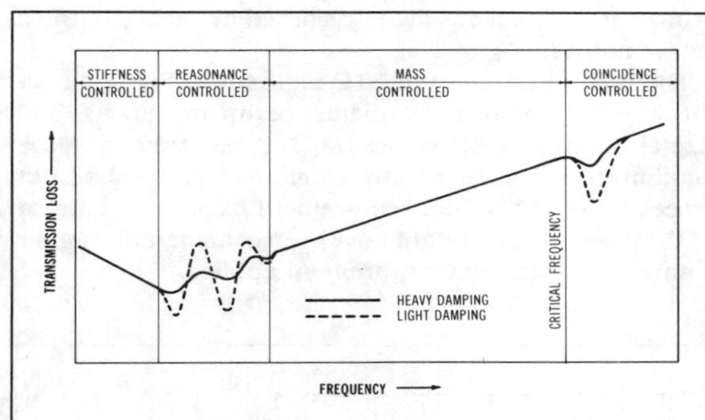

Figure 4-8 The frequency domain of a barrier is divided into four sections controlled by stiffness, resonance, mass, and coincidence of wavelength of impinging sound with surface-wave wavelength in the panel.

The low-frequency resonance effect is due to the mechanical resonance of the barrier. For the heavier barriers useful in audio rooms, the resonance frequency is usually below the audible limit. As the panel resonates at its fundamental mode, a dip in the transmission-loss curve occurs. At frequencies above this, the mass law takes over, but other higher modes of vibration of the panel may cause wiggles in the transmission-loss curve.

The coincidence effect occurs when the wavelength of the incident sound coincides with the wavelength of the bending waves in the panel. For a certain frequency and a certain angle of incidence of the incident sound, the bending oscillations of the panel will be amplified, and the sound energy will be transmitted through the panel with little attenuation. The incident sound covers a wide range of frequencies and arrives at all angles, but the overall result is that the coincidence effect creates an "acoustical hole" over a narrow range of frequencies giving rise to what is called the *coincidence dip* in the transmission-loss curve. This dip occurs above a critical frequency, which is a complex function of the properties of the material. Table 4-3 lists the critical frequency for some common building materials.

Table 4-3. Critical Frequencies*

Material	Thickness (Inches)	Critical Frequency (Hertz)
Brick wall	10	67
Brick wall	5	130
Concrete wall	8	100
Glass plate	1/4	1,600
Plywood	3/4	700

*Calculated from Rettinger.[5]

4.6 SOUND TRANSMISSION CLASS (STC)

The noise criteria approach is convenient and valuable because it defines a typical noise spectrum by a single NC number. It is just as convenient and valuable to be able to classify a barrier transmission loss versus frequency curve by a single number. A standard way of doing this is by using the concept of *sound transmission class (STC)*.[6] A typical standard contour is defined by the values in Table 4-4. A plot of the data in Table 4-4 is shown in Fig. 4-9. The STC-40 contour only is shown, but all other contours have exactly the same shape.

Let us assume that a transmission loss versus frequency plot of a given partition is at hand and that we want to establish the sound transmission class of that partition. The first step is to prepare a transparent overlay of a standard STC contour, say the STC-40 contour of Table 4-4 and Fig. 4-9, to the same frequency and TL scales of the transmission-loss graph on a piece of tracing paper. Then shift this overlay vertically until some of the measured TL values are below the contour and the following conditions are fulfilled: (1) the sum of the deficiencies (i.e., the deviations below the contour) shall not be greater than 32 dB and (2) the maximum deficiency at any single test point shall not exceed 8 dB. When the contour is adjusted to the highest value that meets the above requirements, the sound transmission class of that partition is the TL value corresponding to the intersection of the contour and the 500-Hz ordinate.

Not many readers will have the need to determine STC ratings, but most will need to understand what sound transmission class stands for and some of the inherent problems. An example of the use of STC is given in Fig. 4-10. First, the problem is to determine the STC rating for the measured TL curve shown in Fig. 4-10. The STC overlay is first aligned to 500 Hz and adjusted vertically

Table 4-4. Standard STC Contour

Frequency One-Third Octave (Hertz)	Sound Transmission Loss (Decibels)	
125	24	
160	27	
200	30	
250	33	
315	36	
400	39	
500	40	← Contour identified
630	41	by TL value at
800	42	500 Hz
1000	43	
1250	44	
1600	44	
2000	44	
2500	44	
3150	44	
4000	44	

to read some estimated value, say, STC-44. The number of decibels the measured TL curve is below the STC-44 overlay is read off at each one-third octave point, and all are added together. The total, 47 dB, is more than the 32 dB allowed. The STC overlay is next lowered to an estimated STC-42, and a total of 37 dB results. Lowering the overlay to STC-41 yields a total of 29 dB, which fixes the STC-41 contour as the rating for the TL curve of Fig. 4-10. The number of decibels the measured TL curve is below the STC-41 overlay is recorded at each one-third octave point in Fig. 4-10.

The final illustration of STC methods is Fig. 4-11. In this case, a pronounced coincidence dip appears at 2500 Hz. This illustrates the second STC requirement, "the maximum deficiency at any single test point shall not exceed 8 dB." This 8-dB requirement fixes the overlay at STC-39, although it might have been considerably higher if only the 32-dB sum requirement applied.

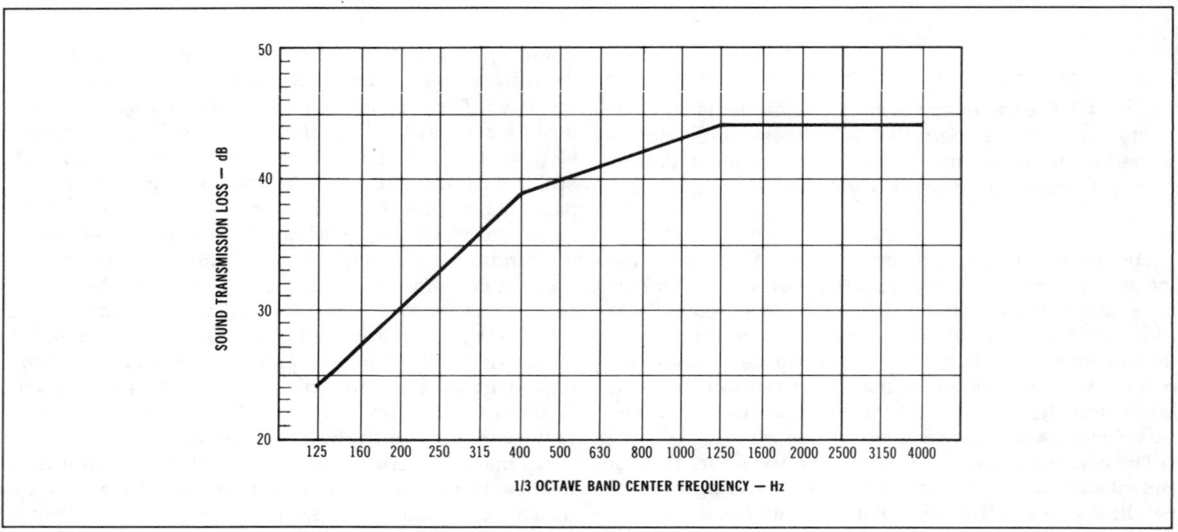

Figure 4-9 The standard shape used in determining the sound transmission class (STC) of a partition.

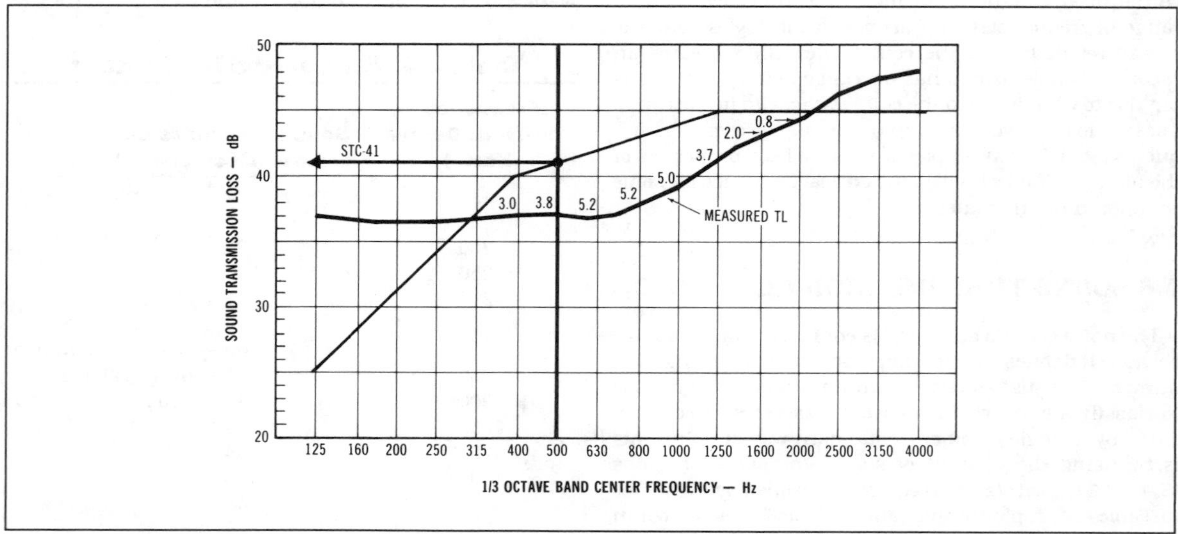

Figure 4-10 Illustration of the method of determining the single-number STC rating from the measured transmission loss (TL) graph.

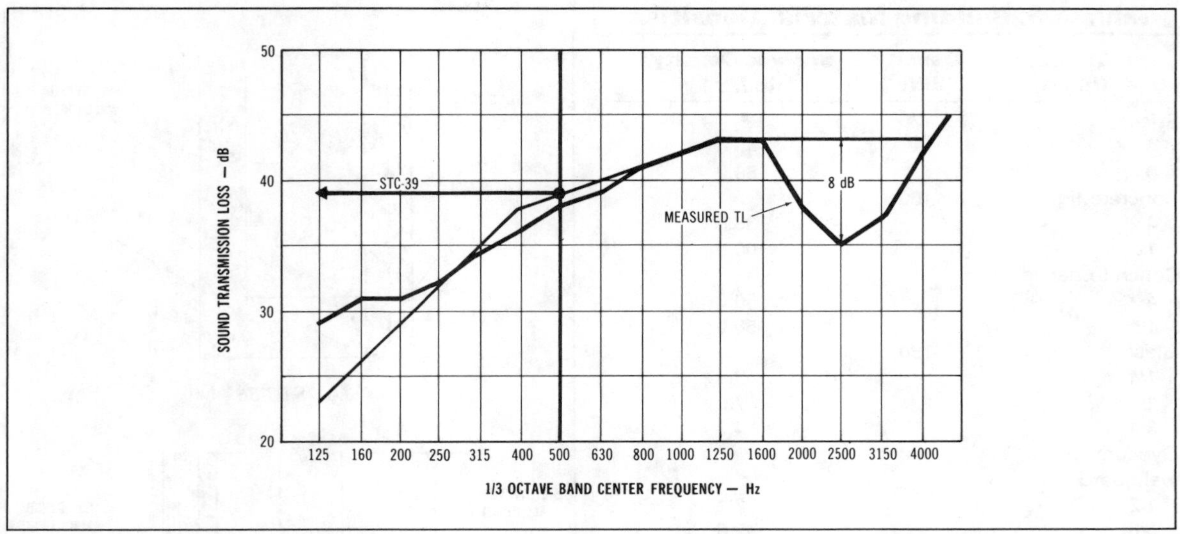

Figure 4-11 Illustrating the second rule for STC determination that a maximum deficiency of 8 dB is allowed.

The shape of the standard STC contour may be very different from the measured transmission-loss curve. For precise work, dealing with measured (or even expertly estimated) TL curves may be desirable rather than relying on STC single-number ratings. Convenience usually dictates use of the STC shorthand system, but it is, at best, a rather crude approximation to the real-world transmission-loss curves.

What wall construction will bring the outdoor jet noise of Fig. 4-5 down to the NC-20 goal we have set for the interior? Fig. 4-12 shows that a wall having a rating of STC-55 is required. The next step is that of exploring the multitude of possible wall configurations to find the STC-55 wall, which meets other needs as well as the acoustical.

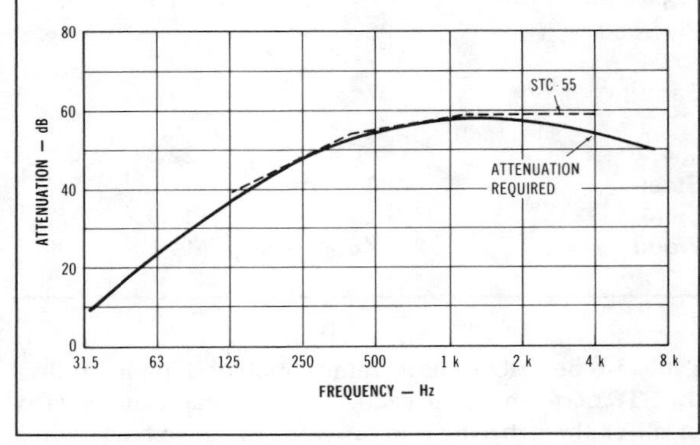

Figure 4-12 The sound barrier attenuation required for the audio room example of Fig. 4-6 is specified here as STC-55.

4.7 WALL CONSTRUCTION

Practical walls for audio rooms are subject to all the effects of the previous section. Diaphragmatic resonance of a wall panel occurs at low frequencies; coincidence dips, at higher frequencies; and a mass-controlled region, between the two, as noted in Fig. 4-8. The more massive the wall and the more highly damped the material, the fewer the problems introduced by diaphragmatic resonance. Coincidence dips in the transmission-loss curve and their resulting transparency to sound in a narrow range of frequencies are a continual source of aggravation, requiring constant attention to their management.

In comparing the relative effectiveness of various wall configurations, the mass law offers the most easily accessible rough approximation. To enter the mass law graphs of Fig. 4-7, the surface density is required. This is simply the weight of a 1-ft^2 wall surface. To assist in computing this, the densities of various common building materials are listed in Table 4-5. An air space, such as between two faces of a 2 × 4-ft frame partition, introduces an element other than mass and generally leads to higher transmission loss.

4.7.1 High-Loss Frame Walls

The literature describing walls for high transmission loss is so extensive and, at times, inconsistent that the challenge here is to get a dependable, highly simplified overview of the field with an emphasis on practical solutions for audio room walls. Jones' summary shown in

Table 4-5. Building Material Densities

Material (in.)	Density (lb/ft^3)	Surface Density (lb./ft^2)
Brick	120	
4		40.0
8		80.0
Concrete:light wt.	100	
4		33.0
12		100.0
Concrete:dense	150	
4		50.0
12		150.0
Glass	180	
1/4		3.8
1/2		7.5
3/4		11.3
Gypsum wallboard	50	
1/2		2.1
5/8		2.6
Lead	700	
1/16		3.6
Particle Board	48	
3/4		1.7
Plywood	36	
3/4		2.3
Sand	97	
1		8.1
4		32.3
Steel	480	
1/4		10.0
Wood	24–48	
1		2–4

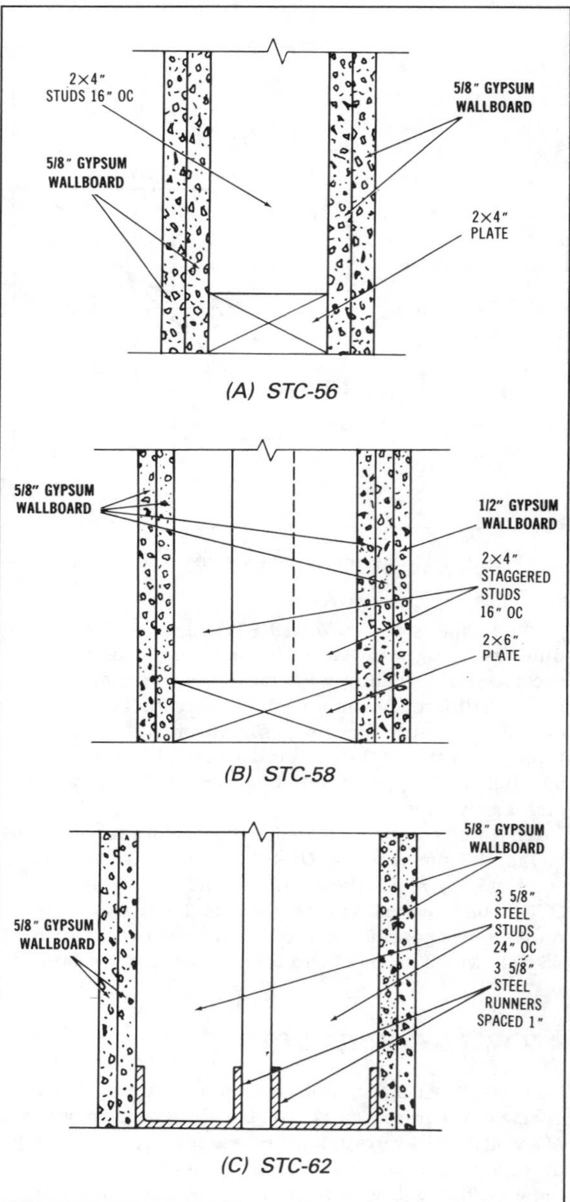

Figure 4-13 Three arrangements of two-leaf partitions using gypsum wallboard having progressively higher STC ratings. *(From data by Green and Sherry, Reference 8.)*

Table 4-6 describes eight frame constructions including the STC performance of each.[7] Gypsum wallboard is used in all of them because it provides an inexpensive and convenient way to get wall mass as well as fire-retardant properties. Two lightweight concrete block walls, systems 9 and 10, fall in the general STC range of the gypsum wallboard walls 1 to 8, inclusive.

The three recent papers by Green and Sherry report measurements on many wall configurations utilizing gypsum wallboard.[8] Fig. 4-13 describes three of them yielding STCs from 56 to 62.

An expression of the empirical mass law in terms of STC rating rather than transmission loss[7] is shown in Fig. 4-14. This makes it easy to evaluate the partitions of Table 4-6 and Fig. 4-13 in terms of partition surface weight. The numbered STC shaded ranges of Fig. 4-14 correspond to the same numbered partitions of Table 4-6, and the A, B, and C points refer to the A, B, and C constructions of Fig. 4-13. Only 1 and 9 fall on the empirical mass law line; all others are 10 to 20 dB better performers than straight mass. This better performance results primarily from decoupling one leaf of a structure from the other, although numerous other factors to be listed are important as well. Here are ten points to remember concerning frame walls for highest STC ratings.

1. It is theoretically desirable to avoid having the coincidence dip associated with one leaf of a wall at the same frequency as that of the other leaf. Making the two leaves different with coincidence dips appearing at different frequencies should render their combined effect more favorable. However, Green and Sherry found this effect negligible when partitions having equivalent surface weights were compared.[8]

2. The two leaves of a wall can be made different by (a) utilizing gypsum board of different thicknesses, (b) mounting a soft fiber (sound-deadening) board under one gypsum board face, and/or (c) mounting gypsum board on resilient channels on one side.

3. Resilient channels are more effective on wood studs than on steel studs.

4. Steel-stud partitions usually have an STC from two to ten points higher than the equivalent wood-stud partition. The flange of the common C-shaped steel stud is relatively flexible and transmits somewhat less sound energy from face to face.

5. If multiple layers of gypsum board are used, mounting the second layer with adhesive rather than screws can affect an STC increase by as much as six points. This is especially helpful with higher density walls.

6. A fiberglass cavity filler (such as R-7) may increase STC by five to eight points. It is more effective in multilayer partitions if the second layer is attached with adhesive.

7. A slight increase in STC results from increasing stud spacing from 16 to 24 in. on center.

8. Increasing stud size from 2½ to 3⅝ in. does not significantly increase either transmission loss or STC in steel-stud partitions with filler in the cavity.

9. Additional layers of gypsum wallboard increase STC and transmission loss, but the greatest improvement is with lighter walls. Adding layers increases stiffness, which tends to shift the coincidence dip to a lower frequency.

10. Attaching the first wallboard layer to studs with adhesive actually reduces STC.

4.7.2 Concrete Block Walls

Concrete block walls behave much like solid walls of the same surface weight and bending stiffness. In Table 4-6, wall system 9 is a lightweight, hollow, concrete block wall with both sides sealed with latex paint. In Fig. 4-14 we see that the performance of this specific wall falls close to pure mass operation. The STC-46 is matched or exceeded by many frame walls listed before it in Table 4-6.

Wall system 10 in Table 4-6 is the same as 9, except wall system 10 has a new leaf, is furred out, and has mineral fiber added to one side in the cavity. These additions increase the STC from 46 to 57, but, again, there are two leaf frame structures before it that can match it. If concrete block walls are dictated by cost or structural factors, their transmission loss can be made to match most double-frame walls by increasing the thickness of the wall, by plastering one or both faces, or by filling the voids with sand or well-rodded concrete, all of which increase wall mass. The STC performance of such walls can be estimated from Fig. 4-14 when the pounds-per-square-foot surface density is calculated. From there on, adding a furred-out facing (such as 10) or adding a second block wall with an air space between the two walls is about the only course of action remaining.

4.7.3 Concrete Walls

The empirical mass law line in Fig. 4-14 goes only to 100 lb/ft^2, only far enough to catch an 8-in. concrete wall of 150 lb/ft^3 density (surface density 100 lb/ft^2). This wall gives a rating close to STC-54. By extending the line we would find that a 12-in. wall would give STC-57, and a concrete wall 24-in. thick, about STC-61. The conclusion is inescapable. This brute-force approach to sound transmission loss is not the best solution, if there is any other alternative. High transmission-loss concrete walls can be improved by introducing air space, for example, two 8-in. walls spaced a foot or so apart. Such a wall requires specialized engineering talent to study damping of the individual leaves of the double wall, the coupling of the two leaves by the air cavity, the critical frequencies involved, the resonances of the air cavity, and so on. Suffice it to say that this type of wall has no ready-made solutions appearing in handbooks.

4.7.4 Wall Caulking

There is a continual movement of all building elements due to wind, temperature expansion and contraction, hygroscopic changes, and deflections due to creep and loading. These movements can open up tiny cracks that are anything but tiny in their ability to negate the effects of a high-loss partition. An acoustical sealant is required to caulk all joints of a partition if highest transmission loss is to be attained. This type of sealant is a specialty product with nonstaining, nonhardening properties that provides a good seal for many years.

Fig. 4-15 calls attention to the importance of bedding steel runners and wood plates in caulking to defeat the irregularities always present on concrete surfaces. A bead

Table 4-6. Sound Transmission Class of Some Common Building Partitions*

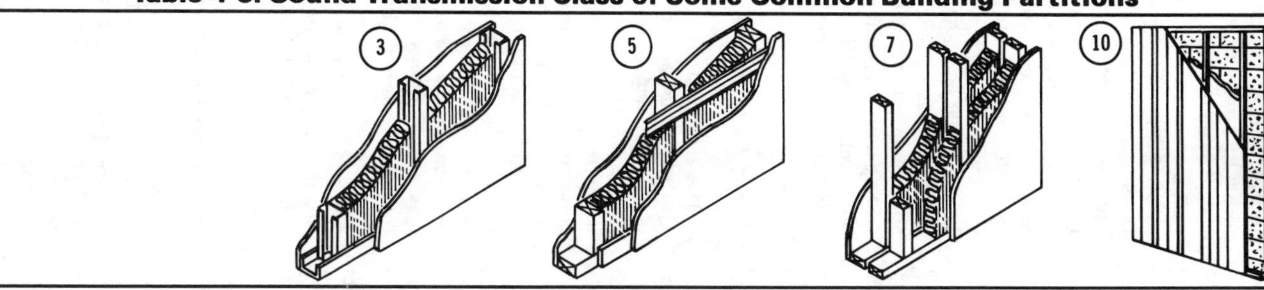

Wall System	Test Sponsor[1]	Laboratory Test Reference	Surface Weight, lb/ft²	STC Rating: *No* Cavity Absorption	STC Rating: Cavity Absorption
1. Single-row 2 × 4 wood stud (16 in. on center), single-layer ⅝-in gypsum board panels each side, *direct attached*	OCF	OCF 424 & OCF 423	—	34	36 (3½-in. glass fiber)
	NGC	NGC 2403 & NGC 2166	6.1	35	38 (3½-in. glass fiber)
2. *Same as 1*, except double-layer ½-in. gypsum board each side	OCF	OCF W-23-69 & OCF W-25-69	—	39	45 (3½-in. glass fiber)
3. Single-row 24-gage 3⅝-in. steel stud (24-in. on center) single ⅝-in gypsum board panels each side, *direct attached.*	NGC	NGC 2385 & NGC 2386	5.2	42	47 (2½-in. glass fiber)
4. *Same as 3*, except double-layer ½-in. gypsum board each side	NGC	NGC 2282 & NGC 2288	8.9	48	53 (3-in. glass fiber)

5. Single-row 2 × 4 wood stud, single-layer ⅝-in. gypsum board panels, *direct attached* one side, attached to metal *resilient channels* other side	FPL	TL 73-72	6.4	—	47 (2¼-in. glass fiber)
	OCF	OCF 431 & OCF 427	—	40	46 (3½-in. glass fiber)
	GA	TL 77-138	—	—	50 (3½-in. glass fiber)
6. *Same as 5*, except double-layer ⅝-in. gypsum board each side	USG	TL 67-212 & TL 67-239	10.6	49	59 (3½-in. mineral fiber)
	NGC	NGC 2368 & NGC 2365	11.3	50	54 (3½-in. glass fiber)
7. Double-row 2 × 4 wood stud, 1-in. plate separation, single-layer ⅝-in. gypsum board each side	FPL	TL 75-83	7.6	—	57 (double 3½-in. glass fiber)
	OCF	OCF W-43-69 & OCF 448	—	45	56 (3-in. glass fiber)
8. *Same as 7*, except double-layer gypsum board each side	FPL	TL 75-82	12.2	—	63 (double 3½-in. glass fiber)
	OCF	OCF W-42-69 & OCF W-40-69	—	58	62 (1½-in. glass fiber)
9. 8-in. lightweight hollow concrete block both sides sealed with latex paint	ABPA	TL 70-16	34	46	—
10. *Same as 9*, with addition of furred out wall: 1⅝-in. 24-gage metal studs, runners placed ¼ in. from concrete wall, covered with ¼-in. prefinished hardboard facing	ABPA	TL 70-14	36	—	57 (1½-in. mineral fiber)

[1]OCF—Owens-Corning Fiberglas Corporation, Box 415, Granville, OH
NGC—Gold Bond Building Products Division, National Gypsum Company, 1650 Military Rd., Buffalo, NY
FPL—USDA Forest Products Laboratory, P.O. Box 5130, Madison, WI
GA—Gypsum Association, 1603 Orrington Ave., Evanston, IL
USG—United States Gypsum, 101 S. Wacker Drive, Chicago, IL
ABPA—American Board Products Association, 205 W. Touhy Ave., Park Ridge, IL

*Source: Reference 7

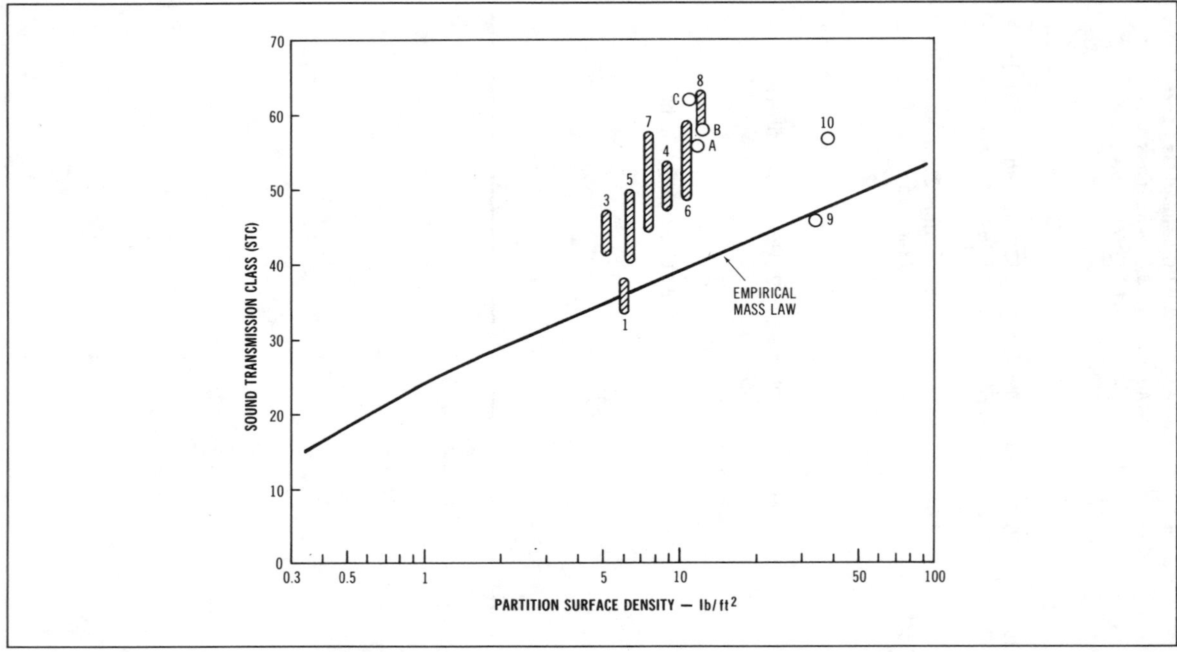

Figure 4-14 A variation of the empirical mass law expressed in terms of sound transmission class rather than sound transmission loss.

of sealant should also be run under the inner layer of gypsum board. The need for such sealing is as important at the juncture of wall-to-wall and wall-to-ceiling as it is at the floor line. The idea is to seal the room hermetically.

4.8 FLOOR AND CEILING CONSTRUCTION

Having high transmission-loss walls around an audio room is futile unless similar attention is given to both the floor and ceiling system above the room, and to the floor of the audio room. Heel and other impact noise on the floor above the room is readily transmitted through the ceiling structure and radiated into the audio room unless precautions are taken. The floor and ceiling structure of Fig. 4-16A is the type common in most existing buildings. Impact noises produced on the floor above are transmitted through the joists to the ceiling diaphragm below and radiated with low loss into the room below. Carpet on the floor above softens heel taps, but its low mass has little effect on transmission loss offered to airborne sounds. Some decoupling of the floor membrane from the ceiling membrane is introduced in Fig. 4-16B in the form of resilient mounting of the ceiling gypsum board. Introduction of absorbent material in the cavity between is also of modest benefit. In Table 4-7 four floor and ceiling structures are described along with STC ratings for each, as determined from field transmission-loss measurements.

Another means of decoupling the floor above from the audio room ceiling is suspending the entire ceiling by a resilient suspension, such as in Fig. 4-17. Very little test work has been conducted to show the effectiveness of such a resiliently suspended ceiling, but Mason Industries, Inc., reports one test.[10] They started out with a 3-in. concrete floor that alone gave STC-41. With a 12-in. air gap, a ⅝-in. gypsum board ceiling was supported on W30N spring and neoprene hangers, resulting in STC-50. By adding a second layer of ⅝-in. gypsum board and a sound-absorbent material in the air space, an estimated STC-55 should be realized. The combination of neoprene and spring in the hanger is most effective over a wide frequency range since the spring is effective at lower frequencies and the neoprene at higher frequencies.

4.9 FLOOR CONSTRUCTION

Building an audio room in an existing building requires very careful attention to the floor. If the audio room is on the ground floor of a frame building, the floor, whatever its construction, is the only barrier between the low-noise room and the environmental airborne noise penetrating to the underside of the floor. Building an audio room on

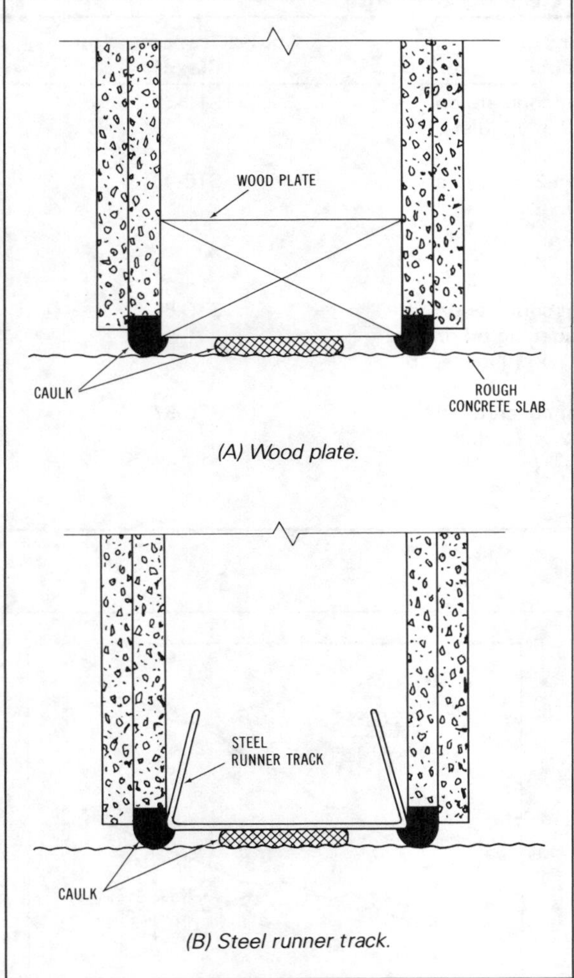

(A) Wood plate.

(B) Steel runner track.

Figure 4-15 Caulking methods used for partitions.

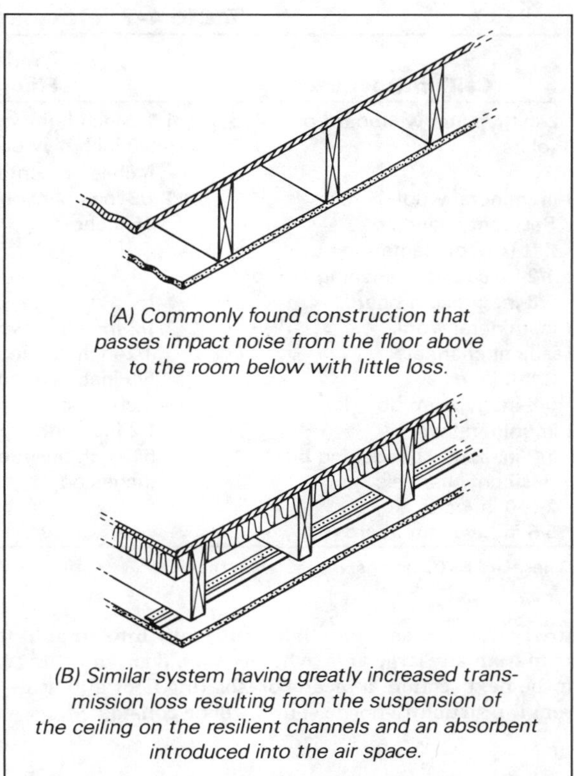

(A) Commonly found construction that passes impact noise from the floor above to the room below with little loss.

(B) Similar system having greatly increased transmission loss resulting from the suspension of the ceiling on the resilient channels and an absorbent introduced into the air space.

Figure 4-16 Floor and ceiling systems.

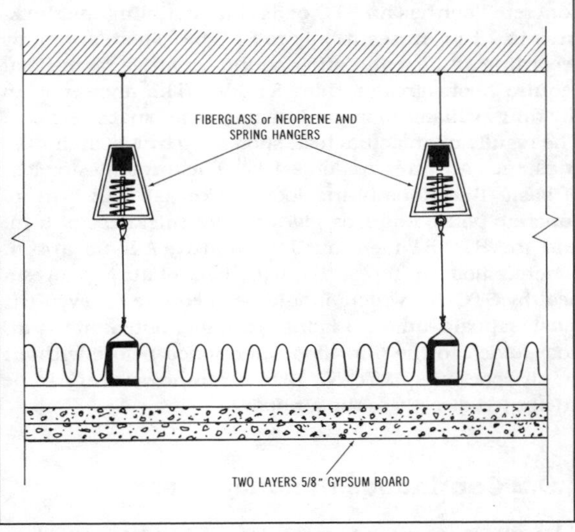

Figure 4-17 A method of suspending a ceiling that gives a great improvement in STC rating of the floor and ceiling combination.

an upper level of an existing frame building means that its floor will be the floor and ceiling structure of the level below with performance approximating that described in Table 4-7.

Adapting an audio room to a steel-frame building with concrete floors has its own peculiar set of problems. Not only must environmental airborne noises be confronted, the noises originating within that very building become a major problem.

Sound transmitted via a solid path requires a different approach in its suppression than airborne sound. Solid-borne sound usually originates as impacts or machinery vibration. Vibrations caused by a waterpipe hammering or a motor mounted rigidly to a building structure are carried throughout a concrete structure with low attenuation and at a speed ten times greater than in air. Struc-

Table 4-7. Floor and Ceiling Systems

Ceiling Treatment	Treatment of Floor Above	Sound Transmission Class*
1/2-in. gypsum wallboard nailed to joists	1 1/2-inch lightweight concrete on 5/8-inch plywood, 2 × 12 joists 16 inches on centers	STC-48
3-in. mineral wool Resilient channels 2 ft-0 in. on center 1/2-in. sound deadening board, 5/8-in. gypsum board	1 1/8-inch plywood on 2 × 10 joists 16 inches oc	STC-46
3-in. mineral wool, Resilient channels 2 ft-0 in. oc 5/8-in. gypsum board	1 1/2-inch lightweight concrete on 1/2-inch sound deadening bd on 5/8-inch plywood, 2 × 10 joists, 16 inches oc	STC-57
2-in. mineral wool 1/2-in. sound deadening bd. Resilient channels 2 ft-0 in. oc 5/8-in. gypsum board	1 1/2-inch lightweight concrete on 5/8-inch plywood, 2 × 10 joists, 16 inches oc	STC-57

*These are FSTC ratings, measured in the field.[9]

ture-borne sounds are radiated efficiently into an audio room from any large area, whether wall, floor, or ceiling. In the next section, a means of isolating floor and walls from the structure-borne sound will be considered.

4.9.1 Floating Floors

Increasing mass is often the least productive way to make significant gains in STC. For example, a 6-in. solid concrete floor has an STC of 54, and doubling the thickness to 12 in. raises it only to STC-59. There are many recording studios and other sound-sensitive rooms that require floors greater than STC-54. The answer is in dividing available mass and placing an air space between. The results of an actual test, sponsored by Mason Industries, Inc., are given in Fig. 4-18.[10] The transmission loss of basic T-sections (4-in. floor thickness) with 2 in. of concrete poured on this gives a total thickness of 6 in. and the STC-54 mentioned previously. Adding a 4-in. concrete floor on top of this with 1 in. of air gap gives a healthy STC-76, which should be adequate for even the most critical studios. It is interesting to note that a 4-in. floor added to the 6-in. floor mentioned before without an air space gives STC-57. A 19 dB improvement can be attributed directly to the air space.

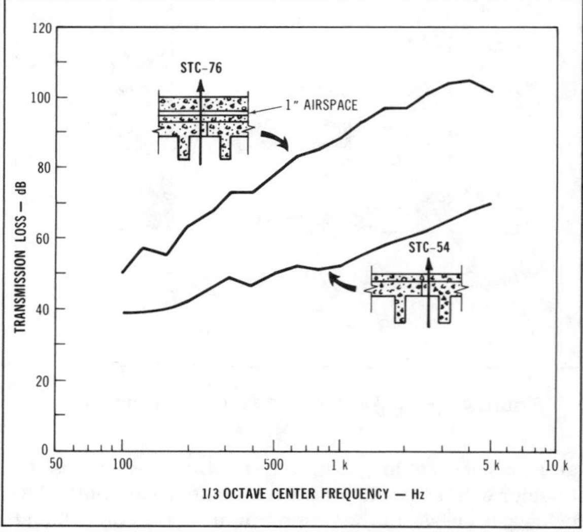

Figure 4-18 The dramatic improvement of standard transmission class from 54 to 76 by adding a 4-in. floating floor with a 1-in. air gap between it and the structural floor. *(Riverband TL-71-247, June, 1971, test reported by Mason Industries, Inc., in Reference 10.)*

4.9.2 Continuous Underlayment

Despite its name, a floating floor of 4-in. concrete does not float in the air with no visible means of support; there must be something between it and the structural floor to carry not only its deadweight but also the liveweight of people. Four ways of supporting a floating floor are shown in Fig. 4-19. What might be termed a primitive type of floating floor, characteristic of early attempts, is described in Fig. 4-19A.[11] Boards of soft vegetable or mineral fiber intended for airborne sound absorption were butted together, completely covering the floor. A covering of building paper, overlapped at the seams, was then placed over the boards, and the concrete was poured on chicken wire for reinforcement. In this case the air space was completely filled with low-density board. This approach usually gave significant improvement over a solid floor; however, its permanency was suspect, and data upon which calculations could be based was unavailable. The method of continuous underlayment is not in favor today.

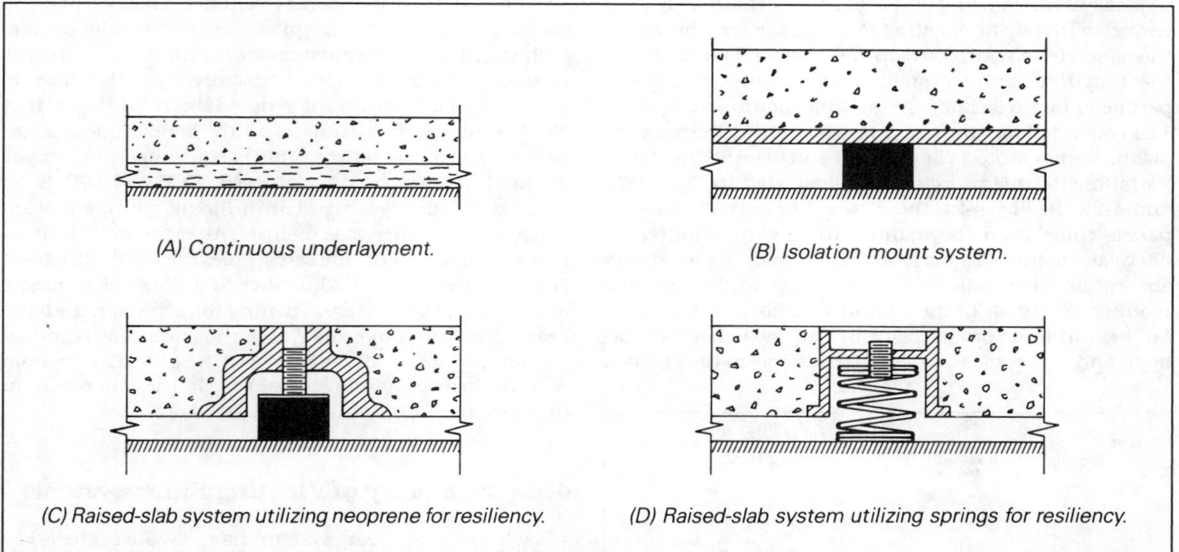

(A) Continuous underlayment.
(B) Isolation mount system.
(C) Raised-slab system utilizing neoprene for resiliency.
(D) Raised-slab system utilizing springs for resiliency.

Figure 4-19 Four methods used in floating floors for increasing transmission loss.

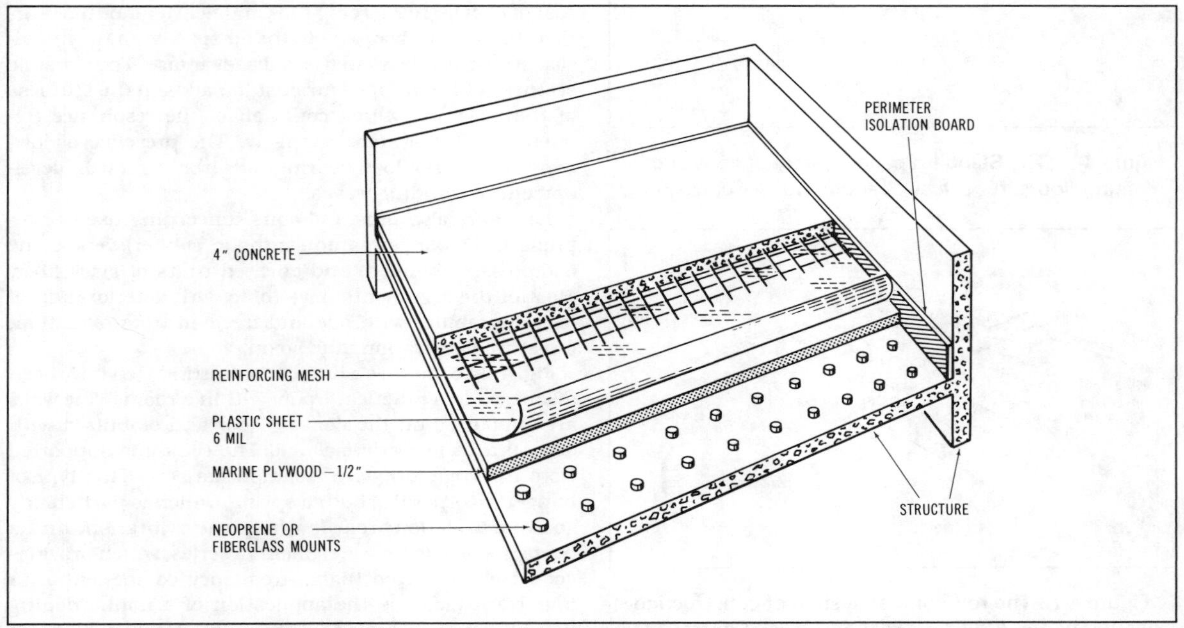

Figure 4-20 Constructional details of a floating floor utilizing neoprene mounts.

4.9.3 Isolation Mount System

A significant improvement in supporting a floating floor is shown in Fig. 4-19B. Here the concrete slab is supported by neoprene "hockey pucks" or by compressed and bonded fiberglass coated with an impervious membrane (typically 2 in. high and on 12- to 24-in. centers). Plywood covered with plastic sheeting provides the form on which the concrete is poured. A typical floating floor based on the isolation mount system is shown in Fig. 4-20. A perimeter board isolates the floating floor from the walls. The concrete is poured on a plywood form covered with plastic film to protect the plywood and to avoid "bridges." Variations of this principle are illustrated in Figs. 4-21 and 4-22. In Fig. 4-21 the plywood or corrugated steel panels come from the manufacturer with compressed fiberglass mounts in place, complete with a low-density absorption fiberglass to fill the air space between the mounts. In Fig. 4-22 the compressed fiberglass mounts are held in their proper place by the low-density absorbent, and it all comes in rolls. When unrolled, the plywood panels are then put in place, the plastic sheet laid over the plywood, and the concrete poured.

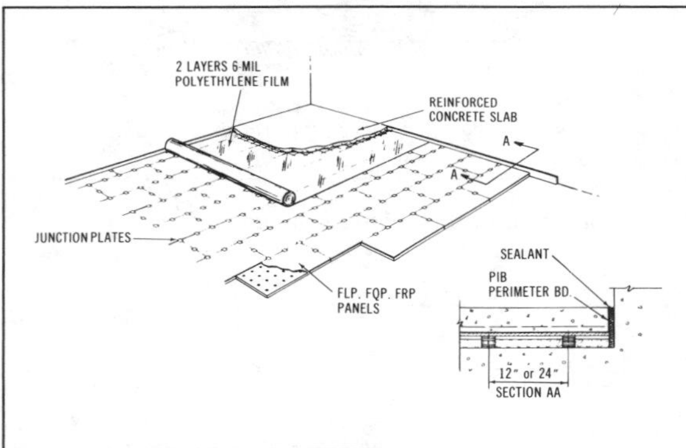

Figure 4-21 The Standard panel system of constructing floating floors. *(Courtesy Peabody Noise Control, Inc.)*

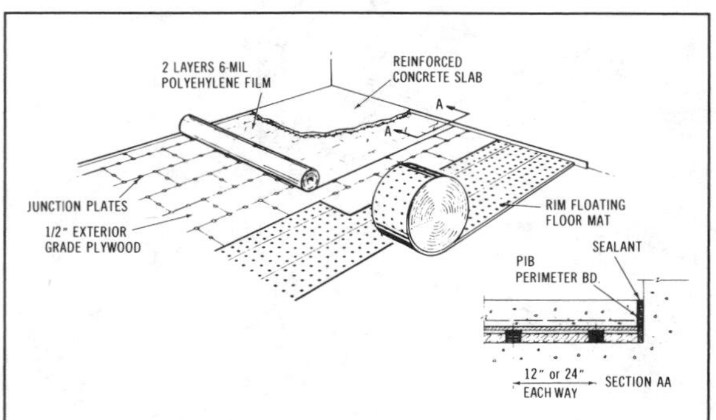

Figure 4-22 The roll-out mat system of constructing floating floors. *(Courtesy Peabody Noise Control, Inc.)*

4.9.4 Raised-Slab System

In Fig. 4-19c the individual isolators are housed in metal canisters that are placed typically on 36- to 48-in. centers each way. The metal canisters are arranged to tie into the steel reinforcing grid and are cast directly in the concrete slab. After sufficient curing time (about 28 days), it is lifted by judicious turning of all the screws one-quarter or one-half turn at a time. This is continued until an air space of at least 1 in. is achieved. In Fig. 4-19D is an alternative raised-slab system utilizing springs instead of neoprene or fiberglass mounts. After the slab is raised to the desired height, the screw holes are filled with grout and smoothed. Fig. 4-23 further describes the elements of the raised-slab system. Turning the screws in the load-bearing isolation mounts raises the cured slab, producing an air space of the required height. This system requires heavier reinforcement rods in the concrete than the systems of Figs. 4-20, 4-21, and 4-22.

4.9.5 Summary of Floating Floor Systems

Each floating floor system has its advocates. For instance, claims of economy for the raised-slab system are based on a lack of pouring forms, a lack of sound-absorbent blanket, and fewer mounts because of greater spacing. All these advantages tend to be offset by the added cost of heavier reinforcing rods and heavier mounts. Further, the lack of absorbent in the air space with the raised-slab system can be viewed as a disadvantage. The dynamic stiffness of the trapped air cushion adds to the stiffness of the isolators, which could affect the resonance frequency of the system adversely. The presence of low-density (but nonload-bearing) absorbent retards development of standing waves.

There are also pros and cons concerning use of neoprene (a Dupont organic synthetic rubber) versus the compressed, bonded, and encased units of glass fiber. Most of the arguments have to do with deterioration of isolating ability with age and freedom from oxidation, moisture penetration, and so on.

Fig. 4-24 combines a number of features that have been discussed in a practical "room within a room." The walls are supported on the floating floor and stabilized with sway braces properly isolated. The ceiling is supported from the structure with isolation hangers. This type of hanger incorporates both a spring, which is particularly good for isolation from low-frequency vibration, and a neoprene or a fiberglass element in series, which provides good isolation from higher-frequency components. An important factor is the application of a nonhardening type of acoustical sealant at the points marked "s." Such a room should provide adequate protection from structure-borne vibrations originating within the building as well as from the seismic type of vibrations transmitted through the ground to the building from nearby truck, surface railroad, or subway sources.

The design of rooms to achieve maximum isolation from airborne and structure-borne sounds is a highly specialized undertaking, ordinarily entrusted to consultants expert in that branch of acoustics. However, an audio engineer, charged with the responsibility of working with a consultant or doing the design personally, is advised to become familiar with the sometimes conflicting claims of

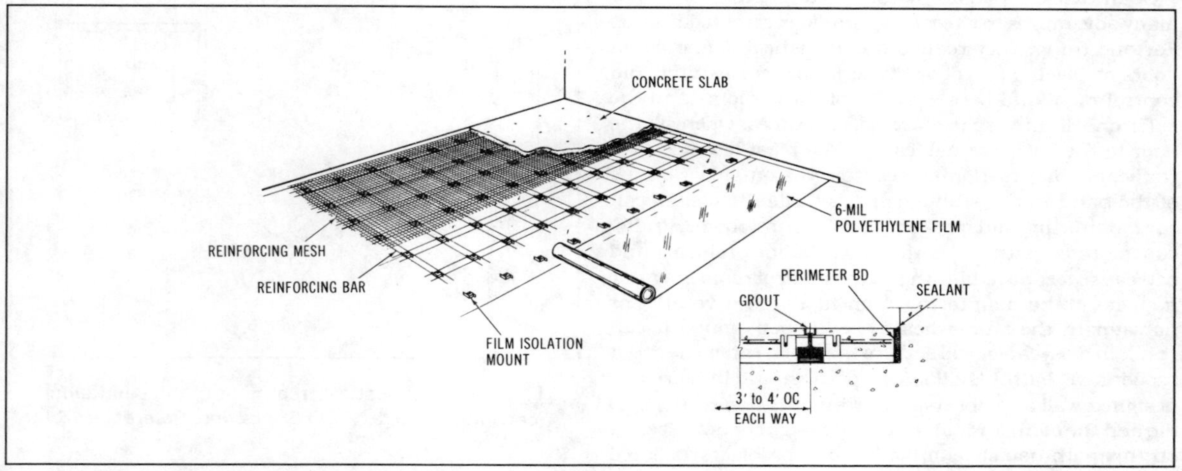

Figure 4-23 The raised-slab system of constructing floating floors. *(Courtesy Peabody Noise Control, Inc.)*

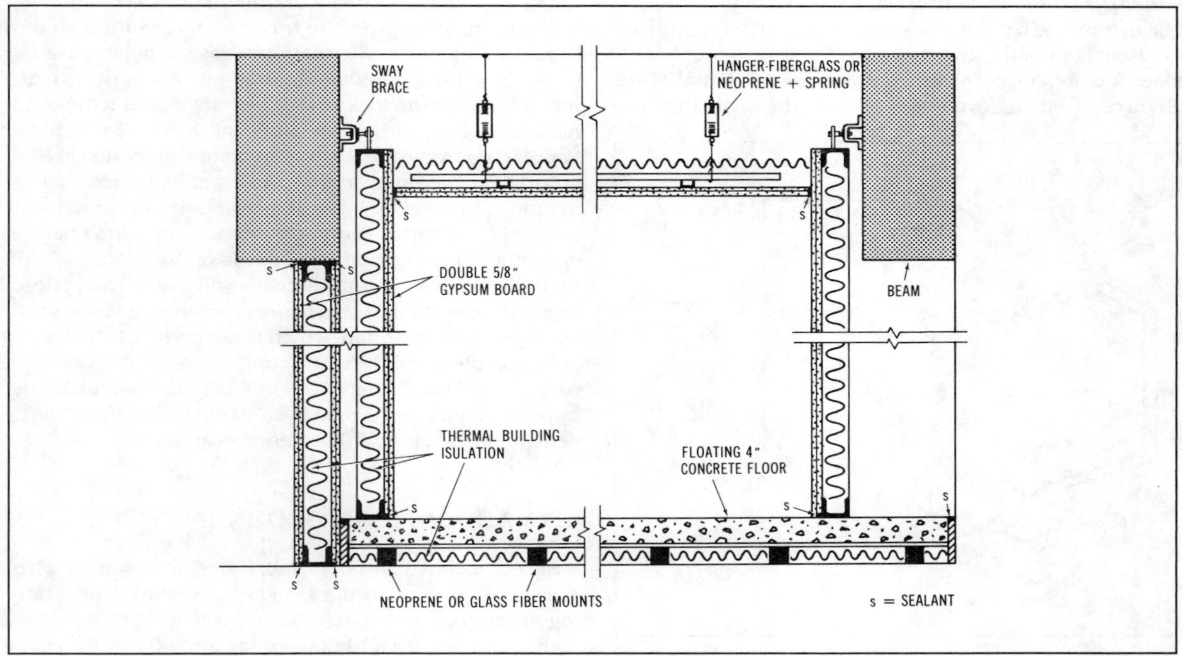

Figure 4-24 A practical "room within a room" exemplifying the principles discussed in the text.

suppliers and the literature on the subject. The references already made and references 12 through 17 should be a start in this preparation.

4.10 SOUND LOCK CORRIDORS

Sound lock corridors, as pictured in Fig. 4-25, offer many advantages to a recording studio/control room suite. For one thing, they reduce the acoustical demands on doors by placing two doors in series between studio and control room and between each of these rooms and the exterior. All three spaces are noise sources. Opening the door to the entrance hall can yield a blast of office, foot traffic, or conversation noises from the outside. Sounds of the band in the studio can reach high levels, as can the monitoring loudspeakers in the control room. Studio/control room path 1 has the potential for problems and can cause feedback howling. If the control room operator happens to be monitoring from tape and a vocalist or narrator in the studio hears the delayed signal, it can result in a psychological seizure that can render the artist inoperative. Path 1 is a flanking path around the carefully designed wall and observation window between the studio and the control room. Having two tight doors in series on this path usually eliminates such problems as listed previously, even though the doors are of modest construction.

Paths 2 and 3 involve blasts of outside noise reaching either the studio or control room. Conversely, it involves blasts from the band in the studio or from the monitoring loudspeakers bothering those hard-working people outside. It is a two-way street in every case. The statistical chances of having two doors open at the same time are

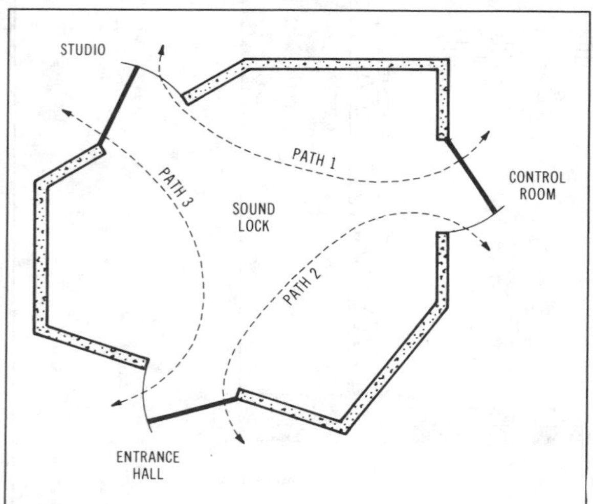

Figure 4-25 The sound lock corridor allows two doors of modest acoustical attenuation to be placed in series between potential noise sources and quiet areas.

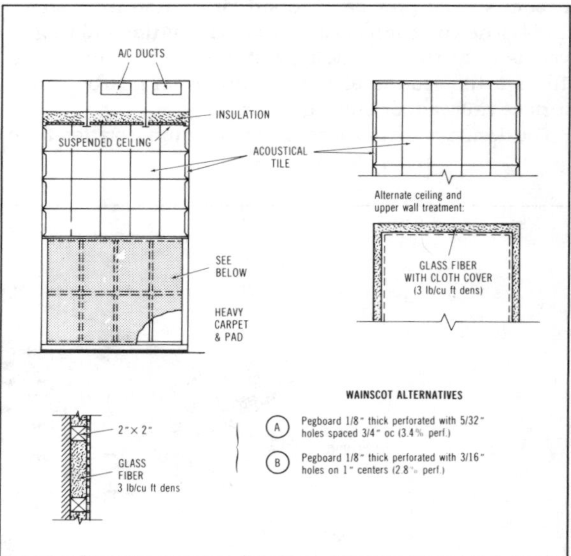

Figure 4-26 Acoustical treatment of the sound lock corridor. *(Courtesy Tab Books, Inc. Reference 18.)*

small, and with two doors in series, the practical degree of isolation achieved over any of the three paths can be very high without taking heroic measures of installing expensive acoustical doors or other barriers.

The more absorptive the inner surfaces of the sound lock, the greater the attenuation of sound (noise) passing through it from one door to another. Acoustical treatment of the sound lock is very uncritical and reduces to making it as absorbent as practical. A few of the many approaches to sound lock treatment are suggested in Fig. 4-26.[18] On the premise that the lower walls are subject to much abrasion, an abrasion-resistant wainscot 3 to 4 ft high is suggested. Perforated wood, composition board, or metal panels having a hole area of 10 to 15% of the total surface results in reasonably wideband absorption. Pegboard with about 3% perforation area gives a midband peak of absorption, which is not perfect, but acceptable. A conventional lay-in ceiling not only hides service runs above but also absorbs well across the band. The upper wall surfaces can be ¾-in. acoustical tile or 3 lb/ft^3 density fiberglass boards covered with fabric.

4.11 ACOUSTICAL DOORS

Special acoustical doors fabricated from metal with special cores, heavy hinges, means of sealing, and latching hardware are available. Their good acoustical performance comes with a high price tag and often with operational inconvenience. There is good reason to design audio room access and egress in such a way that high performance is not required of a single door. Use of the

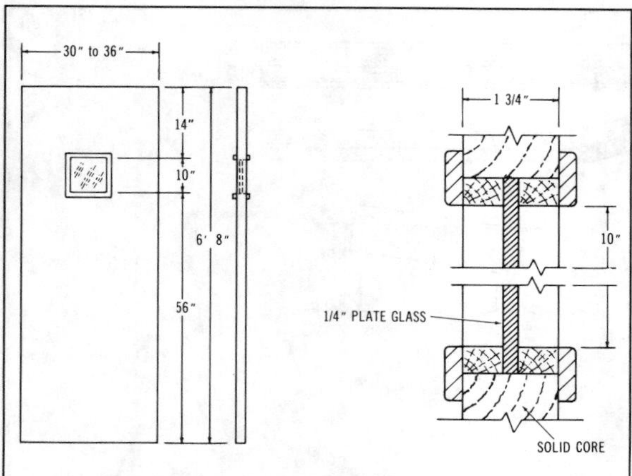

Figure 4-27 An inexpensive door for use in the sound lock corridor based on the commonly available 1 ¾-in. solid-core door. *(Courtesy Tab Books, Inc. Reference 18.)*

sound lock corridor principle discussed in the preceding section places two widely spaced doors in series, relieving the acoustical requirements of each.

An inexpensive door, satisfactory for many but certainly not all applications, is described in Fig. 4-27. It is of solid-core construction in contrast to the usual household doors that approach acoustical transparency. Some solid-core doors are made of laminated wood; others, of particle board with composition board facing. The latter has the greater surface density. The 5.2 lb/ft^2 of the particle-board type gives an STC value of about 35 from Fig. 4-14. An STC-35 does not do justice to, say, STC-55 walls. Nevertheless, for doors separated as they are in the sound lock, the decibels transmission loss of one door comes close to adding arithmetically to the decibels loss of the other door. Two doors, well separated, approach doubling the effect of one.

All this implies a perfect seal around the periphery of the door that could be attained only by nailing the door shut and applying a good bead of acoustical sealant on the crack. A practical, operative door should be sealed with weatherstripping or some other form of sealant. Fig. 4-28 illustrates a number of different approaches to sealing a door.[18] The wiping type requires constant maintenance and occasional replacement. One of the more satisfactory types is the magnetic seal, similar to those on most household refrigerator doors.

4.12 OBSERVATION WINDOW

The observation window between control room and studio can very easily have a weakening effect on the overall transmission loss of the partition separating the rooms. A wall with a rating of STC-60 alone might very well be reduced to STC-50 with even one of the more carefully designed and built windows installed. Just how much the window degrades the overall TL depends on the original TL of the partition, the TL of the window alone, and the relative areas of the two. To understand the factors going into the design of an effective observation window, a good place to start is to study the effectiveness of the glass as a barrier.[19]

4.12.1 Transmission Loss of Single Glass Plates

The measured transmission loss of ¼-, ½-, and ¾-in. single-glass plates (or float) (52 × 76 in. size) is shown in Fig. 4-29. As expected, the thicker the glass plate, the higher the general transmission loss except for a coincidence dip in each graph. Although the heavy ¾-in. plate attains a transmission loss of 40 dB or more above 2 kHz, the general performance is far too low to avoid serious compromise of an STC-50 or STC-55 wall. Considering this general lack of sufficient transmission loss and the complication of the coincidence dip, the single-glass approach is insufficient for most observation window needs. Laminated glass is more of a "limp mass" than glass plate of the same thickness and, hence, has certain acoustical advantages in observation windows. The characteristics of ¼-, ½-, and ¾-in. laminated single-glass plates are shown in Fig. 4-30.

4.12.2 Transmission Loss of Spaced Glass Plates

To isolate the effect on transmission loss of spacing two glass plates, Fig. 4-31 shows three examples.[20] In all cases the same ½- and ¼-in. glass plates are used, but the air space is varied from 2 to 6 in. Above 1500 Hz the effect of spacing is negligible. Below 1500 Hz the effect of spacing is greater. In general, the 2-in. increase from 2 to 4 in. is less effective than the same 2-in. spacing increase from 4 to 6 in. Many observation windows in recording studios utilize spacings of 12 in. or more to maximize the spacing effect.

When two glass plates are separated only a small amount, such as glass widely used for heat insulation, the sound transmission loss is essentially the same as the glass alone from which it is fabricated. There is little advantage using this type of glass in observation windows.

The single case of ½- and ¼-in. laminated glass plates with 6-in. separation is included in Fig. 4-31. The superior performance of laminated glass comes with a higher cost.

4.12.3 Reducing Cavity Resonance

The measured values of transmission loss in Fig. 4-31 have no absorbing material around the periphery of the

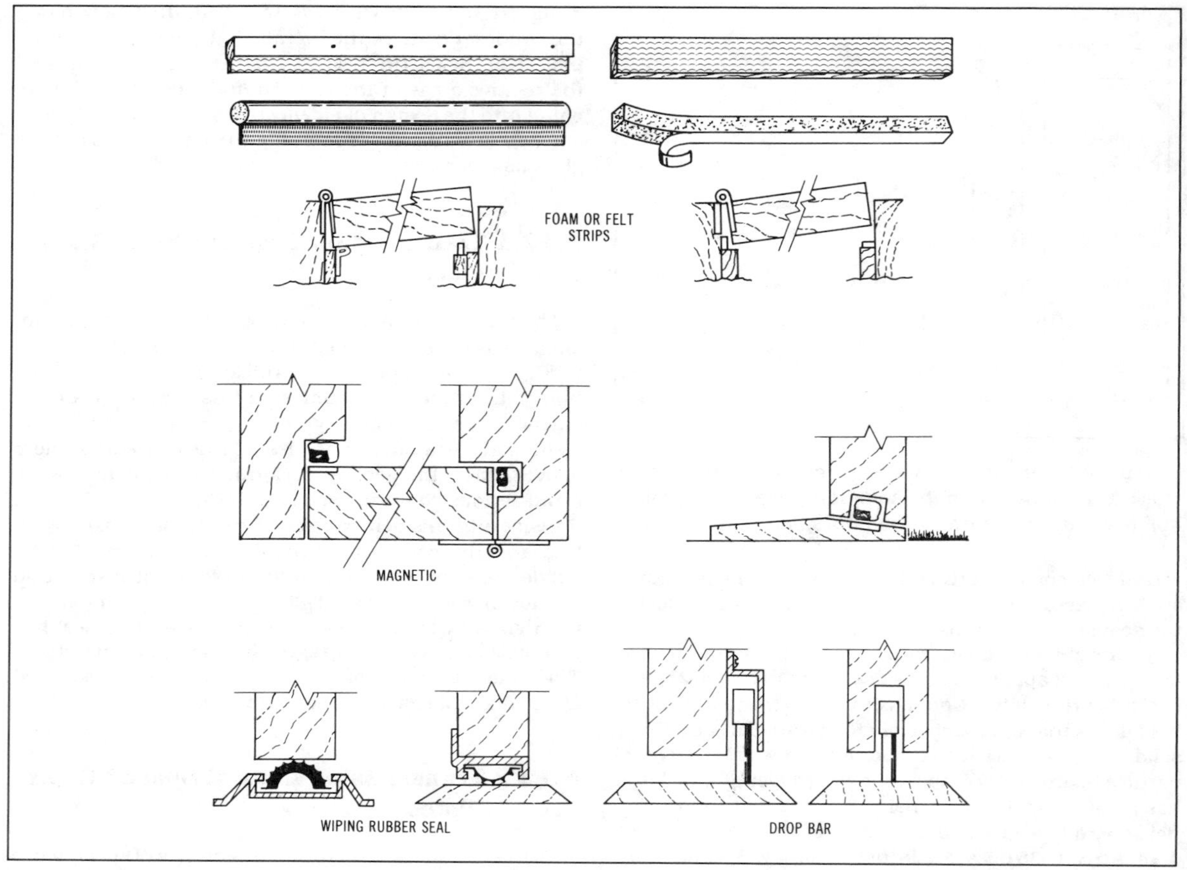

Figure 4-28 Numerous types of weatherstripping can be used for sealing doors to audio rooms. *(Courtesy Tab Books, Inc. Reference 18.)*

space between the two glass plates. An average 5-dB increase in transmission loss can be achieved by installing a minimum of 1-in. absorbent on the "reveals," the edge surfaces of the volume of air between the glass plates. The use of 4-in. of absorbing material, covered with, perhaps, perforated metal, further improves low-frequency transmission loss. The practice of using glass plates of different thicknesses is substantiated by coincidence dips that are shallower in Fig. 4-31 than in Fig. 4-29. By lining the periphery of the space between the glasses with absorbent material, the natural cavity resonance is reduced. The resonance of plates or cavity creates a sort of "acoustical hole" or reduction in transmission loss near each resonance frequency; hence, staggering plate thickness and applying absorbing material are important.

4.12.4 Observation Window Construction

The essential constructional features of two types of observation windows are shown in Fig. 4-32. Fig. 4-32A is typical of the high-transmission-loss type commensurate with high-TL wall construction. The high TL of the window is achieved by using heavy glass, maximum practical spacing of the glass plates, and other important details such as a generous application of acoustical sealant and absorbent reveals between the glass plates.

For a typical frame partition between control room and studio, a more modest window is appropriate, as shown in Fig. 4-32B. The same general demands are placed on this window as on the one in Fig. 4-32A, except that scaled down glass thickness and spacing are employed.

Some confusion seems to exist concerning the inclination of one or both of the glass plates in observation windows. Inclining one of the plates, as shown in Fig. 4-32, may or may not be advisable. Doing so reduces the average spacing, which reduces the TL accordingly. Plate inclination that eliminates a flat acoustical reflection from the glass on the sound source side may be beneficial and appropriate with certain geometry. However, the principal benefit of such plate inclination may be associated with control of light reflections that interfere with visual

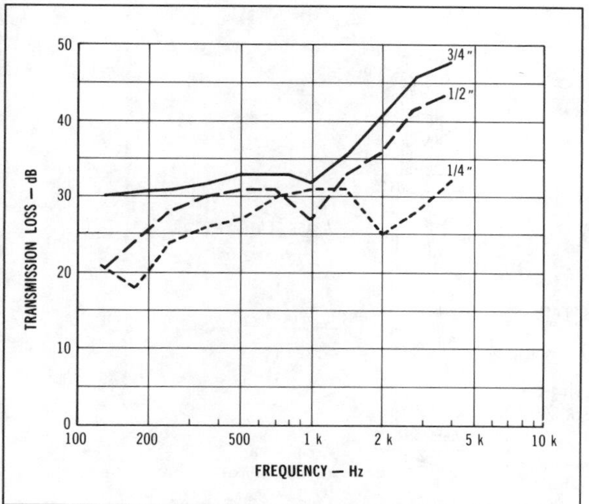

Figure 4-29 Sound transmission loss characteristics of single glass (plate or float) panels. *(Courtesy Libbey-Owens-Ford Co., data from Reference 20.)*

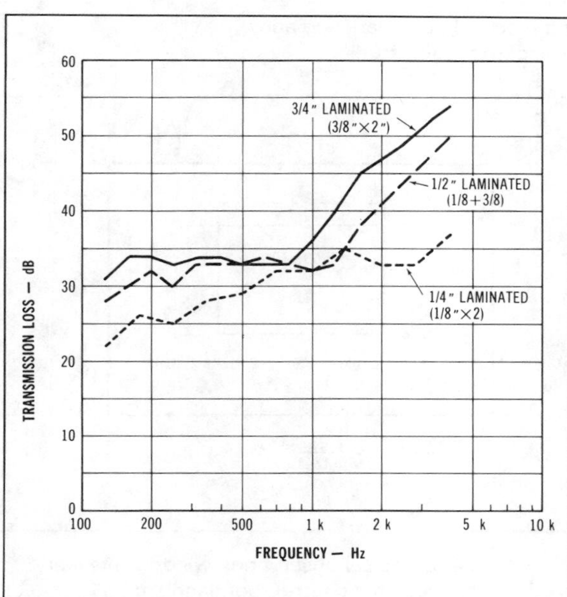

Figure 4-30 Sound transmission loss characteristics of single panels of laminated glass. *(Courtesy Libbey-Owens-Ford Co., data from Reference 20.)*

contact between the rooms. This latter problem is better controlled by using illumination fixtures that conceal the bright light source from the direct line of vision in either direction.

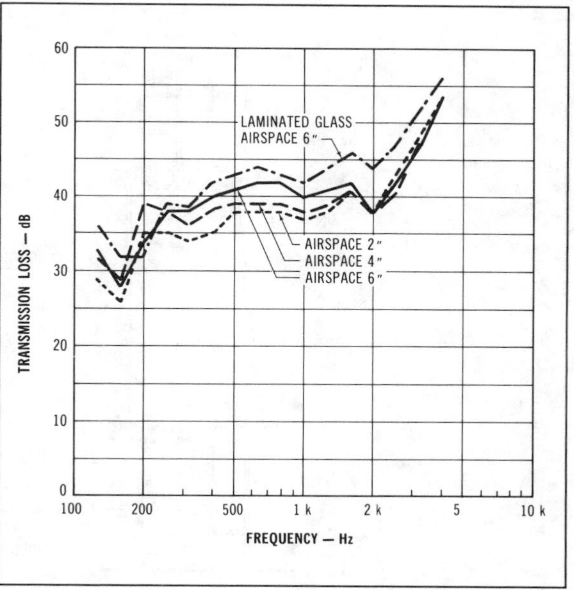

Figure 4-31 Spacing two dissimilar glass plates improves transmission loss. *(Courtesy Libbey-Owens-Ford Co., data from Reference 20.)*

4.13 TRANSMISSION LOSS OF COMPOSITE BARRIER

When an observation window having one transmission loss is set in a wall having another transmission loss, the overall transmission loss is obviously something else, but what is it? It most certainly cannot be obtained by simple manipulation of TLs or STC values. The problem must be referred to basics of sound power transmission. Fig. 4-33 illustrates the case of a 4.4 × 6.4-ft window (the same size as the measured glass of Figs. 4-29, 4-30, and 4-31) set in a 10 × 15-ft partition between control room and studio. The way the transmission loss of the window and the wall affect each other is given by the expression:[21, 22]

$$TL = 10 \log \left[\left(\frac{S_1}{10^{TL_1/10}} \right) + \left(\frac{S_2}{10^{TL_2/10}} \right) \right] \quad (4\text{-}3)$$

where,

TL is the overall transmission loss,
S_1 is the fractional wall surface,
TL_1 is the wall transmission loss in decibels,
S_2 is the fractional window surface,
TL_2 is the window transmission loss in decibels.

As an example let us say that for a given frequency the wall TL_1 = 50 dB and the window TL_2 = 40 dB. From

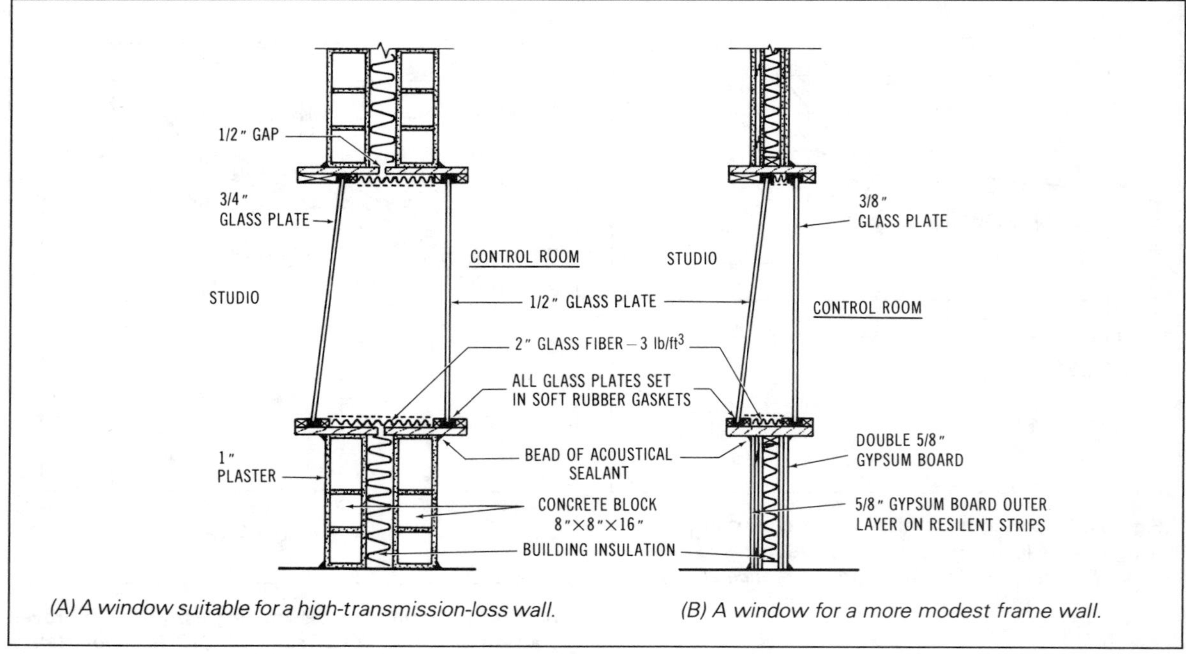

(A) A window suitable for a high-transmission-loss wall. *(B) A window for a more modest frame wall.*

Figure 4-32 Constructional details for a practical observation window set in a partition between control room and studio.

Fig. 4-33 we see that $S_1 = 0.812$ and $S_2 = 0.188$. The overall TL may be found:

$$TL = 10\log\left[\left(\frac{0.812}{10^{50/10}}\right) + \left(\frac{0.188}{10^{40/10}}\right)\right]$$
$$= 45.7\,\text{dB}$$

The 40-dB window has reduced the 50-dB wall to a 45.7-dB overall effectiveness as a barrier. This is for a given frequency. Fig. 4-34 solves Eq. 4-3 in a graphical form using the following steps:

1. Figure the ratio of glass area to total wall area,
2. Subtract window TL from wall TL, and find the intersection of this value with the area from 1,
3. From the intersection, find the reduction of the wall TL from the left scale,
4. Subtract this figure from the original wall TL.

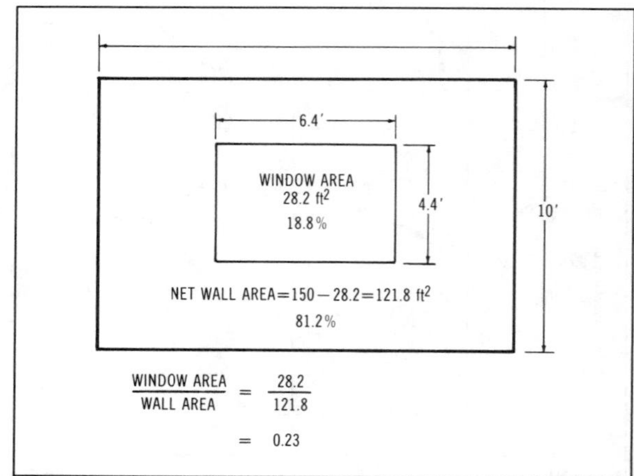

Figure 4-33 Typical observation window in a wall between the control room and studio.

With a ratio of window area to wall area of 0.23 and a 10-dB difference in TL of the two, the graph of Fig. 4-34 is entered at 0.23, and a reduction slightly less than 5 dB is read off the left scale. Subtracting 5 dB from the 50-dB wall TL gives the overall TL with a window of 45 dB. (Calculated from Eq. 4-3 gives 45.7 dB.)

It is easier and more economical to get high transmission loss in wall construction than in window construction. Since this is the case, the possibility arises to compensate for a deficient window by overdesigning the wall. For example, recognizing that an STC-70 masonry wall is possible, how far will it lift an STC-45 window? Using Eq. 4-3 again, we find the overall STC to be 52.2, an increase of over 7 dB over the STC-45 window. Actually using Eq. 4-3 with STC values is a gross oversimplifica-

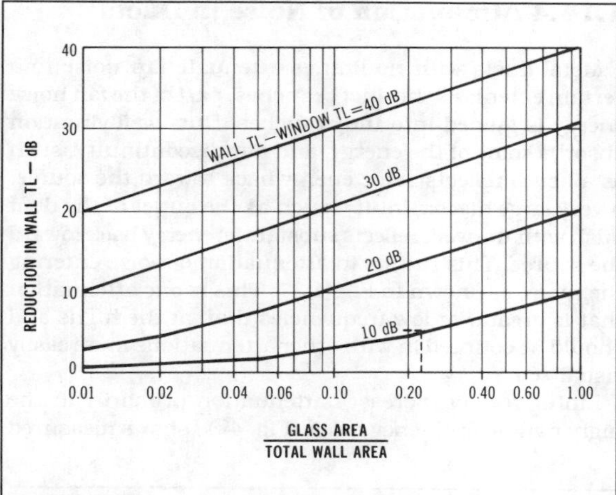

Figure 4-34 Graphical determination of the effect on the overall transmission loss (TL) of a wall by an observation window.

tion embracing all the inaccuracies of fitting measured TL values with a single-number STC rating.

An unusual form of a composite-type barrier is a crack in the wall. Let us assume that an observation window and wall combination has a calculated composite transmission loss of 50 dB. The window, installed with less than ideal craftsmanship, developed a 1/8-in. (0.125-in.) crack around the window frame as the mortar dried and pulled from the frame. Since this is the window of Fig. 4-33, the length of the crack is 21.6 ft, giving a crack area of 0.225 ft^2. What effect will this crack have on the otherwise 50-dB wall? Substituting into Eq. 4-3, we find the new transmission loss of the wall with the crack to be 28 dB. If the crack were only 1/16 in. wide, the TL of the wall would be reduced from 50 to 31.2 dB. A crack only 0.001 in. wide would reduce the TL of 50 dB to 40.3 dB. Such cracks can be eliminated by applying nonhardening sealant, appropriate caulking, or weatherstripping.

4.14 HEATING, VENTILATING, AND AIR-CONDITIONING (HVAC) SYSTEMS FOR LOW NOISE

One of the most ubiquitous sources of noise within the building housing the audio room is the *heating, ventilating, and air-conditioning (HVAC) system*. At the same time it can be the source of greatest comfort and of greatest consternation. Designing of the HVAC system to be installed in the audio suite complex should be left to specialists in that field. Unfortunately, many such designers are not familiar with the stringent requirements of audio rooms, although most are quite capable of achieving low-noise goals if (1) the price is right and (2) someone associated with the audio side of the project reasonably familiar with HVAC factors can "ride herd" on the design and installation. It is this person to whom this section is directed. No better preparation for this responsibility can be obtained than from carefully studying the American Society of Heating, Refrigeration, and Air-Conditioning Engineers (ASHRAE) publications.[23, 24]

4.14.1 Location of HVAC Equipment

From the standpoint of audio room noise, the best location for the HVAC equipment is in the next county. Short of this, a spot should be selected that isolates the inevitable vibration of such equipment from the sound-sensitive area. A good situation is to have the equipment mounted on a concrete pad completely isolated from the structure. In this way, the noise problem is reduced to handling the noise coming through the ducts, a much simpler task than fighting structure-borne vibration.

4.14.2 Identification of HVAC Noise Producers

The various types of HVAC noise producers are identified in Fig. 4-35. The diffusing vanes are right in the room, and the noise produced by air turbulence, principally in the high-frequency region, has only the air path from diffuser to listener or microphone. The only element of control in this case is selecting the most noise-free design of diffuser. Fan noise, on the other hand, travels to the room via both exhaust and supply ducts, and is quite capable of traveling upstream or downstream. The

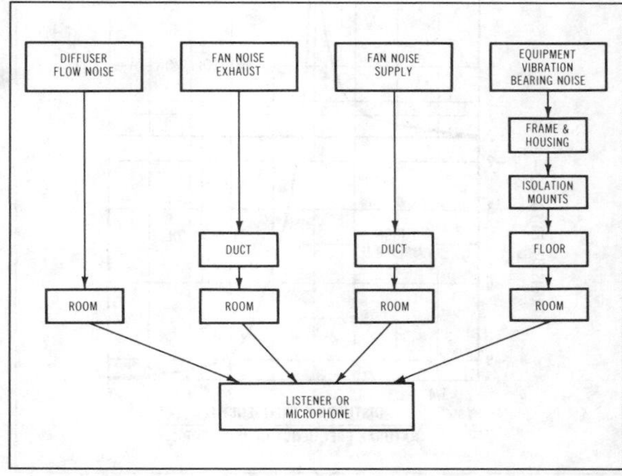

Figure 4-35 Typical paths for interfering noise from HVAC equipment to reach sound sensitive rooms. *(Adapted from ASHRAE, Reference 24.)*

delivery of fan noise over these two paths can be reduced by silencers and/or duct linings. Sizing the ductwork properly is also a means of combating fan noise since sound power output of a fan is fixed largely by air volume and pressure. Assuming that the equipment is far enough removed from the audio room that noise through the walls can be neglected, only equipment vibration and bearing noise remain. These are transmitted first to the equipment frame and housing, then through the vibration isolation mounts to the floor and structure, and finally to the audio room. Control of these vibrations is a complex technique, the principles of which are discussed in the following section.

4.14.3 Vibration Isolation

The general rule is first to do all that can reasonably be done at the source of vibration. The simple act of mounting each HVAC equipment unit on four vibration mounts may help reduce transmitted vibration, may be of no effect at all, or may actually amplify the vibrations, depending on the suitability of the mounts for the job. The isolation efficiency is purely a function of the relationship between the frequency of the disturbing source f_d to isolator natural frequency f_n, as shown by Fig. 4-36. If $f_d = f_n$, a resonance condition exists, and maximum vibration is transmitted. Isolation begins to occur when f_d/f_n is equal to or greater than $\sqrt{2}$. Once in this isolation range, each time f_d/f_n is doubled, the vibration transmission decreases 4 to 6 dB. It is beyond the scope of this treatment to go further than to identify the heart of both the problem and the solution, leaving the rest to experts in the field.

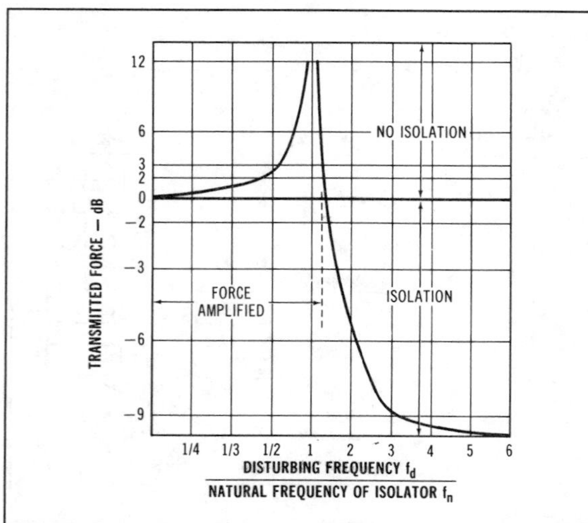

Figure 4-36 Relationships existing in mounting HVAC equipment on vibration isolation mounts. *(After ASHRAE, Reference 24.)*

4.14.4 Attenuation of Noise in Ducts

Metal ducts with no linings attenuate fan noise to a certain extent. As the duct branches, part of the fan noise energy is guided into the branches. Duct wall vibration absorbs some of the energy, and any discontinuity, such as a bend, reflects some energy back toward the source. A very large discontinuity, such as the outlet of the duct flush with the wall, reflects substantial energy back toward the source. This results in attenuation of noise entering the room, as shown in Fig. 4-37. This is one attenuation that is greater at low frequencies than at the highs and should be counted in with other attenuations more easily visualized.

Lining a duct increases attenuation primarily in the higher audio frequency range. Fig. 4-38 shows measured

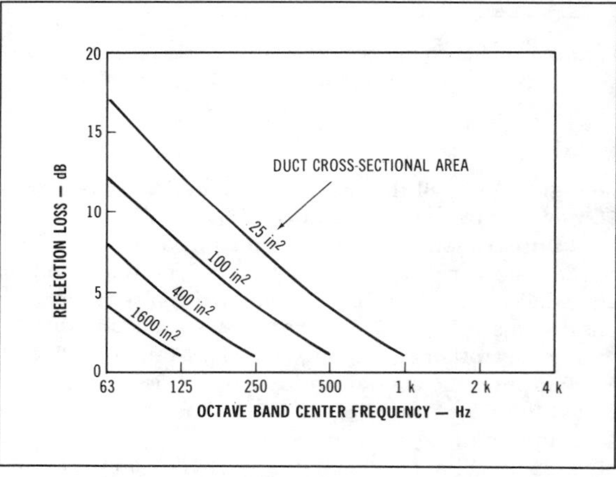

Figure 4-37 Results in the attenuation of HVAC noise entering the room. *(After ASHRAE, Reference 24.)*

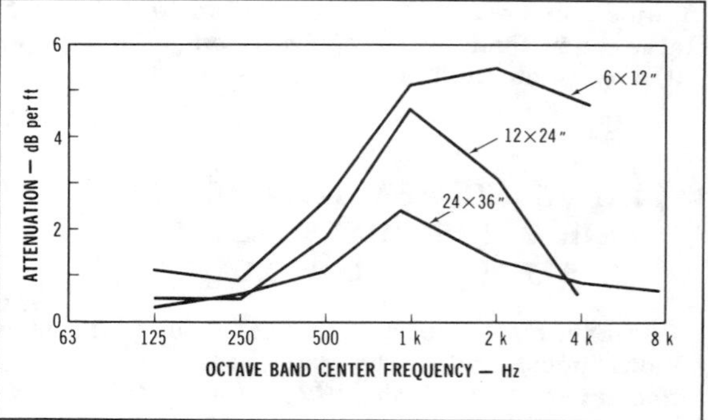

Figure 4-38 Measured attenuation in rectangular ducts. *(After ASHRAE, Reference 24, which attributes Owens-Corning-Fiberglas Corp. Lab Report 32433 and Kodaras Acoustical Laboratories Report KAL-1422-I submitted to Thermal Insulation Manufacturer's Association.)*

duct attenuation with 1-in. duct lining on all four sides. The dimensions shown are for the free area inside the duct. This wall effect attenuation is greatest for the smaller ducts. For midband frequencies, a 10-ft length of ducting can account for 40- or 50-dB attenuation for ducts 12 × 24 in. or smaller. However, higher air velocities are associated with small ducts, which result in producing greater turbulence noise at the grille/diffuser.

Great stress is commonly placed on attenuation contributed by right-angle bends that are lined with duct liner. Fig. 4-39 evaluates attenuation of sound in lined bends. Only lining on the sides is effective, which is the way the elbows of Fig. 4-39 are lined. Here again, attenuation is greater at higher audio frequencies. The indicated duct widths are clear measurements inside the lining. The lining thickness is 10% of the width of the duct and extends two duct widths ahead and two duct widths after the bend. It is apparent that the lining contributes much to attenuation of noise coming down the duct, but less so at lower frequencies.

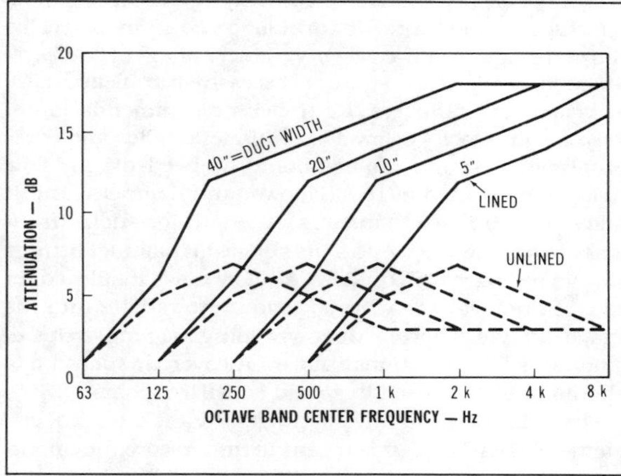

Figure 4-39 Attenuation of sound in HVAC square duct elbows without turning vanes. *(After ASHRAE, Reference 24.)*

4.14.5 Tuned Stubs

Fan blades can produce line spectra or tonal noise at a blade frequency of (RPM × number of blades)/60 Hz. Usually this noise is kept to a minimum when the HVAC engineer selects the right fan. If such tones continue to be a problem, an effective treatment is to install a tuned stub filter someplace along the duct. These can be very effective in reducing fan tones. A typical stub and its attenuation characteristic are shown in Fig. 4-40A. The comparable characteristic of a reactive muffler is also shown in Fig. 4-40B.

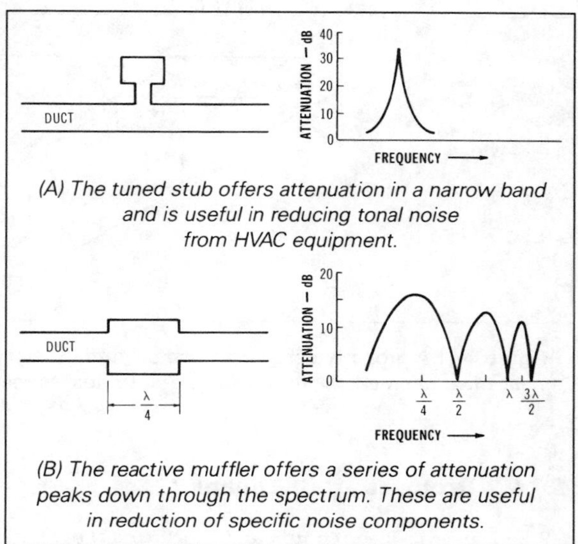

(A) The tuned stub offers attenuation in a narrow band and is useful in reducing tonal noise from HVAC equipment.

(B) The reactive muffler offers a series of attenuation peaks down through the spectrum. These are useful in reduction of specific noise components.

Figure 4-40 The tuned stub and a reactive muffler.

4.14.6 Plenums

As previously stated, a most effective procedure in noise reduction is to reduce the noise at, or very close to, the source. If a system produces a noise level that is too high at the audio room end, one possibility is to install a *plenum* in the supply and another in the return line. Such a plenum is simply a large cavity lined with absorbing material, as shown in Fig. 4-41. Sometimes a nearby room or attic space can be made into a noise attenuating plenum. The attenuation realized from a plenum can be estimated from the following expression[23]:

$$\text{attenuation} = 10\log\left[\frac{1}{S_e\left[\left(\frac{\cos\theta}{2\pi d^2}\right)+\left(\frac{1-a}{S_w a}\right)\right]}\right] \tag{4-4}$$

where,

a is the absorption coefficient of the lining,
S_e is the plenum exit area in square feet,
S_w is the plenum wall area in square feet,
d is the distance between the entrance and exit in feet,
θ is the angle of incidence at the exit (i.e., the angle that the direction d makes with the axis of exit) in degrees.

For those high frequencies where the wavelength is less than plenum dimensions, accuracy is within 3 dB. At lower frequencies Eq. 4-4 is conservative, and the actual attenuation can be 5 to 10 dB higher than the value it gives.

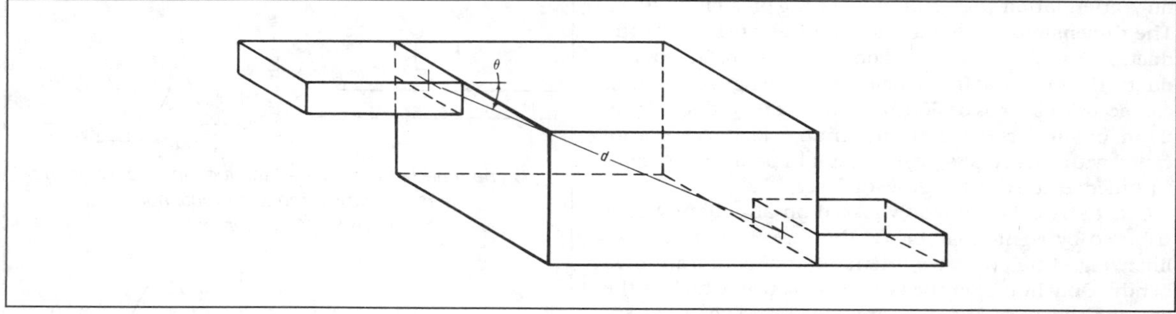

Figure 4-41 A properly designed, lined plenum is a very effective attenuator of HVAC noise and is usually located near the equipment. Unused rooms or attic spaces may sometimes be converted to noise attenuating plenums. *(After ASHRAE, Reference 24.)*

4.14.7 Proprietary Silencers

When space is at a premium and short runs of duct are necessary, proprietary sound-absorbing units can be installed in the ducts at critical points. There is a profusion of configurations available, and many attenuation characteristics can be expected. The extra cost of such units may be offset by economies their use would bring in other ways.

4.14.8 HVAC Systems Conclusion

The intent and purpose of this HVAC section is to emphasize the importance of adequate attention to the design and installation of the heating, ventilating, and air-conditioning system in the construction of studios, control rooms, and listening rooms. HVAC noises commonly dominate in such audio rooms and are often the focus of great disappointment as a beautiful new room is placed into service. The problem is often associated with the lack of appreciation by the architect and the HVAC contractor of the special demands of audio rooms. This blame must ultimately be carried by those representing the owner/client since they did not vigorously fight for low noise from the very beginning and insist on an NC noise clause in the HVAC contract.

Low-cost HVAC systems commonly employ small ducts and high-velocity air. Air turbulence noise increases as the sixth power of the velocity; hence, budget HVAC systems can easily be the source of excessive turbulence noise at grilles and diffusers. Rettinger's recommendation of keeping air velocity below 500 ft/min for studios and other professional sound rooms should be heeded.[5] Air flow noise is generated at tees, elbows, and dampers; and it takes from 5 to 10 diameters in length for such turbulence to be smoothed out. This suggests that duct fittings should be spaced adequately. Air flow noise inside a duct causes duct walls to vibrate, tending to radiate into the space outside. Thermal duct wrapping (lagging) helps to dampen such vibrations, but even covered, such ducts should not be exposed in sound-sensitive rooms.

This "once-over-lightly" approach to a few critical elements of HVAC design is meant to underscore the importance of employing expert design and installation talent, not to create instant experts. The overall HVAC project, however, needs the involvement of the audio engineer at each step.

REFERENCES

1. R. M. LaBreche and M. L. Mendias, *Environmental Noise Assessment*, Lawton, Oklahoma, April 1976. In cooperation with the U.S. EPA, Region VI, Air and Hazardous Materials Division, Dallas, Texas 75270. (The form of Fig. 4-1 is patterned after the noise assessment data sheet included in this report.)
2. L. L. Beranek, "Revised Criteria for Noise in Buildings," *Noise Control*, vol. 3, no. 1, p. 19, January 1957.
3. L. L. Beranek, W. E. Blazier, and J. J. Figwer, *Preferred Noise Criteria (PNC) Curves and Their Application to Rooms*. Presented at the 81st Meeting of the ASA, Washington, DC, April 1971.
4. M. Rettinger, "Noise Level Limits in Recording Studios," *dB the Sound Engineering Magazine*, vol. 12, no. 4, pp. 41–43, April 1978.
5. M. Rettinger, *Acoustic Design and Noise Control*, New York: Chemical Publishing Co., Inc., 1973.

6. *Determination of Sound Transmission Class*, American Society for Testing Materials, designation E413-70T.

7. R. E. Jones, "How to Design Walls for Desired STC Ratings," *Sound and Vibration*, vol. 12, no. 8, pp. 14–17, August 1978.

8. D. W. Green and C. W. Sherry, "Sound Transmission Loss of Gypsum Wallboard Partitions, Report No. 3. 2 × 4 Wood Stud Partitions," *Journal of the ASA*, vol. 71, no. 4, pp. 908–914, April 1982. (*Report No. 1*, vol. 71, no. 1, and *Report 2*, vol. 71, no. 4, also report extensive measurements of transmission loss.)

9. J. B. Grantham, "Airborne Noise Control in Lightweight Floor/Ceiling Systems," *Sound and Vibration*, vol. 5, no. 6, pp. 12–16, June 1971.

10. *Architectural Specifications for Isolated Floors, Walls, and Ceilings*, Bulletin ACS-100, Hollis, New York: Mason Industries, Inc., 1977.

11. C. M. Harris, Editor, *Handbook of Noise Control*, New York: McGraw-Hill, 1957.

12. *Mason Jack-Up Floor Slab System*, Bulletin ACS-101 (13.10/Ma), Hollis, New York: Mason Industries, Inc.

13. *Complete HVAC Engineering Specifications, An Introduction to Vibration Control Specifications*, Bulletin VCS-100 (revised January 1979), Hollis, New York: Mason Industries, Inc.

14. L. Varga, *Comparison and Technical Evaluation of Isolation Media Used in Floating Floor Applications*, Dublin, Ohio: Peabody Noise Control, Inc.

15. *Kinetics Impact and Airborne Noise Control Systems*, Brochure 13.10/Pe, Dublin, Ohio: Peabody Noise Control, Inc.

16. M. Rettinger, "Sound Installation and Isolation of Floating Floors—Practical Engineering for Wood and Concrete," *Recording Engr./Producer*, vol. 12, no. 6, pp. 80, 82, 83, December 1981.

17. M. Rettinger, *Studio Acoustics*, New York: Chemical Publishing Co., Inc., 1981.

18. F. A. Everest, *How to Build a Small Budget Recording Studio from Scratch*, Blue Ridge Summit: Tab Books, Inc.

19. F. A. Everest, "Glass in the Studio," *dB the Sound Engineering Magazine*. Part I, vol. 18, No. 3, pp. 28–33, April 1984; Part II, vol. 18, No. 4, pp. 41–44, May 1984.

20. *Breaking the Sound Barrier*, Publication AR-3, Libby-Owens-Ford Company.

21. M. Rettinger, "Sound Insulation Design for Buildings," *Journal of the ASA*, vol. 56, no. 5, November 1974.

22. M. Rettinger, "Cost Efficient Sound Insulation," *dB Magazine*, vol. 16, no. 8, p. 35, August 1982.

23. *ASHRAE Handbook and Product Directory—1977, Fundamentals*, Chapter 7, "Sound Control Fundamentals," American Society of *HVAC* Engineers, Inc., 345 East 47th St., New York.

24. *ASHRAE Handbook and Product Directory—1976, Systems*, Chapter 35, "Sound and Vibration Control," ASHRAE, see reference 22.

CHAPTER **5**

Acoustical Design of Audio Rooms

by F. Alton Everest

Audio rooms shall be considered under different categories such as recording studios, control rooms, and listening rooms. A wide variety of functions are being served in each type of room, which results in a great diversity of room treatments and physical configurations in practice. For instance, there are recording studios, usually of larger size, dedicated to the recording of classical music in which the more traditional microphone techniques are utilized. Other studios are built specifically for recording contemporary musical groups and use separation-type, multitrack techniques. Still others are video studios in which both picture and sound are recorded simultaneously; stages for motion picture music scoring and dialog replacement; and numerous other specialty studios for producing advertising "jingles," preparing post-recording production, recording of voice-over narration, and so on. The physical manifestation of a studio naturally reflects its designated use, and the architect's dictum that "form follows function" applies specifically in this field. It is obviously impractical to cover in detail the design of rooms in the studio category, and the same limitation applies to control rooms and listening rooms. Instead, we have made a selection that will illuminate principles rather than demonstrate diversity.

5.1 REVERBERATION TIME OF AUDIO ROOMS

A big controversy is in progress as to whether reverberation time is really the single most important parameter in studio acoustics. Perhaps the best summary of present-day expert opinion is that reverberation time is still highly respected as a measure of acoustical quality, but there is also a healthy acknowledgment of other factors, many of which are under intense study and development today. We know a room that is too live is beset with serious acoustical problems, as is one that is too dead. In between there is that degree of reverberation that gives the most pleasing effect. Certainly, a wide range of reverberation time is found in modern studios. Multitrack recording has brought a powerful emphasis on very dead acoustical environments in order to obtain sufficient separation between instruments and vocalists recorded on separate tracks. Without good track separation, freedom of choice is lost in the mixing operation.

Although there is a lack of agreement on the basic value of trying to achieve a certain "optimum" reverberation time, there is good agreement on the desirability of having reverberation time reasonably uniform throughout the audible spectrum. Insofar as this condition prevails, all frequency components of the signal die away at the same rate, and spectral balance is maintained even during the transient decay period.

About the only thing that can be done is to report the range of reverberation times found in existing recording studios, which must be presumed to be satisfactory. Rettinger does this in the form of two statements, RT = 0.2 log Volume and RT = 0.15 log Volume, which are graphed in Fig. 5-1.[1] These two lines seem to embrace general studio practice today. The "live" and "dead" graphs are rough estimates of the extremes in modern practice.

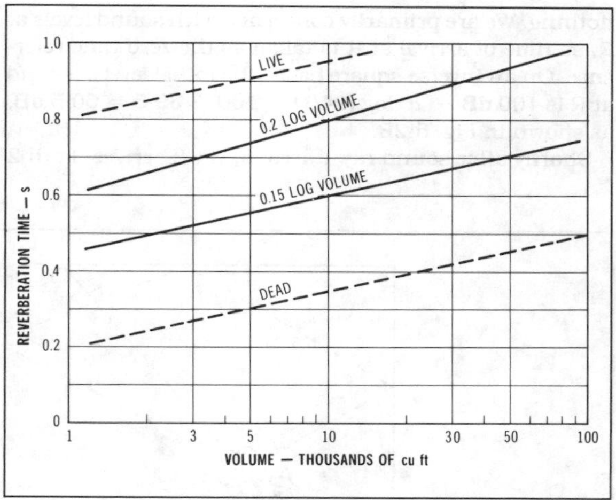

Figure 5-1 Range of reverberation times used in contemporary recording studios. *(After Reference 1.)*

5.1.1 Reverberation via Ray Acoustics

The behavior of sound in an enclosed space can be studied on the basis of ray acoustics as long as the wavelength of the sound under consideration is very short compared to the dimensions of the room. This is the way Sabine, the father of architectural acoustics, did it at the turn of the century, so we have a good precedent. The surfaces of the room of Fig. 5-2A keep the sound energy that radiates from the source S within the confines of the room through numerous reflections. In the interest of simplification, we shall consider the source S, the receiver R, and four room surfaces, neglecting the two side walls.

5.1.2 Buildup of Sound in a Room

To illustrate the buildup of sound in a room, refer to the sketch of Fig. 5-2A. The sound source S is a very special pistol. When the trigger of this pistol is pulled, a pulse of random noise is emitted. The pulse is long enough to give a steady-state sound pressure level measurement of 100 dB at a 1-ft distance. We now move to the receiver R to consider what sound R experiences.

The scale of the sketch of Fig. 5-2A reveals that path 1 is 94 ft from S to R, and it takes sound 94 ft/1130 ft/s = 0.083 s or 83 ms to traverse this distance. Since ray 1 is over the direct, shortest path, for the first 83 ms, R hears nothing. We are primarily concerned with sound levels at R, so time of arrival at R is taken as the zero time reference. On an inverse-square basis, the initial level of sound at R is 100 dB − 20 log (94/1) = 100 − 39.5 = 60.5 dB, as shown in Fig. 5-2B.

Shortly after sound ray 1 arrives, ray 2 arrives. Path 2 is 105 ft long, and assuming perfect reflection on all room surfaces, its level will be 100 − 20 log (105/1) = 100 − 40.4 = 59.6 dB. Ray 2 arrives (105 − 94)/1.13 = 9.7 ms after ray 1. Ray 1 is still arriving at R; hence, ray 2 will increase the level at R. Adding 60.5 dB to 59.6 dB on a power basis, the sum of dB_1 and dB_2 = 10 log ($10^{60.5/10}$

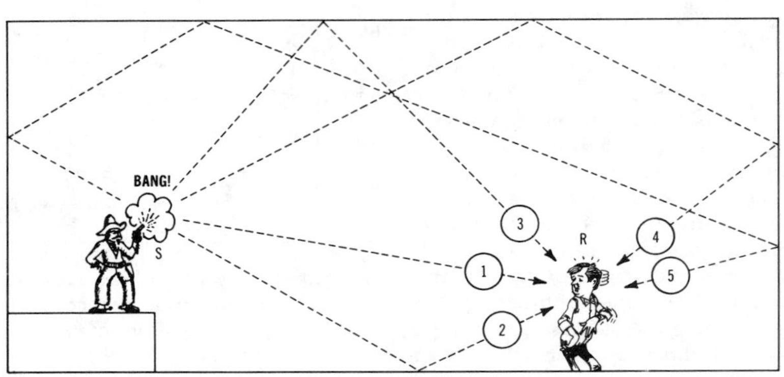

(A) The sound source S gives off a long pulse of random noise, the rays of which travel to receiver R.

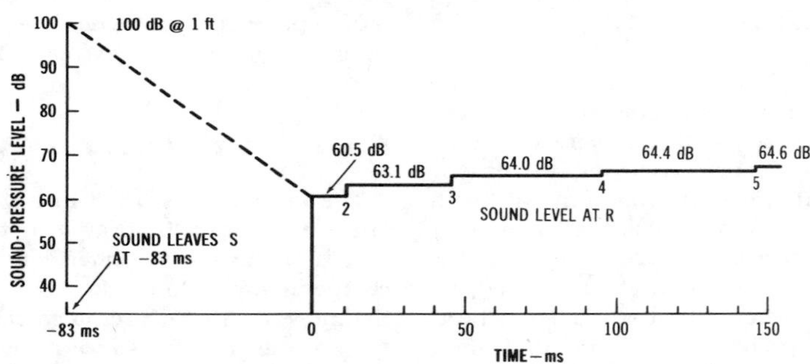

(B) The instant ray 1 arrives at R is taken as time = 0.

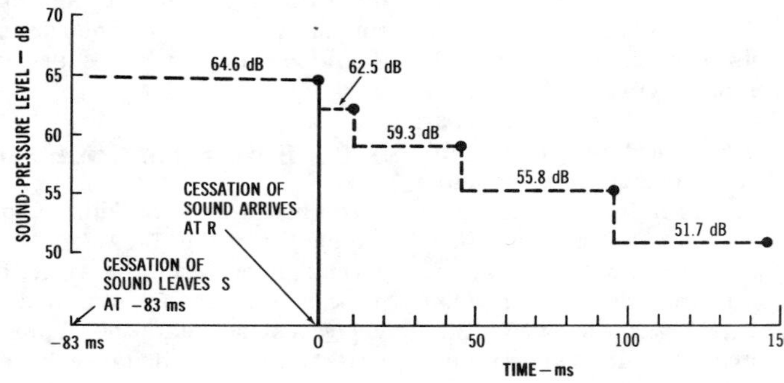

(C) For the decay process, time = 0 is taken as that time the cessation of sound from S arrives at R.

Figure 5-2 A simplified study of the sound buildup and decay in a room.

$+ 10^{59.6/10}) = 63.1$ dB. Ray 3 (traveling 147 ft) arrives at time $t = (147 - 94)/1.13 = 47$ ms, and its level will be

$$100 - 20 \log(147/1) = 100 - 43.3 = 56.7 \text{ dB}$$

Combining ray 3 with rays 1 and 2,

$$(dB_1 + dB_2) + dB_3 = 10 \log(10^{63.1/10} + 10^{56.7/10}) = 64 \text{ dB}$$

Carrying forward similar computations, ray 4 is found to have a level of 53.9 dB arriving at $t = 95$ ms, and ray 5 has a level of 51.7 dB arriving at $t = 146$ ms. As each successive reflection arrives at R, its contribution to the total sound level of R becomes progressively less.

5.1.3 Decay of Sound in a Room

When the random noise pulse from the special pistol suddenly ceases, what happens to the rays of sound on their respective ways but with their support cut off? Obviously, some overall decay process sets in, and it is another worthwhile exercise to examine this in detail with the aid of Fig. 5-2C. In this case, it is expedient to take $t = 0$ as the time at which the cessation of sound arrives at R. We found in Fig. 5-2B that, when all five rays are combined, a level of 64.6 dB is reached. Other rays arriving both before and after ray 5 would increase this level somewhat, but to keep things simple let us say that a level of 64.6 dB prevails at R as the end of the noise pulse first arrives over path 1. The level at R drops instantly as the contribution of ray 1 (60.5 dB) is lost, and the level is sustained only by rays 2 through 5, which are still enroute. The new level at R becomes

$$10 \log(10^{64.6/10} - 10^{60.5/10}) = 62.5 \text{ dB}$$

The next ray to be lost, ray 2, which has contributed a level of 59.6 dB, causes the level to drop to

$$10 \log(10^{62.5/10} - 10^{59.6/10}) = 59.3 \text{ dB}$$

Losing ray 3, which has contributed 56.7 dB, the new level becomes

$$10 \log(10^{59.3/10} - 10^{56.7/10}) = 55.8 \text{ dB}$$

After losing ray 4, which contributed 53.9 dB to the original level, the level of ray 5 is reached, which is about 51.7 dB. Exact agreement with the Fig. 5-2B sound buildup computation requires carrying numbers to more than the three significant places used previously.

Looking at the black dots in Fig. 5-2C, we note that the decay is roughly linear, even though only five of the thousands of reflections are considered. This is, however, the beginning of a reverberatory decay. In fact, if the sound level in this room has decayed $64.6 - 51.7 = 12.9$ dB in 146 ms (0.146 s), a very rough estimate of reverberation time can be set up by the ratio RT:0.146 = 60:12.9. Solving, $RT = (0.146 \times 60)/12.9 = 0.68$ s. As successive rays cease, the level at R drops stepwise. This is a very short reverberation time for the assumed perfectly reflecting room surfaces and the large dimensions implied in our distances, but at least the mechanism of sound decay has been illustrated.

The purpose of the preceding paragraphs centered on Fig. 5-2 is to give an elementary picture of the first few reflections in the growth and decay of the sound field in a room (and also some exercise in the use of the decibel). Fig. 5-3 is the more conventional form of showing the growth and decay curves of the sound field in an enclosed space. The curves of Fig. 5-3A are plotted to a linear vertical scale, and those of Fig. 5-3B, to a logarithmic scale. The linear shape of the exponential decay in the logarithmic form (in decibels) is a convenient form to evaluate reverberation time. As a sound source is suddenly energized, the sound field at any point in the room builds up according to the mechanism studied in Fig. 5-2B, which, however, neglected losses. It does not continue to grow indefinitely any more than an automobile continues to accelerate with a given throttle setting. The growth of the sound field is limited by losses of the enclosure.

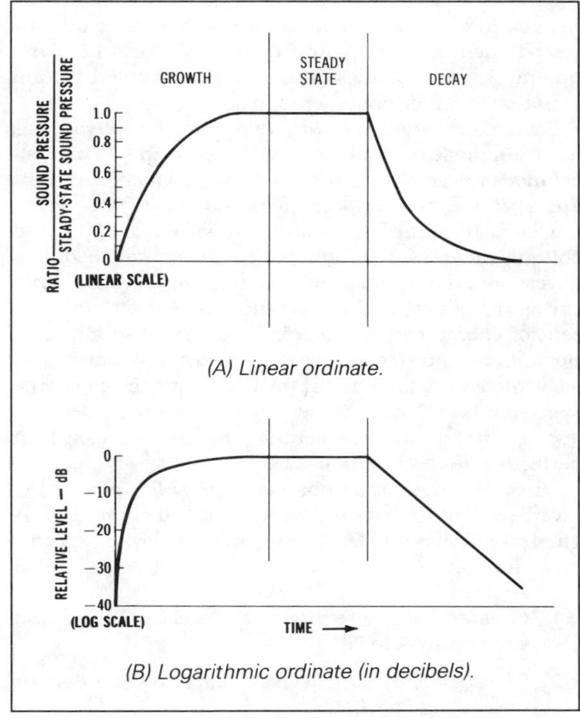

(A) *Linear ordinate.*

(B) *Logarithmic ordinate (in decibels).*

Figure 5-3 The more conventional form of illustrating the growth and decay of sound in a room.

With a given source output, the sound pressure level will increase until absorption in the air, absorbing materials, and structure are equal to the rate of radiation from the source. At this point an equilibrium (steady-state) condition exists as the energy put out by the source is just enough to supply losses. When the source is switched off, sound decays exponentially. This general process is as true of a single mode as it is of the overall composite sound field of the room made up of many modes. Nevertheless the rate of buildup and decay of a single mode will be determined only by the losses applicable to that mode alone rather than the average of the entire room.

5.1.4 Reverberation in Small Rooms

The concept of reverberation is rooted in the concept of a diffuse, reverberant sound field. Such a sound field has a time average of the mean square sound pressure that is the same throughout the room and a flow of energy equally probable in all directions. In small audio rooms dominated by relatively isolated normal modes such conditions do not exist. There is a question as to whether the very term "reverberation" applies in such rooms. As long as energy is not uniformly distributed and the direction of propagation is not random in an audio room, is it proper to use reverberation equations in designing such rooms or to label the results of decay measurements made in such rooms as reverberation time? Schultz eloquently voiced such concerns.[2] And Davis and Davis have frequently warned of the inapplicability of reverberation equations and measurements in small rooms.[3]

Each mode, whether *axial, tangential*, or *oblique*, has a certain angle of incidence associated with it. The easiest mode to visualize is the axial mode, which is at right angles to the two surfaces giving rise to it, but certain angles of incidence are associated with tangential and oblique modes as well. The efficiency of sound absorbers is very much a function of this angle of incidence, and various angles of incidence are inconsistent with the concept of energy flow being equally probable in all directions. In any given octave or one-third octave band, only a few modes are included at the low-frequency end of the spectrum (see Table 3-2), and the fewer the modes, the less applicable are reverberation procedures based on perfectly diffuse conditions.

What are the minimum conditions for measuring reverberation in what might be considered rooms of marginal size? Davis and Davis suggest the following specific procedure:

1. Measure the direct sound level (L_D) close to the sound source, say 4 to 8 ft.
2. Extrapolate by the inverse-square law to a distant measuring point.
3. At the same distant point measure the total sound field (L_T).
4. Find the reverberant sound level (L_R) from

$$L_R = 10 \log (10^{LT/10} - 10^{LD/10})$$

5. Check the value of the reverberant level L_R to see if it is at least 30 dB above the ambient noise level to allow 20 dB of decay and still be 10 dB above the noise level.
6. Reverberation time measurements under such conditions could then be considered valid.[3]

Does all this mean that there should be no use of Sabine's or Eyring's equations in designing an audio room of a size that would definitely not allow a perfectly diffuse field? Should reverberatory decay measurements in such rooms be abandoned completely? Rather than throw out everything associated with the concept of reverberation for small rooms, perhaps a wiser approach would be to gain a thorough understanding of the acoustical anomalies of such rooms as well as the bases of the criticisms. Then we can feel free to use reverberation calculations and measurements, interpreting them with appropriate restraint and with full knowledge. In the 30 × 25 × 19.5-ft control room of Table 3-2, there is one lone axial mode in each of the one-third octave bands centered on 20 and 25 Hz. Obviously, the sound fields represented by the sampling of these bands are about as far from diffuse as we can imagine. However, in the bands centered on 63, 80, and 100 Hz, there are 14, 15, and 17 modes, respectively, with a mix of axial, tangential, and oblique. Although far from a completely diffuse condition, it would seem reasonable to deduce that reverberatory decays in these bands have some meaning as decays of quasi-diffuse fields.

The conclusion of this matter, influenced by highly practical factors, is that measuring the decay of sound in a given room in any octave or one-third octave band in the audible spectrum reveals *how components of the signal in that band will decay in that room.* The variability of the decay rate with location in the room is a natural result of nondiffuse conditions. In the control room mentioned previously, interest is focused on the operator's position.

These factors are of primary interest in this section only for the light they shed on the justification for using Sabine's or Eyring's reverberation time equations in the initial design stages. There is little choice: how else can an initial estimate of the amount of absorption needed at different frequencies be obtained? There is also the matter of experience that must bear some weight. For decades, literally thousands of acoustically small audio rooms have been designed, built, and measured based upon statistical formulas, and their use has proved at least satisfactory enough to fuel an explosive growth in audio. But a new day is approaching as microprocessor-based measuring instruments are revealing an avalanche of new insights into small room acoustics that promise to supplement, but probably not replace, reverberation time and the use of Sabine's statistically based equation.

5.1.5 Sabine's and Eyring's Equations

Reverberation time is generally defined as the time required for the sound pressure level in an enclosed space to decrease 60 dB. Estimations of reverberation time can be made by simple calculations, given the dimensions of the room, the absorption coefficients of the materials lining the room, and a knowledge of the areas of each material. Several equations are available to us for such calculations. Sabine's simple equation is[4]

$$RT = 0.049\,V/Sa \tag{5-1}$$

where,
RT is the reverberation time in seconds,
V is the volume of the room in cubic feet,
S is the surface area of room in square feet,
a is the average absorption coefficient.

A more practical form of Sabine's equation is

$$RT = 0.049\,V/(S_1a_1 + S_2a_2 + S_3a_3 + \cdots) \tag{5-2}$$

where,
RT is the reverberation time in seconds,
V is the volume of the room in cubic feet,
S_1 is the area of material 1,
a_1 is the absorption coefficient of material 1,
S_2 is the area of material 2,
a_2 is the absorption coefficient of material 2 and so on.

Eq. 5-2 is more practical because the absorption coefficients of specific materials (carpets, commercial absorbing materials, and so on) are readily available while the "a" of Eq. 5-1, the average of many things, is accessible only by measuring the room.

Let us consider S_1a_1 of Eq. 5-2. There is a certain area S_1 (100 ft^2) of material (heavy carpet on concrete) in the room. Referring to Table 5-1, the value of 0.14 is the absorption coefficient of a carpet of this type at 500 Hz. The product $S_1a_1 = (100\text{ ft}^2)(0.14) = 14$ sabins (having the dimension of square feet). An absorption coefficient of 1.0 represents the perfect absorber, each square foot being called a sabin of absorption. The sabin is a unit of absorption that may be obtained with 10 ft^2 of a material having an absorption coefficient of 0.1, 2 ft^2 of material with a = 0.5, or 1.25 ft^2 with an a = 0.8. In the present case of $a_1 = 0.14$, the 100 ft^2 yields only 14 sabins.

The Sabine equation, statistically based as it is, works well in large spaces. However, it produces a paradox in very absorptive spaces, and its use with such spaces leads to error. This caused Eyring to rethink the process. He published his equation in the very first volume of the *Journal of the Acoustical Society* in 1930 as follows:

$$RT = \frac{0.049\,V}{-S\log_e(1 - a')} \tag{5-3}$$

where,
RT is the reverberation time in seconds,
V is the volume of the room in cubic feet,
S is the surface area of the room in square feet,
a′ is the average absorption coefficient.[5]

In view of the previous paragraphs, Eyring's equation, like Sabine's, is based on the existence of a perfectly diffuse sound field (i.e., sound intensity uniform throughout the room and particle velocity randomly distributed in all directions).

5.1.6 Calculation of Reverberation Time—Sabine

The 30 × 25 × 19.5-ft room of Table 3-1 and Fig. 3-5 has quite good distribution of modal frequencies. It was considered as a control room in that context, but let us consider it as a studio and follow through the calculations involved with both Sabine's and Eyring's equations. The volume (V) of this room is (30)(25)(19.5) = 14,625 ft^3. The total surface area is (19.5)(25 + 25 + 30 + 30) + (2)(25)(30) = 3645 ft^2. A reverberation time goal of 0.6 s is taken. To achieve this goal of RT = 0.6 s, the absorption units (sabins) required must be calculated. Transposing Eq. 5-1,

$$\begin{aligned}\text{absorption units required} = Sa &= 0.049\,V/RT\\ &= 0.049(14{,}625)/0.6\\ &= 1194 \text{ sabins}\end{aligned}$$

It requires 1194 sabins of absorption to achieve a reverberation time of 0.6 s. It is very desirable to have reverberation time uniform with frequency, and to realize this, 1194 sabins must be in the room for each frequency point (octave) throughout the spectrum. Published absorption coefficients of Table 5-1 are available only from 125 Hz to 4 kHz at octave intervals.

The problem now is that of finding absorption coefficients to fit selected materials to augment Table 5-1. The most extensive source is the *Compendium of Materials for Noise Control* available from the US Government Printing Office.[6] Products of 146 different companies are listed with absorption coefficients for absorbent materials, transmission loss for barrier materials, and performance data on many HVAC components in this 380 page volume. In addition to this material, about 150 pages are devoted to some basic acoustical concepts, the equivalent of a survey course in practical acoustics. Table 5-1 appears on page 55 of the "Compendium."

Following the version of Murphy's law that states, "amenities are more important than acoustics," the owner insists on heavy carpet on 80% of the floor space, leaving a piano area on the remaining parquet flooring. Table 5-1 lists "heavy carpet with 40-oz hairfelt or foam rubber on concrete," and we enter these coefficients on line 1 in

Table 5-2, and multiply each by the 600-ft^2 carpet area to get the sabins at each frequency. Since the remaining 150 ft^2 of parquet flooring is another fixed entity, we enter the coefficients from Table 5-1 for "wood parquet in asphalt on concrete" on line 2 and calculate absorption units for each frequency. Although parquet flooring absorbs very little sound and could well be neglected, it is being included to emphasize that point. It is helpful to carry along a visual image of our approach to the 1194-sabin goal required for the desired reverberation time of 0.6 s; there-

Table 5-1. Absorption Coefficients of General Building Materials and Furnishings

Complete tables of coefficients of the various materials that normally constitute the interior finish of rooms may be found in the various books on architectural acoustics. The following short list will be useful in making simple calculations of the reverberation in rooms.

Materials	Absorption Coefficients (Hz)					
	125	250	500	1000	2000	4000
Brick, unglazed	0.03	0.03	0.03	0.04	0.05	0.07
Brick, unglazed, painted	0.01	0.01	0.02	0.02	0.02	0.03
Carpet, heavy, on concrete	0.02	0.06	0.14	0.37	0.60	0.65
Same, on 40-oz hairfelt or foam rubber	0.08	0.24	0.57	0.69	0.71	0.73
Same, with impermeable latex backing on 40-oz hairfelt or foam rubber	0.08	0.27	0.39	0.34	0.48	0.63
Concrete block, coarse	0.36	0.44	0.31	0.29	0.39	0.25
Concrete block, painted	0.10	0.05	0.06	0.07	0.09	0.08
Fabrics:						
Light velour, 10 oz/yd^2, hung straight, in contact with wall	0.03	0.04	0.11	0.17	0.24	0.35
Medium velour, 14 oz/yd^2, draped to half area	0.07	0.31	0.49	0.75	0.70	0.60
Heavy velour, 18 oz/yd^2, draped to half area	0.14	0.35	0.55	0.72	0.70	0.65
Floors:						
Concrete or terrazzo	0.01	0.01	0.15	0.02	0.02	0.02
Linoleum, asphalt, rubber or cork tile on concrete	0.02	0.03	0.03	0.03	0.03	0.02
Wood	0.15	0.11	0.10	0.07	0.06	0.07
Wood parquet in asphalt on concrete	0.04	0.04	0.07	0.06	0.06	0.07
Glass:						
Large panes of heavy plate glass	0.18	0.06	0.04	0.03	0.02	0.02
Ordinary window glass	0.35	0.25	0.18	0.12	0.07	0.04
Gypsum Board, 1/2 in. nailed to 2 × 4's 16 in. oc	0.29	0.10	0.05	0.04	0.07	0.09
Marble or glazed tile	0.01	0.01	0.01	0.01	0.02	0.02
Openings:						
Stage, depending upon furnishings			0.25—0.75			
Deep balcony, upholstered seats			0.50—1.00			
Grills, ventilating			0.15—0.50			
Plaster, gypsum or lime, smooth finish on tile or brick	0.013	0.015	0.02	0.03	0.04	0.05
Plaster, gypsum or lime, rough finish on lath	0.14	0.10	0.06	0.05	0.04	0.03
Same, with smooth finish	0.14	0.10	0.06	0.04	0.04	0.03
Plywood paneling, 3/8 in. thick	0.28	0.22	0.17	0.09	0.10	0.11
Water surface, as in a swimming pool	0.008	0.008	0.013	0.015	0.020	0.025
Air, sabins/100 ft^3@ 50% RH				0.9	2.3	7.2
Absorption of Seats and Audience, sabins per square foot of seating area						
Audience, seated in upholstered seats, per square foot of floor area	0.60	0.74	0.88	0.96	0.93	0.85
Unoccupied cloth-covered upholstered seats, per square foot of floor area	0.49	0.66	0.80	0.88	0.82	0.70
Unoccupied leather-covered upholstered seats, per square foot of floor area	0.44	0.54	0.60	0.62	0.58	0.50
Wooden pews, occupied, per square foot of floor area	0.57	0.61	0.75	0.86	0.91	0.86
Chairs, metal or wood seats, each, unoccupied	0.15	0.19	0.22	0.39	0.38	0.30

fore, the carpet plus parquet sabins from line 3 are plotted in Fig. 5-4. Above 1 kHz we already have more than a third of the total sabins required, but below 1 kHz the carpet is a poor absorber. Absorption is now unbalanced, and some other material is needed to absorb the primarily low-frequency sound energy and little at higher frequencies.

Looking down the list of materials for something having significant absorption at 125 Hz and much less at 4 kHz, we are attracted to "Gypsum board, ½ in. nailed to 2 × 4's 16 in. oc." This is a reminder that absorption of structural materials must not be neglected. This studio could very well have gypsum board walls and ceiling, a total of 2895 ft². A studio wall would probably have several layers of gypsum board on the studio side, but the greater mass would simply shift its peak of absorbence to a somewhat lower frequency. Let us assume the single layer for the sake of illustration, calculating line 4 and adding lines 3 and 4 for the new total. Plotting this on Fig. 5-4, we find that now we have more low-frequency absorption than needed to compensate for carpet deficiencies.

At 500 Hz we have about 500 sabins and need about 1200 sabins. If the 700 sabins required could be in a material having poor absorbence at 125 Hz but good absorbence at higher frequencies, it would tend to straighten out our total sabins curve. Remember that getting a reverberation time the same at all frequencies requires the same number of sabins at all points. Therefore, a search is initiated for such a material. In the "Com-

Table 5-2. Reverberation Calculations (Sabine's Equation)

		125 Hz		250 Hz		500 Hz		1 kHz		2 kHz		4 kHz	
Material	**Area, ft²**	**a**	**Sa**	**a**	**Sa**	**a**	**Sa**	**a**	**Sa**	**a**	**Sa**	**a**	**Sa**
Heavy carpet on 40-oz foam 80% of floor	600	0.08	48.	0.24	144.	0.57	342.	0.69	414.	0.71	426.	0.73	438.
Parquet on 20% of floor	150	0.04	6.	0.04	6.	0.07	11.	0.06	9.	0.06	9.	0.07	11.
Sum carpet + parquet			54.		150.		353.		423.		435.		449.
Gypsum Board 1/2 in. thick nailed to 2 × 4's, 16 in. oc	2895	0.29	840.	0.10	290.	0.05	145.	0.04	116.	0.07	203.	0.09	261.
Carpet + parquet + gypsum			894.		440.		498.		539.		638.		710.
2-inch 703 Mounting 4 (No airspace)	700	0.22	154.	0.82	574.	0.99	693.	0.99	693.	0.99	693	0.99	693.
Total Sa			1048.		1014.		1191.		1232.		1331.		1403.
Reverberation Time (Sabin), seconds	Ave. 0.60		0.68		0.71		0.60		0.58		0.54		0.51
Eyring's equation													
Total Sa' from above*			1048.		1014.		1191.		1232.		1331.		1403.
Average absorption coefficient $a' = \frac{Sa'}{3645}$		0.29		0.28		0.33		0.34		0.37		0.38	
Reverberation time (Eyring), seconds	Ave. 0.49		0.57		0.60		0.49		0.47		0.42		0.41

*Assuming that Sa' = Sa

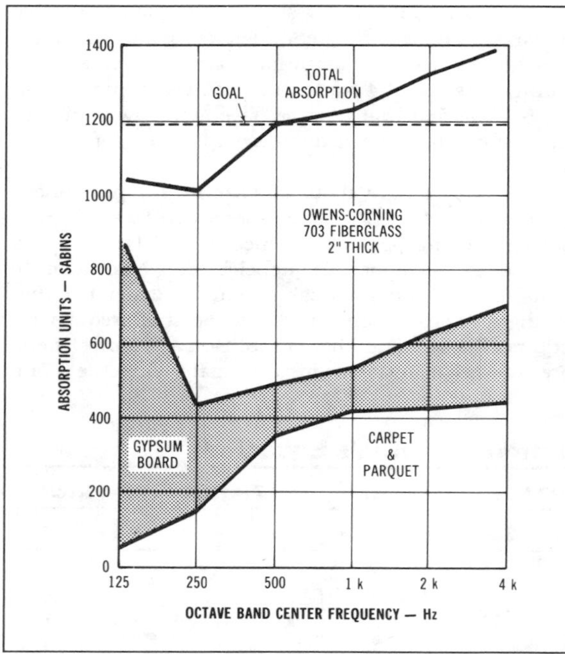

Figure 5-4 Graphical visualization of addition of absorption components in a 30 × 25 × 19.5-ft studio to achieve the 1194 sabins required.

pendium" under "Glass Fiber Materials" (guided by prescience and a bit of experience), we find Owens-Corning™ Type 703 Fiberglas of 2-in. thickness that appears to have the absorption coefficients desired. This material is a semirigid board of 3 lb/ft^3 density widely used in acoustical treatment. Johns-Manville Corp. Spin-Glas 1000 is a similar product, but with twice the absorption at 125 Hz. The 0.99 absorption coefficient of 703 at 500 Hz would call for 700 ft^2 to give about 700 sabins. The coefficients for this 2-in. 703 are entered in Table 5-2, and sabins are calculated for each frequency. The total absorption of carpet + parquet + gypsum board + 2-in. 703 is then plotted in Fig. 5-4. At 500 Hz the total is almost exactly equal to the 1194 required, but the room is somewhat underabsorbed below 500 Hz and somewhat overabsorbed above that frequency. Now is the time to calculate reverberation time and evaluate how closely the goal of 0.6 s is approached. This is done in Table 5-2 and plotted in Fig. 5-5 as the Sabine curve. Although the average reverberation time over the six octaves is 0.60 s, there is what must be termed a modest rise at low frequencies and a modest droop at high frequencies.

At this point in our calculations, attention must be directed to the precision of the calculations just made. First, the coefficients are determined in reverberation rooms by the acoustical laboratories, and they are not highly precise. Furthermore, the measurements of different laboratories on the same material do not always

Table 5-3. Comparison of Absorption Coefficients of Owens-Corning Type 703 Fiberglas Mounting 4 (No Air Space)

Octave Band Center Frequency (Hz)					
125	250	500	1 k	2 k	4 k
0.22	0.82	1.21	1.10	1.02	1.05*
0.22	0.82	0.99	0.99	0.99	0.99†

*From *Noise Control Manual*.[7]

†From "Compendium."[6]

agree. An example of uncertainty in absorption coefficient for the Owens-Corning Type 703 Fiberglas (mounting 4, no air space) is shown in Table 5-3. This has nothing to do with measurement variability, only human judgment. Absorption coefficients greater than unity are a surprise to the newcomer, but they are regularly measured in the acoustical laboratories. A standard 8 × 9-ft sample of the material is laid on the reverberation room floor, and the decay rate of random noise with and without the sample in the room is measured at each band of frequencies using Sabine's equation.[8] Absorption coefficients greater than unity sometimes result. What is to be done about them? Actually, such coefficients indicate that the 8 × 9-ft patch of material is acoustically larger than the geometric 72 ft^2 due to diffraction at the edges of the sample. In Table 5-3 Owens-Corning reports in their publication what came from the acoustical laboratory. The editor of the "Compendium"[6] chose to indicate such coefficients greater than unity as an arbitrary 0.99 to bring consistency with other products listed. Nevertheless, the lesson here is that absorbing material in patches yields greater absorption than the area-coefficient product would indicate. Because diffraction contributes to the diffusion of sound in a room, arranging the 700 ft^2 of 703 absorbing material of Table 5-2 in patches in our studio example would significantly contribute to the diffusion of sound.

Other uncertainties, such as the manner of mounting the absorbing materials, tend to limit the precision of calculations. Above all, not knowing how diffuse the sound field in our studio is underlines the applicability of the Sabine equation. Summing all such variables leads to the decision that there is little point in worrying about the deviations of reverberation time from the goal of 0.6 s in Fig. 5-5.

5.1.7 Calculation of Reverberation Time—Eyring

The design of our studio will now be redone using Eyring's Eq. 5-3. The first step is to compute the average absorption coefficient from which the total sabins required for a reverberation time of 0.6 s can be calculated. Eq. 5-3 can be rearranged as follows:

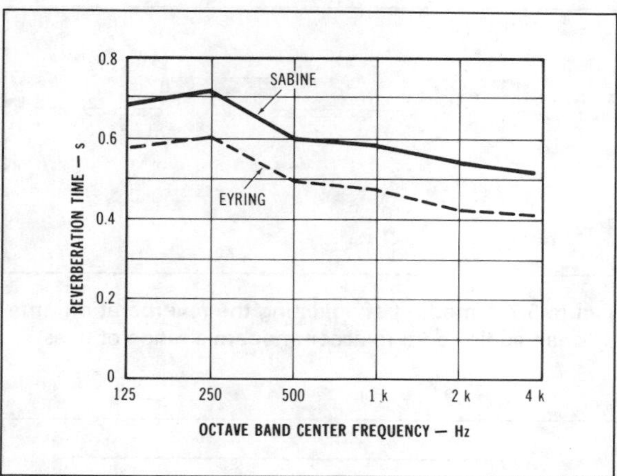

Figure 5-5 Computed reverberation times of a 30 × 25 × 19.5-ft studio comparing the Sabine equation (5-1) and the Eyring equation (5-3).

$$\log_e (1 - a') = 0.049V/-S(RT)$$

substituting,

$$\log_e (1 - a') = 0.049(14{,}625)/-3645(0.6)$$
$$= -0.328$$

Entering −0.328 in an engineering-type calculator and punching the e^x button yields the average absorption coefficient:

$$(1 - a') = 0.72$$
$$a' = 1 - 0.72$$
$$= 0.28$$

By multiplying the total surface area of the room by this average coefficient, the total absorption units required to give a reverberation time of 0.6 s is obtained,

$$Sa' = 3645(0.28) = 1021 \text{ sabins}$$

Compare this to 1194 sabins obtained with the Sabine equation.

Returning to Table 5-2, the total sabins at each frequency can be picked up for this Eyring calculation, and the average absorption coefficient for each frequency, found by dividing total sabins by the wall + ceiling + floor area, 3645 ft^2. Once these average absorption coefficients are found, the reverberation time is calculated from Eq. 5-3 and plotted on Fig. 5-5 for comparison with the Sabine results. The Eyring average across the band is 0.49, as compared to 0.60 s for Sabine, or 18% lower. The logical question at this point is, "Which is the more dependable?"

Young points out that the first two papers presented before the Acoustical Society dealt with absorption coefficients and the buildup and decay of sound in a room.[9] He states, "Many of the difficulties have been largely forgotten—but not overcome . . . ." The problem is largely associated with confusion, even among the experts, regarding absorption coefficients, which are beyond the scope of this treatment. Young's conclusion after detailed study of the problem is that *inasmuch as our published absorption coefficients are Sabine coefficients, the best practice is to use the simple Sabine equation for engineering calculations.*

In summary, we have found that our goal of 0.6-s reverberation time can be at least approximated in the 30 × 25 × 19.5-ft proposed studio (1) by using heavy carpet and pad on 80% of the floor, (2) by utilizing the low-frequency absorption of gypsum-board walls partially to compensate for unbalanced carpet absorption, and (3) by distributing 700 ft^2 of 2-in. thick Type 703 Fiberglas with no air space behind it. These three major elements yield a reasonable reverberation time, as shown by the Sabine curve of Fig. 5-5. This should be considered for what it is, an estimate that will need verification by actual measurements and trimming adjustments on the basis of measured results.

5.1.8 Localization of Reverberation

A common practice in recording studio design is to have some live areas and some dead areas. Musicians need to hear themselves to perform well, and the use of foldback headphones is considered an inferior approach by some. Areas having highly reflective surfaces within an otherwise quite dead room can give the subjective impression of being acoustically live, even though the average effect of the room is much more dead. The sound from some musical instruments is enhanced by local reflecting surfaces; others require less.

Isolation between instruments in multitrack recording of popular musical groups can be a difficult problem. Such isolation is achieved through utilization of microphone directivity, the use of baffles and barriers between sources, the arrangement of acoustics of the studio including reflecting surfaces, the use of electronic circuitry such as noise gates, and the use of contact transducers.[10]

5.1.9 Variable Acoustics

For a recording studio catering to clients with a wide variety of needs because of a wide variety of musical tastes, having some degree of freedom to alter studio acoustics is desirable. There are many ways of building into an audio room variable features that can change reverberation time within limits.

Fig. 5-6 illustrates a clever method devised by Putnam and used in two early studios of the United Recording Corp. in Hollywood.[11] Two perforated panels, one fixed

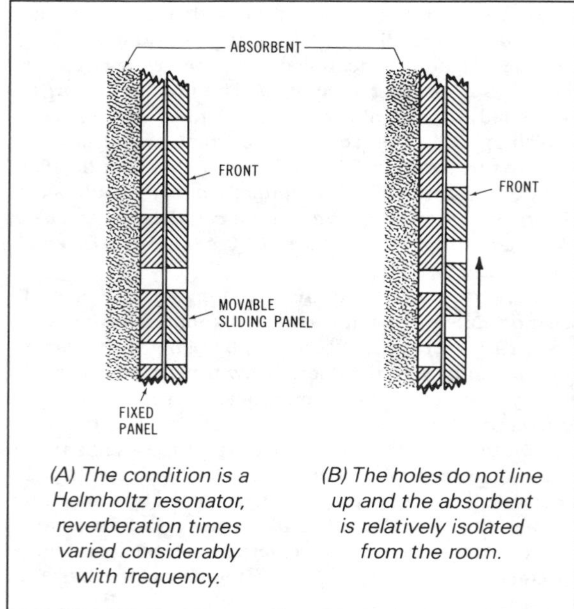

(A) The condition is a Helmholtz resonator, reverberation times varied considerably with frequency.

(B) The holes do not line up and the absorbent is relatively isolated from the room.

Figure 5-6 Putman's method of varying reverberation time in early Hollywood recording studios.

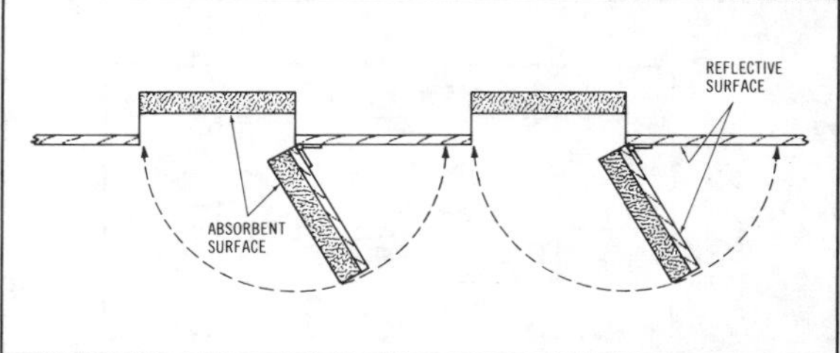

Figure 5-7 A method of adjusting the reverberation time of an audio room to accommodate a range of uses.

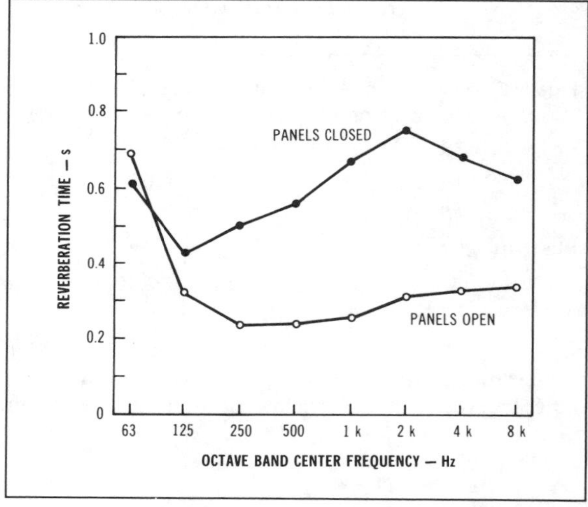

Figure 5-8 Measured reverberation time in a small video studio of 22,000-ft^3 volume with adjustable panels of the type of Fig. 5-7 open and closed.

and one movable, cover the absorbent material. If the holes do not line up, the absorbent is relatively isolated from the room. If they do line up, a Helmholtz resonator effect is obtained. The panels were of ⅛-in. tempered masonite with ⅛-in. holes spaced ½ in. (4.9% perforation area), and the calculated resonance frequency would be about 375 Hz. In a 65,000-ft^3 studio, reverberation time was adjustable from 1.06 to 1.6 s at 500 Hz, a change of 34%. In a smaller studio a change of about 23% was realized. The shortcoming of this method is that the shape of the reverberation-frequency characteristic is drastically altered.

Another method of adjusting acoustics, hoary with age but still useful, is the swinging panel approach of Fig. 5-7. This method yields a more constant reverberation time versus frequency than that of Fig. 5-6. When the panels are closed, the area is highly reflective. When open, most of the area may be made to be predominantly absorbent material. In this case, the shape of the reverberation-frequency curve would be strongly influenced by the thickness of the absorber. Fig. 5-8 shows the open/closed reverberation time versus frequency characteristic for a small 22,000-ft^3 video studio in which everything from dramatics to musical groups must be accommodated. When panels are open, a reverberation time hovering about 0.3 s provides the usual dead general condition to subdue the noise of the moving of cameras and production people and the dragging of cables on the floor. The local acoustical conditions within the setting around the microphone are determined by reflections from the setting panels, props, and so on. When an orchestra or other musical group is to be served, the longer reverberation time resulting from closing the panels is employed.

An excellent modern application of an old method of varying the acoustics of a space is that of Studio D of Fantasy™ Records in Berkeley, California.[12] To accommodate everything from full orchestra film scoring with as many as 80 performers to the more usual rock group requiring extreme separation, numerous features were built into the studio, one of which is the louvered ceiling of Fig. 5-9. The louvers are over that part of the floor left reflective. The 24 louvers, in groups of 6, are flush with the ceiling when closed, each section operable individually. The mechanical plan of the louver is shown in Fig. 5-10.

The louver idea can be applied, on a smaller scale, to walls by using ordinary louvered window hardware with either glass or tempered masonite panels, as shown in Fig. 5-11. Ordinarily, louvers are open (absorptive con-

Figure 5-9 A modern adaptation of an old idea of varying the sound absorption in Studio D, Fantasy Records in Berkeley, California. This room was designed by Sierra Audio. *(Courtesy Fantasy Records)*

dition) or closed (reflective condition). When the louvers are almost closed, however, the crack transforms the installation to slit-type Helmholtz resonators giving peak absorption at some low frequency. The exact frequency, which depends on the depth of the cavity and geometry of the overlap as well as the width of the opening, is rather on the indeterminate and indefinite side but could be controlled by proper attention and mechanical devices.

5.1.10 Subjective Reaction to Reverberation

In concert halls reverberation contributes a richness and fullness that is very important to musical quality. Such audible trailing off of sound is characteristic only of larger spaces and is not discernible as such in small audio rooms. On the other hand, what might be called reverberation in small rooms is that which gives a desirable "room effect" quality to the sound. It can also result in problems such as frequency distortions or colorations that can seriously impair sound quality. Often such colorations can be traced to axial modes or groups of modes widely separated from neighboring modes. This type of distortion could be corrected by placing absorbent materials or structures at high-pressure positions of the offending mode. Some colorations may be traced to early reflections that give rise to comb filter distortion. To reduce such distortions, the offending reflecting surface must be treated. As remedial efforts are made toward reducing distortions observed in a room, the possibility of mechanical vibration of loose objects should be borne in mind, since this is another source of distortions. Slowly sweeping a sine tone at a relatively high level in a room is a favorite method of localizing the source of such vibratory problems.

5.2 SOUND ABSORBERS

Sound may be reflected, refracted, diverged, and diffused, but the only way to get rid of it is to change acoustical energy to another form, usually heat. Sound is absorbed by a carpet through friction offered by the tufts and in glass fiber by the flexing of fibers and the friction offered in the tiny interstices. A panel must be physically fixed to a structure; hence, the losses associated with panel vibration are caused by bending deformations. Metal

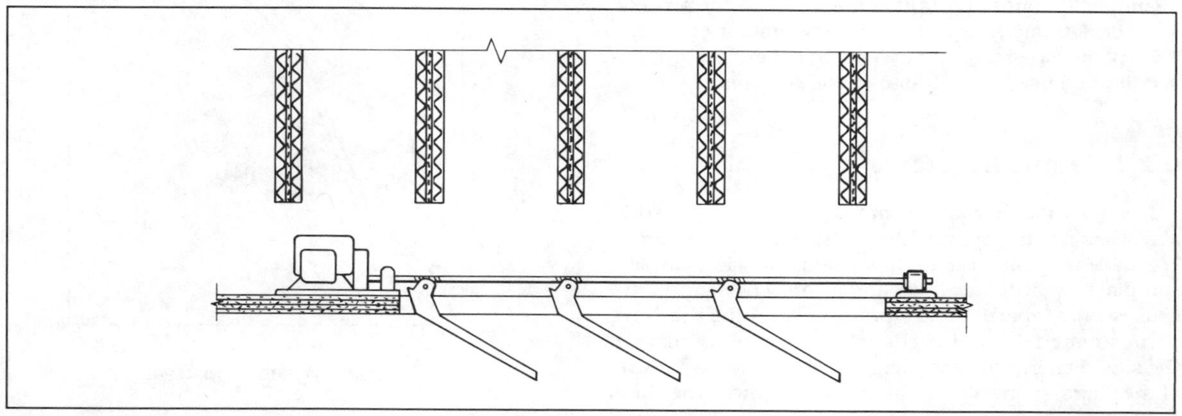

Figure 5-10 The mechanical drive system for controlling position of ceiling louvers in Studio D, Fantasy Records, Berkeley, California. *(Courtesy Fantasy Records)*

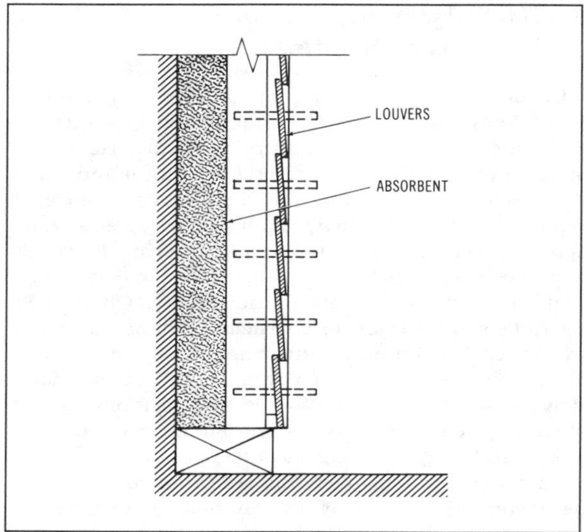

Figure 5-11 An arrangement for varying the absorption in an audio room based on readily available hardware used in household louvered windows.

panels have much lower bending losses than wood or plastic. In perforated panels, losses result from the constriction of air flow through the holes, which increases the effect of air viscosity. Losses are increased for both perforated and unperforated panels by adding porous material in the air space behind them.

In the "Compendium,"[6] Table 5-1, and other listings, the absorption coefficients are given for six standard frequencies (125, 250, 500, 1000, 2000, 4000 Hz). In addition, the *noise reduction coefficient (NRC)* is given. This is simply the average of the coefficients at 250, 500, 1000, and 2000 Hz to give a single-number rating. All single-number systems (NC, STC, and so on) have the advantage of simplicity, but important detail is lost in the process. Most design tasks require the detailed picture of sound absorption variations with frequency; hence, the NRC has very limited use in the design of audio rooms.

5.2.1 Porous Absorbers

The most familiar and commonly available acoustical absorbers are the porous kind. These are fuzzy, fibrous vegetable or mineral materials, foams, fabrics, carpets, soft plasters, acoustical tile, and so on. The sound wave causes the air particles to vibrate down in the depths of porous materials, and frictional losses convert some of the sound energy to heat energy. With very loose packing of the fibers, there is little frictional loss, and if the fibers are compressed into a dense board, there is little penetration and more reflection from the surface. For this reason, density of the porous material is a factor in sound absorption efficiency.

5.2.1.1 Effect of Density

The effect of density of Owens-Corning™ 700 Series of semirigid Fiberglas boards on the absorption of sound is shown in Fig. 5-12. This is a plot of coefficients taken directly from the "Compendium" to provide a visual comparison. For the 1-in. thickness of material, none of the three densities absorb well at frequencies below 500 Hz. At the higher audio frequencies the 6-lb/ft^3 density is better than the 3-lb/ft^3 material, and the lower density 1.58-lb/ft^3 material is poorest of all. The difference, however, is modest. In Fig. 5-13 a comparison of different densities of the 4-in. thick fiberglass boards is made. In this case the 3-lb/ft^3-density board performs better than the 6-lb/ft^3 board. As mentioned previously, boards of density greater than 6 lb/ft^3 have little increase in absorption to offer, and the very dense boards become quite reflective because sound cannot penetrate them well.

Boards of medium density have a mechanical advantage in that they can be cut with a butcher knife and press fitted into place. This is more difficult with materials that have a 1.5-lb/ft^3 density and lower, such as building insulation. The denser the board, the greater the cost. Most acoustical purposes are well served by glass fiber of 3-lb/ft^3 density, although some consultants specify a 6-lb/ft^3 material.

5.2.1.2 Effect of Thickness

Fig. 5-14 explores the effect of thickness of 703 Fiberglas on absorption. Here again the data are taken directly from the "Compendium." [6] The absorption of low-frequency sound energy is very much greater with the thicker materials.

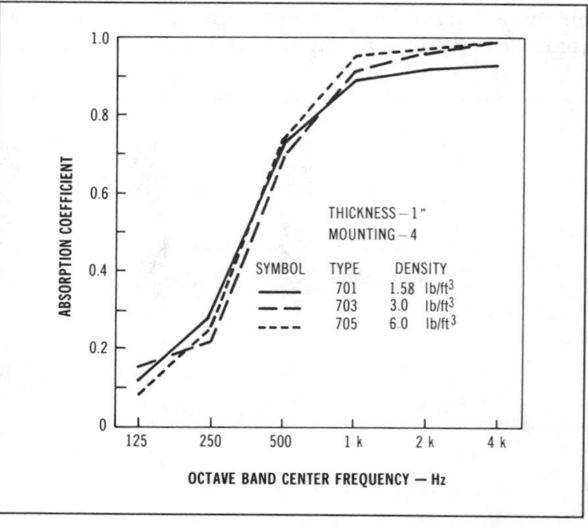

Figure 5-12 The effect of density on the sound absorption properties of Owens-Corning 700 series semirigid Fiberglas boards of 1-in. thickness.

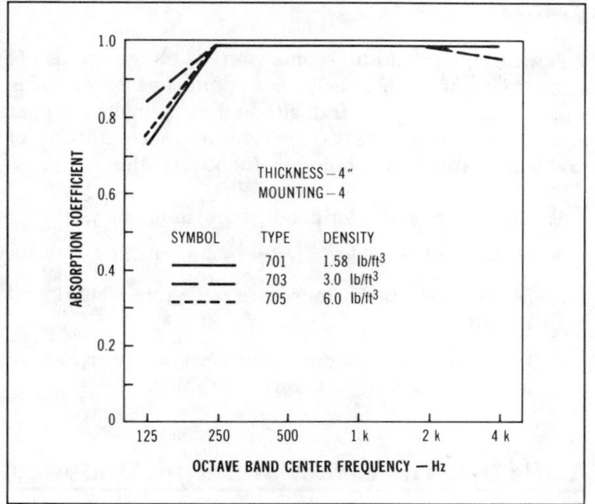

Figure 5-13 The effect of density on sound absorption of Owens-Corning semirigid Fiberglas boards of 4-in. thickness. *(After Reference 6.)*

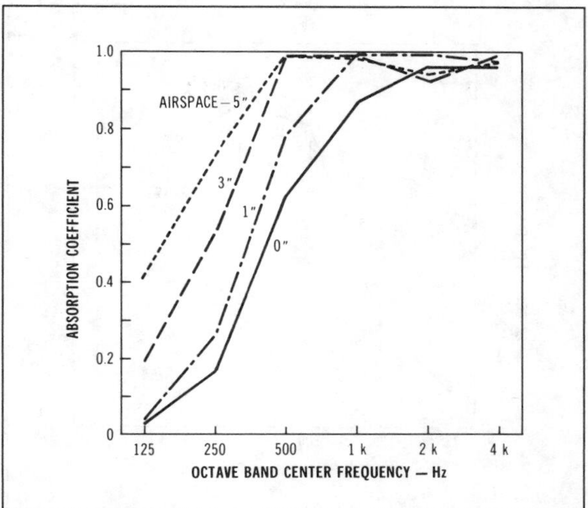

Figure 5-15 The effect of air space behind Owens-Corning Linear Glass Cloth Faced Board of 1-in. thickness. *(After Reference 7.)*

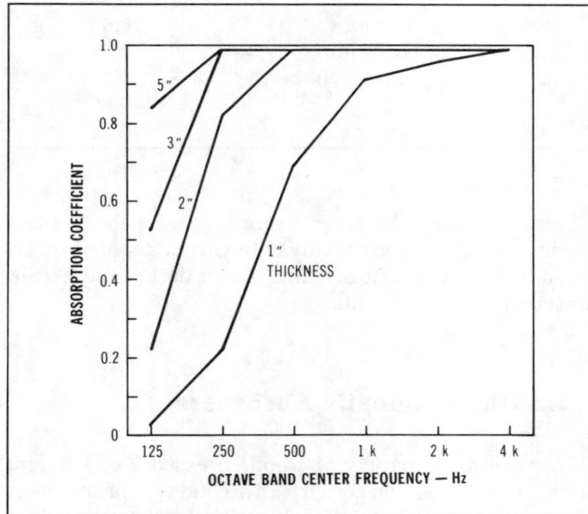

Figure 5-14 The effect of thickness on the sound absorption of Owens-Corning 703 Fiberglas. *(After Reference 6.)*

5.2.1.3 Effect of Air Space

In Fig. 5-15 the effect of air space behind a 1-in. thick Owens-Corning™ Linear Glass Board is shown. With no air space the absorption characteristics are given by the solid line. As the air space is increased in steps to 5 in the lower-frequency absorption increases progressively. Sometimes it is cheaper to use thinner glass fiber and arrange for air space behind it, and sometimes it is cheaper to use glass fiber of greater thickness. At still other times the need for low-frequency absorption is so great that both thick material and air space are required.

5.2.1.4 Tiles and Boards

Acoustical tiles and boards are widely used, primarily for suspended (lay-in) ceiling treatment in noise control. The 12 × 12-in. tile, so popular a generation ago, is available today in a greatly reduced range of choices. In the "Compendium" most sound-absorption coefficients are given for Mounting 7 (lay-in ceiling, 16-in. air space); very few are given for Mounting 4 (directly on wall or ceiling). Fig. 5-16, however, shows the average absorption coefficients of eight 12 × 12-in. acoustical tiles of ¾-in. thickness taken from outdated literature. The vertical lines at each frequency point show the spread of the coefficients for each frequency. Above 500 Hz the absorption is good, with a drooping tendency above 1 kHz.

There are relatively soft fibrous boards, usually in 4 × 8-ft size, that are often used as "sound-deadening" boards in studio treatment. They are often mounted behind or between gypsum-board layers and offer a method of providing some damping effect and of staggering coincidence dips on two sides of a partition for improved transmission loss.

5.2.1.5 Foams

Urethane foams are being used extensively in automotive, machinery, aircraft, and industrial applications. Polyurethane foam is produced in three structural con-

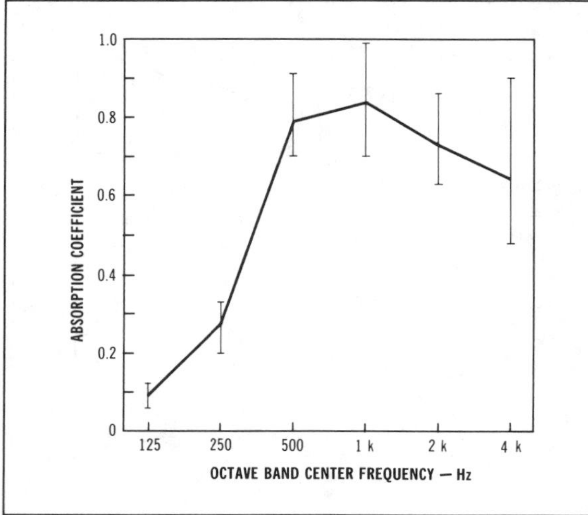

Figure 5-16 The average absorption coefficients of eight acoustical tiles of ¾-in. thickness.

figurations: closed cell, open cell, and reticulated open cell. When the urethane reactants begin to polymerize and generate CO_2 gas, the foam expands into a low-density material. The bubbles formed become distorted into polyhedrons, and the contact points, into planes. These cells are closed, and in this form the material has very poor acoustical absorption properties. It must be possible to force air through a material for it to be an effective sound absorber.

Open-cell foam is produced by collapsing some of the membranes at a certain stage of the process. A reticulated foam has all of the membranes removed, so that only the skeleton remains. Partial reticulation can be controlled to get any degree of openness. It is the partially reticulated foam that finds application as a sound absorber. The number of pores per inch (in the general range of 50 to 100) determines the efficiency as an absorber.

The use of polyurethane foam materials in audio applications has come about in relatively recent times. Sonex, produced by Illbruck, is molded into shapes to simulate the acoustical wedges of the professional anechoic chamber. This material is finding its way into numerous audio rooms. The material comes in nested pairs, each composed of one negative and one positive sheet, as shown in Fig. 5-17. The absorption coefficients for the 2-, 3-, and 4-in. depths are plotted in Fig. 5-18.[14] It is interesting to compare the Sonex absorption characteristics to those of 703 Fiberglas of Fig. 5-14. The performance of the 2-in. depth Sonex is very similar to the 1-in. thick 703, and the 4-in. depth Sonex is similar to the 2-in. thick 703. The more exciting appearance of Sonex, its ease of mounting, and its far higher price must be weighed against the acoustically equivalent glass fiber.

5.2.1.6 Carpets

Few builders of audio rooms want to forego the use of carpeting. Carpet is a visual and comfort asset, and it is a porous absorber of sound, although principally at upper audio frequencies. The "Compendium" quotes the Carpet and Rug Institute on some helpful observations:

1. Cut pile has greater absorption than loop pile,
2. Impermeable backing reduces absorption,
3. Sound absorption increases with pile weight and height,
4. Pad material has significant effect on absorption of a specific carpet, as shown in Table 5-4.

Table 5-4. The Effect of Carpet Underlay

Pad Weight (oz)	Pad Material	Noise Reduction Coefficient (NRC)
—	None	0.35
32	Hair	0.50
40	Hair	0.55
86	Hair	0.60
32	Hair jute	0.55
40	Hair jute	0.60
86	Hair jute	0.65
31	Foam rubber, 3/8 in.	0.60
44	Sponge rubber	0.45

Because of the unbalanced nature of carpet absorption, the designer may wish to reduce the carpet's contribution to room absorption. Controlling the underlay may be the convenient way to do this.

5.2.2 Diaphragmatic Absorbers

Nonperforated panels of wood, pressed wood fibers, plastic, or composition comprise a second type of absorber. When mounted on a solid backing, but separated from it by an air space, the panel will respond to impinging sound waves by vibrating. This results in a flexing of the fibers, and a certain amount of frictional loss results in absorption of some of the sound energy. The mass of the panel and the springiness of the air constitute a resonant system, which results in a peak of absorption at the resonance frequency. Fig. 4.8 is a transmission-loss curve for a panel. If this is inverted, a transmission curve, which applies to the panel under consideration, results. It is stiffness controlled below the resonance frequency (f_0), and mass controlled above. The coincidence effects are usually masked by damping (resistance) of the system.

(A) A Sonex ceiling.

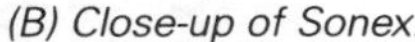

(B) Close-up of Sonex.

Figure 5-17 Sonex, an open-cell polyurethane-foam sound absorber contoured to simulate wedges used in anechoic rooms.

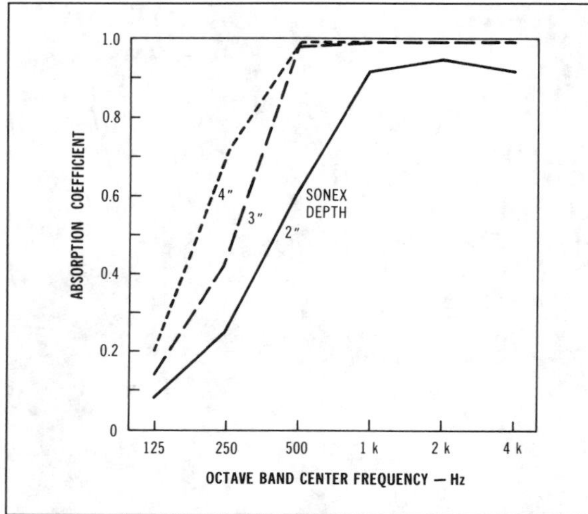

Figure 5-18 Sound absorption characteristics of Sonex of the type shown in Fig. 5-17. *(After Reference 14.)*

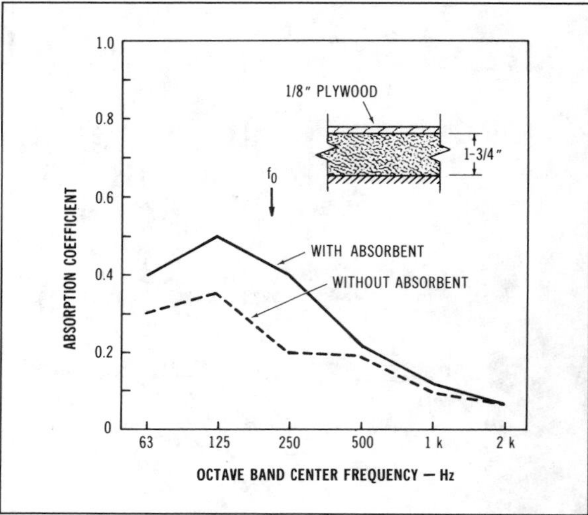

Figure 5-19 Sound absorption characteristics of ⅛-in. plywood in diaphragm action. *(After Reference 15.)*

The approximate frequency of resonance is given by

$$f_o = \frac{170}{\sqrt{MD}} \tag{5-4}$$

where,

f_o is the resonance frequency in hertz,

M is the surface density of the panel in pounds per square foot,

D is the depth of air space in inches.

This is approximate because it is based on normal incidence, but such devices used in a room are subject to random incident sound. Typical absorption curves for panel-type structures are shown in Fig. 5-19,[15] this particular one for ⅛-in. plywood (surface density 0.37 lb/ft^2) and an air space of 1.75 in. Note that a measurement point at 63 Hz is included. The resonance frequency, calculated from Eq. 5-4, gives $f_o = 170/\sqrt{0.37 \times 1.75}$ or $f_o = 211$ Hz. Plotted on Fig. 5-19, this calculated f_o misses the measured one by a considerable margin, which emphasizes the approximate nature of Eq. 5-4. The presence of the absorbent increases the absorption coefficient and broadens the peak somewhat. When the air space equals a quarter wavelength, maximum absorption will occur; with a half wavelength, minimum absorption is achieved.

Panel absorption is an effective method of controlling the modal resonances of rooms at low frequencies, yet providing reflectivity at higher frequencies. These are desirable characteristics for certain types of music. Gypsum-board wall facings, window glass, and doors are all sound absorbers of the panel type.

Membranes are also diaphragmatic absorbers.[16] A very interesting membrane-type low-frequency absorber is available commercially in the form of glass fiber with paper backing. When the paper is exposed to the sound, it acts as a vibrating membrane backed with glass fiber as a damping material. The broken line of Fig. 5-20 is the absorption of 3.5-in. (R-11) Owens-Corning™ Fiberglas building insulation against a solid wall with insulation exposed.[16] The absorption coefficient curve is similar to that of 703 Fiberglas of Fig. 5-14 or Sonex foam of Fig. 5-18. When the same material is flopped over so that the

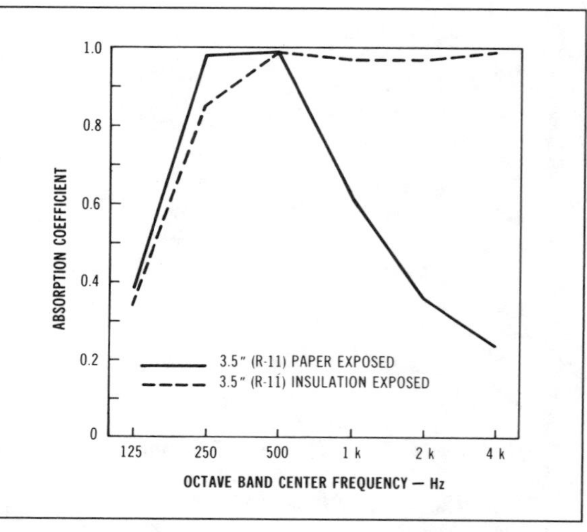

Figure 5-20 Sound absorption of Owens-Corning Fiberglas building insulation of 3.5-in. thickness. *(After Reference 7.)*

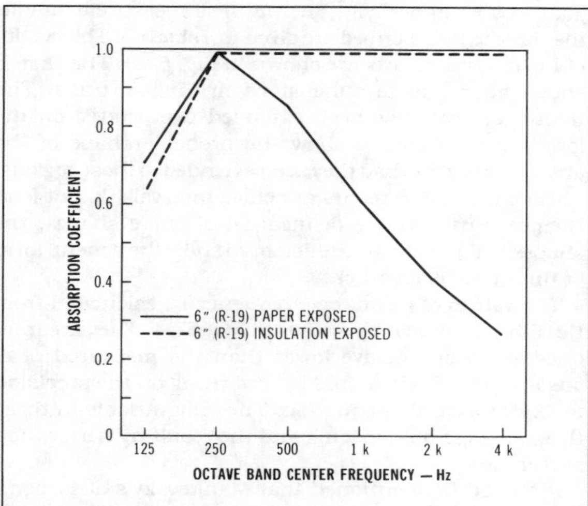

Figure 5-21 Sound absorption of Owens-Corning Fiberglas building insulation of 6-in. thickness. *(After Reference 7.)*

asphalt and kraft paper is exposed to the sound, the solid curve of Fig. 5-20 is obtained. Absorption is greatest in the 250- to 500-Hz region as a membrane resonator. Used as a low-frequency absorber in an audio room, some protection must be provided. Otherwise, it could be mounted on upper walls or on the ceiling out of reach, and if painted flat black, it would essentially be invisible.

Fiberglass building insulation of 6-in. thickness (R-19) can also be used as a membrane resonator.[17] In Fig. 5-21 the broken line shows its absorption characteristic with insulation exposed, and the solid line, with paper exposed. In this case peak absorption occurs at 250 Hz. The 6-in. thickness resonates at a lower frequency than the 3.5-in. thickness.

Such building insulation is also available with a foil-faced laminate with glass-fiber reinforcement and a kraft backing (FRK). Fig. 5-22 shows absorption characteristics for both the 3.5-in. (R-11) and the 6-in. (R-19) with FRK facing exposed to the sound. The FRK acts as a membrane resonating system. The 6-in. has good absorption to lower frequencies; stated another way, its absorption band is wider. These paper-faced building insulation products may find a niche in audio room treatment, especially for budget installations.

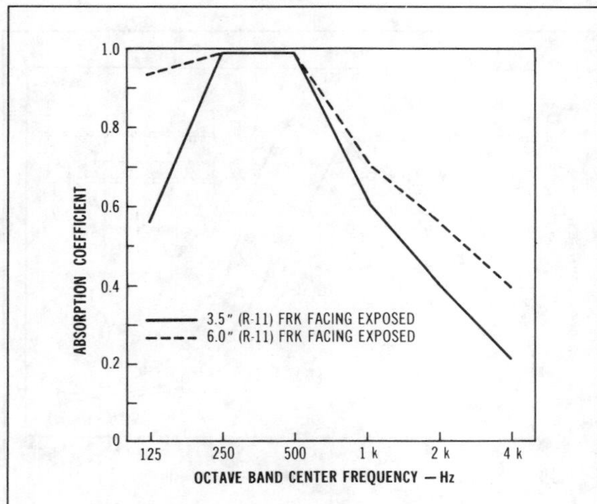

Figure 5-22 Sound absorption of Owens-Corning Fiberglas building insulation *(After Reference 7.)*

5.2.3 Helmholtz Resonators—Perforated Type

Blowing across the mouth of a bottle creates a tone at the frequency of resonance as the mass of air in the neck of the bottle reacts with the springiness of the air inside the bottle. A perforated panel, spaced out from a solid surface, acts like an assemblage of many bottles. Each individual hole in the panel is comparable to the neck of a bottle, and the hole's share of the space behind is comparable to the air within the bottle. In this way a perforated panel can be viewed as a great number of acoustically resonant systems, together displaying the usual phenomena of resonance. The sharpness of the resonance tuning curve is determined by the losses of the overall system, the resistance offered to air flow by the neck, the absorbent material in the cavity, and so on.

As with other resonance systems, the sharpness of the tuning curve is defined by the Q factor. The Q may be found from the expression

$$Q = \Delta f / f_o$$

where,

Δf is the width of the curve at the − 3 dB (half power) points,

f_o is the resonance frequency.

The Q of a Coca-Cola® bottle has been measured at Q = 276. Most Helmholtz resonators used in acoustic treatment have Qs from 1 to 5. Resonators made of ceramic or concrete have been made with much higher Qs. However, a wide resonance curve means absorption over a wide range of frequency, and this is usually the desired characteristic.

The resonance frequency of a perforated panel type of Helmholtz resonator can be calculated from the following expression:

$$f_o = 200\sqrt{p/Dt} \qquad (5\text{-}5)$$

where,

f_o is the frequency of resonance in hertz,

p is the perforation percentage,
t is the effective hole length in inches A_N = (panel thickness) + 0.8 (hole diameter) approximately,
D is the depth of air space in inches.

The perforation percentage (not to be confused with perforation ratio) is computed on a unit basis, as described in Fig. 5-23. Acoustically the hole length appears to be greater than the thickness of the panel; hence, the empirical correction factor related to hole diameter is made. The resonance frequency (f_0) of Helmholtz resonators can be increased by increasing the percent perforation (larger holes, smaller spacing, or both), by decreasing depth of airspace, or by using thinner panels. Resonance frequency f_0 can be lowered by decreasing the percent perforation, by increasing air space depth, or by using thicker panels. The calculated resonance frequency for perforated panels is not very precise, but it is close enough for use in the design stage.

Measured values of absorption coefficients of perforated panel-type Helmholtz resonators have been published by Mankovsky.[17] The physical measurements on the three to be described are given in Table 5-5. The results of his measurements are shown in Fig. 5-24. The sketch shows approximate dimensions in English units. The frequency scale has been extended two octaves on the low-frequency end to show the probable shape of the absorption curves had they been extended to those regions. Although measurements at octave intervals do not lend themselves to precise delineation of curve shapes, the shapes of Fig. 5-24 are sufficient to show the general form of this class of absorber.

The values of resonance frequency f_0, calculated from Eq. 5-5, are shown by arrows in Fig. 5-24. They are from one-half to one octave lower than the measured peak absorption, which should be a warning on the precision to expect from this equation. The only variable in these three cases is hole spacing and the resulting perforation percentage.

It should be mentioned that Mankovsky's absorbent, which was held constant at a 100-mm thickness, is what he called PP-80, but its exact nature is not stated. Neither do we know whether it was against the perforated face, at the back of the air cavity, or in between. Callaway and Ramer have pointed out that for maximum random incidence absorption it is best to position the absorbent away from the perforated panel.[18] For a typical Helmholtz absorber perforated about 1%, a glass-fiber absorber of 3-lb/ft^3 density should be spaced from the perforated panel about ¼ in.

Broadening the absorption curve of perforated Helmholtz resonators may be accomplished by perforating the panel with holes of different diameters and by using variable depth of airspace, which can be accomplished most readily by mounting the panel at an angle to the backing surface. Further consideration of Helmholtz absorbers is given in references 19, 20, 21, 22.

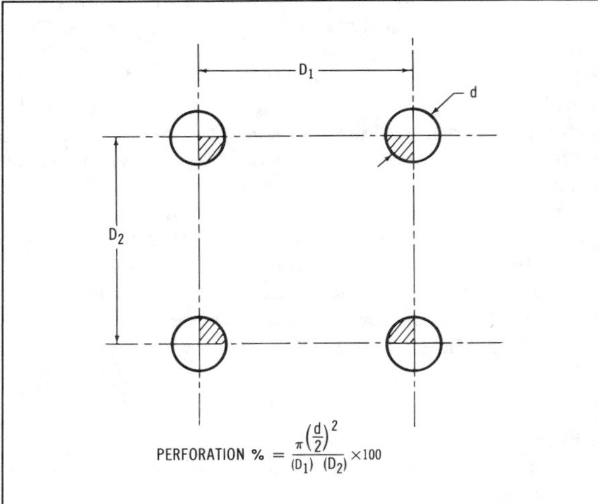

Figure 5-23 The method of figuring perforation percentage on a unit basis.

Table 5-5. Physical Measurements of Helmholtz Resonators*

	Millimeters		
	A	B	C
Panel thickness	4	4	4
Hole diameter	5	5	5
Hole spacing	35	65	100
Depth of air space	200	200	200
Absorbent thickness	100	100	100

*From Acoustics of Studios and Auditoria.[17]

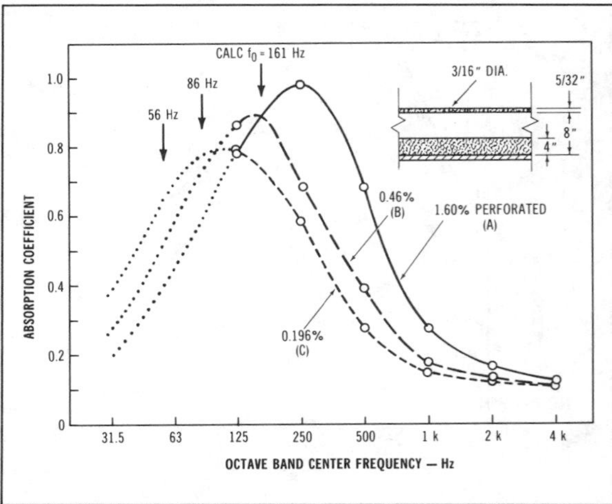

Figure 5-24 Measured absorption coefficients of Mankovsky on three Helmholtz absorbers of the perforated-panel type. *(After Reference 17.)*

5.2.4 Helmholtz Resonators—Slat Type

Helmholtz resonators can be constructed by using spaced slats over an air space. The air mass in the slots between the slats reacts with the springiness of the air in the cavity to form a resonant system, much like that of the perforated panel type. In this case the statement for resonance frequency becomes

$$f_0 = 2160\sqrt{\frac{r}{(d)(D) + (w+r)}} \qquad (5\text{-}6)$$

where,
- f_0 is the frequency of resonance in hertz,
- r is the slot width in inches,
- w is the slat width in inches,
- D is the depth of air space in inches,
- d is the effective depth of the slot in inches, which is 1.2 (thickness of the slat in inches) approximately.

In a practical sense the absorption curve can be broadened by using the variable depth of air space in a structure such as Fig. 5-25. Another approach is using slots of different widths. In the structure of Fig. 5-25, variable air space depth and variable slot width could both be used. The absorbent is shown at the back of the cavity, removed from the slats. This gives a sharper absorption than if the absorbent is in contact with the slats. Having the wide portion above would tend to save floor space. Rettinger has given considerable practical guidance for construction of slat resonators.[23]

The use of Helmholtz resonators to cure "boom" in small rooms is directed toward providing absorption in a narrow frequency band to dampen a specific, identified mode rather than general low-frequency absorption over a broad band. Resonators of high Q and of carefully calculated volume must be constructed for this purpose, and they must be placed, of course, at or near a pressure maximum of that particular mode. van Leeuwen has described the process in detail.[24]

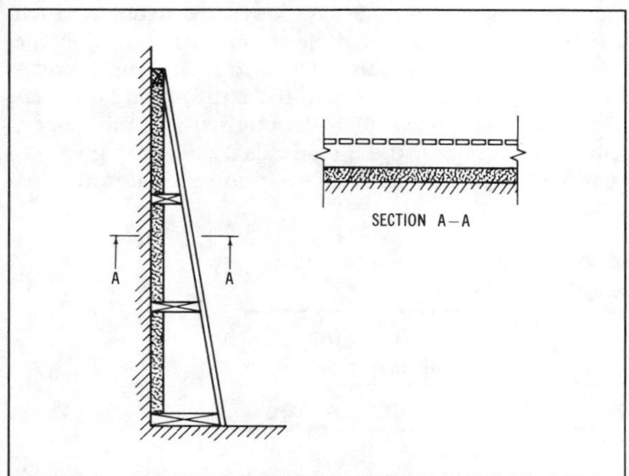

Figure 5-25 A slat-type Helmholtz resonator with varying depth to widen its absorption curve.

5.2.5 Absorption of Sound in Air

In larger rooms the absorption of sound by the air must be considered. The Sabine equation for reverberation time incorporating air absorption is

$$RT = 0.049\,V/(Sa + 4mV) \qquad (5\text{-}7)$$

where,
- RT is the reverberation time in seconds,
- V is the volume of the room in cubic feet,
- S is the surface area of the room in square feet,
- a is the average absorption coefficient,
- m is the attenuation coefficient.

Likewise, the Eyring equation must also have the 4mV term included in the denominator.

The early classical work of Knudsen on the absorption of sound in air has been refined by Harris.[25] The results of Harris are shown in the traditional form in Fig. 5-26 and in the more convenient form in Fig. 5-27. As an exercise in using Fig. 5-27 as well as in gaining some idea of the magnitude of air absorption, an example is given for a room having a volume V = 10,000 ft^3, roughly the size of a professional recording studio. We are interested in a relative humidity range of 20, 40, and 60%. For 2 kHz and 20% relative humidity, Fig. 5-27 is entered and a value of 4mV per 1000 ft^3 of about 7.5 is read off. In a

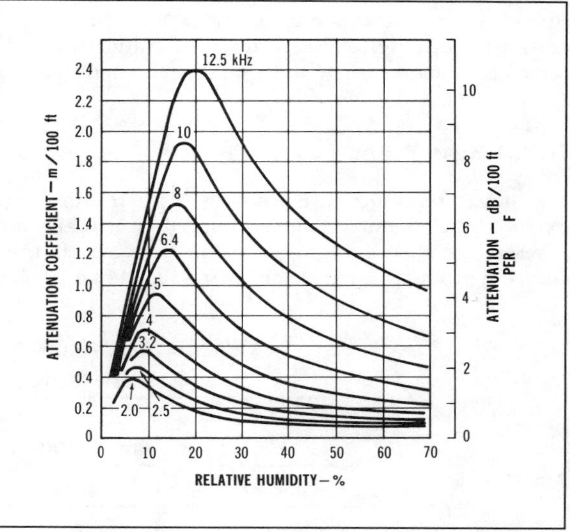

Figure 5-26 Absorption of sound in air as a function of relative humidity and frequency. *(Adapted from Reference 25.)*

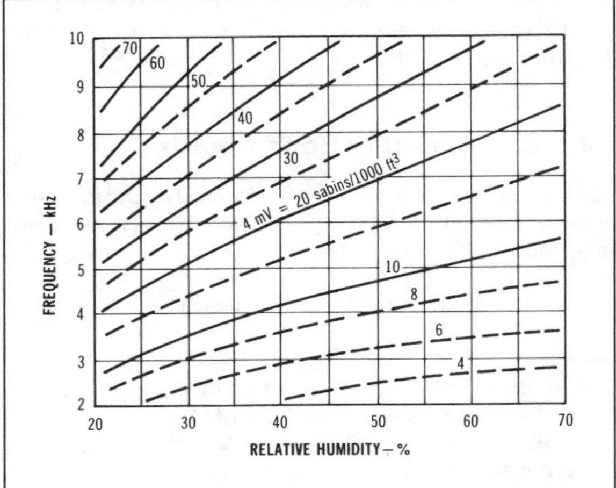

Figure 5-27 An alternate form (from Fig. 5-26) of presenting sound absorption in air. *(Adapted from Reference 25.)*

similar manner the values of 4mV = 1000 ft^3 are read off for 40 and 60% relative humidity. The right-hand part of Table 5-6 is obtained by multiplying the values for 1000 ft^3 on the left by 10 to obtain the total absorption in sabins for the 10,000-ft^3 studio. If a reverberation time of 0.5 s is desired, the total sabins required is (0.049 × 10,000)/0.5 = 980 sabins. Comparing this to the total air absorption of Table 5-6, it is discovered that at 20% relative humidity and 10 kHz, 750 of the 980 sabins required are in air absorption, which would be a factor varying with relative humidity. As noted in Fig. 5-26, the greatest air absorption occurs in the range of 10 to 30% relative humidity and at the higher audio frequencies. Air absorption can radically alter the reverberation time of a room at commonly occurring atmospheric conditions.

5.2.6 Bass Traps

Although *bass traps* are primarily of interest for their extended low-frequency absorption, they actually are excellent absorbers at high audio frequencies as well. They utilize a resonance effect for their exceptional performance at frequencies well below those at which the passive glass fiber or foam absorbers are practical. In Fig. 5-13 we noted that the absorption coefficient of even a 4-in. thickness of glass fiber is headed downward at 125 Hz. The bass trap can introduce significant absorption in the 30- to 100-Hz region.

Bass trap lore pervades the recording industry. Literature on the subject, however, is scarce. Rettinger discussed the fundamentals of bass trap operation, which is explained in Fig. 5-28.[26] In Fig. 5-28A a sound source emits a sinusoidal signal at a given low audio frequency. The wave reflected from the surface interacts with the arriving wave to create a standing-wave effect. The velocity of the air particles at the reflecting surface must, of necessity, be zero because of the solid nature of the reflecting surface and the relatively tenuous nature of the air particles. There is a 90° (quarter-wavelength) phase shift between particle velocity and pressure; hence, pressure is maximum at the reflecting surface where particle velocity is zero. These relationships are graphically presented in Fig. 5-28B. A bass trap is shown in Fig. 5-28C, which is one-quarter wavelength deep at the frequency considered in A and B. This means that at the bottom of the trap the particle velocity is zero and at the trap mouth it is maximum. The cosmetic cloth cover and the glass fiber (or other material) across the opening absorb much sound because of the friction offered the violently vibrating air particles at this position. Pressure, on the other hand, is at a minimum near the mouth of the trap (partial vacuum), tending to divert sound rays from the neighboring region into the trap.

The quarter-wavelength depth of the trap means that it is effective at the resonance frequency and, in diminished form, at nearby frequencies within the scope of its tuning curve. It is also effective at odd multiples of the quarter wavelength. The quarter-wavelength depth of bass traps is listed in Table 5-7, as are the frequencies of the first three odd multiples at which the trap action is also effective. As for dimensions of a bass trap, the quarter-wavelength depth prescribes the lowest frequency at which it is active. The other two dimensions determine only the trap area open to the room. Of course, the trap absorbs sound at frequencies between the multiple odd quarter-wavelength points, well up through the audible spectrum. In summary, then, a so-called bass trap gives (1) peak reactive absorption at the frequency at which its

Table 5-6. Absorption of Sound by Air
Studio Volume = 10,000 cu ft

	4mV/1000 ft^3			Total Sabins Absorption		
Frequency	**20%**	**40%**	**60%**	**20%**	**40%**	**60%**
2 kHz	7.5	3.9	—	75	39	—
5 kHz	29.0	14.2	9.6	290	142	96.0
10 kHz	75.0	45.0	31.0	750	450	310.0

depth is a quarter wavelength, (2) peak reactive absorption at the odd quarter-wavelength frequencies, and (3) general passive absorption in proportion to its opening area up through the spectrum.

The trap is lined with 1- or 2-in. glass fiber boards. The baffles within the trap are usually made up of sound-deadening board core to which glass fiber boards are cemented to both sides. The baffles are commonly suspended by cord or wire to hang freely in the trap.

Placement of the traps in a recording studio is often dictated by architectural considerations, such as placing them under the observation window. Consideration should also be given to the location of nodes and antinodes of pressure distribution in the room at the frequency requiring control. Going to great expense in constructing a bass trap to absorb 80-Hz energy and then placing it where the sound pressure at that frequency is close to zero is futile.

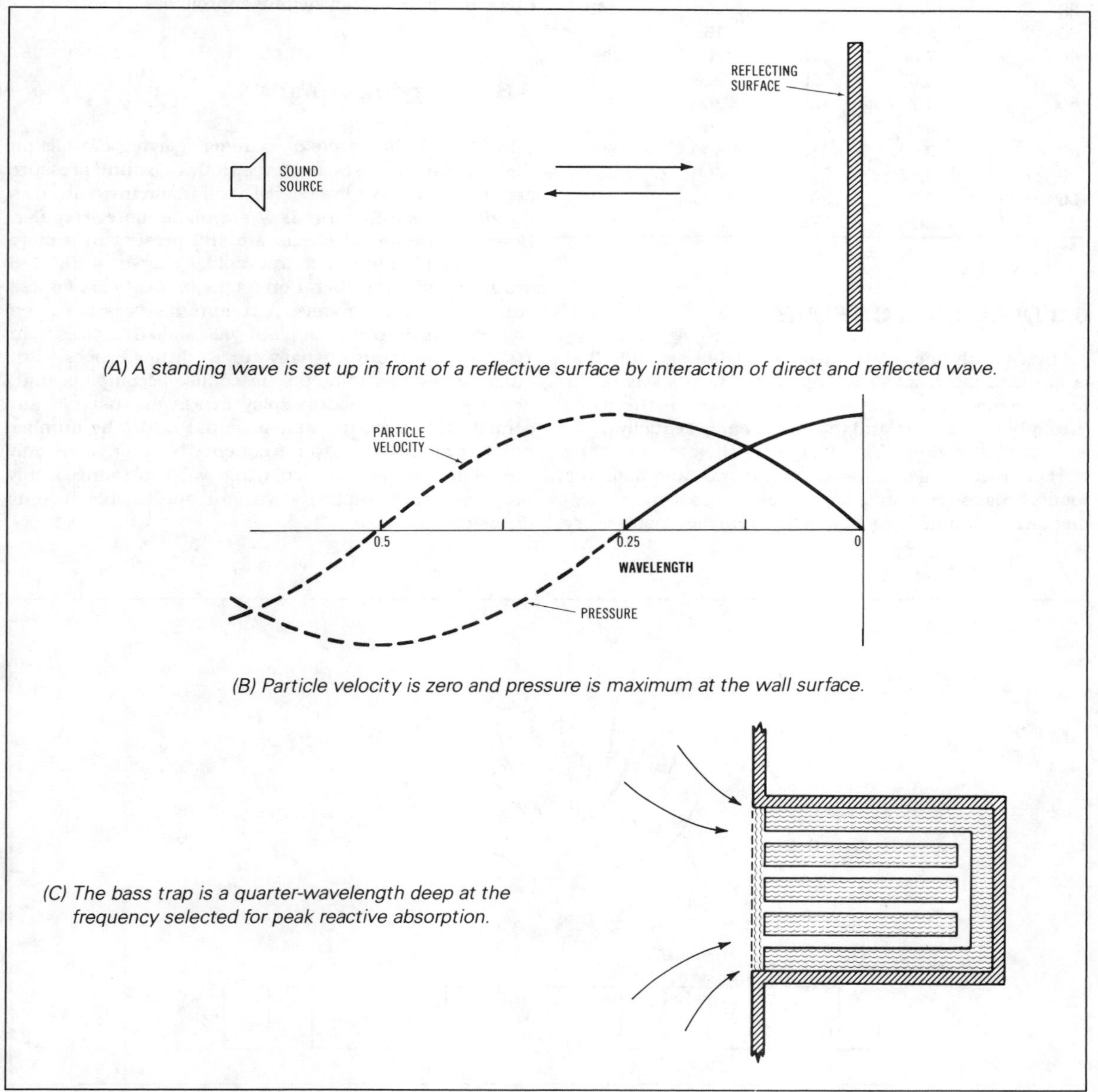

(A) A standing wave is set up in front of a reflective surface by interaction of direct and reflected wave.

(B) Particle velocity is zero and pressure is maximum at the wall surface.

(C) The bass trap is a quarter-wavelength deep at the frequency selected for peak reactive absorption.

Figure 5-28 Bass trap action.

Table 5-7. Bass Trap Quarter-Wavelength Depths (Based on sound velocity of 1130 ft/s)

Frequency (Hertz)	$\frac{\lambda}{4}$ (Feet)	Other Bass Trap Frequencies $\frac{3\lambda}{4}$ (Hertz)	$\frac{5\lambda}{4}$ (Hertz)	$\frac{7\lambda}{4}$ (Hertz)
20	14.13	60	100	140
30	9.42	90	150	210
40	7.06	120	200	280
50	5.65	150	250	350
60	4.71	180	300	420
70	4.04	210	350	490
80	3.53	240	400	560
90	3.14	270	450	630
100	2.83	300	500	700
125	2.26	375	625	875

5.3 DIFFUSION OF SOUND

There is only one way to ensure good diffusion and that is to make the room very large. Only in this way is the time average of the mean square pressure the same throughout the room and the flow of energy equally probable in all directions. This fact is of little comfort in the world of recording studios, control rooms, and listening rooms because economic factors (as well as convenience) dictate much smaller rooms. In these smaller rooms every effort must be made to minimize the problem of quasi-diffuse sound fields.

The problem is compounded by the fact that activities in the small audio room embrace ten octaves of audible sound from 20 to 20,480 Hz, and the bottom four octaves cover sound having wavelengths of the same order of magnitude as the dimensions of the room. This was detailed in Chapter 3. The first and most important step toward adequate diffusion of sound is to distribute the modal frequencies as equitably as possible. Beyond that, there are several other helpful approaches.

5.3.1 Splaying of Walls

In Fig. 3-8 the effects of extreme splaying of walls on the sound field are shown. As contours of sound pressure are distorted, there is a degree of diffusion introduced as the directions of energy flow are made more irregular. However, the modal effects are still present in a more unpredictable form. The trapezoidal shapes of Fig. 3-8 are all right for reverberation rooms, but they are far less suitable for audio rooms. A compromise gesture often suggested is to splay a couple of walls something less than 10°. This procedure usually cures "flutter echoes," but other procedures to be discussed also accomplish that. Actually, such a modest splay makes an insignificant contribution toward a diffuse sound field. The number of room modes in a given frequency band depends only on room volume, thus splaying walls introduces only mathematical complexity without appreciably helping diffusion.

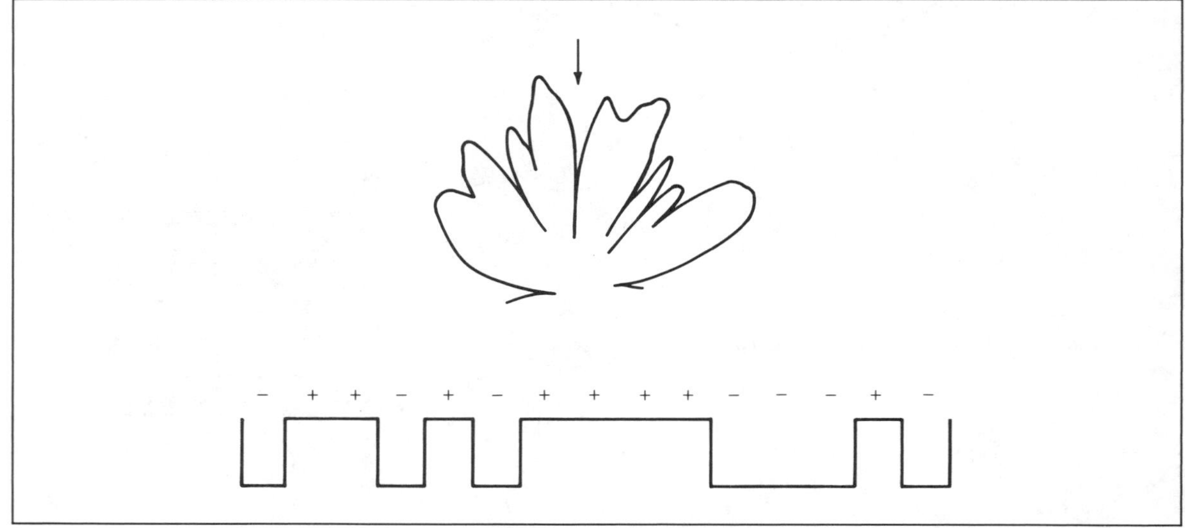

Figure 5-29 The Schroeder diffuser based on maximum length sequence. (After Reference 29.)

5.3.2 Distribution of Absorbing Material

One result of distributing the absorbing material in patches throughout the room is that absorbing efficiency is significantly increased. Remember the absorption coefficients greater than unity in reverberation chamber measurements? They were the result of the diffraction of sound at the edges, making the size of the sample appear acoustically larger than it really was. This effect of increasing absorption is even greater for the smaller patches often used in audio rooms, when compared to the 72-ft^2 areas used in absorption measurements.

Distributing the absorbing material is also beneficial from the standpoint of diffusion of sound in the room. Concentrating absorbence to one or two surfaces of a room results in poor diffusion. In fairness, rooms with nonparallel walls showed less improvement in diffusion when patches of absorbent were employed than rectangular rooms showed.[27]

5.3.3 Geometrical Diffusers

There have been many experiments to determine what geometrical shapes diffuse sound best. It was found that the shapes have to protrude from the wall at least a one-seventh wavelength to be effective as diffusers.[28] It was also determined that ordinary rectangular irregularities were more effective than either a triangular shape or sections of a cylinder. Combining these two observations, a rectangular protuberance would have to be 32 in. deep to be effective at 100 Hz, but only a 6-in. depth would be effective at 300 Hz. Schroeder suggested an entirely new geometric approach to diffusion, which grew out of pseudorandom noise theory.[29] This approach utilizes "maximum length" or "quadratic residue" sequences in the design of "groovy" surfaces, which result in excellent diffusion. Such a wall or ceiling is arranged to have reflection coefficients alternating between +1 and −1 according to the prescribed mathematical sequences. Reflection coefficients of −1 are grooves a quarter-wavelength deep and +1 is simply a hard wall. A wall representing one period of a maximum-length sequence is shown in Fig. 5-29. Designed around 1 kHz, but active over an octave, the quarter-wavelength depths of slots would be 3.39 in. Other arrangements would be necessary to cover the required frequency band. Several octaves can be scattered by alternating between the XZ and the YZ planes. Application of this type of hard wall scattering in audio rooms appears to be very promising in the future.[30,31]

5.4 REFERENCES

1. M. Rettinger, *Studio Acoustics*, New York: Chemical Publishing Co, Inc., 1981.
2. T. J. Schultz, "Problems in the Measurement of Reverberation Time," *Journal of the AES*, vol. 11, no. 4, pp. 307–317, October 1963.
3. D. Davis and C. Davis, "When Not to Make Reverberation Measurements," *Synergetic Audio Concepts Newsletter*, vol. 8, no. 1, p. 14, Fall 1980. (Other comments in vol. 8, no., 3, p. 26, Spring 1981, and vol. 8, no. 4, p. 15, Summer 1981.)
4. W. C. Sabine, *Collected Papers in Acoustics*, Cambridge: Harvard University Press, 1922.
5. C. F. Eyring, "Reverberation Time in Dead Rooms," *Journal of the ASA*, vol. 1, pp. 217–241, January 1930.
6. R. A. Hedeen, *Compendium of Materials for Noise Control*, National Institute for Occupational Safety and Health, NIOSH Publication no. 80–116, May 1980. (Can be ordered from the US Government Printing Office, Washington, DC 20402. It is listed as stock no. 017-033-00359-9. Telephone 202-783-3238.)
7. *Noise Control Manual*, Second Edition, Publication no. 5-BMG-8277-A, June 1980, Toledo, Ohio: Owens-Corning Fiberglas Corp.
8. *Sound Absorption of Acoustical Materials in Reverberation Rooms*, American Society for Testing and Materials, C 423–66, Reapproved 1972.
9. R. W. Young, "Sabine Reverberation Equation and Sound Power Calculations," *Journal of the ASA*, vol. 31, no. 7, pp. 912–921, July 1959.
10. F. A. Everest, *Handbook of Multichannel Recording*, Blue Ridge Summit: Tab Books, 1975. (See especially Chapter 2, "Managing for Track Separation.")
11. M. T. Putnam, "Recording Studio and Control Room Facilities of Advanced Design," *Journal of the AES*, vol. 8, no. 2, April 1960.
12. "Fantasy Records Studio D," *Recording Engineer/Producer*, vol. 11, no. 2, pp. 84–93, April 1980.

13. E. O'Keefe, "Physical and Acoustical Properties of Urethane Foams," *Sound and Vibration*, vol. 12, no. 7, pp. 16–21, July 1978.

14. *Sonex*, (a brochure by) Alpha Audio, Richmond, Virginia (distributors of Sonex).

15. W. E. Purcell, "Materials for Noise and Vibration Control," *Sound and Vibration*, vol. 10, no. 7, pp. 6–33, July 1976.

16. C. L. S. Gilford, "Membrane Sound Absorbers and Their Application to Broadcasting Studios," *B.B.C. Quarterly* (I), pp. 246–256, 1952–1953.

17. V. S. Mankovsky, *Acoustics of Studios and Auditoria*, New York: Hastings House Publishers, 1971.

18. D. B. Callaway and L. G. Ramer, "The Use of Perforated Facings in Designing Low-Frequency Resonant Absorbers," *Journal of the ASA*, vol. 24, no. 3, pp. 309–312, May 1952.

19. F. A. Everest, *Master Handbook of Acoustics*, Blue Ridge Summit: Tab Books, 1981.

20. M. Rettinger, "Low-Frequency Sound Absorbers," *dB The Sound Engineering Magazine*, vol. 4, no. 4, pp. 44–46, April 1970.

21. C. Zwikker and C. W. Kosten, *Sound Absorbing Materials*, New York: Elsevier Publishing Co., Inc., 1949. (Chapter 7, "Absorption by Resonators.")

22. U. Ingård and R. H. Bolt, "Absorption Characteristics of Acoustic Material with Perforated Facings," *Journal of the ASA*, vol. 23, no. 5, pp. 533–540, September 1951.

23. M. Rettinger, "Low-Frequency Slot Absorbers," *dB The Sound Engineering Magazine*, vol. 10, no. 6, pp. 40–43, June 1976.

24. F. J. van Leeuwen, "The Damping of Eigentones in Small Rooms by Helmholtz Resonators," *European Broadcast Union Review*, vol. 62, pp. 155–161, 1960.

25. C. M. Harris, "Absorption of Sound in Air in the Audio Frequency Range," *Journal of the ASA*, vol. 35, no. 1, pp. 11–17, January 1963.

26. M. Rettinger, "Bass Traps," *Recording Engineer/Producer*, vol. 11, no. 4, pp. 46–51, August 1980.

27. K. E. Randall and F. L. Ward, "Diffusion of Sound in Small Rooms," *Proc. IEE* (British), vol 107B, pp. 439–450, September 1960.

28. T. Somerville and F. L. Ward, "Investigation of Sound Diffusion in Rooms by Means of a Model," *Acustica*, vol. 1, no. 1, pp. 40–48, 1951.

29. M. R. Schroeder, "Diffuse Sound Reflection by Maximum-Length Sequences," *Journal of the ASA*, vol. 57, no. 1, pp. 149–150, January 1975.

30. M. R. Schroeder, "Progress in Architectural Acoustics and Artificial Reverberation: Concert Hall Acoustics and Number Theory," Journal of the AES, vol. 32, no. 4, pp. 194–203, April 1984.

31. P. D'Antonio and J. H. Konnert, "The Schroeder Quadratic-Residue Diffuser: Design Theory and Application," 74th Convention of AES, New York, Preprint no. 1999(C-4).

CHAPTER **6**

Recording Studio Design

by F. Alton Everest

6.1 SIGMA SOUND STUDIOS

Sigma Sound Studios, located in Philadelphia, Pennsylvania, is a good example of contemporary studio design.[1] This studio, dating back to 1958 with numerous successful recordings, was given a major redesign in 1981 to keep up with new concepts and developments. Features of the new design were worked out by a small group including Joe Tarsia, president of Sigma Sound; Maurice W. Wasserman, architect; and George L. Augsperger, acoustical consultant.

This project, like others before it, required its share of compromises. The two-story building (about 38 × 95 ft) has brick exterior walls. The new studio was to be on the upper floor with its wood joist floor and roof framing. Originally, the building was two long, narrow row houses with a load-bearing wall down the middle. Later this wall was replaced with steel beams and columns down the middle, which became a challenge to work around. As it worked out, all columns but one were cleverly hidden. Trolley cars on the street in front of the building and a main line railroad a few hundred feet away provided the stimulus for as tight and as massive construction as feasible. In addition to external noise, Studio 2, directly below on the ground floor, provided further impetus for careful design.

The refined and final layout of Studio 1, prepared by the architect after much interaction, is shown in Fig. 6-1. As a buffer against street noise, offices and lounges were placed across the street end of the second floor. Across the rear end are several service rooms, which also serve to protect the noise-sensitive areas. The control room (22 × 20 ft) has one entrance to a private lounge and another to the sound lock. The studio (approximately 1150 ft^2) is a purposefully irregular room, designed to accommodate the various musical groups for maximum acoustical isolation for multitrack recording. Each group, however, is easily visible from the control room through a 14-ft bay window. The studio features variable acoustics so that a wide range of personal tastes and types of music can be served.

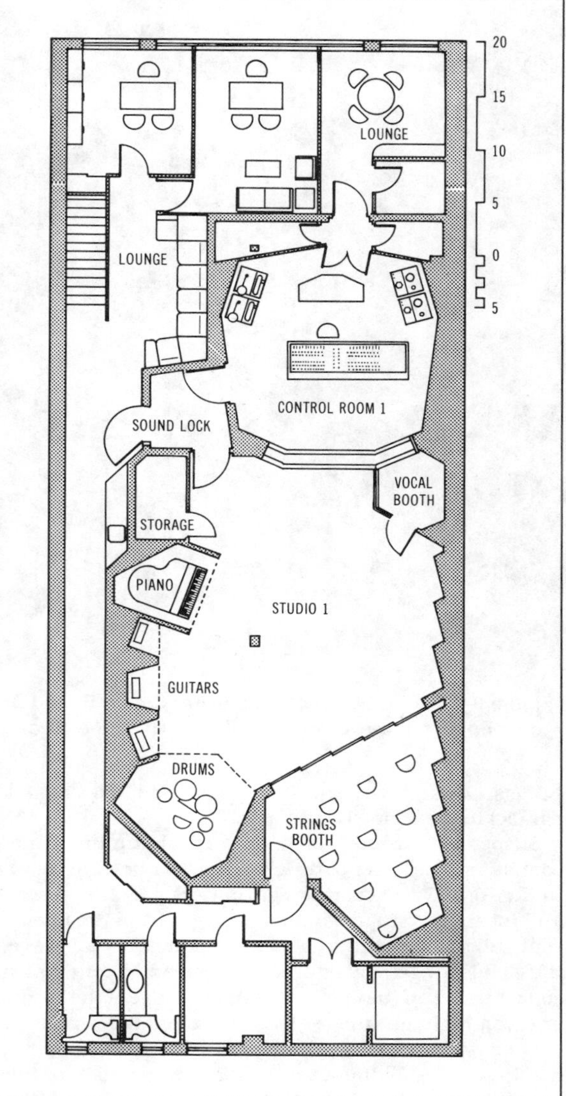

Figure 6-1 Floor plan of Studio 1 and control room of Sigma Sound Studios of Philadelphia. *(Courtesy dB, The Sound Engineering Magazine)*

6.1.1 Constructional Features

For maximum isolation between the studio on the ground floor and the one above it, the floor of Studio 1 is floated. Because of loading limitations, the traditional floating concrete floor was ruled out. A lighter-weight laminate of plywood and gypsum wallboard was substituted, supported on Peabody™ compressed and sealed glass-fiber cubes. To make this floated floor as stiff as possible, the layers were bonded with glue and adhesive staples. The brick exterior walls were strengthened with respect to their transmission loss by a double layer of gypsum wallboard on metal studs fastened to the brick with resilient brackets. To maximize studio volume, a gypsum wallboard sound barrier ceiling follows the sloping roof joists and is supported by resilient isolators.

6.1.2 Studio Features

The string booth of Fig. 6-1 is 220 ft^2 separated from the studio by five 3-ft, 2-in. sliding glass doors, each in its own track so that the string booth can be fully opened to the studio, except for a single door width, as shown in Fig. 6-2.

The vocal booth of Fig. 6-1 is set against the control room observation window. The drum area, the piano alcove, and in between the niches for guitars are shown

Figure 6-2 String booth of Studio 1 of Sigma Sound Studios. Five 3-ft, 2-in. doors, each on a separate track, can be opened to join the string booth's 220-ft^2 to the studio. *(Photo by Arthur Stoppe, engineer, Sigma Sound Studios)*

in Figs. 6-1 and 6-3. The floor is hardwood flooring laid parallel to the string booth door.

Suspended "clouds" of perforated aluminum panels containing glass-fiber batts follow the floor lines, as shown in Fig. 6-3. Two separate lighting systems, fluorescent and incandescent, are employed. Light from the fluorescent tubes illuminates the white ceiling areas between the clouds for general lighting. The incandescent system concentrates on the booths around the edge of the studio, or it can highlight the center of the room if desired.

The sawtooth studio wall shape extending into the string booth includes folding doors that can be partially or fully opened to vary the absorption of the room. This feature is shown most clearly in Fig. 6-2. Fig. 6-4 is a view toward the window end of the studio.

The Sigma Sound Control/Mixdown Room will be described in Section 6.8.

6.2 TRES VIRGOS STUDIO

Like many other successful studios, Tres Virgos had its origin as an eight-track garage studio; this one operating in a residential area of Marin County in Northern California. And, like many others, the neighbors complained, and authorities served eviction papers. The late-night sessions precipitating the issue were tangible evidence of a healthy flow of bookings that introduced a note of encouragement for the future into the general despair resulting from the eviction notice. Future planning was naturally directed toward a new studio, but at first the next step was envisioned as only a modest improvement over the garage facility.

Tres Virgos, located in San Rafael, California, is owned by a consortium of impecunious youths—Jerry Jacob, Michael Stevens, Allen Rice, and Robin Yeager. Most are musicians, and none had experience in the design and construction of professional studios and control rooms, although several did have some experience in general construction. As plans were coming into focus for a new studio, Allen Rice attended a Syn-Aud-Con seminar and heard about the principles of the LEDE™* control rooms. With great enthusiasm they experimented with these principles in their tiny garage control room on a very makeshift basis and were impressed by improvements in sound quality and stereo image. Their goals soared, and they committed themselves to the very best studio and control room the state of the art would allow. At this point they involved Edward Bannon and Chips Davis in the design of the studio and control room. The studio will be described here, and the control room in Section 6.13.

*"LEDE" and "Live End-Dead End" are trademarks of Synergetic Audio Concepts of San Juan Capistrano, CA.

Figure 6-3 View of Studio 1, Sigma Sound Studios, looking into the string booth with sliding glass doors (left), into the piano alcove (right), and the drum and guitar alcoves in between. *(Courtesy dB The Sound Engineering Magazine, Photo by Arthur Stoppe, engineer, Sigma Sound Studios)*

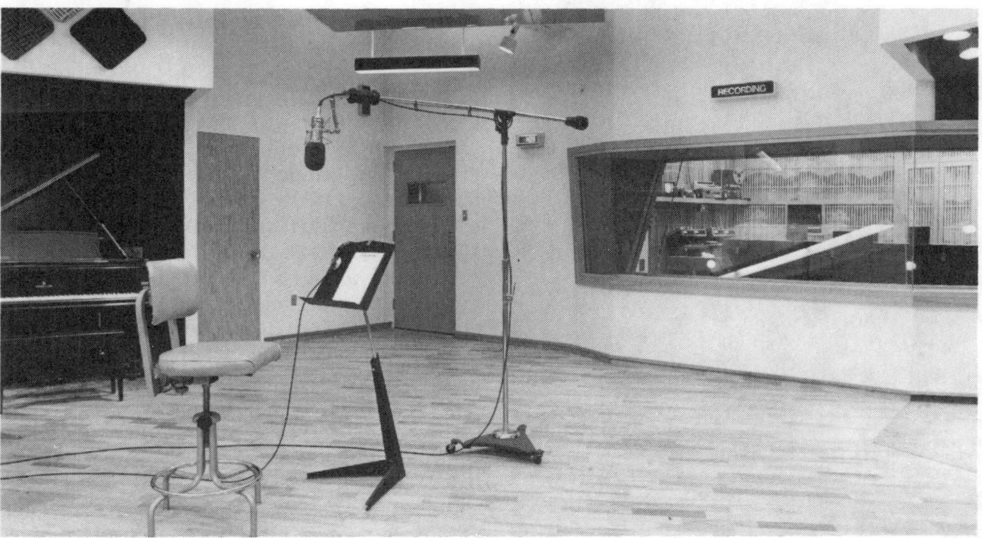

Figure 6-4 View of Studio 1, Sigma Sound Studios, looking into the control room and toward the entrance door. *(Photo by Arthur Stoppe, engineer, Sigma Sound Studios)*

6.2.1. Design Details

The rooms were designed on a walls-within-walls basis. The general floor plan of Fig. 6-5 was adopted to fit in one corner of a large industrial building. Environmental noise exposure was such as to require extreme measures in wall construction. Careful attention to detail was characteristic of every step of the construction phase. Vir-

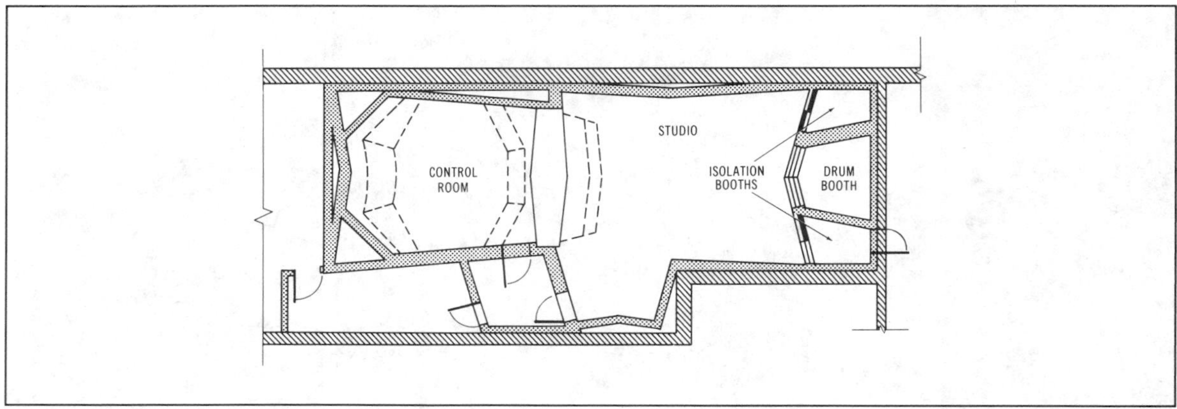

Figure 6-5 Floor plan of Tres Virgos studio and control room, San Rafael, California. (Courtesy Tres Virgos Studio)

tually no nails were used; everything was both screwed and glued. The drum booth, studio, and control room each has its own independent floating floor. Different combinations of soft fiberboard, plywood, gypsum wallboard, ¾-in. high-density industrial-grade particle board, and heavy plaster were used in wall construction. Copious quantities of acoustical sealant assured airtightness. No conduit makes solid contact with framing. Strict attention was given to assure proper polarity from microphone to monitor and tape machines. There is no earth ground; all units are referred to the ac circuit box. Each convenience outlet, even those on the same circuit, has its own three wires running all the way back to the distribution box. This means that devices plugged into different receptacles are referred to the identical ground point.

Figure 6-6 View of Tres Virgos studio during construction. *(Courtesy Tres Virgos Studio)*

6.2.2 Studio Construction

A view of the studio during construction is shown in Fig. 6-6. The studio itself has a floor area of about 900 ft^2. At the end of the studio and facing the control room window is a drum booth flanked by two isolation booths, all with sliding glass doors. These three booths have high ceilings for maximum volume to avoid the usual booth problems of small room effect. The studio arrangement is pictured in Figs. 6-7 and 6-8. A soffit structure over the control room window houses a pair of high-quality monitors for playback. That portion of the floor near the control room window is parquet; the rear portion is carpeted.

A construction time of nine months was projected and realized with a crew of four on a 40-hr week. The cost per square foot was below that of an average single-family California home. The zeal and dedication of all involved have given full satisfaction in the hidden qualities as well as the acoustical, electrical, and functional qualities evident to clients.[2, 3]

6.3 MODULAR STUDIOS

Getting started in the recording studio business requires considerable investment in equipment as well as studio

Figure 6-7 View of completed Tres Virgos studio looking toward the LEDE™ control room. *(Courtesy Tres Virgos Studio)*

Figure 6-8 View of completed Tres Virgos studio. The high-ceilinged drum booth and two isolation booths are visible to the right. *(Courtesy Tres Virgos Studio)*

and control room facilities. Disregarding the equipment aspect for the moment, there are several approaches to building the studio suite. Designing and building your own to save money has many pitfalls and can easily result in a sizable investment in a studio of questionable quality. At the other end of the investment spectrum is the turnkey arrangement that results in a beautiful and functional studio at relatively high cost. Between these extremes is the modular approach introduced in 1978 by a company called Modular Perfection, Inc., of Miami, Florida.

This modular approach is not a "bits-and-pieces" method of solving large-sized problems. For example, studio walls are usually built up from modules 4 ft wide, up to 12 ft high and 12- to 30-in. deep, which have various acoustical characteristics and can be used freestanding or hung on the structural wall. Electrical conduits and pvc conduits for audio lines come with the modules. The size of all modules is arranged so that they can be taken through a standard 3-ft doorway. One of the attractive features of this modular approach is that if the building lease expires or is cancelled, all is not lost. The modules can be taken down and reassembled at another location. There is no denying the appeal of having a studio facility ready for delivery of console, recorders, and ancillary equipment three weeks after the modules are unloaded from three tractor-trailer rigs.

6.3.1 Modules

Fig. 6-9 shows five of the 4-ft wide studio modules that come in lengths of 2, 4, 8, and 12 ft. They come in live, semilive, or dead form. The standard finish for the live modules is pecky cypress; for the semilive modules it is fir strips; and for the dead modules it is double-knit fabric. These modules may be hung on the structural wall or be used as freestanding units. Numerous special-purpose modules are pictured in Fig. 6-10 for framing the observation window, the doorways, and the tape-machine recesses. These are also available in the live or dead acoustical characteristic. All the varied acoustical effects are obtained with the basic two absorption characteristics shown in Fig. 6-11. The live curve is similar to that

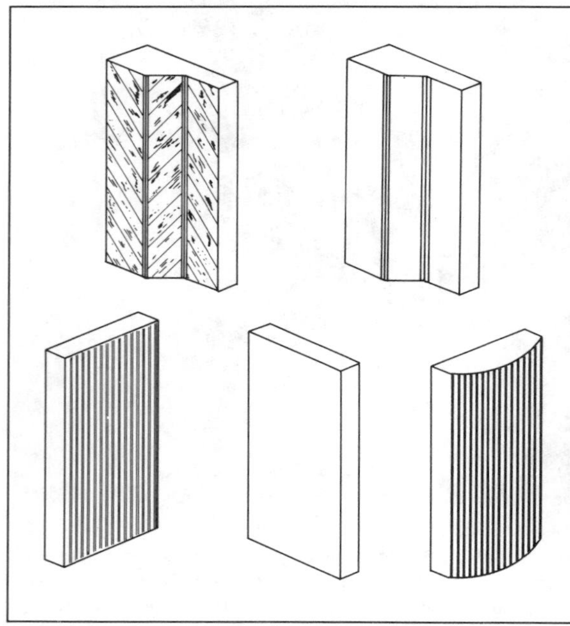

Figure 6-9 The shape of typical Modular Perfection studio modules available in 4-ft widths and in lengths to 12 ft.

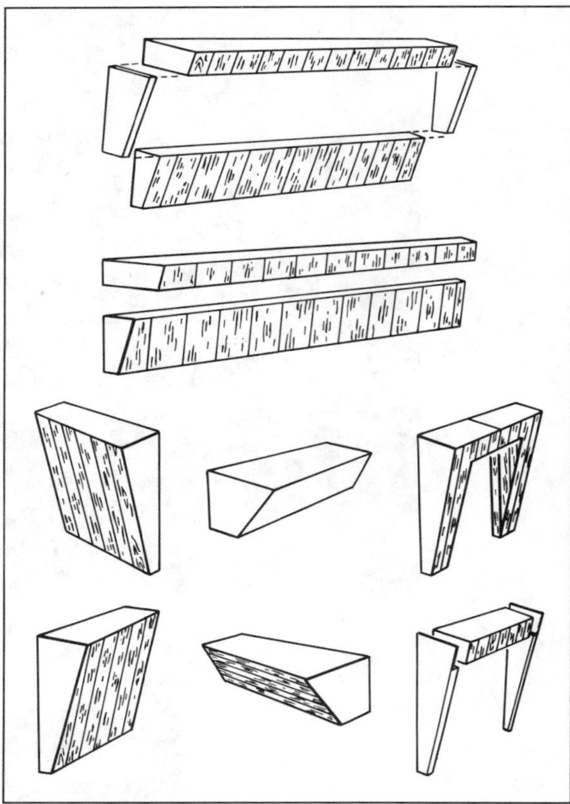

Figure 6-10 Specialized modules for studio window openings, doorways, tape machine recesses, and so on. *(Courtesy Modular Perfection)*

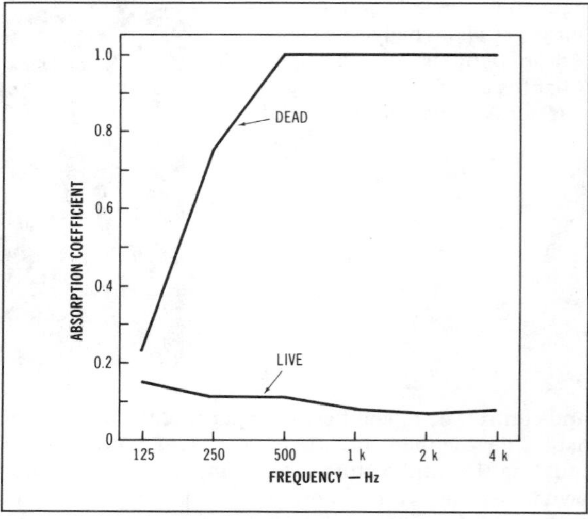

Figure 6-11 Absorption characteristics of live and dead modules.

of plywood backed by some airspace. The dead curve of Fig. 6-11 is similar to that of 2 in. thick glass fiber with a density of 3 lb/ft^3. The semilive module, faced with spaced fir strips, is a combination of the live and dead form. The rear face of all modules for studio applications is the same surface as one of the dead modules. The specifications for a flat, dead module would apply to the rear of any studio module for room calculations.

6.3.2 Ceiling Treatment

Wideband absorption is introduced above the suspended ceiling grid in the form of anechoic-type glass-fiber wedges, as shown in Fig. 6-12. The ceiling grid supports an acoustically transparent screen to hide the wedges and service runs above.

The air-conditioning system provided by Modular Perfection, Inc., uses neither ducts nor fans. Specially made refrigeration pipes are mounted in the ceiling structure, and air circulation is by convection only. The general design of the air-conditioning system is shown in Fig. 6-13. It is completely silent and heats as well as cools. A saving of 30 to 50% is claimed over conventional systems.

6.3.3 Examples of Modular Studios

The acoustical treatment of the dB Recording Studio of North Miami, Florida, using modules from Modular Perfection, Inc., is indicated in the floor plan and views of the studio and control room shown in Figs. 6-14, 6-15, and 6-16. The modular treatment was applied to the main studio, the control room, and the dead isolation room. Further details of this application are given in reference 4. The average reverberation time of the studio was adjusted to 0.4 s, and that of the dead isolation room, to 0.2 s. The studio to control room isolation was measured on a broadband basis and found to be 55 dB; the studio to either isolation room, 50 dB; and the studio to outside of building, 55 dB.

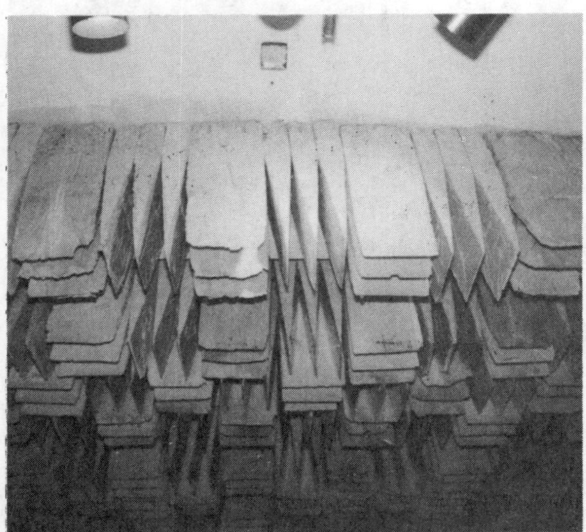

Figure 6-12 Wideband absorption is applied above the ceiling grid in the form of anechoic-type glass-fiber wedges.

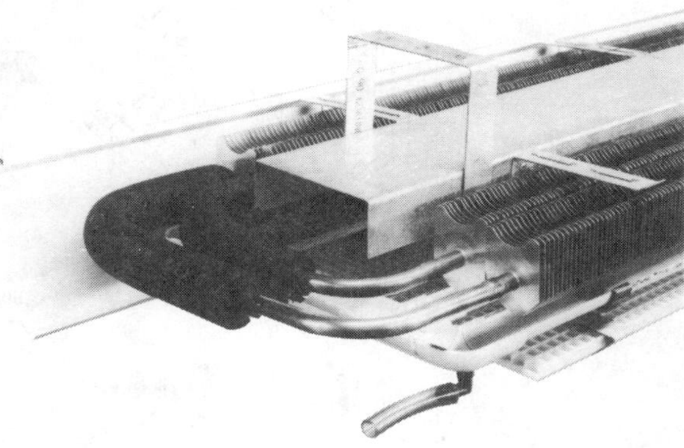

Figure 6-13 Modular air-conditioning system that heats or cools without ducts or fans.

Another modular studio is Middle Ear Studio of Miami Beach, Florida, owned by the Bee Gees. The studio treatment is shown in Fig. 6-17. Two views of the control room are shown in Figs. 6-18 and 6-19.

Two views of a third modular studio are shown in Figs. 6-20 and 6-21. This is Coconuts Recording Studio of North Miami Beach, Florida.

A fourth modular studio is the Stark Lake Studio in the suburbs of Orlando, Florida, as shown in Figs. 6-22 and 6-23. View windows in the control room are an unusual feature.

6.4 A NEW APPROACH TO LISTENING ROOMS

Two types of rooms have traditionally been associated with acoustical measurements, the anechoic room and the reverberation room. The anechoic (echo-free) room is an extremely dead room with absorbent wedges three feet or more in length, protruding into the room on all six surfaces, and these are backed by even more absorbent material. The six surfaces of the reverberation room are hard and reflective. In the anechoic room the reverberant field is essentially eliminated, but in the reverberation room it is maximized. It is very interesting that the latest advancement in the design of rooms for optimum listening conditions is a hybrid, part reverberation room, part

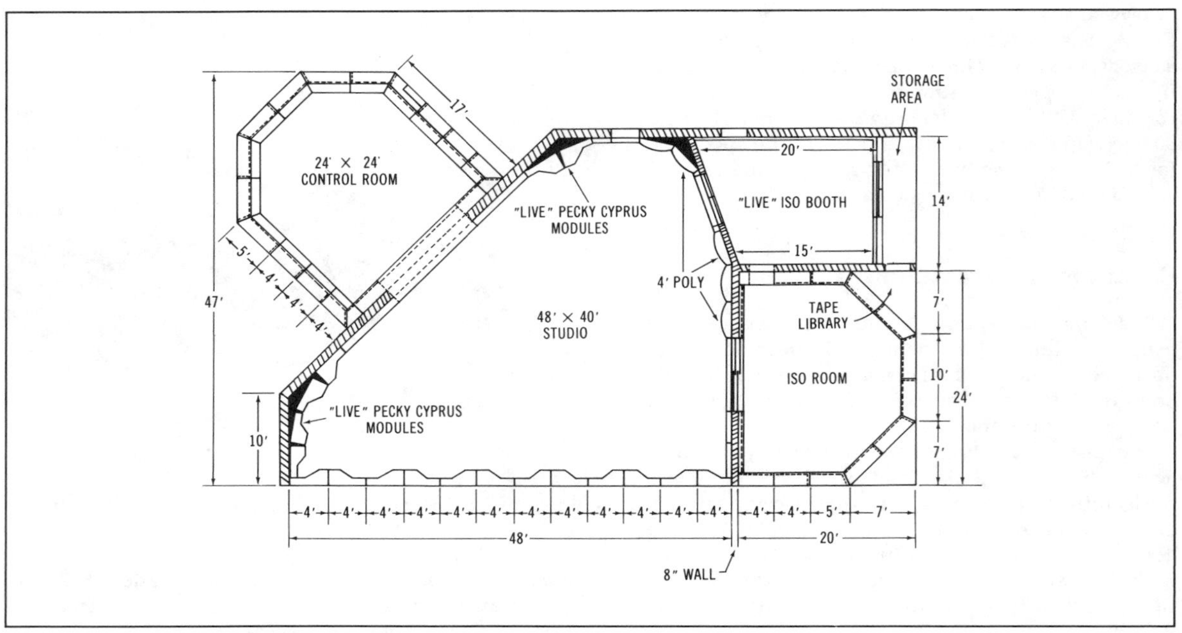

Figure 6-14 Floor plan of dB Studio, North Miami, Florida, which is treated entirely with Modular Perfection, Inc. Modules. *(Courtesy dB Recording Studio)*

Figure 6-15 Control room of dB Recording Studio, North Miami, Florida, treated by the modular approach. *(Courtesy dB Recording Studio)*

Figure 6-16 View of modular treated studio from isolation room of dB Recording Studio, North Miami, Florida. *(Courtesy dB Recording Studio)*

anechoic, so simple as to make the most seasoned designer say, "Why didn't I think of that!"

This new idea in listening rooms was revealed by Ishii and Mizutani of the Matsushita Electrical Industrial Company of Osaka, Japan, at the 72nd Audio Engineering Society convention.[5] They point out once again the commonly observed fact that listening rooms having a favorable reverberation time, quite uniform throughout the audible spectrum, can have a poor quality of sound. They summarize the defects of the conventional listening room. (1) The frequency response of reflections is not flat and varies with angle of arrival. (2) Low-frequency sound

Figure 6-17 Modular treatment of Middle Ear Studio, Miami Beach, Florida, owned by the Bee Gees. *(Courtesy Middle Ear Studio)*

Figure 6-19 Modular rear wall of control room of Middle Ear Studio, Miami Beach, Florida. *(Courtesy Middle Ear Studio)*

Figure 6-18 Operating position with modular control room monitor mountings at Middle Ear Studio, Miami Beach, Florida. *(Courtesy Middle Ear Studio)*

Figure 6-20 Modular treated Coconuts Recording Studio, North Miami Beach, Florida, showing control room window module treatment. *(Courtesy Coconuts Recording Studio)*

tends to be "boomy." (3) The frequency range is too narrow for high-fidelity listening. (4) The design is complicated and time consuming.

To assure that reflections have a flat frequency response irrespective of the angle of arrival, all reflecting surfaces must be of one type, a near-perfect reflector. But therein lies a problem. If all the surfaces of the room are near-perfect reflectors, we are right back to the reverberation room that no one would call a good listening environment. The solution is having two kinds of surfaces, one a near-perfect reflector and the other a near-perfect absorber. Any energy reflected would then have a flat frequency response; the rest would be absorbed. Proportioning the areas of the two types of surfaces is then the means of adjusting reverberation time.

The true significance of this simple, yet revolutionary idea is best appreciated by considering what happens in the conventional listening room (or studio or control room) in which the rays of sound incident on room surfaces A, B, and C are assumed to have a flat-frequency response. The highly idealized listening situation of Fig. 6-24 involves a loudspeaker source, a listener, and the walls treated with patches of acoustical material or structures having different absorption characteristics. Material A is 1-in. glass fiber, B is a perforated-face Helmholtz resonator, and C is a plywood panel spaced out from the wall. Let us assume that the loudspeaker emits a signal with a flat response so that the sound incident on absorbers A, B, and C has a flat characteristic. The direct sound the listener hears would be flat, but the rays reflected from A, B, and C are anything but flat. The reflected ray a′ reflected from material A would have a rapidly falling frequency response because of the increased absorption by A at

Figure 6-21 Studio treated with modular elements, Coconuts Recording Studio, North Miami Beach, Florida. *(Courtesy Coconuts Recording Studio)*

higher frequencies. The absorption peak of the plywood panel B gives a response of reflected ray b′ with a notch taken out of it. The midband absorption peak of resonator C results in a large midband dip in the response of reflected ray c′. The ray reflected from both A and C is sans bass because of the combined effect of reflections from these two surfaces. This hints at the complexity of the frequency response of a ray undergoing reflections from many surfaces, the combined effect of which the listener experiences within the fusion zone of his or her hearing mechanism.

There is a general understanding of the importance of the early arriving sound in establishing the perception of the quality of the sound by the listener. In Fig. 6-24 we note that the direct ray is flat but that all the indicated reflected rays have responses varying wildly. Thus, what arrives after the direct, although still early, sound conflicts with the tendency of the direct ray to give an impression of flat response sound. Fig. 6-24 is based on the ray concept in the interest of simplicity although this concept breaks down at low frequencies.

6.4.1 New Listening Rooms

The appearance of the Ishii-Mizutani listening room is shown in Figs. 6-25 and 6-26. It is relatively easy to get a near-perfect reflecting floor from concrete covered with a thin, hard-wearing surface. The walls and ceiling are made entirely of bands of reflecting surfaces alternating with bands of absorbing surfaces. The near-perfect reflector is constructed of concrete or concrete covered with marble slabs or wooden paneling of a thickness sufficient for it to act more like the concrete surface and less like a wooden panel that vibrates. Surely wood 1-in. thick would be the minimum thickness to be considered. The near-perfect absorber is glass fiber of 2-lb/ft^3 density in thickness up to 5.5 ft. The reflecting surfaces are placed at angles to discourage flutter echoes between opposite walls.

The ideal form of this listening room is outlined in Fig. 6-27. The near-perfect absorbers are dissipative glass fiber absorbers, a minimum of 5.5 ft deep. Augmenting the dissipative aspect is a reactive bass trap effect for the

Figure 6-22 Studio view of the Stark Lake Modular Studio in the suburbs of Orlando, Florida. *(Courtesy Stark Lake Modular Studio)*

Figure 6-23 Stark Lake Recording Studio in the outskirts of Orlando, Florida, showing the modular treatment. *(Courtesy Stark Lake Modular Studio)*

frequency at which the depth is a quarter wavelength. A depth of 5.5 ft (a quarter wavelength at about 50 Hz) assures good absorption down to a frequency somewhat below 50 Hz. Rettinger suggests making a sloping bottom to the pit to widen this trap effect.

The other surfaces of the room of Fig. 6-27 are near-perfect reflectors, sturdy and massive enough to reflect sound only and to avoid absorption and reradiation that would accompany the vibration of these surfaces in response to impinging sound energy. The end of the room near the loudspeakers should also be a near-perfect reflector to avoid complicating the radiation character-

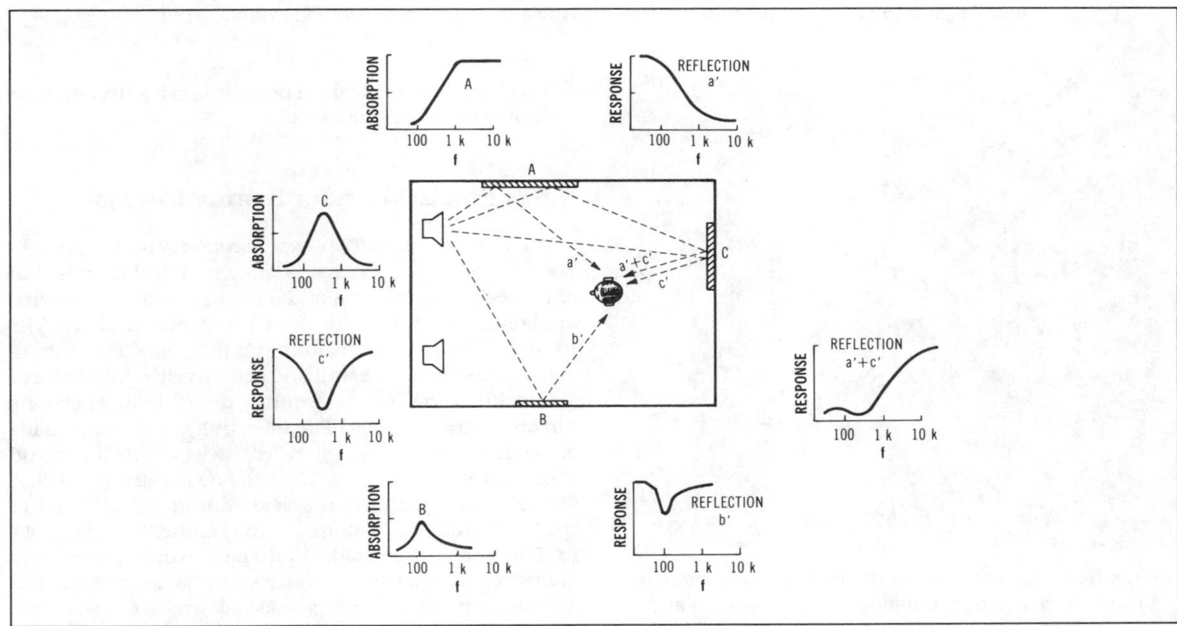

Figure 6-24 A highly idealized listening situation with a loudspeaker source, a listener, and the walls with patches of acoustical material having different absorption characteristics.

Figure 6-25 The front part of the Ishii-Mizutani listening room, which is designed as a hybrid between the anechoic chamber and the reverberation room. *(Courtesy Matsushita Electrical Industrial Co., Ltd.)*

Figure 6-26 The rear part of the Ishii-Mizutani listening room with alternating near-perfect absorbers and reflectors. *(Courtesy Matsushita Electrical Industrial Co., Ltd.)*

istics of the loudspeakers. The floor is reflective, and the ceiling is built like the walls.

6.4.2 Practical Audio Testing Rooms

The room of Fig. 6-27 is expensive because the absorbers require so much space. A more practical form is that of Fig. 6-28, which is an audio testing room constructed at Matsushita, principally for testing loudspeakers. The front wall is all reflective to minimize the effect of loudspeaker position. The wall and ceiling reflecting surfaces are inclined toward the front to direct first reflections directly to the listeners. The reflecting surfaces are made of a combination of two-ply ¾-in. thick particle board and ¼-in. thick plasterboard. The thickness of the glass fiber (2-lb/ft^3 density) on the sides varied from 12 to 35 in.; at the back, from 24 to 32 in.; at the ceiling, from 32 to 47 in. The room is trapezoidal in shape to avoid the necessity of making splayed sections to reduce flutter hazard. The general trend of the ceiling slopes downward toward the rear of the room. It is obvious that a few compromises have been made to make it practicable. A study of the

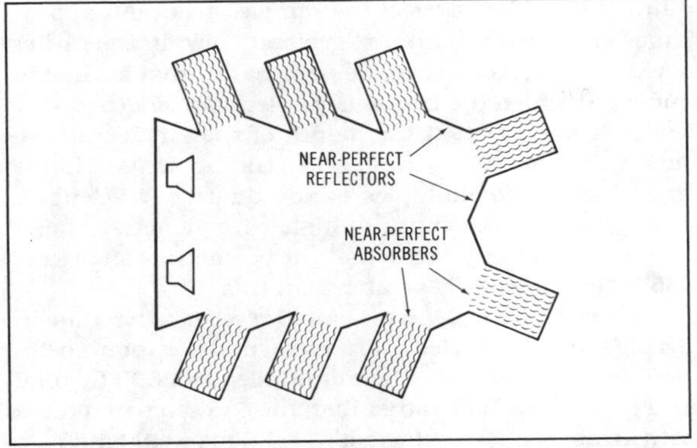

Figure 6-27 Outline of the Ishii-Mizutani type listening room. *(After AES, Reference 5.)*

results of acoustical tests made in the room will give some basis of judgment as to the effect of such compromises and the overall performance of the room.

6.4.3 Test Results

The pertinent data on the room are

Surface area	2605 ft^2
Room volume	8122 ft^3
Absorbing area	635 ft^2
Target reverberation time	0.5 s

The absorption coefficient for surfaces in the room varies from an assumed zero for the rigid reflecting surfaces to an assumed unity for the absorbent area. The average absorption coefficient is 635/2605 = 0.244 assuming 1.0

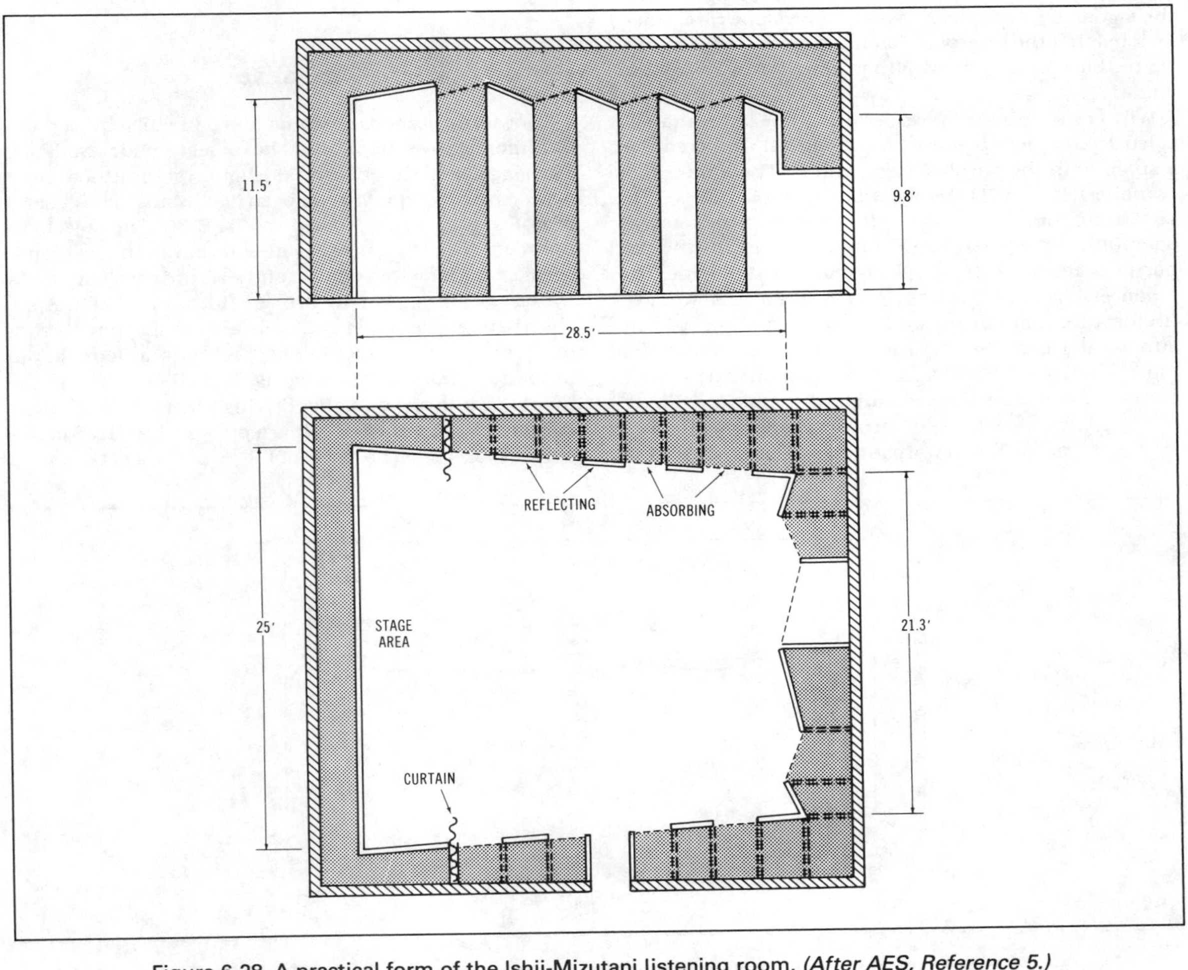

Figure 6-28 A practical form of the Ishii-Mizutani listening room. *(After AES, Reference 5.)*

coefficient for the absorbent areas. Using the Eyring form of the reverberation equation (Eq. 5-3), we get

$$RT = (0.049 \times 8122)/[(-2605)\log_{\epsilon}(1 - 0.244)]$$
$$= 0.547\,s$$

As a further exercise, the reverberation time calculated from the Sabine form of the equation (Eq. 5-1) is

$$RT = (0.049 \times 8122)/(635 \times 1.0)$$
$$= 0.627\,s$$

The two are not very far apart, but what do the measurements tell us? Measured reverberation times are plotted in Fig. 6-29, and in this we see one of the flattest reverberation time versus frequency graphs extant due to the use of only very thick dissipative-type absorbing material. With such characteristics, all components of the signal die away at very close to the same rate. But, it is noted that the reverberation time is close to 0.4 s, lower than that predicted by either the Eyring or Sabine equations.

Why is the observed reverberation time lower than the calculated? There is more absorbence in the room than visualized in the previous calculations. There seem to be two alternatives: (1) the rigid portions of the room are absorbing sound or (2) the soft portions of the room are absorbing better than 100%. Any absorption by the rigid portions must be by diaphragmatic action, and it is inconceivable that this form of extra absorption would be uniform throughout the audible spectrum to yield measured values of reverberation time as flat as that of Fig. 6-29. On the other hand, it is common experience in testing laboratories for the standard sample size (72 ft^2) of a good absorber to yield absorption coefficients of 1.1 or 1.2 or more. This is attributed, at least in part, to diffraction at the edges of the sample, making it appear larger acoustically than it is geometrically. In the earlier discussion on bass traps, we pointed out that at the frequency at which the trap is a quarter wavelength, a very low pressure exists at the mouth of the pit, tending to suck in sound energy from surrounding areas. This is true also at odd multiples of the quarter wavelength, extending the effect up into higher frequencies. Therefore, the possibility exists that the geometric soft area of 635 ft^2 is acoustically greater than this.

Substituting the 0.4-s measured reverberation time in Eyring's equation yields an average absorption coefficient of 0.317, which, when multiplied by 2605 ft^2 total area gives 827 sabins rather than the 635 sabins expected with an absorption coefficient of 1.0. This would indicate that either the effective absorption coefficient of the soft areas is about 1.30 or the 635 ft^2 appears acoustically to be 827 ft^2, an increase in effective area of 30%. Using the Sabine equation, these figures are a = 1.57 or 57% increase in effective area.

6.4.4 Transient Response

Tone burst response records taken in still a third room of a more conventional type have been made available. These cast some interesting sidelights on the functioning of rooms of the type we have been discussing. The general layout of the room is shown in Fig. 6-30. The objects in the room (five loudspeakers in addition to the test loudspeaker, a piano, ten chairs, and a record rack with glass windows) are shown in broken lines. Four of the six absorbent elements on the walls are equipped with sliding panels. The five microphone positions are letter keyed to the tone burst records of Fig. 6-31. Fig. 6-31A is the input to the power amplifier driving the test loudspeaker, crosshatched in Fig. 6-30. It is a pulse of 100 Hz, 8 cycles on, 26 cycles off. The pulse of Fig. 6-31C was taken with

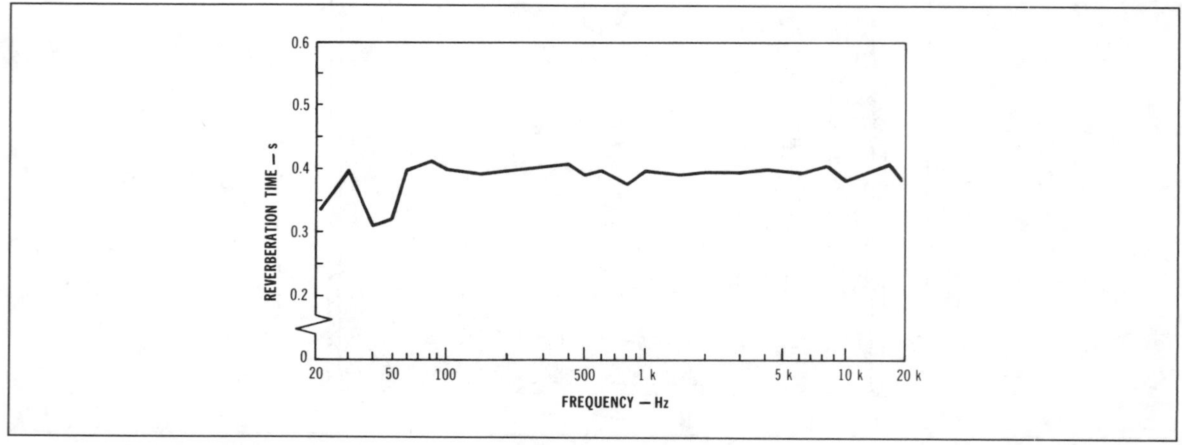

Figure 6-29 Reverberation time versus frequency plot for the room of Fig. 6-29. *(After AES, Reference 5.)*

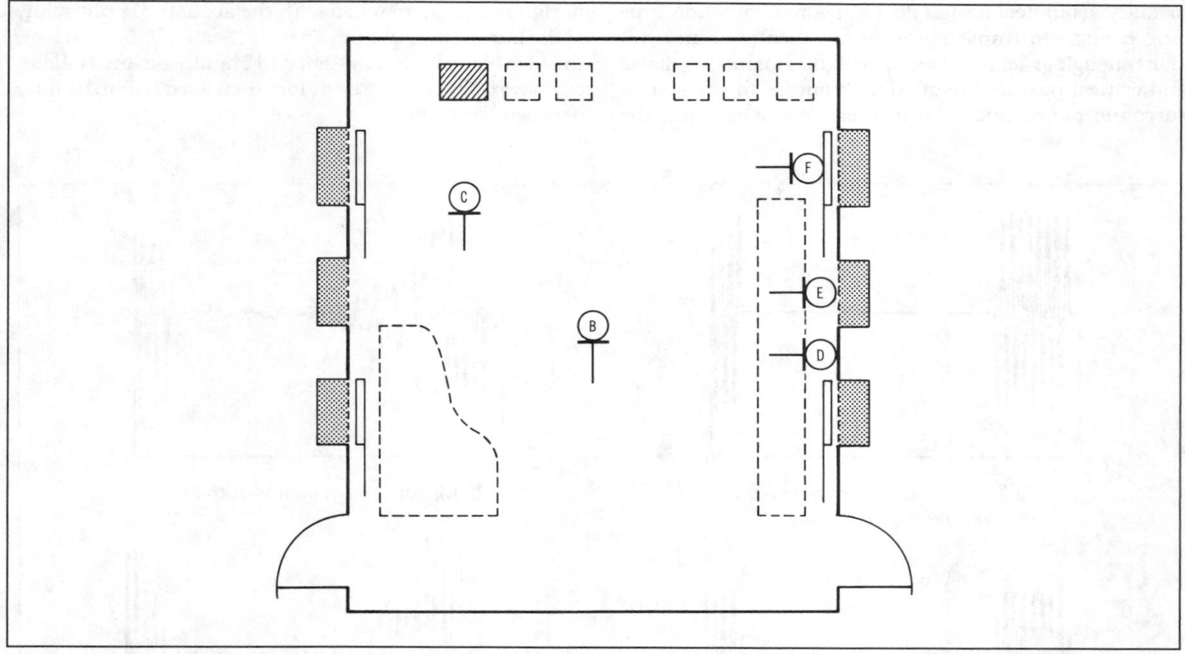

Figure 6-30 Microphone positions and general layout of the listening room in which the tone pulse records of Fig. 6-31 were recorded. *(Courtesy Matsushita Electrical Industrial Co., Ltd.)*

the microphone 1 m from the loudspeaker. For Fig. 6-31B the microphone was in the center of the room, as shown in Fig. 6-30. The pulse of Fig. 6-31D was taken with the microphone close to the reflective portion of the wall. For the pulse of Fig. 6-31E, the microphone was close to an absorptive section of the wall. The pulse of Fig. 6-31F was opposite one of the sliding panels. Fig. 6-31G is the background noise to the same scale as the other pulses.

These pulses revealed that the sliding panels vibrated excessively and that they required replacement by more rigid panels. The tailing off of panel vibration is evident in Figs. 6-31B, D, and F. It is also interesting to note the very low amplitude in front of the absorbent area as energy is "soaked up" by the deep absorber.

6.5 FACILITIES FOR MIXING FILM SOUND

The persons charged with mixing dialog, music, and sound effects for film must adjust the relative levels of these three audible components so that the resulting product is intelligible and has the full emotional impact envisioned by the director. Music that is too loud calls attention to itself rather than heightening the response to the visual scene. If it is not loud enough to serve its intended purpose, it is money spent with value not received. Speech intelligibility is vital to the storyline, and sound effects must be perfect in timing and acoustical perspective to make their full contribution to the illusion of reality that is the motion picture.

The sound-dubbing stage has specific acoustical requirements. The sound mixers must hear the sound as reproduced, as the consumer will hear it in the theater or over television. It is most unfair to mixers to ask them to make arbitrary adjustments to compensate for deficiencies of the dubbing environment. The task of mixers demands extensive experience, keen hearing, and an esthetic sense usually attributed only to the more visible and appreciated artists.

Film sound-mixing environments in Hollywood and elsewhere are often relics of a less-sophisticated age, but here three modern examples embodying the copyrighted acoustical designs of Jeff Cooper are described.

6.5.1 Warner Dubbing Stage A

Warner dubbing Stage A in Hollywood (Fig. 6-32), represents a new generation of film-dubbing studios for the production of critical sound tracks for all formats, including Dolby stereo-surround films. The reverberation versus frequency curve is designed to be smooth between 250 and 4000 Hz within a reputed $\pm$ 0.1 s. The curve is designed to slope gently upwards below 250 Hz at a rate of 150% per octave to provide warmth and sonority. The primary acoustical design goal was a reverberation time long enough to transfer well to full theater sound, yet short enough to achieve good articulation for mixing dialog and critical positioning of sound sources in the stereo-surround panoramic field. In these characteristics, the design has been matched with the acoustical philosophy of the Lucasfilm Dubbing Theater (Section 6.5.3). In fact, the identical monitor system and Tomlinson and Holman crossover (THX) is used for increased compatibility between the facilities.

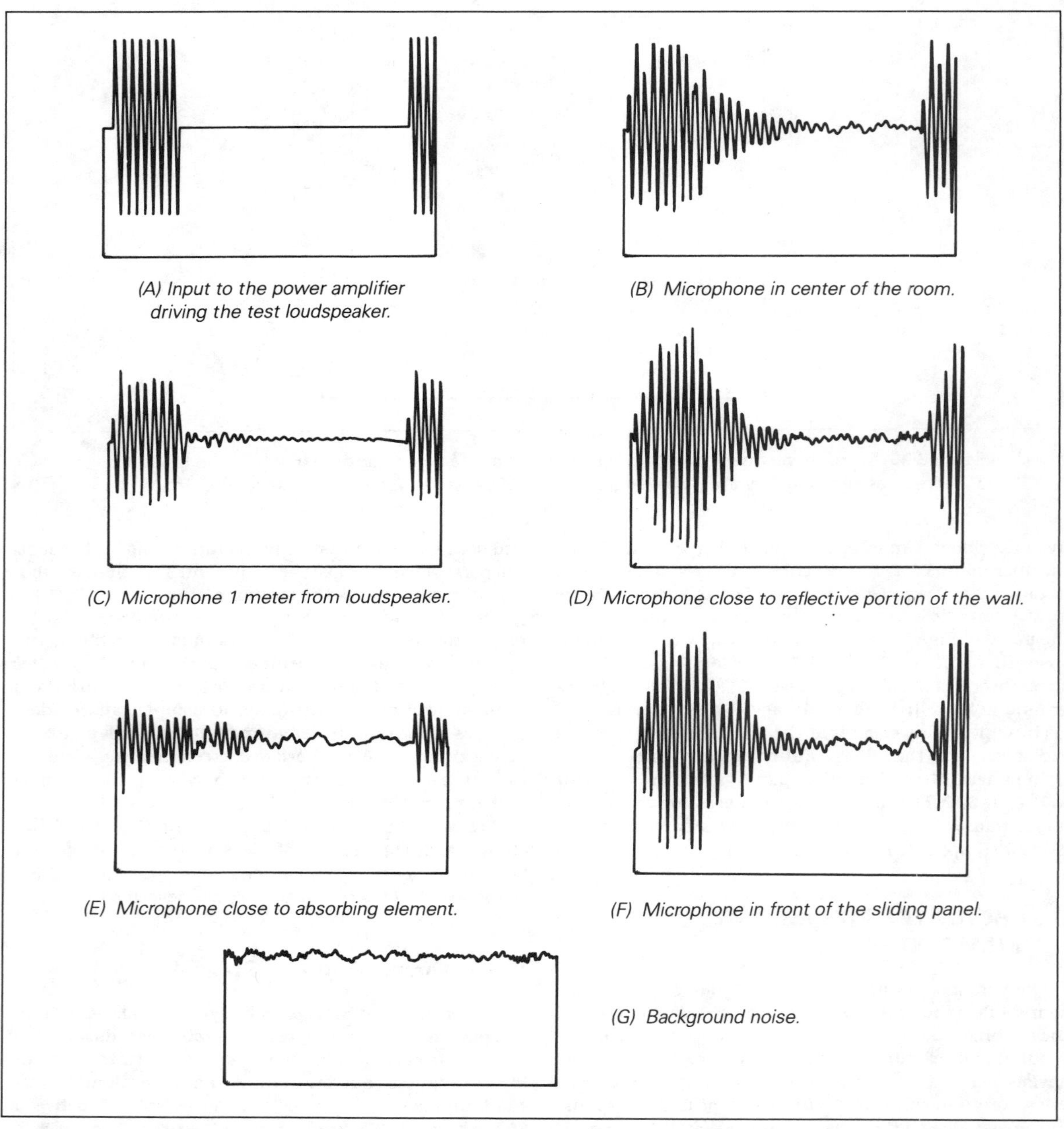

(A) Input to the power amplifier driving the test loudspeaker.

(B) Microphone in center of the room.

(C) Microphone 1 meter from loudspeaker.

(D) Microphone close to reflective portion of the wall.

(E) Microphone close to absorbing element.

(F) Microphone in front of the sliding panel.

(G) Background noise.

Figure 6-31 Tone pulse records made with the microphone in the positions of Fig. 6-30. Panel vibration tailing off is evident in B, D, and F. *(Courtesy Matsushita Electrical Industrial Co., Ltd.)*

Figure 6-32 Warner Dubbing Stage A in Hollywood. *(Courtesy Acoustic Design © Jeff Cooper, photo by Bill Lovi)*

6.5.2 Fantasy Films/Saul Zaentz Film Center

The Fantasy Films/Saul Zaentz Film Center, in Berkeley, California (Figs. 6-33 and 6-34), represents a new breed of studios combining film-mixing and music-recording technology. The facility actually serves four functions: (1) a 50-seat theater for viewing films, (2) a Dolby surround film-dubbing stage using up to nine discrete loudspeaker locations, (3) a "foley" stage and sound effects recording room, and (4) a stage for dialog replacement.

One innovative feature, not shown in the photographs, is an adjacent acoustical simulation chamber in which various acoustical environments can be set up for purposes of realism in film dubbing.

The sawtooth-shaped balconies are actually huge Helmholtz resonators designed to aid diffusion. Air distribution is accomplished inside the infrastructure via the ceiling resonators. The 1-in. × 40-ft slots are barely visible in Fig. 6-34.

A 12 × 20-ft area at the front of the theater is treated with a hardwood floor, as shown in Fig. 6-33, to be used for dialog replacement. Actors in this area can overdub dialog while watching their own movements on the screen. Further details are covered in references 6 and 7.

6.5.3 Lucasfilm Mixing Theater

Figs. 6-35 and 6-36 show the Lucasfilm Mixing Theater, located in Marin County across the bay from San Francisco. It features a copyrighted system of acoustical diffusers of revolutionary design with soft-scapes, continuous surfaces, and no corners; the architecture, air,

Figure 6-33 Film mixing facility at Fantasy Films/Saul Zaentz Film Center, Berkeley, California. *(Courtesy Acoustic Design ©Jeff Cooper, photo by Bill Lovi)*

acoustical treatment, and lighting are all in fluid motion. The absence of ornamentation or exposed structures lends a futuristic feel to the room, while the symmetrical light diffusers draw on classical influences.

The frame of the room is actually a floating soundproof room, jacked up to provide 2 in. of airspace. Cooper has used wood framing to achieve a damping effect to avoid steel framework that sometimes "rings." The walls are constructed of continuous handcrafted plaster diffusers, with insets of stretched velvet over acoustical panels.

The repetitive columnar motif of the diffusers serves several functions. First the curved plaster portions contour the room's reflective surfaces, providing a homogeneity of sound fields to assure a good balance at every seat. Second, via a membrane absorber inset into each column, the diffusers provide tuned bass absorption to ensure definition and clarity at the low end of the spectrum. These bass traps are then covered with compressed fiberglass and velvet to help absorb high and mid frequencies and thereby balance the overall absorption characteristics of the room.

Finally, in addition to these acoustical functions, the diffusers provide the sole source of all recessed lighting and a truly silent, well-dispersed air-conditioning system. Yet, in true marriage of function and form, the diffusers manage to evoke an esthetic atmosphere that can only be described as acoustical sculpture.

6.6 CONTROL ROOMS

There is a wide range of opinion among the experts in just how a control room should be built and treated. Viewing modern control rooms with their beautiful, subdued, colored lighting; pecky cedar panels; slabs of ornamental stone; and angled wall and ceiling surfaces of lavish texture; it seems cruel to classify them as primitive. On the other hand, studying the philosophies and control rooms of the top technical designers and finding wide divergence of approach among them, we can conclude that our understanding of the acoustics of small rooms and the functioning of our hearing mechanism is so lim-

Figure 6-34 Another view of Fantasy Films/Saul Zaentz Film Center, Berkeley. *(Courtesy Acoustic Design © Jeff Cooper, photo by Bill Lovi)*

ited that the word "primitive" makes reasonably good sense. Certainly, if our understanding of all the factors involved were complete, the experts would be following a common path. Disagreement on Ohm's law ended long ago. A key to future development in the acoustics of control, mixdown, and other listening rooms may well be in the new microprocessor-based, sophisticated measuring instruments now beginning to appear, coupled with ongoing research in the psychophysics of hearing.

6.6.1 Control Room Philosophy

In the following sections, the approach of several authorities in control room design will be reviewed in some detail. True, their recommendations take diverse, and sometimes opposite, directions, but each has solid acoustical and psychoacoustical reasoning behind his point of view. Each has extensive experience in the field; each is highly respected in the audio fraternity.

6.6.2 Concurrence on Psychoacoustical Factors

Despite different approaches to control room design taken by various practitioners, there is reasonable agreement on the basics of psychoacoustics. Before considering the divergences, let us review this area of general agreement. Viewing a projected motion picture, we realize that the motion is only an illusion. The projected pictures are all stills, albeit sequential stills, of real-life action. The eye-brain mechanism fuses the stills into smooth-flowing action as long as the frame rate is about 16 per second (one every 65 ms) or greater. The ear-brain mechanism exhibits a similar fusion effect in the perception of sound. Reflected speech or music sounds arriving within about 30 ms of the direct sound are fused (integrated) with the direct sound in a generally desirable and helpful fashion. Single, reflected sounds arriving more than 30 ms (or 80 or 100 ms) later are generally perceived as undesirable discrete echoes. Time differences between direct and reflected sound in the range of a few milliseconds result in comb filter distortion in the form of dips and peaks of response that can cause audible colorations of the sound. There may be disagreements on the relative subjective importance of some of these psychoacoustical effects, but not on their existence.

6.7 INTEGRATION OF LOUDSPEAKER AND CONTROL ROOM

The "eternal triangle" of the control room is the ever-present conflict between the visual, aural, and operational functions. The reluctance to trade a good view of what is happening in the studio for the limitations surrounding almost any conceivable type of video image keeps that glass window solidly rooted in place. This is despite the problems such an expanse of reflective glass brings to other aspects of the control room job. A basic tenet of the control room is to provide the operator with as close to optimum listening conditions as possible. The operator's job is then to record and assemble the component

Figure 6-35 Lucasfilm Mixing Theater, Marin County, near San Francisco.
(Courtesy Acoustic Design ©Jeff Cooper, photo by Bill Lovi)

parts of the production, and this involves equipment. To perform the job well and efficiently requires the right equipment conveniently accessible. Microprocessor control is bringing a new era of freedom from the mechanics to enable the operator to concentrate on the esthetics.

The Japanese were early users of large horns in monitor rooms and in the more elaborate audiophile listening rooms. As early as 1955 long, straight horns were used as woofers in many indoor installations. A typical Japanese home high-fidelity installation of the 1960s is shown in Fig. 6-37. Some are still in use today. In many designs of this type, the necks of the horns protruded into the back yard, far beyond the exterior wall of the house; the weatherproof drivers were supported on pedestals. According to Teppei Kado of Nihon Audio Co., Ltd., of Tokyo, some large horns are still used in home listening rooms but have passed from the scene in monitor rooms. Such horn systems have both supporters and detractors in Japan, although Mr. Kado, an audio consultant and listening room designer, has personally abandoned their use because of "directivity problems, incomplete wavefront, and horn resonances."

Putnam has recently placed renewed emphasis on the aural problem of integrating the loudspeakers within the control room.[8] As far back as 1959 he made a beginning in this direction in an early United Recording Corp. studio in Hollywood.[9] A large, inclined soffit in the control room to house the loudspeakers protruded into the studio in an unusual way. The purpose of this was to accommodate the transition from monaural to stereophonic recording. The result was a significant increase in loudspeaker radiating efficiency. The console was moved back from the traditional location against the observation window. This created new low-frequency anomalies and a

Figure 6-36 View from the screen of Lucasfilm Mixing Theater, Marin County, California. *(Courtesy Acoustic Design © Jeff Cooper, photo by Bill Lovi)*

Figure 6-37 A typical horn woofer installation common in the more elaborate Japanese home listening rooms of the 1960s. *(Courtesy Yoshikatu Demiya, owner)*

troublesome new transmission path under the console. In the intervening years, many new ideas in control room design were introduced, and new sophisticated instrumentation appeared to undergird the various new philosophies. Putnam's emphasis was placed on the loudspeakers.

Putnam realized that a further increase in radiation efficiency of the loudspeaker system would result in reduced cone excursion, which would bring lower distortion and better linearity at the low frequencies as well as lower power requirements of the driving amplifiers. He envisioned a physical coupling of the mouth of loudspeaker horns to the room to attain a larger optimum listening area. Such large horns gave promise of better control of undesirable acoustical effects in the amplitude and time domains. The need for some control over the ratio of direct-to-indirect sound and diffusion in the listening area was also recognized.

The prototype Hypex horn in use in the control room of United/Western Studio 1 in Hollywood since August 1981 is shown in Fig. 6-38. The lower horizontal flare section of the horns, which would interfere with viewing the studio through the control room window, is made of ¼-in. plexiglass. The geometry of the horn arrangements is shown in the sketch of Fig. 6-39.

The responses of the equalized and unequalized Hypex horn system are shown in Fig. 6-40. These curves were traced with a 60-s sweep of one-third-octave warble tone. The peak, of course, is the result of radiating into a much smaller, solid angle than the half-space case of a loudspeaker in a baffle.

There are certain compromises in horn shape to accommodate the optical, architectural, and acoustical parameters. For example, the top horizontal flare section is somewhat different from the bottom. The ¼-in. plexiglass was cold formed using the technique of constructing a "ribless" boat hull. The console face, usually the source of comb filter distortion, in this case provides an

(A) Front view.

(B) Side view.

Figure 6-38 Two view of prototype Hypex horn loudspeakers integrated into control room. *(After AES, Reference 8.)*

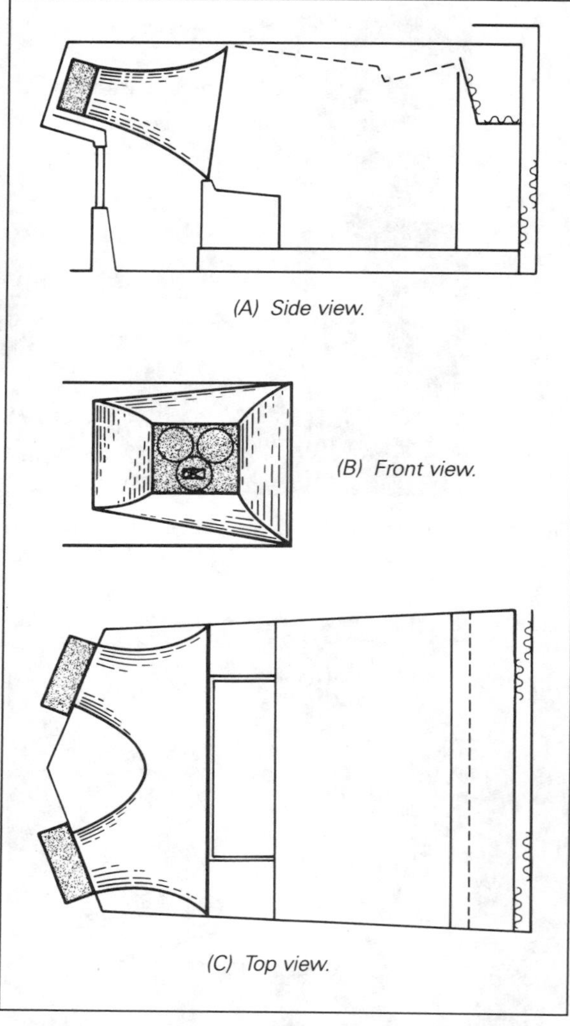

(A) Side view.

(B) Front view.

(C) Top view.

Figure 6-39 Drawing showing horn and room geometry. *(After AES, Reference 8.)*

extension of the lower horizontal flare section, and the horn is fastened to the console with foam between. Accelerometer measurements made possible the damping of diaphragmatic modes of vibration that resulted in improvements as much as 15 dB at certain frequencies.

To achieve the widest possible dispersion of high-frequency energy over the audition area, the maximum length of the central flare section was limited. This is evident from a study of the plan view of Fig. 6-39. The size of this center flare section was also limited by the desire for a good stereophonic image over a maximum area of the room. The sound path under the console is blocked, and interference effects from this possible source were not detected.

The minimum usable frequency for low distortion was extended by the use of a vented horn constituted by the vent coupling to the center flare section, which provides a left and right vent. The extension of the effective length of the horn mouth by ceiling, walls, and console face also works to lower the minimum usable frequency. The drivers in this prototype are a modified version of the TA® UREI Model 815A. The volume of the control room is about 3700 ft^3. The rear wall is made as absorptive as was practical to do so.

About 60% of the total available sidewall area is covered with hinged panels having 2-in. glass fiber of 3-lb/ft^3 density on the back surfaces. These can be hinged out to about 25° from the wall surface. The effective room absorption can be increased by opening these hinged panels and reduced by closing them. Low-frequency absorption can be varied from 20 to 55% at 125 Hz by

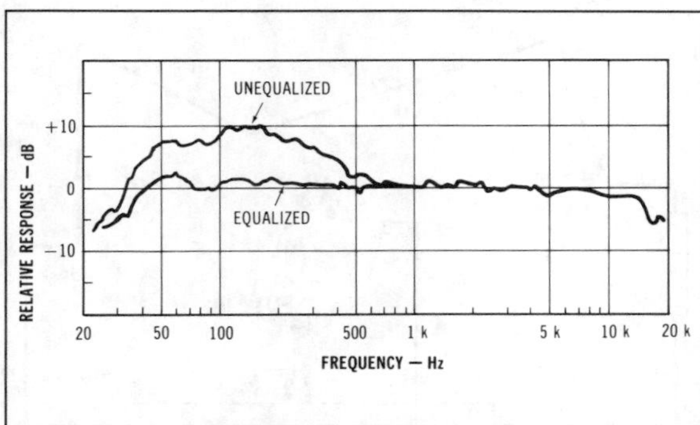

Figure 6-40 Unequalized and equalized response of prototype Hypex horn of Fig. 6-39 at mixer position. *(After AES, Reference 8.)*

raising or lowering ceiling sections. These variable acoustical entities facilitate experimentation and evaluation of the prototype Hypex horn idea.

What are the objective and subjective results? Efficiency is indeed high, which means that a given sound pressure level can be obtained with lower amplifier power and lower cone excursion. Perhaps the most valuable result is that the audition area is greatly increased over conventional loudspeaker arrangements. Subjective reactions of persons of both artistic and technical backgrounds have been favorable enough to encourage further development of the horn system. Work is in progress to improve the horn/driver match at low frequencies and to improve damping of plates forming the horn.

6.8 AUGSPERGER'S APPROACH—SIGMA SOUND CONTROL ROOM

Since 1975, George Augsperger has been directly involved in the design of more than one hundred control or mixdown rooms. He has also tested monitor loudspeakers and made acoustical corrections in another hundred rooms. Out of this wealth of experience, his words are worthy of our consideration. That which follows is based on his detailed description of his experience in "tuning" the Sigma Sound Studio 1 control and mixdown room.[10] Most recording studio control rooms are used both for recording and mixdown, the latter function being the more demanding of the two.

". . . good mixdown rooms are not intended to be 'perfect' listening rooms . . . . Instead, the mixdown room is used as a working tool. It should enable the engineer to assemble a final product that may be multilayered and very complex yet which retains its integrity when heard in a wide variety of listening conditions."[10] Of course, comfort and quietness from distractions are highly desirable, but beyond these basics, there is not a great difference between rooms judged as "good" by professionals active in the field.

6.8.1 Monitor Geometry

Augsperger pinpoints one characteristic of a good mixdown room as one having the proper geometrical relationship between the monitor loudspeakers and the operator. Although Sigma Sound Studios use UREI 813s, he feels there is little difference between the top three or four highly regarded loudspeaker systems. The distance between mix center and each of the monitors should be 10 to 11 ft and subtend 60° in the plan view. The loudspeaker axes cross about 3 ft behind the console as shown in Fig. 6-41. The alcove above the observation window should be left open until the positioning of the monitors is completely finalized. Once positioned, the baffle surface is developed by trial and error for best results.

If the front corners of the control mixdown room are not used for doors, the monitor shelf can be lower than door height. The Sigma shelf is about 76 in. above the

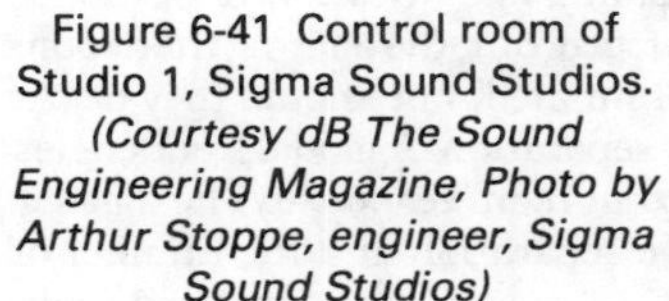
Figure 6-41 Control room of Studio 1, Sigma Sound Studios. *(Courtesy dB The Sound Engineering Magazine, Photo by Arthur Stoppe, engineer, Sigma Sound Studios)*

floor, 46 in. (20°) above ear level. This is, of course, a compromise between visibility and best listening conditions, but 10° is closer to optimum.

6.8.2 Control Room Shape

"The more successful mixdown rooms are bilaterally symmetrical, 16–19 ft wide at the front and 20–24 ft wide near the rear."[10] This statement refers to the inner, visible surfaces of the room. The structural outer shell, providing the ultimate low-frequency boundaries, is beyond these inner walls. Control/mixdown room volume usually falls between 4000 and 6000 ft^3. At Sigma the rear wall and rear side splays are made of wooden grillwork, as shown in Fig. 6-41, acoustically transparent for maximum flexibility of adjusting room acoustics later without disturbing appearance. Although Augsperger has not commented on it, such a uniform wooden grillwork is considered a potential problem in architectural acoustics. For example, reflections from stairs may have a tonal character. The uniform slat spacing acts as a diffraction grating at frequencies at which spacing is comparable to the wavelength of the impinging sound. At the higher audio frequencies the grillwork may not be uniformly transparent acoustically.

There are two general schools of thought on control room ceiling shape. Fig. 6-42A illustrates what is termed the "compression ceiling"; Fig. 6-42B shows the "expansion ceiling." Each has its devotees. A third variation is a level ceiling with certain distribution of absorptive and reflective areas. Augsperger's reaction is that the compression ceiling gives the "punchier" sound; it also produces short delay reflections that result in comb filter distortion. The ceiling of Sigma Sound Studios was, after pro-and-con discussion, made in the compression form.

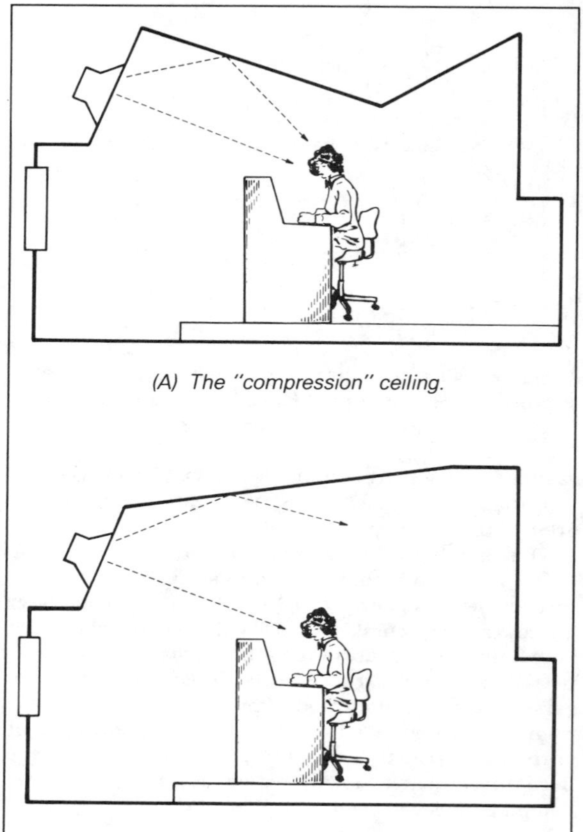

(A) The "compression" ceiling.

(B) The "expansion" ceiling.

Figure 6-42 The effect of control/mixdown ceiling shape on reflection pattern.

6.8.3 Control Room Acoustical Treatment

Reverberation time of mixdown rooms is typically between 0.25 and 0.3 s at midband. The average absorption coefficient is around 0.33. The directivity of the monitors is such that the ratio of direct-to-reflected midband sound is close to unity, which is considered favorable.

As will be discussed more fully in a later section, there is a great lack of agreement on how the absorptive and reflective areas should be distributed. Some say absorptive front and reflective rear; others say the opposite. Still others recommend uniform distribution over all surfaces. Augsperger prefers the front of the room slightly more live than the rear. He designs for similar absorption in all three orthagonal axes: front to back, side to side, and top to bottom. This is then trimmed with small absorptive and reflective patches until typical musical passages sound right.

6.8.4 Problems at Low Frequencies

Substantial absorption below 125 Hz is a must, even though difficult to achieve. Rooms judged to be of good quality rarely have reverberation times near 40 Hz more than twice that at midband. The question of standing waves must be bravely faced but the fact is that room resonances cannot be eliminated, nor should they be. At very low frequencies the separation of modal frequencies results in peaks and dips in room response. The smaller the room, the greater the separation and the number of irregularities. On top of this, seating the operator at room center guarantees that nulls occur there at certain bass frequencies. Augsperger at one time thought that making the structural walls irregular and the inner surfaces symmetrical would be best, but experience has taught him that the idea is faulty.

The very nature of stereo reproduction requires bilateral symmetry. Bass summation turns out to be more important than good imaging and phantom center stability. Panning the kick drum center should not change its tonal quality but should be about 6 dB louder than full left or full right. With a nonsymmetrical room this does not happen. In some rooms the kick drum disappears when panned center!

Adequate low-frequency absorption tends to minimize many of the problems of that region of the spectrum. Augsperger has found that low-frequency absorption under the window, across the rear wall, and in the rear corners is most effective. At Sigma, sub-woofers were installed under the studio window in part of the trap space, but finding the proper place for them and getting them to blend with the monitors is difficult.

6.8.5 Diffusion, Reflections, and Comb Filters

Diffusion of sound is helped by distributing absorptive and reflective surfaces. If any major surface of the room is totally absorptive, sound diffusion suffers. On the other hand, reflective surfaces near the loudspeaker can result in audible colorations as a result of the comb filter effect. If the upward sloping ceiling were to result in an audible peak or dip in response, its contour would have been changed or it would have been vented. Often such reflection effects are masked by other reflections.

6.9 QUEEN'S APPROACH

Daniel Queen points out that in small rooms, such as a control room, the reverberant field builds up quickly, making the reverberant field a component of the early sound fused with the original impulse.[11] The room itself distorts the signal spectrum as frequency-dependent room modes cause the level of sound to vary with position. In addition to this effect, the sound absorbers in the room are frequency dependent. The best cure of room modes is to shift activity to a large room, but this is usually impractical. Queen suggests the following steps:

1. Select monitor loudspeakers having the same amplitude-frequency response curves (though not necessarily reference levels) on axis, 45° off axis, and in the reverberant field.
2. Choose as large a control room as possible with favorable proportions.
3. Place the loudspeakers to provide most favorable directional cues.
4. Provide as much absorption as practical, but apply it uniformly to all surfaces.

He suggests an indoor-outdoor carpet on an open-cell foam pad on walls and ceiling. He then gives a step-by-step procedure for matching room characteristics in all octave bands and for equalizing the system. The main point to be emphasized here is that Queen recommends room absorption to be applied uniformly to all surfaces.

6.10 RETTINGER'S APPROACH

The late Michael Rettinger's numerous papers in technical journals on the subject of control room treatment are given in references 12 to 16 and are concisely summarized in his book, *Studio Acoustics*.[17] He suggests:

1. A trapezoidal room shape, or at least avoiding parallel front sidewalls. By shaping the front sidewalls linearly or curvilinearly like a horn, a tendency toward avoiding coincidental reinforcement of normal modes and avoidance of flutter echoes is achieved.
2. The frontal part of the horizontal cross section of the room should display some reflective panels, comparable to an exponential horn. This serves to direct sound to the operator and to load the monitors at low frequencies.
3. The vertical cross section of the room should have reflective areas near the front.
4. The rear sidewalls and rear ceiling should be moderately absorptive, but the rear wall should be near anechoic. The room contours are visualized in Fig. 6-43.

The rear wall treatment suggested by Rettinger is illustrated in Fig. 6-44. Multiple layers of 2-in. glass-fiber boards are arranged in depth to attain significant absorbence to lower frequencies. A cosmetic fabric cover such as loudspeaker grille cloth may be used as a facing.

6.11 VEALE'S APPROACH

Edward J. Veale, an acoustical consultant in England, has also presented his ideas on control room design.[18] He emphasizes the importance of using only dissipative acoustical absorbers rather than reactive types such as Helmholtz resonators. He guards against any absorber that will introduce an addition or nonlinear modification to the sound in the control room. (Although bass traps are based on reactive, quarter-wave resonance phenomena, they are such effective "sound sinks" that little, if any, energy is returned to the room and, hence, would presumably be acceptable to Veale. However, diaphragmatic absorbers, such as wooden decks and plasterboard walls, would not qualify.)

Veale's main concern is centered on early (but not too

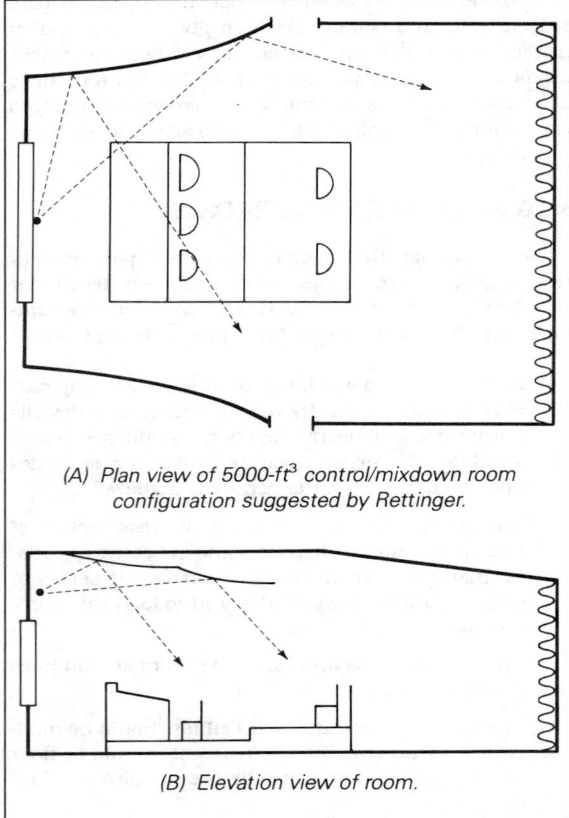

(A) Plan view of 5000-ft³ control/mixdown room configuration suggested by Rettinger.

(B) Elevation view of room.

Figure 6-43 Rettinger control room contours.

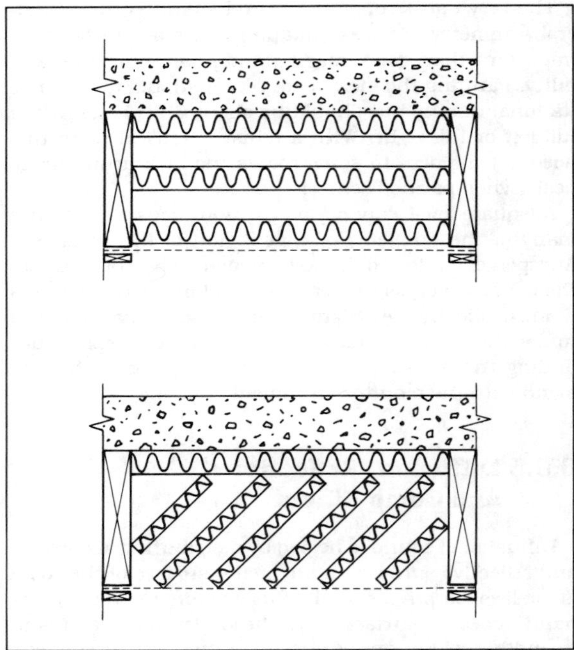

Figure 6-44 Rettinger's two suggestions for a highly absorptive rear wall in a control/mixdown room. *(After Reference 12.)*

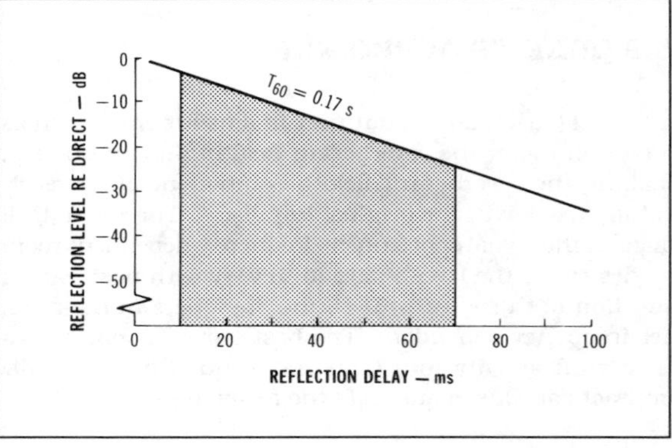

Figure 6-45 Veale's area of acceptable control room reflections at the position of the mixer. *(After Reference 18.)*

early) reflections, and apparently he has devised his plan on the basis of subjective judgment with instrumental measurements to evaluate conformance to the plan. He claims that it has been established that reflections arriving at the ear within 8 ms after the direct "serve no purpose." We suppose that it is to serve no good purpose, for this is the delay region in which dense comb filter effects appear. Reflections arriving between 10 and 70 ms "are useful." Experiments were made in comparing the reflection pattern of the control room to the results of mixed sound when listened to in an average domestic environment. He concluded that between 4 and 7 reflections are required to give a complete sound picture to the ear. The first reflection should arrive 10 to 15 ms after the direct and be 4 to 6 dB down. The other reflections should be reasonably evenly spaced on up to about 50 to 70 ms each 4 to 10 dB down from the preceding one. When the amplitudes of the reflections are plotted against delay, they should follow a reverberant decay corresponding to an RT of 0.17 s. In Fig. 6-45 the shaded area encompasses the region Veale says would provide the most favorable reflection configuration.

Veale's plan does not explicitly state where absorbent materials are to be placed. However, he does require low-frequency reflective surfaces in the vicinity of the monitor loudspeakers, which agrees with Rettinger and others. From there on it is a matter of placing absorbing materials of the right area and absorption coefficient to achieve the stated reflection amplitudes. As delays out to 70 ms are involved, reflections from the rear surfaces as well as sidewalls and ceilings must be carefully controlled. A control room treated according to Veale's plan would have patches of absorbent of varying thickness placed strategically.

6.12 DON DAVIS'S APPROACH

In 1978 Don Davis introduced a new approach to the acoustical treatment of control rooms.[19] Through Heyser's time-delay spectrometry, the prolific production of audible comb-filter distortion at the operator's position was made vividly evident.[20] These are caused by interference (superposition) of very early reflections with the direct sound from the monitor loudspeakers. These reflections originate at hard surfaces around the loudspeakers, the console face, and so on. Davis suggested a rather radical approach to the distribution of absorbing surfaces; he made the front end of the control room dead and the rear end live. The reason given for this was that current practice "created environments rife with response anomalies" caused by the mixer hearing "too many early reflections and too few, relatively speaking, later ones."[19] Although the subsequent discussion in the 1978 publication is a mixture of new developments in monitors and microphones and the need for semireverberant conditions, the reduction of "response anomalies" from the front plus the addition of delayed reflections from the rear combine to give "the mixer the subjective feeling the monitors are the only sound source." Here is the birth of the Live End–Dead End™ control room rationale, which was much better understood and elaborated in the following months.[21]

It is Don Davis's intention to limit the use of the LEDE™ designation to control rooms that have the following:

1. A nonsymmetrical bass-containing outer shell, free of pronounced low-frequency resonances, large enough to support the low frequencies needed for music. (Actually, the LEDE™ concept applies only to geometric frequencies at which ray acoustics apply.)
2. A symmetrical inner shell effective at geometric frequencies above (3)(velocity of sound)/(smallest room dimension) Hz.
3. An effective anechoic path between the monitor loudspeakers and the mixer's ears that extends at least 2 to 5 ms beyond the initial time-delay gap of the studio.
4. A highly diffused (at geometrical frequencies) sound field present during the onset of the so-called Haas effect.
5. No "early-early" sound via structure-borne paths reaching the mixer's ears before the direct sound arrives.
6. Hard-surfaced rear and rear-side walls and rear ceiling so arranged as to yield an interwoven, high-density comb filter pattern.

When time-energy-frequency measurements made by a qualified technician confirm these factors, authorization to use the LEDE™ acronym will be given with no fee.

To understand the Live End–Dead End™ principles, we must review several basic phenomena.

6.12.1 Comb-Filter Distortions

Heyser's time-delay spectrometry (TDS) has given audio engineers a powerful tool.[20] An acoustical frequency sweep signal of a given (usually flat) spectrum can be radiated into a room, and by a special offset system the spectrum (or frequency response, if you will) of any reflected component can be selected and displayed. The microphone feeding the TDS equipment accepts the entire bewildering cacophony of reflected sound energy from all surfaces, but the equipment accepts only that which arrives at a given, adjustable time after the exciting signal went out. For example, if it is desired to see what the output of the left monitor looks like 10 ft away at the ear position of the mixer, the right monitor is deactivated and the TDS gate set to accept only the direct ray arriving (10 ft/1130 ft/s) 8.8 ms after the signal left the loudspeaker. The trace would show a nice, relatively flat, combined response of the power amplifier and loudspeakers. Introducing a reflecting surface (such as the console face), the TDS system now picks up the direct ray combined acoustically with the reflected ray of essentially the same amplitude (process of interference or superposition), and the flat response becomes highly contorted. If the difference between the path lengths of the direct and reflected components is 1 in. (0.0737 ms), the response of Fig. 6-46A[21] is produced with two dips of about 20-dB magnitude removed from our precious spectrum. If the path difference between direct and reflected rays is 12 in., the reflected ray arrives (1 ft/1130 ft/s) = 0.88 ms later. The effect on system frequency response is as shown in Fig. 6-46B. Short delays of this type create serious comb filter interference effects and may be caused by reflections from walls, ceiling, or console face. The greater the path differential between direct and reflected rays, the closer together the nulls, and the less audible the effect will be. will be.

These comb filters are not all bad; they are very much a part of our everyday experience. When the delays are

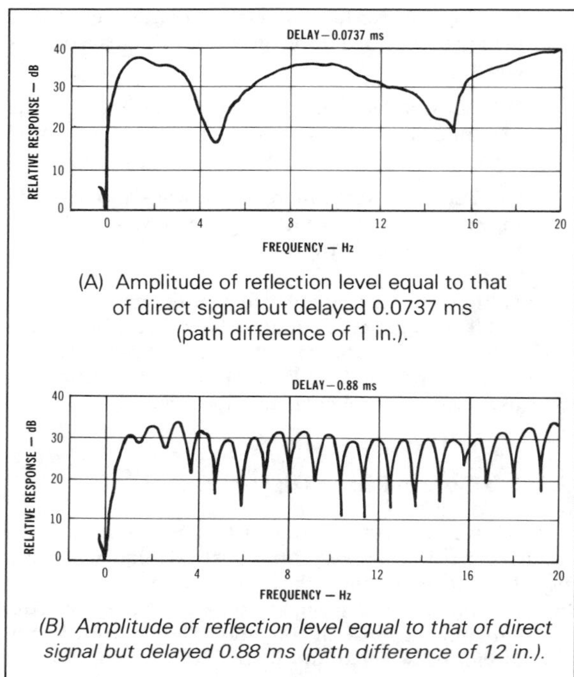

(A) Amplitude of reflection level equal to that of direct signal but delayed 0.0737 ms (path difference of 1 in.).

(B) Amplitude of reflection level equal to that of direct signal but delayed 0.88 ms (path difference of 12 in.).

Figure 6-46 Simulation of the effect of very early reflections on the system frequency response at the ear position of the mixer. *(After Reference 21.)*

small, however, the large parts of the spectrum gouged out at the nulls definitely degrade sound quality. The nulls are formed when the direct and delayed signals are in phase opposition (180° out of phase). When they are in phase, peaks 6 dB higher than either are formed. A study by Bucklein indicates that peaks are even more audible than dips.[22] We must condition ourselves to think of two types of comb filter effects: (1) those producing audible coloration, and (2) the benign inaudible effects. Reflections of short delays produce audible colorations.

6.12.2 Geometric Frequencies

At low audio frequencies the monitor loudspeakers are essentially nondirectional, which means that significant energy is directed to adjoining walls, ceiling, and window glass. Any practical treatment applied to the front dead end is quite transparent and ineffective as an absorber at these low frequencies. The Live End–Dead End™ control room design considers only geometric frequencies.

The boundary between regions A and B of Fig. 3-1 for a 30 × 25 × 19.5-ft outer shell of a control room with a reverberation time of 0.5 s can be computed from Eq. 3-1:

$$f = 11{,}250\sqrt{\frac{RT}{V}}$$

$$= 11{,}250\sqrt{\frac{0.5}{14{,}625}}$$

$$= 66\,\text{Hz}$$

The lower boundary of geometric region C, 4f = 263 Hz. The transition between regions B and C is gradual, but we can safely say that for this room, geometric acoustics take over above about 263 Hz (wavelength 5 ft). For a control room of the more common outer shell dimensions of 24 × 20 × 15.6 ft and a reverberation time of 0.4 s, 4f = 329 Hz. Above frequencies in this range, the Live End–Dead End™ principle is effective, and adequate absorption can be obtained by absorbers of reasonable thickness.

6.12.3 Initial-Time-Delay Gap

In listening to music, we receive a distinct impression of the size of the hall in which the music was played. The cue for such perception is the *initial time delay*, which is the length of time between the arrival at the microphone of the direct sound and the first reflected sound. Beranek in his detailed study of the acoustics and reputations of many concert halls emphasized the importance of this initial time delay.[23] As applied to control rooms, controlling the initial time delay of the room is the way to control the *psychoacoustical size* of the room (i.e., the size the room seems to be from the aural cues received).

The general arrangements of the Live End–Dead End™ control room are shown in Fig. 6-47. The sound (of geometric frequencies) traveling toward the room surfaces surrounding the mixer is absorbed. The direct sound received by the mixer indicates that the loudspeakers are the source of the sound. Sound traveling to the rear portion of the room is reflected and returned toward the source and tends to be dissipated by the dead-end absorbent. The splayed and protruding reflectors at the live end diffuse the sound. Some rays are reflected many times, tending to spread out in time the energy returned to the mixer. The direct path length is shorter than the others; hence, it arrives at the ears of the mixer first. The diffuse sound from the rear arrives considerably later.[24, 25]

In the studio, the initial time-delay gap between the arrival of direct sound at the microphone and the arrival of reflections is quite short. Don Davis reports that studies with volumes of 6000 and 200,000 ft^3 exhibit the same initial time-delay gap within 1 ms.[26] He also states that in studios with such a wide size range, the ratio of direct signal to the first significant reflection were within 1 dB of each other. As shown in Fig. 6-48, these early reflections come from the floor, music stand, and other nearby

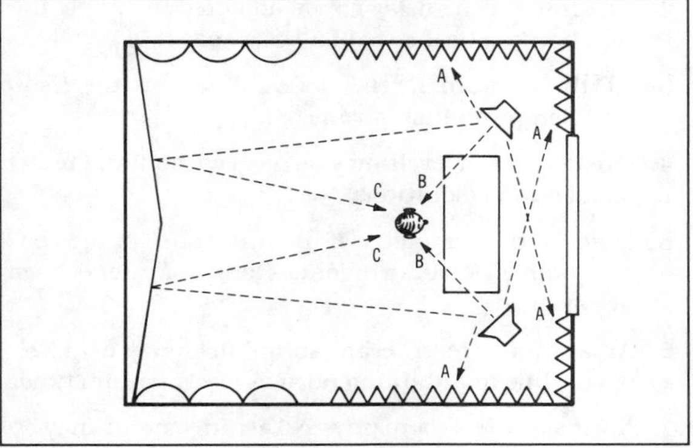

Figure 6-47 Conceptual layout of Live End-Dead End™ control room. (A) Absorption of early reflections by dead-end treatment. (B) The direct sound reaching the mixer's ears unencumbered with the reflections of A. (C) Reflections from the live rear delayed 10 to 20 ms, giving the mixer the impression of being in a larger space.

objects and are largely independent of the size of the studio. In the control room, if similar early reflections are not suppressed, the short initial time gap of the mixer will mask that of the studio. In the Live End–Dead End™ control room, the dominant reflections arriving at the ears of the mixer are from the rear of the room some 15 or 20 ms later. This delay enables the mixer to hear clearly the early reflections of the sound of the performer. The initial time-delay gap of the Live End–Dead End™ control room is purposely made greater to avoid masking that of the studio. The comb filter effects with such long delays are completely inaudible because the interference peaks and nulls are so closely spaced that they are undetectable.

6.12.4 Haas Fusion Zone

The direct sound, arriving first, dominates the impression the mixer receives. The delayed diffuse sound from the rear does not sound like an echo because it arrives within the Haas fusion zone.[27] It makes the perceived sound seem louder and is especially beneficial in making the mixer feel as if it is in a larger space. The sound reflected from the rear, delayed 15 to 20 ms, provides cues normally associated with larger rooms.

6.12.5 Energy-Time Curve

The instrumentation for measuring the energy-time curve (ETC) must also be attributed to Heyser. Briefly, this equipment utilizes a time-delay spectrometer as a "front-end" and a fast Fourier transform analyzer as a demodulator and "storage bin." The graph of Fig. 6-49 is an idealized, yet typical, record available through such a system.[24] In this case the test signal frequency sweep is applied to one monitor, and the test microphone feeding the equipment is placed in the region occupied by the ears of the sound mixer. The received energy density is then displayed against time as shown in Fig. 6-49. This display is especially helpful in setting up an LEDE™ control room. The time from 0 to t_1 is the transit time for the sound to travel from the loudspeaker to the microphone at which time the direct sound is displayed as a relatively

Figure 6-48 The initial time-delay gap in the studio is short.

intense peak. The early reflections from the front surfaces of the room arriving at the microphone between t_1 and t_2 are reduced in level in the Live End–Dead End™ control room by the absorbent covering critical areas. At t_2 the first significant reflection from the rear arrives at the microphone (the mixer's ears), followed by a second at t_3 and a third at t_4. Beyond t_4 the decay of the diffuse, reverberant field of the room is displayed.

There is an advantage in having the significant reflections after t_2 spread out in time. Kuttruff describes the work of Seraphim on the extension of Haas's fusion zone by consecutive, spaced echoes.[28] While a single reflection might result in a fusion zone to 30 ms, a series of four spaced reflections might extend it to 85 ms. This places a distinct premium on managing live-end reflecting surfaces to obtain three or four significant reflections, as shown in Fig. 6-49. The work of both Haas and Seraphim was done with direct and delayed signals arriving from the front quadrant of the observers—in the Live End–Dead End™ room the comparable reflections arrive from the rear. Further study is needed to demonstrate that the effect of extending the Haas zone is the same as for the reflections arriving from the rear.

6.12.6 Advantage of LEDE™

Don Davis lists the acoustical features of the LEDE™ (Live End–Dead End™) concept.[21]

1. The comb filter irregularities (peaks and dips) resulting from reflections from the rear are so tightly packed in frequency that they are inaudible.
2. The initial time-delay gap is adjusted to supply the psychoacoustical cues of a large space.
3. All the first-order reflections fall within the Haas and Seraphim fusion zone.
4. Greater sound levels may be used without the usual small room colorations.
5. Need for the symmetry of the inner shell of the control room is not as stringent as long as flutter echoes are avoided.
6. An adequate reverberant sound field may be developed while maintaining normal reverberation time.
7. Normal control room physical arrangements may be followed.

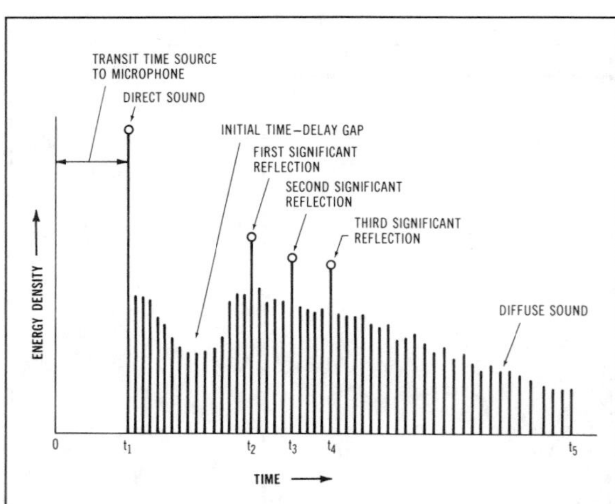

Figure 6-49 The energy-time curve displayed by the combination of time-delay spectrometry and fast Fourier transform type of equipment. *(After References 17 and 18.)*

6.12.7 Reactions to LEDE™ Listening Environment

Stepping outside the rather emotionally charged recording industry, the reaction of Bert Whyte to his newly installed Live End–Dead End™ treatment in his listening room is interesting.

> . . . one is immediately aware of the great increase in clarity and cleanness. Bass is singularly free of boominess or overhang. Instruments seem more clearly defined. Dense and complex musical textures are more articulate. Depth perception is greatly enhanced, as is the sense of ambience and the reverberant characteristics of the recording hall.
>
> —Bert Whyte, *Audio*, July, 1982

Within the industry, Richards and Nichols record their reaction to their LEDE™ control room.[29] They admit that it takes time to adjust to the room, but once accomplished, a new "transparency" results, as though the glass is taken out of the window and the mixer is in the studio with the musicians. A wide, good stereo image prevails. A much more critical approach to microphone selection and placement is possible now that such problems are not masked by other problems. It is a "strictly clinical atmosphere; there's no hype," and they feel the LEDE™ control room is a significant step toward standardization. Along with such favorable reactions, many are less enthusiastic. It will take some time to sort out the lasting qualities of all of the ideas on control rooms that have been presented.

6.13 CHIPS DAVIS'S APPROACH—TRES VIRGOS CONTROL ROOM

It is fitting that the one who did the first retrofit Live End–Dead End™ control room be involved in the design of the control room to be described, that of the Tres Virgos

Figure 6-50 The front, dead-end of the Tres Virgos LEDE™ control room.

Figure 6-51 The Tres Virgos LEDE™ control room showing both absorbent panels associated with the dead front end and the carefully oriented reflecting panels at the live rear end.

Studio. After hearing Don Davis suggest (at the Synergetic Audio Concepts seminar, February, 1978) that, perhaps, better control rooms could be built by a different distribution of absorbing surfaces, Chips Davis immediately applied the theory to the control room of his own studio in Las Vegas. The results were most encouraging, and retrofitting existing control rooms and designing and building new LEDE™ control rooms accelerated. Tres Virgos control room was one of the first conceived in LEDE™ lore and dedicated to the proposition that all control room reflections are not equal.

First, a geometrical study was made to determine the optimum inner shell shape. This included (1) the orientation of the monitor loudspeakers, (2) the splayed sidewalls, and (3) the diffusing surfaces at the rear of the room. The loudspeaker axes crossed somewhat behind the head position of the operator. The "LEDE™ line" was then established at the ears of the operator, which was to be the general demarcation between the front soft and the rear hard areas. There is nothing magical about this line. The important thing is the final distribution of reflections on the ETC display, and later adjustments to optimize this are to be expected. The rear surfaces were then considered one by one by the ray tracing method to establish an advantageous distribution of echoes to take advantage of the Seraphim effect.

An anechoic response was sought for the 12- to 15-ms time interval immediately after the arrival of the direct ray from the monitor. "Anechoic" is really too strict a term because reflections at least 12 dB below the direct ray are sufficiently anechoic. The next important reflection is one arriving 15 ms after the direct ray to initiate the Haas fusion process in the ear-brain system of the operator. Other spaced reflections should stand out from the reverberant field 6 dB or so to extend the Haas zone after the manner of Fig. 6-49.

The practical realization of the Tres Virgos control room is shown in the photographs of Figs. 6-50 and 6-51. The rear reflecting panels, carefully positioned and inclined according to the reflection analysis described, yielded the dominant reflection sequence in both time and energy density as checked by ETC verification. The photographs do not show an acoustical shield, which is required to reduce console face reflections and the resulting pronounced coloration described in reference 30. Further details are given in references 31 and 32.

REFERENCES

1. M. W. Wasserman, "Architectural Design for Studio One Sigma Sound Studios," *dB The Sound Engineering Magazine*, vol. 15, no. 11, pp. 50–51, November 1981.

2. J. Jacob and R. Millward, "Building Tres Virgos," *dB The Sound Engineering Magazine*, vol. 15, no. 11, pp. 36–40, November 1981.
3. R. Hodas, "Tres Virgos—One of the First Examples of a Complete Live-End/Dead-End Control Room Installation," *Recording Engineer/Producer*, vol. 13, no. 6, pp. 78–85, December 1982.
4. T. Paine, "A Novel Modular Construction Technique for dB Recording Studios, Florida," *Recording Engineer/Producer*, vol. 13, no. 4, pp. 38–45, August 1982.
5. S. Ishii and T. Mizutani, "A New Type of Listening Room and Its Characteristics—A Proposal for a Standard Listening Room," presented at the 72nd convention of the AES, preprint 1887 (B-4), October 1982.
6. J. Cooper, "The Construction of the Saul Zaentz Film Center," *dB The Sound Engineering Magazine*, vol. 14, no. 7, pp. 32–37, July 1980.
7. L. Zide, "Fantasy Recording/Zaentz Film Center: A Candy Store for the 80's," *dB The Sound Engineering Magazine*, vol. 14, no. 8, pp. 38–42, August 1980.
8. M. T. Putnam, "The Loudspeaker and Control Room as a Wholly Integrated System," *Journal of the AES*, vol. 31, no. 4, pp. 239–245 April 1983.
9. M. T. Putnam, "Recording Studio and Control Room Facilities of Advance Design," *Journal of the AES*, vol. 8, no. 2, p. 111 April 1960.
10. G. L. Augsperger, "Contemporary Mixdown Room Design," *dB The Sound Engineering Magazine*, vol. 15, no. 11, pp. 54–59, November 1981.
11. D. Queen, "Monitoring Room Acoustics," *dB The Sound Engineering Magazine*, vol. 7, no. 5, pp. 24–26, May 1973.
12. M. Rettinger, "On the Acoustics of Control Rooms," presented at the 57th convention of the AES, preprint 1261 (J-1), May 1972.
13. M. Rettinger, "Control Room Acoustics," *dB The Sound Engineering Magazine*, vol. 11, no. 4, pp. 26–29, April 1977.
14. M. Rettinger, "The LEDE Acoustical Concept," (letter to the editor) *Recording Engineer/Producer*, vol. 11, no. 2, April 1980.
15. M. Rettinger, "A Live-End Environment for Control Room Loudspeakers," *dB The Sound Engineering Magazine*, vol. 14, no. 6, pp. 42–43, June 1980.
16. M. Rettinger, "Control Room Acoustics," *dB The Sound Engineering Magazine*, vol. 15, no. 10, pp. 57–61, October 1981.
17. M. Rettinger, *Studio Acoustics*, New York: Chemical Publishing Company, Inc., 1981.
18. E. J. Veale, "The Environment Design of a Studio Control Room," presented at the 49th Convention of the AES in Rotterdam, preprint A-2 (R), February 1973.
19. D. Davis, "Putting It All Together in a Control Room," *Synergetic Audio Concepts Tech Topic*, vol. 5, no. 7, April 1978.
20. R. C. Heyser, "Acoustical Measurements by Time Delay Spectrometry," *Journal of the AES*, vol. 15, no. 4, p. 370, April 1967.
21. C. Davis and D. Davis, "(LEDE) Live End-Dead End Control Room Acoustics . . . (TDS) Time-Delay Spectrometry . . . (PZM) Pressure-Zone Microphones," *Recording Engineer/Producer*, vol. 10, no. 1, p. 41, February 1979.
22. R. Bucklein, "The Audibility of Frequency Response Irregularities," *Journal of the AES*, vol. 29, no. 3, pp. 126–131, March 1981.
23. L. L. Beranek, *Music, Acoustics and Architecture*, New York: John Wiley & Sons, Inc., 1962.
24. D. Davis and C. Davis, "The LEDE™ Concept for the Control of Acoustic and Psychoacoustic Parameters in Recording Control Rooms," *Journal of the AES*, vol. 28, no. 9, pp. 585–595, September 1980.
25. D. Davis, "The Role of the Initial Time-Delay Gap in the Acoustic Design of Control Rooms for Recording and Reinforcing Systems," presented at the 64th convention of the AES, preprint 1547 (F-3), November 1979.

26. D. Davis, "Engineering an LEDE™ Control Room for a Broadcasting Facility," presented at the 67th convention of the AES, New York, preprint 1688 (I-1), October–November 1980.

27. H. Haas, "The Influence of a Single Echo on the Audibility of Speech," *Acustica*, vol. 1, no. 2, 1951, in German. (An English translation for Dr. Ing. K. P. R. Ehrenberg appears in the *Journal of the AES*, vol. 20, no. 2, pp. 146–159, March 1972.)

28. H. P. Seraphim, "Uber Die Wahrnehmbarkeit Mehrerer Ruckwurfe Von Sprachschall," *Acustica*, vol. 11, pp. 80–91, 1961. (A brief summary of Seraphim's paper given [in English] in H. Kuttruff, *Room Acoustics*, Second Edition, 1979, Barking, Essex, England: Applied Science Publishers, Ltd.)

29. R. Richards and G. Nichols, "Translating LEDE™ Control Room Design into Practical Experience," presented at the 66th convention of the AES, Los Angeles, California, preprint 1631 (G-3), May 1980.

30. C. Davis and G. E. Meeks, "History and Development of the LEDE Control Room Concept," presented at the 72nd convention of the AES, Anaheim, California, preprint 1954 (B-5), October 1982.

31. C. Davis, "LEDE Comes of Age," *The Mix*, vol. 6, no. 7, pp. 23, 24, 71, July 1982.

32. C. Davis and E. Bannon, "Designing for a Quiet Control Room," *The Mix*, vol. 5, no. 8, pp. 46–51, August 1981.

CHAPTER **7**

Rooms for Speech, Music, and Cinema

by Rollins Brook and Ted Uzzle*

*Sections 7.1 through 7.13 are by Rollins Brook. Section 7.14 is by Ted Uzzle.

The first part of this chapter presents the principles of acoustical design of rooms for speech activities: classrooms, meeting rooms, board rooms, lecture halls, drama theaters, churches, and auditoriums. The latter two almost always include the need for good acoustics for music. The acoustical design for music is discussed next, and accommodations for combined speech and music functions are also discussed. Finally, acoustics for the cinema is discussed.

7.1 SPEECH INTELLIGIBILITY

The goal of an acoustical design for optimum speech performance is to provide for maximum intelligibility of the speech while also maintaining a natural voice quality. Intelligibility is directly dependent upon the signal level, the background noise level, and the reverberation level in the room. The natural voice quality is controlled by the spectral uniformity of the reflections and absorption of the room surfaces and furnishings and by the effort required of the talker. In larger rooms the sound system will have a major effect on the quality and intelligibility of speech.

Establishing specific signal-to-noise and reverberation design goals is not a simple task. Over the past half century a number of psychoacoustical studies have attempted to quantify the dependence of intelligibility on background noise and reverberation. The data and conclusions have varied considerably.[1–5] Some of the variations can be attributed to the difficult task of testing for speech intelligibility and of establishing task-related measures of acceptability. In addition to the acoustical variables, there are also variations in the skills of talkers and listeners as well as in the level of difficulty of the speech content.

The acoustical design of small rooms and rooms with short reverberation times (less than 1.5 s) is rather simple. However, the acoustical and electroacoustical design of large rooms and rooms with a long reverberation time (RT) is much more complex. It also is still somewhat of an inexact science because of the problems in quantifying and specifying intelligibility. The acoustical design procedures and the parameter values presented in this chapter, while not supported by all the literature on the subject, have been found to be reliable in designing rooms for speech.

7.1.1 Background Noise

Intelligibility is hampered, sometimes prevented, by background noise—traffic, machinery in the room or nearby, the heating and air-conditioning system (HVAC), airplane flyovers, rain, and so on. (Techniques for controlling these problems are discussed in Chapter 4.) Control of background noise is always costly, so it is important to establish design goals that are realistic and based upon need.

Background noise has no effect upon intelligibility when the noise is 25 dB below the speech level, though it may still be an annoyance. When the signal-to-noise ratio is less than 25 dB, the magnitude of the reduction in intelligibility is dependent upon four factors:

1. Spectral content of the noise signal,
2. Signal-to-noise ratio,
3. Reverberation time,
4. Distance between source and listener.

Auditory interference from background noise is called *masking*. While the masking effect is greatest at the frequency of the noise, there will also be some masking of perception of sounds for several octaves above the noise frequency. This effect, called *upward masking*, can be a particular problem with heavy machinery that generates a loud low-frequency noise. The louder the noise level, the greater will be the upward masking.

For the best speech intelligibility, it is important to minimize noise in the main intelligibility range from 500 to 4000 Hz (usually produced by air flow through the HVAC system). Comfortable listening conditions also require the control of low-frequency rumble from building machinery.

In small rooms and in rooms with a reverberation time of less than 1.5 s, intelligibility can be good with a signal-to-noise ratio of only +10 dB. In large rooms, especially where the reverberation time exceeds 1.5 s, it is important to maintain a minimum signal-to-noise ratio of 25 dB. The establishment of a signal-to-noise design goal also requires a value judgment about the degree to which noise is a distraction. Although good intelligibility can

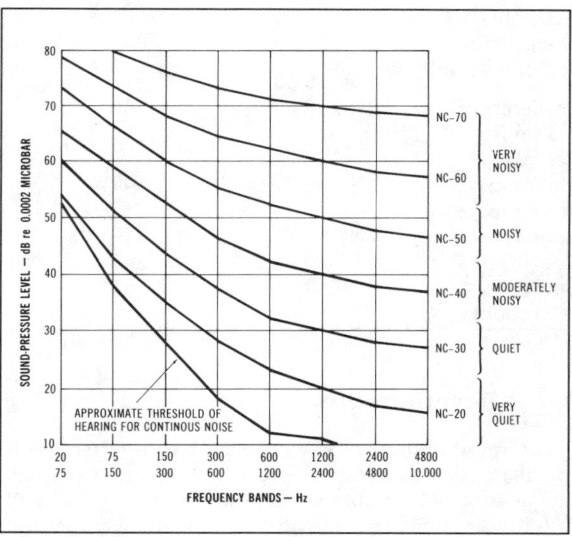

Figure 7-1 Noise criteria curves.

be achieved with a signal-to-noise ratio of 25 dB and sometimes less, still the noise level may be high enough to intrude on quiet moments, such as in a theater or in a church. Low-level intruding noises, such as talking in the lobby, aircraft flyovers, and sirens passing by, may be regarded as tolerable nuisances in a classroom or lecture hall; however, they would be intolerable in a drama theater or concert hall. Noise criteria curves are shown in Fig. 7-1. Table 7-1 lists recommended background noise levels for a variety of spaces. These recommendations consider both intelligibility and dramatic effect.

Table 7-1. Recommended Noise Criteria for Rooms

Type of Space	Recommended Noise Criterion Curve	Computed Equivalent Sound-Level Meter Readings (A scale readings in decibels)
Broadcast studios	NC 15-25	25-35
Concert halls	NC 20	30
Drama theaters	NC 20-25	30-35
Music rooms	NC 25	35
School rooms	NC 25	35
Large conference and boardrooms (for about 50 or more people)	NC 25	35
Assembly halls (with amplification)	NC 25-30	35-40
Conference room (for 20 or less)	NC 30	40
Motion picture theaters	NC 30	40
Churches	NC 30	40
Courtrooms	NC 30	40
Sports Coliseums	NC 50	60

7.1.2 Reverberation

The reverberation of speech begins to interfere with intelligibility after a few milliseconds. Listeners with normal hearing will combine (fuse) the direct sound and all of its reflections arriving within approximately the first 40 ms. These early reflections add to the perceived level of the direct sound. After about 40 ms the brain is no longer able to fuse the reflections fully, and they begin to degrade intelligibility by causing the sound of syllables to run together. Still later reflections, will cause whole words to blur together. These late reflections, if loud enough, begin to be heard as separate echoes. There is substantial disagreement among researchers as to the quantifying details, but there is general agreement that late reflections degrade intelligibility in proportion to their intensity and arrival time.

In very reverberant, medium-sized rooms, such as many older churches, a strong voice may be able to excite echoes of sufficient delay and intensity to be both annoying and detrimental to good communication. In very large rooms, the natural voice does not have sufficient energy to create echoes with enough level to be troublesome. Here, echo problems are more likely to be caused by the much higher levels produced by the speech reinforcement system.

The problems of echoes can be especially acute where supplementary loudspeaker clusters are used to cover the rear of the room and balconies. Many large auditoriums have been plagued with echoes heard in the main floor seating area coming from sound system reflections off follow-spot and control booth windows, rear walls of balconies, and balcony fronts. High-level returns off the rear wall are a common cause of failure with church and gym sound systems.

In general, speech intelligibility is improved by lowering the reverberation time. However, there is a point of diminishing or even negative returns. When the reverberation time falls below about 0.5 s, it is likely that useful speech energy is being absorbed when it could be directed to the audience to enhance the direct sound level. As a room increases in size (volume), it is natural for the reverberation to increase. This increasing reverberation time is useful in helping to sustain the speech level to the audience up to about 1.5 s. With a reverberation time of 1.5 to 2.0 s, it is necessary to take all available architectural design options (discussed later) to ensure acceptable intelligibility. In rooms with a time longer than 2 s, a sound-reinforcement system will almost

Table 7-2. Optimal Reverberation Time for Speech Rooms

Speech Room	1000-Hz Octave Band Reverberation Time
Classrooms:	
Hearing impaired	≤0.4
Children	0.3–0.6
High school and adults	0.5–1.0
Conference and boardrooms	0.4–0.8
Drama theaters	0.8–1.4
Courtrooms	0.6–1.0
General-purpose auditoriums*	0.8–1.8
Churches*	1.4–2.2

*While the optimal reverberation time for speech is always less than 1.5 s, longer times are often necessary in rooms where music is important.

always be required. The general recommendations for reverberation time in various speech rooms are shown in Table 7-2.

Although it is customary to relate the degrading effects of reverberation with reverberation time, the level of the reflections heard after about 40 ms is actually more important than the specific reverberation time of the room. In most cases, there is a predictable relationship between the level of these signals and the reverberation time of the space. There are cases, however, where the reverberation decay is not linear, causing the level of the reflections to remain higher, or fall faster, than the reverberation time would suggest. (Reverberation decays exponentially. The decay appears as a straight line when drawn on log scale paper; hence, we hear the common expression, a "linear" decay.)

The concept of reverberation time is based upon the premise that the sound field is completely diffuse. This condition may not exist in very "dead" rooms or in rooms that have been designed to have carefully controlled reflections and absorption. In these special cases, the decay time may not be linear, and it may vary with the location of the sound source and the test microphone. Large auditoriums with architectural structures, such as stage houses, balcony overhangs, and large curved surfaces, will also exhibit nonlinear decay rates. This nonlinear decay is not apparent from RT- measuring devices that provide only a numerical result. For a complete understanding of the reverberant behavior of a room, it is necessary to examine a graphical display of octave bands of decay, as illustrated in Fig. 7-2.

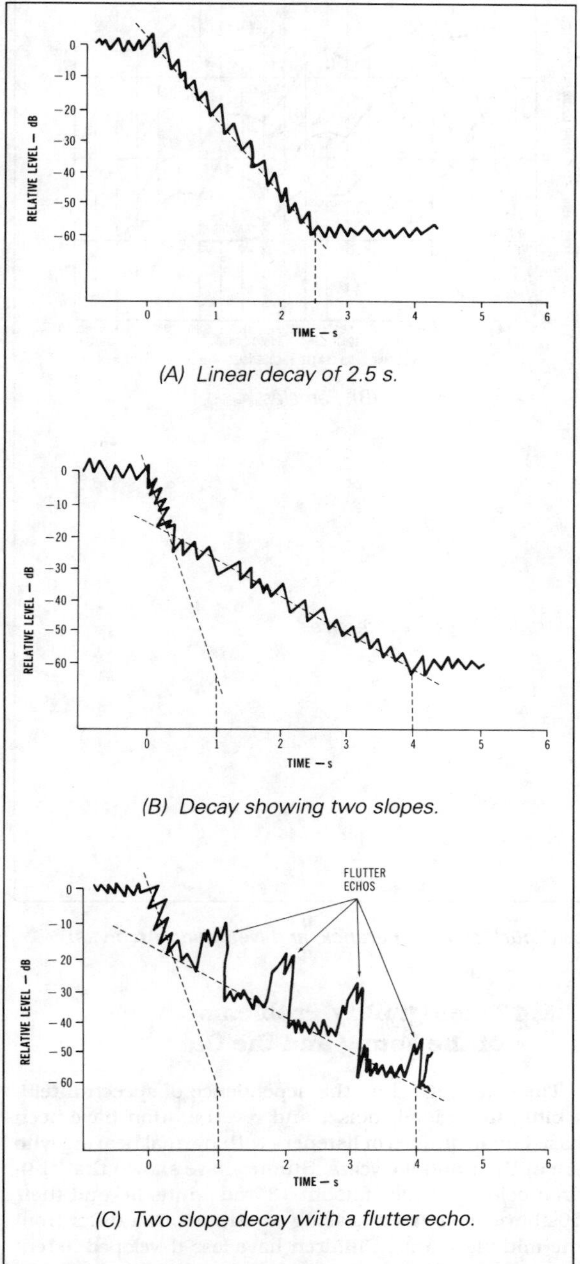

Figure 7-2 Graphical display of reverberation decay.

7.1.3 Speech Level

Speech intelligibility is a function of signal level even in the absence of noise or reverberation.[2] Intelligibility is at a maximum with sound pressure levels from about 70 to 90 dB with a small decline in intelligibility at higher levels. Below 70 dB, intelligibility begins to decline, and it falls off rapidly with sound pressure levels below about 40 dB. A typical plot of intelligibility as a function of level is shown in Fig. 7-3.

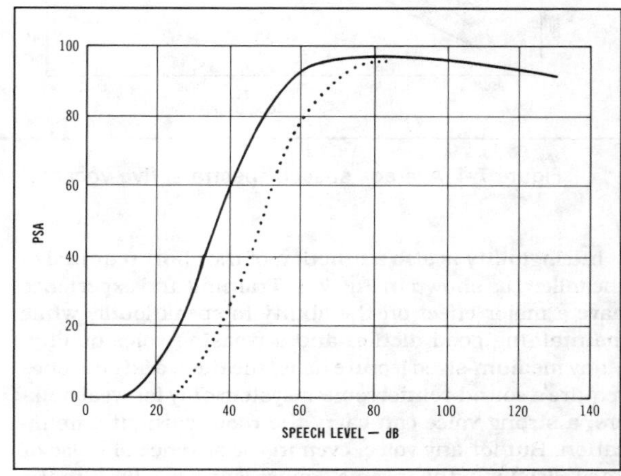

Figure 7-3 Dependence of the percentage syllable articulation (PSA) on the loudness level of speech-quiet room, . . . 40-dBA background level. *(After Reference 2.)*

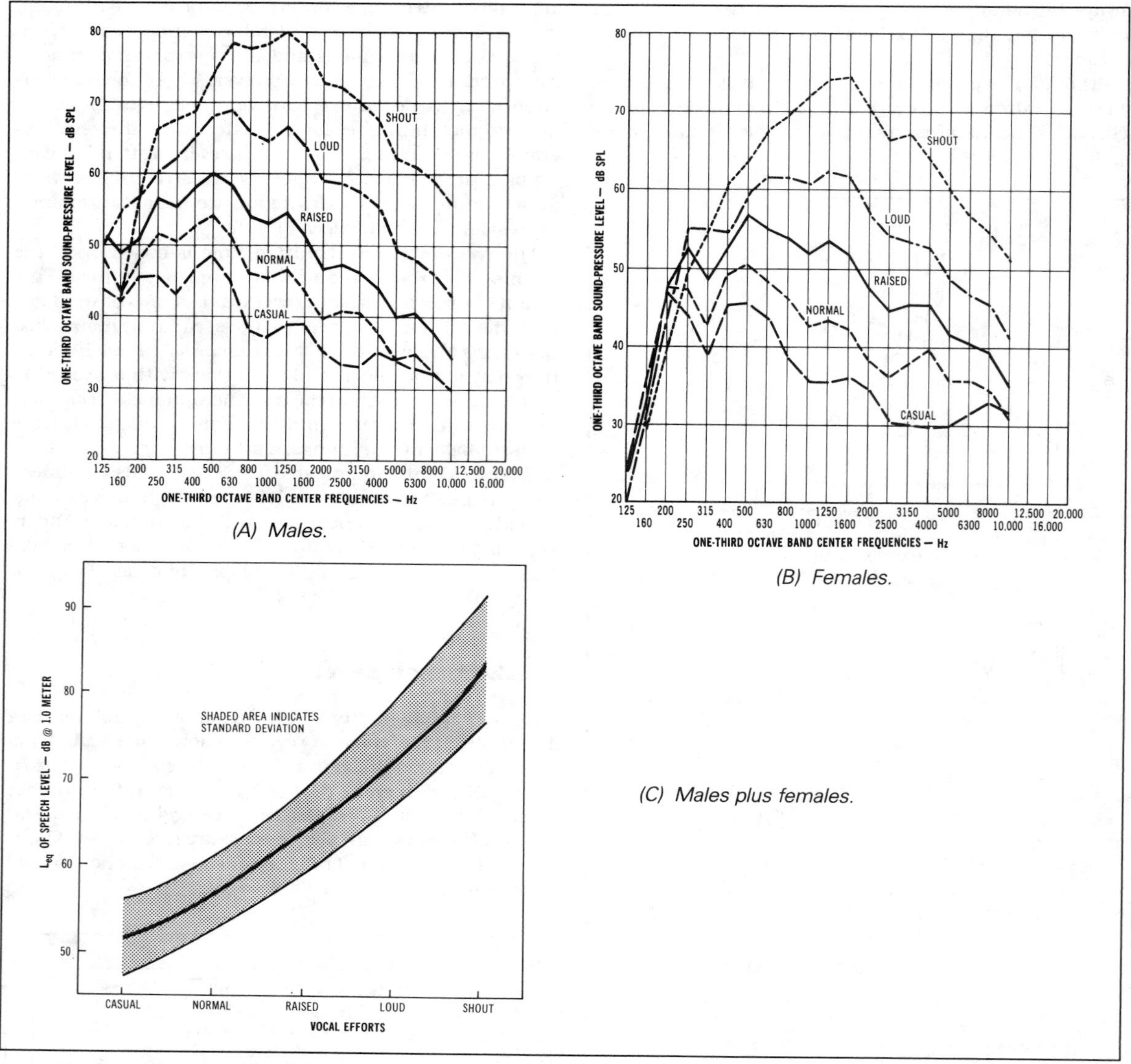

(A) *Males.*

(B) *Females.*

(C) *Males plus females.*

Figure 7-4 Average speech spectra at five vocal efforts. *(Courtesy Bolt, Beranek, and Neumann Archives)*

Intelligibility is also a function of the effort required of the talker, as shown in Fig. 7-4. Training and experience have a major effect on the ability to speak loudly while maintaining good diction and a pleasing voice quality. Many medium-sized lecture halls, theaters, and churches require a sound-reinforcement system only for weak talkers; a strong voice can carry the room without amplification. But for any voice, even in the absence of noise or late reflections, the inverse-square law sets a limit to the distance at which speech has sufficient level to be understood clearly.

7.1.4 Intelligibility Problems of the Young and the Old

The rules regarding the dependence of speech intelligibility upon level, noise, and reverberation have been based upon studies of listeners with normal hearing who are in their mid-life years. Studies have shown that children below the age of about 13 and adults beyond their 50s have age-related hearing conditions that differ from the mid-life years.[6] Children have less-developed listening and language skills than adults. Older people have

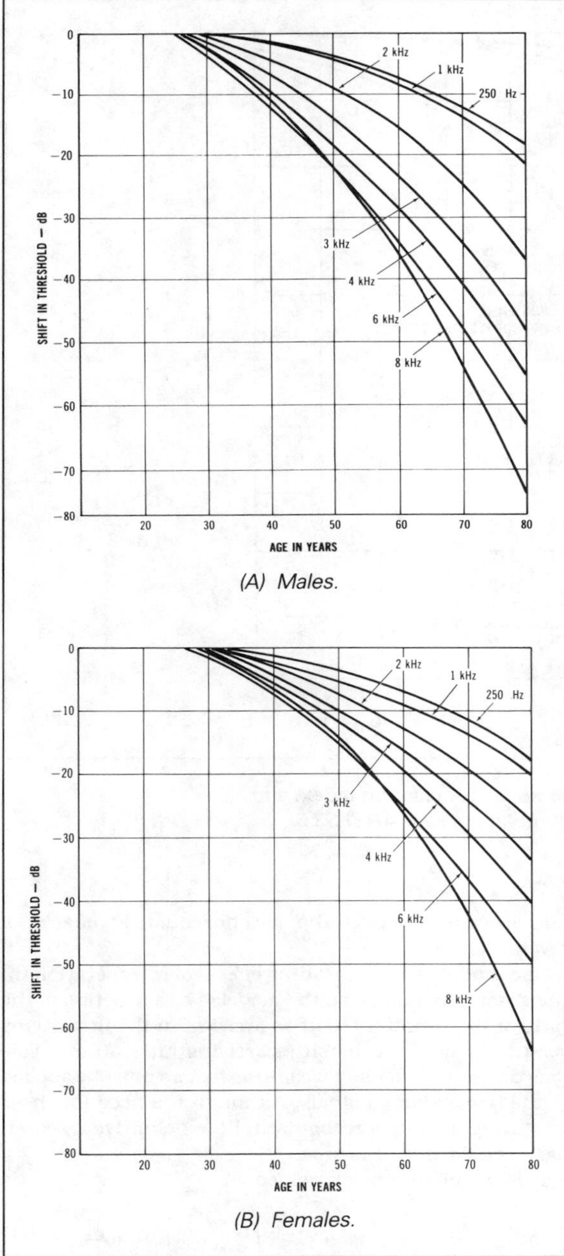

(A) Males.

(B) Females.

Figure 7-5 Shift in threshold of hearing with age (zero shift = 25-year-old males).

high-frequency hearing losses that degrade intelligibility (see Fig. 7-5). Although the hearing acuity and the signal-processing abilities of the old and the young are different, both groups require a higher direct sound level in order to have good speech intelligibility. Both are also more susceptible to the degrading effects of noise and reverberation.

It is evident that classrooms for elementary and junior high-school students should be carefully designed to meet the specialized hearing needs of this age group. Reasonable design criteria include a minimum signal-to-noise ratio of 30 dB and a maximum reverberation time of 0.4 s. The ceiling should be hard (reflective) to provide useful early reflections, and the floor should be carpeted. No dimension of the room should exceed 30 ft unless sound reinforcement is provided. Meeting rooms and social halls for the elderly should meet these same criteria. Room designs based upon these criteria would also be appropriate for use by persons with nonage-related hearing impairments.

7.1.5 Intelligibility Testing and Predicting

Speech intelligibility tests were originally developed for evaluating the performance of communication systems, such as telephone, radio, and so on, as functions of restricted bandwidth and background noise levels. These tests consist of trained auditors checking multiple choice answers or writing down the words or sentences understood through the system under evaluation. A variety of test materials has been employed, as shown in Fig. 7-6. Tests using complete sentences are generally not very discriminating because of the multiple clues contained within the meaning of the sentence. Phonetically balanced words, either real words or nonsense syllables, provide a more stringent test. A testing procedure has been standardized by the American National Standards Institute (ANSI).

From these communications studies of speech intelligibility, there were developed procedures for evaluation and prediction based upon signal-to-noise ratios. The most widely used of these is the *Articulation Index (AI)* for which standard methods for calculation have been established by ANSI.[4] In this system, octave or one-third-octave bands of speech (peak levels) and noise (rms levels) are compared. These band-limited signal-to-noise ratios are multiplied by a weighting factor based upon relative contribution to intelligibility, as shown in Table 7-3. These weighted-band figures are summed to yield an AI rating. Fig. 7-6 shows the relationship between signal-to-noise (broadband noise), AI, and various intelligibility tests.

A room may be regarded as a communication system, and the signal-to-noise criteria established for electronic systems are equally applicable to rooms. Most rooms, however, have an added degree of complexity—reverberation. The signal-to-noise studies and the resulting performance criteria have dealt almost exclusively with noise in a nonreverberant setting. Thus, the great body of literature on noise-degraded intelligibility is of little value in quiet (low noise) but reverberant rooms. Although some AI derating scales based on reverberation time have been proposed, they are of limited usefulness because they do

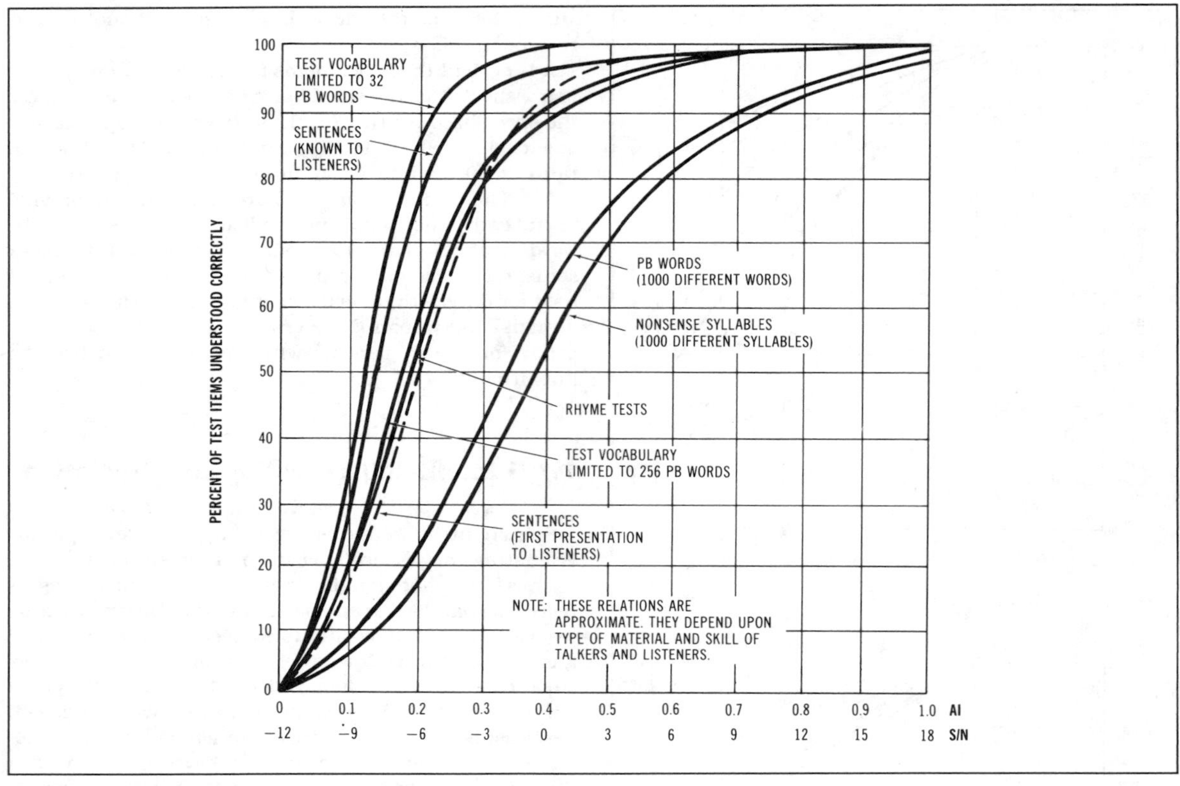

Figure 7-6 Relation between signal to noise, articulation index, and various measures of speech intelligibility. *(From ANSI S3.5)*

Table 7-3. Percentage Contribution to Intelligibility (Interpolated from ANSI S3.5)

Band Center Frequency Hz	% Contribution One-Third Octave	Octave
200 and below	1.2	
250	3.0	7.2
315	3.0	
400	4.2	
500	4.2	14.4
680	6.0	
800	6.0	
1 kHz	7.2	22.2
1.25 kHz	9.0	
1.6 kHz	11.2	
2 kHz	11.4	32.8
2.5 kHz	10.2	
3.15 kHz	10.2	
4 kHz	7.2	23.4
5 kHz and above	6.0	

not accurately model the psychoacoustical effects of reverberation.

The intelligibility-degrading effects of reverberation (in the absence of noise) may be modeled as a function of the ratio of the sound intensities arriving in the first 40 ms versus the sound intensities arriving after 40 ms. Various times and intensity-weighting factors must be applied to the late-arriving signals. Although the need for these weighting factors is recognized, little definitive research has been done in this area.[7–9]

This model may be expressed as

$$A_{ob} = \int_{0}^{40\text{ ms}} p^2_{ob(t)}dt \Big/ \int_{40\text{ ms}}^{\infty} p^2_{ob(t)}W_{ob(t)}dt \qquad (7\text{-}1)$$

where,

A_{ob} is the articulation factor by octave band at a point in the room,

$p_{ob(t)}$ is the sound pressure by octave band at time t,

$W_{ob(t)}$ is the weighting factor by octave band at time t.

The A_{ob} figures would need to be weighted according to the contribution of each octave band to intelligibility and then summed to yield a final intelligibility rating.

Even if the required weighting factors for the late signals were in hand, this approach would not be easy to apply. In an existing room, the early and late levels may be determined by using time-window measurements, but in the architectural design stage, ray-tracing techniques would be required. Trials have shown that a minimum of 2000 ray studies would be required for a simple study of a typical auditorium. Such a procedure is, at best, very complex.

Simplified techniques have been proposed as practical working tools for the prediction of intelligibility in reverberant rooms.[5,10] At this writing, the most widely used procedure was developed by Peutz[5,11] with elaborations by Davis and Davis.[12] The Peutz method was empirically derived from a large number of listening tests conducted in many locations in a variety of rooms with different reverberation times. It is important to understand that the procedure is based upon statistical analyses and curve-fitting techniques; therefore, it is subject to error when applied to nonuniform reverberant fields as may be found in rooms with unusual architectural features.

The Peutz method examines the *percentage articulation loss of consonants* ($\%AL_{cons}$) based upon the observation that the loss of consonant sounds is more degrading to intelligibility than is the loss of vowel sounds. Also, consonants are voiced at lower levels than vowels and thus are more easily masked by reverberation.

The Peutz system employs two basic principles. The first states that the loss of intelligibility increases as the distance between the source and the listener increases up to the point at which the reverberant level L_R is about 10 dB greater than the direct level L_D. Beyond this limiting distance ($L_R - L_D > 10$ dB), there is no further increase in intelligibility loss. The maximum loss is

$$\%AL_{cons} = 9RT \tag{7-2}$$

The second principle states that for distances less than this limiting distance

$$\%AL_{cons} = (656D^2RT^2)/VQ) \tag{7-3}$$

where,

D is the source-to-listener distance in feet,
RT is the reverberation time,
V is the volume of the room in cubic feet,
Q is the directivity ratio of the source.

$\%AL_{cons} = 15$ is widely regarded as the limit for good intelligibility. Substituting 15 into Eq. 7-2 yields a reverberation time of 1.67 s. In essence this means that for $RT < 1.67$ s (or more conservatively, 1.5 s), intelligibility is independent of listener distance D, room volume V, or source directivity Q. A further implication is that AI measures may be applied without regard to RT with an error < 0.1 AI where $RT < 1.5$ s.

It would, however, be a mistake to conclude that every quiet room with an $RT < 1.5$ s will have acceptable speech intelligibility. Loud echoes, focusing from curved surfaces, and other acoustical anomalies can still produce speech garbling despite an apparently low reverberation time. Acceptable levels of reverberation also depend upon the user group. The special needs of the old, the young, and the hearing impaired have already been noted. Times between 1.0 and 1.5 s, although yielding acceptable intelligibility, may also be fatiguing to some listeners and inappropriate for some programs (for example, an intimate drama).

Either the AI method (where $RT < 1.5$ s) or the Peutz method (where $RT > 1.5$ s), especially with the refinements of Davis and Davis,[12] can provide a useful guide in most rooms. However, bear in mind that intelligibility testing and predicting at the present state of the art are still approximate and not exact. All prediction computations should be viewed as a general guide and should be weighed in terms of intended use as well as in consideration of any nonaverage acoustical conditions present. A difficult speech message (say a technical lecture to beginning students) will be more degraded by reverberation or noise than a simple, familiar message.

7.2 SOUND REFLECTIONS IN ROOMS FOR SPEECH

The acoustical design of a room should be planned to make use of all available speech energy to provide the best possible signal-to-noise and direct-to-reverberant ratios. This is accomplished by selecting wall and ceiling finishing materials that are sound reflecting and by angling or contouring these surfaces to reflect speech energy into the audience while also avoiding late-arriving reflections. Careful use of reflecting surfaces can raise the direct sound level to the audience by 10 dB. (In effect, the Q of the sound source is increased. A front-facing talker has a Q of about three in a nonreverberant room.)

To be most effective, the pattern of reflections must be arranged to meet three criteria:

1. Only reflections arriving within the fusion zone should be allowed to reach the audience.
2. The pattern of reflections reaching the audience should be uniform and without dead spots or hot spots.
3. The density of reflections (in both time and space) should increase toward the rear of the audience to help compensate for the natural fall-off of the direct sound level with distance.

7.2.1 Flat Reflectors

In order to provide a controlled reflection (the angle of reflection equal to the angle of incidence), the smallest dimension of the reflecting surface must be large compared to the wavelength of the sound to be reflected. The relationship between the size of the reflecting surface and the wavelength has not been quantified through objective tests, although a testing procedure should soon be available using recently developed techniques of adjustable time-window observation. A useful, empirically derived rule is that to be an effective reflector, the minimum dimension of a surface must be at least twice the longest wavelength to be reflected. For longer wavelengths, there will be some controlled reflection and some uncontrolled diffusion. As the wavelength reaches equality with the smallest dimension, controlled reflection ends, and the returned sound becomes completely diffuse. In a period of only one octave, a surface can change from a controlled reflector to a diffuser.

As the wavelength becomes larger than an obstacle in its path, the sound begins to bend (diffract) around the obstacle. A surface suspended in air may be a reflector at higher frequencies, a diffuser in the midband, and acoustically invisible at low frequencies. If the reflector is located near or attached to a large surface such as a wall or ceiling, the large surface will control the low-frequency sounds while the midbands and highbands are diffused or reflected according to the dimensions of the smaller reflector surfaces. It is possible to construct a surface large enough to be a reflector at all frequencies, but a diffuser or a diffractor will always be band limited in performance. A surface that is a diffuser at 1000 Hz will be a controlled reflector at 2000 Hz and invisible below about 250 Hz. These principles are illustrated in Fig. 7-7.

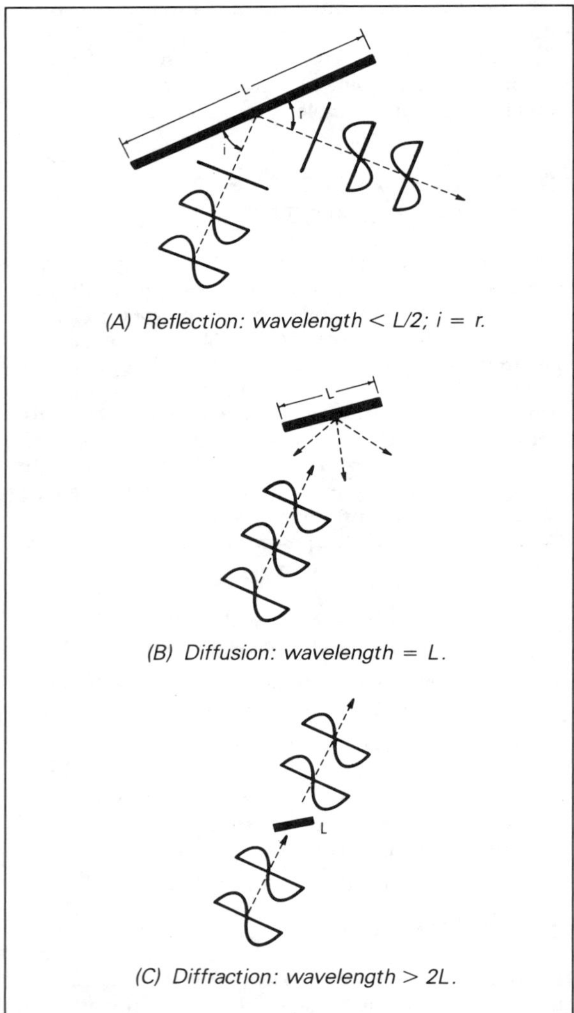

Figure 7-7 Principles of reflection, diffusion, and diffraction.

To ensure good speech intelligibility, reflectors should be sized to reflect sound above 500 Hz. This requires that the reflector be at least 4.5 ft in the smallest dimension. Larger surfaces will add more bass to the early reflections. Although this may add warmth to the male voice, it does not provide any additional intelligibility. It is a good practice to avoid the excessive use of small reflecting surfaces since these can impart an overemphasis of the high frequencies, thus producing a harsh or shrill sound quality.

7.2.2 Diffusion

Most rooms intended for speech activities do not have much need for sound diffusion; it is more important to concentrate the available energy as useful reflections to the audience. Where diffusion occurs below 500 Hz, speech intelligibility is little affected, and a small amount of low-frequency diffusion may enhance the sense of warmth.

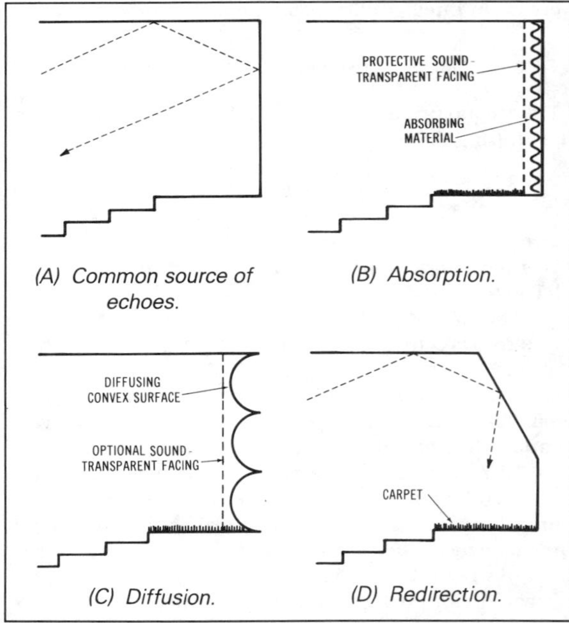

Figure 7-8 Solutions for echo-producing surfaces.

Too much low-frequency diffusion, especially when combined with a longer low-frequency reverberation time, will cause the room to sound boomy. In large rooms with a very long low-frequency reverberation time, it is often necessary to filter the low end out of the reinforcement sound in order to avoid upward masking by the excessive low-frequency reverberant field.

When a boundary surface (usually the rear wall or widely spaced side walls) is a source of echoes and if it cannot be reshaped into a useful reflector, there is a choice of corrective measures between making the offending surface absorptive or diffusing. Where there is also a need to reduce reverberation time, absorption should be selected. If the reverberation time does not require further reduction, a diffusing surface may be used (see Fig. 7-8).

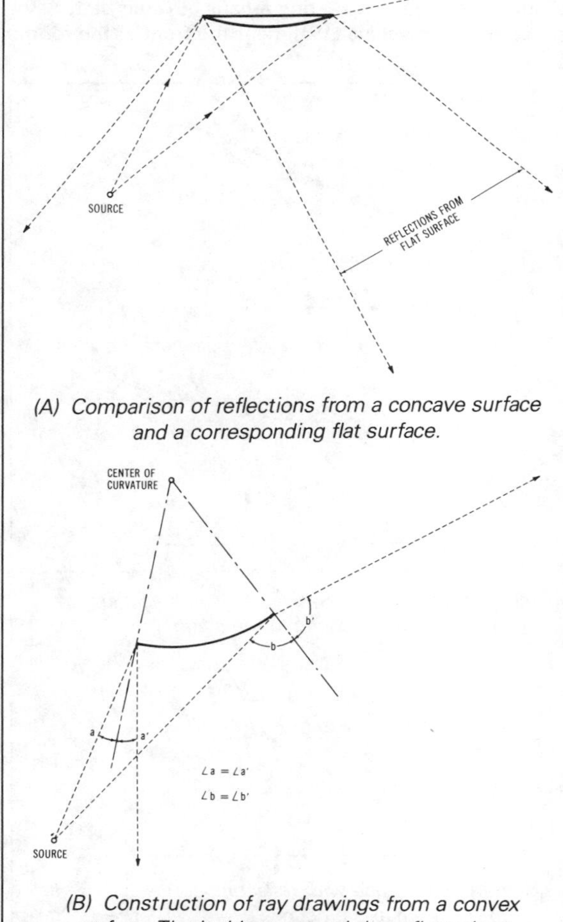

(A) Comparison of reflections from a concave surface and a corresponding flat surface.

(B) Construction of ray drawings from a convex surface. The incident ray and the reflected ray from equal angles with a radius of the curve.

Figure 7-9 Use of wide-angle reflectors.

7.2.3 Curved Surfaces

Convex curves with long radii and chords (> 2 wavelengths) may be used as wide-angle reflectors, as shown in Fig. 7-9. Such wide-angle reflections are of limited usefulness in rooms for speech. The reflections (hence, energy) from a convex surface are spread so much wider than from a flat surface of equivalent chord size that the sound pressure level of the reflection is lower—more like a diffuse reflection. It is the diffusing qualities of convex curves that make them important in rooms for music.

A concave surface is an acoustical liability because it focuses sound reflections causing hot spots and sometimes intense, long-delayed echoes. The concave surface must be broken up with a smaller plane or convex surfaces that will redirect or diffuse the sound and interrupt the focusing of the reflections. Application of highly absorbent material (a > 0.95) is sometimes acceptable, but redirection of the sound is usually more effective.

A useful test to determine whether a concave surface is going to be an acoustical problem is to complete the circle or ellipse. If any part of the audience or stage is included, the convex surface will be an acoustical problem.

7.3 SOUND ABSORPTION IN ROOMS FOR SPEECH

Sound-absorbing material is needed to control unwanted reflections and to reduce the overall reverberation time of the room for speech to the desired value. The spectral performance of the absorptive surfaces of a room will have a major influence on the tonal quality of the room. This influence may be seen in a graph of the reverberation time versus frequency. For good speech sound quality, the reverberation time should be uniform from 200 to 4000 Hz, although a small increase in reverberation time below 500 Hz is acceptable. Large rooms will show the effect of air absorption above about 2000 Hz.

Absorption is present in every room in three forms:

1. That which comes from construction techniques and materials (including the air within the room);
2. That which is intentionally applied to room surfaces;
3. That which comes from room furnishings and the audience.

A general rule of thumb for rooms for speech is to make all surface areas that do not provide useful reflections absorbent and, conversely, not to cover any useful reflectors. The latter is widely violated. Almost every classroom and many conference rooms have absorbent ceilings and hard floors, yet the reverse would provide far better room acoustics. Carpet on the floor not only covers a useless reflecting surface, it also greatly reduces audience noise. The elimination of footfall and chair- or desk-moving noises would be an important contribution to quieter classrooms.

It is distracting to performers, audience, and sound

system operators to have an auditorium or theater that changes in reverberant quality, depending upon the size of the audience. Metal or wooden seats, when empty, are useless reflecting surfaces. The seats should be upholstered in order to provide an unoccupied reverberation time close to that with a full audience. This approach will provide a room that is more acoustically consistent regardless of audience size. (Contrary to popular myth, it is not possible to have an empty seat exactly match the absorption of an occupied seat.)

The mass and stiffness of walls and ceiling will have a major effect upon the amount of bass absorption, that is built into the room. Heavy concrete walls will provide negligible low-frequency absorption, although thin wood paneling on furring strips, so common in churches and boardrooms, can contribute significant bass absorption. This problem is discussed in detail in Section 5.2.

Sound absorption by the air in the room is significant only in very large rooms and for large outdoor events. The absorbing properties of air are discussed in Section 5.2.5.

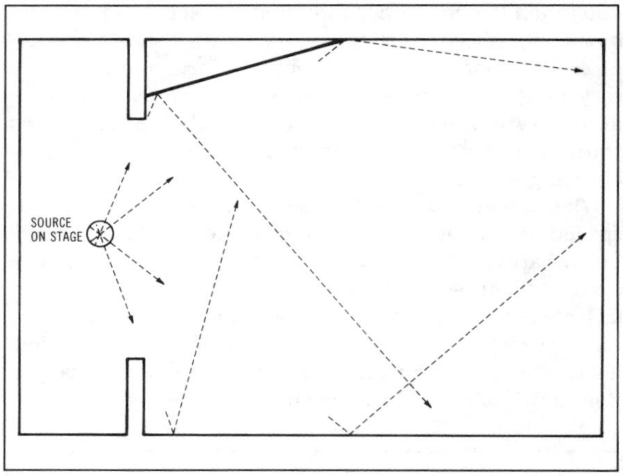

SOURCE ON STAGE

Figure 7-10 The rear seating area is covered better by reflections from splayed wall near the front of the room.

7.4 ROOM SHAPE FOR SPEECH

The shape of the room plays an important role by defining the relationship between the audience and the sound source and between the audience and the reflecting surfaces of the walls and ceiling. The side walls and ceiling are potentially useful reflecting surfaces and should be carefully designed to maximize their usefulness. The rear wall and floor are potential sources of useless or harmful reflections and require attention to prevent a negative contribution.

The flutter echo problem created by parallel hard walls is well known, yet classroom and lecture halls continue to be built with parallel walls. In many of these rooms, the use of splayed walls, at least in the "sending end" of the room, would greatly increase the acoustical quality of the room. Wide splaying of the audience area, however, is not always desirable. The side walls of a wide, fan-shaped room may provide some useful early reflections in the seating areas near the walls, but the center of the room will either be out of the reflection pattern or, worse, will receive late-arriving reflections. These problems are shown in Figs. 7-10 and 7-11.

If the ceiling is too high, it will provide little in the way of useful early reflections. It is sometimes possible to lower the effective height of the ceiling by using a reflecting panel hung over the talker, such as a canopy over the pulpit in a church or a reflecting panel constructed in front of a stage opening. An example is shown in Fig. 7-12.

The vertical angular relationship between the sound source and the audience will have a major effect upon the absorption factor of the audience. Sound traveling across an audience at an angle of less than about 10° (called grazing incidence) will be reduced in level more than would be predicted by the inverse-square law. This extra audi-

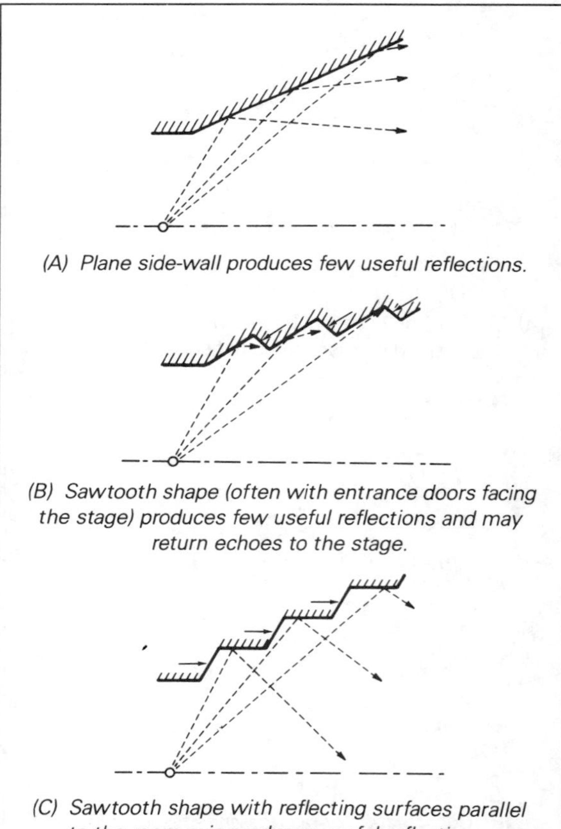

(A) Plane side-wall produces few useful reflections.

(B) Sawtooth shape (often with entrance doors facing the stage) produces few useful reflections and may return echoes to the stage.

(C) Sawtooth shape with reflecting surfaces parallel to the room axis produces useful reflections.

Figure 7-11 Partial plan of side walls in a wide, fan-shaped room.

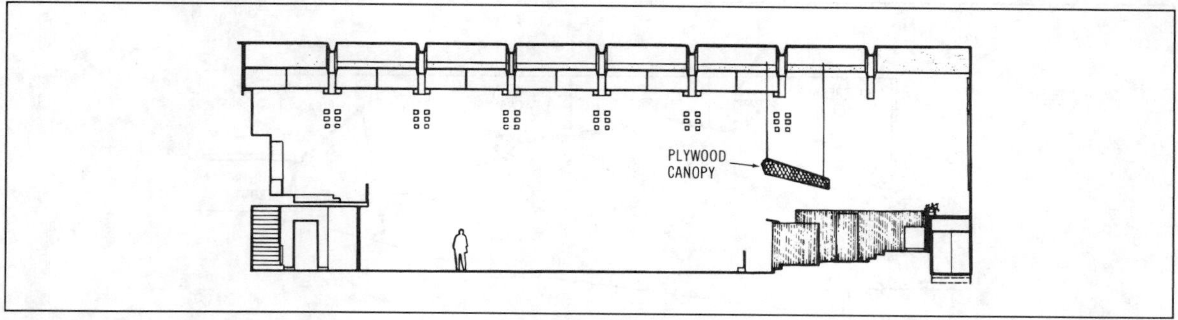

Figure 7-12 In a room with a high ceiling, a hanging reflecting panel (canopy) over and in front of the speaking area can provide useful early reflections. It can also sometimes be used to hide a reinforcement loudspeaker.

ence absorption is the main reason that a talker standing before an audience on a flat floor will be poorly heard beyond the first several rows. Except in small rooms, elevation of the sound source is vital to success with flat audience seating. The required elevation may come from placing the talker on a platform; it may come, indirectly, from using an overhead reflector or, for best results, from using a combination of a platform with reflectors. A sound-reinforcement system is often required only to make up for the shortcomings of a poor acoustical design.

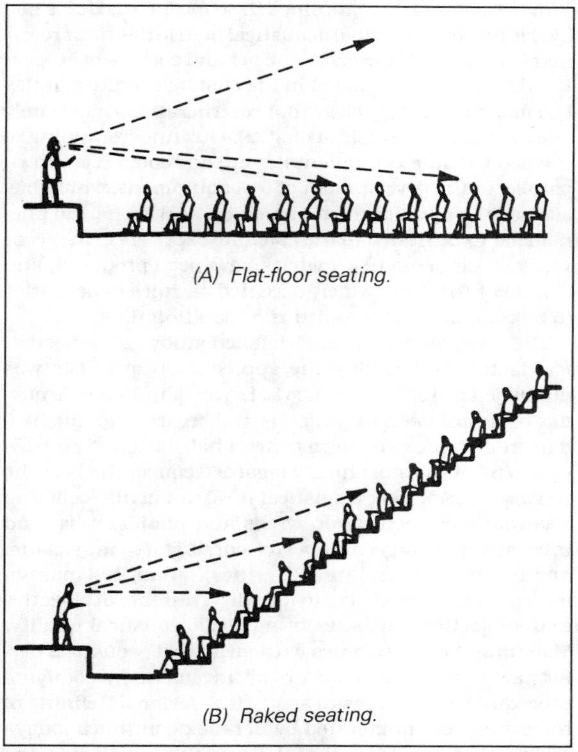

There is a strong relationship between good hearing and good sightlines, as shown in Fig. 7-13. Flat-floor seating of more than a few rows has neither. Raked (sloped-floor) seating is essential in order for a large audience to have good sightlines and good, natural acoustics. With raked seating, the reduction in level of the sound passing over the audience will be governed by the inverse-square law, and the listener will not be acoustically shadowed by the person seated in front.

(A) Flat-floor seating.

(B) Raked seating.

Figure 7-13 Raked seating provides better sight lines and better hearing than flat-floor seating.

7.5 AMPLIFICATION IN ROOMS FOR SPEECH

The need for playback of recorded media is so common that it has become a standard procedure to install an amplification system in most meeting rooms, boardrooms, and lecture halls. The playback system is also available for speech reinforcement when required. The actual need for amplification to ensure good speech intelligibility depends upon:

1. Level of the background noise,
2. Level of the direct speech signal combined with the early reflections,
3. Level of the late reflections,
4. Difficulty of the message to the listeners,
5. Age of the listeners.

These five conditions can vary so widely that it is not practical to establish simple rules defining when amplification should be included in a room design. A general guideline is possible: well-designed rooms smaller than 25,000 ft^3 will rarely need amplification, but a room larger than 250,000 ft^3 will always require a reinforcement system. For rooms between 25,000 and 250,000 ft^3, the five parameters listed previously must be considered to determine the need for amplification.

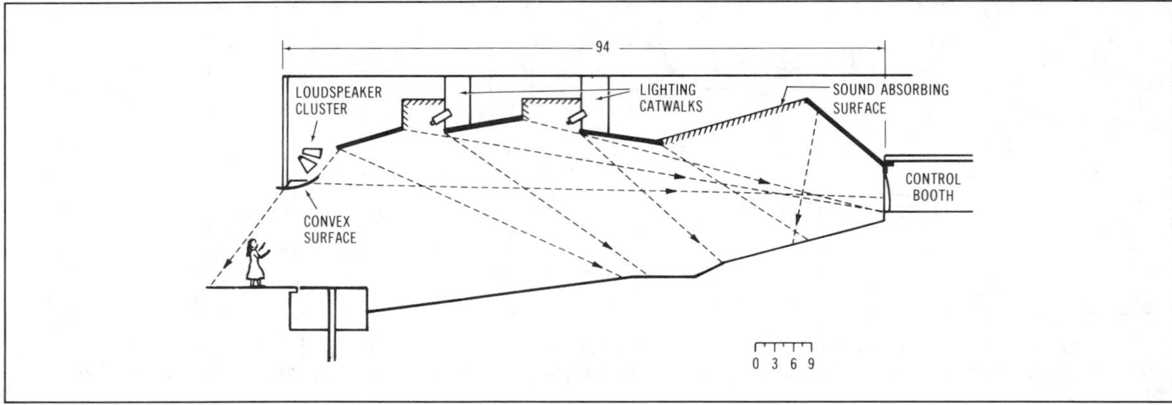

Figure 7-14 Center-line section through a large drama theater showing a ceiling shaped to reflect sound energy into the rear seating area.

In these intermediate-sized rooms, a strong voice delivering a nontechnical message in an acoustically well-designed room should be able to speak to 1000 people or more without the need for amplification, as in Fig. 7-14. On the other hand, a weak voice delivering a complex or difficult lecture in a poorly designed room could require amplification for fewer than 50 listeners.

7.6 MUSIC AND ACOUSTICS

Because the acoustical needs of speech and music differ, the acoustical design of rooms for music differs in several important ways from the design of rooms for speech. The extent and significance of the differences are presented in this section with references to the preceding and following sections.

Rooms for music can take many forms: a 300-seat recital room in a school, a general-purpose auditorium where the community orchestra performs, a concert hall with a resident symphony orchestra, a large sports arena in which touring popular music groups perform, and so on. The following sections will focus on rooms dedicated to the performance of instrumental music only—pure concert and recital halls—in order to clearly present the principles of music acoustics. Only secular concert music is considered in this section; opera and music for church are covered in Sections 7.11.4 and 7.11.5, respectively, since these forms must be considered in relation to speech. Sections 7.11, 7.12, and 7.13 will consider the adjustments and compromises required to accommodate a variety of forms.

In rooms for speech, the prime requisite is intelligibility, followed by freedom from distracting noise and naturalness of sound quality. In rooms for music, establishing an order of performance requisites is not nearly as simple and clear-cut. Enjoyment of music is, apparently, a good bit more complex than speech communication—certainly the acoustics of music are a good bit more complex.

7.6.1 Evaluation

In the nearly 100 years since the concept was described by Sabine, our principal acoustical metric has been reverberation time. However, as the art and science of acoustical design have developed in the past half century, it has become increasingly clear that reverberation time is only one part of good music acoustics. Our understanding of the acoustical requirements of music rooms has grown parallel to the development of test equipment, which has allowed the measurement of musical and acoustical phenomena to be related to the listening experience. In recent years a number of new metrics have been proposed, and several of them are widely accepted as rules of acoustics to be considered along with reverberation time.

The most ambitious and detailed study of the acoustical factors influencing the appreciation of music was published in 1962 by Dr. Leo L. Beranek in *Music, Acoustics and Architecture,* which is still regarded as the fundamental guide to modern concert hall design.[13] He traveled to 54 of the most highly regarded concert halls in the Western world, took acoustical measurements, collected accurate architectural drawings and photographs, and interviewed a large number of conductors, musicians, and trained listeners (music critics). From this mass of information, he was able to identify a number of objective and subjective attributes of musical-acoustical quality. Matching these attributes with measured acoustical performance provided a major advancement in codifying procedures for successful acoustical designs. Refining of the principles enumerated by Beranek continues today.

One of the outgrowths of Beranek's study was the development of a rating scheme for assigning a single-number quality judgment for concert halls. His system, like several others that have been offered by other acousticians, suffers from two as-yet-unsolved flaws:

1. It is very hard (impossible?) to reach a consensus on the relative weight to assign to various musical-acoustical variables.

2. It appears that the relative values of different variables do not combine in a linear manner. A low rating in an important quality cannot be fully compensated for by excellence in other qualities. Thus, two halls may have the same rating number but still sound different.[14,15]

Despite their basic flaws, rating schemes do play a useful role in helping to focus attention on the variety of factors that must all be right in order to achieve acoustical excellence. A summary of Beranek's rating system is shown in Fig. 7-15. It will be used in this text as a practical example, not as gospel.

Beranek's research techniques have been criticized for relying upon memory in making comparative judgments among halls. Although we often are slow to admit it, human auditory memory is not very reliable. It is easily confused by visual distractions, differences in performance and repertoire, even by our mood or health. Since the advent of high-quality tape recording equipment, researchers have established evaluation procedures using binaural recordings made with a dummy head and reproduced via earphones or via loudspeakers in an anechoic room. This procedure makes possible direct A to B comparisons of different halls or of different seats in a hall. It also allows a large number of subjects to hear the same performance free of outside distractions.

(Cremer and Müller have compiled and reviewed a great deal of this new work.[16] The reader interested in the mathematical details of the physical and psychoacoustical base for music acoustics is encouraged to read Cremer.)

As a result of this continuing research and of the experience of building a large number of concert halls in the past half century, acousticians are in general agreement about many basic technical parameters and attributes of the music-listening experience. Among these are some basic, self-evident principles:

1. Different kinds of music have different acoustical needs,

2. There are differences in the needs of the players and the listeners,

3. A successful concert hall must meet the acoustical needs of the musical performance for both the audience and the performers,

4. There is no single best design for a concert hall; there are a variety of architectural solutions for most acoustical requirements,

5. The design of concert halls is still a science-based art.

7.6.2 Language of Music and Acoustics

The disciplines of acoustics and music have evolved separately over the years and only rather recently have the two come to be considered together. Not surprisingly, their technical vocabularies are not consistent with each other; they sometimes use the same word with different meanings (*resonance* and *intensity*, for example, have different meanings to the musician and the acoustician). The following definitions are drawn from Beranek's list[13] of attributes of musical and acoustical qualities (also see Fig. 7-16).

Loudness of the direct sound is our perception of the direct signal combined with its reflections arriving within the first 70 ms. This loudness is partly controlled by the construction of the orchestra enclosure, or sending end of the room, but it is largely a matter of distance from the orchestra. The best seats are usually about 60 ft from the conductor, seats beyond about 100 ft on the main floor are likely to be judged deficient in direct sound level. In rooms for speech, reflections can be used to increase the apparent direct level by aiming early reflections into the rear seats. This technique is also used in music rooms, but it has more limitations because of the need for diffusion and because the timing and intensity of the early reflections have subtle effects in music that are not significant in speech communication.

Loudness of the reverberant sound is determined by the absorption present and the reverberation time. The study of music acoustics is basically the study of the relationship between the direct and reverberant fields: the difference in levels, arrival times, and direction of arrival.

Intimacy or *presence* of a hall is generally regarded as the single most important factor. The intimacy of a hall is measured partly by the ratio of direct-to-reverberant sound levels and, more importantly, by the *initial-time-delay gap (ITDG)*, discussed in Section 6.12.3. The ITDG is the interval between the arrival of the direct sound from the stage and the arrival of the first reflection from the walls or ceiling. We shall dwell at length on the initial-time-delay gap in Section 7.7.

Definition or *clarity* in music can be compared to intelligibility in speech. It is, like intimacy, affected by the arrangement and timing of early reflections. It is also related to reverberation time and to the distance from the performer, thus it is a function of the ratio of the direct-to-reverberant levels. As we shall see, the importance of definition is dependent upon the type of music.

Fullness of tone is the change in the original (direct) sound from an instrument after reverberation is added. Reverberation sustains the notes and fills the space between them, causing a blending of successive notes. Certain types of music are very dependent upon this blending, and some instruments, especially the organ, need reverberation to achieve their full musical potential. Fullness of tone is the inverse of definition. The type of musical composition as well as the tempo and the phrasing in the performance is interrelated with definition and

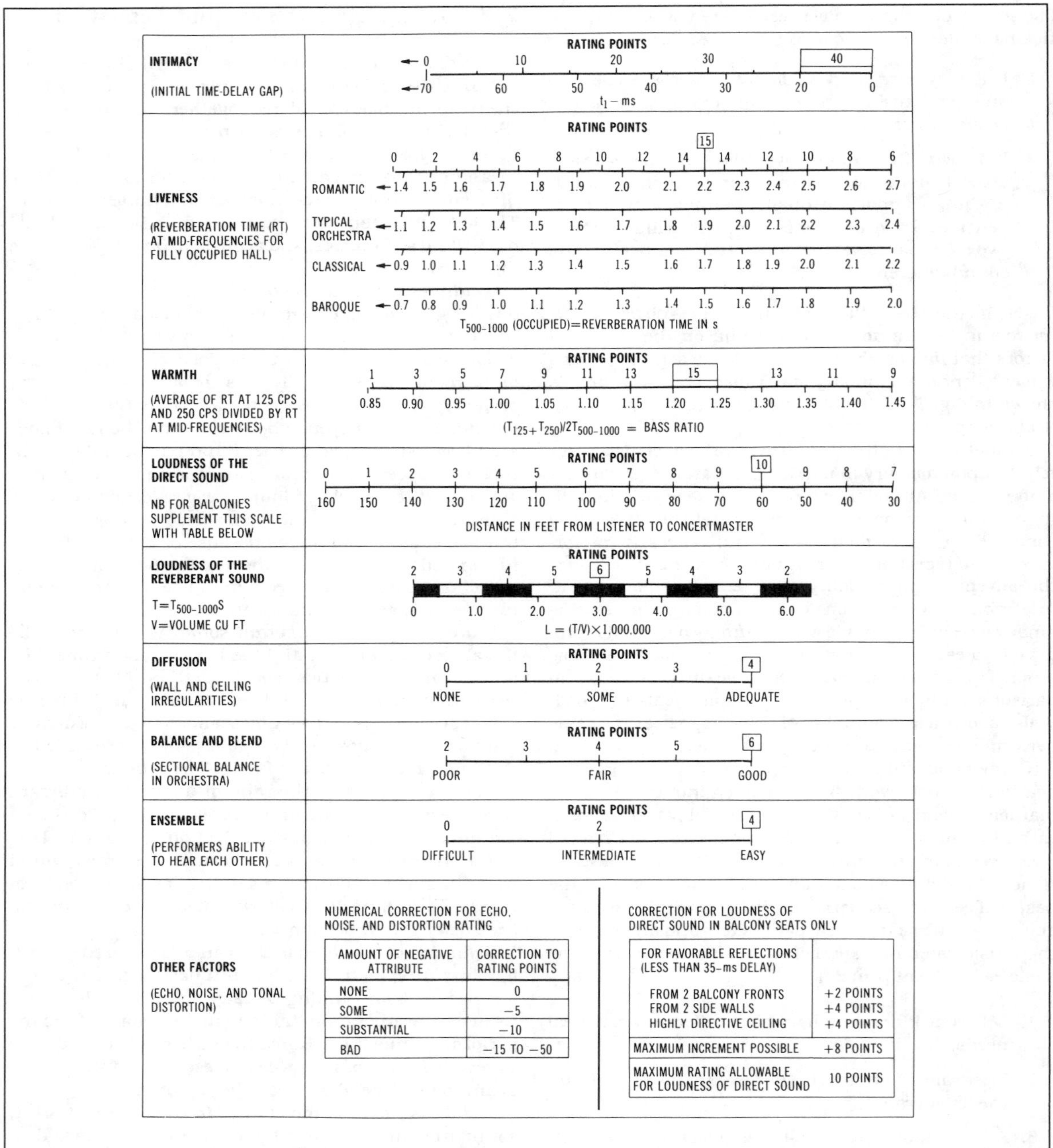

Figure 7-15 Rating scale for orchestra concert halls. *(After Reference 13.)*

fullness of tone. Fig. 7-17 diagrams the relationships between definition/fullness of tone, direct/late loudness, and music composition.

Liveness is related primarily to the average reverberation time of the middle octaves centered at 500 and 1000 Hz and to the balance between the direct and reverberant sound levels. Liveness is also related to the volume of the hall relative to the audience area; this relationship can also be expressed as a function of the room ceiling height. It is a useful rule of thumb that in a hall where the only significant absorption is the audience and performers, the midband reverberation time will be approximately

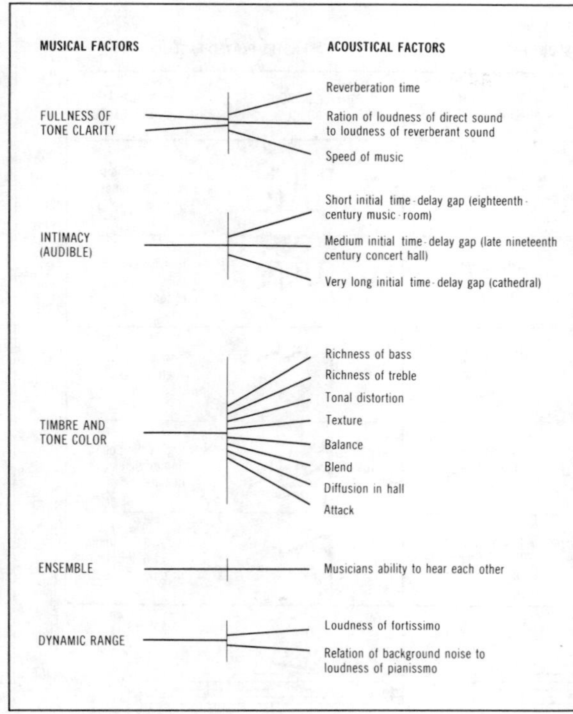

Figure 7-16 Musical qualities affected by acoustics. *(After Reference 13.)*

$$RT = (H/27) + 0.35 \tag{7-4}$$

where,
H is the average ceiling height in feet.

When $H < 40$ ft, the rule can be rounded off to

$$RT = H/20 \tag{7-5}$$

Warmth is created by a longer reverberation time in the lower frequencies relative to the midband. Warmth, or fullness of bass tone, requires the reverberation time average of the 125- and 250-Hz octave bands to be at least 1.25 times the midband time. The sound is said to be *brittle* if the low-frequency reverberation time is shorter than the midband. Deficiencies in low frequencies are usually the result of excessive absorption due to such constructions as thin wood panels on furring strips. The special problem of low-frequency loss due to audience seating will be discussed in Section 7.8. Small rooms (less than about 15,000 ft^3) are subject to problems with standing waves, which may cause considerable irregularities in bass response. (See Section 3.4 and 3.5.) Standing waves are seldom a problem in larger rooms.

Brilliance is a measure of the high-frequency response. It describes a sound rich in harmonics and high frequencies. In large halls, brilliance will be noticeably affected by air absorption. It is also governed by the ratio of high-frequency reverberation time to the midband time. The sound is likely to be overly bright and harsh unless the high frequency (4 to 8 kHz) reverberation time is less than the midband. In large halls, air absorption usually provides the needed rolloff.

Diffusion is a measure of the spatial orientation of the reflected sound. Music is enhanced by highly diffuse reflections, especially in the lateral plane. The diffusion should be so great that the sound field is substantially different at each ear. Our hearing mechanism is very sensitive to direction of arrival, and music enjoyment is strongly related to early reflections arriving from the sides.[17] Early reflections arriving from above, in front, or from behind are less important than those from the sides.

Attack is used to indicate the performer's perception of the response of the hall. To perform well, the musician must have some reverberant sound returned from the hall. If this return is too strong and early, as from the orchestra enclosure only, it does not give a feeling of the hall. If the return is late, it becomes a distracting echo—though musicians appear to tolerate echoes better than the average listener.

Balance, blend, and *ensemble* are all influenced by patterns of reflections near the orchestra, the arrangement of the players on the stage, and the control of the conductor. Balance governs the relative loudness of the sections of the orchestra and the relative loudness of the orchestra and soloists. Blend is the mixing of sound from individual instruments to form a pleasing whole. Ensemble is the ability of the performers to play in unison, which is heavily dependent upon the ability of the players to hear each other.

Texture is the spacing and quantity (hence density) of reflections between the initial-time-delay gap and the onset of diffuse (or statistical) reverberation. Although texture is regarded as an important parameter, there has been little published research into its ideal structure. Beranek suggests there should be at least five reflections in the first 70 ms after the direct sound. These early reflections should be fairly evenly spaced, have diminishing amplitudes, and arrive from the sides.

Tonal quality of a concert hall is a measure of the effect of the room upon the reverberant field. It is usually noticed as a negative attribute such as nonuniform absorption of certain tones or the addition of spurious rattles or sympathetic vibrations.

Uniformity of sound quality in a hall is important and should be a major design goal, but the quest for uniformity must be tempered by the knowledge that it can never be fully achieved. No two seats in any room will have *exactly* the same sound field, but in a good room an experienced listener should not be able to hear a difference from the seat in front, the seat behind, and two seats on either side. Deep balcony overhangs usually create poor hearing conditions by shielding the rear-most listeners from early reflections and from direct contact with the reverberant field of the room. Rooms that are more than about 65 ft

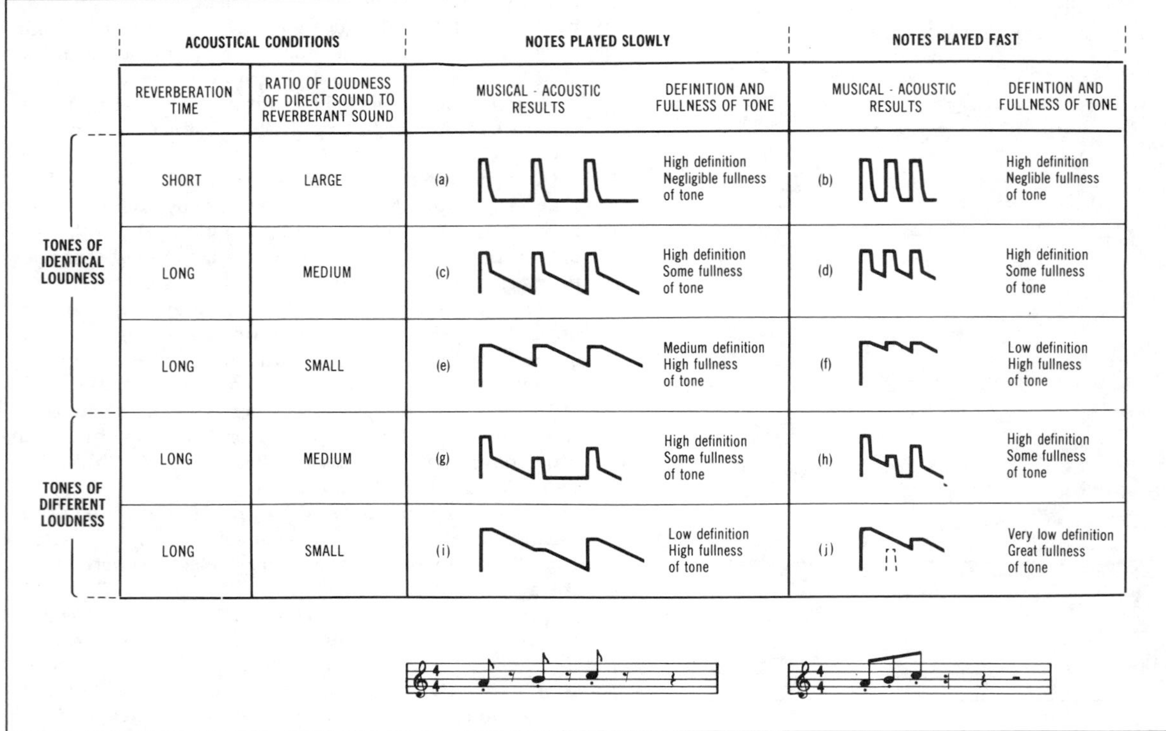

Figure 7-17 Interrelations of composition, tempo, reverberation time, and reverberant to direct loudness. *(After Reference 13.)*

wide or have seats more than about 100 ft from the stage are likely to have uniformity problems. The requirements of uniformity are met when intimacy and texture are satisfactory at all seats.

7.6.3 Acoustics and the Composer

Long before the electronic age gave us tools with which to measure the relationship between music and acoustics, musicians had come to understand certain basic relationships between musical qualities and their performance spaces. The great stone medieval churches required a different type of musical composition than the intimate music rooms in the homes of the nobility. Throughout the history of music, there is a strong correspondence between style of composition and the customary performance place.

The beginning of our concert music heritage lies in the baroque period (approximately 1600–1750) of which Handel and J. S. Bach are the two giants. The concerto and sonata were the principal instrumental music forms that developed in this period. The baroque musical style is highly ornamental and largely contrapuntal. The several independent lines running in counterpoint require that the listener be able to hear the detail of the music very clearly; there must be no masking of sound by reverberation. This attention to detail was made possible by the fairly small music rooms (RT < 1.5 s, intimate, and high definition) at court and in the homes of the rich where instrumental music was usually performed. Orchestral performances in large public halls did not develop until much later.

The classical period (1750–1820) dates from the death of Bach. The major composers of the period were Beethoven, Haydn, and Mozart. They continued the development of the sonata and introduced a new form, the symphony, which grew to dominate musical form and is still popular today. The symphony required a larger group of performers and, in turn, a larger performance hall. Public orchestral performances began in the late 18th century, mostly from the stages of opera houses. It was not until the mid-19th century that large halls began to be built especially for orchestras. As the halls grew in size, the reverberation time became longer; the classical period has come to be associated with a reverberation time of about 1.7 s.

Clarity of detail remained as important as it had been in the baroque era; but with longer reverberation time and larger orchestra, fullness of tone began to acquire greater importance. The later Beethoven symphonies began the transition from the formal structure of the classical style to the more emotional music of the romantic period.

The romantic style (1820–1890+) saw ever larger orchestras playing complex harmonics intended to convey rich emotional experiences rather than the intellectually appealing counterpoint detail of the baroque and classical styles. The great concert halls built in the last half of the 19th century (average RT = 2.2 s) reflect the desire of the musicians to provide fullness of tone and loudness even with a corresponding loss of definition.

The 20th century has produced several changes in music style. In addition to the continuation of the emotionalism and experimentation of the late romantic period, there has been a revival of interest in the music of earlier eras. Until this century, concert programs were usually made up of contemporary works with great emphasis on performance of new compositions, often commissioned by a wealthy patron. Older music, even of only a generation earlier, was rarely performed. Bach, for example, was unperformed from his death in 1750 until Mendelssohn performed his *St. Matthew Passion* in 1829.

Today's orchestral repertoire spans 400 years of musical development. It also spans 400 years of acoustical change, including a greater than 1-s range of preferred reverberation time. Consequently, more is expected of today's concert hall than at any time in the past.

7.6.4 Acoustics and the Performer

Just as composers tailor their style to the acoustics of the performance space, so the performers are influenced by the acoustical qualities of the concert hall as well. Conductor Leopold Stokowski wrote, "My experience has been that every concert hall in the world has different acoustical qualities and, as a concert hall is really an instrument for sound of music, the differences of each hall must be taken care of during rehearsals and concerts." It is widely acknowledged that an orchestra on tour will rarely achieve the same level of performance excellence as in its home hall.

The design of the orchestra enclosure, or the sending end of the room, will have a profound effect upon the sound heard by the audience and upon the performance of the orchestra. The near-field acoustics must be arranged so that all parts of the orchestra can hear each other. Without good internal communication, ensemble will be poor, intonation may suffer, and the overall performance is likely to be muddy and lifeless. If conductors cannot hear an accurate balance and blend, they cannot be expected to provide a correct balance among the instruments for the audience.

The players as well as conductors rely upon the return sound from the hall to provide them with a feeling of loudness and fullness of tone. If the nearby reflecting surfaces, which are vital to communication, return too much sound, the orchestra's sense of its own loudness will be thrown off. An overly loud near-field sound acts to dampen the orchestra and may rob the performance of needed loudness. The design of the orchestra enclosure is just as important as the design of the audience chamber.

7.7 REVERBERATION IN ROOMS FOR MUSIC

Almost every parameter in music/acoustics is influenced by the relationship between the direct and the reflected sound fields. The reflected field is entirely the creation of the room architecture and the seating pattern of the audience. The direct sound is not influenced by the architecture, although it is influenced by interaction with the audience. The perceived loudness of the direct sound, which includes the early reflections, is a product of a part of the room architecture. In large rooms, the high frequencies of both the direct and reflected sound are subject to the effects of temperature and humidity.

7.7.1 Anatomy of Reverberation

Reverberation starts with a few early reflections that rapidly increase in quantity until the density is so great that the room is filled with a homogeneous reverberant field. Fig. 7-18 diagrams a typical reverberation event. The lower scale divides the event into four periods important to understanding the texture of the reverberation.

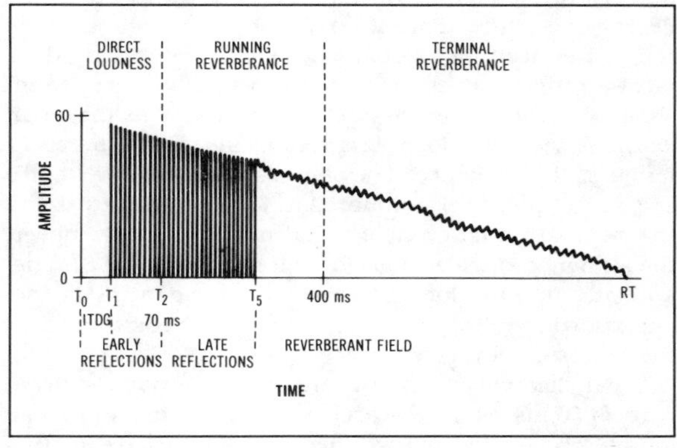

Figure 7-18 The anatomy of a reverberation event.

1. The *initial-time-delay gap*, that is the time between the arrival of the direct sound t_0 and the arrival of the first reflection t_1.
2. The early reflections arriving between t_1 and about 70 ms or t_2.
3. The late reflections arriving between 70 ms and the start of the statistical (or uniform) reverberant field t_s.

4. The statistical reverberant field that is decaying at a rate set by the reverberation time of the room.

Each of these periods has its own unique contribution to the enjoyment of music.

The length of the ITDG is widely regarded as one of the most critical factors in hall design. The rating scale for intimacy (Fig. 7-15) shows 40 out of 100 rating points for an ITDG of up to 20 ms. (Recent research indicates that an ITDG of less than about 5 ms is somewhat less desirable because the audible comb filter effects caused by phase cancellations are more noticeable at short delays.) If the first reflection is lower in level than a later reflection, the louder reflection will usually determine t_1 and thus the ITDG. So it is important that the desired first reflection be as strong as possible.

Actually, this "first" reflection should not be a single reflection but rather a burst of very closely spaced reflections arriving from different surfaces. If the reflecting surfaces were replaced by mirrors, a listener in the audience should be able to see the orchestra from six to eight different angles with each visual path nearly equal in distance. The fewer the components in this "first" reflection burst, the less pleasing the sound.

The direction of arrival of the early reflections has been found to be very important.[17] Lateral reflections off the side walls are more important than those from above, front, or rear. The importance of this directional factor had not been recognized at the time Beranek prepared his rating system. He has since suggested that the intimacy rating could be divided to rate both the initial-time-delay gap and the angle of arrival.

It is the need for strong, early lateral reflections that most strongly argues for a narrow room, no more than about 65 ft wide—the classic shoe-box design. As the room becomes wider, the lateral reflections take longer to reach much of the audience. They are also lower in level both because of the inverse-square law losses and because of the extra attenuation as a result of having passed over the audience at a low angle (detailed in Section 7.8). The audience attenuation is frequency-dependent as is the air absorption. Together they act to alter the timbre of the reflected sound.

The division between early and late reflections is given here as 70 ms. Some researchers prefer 80 ms. In rooms for speech, the figure is 40 ms. These times are for the threshold of perceptibility of reflections as separate sounds. The threshold is not sharp; it depends upon the length of the original sound, its direction of arrival, and individual differences in listeners. Although we do not perceive early reflections as separate sounds, we are very aware of their presence. Our impression of the loudness of the direct sound results from the integration of the direct sound with all the reflections prior to t_2.

Just as it is desirable for most of the early reflections to arrive laterally, it is equally important that the late reflections arrive from all directions. It is largely these late, nondirectional reflections that create fullness of tone and give music its sense of liveness.

The dividing line between late reflections and the statistical field t_s is rather arbitrary. Cremer has suggested that t_s be defined as occurring at the point where a listener can no longer distinguish an increase in the density of reflections. Since the average listener's limit for perceiving the presence of a reflection (not as a separate sound) is a time interval of 0.5 ms, the maximum distinguishable density of reflections is about 2000. Cremer demonstrates that this density will be achieved at

$$t_s = \frac{\sqrt{V}}{3} \qquad (7.6)$$

where,

V is the volume in cubic feet,

t_s is in milliseconds.

It is interesting to note that t_s is dependent only on volume. It is independent of absorption and, hence, of reverberation time. The significance of this relationship will become clearer later when we consider the use of variable areas of absorption to adjust the reverberation time of a room. It should also be evident that rooms with different volumes will sound different; the texture of the sound will be different even if the initial-time-delay gap and reverberation time are identical in the rooms.

7.7.2 Loudness of Reverberation

The upper scale in Fig. 7-18 shows a set of time-based divisions of the reverberation event, which are related to perceived loudness and its effect on music. The first division from t_0 to t_2 combines, as our hearing does, the direct sound and the early reflections. The second period, from t_2 to 400 ms, is called *running reverberance*. The last period from 400 ms to the end of the reverberation time is called *terminal reverberance*.

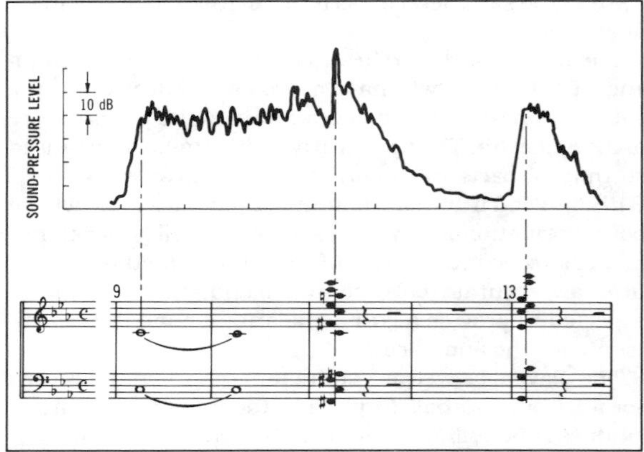

Figure 7-19 Relation between music and running reverberance (first two measures) and terminal reverberance (last three measures). *(After Reference 16.)*

Running reverberance is perceived as liveness, adds fullness of tone, and degrades definition. Terminal reverberance is the lingering (and often thrilling) sound that persists after an abrupt stop in the music. Fig. 7-19 shows the effect of these two periods on music. This excerpt from Beethoven's *Coriolanus Overture* (Op. 62, measures 9–13) clearly shows the terminal reverberation following the two stopped fortissimo chords. The first two measures are well blended by the running reverberance.

The relation between the loudness of the direct and running periods is the most delicate balance in music and acoustics. This balance influences almost every other parameter.

Schultz has proposed a parameter R to describe the ratio of running reverberance to direct loudness[18]:

$$R = \int_{50\text{ ms}}^{400\text{ ms}} p^2_{(t)}\,dt \Big/ \int_{0}^{50\text{ ms}} p^2_{(t)}\,dt \qquad (7\text{-}7)$$

where,

$p_{(t)}$ is the sound pressure by octave bands at time t,

50 ms is the limit for integration of early sound.

Fig. 7-20 shows plots of 10 log R versus frequency for four concert halls. The sounds of these halls are recognized as nearly spanning the accepted range between live and dry. The sound in each hall relates well to the ratio of running reverberance to direct loudness (R) index. The larger the value of R in the midband, the greater the perceived liveness and fullness of tone. A midband rating of + 10 would be much too live, while a rating near zero or below would be a very dry room, a good speech room.

Listening experience in a large number of halls indicates that the acceptable range for the R index is only about 7 dB and that a difference as small as 2 dB can be clearly heard. Our present methods of design and performance prediction do not yet have a 2-dB resolution. It is, therefore, useful to include some adjustable reflecting elements in the architectural design. With these adjustable reflectors, it is possible to "tune" the hall in order to achieve an optimum R index. The tuning is accomplished by adjustments to the early reflections, thus varying the loudness of the direct field. Tuning by introducing more absorption to adjust the loudness of the reverberant field is impractical because it would also change reverberation time and thus create a ripple effect through the other parameters that are a function of reverberation time. (Adjustments to reverberant time are discussed in Sections 7.11 through 7.13.)

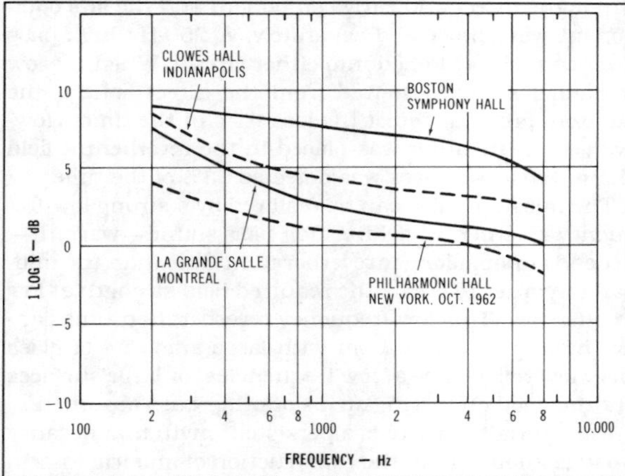

Figure 7-20 Reverberant to direct loudness in four halls. *(After Reference 11.)*

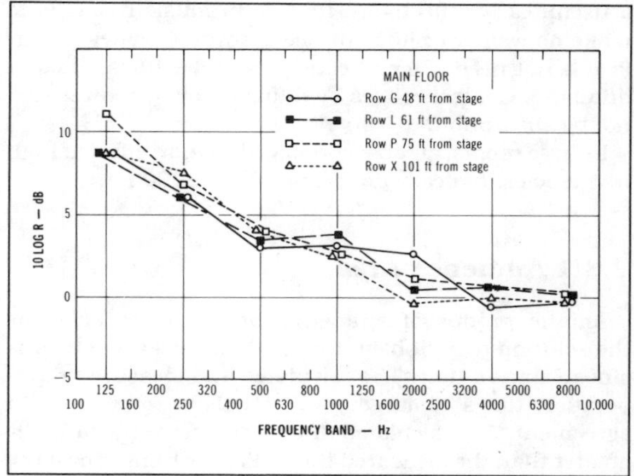

Figure 7-21 Variation of R with distance from the stage in La Grande Salle, Montreal. *(After Reference 11.)*

By carefully structuring the early reflections, it is possible to achieve a nearly uniform ratio of reverberant to direct loudness over almost all the audience area. Little can be done with the front few rows in the direct field of the orchestra, and rows under deep balcony overhangs may be shielded from full participation in the reverberant field. Fig. 7-21 shows the 10 log R curves taken at four different distances from 48 to 101 ft from the stage of a well-designed hall. The variation does not exceed 3 dB.

Schultz has observed, "No one would dream of manufacturing an automobile engine without any adjustable devices to be correctly set during an engine tune-up, even though internal combustion engines are mass produced by the thousands in a completely developed technology. Why should a wholly unique concert hall not have similar provisions for optimizing its performance?"[19]

7.8 ABSORPTION IN ROOMS FOR MUSIC

Reverberation time is determined by the ratio of volume to the absorption present in the room. In concert hall design, the basic goal set by economic realities is to get as much reverberation time per volume unit as possible. This can only be accomplished by confining the absorption to the audience and performers. In speech rooms the rule is to make absorptive any surface that does not return a useful early reflection. The rule in music rooms is to make no wall or ceiling surface absorptive; where a surface is not needed for directed early reflections, make it diffusing. Control echoes by diffusion or by redirection, not by absorption.

In large rooms, air absorption will have an effect at high frequencies, typically noticeable above 2000 Hz.

7.8.1 Audience Area

Another product of Beranek's study of concert halls was the solution to a problem that had plagued acousticians since Sabine's time. The calculated and measured reverberation times in large concert halls were seldom in agreement. The calculated times were often substantially greater than the measured times. Sabine himself cast the seed for both the problem and its solution when he stated that the absorption of the audience could be calculated on a per-person basis or by audience area. He chose the per-person method as did almost everyone else thereafter. However, Beranek demonstrated that per-person calculations were unreliable, whereas calculations based on audience area can be very accurate.[20]

The absorption of the audience and performance areas with different kinds of seating and percent of occupancy can be calculated from the data given in Table 5.1. The absorption coefficients for audience areas include the first 3.5 ft of carpeted aisle width. Absorption for additional aisle widths should be calculated separately. Carpet under occupied seats will not contribute significant additional absorption, although it will make the absorption of unoccupied seating areas more nearly equal to occupied areas. The use of carpet under cloth-covered, well-upholstered seats is not usually acoustically cost effective. However, its use under wooden pews or lightly upholstered seats may be desirable in order to make the reverberation time more nearly constant with changing audience size—often important in churches.

7.8.2 Mystery of the Missing Cellos

A vexing problem in many concert halls has been referred to as the "mystery of the missing cellos." The cellos are right there on stage, playing away, but much of the audience cannot hear them. The typical hall with missing cellos will have a generally weak bass. It probably has large areas of thin wood paneling and a flat or low-slope floor. Schultz and Watters conducted a series of tests and experiments that explain this problem and offer solutions.[21]

When sound travels at grazing incidence across the audience, two forces act to change the frequency response of the sound. One is the absorption of mostly mid and higher frequencies by the heads and shoulders of the audience. Second is the rather surprising loss of mid-lows due to the interference effect of the seat backs—whether occupied or not. This seat effect can cause a loss of as much as 20 dB in the general area of 150 Hz, as shown in Fig. 7-22. The width, as well as depth of the loss, can be increased by large-area, long, slotted return-air grilles under the seats (common in many older halls). The seating effect occurs only at grazing incidence; the steeply raked seating of balconies rarely exhibits this bass absorption (another reason why balcony seats are often better than the main floor).

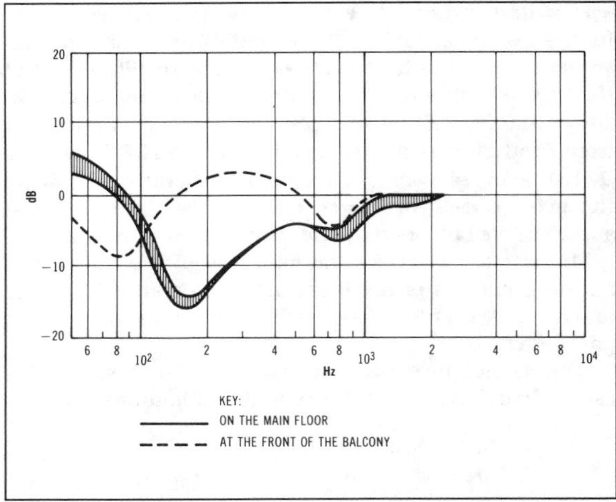

Figure 7-22 Attenuation due to seat effect. *(After Reference 11.)*

Despite the seating effect, not all halls have an aurally noticeable low-frequency bass, or missing cellos. Schultz found that our perception of bass tones does not require the tones to be present in the direct signal if they are richly present in the reverberant signal.[18] In a series of listening tests, subjects were instructed to listen for a change in bass as test samples were presented in quick succession. The subjects were presented with sounds where the direct and early component and the late component were processed separately. A 250-Hz high-pass filter could be switched into either circuit. When the low frequencies were removed from the direct sound, the auditors failed to detect the loss 61% of the time. However, when the filter was placed in the reverberant field chain, the loss of bass was detected 93% of the time.

The missing cellos can be restored by a strong low-frequency reverberant field. A rich bass sound—warmth—depends upon a longer reverberation time than the mid-band in order to create the required field strength at low frequencies. This low-frequency reverberation time cannot be attained in a room with large amounts of glass (very low reflectance at low frequencies) or large surfaces of thin wood on furring strips or other bass absorbers.

Unfortunately, there is a persistent myth that because wood is important in the construction of musical instruments, it must also be useful in the construction of music rooms. The flaw in this reasoning is that the instrument and the room have entirely different roles and, therefore, are not to be built in the same manner. The thin wood of the violin is set in vibration by the strings; this adds body and timbre as well as loudness to the soft vibrations of the strings. The room's role is to contain and reflect this sound unchanged, not to add to it or subtract from it. To accomplish this goal, especially at low frequencies, the walls and ceiling must be too hard for the sound to penetrate and too stiff for the sound to move. If a wood finish is desired, it should be tightly glued to massive masonry walls.

7.9 CONCERT HALL DESIGN

The design and construction of a new concert hall, or even a major remodeling of an existing hall, is a major event in any community. It represents the investment of a large amount of money and is, probably, the culmination of years of effort by a large group of civic leaders. The building will be a significant addition to the cultural and social life of the community. The project will also provide the architect with an opportunity to make a major (perhaps, *the* major) architectural statement of his or her professional career.

The architects are assisted in their work by an army of technical specialists working on structural problems, the HVAC system, the electrical layout, acoustical recommendations, and others. The architects are personally most concerned with the visual design. It is here that the visions of the architects and the calculations of the acoustical consultants are likely to come into conflict. The visions of the architects are probably also shared by the funding authority—civic committee, philanthropist, or school board. Indeed, often architects are chosen through a design competition; thus, the basic design for the hall may be well set before the acoustical consultant is hired. More often than not, the final acoustical design is a product of what is possible rather than what is best.

7.9.1 Music, Acoustics, and Economics

A large concert hall is costly to build and costly to maintain and operate. It has always been so and probably always will be. Historically, concert halls have been built and the operation of their resident orchestras largely subsidized by the government and the very rich. Such facilities are rarely completely self-supporting even in the largest cities of the world. Except as part of a school, halls dedicated only to use by an orchestra are rarely built. Even when a pure concert hall is built, the high costs of such specialized construction are often mitigated by compromising acoustical goals.

The first conflict is between the need to have a large number of seats in order to generate revenue versus the acoustical goals of a more limited audience area. It is a widely accepted axiom that good natural (nonelectronic) acoustics cannot support an audience of more than 2200 to 2500 with today's chair sizes and safety code requirements. Both the width and the length of a concert hall have optimum values. Larger audience areas are acoustically poorer and require additional (costly) acoustical devices to help compensate for excessive width or length.

The other major acoustical cost conflict arises over the maximum reverberation time to be provided, and the companion question, Shall lesser reverberation times be selectable by adjustable acoustics? With the audience area fixed by the seating mandate and absorption present only in the audience and performers, the reverberation time will vary directly with the average ceiling height. To provide the optimum acoustics for music of the Romantic period as well as much modern music and all organ music, the average ceiling height must be in excess of 45 ft. Where two or three balconies are included, the required height over the main floor will be substantially more than 45 ft. It is an unfortunate economic reality that such large structures are often beyond the funds available. There are many good music rooms that would be excellent if the ceiling were another 10 or 15 ft higher.

7.9.2 Sending End

In the pure concert or recital hall, there is no requirement for a stage house. The orchestra can be, as it should be, in the same room with the audience. The orchestra performing area, or sending end of the room, must be designed to provide good internal communication and to direct a well-balanced and blended sound to the audience.

The width and depth of the orchestra area are influenced by the number of players (about 20 ft^2 each) and the height of the ceiling. Where the ceiling is low (less than 30 ft), it can be used for internal communication as well as directing sound to the audience, so the side walls may be set to give a wide and deep orchestral area. If, on the other hand, the ceiling is high, the side walls should be less than 50 ft apart, and the depth of the orchestra, no more than 30 ft. Neither of these arrangements is really optimum.

A wide or deep orchestra under a low ceiling has several limitations. The low ceiling, while providing good early reflections to the orchestra and audience, cuts off the sound from the volume above the orchestra—volume needed for a longer reverberation time. Audience members seated near the front sides do not hear a good balance between the sides of the orchestra. The difference in arrival times of sounds from each side may be great enough to give the illusion of poor ensemble. This illusion of poor ensemble also occurs if the orchestra seating arrangement is too deep. For oratorios with a large chorus and orchestra, this problem probably has no solution.

If the ceiling is made high in order to favor the reverberation time, the side and rear walls must be used to meet the needs of the orchestra and audience. Locating the walls to provide the early reflections and orchestra communication will limit the orchestra area to about 1500

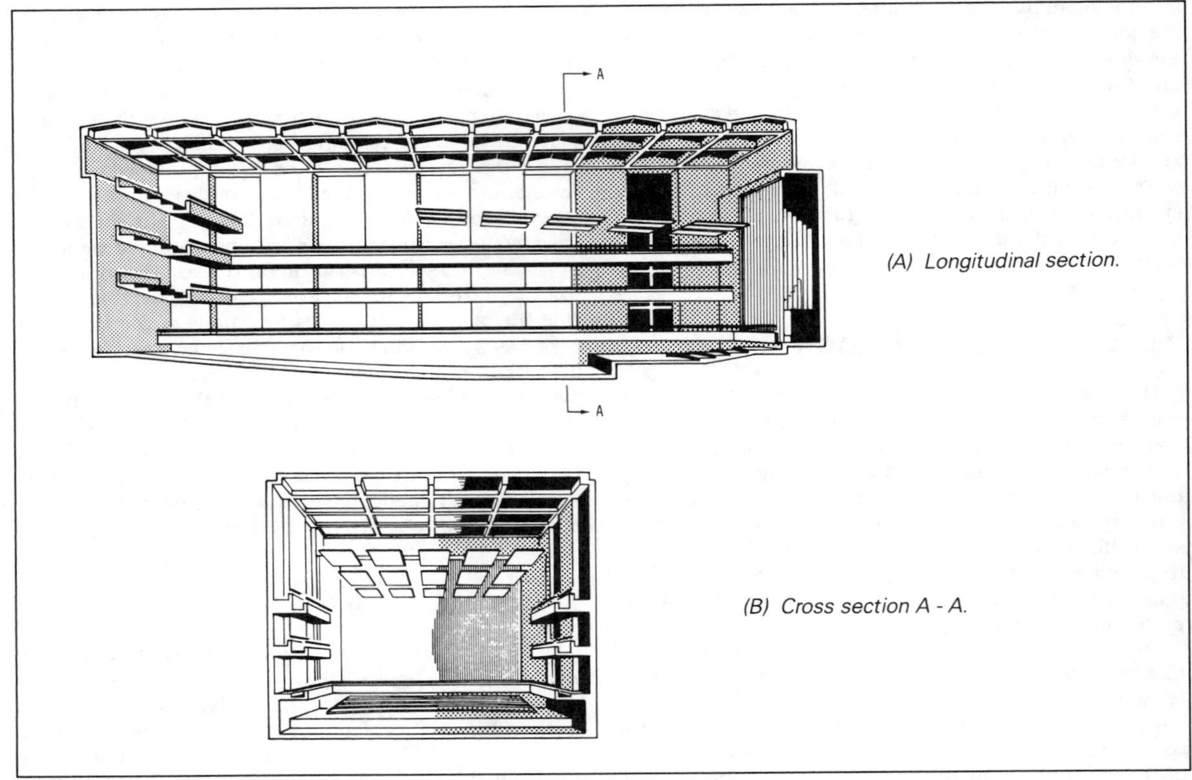

Figure 7-23 Idealized concert hall design.
(After Reference 13.)

ft^2. Such a limited area is acceptable for 75 to 80 players. Larger groups will be too crowded.

A popular modern solution is to provide a large orchestra area under a composite ceiling that is high to the reverberant sound and low to a controlled amount of the direct sound. Such an idealized hall is shown in Fig. 7-23. The acoustical panels (often called clouds) hanging over the orchestra and front of the audience are located, shaped, and tilted to provide on-stage communication and to provide directed early reflections to the audience. By making the panels adjustable, the R index can be set as desired. The panels need not be large; these early reflections do not need to include frequencies much below about 500 Hz.

7.9.3 The Main Floor

The main floor audience area in the idealized hall (Fig. 7-23) is 65 ft wide and 100 ft from the stage to the rear row. A public, nonschool-based concert hall of this design is not likely to be built today because the seat count is too low to generate enough revenue. In a modern civic hall, the main floor will be wider, probably in a fan shape, and the balconies will be deeper. Although such a wide hall can be made to work acoustically, in order to be successful, the working balance between the architect's vision and the acoustician's calculations will have to tilt more toward the acoustician. As the hall grows wider, the overhead panels must extend over more of the audience and must be more carefully adjusted, and the shaping of the side walls becomes more critical.

As the side walls move out, no matter how exacting the wall design, an increasingly large part of the center of the audience is too far away to receive useful lateral reflections. Although careful shaping of the clouds can produce some useful laterals, this technique is limited and cannot be expected to replace well-located walls. A few recent large hall designs have used, with some success, multiple audience levels or low, railing-like walls in the audience to provide surfaces from which lateral reflections may be directed. Such solutions have an enormous visual impact and require great skill from both the architect and the acoustician.

7.9.4 Balconies

Balconies are used to locate listeners closer to the stage and are much better than a very long main floor. Unfortunately, balconies are often regarded by architects as second-class seats and are carelessly designed. In fact, good balcony seats are often better than main-floor seats. Figs. 7-24 and 7-25 illustrate basic criteria for good balconies and some common faults.

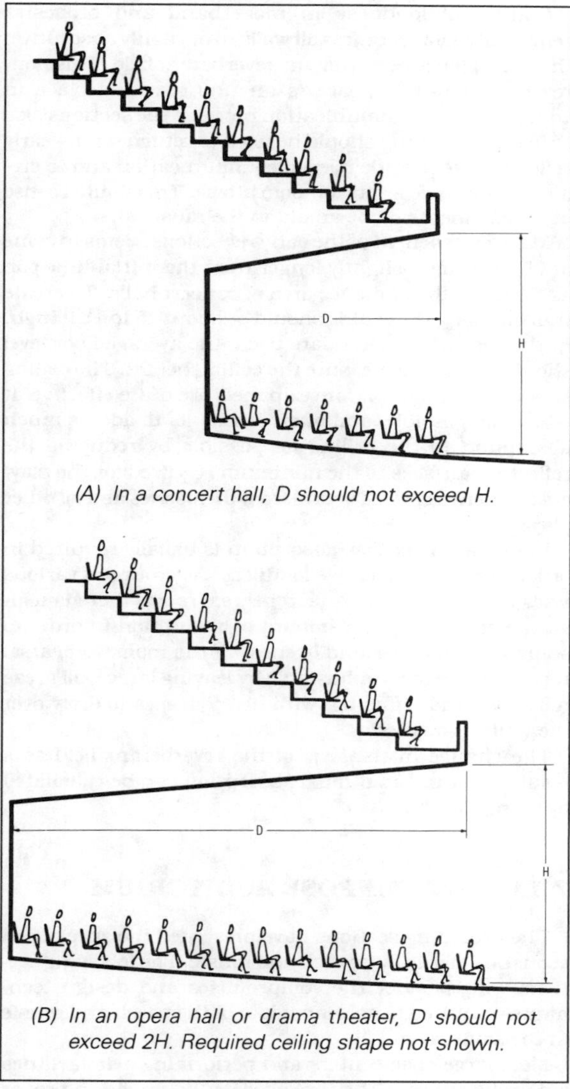

(A) In a concert hall, D should not exceed H.

(B) In an opera hall or drama theater, D should not exceed 2H. Required ceiling shape not shown.

Figure 7-24 Guide to balcony design. (After Reference 13.)

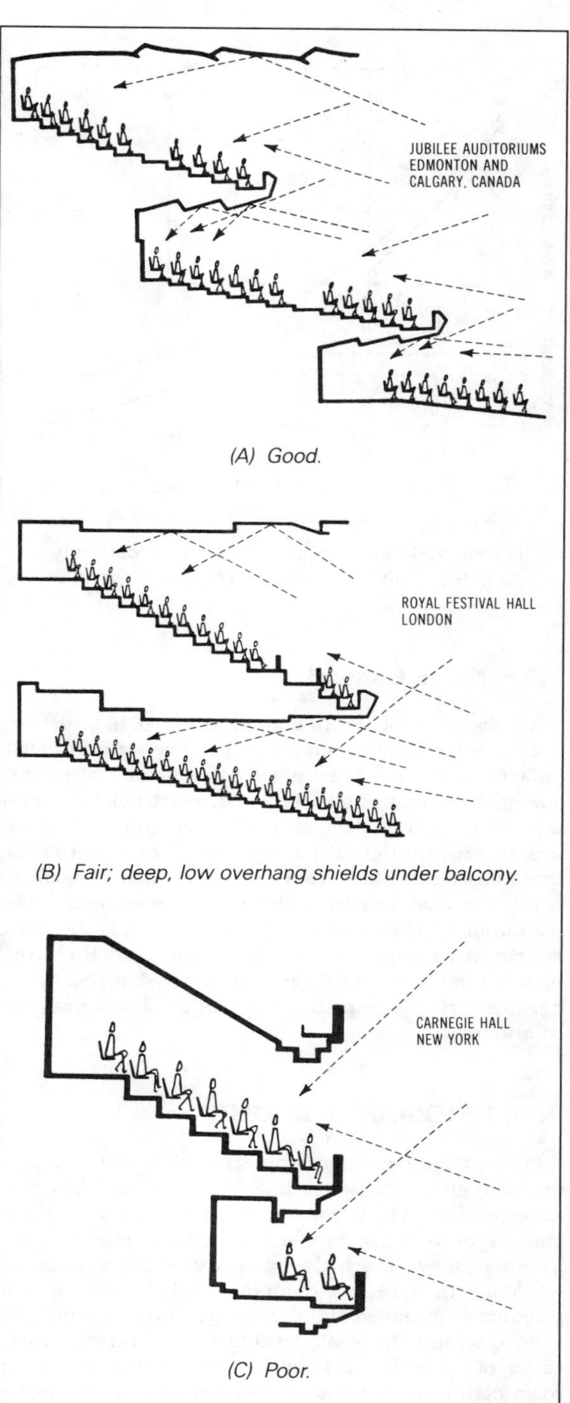

(A) Good.

(B) Fair; deep, low overhang shields under balcony.

(C) Poor.

Figure 7-25 Three typical balcony designs. (After Reference 13.)

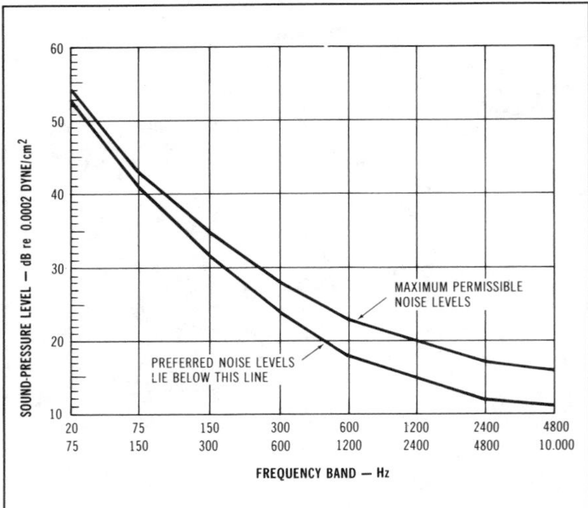

Figure 7-26 Noise level criteria for concert halls. *(Courtesy Bolt, Beranek, and Neumann Archives)*

7.9.5 Noise Control

A successful concert hall must be free of all intruding noises. Achieving this simple goal can be extraordinarily difficult and costly. There are very few quiet places left in our cities. Heavy traffic including buses, trucks, and subways along with police and medical evacuation helicopters all contribute to the noise and vibration problems that must be excluded from the concert hall. In addition to these external problems, there are noise sources within the building. The most obvious, and costly, is the HVAC system. Attention must also be given to elevators, rest rooms, dimmers, and stage machinery. Fig. 7-26 gives noise criteria by frequency for both good and marginal conditions.

7.10 REHEARSAL ROOMS

Professional symphony orchestras will usually have the use of their performance hall for rehearsals. The vast majority of school and community orchestras, bands, and choral groups do not have this benefit and must rehearse in other places. Given the opportunity, every musician would like the rehearsal room to sound like the principal place of performance. Unfortunately, it is usually not possible to achieve this goal; it would require a virtual duplication of the performance space. Architecturally, a small room cannot be made to sound like a large hall, but it might be possible with the aid of electronics. Although the initial-time-delay gap could probably be duplicated, the early reflection patterns, timing, and the texture of the sound (t_s) would still be noticeably different. It is unlikely that the reverberation time of the large room could be duplicated in the smaller room—the absorption of the musicians would be too great.

In the performance hall, the orchestra or choir is usually enclosed on three sides by hard reflective surfaces. If this arrangement is applied in the rehearsal room, it is likely that the sound level heard by the performers will be too loud. It will be louder, perhaps much louder, than they hear in the performance hall. There is, therefore, a tendency to play softer—particularly when the loudness becomes uncomfortable. It is necessary to introduce absorptive surfaces to control the level.

Control of loudness in most band and orchestra rehearsal rooms requires all walls to be highly absorptive, thus completely removing the reverberant field. This non-reverberation-time space is an uninteresting place in which to play. Communication between the sections also suffers. The ceiling should be used to return strong early reflections to provide needed communication and to create at least some feeling of room attack. This limited sense of envelopment will be an aid to the musicians.

Maximum benefit of the early reflections seems to come at 25 to 30 ms—slightly longer than the initial-time gap as found in the audience area of concert halls. To create this time gap, the ceiling should be about 15 to 18 ft high. In the case where risers are used, the average floor level should be used to measure the ceiling height. The ceiling should be diffusing. Convex panels are quite effective. It is usually possible, and often desirable, to add as much absorption to the ceiling as possible by reducing the reflective surfaces to the minimum required for the players to receive reflected sound from themselves and all other players.

In choral rooms less absorption is usually required in order to control excessive loudness. As groups of various sizes often share the same rehearsal room, there is usually a need to vary the amount of absorption in order to adjust the loudness and liveness of the room. Rehearsal rooms can be made adjustable by leaving large wall areas reflective (and diffusing) with heavy drapes to draw over the walls as desired.

The change in the level of the reverberant field as a result of adding additional absorption can be calculated by using Eq. 7-8.

7.11 MULTIPURPOSE AUDITORIUM

The preceding sections have presented the specialized acoustical needs for speech and music. The following sections will consider the compromises and design techniques required to accommodate both speech and music in the same room.

Most large civic centers and performing arts facilities are multipurpose. They are expected to provide a proper performing environment for symphony orchestra, popular music, opera, drama, and a host of commercial events (largely speech type). Also included in this combined speech and music group are churches and the rarely seen pure opera house.

7.11.1 Establishing Acoustical Priorities

The first step in designing a multipurpose hall is to establish a list of priorities. Is the facility basically a concert hall that will be used secondarily for other events in the orchestra's off season? Or is it a road house used mostly for popular music touring groups with symphony or opera a few times each year? Perhaps it is really a drama theater with an orchestra pit for opera or musicals. The answers to the use question will determine the longest and shortest reverberation times and their relative importance.

The acoustical needs of speech and music are summarized in Table 7-4. From this comparison, it is evident that the most significant differences are reverberation time, concentration of early reflections, and use of diffusion. These three factors also control the R index and texture.

There are two important attributes of speech that make combined-use rooms possible. If the direct signal is loud enough to hear well and if the articulation loss is low enough for good intelligibility, the needs for speech are largely met. These requirements suggest that a multipurpose room can be designed with good natural acoustics for music and then equipped to meet the needs of speech by the addition of a reinforcement system and a means of lowering the reverberation time. Another approach would be to design the acoustics of the room for good speech activities and provide a means of raising the reverberation time (and other parameters) to the desired value for music. Both plans or combinations are practical; both have limitations.

Table 7-4 Acoustical Needs of Speech and Music Compared

Acoustical Factors	Speech	Music
RT	< 1.5 s	> 1.5 s
RT versus frequency	nearly flat	carefully contoured
ITDG	not important	very important
Early reflections	0 to 40 ms; as many as possible, especially directed to the rear; arrival direction not important	0 to 70 ms; some carefully planned; lateral arrival very important
Late reflections	after 50 ms; avoid as much as possible	after 70 ms; as much as RT will support; diffuse
R index	low as possible	> 0, < 10; carefully adjusted
Diffusion	minor usefulness	major usefulness
Added absorption	much; on any surface that does not produce an early reflection	none; diffusion to control unwanted reflections
General relation to room's acoustics electronic reinforcement	broad range of acceptable conditions acceptable, but not always practical for drama	narrow range of acceptable conditions generally unacceptable for concert music, acceptable for popular music shows
Maximum distance from stage	< 75 ft	> 100 ft
Good sightlines	important	important
Width of audience	limited by sightlines	optimum < 65 ft
Background noise	low	very low

7.11.2 Electronic Reinforcement

Certain types of events will usually require reinforcement: lectures, popular music, and most musical comedies. Reinforcement for drama and opera will depend upon the R index or %AL_{cons}, the size of the audience, the skill of the performers, and, often most importantly, the desires of the producer. A vocalist performing with a concert orchestra may require electronic assistance in a large hall. Since most of this book deals with the application of electronic systems to augment or to create direct sound fields, this section will consider only the control of the reflected sound. Before leaving the subject of amplified direct sound, however, here are some useful observations:

1. The accomplishment of good speech intelligibility, including vocal music, in a reverberant space requires the use of high-frequency horns with high directivity (Q).
2. The needs of amplified instrumental music are usually better served with a low-Q horn. In general, a horn with a low Q will sound more musical than a high-Q horn.
3. In order to keep the sound associated with its origin, the reinforcement loudspeaker cluster should be no more than about 30 ft above the stage floor. When sounds originating upstage are reinforced, it

is likely that much of the audience will hear the first arrival from the loudspeaker rather than from the actual source. Amplified stage events will often sound more realistic if the reinforcement signal is delayed.

4. For the best realism, any electronic augmentation of the reverberant sound field should not be reproduced through the reinforcement system; the two functions should be independent.

5. When loudspeakers are used to provide foldback monitoring for musicians on stage, the introduction of 20 to 25 ms of delay will usually allow the performer's listening needs to be met with about 6 dB less level from the loudspeakers. This level reduction is often important in feedback control.

7.11.3 Stage House and Orchestra Shell

The stage house is important for drama and opera to accommodate hanging scenery, curtains, and lighting. Acoustically, a stage house is a liability. It provides no overhead reflecting surfaces. In most cases, the sets on stage are made of canvas with no nearby hard reflecting surfaces. Thus, the performers have no acoustical support behind the proscenium.

When an orchestra or other music performers are located on stage, an acoustical shell should be placed around them to provide internal communication and to couple the sound to the audience chamber. In order to couple well, the proscenium opening should be more than 30 ft high. Because the visual needs of drama and opera usually require a lower proscenium opening, it is often necessary for the proscenium as well as the reflector panels, loudspeakers, and lighting over the forestage to be adjustable in height.

The orchestra shell presents several design problems. It must be massive in order to be an effective reflector at low frequencies. Its surface must be carefully structured to provide internal communication to the orchestra while also reflecting a well-balanced and blended sound into the audience. The shell must be demountable for storage. The roof of the shell is typically divided into sections that can be tilted up vertically and retracted into the fly space of the stage house. The sides usually are made up of a number of tall but narrow sections (called towers) that can be rolled across the stage to be stored nested together in a rear or side stage storage area.

If the proscenium is low, less than about 25 ft, the shell roof probably cannot be adjusted to reflect sound into the rear of the audience or into the balconies. The low roof will also return too much sound to the orchestra. The brass and percussion will overpower the strings unless the rear roof area is made absorptive or partly open to the fly gallery to "dump" the excessive power of the brass and percussion. When the proscenium is 30 ft or higher, there will be height enough to angle the roof to provide reflections into the balconies. Then the shell roof can be tightly fitted, and no sound will need to be wasted into the stage house.

7.11.4 Opera

Opera was invented in 1597 by a group of musicians and poets (including the father of Galileo) as a revival of classical Greek drama as they thought it might have been staged. This combining of drama and music with a new vocal form (very different from the then common madrigal) was an immediate success. In a single generation, it swept Europe and became the dominant form of public musical performance. From the opera's overture grew the symphony. In the 19th century the opera orchestra moved out of the pit onto the stage as the concert or symphonic orchestra we know today.

Because opera is a dramatic and a visual art form, it is important that the audience be close enough to see the singers. About 75 ft is the maximum distance for good visual contact. The traditional horseshoe shape of the opera house with rows of shallow boxes built into the rear and side walls evolved as the most efficient way to locate a large audience close to the stage. This scheme resulted in a room with much absorption on the floor and walls, thus maintaining a reverberation time compatible with good speech intelligibility and high definition in the music.

Unlike orchestral music, the acoustical needs for opera have not changed in the past 400 years. Only Wagner has strayed far from the original baroque-Italian opera form. Wagnerian opera is intended for performance in a more reverberant hall—about 1.7 s rather than the usual 1.5 s.

Fig. 7-27 shows the factors on Beranek's rating scale where the needs for opera differ from orchestral music. Because opera is more speech oriented, the initial-time-delay gap is slightly longer: up to 24 ms for the first arrival. Balance between singers and orchestra is important. For the early operas, the orchestra was quite small and played from the floor in front of the stage. As the orchestra grew in size, it became necessary to locate it in a pit to help control the loudness balance. Wagner went even farther by closing the top of the pit, leaving only a small opening for the sound to emerge. Today it is common to locate the orchestra on an elevator platform so it may be raised or lowered to meet varying performance and acoustical needs. Obviously, an orchestra playing in a pit will have a very different sound than when playing on stage under a shell.

7.11.5 Church

The medieval and Renaissance origins of some of our church musical and architectural styles are still evident today. The great stone cathedrals with their enormous reverberation times provided a majestic sound for the organ and the chants of the choir. It was a magnificent stage for the pageantry of the Mass. The proceedings were conducted in Latin, so intelligibility was of little importance. After the Reformation, at least in the protestant churches, pageantry declined and the need for speech intelligibility increased, so church architecture began to

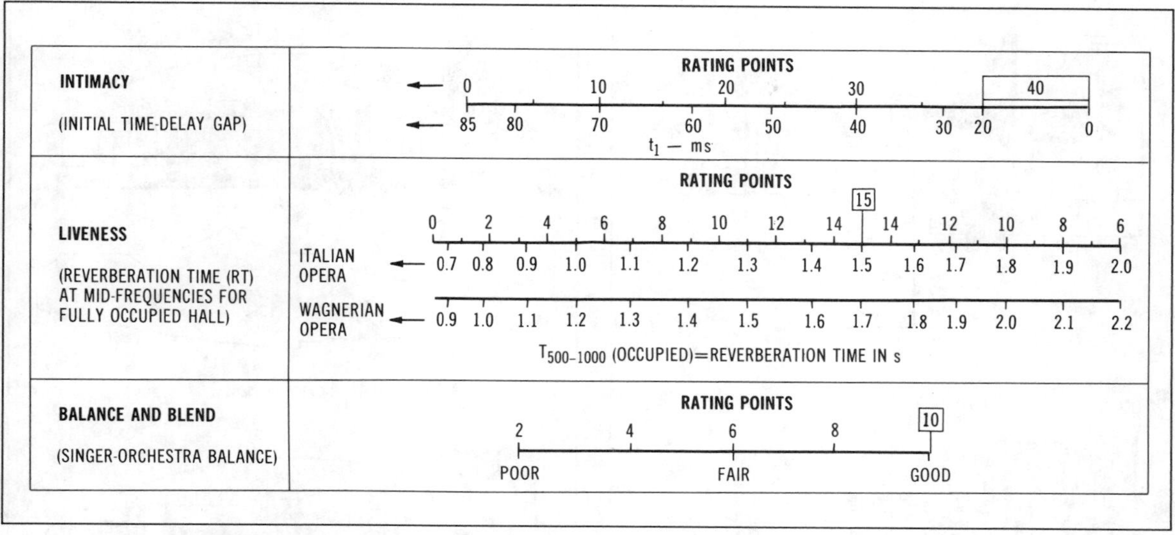

Figure 7-27 Rating scale for opera; identical to rating for orchestra except as shown. *(After Reference 13.)*

change. But even today there still exists a dichotomy of acoustical needs in the church.

The design of a modern church is most challenging because of the variety of acoustical needs occurring in rapid succession during a single service. A typical program might include organ music (RT > 2.5 s), a piano solo or small instrumental group (RT = 1.4 s), a dramatic reading (RT < 1 s), an anthem by the choir (RT = 1.8 s), and congregational singing (RT = 1.6 s). In a single hour's program, the reverberation time requirements span from less than 1 s to more than 2.5 s.

Unlike any other performance space, the audience (congregation) is an active participant with spoken responses and group singing. If the reverberation time is too low, congregational participation will be depressed and weak; organ and choir music will also be uninteresting. On the other hand, with a music-supporting reverberation time, speech will have to be reinforced. Microphones on the pulpit and altar are simple to arrange; not so simple is the pickup for dramatic vignettes that often are part of religious services. Even more difficult is finding a visually and acoustically acceptable place to locate loudspeaker clusters with large high-Q horns. Probably the best hope for meeting all the acoustical needs of a church is programmable electronic reverberation.

7.12 CHANGING REVERBERATION TIME ARCHITECTURALLY

Reverberation time is directly dependent upon the volume and inversely dependent upon the total absorption of the room; changing either will change reverberation time. There are, however, subtle differences in the sonic effect between the two. They do not each affect the reverberant field in quite the same way.

When the volume is changed, not only does the reverberation time change but also all parts of the reverberation event after t_2 (see Fig. 7-18): the density of the late reflections, the time of t_s, and the loudness of the running and terminal reverberance. Changing absorption has less effect upon the texture of the reverberant field; it principally affects the running loudness (hence, the R index) and the slope of the terminal decay.

7.12.1 Adjustable Volume

In theory, reducing reverberation time by reducing volume seems to be more desirable; in actual fact, the cost is so great that it is rarely done. A practical scheme for changing volume only is probably not possible because changing volume almost always creates significant changes in the total absorption left in the room.

A common application of variable-volume rooms is dividing the room into separate spaces for both altered acoustics as well as simultaneous usage for different events. In schools (Fig. 7-28) or convention centers (Fig. 7-29), the balcony or under balcony may be cut off from the auditorium by a folding wall in order to form separate smaller meeting rooms. Such divisions may leave the remaining auditorium with acoustical changes ranging from minimal to drastic. (The sound isolation problems between the divided rooms are usually very significant.)

Lowering the ceiling to reduce the volume is structur-

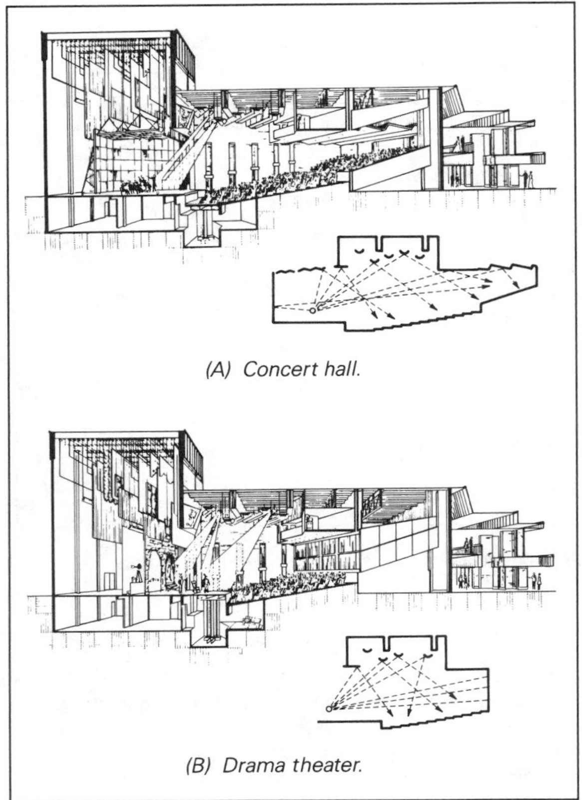
(A) Concert hall.

(B) Drama theater.

Figure 7-28 A 900-seat school auditorium with a folding wall to separate the balcony from classroom use. Grosse Pointe Michigan High School North.

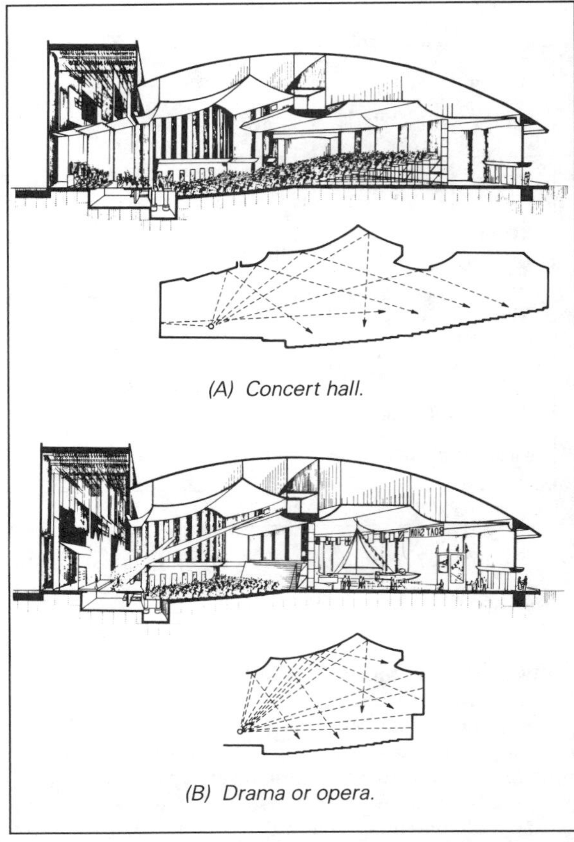
(A) Concert hall.

(B) Drama or opera.

Figure 7-29 Veteran's Memorial Auditorium, 2100 or 800 seats, San Rafael, California.

ally complex and costly. In addition, there are the problems of lighting catwalks and room ventilation that must operate from any ceiling setting. Fig. 7-30 illustrates a practical solution to these problems. Here, large sections of the ceiling can be lowered to close off one or both balconies, while other panels are tilted to change the pattern of the early reflections. The lighting catwalks and proscenium are also lowered as required for different kinds of events. In this design any sound entering the upper volume through openings between the ceiling panels is largely trapped and unable to return to the audience. Fine adjustments in reverberation time are accomplished by lowering heavy curtains along the side and rear walls. This combination of variable volume and absorption provides a range of reverberation time from 1.2 to 1.8 s, as the seating capacity changes from 850 to 3000.

A simpler construction in a smaller hall is illustrated in Fig. 7-31. Here, a system of acoustical reflector panels can be lowered to redirect the early reflections and to choke off much of the energy from entering the upper volume of the hall. For full effectiveness, it is necessary to introduce additional absorption into the upper cavity to absorb the sound that is able to reach that area. In this scheme, the real volume remains large while the effective and the visual volume is made smaller.

Another form of variable volume has been attempted, usually with little success, by coupling one or more very reverberant chambers with the main auditorium. The coupling between the rooms is usually via an adjustable shutter. With the shutter closed, the auditorium has its natural reverberation time. As the shutter is opened, there is a varying degree of coupling between the rooms, which allows the longer reverberation time of the chamber to be returned to the auditorium. Because of the limited amount of energy that can be transferred, there is little, if any, noticeable effect on the level of the running reverberance. The principal contribution will be to make the terminal reverberance longer. The audible effect will be most noticeable on stopped chords.

7.12.2 Adjustable Absorption

One important advantage of movable ceiling schemes is psychological rather than acoustical: the room can be made to appear smaller and more intimate as the rever-

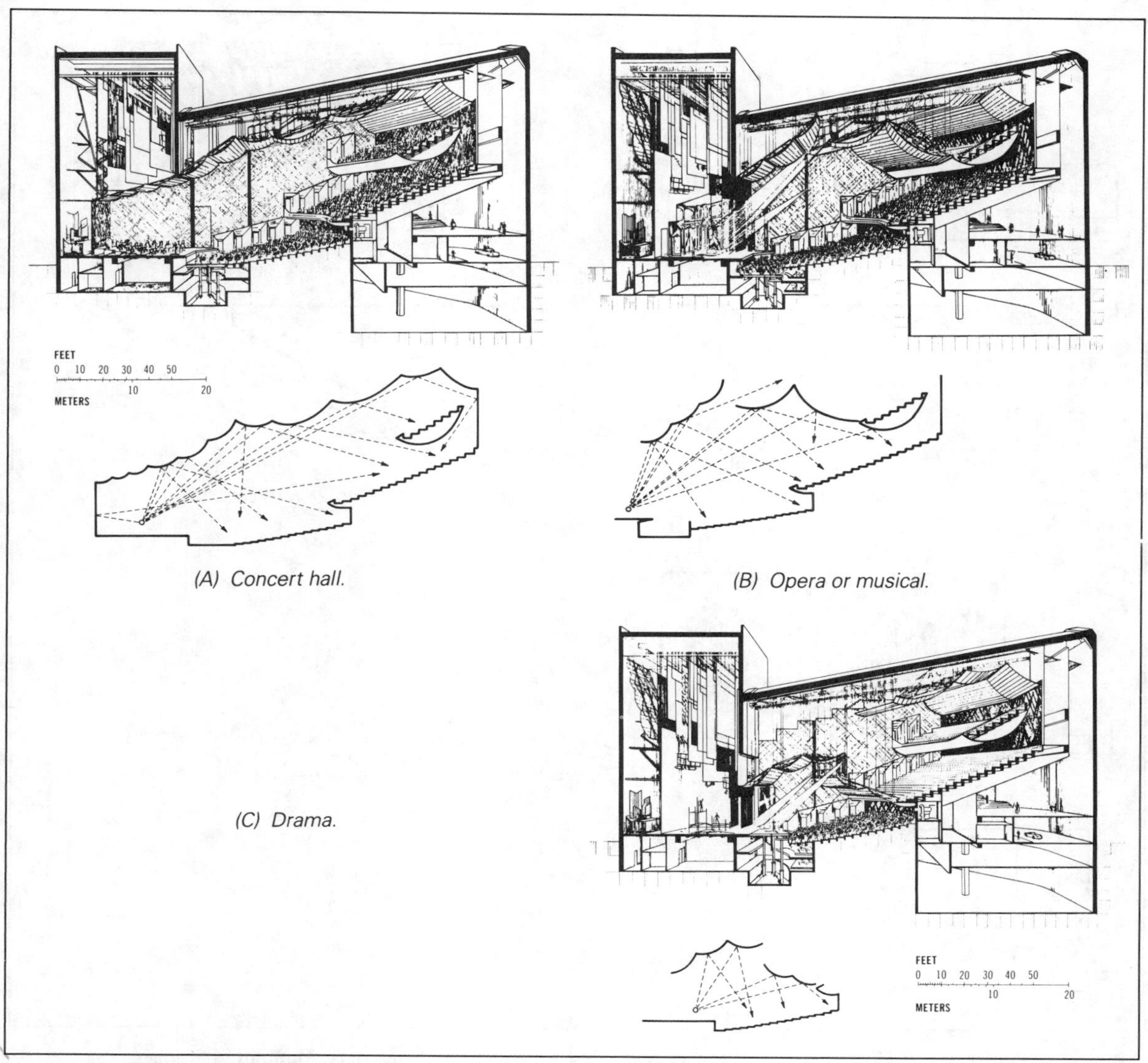

Figure 7-30 Edwin Thomas Performing Arts Hall, 3000, 2100, or 850 seats, University of Akron, Ohio.

beration time is made shorter; our eyes and ears receive the same impressions. This benefit is less likely to be achieved by variable absorption techniques. Fig. 7-32 shows an auditorium that has some increase in visual intimacy as its seating area is reduced by a half by a dividing curtain. The reverberation time is adjustable from 1.4 to 1.7 s, partly by using retractable side wall curtains disguised behind a metal grillework.

When the purpose of the added absorption is to reduce the reverberation time in order to increase the definition of music (lower the R index) or to increase speech intelligibility (lower $\%AL_{cons}$), the effectiveness of the added absorption can be increased by simultaneous adjustments of the early reflection patterns. The hall illustrated in Fig. 7-33 has acoustical clouds that can be lowered and tilted to create optimum reflection patterns for concert, opera, or drama modes. This is a simplification of the design shown in Fig. 7-31. Note the use of two sections of orchestra pit lifts and four stage lifts. The stage, one of the world's largest, is 168 ft deep with the rear wall open. The proscenium is 95 ft wide and has a maximum adjustable height of 35 ft.

The illustrations of auditoriums in this section are based upon drawings from Dr. George C. Izenour's *Theater Design*,[22] which is to theater architecture as Beranek's book[13] is to concert hall acoustics. The examples are selected to demonstrate how variable acoustics systems can be implemented. These halls, interesting as they are,

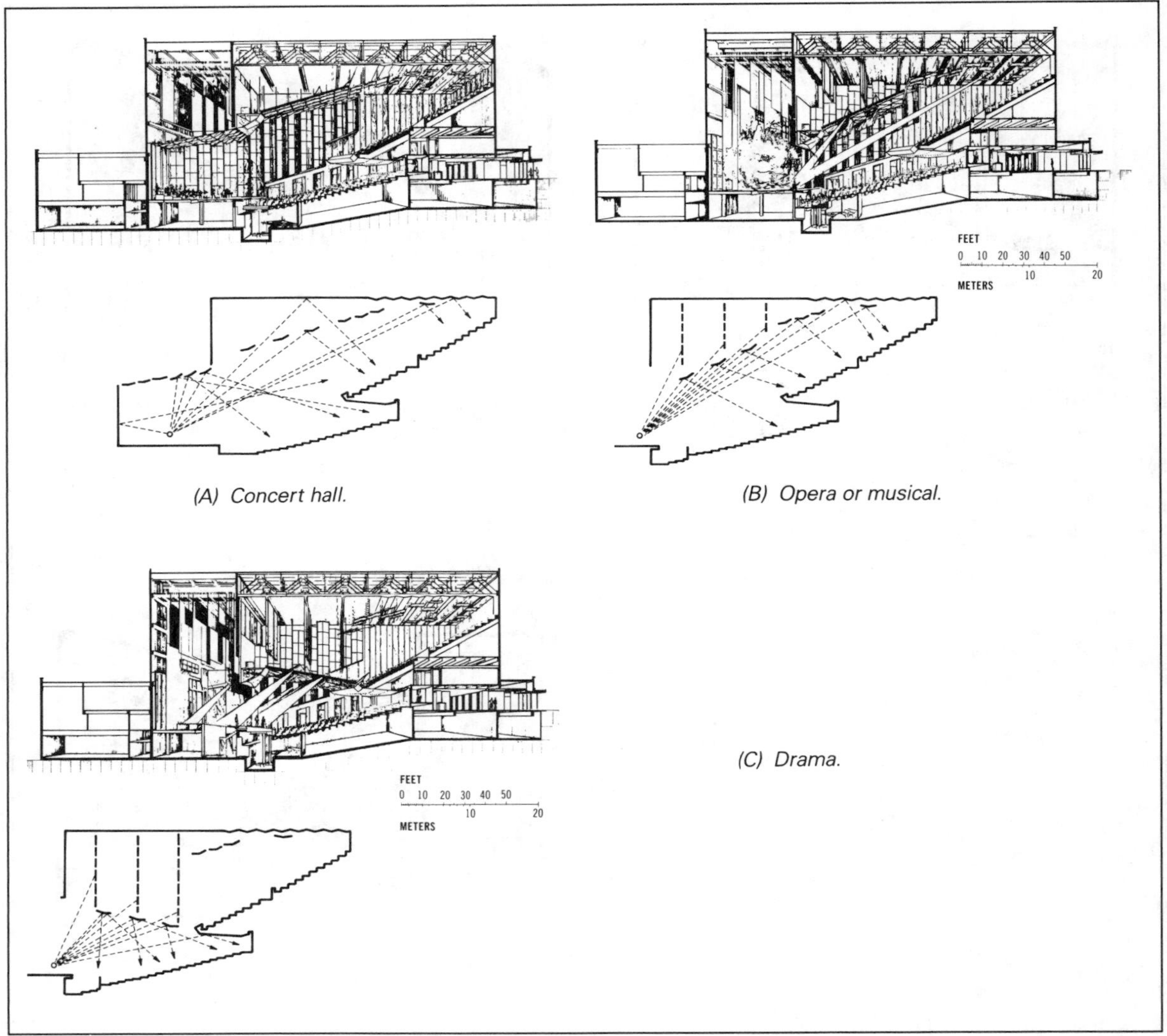

Figure 7-31 Cain Auditorium, 1800 or 950 seats, Kansas State University, Manhattan, Kansas.

generally represent the exceptions rather than usual design practice.

The most common means of adjusting reverberation time is by using retractable curtains that may be lowered to cover part of the side or the rear walls. Sometimes these drapes are concealed behind an acoustically transparent screen. Another common technique is to extend curtains horizontally across the hall in the attic space between an acoustically transparent visual ceiling and the real acoustical ceiling above.

A significant design problem is to ensure that low-frequency absorption is added in sufficient amounts to maintain the desired low/mid-band reverberation time ratio. Providing deep and irregular cavities behind the curtains is often helpful in securing low-frequency absorption.

The change in reverberation time after volume or absorption changes can be calculated using the standard reverberation time equation. The change in the level of the running reverberance may be calculated by

$$\Delta L_R = 10 \log (S\bar{a}_1/S\bar{a}_2) \text{dB} \tag{7-8}$$

or,

$$\Delta L_R = 10 \log (RT_2/RT_1) \text{dB} \tag{7-9}$$

where,

$S\bar{a}_1$ or RT_1 is the condition before change,
$S\bar{a}_2$ or RT_2 is the condition after change.

7.13 CHANGING REVERBERATION TIME ELECTRONICALLY

Architectural control of reverberation time consists of setting it to the longest useful time and reducing it as desired by adjusting volume, absorption, or both. The reverberation time of a room may also be adjusted electronically, in which case the architectural reverberation time is set to its lowest useful value and then adjusted upward by electronic means. The electronic reverberation may be an enhancement of the natural reverberation of the room, or it may be a wholly new creation.[23] It is widely expected that the last decade of the 20th century will see electronics largely replace architecture as the controller of acoustics in churches and multipurpose auditoriums.

7.13.1 Enhanced Reverberation

There are two basic methods of achieving reverberation enhancement. Both systems operate by sampling the architectural reverberant field, amplifying and processing the signal, then adding it back to the existing field. Either system is capable of providing a small amount of assistance to the room. Unfortunately, both systems are very expensive to install. Principally because of the cost, each system has been installed in only a few halls.

The *sound field amplification system*, as developed by the Philips Company of Holland, employs a large number of individual microphone-amplifier-loudspeaker channels that are located in the walls and ceiling. The sound picked up by a surface-mounted microphone is reproduced, broadband, by a loudspeaker located some distance away. As many as 100 or more independent channels, each operating at a very low gain, may be required in order to keep the system stable and free of coloration caused by edge-of-feedback operation.

The gain required may be estimated by using Eq. 7-9. For example, if the reverberation time is to be changed from 1.2 to 2.2 s, the gain (G) required of the system will be

$$G = 10 \log(2.2/1.2)$$
$$= 2.6 \text{ dB}$$

or, say, 3 dB. The Philips Co. recommends that the number of channels (N) required to keep the system stable is

$$N = 50G - 50 \qquad (7\text{-}10)$$

or,

$$N = 500 \log\ (RT_2/RT_1) - 50 \qquad (7\text{-}11)$$

Continuing the example with a required gain of 3 dB, the minimum number of channels would be 100.

The *assisted resonance (AR) system* is similar, except the feedback problem is reduced by operating each channel as a narrowband system rather than full bandwidth. This is accomplished by locating each microphone in an individually tuned resonator. The assisted resonance system generally is operated over only a part of the audio spectrum. The best-known AR system is in the Royal Festival Hall in London.[24] There, 172 channels cover the range from about 60 to 700 Hz to provide additional low-frequency reverberation time. Without this assistance, the hall has a noticeable lack of warmth. A 90-channel system operating from 40 Hz to 1.8 kHz has been installed in the very successful Silva Concert Hall (Eugene, Oregon).[25] This system can vary the midband reverberation time from 1.5 to 2.5 s under the control of a small computer.

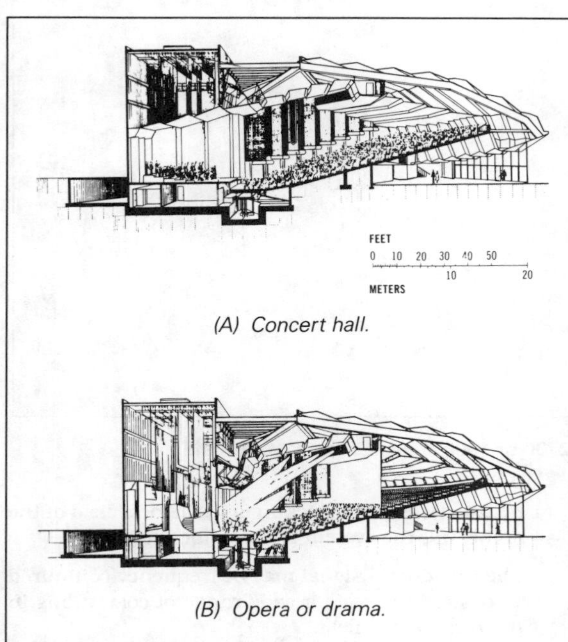

(A) Concert hall.

(B) Opera or drama.

Figure 7-32 Eugenia Van Wezel Auditorium, 1800 or 850 seats, Sarasota, Florida.

7.13.2 Created Reverberation

Created reverberation[26,27] does not reproduce and enhance the room's architectural reverberance; rather, it creates a whole new reverberant field. One or a few microphones are located on stage in the near sound field. Their broadband pickup is processed through a reverberation device and then applied to the room by a moderate num-

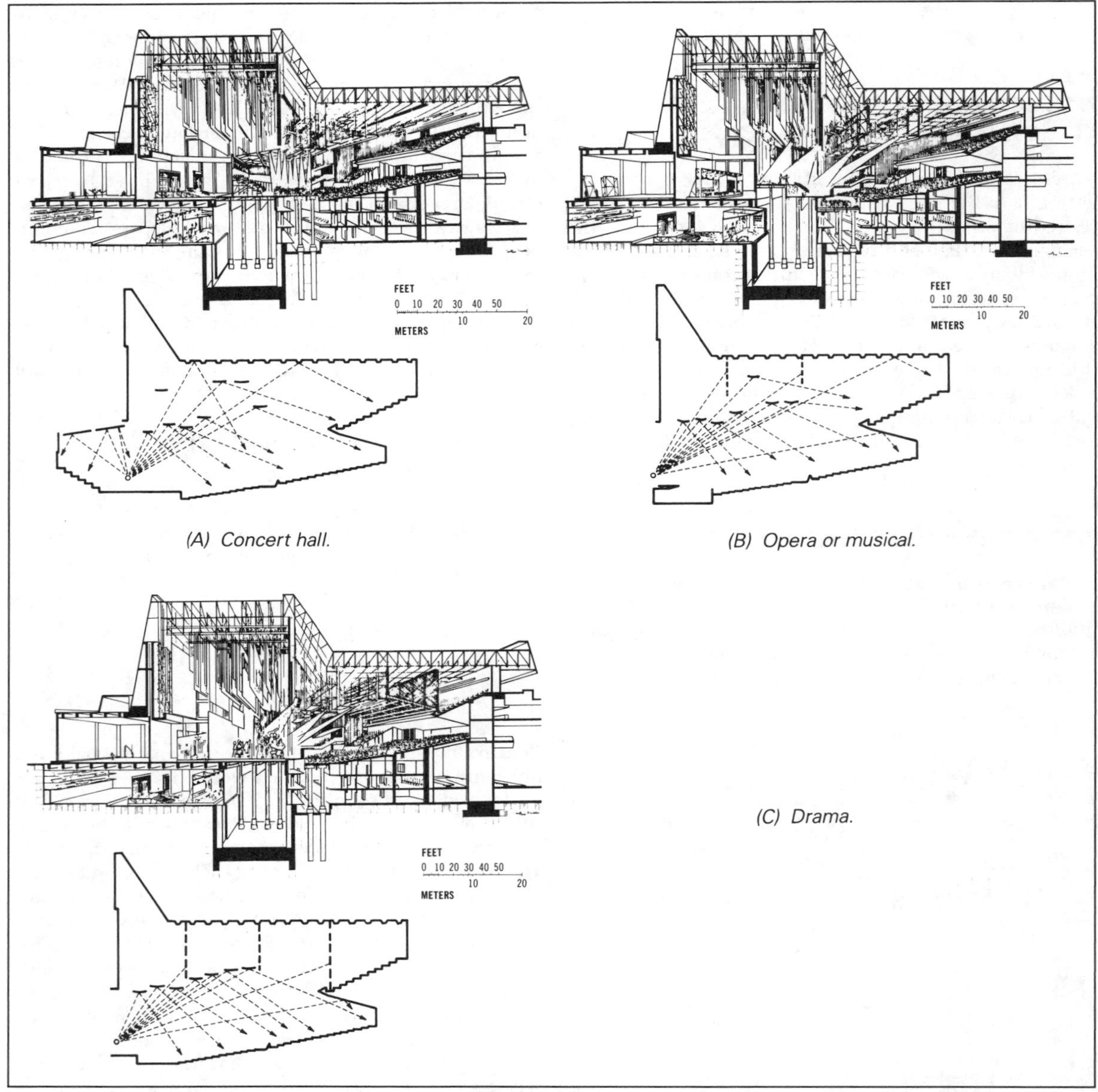

Figure 7-33 Sala de Conciertos Rios Reyna, 2700 or 1500 seats, Caracas, Venezuela.

ber of loudspeakers so located and operating at levels such that they cannot be localized. Before the advent of high-quality digital delay systems, the reverberation device was a chamber. Chambers have the disadvantages of creating a texture that does not sound like a large room and of being hard to make adjustable. With modern programmable digital reverberation synthesizers, texture can be precisely structured as desired. This system has several distinct advantages:

1. Because the sound pickup is in the near field of the orchestra, the system is much more stable.
2. The broadband signal may be frequency contoured as desired to create a wide range of colorations in the reverberant field.
3. The system does not rely upon the architectural reverberant field so it may be employed in a very dead room or outdoors.

4. By use of the enormous flexibility of the digital processor, a large number and variety of reverberation conditions may be preprogrammed and stored in memory to be recalled by the push of a switch.
5. Because the system is largely software controlled, improvements and additional features can be easily added in the future.
6. And, perhaps most important of all, the system is affordable. A few tens of thousands of dollars rather than a few hundreds of thousands of dollars as required for systems that enhance the existing reverberant field.

The acoustical power required from the system will depend upon the energy required to bring the existing reverberant field up to the desired reverberation time. In a 250,000-ft^3 room with an architectural reverberation time of 1.2 s, raising the reverberation time to 2.2 s for a symphony orchestra would require about 30 acoustical watts from the system. If this power requirement were divided among ten loudspeakers, each unit would produce about 3 acoustic watts, which is not a large demand. If a reverberant field is to be created outdoors, very much more power and, probably, more loudspeakers will be required.

The number and location of the loudspeakers should be selected so that the reverberant field is very diffuse and the audience is unable to localize a source. The signals to the loudspeakers should be carefully delayed so that the reverberant field starts at the correct time relative to the arrival of the direct signal.

7.13.3 Early Reflections

The reverberant field, whether enhanced or created, occurs after t_2 (see Fig. 7-18). The sound field between t_1 and t_2 is created by the early reflections. These early reflections may be augmented or created electronically.

The early reflections system can share near-field microphone signals with the created reverberation system. Of course, the signals are processed differently by each system. The ideal early reflection synthesizer should allow the setting of the time and intensity of each reflection. After the t_1 to t_2 period is synthesized, it is sent via proper delays to loudspeakers arranged to provide mostly laterally arriving sound to the audience. Considerable ingenuity will be required to serve the center area of a wide hall with laterally arriving sounds.

The electronic signals of the two systems can be mixed to feed most of the loudspeakers, although a few locations will want only the early or only the late signals. In both systems the levels from the loudspeakers must be carefully adjusted to provide reflections at the correct level in order to sound realistic and to maintain the desired R index in all parts of the hall.

7.14 CINEMAS

7.14.1 Noise Control in Cinemas

Sound obeys the same physics in cinema theaters as in other places of public assembly, and its generation and behavior are described throughout this book. Particular demands are made on motion-picture sound, however, and sound motion picture theaters have evolved over more than 50 years to meet these demands as the recording processes and artistic and dramatic requirements have changed. The remaining sections in this chapter will describe the solutions and practices common today.

Sound in the cinema theater must be under the creative control of studio personnel charged with producing the finished sound track, and ultimately under the control of the actors, musicians and operators of the effects who generated the original sound. The first requirement of theater acoustics is that extraneous noises not contemplated at the time of recording or mixing be excluded from the theater.

The simplest way to control site noises is to locate the theater in a quiet areas. This is a benefit of today's common practice of building cinemas in shopping malls, usually set apart from the other stores and surrounded by their own parking lot. In much noisier urban environments, the preferred solution is to surround the auditorium with less noise-sensitive offices or shops. Here again, theater economics work well with acoustical needs. Often the cinema auditorium is set back from the street so that the commercially valuable sidewalk and street frontage can be let to a row of shops and higher floors can be let as offices. The cinema patron walks through a lobby going away from the street and its noises and enjoys a quiet auditorium; after the show the exit doors the patron uses open onto smaller side streets. This type of theater site usage has been employed for many centuries and works well if handled with a sensitivity to noise problems during the design stage.

Walls and partitions must be designed and constructed with sufficient sturdiness, mass, and closure so that sound can neither be transmitted through their structure nor enter them at one unintended aperture and leave them at another. This last consideration deserves a word of explanation. Flanking paths for noise transmission exist where airborne sound can enter the construction on one side, for example, around a ventilation duct, travel through an interior cavity, and exit audibly on the other side. When carpenters construct cabinets or furniture, they usually see to it that all the pieces fit exactly square and tight. When the same carpenters construct a partition, it isn't possible for them to make the pieces fit as tightly together or around utility openings without exercising great care. Architects or building contractors and their job captains must understand which walls are most sensitive to noise transmission and take all the care needed that everything is sealed tightly. Wall construction details are given in the standard noise control handbooks.[28,29]

Noise control problems of particular importance for the cinema theater arise when multiple auditoriums are housed in one building and with the isolation of projection noise from the auditorium. Partitions between multicinemas should achieve STC-55, and structural transmission from a loudspeaker should be tested for and solved, if necessary, by isolation mounts for the loudspeakers. This can be a great problem with surround and subwoofer loudspeakers when these are used. Since the wall between the auditorium and the projection booth must be pierced for windows for the image to be projected through, special attention must be paid to its construction and treatment. Fig. 7-34 shows the type of problem that can arise. In this cinema the concrete block wall enclosing the projection booth did not meet the coffered, cast concrete roof perfectly, and projector noise was transmitted by flanking path down the hollow chambers of the wall blocks and out through the projection ports. Once these paths are sealed, transmission through the glass itself must be dealt with. Sometimes a small balcony, lined with absorption material and with a small vertical lip at the edge toward the auditorium, is built just outside the projection ports. A somewhat simpler solution is shown in Fig. 7-35, which shows the wall opening closed with a series of stiff absorbing panels, each pierced with an opening just large enough not to cause image vignetting and with spacing between each of the panels to create a group of noise traps. This method was described in the year 1916 for use in the silent cinema.[30]

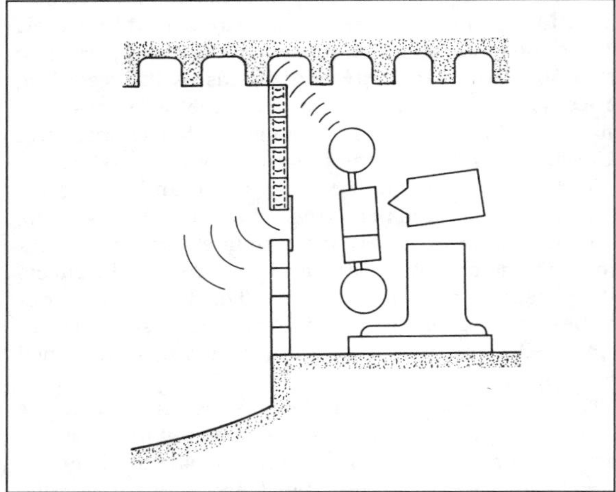

Figure 7-34 Flanking noise transmission through a wall between an auditorium and its projection booth.

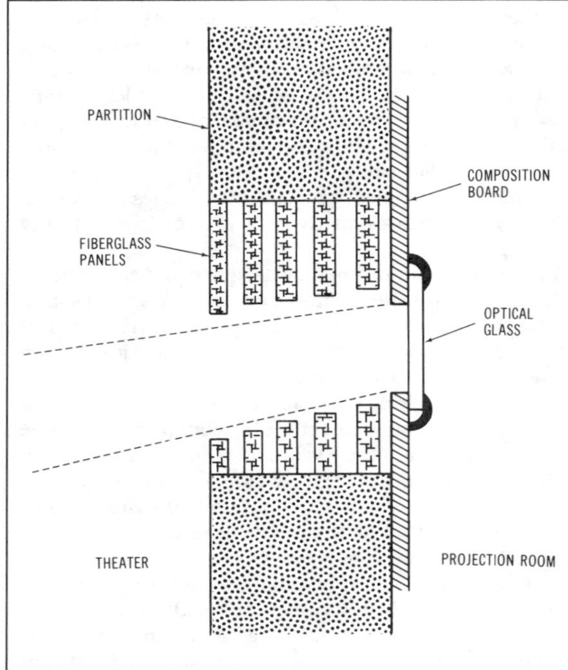

Figure 7-35 Lining a projection port to reduce noise transmission.

Structural vibration from the projectors must be dealt with by means of an isolating footing for the projector pedestals, an example of which is shown in Fig. 7-36, although this treatment must not be permitted to introduce unsteadiness in the projected image. Of course, the best course is to demand, and get, quiet, smooth-running projectors.[31]

All furnishings and equipment in the theater must be able to operate quietly, particularly seats, doors between the auditorium and the lobby or projection room, and the ventilation system. Excellent noise isolation between the lobby and the auditorium can be achieved without any door in place if an entryway with several turns and absorptive linings is used. These are also useful for allowing the patron's eyes to adjust slowly to the lower illumination in the theater.

The subject of audience noise was studied by W. A. Müeller and described by him in a classic paper.[32] Noisy audiences are not necessarily an evil to be combated at all costs. Immersion in the thunder of the laughter of hundreds of other people is very pleasant, as is the sound of many others applauding or the hush of many others holding their breath at a particularly dramatic moment. One of broadcasting's most despicable inventions, the recorded laugh track, acknowledges this phenomenon. Nevertheless, extra absorption should not be introduced into a cinema auditorium just to reduce audience noise. Many of the early film comedians became adept at handling the pause that must follow a funny line, and the Marx Brothers often introduced a visual bit there in case the theater was not full or the audience was unresponsive. Margaret Dumont's slow double-takes were carefully crafted artifacts of the sound motion-picture comedy.

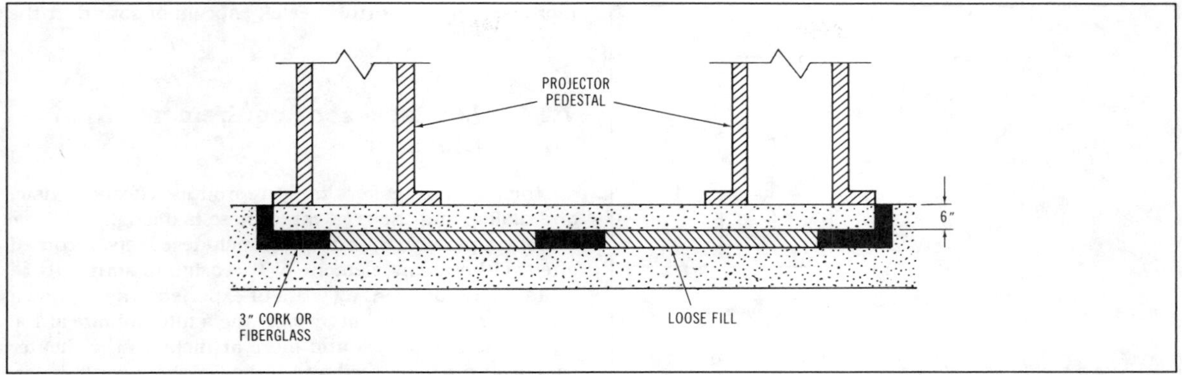

Figure 7-36 Vibration isolation for motion picture projectors. *(After Rettinger.)*

After all the intruding noises have been identified and isolated, the background noise level of the cinema must be NC-30, as shown in Fig. 7-37.

7.14.2 Reflected and Reverberant Sound in Cinemas

Echoes created by long transit times to and from an untreated rear wall in the cinema are enormously destructive of dialog intelligibility and must be dealt with vigorously and effectively. One low-cost solution to this problem is shown in Fig. 7-38. The vertical wall between the auditorium and the projection room is covered with tilted paneling A to A′, which is itself pierced for the projection ports. These panels, depending on their materials, will absorb some of the direct sound from the loudspeakers and reflect the rest into the last few rows of seats, where the short extra transit times will make them indistinguishable from the direct sound.

Large, reflective, parallel side walls create flutter echoes between them, and these are harmful for many types of buildings, but ordinarily not for cinemas. Noises originating in these auditoriums, such as laughter, applause, or the munching of popcorn, are sharp and staccato in nature, and flutter echo has little effect on them.

The reverberative decay of sound in rooms used for playback of recordings poses some special problems: not only does a decay take place in the room, but there are also decays recorded on the sound track, originating in the studio (or perhaps deliberately introduced in the mixing electronics). This was the subject of considerable study in the early days of motion-picture sound recording.[33–35] When sound is recorded in a room of reverberation time RT_1 and played back in a room of reverberation time RT_2, the resulting reverberation time was empirically found to be approximately

$$\sqrt[3]{RT_1{}^3 + RT_2{}^3} \tag{7-12}$$

This analysis, as well as practical experience with putting talkies into the large movie palaces of the time, suggested the desirability of introducing as much absorption into theater auditoriums as possible. Eventually Potwin formulated curves of desired reverberation time over theater volume, which were approximately

$$0.2\log V + 0.1 \tag{7-13}$$

for midrange frequencies (volume in cubic feet).[36]

As years passed, it became common practice to intro-

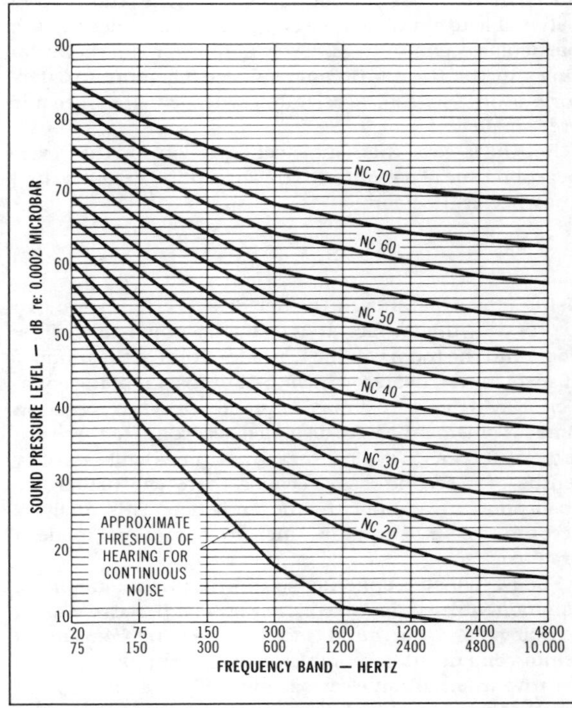

Figure 7-37 Noice criteria curves.

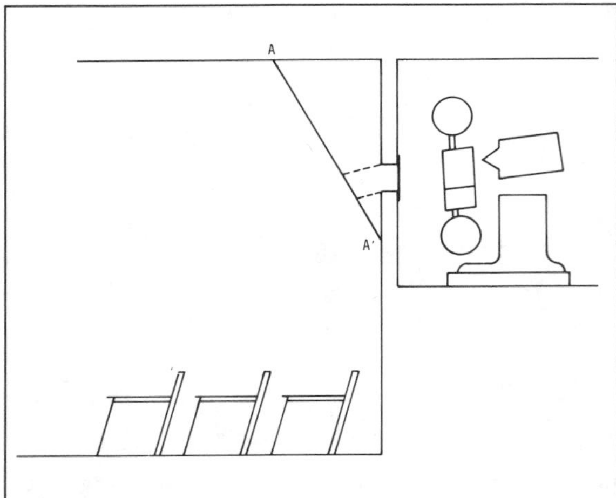

Figure 7-38 Tilted facia panel, A to A', throws echoes harmlessly down into the last rows of seats rather than back toward the front of the theater.

duce as much absorption as possible into cinema theaters, the most popular materials being fiberglass blankets behind corrugated, perforated aluminum facings or burlap draperies pleated to 50% fullness over a wall or more absorbing blankets. When stereophonic sound was introduced in the 1950s and sound mixers in the studios were better able to simulate the reverberation they desired the particular scene to have, lower and lower reverberation times in the theater became subjectively more satisfactory, a process that accelerated when cinemas became ever smaller.

Rettinger gave this empirical equation for the reverberation time of a room with no absorption except seated audience at the floor[37]

$$(18.2S_a/V + 0.1)^{-1} \tag{7-14}$$

Using modern standard theater design criteria, we can express S_a, the surface area of the occupied area of the floor, and the room volume V as a function of the number of seats in the theater, which then drops out of the equation, leaving us with a maximum practical reverberation time for cinema theaters designed according to these criteria of 0.85 s.[38] Typical measured times will be a few tenths of a second less, because there will usually be absorption in addition to the audience. This analysis accords well with many measurements of modern practice.[39]

Today, as stereophonic soundtracks become more common with compatible stereo optical processes such as Dolby SVA™, surround tracks are evolving from effects reinforcement into an ambience track, supplying reverberative information electroacoustically from all around the theatergoer. This development is to be expected as creative sound recordists and mixers demand, and expect, more and more control over all aspects of sound in the cinema.

7.14.3 Loudspeaker Requirements for Cinemas

Cinema loudspeakers must reproduce effects, music, and dialog, and the greatest of these is dialog.

Motion-picture soundtracks include effects recorded often without any element of the original sound to be imitated, because many years of experience have shown that recording an effect by pointing a microphone at the natural source may sound more artificial in the theater than a sound generated by a Rube Goldberg contraption on a Foley stage. Soundtracks include title and background music mixed in (usually) long after photography. These are not included to amaze audiences and instill in them a keen appreciation of the sound equipment employed in the theater; they are used as part of a larger dramatic purpose. Effects must be convincing and music must be satisfying, but audiences come into the theater primarily to hear the dialog of the actors, not the effects or music. The loudspeakers must be capable of projecting intelligible speech *through* convincing effects and satisfying music.

In the celebrated scene of the helicopter attack on the village in the film *Apocalypse Now*, we are inundated by

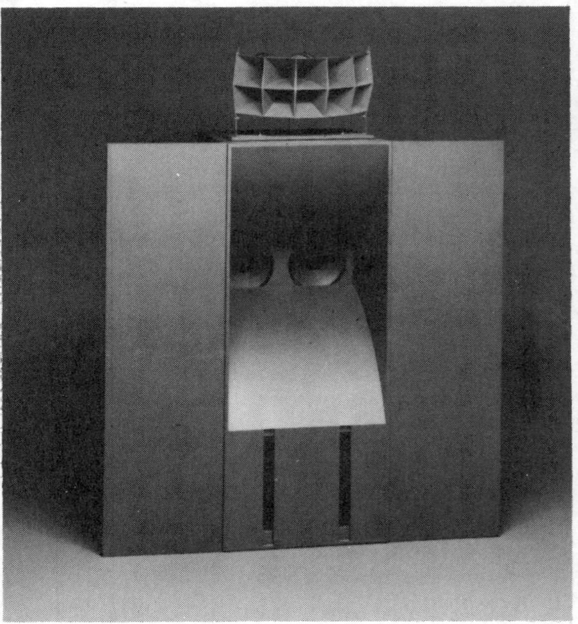

Figure 7-39 Hybrid bass horn and bass-reflex cabinet used in the most popular motion picture sound loudspeaker system.

helicopter noises and by music (Wagner's *Ride of the Valkyries*), both at high levels, but we must always be able to understand each word of dialog spoken in the helicopter.

When accompanying dialog, music, and effects must have restricted high-frequency response to avoid masking effects that would reduce the intelligibility of speech, this condition imposes certain requirements on the bandwidth of the reproduced sound and on the characteristics of the loudspeaker used. If possible, the loudspeaker should be able to offer a higher direct-to-reverberant sound ratio in the intelligibility-sensitive frequency region of speech, than it offers below. One solution to this problem is the vented horn bass cabinet, shown in Fig. 7-39 (for a discussion of this type of cabinet, see section 14.16).

Theater loudspeaker systems will be placed behind projection screens, usually extruded or cast from polyvinyl chloride (pvc) about 15 mils thick, with many small circular perforations comprising about 8 or 8.5% open area. Modern measurements indicate this screen has no effect below about 1 kHz, but above that frequency it acts as a beam spreader or acoustic lens.[40] Fig. 7-40 shows this effect for a typical theater loudspeaker, and Fig. 7-41 shows it for a planar mouth high-frequency horn ¼ in. away from the screen. In addition to this effect, perforated theater screens introduce a roughness into the frequency response of the loudspeakers behind them, a representative example of which is shown in Fig. 7-42. New theoretical work points the way to improved transmission performance of theater screens, particularly if more, but smaller, perforations can be used.[41]

When loudspeakers are placed behind the screen in a theater, they should be raised as high as possible so that the high-frequency horn just looks out below the masking or border at the top of the screen. Loudspeaker height has very little psychoacoustic effect on localization of the apparent source of the sound, because of the relative insensitivity of the ears to vertical localization (compared to horizontal localization) and the strength of the ventriloquism effect created by the projected image. Lifting the loudspeakers as high as possible will generally improve the uniformity of direct sound distribution in the seating area.

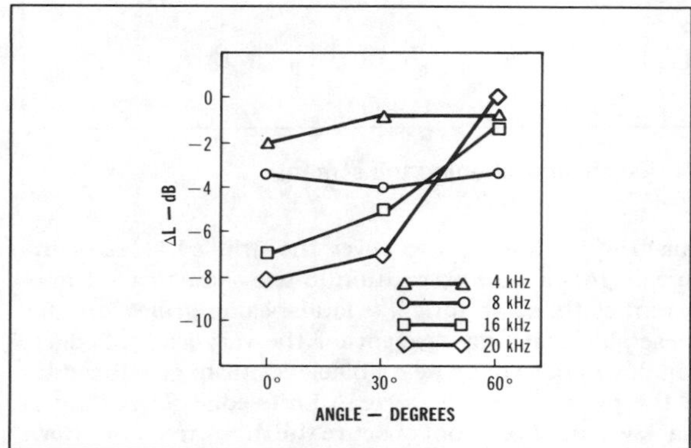

Figure 7-40 Beam spreading effect of theater projection screen.

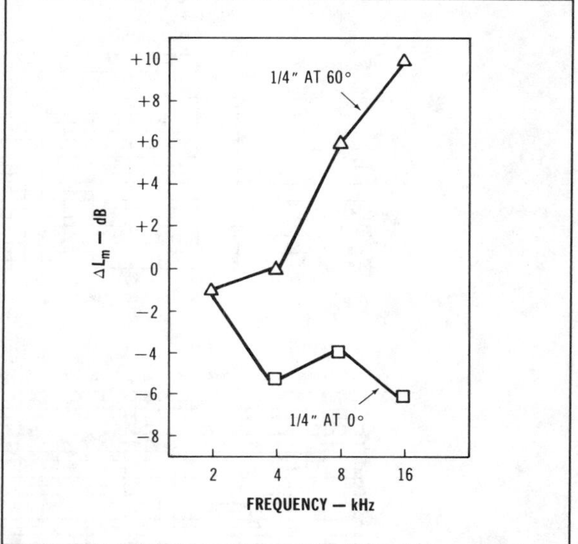

Figure 7-41 Gain achieved off-axis when theater projection screen is placed ¼ inch from planar mouth high-frequency horn.

The ear is quite sensitive to localization of apparent sound sources in the horizontal plane, and horizontal placement of loudspeakers behind the screen requires some attention. Ordinarily, if there are to be three loudspeakers behind the screen, the center channel loudspeaker is placed in the center (of course), and the centerlines of the left and right channel loudspeakers are placed one-sixth of the width of the open area of the screen inside its left and right edges. This arrangement is shown in Fig. 7-43. In the same way, if there are to be five loudspeakers behind the screen, as shown in Fig. 7-44, the two outside loudspeakers are usually placed one-tenth the open width of the screen inside its edges, and the additional channels 2 and 4 are separated from the others by one-fifth the open width of the screen.[42] Sometimes, particularly in long theaters with narrow screens, the stereophonic channels are separated more than these proportions to enhance the stereophonic effect at the center and rear of the theater.

If a partition is constructed flush with the front edges of the loudspeaker system's bass cabinets, with openings for the high-frequency horns to look through, the bass response of the loudspeakers used will be enhanced. This technique has been used for some years in the studios and, of course, is the reason why some loudspeaker manufacturers supply wings with their theater systems, as shown in Fig. 7-39. Sometimes in very small cinemas,

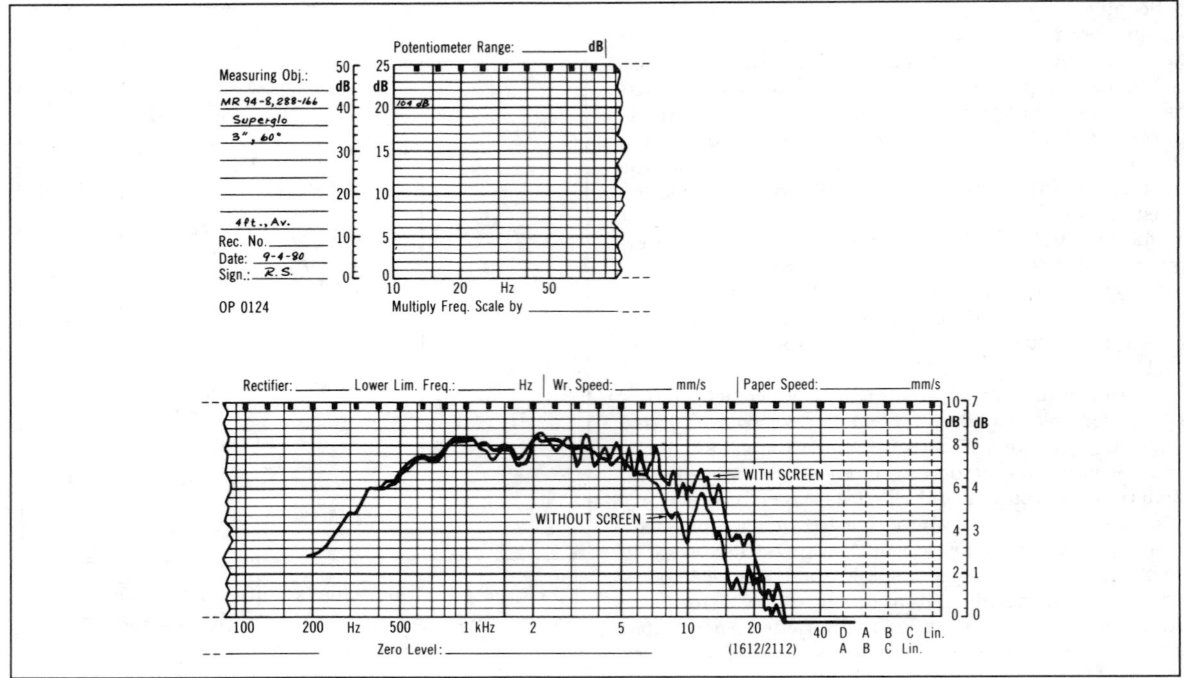

Figure 7-42 Frequency response roughness introduced by a perforated theater screen.

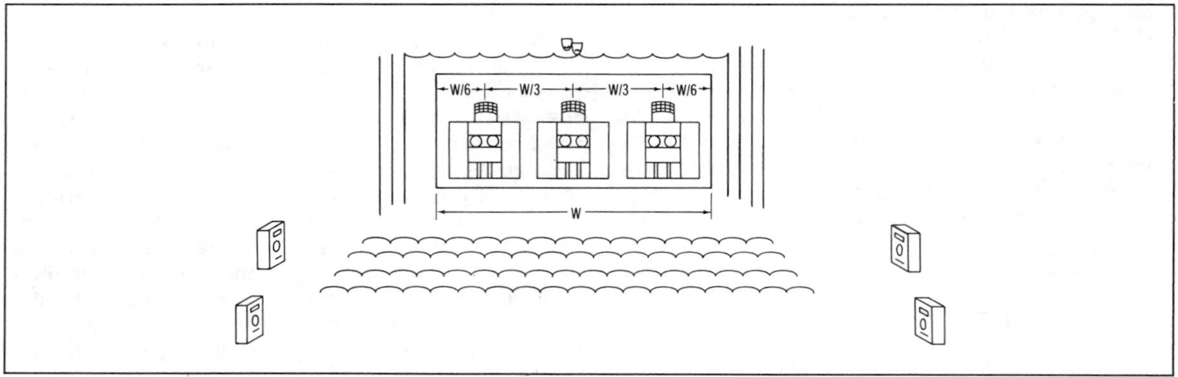

Figure 7-43 Loudspeaker placement for three channels behind the screen.

the exterior wall behind the screen will be pierced and a loudspeaker housing constructed that protrudes into the alley or parking lot behind the theater. This is not a bad idea from the standpoint of loudspeaker performance, but special care must be taken that the loudspeakers are secure from theft and accessible for service.

More and more often today, films not photographed in widescreen processes (anamorphic or 70 mm) are released with stereophonic sound. The theater must draw inside masking or draperies to cover the unused sides of the screen. It is a wise precaution to use acoustically transparent cloth, something like loudspeaker grille cloth, for these side maskings, except for the very leading edges, which will have to be heavy black velour to give the sides of the projected image a clean knife-edge. This strip of black velour should not obscure the high-frequency horn of any of the loudspeakers behind the screen.

The placement of surround loudspeakers in the theater

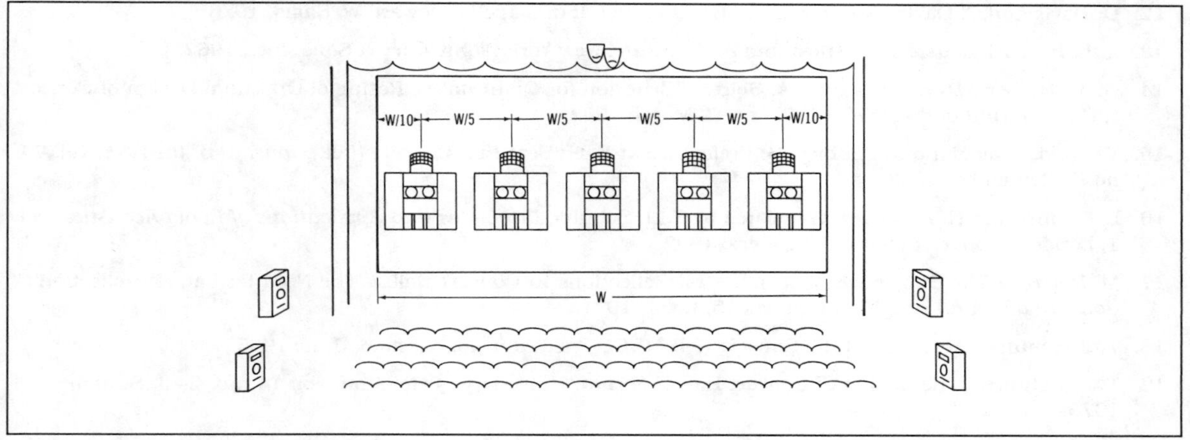

Figure 7-44 Loudspeaker placement for five channels behind the screen.

is the subject of considerable alchemy and dispute. Clearly, there should be many of them, each operating at low levels, around the sides and rear of the theater to confuse the listener's sense of direction (this is only to say that "surrounds" should surround). This consideration often militates against larger, higher-cost surround loudspeakers, and clearly with modern soundtracks, many smaller surround loudspeakers will usually sound better than fewer larger loudspeakers, where the total costs are about the same.

REFERENCES

1. V. O. Knudsen and C. M. Harris, *Acoustical Designing in Architecture*, New York: Acoustical Society of America, 1978.
2. L. Cremer and H. A. Müller, translated by T. J. Schultz, *Principles and Applications of Room Acoustics*, vol. 1, London: Applied Science Publishers, 1982.
3. H. G. Latham, "The Signal-to-Noise Ratio for Speech Intelligibility—an Auditorium Design Index," *Applied Acoustics*, vol. 12, July 1979.
4. "Methods for the Calculation of the Articulation Index," New York: American National Standards Institute, ANSI S3.5, 1969.
5. V. M. A. Peutz, "Articulation Loss of Consonants as a Criterion for Speech Transmission in a Room," *Journal of the AES*, vol. 19, no. 11, pp. 915–919, December 1971.
6. A. L. Nabelek and P. K. Robinson, "Monaural and Binaural Speech Perception in Reverberation for Listeners of Various Ages," *Journal of the ASA*, vol. 71, no. 5, May 1982.
7. J. P. A. Lochner and F. F. Burger, "The Influence of Reflections on Auditorium Acoustics," *Journal of Sound and Vibration*, vol. 4, October 1964.
8. B. Nordlud, T. Kihlman, and S. Lundblad, "Use of Articulation Tests in Auditorium Studies," *Journal of the ASA*, vol. 44, no. 1, July 1968.
9. F. Santon, "Numerical Prediction of Echograms and of the Intelligibility of Speech in Rooms," *Journal of the ASA*, vol. 59, no. 6, June 1976.
10. T. Houtgast, H. J. M. Steeneken, and R. Plomp, "Predicting Speech Intelligibility in Rooms from the Modulation Transfer Function," *Acustica*, vol. 46, September 1980.
11. W. Klein, "Articulation Loss of Consonants as a Basis for Design and Judgment of Sound Reinforcement Systems," *Journal of the AES*, vol. 19, no. 11, pp. 920–922, December 1971.

12. D. Davis and C. Davis, *Sound System Engineering*, Indianapolis: Howard W. Sams, 1976.

13. L. L. Beranek, *Music, Acoustics, and Architecture*, New York: John Wiley & Sons, Inc., 1962.

14. G. M. Hulbert, D. E. Baxa, and A. Seireg, "Criterion for Quantitative Rating of Optimum Design of Concert Halls," *Journal of the ASA*, vol. 71, no. 3, March 1982.

15. Y. Ando, "Calculation of Subjective Preference at Each Seat in a Concert Hall," *Journal of the ASA*, vol. 74, no. 3, September 1983.

16. L. Cremer and H. A. Müller, translated by T. J. Schultz, *Principles and Applications of Room Acoustics*, vol. 1, London: Applied Science Publishers, 1982.

17. M. Barron, "The Subjective Effects of First Reflections in Concert Halls—The Need for Lateral Reflections," *Journal of Sound and Vibration*, vol 15, no. 4, 1971.

18. T. J. Schultz, "Acoustics of the Concert Hall," *IEEE Spectrum*, vol. 2, no. 6, June 1965.

19. T. J. Schultz, "The Design of Concert Halls," *Forum*, University of Houston, vol. 14, no. 2–3, Summer/Fall 1976.

20. L. L. Beranek, "Audience and Seat Absorption in Large Halls," *Journal of the ASA*, vol. 32, no. 6, June 1960.

21. T. J. Schuitz and B. G. Watters, "Propagation of Sound Across Audience Seating," *Journal of the ASA*, vol. 36, no. 9, May 1964.

22. G. C. Izenour, *Theater Design*, New York: McGraw-Hill, 1977.

23. J. Eargle, "Sound Fields, Part 3," *dB The Sound Engineering Magazine*, vol. 16, no. 12, December 1982.

24. P. Parkin and K. Morgan, "Assisted Resonance in the Royal Festival Hall, London; 1965–1969," *Journal of the ASA*, vol. 48, no. 5, 1970.

25. "Sound System Design for the Eugene Performing Arts Center," *Recording Engineer/Producer*, vol. 13, no. 6, December 1982.

26. K. Yamaguchi, T. Fujita, F. Kawakami, and H. Sotome, "Design of an Auditorium Where Electroacoustical Technology is Fully Available: Exhibition Hall of Yamaha Sportland TSUMAGOI," *Journal of the ASA*, vol. 62, no. 5, November 1977.

27. H. Chaudiere, "Ambiophony, Has Its Time Finally Arrived?" AES Preprint 1492 (F-12), 63rd Convention, May 1982.

28. L. L. Doelle, *Environmental Acoustics*, New York: McGraw-Hill, 1972.

29. C. M. Harris, *Handbook of Noise Control*, Second Edition, New York: McGraw-Hill, 1979.

30. F. H. Richardson, *Motion Picture Handbook*, New York: Chalmers Publishing, p. 217, 1916.

31. H. C. Hardy, "Acoustical Factors in the Design of Motion Picture Equipment," *Journal of the SMPTE*, vol. 50, no. 2, p. 139, February 1948.

32. W. A. Müeller, "Audience Noise as a Limitation to the Permissible Volume Range of Dialogue in Sound Motion Pictures," *Journal of the SMPE*, vol. 35, no. 1, p. 48, July 1940.

33. A. P. Hill, "Combined Reverberation Time of Electrically Coupled Rooms," *Journal of the ASA*, vol. 4, no. 1, part 1, p. 63, July 1932.

34. V. S. Mankovsky, *Acoustics of Studios and Auditoria*, New York: Focal Press, pp. 47–50, 1971.

35. J. P. Maxfield, "Some Physical Factors Affecting the Illusion in Sound Motion Pictures," *Journal of the ASA*, vol. 3, no. 1, part 1, p. 69, July 1931.

36. C. C. Potwin, "The Control of Sound in Theaters and Preview Rooms," *Journal of SMPE*, vol. 32, no. 2, p. 119, August 1940.

37. M. Rettinger, *Acoustic Design and Noise Control*, Second Edition, New York: Chemical Publishing, p. 97, 1973.

38. As given for instance in *Planning a Cinema*, Eindhoven, N. V. Philips Gloeilampenfabrieken, 1964, *passim*.

39. T. Uzzle, "Acoustics and Electroacoustics of the Cinema Theatre," read before the 100th meeting of the ASA, November 18, 1980.

40. T. Uzzle and R. Sinclair, "Sound Transmission of Perforated Theatre Screens: a Preliminary Study," read before the 69th meeting of the AES, May 12, 1981.

41. M. Rettinger, "Sound Transmission Through Perforated Screens," *Journal of SMPTE*, vol. 91, no. 12, p. 1171, December 1982.

42. M. Z. Wysotsky, *Wide-Screen Cinema and Stereophonic Sound*, New York: Focal Press, pp. 123–124, 1971.

ADDITIONAL BIBLIOGRAPHY FOR ROOMS FOR SPEECH

R. H. Bolt and R. B. Newman, "Architectural Acoustics," *Architectural Record*, April, June, September, and November 1950.

M. D. Egan, *Concepts in Architectural Acoustics*, New York: McGraw-Hill, 1972.

R. B. Newman, "Acoustics," *Time Saver Standards for Architectural Design Data*, New York: McGraw-Hill, 1974.

ADDITIONAL BIBLIOGRAPHY FOR ROOMS FOR MUSIC

Y. Ando, M. Takaiski, and K. Toda, "Calculations of the Sound Transmission over Theatre Seats and Methods for Its Improvement in the Low-Frequency Range," *Journal of the ASA*, vol. 72(2), August 1982.

D. Dutsch, editor, *The Psychology of Music*, New York: Academic Press, 1982.

C. M. Hutchins, editor, *The Physics of Music*, Readings from *Scientific American*, San Francisco: W. H. Freeman and Co., 1978.

V. O. Knudsen and C. M. Harris, *Acoustical Designing in Architecture*, New York: ASA, 1978.

M. R. Schroeder, "Binaural Dissimilarity and Optimum Ceilings for Concert Halls: More Lateral Sound Diffusion," *Journal of the ASA*, vol. 65, no. 4, pp. 958–963, April 1979.

T. J. Schultz, *Concert Hall Tour of North America*, monograph by Bolt Beranek and Newman, Cambridge, Massachusetts, October 1980.

ADDITIONAL BIBLIOGRAPHY FOR ROOMS FOR CINEMA

L. L. Beranek, moderator, "Forum on Motion Picture Theatre Acoustics," *Journal of the SMPTE*, vol. 57, no. 2, pp. 145–169, August 1951.

R. Stoddard, *Theatre and Cinema Architecture: a Guide to Information Sources*, Detroit: Gale Research, 1978. (A book-length bibliography of books and articles.)

H. Stote, editor, *The Motion Picture Theater*, New York: SMPTE, pp. 151–186, 1948.

CHAPTER **8**

Acoustics of Open Plan Rooms

by Rollins Brook*

8.1 SPEECH PRIVACY IN OPEN PLAN ROOMS

Open plan offices have become very popular because of their lower construction costs and their continuing efficiencies in maintenance and ease of rearrangement with changing needs and changing tenants. The principal disadvantage of the open arrangement is the lack of aural privacy. Workers are distracted, sometimes annoyed, by overheard conversations and noise from nearby workstations. More serious is the lack of speech privacy where some degree of confidentiality is required.

Relief from the distractions of intruding noise and conversations as well as the need for speech privacy can be achieved through a combination of careful architectural planning, application of a low-level masking noise, and proper arrangement and use of the space. None of these alone is likely to be successful; they must be applied together in a carefully planned synergism.

The required architectural planning consists of two basic steps:

1. Provide an acoustical barrier in the direct sound path between the workstations that are to be protected from each other,
2. Eliminate reflected sound paths between the stations.

The masking noise system should be adjusted to provide:

1. A spectrum shape designed to provide maximum degradation of speech intelligibility,
2. An overall sound quality and loudness that is not itself a source of annoyance.

One of the chief advantages of the open plan is the ease of reconfiguring the office. The user, therefore, has some responsibilities in establishing and maintaining acceptable speech privacy. These are:

1. Adequate separation between workstations,
2. Proper orientation of the workstations to each other,
3. Speech effort (level) of the workers,
4. Defining the degree of privacy required for each worker.

8.2 RATING SCALE FOR OPEN PLAN ROOMS

Each of the factors contributing to speech privacy can be indexed to a rating scale. The individual ratings add together to yield an overall rating that can be equated with a level of speech privacy and a prediction of acceptability. Several rating scales have been developed.[1–3] One that has been shown to be effective relates all parameters to the articulation index (AI).[1] (AI is discussed in Chapter 7). A simple procedure for estimating speech privacy has been developed based upon this AI rating system.

Speech privacy is basically a study in signal-to-noise. It has been shown that annoyance as well as speech intelligibility are functions of signal-to-noise and, within broad limits, are not functions of absolute signal level. If speech cannot be understood, it is not very distracting to nearby workers. Studies of the subjective perception of privacy by workers in open plan offices have established the ratings shown here:

Articulation Index	**Perception**
0.00–0.05	confidential privacy, no distraction
0.05–0.20	normal privacy, little distraction
0.20–0.35	marginal privacy, some distraction
0.35–0.50	no privacy, substantial distraction
0.50–1.00	no privacy, good communication

8.3 ACOUSTICAL DESIGN OF BARRIERS IN OPEN PLAN ROOMS

In an open plan office, a *barrier* is, by definition, a partial-height device. It must be high enough to provide an acoustical line-of-sight interruption between workstations, usually about 5 ft for seated workers and higher for standees. Additional height is desirable for increased effectiveness. In order to provide good isolation, if the barrier does not turn around the workstation forming a partial box, it should be the longer of 10 ft or twice the barrier height. The transmission loss of the barrier is provided by a dense inner core weighing at least 1 lb/ft^2. This core should be covered on both sides with an effective sound-absorbing material (a $\geq$ 0.9 in the speech frequencies) in order to prevent reflections off the surface of the barrier.

There will be a diffraction of sound, especially the lower and middle frequencies, over the top of the barrier. In an otherwise properly treated room, this diffraction effect will set the limit of the insertion loss of the barrier. Under the best of conditions, the practical limitation on the insertion loss will be about 12 dB (AI loss of 0.4) in the speech intelligibility range. There are many barriers on the market with poorer performance. Fig. 8-1 shows the typical range of insertion loss in decibels to be expected from barriers. Fig. 8-2 shows the barrier performance expressed in terms of AI loss. Note that the contribution of the barrier to AI loss is not a linear function and that it is dependent upon the AI extant without the barrier in place.

It is evident from these charts that although a barrier is vital to the success of an open plan design, its contribution is not always as significant as we might expect. Maximum effectiveness is often not achieved because of

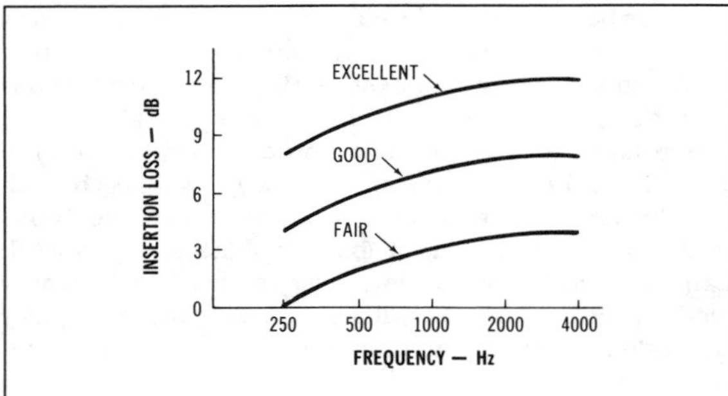

Figure 8-1 Typical insertion loss curves for barriers used in open plan rooms. *(After Reference 1.)*

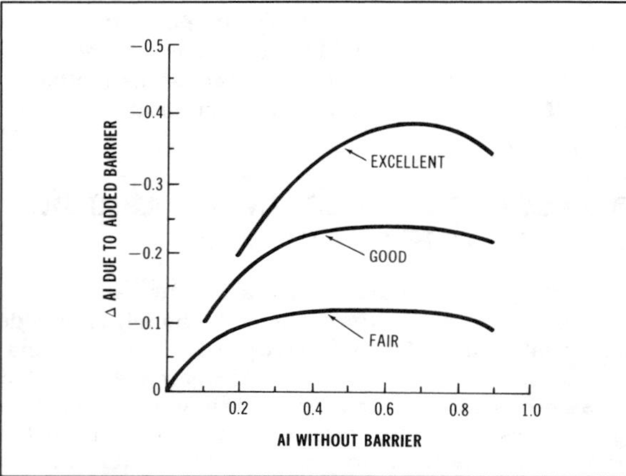

Figure 8-2 Articulation indexes change with barriers of different performance qualities. *(After Reference 1.)*

an esthetic desire to keep the height low or because low-cost, lower-mass construction is used. Do not assume an AI loss greater than about 0.25 unless a higher figure is supported by test data.

8.4 ACOUSTICAL DESIGN OF REFLECTION PATHS IN OPEN PLAN ROOMS

The architectural design goal should be to eliminate all reflection (flanking) paths around barriers by providing a room with no sound-reflecting surfaces. In such a perfect room, sound will diminish at a rate of 20 log (distance ratio) or a 6-dB reduction with each doubling of distance (the inverse-square law). In very good actual construction, fall-off rates of 4 to 5 dB per distance doubled are achieved [13 to 17 log (distance ratio)]. Rates of 2- to 3-dB reduction per distance doubled are found in poor rooms [7 to 10 log (distance ratio)].

The floor, ceiling, walls, and windows are potential surfaces that may provide reflection paths around barriers. Barriers, file cabinets, and other large furniture items should be considered in the category with walls. It is a basic assumption that the floor will be carpeted and that the ceiling will be treated with an effective sound-absorbing material. Hard walls and windows will become significant reflecting surfaces unless they are covered with absorbent material, shielded by the arrangement of the barriers, or angled to reflect only into an absorbent material.

The most difficult flanking path to eliminate is often that provided by the plastic lens on a ceiling-mounted lighting fixture. A 2 × 4-ft lighting fixture located in the ceiling midway between two workstations can destroy an otherwise successful isolation plan, as illustrated in Fig. 8-3. The ideal arrangement would be to provide indirect lighting from recessed coves that do not expose any reflective surfaces in the ceiling. Another commonly used indirect lighting approach, called task-ambient lighting, incorporates up-lighting fixtures in the barriers or other office furniture. Where these acoustically neutral lighting systems cannot be employed, locating the ceiling fixture directly over the workstation is better than a location between stations, but this may be a poor long-term solution because the workstation layouts may be changed in the future.

8.5 MASKING NOISE IN OPEN PLAN ROOMS

To provide effective speech masking, the noise should have a spectrum shape similar to that of average speech, especially in the main intelligibility range above 500 Hz. The spectrum must also have a balanced, nonirritating quality. The spectrum shown in Fig. 8-4 has been found to be effective and acceptable in hundreds of offices over a period of 20 years of testing. The range below about 250 Hz will almost always be filled in by the rumble of the heating, ventilating, and air-conditioning system.

The sound pressure level must be high enough to provide useful masking but not so high as to be annoying. A sound pressure level of 40 dB in the octave band centered at 1000 Hz is a common design goal. A level of 45 dB is likely to be judged as too loud, whereas 35 dB probably will not provide a useful degree of masking. There is a linear relationship between the articulation index and the masking noise level; a 3-dB change in the noise level produces a 0.1 change in the articulation index.

The sound field should be uniform throughout the office, not only to maintain uniform effectiveness but also because a lack of uniformity will make the noise more noticeable as workers move about the office. A uniformity of ±2 dB is an attainable and useful goal in most spaces. The question often arises whether the masking noise should be extended into support spaces such as store rooms, restrooms, corridors, or nearby enclosed offices. While

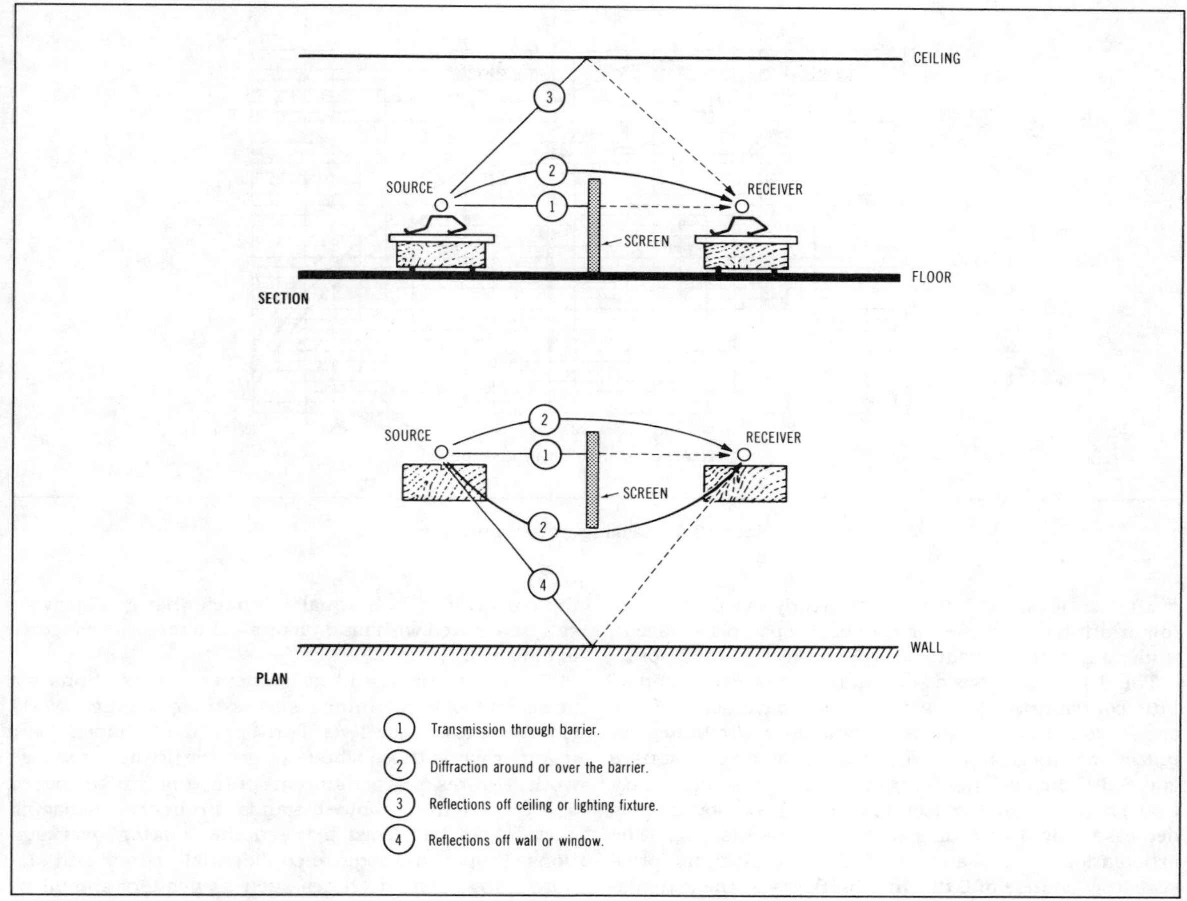

Figure 8-3 Typical sound paths.

extending the noise system into these areas is costly, such extended coverage is useful in maintaining an easily ignored background status for the noise. This factor grows in significance when noise levels above 40 dB (1-kHz octave band) are employed.

In order to be effective and to remain in the ignored background, the masking noise must be continuous. Intermittent sounds such as traffic or typewriter noise do not provide effective masking. Background music systems are sometimes used for masking. Because music has natural variations in level, it is often necessary to have the peak levels rather high in order to have effective masking during low passages. Many people find background music distracting or annoying.

Although the ideal masking noise spectrum sounds similar to the air register noise of many HVAC systems, air noise is rarely a reliable masking source. In many air systems the rate of flow—hence, the noise level—will vary with the load demand. Also, the noise field produced rarely meets the uniformity requirement.

It is evident that only an electronically produced noise will meet the criteria for adjustable spectrum and level. Although this masking noise is sometimes referred to as white noise, it actually has a carefully adjusted spectrum that is neither white nor pink noise. The subjective evaluation of the sound generated by a masking system is enhanced by the use of two or three separate noise channels. In such systems, adjacent loudspeakers receive noise from different generators. The multichannel system produces a noncoherent sound field that is more "listenable" than a single-channel system. Careful planning and installation of the loudspeakers are necessary to provide the required uniformity in the sound field.

8.6 USE RESTRICTIONS IN OPEN PLAN ROOMS

The arrangement of workstations within an open plan space can have a profound impact upon the effectiveness

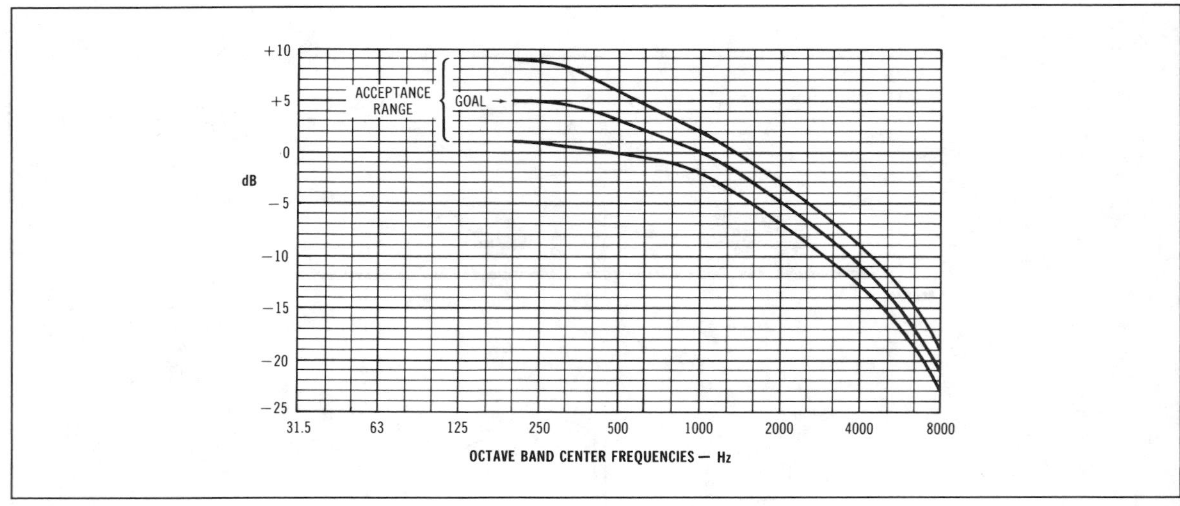

Figure 8-4 Masking noise spectrum.

of the privacy control measures already discussed. It is important for the owner or user of an open plan office to understand the consequences of changes in the layout.

The distance between workstations makes an important contribution to privacy. As we have seen, if the absorption in the room has completely eliminated all reflections, then sound will decay by the inverse-square law, 6 dB with each doubling of distance. It is more likely that some low-level reflections remain, so sound may decrease only 4 or 5 dB per doubling of distance. The articulation index changes by 0.2 with each sound pressure level change of 6 dB. In a 5-dB space, the articulation index change is 0.166.

When devoid of acoustical reflections, the level of speech perceived by the listener will change about 10 dB (an articulation index change of 0.3) as the talker changes orientation from 0° (face-to-face) to 180°. If the talker remains fixed while the listener turns away, the listener will not perceive much change in level, but the ability to judge the direction of origin will be degraded. Privacy may be improved by as much as 0.3 articulation index points by having the talker face away from a nearby workstation. It is, of course, impossible to arrange an office (greater than two workers) where all workstations can be oriented at 180°. The orientation among workstations throughout an office will vary from 0° to 180°.

How loudly a person talks will have a profound effect upon the degree of speech privacy available. Even "normal" speech effort varies in sound pressure level among people, and there certainly will be a considerable range between low and raised speech efforts. Variations in speech levels from low to normal to raised may yield an articulation index range of 0.6. Planning should be based upon a normal voice effort. If the design were based on low-level speech, it is unlikely that the workers would long accept the constraints. It is equally unlikely that good privacy can be assured with loud talkers—the range of remedies is too small.

The arrangement and assignment of workstations is a powerful tool in planning a successful open office. Workers who require a low level of privacy can be grouped closer together while those who need greater privacy or whose work requires a larger amount of talking can be spaced apart. Often filing cabinet islands or other extra-spacing devices can be placed between the "talking" workstations. People who require confidential privacy and stations with noisy machines such as printers should be very much removed from all others or placed in fully enclosed rooms.

8.7 ANALYSIS PROCEDURE FOR OPEN PLAN ROOMS

The five basic variables discussed previously are shown in a normalized position on a scale in Fig. 8-5, where the relative value of AI = 0 is the starting point. This arrangement yields an actual AI of 0.72, which is completely unacceptable for speech privacy. The analysis or design process begins by adjusting each of the five variables and combining the AI changes with the base 0.72 until the final AI rating falls within the design goal range selected from the previous list of the relationships between AI and average perception of speech privacy and distraction.

For example, with the addition of a barrier of good quality, the 0.72 base will be diminished by 0.25. Another −0.15 will come from increasing the masking noise level to 40 dB. The articulation index at the subject workstation is now 0.32. Another −0.15 is required to be well into the normal privacy range. This additional reduction

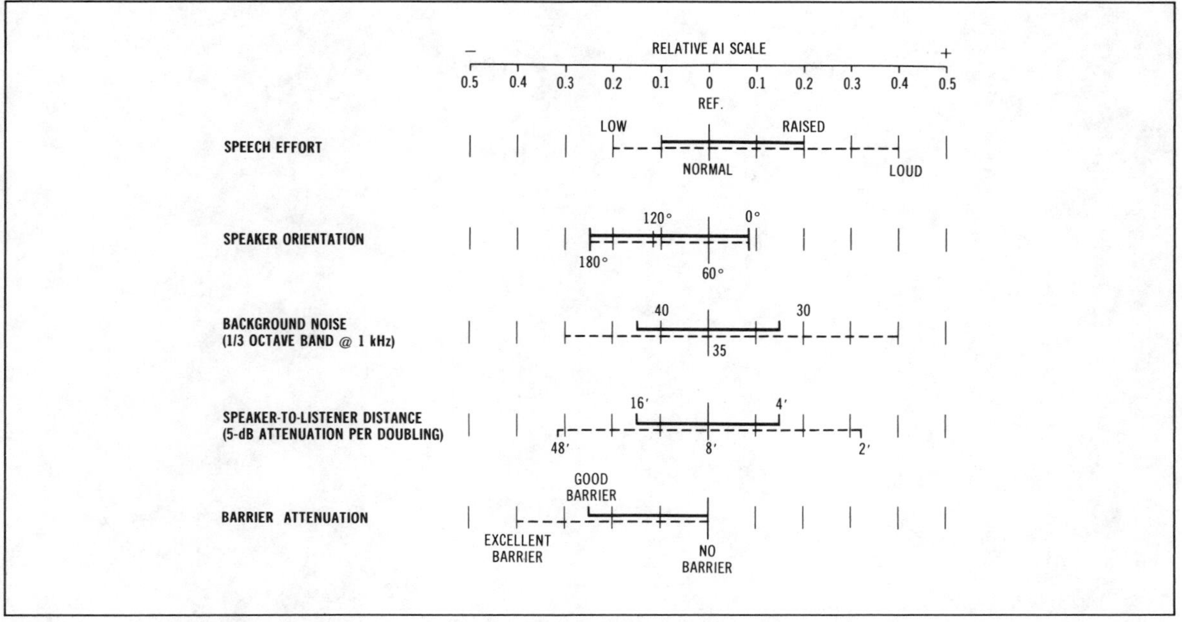

Figure 8-5 Summary of five variables. Typical ranges in the value of AI are indicated by the solid bars. Broken bars show extreme ranges. *(After Reference 1.)*

could come by changing the orientation between workstations, by a doubling of the distance between stations, by an improvement in the quality of the barrier, or by a combination of actions.

The analysis continues station by station until the entire office area has been examined. There is no reliable shortcut that allows the whole space to be analyzed in one computation. A careful examination of Fig. 8-5 will show that it is very difficult, but possible, to design an open plan office with effective speech privacy.

REFERENCES

1. R. Pirn, "Acoustical Variables in Open Planning," *Journal of the ASA*, vol. 49, pp. 1339–1345, May 1971.
2. W. J. Cavanaugh, W. R. Farrell, P. W. Hirtle, and B. G. Watters, "Speech Privacy in Buildings," *Journal of the ASA*, vol. 34, pp. 475–492, April 1962.
3. M. D. Egan, *Concepts in Architectural Acoustics*, New York: McGraw-Hill, 1972.

PART 2

Electronic Components for Sound Engineering

CHAPTER **9**

Resistors, Capacitors, and Inductors

by Glen Ballou

9.1 RESISTORS[1–3]

Resistance is associated with the phenomenon of energy dissipation. In its simplest form, it would be a measure of the opposition to the flow of current by a piece of electric material. Resistance dissipates energy in the form of heat; the best conductors have low resistance and produce little heat, whereas the poorest conductors have high resistance and produce the most heat. For instance, if a current of 10 A flowed through a resistance of 1 Ω, the heat would be 100 W. If the same current flowed through 100 Ω, the heat would be 10,000 W, which is determined by the formula

$$P = I^2R \tag{9-1}$$

where,
P is the power in watts,
I is the current in amperes,
R is the resistance in ohms.

In a pure resistance, the voltage and current relationship remains the same; therefore, the voltage drop across the resistor is

$$V = IR \tag{9-2}$$

where,
V is the voltage in volts,
I is the current in amperes,
R is the resistance in ohms.

Resistors are normally either fixed or variable and have tolerances from 1 to 20% and power ranges from 0.1 W to hundreds of watts.

9.1.1 Resistor Characteristics

Resistors will change value as a result of applied voltage, power, ambient temperature, frequency change, mechanical shock, or humidity.

The *voltage coefficient* is the rate of change of resistance due to an applied voltage, given in percent parts per million per volt (% ppm/V). Normally negative for most resistors, some semiconductor devices increase in resistance with applied voltage.The voltage coefficient of very high-valued carbon-film resistors, for instance, is rather large, and that for wirewound resistors is usually negligible. *Varistors* are resistive devices designed to have a large voltage coefficient.

The *temperature coefficient (TC)* is the rate of change in resistance with ambient temperature, usually stated as parts per million per degree celsius (ppm/°C). Many types of resistors increase in value as the temperature increases, while others, particularly hot-molded carbon types, have a maximum or minimum in their resistance curves that gives a zero temperature coefficient at some temperature. Metal film and wirewound types have temperature coefficient values of less than 100 ppm/°C. Thermistors are resistance devices designed to have a large temperature coefficient.

The *power coefficient* is the product of the temperature coefficient and temperature rise per watt, which gives a power coefficient in percent per watt (%/W), indicating the change in value resulting from applied power.

The ac resistance value changes with frequency because of the inherent inductance and capacitance of the resistor plus the skin effect, eddy current losses, and dielectric loss.

All resistors have one by-product in common when put into a circuit: they produce heat, because power is dissipated any time a voltage, V, is impressed across a resistance R. This power is calculated from Eq. 9-1 or

$$P = V^2/R \tag{9-3}$$

where,
P is the power in watts,
V is the voltage in volts,
R is the resistance in ohms.

As can be seen, changing the voltage, while holding the resistance constant, changes the power by the square of the voltage. For instance, a voltage change from 10 to 12 V changes the power 44%. Changing the voltage from 10 to 20 V changes the power 400%.

Changing the current while holding the resistance constant has the same effect as a voltage change. For instance, changing the current from 1 to 1.2 A increased the power 44%, whereas changing from 1 to 2 A increases the power 400%.

Changing the resistance while holding the voltage or current constant changes the power linearly. If the resistance is changed from 1 kΩ to 800 Ω and the voltage remains the same, the power will increase 20%. If the resistance is changed from 500 Ω to 1 kΩ, the power will change 50%. Note that an increase in resistance causes a decrease in power.

Changing the resistance while holding the current constant is also a linear power change. In this example, increasing the resistance from 1 to 1.2 kΩ increases the power 20%, whereas increasing the resistance from 1 to 2 kΩ increases the power 100%.

It is important to size resistors to take into account changes in voltage or current. Remember, if the resistor remains constant and voltage is increased, current also increases linearly. This is determined by using Ohm's law (Eq. 9-1) or

$$R = V/I \tag{9-4}$$

or,

$$I = V/R$$

When carbon resistors operate, they are normally cool to touch (40°C), while wirewound or ceramic resistors are designed to operate at temperatures up to 140°C. Wherever power is dissipated, it is imperative that adequate ventilation is provided to eliminate thermal destruction of the resistor and surrounding components.

The values of the resistor are either printed on the resistor, as in power resistors, or are color coded on the resistor. The color code for resistors is shown in Fig. 9-1.

9.1.2 Types of Resistors[1]

Every material that conducts electrical current has *resistivity*, which is defined as the resistance of a material to electric current. Resistivity is normally defined in terms of the resistance (in ohms) of a 1-cm per side cube of the material measured from one surface of the cube to the opposite surface. The measurement is stated in ohms per centimeter cubed (Ω/cm^3). The inverse of resistivity is conductivity. Good conductors have low resistivity, and good insulators have high resistivity. Resistivity is important because it shows the difference between materials and their opposition to current, making it possible for resistor manufacturers to offer products with the same resistance but differing electrical, physical, mechanical, or thermal features. The following is the resistivity of various materials:

Material	Resistivity
Aluminum	0.0000028
Copper	0.0000017
Nichrome	0.0001080
Carbon	0.0001850 (varies)
Typical Ceramic	100,000,000,000,000 or (10^{14})

9.1.2.1 Carbon-Composition Resistors

Carbon-composition resistors are the least expensive resistors and are widely used in circuits that are not critical to input noise and do not require tolerances better than ± 5%.

The carbon-composition, hot-molded version is basically the same product it was more than 40 years ago. Both the hot- and cold-molded versions are made from a mixture of carbon and a clay binder. In some versions, the composition is applied to a ceramic core or armature. Although in the inexpensive version, the composition is a monolithic rigid structure. Carbon-composition resistors may be from 5 Ω to many megohms and 0.1 to 4 W. The most common power rating is ¼ and ½ W with resistance values from 220 to 470,000 Ω.

Carbon-composition resistors offer well-established reliability and are still being specified for military and aerospace equipment. They also can withstand higher surge currents than carbon-film resistors. Resistance values, however, are subject to change upon absorption of moisture and increase rapidly at temperatures much above 60°C. Noise also becomes a factor when carbon-composition resistors are used in hi-fi and communication applications. A carbon-core resistor, for example, generates electronic noise that can reduce the readability of a signal or even mask it completely.

9.1.2.2 Carbon-Film Resistors

Carbon-film resistors are leaded ceramic cores with thin films of carbon applied. Although carbon films offer closer tolerances and better temperature coefficients than carbon compositions, most characteristics are virtually identical for a large number of general purpose, noncritical applications where neither reliability, surge currents, or noise are crucial factors.

9.1.2.3 Metal-Film Resistors

Metal film resistors are discrete devices formed by depositing metal or metal oxide films on an insulated core.

The metals are usually either nichrome sputtered on ceramic or tin oxide on ceramic or glass. Another method is to screen or paint powdered metal and powdered glass that is mixed in an ink or paste-like substance on a porous ceramic substrate. Firing or heating in an oven bonds the materials together. This type of resistor technology is called *cermet technology*.

Metal film resistors are most common in the 1- to 100-kΩ range and ¼ to ½ W with tolerances of ± 1%.

The temperature coefficient of resistance (TCR) is in the ± 100 ppm/°C range for all three technologies. Yet there are subtle differences:

- Cermet covers a wider resistance range and handles higher power than nichrome deposition.
- Nichrome is generally preferred over tin oxide in the upper and lower resistance ranges and can provide TCRs that are lower than 50 ppm/°C.
- Tin oxide is better able to stand higher power dissipation than nichrome.

9.1.2.4 Wirewound Resistors

Wirewound resistors have resistive wire wound on a central ceramic core. One of the oldest technologies, wirewounds provide the best-known characteristics of high-temperature stability and power-handling ability.

Nichrome, Manganin, and *Evanohm* are the three most widely used wires for wirewound resistors.

Wirewound resistors in the 0.01-Ω to 1-MΩ range are common. Tolerance is ±2% and TCR is ± 10 ppm/°C.

Wirewound resistors are generally classed as *power* or *instrument-grade products*. Power wirewounds, capable of handling as much as 1500 W, are wound from uninsulated coarse wire to provide better heat dissipation. The unit is given an overall electrical insulation coating of silicone.

Instrument-grade precision wirewound resistors are made from long lengths of finely insulated wire. After

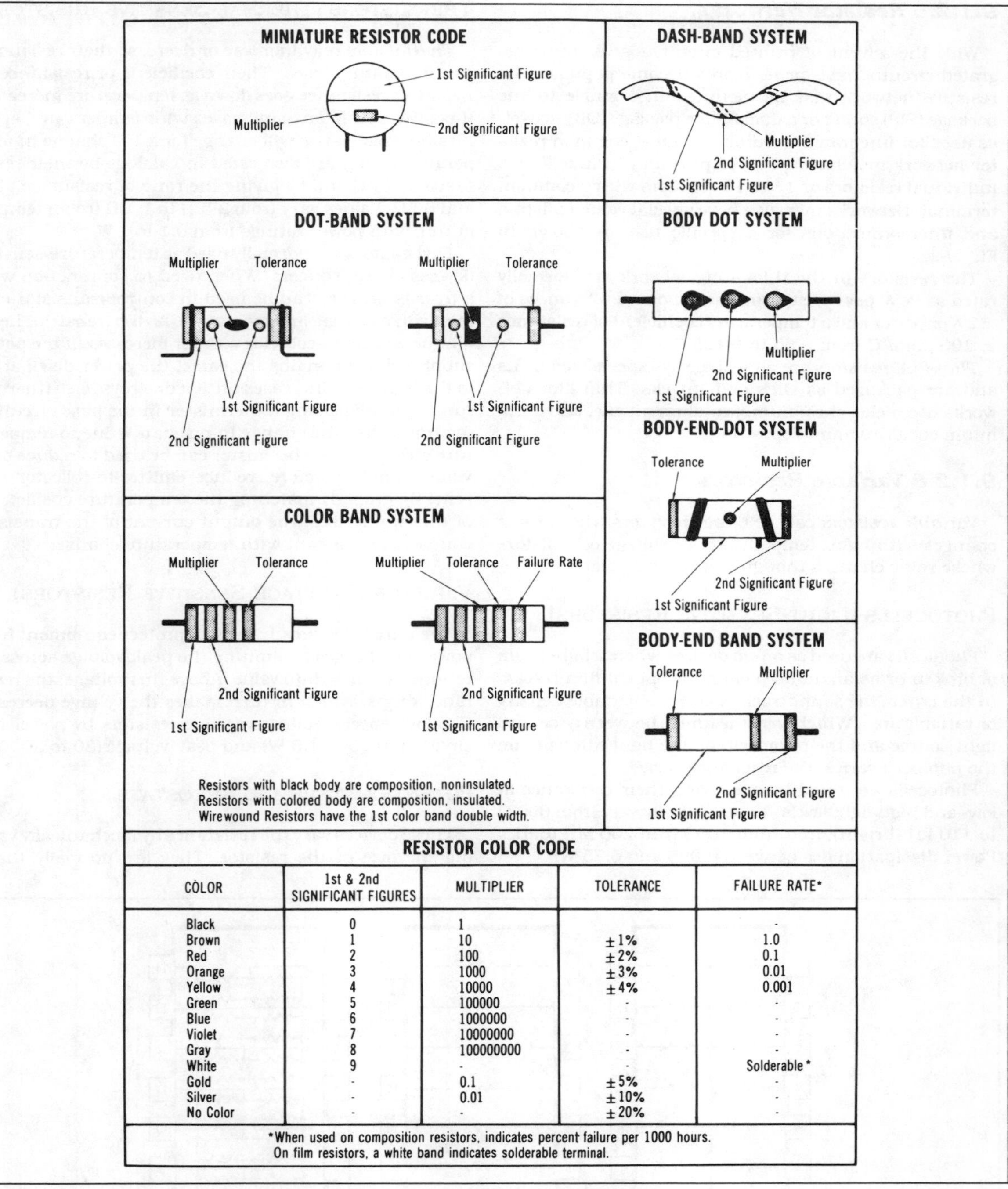

RESISTOR COLOR CODE

COLOR	1st & 2nd SIGNIFICANT FIGURES	MULTIPLIER	TOLERANCE	FAILURE RATE*
Black	0	1		-
Brown	1	10	±1%	1.0
Red	2	100	±2%	0.1
Orange	3	1000	±3%	0.01
Yellow	4	10000	±4%	0.001
Green	5	100000	-	-
Blue	6	1000000	-	-
Violet	7	10000000	-	-
Gray	8	100000000	-	-
White	9	-	-	Solderable*
Gold	-	0.1	±5%	-
Silver	-	0.01	±10%	-
No Color	-	-	±20%	-

*When used on composition resistors, indicates percent failure per 1000 hours. On film resistors, a white band indicates solderable terminal.

Figure 9-1 Color codes for resistors and capacitors.

winding, these are usually conformally coated with a ceramic material.

All wirewound resistors are classed as air-core inductors of the solenoid type; therefore, inductive reactance at high frequency alters the resistive value. The seriousness of this problem is directly proportional with frequency. Special winding is useful to cancel reactance at low frequencies.

9.1.2.5 Resistor Networks

With the advent of printed circuit boards and integrated circuits, *resistor networks* became popular. The resistive network may be mounted in a single in-line package (SIP) socket or a dual in-line package (DIP) socket, as used for integrated circuits. The most common resistor network may have 14 or 16 pins and include 7 or 8 individual resistors or 12 to 15 resistors with a common terminal. Networks may also have special value resistors and interconnections for a specific use, as shown in Fig. 9-2.

The resistors in the thick-film network are normally rated at ⅛ W per resistor and have normal tolerances of ±2% or better and a temperature coefficient of resistance ± 100 ppm/°C from −55 to +125°C.

Thin-film resistors are almost always specialized units and are packaged as DIPs or flatpacks. Thin-film networks use nickel chromium, tantalum nitride, and chromium cobalt vacuum depositions.

9.1.2.6 Variable Resistors

Variable resistors can be either resistors whose value changes with light, temperature, or voltage or resistors whose value changes though mechanical means.

Photocells (Light-Sensitive Resistors)

Photocells are used as off-on devices where a light beam is broken or as an audio pickup for optical film tracks. In the latter, the soundtrack is either a variable density or variable area. Whichever, the film is between a focused light source and the photocell. As the light intensity on the photocell varies, the resistance varies.

Photocells are rated by specifying their resistance at low- and high-light levels. These typically vary from 600 Ω to 110 kΩ (bright), and from 100 kΩ to 200 MΩ (dark). Power dissipation lies between 0.005 and 0.75 W.

Thermistors (Thermal-Sensitive Resistors)

Thermistors may increase or decrease their resistance as temperature rises. Their coefficient of resistance (if negative, resistance goes down as temperature increases; if positive, resistance increases with temperature) specifies how resistance will change for a 1°C change in temperature. They are also rated in catalogs by their resistance at 25°C and by giving the ratio of resistance at 0° and 50°C. Values vary from 2.5 Ω to 1 MΩ (room temperature), with power ratings from 0.1 to 1 W.

Thermistors are normally used as temperature-sensing devices or transducers. When used in conjunction with a transistor, they can be used to control transistor current with a change in temperature. As the transistor heats up, the emitter-to-collector current increases. If the power supply voltage remains the same, the power dissipation in the transistor increases until it destroys itself (thermal runaway). By placing a thermistor in the base circuit of the transistor, the change in resistance due to temperature change of the thermistor can be used to reduce base voltage and, therefore, reduce emitter-to-collector current. By properly matching the temperature coefficients of the two devices, the output current of the transistor can be held constant with temperature change.

Varistors (Voltage-Sensitive Resistors)

The *varistor* is mostly used to protect equipment from power-line surges by limiting the peak voltage across its terminals to a certain value. Above this voltage, the resistance drops, which in turn makes the voltage decrease. Catalogs specify voltage-variable resistors by power dissipation (0.25 to 1.5 W) and peak voltage (30 to 300 V).

Potentiometers and Rheostats

These devices vary the resistance by mechanically varying the size of the resistor. They are normally three-

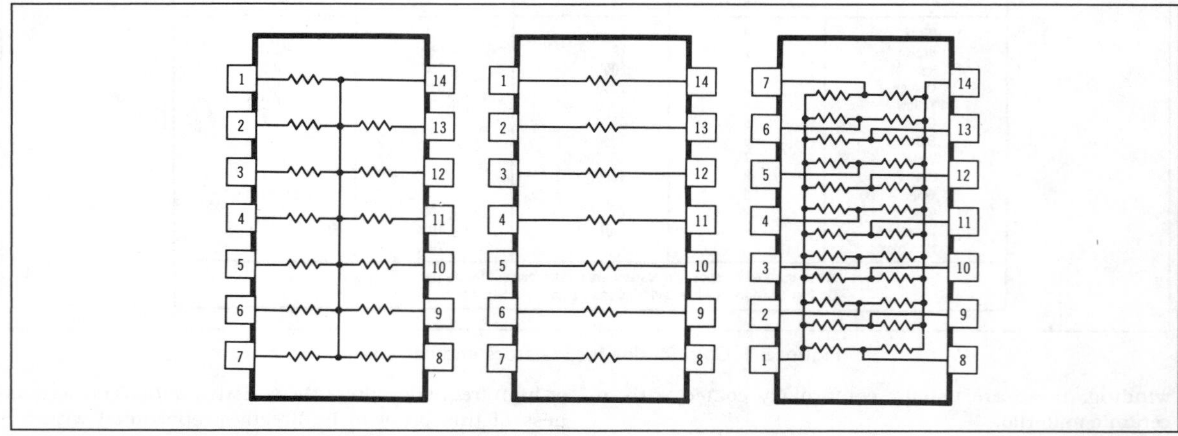

Figure 9-2 Various types of resistor networks.

terminal devices, two ends and one wiper, as shown in Fig. 9-3. By varying the position of the wiper, the resistance between either end and the wiper changes. Potentiometers may be wirewound or nonwirewound. The nonwirewound resistors usually have either a carbon or a conductive plastic coating. Potentiometers or pots may be 300° single turn or multiple turn, the most common being 1080° three turn and 3600° ten turn.

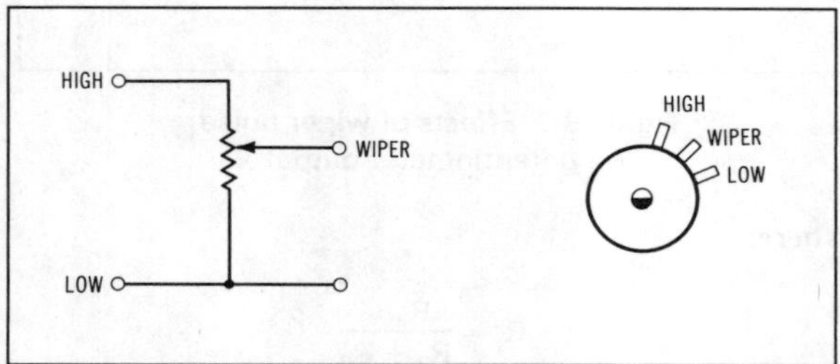
HIGH
WIPER
LOW
HIGH
WIPER
LOW

Figure 9-3 Standard three-terminal potentiometer.

Wirewound elements offer temperature coefficients of resistance (TCs) of ±50 ppm/°C and tolerances of ±5%. Resistive values are typically 10 Ω to 100 kΩ, with power ratings from 1 to 200 W.

Carbon elements have TCs of ±400 to ±800 ppm/°C and tolerances of ±20%. The resistive range spans 50 Ω to 2 MΩ, and power ratings are generally less than 0.5 watt.

Potentiometers may be either linear or nonlinear, as shown in Fig. 9-4. The most common nonlinear pots are counterclockwise semilog and clockwise semilog. The counterclockwise semilog pot is also called an audio taper pot because when used as a volume control, it follows the human hearing equal loudness curve. If a linear pot were used as a simple volume control, the first 20% of the pot would control the volume of the sound system. By using an audio taper pot (Fig. 9-4) the entire pot is used. Note that there is only a 10 or 20% change in resistance value between the common and wiper when the pot is 50% rotated. Pots are also produced with various taps. These taps are often used in conjunction with "loudness" controls.

Potentiometers also come in combinations of two or more units assembled for operation by a single control shaft or separately controlled by concentric shafts. Switches with various contact configurations can also be assembled to single or ganged potentiometers and arranged for actuation during the first few degrees of shaft rotation.

A *wirewound potentiometer* is made in the following manner.[2] A resistor is wound on a piece of insulating material in the form of a thin card, as shown in Fig. 9-5. After winding, the card is formed into a circle and fitted around a form. The card may be tapered to permit various rates of change of resistance for variable controls, as shown in Fig. 9-6. The wiper presses along the wire on the edge of the card.

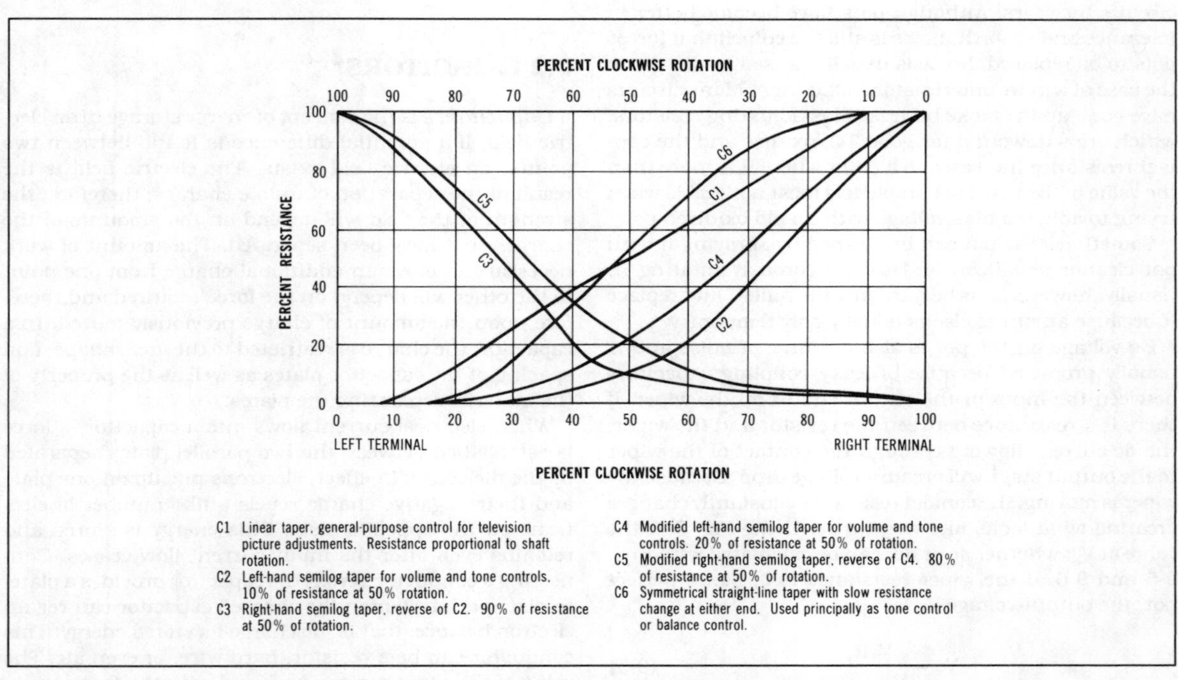
PERCENT CLOCKWISE ROTATION
100 90 80 70 60 50 40 30 20 10 0
PERCENT RESISTANCE
100
80
60
40
20
0
C1
C2
C3
C4
C5
C6
0 10 20 30 40 50 60 70 80 90 100
LEFT TERMINAL
RIGHT TERMINAL
PERCENT CLOCKWISE ROTATION
C1 Linear taper, general-purpose control for television picture adjustments. Resistance proportional to shaft rotation.
C2 Left-hand semilog taper for volume and tone controls. 10% of resistance at 50% rotation.
C3 Right-hand semilog taper, reverse of C2. 90% of resistance at 50% of rotation.
C4 Modified left-hand semilog taper for volume and tone controls. 20% of resistance at 50% of rotation.
C5 Modified right-hand semilog taper, reverse of C4. 80% of resistance at 50% of rotation.
C6 Symmetrical straight-line taper with slow resistance change at either end. Used principally as tone control or balance control.

Figure 9-4 Standard resistance taper (resistivity versus rotation) curve.

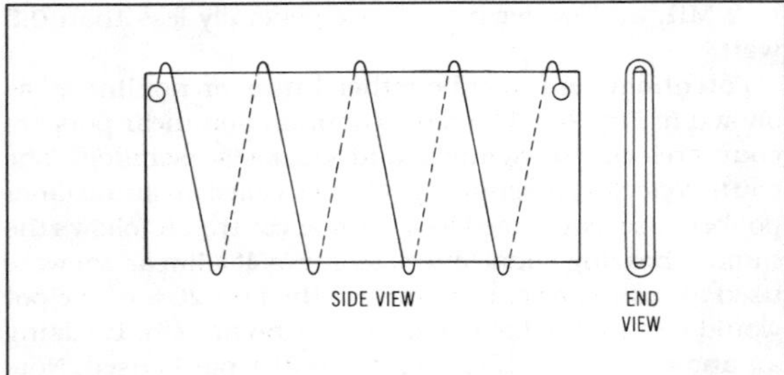

Figure 9-5 Construction of a fixed card wirewound resistor.

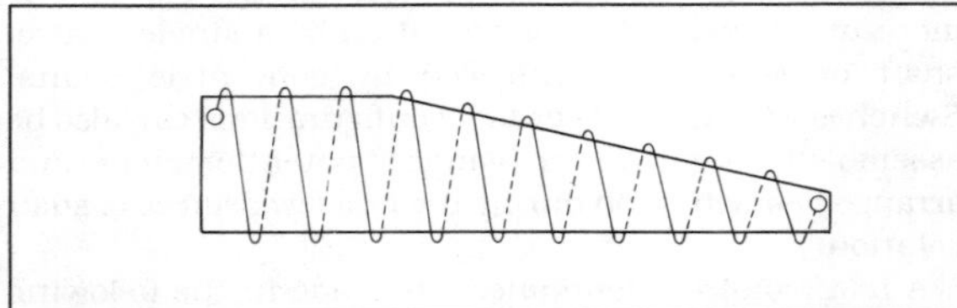
Figure 9-6 Construction of a tapered card wirewound resistor.

Contact Resistance

Noisy pots have been a problem that has plagued audio circuits for years. Although pots have become better in tolerance and so forth, noise is still the culprit that forces pots to be replaced. Noise is usually caused by dirt or, in the case of wirewound resistors, oxidation. Many circuits have gone up in smoke because bias-adjusting resistors, which are wirewound for good TC, oxidize and the contact resistance increases to a point where it is more than the value of the pot. This problem is most noticeable when trying to adjust a bias voltage with an old oxidized pot.

Sometimes the pot can be cleaned by spraying it with pot cleaner or silicon and then vigorously rotating it. Usually, however, it is best to "bite the bullet" and replace it because anything else is usually only temporary.

Dc voltage on the pot is also a source of noise and is usually produced because of leaky coupling capacitors between the input or the output circuit on the wiper. If there is a resistance between the resistor and the wiper, the dc current flowing through the contact of the wiper to the output stage will create a voltage drop. Because the wiper is moving, the contact resistance constantly changes creating what looks like varying ac. Using Fig. 9-7, the value at V_x, whether ac or dc, can be calculated with Eqs. 9-5 and 9-6. If the wiper resistance is 0, i.e., a perfect pot, the output voltage V_x is

$$V_x = \frac{V_1 R_y}{R_1 + R_y} \qquad (9\text{-}5)$$

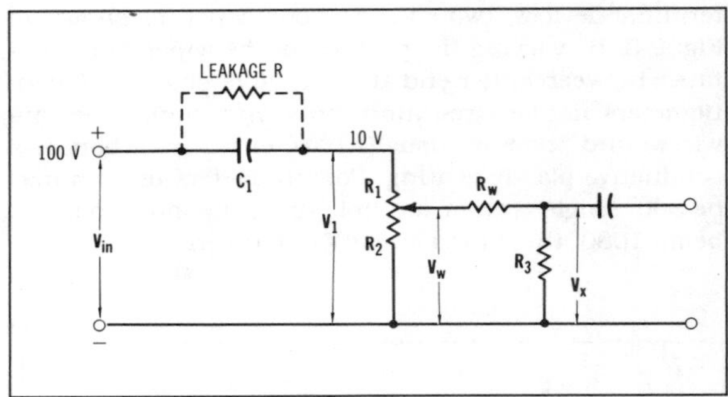

Figure 9-7 Effects of wiper noise on potentiometer output.

where,

$$R_y = \frac{R_2 R_3}{R_2 + R_3}$$

If a pot wiper has a high resistance, R_w, the output voltage V_x is

$$V_x = \frac{V_w R_3}{R_w + R_3} \qquad (9\text{-}6)$$

where,

$$V_w = \frac{V_1 R_2 (R_w + R_3)}{R_2 + R_w + R_3}$$

9.2 CAPACITORS[4–6]

Capacitance is the concept of energy storage in an electric field. If a potential difference is found between two points, an electric field exists. The electric field is the result of the separation of unlike charges; therefore, the strength of the field will depend on the amounts of the charges that have been separated. The amount of work necessary to move an additional charge from one point to the other will depend on the force required and therefore upon the amount of charge previously moved. In a capacitor, the charge is restricted to the area, shape, and spacing of the capacitor plates as well as the property of the material separating the plates.

When electrical current flows into a capacitor, a force is established between the two parallel plates separated by the dielectric. In effect, electrons pile up on one plate and their negative charge repels a like number of electrons on the opposite plate. This energy is stored and remains even after the input current flow ceases. Connecting a conductor across the capacitor provides a plate-to-plate path by which the charged capacitor can regain electron balance; that is, discharge its stored energy. This conductor can be a resistor, hard wire, or even air. The value of the capacitor can be found with the formula

$$C = AK/4.45D \quad (9\text{-}7)$$

where,
C is the value of the capacitor in picofarads,
A is the area of the plate in square inches,
K is the dielectric constant of the insulation,
D is the spacing in inches.

The work necessary to transport a unit charge from one plate to the other is

$$e = kg \quad (9\text{-}8)$$

where,
e is the energy per unit charge in volts,
g is the charge already transported in coulombs,
k is the proportionality factor between the work necessary to carry a unit charge between the two plates and the charge already transported; therefore:

$$k = 1/C,$$

where,
C is the capacitance in farads.

The value of a capacitor can now be calculated from the formula

$$C = q/e \quad (9\text{-}9)$$

where,
q is the charge in coulombs.

The *dielectric constant* is the property of a given material that determines the amount of electrostatic energy that may be stored in that material per unit volume for a given voltage. The value of the dielectric constant expresses the ratio of a capacitor in a vacuum to one using a given dielectric. The dielectric of air is one and is the reference unit employed for expressing the dielectric constant. If the dielectric constant of the capacitor is increased or decreased, the capacitance will increase or decrease, respectively. Table 9-1 lists the dielectric constants of various materials.

The dielectric constant of materials is generally affected by both temperature and frequency, except for quartz, Styrofoam®, and Teflon®, whose dielectric constants remain essentially constant. Small differences in the composition of a given material will also affect the dielectric constant.

Capacitors are used for both ac and dc applications. In dc circuits they are used to store and release energy, such as filtering power supplies, and for providing on demand, a single high-voltage pulse of current.

In ac circuits, they are used to block dc, allowing only ac to pass, bypassing ac frequencies, or discriminating between higher and lower ac frequencies. In a circuit with a pure capacitor, the current will lead the voltage by 90°.

Table 9-1. Dielectric Constants of Materials

Materials	Dielectric Constant (Approx)
Air	1.0
Amber	2.6–2.7
Bakelite (asbestos base)	5.0–22
Bakelite (mica filled)	4.5–4.8
Beeswax	2.4–2.8
Cambric (varnished)	4.0
Celluloid	4.0
Cellulose Acetate	3.1–4.5
Durite	4.7–5.1
Ebonite	2.7
Fiber	5.0
Formica	3.6–6.0
Glass (electrical)	3.8–14.5
Glass (photographic)	7.5
Glass (Pyrex)	4.6–5.0
Glass (window)	7.6
Gutta Percha	2.4–2.6
Isolantite	6.1
Lucite	2.5
Mica (electrical)	4.0–9.0
Mica (clear India)	7.5
Mica (filled phenolic)	4.2–5.2
Micarta	3.2–5.5
Mycalex	7.3–9.3
Neoprene	4.0–6.7
Nylon	3.4–22.4
Paper (dry)	1.5–3.0
Paper (paraffin coated)	2.5–4.0
Paraffin (solid)	2.0–3.0
Plexiglass	2.6–3.5
Polyethylene	2.3
Polystyrene	2.4–3.0
Porcelain (dry process)	5.0–5.5
Porcelain (wet process)	5.8–6.5
Quartz	5.0
Quartz (fused)	3.78
Rubber (hard)	2.0–4.0
Ruby Mica	5.4
Shellac (natural)	2.9–3.9
Silicone (glass) (molding)	3.2–4.7
Silicone (glass) (laminate)	3.7–4.3
Slate	7.0
Steatite (ceramic)	5.2–6.3
Steatite (low loss)	4.4
Styrofoam	1.03
Teflon	2.1
Vaseline	2.16
Vinylite	2.7–7.5
Water (distilled)	34–78
Wood (dry)	1.4–2.9

The value of a capacitor is normally written on the capacitor, and the sound engineer is only required to determine their effect in the circuit. Where capacitors are connected in series with each other, the total capacitance is

$$C_T = 1/[(1/C_1) + (1/C_2) + (1/C_n)] \quad (9\text{-}10)$$

and is always less than the value of the smallest capacitor. When connected in parallel, the total capacitance is

$$C_T = C_1 + C_2 + C_n \quad (9\text{-}11)$$

and is always larger than the largest capacitor.

When used in an ac circuit, the capacitive reactance, or the impedance the capacitor injects into the circuit, is important to know and is found with the formula

$$X_C = 1/2\pi fC \quad (9\text{-}12)$$

where,
f is the frequency in hertz,
C is the capacitance in farads.

When a dc voltage is impressed across a capacitor, a time (t) is required to charge the capacitor to the voltage, which is determined with the formula

$$t = RC \quad (9\text{-}13)$$

where,
R is the resistance in ohms,
C is the capacitance in farads.

In a circuit consisting of only resistance and capacitance, the time constant t is defined as the time it takes to charge the capacitor to 63.2% of the maximum voltage. In a circuit containing inductance and resistance, the time constant is defined as the time it takes for the current to reach 63.2% of its maximum value.

During the next time constant, the capacitor is charged or the current builds up to 63.2% of the remaining difference of full value, or to 86.5% of the full value. Theoretically, the charge on a capacitor or the current through a coil can never actually reach 100%, but it is considered to be 100% after five time constants have passed. When the voltage is removed, the capacitor discharges, and the current decays to 63.2% of the full value.

These two factors are shown graphically in Fig. 9-8. Curve A shows the voltage across a capacitor when charging, or the current through an inductance on buildup. Curve B shows the capacitor voltage when discharging or an inductance current decay. It is also the voltage across the resistor on charge or discharge.

Network transfer functions are the ratio of the input to output voltage for a given type of network containing resistive and reactive elements. The transfer functions for networks consisting of resistance and capacitance are given in Fig. 9-9. The expressions for the transfer functions of the networks are A equals 6.28 f, B equals RC, C equals R_1C_2, D equals R_2C_2, n is a positive multiplier. C is expressed in farads; f, in hertz; and R, in ohms.

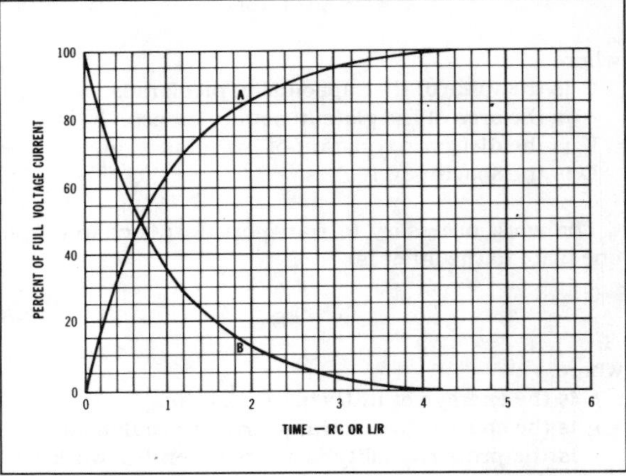

Figure 9-8 Universal time graph.

9.2.1 Characteristics

Various types of capacitors are shown in Fig. 9-10 along with a color code to indicate a certain capacitance and tolerance.

9.2.1.1 Capacitance

The capacitance of a capacitor is normally expressed in microfarads (μF or 10^{-6} farads) or picofarads (pF or 10^{-12} farads) with a stated accuracy or tolerance. Tolerance is expressed as ± (plus or minus) a certain percentage of the nominal or nameplate value. There is also a tolerance rating called *GMV*, an abbreviation for *guaranteed minimum value*, sometimes referred to as *MRV* or *minimum rated value*, which means that the capacitance is never less than the marked value when used under specified operating conditions, although it may amount to more than the nameplate value.

9.2.1.2 Equivalent Series Resistance

All capacitors have an *equivalent series resistance (ESR)* expressed in ohms or milliohms. This loss comes from lead resistance, termination losses, and dissipation in the dielectric material.

9.2.1.3 Equivalent Series Inductance

The *equivalent series inductance (ESL)* can be useful or detrimental. It does reduce the high-frequency use of the capacitor; however, it can be used in conjunction with the capacitor's capacitance to form a resonant circuit useful, for instance, for switcher-power supply filtering.

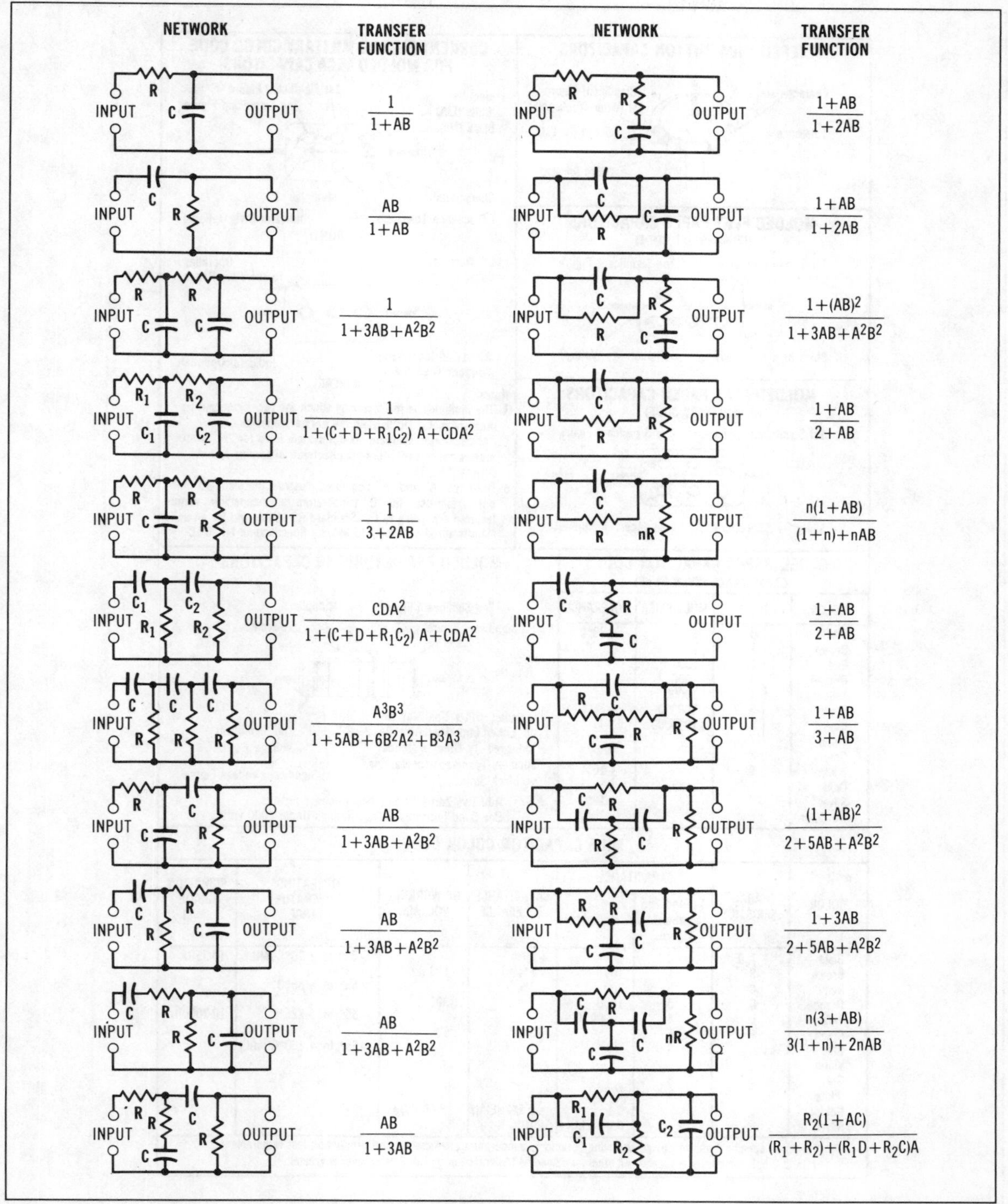

Figure 9-9 Resistance-capacitance network transfer functions.

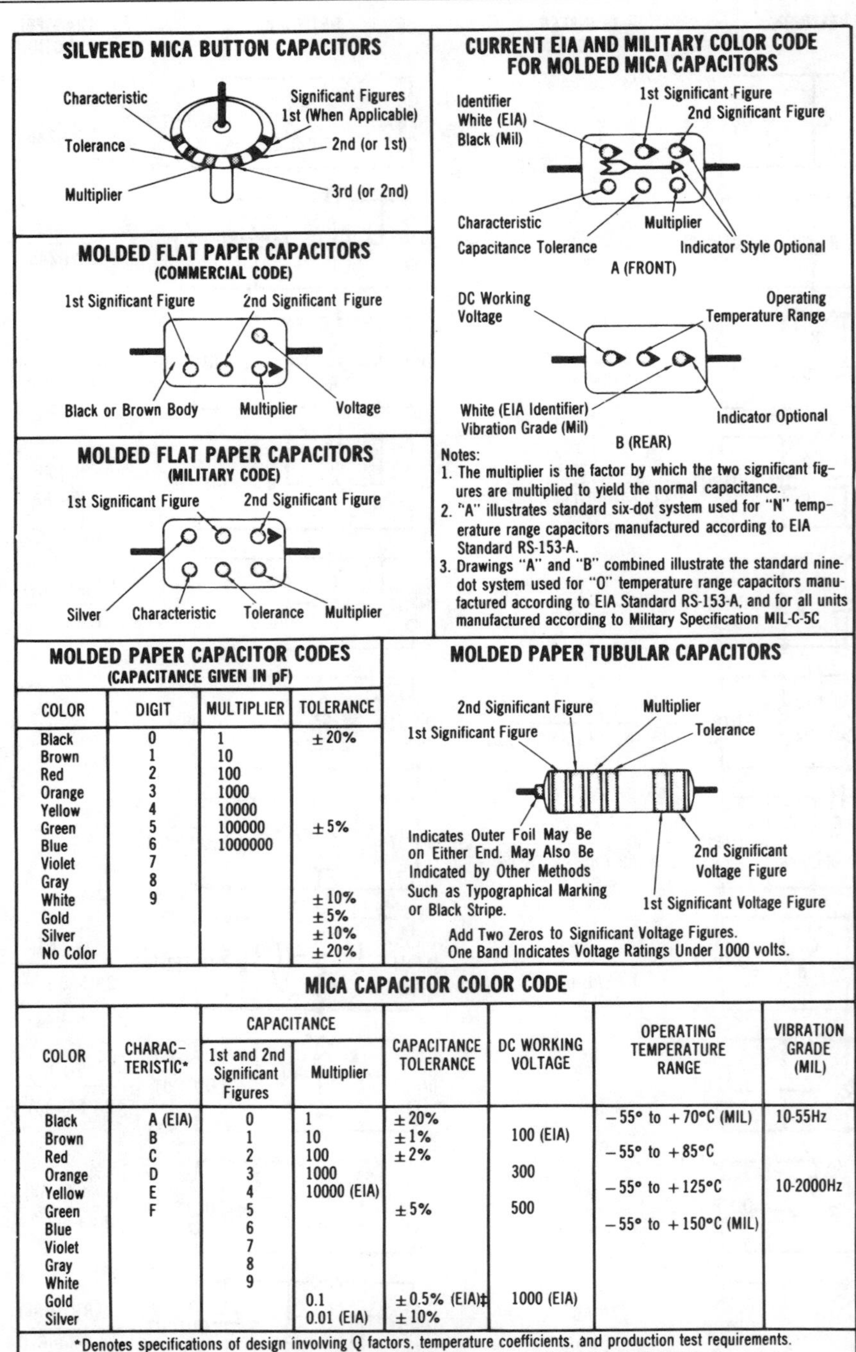

Notes:
1. The multiplier is the factor by which the two significant figures are multiplied to yield the normal capacitance.
2. "A" illustrates standard six-dot system used for "N" temperature range capacitors manufactured according to EIA Standard RS-153-A.
3. Drawings "A" and "B" combined illustrate the standard nine-dot system used for "O" temperature range capacitors manufactured according to EIA Standard RS-153-A, and for all units manufactured according to Military Specification MIL-C-5C

MOLDED PAPER CAPACITOR CODES
(CAPACITANCE GIVEN IN pF)

COLOR	DIGIT	MULTIPLIER	TOLERANCE
Black	0	1	±20%
Brown	1	10	
Red	2	100	
Orange	3	1000	
Yellow	4	10000	
Green	5	100000	±5%
Blue	6	1000000	
Violet	7		
Gray	8		
White	9		±10%
Gold			±5%
Silver			±10%
No Color			±20%

MICA CAPACITOR COLOR CODE

COLOR	CHARACTERISTIC*	CAPACITANCE: 1st and 2nd Significant Figures	CAPACITANCE: Multiplier	CAPACITANCE TOLERANCE	DC WORKING VOLTAGE	OPERATING TEMPERATURE RANGE	VIBRATION GRADE (MIL)
Black	A (EIA)	0	1	±20%		−55° to +70°C (MIL)	10-55Hz
Brown	B	1	10	±1%	100 (EIA)		
Red	C	2	100	±2%		−55° to +85°C	
Orange	D	3	1000		300		
Yellow	E	4	10000 (EIA)			−55° to +125°C	10-2000Hz
Green	F	5		±5%	500	−55° to +150°C (MIL)	
Blue		6					
Violet		7					
Gray		8					
White		9					
Gold			0.1	±0.5% (EIA)‡	1000 (EIA)		
Silver			0.01 (EIA)	±10%			

*Denotes specifications of design involving Q factors, temperature coefficients, and production test requirements.
‡On ±0.5pF, whichever is greater. All others are specified tolerance or ±1.0pF, whichever is greater.

Figure 9-10 Capacitor

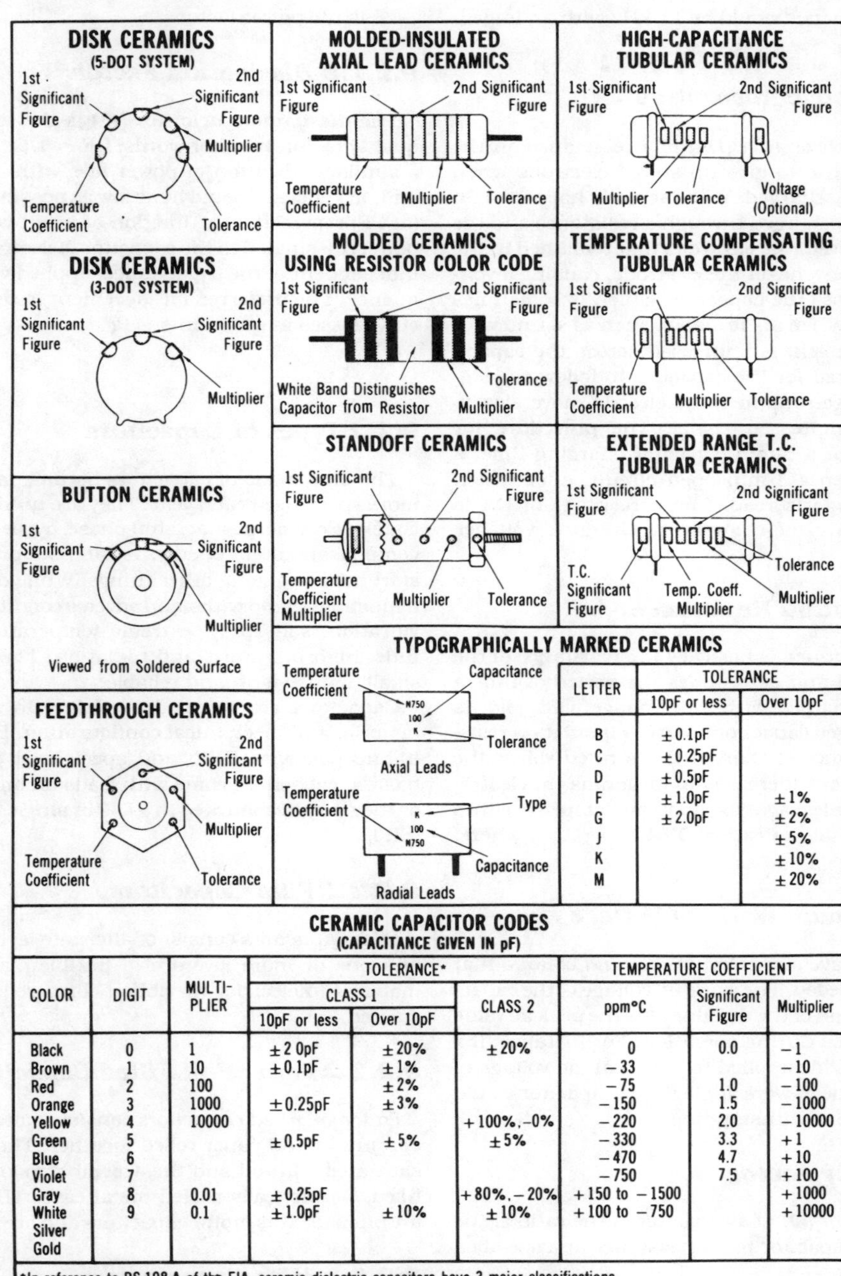

LETTER	TOLERANCE	
	10pF or less	Over 10pF
B	±0.1pF	
C	±0.25pF	
D	±0.5pF	
F	±1.0pF	±1%
G	±2.0pF	±2%
J		±5%
K		±10%
M		±20%

CERAMIC CAPACITOR CODES
(CAPACITANCE GIVEN IN pF)

COLOR	DIGIT	MULTI-PLIER	TOLERANCE* CLASS 1		TOLERANCE* CLASS 2	TEMPERATURE COEFFICIENT ppm°C	Significant Figure	Multiplier
			10pF or less	Over 10pF				
Black	0	1	±2 pF	±20%	±20%	0	0.0	−1
Brown	1	10	±0.1pF	±1%		−33		−10
Red	2	100		±2%		−75	1.0	−100
Orange	3	1000	±0.25pF	±3%		−150	1.5	−1000
Yellow	4	10000			+100%,−0%	−220	2.0	−10000
Green	5		±0.5pF	±5%	±5%	−330	3.3	+1
Blue	6					−470	4.7	+10
Violet	7					−750	7.5	+100
Gray	8	0.01	±0.25pF		+80%,−20%	+150 to −1500		+1000
White	9	0.1	±1.0pF	±10%	±10%	+100 to −750		+10000
Silver								
Gold								

*In reference to RS-198-A of the EIA, ceramic dielectric capacitors have 3 major classifications
Class 1, temperature compensating ceramics requiring high Q and capacitance stability.
Class 2, where Q and stability of capacitance are not required.
Class 3, low voltage ceramics, where dielectric losses, high insulation resistance, and capacitance stability are not of major importance. Tolerance on Class 3 Ceramic Capacitors is indicated by code, either ±20% (Code M) or +80%, −20% (Code Z).

color codes.

If a 10,000 μF capacitor had an inductance of 11.5 mH, the resonant frequency would be 11 kHz with an impedance of 0.005 Ω.

9.2.1.4 Dielectric Absorption[7]

The *dielectric absorption (DA)* is a reluctance on the part of the dielectric to give up stored electrons when the capacitor is discharged. What actually happens is if the capacitor is discharged through a resistance and the resistance is removed, the electrons that remained in the dielectric will reconvene on the electrode, causing a voltage to appear across the capacitor, which is sometimes called "memory." When an ac signal, such as sound with its high rate of attack, is impressed across the capacitor, time is required for the capacitor to follow the signal as the free electrons in the dielectric move slowly. The result is compressed signal. The procedure for testing DA calls for a 5-min capacitor charging time, a 5-s discharge, then a 1-min open circuit, after which the recovery voltage is read. The percentage of DA is defined as the ratio of recovery to charging voltages times 100.

9.2.1.5 Insulation Resistance

Insulation resistance is basically the resistance of the dielectric material and determines the period of time a capacitor, once charged with a dc voltage, will hold its charge. A discharged capacitor has a low insulation resistance; however, once it charges to its rated value, the insulation resistance increases to megohms. In electrolytic capacitors, the leakage current in milliamperes within the capacitor should not exceed 0.04(C) + 0.30, where, C is in microfarads.

9.2.1.6 Maximum Working Voltage

All capacitors have a *maximum working voltage* that should not be exceeded. The working voltage of the capacitor is a combination of the dc value plus the peak ac value that may be applied during operation. For instance, if a capacitor has 10-V dc applied to it and an ac voltage of 10-V rms or 14-V peak were applied, the capacitor would have to be capable of withstanding 24 V.

9.2.1.7 Quality Factor

The *quality factor (Q)* of a capacitor is the ratio of the reactance of the capacitor to its resistance at a specified frequency.

Q is found by the formula

$$Q = 1/(2\pi fCR) = 1/PF \tag{9-14}$$

where,

Q is the quality factor,
f is the frequency in hertz,
C is the value of capacitance in farads,
R is the internal resistance in ohms,
PF is the power factor.

9.2.1.8 Dissipation Factor

The *dissipation factor* (or DF) is the reciprocal of the quality factor. In other words, DF = 1/Q. It is, therefore, a similar indication of power loss within the capacitor and, in general, should be as low as possible. Power factor (or PF) represents the fraction of input volt-amperes (or power) dissipated in the capacitor dielectric. It is virtually independent of the capacitance, applied voltage, and frequency. The preferred measurement in describing capacitive losses in ac circuits is PF.

9.2.2 Types of Capacitors

The uses made of capacitors become more varied and more specialized each year. They are used to filter, tune, couple, block dc, pass ac, shift phase, bypass, feed through, compensate, store energy, isolate, suppress noise, and start motors among other things. While doing this, they frequently have to withstand adverse conditions like shock, vibration, salt spray, extreme temperatures, high altitude, high humidity, and radiation. They must also be small, lightweight, and reliable.

Capacitors are grouped according to their dielectric material and mechanical configuration. Because of dual in-line packages (DIP) and specialized printed circuit boards, capacitors come with leads on one or, two ends, or they may be mounted in a DIP or single in-line package (SIP).

9.2.2.1 Film Capacitors

Film capacitors consist of alternate layers of metal foil and one or more layers of a flexible plastic-insulating material (dielectric) in ribbon form rolled and encapsulated.

9.2.2.2 Paper Foil Filled Capacitors

Paper foil filled capacitors consist of alternate layers of aluminum and paper rolled together. The paper may be saturated with oil and the assembly mounted in an oil-filled, hermetically sealed metal case. These capacitors are often used as motor capacitors and are rated at 60 Hz.

9.2.2.3 Mica Capacitors

Mica capacitors are either alternate layers of metal foil and mica insulation, which are stacked together and encapsulated, or they are silvered mica. In the latter case, a silver electrode is screened on the mica insulators that are then assembled and encapsulated.

Mica capacitors have small capacitance values and are usually used in high-frequency circuits.

9.2.2.4 Ceramic Capacitors

Ceramic capacitors are the most popular capacitor for bypass and coupling application because of their variety of sizes, shapes, and ratings.

Ceramic capacitors also come with a variety of K values (dielectric constant).

The higher the K value, the smaller the size of the capacitor; however, it also means the capacitor is less stable. High-K capacitors have a dielectric constant in excess of 3000, are very small, and have values between 0.001 μF to several microfarads.

When temperature stability is important, capacitors with lower Ks, in the 10 to 200 region, are required. If a high-Q capacitor is also required, it will have to be physically larger. Ceramic capacitors can be made with a zero temperature change. These are called negative-positive-zero (NPO). They come in a capacitance range of 1.0 pF to 0.033 μF.

One temperature-compensated capacitor with a designation of N750 is used when accurate capacitance is required. The 750 means the decrease in capacitance with increase in temperature will be a 750 ppm/°C temperature rise. Translated, this means the capacitance value will decrease 1.5% for a 20°C temperature increase. N750 capacitors come in values between 4.0 and 680 pF.

9.2.2.5 Electrolytic Capacitors[7]

About 150 years after the Leyden jar (1745), the first electrolytic capacitor was made in Germany; its principle was discovered some 25 years earlier, in about 1870. Not until the late 1920s (after World War I), when power supplies replaced batteries in radio receivers, were aluminum electrolytics used in any quantities. At first, the electrolytics contained liquid electrolytes. These "wet" units disappeared during the late 1930s when the "dry" gel types took over.

But low temperatures still reduce performance and can even freeze electrolytes, while high temperatures can dry them out. What is more, the electrolytes themselves can leak and corrode the equipment. Also, repeated surges over the rated working voltage, excessive ripple currents, and high operating temperature reduce performance and shorten capacitor life. Much room is left for improvement.

However, to improve electrolytics much further, materials other than aluminum are probably required. Only tantalum, of all the possibilities, has proved to be commercially practical so far; unfortunately, the rapidly rising cost of tantalum has slowed its applications substantially.

The aluminum electrolytic is made up of two aluminum ribbons rolled up with a porous separator that has a fluid, gel, or paste electrolyte suspended in it. One foil is the positive plate, the electrolyte is the negative plate, and the second aluminum ribbon is the negative contact foil. The dielectric is a nonconductive aluminum oxide electrochemically formed on the surface of the positive foil.

Tantalum electrolytics are made like aluminum electrolytics, except a tantalum metal foil is used rather than aluminum. Solid-sintered anode types have the highest capacitance per unit volume. They use a porous tantalum slug as the positive plate with a tantalum oxide dielectric.

Solid-electrolyte tantalums contain no liquids or volatile constituents. A solid semiconductor is used rather than a liquid electrolyte. These capacitors are considered dry.

Electrolytic capacitors are inherently polarized. If the capacitor is installed in the circuit backwards, it will self-destruct, often shorting out. If an electrolytic capacitor is required in a nonpolarized installation, for instance, as capacitors in loudspeaker crossover networks, nonpolarized (NP) capacitors can be purchased. These capacitors basically are two capacitors back to back in one case.

New capacitors or capacitors that have not been used for a long time require "forming." Electrolytic capacitors that have been on the shelf or out of service for some time may measure only 40 to 60% of their rated capacitance. After they have been in use at their normal operating voltage for a short period, the capacitance will return to its normal value. Electrolytic capacitors should be reformed by operating them at their rated voltage before measuring the capacitance.

In general, electrolytic capacitors measuring 75% of their rated value should be replaced. In the use of bypass capacitors there is, from the application standpoint, usually no upper limit on the value. This is reasonably true for all filter capacitors, except for input capacitors used in power supplies. Here the limit is set by the permissible current through the rectifier element.

Electrolytic capacitors are quite satisfactory for frequencies below 500 kHz. However, at frequencies above 500 kHz, they lose their effectiveness quite rapidly. As an example, a 10-μF electrolytic capacitor at frequencies above 500 kHz will have an effective capacitance of only 0.5 μF.

It is customary, when electrolytic capacitors are used in circuits where the frequency may run from zero to several hundred thousand hertz, such as in a video amplifier, to connect additional paper and a mica capacitor in parallel with the electrolytic capacitor. The electrolytic capacitor operates quite effectively at audio frequencies, the paper capacitor operates through the middle range of radio frequencies, and the mica capacitors operate at the extremely high frequencies.

9.2.3 Identification

Capacitors are identified as to value, voltage, and tolerances either by their numeric values stamped on the case, such as electrolytics, or by a color code, as shown in Fig. 9-10.

9.3 INDUCTORS

Inductance is used for the storage of magnetic energy. Magnetic energy is stored as long as current keeps flowing through the inductor. The current of a sine wave lags the voltage by 90° in a perfect inductor.

The impedance of an inductor to an ac signal, inductive reactance (X_L), is found by the following formula

$$X_L = 2\pi fL \quad (9\text{-}15)$$

where,
f is the frequency in hertz,
L is the inductance in henrys.

The inductance of a coil is not affected by the type of wire used for its construction. However, the Q of the coil will be governed by the ohmic resistance of the wire. Coils wound with silver or gold wire have the highest Q for a given design.

To increase the inductance, place inductors in series. The total inductance will be

$$L_T = L_1 + L_2 + L_n \quad (9\text{-}16)$$

and will always be greater than the largest inductor.

To reduce the total inductance, place the inductors in parallel

$$L_T = 1/[(1/L_1) + (1/L_2) + (1/L_n)] \quad (9\text{-}17)$$

and the total inductance will always be less than the value of the lowest inductor.

The following is the relationship of the turns in a coil to its inductance:

1. The inductance is proportional to the square of the turns.
2. The inductance is increased as the permeability of the core material is increased.
3. The inductance increases as the cross-sectional area of the core material is increased.
4. The inductance is increased as the length of the winding is increased.
5. A shorted turn decreases the inductance. In an audio transformer, the frequency characteristic will be affected, and the insertion loss increased.
6. Inserting an iron core in a coil increases the inductance; hence, its inductive reactance is increased.
7. Introducing an air gap in an existing choke reduces the inductance.

The maximum voltage induced in a conductor moving in a magnetic field is proportional to the number of magnetic lines of force cut by the conductor moving in the field. A conductor moving parallel to the lines of force cuts no lines of force; therefore, no current is generated in the conductor. A conductor moving at right angles to the lines of force will cut the maximum number of lines per inch per second; therefore, the voltage will be at the maximum.

A conductor moving at any angle to the lines of force cuts a number of lines of force proportional to the sine of the angles. Thus,

$$E = BLv\sin\theta \times 10^{-8} \quad (9\text{-}18)$$

where,
B is the flux density,
L is the length of the conductor in centimeters,
v is the velocity in centimeters per second of the conductor moving at an angle θ.

The direction of the induced electromotive force (emf) is in the direction in which the axis of a right-hand screw, when turned with the velocity vector, moves through the smallest angle toward the flux density vector. This is called the right-hand rule.

The magnetomotive force produced by a coil is derived by multiplying the number of turns of wire (T) in the coil by the current (I in amperes) flowing through it. It is given in ampere turns:

$$\text{ampere turns} = T(V/R) = TI \quad (9\text{-}19)$$

The inductance of a single layer, a spiral, and multilayer coils can be calculated by the following methods. They may be calculated by using either Wheeler's or Nagaoka's formulas. The accuracy of the calculation will vary between 1 and 5%. Using Wheeler's formula for a single layer coil, as shown in Fig. 9-11A, the inductance may be calculated as follows:

$$L = B^2N^2/(9B + 10A)\,\mu H \quad (9\text{-}20)$$

For the multilayer coil, as shown in Fig. 9-11B,

$$L = 0.8B^2N^2/(6B + 9A + 10C)\,\mu H \quad (9\text{-}21)$$

For the spiral coil, as shown in Fig. 9-11C,

$$L = B^2N^2/(8B + 11C)\,\mu H \quad (9\text{-}22)$$

where,
B is the radius of the winding,
N is the number of turns in the coil,
A is the length of the winding,
C is the thickness of the winding.

9.3.1 Q

Q is the ratio of the inductive reactance to the internal resistance of the coil. The principal factors that affect Q are frequency, inductance, dc resistance, inductive reactance, and the type of winding. Other factors are the core

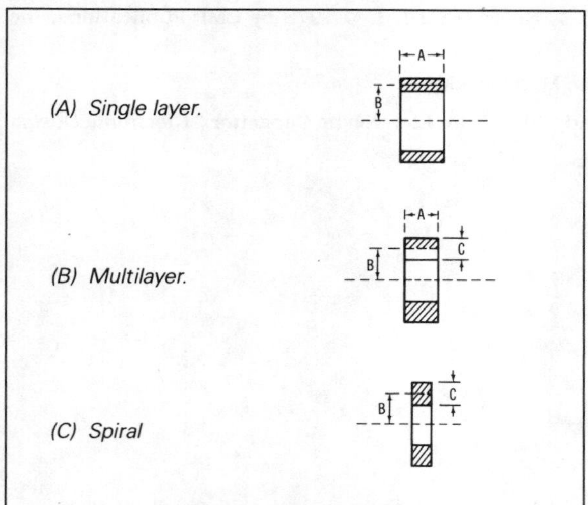

Figure 9-11 Single- and multiple-layer inductors.

losses, the distributed capacity, and the permeability of the core material.

The Q of the coil can be measured as follows. Using the circuit of Fig. 9-12, Q of a coil may be easily measured for frequencies up to 1 MHz. Since the voltage across an inductance at resonance equals QV (where, V is the voltage developed by the oscillator), it is necessary only to measure the output voltage from the oscillator and the voltage across the inductance.

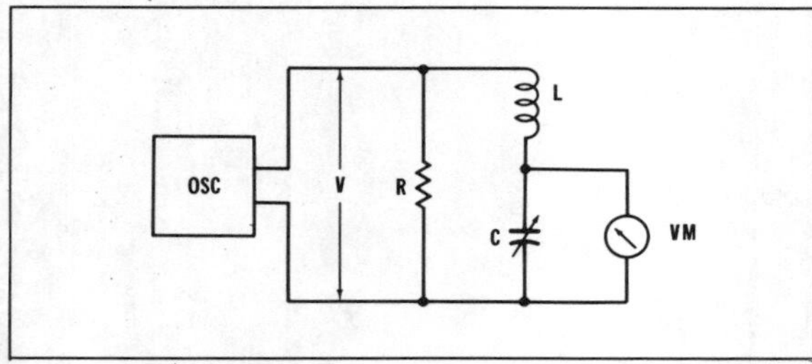

Figure 9-12 Circuit for measuring the Q of a coil.

The voltage from the oscillator is introduced across a low value of resistance R, about 1/100 of the anticipated radio-frequency resistance of the LC combination, to assure that the measurement will not be in error by more than 1%. For average measurements, resistor R will be on the order of 0.10 Ω. If the oscillator cannot be operated into an impedance of 0.10 Ω, a matching transformer may be employed. It is desirable to make C as large as convenient to minimize the ratio of the impedance looking from the voltmeter to the impedance of the test circuit. The voltage across R is made small, on the order of 0.10 V. The LC circuit is then adjusted to resonate and the resultant voltage measured. The value of Q may then be equated:

$$Q = \text{Resonant voltage across C/Voltage across R} \quad (9\text{-}23)$$

The Q of a coil may be approximated by the equation:

$$\begin{aligned} Q &= 2\pi fL/R \\ &= X_L/R \end{aligned} \quad (9\text{-}24)$$

where,

f is the frequency,
L is the inductance,
R is the dc resistance (as measured by an ohmmeter),
X_L is the inductive reactance of the coil.

9.3.2 Right-Hand Rule

The *right-hand rule* is a method devised for determining the direction of a magnetic field around a conductor carrying a direct current. The conductor is grasped in the right hand with the thumb extended along the conductor. The thumb points in the direction of the current. If the fingers are partly closed, the finger tips will point in the direction of the magnetic field.

Maxwell's rule states, "If the direction of travel of a right-handed corkscrew represents the direction of the current in a straight conductor, the direction of rotation of the corkscrew will represent the direction of the magnetic lines of force."

REFERENCES

1. "Basic Resistive Technology," *Hewlett-Packard Bench Briefs*, January, February, 1981. Sections reprinted with permission from *Bench Briefs*, a Hewlett-Packard service publication.
2. H. M. Tremaine, *Audio Cyclopedia*, Indianapolis: Howard W. Sams & Co., Inc., 1969.
3. "Resistive Components," *1979 Electronic Buyer's Handbook and Directory*, vol. 2, December 1978.
4. "Exploring the Capacitor," *Hewlett-Packard Bench Briefs*, September, October, 1979. Sections reprinted with permission from *Bench Briefs*, a Hewlett-Packard service publication.

5. "Capacitors," *1979 Electronic Buyer's Handbook,* vol. 1, November 1978. © 1978 by CMP Publications, Inc. Reprinted with permission.

6. W. G. Jung and R. March, "Picking Capacitors," *Audio,* March 1980.

7. "Electrolytic Capacitors: Past, Present and Future," and "What Is an Electrolytic Capacitor," *Electronic Design,* May 28, 1981.

CHAPTER **10**

Transformers

by Glen Ballou

A *transformer* is an electrical device consisting of one or more coils of wire wound on a magnetic material core. Electrical energy may be transmitted between one or several of the windings. Transformers designed for audio-frequency use must be capable of transmitting currents over a wide frequency range, in contrast to a power transformer that transmits currents over a narrow frequency band. Transformers for either service may be designed to step up or step down the current. Typical schematics for an audio and a power transformer are shown in Fig. 10-1A and B.

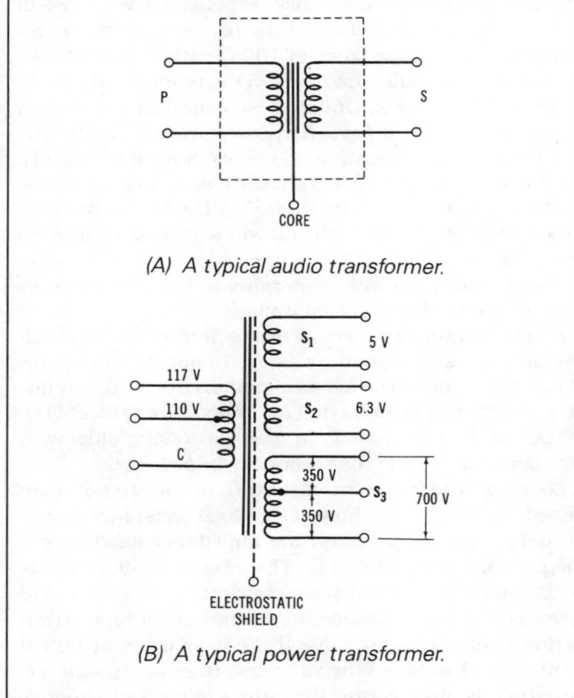

Figure 10-1 An audio transformer and a power transformer.

An *autotransformer* is a transformer with a single winding, as shown in Fig. 10-2. Such transformers may be designed for stepping the voltage up or down and may be used with any type equipment. Autotransformers are also constructed to be continuously variable over their entire range. The interior construction of a variable autotransformer manufactured by Gen Rad Co. and sold under the tradename of Variac® is pictured in Fig. 10-3.

The autotransformer used in this device consists of a single-layer winding on a toroidal core. As the shaft is rotated, a brush contact traverses the winding turn by turn; thus, the voltage may be varied from zero to full voltage. A tap on the winding permits the input voltage (line) to be changed, resulting in an overvoltage connection (0 to 140 V for a line voltage of 117 V). Autotransformers are sometimes used in audio amplifiers for interstage coupling and for impedance matching in loudspeaker systems.

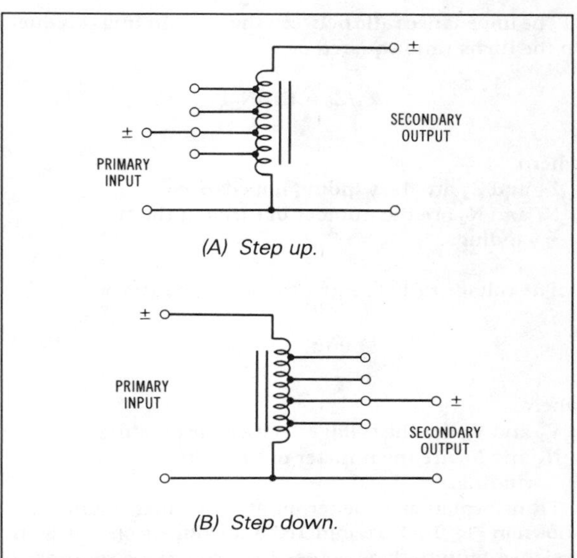

Figure 10-2 Two types of autotransformers.

Figure 10-3 Interior construction of a Gen Rad Variac® showing the autotransformer winding.

10.1 TRANSFORMER IMPEDANCE

A *transformer* is an impedance-matching device. Because it is connected between impedances of different values or to unterminated impedances, it is also used as a voltage or current multiplier or divider.

The impedance ratio between the two windings is equal to the turns ratio squared or

$$Z_1/Z_2 = (N_1/N_2)^2 \quad (10\text{-}1)$$

where,
Z_1 and Z_2 are the winding impedances,
N_1 and N_2 are the number of turns in the two windings.

The voltage ratio is equal to the turns ratio or

$$V_1/V_2 = N_1/N_2 \quad (10\text{-}2)$$

where,
V_1 and V_2 are the voltages across the winding,
N_1 and N_2 are the number of turns in the two windings.

Transformers may be terminated or unterminated, as shown in Fig. 10-4. Terminated transformers operate with resistive terminations across the primary or secondary or both, as shown in Fig. 10-4B to D. If a 500- to 50,000-Ω transformer is terminated on the secondary side with 50,000 Ω, looking into the primary will show an impedance of 500 Ω. The frequency response will show a loss of 1 dB at 80 and 7000 Hz. If the transformer is terminated by a 1000-Ω source impedance, the low-frequency response will be better than normal, or a loss of 1 dB at around 15,000 Hz.

Terminated transformers are used in circuits requiring a solid termination, such as a line, equalizer, filter, or similar devices.

An unterminated transformer is used to feed the input of a high-impedance, low-noise circuit. This connection is often referred to as an open-circuit connection and is generally employed in microphone and photocell preamplifiers. The source feeding the transformer is considered to be the transformer termination. An unterminated transformer should not be used to feed an equalizer, a filter, or an amplifier requiring a solid termination.

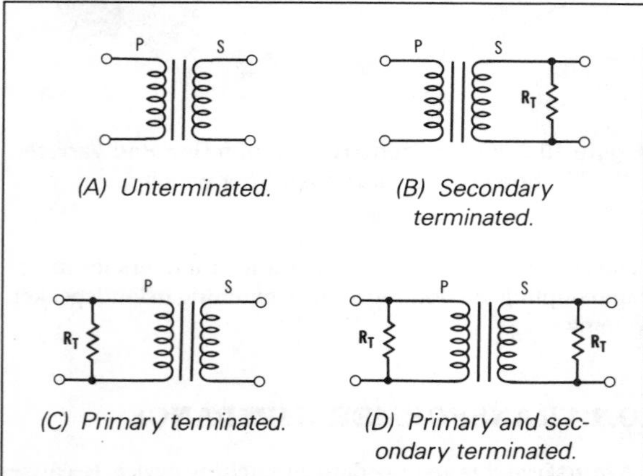

(A) Unterminated.

(B) Secondary terminated.

(C) Primary terminated.

(D) Primary and secondary terminated.

Figure 10-4 Transformer terminations.

The frequency characteristics of an unterminated transformer differ somewhat from those of a terminated transformer and are as follows: Assume a high-quality line-to-input transformer is designed to operate from a source impedance of 500 Ω, having a secondary impedance of 50,000 Ω, and the secondary is left unterminated. Under normal operating conditions, when the primary is terminated by a source impedance of 500 Ω, it will be assumed the frequency response shows a loss of 1 dB at 40 and 12,000 Hz. If the primary is now terminated by a line impedance of 100 Ω rather than 500 Ω, the loss of 1 dB will appear at 1/5 (by reducing 100/500) of 40 Hz, or at 8 Hz. Under these conditions, the high end may resonate at some frequency around 12,000 Hz.

If the primary termination is now changed to 1000 Ω, the frequency response will show a loss of 1 dB at 80 Hz, or the lowest frequency multiplied by the new impedance ratio (1000/500). The high end will start to drop around 7000 Hz.

These values are only approximate but are generally true of unterminated transformers.

A split-terminated transformer is terminated on both the primary and secondary sides, as shown in Fig. 10-4D. To illustrate how such terminations are used, assume an input transformer having an impedance ratio of 600/50,000 Ω is terminated on the secondary side with 100,000 Ω or double the secondary impedance.

Looking into the normal 600-Ω primary shows an impedance of 1200 Ω. Now, if a 1200-Ω resistance is connected across the primary, the impedance looking into the primary is again 600 Ω. The advantage of such termination is that the transformer primary presents a solid termination to the source impedance. This type termination is of particular value if the primary is being fed from a matched line. When a transformer using split termination is first connected into a circuit, frequency response measurements should be made to determine whether the frequency characteristics have materially changed from the original specifications.

The unknown impedance between taps of a transformer can be calculated with the formula

$$Z_3 = Z_2(\sqrt{Z_1/Z_2} - 1)^2$$

or, (10-3)

$$Z_3 = (\sqrt{Z_1} - \sqrt{Z_2})^2$$

where,
Z_3 is the unknown impedance,
Z_2 is the lower impedance tap,
Z_1 is the higher impedance tap.

As an example, assume it is desired to know the imped-

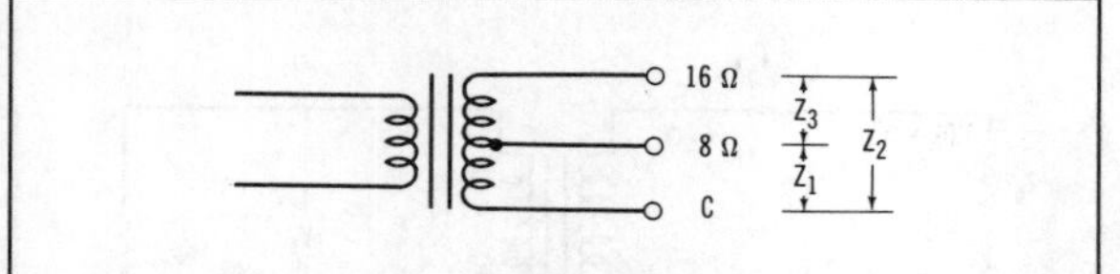

Figure 10-5 Impedances between taps of transformers.

ance Z_3 between the 8- and 16-Ω taps on the transformer illustrated in Fig. 10-5.

$$Z_3 = 8(\sqrt{16/8} - 1)^2$$
$$= 8(\sqrt{2} - 1)^2$$
$$= 8(1.41 - 1)^2$$
$$= 8(0.41)^2$$
$$= 8(0.1716)$$
$$= 1.37\ \Omega$$

Thus, the impedance between the 8- and 16-Ω taps is 1.37 Ω.

Transformers are generally used to step up or step down a voltage or to transfer power from one circuit to another. Because circuits differ in their impedance, if the maximum transfer of power is to take place, the turns ratio of the transformer must be such that an impedance match is effected between the two circuits, the source, and the load.

As an example, assume the 70-V output circuit of an amplifier is to be connected to a loudspeaker. Because an output may be 100 Ω and the loudspeaker only a few ohms, the transformer will have to be of such a turns ratio that the impedance reflected back by the loudspeaker will cause the primary of the transformer to present the correct load impedance to the amplifier. If the amplifier requires a load impedance of 100 Ω and the speaker is 8 Ω, the impedance ratio is 100/8 or 12.5/1.

For a transformer of this design, if an 8-Ω resistance is connected across the output winding, the reflected impedance seen by the amplifier will be 100 Ω. The turns ratio of the coils is 3.54 or the square root of 12.5. Thus, it may be said,

$$Z_s/Z_p = (N_s/N_p)^2 \tag{10-4}$$

or,

$$N_s/N_p = \sqrt{Z_s/Z_p} \tag{10-5}$$

where,

Z_s is the impedance of the secondary,
Z_p is the impedance of the primary,
N_s is the number of turns in the secondary winding,
N_p is the number of turns in the primary winding.

In a well-designed transformer, the impedance ratio will remain the same throughout the normal frequency band. If a pure capacitance or inductance is connected across the transformer rather than a resistance, the impedance seen by the primary will appear as a capacitance or inductance.

10.2 REFLECTED IMPEDANCE

The *reflected impedance* is the impedance seen when looking into a given winding of a transformer with one or more of the other windings terminated in a given load resistance.

To illustrate how the reflected impedance of a transformer winding is calculated, assume an ideal transformer (one with no losses) is available with a turns ratio of 20:1. The secondary winding (the smaller of the two) is terminated with a resistive load of 10 Ω, as shown in Fig. 10-6A. This is considered a step-down transformer since the secondary voltage is less than the primary voltage. The reflected impedance to the primary winding may be calculated

$$Z_1 = N^2R_L$$

or, (10-6)

$$Z_1 = N^2Z_2$$

where,

Z_1 is the primary impedance,
N is the turns ratio,
R_L is the load resistance in ohms across the secondary,
Z_2 is the secondary impedance.

The impedance seen by the input is the turns ratio (20) squared, or 400 times the impedance of (10 Ω) of the secondary. The 4000 Ω seen at the primary winding is the reflected impedance caused by the 10-Ω secondary terminating resistance. The 4000 Ω will only be seen when the secondary is terminated in 10 Ω. If the primary impedance is measured with the secondary unterminated, only the actual inductive reactance of the primary coil will be measured. For the step-up transformer shown in Fig. 10-6B, the equation is

$$Z_1 = Z_2/N^2$$
$$= R_L/N^2 \tag{10-7}$$

where,

Z_1 is the smaller impedance of the two windings,
Z_2 is the larger impedance of the two windings,
N^2 is the impedance ratio (turns ratio squared),
R_L is the load resistance in ohms.

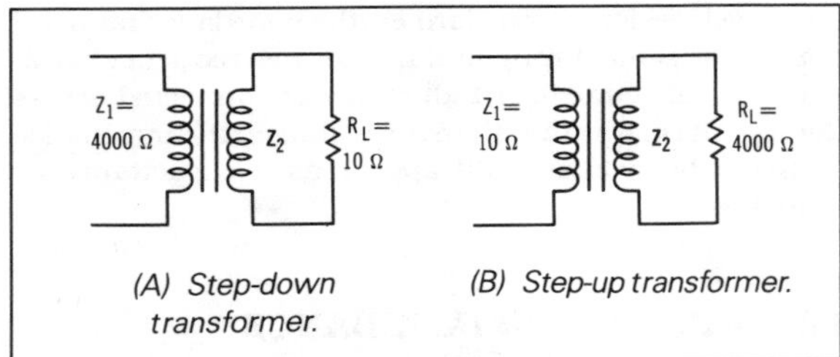

(A) Step-down transformer.
(B) Step-up transformer.

Figure 10-6 Reflected impedance by termination of a transformer winding.

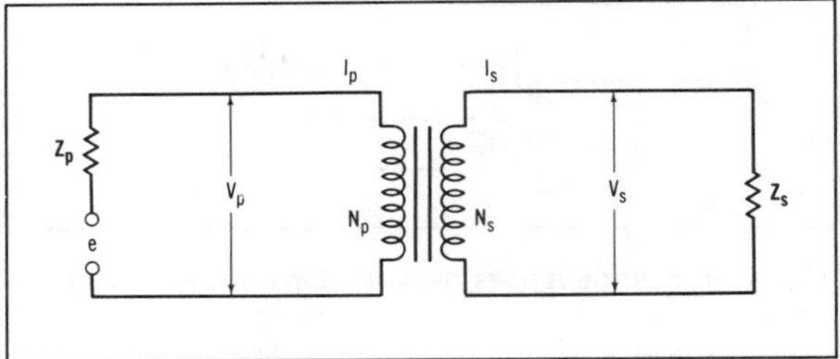

Figure 10-7 The electrical circuit of an ideal transformer with 100% efficiency.

A transformer does not supply an impedance but is designed to effect an impedance match between two circuits by supplying the correct turns ratio between the source and load impedances. Transformers will only present the correct impedance match when they are properly terminated. If the transformer is of the correct turns ratio, the correct load impedance will be reflected by the secondary winding load resistance. If the transformer has more than one winding, only one must be terminated, unless the transformer is designed to operate with a double termination. In the practical transformer, the distributed capacity and leakage are also reflected to the primary side.

10.3 TRANSFORMER LOSSES

An ideal transformer (Fig. 10-7) has no electrical losses. None of the electrical energy is lost in producing the magnetic field in the iron core, nor as heat in the windings. Furthermore, all the lines of flux of the changing current in one winding link all the turns of the other winding. Actually, this is not possible because there are always some losses regardless of the design and materials used; therefore, all transformers have losses.

A simple transformer with its various parameters is shown in Fig. 10-8A and B. In addition to the power transfer characteristics, the primary inductance L_m shunts the source impedance shown in Fig. 10-8C. A leakage reactance L_L, which in effect is in series with the load, and a distributed capacity C (due to the winding of the coils) are also in shunt with the source impedance.

As the frequency of the input signal decreases, the primary inductance also decreases. This decrease of inductance may reach a point where some of the power that is normally transferred from the primary to the secondary is shunted through the inductance, as shown in Fig. 10-9A. If the frequency of the signal voltage is increased, the impedance of the distributed capacity decreases and shunts a portion of the power that would normally be passed to the load, as shown in Fig. 10-9B.

The transfer of electrical energy from the primary to the secondary of a transformer depends on the magnetic lines of force linking both the primary and secondary windings. In an ideal transformer, 100% of the lines of force would be utilized, and the maximum transfer of energy would take place without loss.

The foregoing situation can never be achieved because a certain number of the magnetic lines of force leak off into the air. This leakage is called leakage reactance. Leakage reactance is reduced in a transformer by the core material, core design, and the geometry of the coils.

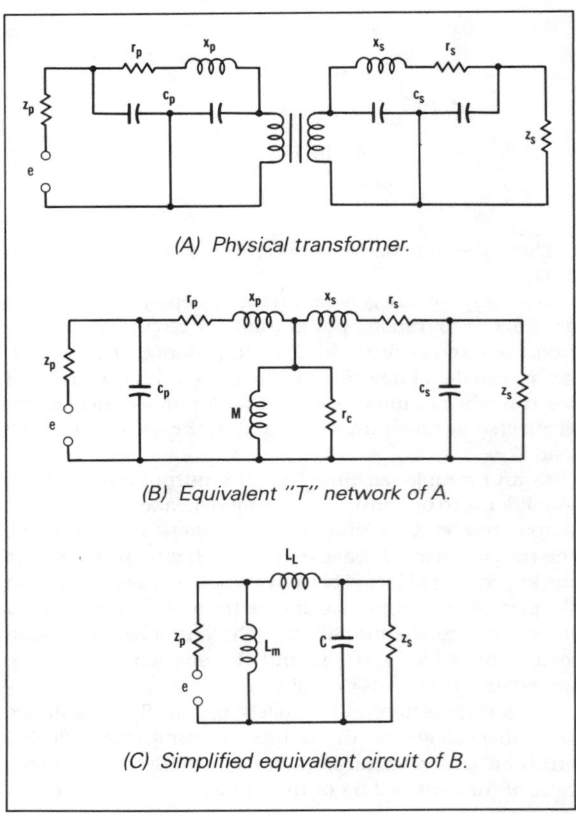

(A) Physical transformer.
(B) Equivalent "T" network of A.
(C) Simplified equivalent circuit of B.

Figure 10-8 Equivalent circuits of an audio transformer.

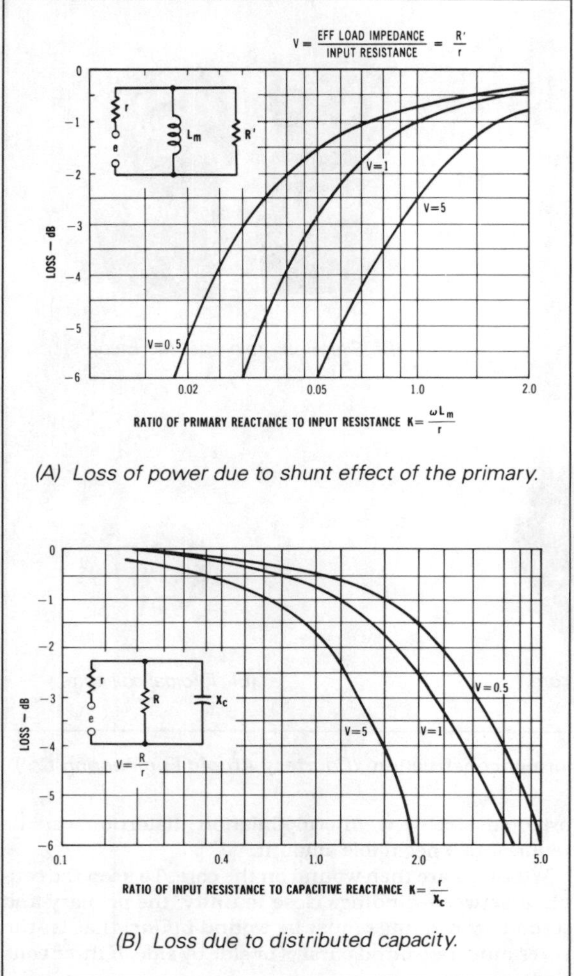

(A) Loss of power due to shunt effect of the primary.

(B) Loss due to distributed capacity.

Figure 10-9 Loss curves of an audio transformer.

In conventional push-pull output transformers, the magnetic lines of force do not completely couple both halves of the primary winding. Lines of force coupled to one coil but not to the other cause a counter electromotive force to be generated.

The *reflection losses* is the transmission loss resulting from a portion of the transmitted signal being reflected back toward the signal source. Reflection losses may be the result of mismatched impedances or of a discontinuity in the transmission line. In the case of an improperly terminated line, not all of the signal energy is transmitted to the load. The portion not absorbed by the load is reflected back toward the source, meets the energy from the source, and causes a loss of power. The greater the mismatch of the termination at the load end of the line, the greater will be the losses because of reflection.

The *copper loss* is a power loss caused in a power transformer by the dc resistance of the coils. The loss varies as the square of the current.

The *iron* or *core loss* is the loss of energy due to eddy currents in the core material. In practical transformers, the core loss remains almost constant from no load to full load, under normal conditions.

Eddy currents are circulating currents induced in a conducting material as the result of the rapid reversal of the magnetic field. To reduce eddy-current loss in the core material, laminated cores are used, thereby improving the transformer characteristics. *Hysteresis losses* in the core are caused by molecular friction and are reduced by the use of alloy steel, such as silicon, Hypersil®, and Hypernic®. The latter two metals are manufactured by Westinghouse.

The *insertion loss* in a transformer is the loss caused by the shunt reactance, distributed capacitance, dc resistance of the coils, core material, and other losses due to the geometry of the coils. In the average audio transformer, this loss is not too important unless the power in the transformer is large, such as in an output transformer. When the core becomes saturated in a power transformer, it is no longer able to produce additional lines of force. Hysteresis losses occur, the coils become overheated, and damage to the winding may take place under these circumstances.

In an audio-frequency transformer, if the core cannot produce the required lines of force, the inductance drops. Because of the core saturation, the core losses increase, and the frequency response is affected, particularly at frequencies below 100 Hz.

10.4 TRANSFORMER CONSTRUCTION

Transformer laminations and cores are many and varied. High-quality audio transformers often use the C and E type, grain-oriented steel cores, as shown in Fig. 10-10A and B. Grain-oriented steel is a cold-rolled grade of 3% silicon steel, manufactured by the Allegheny Ludlum Steel Corp. It has high-saturation flux density, lower core losses, and lower exciting volt-amperes than regular silicon steel. This high degree of orientation is preserved by the cutting of the core and the gapless construction. The steel strip is coated on both sides to provide good interlamination resistance with a negligible effect on the space factor. The strip is slit to the proper width and wound on a mandril to make a gapless core. The core is then annealed to relieve winding stresses and cut to produce two core halves. The effective air gap, when the surfaces are placed together, is 0.001 inch.

Similar cores manufactured by Westinghouse are known under the tradename of Hipersil®. The magnetic properties of grain-oriented steel are achieved by the orientation of the steel crystals through rolling and heat treatment. Individual crystals line up with their edges

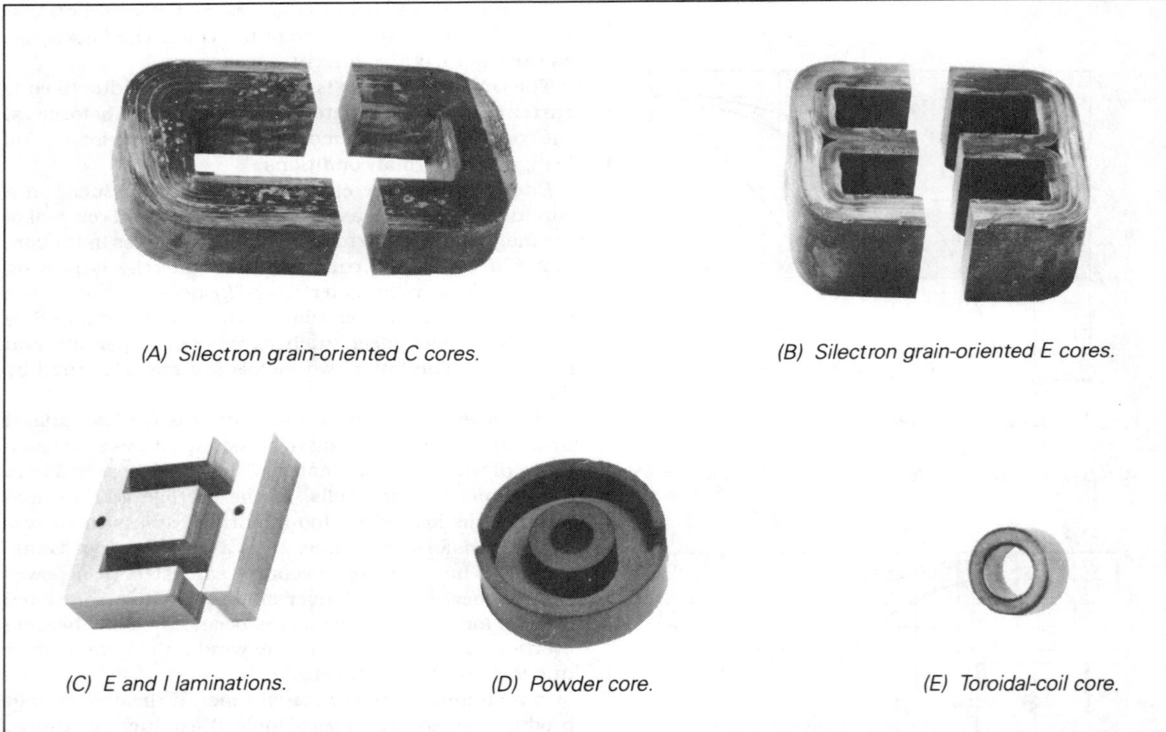
(A) Silectron grain-oriented C cores.
(B) Silectron grain-oriented E cores.
(C) E and I laminations.
(D) Powder core.
(E) Toroidal-coil core.

Figure 10-10 Typical cores used for power and audio transformer construction. ***(Courtesy Arnold Engineering Co.)***

essentially parallel to each other and parallel to the direction of the rolling sheets. When crystals are oriented in one direction, the steel has a much higher magnetic permeability than steel with crystals pointing at random. Grain-oriented steel requires a smaller external magnetizing force to produce a given flux than does unoriented steel. This results in a very high high-density permeability, high low-density permeability, high incremental permeability, and very low losses in the direction of the rolling. For comparative grain arrangement of ordinary silicon steel, refer to Fig. 10-11. Each arrow represents the direction of easiest magnetization of the individual crystals forming the steel.

The E-shaped cores in Fig. 10-10B are used for shell-type transformers, where the coil is placed over the center leg. The E and I laminations shown in Fig. 10-10C are used for both audio and power transformers. The powder core shown in Fig. 10-10D is designed for two halves, one over the other, completely enclosing the coil. The toroidal core shown in Fig. 10-10E supports the coil, which is shuttle wound around the core. The C and E cores are also used for pulse transformers and for 400- to 3000-Hz power transformers.

The manner in which the core laminations are stacked can have quite an effect on the intermodulation distortion induced by a transformer. By the proper design of the coils, the method of stacking, and the use of grain-oriented steel, the intermodulation distortion can be reduced to a negligible amount.

Windings are then wound on the core. To keep the coupling between windings close to unity, the primary and secondary windings must be wound *bifilar;* that is, the wires must be wound parallel or side by side. If three coils

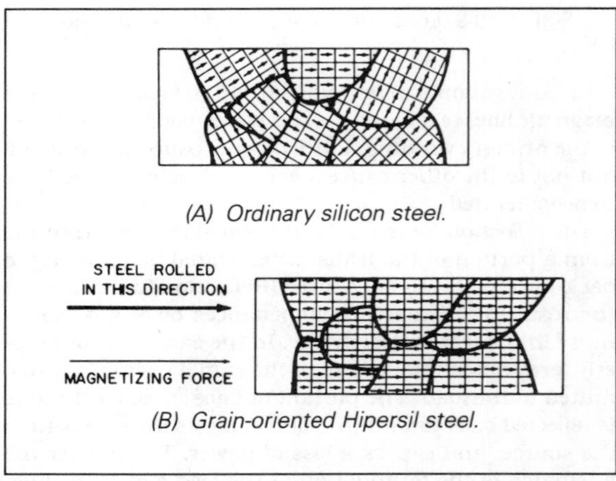

(A) Ordinary silicon steel.
(B) Grain-oriented Hipersil steel.

Figure 10-11 Comparative grain arrangements. ***(Courtesy Westinghouse Electric Co.)***

are wound together, it would be called *trifilar*, and five wires, *penafilar*.

The following is an example of a transformer construction.

A typical bifilar-wound transformer that may be used as the driver transformer for a transistor amplifier is wound, using a split-primary bifilar wound with two secondaries. A 600-turn number 30 enameled wire primary is first wound on a ¾-in.^{2} nylon bobbin. Next, two secondaries are wound, two 200-turn simultaneous windings (bifilar) of number 27 enameled wire. The primary is then continued by winding another 600 turns over the top of the other windings. The ends are brought out, and the starts and ends identified. The approximate dc resistance of the primary is 45 Ω and of the secondaries, 3.3 Ω each. The core is made of EL-75, grade M-19 silicon steel E and I laminations as shown in Fig. 10-12, using a 1-mil air gap. Enough laminations are used to fill the hole in the bobbin (¾ in.), resulting in a transformer with a turns ratio of 6:1:1. In using the transformer, the proper polarities must be observed (Fig. 10-13).

In modern high-gain amplifiers, the input transformer is generally required to work from a very low-level signal input. Under these conditions of high gain and a low-level signal, it is necessary to make use of specially designed input transformers that will not be affected by extraneous magnetic fields and strong electrostatic fields caused by switching circuits and radio transmissions.

Hum pickup may be reduced to a great extent by the design of the coils, core, and general construction of the transformer.

Any hum voltage induced in the core from an outside source, such as through the chassis or from an adjacent transformer, will induce a hum voltage in the windings. If two identical coils are wound on opposite legs of the transformer core, and the direction of one of the coils is reversed from the other, and if the two coils are connected in series by reversing their connections, equal hum voltage is induced in the coils on each leg 180° out of phase with the other, cancelling out the hum pickup.

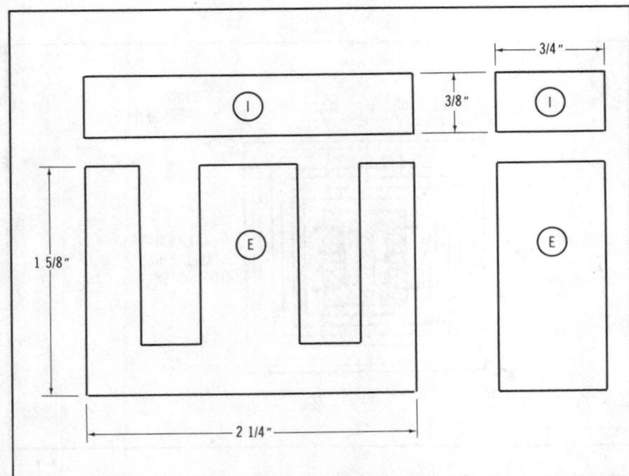

Figure 10-12 E and I core laminations used in Class-B driver transformers for transistor power amplifier.

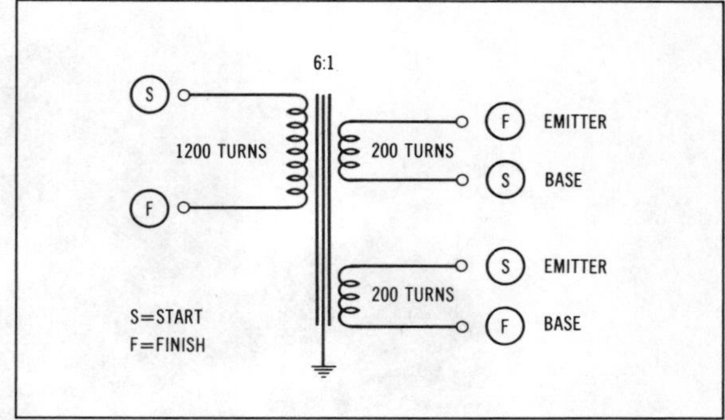

Figure 10-13 Driver transformer coil configuration for transistor Class-B push-pull amplifier stages.

10.5 TRANSFORMER SHIELDING

Transformers often require *shielding*, either to reduce the effects of the transformer on the environment or to reduce the effects of the environment on the transformer and, hence, the signal.

10.5.1 Electrostatic Shielding

An *electrostatic shield* consists of a single turn of copper or brass covering the entire length of the primary winding. The ends of the shield are insulated from each other to prevent the shield from acting as a shorted turn. A connection to the shield is to prevent the passage of line noises and radio-frequency signals from the transformer into the power supply and other parts of the equipment. Electrostatic shields are also used in audio transformers to prevent capacity coupling between windings, thus permitting only inductive coupling.

10.5.2 Magnetic Shielding

Permeability is a measure of the ease with which a magnetic material will pass lines of force. High-quality transformers, shields, and other electrical equipment use high-permeability magnetic iron made of various alloys.

$$\text{Permeability}(\mu) = B/H \qquad (10\text{-}8)$$

where,

B is the magnetic induction in gauss,

H is the magnetizing force in oersteds, the μ of air is one.

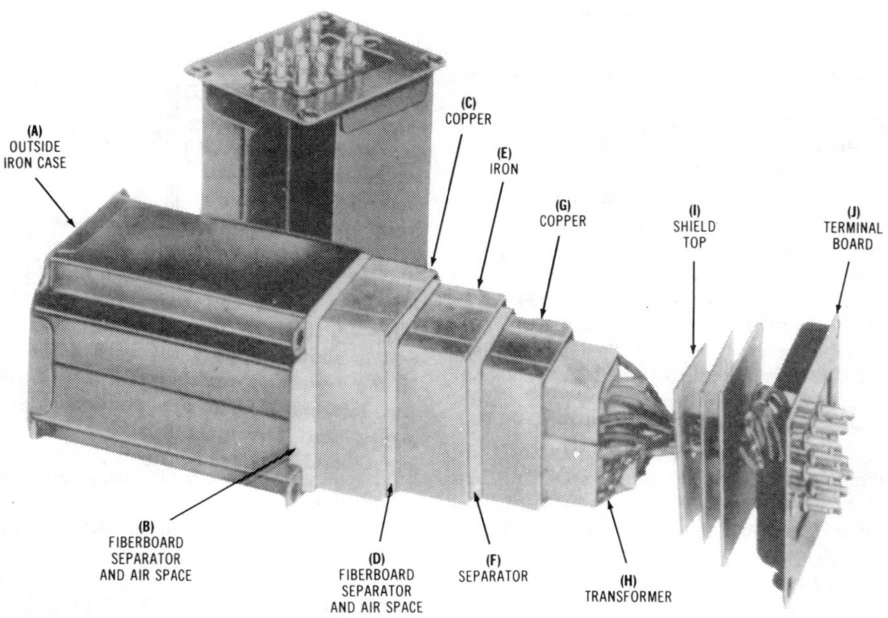

Figure 10-14 Transformer encased in nested-shield. *(Courtesy Kenyon Electronics Inc.)*

An audio-transformer case consisting of alternate iron and copper shields separated by an air space, as shown in Fig. 10-14, is called a nested shield. Referring to Fig. 10-15, when a magnetic field encounters the outside high permeability iron case (A) of the transformer, it will travel through the case and be deflected around the transformer mounted inside the case because iron offers a path of lower resistance to magnetic lines of force than air offers. Also, in passing through the iron case, a portion of the field is dissipated in the form of heat due to friction and the short-circuiting effect of the case. The now reduced field continues through the air space filled by the fiberboard spacers (B), then through the copper shield (C). The field again passes through an air space (D) to a high-permeability iron shield (E), which again reduces the field strength. Leaving this shield, the field passes through air space (F) to copper shield (G), which houses the transformer (H). At the top of each shield are covers (I) (shown in Fig. 10-14), which, in effect, provide watertight shields around the transformer. The copper shields have little or no effect on the reduction of the magnetic field. Their purpose is to reduce the effects of electrostatic fields and disturbances caused by the breaking of electrical circuits and radio transmissions.

To secure a further reduction from the effects of external magnetic fields, the coils of the transformer are wound hum-bucking, which neutralizes the effects of any magnetic field that may reach the transformer coils after passing through the multiple shielding. Using the construction illustrated in Figs. 10-14 and 10-15, hum and noise pickup may be reduced 120 dB relative to the strength of the interfering magnetic field.

The core of the transformer is brought to a separate terminal for connection to a transmission ground system. The outer iron case is completely insulated from the internal shields and transformer core.

Low-level input transformers operating ahead of a considerable amount of gain and near ac-operated equipment require nested shielding. *Mumetal* is a metallic alloy with a high permeability and a low hysteresis loss that makes it excellent for magnetic shielding.

Magnetic shielding is often 120 dB, which means for a given external magnetic field surrounding the transformer, the strength of the magnetic field will be reduced

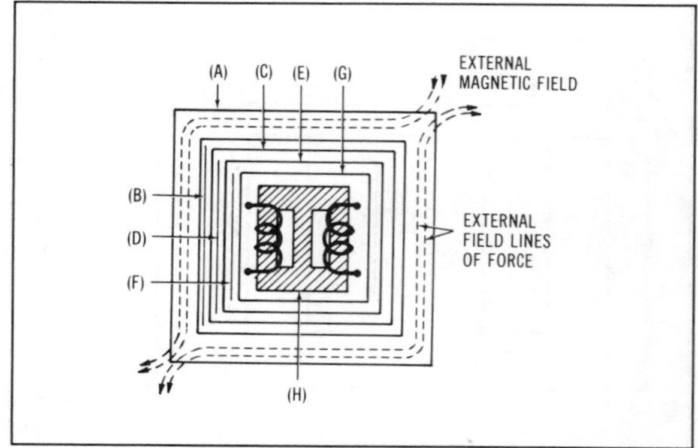

Figure 10-15 External magnetic lines of force deflected by an iron case and a nested-shield around a transformer.

120 dB at the transformer windings. The amount of reduction is fixed, and the actual hum pickup can vary with the change in the external magnetic field strength. However, with 120 dB of hum reduction, generally little difficulty is encountered. A single ⅛-in.-thick single cast-iron case will only reduce the magnetic field 12 dB.

10.6 TYPES OF TRANSFORMERS

There are many types of transformers used in audio, from power supply transformers to input transformers and output transformers and special transformers.

10.6.1 Power Transformers

A *power transformer* is used to provide power to a circuit. The input to the transformer is usually 50 or 60 Hz, 110 to 220 V ac from the power line. The output may be either high or low or both and may have single or multiple outputs. Output voltages may be 300 to 600 V with 6.3- or 12.6-V windings for tube circuits or, more commonly, 24- to 60-V single or multiple circuits for solid-state circuits. The voltage output of 6 to 12 V is often used for integrated circuit preamplifiers. Output current capabilities range from milliamperes to 20 A.

Power transformers may be designed for 50 to 60 Hz or 400-Hz input. The 400 Hz used in aviation is not common among sound systems. The higher the frequency, the smaller the transformer core can be without saturation. As the input frequency decreases, the amount of core iron must increase to assure the core will not saturate. When the core saturates, the heat rise in the transformer increases and eventually causes the transformer to become brittle and probably short out. Therefore, it is imperative that transformers designed for 60 Hz are not operated on 50 Hz. Without any side effects, 50-Hz transformers, however, can be operated on 60 Hz. The disadvantage of this is increased size.

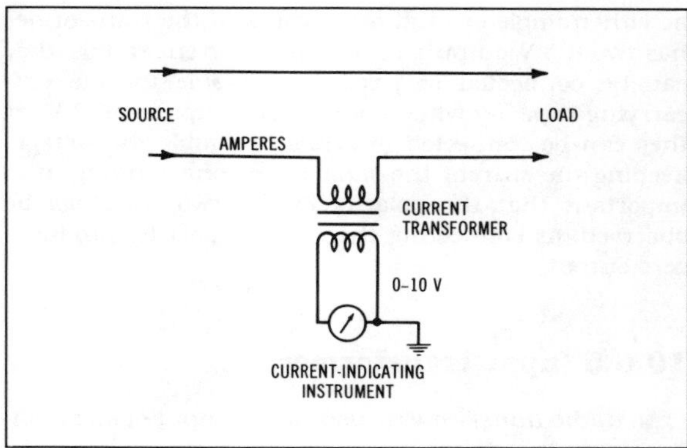

Figure 10-16 Current transformer connected to indicate load current.

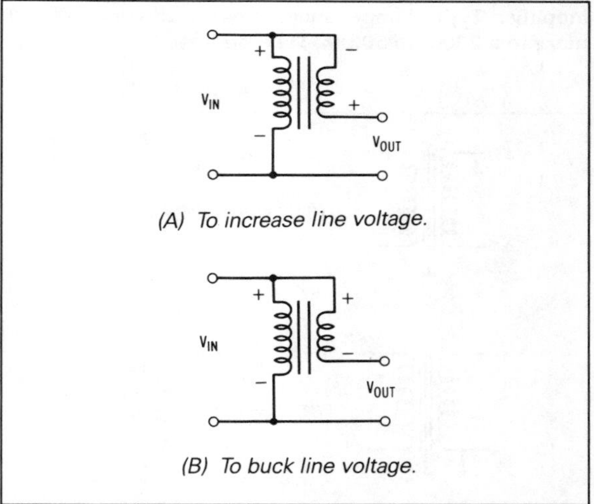

Figure 10-17 Booster transformer connections.

10.6.2 Current Transformers

A *current transformer* is designed to work with a current-indicating instrument. The primary of the transformer is connected in series with the load, and the indicating instrument is connected to the secondary, as shown in Fig. 10-16. In this manner, the transformer carries the load while the instrument is completely isolated. The indicating instrument is actually a voltmeter calibrated in amperes.

10.6.3 Buck-Boost Transformers

A *buck-boost transformer* is used in power transmission work to increase or decrease the line voltage where a conventional transformer would be impractical or too costly. The connections for boosting the line voltage are shown in Fig. 10-17A, and the connections for decreasing the line voltage are shown in Fig. 10-17B. When reducing the line voltage, the secondary coil is connected to buck the line voltage, thus reducing it. The coils of the booster transformer must be capable of carrying the full-load current. For light loads, a filament or bell-ringing transformer may be used as a buck-boost transformer.

10.6.4 Filament Transformers

A *filament transformer* is a transformer used for supplying a source of voltage to the filament or heater circuit of a vacuum tube. They can also be used for indicator lamps and low-voltage power supplies. The output voltage of filament transformers is usually 6.3 or 12.6 V and can be either single or multiple outputs. If the transformer has two 6.3-V outputs of the same current rating, they can be connected in parallel to double the current-carrying capacity while holding the output to 6.3 V, or they can be connected in series to double the voltage, keeping the current the same as for one winding. It is important that the polarity of the two windings be observed, as connecting them out of polarity produces zero output.

10.6.5 Input Transformers

An *audio transformer* is used at the input of an amplifier or similar device. Input transformers are generally better shielded from magnetic fields since they are required to operate in low-level circuits. Input transformers, as a rule, are designed to match the low impedance of a transmission line or microphone to the input of a low-level amplifier. Typical impedance ratios are 250 or 600 Ω primary to a 2000- to 50,000-Ω secondary.

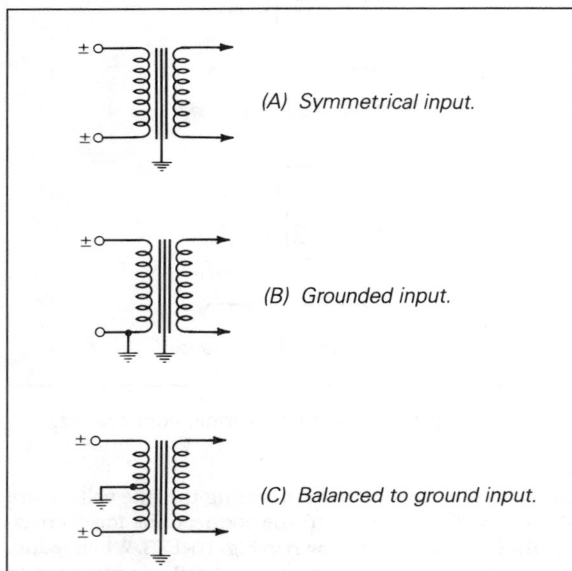

Figure 10-18 Three different types of transformer input circuits.

Terminology used with input transformers is often misused, especially when referring to grounded-input circuits. Fig. 10-18 illustrates three methods most commonly employed. Fig. 10-18A shows an ungrounded symmetrical input, often erroneously referred to as a balanced input. A true balanced circuit is one using an input transformer with a center tap to ground, as shown in Fig. 10-18C. For the circuit of Fig. 10-18A to be truly balanced (although no ground is used), the transformer windings must be wound so that the distributed capacitance to ground is the same for each coil. Also, each coil must have identical inductance and dc resistance and be physically interleaved to reduce the effects of leakage inductance. If all these conditions are met, the coil may be said to be balanced. However, in the average coil these conditions do not always prevail; therefore, this circuit is said to be *symmetrical*.

The circuit in Fig. 10-18B is an unbalanced input with one side of the input winding connected to ground. This input is often used with circuits such as a high-impedance microphone employing a single conductor and shield. The shield is connected to the ground side of the transformer.

10.6.6 Repeat or Isolation Transformers

A *repeat* or *isolation coil* is an audio transformer consisting of two windings usually with a one-to-one impedance ratio. Repeat coils can also be designed with taps at various points on the coils to provide impedance matching between circuits of unequal impedance. A typical schematic of a repeat coil is shown in Fig. 10-19. The coil is designed for an impedance of 600 Ω, ranging downward to 250 Ω; the center tap is always balanced with respect to the center of the coil.

The windings consist of several separate coils, each with the same number of turns and connected in series in such a manner that the capacitance between coils is reduced to a minimum. This method of construction permits the various impedance taps to be taken at the exact electrical center, resulting in a well-balanced design. The

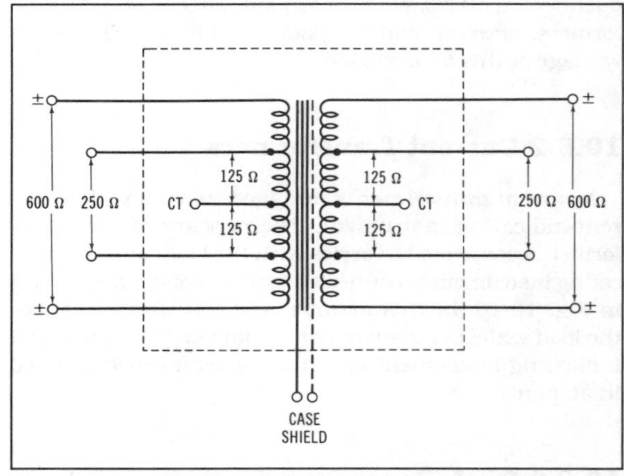

Figure 10-19 Typical 600:600-Ω repeat or isolation coil. In-between impedances are indicated for ready reference.

insertion loss of the average repeat coil is about 0.10 to 0.5 dB.

10.6.7 Bridging Transformers

A *bridging transformer* is a special transformer with a high-impedance primary designed to be operated from a low source impedance. Many amplifiers used in recording systems and broadcasting make use of bridging transformers since these transformers permit several amplifiers to be connected across a line as shown in Fig. 10-20 without upsetting the impedance match of the other equipment.

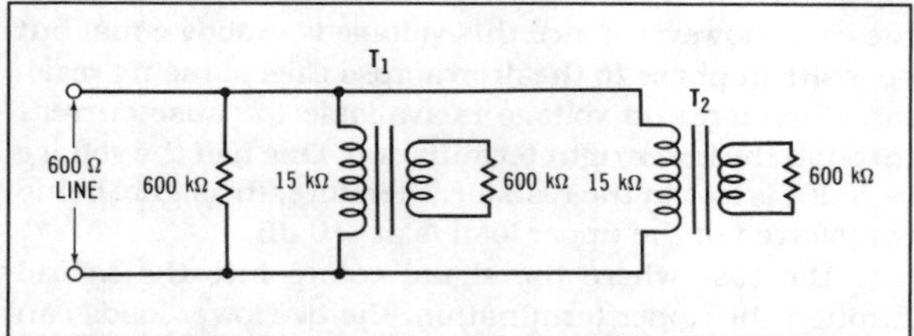

Figure 10-20 Bridging transformers.

Transformers with a very high input impedance (primary) are not used for bridging transformers because the high impedance has capacitance and inductance that creates poor frequency response.

A transformer with a low-impedance primary may often be converted for bridging use by the addition of resistors, as shown in Fig. 10-21. In Fig. 10-21A two resistors R_B have been added in series with a 600-Ω primary to raise the input impedance to the desired bridging impedance. In Fig. 10-21B the same method has been used, except the circuit is unbalanced. In Fig. 10-21C resistor R_B has been connected in series with the return of a split-primary transformer. In this case the transformer may only be used for bridging purposes. Transformers converted to bridging inputs, as shown, will show a considerable insertion loss because of the resistance R_B in series with the windings. This loss will vary depending on the impedance ratio of the transformer and the value of the resistors. Transformers designed expressly for bridging service do not, as a rule, make use of resistors.

It may be necessary when using a transformer with a 600-Ω primary for bridging purposes to add an additional resistor in shunt with the primary winding, as shown by the dotted-line resistor in Fig. 10-21A and B, to preserve the frequency response of the coil. The addition of this shunt resistor will increase the insertion loss of the transformer as a whole, the amount depending on the impedance ratio between the bridging source and the impedance of the transformer primary.

The three resistors form a bridging pad. The loss for Fig. 10-21 may be calculated with the formula

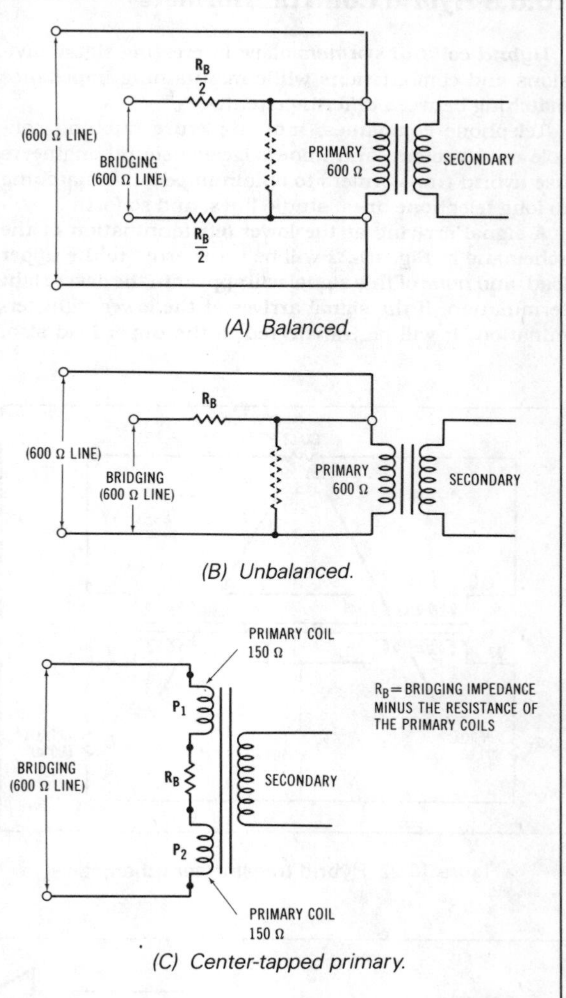

Figure 10-21 Methods of converting low-impedance transformers to bridging inputs.

$$db_{ATT} = 10 \log 4 \frac{\left(R_B + \frac{Z_P Z_L}{Z_P + Z_L}\right)^2}{(R_B + Z_P)Z_L} \qquad (10\text{-}9)$$

where,

dB_{ATT} is the decibels attenuation,
R_B is the bridging resistor value in ohms,
Z_p is the primary impedance of the transformer,
Z_L is the secondary load to the transformer,

The standard bridging input impedances used in the sound industry are 7500, 10,000, 15,000, 25,000, and 30,000 Ω.

10.6.8 Hybrid Coil Transformers

Hybrid coil transformers allow interesting signal divisions and combinations while maintaining impedance matching between differing circuits.

Telephone companies, motion-picture dubbing console constructors, and knowledgeable sound engineers use hybrid transformers to obtain impedance matching to long telephone lines, studio lines, and so forth.

A signal arriving at the lower left termination of the schematic in Fig. 10-22 will be transferred to the upper load, and none of this signal will appear in the lower right termination. If the signal arrives at the lower right termination, it will be transferred to the upper load also, and none of it will appear at the lower left termination. In order to obtain these characteristics, the balancing resistor connected to the center point of the transformer winding must be set to the proper value relative to the upper termination. (In the case of long transmission lines with complex impedances, precision balance networks can replace the balance resistors. Impedances of 300, 600, 900, 1200 Ω, and so forth, are routinely handled by readily available hybrids.)

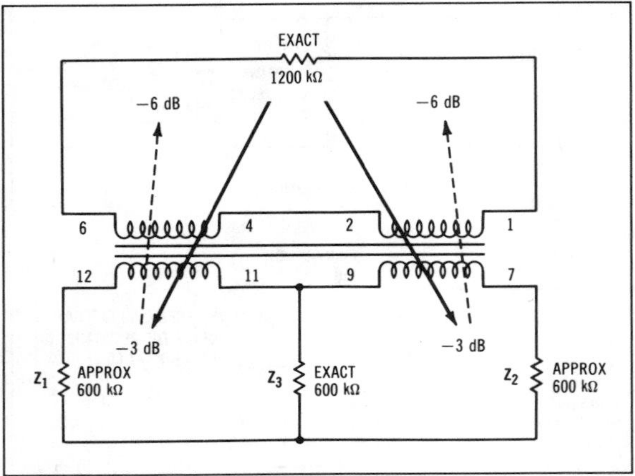

Figure 10-22 Hybrid transformer schematic.

To better understand the operation of this device, assume a signal originates from the lower left, and assume the impedance looking into 11 and 12 to be exactly equal to the value of the 600-Ω balancing resistor. If this is so, then the voltage drop from 12 to 11 will be exactly duplicated across 9 to 7, which would seem to induce a voltage in the circuit of the lower right termination. This is not the case, however, since this voltage is exactly equal but opposite in phase to the drop across the balancing resistor. Therefore, no voltage is available to cause current through the lower right termination. One half the voltage (−6 dB) is lost in the resistor; therefore, the signal being transferred to the upper load is at −6 dB.

In the case where the signal comes into the hybrid through the upper termination, the two lower loads can be considered in series; consequently, no voltage appears across the balancing resistor. Therefore, there is no voltage loss in transmission. However, because of the equal division of the upper signal between the lower right and the lower left loads, each load will receive one half the power, or 3 dB less than the original.

Fig. 10-23 shows how hybrid coils are employed in the telephone industry to permit a single line to be used for two-way conversation. It is the practice to use two amplifiers to make up a repeater station: one amplifier providing amplification in one direction and the second, in the

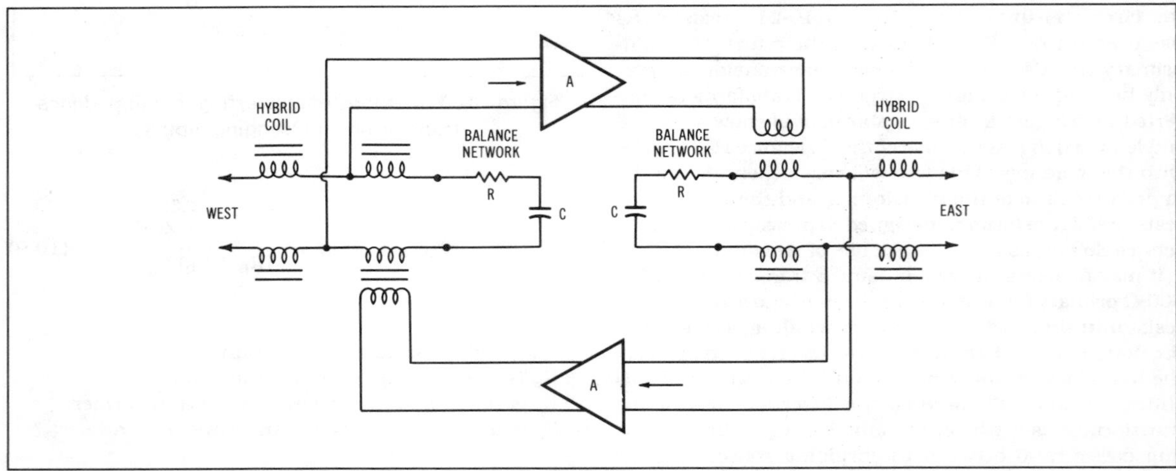

Figure 10-23 Hybrid coils used in a telephone-repeater station to permit using a single pair transmission line for east-west conversation.

opposite direction. When the lines are properly terminated and the balancing networks adjusted, both amplifiers may be used without producing a howl or singing.

The sum of the gains of the two amplifiers must always be less than the sum of the losses across the two hybrid coils to prevent unbalance and singing. For telephone transmission the frequency bandwidth is limited to frequencies between 200 and 3000 Hz. Filters are employed to prevent singing at frequencies outside this band. The balancing networks consist of a resistance and a capacitor connected in series across one pair of terminals of the hybrid coil. In some instances an inductance is employed.

10.6.9 70.7-V Transformers

A 70.7-V transformer is one used to match a 4-, 8-, or 16-Ω loudspeaker to a 70.7-V line. In sound systems, many loudspeakers of different power requirements and different distances from the source are often connected to a single amplifier output. Professional sound system amplifiers include a 70.7-V output. The output of 70.7 V was decided upon as it allowed for Class-II wiring of the loudspeaker line. The actual output impedance of the amplifier is determined by the formula

$$\begin{aligned} Z &= V^2/P \\ &= (70.7)^2/P \\ &= 5000/P \end{aligned} \tag{10-10}$$

where,
P is the output power.

70.7-V transformers are designed to transfer a specific output power to the loudspeaker whenever the transformer input voltage is equal to 70.7 V. The transformer in Fig. 10-24 has outputs of 2, 4, and 8 Ω and wattage taps of 1, 2, and 4 W. If this transformer is connected to an 8-Ω loudspeaker, and the 4-W primary is connected to a 70.7-V line, the transformer will deliver 4 W to the loudspeaker when the amplifier delivers 70.7 V. The actual primary impedance of the transformer is calculated from the power delivered to the loudspeaker plus the *insertion loss* of the transformer.

The use of the 70.7-V transformer allows easy adjusting of power to each loudspeaker and produces minimum line loss as the 70.7-V line has a relatively high impedance.

10.6.10 Three-Phase Transformers

Several methods used for connecting three-phase power transformers for commercial services are shown in Figs. 10-25 to 10-29. An open-delta connection is the simplest of all three-phase transformer connections since each winding consists of only two coils, as shown in Fig. 10-25. Fig. 10-26 is a six-winding transformer connected in delta. Figs. 10-27 and 10-28 illustrate two transformers connected in a star or wye configuration using a three-

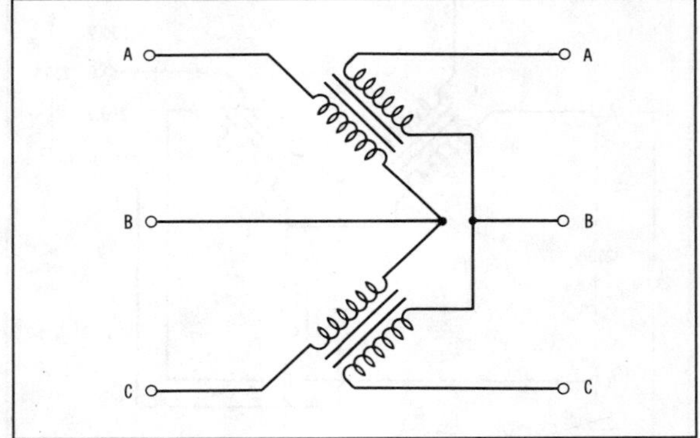

Figure 10-25 Three-phase transformer open-delta connection.

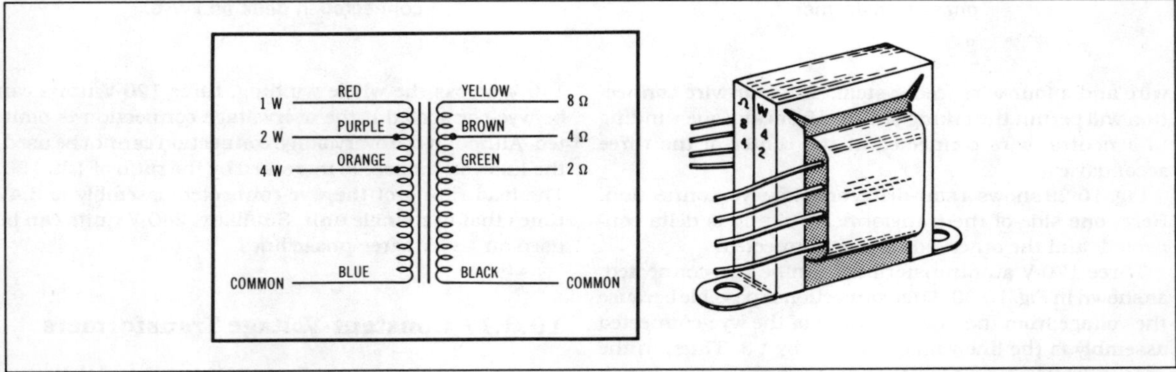

Figure 10-24 A 70.7-V loudspeaker transformer.

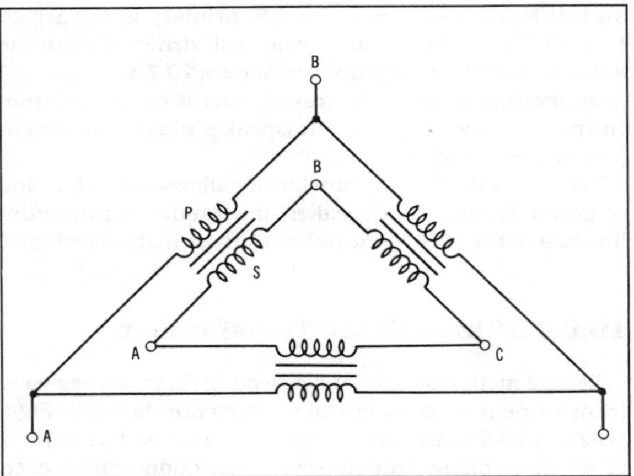

Figure 10-26 Three-phase transformer delta connected.

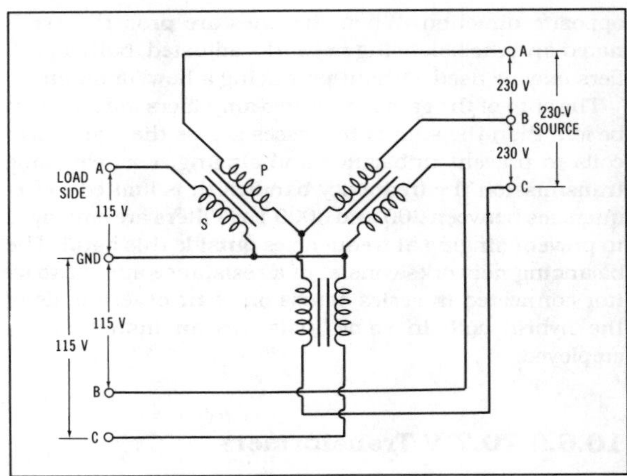

Figure 10-28 Star-connected, four-wire, three-phase transformer.

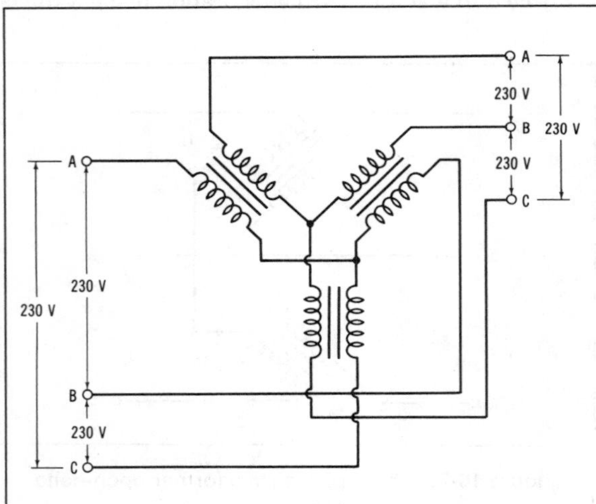

Figure 10-27 Star- or wye-connected three-wire, three-phase transformer.

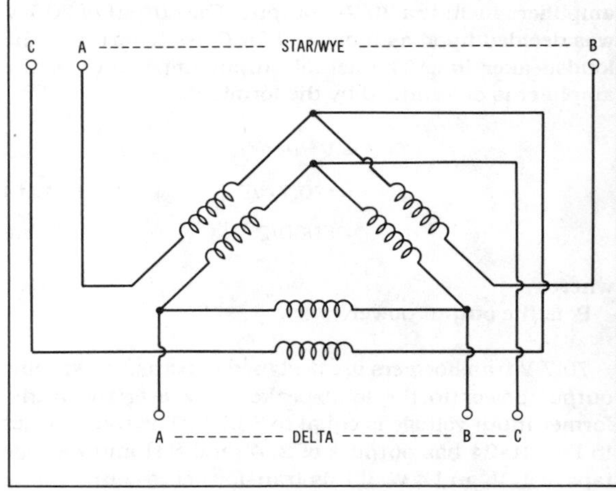

Figure 10-29 Three-phase transformer with windings connected in delta and wye.

wire and a four-wire feed system. The four-wire connection will permit the taking of 115 V from any one winding to a neutral wire connected at the center of the three secondaries.

Fig. 10-29 shows a star-delta, or delta-wye, connection. Here, one side of the transformer winding is delta connected, and the other side is star connected.

Three 120-V autotransformers can be wye-connected, as shown in Fig. 10-30. This connection is possible because the voltage from the line to neutral of the wye-connected assembly is the line voltage divided by $\sqrt{3}$. Thus, in the case of the 240-V three-phase line, the voltage across each unit will be 138 V. Since each single unit is wound for 140 V across the whole winding, three 120-V units can be wye-connected if the overvoltage connection is omitted. Although the overvoltage connection cannot be used, the kilo-volt-ampere is increased by the ratio of 138:120. The load rating of the wye-connected assembly is 3.47 times that of a single unit. Similarly, 240-V units can be used on 480-V three-phase lines.

10.6.11 Constant-Voltage Transformers

Constant-voltage transformers are a special type of transformer, containing voltage-regulating circuits, which

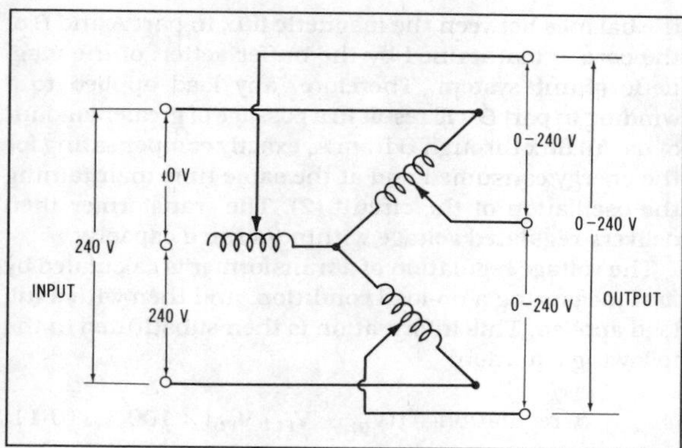

Figure 10-30 Three 120-V autotransformers connected for 240-V, three-phase operation.

automatically correct for line-voltage changes, thus maintaining the load voltage constant. These transformers have no mechanical parts and, except for a slight hum, are noiseless. These devices do have fairly strong magnetic fields and, when installed, should be placed at some distance from equipment sensitive to such magnetic fields, particularly magnetic-recording equipment.

A model CVS constant-voltage transformer, manufactured by Sola Electric Co., is shown in Fig. 10-31.

Figure 10-31 Constant-voltage transformer-type CVS. *(Courtesy Sola Electric, division of General Signal Corp.)*

Constant-voltage transformers by Sola are manufactured in two types: the sinusoidal type CVS and the normal-harmonic type CVN. Both transformers will regulate the output voltage to within 1% or less for a line-voltage variation between 95 and 130 V at the primary. The type CVN has about 14% total harmonic distortion (THD) and is used where line-frequency harmonics are of little consequence. Type CVS contains, besides the voltage regulating circuits, a harmonic-suppression circuit that reduces the internally generated harmonics to 1.5 to 3%, depending on the load conditions. Since the basic principle of operation is the same for both type regulators, the normal harmonic type (CVN) will be discussed.

Referring to Fig. 10-32, the voltage-regulating circuit involves the use of three coils: a primary (1), a compensating winding (3), and a resonant winding (2), connected in parallel with capacitor C. A cross-sectional view of the internal construction appears in Fig. 10-33. Primary winding (1) and compensating coil (3) are layer wound one over the other on part A, of the center leg of the core. Resonant winding (2) is wound on part B of the same leg but isolated from the primary and compensating winding by a magnetic shunt.

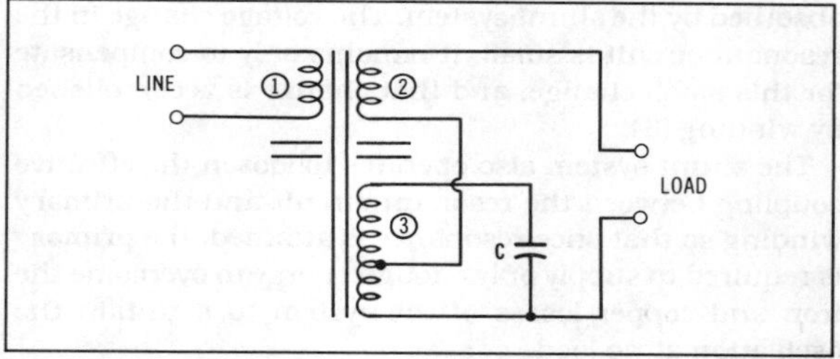

Figure 10-32 Basic circuit for Sola Electric Co. constant-voltage transformer using three coils. *(Courtesy Sola Electric, division of General Signal Corp.)*

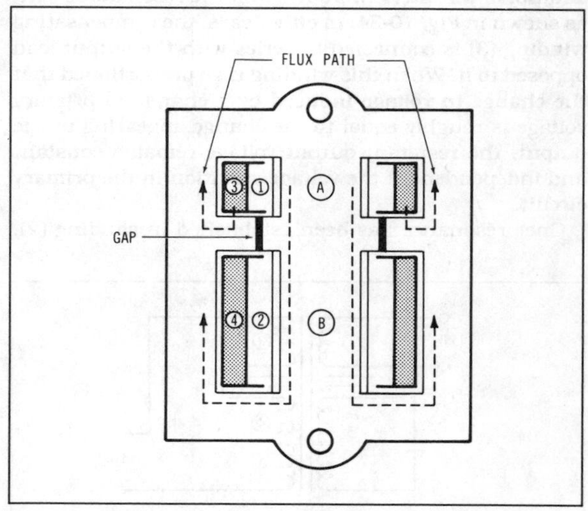

Figure 10-33 Cross-sectional view of the core and coil construction of a Sola Electric Co. constant-voltage transformer. *(Courtesy of Sola Electric, division of General Signal Corp.)*

When an alternating current of low voltage is impressed across the primary winding, the resulting magnetic flux induces a voltage in winding (2). Because of the reluctance of the air gaps in the shunt path, this voltage roughly approximates the turn-ratio voltage. As the voltage across the primary is increased, more flux threads through part B of the core structure. When this flux density becomes such that the inductive reactance of winding (2) approaches the value of the capacitive reactance of C at the frequency of the exciting voltage, this circuit becomes resonant, and the voltage appearing across winding (2) rises rapidly to a stable, predetermined value that is higher than the calculated turn-ratio voltage. This has the effect of increasing the magnetic density in that portion of the magnetic circuit on which the resonant winding is wound (part B) and of greatly reducing the relative reluctance of the shunt system so that subsequent variations in flux, produced by changes in the primary circuit, are largely absorbed by the shunt system. The voltage change in the resonant circuit is small. It remains only to compensate for this small change, and that change is accomplished by winding (3).

The shunt system also operates to loosen the effective coupling between the resonant circuit and the primary winding so that once resonance is attained, the primary is required to supply only enough energy to overcome the iron and copper losses of the system to maintain the oscillation at no load.

Since the voltage across winding (2) is stable once resonance is attained, it may be used as a basis of constant-output voltage of the transformer. The output voltage is obtained by tapping across a portion (or all) of the resonant winding coil (2), as shown in Fig. 10-32, or from an additional winding (4), wound over the resonant circuit, as shown in Fig. 10-34. In either case, the compensating winding (3) is connected in series with the output load opposed to it. When this winding is so proportioned that the change in voltage induced by a change in primary voltage is roughly equal to the change appearing in the output, the resultant output voltage remains constant and independent of the voltage variation in the primary circuit.

Once resonance has been established in winding (2),

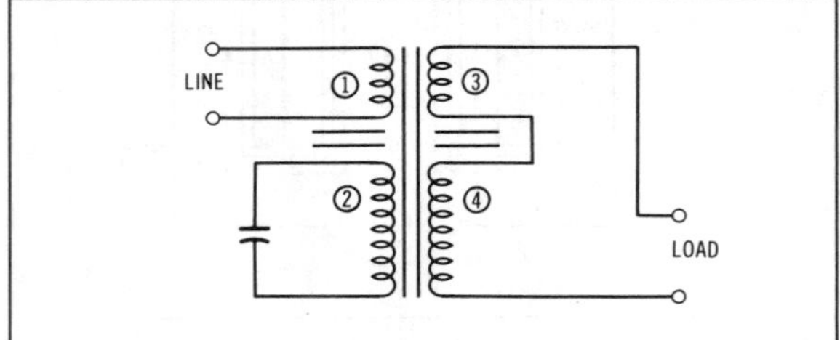

Figure 10-34 Basic circuit for Sola Electric Co. constant-voltage transformer using four coils. *(Courtesy Sola Electric, division of General Signal Corp.)*

the balance between the magnetic flux in part A and B of the core is maintained by the buffer action of the magnetic shunt system. Therefore, any load applied to a winding in part B will result in a passage of greater amount of useful flux through B from A, exactly compensating for the energy consumed and at the same time maintaining the oscillation of the circuit (2). The transformer then delivers regulated voltage within its rated capacity.

The voltage regulation of a transformer is calculated by first measuring a no-load condition, and then with a full load applied. This information is then substituted in the following equation:

$$\% \text{ regulation} = [(V_{NL} - V_{FL})/V_{FL}] \times 100 \qquad (10\text{-}11)$$

where,

V_{NL} is the no-load voltage,
V_{FL} is the full-load voltage.

10.6.12 Electromechanical Voltage Regulators

Electromechanical line-voltage regulators combine the power-handling capabilities of a motor-driven variable autotransformer with the fast response and accuracy of an electronic feedback loop, Fig. 10-35. This type regulator introduces no harmonic distortion and is totally unaffected by changes in load power factor, from zero leading, to zero lagging, and is insensitive to load currents. With proper design it can hold the output voltage constant with wide swings of line frequency, a factor most important in the regulation of voltage from portable and emergency generators. It is well suited for applications involving heavy starting currents and can withstand overloads up to 10 times the rated output current. Such regulators may be obtained with power-handling capabilities up to several kilovoltamperes, for either single- or three-phase operation. The main drawback is the reaction time due to the required movement of the autotransformer.

10.7 INSERTION LOSS

All transformers have *insertion loss* that must be taken into account when either determining the actual power delivered to the load or the actual power taken from the line.

Two major possibilities enter into the calculation of the effect of the insertion loss of a 70-V transformer when planning the *electrical power required (EPR)* from the power amplifier or amplifiers.

In the first case, the manufacturer of the transformer recognizes that the loudspeaker should receive the power stated on the primary taps of the transformer since the sound-system designer will have planned the required sound levels on the basis of that wattage value to the

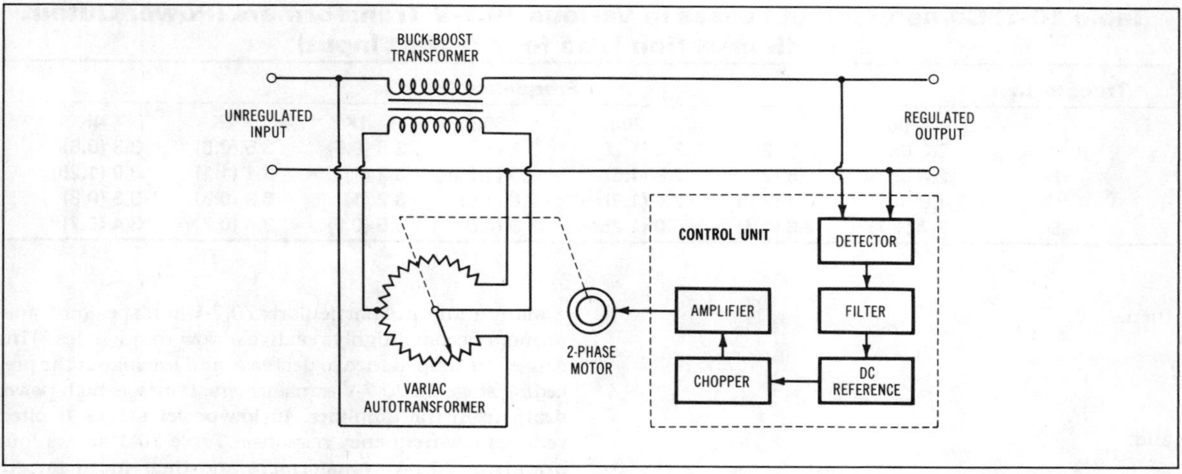

Figure 10-35 Block diagram of an electromechanical voltage regulator. *(Courtesy Gen Rad Inc.)*

loudspeakers. The manufacturer states what the insertion loss is (usually in decibels) and, just as important, adjusts the windings internally to compensate for the stated insertion loss, thereby insuring that the stated primary wattage appears at the loudspeaker terminals. When this is the case the input power and the actual primary impedance, Z, of the transformer can be found by the formula:

$$\text{input power}_{dBm} = \text{loudspeaker power}_{dBm} + \text{power loss in transformer}_{dBm} \quad (10\text{-}11)$$

and,

$$\begin{aligned}\text{input Z} &= (70.7)^2/\text{total power}_{watts} \\ &= 5000/\text{power to speaker}_{watts}\,(10^{\text{insertion loss dB}/10}) \quad (10\text{-}12)\end{aligned}$$

For example, a transformer with a 10-W primary tap and a 1.5-dB insertion loss, would actually draw 14.13 W from the line.

$$\begin{aligned}\text{Total power} &= \text{power to speaker}\,(10^{\text{insertion loss dB}/10}) \\ &= 10(10^{1.5/10}) \\ &= 14.13\,\text{W} \quad (10\text{-}13) \\ &= 5000/14.13 \\ &= 354\ \Omega\end{aligned}$$

instead of

$$5000/10\ \text{W} = 500\ \Omega$$

In the second case, the manufacturer has made no compensation for the insertion loss. One of the problems the manufacturer presents is the fact that the 70-V line impedance seems correct when measured with an impedance meter, but the acoustic output is too low. In a typical case, the insertion losses can be quite high, but for the sake of an example, again choose an insertion loss of 1.5 dB. This time the primary impedance remains at its rating (usually), and the power at the secondary taps is off by 1.5 dB. The power to the speakers where the transformer insertion loss is not compensated for in the transformer windings is

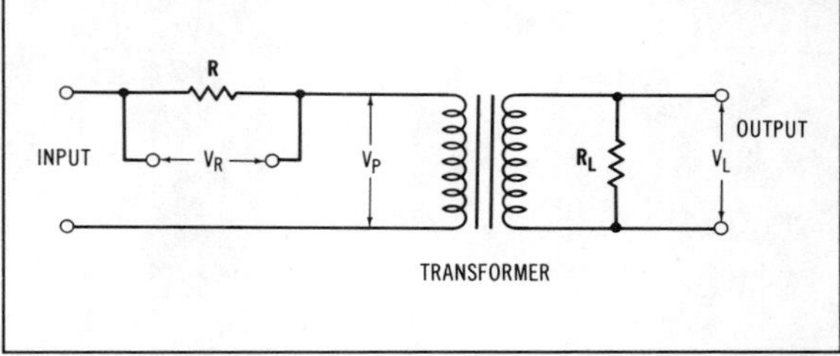

Figure 10-36 Test setup for determining insertion losses in a 70.7-V constant voltage loudspeaker transformer.

$$\begin{aligned}\text{Power to loudspeaker}_{watts} &= \frac{\text{Input power}_{watts}}{10^{\text{insertion loss dB}/10}} \\ &= 10/10^{1.5/10} \quad (10\text{-}14) \\ &= 7.08\,\text{W}\end{aligned}$$

The insertion loss in constant voltage transformers can be measured with the test circuit in Fig. 10-36. In effect, the input and output power is measured and/or calculated, and the insertion loss is calculated as the log of the ratio of input to output. Since

$$I = V_R/R$$

Table 10-1. Comparison of Losses in Various 70.7-V Transformers (Power Output and, dB Insertion Loss for a 4-Watt Input)

Transformer	Frequency (Hz)						
	50	100	200	500	1K	2K	4K
A	2.0 (3)	2.5 (2)	3.0 (1.25)	3.2 (1)	3.5 (0.6)	3.5 (0.6)	3.3 (0.8)
B	2.4 (2.2)	2.5 (2)	2.8 (1.5)	3.0 (1.25)	3.2 (1)	3.1 (1.1)	3.0 (1.25)
C	1.0 (6)	2.1 (2.8)	2.6 (1.9)	2.8 (1.5)	3.2 (1)	3.3 (0.8)	3.3 (0.8)
D	2.7 (1.7)	2.9 (1.4)	3.0 (1.25)	3.3 (0.8)	3.5 (0.6)	3.4 (0.7)	3.4 (0.7)

then,

$$VI = W_{in}$$

$$= (V_R/R)V_P$$

and,

$$W_{out} = (V_L)^2/R_L$$

$$\text{Insertion loss} = 10 \log (W_{in}/W_{out}) \qquad (10\text{-}15)$$

$$= N \text{ dB}$$

Many audio and particularly 70.7-V loudspeaker transformers become highly reactive at low frequencies. This causes the impedance to decrease and mismatch the preceding stage. In 70.7-V transformers, it means high power drain from the amplifier. In low-power stages it often reduces low-frequency response. Table 10-1 shows four brands of 70.7-V transformers and their input impedance versus frequency characteristics with a constant impedance load.

CHAPTER **11**

Tubes, Discrete Solid-State Devices, and Integrated Circuits

by Glen Ballou

11.1 TUBES[1]

In 1883, Edison discovered that electrons flowed in an evacuated lamp bulb, from a heated filament to a separate electrode (the Edison effect). Fleming, making use of this principle, invented the "Fleming Valve" in 1905, but when DeForest, in 1907, inserted the grid, he opened the door to electronic amplification with the "Audion." The millions of vacuum tubes are an outgrowth of the principles set forth by these men.

11.1.1 Tube Elements

Vacuum tubes consist of various elements or electrodes. The symbols for these elements are shown in Fig. 11-1, and they are defined as follows.

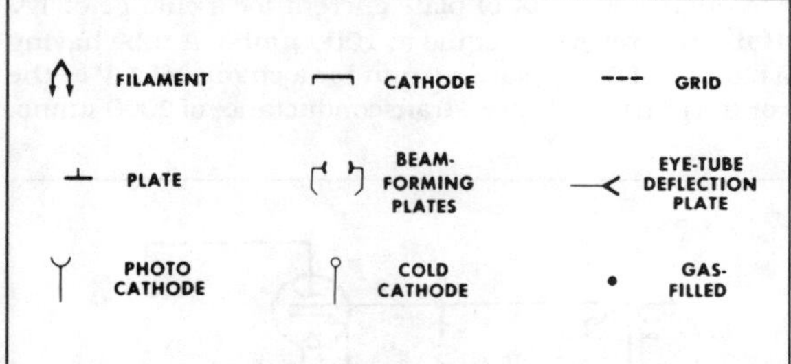

Figure 11-1 Tube elements and their designations.

The *filament* is the element in a directly heated vacuum tube that emits electrons. The *heater* is a coiled element used to heat the cathode element in an indirectly heated vacuum tube. The *cathode* is a sleeve surrounding the heater in a vacuum tube. The surface of the cathode is coated with barium oxide or thoriated tungsten to increase the emission of electrons.

The *plate* is the positive element in a vacuum tube, the element from which the output signal is usually taken. It is also called an *anode*.

The *control grid* is a spiral wire element placed between the plate and cathode elements of a vacuum tube to which the input signal is generally applied. This element controls the flow of electrons between the cathode and the plate elements.

The *screen grid* is an element in a pentode-type vacuum tube that is situated between the control grid and the plate elements. This screen grid is maintained at a positive potential to reduce the capacitance existing between the plate and the control-grid elements. It thus acts as an electrostatic shield and prevents self-oscillation and feedback within the tube.

The *suppressor grid* is a gridlike element situated between the plate and screen elements in a vacuum tube to prevent secondary electrons emitted by the plate from striking the screen grid. The suppressor is generally connected to the ground or cathode circuit.

11.1.2 Tube Types

There are many types of tubes, each used for a particular purpose. All tubes require a type of heater to permit the electrons to flow.

A *diode* is a two-element vacuum tube consisting of a plate and a cathode. Diodes are normally used for rectifying or controlling the polarity of a signal.

A three-element vacuum tube is a *triode*. This is the simplest of the tubes used to amplify a signal. A triode consists of cathode, control grid, and plate. A *tetrode* is a four-element vacuum tube containing a cathode, a control grid, a screen grid, and a plate. It is frequently referred to as a screen-grid tube. A *pentode* is a five-element vacuum tube containing a cathode, control grid, screen grid, suppressor grid, and plate.

A *hexode* is a six-element vacuum tube consisting of a cathode, control grid, suppressor grid, screen grid, injector grid, and plate. A *heptode* is a seven-element vacuum tube consisting of a cathode, control grid, four grids, and plate. A *pentagrid* is a seven-element vacuum tube consisting of a cathode, five grids, and plate.

A *beam-power tube* is a power-output tube having the advantage of both the tetrode and pentode tubes. Beam-power tubes are capable of handling relatively high levels of output power for application in the output stage of an audio amplifier. The power-handling capabilities stem from the concentration of the plate-current electrons into beams of moving electrons. In the conventional tube the electrons flow from the cathode to the plate, but they are not confined to a beam. In a beam-power tube the internal elements consist of a cathode, control grid, screen grid, and two beam-forming elements that are tied internally to the cathode element.The cathode is indirectly heated as in the conventional tube.

11.1.3 Symbols and Base Diagrams

Although there are many symbols used, the following are the basic symbols used for tube circuits:

C	Coupling capacitor between stages
C_{g2}	Screen grid bypass capacitor
C_k	Cathode bypass capacitor
E_{bb}	Supply voltage
E_{ff}	Plate efficiency
E_p	Actual voltage at plate
E_{sg}	Actual voltage at screen grid
E_o	Output voltage
E_{sig}	Signal voltage at input
E_g	Voltage at control grid
E_f	Filament or heater voltage

I_f Filament or heater current

I_p Plate current

I_k Cathode current

I_{sg} Screen-grid current

I_{pa} Average plate current

I_{ka} Average cathode current

I_{sga} Average screen grid current

g_m Transconductance (mutual conductance)

mu Amplification factor (μ)

P_{sg} Power at screen grid

P_p Power at plate

P-P Plate-load, plate-to-plate, or push-pull amplifier

R_g Grid resistor

R_k Cathode resistor

R_l Plate-load impedance or resistance

R_p Plate-load resistor

R_{sg} Screen-dropping resistor

R_d Decoupling resistor

r_p Internal plate resistance

V_g Voltage gain

The basing diagrams are shown in Fig. 11-2.

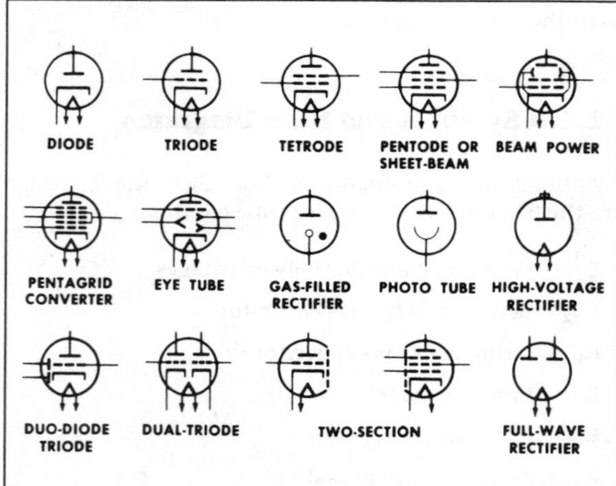

Figure 11-2 Basing diagrams for popular tubes.

11.1.4 Transconductance

Transconductance is the change in the value of plate current expressed in microamperes divided by the signal voltage at the control grid of a vacuum tube, and it is expressed by conductance. *Conductance* is the opposite of resistance, and the name *mho* (ohm spelled backward) was adopted for this unit of measurement. *Siemans* (S) have been adopted as the SI standard for conductance and are currently replacing mhos in measurement.

The basic mho is too large for practical usage; therefore, the term *micromho* is used. One micromho is equal to one-millionth of a mho.

The transconductance (g_m) of a tube may be found with the formula

$$g_m = \Delta I_p / \Delta E_{sig} \,(E_{bb} \text{ held constant}) \qquad (11\text{-}1)$$

where,

ΔI_p is the change of plate current,
ΔE_{sig} is the change of control-grid signal voltage,
E_{bb} is the plate supply voltage.

A change of 1 mA of plate current for a change of 1 V at the control grid is equal to 1000 μmho. A tube having a change of 2 mA plate current for a change of 1 V at the control grid would have a transconductance of 2000 μmho.

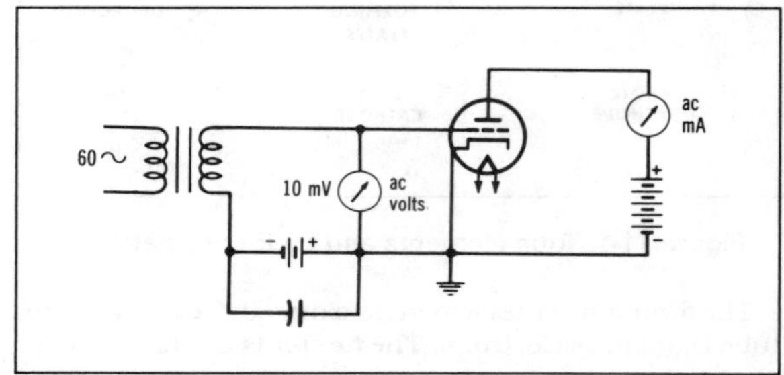

Figure 11-3 Circuit for measuring the transconductance (G_m) of a typical vacuum tube.

Transconductance is measured by the use of a circuit such as that shown in Fig. 11-3. Normal grid and plate voltages are applied as indicated. The signal voltage is adjusted at the control grid of the tube. An ac milliammeter, calibrated in transconductance, is connected in the plate circuit:

$$g_m = I_{pac} \times 1000 \qquad (11\text{-}2)$$

11.1.5 Amplification Factor

Amplification factor or *voltage gain* is the amount the signal at the control grid is increased in amplitude after passing through the tube, which is also referred to as the Greek letter μ (mu) or voltage gain (V_g) of the tube.

Tube voltage gain may be computed using

$$V_g = (g_m r_p R_p)/(r_p R_p 10^6) \qquad (11\text{-}3)$$

or

$$V_g = (\mu R_p)/(r_p R_p)$$

where,
g_m is the transconductance in micromhos,
r_p is the plate resistance in ohms,
R_p is the load resistance in ohms,
μ is the voltage gain.

If the amplifier consists of several stages, the amount of amplification is multiplied by each stage. The gain of an amplifier stage varies with the type tube and the interstage coupling used. The general equation for voltage gain is

$$V_{gt} = V_{g1}(V_{g2})V_{g3} \cdot \cdot \cdot \qquad (11\text{-}4)$$

where,
V_{gt} is the total gain of the amplifier,
V_{g1}, V_{g2}, and V_{g3} are voltage gain of the individual stages.

Triode tubes are classified by their amplification factor. A low-μ tube is one having an amplification factor less than 10. Medium-μ tubes have an amplification factor of from 10 to 50, with a plate resistance of 5 to 15,000 Ω. High-μ tubes have an amplification factor of 50 to 100 with a plate resistance of 50,000 to 100,000 Ω.

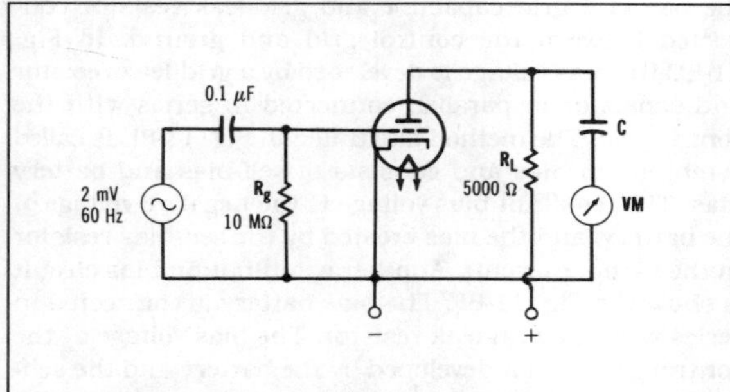

Figure 11-4 The Electronic Industries Association (EIA) method of measuring the ac amplification factor of triodes and pentodes. The internal impedance of the signal source should not exceed 2500 Ω.

A simple test for measuring the ac amplification factor is shown in Fig. 11-4. The ratio of the output voltage to the input voltage is a measure of the amplification factor. This test is used for both triodes and pentodes.

11.1.6 Phase

Phase reversals take place in a tube. The phase reversal in electrical degrees between the elements of a self-biased pentode for a given sine at the control grid is shown in Fig. 11-5. Note that, for an instantaneous positive voltage at the control grid, the voltage phase between the grid and plate is 180° and will remain so for all normal operating conditions. The control grid and cathode are in

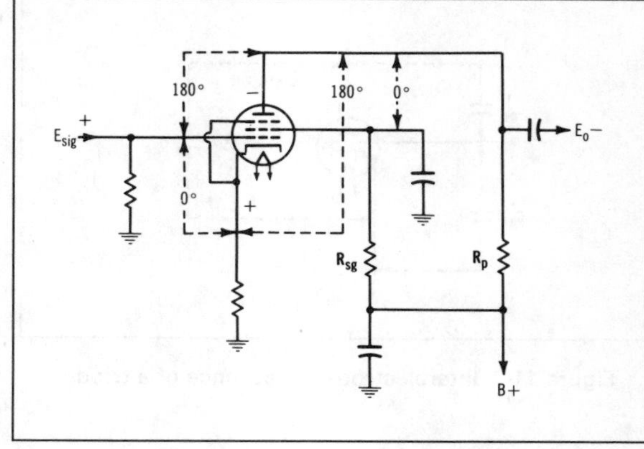

Figure 11-5 Phase reversal of the signal between the elements of a pentode vacuum tube. The reversals are the same for a triode.

phase. The plate and screen-grid elements are in phase with each other. The cathode is 180° out of phase with the plate and screen-grid elements.

The phase reversal of the voltage and current for each element is shown in Fig. 11-6. For an instantaneous positive sine wave at the control grid, the voltages at the plate and screen grid are negative, and the currents, positive. The voltage and current are both positive in the cathode resistor and are in phase with the voltage at the control grid.

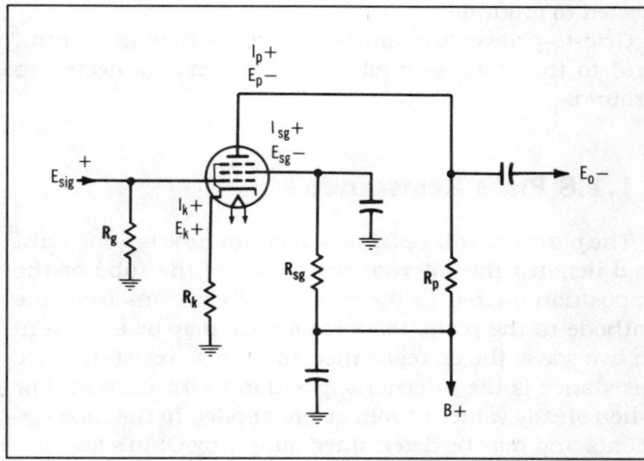

Figure 11-6 Phase reversal of the current and voltage in a pentode vacuum tube. The reversals are the same in a triode for a given element.

11.1.7 Internal Capacitance

The *internal capacitance* of a vacuum tube is created by the close proximity of the internal elements, as shown in Fig. 11-7. Unless otherwise stated by the manufacturer, the internal capacitance of a glass tube is mea-

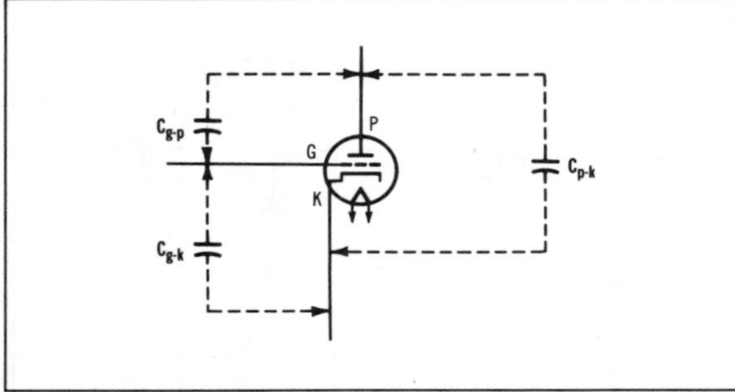

Figure 11-7 Interelectrode capacitance of a triode.

sured using a close-fitting metal tube shield around the glass envelope connected to the cathode terminal. Generally, the capacitance is measured with the heater or filament cold and with no voltage applied to any of the other elements.

In measuring the capacitance, all metal parts, except the input and output elements, are connected to the cathode. These metal parts include internal and external shields, base sleeves, and unused pins. In testing a multisection tube, elements not common to the section being measured are connected to ground.

Input capacitance is measured from the control grid to all other elements, except the plate, which is connected to ground.

Output capacitance is measured from the plate to all other elements, except the control grid, which is connected to ground.

Grid-to-plate capacitance is measured from the control grid to the plate with all other elements connected to ground.

11.1.8 Plate Resistance

The *plate resistance* (r_p) of a vacuum tube is a constant and denotes the internal resistance of the tube or the opposition offered to the passage of electrons from the cathode to the plate. Plate resistance may be expressed in two ways: the dc resistance and the ac resistance. Dc resistance is the internal opposition to the current flow when steady values of voltage are applied to the tube elements and may be determined simply by Ohm's law:

$$r_p(\text{dc}) = E_p/I_p \quad (11\text{-}5)$$

where,
E_p is the dc plate voltage,
I_p is the steady value of plate current.

The ac resistance requires a family of plate-current curves from which the information may be extracted. As a rule, this information is included with the tube characteristics and is used when calculating or selecting components for an amplifier. The equation for calculating ac plate resistance is

$$r_p(\text{ac}) = \Delta E_p/\Delta I_p\,(E_{sig}\text{ held constant}) \quad (11\text{-}6)$$

where,
E_p is the voltage at the plate,
I_p is the plate current,
Δ is the change in E_p and I_p,
E_{sig} is the control grid signal voltage.

The values of E_p and I_p are those taken from the family of curves supplied by the manufacturer for the particular tube under consideration.

11.1.9 Grid Bias

Increasing the plate voltage or decreasing the grid-bias voltage decreases the plate resistance.

The six methods most commonly used to bias a tube are illustrated in Fig. 11-8. In Fig. 11-8A a bias cell is connected in series with the control grid. In Fig. 11-8B the tube is self-biased by the use of a resistor connected in the cathode circuit. In Fig. 11-8C the circuit is also a form of self-bias; however, the bias voltage is obtained by the use of a grid capacitor and grid-leak resistor connected between the control grid and ground. In Fig. 11-8D the bias voltage is developed by a grid-leak resistor and capacitor in parallel, connected in series with the control grid. The method illustrated in Fig. 11-8E is called combination bias and consists of self-bias and battery bias. The resultant bias voltage is the negative voltage of the battery, and the bias created by the self-bias resistor in the cathode circuit. Another combination bias circuit is shown in Fig. 11-8F. The bias battery is connected in series with the grid-leak resistor. The bias voltage at the control grid is that developed by the battery and the self-bias created by the combination of the grid resistor and capacitor.

If the control grid is permitted to become positive with respect to the cathode, it results in a flow of current between the control grid and the cathode through the external circuits. This condition is unavoidable because the wires of the control grid, having a positive charge, attract electrons passing from the cathode to the plate; therefore, the control-grid voltage is normally kept negative, reducing grid current and distortion.

Grid-current flow in a vacuum tube is generally thought of as being caused by only driving the control grid into the positive region and causing the flow of grid current.

The grid voltage, plate-current characteristics are found through a series of curves supplied by the tube manufacturer, as shown in Fig. 11-9.

The curves indicate that for a given plate voltage the plate current and grid bias may be determined. For example, the manufacturer states that for a plate voltage of 250 V and a negative grid bias of −8 V, the plate current will be 9 mA, which is indicated at point A on the 250-V

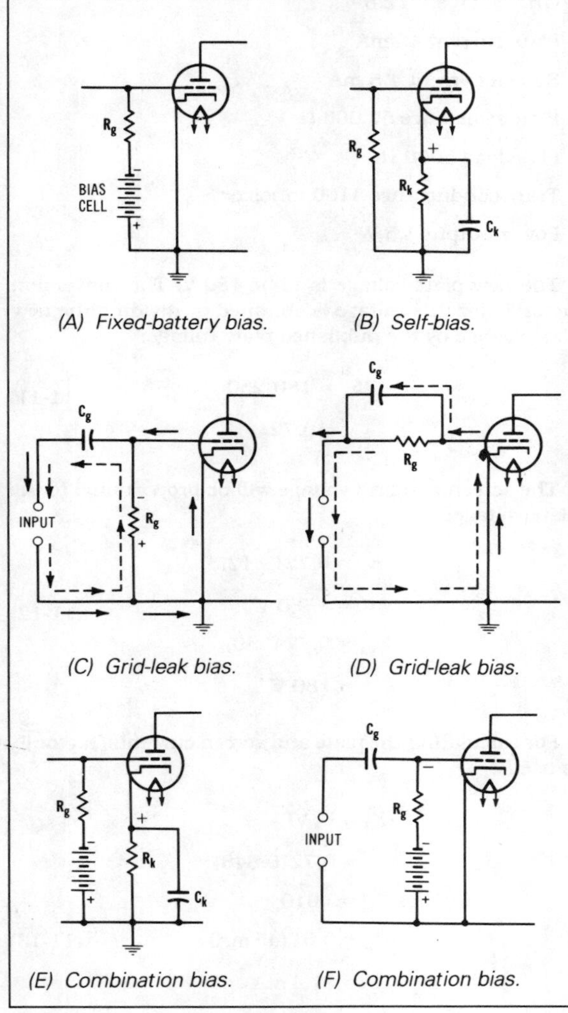

Figure 11-8 Various methods of obtaining grid bias.

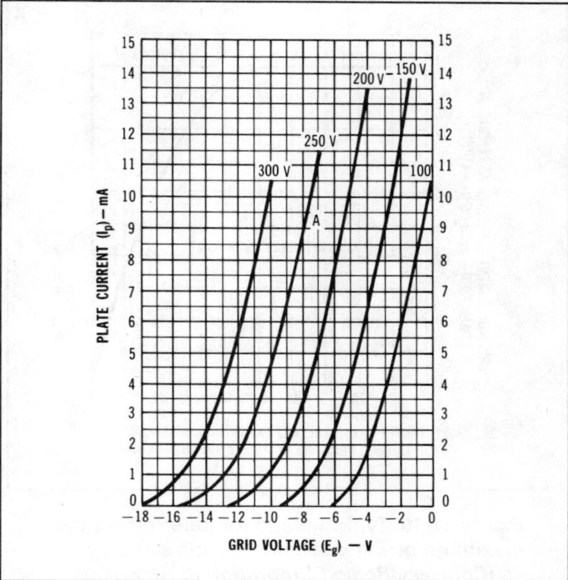

Figure 11-9 Grid voltage, plate-current curves for a triode tube.

curve. If it is desired to operate this tube with a plate voltage of 150 V and still maintain a plate current of 9 mA, the grid bias will have to be changed to a −3 V.

11.1.10 Plate Efficiency

The *plate efficiency* (E_{ff}) is calculated by the formula:

$$E_{ff} = [\text{watts}/(E_{pa} I_{pa})] \times 100 \qquad (11\text{-}7)$$

where,

watts is the power output,
E_{pa} is the average voltage at the plate,
I_{pa} is the average plate current.

The measurement is made with a load resistance in the plate circuit equal in value to the plate resistance stated by the manufacturer.

11.1.11 Power Sensitivity

Power sensitivity is the ratio of the power output to the square of the input voltage, expressed in mhos:

$$\text{Power sensitivity} = P_o/(E_{in})^2 \qquad (11\text{-}8)$$

where,

P_o is the power output of the tube in watts,
E_{in} is the rms signal voltage at the input.

11.1.12 Screen Grid

The *screen-grid series-dropping resistance* is calculated by referring to the data sheet of the manufacturer and finding the maximum voltage that may be applied and the maximum power that may be dissipated by the screen grid. These limitations are generally shown graphically as in Fig. 11-10. The value of the resistor may be calculated using

$$R_{sg} = E_{sg}(E_{bb} - E_{sg})/P_{sg} \qquad (11\text{-}9)$$

where,

R_{sg} is the minimum value for the screen-grid voltage-dropping resistor in ohms,

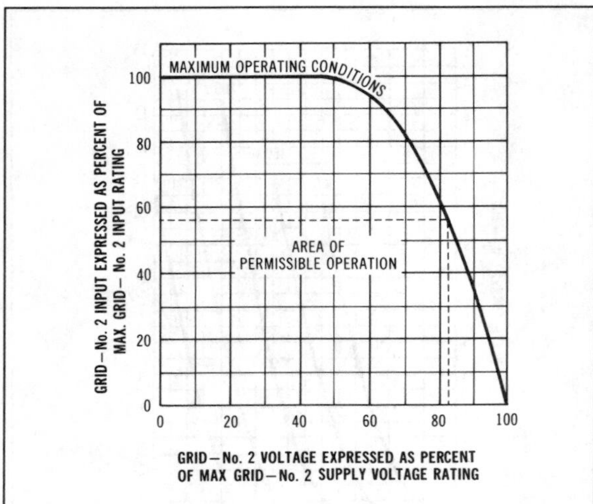

Figure 11-10 Typical graph for determining the maximum power dissipated by the screen grid. *(Courtesy Radio Corporation of America)*

E_{sg} is the selected value of screen-grid voltage,
E_{bb} is the screen-grid supply voltage,
P_{sg} is the screen-grid input in watts corresponding to the selected value of E_{sg}.

11.1.13 Plate Dissipation

Plate dissipation is the maximum power that can be dissipated by the plate element before damage:

$$\text{watts dissipation} = E_p I_p \tag{11-10}$$

where,
E_p is the voltage at the plate,
I_p is the plate current.

11.1.14 Changing Parameters

If a tube is to operate at a different plate voltage than published, the new values of bias, screen voltage, and plate resistance can be calculated by the use of conversion factors F_1, F_2, F_3, F_4 and F_5. Assume the following conditions are specified for a single beam-power tube:

Plate voltage 250 V

Screen voltage 250 V

Grid voltage − 12.5 V

Plate current 45 mA

Screen current 4.5 mA

Plate resistance 52,000 Ω

Plate load 5000 Ω

Transconductance 4100 mhos or S

Power output 4.5 W

The new plate voltage is to be 180 V. The conversion factor F_1 for this voltage is obtained by dividing the new plate voltage by the published plate voltage:

$$\begin{aligned} F_1 &= 180/250 \\ &= 0.72 \end{aligned} \tag{11-11}$$

The screen and grid voltage will be proportional to the plate voltage:

$$\begin{aligned} E_g &= 0.72(-12.5) \\ &= -9.0\text{ V} \\ E_{sg} &= 0.72\ (250) \\ &= 180\text{ V} \end{aligned} \tag{11-12}$$

For calculating the plate and screen currents, factor F_2 is used:

$$\begin{aligned} F_2 &= F_1\sqrt{F_1} \\ &= 0.72(0.848) \\ &= 0.610 \\ I_p &= 0.61(45\text{ mA}) \\ &= 27.4\text{ mA} \\ I_{sg} &= 0.61(4.5\text{ mA}) \\ &= 2.74\text{ mA} \end{aligned} \tag{11-13}$$

The plate load and plate resistance may be calculated by use of factor F_3:

$$\begin{aligned} F_3 &= F_1/F_2 \\ &= 0.720/0.610 \\ &= 1.18 \\ r_p &= 52{,}000(1.18) \\ &= 61{,}360\ \Omega \\ R_L &= 5000(1.18) \\ &= 5900\ \Omega \end{aligned} \tag{11-14}$$

The power output is found by the use of the factor F_4:

$$F_4 = F_1 F_2$$
$$= 0.72(0.610) \quad (11\text{-}15)$$
$$= 0.439$$
$$\text{Power Output} = 0.439(4.5)$$
$$= 1.97 \text{ W}$$

The transconductance is determined by the aid of factor F_5:

$$F_5 = 1/F_3$$
$$= 1/1.18 \quad (11\text{-}16)$$
$$= 0.847$$
$$\text{transconductance} = 0.847(4100)$$
$$= 3472\ \mu\text{mho}$$

The foregoing method of converting for voltages other than those originally specified may be used for triodes, tetrodes, pentodes, and beam-power tubes, provided the plate and grid-1 and grid-2 voltages are changed simultaneously by the same factor. This will apply to any class of tube operating, such as class A, AB_1, AB_2, B, or C. Although this method of conversion is quite satisfactory in most instances, the error will be increased as the conversion factor departs from unity. The most satisfactory region of operation will be between 0.7 and 2.0. When the factor falls outside this region, the accuracy of operation is reduced.

11.1.15 Tube Heater

The data sheets of tube manufacturers generally contain a warning that the heater voltage should be maintained within ±10% of the rated voltage. As a rule, this warning is taken lightly, and little attention is paid to heater voltage variations, which have a pronounced effect on the tube characteristics. Internal noise is the greatest offender. Because of heater-voltage variation, emission life is shortened, electrical leakage between elements is increased, heater-to-cathode leakage is increased, and grid current is caused to flow. Thus, the life of the tube is decreased with an increase of internal noise.

11.2 DISCRETE SOLID-STATE DEVICES

11.2.1 Semiconductors[1,2]

Conduction in solids was first observed by Munck and Henry in 1835, and later in 1874 by Braum. In 1905, Col. Dunwoody invented the crystal detector, used in the detection of electromagnetic waves. It consisted of a bar of silicon carbide or carborundum held between two contacts. However, in 1903, Pickard filed a patent application for a crystal detector in which a fine wire was placed in contact with the silicon. This was the first mention of a silicon rectifier and was the forerunner of the present-day silicon rectifier. Later, other minerals such as galena (lead sulphide) were employed as detectors. In 1883, Edison observed the flow of current between a hot filament and an anode placed in an evacuated bulb (Edison effect). In 1903 Fleming made use of Edison's discovery and devised the first vacuum diode detector. In 1906, Dr. Lee DeForest invented the three-element vacuum tube. During World War II, intensive research was conducted to improve crystal detectors used for microwave radar equipment. As a result of this research, the original point-contact transistor was invented at the Bell Telephone Laboratories in 1948.

A *semiconductor* is an electronic device whose main functioning part is made from materials, such as germanium and silicon, whose conductivity ranges between that of a conductor and an insulator.

Germanium is a rare metal discovered by Winkler in Saxony, Germany, in the year 1896. Germanium is a by-product of zinc mining. Germanium crystals are grown from germanium dioxide powder. Germanium in its purest state behaves much like an insulator because it has very few electrical charge carriers. The conductivity of germanium may be increased by the addition of small amounts of an impurity.

Silicon is a nonmetallic element used in the manufacture of diode rectifiers and transistors. Its resistivity is considerably higher than that of germanium.

The relative position of pure germanium and silicon is given in Fig. 11-11. The scale indicates the resistance of conductors, semiconductors, and insulators per cubic centimeter. Pure germanium has a resistance of approximately 60 Ω/cm^3. Germanium has a higher conductivity or less resistance to current flow than silicon and is used in low- and medium-power diodes and transistors.

The base elements used to make semiconductor devices are not usable as semiconductors in their pure state. They must be subjected to a complex chemical, metallurgical, and photolithographical process wherein the base element is highly refined and then modified with the addition of specific impurities. This precisely controlled process of diffusing impurities into the pure base element is called *doping* and converts the pure base material into a semiconductor material.

The semiconductor mechanism is achieved by the application of a voltage across the device with the proper polarity so as to have the device act either as an extremely low resistance (the forward biased or conducting mode) or as an extremely high resistance (reversed bias or nonconducting mode). Because the device is acting as both a good conductor of electricity and also, with the proper reversal of voltage, as a good electrical nonconductor or insulator, it is called a semiconductor.

Some semiconductor materials are called *p* or positive

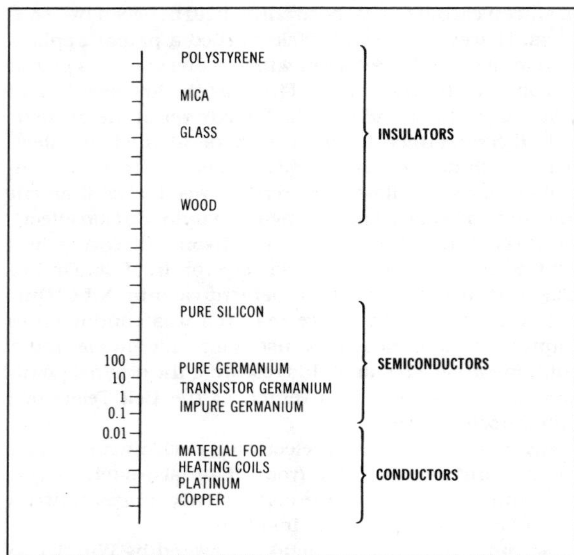

Figure 11-11 Resistance of various materials per cubic centimeter. Pure germanium has about 60 Ω of resistance per cubic centimeter.

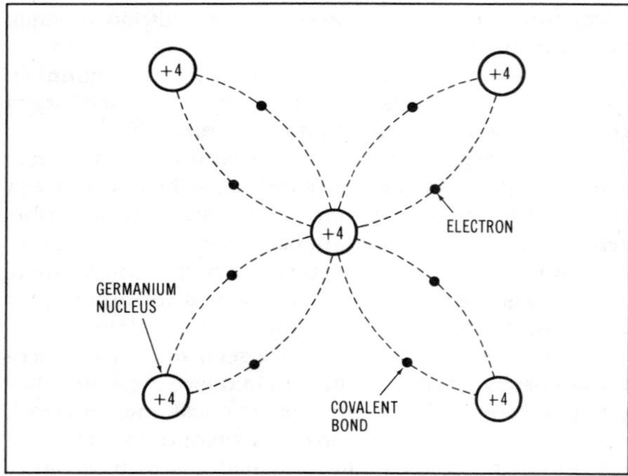

Figure 11-12 Atomic structure of a pure germanium crystal. In this condition germanium is a poor conductor

type because they are processed to have an excess of positively charged ions. Others are called *n* or negative type because they are processed to have an excess of negatively charged electrons. When a p-type of material is brought into intimate contact with an n-type of material, a *pn junction* is formed. With the application of the proper external voltage, a low resistance path is produced between the n and p material. By reversing the previously applied voltage, an extremely high resistance called the *depletion layer* between the p and n types results. This device, whose

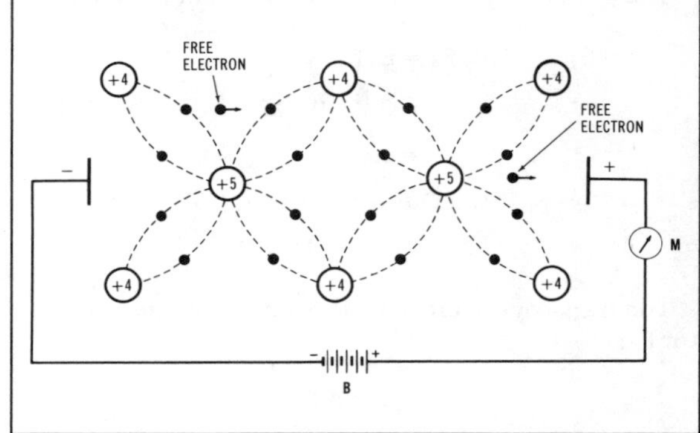

Figure 11-13 Atomic structure of an n-type germanium crystal when a doping agent containing five electrons is induced.

conduction depends upon the polarity of the externally applied voltage, is known as a diode. By combining several of these pn junctions together in a single device, many other semiconductor products with extremely useful electrical properties have also been developed.

The theory of operation of a semiconductor device should be approached from its atomic structure.

The outer orbit of a germanium atom contains four electrons. The atomic structure for a pure germanium crystal is shown in Fig. 11-12. Each atom containing four electrons forms covalent bonds with adjacent atoms. Therefore, there are no "free" electrons, and germanium in its pure state is a poor conductor of electricity, as shown in Fig. 11-11. If a piece of "pure" germanium (the size used in a transistor) has a voltage applied to it, only a few microamperes of current caused by electrons that have been broken away from their bonds by thermal agitation will flow in the circuit. This current will increase at an exponential rate with an increase of temperature.

When an atom with five electrons, such as antimony or arsenic, is introduced into the germanium crystal, the atomic structure is changed to that of Fig. 11-13. The extra electrons (called free electrons) will move toward the positive terminal of the external voltage source.

When an electron flows from the germanium crystal to the positive terminal of the external voltage source, another electron enters the crystal from the negative terminal of the voltage source. Thus, a continuous stream of electrons will flow as long as the external potential is maintained.

The atom containing the five electrons is the *doping agent* or *donor*. Such germanium crystals are classified as *n-type germanium*.

Using a doping agent of indium, gallium, or aluminum, each of which contains only three electrons in its outer orbit, causes the germanium crystal to take the atomic structure of Fig. 11-14. In this structure, there is a *hole* or *acceptor*. The term *hole* is used to denote a mobile

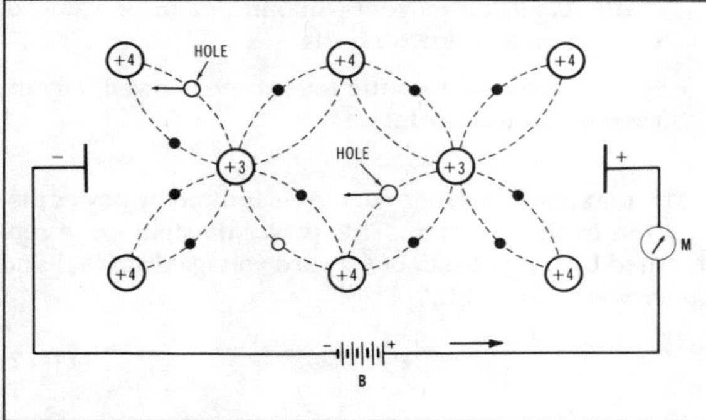

Figure 11-14 Atomic structure of a p-type germanium crystal when a doping agent containing three electrons is induced.

particle that has a positive charge and that simulates the properties of an electron having a positive charge.

When a germanium crystal containing holes is subjected to an electrical field, electrons jump into the holes, and the holes appear to move toward the negative terminal of the external voltage source.

When a hole arrives at the negative terminal, an electron is emitted by the terminal, and the hole is canceled. Simultaneously, an electron from one of the covalent bonds flows into the positive terminal of the voltage source. This new hole moves toward the negative terminal causing a continuous flow of holes in the crystal.

Germanium crystals having a deficiency of electrons are classified *p-type germanium*. Insofar as the external electrical circuits are concerned, there is no difference between electron and hole current flow. However, the method of connection to the two types of transistors differs.

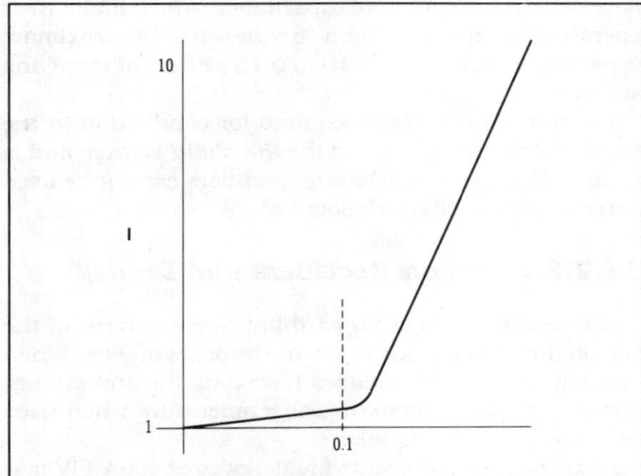

Figure 11-15 Voltage-versus-current characteristic of the junction.

When a germanium crystal is doped so that it abruptly changes from an n-type to a p-type, a positive potential is applied to the p-region, and a negative potential is applied to the n-region, the holes move through the junction to the right and the electrons move to the left, resulting in the voltage-current characteristic shown in Fig. 11-15. If the potential is reversed, both electrons and holes move away from the junction until the electrical field produced by their displacement counteracts the applied electrical field. Under these conditions, zero current flows in the external circuit. Any minute amount of current that might flow is caused by thermal-generated hole pairs. Fig. 11-16 is a plot of the voltage versus current for the reversed condition. The leakage current is essentially independent of the applied potential up to the point where the junction breaks down.

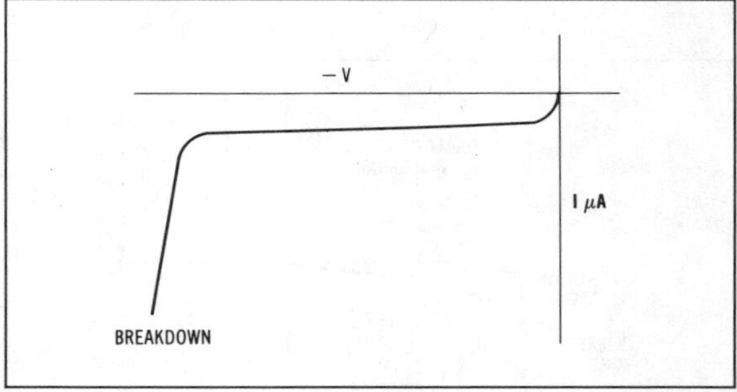

Figure 11-16 Voltage-versus-current characteristic of the junction transistor with the battery polarities in the reverse condition.

11.2.2 Diodes

The *diode* is a device through which current can flow easily from one terminal to another, but cannot flow in the other direction under a reversed-bias condition. Another way of defining a diode is to say that it exhibits a low resistance to current flow in one direction and a high resistance in the other.

Fig. 11-17 shows the ideal *diode characteristics*. Ideally, when *reverse biasing* the diode (connecting the negative of the supply to the diode anode), no current should flow regardless of the value of voltage (V) impressed across the diode. With the diode *forward-biased* current should flow even at very low resistance to current flow. Fig. 11-18 shows the actual diode characteristics. The behavior of an actual diode is not quite as simple as that shown for an ideal case. Starting with the diode reverse biased, a small reverse current does flow. The size of this *reverse-leakage current* has been exaggerated for clarity and typically is in the order of nanoamperes. Note also that the forward resistance is not constant and, therefore, does not yield a straightline forward-conduction curve. Instead,

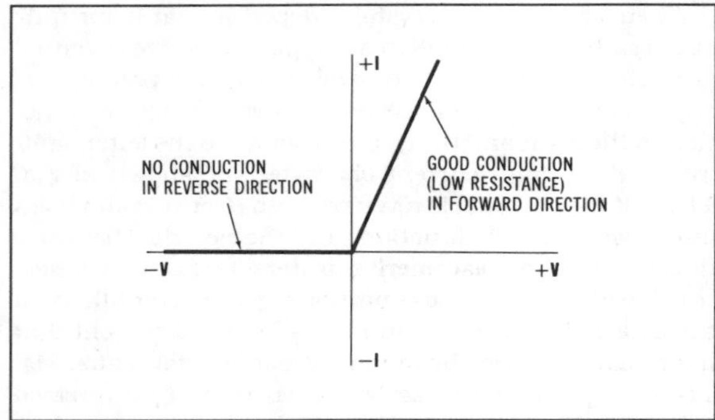

Figure 11-17 Ideal diode characteristics with good conduction in the forward direction and no conduction in the reverse direction.

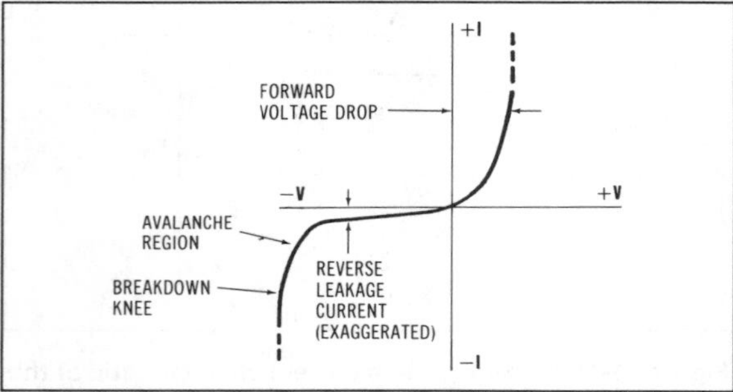

Figure 11-18 Actual diode characteristics.

it begins high and drops rapidly at relatively low applied voltage. Above about a 1-V drop, however, it does approach a steep straightline slope (i.e., low resistance).

In the reverse-biased region of Fig. 11-18, note that when the applied voltage (−V) becomes large enough, the leakage current suddenly begins to increase very rapidly, and the slope of the characteristic curves becomes very steep. Past the so-called "knee" in the characteristic, even a small increase in reverse voltage causes a large increase in the reverse current. This steep region is called the *breakdown* or *avalanche* region of the diode characteristic.

The application of high reverse voltage causes the diode to break down and stop behaving like a diode. This is helpful in understanding why one of the two most important diode parameters is the *peak-reverse-voltage rating* or *PRV*. This is also referred to as the *peak-inverse-voltage rating* or *PIV*. This rating indicates how high the reverse voltage can be without approaching the knee and risking breakdown.

Additional diode parameters are:

- *Maximum average current*—causes overheating of the device.
- *Peak repetitive current*—maximum peak value of current on a repetitive basis.
- *Surge current*—absolute maximum allowed current even if just momentary.

The maximum average current is limited by power dissipation in the junction. This power dissipation is represented by the product of forward voltage drop (V_F) and the forward current (I_F):

$$P = V_F I_F \tag{11-17}$$

11.2.2.1 Selenium Rectifiers and Diodes

A *selenium rectifier cell* consists of a nickel-plated aluminum-base plate coated with selenium, over which a low-temperature alloy is sprayed. The aluminum base serves as a negative electrode, and the alloy, as the positive. Current flows from the base plate to the alloy but encounters high resistance in the opposite direction. The efficiency of conversion depends to some extent on the ratio of the resistance in the conducting direction to that of the blocking direction. Conventional rectifiers generally have ratios from 100:1 to 1000:1.

Selenium rectifiers may be operated over temperatures of −55 to +150°C. Rectification efficiency is in the order of 90% for three-phase bridge circuits and 70% for single-phase bridge circuits. As a selenium cell ages, the forward and reverse resistance increases for approximately one year, then stabilizes, decreasing the output voltage by approximately 15%. The internal impedance of a selenium rectifier is low and exhibits a nonlinear characteristic with respect to the applied voltage, thus maintaining a good voltage regulation. Therefore, it is often used for battery charging.

By the nature of their construction, selenium rectifiers have considerable internal capacitance, which limits their operating range to audio frequencies. Approximate capacitance ranges are 0.10 to 0.15 μF/in.^{2} of rectifying surface.

The minimum voltage required for conduction in the forward direction is termed the *threshold voltage* and is about 1 V; therefore, selenium rectifiers cannot be used successfully at voltages below 1 V.

11.2.2.2 Silicon Rectifiers and Diodes

Because of the high forward-to-reverse current of the silicon diode, the efficiency is in the order of 99%. When properly used, silicon diodes have long life and are not affected by aging, moisture, or temperature when used with the proper heat sink.

As an example, four individual diodes of 400 V PIV may be connected in series to withstand a PIV of 1600 V. In a series arrangement, the most important consideration is that the applied voltage be equally distributed between the several units. The voltage drops across each individual unit must be very nearly identical. If the instantaneous voltage is not equally divided, one of the units may be subjected to a voltage exceeding its rated value, causing it to fail. This then causes the other rectifiers to absorb the PIV, often creating destruction of all the rectifiers.

Uniform voltage distribution can be obtained by the connection of capacitors or resistors in parallel with the individual rectifier unit. Shunt resistors are used for steady-state applications, and shunt capacitors are used in applications where transient voltages are expected. If the circuit is exposed to both dc and ac, both shunt capacitors and resistors should be employed.

When the maximum current of a single diode is exceeded, two or more units may be connected in parallel. To avoid differences in voltage drop across the individual units, a resistor or small inductor is connected in series with each diode. Of the two methods, the inductance is favored because of the lower voltage drop and consumption of power.

11.2.2.3 Zener and Avalanche Diodes

When the reverse voltage is increased beyond the breakdown knee of the diode characteristics as shown in Fig. 11-18, the diode impedance suddenly drops sharply to a very low value. Provided that the current is limited by an external circuit resistance, this need not cause harm to the diode; in fact, operation in the "zener region" is normal for certain diodes specifically designed for the purpose. In zener diodes, sometimes simply called "zeners," the breakdown characteristic is deliberately made as vertical as possible in the zener region so that the voltage across the diode is essentially constant over a wide reverse-current range. Thus, the zener acts as a voltage regulator. Since its zener-region voltage can be made highly repeatable and very stable with respect to time and temperature, the zener diode can also function as a voltage reference. Zener diodes come in a wide variety of voltages, currents, and powers, ranging from 3.2 V to hundreds of volts, from a few milliamperes to 10 A or more, and from about 250 mW to over 50 W.

Avalanche diodes are diodes in which the shape of the breakdown knee has been controlled, and the leakage current before breakdown has been reduced so that the diode is especially well suited to two applications: high-voltage stacking and clamping. In other words, they prevent a circuit from exceeding a certain value of voltage by causing breakdown of the diode at or just below that voltage.

11.2.2.4 Small-Signal Diodes

Small-signal diodes are low-level devices with the same general characteristics as power diodes. They are smaller, dissipate much less power, and are not designed for high-voltage, high-power operation. Another name for them is *general-purpose diodes*. Typical rating ranges are

I_F (forward current): 1 to 500 mA

V_F (forward voltage drop at I_F): 0.2 to 1.1 V

piv (peak inverse voltage) or

prv (peak reverse voltage): 6 to 1000 V

I_R (leakage current at 80% or prv): 0.1 to 1.0 μA

11.2.2.5 Switching Diodes

Switching diodes are small-signal diodes used primarily in digital-logic and control applications in which the voltages may change very rapidly so that speed, particularly reverse-recovery time, is of paramount performance. Other parameters of particular importance are low shunt capacitance, low and uniform V_F (forward voltage drop), low I_R (reverse leakage current) and, in control circuits, prv.

11.2.2.6 Noise Diodes

These silicon diodes are used in the avalanche mode (reverse biased beyond the breakdown knee) to generate broadband noise signals. All diodes generate some noise; these, however, have special internal geometry and are specially processed so as to generate uniform noise power over very broadbands. They are low-power devices (typically, 0.05 to 0.25 W) and are available in several different bandwidth classes from as low as 0 to 100 kHz to as high as 1,000 to 18,000 MHz.

11.2.2.7 Varactor Diodes

Varactor diodes are made of silicon or gallium arsenide and are used as adjustable capacitors. Certain diodes, when operated in the reverse-biased mode at voltages below the breakdown value, exhibit a shunt capacitance that is inversely proportional to the applied voltage. By varying the applied reverse voltage, the capacitance of the varactor may be varied, and this effect can be used to tune circuits, to modulate oscillators, to generate harmonics, and to mix signals. Varactors are often referred to as *voltage-tunable trimmer capacitors*.

11.2.2.8 Tunnel Diodes

The *tunnel diode* takes its name from the *tunnel effect*, a process where a particle can disappear from one side of a barrier and instantaneously reappear on the other side as though it had tunneled through the barrier element.

Tunnel diodes are made by heavily doping both the p and n materials with impurities, thus giving them a completely different voltage-current characteristic from regular diodes. This characteristic, which is shown in Fig. 11-19, makes them uniquely useful in many high-frequency amplifiers as well as pulse generators and radio-frequency oscillators.

The thing that makes the tunnel diode work as an active

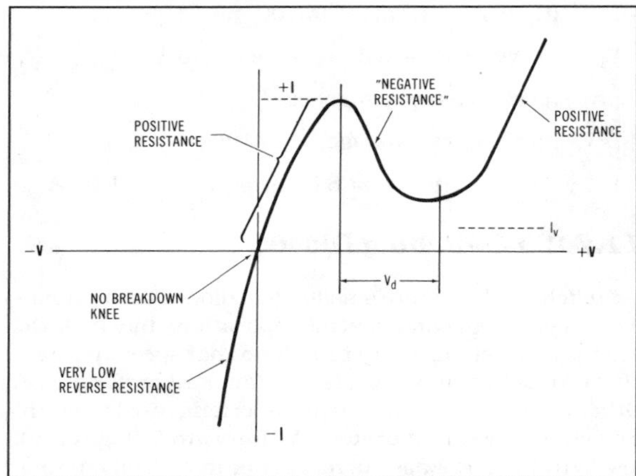

Figure 11-19 Tunnel-diode characteristics showing negative region (tunnel region).

element is the "negative resistance region" over the voltage range V_d *(a small fraction of a volt)*. In this region, increasing the voltage decreases the current, the opposite of what happens with a normal resistor. Note also that tunnel diodes conduct heavily in the reverse direction; in fact, there is no breakdown knee or leakage region.

11.2.3 Thyristors[3]

Stack four properly doped semiconductor layers in series, pnpn (or npnp), and the result is a four-layer, or Shockley, breakover diode. Adding a terminal (gate) to the second p-layer creates a gate-controlled, reverse-blocking thyristor, or silicon-controlled rectifier (SCR), as shown in Fig. 11-20A.

The four-layer diode connects (fires) above a specific threshold voltage. In the SCR, the gate controls this firing threshold voltage, called the forward-blocking voltage.

To understand how four-layer devices work, mentally separate the material of the layers into two three-layer transistor devices, as in Fig. 11-20B. Fig. 11-20C is an equivalent two-transistor representation in a positive-feedback connection. Assuming a_1 and a_2 are the current gains of the two transistor sections with each gain value less than unity, the total base current I_b into the $n_1p_2n_2$ transistor is

$$I_b = a_1a_2I_b + I_O + I_g \qquad (11\text{-}18)$$

where,

I_O is the leakage current into the base of the $n_1p_2n_2$ transistor,

I_g is the current into the gate terminal.

The circuit fires (turns on) and becomes self-feeding (or self-latching) after a certain turn-on time needed to stabilize the feedback action, when the equality of Eq. 11-18 is achieved. This result becomes easier to understand by solving for I_b, which gives

$$I_b = (I_O + I_g)/(1 - a_1a_2) \qquad (11\text{-}19)$$

When the product a_1a_2 is close to unity, the denominator approaches zero; then, not only does I_b approach a large value, but for a given leakage current I_O, the gate current to fire the device can be extremely small. More-

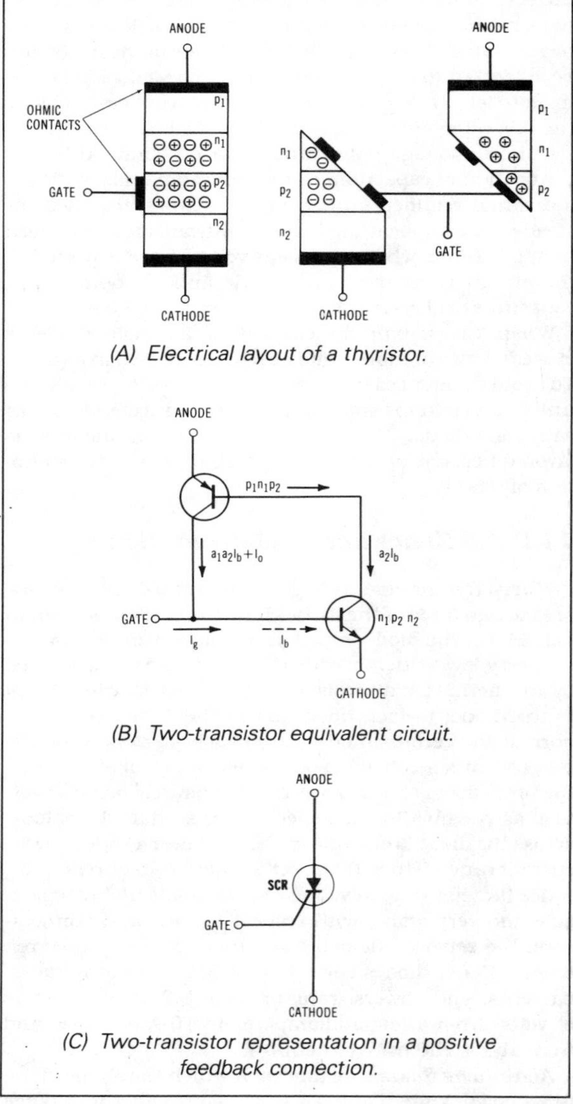

Figure 11-20 Thyristor schematics. *(Courtesy Electronic Design)*

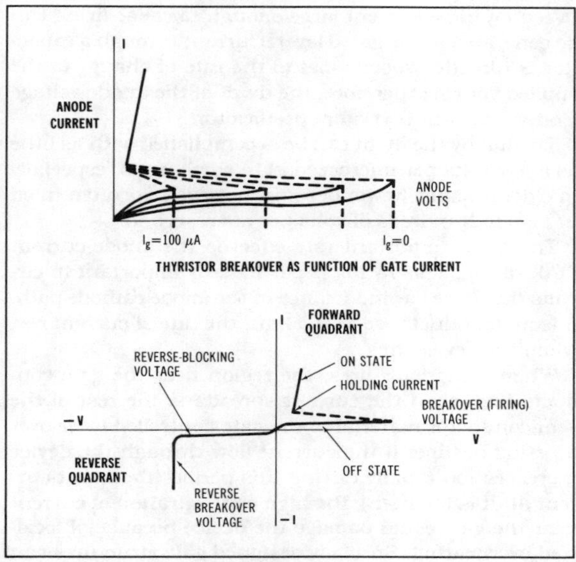

Figure 11-21 Thyristor breakover as a function of gate current and forward voltage. *(Courtesy Electronic Design)*

over, as I_b becomes large, I_g can be removed, and the feedback will sustain the on condition, since a_1 and a_2 then approach even closer to unity.

Accordingly, in the breakover diode (where I_g is absent) as applied anode voltage increases, I_O also increases. When the quality of Eq. 11-18 is established, the diode fires. The thyristor fires when the gate current I_g rises to establish equality in the equation (with the anode voltage fixed). Or, for a fixed I_g the anode voltage can be raised (as for the diode) until the thyristor fires, with I_g determining the firing voltage, as shown in Fig. 11-21.

Once fired, a thyristor stays on until the anode current falls below a specified minimum holding current for a certain turnoff time. In addition, the gate loses all control once a thyristor fires. Removal or even reverse biasing of the gate signal will not turn off the device (although reverse biasing can help speed turnoff). Of course, when the device is used with an ac voltage on the anode, the unit automatically turns off on the negative half of the voltage cycle. In dc switching circuits, however, complex means must often be used to remove, reduce, or reverse the anode voltage for turnoff.

Fig. 11-22 shows a bilaterally conductive arrangement that behaves very much like two four-layer diodes (*diacs*), or two SCRs (*triacs*), parallel and oppositely conductive. When terminal A is positive and above the breakover volt-

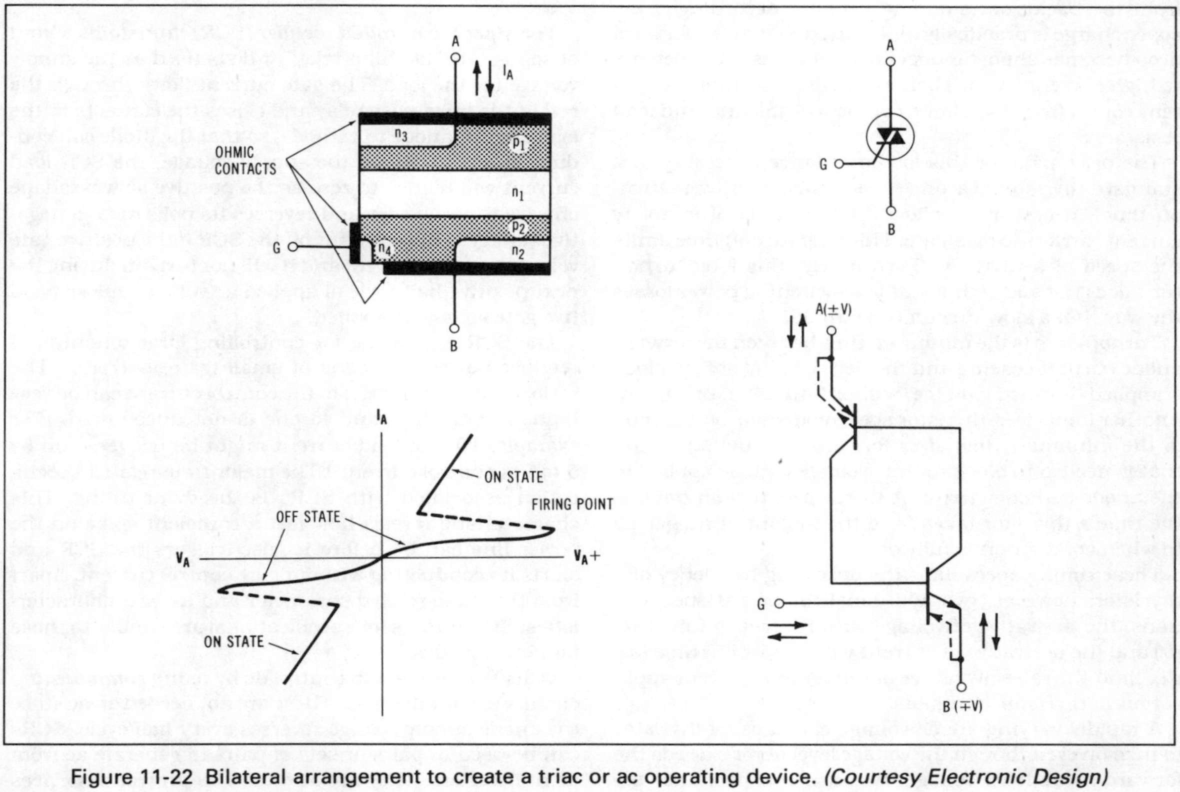

Figure 11-22 Bilateral arrangement to create a triac or ac operating device. *(Courtesy Electronic Design)*

age, a path through $p_1n_1p_2n_2$ can conduct; when terminal B is positive, path $p_2n_1p_1n_3$ can conduct. When terminal A is positive, a third element (terminal G), when sufficiently positive, will enable the $p_1n_1p_2n_2$ path to fire at a much lower voltage than when G is zero. This action is almost identical with that of the SCR. When terminal G is made negative and terminal B is made positive, the firing point is lowered in the reverse, or $p_2n_1p_1n_3$, direction.

Because of low impedances in the on condition, four-layer devices must be operated with a series resistance in the anode (and gate) that is large enough to limit the anode-to-cathode (or gate) current to a safe value.

To understand the low-impedance, high-current capability of the thyristor, the device must be examined as a whole rather than by the two-transistor model. In Fig. 11-20B the $p_1n_1p_2$ transistor has holes injected to fire the unit, and the $n_1p_2n_2$ transistor has electrons injected. Considered separately as two transistors, the space-charge distributions would produce two typical, transistor saturation-voltage forward drops, which are quite high when compared with the actual voltage drop of a thyristor.

However, when the thyristor shown in Fig. 11-20A is considered, the charges of both polarities exist simultaneously in the same n_1 and p_2 regions. Therefore, at the high injection levels that exist in thyristors, the mobile-carrier concentration of minority carriers far exceeds that from the background-doping density. Accordingly, the space charge is practically neutralized so that the forward drop becomes almost independent of the current density to high current levels. Then, the major resistance to current comes from the ohmic contacts of the unit and load resistance.

The price paid for this low-impedance capability in a standard thyristor is a long turnoff time (relative to turn-on time), necessary to allow the high level of minority current carriers to dissipate. This long turnoff time limits the speed of a thyristor. Fortunately, this long turnoff time does not add significantly to switching power losses the way that a slow turnon time would.

Turnoff time is the minimum time between the forward anode current ceasing and the device being able to block reapplied forward voltage without turning on again. Another important thyristor spec, *reverse-recovery time*, is the minimum time after forward conduction ceases that is needed to block reverse-voltage with ac applied to the anode-cathode circuit. A third spec, *turnon time*, is the time a thyristor takes from the instant of triggering to when conduction is fully on.

These timing specs limit the operating frequency of a thyristor; however, two additional important specifications, the derivative of voltage with respect to time (*dv/dt*) and the derivative of current with respect to time (*di/dt*), limit the rates of change of voltage and current application to thyristor terminals.

A rapidly varying anode voltage can cause a thyristor to turn on even though the voltage level never exceeds the forward breakdown voltage. Because of capacitance between layers, a current large enough to cause firing can be generated in the gated layer. Current through a capacitor is directly proportional to the rate of change of the applied voltage; therefore, the dv/dt of the anode voltage is an important thyristor specification.

Turnon by the dv/dt can be accomplished with as little as a few volts per microsecond in some units, especially in older designs. Newer designs, however, are often rated in tens to hundreds of volts per microsecond.

The other important rate effect is the anode-current di/dt rating. This rating is particularly important in circuits that have low inductance in the anode-cathode path. Adequate inductance would limit the rate of current rise when the device fires.

When a thyristor fires, the region near the gate conducts first; then the current spreads to the rest of the semiconductor material of the gate-controlled layer over a period of time. If the current flow through the device increases too rapidly during this period (the input-current di/dt is too high), the high concentration of current near the gate could damage the device because of localized overheating. Specially designed gate structures can speed up the turnon time of a thyristor, and thus its operational frequency, as well as alleviate this hot-spot problem.

11.2.3.1 Silicon-Controlled Rectifiers

The *silicon-controlled rectifier (SCR) thyristor* is a kind of solid-state "latching relay" if dc is used as the supply voltage for the load. The gate current flows through the coil of the imaginary relay and closes the contacts in the load circuit (anode to cathode) so that the diode can conduct. If ac is used as the supply voltage, the SCR load current will reduce to zero as the positive ac waveshape crosses through zero and reverses its polarity to a negative voltage. This will shut off the SCR if the positive gate voltage is also removed, and it will not turn on during the next positive half cycle of applied ac voltage unless positive gate voltage is applied.

The SCR is suitable for controlling large amounts of rectifier power by means of small (gate) currents. The ratio of the load current to the control current can be very high, several thousand to one is not uncommon. (For example, 10 A of load current might be triggered on by 5 mA of control current.) The major time-related specification associated with SCRs is the dv/dt rating. This characteristic reveals how fast a transient spike on the power line can be before it false-triggers the SCR and starts its conducting without gate control current. Apart from this time-related parameter and its gate characteristics, SCR ratings (or specifications) are similar to those for power diodes.

SCRs can be used to control dc by using *commutating circuits* to shut them off. These are not needed on ac since the anode supply voltage reverses every half cycle. SCRs can be used in pairs or sets of pairs to generate ac from dc in inverters. They are also used as protective devices to protect against excessive voltage by acting as a short-circuit switch. These are commonly used in power supply "crowbar" overvoltage protection circuits. SCRs are also used to provide "switched power amplification," such as in solid-state relays.

11.2.3.2 Triacs

Fig. 11-23 shows a three-terminal semiconductor that behaves like two SCRs connected back to front in parallel so that they conduct power in both directions under control of a single gate-control circuit. A simple way of thinking of the triac is to visualize it as a kind of solid-state double-pole relay. Triacs are widely used to control ac power by phase shifting (delaying) the gate-control signal for some fraction of the half cycle during which the power diode could be conducting. (Light dimmers found in homes and offices and variable-speed drills are good examples of triac applications.)

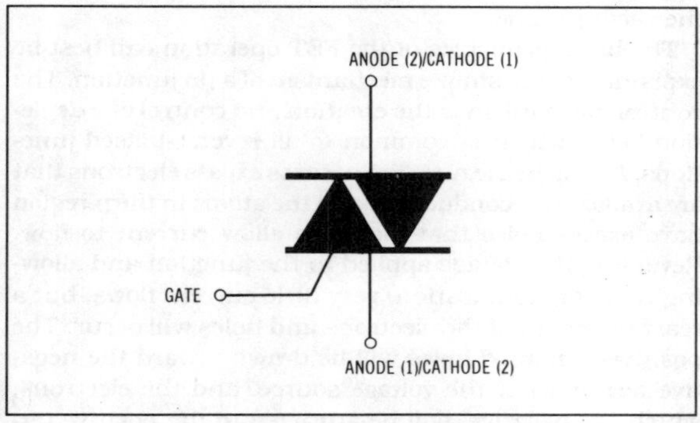

Figure 11-23 Schematic of a triac.

11.2.3.3 Light-Activated Silicon-Controlled Rectifiers

When sufficient light falls on the exposed gate junction, the silicon-controlled rectifier (SCR) is turned on just as if the gate-control current were flowing. (The gate terminal is also provided for optional use in some circuits.) These devices are used in projector controls, positioning controls, photorelays, "slave" flashes, and security protection systems.

11.2.3.4 Diacs

The *diac* is shown in Fig. 11-24. Think of it as two zener (or avalanche) diodes connected in series, back to back. When the voltage across the diac (in either direction) gets large enough, one of the zeners breaks down. This action drops the voltage to a lower level, causing a current increase in the associated circuit. This device is used to trigger SCRs or triacs.

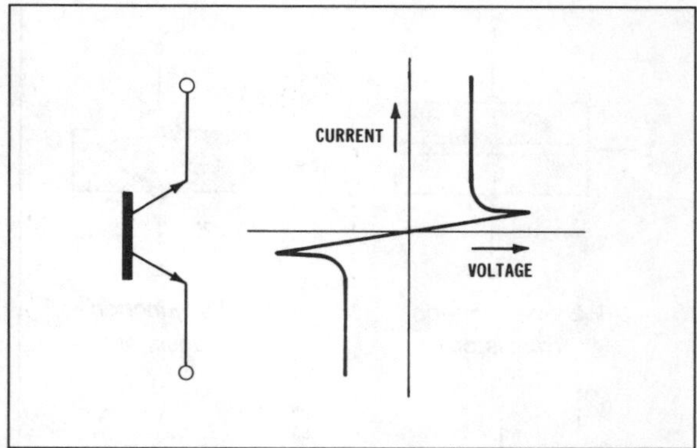

Figure 11-24 Schematic of a diac.

11.2.3.5 Opto-Coupled Silicon-Controlled Rectifiers

The *opto-coupled SCR* is a combination of a light-emitting diode (LED) and a photo silicon-controlled rectifier (photo-SCR). When sufficient current is forced through the LED, it emits an infrared radiation that triggers the gate of the photo-SCR. Thus, a small control current can regulate a large load current, and the device provides insulation and isolation between the control circuit (the LED) and the load circuit (the SCR). Opto-coupled transistors and Darlington transistors that operate on the same principle will be discussed later.

11.2.4 Transistors[1]

There are many different types of transistors, and they are named by the way they are grown, or made. In Fig. 11-25A is shown the construction of a *grown-junction transistor.* An *alloy-junction transistor* is shown in Fig. 11-25B. During the manufacture of the material for a grown junction, the impurity content of the semiconductor is altered to provide npn or pnp regions. The grown material is cut into small sections, and contacts are attached to the regions. In the alloy-junction type, small dots of n- or p-type impurity elements are attached to either side of a thin wafer of p- or n-type semiconductor material to form regions for the emitter and collector junctions. The base connection is made to the original semiconductor material. *Drift-field transistors* employ a modified alloy junction in which the impurity concentration in the wafer is diffused or graded, as shown in Fig. 11-25C. The drift field speeds up the current flow and extends the frequency response of the alloy-junction transistor.

A variation of the drift-field transistor is the *microalloy diffused transistor,* as shown in Fig. 11-25D. Very narrow base dimensions are achieved by etching techniques, resulting in a shortened current path to the collector.

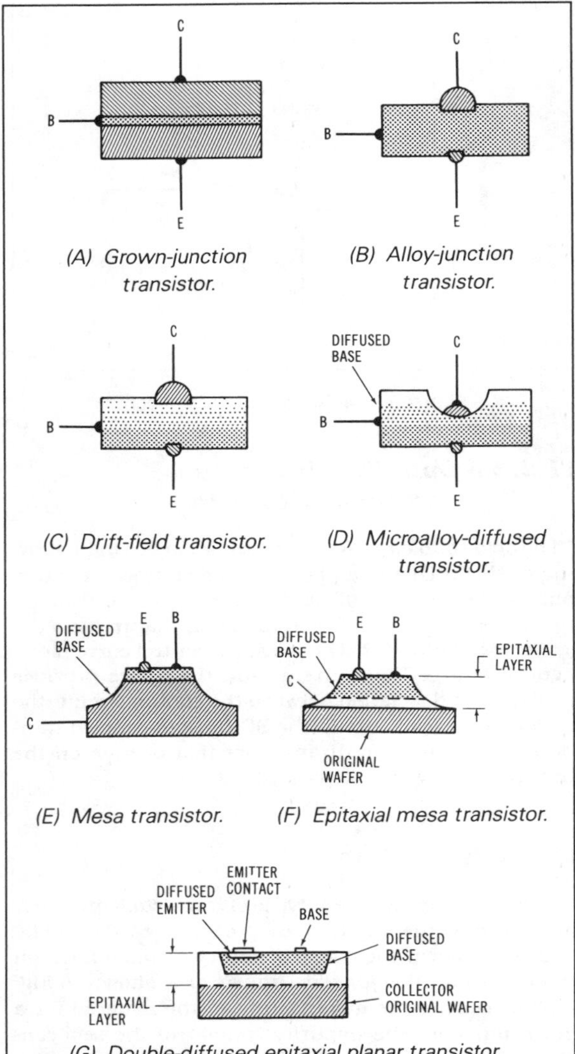

Figure 11-25 Transistor construction.

Mesa transistors shown in Fig. 11-25E use the original semiconductor material as the collector, with the base material diffused into the wafer and an emitter dot alloyed into the base region. A flat-topped peak or mesa is etched to reduce the area of the collector at the base junction. Mesa devices have large power-dissipation capabilities and can be operated at very high frequencies. Double-diffused epitaxial mesa transistors are grown by the use of vapor deposition to build up a crystal layer on a crystal wafer and will permit the precise control of the physical and electrical dimensions independently of the nature of the original wafer. This technique is shown in Fig. 11-25F.

The planar transistor is a highly sophisticated method of constructing transistors. A limited area source is used for both the base diffusion and emitter diffusion, which provides a very small active area, with a large wire contact area. The advantage of the planar construction is its high dissipation, lower leakage current, and lower collector cutoff current, which increases the stability and reliability. Planar construction is also used with several of the previously discussed base designs. A double-diffused epitaxial planar transistor is shown in Fig. 11-25G.

The *field-effect transistor*, or *FET* as it is commonly known, was developed by the Bell Telephone Laboratories in 1946, but it was not put to any practical use until about 1964. The principal difference between a conventional transistor and the FET lies in the fact that the transistor is a *current-controlled* device, while the FET is *voltage controlled*, similar to the vacuum tube. Conventional transistors also have a low input impedance, which may at times complicate the circuit designer's problems. The FET has a high input impedance with a low output impedance; this characteristic caused it to be likened to the vacuum tube.

The basic principles of the FET operation can best be explained by the simple mechanism of a pn junction. The control mechanism is the creation and control of a depletion layer, which is common to all reverse-biased junctions. Atoms in the n-region possess excess electrons that are available for conduction, and the atoms in the p-region have excess holes that may also allow current to flow. Reversing the voltage applied to the junction and allowing time for stabilization, very little current flows, but a rearrangement of the electrons and holes will occur. The positively charged holes will be drawn toward the negative terminals of the voltage source, and the electrons, which are negative, will be attracted to the positive terminal of the voltage source. This results in a region being formed near the center of the junction having a majority of the carriers removed and therefore called the *depletion regions*.

Referring to Fig. 11-26A, a simple bar composed of n-type semiconductor material is shown, with two nonrectifying contacts at each end. Because there is always a certain amount of resistance R between the two end electrodes, P is the function of the material sensitivity, L is the length of the bar, W is the width, and T is the thickness. Resistivity may be equated

$$R = (PL)/(WT) \tag{11-20}$$

By varying one or more of the variables of the resistance of the semiconductor, the bar may be changed. Assume a p-region in the form of a sheet is formed at the top of the bar shown in Fig. 11-26B. This may be accomplished by diffusion, alloying, or epitaxial growth, and a pn junction is formed. Thus, a reverse voltage appearing between the p- and n-material produces two depletion regions. Current in the n-material is caused primarily by means of excess electrons. By reducing the concentration of electrons or majority carriers, the resistivity of the material is increased. Removal of the excess electrons by means of the depletion region causes the material to become practically nonconductive.

Disregarding the p-region and applying a voltage to the ends of the bar cause a current and create a potential gradient along the length of the bar material, with the voltage increasing toward the right, with respect to the negative end or ground. Connecting the p-region to ground causes varying amounts of reverse-bias voltage across the pn junction, with the greatest amount developed toward the right end of the p-region. A reverse voltage across the bar will produce the same depletion regions. If the resistivity of the p-type material is made much smaller than that of the n-type material, the depletion region will then extend much farther into the n-material than into the p-material. To simplify the following explanation, the depletion of p-material will be ignored.

The general shape of the depletion is that of a wedge, increasing the size from left to right. Since the resistivity of the bar material within the depletion area is increased, the effective thickness of the conducting portion of the bar becomes less and less, going from the end of the p-region to the right end. This indicates the overall resistance of the semiconductor material is larger because the effective thickness is being reduced. Continuing to increase the voltage across the ends of the bar, a point is reached where the depletion region is extended practically all the way through the bar, reducing the effective thickness to zero. Increasing the voltage beyond this point produces little change in current.

Because of the controlling action of the p-region, it is termed a gate. The left end of the bar, being the source of majority carriers, is termed the source. The right end, being where the electrons are drained off, is called the drain. A cross-sectional drawing of a typical FET is shown

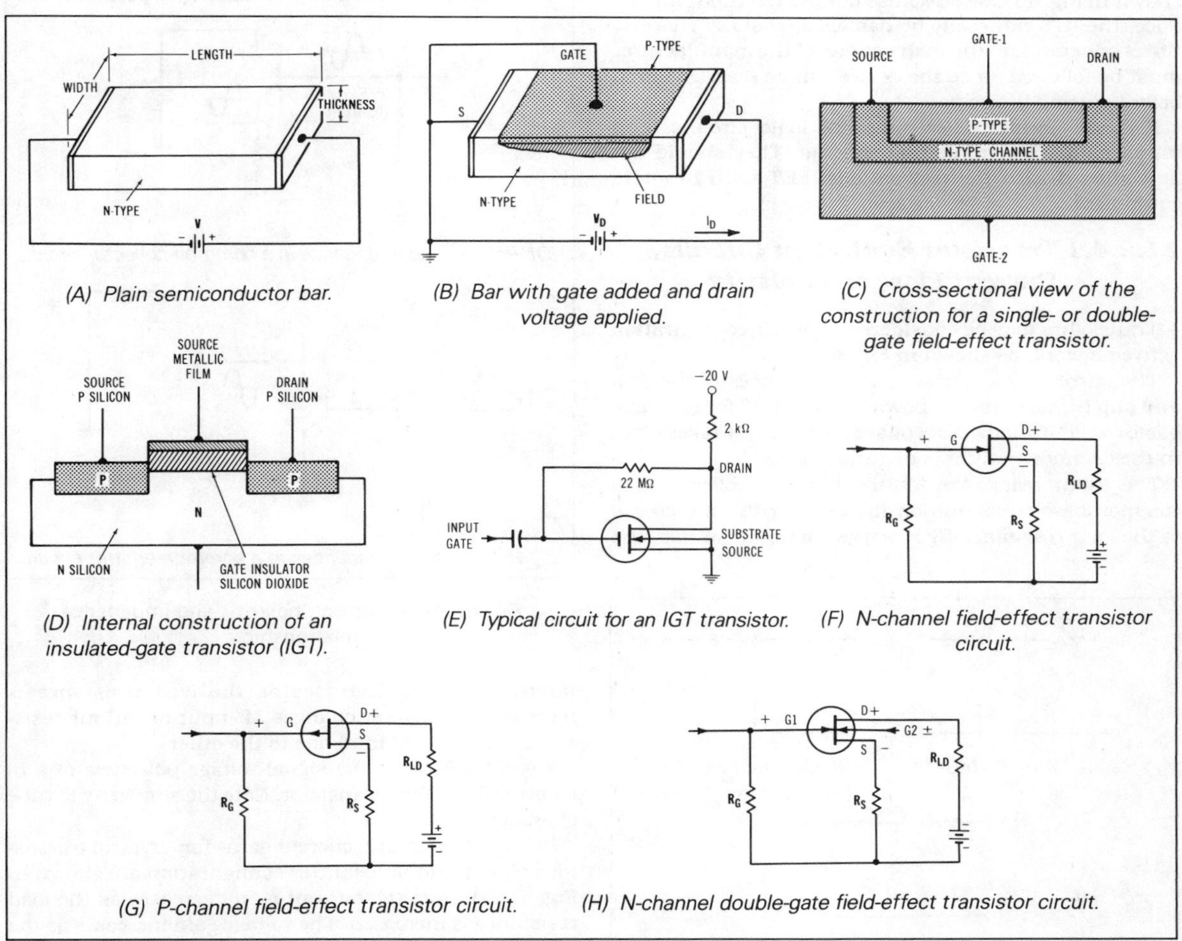

(A) Plain semiconductor bar.

(B) Bar with gate added and drain voltage applied.

(C) Cross-sectional view of the construction for a single- or double-gate field-effect transistor.

(D) Internal construction of an insulated-gate transistor (IGT).

(E) Typical circuit for an IGT transistor.

(F) N-channel field-effect transistor circuit.

(G) P-channel field-effect transistor circuit.

(H) N-channel double-gate field-effect transistor circuit.

Figure 11-26 Field-effect transistors (FETs).

in Fig. 11-26C, and three basic circuits are shown in Fig. 11-26F through H.

Insulated-gate transistors (IGT) are also known as field-effect transistors, metal-oxide silicon or semiconductor field-effect transistors (MOSFET), metal-oxide silicon or semiconductor transistors (MOST), and insulated-gate field-effect transistors (IGFET). All these devices are similar and are simply names applied to them by the different manufacturers.

The outstanding characteristics of the IGT are its extremely high input impedance, running to 10^{15} Ω. IGTs have three elements but four connections—the gate, the drain, the source, and an n-type substrate, into which two identical p-type silicon regions have been diffused. The source and drain terminals are taken from these two p-regions, which form a capacitance between the n-substrate and the silicon-dioxide insulator and the metallic gate terminals. A cross-sectional view of the internal construction appears in Fig. 11-26D, with a basic circuit shown in Fig. 11-26E. Because of the high input impedance, the IGT can easily be damaged by static charges. Strict adherence to the instructions of the manufacturer must be followed since the device can be damaged even before putting it into use.

IGTs are used in electrometers, logic circuits, and ultrasensitive electronic instruments. They should not be confused with the conventional FET used in audio equipment.

11.2.4.1 Transistor Equivalent Circuits, Current Flow, and Polarity

Transistors may be considered to be a T configuration active network, as shown in Fig. 11-27.

The current flow, phase, and impedances of the npn and pnp transistors are shown in Fig. 11-28 for the three basic configurations. Note phase reversal only takes place in the common-emitter configuration.

The input resistance for the common-collector and common-base configuration increases with an increase of the load resistance R_L. For the common emitter, the input resistance decreases as the load resistance is increased; therefore, changes of input or output resistance are reflected from one to the other.

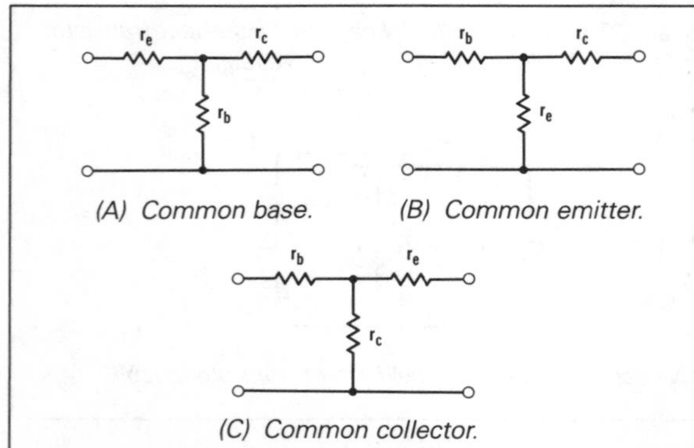

Figure 11-27 Equivalent circuits for transistors.

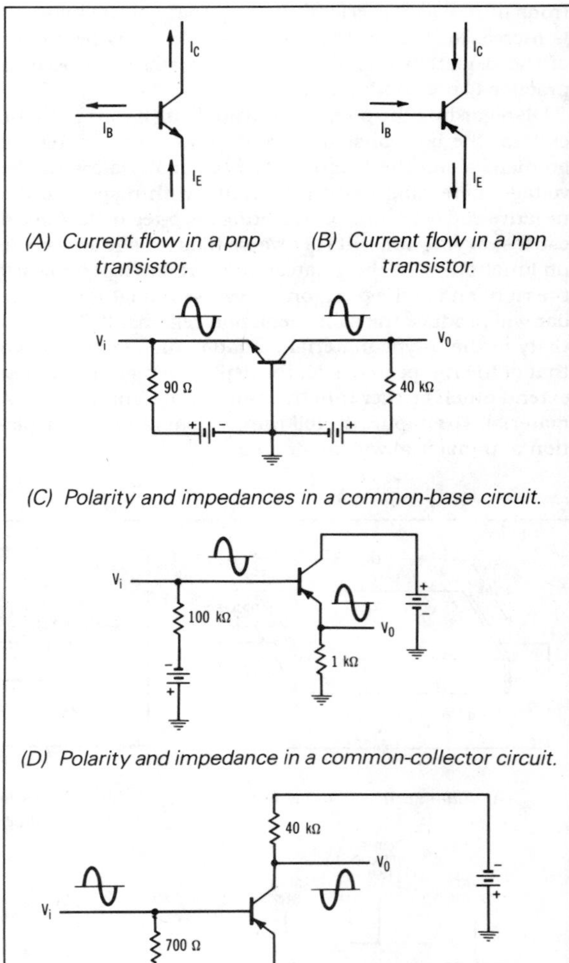

I_C
I_B
I_E
(A) Current flow in a pnp transistor.
(B) Current flow in a npn transistor.
V_i
V_o
90 Ω
40 kΩ
(C) Polarity and impedances in a common-base circuit.
100 kΩ
1 kΩ
(D) Polarity and impedance in a common-collector circuit.
40 kΩ
700 Ω
(E) Polarity and impedances in a common-emitter circuit.

Figure 11-28 Current, polarity, and impedance relationships.

Fig. 11-29 shows the signal-voltage polarities of a p-channel field-effect transistor. Note the similarity to tube characteristics.

Voltage, power, and current gains for a typical transistor using a common-emitter configuration are shown in Fig. 11-30. Note the current gain decreases as the load resistance is increased. The voltage gain increases as the load resistance is increased. Maximum power gain occurs when the load resistance is approximately 40,000 Ω, and it may exceed unity. For the common-collector connec-

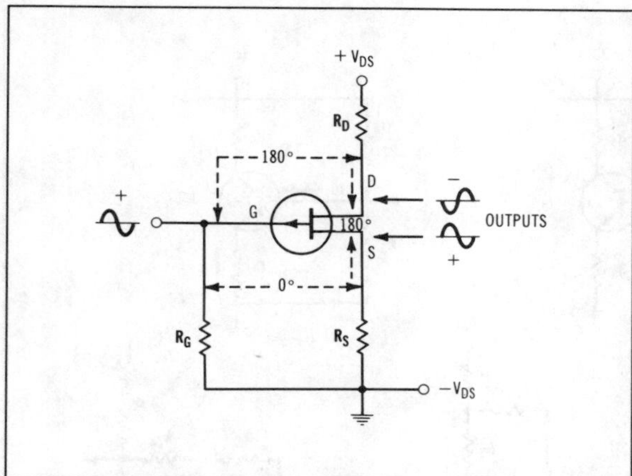

Figure 11-29 Signal-voltage polarities in a p-channel field-effect transistor (FET).

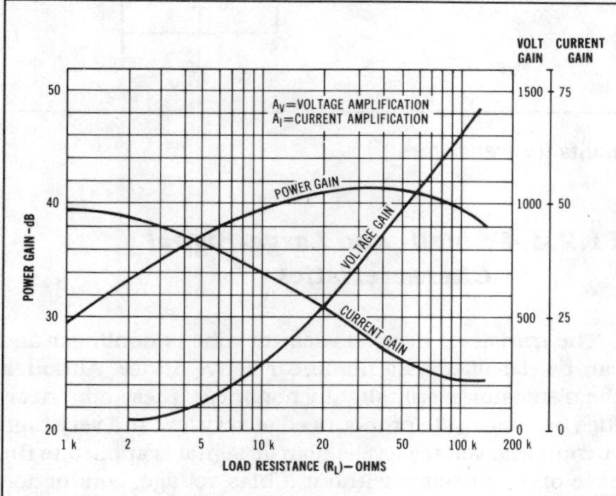

Figure 11-30 Typical voltage, power, and current gains for a conventional transistor using a common-emitter configuration.

tion, the current gain decreases as the load resistance is increased. While the voltage gain increases as the load resistance is increased, it never exceeds unity. Curves such as these help the designer to select a set of conditions for a specific result.

The power gain varies as the ratio of the input to output impedance and may be computed with the formula

$$dB = 10 \log(Z_o/Z_{in}) \quad (11\text{-}21)$$

where,

Z_o is the output impedance in ohms,

Z_{in} is the input impedance in ohms.

11.2.4.2 Forward-Current-Transfer Ratio

An important characteristic of a transistor is its *forward-current-transfer ratio*, or the ratio of the current in the output to the current in the input element. Because of the many different configurations for connecting transistors, the forward transfer ratio is specified for a particular circuit configuration. The forward-current-transfer ratio for the common-base configuration is often referred to as *alpha* (α) and the common-emitter forward-current-transfer ratio as *beta* (β). In common-base circuitry, the emitter is the input element, and the collector is the output element. Therefore, the dc alpha is the ratio of the dc collector current I_C to the dc emitter current I_E. For the common emitter, the dc beta is then the ratio of the dc collector current I_C to the base current I_B.

Because the ratios are based on the dc currents, they are termed *alpha* and *beta*. The ratios are also given in terms of the ratio of signal current, relative to the input and output, or in terms of ratio of change in the output current to the input current, which causes the change.

The term alpha is also used to denote the frequency cutoff of a transistor and is defined as the frequency at which the value of alpha for a common-base configuration, or beta for a common-emitter circuit, falls to 0.707 times its value at a frequency of 1000 Hz.

Gain-bandwidth product is the frequency at which the common-emitter forward-current-transfer ratio beta is equal to unity. It indicates the useful frequency range of the device and assists in the determination of the most suitable configuration for a given application.

11.2.4.3 Bias Circuits

Several different methods of applying bias voltage to transistors are shown in Fig. 11-31, with a master circuit for aiding in the selection of the proper circuit shown in Fig. 11-32. Comparing the circuits shown in Fig. 11-31, their equivalents may be found by making the resistors in Fig. 11-32 equal to zero or infinity for analysis and study. As an example, the circuit of Fig. 11-31D may be duplicated in Fig. 11-32 by shorting out resistors R_4 and R_5.

The circuit Fig. 11-31G employs a split voltage divider for R_2. A capacitor connected at the junction of the two resistors shunts any ac feedback current to ground. The stability of circuits A, D, and G in Fig. 11-31 may be poor unless the voltage drop across the load resistor is at least one-third the value of the power supply voltage V_{cc}. The final determining factors will be *gain* and *stability*.

Stability may be enhanced by the use of a thermistor to compensate for increases in collector current with increasing temperature. The resistance of the thermistor decreases as the temperature increases; thus, the bias voltage is decreased, and the collector voltage tends to remain constant. Diode biasing may also be used for both temperature and voltage variations. The diode is used to establish the bias voltage, which sets the transistor idling current or the current flow in the quiescent state.

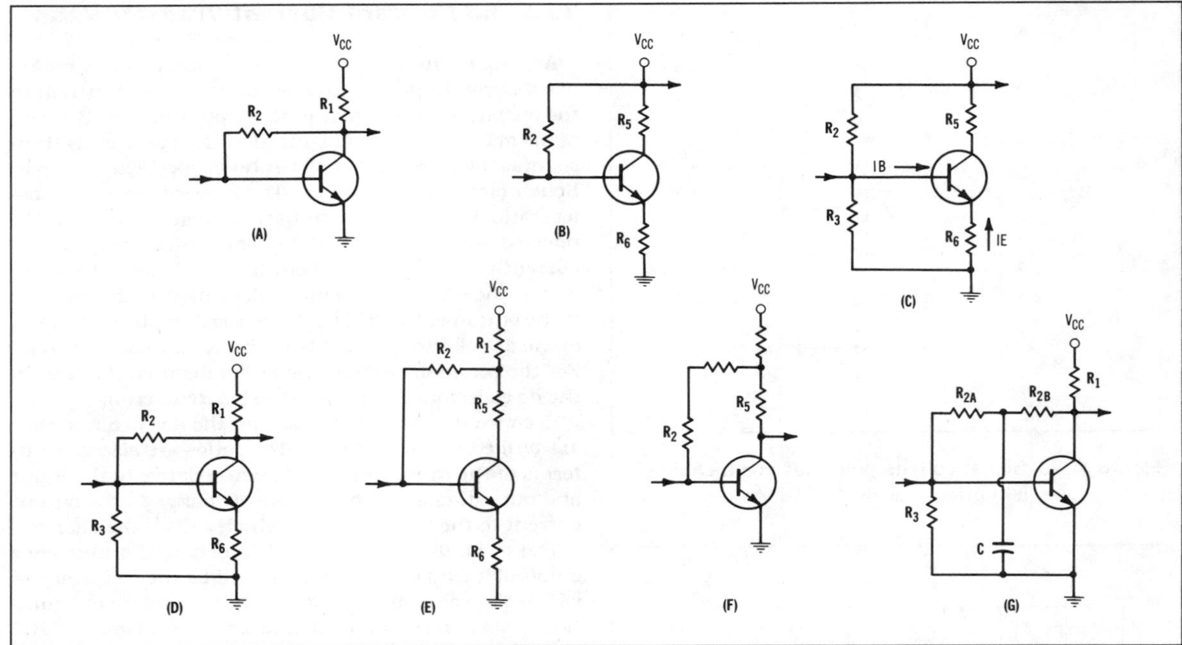

Figure 11-31 Basic bias circuits for transistors.

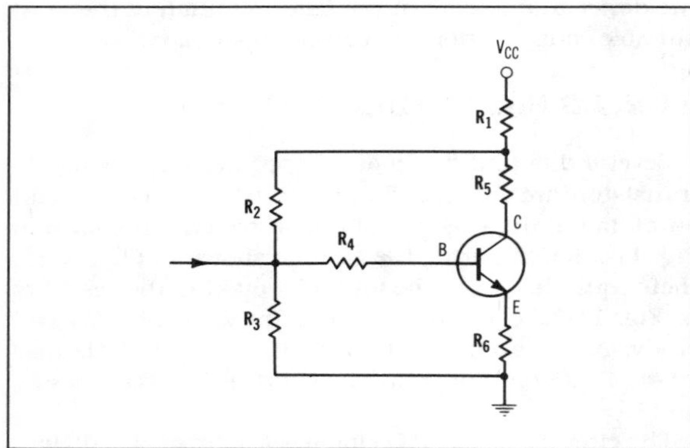

Figure 11-32 Basic design circuit for transistor bias circuits.

When a transistor is biased to a nonconducting state, small reverse dc currents flow, consisting of leakage currents that are related to the surface characteristics of the semiconductor material and saturation currents. Saturation current increases with temperature and is related to the impurity concentration in the material. Collector-cutoff current is a dc current caused when the collector-to-base circuit is reverse biased and the emitter-to-base circuit is open. Emitter-cutoff current flows when the emitter to base is reverse biased and the collector-to-base circuit is open.

11.2.4.4 Small- and Large-Signal Characteristics

The transistor like the vacuum tube is nonlinear and can be classified as a nonlinear active device. Although the transistor is only slightly nonlinear, these nonlinearities become quite pronounced at very low and very high current and voltage levels. If an ac signal is applied to the base of a transistor without a bias voltage, conduction will take place on only one-half cycle of the applied signal voltage, resulting in a highly distorted output signal. To avoid high distortion, a dc-biased voltage is applied to the transistor, and the operating point is shifted to the linear portion of the characteristic curve. This improves the linearity and reduces the distortion to a value suitable for small-signal operation. Even though the transistor is biased to the most linear part of the characteristic curve, it can still add considerable distortion to the signal if driven into the nonlinear portion of the characteristic.

Small-signal swings generally run from less than 1 μV to about 10 mV under normal operation conditions. Therefore, it is highly important that the dc-biased voltage be of sufficient value so that the applied ac signal is small compared to the dc-bias current and voltage. Transistors are normally biased at current values between 0.1 and 10 mA. For large-signal operation, the design procedures become quite involved mathematically and require a considerable amount of approximation and the use of nonlinear circuit analysis.

Because of the wide difference of impedance between the input and output circuits of transistors, care must be taken to provide an impedance match between cascaded stages. Otherwise, an appreciable loss of power will take place.

The maximum power amplification is obtained with a transistor when the source impedance matches the internal input resistance, and the load impedance matches the internal output resistance. The transistor is then said to be image matched.

If the source impedance is changed in value, it affects the internal output resistance of the transistor, necessitating a change in the value of the load impedance. When transistor stages are connected in tandem, except for the grounded-emitter connection, the input impedance is considerably lower than the preceding stage output impedance. Therefore, the interstage transformer must supply an impedance match in both directions.

When working between a grounded base and a grounded-emitter circuit, a step-down transformer must be used. Working into a grounded-collector stage, a step-up transformer is used. Grounded-collector stages are sometimes used as an impedance-matching device between other transistor stages.

When adjusting the battery voltages for a transistor amplifier employing transformers, the battery voltage must be increased to compensate for the dc voltage drop across the transformer windings. The data sheets of the manufacturer should be consulted before selecting a transformer to determine the source and load impedances.

11.2.4.5 Transistor Noise Factor

In a low-level amplifier, such as a preamplifier, noise is the most important single factor and is stated as the signal-to-noise ratio or noise factor. Most amplifiers employ resistors in the input circuit, which contribute a certain amount of measurable noise because of thermal activity. This power is generally about −160 dB, re: 1 W for a bandwidth of 10,000 Hz. When the input signal is amplified, the noise is also amplified. If the ratio of the signal power to noise power is the same, the amplifier is noiseless and has a noise figure of unity or more. However, in a practical amplifier some noise is present, and the degree of impairment is called the noise figure (nf) of the amplifier, expressed as the ratio of signal power to noise power at the output:

$$nf = (S_1/N_1)/(S_o/N_o) \qquad (11\text{-}22)$$

where,

S_1 is the signal power,
N_1 is the noise power,
S_o is the signal power at the output,
N_o is the noise at the output.

$$nf_{dB} = 10 \log nf \text{ of the power ratio} \qquad (11\text{-}23)$$

Thus, for an amplifier with a 1-dB noise figure, the signal-to-noise ratio decreases by a factor of 1.26, a 3-dB nf by a factor of 2, a 10-dB nf by a factor of 10, and a 20 dB nf by a factor of 100. Amplifiers with an nf below 6 dB are considered excellent.

Low-noise factors can be obtained by the use of an emitter current of less than 1 mA, a collector voltage of less than 2 V, and a signal-source resistance below 2000 Ω.

11.2.4.6 Internal Capacitance

The paths of internal capacitance in a typical transistor are shown in Fig. 11-33. Since the width of the pn junction in the transistor will vary in accordance with voltage and current, the internal capacitance also varies. Variation of collector-base capacitance C with collector voltage and emitter current is shown in Figs. 11-33B and C. The increase in the width of the pn junction between the base and collector, as the reverse bias voltage (V_{CB})

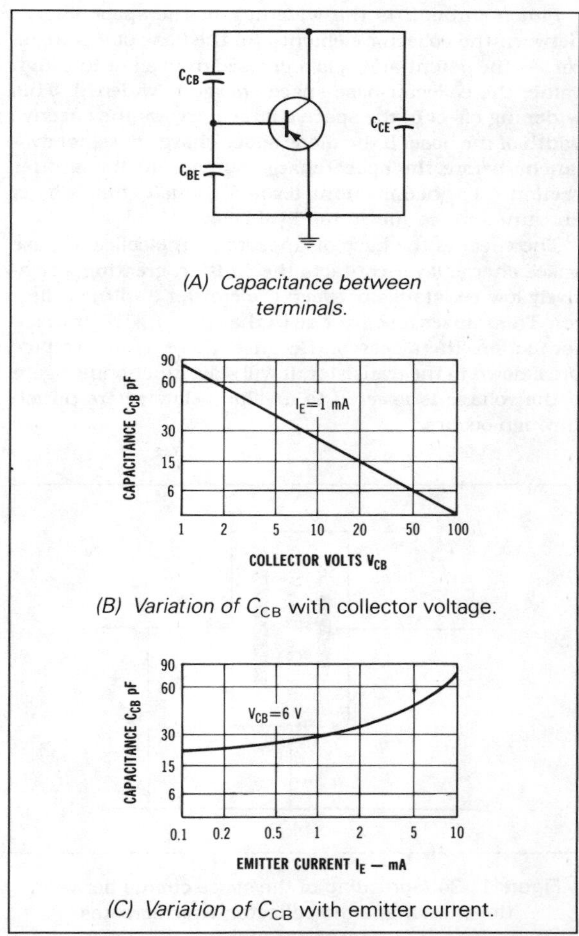

Figure 11-33 Internal capacitance of a transistor.

is increased, is reflected in lower capacitance values. This phenomenon is equivalent to increasing the spacing between the plates of a capacitor. An increase in the emitter current, most of which flows through the base-collector junction, increases the collector-base capacitance (C_{CB}). The increased current through the pn junction may be considered as effectively reducing the width of the pn junction. This is equivalent to decreasing the spacing between the plates of a capacitor, therefore, increasing the capacitance.

The average value of collector-base capacitance (C_{CB}) varies from 2 to 50 pF, depending on the type transistor and the manufacturing techniques. The collector-emitter capacitance is caused by the pn junction. It normally is five to ten times greater than that of the collector-base capacitance and will vary with the emitter current and collector voltage. For certain applications advantage is taken of this effect for control purposes.

11.2.4.7 Punch Through

Punch through is the widening of the space charge between the collector element and the base of a transistor. As the potential V_{CB} is increased from a low to a high value, the collector-base space charge is widened. This widening effect of the space charge narrows the effective width of the base. If the diode space charge does not avalanche before the space charge spreads to the emitter section, a phenomenon termed *punch through* is encountered, as shown in Fig. 11-34.

The effect is the base disappears as the collector-base space charge layer contacts the emitter, creating a relatively low resistance between the emitter and the collector. This causes a sharp rise in the current. The transistor action then ceases. Because there is no voltage breakdown in the transistor, it will start functioning again if the voltage is lowered to a value below where punch through occurs.

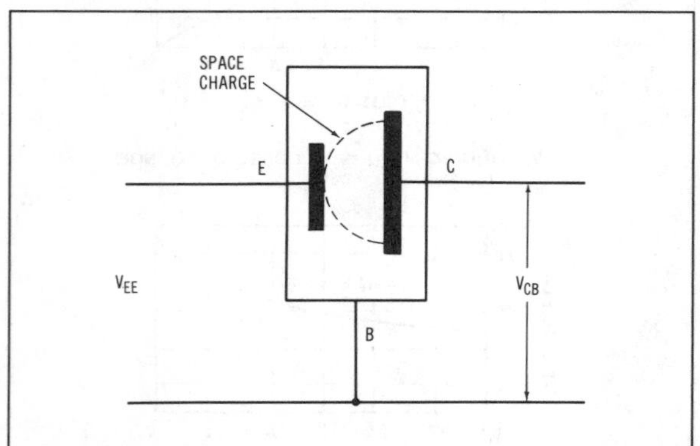

Figure 11-34 Spreading of the space charge between the emitter and the collector, which creates "punch-through."

When a transistor is operated in the punch-through region, its functioning is not normal, and heat is generated internally that can cause permanent damage to the elements.

11.2.4.8 Breakdown Voltage

Breakdown voltage is that voltage value between two given elements in a transistor at which the crystal structure changes and current begins to increase rapidly. Breakdown voltage may be measured with the third electrode open, shorted, or biased in either the forward or reverse direction. A group of collector characteristics for different values of base bias are shown in Fig. 11-35. The collector-to-emitter breakdown voltage increases as the base-to-emitter bias is decreased from the normal forward values through zero to reverse. As the resistance in the base-to-emitter circuit decreases, the collector characteristics develop two breakdown points. After the initial breakdown, the collector-to-emitter voltage decreases with an increasing collector current, until another breakdown occurs at the lower voltage.

Breakdown can be very destructive in power transistors. A breakdown mechanism, termed *second breakdown*, is an electrical and thermal process in which current is concentrated in a very small area. The high current, together with the voltage across the transistor, causes intense heating, melting a hole from the collector to the emitter. This causes a short circuit and internal breakdown of the transistor.

The fundamental limitation to the use of transistors is the breakdown voltage (BV_{cer}). Because the breakdown voltage is not sharp, it is necessary to specify the value of collector current at which breakdown will occur. This data may be obtained from the data sheet of the manufacturer.

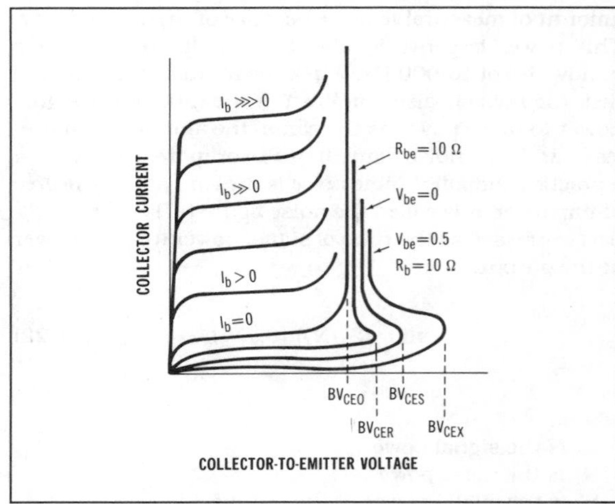

Figure 11-35 Typical collector characteristic curves showing locations of various breakdown voltages.

11.2.4.9 Transistor Load Lines

Transistor load lines are used to design circuits. An example of circuit design uses a transistor with the following characteristics:

Maximum collector current: 10 mA;

Maximum collector voltage: −22 V;

Base current: 0 to 300 μA;

Maximum power dissipation: 300 mW.

The base-current curves are shown in Fig. 11-36A. The amplifier circuit is to be Class A, using a common-emitter circuit, as shown in Fig. 11-36B. By proper choice of the operating point, with respect to the transistor characteristics and supply voltage, low distortion, Class-A performance is easily obtained within the transistor power ratings.

The first requirement is a set of collector-current, collector-voltage curves for the transistor to be employed. Such curves can generally be obtained from the data sheets of the manufacturer. Assuming that such data are at hand and referring to Fig. 11-36A, a curved line is plotted on the data sheet, representing the maximum power dissipation by the use of the equation

$$I_c = P_c/V_c$$

or

$$V_c = P_c/I_c$$

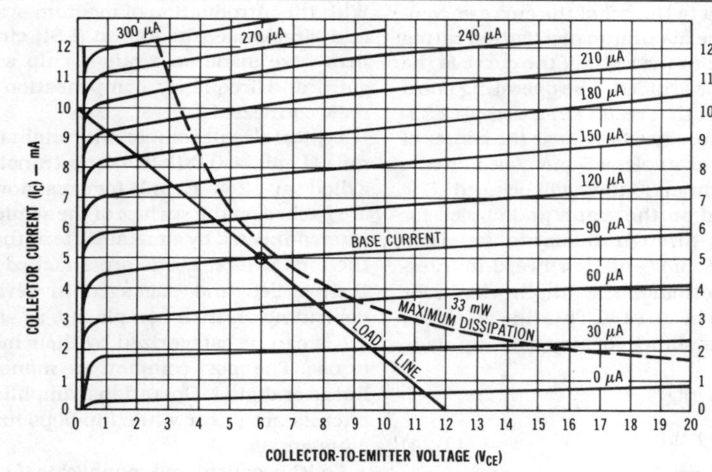

(A) Common-emitter-collector family of curves, with load line and maximum dissipation power curve.

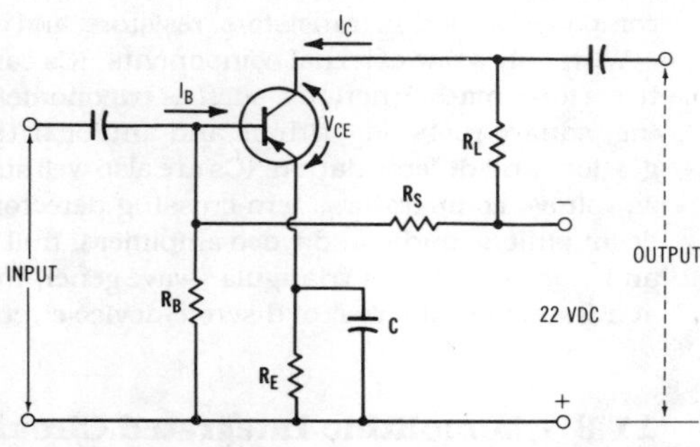

(B) Amplifier circuit used for load-line calculations.

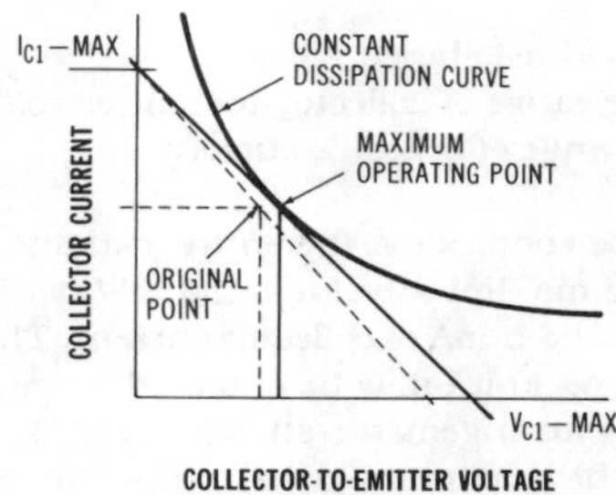

(C) Load line moved to right for maximum power output. Dotted lines are the original load line and operating point.

Figure 11-36 Load-line calculation curves.

where,
I_c is the collector current,
P_c is the maximum power dissipation of the transistor,
V_c is the collector voltage.

At any point on this line at the intersection of V_cI_c, the product equals 0.033 W or 33 mW. In determining the points for the dissipation curve, voltages are selected along the horizontal axis and the corresponding current is equated using:

$$I_c = P_c/V_{CE}$$

The current is determined for each of the major collector-voltage points, starting at 16 V and working backward until the upper end of the power curve intersects the 300-μA base-current line.

After entering the value on the graph for the power dissipation curve, the area to the left of the curve encompasses all points within the maximum dissipation rating of the transistor. The area to the right of the curve is the overload region and is to be avoided. The operating point is next determined. A point that results in less than a 33-mW dissipation is selected somewhere near the center of the power curve. For this example, a 5-mA collector current at 6 V, or a dissipation of 30 mW, will be used. The selected point is indicated on the graph and circled for reference. A line is drawn through the dot to the maximum collector current, 10 mA, and downward to intersect the V_{CE} line at the bottom of the graph, which, for this example, turns out to be at 12 V. This line is termed the *load line*. The load resistance R_L may be computed:

$$\begin{aligned} R_L &= dV_{CE}/dI_C \\ &= (0 - 12)/(0 - 0.01) \qquad (11\text{-}24) \\ &= 12/0.01 \\ &= 1200\ \Omega \end{aligned}$$

where,
R_L is the load resistance,
dV_{CE} is the range of collector-to-emitter voltage,
dI_C is the range of collector current.

Under these conditions, the entire load line dissipates less than the maximum value of 33 mW, with 90 μA of base current and 5 mA of collector current. The required base current of 90 μA may be obtained by means of one of the biasing arrangements shown in Fig. 11-31.

To derive the maximum power output from the transistor, the load line may be moved to the right and the operating point placed in the maximum dissipation curve, as shown in Fig. 11-36C. Under these conditions, an increase in distortion may be expected. As the operating point is now at 6.5 V and 5 mA, the dissipation is 33 mW. Drawing a line through the new operating point and 10 mA (the maximum current), the voltage at the lower end of the load line is 13.0 V; therefore, the load impedance is now 1300 Ω.

Values shown on the graph are for a particular type of transistor. Other types will have a similar family of curves, but not of the same values.

11.3 INTEGRATED CIRCUITS[2]

An *integrated circuit (IC)* is a device consisting of hundreds and even thousands of components in one small enclosure, and it came into being when manufacturers learned how to grow and package semiconductors and resistors.

The first ICs were small scale and usually too noisy for audio circuits; however, as time passed, the noise was reduced, stability increased, and the operational amplifier IC became an important part of the audio circuit. With the introduction of medium-scale integration (MSI) and large-scale integration (LSI) circuits, power amplifiers were made on a single chip with only capacitors, gain, and frequency compensation components externally connected.

Typical circuit components might use up a space 4 × 6 mils (1 mil = 0.001 in.) for a transistor, 3 × 4 mils for a diode and 2 × 12 mils for a resistor. These components are packed on the surface of the semiconductor wafer and interconnected by a metal pattern that is evaporated into the top surface. Leads are attached to the wafer that is then sealed and packaged in several configurations, depending on their complexity, as shown in Fig. 11-37.

ICs can be categorized by their method of fabrication or use. The most common are monolithic or hybrid and linear or digital. Operational amplifiers and most analog circuits are linear while flip-flops and on-off switch circuits are digital.

An IC is considered *monolithic* if it is produced on one single chip and *hybrid* if it consists of more than one monolithic chip tied together and/or includes discrete components such as transistors, resistors, and capacitors.

With only a few external components, ICs can be made to perform math functions, such as trigonometry, squaring, square roots, logarithms and antilogarithms, integration, and differentiation. ICs are also well suited to act as voltage comparators, zero-crossing detectors, ac and dc amplifiers, audio and video amplifiers, null detectors, and sine-, square-, or triangular-wave generators, and all at a fraction of the cost of discrete-device circuits.

11.3.1 Monolithic Integrated Circuits

All circuit elements, both active and passive, are formed at the same time on a single wafer. The same circuit can be repeated many times on a single wafer and then cut to form individual 50-mil^2 ICs.

Bipolar transistors are often used in ICs and are fabricated much like the discrete transistor by the planar process. The differences are the contact-to-the-collector region is through the top surface rather than the substrate, requiring electrical isolation between the substrate and the collector. The integrated transistor is isolated from other components by a pn junction that creates capacitance, reducing high-frequency response and increasing leakage current, which in low-power circuits can be significant.

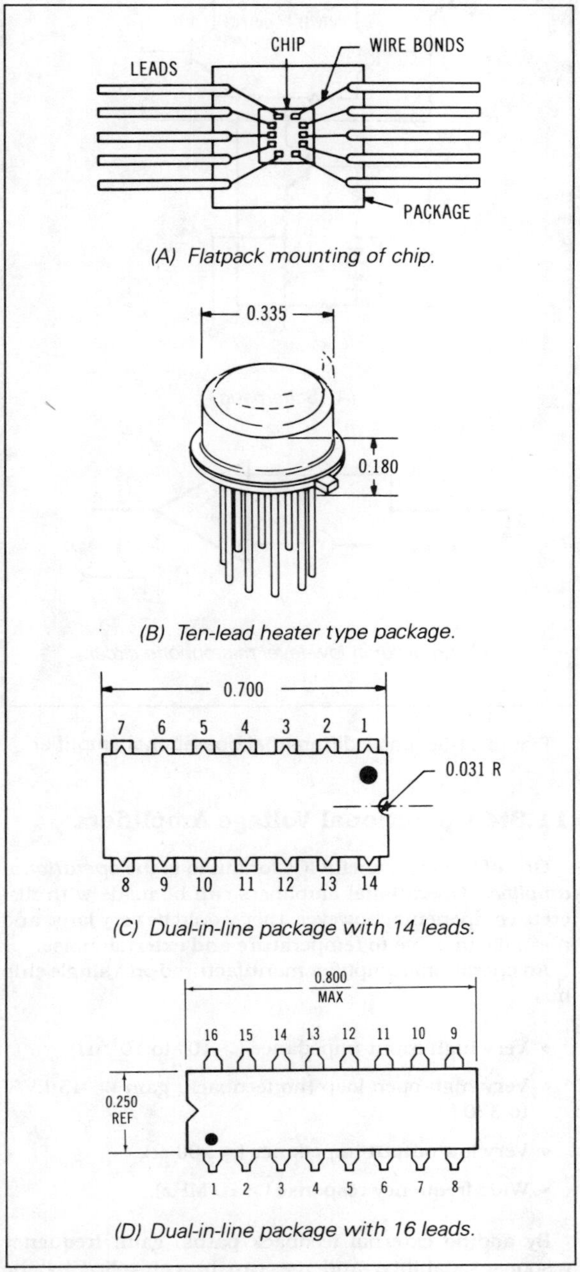

(A) *Flatpack mounting of chip.*

(B) *Ten-lead heater type package.*

(C) *Dual-in-line package with 14 leads.*

(D) *Dual-in-line package with 16 leads.*

Figure 11-37 Various configurations of integrated circuits.

Integrated diodes are produced the same way as transistors and can be regarded as transistors whose terminals have been connected to give the desired characteristics.

Resistors are made at the same time as transistors. The resistance is characterized in terms of its sheet resistance, which is usually between 100 and 200 Ω/square material for diffused resistors and between 50 and 150 Ω/square material for deposited resistors. To increase the value of a resistor, square materials are simply connected in series.

It is very difficult to produce resistors with much closer tolerance than 10%; however, it is very easy to produce two adjacent resistors to be almost identical. Therefore, when making comparator-type circuits, the circuits are balanced. Because of this, circuits are made to perform on ratios rather than absolute values. Another advantage is uniformity in temperature. As the temperature of one component varies, so does the temperature of the other components, allowing good tracking between components and circuits. Therefore, integrated circuits are usually more stable than discrete circuits.

Capacitors are made as thin-film integrated capacitors or junction capacitors. The thin-film integrated capacitor has a deposited metal layer and a n+ layer isolated with a carrier-free region of silicon dioxide. In junction capacitors, both layers are diffused low-resistance semiconductor material. Each layer has a dopant of opposite polarity; therefore, the carrier-free region is formed by the charge depleted area at the pn junction.

The MOSFET transistor has many advantages over the bipolar transistor for use in ICs as it occupies only 1/25 the area of the bipolar equivalent due to lack of isolation pads. The MOSFET acts like a variable resistor; therefore, it can also be used as a high-value resistor. For instance, a 100-kΩ resistor might occupy only 1 mil^2 as opposed to 250 mil^2 for a diffused resistor.

The chip must finally be connected to terminals or have some means of connecting to other circuits, and it must also be packaged to protect it from the environment. Early methods included using fine gold wire to connect the chip to contacts. This was later replaced with aluminum wire ultrasonically bonded.

Flip-chip and beam-lead methods eliminate the problems of individually bonding wires. Relatively thick metal is deposited on the contact pads before the ICs are separated from the wafer. The deposited metal is then used to contact a matching metal pattern on the substrate. In the flip-chip method, globules of solder deposited on each contact pad ultrasonically bond the chip to the substrate.

In the beam-lead method, thin metal tabs lead away from the chip at each contact pad. The bonding of the leads to the substrate reduces heat transfer into the chip and eliminates pressure on the chip.

The chip is finally packaged in either hermetically sealed metal headers or is encapsulated in plastic, which is an inexpensive method of producing ICs.

11.3.2 Hybrid Integrated Circuits

Hybrid circuits combine monolithic and thick- and thin-film discrete components for obtaining the best solution to the problem.

Active components are usually formed as monolithics; however, sometimes discrete transistors are soldered into the hybrid circuit.

Passive components such as resistors and capacitors are made with thin- and thick-film techniques. Thin films are 0.001 to 0.1 mil thick, while thick films are normally 60 mils thick.

Resistors can be made with a value from ohms to megohms with a tolerance of 0.05% or better.

High-value capacitors are generally discrete, miniature components that are welded or soldered into the circuit, and low-value capacitors can be made as film capacitors and fabricated directly on the substrate.

Along with being certain that the components will fit into the hybrid package, the temperature must also be taken into account. The temperature rise T_R of the package can be calculated with the following formula:

$$T_R = T_C - T_A$$
$$= P_T \theta_{CA}$$

where

T_C is the case temperature,
T_A is the ambient temperature,
P_T is the total power dissipation,
θ_{CA} is the case-to-ambient thermal resistance.

The θ_{CA} for a package in free air can be approximated at 35°C/watt/in.^{2} or a device will have a 35°C rise in temperature above ambient if 1 watt is dissipated over an area of 1 in.^{2}

11.3.3 Differential Amplifiers[4]

The *differential amplifier* shown in Fig. 11-38A includes two identical linear circuits. Each of the circuits is connected so the output between them is zero when the inputs are identical, and the output is maximum when the inputs are opposite in polarity.

The ability of the differential amplifier to block identical signals is useful to reduce hum and noise that is picked up on input lines such as in low-level microphone circuits, as shown in Fig. 11-38B. This rejection is called common-mode rejection and often eliminates the need for an input transformer.

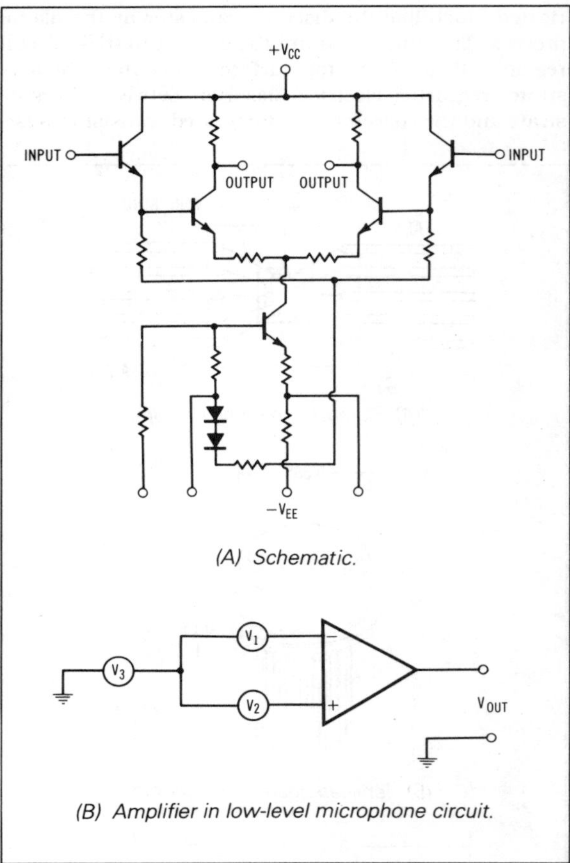

(A) Schematic.

(B) Amplifier in low-level microphone circuit.

Figure 11-38 Basic differential operational amplifier.

11.3.4 Operational Voltage Amplifiers

One of the most useful ICs for audio is the *operational amplifier*. Operational amplifiers can be made with discrete components; however, they would be very large and normally instable to temperature and external noise.

An operational amplifier manufactured on a single chip has

- Very high input impedance (> 10^6 to 10^{12} Ω),
- Very high open-loop (no feedback) gain (> 45 kV/V to 320 kV/V),
- Very low output impedance (< 200 Ω),
- Wide frequency response (> 10 MHz),

By adding external feedback paths, gain, frequency response, stability, and use can be controlled by the designer.

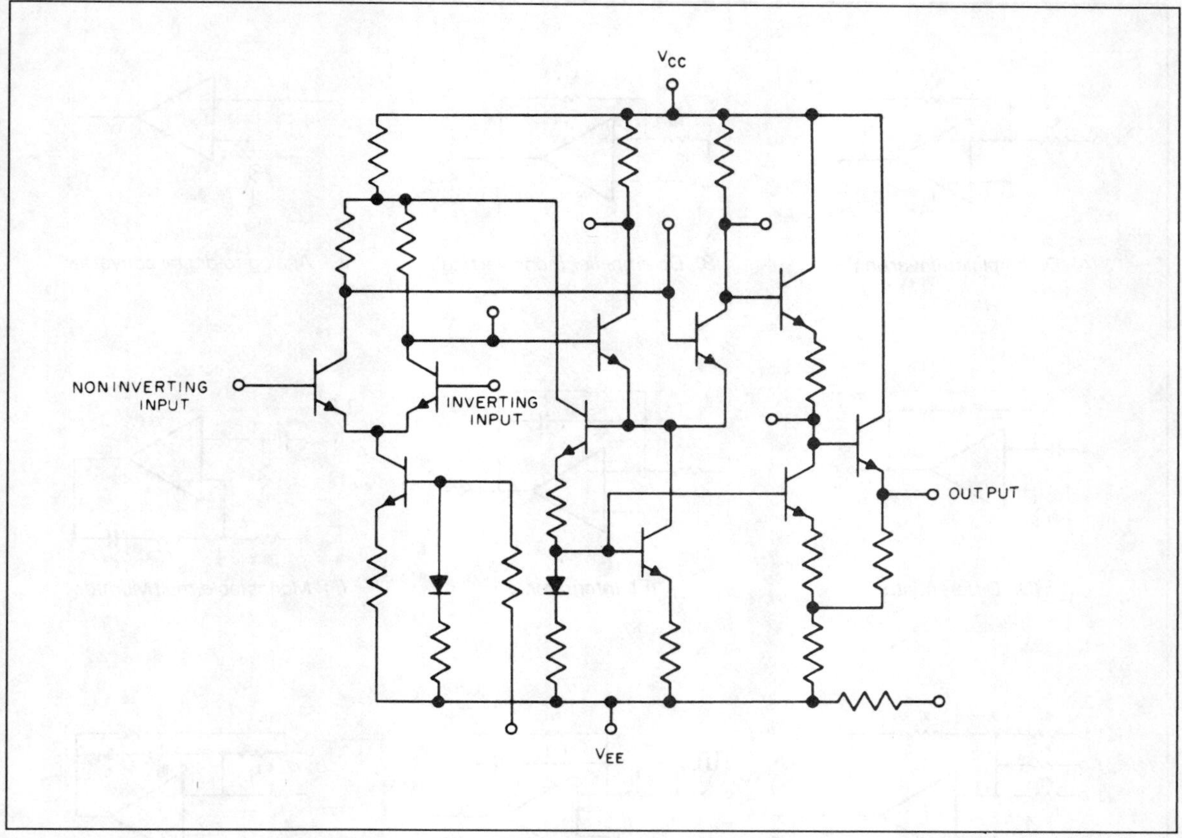

Figure 11-39 Schematic of a typical operational amplifier.

Op amps are normally two-input differential devices; one input inverting the signal, and the second input not inverting the signal hence called *noninverting*, as shown in Fig. 11-39. Several typical op amp circuits are shown in Fig. 11-40.

Because there are two inputs of opposite polarity, the output voltage is the difference between the inputs:

$$E_{o(+)} = A_v E_2 \quad (11\text{-}25)$$

$$E_{o(-)} = A_v E_1 \quad (11\text{-}26)$$

E_o can, therefore, be calculated from

$$E_o = A_v \times (E_1 - E_2) \quad (11\text{-}27)$$

Often one of the inputs is grounded, either through a direct short or a capacitor, therefore, the gain is either

$$E_o = A_v E_1$$

or (11-28)

$$E_o = A_v E_2$$

To provide both a positive and negative output with respect to ground, a positive and negative power supply is required, as shown in Fig. 11-41. The supply should be regulated and filtered. Often a + and − power supply is not available, such as in an automobile, so the IC must operate on a single supply, as shown in Fig. 11-42. In this supply, the output dc voltage is set by adjusting R_1 and R_2 so the voltage at the noninverting input is about one-third the power supply voltage.

The diodes and zener diodes in Fig. 11-43 are used to protect the IC from damage caused by transients, reverse voltage, and overdriving. D_6 and D_7 clip the inputs before overdriving, D_1 and D_2 protect against reverse polarity, D_4 and D_5 regulate the supply, and D_3 limits the total voltage across the IC.

Dc error factors result in an output offset voltage E_{oo}, which exists between the output and ground when it

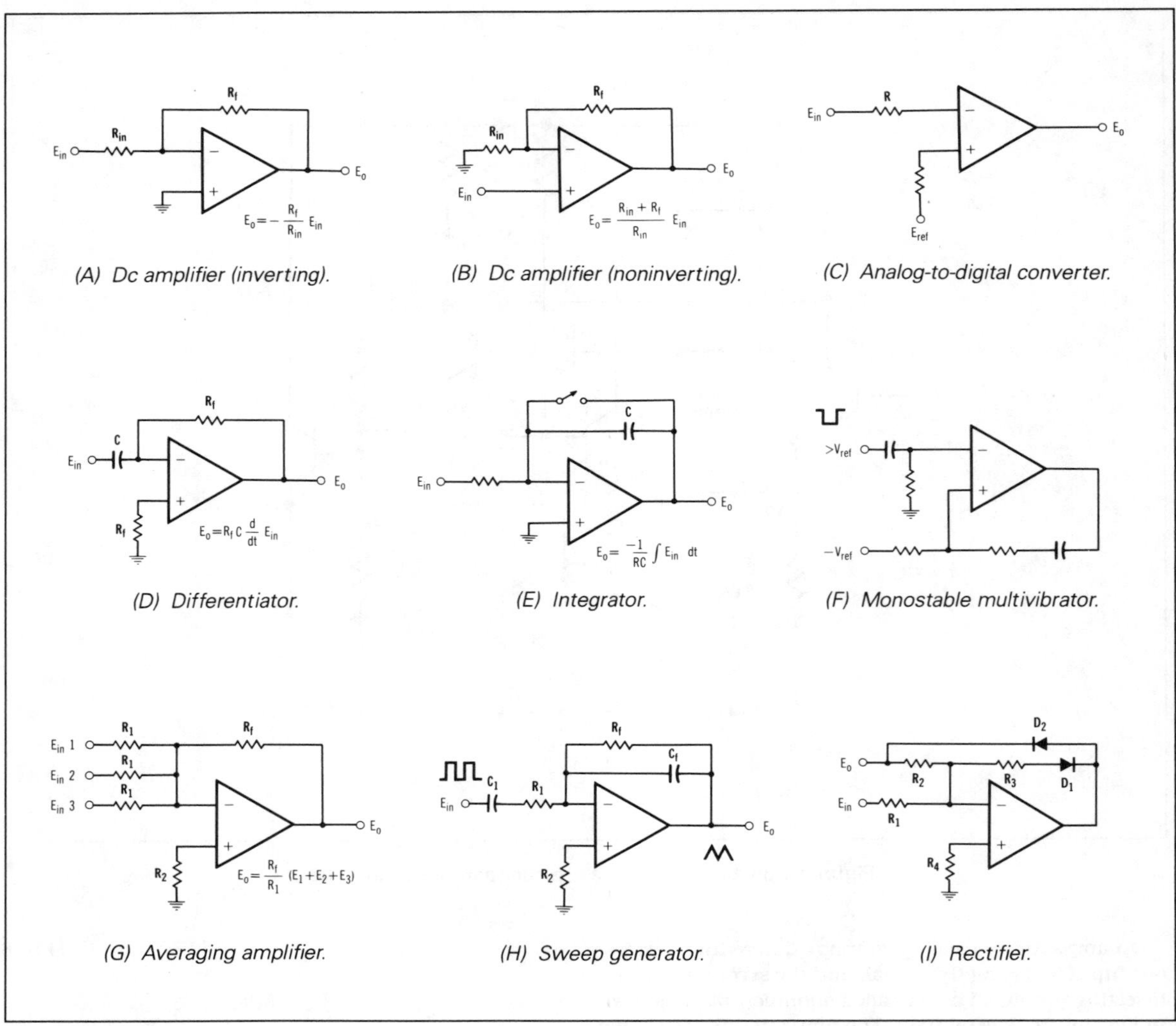

(A) Dc amplifier (inverting).
(B) Dc amplifier (noninverting).
(C) Analog-to-digital converter.
(D) Differentiator.
(E) Integrator.
(F) Monostable multivibrator.
(G) Averaging amplifier.
(H) Sweep generator.
(I) Rectifier.

Figure 11-40 Typical op-amp circuits.

should be zero. Dc offset error is most easily corrected by supplying a voltage differential between the inverting and noninverting inputs, which can be accomplished by one of several methods, as shown in Fig. 11-44. Connecting the feedback resistor R_F usually causes an offset and can be found with the formula

$$E_{oo} = I_{bias} R_F \tag{11-29}$$

By making the compensating resistor shown in Fig. 11-44A equal to

$$R_C = R_F R_{IN}/(R_F + R_{in}) \tag{11-30}$$

offset will be a minimum. If this method is not satisfactory, the methods of Figs. 11-43B or C might be required.

Operational amplifier circuits can be found in Chapters 15, 17, 19, and 22.

11.3.5 Operational Transconductance Amplifiers

The *operational transconductance amplifier (OTA)* provides transconductance gain and current output rather than voltage gain and output as in an operational amplifier. The output is the product of the input voltage and amplifier transconductance, and it can be considered an infinite impedance current generator.

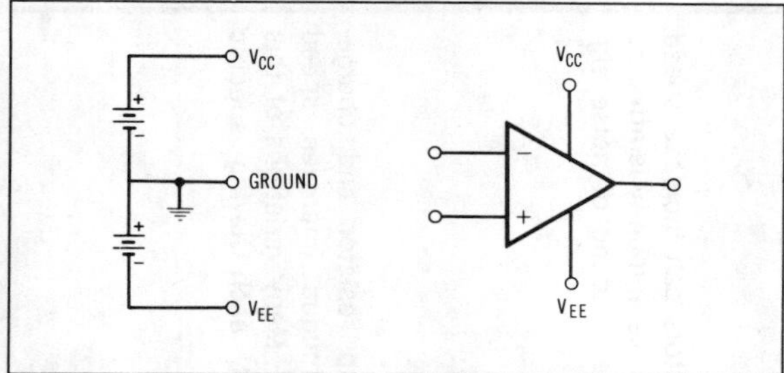

Figure 11-41 Positive- and negative-type power supply.

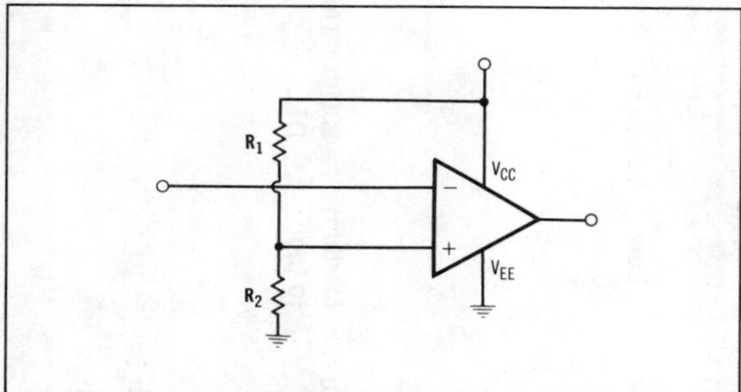

Figure 11-42 Simple circuit for operating on a single-ended power supply.

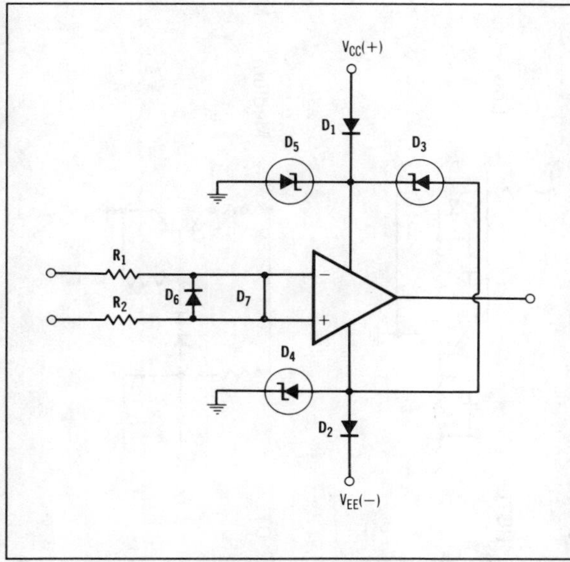

Figure 11-43 Diode protection circuits for integrated circuits.

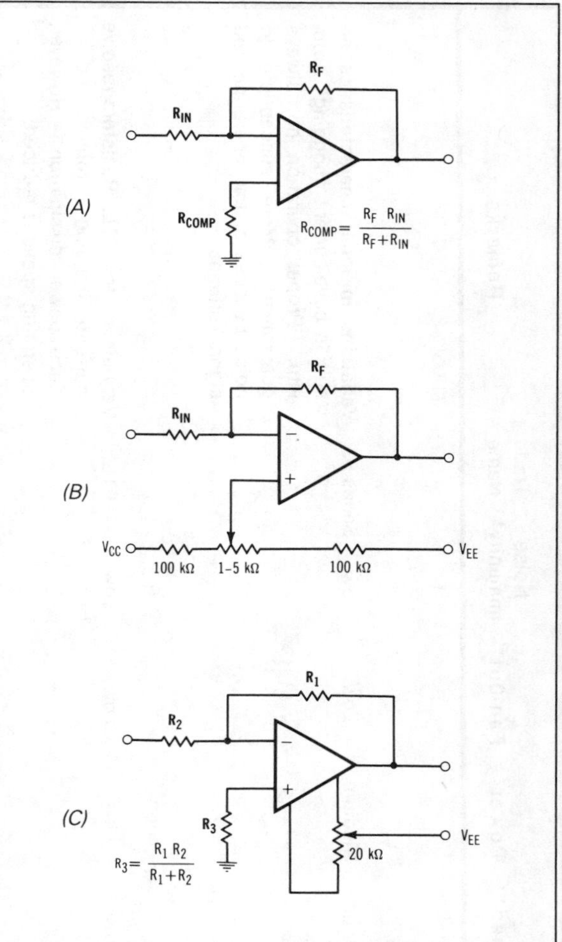

Figure 11-44 Various methods for correcting dc error.

Varying the bias current on the OTA can completely control the open-loop gain of the device and can also control the total power input.

OTAs are useful as multipliers, automatic gain control (agc) amplifiers, sample and hold circuits, multiplexers, and multivibrators to name a few.

11.3.6 Digital Integrated Circuits[4]

Digital ICs produce an output of either 0 or 1. With digital circuits, when the input reaches a preset level, the output switches polarity. This makes digital circuitry relatively immune to noise.

Bipolar technology is characterized by very fast propagation time and high power consumption, while MOS technology has relatively slow propagation times, low power

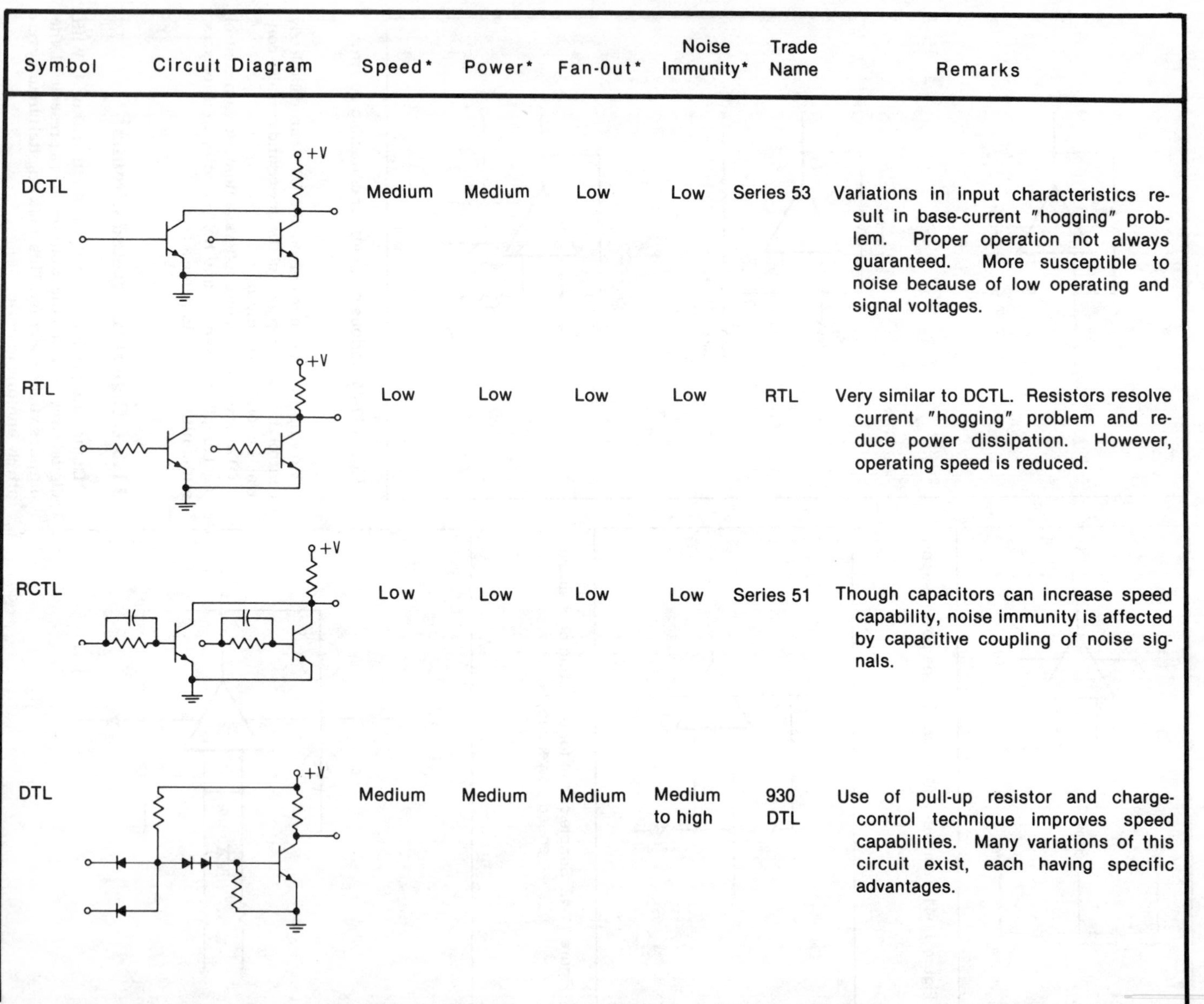

Symbol	Circuit Diagram	Speed*	Power*	Fan-Out*	Noise Immunity*	Trade Name	Remarks
DCTL		Medium	Medium	Low	Low	Series 53	Variations in input characteristics result in base-current "hogging" problem. Proper operation not always guaranteed. More susceptible to noise because of low operating and signal voltages.
RTL		Low	Low	Low	Low	RTL	Very similar to DCTL. Resistors resolve current "hogging" problem and reduce power dissipation. However, operating speed is reduced.
RCTL		Low	Low	Low	Low	Series 51	Though capacitors can increase speed capability, noise immunity is affected by capacitive coupling of noise signals.
DTL		Medium	Medium	Medium	Medium to high	930 DTL	Use of pull-up resistor and charge-control technique improves speed capabilities. Many variations of this circuit exist, each having specific advantages.

Figure 11-45 Typical digital circuits and their characteristics for

TTL	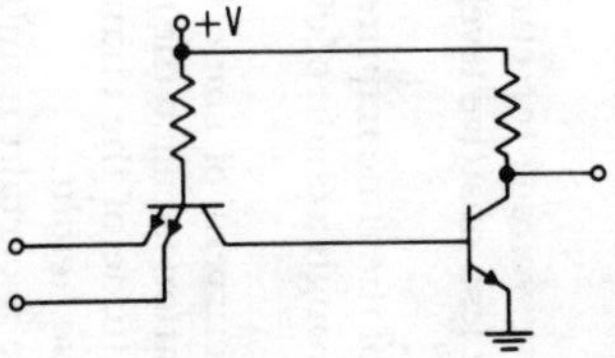 High	Medium	Medium	Medium to high	SUHL Series 54/74	Very similar to DTL. Has lower parasitic capacity at inputs. With the many existing variations, this has become very popular.
CML (ECL)	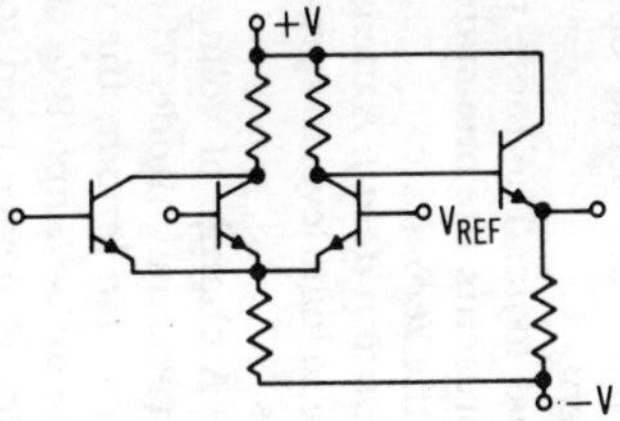 High	High	High	Medium to high	MECL ECCSL	Similar to a differential amplifier, the reference voltage sets the threshold voltage. High-speed, high fan-out operation is possible with associated high power dissipation. Also known as emitter-coupled logic (ECL).
CTL	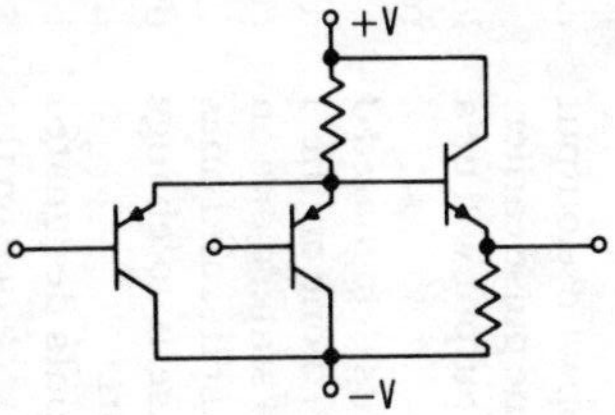 High	High	Medium	Medium	CTML	More-difficult manufacturing process results in compromises of active device characteristics and higher cost.
I^2L	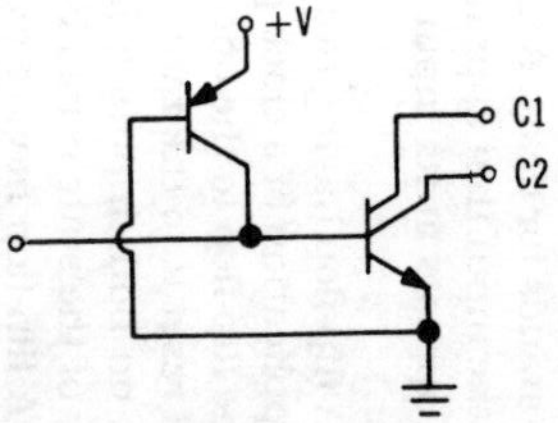 High	Low	High	Medium	I^2L	Provides smallest and most dense bipolar gate. Simple manufacturing process and higher component packing density than any MOS process. Also known as merged-transistor logic (MTL).
*Low =	<5 MHz	<5 mW	<5	<300 mV		
Medium =	5 to 15 MHz	5 to 15 mW	5 to 10	300 to 500 mV		
High =	>15 MHz	>15 mW	>10	>500 mV		

the major bipolar logic families. *(Adapted from Reference 4)* consumption, and high circuit density. Fig. 11-45 shows typical circuits and characteristics of the major bipolar logic families.

The following is some of the terminology common to digital circuitry and digital ICs:

Adder: Switching circuits that generate sum and carry bits.

Address: A code that designates the location of information and instructions.

AND: A Boolean logic operation that performs multiplication. All inputs must be true for the output to be true.

Asynchronous: A free-running switching network that triggers successive instructions.

Bit: Abbreviation for binary digit; a unit of binary information.

Buffer: A noninverting circuit used to handle fan-out or convert input and output levels.

Byte: A fixed-length binary-bit pattern (word).

Clear: To restore a device to its standard state.

Clock: A pulse generator used to control timing of switching and memory circuits.

Clock rate: The frequency (speed) at which the clock operates. This is normally the major speed of the computer.

Counter: A device capable of changing states in a specified sequence or number of input signals.

Counter, binary: A single input flip-flop. Whenever a pulse appears at the input, the flip-flop changes state (called a *T flip-flop*).

Counter, ring: A loop or circuit of interconnected flip-flops interconnected so that only one is on at any given time. As input signals are received, the position of the on state moves in sequence from one flip-flop to another around the loop.

Fan-in: The number of inputs available on a gate.

Fan-out: The number of gates that a given gate can drive. The term is applicable only within a given logic family.

Flip-flop: A circuit having two stable states and the ability to change from one state to the other on application of a signal in a specified manner.

Flip-flop D: D stands for delay. A flip-flop whose output is a function of the input that appeared one pulse earlier; that is, if a one appears at its input, the output will be a one a pulse later.

Flip-flop JK: A flip-flop having two inputs designated J and K. At the application of a clock pulse, a one on the J input will set the flip-flop to the one or on state; a one on the K input will reset it to the zero or off state; and ones simultaneously on both inputs will cause it to change state regardless of the state it had been in.

Flip-flop RS: A flip-flop having two inputs designated *R* and S. At the application of a clock pulse, a one on the S input will set the flip-flop to the one or on state, and a one on the *R* input will reset it to the zero or off state. It is assumed that ones will never appear simultaneously at both inputs.

Flip-flop R, S, T: A flip-flop having three inputs, *R, S,* and *T*. The R and S inputs produce states as described for the RS flip-flop above; the T input causes the flip-flop to change states.

Flip-flop T: A flip-flop having only one input. A pulse appearing on the input will cause the flip-flop to change states.

Gate: A circuit having two or more inputs and one output, the output depending on the combination of logic signals at the inputs. There are four gates: AND, OR, NAND, NOR. The definitions below assume positive logic is used.

Gate, AND: All inputs must have one-state signals to produce a zero-state output.

Gate, NAND: All inputs must have one-state signals to produce a one-state output.

Gate, NOR: Any one input or more having a one-state signal will yield a zero-state output.

Gate, OR: Any one input or more having a one-state signal is sufficient to produce a one-state output.

Inverter: The output is always in the opposite logic state as the input. Also called a NOT circuit.

Memory: A storage device into which information can be inserted and held for use at a later time.

NAND gate ($D = ABC$ for positive inputs): The simultaneous presence of all inputs in the positive state generates an inverted output.

Negative logic: The more negative voltage (or current) level represents the one-state; the less negative level represents the zero-state.

NOR gate ($D = A + B + C$ for positive inputs): The presence of one or more positive inputs generates an inverted output.

NOT: A Boolean logic operator indicating negation. A variable designated NOT will be the opposite of its AND or OR function. A switching function for only one variable.

OR: A Boolean operator analogous to addition (except that two truths will only add up to one truth). Of two variables, only one need be true for the output to be true.

Parallel operation: Pertaining to the manipulation of information within computer circuits in which the digits of a word are transmitted simultaneously on separate lines. It is faster than serial operation but requires more equipment.

Positive logic: The more positive voltage (or current) level represents the one-state; the less positive level represents the zero-state.

Propagation delay: A measure of the time required for a change in logic level to spread through a chain of circuit elements.

Pulse: A change of voltage or current of some finite duration and magnitude. The duration is called the *pulse width* or *pulse length;* the magnitude of the change is called the *pulse amplitude* or *pulse height.*

Register: A device used to store a certain number of digits in the computer circuits, often one word. Certain registers may also include provisions for shifting, circulating, or other operations.

Rise time: A measure of the time required for a circuit to change its output from a low level (zero) to a high level (one).

Serial operation: The handling of information within computer circuits in which the digits of a word are transmitted one at a time along a single line. Though slower than parallel operation, its circuits are much less complex.

Shift register: An element in the digital family that uses flip-flops to perform a displacement or movement of a set of digits one or more places to the right or left. If the digits are those of a numerical expression, a shift may be the equivalent of multiplying the number by a power of the base.

Skew: Time delay or offset between any two signals.

Synchronous timing: Operation of a switching network by a clock pulse generator. Slower and more critical than asynchronous timing but requires fewer and simpler circuits.

Word: An assemblage of bits considered as an entity in a computer.

REFERENCES

1. H. Tremaine, *Audio Cyclopedia*, Howard W. Sams & Co., Inc. 1969.
2. "Semiconductors: Discrete and ICs," *Electronic Buyers Handbook*, Vol. 6, Sept. 1978. Copyright 1978 by CMP Publications. Reprinted with permission.
3. What's a Thyristor, *Electronic Design*, Sept. 3, 1981.
4. *Reference Data for Radio Engineers*, Indianapolis: Howard W. Sams & Co., Inc., 1975.

ADDITIONAL BIBLIOGRAPHY

P. B. Brown, G. N. Franz, and H. Moraff, *Electronics for the Modern Scientist*, Elsevier Science Publishers, B.V., 1982.

W. H. Buchsbaum, *Encyclopedia of Integrated Circuits: A Practical Handbook of Essential Reference Data*, Englewood Cliffs: Prentice-Hall, Inc., 1981.

R. Colen (Microelectronic editor), *Electronic Design*, New York: Hayden Publishing, 1966, p. 171.

M. Grossman, *Technician's Guide to Solid-State Electronics*, West Nyack: Parker Publishing Co., 1976.

J. Carr, *OP AMP Circuit Design & Applications*, Blue Ridge Summit: Tabs Books, Inc., 1976.

CHAPTER **12**

Heat Sinks, Wire, and Relays

by Glen Ballou

12.1 HEAT SINKS

Heat sinks are used to radiate heat from solid-state devices. They are generally made from extruded aluminum or copper and are painted black, except for the areas in which the heat-producing device is mounted. The size of heat sinks will vary with the amount of heat to be radiated, the ambient temperature, and the maximum average forward current through the element. Several different types of heat sinks are pictured in Fig. 12.1. The basic relation for heat transfer is

$$P_D = \Delta T / \Sigma R_\theta \qquad (12\text{-}1)$$

where,

P_D is the power dissipated in watts,
ΔT is the temperature difference created,
ΣR_θ is the sum of the thermal resistances across which the heat transfer exists.

Heat sinks operate on three modes of heat transfer: (1) conduction, (2) radiation, and (3) convection.

The rate of heat flow from an object is

$$Q = (KA\Delta T)/L \qquad (12\text{-}2)$$

where,

Q is the rate of heat flow,
K is the thermal conductivity of the material
A is the cross-sectional area,
ΔT is the temperature difference,
L is the length of the heat flow.

For the best conduction of heat, the material should have a high thermal conductivity and have a large cross-sectional area. The ambient or material temperature should be maintained as low as possible, and the thermal path should be short.

The heat also may be transferred by convection and radiation. When a surface is hotter than the air about it, the density of the air is reduced. Therefore, it rises, taking with it heat. The amount of heat (energy) radiated by a body is dependent upon its surface area, temperature, and emissivity.

For best results, the heat sink should:

1. Have maximum surface area and volume (hence the use of vertical fins).
2. Be made of a high thermal conductivity material.
3. Have material of high emissivity (painted aluminum or copper).
4. Have proper ventilation and location (should be below, not above, other heat radiators).
5. Be placed so that the lowest power device is below the higher power devices, and all devices should be as low as possible on the heat sink.

(A) *Small heat sinks used with diodes and transistors. Their diameter is less than a dime.*

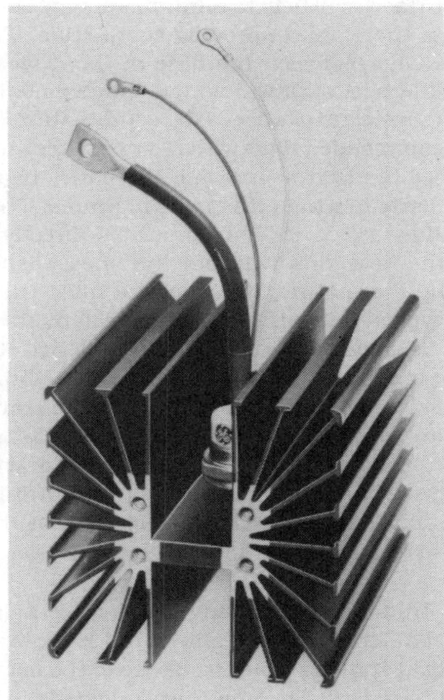

(B) *Large heat sink for use with heavy-current diode rectifiers. The stud of the diode is screwed into the center fin of the sink.*

Figure 12-1 Conduction-type heat sinks used for cooling diodes and transistors. *(Courtesy Wakefield Engineering Inc.)*

The overall effectiveness of a heat sink is dependent, to a great extent, on the intimacy of the contact between the device to be cooled and the surface of the sink. Intimacy between these two is a function of the degree of conformity between the two surfaces and the amount of pressure that holds them together. The application of a silicone oil

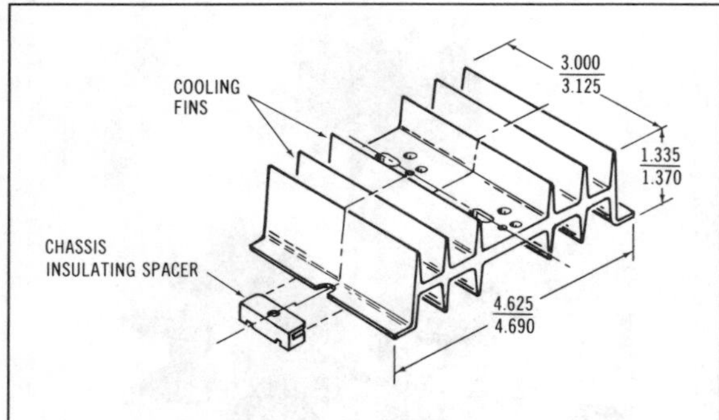

Figure 12-2 Typical heat sink for mounting two transistors. *(Courtesy AC-Delco, Division of General Motors Corp.)*

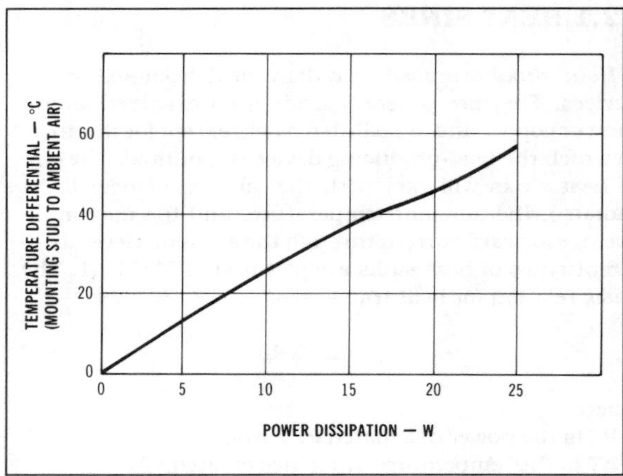

Figure 12-3 Thermal characteristics for the heat sink shown in Fig. 12-2, with convection flow of air. *(Courtesy AC-Delco, Division of General Motors Corp.)*

to the two surfaces will help to minimize air gaps between the surfaces, therefore, improving conduction. The use of a mica washer between the base of the device to be cooled and the heat sink will add as much as 0.5°C per watt to the thermal resistance of the combination. Therefore, it is recommended that (whenever possible) an insulating washer be used to insulate the entire heat sink from the chassis to which it is to be mounted. This permits the solid-state device to be mounted directly to the surface of the heat sink (without the mica washer). In this way, the thermal resistance of the mica washer is avoided. A typical heat sink manufactured by the Delco Radio Corp. is shown in Fig. 12-2. This sink has 165 in.^{2} of radiating surface. The graph in Fig. 12-3 shows the thermal characteristics of a heat sink with a transistor mounted directly on its surface. A silicone oil is used to increase the heat transfer. This graph was made with the heat-sink fins in a vertical plane, with air flowing from convection only. Fig. 12-4 shows the effect of thermal resistance with forced air blown along the length of the fin.

A typical transistor mounting kit is shown in Fig. 12-5. Several different types of silicon fluids are available to improve heat transfer from the device to the heat sink. Among them are Dow Corning Corp.'s Type-200, Wakefield Engineering Co. Thermal compound, and CG Electronics' Z5 Silicone compound. The fluid is applied between the base of the transistor and the surface of the heat sink or, if the sink is insulated, between the base and the mica washers. For diodes pressed into a heat sink, the silicone fluid is applied to the surface of the diode case before pressing it into the heat sink. The purpose of the silicone fluid is to provide good heat transfer by eliminating air gaps.

The thermal capacity of a cooling fin or heat sink must be large compared to the thermal capacity of the device and have good thermal conductivity across its entire area. Since the surface conditions create differences in the emissivity, it becomes important to select or create a surface that provides the greatest emissivity. The average

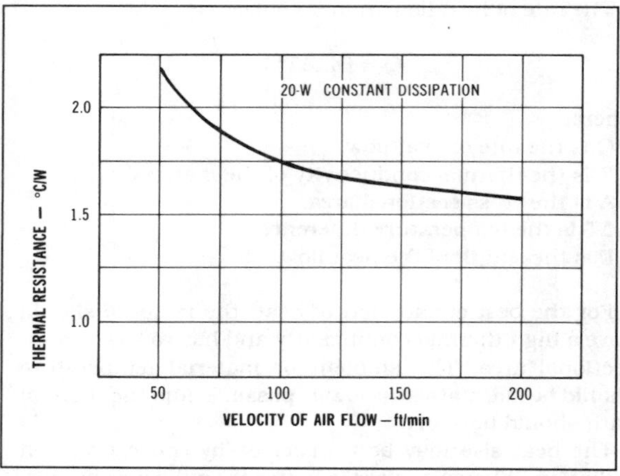

Figure 12-4 Thermal characteristics for the heat sink shown in Fig. 12-2, with forced-air cooling. *(Courtesy AC-Delco, Division of General Motors Corp.)*

emissivity is expressed in watts per degree centigrade per square inch (W/°C/in.^{2}). The average emissivity for different materials and surfaces is:

Aluminum anodized	0.8 (black)
Aluminum paint	0.50
Aluminum painted	0.9 (black)
Aluminum polished	0.05
Copper oxidized	0.7
Copper painted	0.9 (black)
Copper polished	0.05
Steel painted	0.9 (black)
Steel sheet	0.65

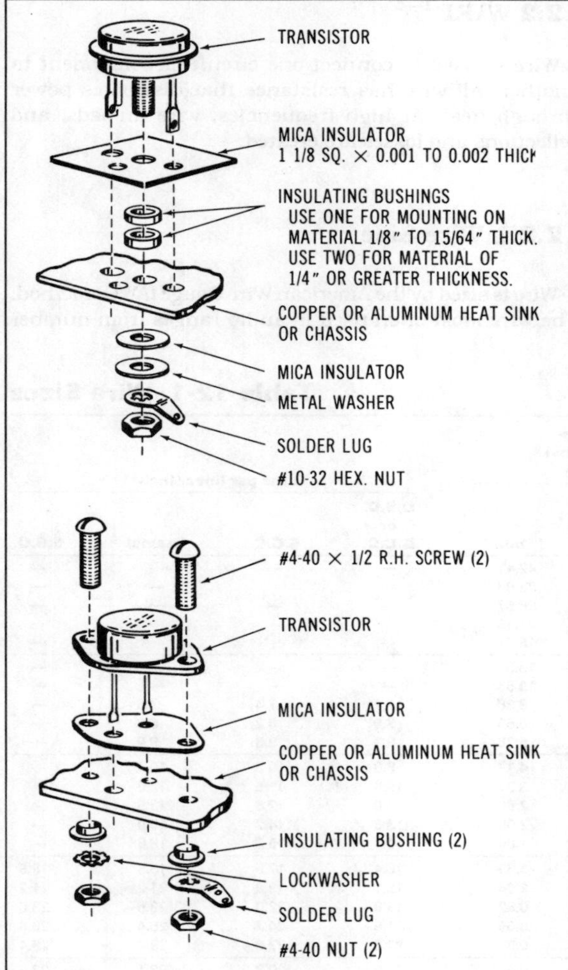

Figure 12-5 Transistor mounting kits for heat-sink operation. *(Courtesy AC-Delco, Division of General Motors Corp.)*

In the selection of a heat sink material, thermal conductivity of the material must be considered. This determines the thickness required to eliminate thermal gradients and the resultant reduction in emissivity. An aluminum fin must be twice as thick as a comparable copper fin, and steel must be eight times as thick.

Except for the smallest solid-state devices, most devices must use a heat sink, either built in or external.

Space for heat sinks is generally limited, so the minimum surface area (in square inches) permissible may be approximately calculated for a flat aluminum heat plate by the following equation:

$$A = 133 \times (W/\Delta T)\ \text{in.}^2 \qquad (12\text{-}3)$$

where,

W is the power dissipated by the device,

ΔT is the difference between the ambient and case temperatures in degrees Celsius.

The approximate wattage dissipated by the device can be calculated from the load current and the voltage drop across it:

$$W = I_L V_D \qquad (12\text{-}4)$$

For a triac, V_D is about 1.5 V; for SCRs, about 0.7 V. For transistors it could be from 0.7 V to more than 100 V.

To determine the minimum surface area for a flat aluminum heat sink required for a typical reflection with a load current of 15 A, at 25°C ambient for a triac of 1.5 V:

$$\Delta T = T_{case} - T_{ambient}$$
$$= 75°C - 25°C$$
$$= 50°C$$
$$W = V_D I_L$$
$$= 1.5(15)$$
$$= 22.5\ \text{W}$$

Using Eq. (12-3)

$$A = 133 \times (22.5)/50$$
$$= 59.85\ \text{in.}^2$$

It is important that the case temperature T_{case} does not exceed the maximum allowed for a given load current I_L (see typical derating curves in Fig. 12-6).

Eq. 12-3 gives the surface area needed for a vertically mounted heat sink. With free air convection, a vertically

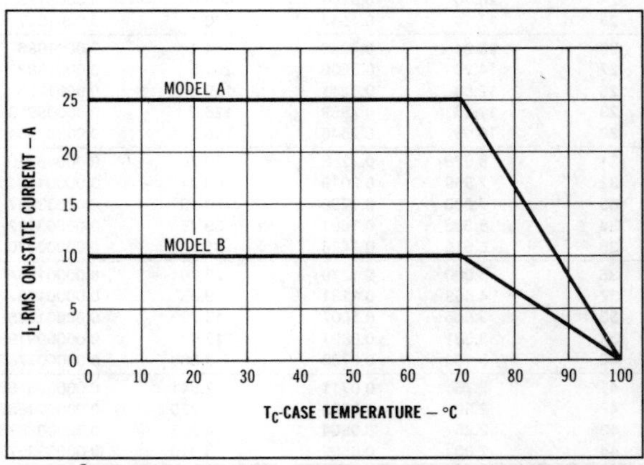

Figure 12-6 A typical derating curve for solid-state devices.

mounted heat sink has a thermal resistance approximately 30% lower than with horizontal mounting, as shown in Fig. 12-7. In restricted areas, forced-convection cooling may be necessary to reduce the effective thermal resistance of the heat sink.

When forced-air cooling is used to cool the component, the cubic feet per minute (cfm) required is determined by the following formula:

$$\text{cfm} = [(\text{Btu/hr})/60] \times (0.02 \times \text{temp rise}) \qquad (12\text{-}5)$$

where,
1 W = 3.4 Btu.

12.2 WIRE[1–4]

Wire is used to connect one circuit or component to another. All wire has resistance that dissipates power through heat. At high frequencies, wire unloads, and reflections and losses are created.

12.2.1 Wire Size

Wire is sized by the American Wire Gauge (AWG) method. The wire most often used in audio ranges from number

Table 12-1. Wire Sizes

AWG No. (B&S)	Diam mils*	Diam mm	Cir mils	Cross-sectional area In.²	Cross-sectional area mm²	Turns per linear inch** D.S.C. or D.C.C.	Turns per linear inch** S.C.C.	Turns per linear inch** Enamel	Turns per linear inch** S.S.C.
1	289.3	7.348	83690	0.06573	42.41	—	—	—	—
2	257.6	6.544	66370	0.05213	33.63	—	—	—	—
3	229.4	5.827	52640	0.04134	26.67	—	—	—	—
4	204.3	5.189	41740	0.03278	21.15	—	—	—	—
5	181.9	4.621	33100	0.02600	16.77	—	—	—	—
6	162.0	4.115	26250	0.02062	13.3	—	—	—	—
7	144.3	3.665	20820	0.01635	10.55	—	—	—	—
8	128.5	3.264	16510	0.01297	8.36	7.1	7.4	7.6	—
9	114.4	2.906	13090	0.01028	6.63	7.8	8.2	8.6	—
10	101.9	2.588	10380	0.008155	5.26	8.9	9.3	9.6	—
11	90.74	2.305	8234	0.006467	4.17	9.8	10.3	10.7	—
12	80.81	2.053	6530	0.005129	3.31	10.9	11.5	12.0	—
13	71.96	1.828	5178	0.004067	2.62	12.0	12.8	13.5	—
14	64.08	1.628	4107	0.003225	2.08	13.3	14.2	15.0	—
15	57.07	1.450	3257	0.002558	1.65	14.7	15.8	16.8	—
16	50.82	1.291	2583	0.002028	1.31	16.4	17.9	18.9	18.9
17	45.26	1.150	2048	0.001609	1.04	18.1	19.9	21.2	21.2
18	40.30	1.024	1624	0.001276	0.82	19.8	22.0	23.6	23.6
19	35.89	0.9116	1288	0.001012	0.65	21.8	24.4	26.4	26.4
20	31.96	0.8118	1022	0.0008023	0.52	23.8	27.0	29.4	29.4
21	28.46	0.7230	810.1	0.0006363	0.41	26.0	29.8	33.1	32.7
22	25.35	0.6438	642.4	0.0005046	0.33	30.0	34.1	37.0	36.5
23	22.57	0.5733	509.5	0.0004002	0.26	31.6	37.6	41.3	40.6
24	20.10	0.5106	404.0	0.0003173	0.20	35.6	41.5	46.3	45.3
25	17.90	0.4547	320.4	0.0002517	0.16	38.6	45.6	51.7	50.4
26	15.94	0.4049	254.1	0.0001996	0.13	41.8	50.2	58.0	55.6
27	14.20	0.3606	201.5	0.0001583	0.10	45.0	55.0	64.9	61.5
28	12.64	0.3211	159.8	0.0001255	0.08	48.5	60.2	72.7	68.6
29	11.26	0.2859	126.7	0.00009953	0.064	51.8	65.4	81.6	74.8
30	10.03	0.2546	100.5	0.00007894	0.051	55.5	71.5	90.5	83.3
31	8.928	0.2268	79.70	0.00006260	0.040	59.2	77.5	101.	92.0
32	7.950	0.2019	63.21	0.00004964	0.032	62.6	83.6	113.	101.
33	7.080	0.1798	50.13	0.00003937	0.0254	66.3	90.3	127.	110.
34	6.305	0.1601	39.75	0.00003122	0.0201	70.0	97.0	143.	120.
35	5.615	0.1426	31.52	0.00002476	0.0159	73.5	104.	158.	132.
36	5.000	0.1270	25.00	0.00001964	0.0127	77.0	111.	175.	143.
37	4.453	0.1131	19.83	0.00001557	0.0100	80.3	118.	198.	154.
38	3.965	0.1007	15.72	0.00001235	0.0079	83.6	126.	224.	166.
39	3.531	0.0897	12.47	0.000009793	0.0063	86.6	133.	248.	181.
40	3.134	0.0799	9.888	0.000007766	0.0050	89.7	140.	282.	194.
41	2.75	0.0711	7.841	0.000006160	0.0040	—	—	—	—
42	2.50	0.0633	6.220	0.000004885	0.0032	—	—	—	—
43	2.25	0.0564	4.933	0.000003873	0.0025	—	—	—	—
44	2.00	0.0502	3.910	0.000003073	0.0020	—	—	—	—

*A mil is 1/1000 inch.

**Approximate only—thickness of insulation varies.

Source: Radio Electronics

4 to number 24. Wire with a number less than number 4 is very heavy and cumbersome while wire greater than number 24 is extremely fragile and has a high resistance. Table 12-1 is a table of the AWG wire sizes between numbers 1 and 44. Resistance is an important factor in determining wire size in the audio circuit. For instance, if an 8-Ω loudspeaker is being connected to an amplifier 500 ft away through a number 19 wire, 50% of the power would be dropped in the wire in the form of heat. A handy rule of thumb to remember is that 1000 ft of number 16 wire has a resistance of 4 Ω. Each time the wire size changes three numbers (i.e., from number 16 to 19 or 13), the resistance doubles or halves.

12.2.2 Wire Resistance

When using a 70-V loudspeaker system, the choice of wire size for loudspeaker lines is determined by an economic balance of the cost of copper against the cost of power lost in the line. Table 12-2 gives the length of cable that causes a reduction of 0.5 dB (12½%) power in the load. Half of this reduction is actually a line loss. The other half is power not taken from the amplifier because the load at the amplifier is not the design load, for example, 122 Ω (40 W for 70 V), but greater by the line resistance. As an example, consider a 4000-ft pair of number 10s, with a total resistance of 8 Ω and a load intended to

Between AWG No. 1 and 44

Turns per Sq In**			Feet per pound				Current-carrying capacity (amperes)		
SCC	Enamel	DCC	DCC	SCC	Bare	Ohms per 1000 ft	At 1000 C.M. per amp	At 1500 C.M. per amp	Nearest British S.W.G.
—	—	—	—	—	3.947	0.1260	83.7	55.7	1
—	—	—	—	—	4.977	0.1592	66.4	44.1	3
—	—	—	—	—	6.276	0.2004	52.6	35.0	4
—	—	—	—	—	7.914	0.2536	41.7	27.7	5
—	—	—	—	—	9.980	0.3192	33.1	22.0	7
—	—	—	—	—	12.58	0.4028	26.3	17.5	8
—	—	—	—	—	15.87	0.5080	20.8	13.8	9
—	58	—	19.6	19.9	20.01	0.6045	16.5	11.0	10
—	74	—	24.6	25.1	25.23	0.8077	13.1	8.7	11
87.5	92	80.0	30.9	31.6	31.82	1.018	10.4	6.9	12
110	114	95.5	38.8	39.8	40.12	1.284	8.2	5.5	13
136	144	121	48.9	50.2	50.59	1.619	6.5	4.4	14
170	182	150	61.5	63.2	63.80	2.042	5.2	3.5	15
211	225	183	77.3	79.6	80.44	2.575	4.1	2.7	16
262	282	223	97.3	100	101.4	3.247	3.3	2.2	17
321	357	271	119	124	127.9	4.094	2.6	1.7	17–18
397	450	329	150	155	161.3	5.163	2.0	1.3	18
493	558	399	188	196	203.4	6.510	1.6	1.1	19
592	708	479	237	247	256.5	8.210	1.3	0.86	20
775	868	625	298	311	323.4	10.35	1.0	0.68	21
940	1090	754	370	389	407.8	13.05	0.81	0.54	22
1150	1368	910	461	491	514.8	16.46	0.64	0.43	23
1400	1640	1080	584	624	648.4	20.76	0.51	0.34	24
1700	2140	1260	745	778	817.7	26.17	0.41	0.27	25
2060	2530	1510	903	958	1031	33.00	0.32	0.21	26
2500	3340	1750	1118	1188	1300	41.62	0.25	0.17	27–28
3030	4145	2020	1422	1533	1639	52.48	0.20	0.13	29
3670	5250	2310	1759	1903	2067	66.17	0.16	0.11	30
4300	6510	2700	2207	2461	2607	83.44	0.13	0.084	31–32
5040	8175	3020	2534	2893	3287	105.20	0.10	0.067	33
5920	10220	—	2768	3483	4145	132.70	0.079	0.053	34–35
7060	12650	—	3137	4414	5227	167.30	0.063	0.042	36
8120	16200	—	4697	5688	6591	211.00	0.050	0.033	36–37
9600	19950	—	6168	6400	8310	266.00	0.039	0.026	37–38
10900	25000	—	6737	8393	10480	335.00	0.032	0.021	38–39
12200	31700	—	7877	9846	13210	423.00	0.025	0.017	39–40
14000	39600	6510	9309	11636	16660	533.40	0.020	0.013	41
16600	49100	6950	10666	13848	21010	672.60	0.016	0.010	42–43
18000	62600	7450	11907	18286	26500	848.10	0.012	0.008	43
—	77600	—	14222	24381	33410	1069.00	0.009	0.006	44
—	97500	—	17920	30610	42130	1323.00	0.008	0.005	45
—	122000	—	22600	38700	53100	1667.00	0.006	0.004	45–46
—	152000	—	28410	48600	66970	2105.00	0.005	0.003	46–47
—	190000	—	35950	61400	84460	2655.00	0.004	0.0025	47

*A mil is 1/1000 inch.

**Approximate only—thickness of insulation varies.

Source: Radio Electronics

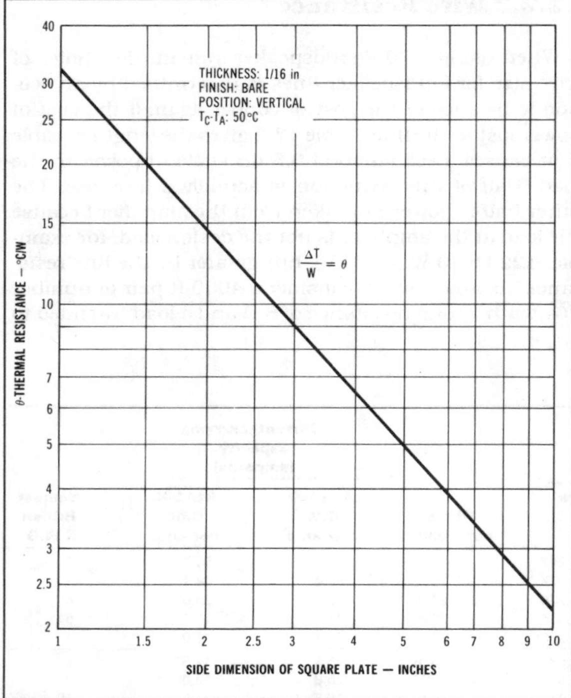

Figure 12-7 Thermal resistance for a 1⁄16-in. aluminum plate of various dimensions.

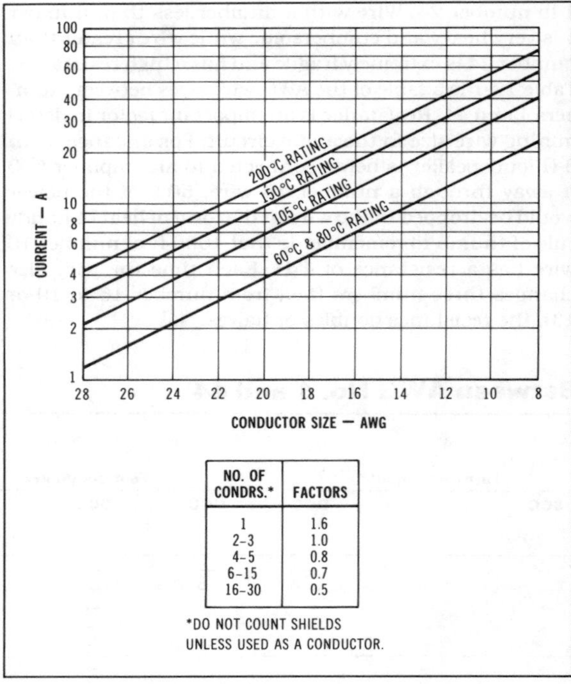

NO. OF CONDRS.*	FACTORS
1	1.6
2–3	1.0
4–5	0.8
6–15	0.7
16–30	0.5

*DO NOT COUNT SHIELDS UNLESS USED AS A CONDUCTOR.

Figure 12-8 Current capabilities for wire.

be 40 W at 70 V (impedance 122 Ω). The power delivered by the amplifier into its load of 122 plus 8 Ω is 37.7 W. The drop in the line is 4.3 V, the power lost in the line is 2.3 W. The voltage at the speaker is 65.7, and the power taken by the speaker is 35 W, which is 5 W or 12½% or 0.5 dB less than intended. However, only half of this is actually lost; the rest is simply not taken from the amplifier. An additional load of 2.3 W may, therefore, be connected to the amplifier.

12.2.3 Wire Current Ratings

The maximum continuous current rating for an electronic cable is limited by conductor size, number of conductors contained within the cable, maximum temperature rating of the cable, and environment conditions, such as ambient temperature and air flow. A general chart has been made to simplify the number of cables in a conduit and the current-carrying capacity of each conductor. To use the current capacity chart in Fig. 12-8, first determine the conductor gage, the temperature rating, and the number of conductors from the applicable product description for the cable of interest.

Next, find the current value on the chart for the proper temperature rating and conductor size. To calculate the maximum current rating per conductor, multiply the chart value by the appropriate conductor factor. The chart assumes the cable is surrounded by still air at an ambient temperature of 25°C. Current values are in rms amperes and are valid for copper conductors only.

The current ratings of Fig. 12-8 are intended as general guidelines for low-power electronic communications and control applications. Current ratings for power applications generally are set by regulatory agencies such as Underwriters Laboratories (UL), Canadian Standards Association (CSA), National Electronics Commission (NEC), and others.

12.2.4 Wire Flexibility

Wire flexibility is controlled by the stiffness of the wire and the covering. Table 12-3 gives suggested conductor strandings for various degrees of flexibility.

12.2.5 Wire Jackets and Insulation Characteristics

The jackets and insulation characteristics determine the resistance of the wire or cable to the environment and the flexibility of it, especially at low temperatures. Tables 12-4 and 12-5 give the comparative properties of rubber insulation and plastic insulation.

Table 12-2. Length of Two-Wire 70-V Line Delivering Various Values of Power at 0.5 dB (12.5%) Loss

Wire Size AWG	Resistance per 1000′ Wire Pair	Max Safe Current	Max Safe Power	Nominal Power in the Load									
				10 W	**15 W**	**20 W**	**30 W**	**40 W**	**60 W**	**100 W**	**200 W**	**400 W**	**1000 W**
# 6	0.8 ohms	50 Amp	3500 W	(Length of Line)				9100	6200	3640	1820	910	360 ft
# 8	1.28	35	2450				7800	5700	3900	2280	1140	570	230 ft
#10	2.0	25	1750		9900	7300	5000	3700	2500	1450	730	370	150 ft
#12	3.2	20	1400	9100	6200	4600	3100	2300	1600	910	460	230	90 ft
#14	5.2	15	1000	5600	3800	2800	1900	1400	950	560	280	140	56 ft
#16	8.0	6	420	3600	2400	1800	1200	900	600	370	180	90 ft	
#18	13.0	3	210	2300	1500	1100	750	560	370	230 ft			
#20	20.6	1	70	1400	960	710	480	350	240	110 ft			
#22	32.6	0.5 Amp		900	600	450	300 ft						
	Load Impedance (ohms)			**490**	**327**	**245**	**163**	**122**	**81**	**49**	**24.5**	**12.2**	**4.9**

For 1-dB loss, double all lengths. *For 25-V line*: divide all lengths by 8, divide maximum safe power by 2.8, and divide load impedance by 8.
(Courtesy Altec Lansing)

Table 12-3. Suggested Conductor Strandings for Various Degrees of Flexing Severity

Typical Applications	12 AWG Stranding		14 AWG Stranding		20 AWG Stranding		22 AWG Stranding	
	AWG	mm	AWG	mm	AWG	mm	AWG	mm
Fixed Service (Hook-up Wire Cable in Raceway)	19 × 25*	19 × 0.455*	Solid or 19 × 27	19 × 0.361	Solid or 7 × 28 or 10 × 30	7 × 0.320 or 10 × 0.254	Solid or 7 × 30	7 × 0.254
Moderate Flexing (Frequently Disturbed for Maintenance)	65 × 30	65 × 0.254	19 × 27 or 41 × 30	19 × 0.361 or 41 × 0.254	7 × 28 or 10 × 30 or 19 × 32 or 26 × 34	7 × 0.320 or 10 × 0.254 or 19 × 0.203 or 26 × 0.160	7 × 30 or 19 × 34	7 × 0.254 or 19 × 0.160
Severe Flexing (Microphones Test Prods)	165 × 34	165 × 0.160	104 × 34	104 × 0.160	26 × 34 or 42 × 36	26 × 0.160 or 42 × 0.127	19 × 34 or 26 × 36	19 × 0.160 or 26 × 0.127
Most Severe Duty (Mercury Switches)	259 × 36 (7⁄8 × 37*** Rope Lay)	259 × 0.127	168 × 36 (7 × 24 Rope lay)	168 × 0.127	105 × 40 (3 × 35 Rope Lay)	105 × 0.079	(Consider braid or tinsel)	

Typical Applications	16 AWG Stranding		18 AWG Stranding		24 AWG Stranding		26 AWG Stranding	
	AWG	mm	AWG	mm	AWG	mm	AWG	mm
Fixed Service (Hook-up Wire Cable in Raceway)	Solid or 19 × 29	19 × 0.287	Solid or 7 × 26 or 16 × 30	7 × 0.404 or 16 × 0.254	Solid or 7 × 32	7 × 0.203	Solid or 7 × 34	7 × 0.160
Moderate Flexing (Frequently Disturbed for Maintenance)	19 × 29 or 26 × 30	19 × 0.287 or 26 × 0.254	16 × 30 or 41 × 34	16 × 0.254 or 41 × 0.160	7 × 32 or 10 × 34	7 × 0.203 or 10 × 0.160	7 × 34	7 × 0.160
Severe Flexing (Microphones Test Prods)	65 × 34 or 104 × 36	65 × 0.160 or 104 × 0.127	41 × 34 or 65 × 36	41 × 0.160 or 65 × 0.127	19 × 36 or 45 × 40**	19 × 0.127 or 45 × 0.079**	7 × 34 or 10 × 36**	7 × 0.160 or 10 × 0.127**
Most Severe Duty (Mercury Switches)	105 × 36 (7 × 15 Rope Lay)	105 × 0.127	63 × 36 (7 × 9 Rope Lay)	63 × 0.127		(Consider braid or tinsel)		

*19 strands of 25 AWG or 19 strands of 0.455 mm wire.

(Courtesy Belden Corp.)

**Composite constructions consisting of 4 strands copper-covered steel and 3 strands copper are frequently used for severe flexing in small-sized cables. No. 25 AWG (4 × 33 copper-covered steel + 3 × 33 copper) is popular in microphone cables.

***Rope lay is several stranded groups cabled together. For example: No. 12 AWG. 259 × 36 is 7 cords each consisting of 37 strands of No. 36 AWG.

Table 12-4. Comparative Properties of Rubber Insulation

Properties	Rubber	Neoprene	Hypalon (Chloro-sulfonated Polyethylene)	EPDM (Ethylene Propylene Diene Monomer)	Silicone
Oxidation Resistance	F	G	E	G	E
Heat Resistance	F	G	E	E	O
Oil Resistance	P	G	G	F	F-G
Low Temperature Flexibility	G	F-G	F	G-E	O
Weather, Sun Resistance	F	G	E	E	O
Ozone Resistance	P	G	E	E	O
Abrasion Resistance	E	G-E	G	G	P
Electrical Properties	E	P	G	E	O
Flame Resistance	P	G	G	P	F-G
Nuclear Radiation Resistance	F	F-G	G	G	E
Water Resistance	G	E	G-E	G-E	G-E
Acid Resistance	F-G	G	E	G-E	F-G
Alkali Resistance	F-G	G	E	G-E	F-G
Gasoline, Kerosene, Etc. (Aliphatic Hydrocarbons) Resistance	P	G	F	P	P-F
Benzol, Toluol, Etc. (Aromatic Hydrocarbons) Resistance	P	P-F	F	F	P
Degreaser Solvents (Halogenated Hydrocarbons) Resistance	P	P	P-F	P	P-G
Alcohol Resistance	G	F	G	P	G

P = poor F = fair G = good E = excellent O = outstanding *(Courtesy Belden Corp.)*

These ratings are based on average performance of general-purpose compounds. Any given property can usually be improved by the use of selective compounding.

Table 12-5. Comparative Properties of Plastic Insulation

Properties	PVC	Low-Density Polyethylene	Cellular Polyethylene	High-Density Polyethylene	Polypropylene	Polyurethane	Nylon	Teflon®
Oxidation Resistance	E	E	E	E	E	E	E	O
Heat Resistance	G–E	G	G	E	E	G	E	O
Oil Resistance	F	G	G	G–E	F	E	E	O
Low Temperature Flexibility	P–G	G–E	E	E	P	G	G	O
Weather, Sun Resistance	G–E	E	E	E	E	G	E	O
Ozone Resistance	E	E	E	E	E	E	E	E
Abrasion Resistance	F–G	F–G	F	E	F–G	O	E	E
Electrical Properties	F–G	E	E	E	E	P	P	E
Flame Resistance	E	P	P	P	P	P	P	O
Nuclear Radiation Resistance	G	G	G	G	F	G	F–G	P
Water Resistance	E	E	E	E	E	P–G	P–F	E
Acid Resistance	G–E	G–E	G–E	G–E	E	F	P–F	E
Alkali Resistance	G–E	G–E	G–E	G–E	E	F	E	E
Gasoline, Kerosene, Etc. (Aliphatic Hydrocarbons) Resistance	P	P–F	P–F	P–F	P–F	G	G	E
Benzol, Toluol, Etc. (Aromatic Hydrocarbons) Resistance	P–F	P	P	P	P–F	P	G	E
Degreaser Solvents (Halogenated Hydrocarbons) Resistance	P–F	P	P	P	P	P	G	E
Alcohol Resistance	G–E	E	E	E	E	P	P	E

P = poor F = fair G = good E = excellent O = outstanding *(Courtesy Belden Wire & Cable)*

These ratings are based on average performance of general purpose compounds. Any given property can usually be improved by the use of selective compounding.

Typical characteristics of popular insulation and jacket compounds follow.

12.2.5.1 Vinyl

Vinyl is sometimes referred to as pvc or polyvinylchloride. Extremely high or low temperature properties cannot be found in one formulation, therefore, formulations may have a −40 to +105°C rating, while other common vinyls may have −20 to +60°C. The many varieties of vinyl also differ in pliability and electrical properties fitting a multitude of applications. The price range can vary accordingly. Typical dielectric constant values can vary from 3.5 to 6.5.

12.2.5.2 Polyethylene

A very good insulator in terms of electrical properties, polyethylene has a low constant dielectric value over all frequencies and very high insulation resistance. In terms of flexibility, *polyethylene* can be rated stiff to very hard, depending on molecular weight and density. Low density is the most flexible, whereas a high-density high-molecular-weight formulation is rock hard. Moisture resistance is rated excellent. Correct brown and black formulations have excellent weather resistance. The dielectric constant is 2.3 for solid insulation and 1.64 for cellular designs.

12.2.5.3 Teflon®

Teflon® has excellent electrical properties, temperature range, and chemical resistance. It is not suitable where subjected to nuclear radiation, and it does not have good high-voltage characteristics. FEP Teflon® is extrudable in a manner similar to vinyl and polyethylene; therefore, long wire and cable lengths are available. TFE Teflon® is extrudable in a hydraulic ram-type process, and lengths are limited due to amount of material in the ram, thickness of the insulation, and core size. TFE must be extruded over silver- or nickel-coated wire. The nickel- and silver-coated designs are rated +260 and +200°C maximum, respectively. The cost of Teflon® is approximately eight to ten times more per pound than vinyl insulations.

12.2.5.4 Polypropylene

Similar in electrical properties to polyethylene, polypropylene is primarily used as an insulation material. Typically, it is harder than polyethylene, which makes it suitable for thin wall insulations. UL maximum temperature rating may be 60 or 80°C. The dielectric constant is 2.25 for solid and 1.55 for cellular designs.

12.2.5.5 Silicone

This is a very soft insulation that has a temperature range from −80 to +200°C. It has excellent electrical properties plus ozone resistance, low moisture absorption, weather resistance, and radiation resistance. It typically has low mechanical strength and poor scuff resistance.

12.2.5.6 Neoprene

The maximum temperature range of this material can vary from −55 to +90°C. The actual range would depend on the formulation used. Neoprene is both oil resistant and sunlight resistant making it ideal for many outdoor applications. The most stable colors are black, dark brown, and gray. The electrical properties are not as good as other insulation material; therefore, thicker insulation should be used.

12.2.5.7 Rubber

The description of rubber normally includes natural rubber and SBR compounds. Both can be used for insulations and jackets. There are many formulations of these basic materials, and each formulation is for a specific application. Some formulations are suitable for −55°C minimum, while others are suitable for + 75°C maximum.

12.2.6 Insulation Color Codes

The wire insulation colors help trace conductors or conductor pairs. There are many color tables; however, Tables 12-6 and 12-7 are the common ones used.

12.2.7 Multiconductor Cables

When a plurality of lines, carrying different programs or signals, are run together in the same conduit, they tend to induce crosstalk currents into each other. When planning such a run, answers are needed for several questions:

1. Must the cost be paid for shielded cables or will twisted pairs suffice?
2. Should transformers be used?
3. Should the circuit be grounded?
4. What about capacity?
5. What about line loss? Selection of conductor size?

Crosstalk is induced (1) electromagnetically, due to unbalanced coupling between one circuit and others; (2) electrostatically, due to unbalanced capacitance to other circuits, to the conduit if it carries current and thus develops a voltage difference between one circuit and the others, or to its own or other shields carrying current.

Shielded, two-conductor cable has leakage between the conductors and the surrounding shield. A number 20 AWG, for instance, will have a leakage between 40 and 60 MΩ.

Table 12-6. Color Code for Nonpaired Cables

Conductor	Color	Conductor	Color	Conductor	Color	Conductor	Color
1st	Black	1st	Black	18th	Orange/Red	35th	Wht/Red/Org
2nd	White	2nd	White	19th	Blue/Red	36th	Org/Wht/Blue
3rd	Red	3rd	Red	20th	Red/Green	37th	Wht/Red/Blue
4th	Green	4th	Green	21st	Orange/Green	38th	Blk/Wht/Grn
5th	Brown	5th	Orange	22nd	Blk/Wht/Red	39th	Wht/Blk/Grn
6th	Blue	6th	Blue	23rd	Wht/Blk/Red	40th	Red/Wht/Grn
7th	Orange	7th	White/Black	24th	Red/Blk/Wht	41st	Grn/Wht/Blue
8th	Yellow	8th	Red/Black	25th	Grn/Blk/Wht	42nd	Org/Red/Grn
9th	Purple	9th	Green/Black	26th	Org/Blk/Wht	43rd	Blue/Red/Grn
10th	Gray	10th	Orange/Black	27th	Blue/Blk/Wht	44th	Blk/Wht/Blue
11th	Pink	11th	Blue/Black	28th	Blk/Red/Grn	45th	Wht/Blk/Blue
12th	Tan	12th	Black/White	29th	Wht/Red/Grn	46th	Red/Wht/Blue
		13th	Red/White	30th	Red/Blk/Grn	47th	Grn/Org/Red
		14th	Green/White	31st	Grn/Blk/Org	48th	Org/Red/Blue
		15th	Blue/White	32nd	Org/Blk/Grn	49th	Blue/Red/Org
		16th	Black/Red	33rd	Blue/Wht/Org	50th	Blk/Org/Red
		17th	White/Red	34th	Blk/Wht/Org		

Table 12-7. Color Codes for Paired Cables

Pair No.	Color Combination	Pair No.	Color Combination	Pair No.	Color Combination	Pair No.	Color Combination
1	Black paired with Red	10	Red paired with Blue	19	White paired with Blue	28	Orange paired with Yellow
2	Black paired with White	11	Red paired with Yellow	20	White paired with Yellow	29	Purple paired with Orange
3	Black paired with Green	12	Red paired with Brown	21	White paired with Brown	30	Purple paired with Red
4	Black paired with Blue	13	Red paired with Orange	22	White paired with Orange	31	Purple paired with White
5	Black paired with Yellow	14	Green paired with White	23	Blue paired with Yellow	32	Purple paired with Dark Green
6	Black paired with Brown	15	Green paired with Blue	24	Blue paired with Brown	33	Purple paired with Light Blue
7	Black paired with Orange	16	Green paired with Yellow	25	Blue paired with Orange	34	Purple paired with Yellow
8	Red paired with White	17	Green paired with Brown	26	Brown paired with Yellow	35	Purple paired with Brown
9	Red paired with Green	18	Green paired with Orange	27	Brown paired with Orange	36	Purple paired with Black
						37	Gray paired with White

(Courtesy Belden Wire & Cable)

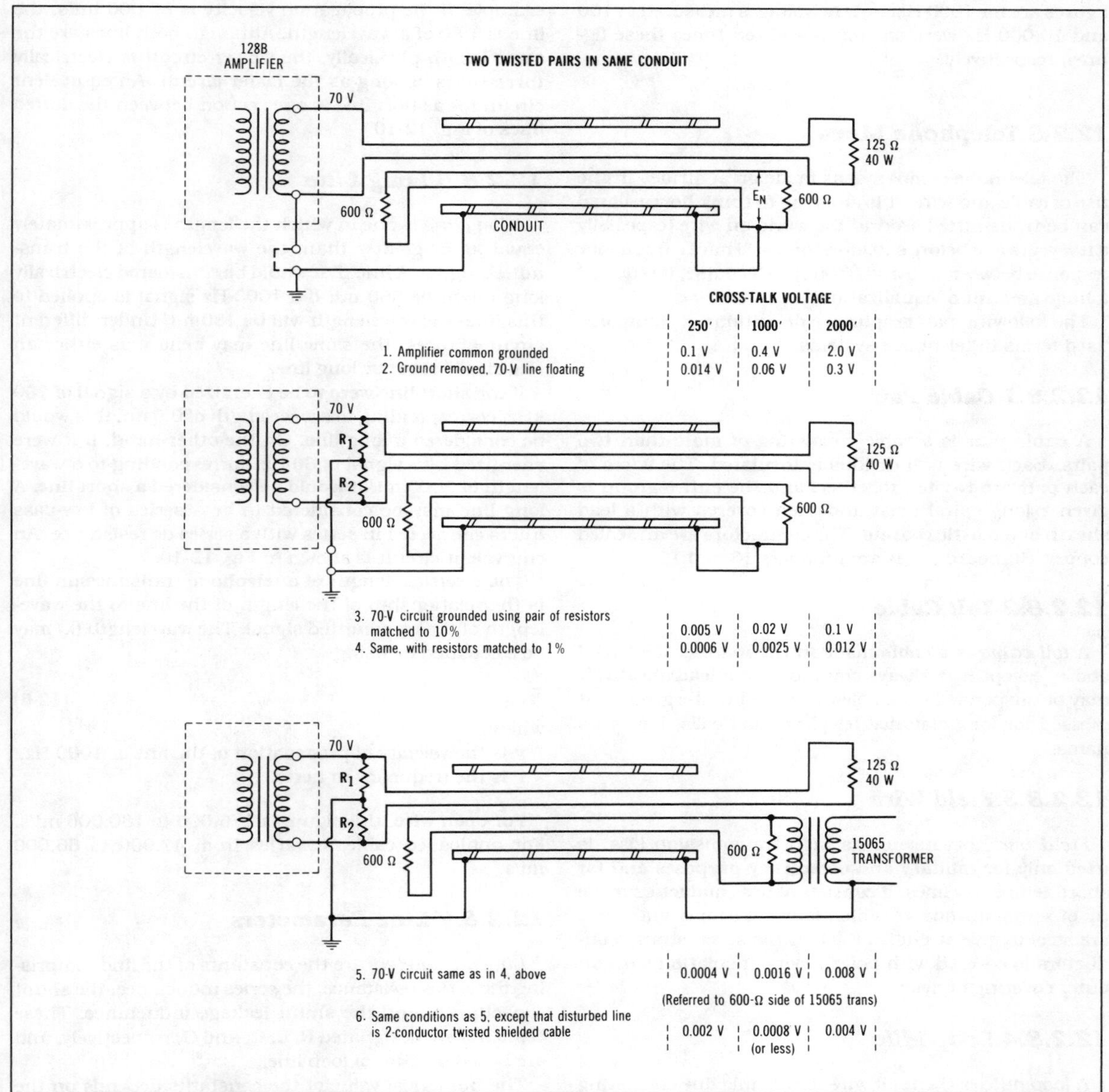

Figure 12-9 Effect of grounding on crosstalk. *(Courtesy Altec Lansing Corp.)*

Two wires of a pair *must* be twisted; this ensures close spacing and aids in cancelling pickup by transposition. In the measurements in Fig. 12-9, all pickup was capacitive because the twisting of the leads effectively eliminated inductive coupling.

Measurements were made on a twisted pair run in the same conduit with a similar twisted pair, the latter carrying signals at 70 V. The length measured was 250 ft. Since measurements made for half this length produced half the voltages, the results to be expected with longer runs are increased in proportion in the following manner. The disturbing line was driven from the 70-V terminals of an Altec 128B amplifier, and the line was loaded at the far end with 125 Ω, thus transmitting 40 W. The figures are for 1000 Hz, but the voltages measured at 100 and 10,000 Hz were one-tenth and ten times these figures, respectively.

12.2.8 Telephone Lines

The telephone company has made great strides in the use of cable and wire. It is amazing to think how a signal can be transmitted around the world on wire (especially a few years ago before satellites) and still have a frequency response between 300 and 3500 Hz. Of course, it required a huge amount of equalization.

The following paragraphs are definitions of commonly used terms in telephone systems.

12.2.8.1 Cable Pair

A *cable pair* is a cable consisting of more than two pairs. Each wire is individually insulated. The wires of each pair are twisted together, and the entire group is given a long spiral twist and then covered with a lead sheath or a plastic coating. The conductors are annealed copper. Standard gages are numbers 16 and 19.

12.2.8.2 Toll Cable

A *toll cable* is a cable made in the manner described above, except it is always covered with a lead sheath. It may be suspended from poles or buried in the ground. It is used for long-distance telephone toll calls, hence its name.

12.2.8.3 Field Wire

Field wire, because of its high transmission loss, is used only for military and emergency purposes and for short, temporary lines. It consists of two conductors made up of seven strands, of which four are copper and three are steel to give strength. Each of the seven-strand conductors is covered with polyethylene insulation with an outer covering of nylon.

12.2.8.4 Loop Mile

A *loop mile* is the total wire in a 1-mile line consisting of two conductors, or 2 mile of wire.

12.2.8.5 Short Line

A *short line* is one in which the electrical length of the line is considerably shorter than the wavelength of the transmitted signal. An electrically short line represents a loop mile of line. If a signal of 1000 Hz is sent through the line and the velocity of the signal in the line is assumed to be 180,000 mi/s, the wavelength of the signal is 180 mi, or the line is 1/180 of a wavelength. Consider a second example: If the propagation velocity is 60,000 mi/s, the line is 1/60 of a wavelength. Although both lines are the same length physically, the slower circuit is electrically three times as long as the faster circuit. An equivalent circuit for a short line is one section between the dotted lines of Fig. 12-10.

12.2.8.6 Long Line

A *long line* is one in which the length is approximately equal to, or greater than, the wavelength of the transmitted signal. A line that would be considered electrically long might be 360 mi. If a 1000-Hz signal is applied to this line, the wavelength will be 180 mi. Under different circumstances, the same line may behave as either an electrically short or long line.

If the short line were to be energized by a signal of 200 kHz, corresponding to a wavelength of 0.9 mi, this would be considered a long line. On the other hand, if it were energized by a signal of 60 Hz, corresponding to a wavelength of 3000 mi, it would be considered a short line. A long line may be considered to be a series of low-pass filters connected in series with a series dc resistance. An equivalent circuit is shown in Fig. 12-10.

The electrical length of a telephone transmission line is the relationship of the length of the line to the wavelength of the transmitted signal. The wavelength (λ) may be calculated by using

$$\lambda = v/f \tag{12-6}$$

where,

v is the velocity of propagation of the line at 1000 Hz,

f is the frequency in hertz.

For open wire, this figure is 176,000 to 180,000 mi/s. For nonloaded cable, it varies from 47,000 to 66,000 mi/s.

12.2.8.7 Line Parameters

Line parameters are the constants of the line comprising the series resistance, the series inductance, the shunt capacitance, and the shunt leakage inductance. These elements are designated R, L, C, and G, respectively, and are based on 1 mi of loop line.

The numerical value of the constants depends on the size of the conductors, their spacing, the insulation, the frequency of the transmitted signal, and the weather conditions. The previously mentioned parameters are distributed along the entire length of the line. The parameters of the line cause delay in the signal.

The attenuation for a loop mile of line is calculated by

$$\text{dB Atten.} = \left[\left(\frac{R}{2}\right)\left(\sqrt{\frac{C}{L}}\right)\right] + \left[\left(\frac{G}{2}\right)\left(\sqrt{\frac{L}{C}}\right)\right] \times 8.686 \tag{12-7}$$

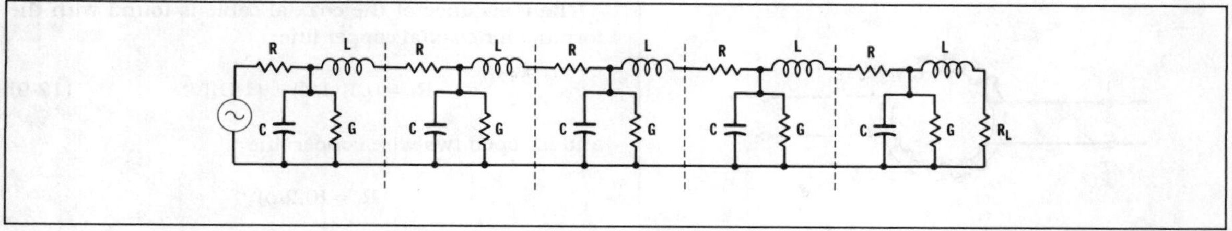

Figure 12-10 Equivalent circuit for a long transmission line.

where,

$\left(\frac{R}{2}\right)\left(\sqrt{\frac{C}{L}}\right)$ is the series loss.

$\left(\frac{G}{2}\right)\left(\sqrt{\frac{L}{C}}\right)$ is the shunt loss.

Generally, the series loss exceeds the shunt loss. Increasing the series loading inductance decreases the series loss but increases the shunt loss.

12.2.8.8 Artificial Line

An *artificial line* is a unit containing the equivalent constants of 1 mi of standard telephone line or cable. The parameters may be represented as shown in Fig. 12-10. A long line may be considered to be made up of a series of unit sections. Thus, a 360-mi line would consist of five 72-mi units. Such setups are used in the laboratory to study the behavior of transmission lines.

12.2.8.9 Characteristic Impedance

The *characteristic impedance* of a transmission line is equal to the impedance that must be used to terminate the line in order to make the input impedance equal to the terminating impedance. For a long line the input impedance will equal the characteristic impedance of the line, irrespective of the terminating impedance.

The characteristic impedance will also depend on the parameters of the pair and the applied frequency. The resistive component of the characteristic impedance is generally high at the low frequencies, falling off with an increase of frequency. The reactive component is high at the low frequencies and falls off as the frequency is increased.

The impedance of a uniform line is the impedance obtained for a long line (infinite length). It is apparent that for a long line, the current in the line is little affected by the value of the terminating impedance at the far end of the line. If the line has an attenuation of 20 dB and the far end is short circuited, the characteristic impedance as measured at the sending end will not be affected by more than 2%.

In practice, a transmission line is seldom uniform. The terminating equipment impedance will vary from that of the line. This may be corrected by the use of a repeat coil that may be matched to the line on one side and to the terminating equipment on the other.

12.2.8.10 Velocity of Propagation

Velocity of propagation is the velocity of the signal as it travels from one end of the line to the other end and is caused because a transmission line possesses three inherent properties that are the characteristics of all electrical circuits: resistance, inductance, and capacitance.

All three of these properties will exist regardless of how the line is constructed. Lines cannot be constructed to eliminate these characteristics.

Under the foregoing conditions, the velocity of the electrical pulses applied to the line are slowed down in their transmission. The elements of the line are distributed evenly and are not localized or present in a lumped quantity.

The velocity of propagation will vary from 10,000 to about 90,000 mi/s, depending on the construction of the line.

A transmission line is loaded at stated intervals by connecting an inductance in series with the line. Two types of loading are in general usage: lumped and continuous. Loading a line increases the impedance of the line, thereby decreasing the series loss because of the conductor resistance.

Although loading decreases the attenuation and distortion and permits a more uniform frequency characteristic, it also increases the shunt losses caused by leakage. Loading also causes the line to have a cutoff frequency above which the loss becomes excessive. In a continuously loaded line, loading is obtained by wrapping the complete cable with a high-permeability magnetic tape or wire. The inductance is distributed evenly along the line, causing it to behave as a line with distributed constants.

In the lumped loading method, toroidally wound coils are placed at equally spaced intervals along the line coils as shown in Fig. 12-11. Each coil has an inductance in the order of 88 mH. The insulation between the line conductors and ground must be extremely good if the coils

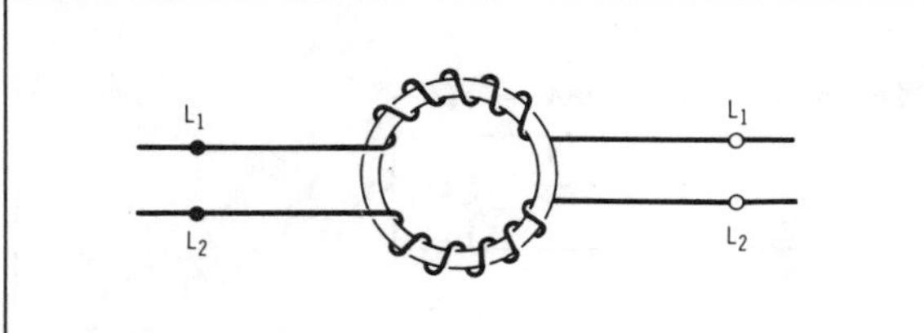

Figure 12-11 A loading coil connected in a transmission line.

are to function properly. Loading coils will increase the talking distance by 35 to 90 mi for the average line.

If a cable is not properly terminated, some of the transmitted signal will be reflected back toward the transmitter, reducing the output.

12.2.9 Coaxial Cable

Coaxial cable is a cable in which one conductor is accurately centered inside another. It is used for the transmission of television signals and other high frequencies.

Coaxial cable is used quite extensively with various types of test equipment. When such cable is replaced, the capacitance per foot must be taken into consideration, particularly for oscilloscope probes. The capacitance value per foot is given in Table 12-8. The various types of cable may be identified from their coding:

R Radio frequency,

G Made for US Government,

– Number assigned by government approval,

U Universal specification.

Thus, a cable marked RG-11a/U means radio frequency, government approval number, with a universal specification. The letter appearing before the slash (/) is a specification modification.

Attenuation expressed in decibels per 100 ft can be found with the formula

$$A = (4.35R_t/Z_O) + 2.78fp\sqrt{\epsilon} \qquad (12\text{-}8)$$

where,
- A is the attenuation in dB/100 ft,
- R_t is the total line resistance in Ω/100 ft,
- Z_O is the characteristic impedance of the line,
- f is the frequency in 10^6 Hz,
- p is the power factor of the dielectric medium,
- ε is the dielectric constant of transmission line insulation.

The resistance of the coaxial cable is found with the formula for coaxial copper line:

$$R_t = 0.1[(1/d) + (1/D)]\sqrt{f} \qquad (12\text{-}9)$$

and for open two-wire copper line

$$R_t = (0.2/p)\sqrt{f}$$

where,
- d is the diameter of conductors (center conductor for coaxial line in inches),
- D is the diameter of inner surface of outer coaxial conductor in inches,
- f is the frequency in 10^6 Hz.

The characteristic impedance of the cable is equal to

$$Z_O = (138/\sqrt{\epsilon})\log(D/d) \qquad (12\text{-}10)$$

where,
- ε is the dielectric constant.

The velocity of propagation of coaxial cables is the ratio of the dielectric constant of air to the square root of the dielectric constant of the insulator and is expressed in percent

$$v_L/v_S = 1/\sqrt{\epsilon} \qquad (12\text{-}11)$$

where,
- v_L is the velocity of propagation in the transmission line,
- v_S is the velocity of propagation in free space,
- ε is the dielectric constant of transmission line insulation.

12.3 RELAYS

A *relay* is an electrically operated switch connected to or actuated by a remote circuit. The relay causes a second circuit or group of circuits to operate. The relay may have any number of circuits connected to it. These circuits may consist of motors, bells, lights, audio circuits, and so on, or the relay may be used to switch a number of other circuits.

Relays may be electromechanical or solid state. Both have advantages and disadvantages.

12.3.1 Electromechanical Relays

Regardless of whether the relay operates on ac or dc, it will consist of an actuating coil, a core, an armature, and a group of contact springs that are connected to the circuit or circuits to be controlled. Associated with the

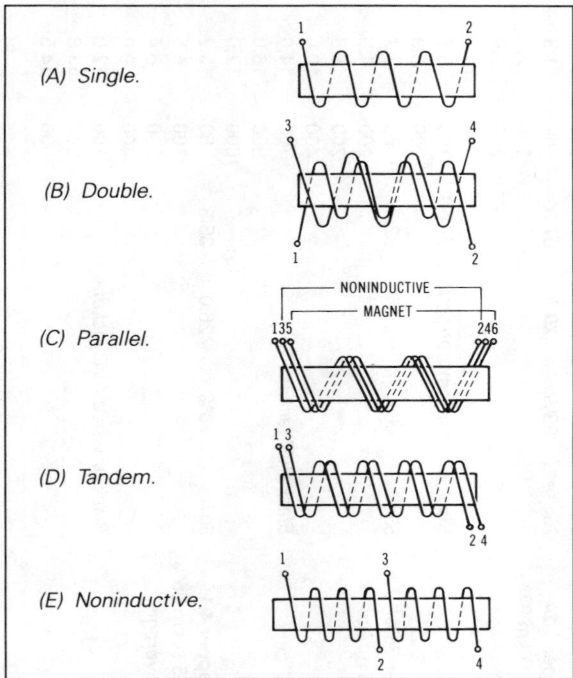

Figure 12-12 Types of relay coil windings.

armature are mechanical adjustments and springs. The mechanical arrangement of the contacts may be such that when the relay is at rest, certain circuits are either open or closed. If the circuits are closed when the relay is at rest, the relay is said to be normally closed. If the circuits are open, it is called a normally open relay.

Relays are wound in many different manners. Among them are the single wound, double wound, parallel wound, tandem wound, and noninductively wound, as shown in Fig. 12-12.

12.3.1.1 DC Relays

Direct current (dc) relays differ in the amount of current and voltage required to operate them. Also, the dc resistance of the actuating coils may vary from a few to several thousand ohms. In addition, they may be of many different types including the *marginal, quick-operate, slow-operate,* and *polarized* varieties.

A *marginal relay* is one that operates when the current through its winding reaches a specified value, and it releases when the current falls to a given value. In the quick-operate type, the armature is attracted immediately to the pole piece of the electromagnet when the control circuit is closed.

Slow-operate relays have a time-delay characteristic; the armature is not attracted immediately to the pole piece of the electromagnet when the control circuit is closed. These relays employ a copper collar around the armature end of the pole piece and differ from the slow-release variety in that the latter type has the copper collar around the end of the pole piece opposite from the armature.

A polarized relay is designed to react to a given direction of current and magnitude. Polarized relays use a permanent magnet core. Current in a given direction increases the magnetic field, and in the opposite direction it decreases the field. Thus, the relay will operate only for a given direction of current through the coil.

A *latching relay* is a relay containing two separate actuating coils, Fig. 12-13. Actuating one coil latches the relay in one position; where it remains until it is unlatched by energizing the other coil.

Figure 12-13 Latching relay using two coils.

12.3.1.2 AC Relays

Alternating-current (ac) relays are similar in construction to the dc relays. Since alternating current has a zero value every half cycle, the magnetic field of an ac-operated relay will have corresponding zero values in the magnetic field every half cycle.

At and near the instants of zero current, the armature will leave the core, unless some provision is made to hold it in position. One method consists of using an armature of such mass that its inertia will hold it in position. Another method makes use of two windings on separate cores. These windings are connected so that their respective currents are out of phase with each other. Both coils effect a pull on the armature when current flows in both windings.

A third type employs a split pole piece of which one part is surrounded by a copper ring acting as a shorted turn. Alternating current in the actuating coil winding induces

Table 12-8. Characteristics of Coaxial Cable

Description	Trade & UL Type Number	AWG (Stranding) [Dia. in mm] Nom. D.C.R.	Nominal OD		No. of Shields and Material Nom. D.C.R.	Nom. Imp. (ohms)	Nom. Vel. of Prop	Nominal Capacitance		Nominal Attenuation		
			In.	mm				pF/ft	pF/m	MHz	dB/ 100 ft	dB/ 100 m
RG-8U	9208	13 (7 × 21) [2.17] bare copper 1.87 Ω/M′ 6.1 Ω/km	.397	10.1	1 bare copper 80% shield coverage	57	78%	22.6	74.1	50	1.2	3.9
										100	1.8	5.9
										200	2.7	8.9
										400	4.2	13.8
						Black PVC jacket.				700	5.8	19.0
										900	6.7	22.0
										1000	7.1	23.3
RG-9U	8242	13 (7 × 21) [2.17] silver-coated copper 1.87 Ω/M′ 6.1 Ω/km	.420	10.67	2-inner-silver-coated outer bare copper 0.7 Ω/M′ 2.3 Ω/km 97% shield coverage	51	66%	30.0	98.4	50	1.6	5.2
										100	2.2	7.2
										200	3.2	10.5
										400	4.7	15.4
										700	6.9	22.6
						Gray noncontaminating PVC jacket.				900	8.0	26.3
										1000	8.9	29.2
										4000	21.5	70.5
RG-11U	9212	18 (7 × 26) [1.22] tinned copper 6.06 Ω/M′ 19.9 Ω/km	.405	10.29	1 bare copper 1.24 Ω/M′ 4.1 Ω/km 97% shield coverage	75	66%	20.5	67.3	50	1.3	4.2
										100	2.0	6.6
										200	2.9	9.5
										400	4.2	13.8
						Black noncontaminating PVC jacket.				700	5.8	19.0
										900	6.9	22.6
RG-58U	9201	20 (Solid) [.81] bare copper 10.1 Ω/M′ 33.1 Ω/km	.193	4.90	bare copper 78% shield coverage	53	66%	28.5	92.4	1000/50	[illegible]	[illegible]
										100	4.5	14.8
										200	6.8	22.3
										400	10.0	32.8
						Black PVC jacket.				700	14.0	45.9
										900	16.0	52.5
										1000	17.0	55.8
RG-58 A/U	8219	20 (19 × 32) [.94] tinned copper 8.8 Ω/M′ 28.9 Ω/km	.193	4.90	1 tinned copper 4.1 Ω/M′ 13.5 Ω/km 96% shield coverage	50	78%	26.0	85.3	50	3.2	10.5
										100	4.5	14.8
										200	6.4	21.0
										400	9.0	29.5
						Black or white PVC jacket.				700	12.0	39.4
										900	13.8	45.3
										1000	14.5	47.6

RG-59U	9240	22 (Solid) [.8] bare-braid-covered steel 61.5 Ω/M′ 201.8 Ω/km	.240	6.10	80% 1 bare copper braid 56 Ω/M′ 16.4 Ω/km	75	78%	17.3	56.7	50	1.8	5.9
										100	2.6	8.5
										200	3.8	12.5
						Black PVC jacket.				500	6.2	21.0
										900	8.4	27.6
										1000	8.8	28.9
RG-62 A/U	9268	22 (Solid) [.64] bare-copper-covered steel 41.2 Ω/M′ 135.2 Ω/km	.260	6.60	1 bare copper 2.6 Ω/M′ 8.5 Ω/km 95% shield coverage	93	84%	13.5	44.3	50	1.9	6.2
										100	2.7	8.9
										200	3.8	12.5
										400	5.4	17.7
						Black PVC jacket.				700	7.3	24.0
										900	8.3	27.2
										1000	8.7	28.5
RG-122 U	9252	22 (27 × 36) [.71] tinned copper 17.1 Ω/M′ 56.1 Ω/km	.160	4.06	1 tinned copper 5.2 Ω/M′ 17.1 Ω/km 97% shield coverage	50	66%	30.8	101.0	50	4.5	14.8
										100	7.0	23.0
										200	10.0	32.8
										400	15.2	49.9
						Black noncontaminating PVC jacket.				700	21.2	69.6
										900	25.0	82.0
										1000	26.5	87.0
RG-141 A/U	83241	18 (Solid) [1.02] silver-coated copper-covered steel 16.3 Ω/M′ 53.5 Ω/km	.190	4.83	1 silver-coated copper 4.26 Ω/M′ 14.0 Ω/M′ 97% shield coverage	50	69.5%	29.0	95.1	50	2.1	6.9
										100	3.2	10.5
										200	4.7	15.4
										400	6.9	22.6
						Brown fiber glass jacket.				700	10.0	32.8
										900	12.0	39.4
										1000	13.0	42.7
RG-174U	8216	26 (7 × 34) [.48] bare-copper-covered steel 97 Ω/M′ 318.3 Ω/km	.101	2.56	1 tinned copper 10.3 Ω/M′ 33.8 Ω/km 88% shield coverage	50	66%	30.8	101.0	50	6.6	21.7
										100	8.9	29.2
										200	12.0	39.4
										400	17.5	57.4
						Black PVC jacket.				700	24.1	79.1
										900	28.2	92.5
										1000	30.0	98.4
RG-178 B/U	83265	30 (7 × 38) [.31] silver-coated copper-covered steel 250 Ω/M′ 820.2 Ω/km	.070	1.78	1 silver-coated copper 14.6 Ω/M′ 47.9 Ω/km 96% shield coverage	50	69.5%	29.0	95.1	50	10.5	34.4
										100	14.0	45.9
										200	19.0	62.3
										400	28.0	91.9
						Tinted brown FEP Teflon jacket.				700	37.0	121.4
										900	42.5	139.4
										1000	46.0	150.9

Table 12-8—cont. Characteristics of Coaxial Cable

Description	Trade & UL Type Number	AWG (Stranding) [Dia. in mm] Nom. D.C.R.	Nominal OD		No. of Shields and Material Nom. D.C.R.	Nom. Imp. (ohms)	Nom. Vel. of Prop	Nominal Capacitance		Nominal Attenuation		
			In.	mm				pF/ft	pF/m	MHz	dB/ 100 ft	dB/ 100 m
RG-179 B/U	83264	30 (7 × 38) [.31] silver-coated copper-covered steel 250 Ω/M′ 820.3 Ω/km	.100	2.54	1 silver-coated copper 8.5 Ω/M′ 27.9 Ω/km 94% shield coverage	75	69.5%	19.5	64.0	50	8.5	27.9
										100	10.0	32.8
										200	12.5	41.0
										400	16.0	52.5
										700	19.7	64.6
										900	22.3	73.2
										1000	24.0	78.7
RG-180 B/U	83266	30 (7 × 38) [.31] silver-coated copper-covered steel 250 Ω/M′ 820.3 Ω/km	.140	3.56	1 silver-coated copper 6.5 Ω/M′ 21.3 Ω/km 93% shield coverage	95	69.5%	15.0	49.21	50	4.6	15.1
										100	5.7	18.7
										200	7.6	24.9
										400	10.7	35.1
						Tinted brown FEP Teflon jacket.				700	14.9	48.9
										900	15.9	52.2
										1000	17.0	55.8
RG-187 A/U	83267	30 (7 × 38) [.31] silver-coated copper-covered steel 250 Ω/M′ 820.3 Ω/km	.105	2.66	1 silver-coated copper 8.5 Ω/M′ 27.9 Ω/km 94% shield coverage	75	69.5%	19.5	64.0	50	7.9	25.9
										100	9.8	32.2
										200	12.7	41.7
										400	15.8	51.8
						White TFE tape wrapped jacket.				700	20.5	67.3
										900	23.7	77.7
										1000	25.0	82.0
RG-188 A/U	83269	26 (7 × .0067) [.51] silver-coated copper-covered steel 91.2 Ω/M′ 299.4 Ω/km	.102	2.59	1 silver-coated copper 8.51 Ω/M′ 27.9 Ω/km 95% shield coverage	50	69.5%	29.0	95.2	50	7.9	25.9
										100	9.8	32.2
										200	12.7	41.7
										400	15.8	51.8
										700	20.5	67.3
						White TFE tape wrapped jacket.				900	23.7	77.7
										1000	25.0	82.0

RG-196 A/U	83270	30 (7 × 38) [.31] silver-coated copper-covered steel 250 Ω/M′ 820.2 Ω/km	.076	1.93	1 silver-coated copper 14.6 Ω/M′ 47.9 Ω/km 96% shield coverage	50	69.5%	29.0	95.1	50	7.9	25.9
										100	9.8	32.2
										200	12.7	41.7
										400	15.8	51.8
						White TFE tape wrapped jacket.				700	20.5	67.3
										900	23.7	77.7
										1000	25.0	82.0
RG-213U	8267	13 (7 × 21) [2.17] bare copper 1.87 Ω/M′ 6.1 Ω/km	.405	10.29	1 bare copper 1.2 Ω/M′ 3.9 Ω/km 97% shield coverage	50	66%	30.8	101.0	50	1.6	5.2
										100	2.2	7.2
										200	3.2	10.5
										400	4.7	15.4
										700	6.9	22.6
						Black noncontaminating PVC jacket.				900	8.0	26.3
										1000	8.9	29.2
										4000	21.5	70.5
RG-214U	8268	13 (7 × .0296) [2.26] silver-coated copper 1.73 Ω/M′ 5.7 Ω/km	.425	10.80	2 silver-coated copper .7 Ω/M′ 2.3 Ω/km 98% shield coverage	50	66%	30.8	101.0	50	1.6	5.2
										100	2.2	7.2
										200	3.2	10.5
										400	4.7	15.4
										700	6.9	22.6
						Black noncontaminating PVC jacket.				900	8.0	26.3
										1000	8.9	29.2
										4000	21.5	70.5
RG-223U	9273	19 (Solid) [.91] silver-coated copper 8.05 Ω/M′ 26.4 Ω/km	.212	5.38	2 silver-coated copper 2.5 Ω/M′ 8.3 Ω/km 97% shield coverage	50	66%	30.8	101.0	50	3.1	10.1
										100	4.5	14.8
										200	6.4	21.0
										400	9.2	30.2
						Black noncontaminating PVC jacket.				700	12.5	41.0
										900	14.3	46.9
										1000	16.3	52.5

a current in the copper coil. This current is out of phase with the current in the actuating coil and does not reach the zero value at the same instant as the current in the actuating coil. As a result, there is always enough pull on the armature to hold it in the operating position.

An ac differential relay employs two windings exactly alike, except they are wound in opposite directions. Such relays operate only when one winding is energized. When both windings are energized in opposite directions, they produce an aiding magnetic field, since the windings are in opposite directions. When the current through the actuating coils is going in the same direction, they produce opposite magnetic fields. If the current through the two coils is equal, the magnetic fields neutralize each other and the relay is nonoperative.

A differential polar relay employs a split magnetic circuit consisting of two windings on a permanent magnet core. In reality a differential polar relay is a combination of a differential and a polarized relay.

12.3.1.4 Thermal Time-Delay Relay[10]

Reed relays were developed by the Bell Telephone Laboratories in 1960 for use in the Bell System central offices. The device shown in Fig. 12-14 consists of two magnetic reeds in a glass capsule with a nitrogen atmosphere. The glass envelope is surrounded by an electromagnetic coil connected to a control circuit. Although originally developed for the telephone company, such devices have found many uses in the electronics industry.

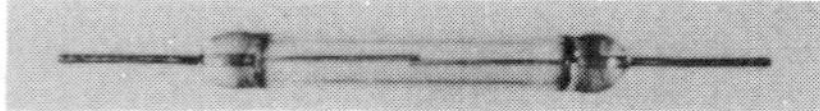

Figure 12-14 Reed relay encased in an envelope of glass filled with nitrogen. Contact capacitance is 0.1125 pF. *(Courtesy AT&T Bell Laboratories)*

Fig. 12-15 shows the concept of the ferreed relay in a simplified form. Windings around the glass-envelope-enclosed reed are arranged in such a way that the contact is open or closed in response to pulses of current in the X and Y leads. For the closed state shown, simultaneous pulses in both the X and Y leads effectively cause the Remendur to become one magnet. The two reeds are now magnetically attracted, and the contact is closed. To open, a pulse is applied to either the X or Y windings, which effectively divides the Remendur into two magnets at the magnetic shunt plate. Since the ends of the Remendur are both north (or both south) poles, they repel each other and the contact is opened.

Remendur is a cobalt-iron-vanadium alloy, developed by Bell Telephone Laboratories. It has a square hysteresis loop with values of coercive force between those of a soft magnetic material and a permanent magnet. The reed may be closed in ½ ms and have an intercapacitance of 0.1125 pF and an ac contact resistance of 50 mΩ. The

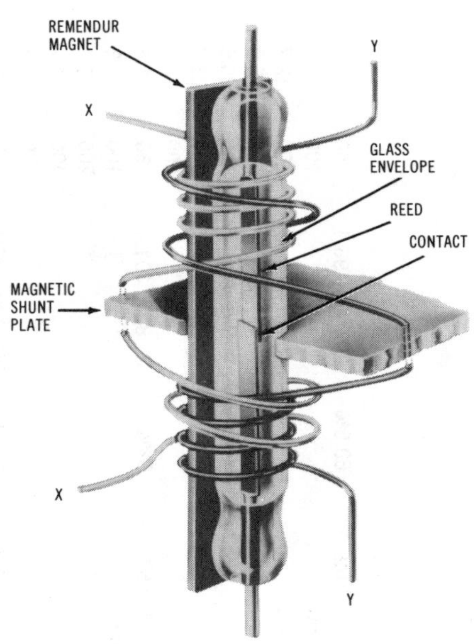

Figure 12-15 Ferreed relay, showing the coils and the Rememdur magnet. The actual size of the relay is 1 × 0.150 in. *(Courtesy Bell Telephone Laboratories Record)*

advantages of such relays are their low internal capacitance, low contact resistance, and high speed of operation.

Reed relays are also manufactured without the magnet, so that when the coils are energized, the reed snaps closed. The coil actuation is limited to low dc ripple current. However, an ac control voltage may be used in conjunction with a diode and filter capacitor. Depending on the design, the reeds will follow an ac coil input or dc pulses up to 400 Hz, provided the time on does not exceed 50%. Because of the fast action of the reed relays, they are ideal for use with semiconductor devices. Coils range from 1700 to 30,000 turns, with a dc resistance of 100 to 10 kΩ. Operating voltages range from 6 to 110 V. Up to three internal contacts are available; thus, single-pole, double-throw action can be obtained. The relays may be obtained with dry or wetted contacts and will withstand shock (up to about 40 g's), without false operation. Typical contact ratings are 15 VA, 1-A switching, and 3-A carry.

12.3.1.4 Thermal Time-Delay Relay[5]

A *thermal time-delay relay* is a relay with a thermal unit so designed that a delay period of from 2 s to 5 min may be induced in an electrical circuit. Fig. 12-16 shows a thermal delay relay manufactured by Thomas A. Edison, Inc. It consists of two bimetallic strips, each rigidly supported at one end with contacts at the other end. An electrical heater is wound around the primary bimetal member, which is deflected by the application of heater

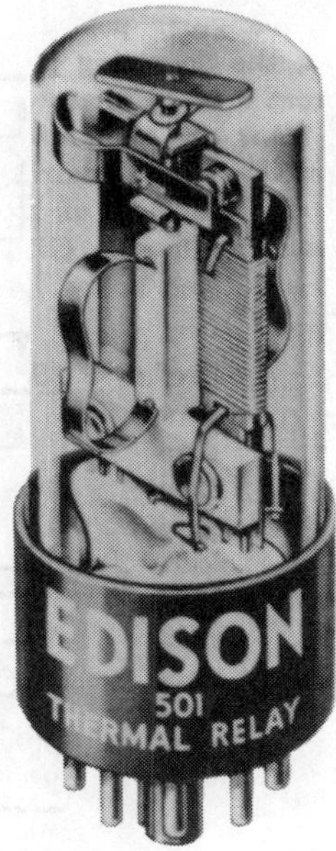

Figure 12-16 Interior view of a Model 501 thermal time-delay relay. *(Courtesy Thomas A. Edison Instrument Division)*

current to mate with the contact mounted on the other bimetal strip. The use of the second bimetal strip, which supports the preloaded spring contact, provides compensation for ambient temperature changes from −60 to +85°C.

One contact is mounted on a spring attached to the compensating bimetal strip. This spring is restrained until the primary bimetal is deflected sufficiently to cause contact. After the contacts close, the spring lifts from its restraining support and applies force to hold the contact firmly together.

Factors controlling the deflection of the bimetal are stable, and the original setting of the contacts permanently fixes the timing characteristics of the relay. The structure of the elements is such that the contacts will not close under vibration (1/16 in. at 55 Hz) with the heater unexcited, nor will the contacts open under the same condition at saturation temperature.

12.3.2 Contact Characteristics[5, 6]

Contacts may switch either power or "dry" circuits. A power circuit always has current flowing, while a dry circuit has minimal or no current flowing, such as an audio circuit. A dry or low-level circuit typically is less than 100 mV or 1 mA.

The mechanical design of the contact springs is such that when the contacts are closed, they slide for a short distance over the surfaces of each other before coming to rest. This is called a wiping contact, and it ensures good electrical contact.

Contacts are made of silver, palladium, rhodium, or gold and may be smooth or bifurcated. Bifurcated contacts have better wiping and cleaning action than smooth contacts and, therefore, are used on dry circuits.

As contacts close, the initial resistance is relatively high, and any films, oxides, and so on further increase the contact resistance. Upon closing, current begins to flow across the rough surface of the contacts, heating and softening them until the entire contact is mating, which reduces the contact resistance to milliohms. When the current through the circuit is too low to heat and soften the contacts, gold contacts should be used since the contacts do not oxidize and, therefore, have low contact resistance. On the other hand, gold should not be used in power circuits where current is flowing.

The contact current specified is the maximum current, often the make-or-break current. For instance, the make current of a motor or capacitor may be 10 to 15 times as high as its steady-state operation. The contact voltage specified is the maximum voltage allowed during arcing during break. The break voltage of an inductor can be 50 times the steady-state voltage of the circuit.

To protect the relay contacts from high transient voltages, arc suppression should be used. This may be in the form of a reverse-biased diode (rectifier), variable resistor (varistor), or RC network, as shown in Fig. 12-17.

The R and C in an RC circuit are calculated with the following formulas:

$$C = (I^2/10)\ \mu F \tag{12-12}$$

$$R = \frac{E}{10I(1 + 50/E)} \tag{12-13}$$

When using a rectifier, the rectifier is an open circuit to the power source because it is reverse biased; however, when the circuit breaks, the diode conducts. This tech-

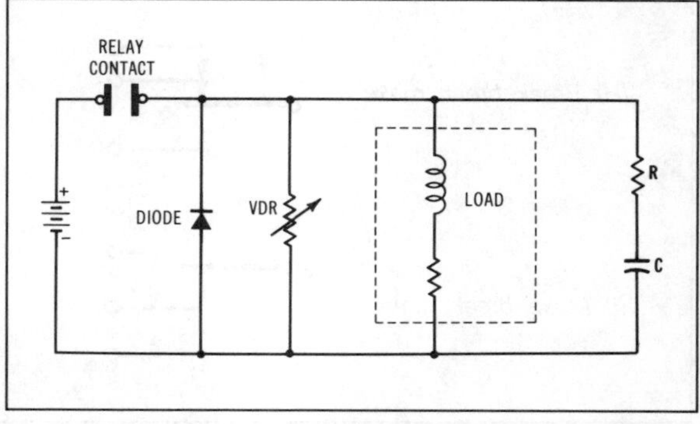

Figure 12-17 Methods of suppressing transients across contacts.

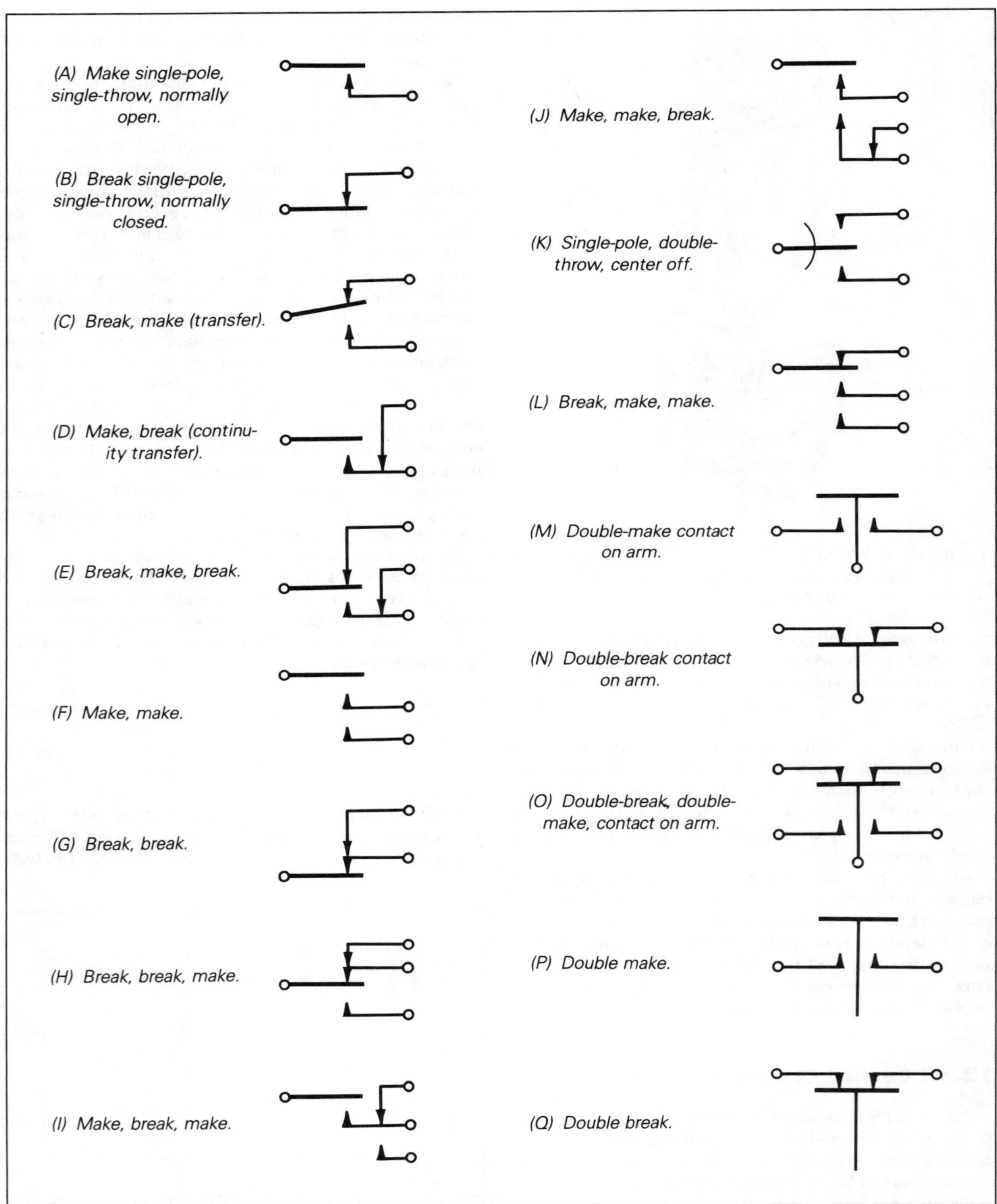

Figure 12-18 Various contact arrangements of common relays. *(From American National Standard Definitions and Terminology for Relays for Electronics Equipment C83.16-1971)*

nique depends on a reverse path for the diode to conduct; otherwise, it will flow through some other part of the circuit. It is important that the rectifier have a voltage rating equal to the transient voltage.

Contact bounce occurs in all mechanical-type relays except the mercury-wetted types that, because of the thin film of mercury on the contacts, do not break during make. Bounce creates noise in the circuit, particularly when switching audio where it acts as a dropout.

There are various combinations of contact springs making up the circuits that are operated by the action of the relay. Typical spring piles are shown in Fig. 12-18.

12.3.3 Relay Loads[7]

Never assume that a relay contact can switch its rated current no matter what type of load it sees (Fig. 12-19). High in-rush currents or high induced back electromotive force (emf) can quickly erode or weld electromechanical relay contacts and destroy solid-state relays.

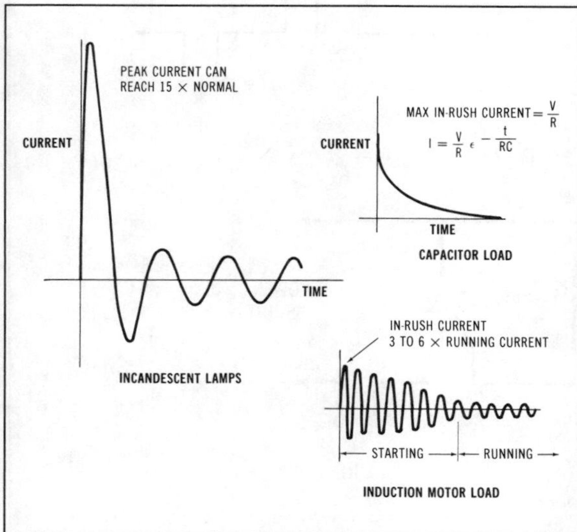

Figure 12-19 High in-rush current on turn-on can damage relays.

The Effects of Various Loads:

- Incandescent Lamps: The cold resistance of a tungsten-filament lamp is extremely low, resulting in in-rush currents as much as 15 times the steady-state current. This is why lamp burnout almost always occurs during turnon.
- Capacitive Loads: The initial charging current to a capacitive circuit can be extremely high, since the capacitor acts as a short circuit, and current is limited only by the circuit resistance. Capacitive loads may be long transmission lines, filters for electromagnetic interference (emi) elimination and power supplies.
- Motor Loads: High in-rush current is drawn by most motors, because at standstill their input impedance is very low. When the motor rotates, it develops an internal back emf that reduces the current. Depending on the mechanical load, the starting time may be very long and produce a relay-damaging in-rush current.
- Inductive Loads: In-rush current is limited by inductance; however, when turned off, energy stored in magnetic fields must be dissipated.
- DC Loads: These are harder to turn off than ac loads because the voltage never passes through zero. When electromagnetic radiation (emr) contacts open, an arc is struck that may be sustained by the applied voltage, burning contacts.

12.3.4 Solid-State Relays[8]

Solid-state relays (SSRs) utilize the on-off switching properties of the transistor and the silicon-controlled rectifier (SCR) for opening and closing dc circuits. They also use triacs for switching ac circuits.

12.3.4.1 Advantages

SSRs have several advantages over their electromechanical counterparts: no moving parts, arcing, burning, or wearing of contacts; and the capacity for high-speed, bounceless, noiseless operation. Some SSRs are available with the unique feature of optical coupling: the signal circuit includes a lamp or light-emitting diode that shines on a phototransistor serving as the actuating device. In other types of SSRs, a small reed relay or transformer may serve as the actuating device, while a third type is direct coupled. These are shown in Fig. 12-20.

Ac relays turn on and off to zero crossing; therefore, they have reduced dv/dt. However, this does slow down the action to the operating frequency.

12.3.4.2 Disadvantages and Protection[8]

Solid-state relays also have some inherent problems as they are easily destroyed by short circuits, high surge current, high dv/dt, and high peak voltage across the power circuit.

Short-Circuit Protection

Short-circuit and high-surge current protection is performed with fast blow fuses or series resistors. A standard fuse normally will not blow before the SCR or triac

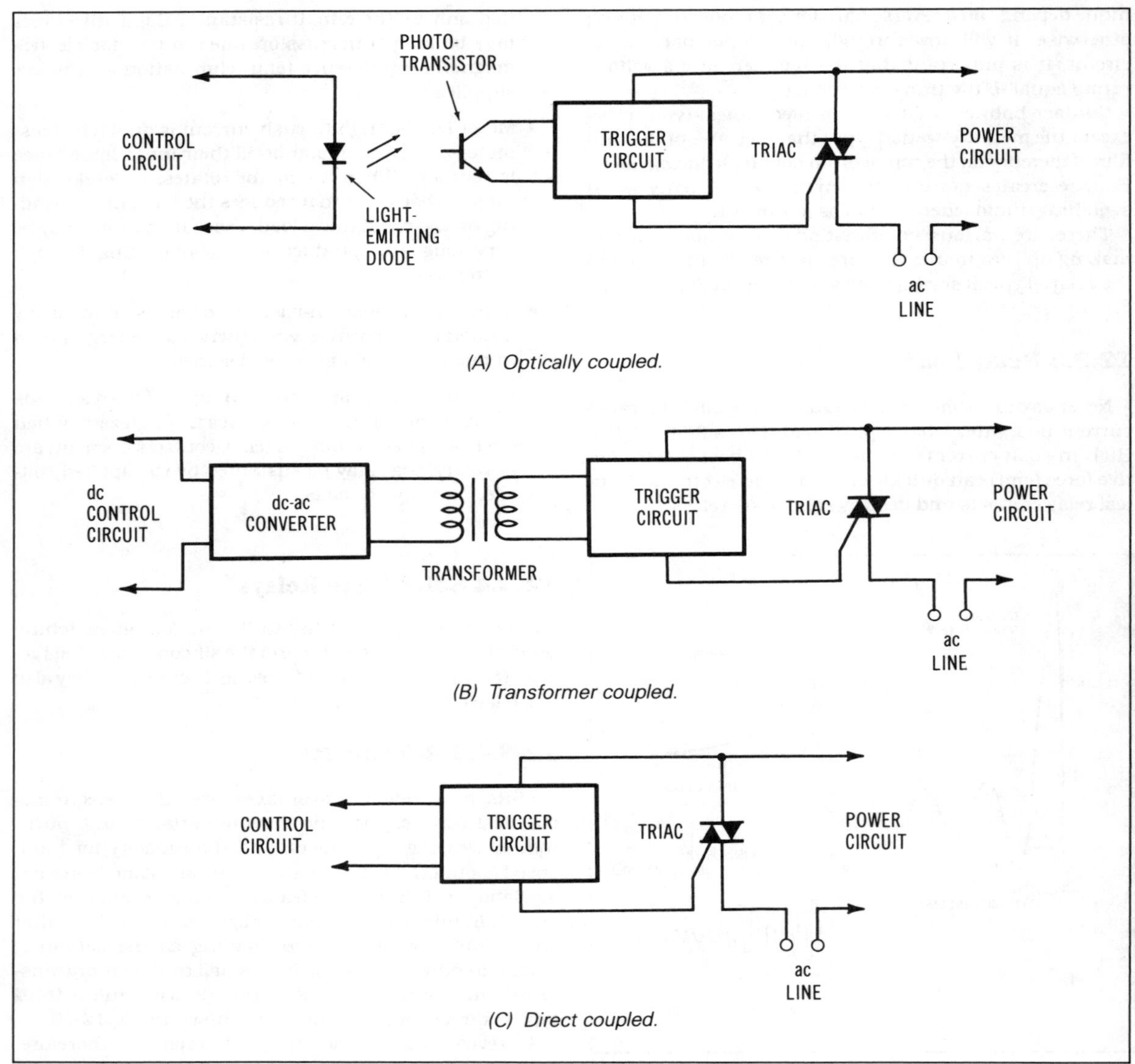

Figure 12-20 Various types of solid-state relays.

since the fuses are designed to withstand surge currents. Fast blow fuses will act on high in-rush currents and, therefore, protect solid-state devices.

Using a current-limiting resistor will protect the SSR; however, it creates a voltage drop that is current dependent and, at high current, dissipates high power.

High DV/DT Protection

A common technique for protecting solid-state switching elements against high dv/dt transients is by shunting the switching element with an RC network (snubber), as shown in Fig. 12-21. The following equations provide effective results:

$$R_2 = (L/V)(dv/dt) \tag{12-14}$$

$$R_2 = (\sqrt{1-(pf)^2}/2\pi I)(dv/dt) \tag{12-15}$$

$$C = 4L/(R_2)^2 \tag{12-16}$$

$$C = (4/R_2^2)(V/I)[(\sqrt{1-(pf)^2}/2\pi f) \tag{12-17}$$

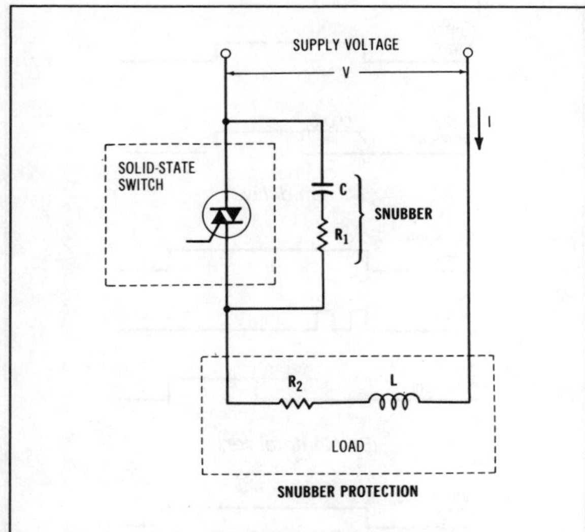

Figure 12-21 Snubber circuit for solid-state relay protection.

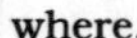

where,

L is the inductance in henrys,
V is the line voltage,
dv/dt is the maximum permissible rate of change of voltage in volts per microsecond,
I is the load current,
pf is the load power factor,
C is the capacitance in microfarads,
R_1, R_2 are the resistance in ohms,
f is the line frequency.

High Peak-Transient-Voltage Protection

Where high peak-voltage transients occur, effective protection can be obtained by using metal-oxide varistors (MOV). The MOV is a bidirectional voltage-sensitive device that becomes low impedance when its design voltage threshold is exceeded.

Fig. 12-22 shows how the proper MOV can be chosen. The peak nonrepetitive voltage (V_{DSM}) of the selected relay is transposed to the MOV plot of peak voltage versus peak amperes. The corresponding current for that peak voltage is read off the chart. Using this value of current (I) in

$$IR = V_P - V_{DSM} \tag{12-18}$$

where,

R is the load plus source resistance,
V_P is the peak instantaneous voltage transient.

see that the V_{DSM} peak nonrepetitive voltage of the SSR is not exceeded.

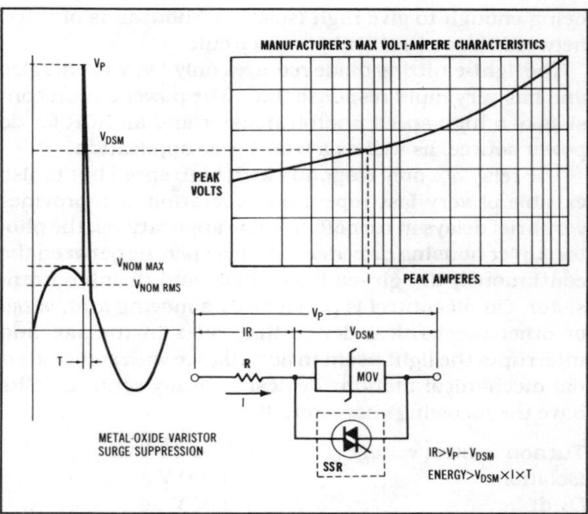

Figure 12-22 Metal-oxide varistor peak transient protector.

The energy rating of the MOV must not be exceeded by the value of

$$E = V_{DSM}(I)(t) \tag{12-19}$$

Low Load Current Protection

If the load current is low, it may be necessary to take special precautions to ensure proper operation. Solid-state relays have a finite off-state leakage current.

If the off-state voltage across the load is very high, it could cause problems with circuit dropout and component overheating. In these applications a low-wattage incandescent lamp in parallel with the load offers a simple remedy. The nonlinear characteristics of the lamp allow it to be of lower resistance in the off state while conserving power in the on state. It must be remembered to size the SSR for the combined load.

12.3.4.3 Optically Coupled Solid-State Relays

The optically coupled solid-state relay arrangement (SSR) shown in Fig. 12-20A is capable of providing the highest control/power-circuit isolation—many thousands of volts—in compact, convenient form. The triac trigger circuit is energized by a phototransistor, a semiconductor device (encapsulated in transparent plastic) whose collector-emitter current is controlled by the amount of light falling on its base region.

A phototransistor is mounted in a light-tight chamber with a light-emitting diode, the separation between them being enough to give high isolation (thousands of volts) between the control and power circuit.

The light-emitting diode requires only 1½ V to energize and has very rapid response time. The power circuit consists of a high-speed phototransistor and an SCR for dc power source, as well as a triac for ac application.

The relay not only responds with high speed but is also capable of very fast repetitious operation and provides very brief delays in turnoff. In some applications, the photocoupler housing provides a slotted opening between the continuously lit light-emitting diode and the phototransistor. On-off control is provided by a moving arm, vane, or other mechanical device that rides in the slot and interrupts the light beam in accordance with some external mechanical motion. Typical optically coupled SSRs have the following characteristics:

Turnon control voltage	3 to 30 V dc
Isolation	1500 V ac
Dv/dt	100 V/μs
Pickup control voltage	3 V dc
Dropout control voltage	1 V dc
One-cycle surge (rms)	7 to 10 times nominal
1-s overload	2.3 times nominal
Maximum contact voltage drop	1.5 to 4 V

12.3.4.4 Transformer-Coupled Solid-State Relays

In Fig. 12-20B, the dc control signal is changed to ac in a converter circuit, the output of which is magnetically coupled to the triac trigger circuit by means of a transformer. Since there is no direct electrical connection between the primary and secondary of the transformer, control/power-circuit isolation is provided up to the voltage withstanding limit of the primary/secondary insulation.

12.3.4.5 Direct-Coupled Solid-State Relays

The circuit shown in Fig. 12-20C is the simplest configuration; no coupling device is interposed between the control and actuating circuits, so no isolation of the control circuit is provided.

One other variation of these solid-state circuits is occa-

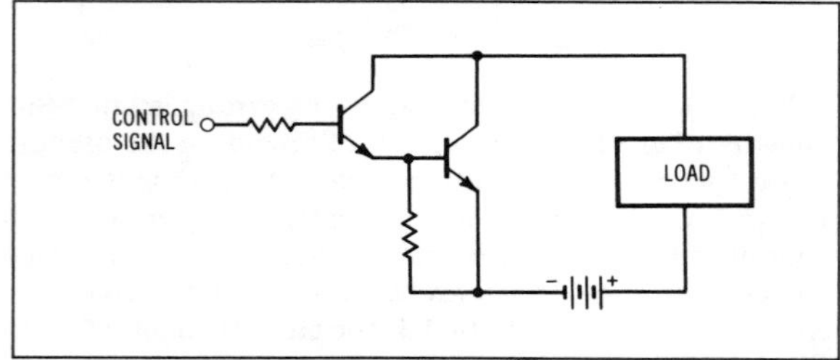

Figure 12-23 Darlington direct-coupled solid-state relay.

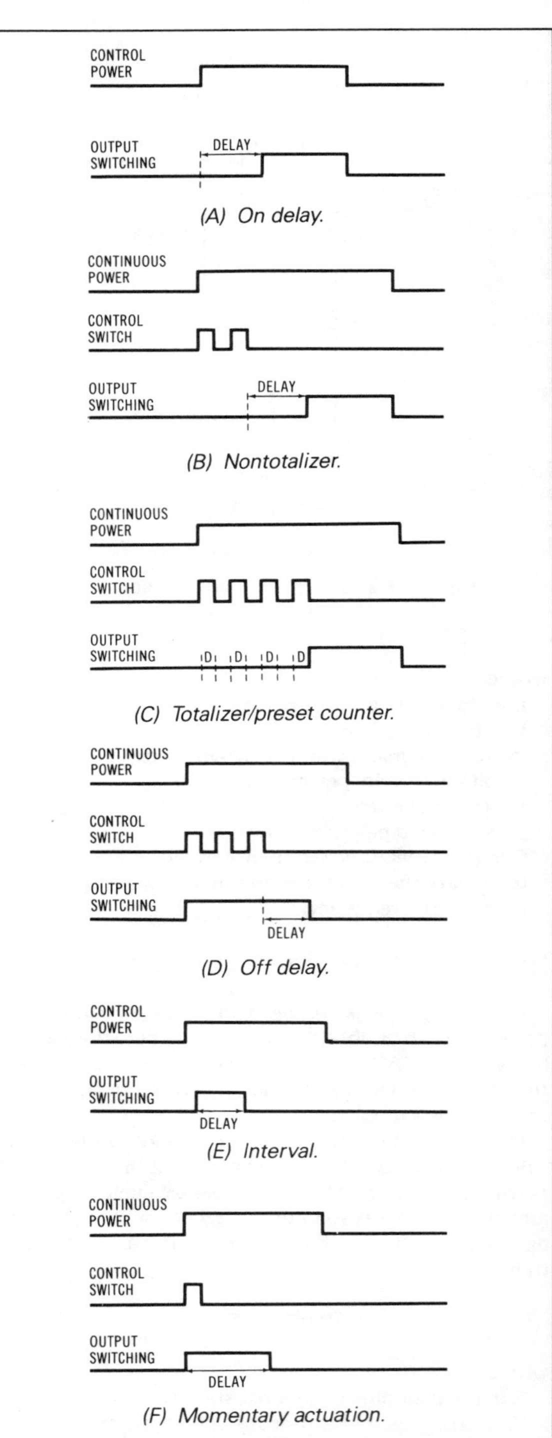

Figure 12-24 Types of time-delay relays.

sionally encountered—the *Darlington* circuit. A typical arrangement is shown in Fig. 12-23. Actually, a pair of cascaded power transistors, this circuit is used in many solid-state systems to achieve very high power gain—1000 to 10,000 or more. Now marketed in single-transistor cases, it can be obtained as what appears to be a single transistor with high operating voltage ratings that control high amperage loads with only a few volts at the base connection and draw only a few milliamperes from the control circuit. It can be used for relay purposes in a dc circuit the same way, either by direct control signal coupling or with intermediate isolation devices like those described. It is not usable in ac power circuits.

12.3.4.6 Solid-State Time-Delay Relays[9]

Solid-state time-delay relays can operate in many different modes since they do not rely on heaters or pneumatics. The simple ICs allow the relays to do standard functions plus totaling, intervals, and momentary action.

On-Delay

Upon application of control power, the time-delay period begins. At the end of time delay, the output switch operates. When control power is removed, the output switch returns to normal, (Fig. 12-24A).

Nontotalizer

Upon the opening of the control switch, the time-delay period begins. However, any control switch closure prior to the end of the time delay will immediately recycle the timer. At the end of the time-delay period, the output switch operates and remains operated until the required continuous power is interrupted, as shown in Fig. 12-24B.

Totalizer/Preset Counter

The output switch will operate when the sum of the individual control switch closure durations equal the preset time-delay period. There may be interruptions between the control switch closures without substantially altering the cumulative timing accuracy. The output switch returns to normal when the continuous power is interrupted, as shown in Fig. 12-24C.

Off-Delay

Upon closure of the control switch, the output switch operates. Upon opening of the control switch, the time-delay period begins. However, any control switch closure prior to the end of the time-delay period will immediately recycle the timer. At the end of the time-delay period, the output switch returns to normal. Continuous power must be furnished to this timer, as shown in Fig. 12-24D.

Interval

Upon application of the control power, the output switch operates. At the end of the time-delay period, the output switch returns to normal. Control power must be interrupted in order to recycle, as shown in Fig. 12-24E.

Momentary Actuation

Upon closure of the control switch, the output switch operates, and the time-delay period begins. The time-delay period is not affected by duration of the control switch closure. At the end of the time-delay period, the output switch returns to normal. Continuous power must be furnished to this timer, as shown in Fig. 12-24F.

REFERENCES

1. *Guide to Coaxial Cable*, Electronic Capabilities, Summer 1968.
2. *Wire and Cable Glossary*, Pawtucket, Rhode Island: American Insulated Wire Corp.
3. "Altec Engineering News," *Altec Lansing Technical Letter*, no. 141. Altec Corp., Oklahoma City, OK
4. "Altec Engineering Notes," *Altec Lansing Technical Letter*, no. 167. Altec Corp., Oklahoma City, OK
5. *Designer's Handbook and Catalog of Reed and Mercury Wetted Contact Relays*, Chicago, Illinois: Magnecraft Electric Co.
6. "Relays, Solenoids, Timers, and Motors," *Electronic Buyer's Handbook*, 1978. Copyright 1978 by CMP Publications. Reprinted with permission.
7. "Relay Loads" *Electronic Design* 26, December 20, 1978.
8. *Solid-State Relays*, Chicago, Illinois: Magnecraft Electric Co.
9. *Designer's Handbook and Catalog of Time-Delay Relays*, Chicago, Illinois: Magnecraft Electric Co.
10. H. Tremaine, *Audio Cyclopedia*, Indianapolis: Howard W. Sams & Co., Inc., 1969.

PART 3

Electroacoustic Devices

CHAPTER 13

Microphones

by Glen Ballou*

*Section 13.9 is by Dr. Clay Barkley, Crown International; sections 13.10 through 13.11 are by Bill Swintek, Swintek Enterprises; and section 13.17 is by Doug Fearn.

Microphones are electroacoustic devices that convert acoustical energy into electrical energy. All microphones have some type of diaphragm or moving surface that is excited by the acoustical wave that hits it. The output is an electrical signal that is essentially equivalent in shape and amplitude to the acoustical input.

Microphones fall into two classes: *pressure* and *velocity*. In a pressure microphone the diaphragm has only one surface exposed to the sound source; therefore, the output corresponds to the instantaneous sound pressure of the impressed sound waves. A pressure microphone is a *zero-order gradient microphone*, which is the most common type of microphone, and includes carbon, crystal, dynamic, pressure, and capacitor types.

The second class of microphone is the velocity microphone, also called a *first-order gradient microphone*. With this microphone, the effect of the sound wave is the difference or gradient between the sound wave that hits the front and the rear of the diaphragm. In this type, the electrical output corresponds substantially to the instantaneous particle velocity in the impressed sound wave. Ribbon microphones as well as pressure microphones that are altered to produce front-to-back discrimination are of the velocity type.

Another method of classifying microphones is by their pickup pattern (i.e., whether or not they discriminate between the various directions the sound source comes from). These classifications (Fig. 13-1) are:

Omnidirectional—pickup is equal in all directions.

Bidirectional—pickup is equal from the front and back and zero from the sides.

Unidirectional—pickup is from the front only, the pickup appearing cardioid or heart-shaped.

13.1 CARBON MICROPHONES

One of the earliest types of microphones the *carbon microphone* is still in use today mostly in telephone handsets.

A carbon microphone[1] is shown in Fig. 13-2 and operates in the following manner.

Several hundred small carbon granules are held in close contact in a brass cup called a button which is attached to the center of a metallic diaphragm. Sound waves striking the surface of the diaphragm disturb the carbon granules, thus changing the contact resistance between their surfaces. A battery or dc power source is connected in series with the carbon button and the primary of an audio impedance-matching transformer. The change in contact resistance causes the current from the power supply to vary in amplitude resulting in a current waveform similar to the acoustic waveform striking the diaphragm.

The impedance of the carbon button is low; therefore, a stepup transformer is used to increase the impedance and voltage output of the microphone and to eliminate dc from the output circuit.

The current through the buttons should not exceed that recommended by the manufacturer, or the carbon granules may be fused. If the microphone is of the double-button type, the currents through each button must be the same when the diaphragm is at rest. Carbon micro-

MICROPHONE	OMNIDIRECTIONAL	BIDIRECTIONAL	DIRECTIONAL	"SUPER-CARDIOID"	"HYPER-CARDIOID"
Directional Response Characteristic					
Voltage Output	$E=E_0$	$E=E_0 \cos\theta$	$E=\frac{E_0}{2}(1+\cos\theta)$	$\frac{E_0}{2}[(\sqrt{3}-1)+(3-\sqrt{3})\cos\theta]$	$E=\frac{E_0}{4}(1+3\cos\theta)$
Random Energy Efficiency (%)	100	33	33	27	25
Front Response / Back Response	1	1	∞	3.8	2
Front Random Response / Total Random Response	0.5	0.5	0.67	0.93	0.87
Front Random Response / Back Random Response	1	1	7	14	7
Equivalent Distance	1	1.7	1.7	1.9	2
Pickup Angle (2 θ) For 3-dB Attenuation		90°	130°	116°	100°
Pickup Angle (2 θ) For 6-dB Attenuation		120°	180°	156°	140°

Figure 13-1 Performance characteristics of various microphones.

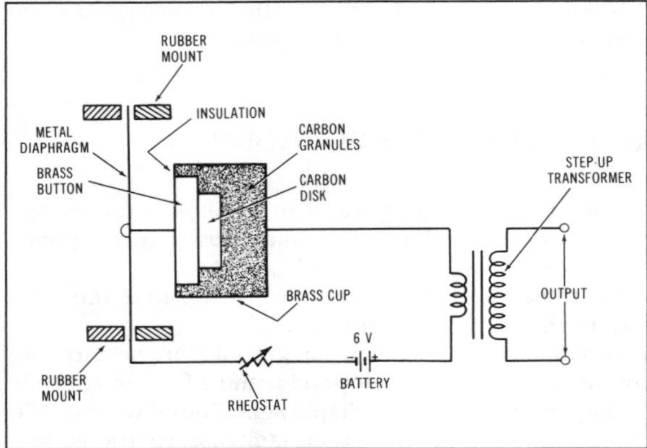

Figure 13-2 Connection and construction of a single-button carbon microphone.

phones should not be subjected to heavy jolts when the current is flowing unless they are designed for such service.

The principal disadvantages of the carbon microphone are:

1. Continuous high-frequency hiss caused by the changing contact resistance between the carbon granules.
2. The frequency response is limited.
3. The distortion is rather high.

For these reasons, carbon microphones are not used today for sound reinforcement recording or any situation requiring quality or wide frequency response.

13.2 CRYSTAL AND CERAMIC MICROPHONES

Crystal and *ceramic microphones* were once popular because they were inexpensive and their high-impedance high-level output allowed them to be connected directly to the input grid of a tube amplifier. They were most popular in such equipment as home tape recorders where microphone cables were short and input impedances, high.

Crystal and ceramic microphones operate as follows:[2]

Piezoelectricity is "pressure electricity" and is a property of certain crystals such as Rochelle salt, tourmaline, barium titanate, and quartz. When pressure is applied to any of these crystals, electricity is generated, or if an electrical charge is applied to the crystal, it changes shape and can be used to impart motion. The piezoelectric effect was discovered in 1880 by Pierre and Jacques Curie. Present-day commercial materials have been especially developed for their piezoelectric qualities. Among them are ammonium dihydrogen phosphate (ADP), lithium sulphate (LN), dipotassium tartrate (DKT), potassium dihydrogen phosphate (KDP), lead zirconate, and lead titanate (PZT). Ceramics do not have piezoelectric characteristics in their original state, but the characteristics are introduced in the materials by a polarizing process. In piezoelectric ceramic materials the direction of the electrical and mechanical axes depend on the direction of the original dc polarizing potential. During polarization a ceramic element experiences a permanent increase in dimensions between the poling electrodes and a permanent decrease in dimension parallel to the electrodes.

The crystal element can be cut as a bender element that is only affected by a bending motion or as a twister element that is only affected by a twisting motion, as shown in Fig. 13-3.

The normal crystal microphone is made from Rochelle salt, which is grown from a supersaturated solution of sodium potassium tartrate tetrahydrate by cooling at a temperature of 40°C. Such microphones should not be stored or operated at high temperatures.

Crystal and ceramic microphones may be manufactured as a direct actuating type where the sound wave

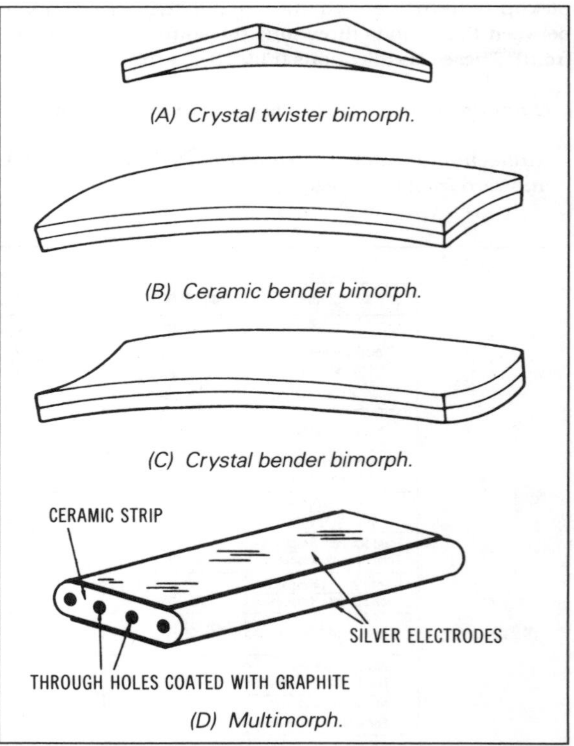

Figure 13-3 Curvatures of bimorphs and multimorph. *(Courtesy Clevite Corp., Piezoelectric Div.)*

hits the crystal directly, as an indirectly actuated type where the sound wave hits a diaphragm that is connected to the crystal, or as a sound cell where a number of crystal elements are stacked in a pile, as shown in Fig. 13-4.

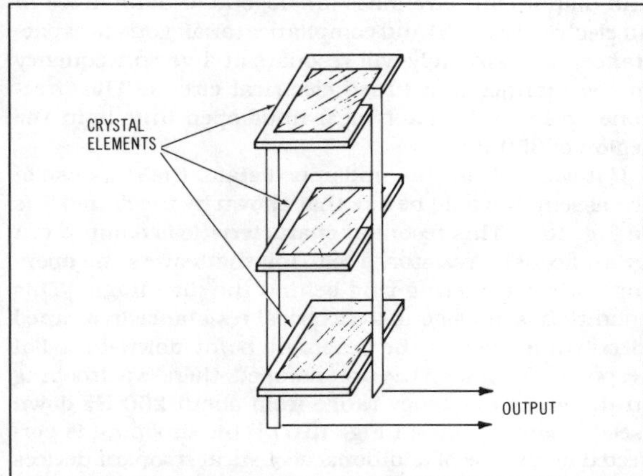

Figure 13-4 Crystal sound-cell configuration used in microphone construction.

The internal capacitance of a crystal microphone is about 0.03 μF for the diaphragm-actuated type and 0.0005 to 0.015 μF for the sound-cell type.

The ceramic microphone operates like a crystal microphone except that it employs a barium titanate slab in the form of a ceramic. Because it has better temperature and humidity characteristics than the crystal microphone, it has replaced it.

Crystal and ceramic microphones normally have a frequency response from 80 to 6500 Hz; however, they can be made to have a flat response to 16 kHz. Their output impedance is about 100 kΩ, and they require a load of 1 to 5 MΩ to produce a level of about −50 dB re 1 V/μbar.

13.3 DYNAMIC MICROPHONES

The *dynamic microphone* is also referred to as a *pressure* or *moving-coil microphone.* It employs a small diaphragm and a voice coil, moving in an intense permanent magnetic field. Sound waves striking the surface of the diaphragm cause the coil to move in the magnetic field, thus generating a voltage proportional to the sound pressure at the surface of the diaphragm.

In a dynamic pressure unit, as shown in Fig. 13-5, the magnet and its associated parts (magnetic return, pole piece, and pole plate) produce a concentrated magnetic flux of approximately 10,000 G in a small gap.

The diaphragm, a key item in the performance of a microphone, supports the voice coil centrally in the magnetic gap, maintaining that center condition with a gap of only 0.006 in. on either side of the voice coil.

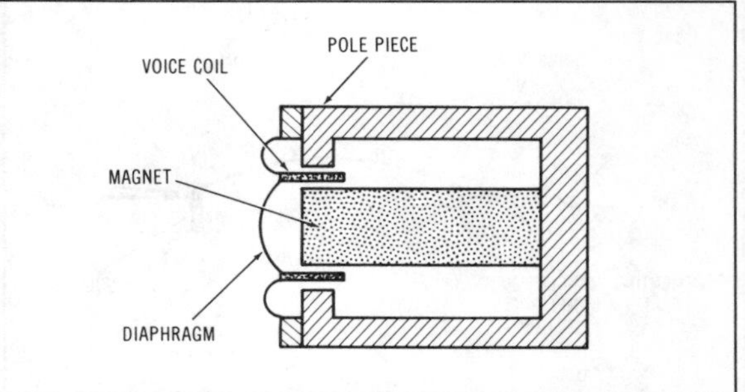

Figure 13-5 A simplified drawing of a dynamic microphone.

An omnidirectional diaphragm and voice-coil assembly[3,4] is shown in Fig. 13-6. The compliance section has two hinge points. Between these points is a section made up of tangential corrugated, triangular sections that stiffen this portion. The hinge points are designed to permit high-compliance action. A spacer supports the moving part of the diaphragm away from the top pole plate to provide room for its movement. The cementing flat is bonded to the face plate. A stiff hemispherical dome is designed to provide adequate acoustical capacitance. The coil seat is a small step where the voice coil is mounted, centered, and bonded on the diaphragm.

In early microphones, most diaphragms were made of aluminum and usually were less than 1 mil (0.001 in.) in thickness. Aluminum, once considered the best material available, is light in weight, fairly easy to form, and maintains its dimensional stability after it is molded. Unaffected by extremes in temperature or humidity, aluminum, in general, serves the purpose. But that 1-mil thickness makes the diaphragms fragile, a fragility that has ruined many dispositions. When it is touched or otherwise deformed by excessive pressure, an aluminum diaphragm is dead.

A great deal of research was performed in an attempt to find another material that had the acoustical advantages of aluminum but yet was tough enough to withstand abnormal deformation. The material turned out to be a polyester film manufactured by the DuPont Company and known by its trade name, Mylar™.

Mylar[5] is a unique plastic. Extremely tough, it has high tensile strength, high resistance to wear, and outstanding flex life. Capable of withstanding high temperatures, it is used in motors, transformers, and other critical applications. Mylar diaphragms have been tested with temperature variations from −40 to +170°F (−40 to +77°C) cycled over long periods without any impairment to the diaphragm. Since Mylar is extremely stable, its properties will not change within the temperature and humidity range in which microphones are used.

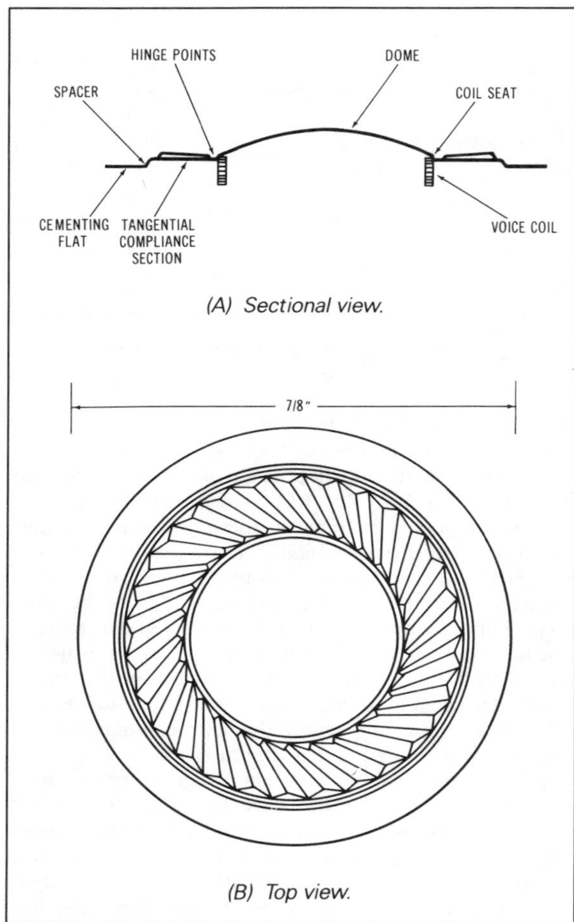

Figure 13-6 Omnidirectional diaphragm and voice coil assembly.

The specific gravity of Mylar is approximately 1.3 (as compared to 2.7 for aluminum); therefore, a Mylar diaphragm may be made considerably thicker without upsetting the relationship of the diaphragm mass to the voice-coil mass. (In the case of the omnidirectional diaphragm, the thickness is 1½ mils.) Mylar diaphragms are formed under high temperature and high pressure, a process in which the molecular structure is formed permanently to establish a "dimensional memory" that is highly retentive. Unlike aluminum, Mylar diaphragms will retain their shape and dimensional stability although they may be subjected to drastic momentary deformations. Such a diaphragm may be bent at right angles and, when allowed to spring back, will still operate. It may not remain acoustically perfect, but the microphone will continue to function. Diaphragms have been flattened against the supporting structure by pressure from the palm of a hand and yet the microphone functioned properly.

The voice coil is the controlling part of the mass involved in the diaphragm voice-coil assembly, inasmuch as it weighs more than the diaphragm. Because the voice coil and diaphragm have mass (analogous to inductance in an electrical circuit) and compliance (analogous to capacitance), the assembly will resonate at a given frequency in the manner of a tuned electrical circuit. The "free-cone" resonance of a typical undamped unit is in the region of 350 Hz.

If it were left in this undamped state, the response of the assembly would be like that shown by the dotted line in Fig. 13-7. This resonant characteristic is damped out by an acoustic resistor, a felt ring that covers the openings in the centering ring behind the diaphragm. This condition is analogous to electrical resistance in a tuned circuit and damps the resonant point down to a flat response. Even with the unit damped, there is a drooping in the lower frequency range from about 200 Hz down (see the dotted line in Fig. 13-7). This drooping is corrected by the use of additional acoustical resonant devices inside the microphone case. A cavity behind the unit (analogous to capacitance) helps resonate at the low frequencies with the mass (inductance) of the diaphragm and voice-coil assembly.

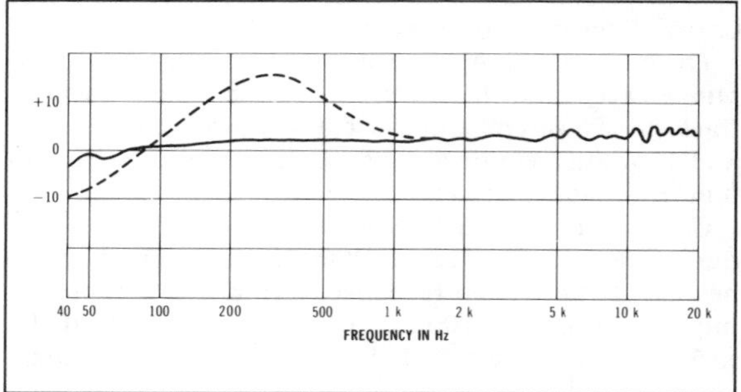

Figure 13-7 Diaphragm and voice-coil assembly response curve.

Still another tuned resonant circuit is added in the form of a tube, which couples the inside cavity of the microphone housing to the outside, as shown in Fig. 13-8. This tube has an acoustic inductance that is tuned to a low frequency, around 50 Hz, so that a flat response extending down to 35 Hz may be obtained.

The radius of the dome provides stiffness and an acoustic capacity in the form of an air cavity between the diaphragm and the dome of the pole piece. This capacitance resonates with the mass (inductance) of the assembly and helps extend the response up to 20,000 kHz.

To control this high-frequency resonance, an acoustic resistance in the form of a sintered-bronze filter or equiv-

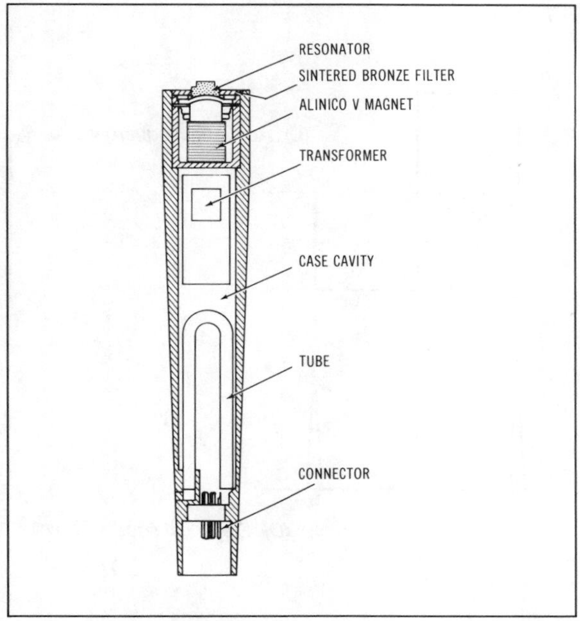

Figure 13-8 Omnidirectional microphone cross-section view.

alent is placed in front of the diaphragm shown in Fig. 13-8. This filter also serves as an effective protection device.

Sintered bronze is composed of bronze spheres that are pressed to form a porous sheet of material. Used as a filter, it prevents dirt particles, magnetic chips, and moisture from gravitating to the inside of the unit. Magnetic chips, if allowed to reach the magnetic gap area, eventually will accumulate on top of the diaphragm and impair the frequency response. It is possible for such chips to "pin" the diaphragm to the pole piece and thereby render the microphone inoperative.

If we assume that the sound pressure the microphone sees is a plane wave in the far field, the relationship of the air particle displacement to its velocity and its acceleration is shown in Fig. 13-9.

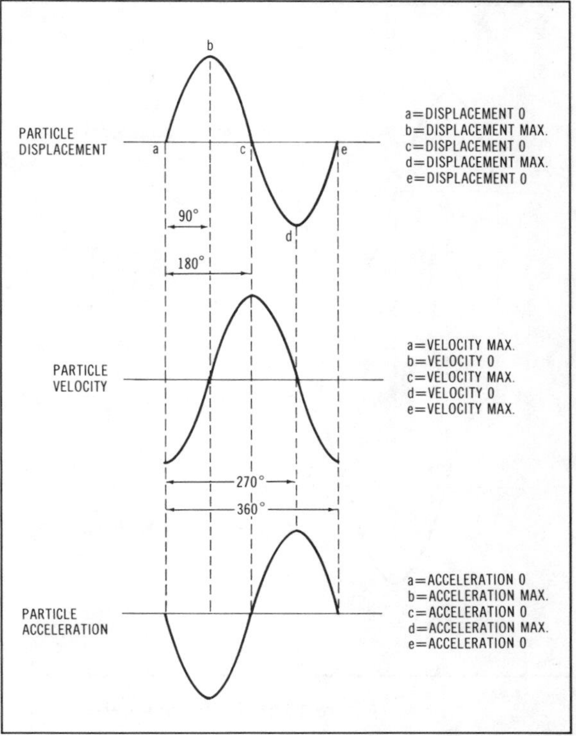

Figure 13-9 Air particle motion in a sound field, showing relationship to velocity and acceleration.

Fig. 13-10 illustrates the effect of a varying sound pressure on a moving-coil microphone. (For this brief and admittedly simplified explanation, assume that a massless diaphragm voice-coil assembly is used.) The acoustical waveform shown in Fig. 13-10A is one cycle of an acoustic waveform, where *a* indicates atmospheric pressure AT; and *b* represents atmospheric pressure plus a slight over pressure increment Δ or AT + Δ.

Looking at Fig. 13-10B, we see that the electrical waveform output from the moving-coil microphone does not follow the phase of the acoustic waveform because at maximum pressure, AT + Δ or *b*, the diaphragm is at rest (no velocity). Further, the diaphragm and its attached coil reach maximum velocity, hence maximum electrical amplitude, at point *c* on the acoustical waveform, which is of no consequence unless another microphone is being used along with the moving-coil microphone in a stereo system where the other microphone does not see the same 90° displacement. Due to this phase displacement, condenser microphones should not be mixed with moving-coil or ribbon microphones. (Sound pressure can be proportional to velocity in many practical cases.[6])

Looking at Fig. 13-10C, let us assume that we can create a steady overpressure and hold it (generate an acoustic square wave), and that we still have a massless-diaphragm voice-coil microphone as well as a massless loudspeaker. The result would be as shown in Fig. 13-10D. As the acoustic pressure rises from *a* to *b*, it represents a velocity; and voltage output from the microphone appears. Then, as the diaphragm reaches its maximum displacement and stays there during the time interval represented by the distance between *b* and *c*, no voice-coil velocity exists; hence, the electrical output voltage ceases. The same situation would repeat itself from *c* to *e*, and from *e* to *f* on the acoustic waveform. It can be readily seen that no moving-coil microphone can reproduce a square wave, which, again, is of no real con-

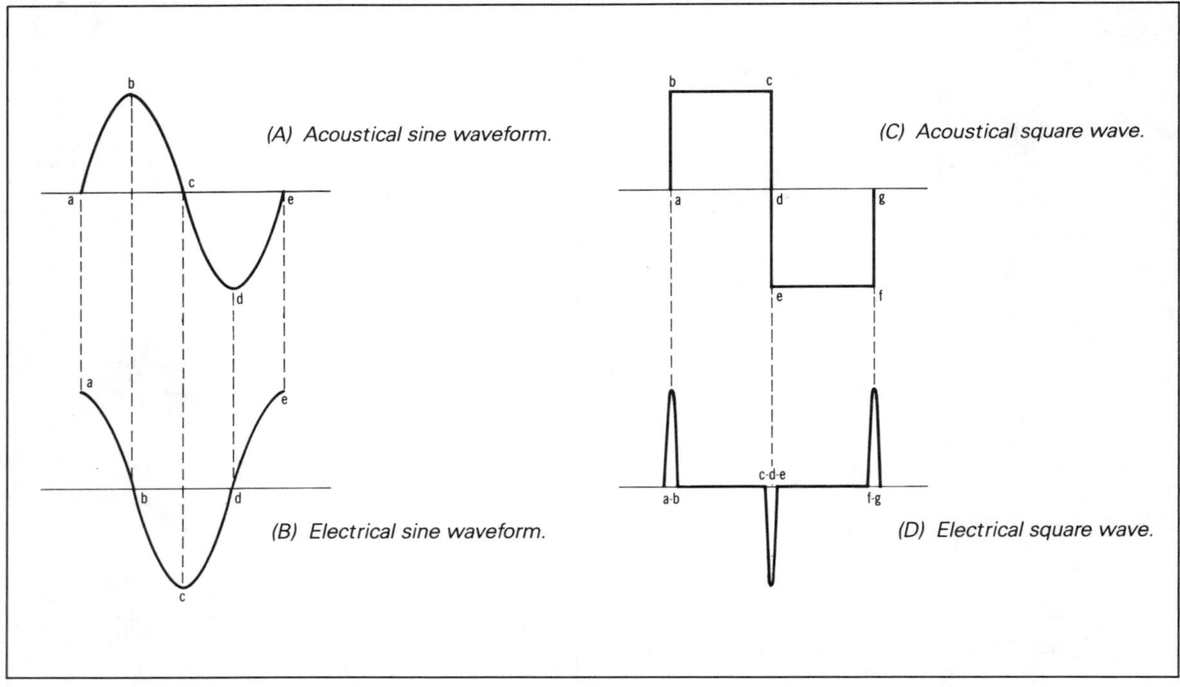

Figure 13-10 Effect of a varying sound pressure on a moving-coil microphone.

sequence, but it does give some insight into the method of transduction.

Fig. 13-11 shows another interesting theoretical consideration of the moving-coil microphone mechanism. In this case, we are going to assume a sudden transient condition. Starting at *a* on the acoustic waveform, the normal atmospheric pressure is suddenly increased by the first wavefront of a new signal and proceeds to the first overpressure peak, AT + Δ or *b*. The diaphragm will reach a maximum velocity halfway to *b* and then return to zero velocity at *b*. This will result in a peak *a′* in the electrical waveform. From *b* on, the acoustic waveform and the electrical waveform will proceed as before, cycle for cycle, but 90° apart.

In this special case, peak *a′* represents something extra. It may well be that, due to the myriad other problems (especially mass) encountered in a practical moving-coil microphone, this minute effect is swamped. It does illustrate, however, that even with a "perfect," massless, moving-coil microphone, "perfect" electrical waveforms will not be produced.

When sound waves vibrate the diaphragm, the voice coil moving in the magnet gap has a voltage induced in it proportional to the magnitude and at the frequency of the vibrations. However, the voice coil and diaphragm, lightweight as they may be, have some finite mass. Any mass has inertia. If the so-called stationary part of our

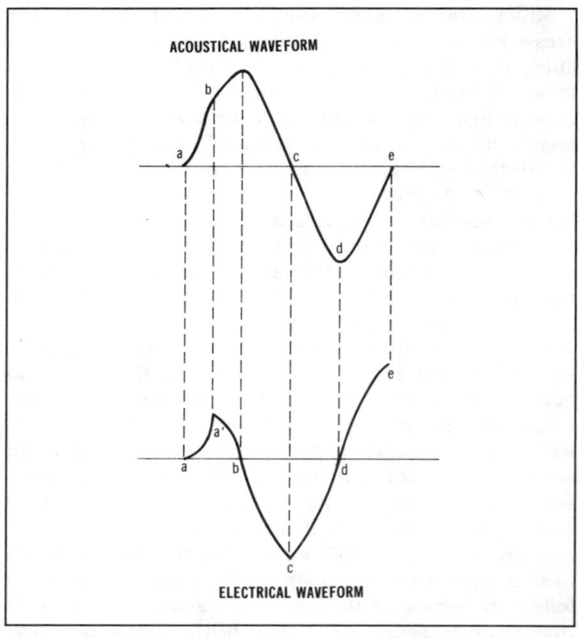

Figure 13-11 Effect of a transient condition on a moving-coil microphone.

two systems, the magnetic circuit, is moved in space, the inertia of the diaphragm and coil cause them to try to remain fixed in space. Just as when acoustically actuated, there will be relative motion between the two systems with a resultant electrical output. In such a microphone, therefore, electrical output can be obtained in two ways, by motion of the diaphragm from airborne acoustical energy and by motion of the magnet circuit by structure-borne vibration. The former is the desired output; the latter is undesired.

Several things may be tried to eliminate the undesired output. The mass of the diaphragm and voice coil may be reduced, but there are practical limits, or the frequency response may be limited mechanically such as with stiffer diaphragms or electronically with filter circuits. However, this limited response makes the microphone unsuitable for broad-range applications.

To reject unwanted acoustical noise, unidirectional microphones are used. Unidirectional microphones are much more sensitive to vibration relative to their acoustic sensitivity than omnidirectional types. Fig. 13-12 shows a plot of vibration sensitivity versus frequency for a typical omnidirectional and unidirectional microphone with the levels normalized with respect to acoustical sensitivity.

Note that the vibration sensitivity of the unidirectional microphone is about 15 dB higher than the omnidirectional and that there is a peak at about 150 Hz. The peak gives us a clue to help explain the difference.

Unidirectional microphones are usually differential microphones; that is, the diaphragm responds to a pressure differential between its two surfaces. The oncoming sound wave is not only allowed to reach the front of a diaphragm but, through one or more other openings and appropriate acoustical phase-shift networks, also reaches the rear of the diaphragm. At low frequencies, the net instantaneous pressure differential causing the diaphragm to move is small compared to the absolute sound pressure. This is illustrated in Fig. 13-13, where the upper curve shows the pressure wave that arrives at the front entry to the diaphragm. The middle curve shows the pressure wave that reaches the rear of the diaphragm after a slight delay due to the greater distance the sound had to travel to reach the rear entry and some additional phase shift it encounters after entering. The net pressure actuating the diaphragm is the bottom curve, which is the instantaneous difference between the two upper curves. In a typical unidirectional microphone, the differential pressure at 100 Hz will be only about one-tenth of the absolute pressure or 20 dB down from the pressure an omnidirectional microphone would experience.

To get a reasonable electrical output from a unidirectional microphone, the diaphragm must move more easily for a given low-frequency sound pressure. This is accomplished partly by reducing the damping resistance to less than one-tenth of that normally used in an omnidirectional microphone, the reason a peak occurred at around 150 Hz in Fig. 13-12. This is the mechanical resonant frequency of the diaphragm and voice coil, which is emphasized because of lack of damping. Since the diaphragm of an omnidirectional microphone is much more heavily damped, it follows that it will respond less to inertial or mechanical vibration forces.

From the foregoing it is clear that there is a need for some kind of isolation to prevent the microphone cartridge from experiencing mechanical shock and vibration.

13.4 CAPACITOR MICROPHONES

A *capacitor* or *condenser microphone* is one where the sound pressure level varies the head capacitance of the microphone by deflecting one plate of the capacitor, caus-

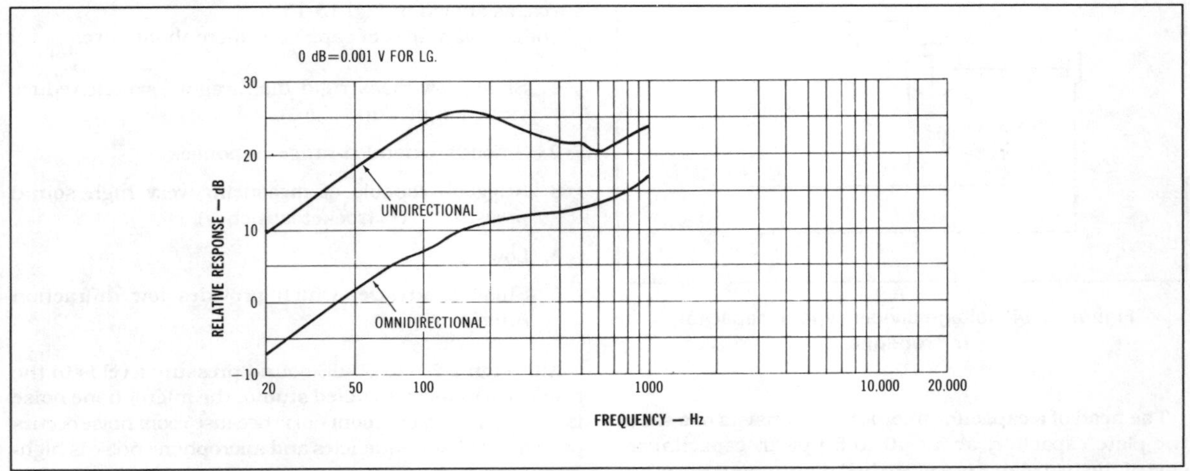

Figure 13-12 Vibration sensitivity of a microphone cartridge.

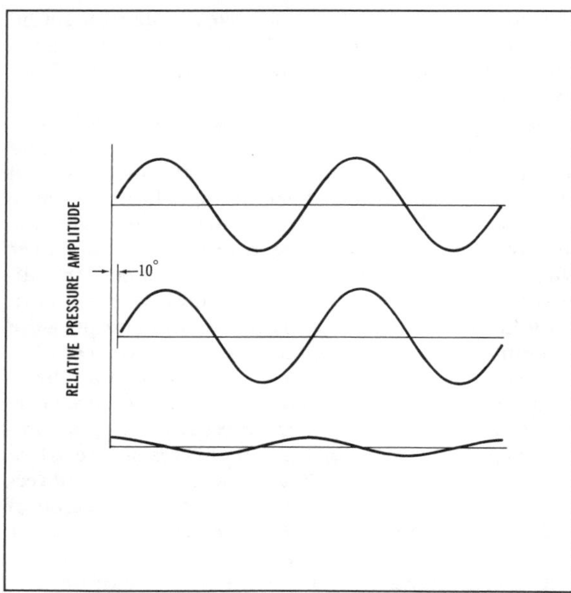

Figure 13-13 Differential pressure at low frequencies on unidirectional microphones.

ing an electrical signal that varies with the acoustical signal. The varying capacitance can be used to vary a radio-frequency signal that is later demodulated as a frequency-modulated transmitter or, more conventionally, as one leg of a voltage divider, shown in Fig. 13-14, where R and C form the voltage divider of the power supply + + to −.

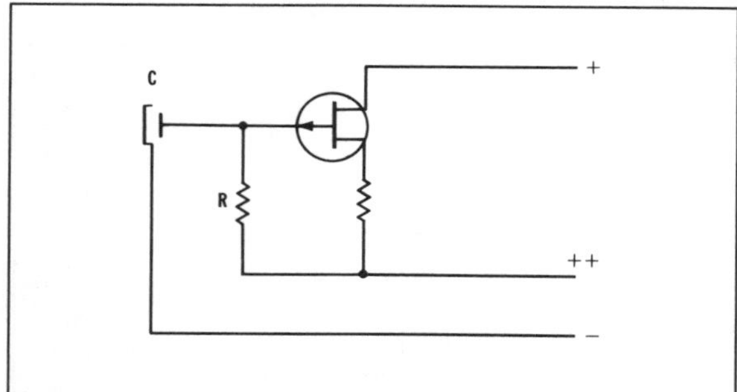

Figure 13-14 Voltage divider type of capacitor microphone.

The head of a capacitor microphone consists of a small two-plate capacitor, about 40 to 50 pF in capacitance. One of the two plates is a stretched diaphragm; the other is a heavy back plate or center terminal, as shown in Fig. 13-14. The back plate is insulated from the diaphragm and spaced approximately 0.001 in. from, and parallel to, the rear surface of the diaphragm. Mathematically the output from the head may be calculated using:

$$E_o = (E_0 a^2 P)/(8dt) \qquad (13\text{-}1)$$

where,

E_o is the output voltage,
E_0 is the dc polarizing voltage in volts,
a is the radius of active area of the diaphragm in centimeters,
P is the pressure in dynes per square centimeter,
d is the spacing between the back plate and diaphragm in centimeters,
t is the diaphragm tension in dynes per centimeter.

Capacitor microphones require a preamplifier as an integral part of the housing and a source of polarizing voltage for the head, plus a source of power. Such microphones, if operated in a high humidity, may develop noise due to moisture getting into the head and cause arcing between the diaphragm and back plate; however, in present-day microphone's, this has been almost completely eliminated. If the device is being operated in high humidity, the head should be stored in a desiccator jar when not in use.

The capacitor microphone has a much faster rise time than the dynamic microphone because of the dynamic microphone's larger diaphragm and the inductance of the moving coil. The capacitor rise time rises from 10% of its rise time to 90% in approximately 15 μs, while the rise time for the dynamic microphone is in the order of 40 μs.

Capacitor microphones generate an output electrical waveform in step or phase with the acoustical waveform and can be adapted to measure essentially dc overpressures, as shown in Fig. 13-15.

Some advantages of capacitor microphones are:

1. Small, low-mass rigid diaphragms, which reduce vibration pickup,
2. Smooth, extended-range response,
3. Rugged—capable of measuring very high sound pressure levels (rocket launches),
4. Low noise,
5. Small head size, which provides low diffraction interference,

Although a 20- to 30-dB sound pressure level is in the range of a well-constructed studio, the microphone noise is not masked by the room noise because room noise occurs primarily at low frequencies and microphone noise is high-frequency hiss.

Many capacitor microphones operate with an equiva-

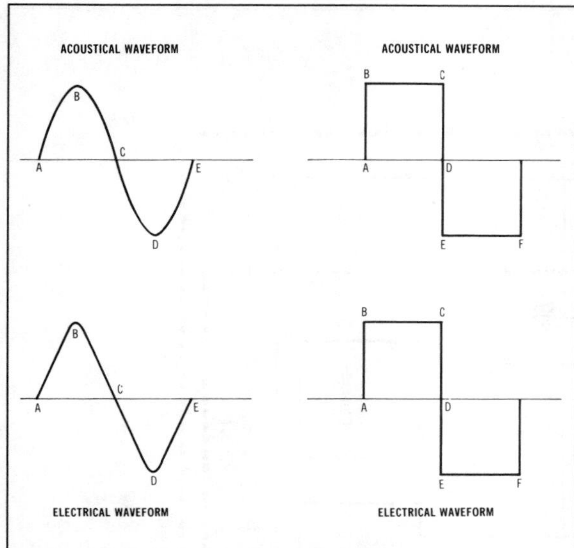

Figure 13-15 Capacitor microphone acoustic wave and electrical signals. Note the in-phase condition.

lent noise level of 20- to 30-dB sound pressure level. The following is a microphone designed by Richard Burwen with an A-weighted sound pressure level of 15 dB and is typical of low-noise capacitor microphones.[7]

Fig. 13-16 shows the principal electronic noise sources in the capacitor microphone system. The desired signal is generated by the variable microphone capacitance that is biased by high voltage. In this particular microphone, the capacitance is approximately 43 pF, which is fairly high for a capacitor microphone. One of the principal sources of noise is the voltage noise E_{N4} generated within the amplifier A1. Also the amplifier has an input current noise I_{N1}, which develops a voltage across the source capacitance. Another factor that influences the signal and, therefore, influences the signal-to-noise ratio is the input capacitance of the amplifier system. This loads the microphone capacitance and attenuates the input signal, thereby making the voltage noise of the amplifier more significant relative to the microphone signal.

Hum pickup due to stray capacitance to an ac source E_{N2} can be very serious if the microphone is not tightly shielded. Similarly, stray capacitance to any noise source such as a power supply lead or even a zener diode can introduce significant noise into the microphone capacitance. Furthermore, capacitance to any dc source constitutes an unwanted capacitor microphone that must be rigidly supported and adequately damped mechanically to prevent vibration from altering the system frequency response.

One of the largest sources of noise in capacitor microphone systems is the load resistor used for biasing the capsule. In a typical capacitor microphone system this resistor is about 250 MΩ. This value is so low that it delivers an appreciable noise current into the microphone capacitance from its thermal agitation noise generator E_{N3}. By increasing the value of this resistance to 20,000 MΩ, the current delivered into the microphone capacitance can be reduced by the square root of the resistance ratio.

A block diagram of the model 3000 low-noise capacitor microphone system is shown in Fig. 13-17. The system is designed around the Schoeps MKT-45, 60-V capacitor capsule, which was chosen for several reasons. This capsule has a pleasing subjective quality, excellent frequency response, high capacitance that attenuates input noise currents previously described, and fairly high output.

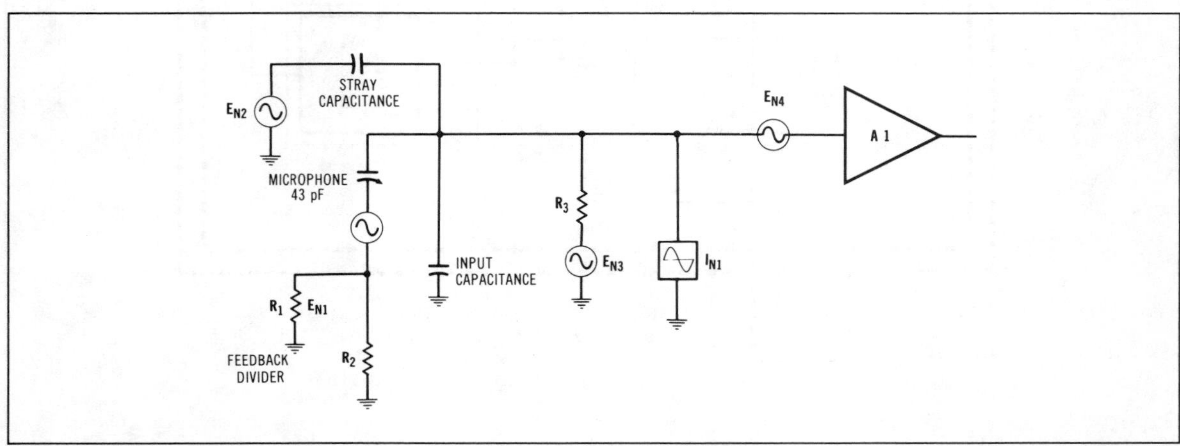

Figure 13-16 Condenser microphone noise sources.

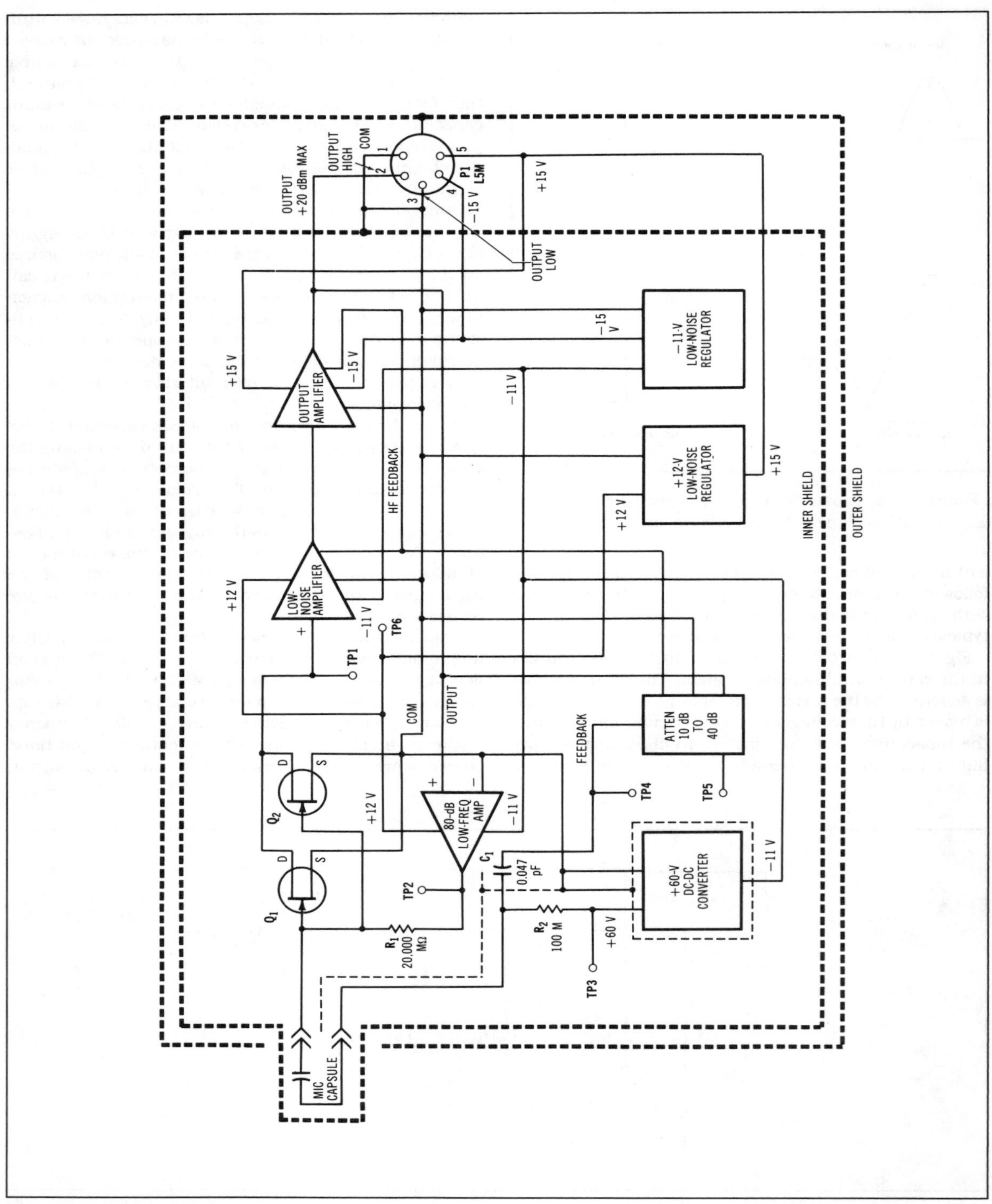

Figure 13-17 Richard Burwen microphone amplifier block diagram. *(Courtesy Richard Burwen)*

Another important advantage is the three-wire floating capacitance arrangement that permits a feedback voltage to be added into the input by feeding it in series with the capsule. The capsule is manufactured with single or switchable directional patterns including onmidirectional, bidirectional, cardioid, and hypercardioid.

The system consists of an input preamplifier having two high transconductance field-effect transistors (FETs) in parallel, a second-stage, a low-noise amplifier, and a final output amplifier. This output amplifier is dc coupled to the load and delivers 7.7 V rms into 200 Ω or more. Feedback around the entire system comes from the output through an attenuator to the low side of the capsule. To stabilize the dc output level, additional feedback at subaudio frequencies, which are amplified 80 dB in a low-frequency amplifier, is delivered to the 20,000-MΩ capsule load resistor to bias the FETs.

In the FET preamplifier, noise is minimized by using low-capacitance high-transconductance FETs. The equivalent short-circuited input noise voltage in the upper audio bandwidth is approximately ⅓ μV. A voltage is required at R_1 to offset leakage current and properly bias the FETs. This voltage is supplied by the 80-dB low-frequency amplifier that senses the output dc offset and delivers 0 to −9 V into resistor R_1. The amplifier provides no feedback within the audio range, but only at direct current.

Low power-supply noise is important so the power for the first stage comes from a +12-V regulator that has only 0.5 μV of noise output. The attenuation of noise from the external +15-V supply is 100 dB. The −11-V regulator has approximately 2 μV output noise and attenuates ripple and noise from the −15-V external supply by 90 dB. A +60-V dc to dc converter is used to bias the capsule and is powered from the −11-V regulator.

Because of system design, the second amplifier must be a low-noise type and, therefore, has been designed for only 0.5-μV input noise.

A unity gain dc output amplifier provides high output current capability along with low open-loop distortion and short-circuit protection. The overall gain of the amplifier system is determined by the feedback from this output amplifier through a three position 10-, 25-, and 40-dB attenuator that feeds the low side of the microphone capsule providing the full +20-dBm output at sound pressure levels of 140, 125, or 110 dB, respectively.

Bias for the capsule is produced by a shielded +60-V dc to dc converter. It operates just below 500 kHz and has decoupling on the input power supply leads as well as good output filtering and less than 0.1-μV leakage; therefore, the power converter has no effect on the system noise.

The output signal and input power comes from a five-pin audio connector. The system has a single-ended output, but it can feed either a single-ended input amplifier, if the cable is short, or preferably a differential input amplifier. The entire system is double shielded in order to reduce the effects of hum pickup and radio-frequency pickup from switches on power lines and from light dimmers. The amplifier is contained within an inner shield that is the basic ground for the system, and the outer shield is completely isolated and grounded at a single point back at the studio console. The only portion of the inner shield that is exposed when handling the microphone is the capsule itself. To eliminate noise pickup, the capsule has to be mounted on the inner shield rather than on the outer shield.

The output noise level of the microphone system measured in one-third-octave bands is plotted in Fig. 13-18. Fig. 13-18C shows the spectrum for the amplifier alone when connected to a 40-pF source capacitance. Figs.

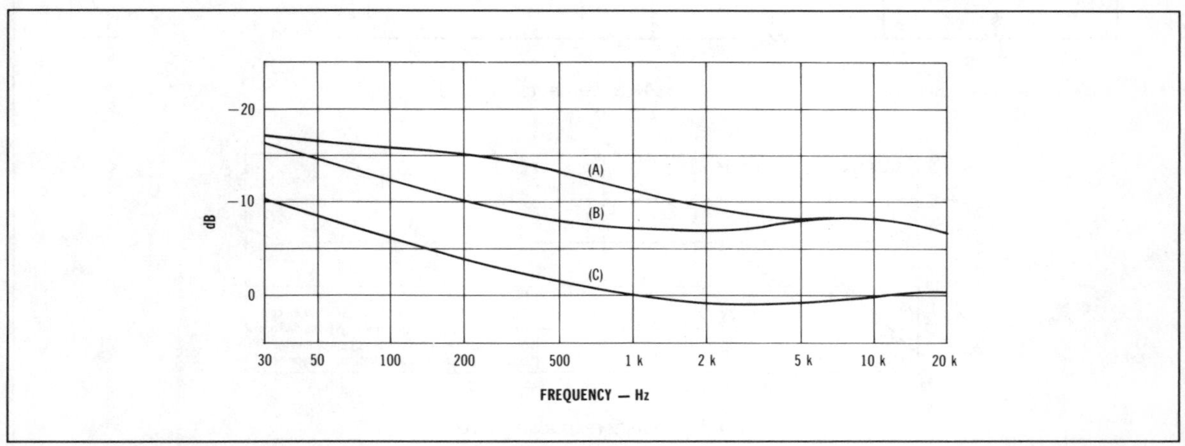

Figure 13-18 Noise spectrum measured in one-third octave bands. (A) Two-way capsule switched to cardioid. (B) Sample capsule switched to omnidirectional. (C) Amplifier noise with 40-pF source. *(Courtesy Richard Burwen)*

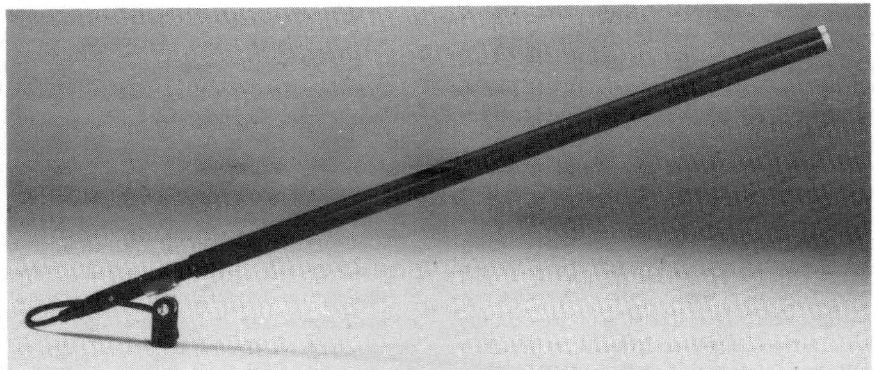

Figure 13-19 AKG C-451E microphone with shotgun extension. *(Courtesy AKG Acoustics, Inc.)*

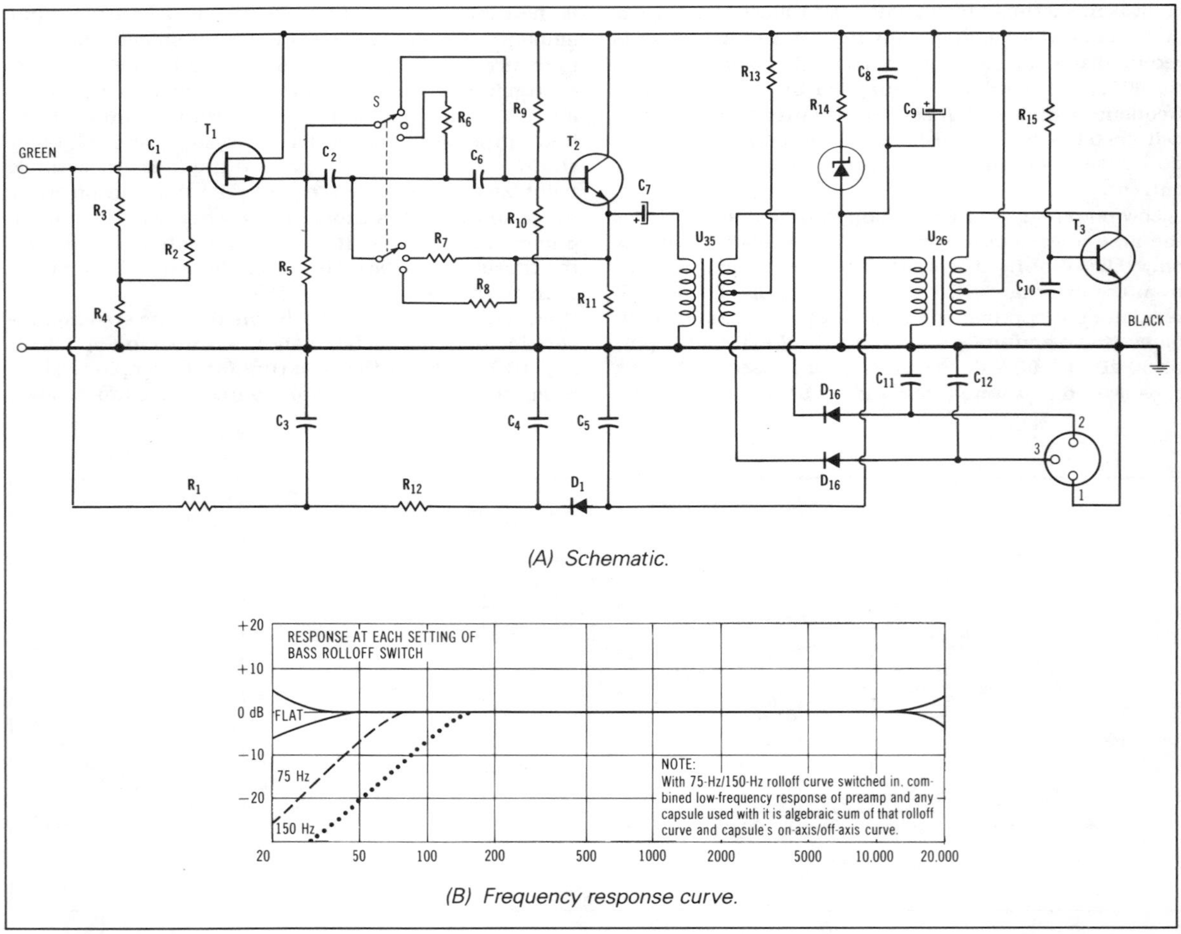

(A) Schematic.

RESPONSE AT EACH SETTING OF BASS ROLLOFF SWITCH

NOTE: With 75-Hz/150-Hz rolloff curve switched in, combined low-frequency response of preamp and any capsule used with it is algebraic sum of that rolloff curve and capsule's on-axis/off-axis curve.

(B) Frequency response curve.

Figure 13-20 AKG C-451EB microphone schematic and frequency response curve. *(Courtesy AKG Acoustics, Inc.)*

13-18A and B show the noise levels produced with an omnidirectional, cardioid two-way switchable capsule mounted. These curves were measured by inserting the microphone into a soundproof metal tank lined with absorptive material. They show that the major contributor of noise is the capsule itself, which has some 6 to 12 dB more noise than the amplifier. In the capsule, noise may be contributed by the thin layer of air between the diaphragm and its back plate. However, the mechanical venting used to change the directional pattern has a considerable effect, as shown by Fig. 13-18A for the cardioid pattern, which is as much as 5 dB above the omnidirectional pattern in the vicinity of 300 Hz.

Another high-quality capacitor microphone, the AKG C-451E is suitable for recording studios, television and radio broadcast, motion picture studios, and stage and concert hall applications, as well as high-quality commercial sound installations.

The AKG C-451EB is a *capacitor microphone system* (CMS) (Fig. 13-19) that uses audio frequency circuitry with field-effect transistors as shown in Fig. 13-20. Low-noise level, extremely high reliability, and life-long stability are inherent features of this microphone. Low-current consumption at low voltage and phantom circuit powering permits feeding the microphone supply voltage via a standard two-conductor shielded audio cable.

The miniature capacitor microphone transducer incorporated into the capsule of the CMS consists of a gold-vapored ceramic electrode and a permanently fixed metallic diaphragm. The ceramic electrode is provided with an insulating coating, preventing short circuits of electrode and diaphragm.

The results are extremely reliable capacitor microphone capsules, impervious to a wide range of temperature and humidity fluctuations and free of deterioration and hysteresis.

The C-451E offers interchangeable capsules, allowing the selection of different response characteristics from omnidirectional to cardioid to hyper-cardioid to adapt the microphone to various types of environments and recording applications.

Because of the new PCM recorders, signal-to-noise ratio has reached a level of 90 dB, requiring capacitor microphones to increase their signal-to-noise level to match the recorder. The new AKG C-460B microphone[8] shown in Fig. 13-21 has an equivalent noise level of 15-dB sound pressure level (IEC 179A), which is a weighted noise level of the amplifier of 0.7 rms μV (IEC 179A). The system uses the same transducers as the existing 450 series, even though the diameter of the amplifier is slightly larger. To increase the signal-to-noise ratio, lower the distortion, and improve dynamic range, the electronics had to be redesigned, as shown in Fig. 13-22. As in most circuitry, the input stage is the stage that creates the most noise; therefore, a novel circuit, as shown in Fig. 13-23, was used. It is important that the voltage on the transducer does not change. This is normally accomplished by controlling the input current, being sure it is constant. In the circuit of the AKG C-460B, the voltages V_{in}, V_o, and V_D are within 0.1% of each other. Noise, which might come into the circuit as V_{in} through the operational amplifier, is only 1/91 of the voltage V_o. A second-order Butterworth filter of minimum phase design has been installed with the 3-dB down points at 50, 70, or 150 Hz. The output stage is coupled to the line through a transformer that, because of its large section iron core, can be driven to the high levels at low frequencies.

Pre-attenuation, that is, attenuation between the capacitor and the amplifier, is normally achieved by connecting parallel capacitors to the input or by reducing the input stage gain by means of capacitors in the negative feedback circuit. This normally causes parasitic

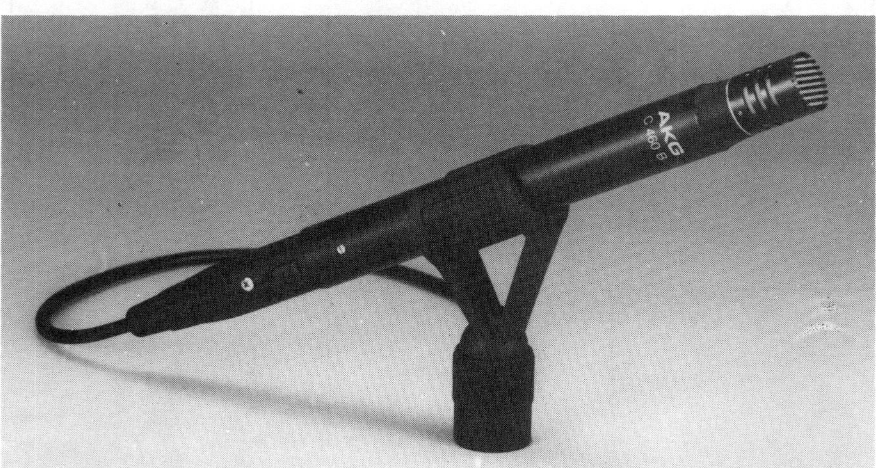

Figure 13-21 AKG C-460B condenser microphone. *(Courtesy AKG Acoustics, Inc.)*

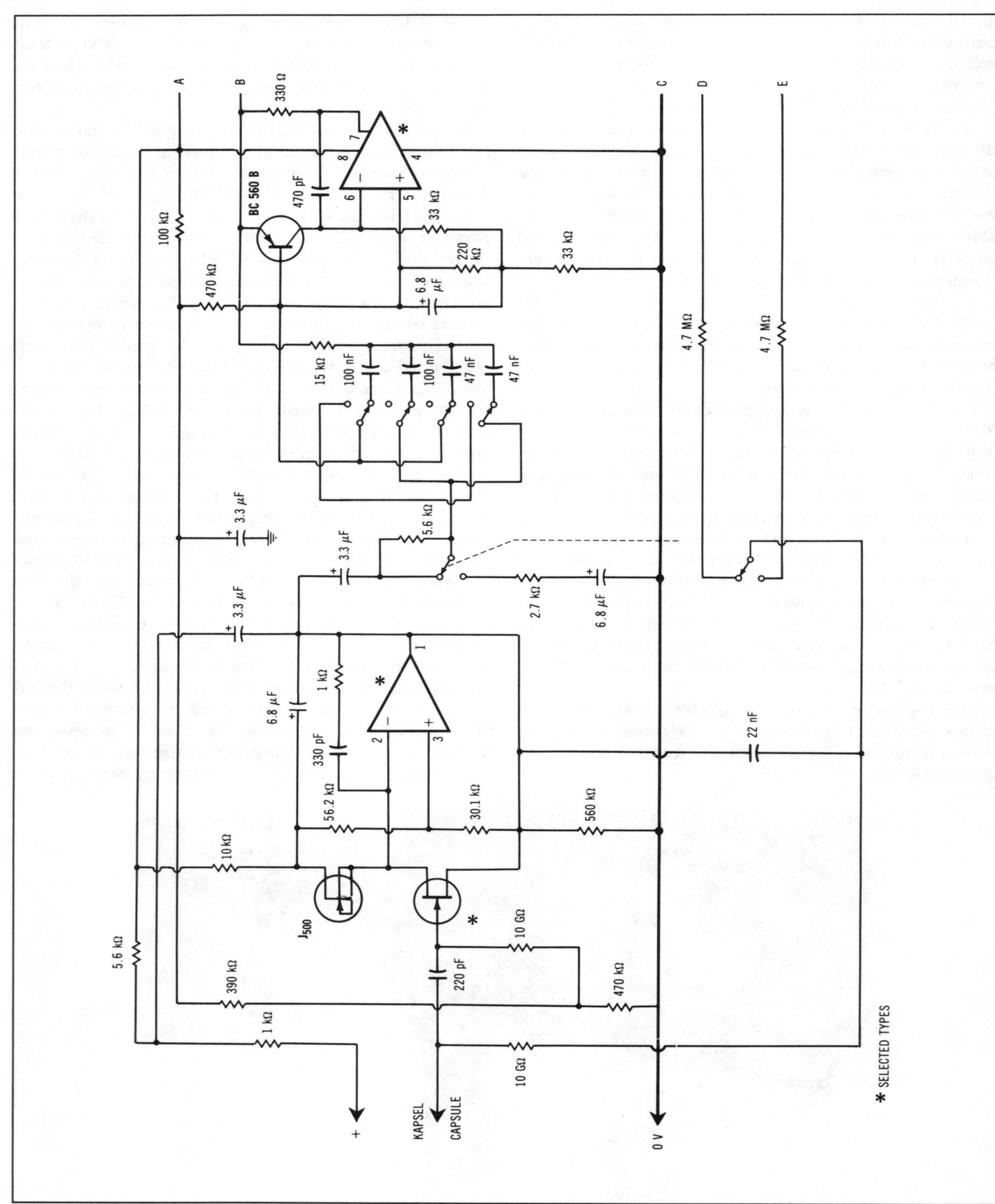

Figure 13-22 AKG C-460B microphone schematic.

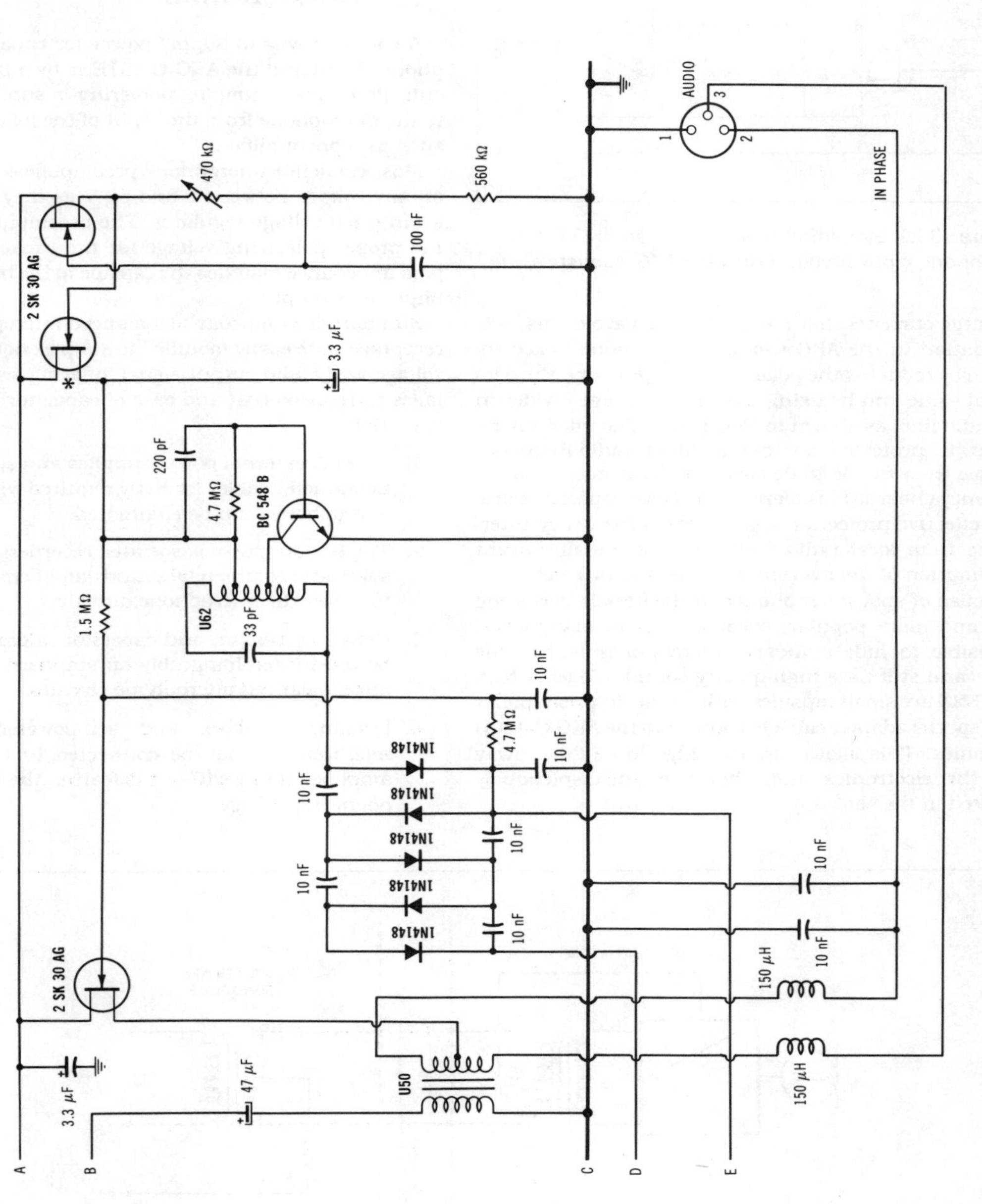

(Courtesy AKG Acoustics, Inc.)

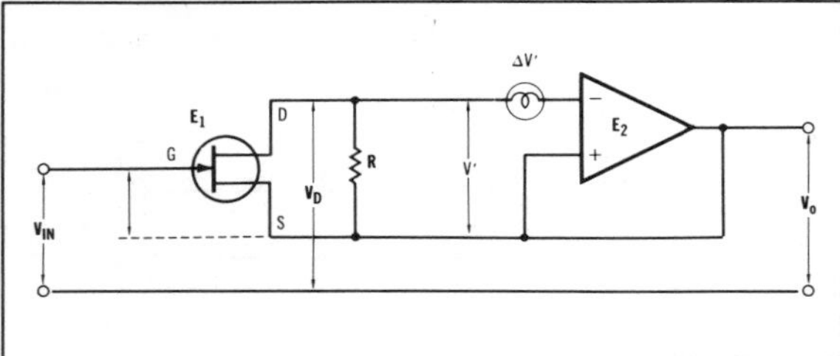

Figure 13-23 Simplified schematic of an AKG C-460B microphone input circuit. *(Courtesy AKG Acoustics, Inc.)*

discharge currents that create noise. To avoid this, pre-attenuation in the AKG C-460B microphone is accomplished by reducing the polarizing voltage to one-third its normal value and by using a resistive voltage divider in the audio line, as shown in Fig. 13-22. The microphone output is protected against residual radio-frequency voltages from the dc to dc converter by means of radio-frequency chokes. This along with shunt capacitors provides effective protection against radio-frequency interference from local radio stations. The overall current consumption of the microphone is less than 1 mA.

The use of spot microphones in theaters is becoming more and more popular, because it is in many cases impossible to hide standard microphones within the scenes and still have high-quality sound. Models CK1X and CK2X are small capsules with a built-in preamplifier and a special adapter cable to connect to the AKG C-460B electronics. This allows the cartridge to be 20 ft away from the electronics and, therefore, inconspicuously mounted in the set.

13.5 PHANTOM POWER FOR CAPACITOR MICROPHONES

A common way to supply power for capacitor microphones including the AKG C-451E is by a *phantom circuit. Phantom* or *simplex powering* is supplying power to the microphone from the input of the following device such as a preamplifier.

Most capacitor microphone preamplifiers can operate on any voltage between 9 and 52 V as they incorporate an internal voltage regulator. The preamplifier supplies the proper polarizing voltage for the capacitor capsule plus impedance matches the capsule to the balanced low-impedance output.

Standard low-impedance, balanced microphone input receptacles are easily modified to simplex both operating voltage and audio output signal, offering several advantages in reduced cost and ease of capacitor microphone operation:

1. Special, external power supplies and separate multiconductor cables formerly required with capacitor microphones can be eliminated.
2. The B+ supply in associated recorders, audio consoles, and commercial sound amplifiers can be used to power the microphone directly.
3. Dynamic, ribbon, and capacitor microphones can be used interchangeably on standard, low-impedance, balanced microphone circuits.
4. Dynamic, ribbon, and self-powered capacitor microphones may be connected to the modified amplifier input without defeating the microphone operating voltage.

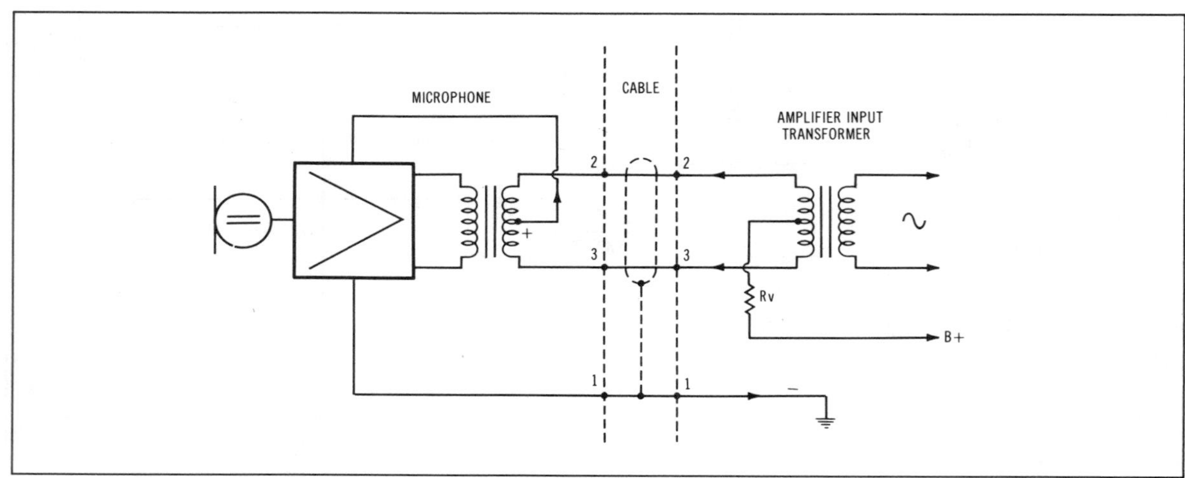

Figure 13-24 Direct center-tap connection method of phantom powering capacitor microphones. *(Courtesy AKG Acoustics, Inc.)*

5. Any recording, broadcast, and commercial installation can be inexpensively upgraded to capacitor microphone operation using existing, two-conductor microphone cables and electronics.

Phantom circuit use requires only that the microphone operating voltage be applied equally to pins 2 and 3 of the amplifier low-impedance input receptacle. Pin 1 remains ground and circuit minus. The polarity of standard microphone cable wiring is not important except for the usual audio-phasing requirement. Two, equally effective methods of amplifier powering can be used.

1. Connect an amplifier B+ supply of 9 to 12 V directly to the ungrounded center tap of the microphone input transformer, as shown in Fig. 13-24. A series-dropping resistor is required for above 12 and up to 52 V. Fig. 13-25 is a resistor value chart for the AKG C-451E microphone.
2. A two-resistor, artificial center powering circuit is required when the microphone input transformer is not center-tapped, or input attenuation networks are used across the input transformer primary. Connect a B+ supply of 9 to 12 V directly to the artificial center of two 332-Ω, 1% tolerance precision resistors, as shown in Fig. 13-26. Any transformer center taps should not be grounded. For voltages above 12 and up to 52 V, double the chart resistor value of Fig. 13-25.

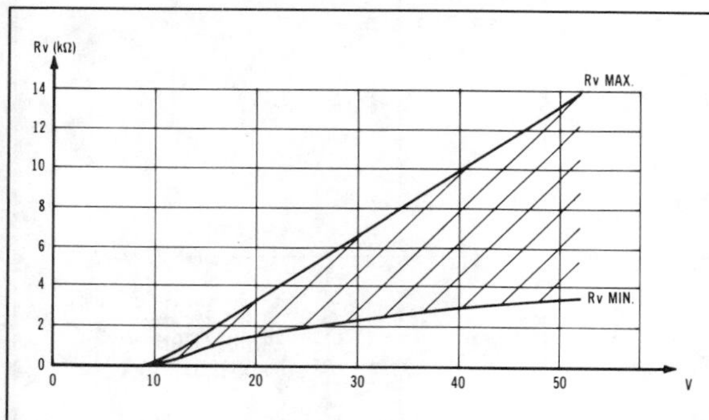

Figure 13-25 Dropping resistor value chart for phantom powering AKG C-451E microphones. *(Courtesy AKG Acoustics, Inc.)*

Any number of capacitor microphones may be powered by either method from a single B+ source according to the current available. Use of the largest resistor value shown (Rv maximum) for various voltages in Fig. 13-25 is recommended for minimum current consumption.

These same methods can be used to phantom power the capacitor microphones of other manufacturers.

13.6 CAPACITOR RADIO-FREQUENCY, FREQUENCY-MODULATED MICROPHONES

A *frequency-modulated microphone* is a capacitor microphone that is connected to a radio-frequency oscillator. Pressure waves striking the diaphragm cause variations in the capacity of the microphone head, which frequency modulates the oscillator. The output of the modulated oscillator is passed to a discriminator and amplified in the usual manner.

Capacitor microphones using a radio-frequency oscillator are not entirely new to the recording profession, but since the advent of solid-state devices, considerable improvement has been achieved in design and characteristics. An interesting microphone of this design is the Schoeps Model CMT26U manufactured in West Germany by Schall-Technik, and named after Dr. Carl Schoeps, the designer.

The basic circuitry is shown in Fig. 13-27.[9] By means of a single transistor, two oscillatory circuits are excited and tuned to the exact same frequency of 3.7 MHz. The output voltage from these circuits is rectified by a phase-bridge detector circuit, which operates over a large linear modulation range with very small radio-frequency voltages from the oscillator. The amplitude and polarity of the output voltage from the bridge depend on the phase angle between the two high-frequency voltages. The microphone capsule (head) acts as a variable capacitance in one of the oscillator circuits. When a sound wave impinges on the surface of the diaphragm of the microphone head, the vibrations of the diaphragm are detected by the phase curve of the oscillator circuit, and an audio frequency voltage is developed at the output of the bridge circuit. The microphone-head diaphragm is metal to guarantee a large constant capacitance. An automatic frequency control (afc) with a large range of operation is provided by means of capacitance diodes to preclude any influence caused by aging or temperature changes on the frequency determining elements, which might throw the circuitry out of balance.

The internal output resistance is 200 Ω. The signal is fed directly from the bridge circuit through two capacitors and delivers an output level of −51 to −49 dB (depending on the polar pattern used) into a 200-Ω load for a sound pressure level of 10 dynes/cm^2. The signal-to-noise ratio and the distortion are independent of the load because of the bridge circuit; therefore, the microphone may be operated into load impedances ranging from 30 to 200 Ω.

13.7 CAPACITOR RADIO-FREQUENCY MICROPHONES

A capacitor microphone of somewhat different design, manufactured by Sennheiser of West Germany and also employing a crystal-controlled oscillator, is shown in Fig. 13-28.[9] In the conventional capacitor microphone (without oscillator) the input impedance of the preamplifier is in the order of 100 MΩ; therefore, it is necessary to place the capacitor head and preamplifier in close proximity. In the Sennheiser microphone, the capacitive element (head) used with the radio-frequency circuitry is of lower impedance since the effect of a small change in capacitance at radio frequencies is considerably greater than at audio frequencies. Instead of the capacitor head being

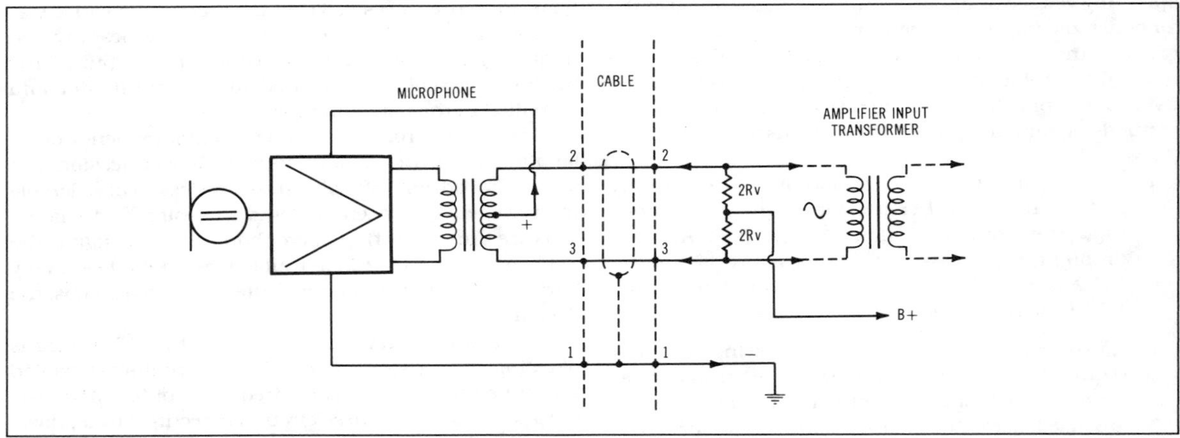

Figure 13-26 Artificial center tap connection method of powering capacitor microphones. *(Courtesy AKG Acoustics, Inc.)*

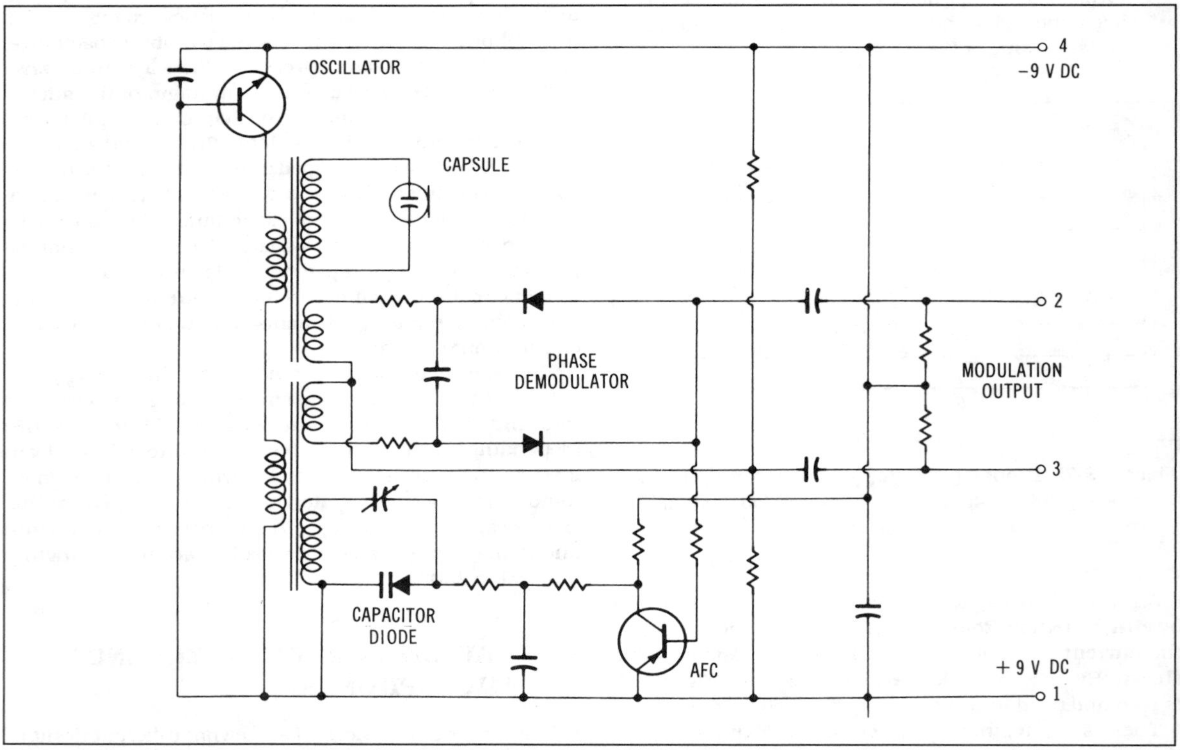

Figure 13-27 Basic circuit for the Schoeps radio-frequency capacitor microphone, series CMT.

subjected to a high dc polarizing potential, the head in this microphone is subjected to radio-frequency voltage of only a few volts.

Since the preamplifier and crystal-controlled oscillator are of transistor design, they are assembled in an integral unit. An external power supply of 12 V dc is required.

Referring to Fig. 13-28, the output voltage of the 10-MHz oscillator is periodically switched by diodes D_1 and D_2 to capacitor C. The switching phase is shifted 90° from that of the oscillator by means of loose coupling and aligning the resonance of the microphone circuit M under a no-sound condition. As a result, the voltage across capacitor C is zero. When a sound impinges on the diaphragm, the switching phase changes proportionally to the sound pressure, and a corresponding audio voltage appears across capacitor C. The output of the switching diodes is directly connected to the transistor-amplifier stage, whose gain is limited to 12 dB by the use of negative feedback.

To eliminate the effects of radio-frequency oscillator noise, the oscillator circuit is crystal controlled. Noise in an oscillatory circuit is inversely proportional to the Q of the circuit. Because of the high Q of the crystal and its stability, compensating circuits are not required, resulting in low internal noise.

The output stage is in reality an impedance-matching transformer adjusted for 100 Ω, for a load impedance of 2000 Ω or greater. Radio-frequency chokes are connected in the output circuit to prevent radio-frequency interference and also to prevent external radio-frequency fields from being induced into the microphone circuitry.

13.8 ELECTRET MICROPHONES

An *electret microphone* is a capacitor microphone in which the head capacitor has a permanent charge on it, therefore, eliminating the high-voltage bias supply.

From a design viewpoint a microphone intended to be used for critical recording, broadcast, or sound reinforcement represents a challenge involving minimal performance compromise. For this reason microphone designs using electret transducers have developed relatively slowly where high performance is a prime consideration. Early electrets did offer the microphone designer a means of reducing the complexity of a condenser microphone by eliminating the high-voltage bias supply, but serious environmental stability problems negated this advantage, which is not the case today. Well-designed electret microphones can be stored at 50°C (122°F) and 95% relative humidity for about a year with a sensitivity loss of only 1 dB. Under normal conditions of temperature and humidity, electret transducers will demonstrate a much lower charge reduction versus time than under the severe conditions indicated. Even as early as 1925 when Egushi was experimenting with wax electrets, he found no evidence of charge decay after a period of three years for those electrets stored in a short-circuited condition in a

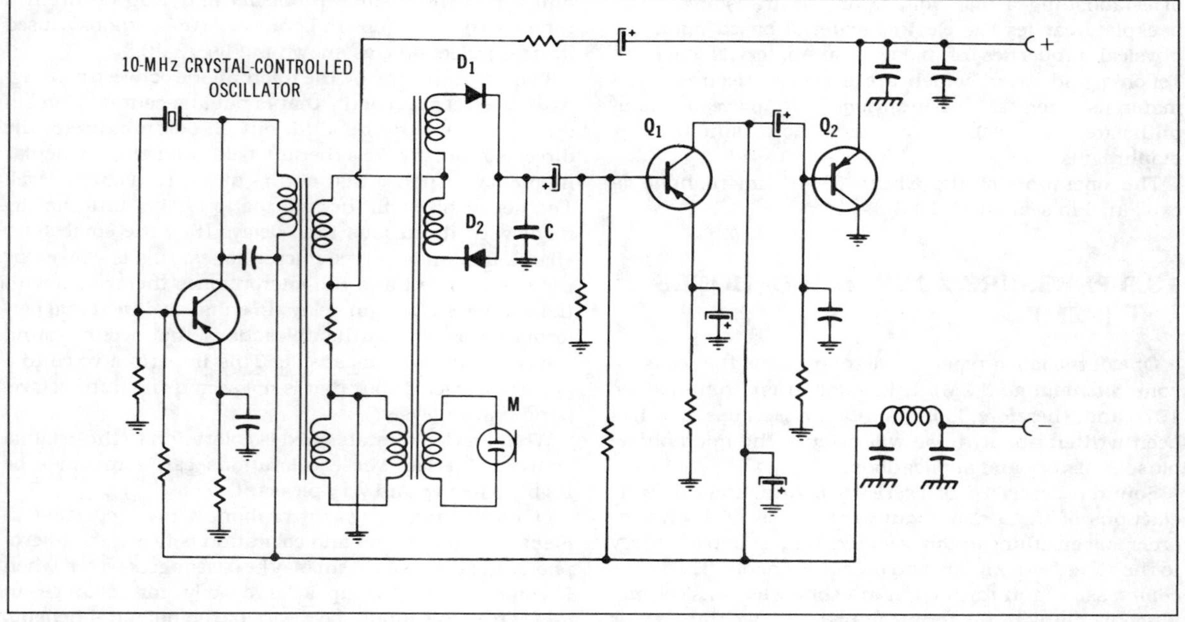

Figure 13-28 Basic circuit for the Sennheiser model 405 and 805 capacitor microphones. *(Courtesy Sennheiser Electronic Corp.)*

dry atmosphere at room temperature, which is not to say, however, that all electret transducers are the same in terms of charge stability. Even if a proper electret material is used, there are many steps in the fabricating, cleaning, and charging processes that greatly influence charge stability.

Properly constructed electrets can simplify the design of a condenser microphone by eliminating the need for dc to dc voltage converters or complex circuit configurations, or the need to operate at a specific simplex voltage to bias the transducer properly.

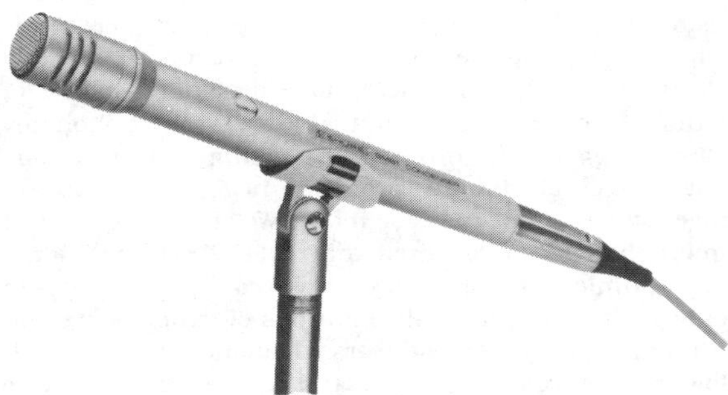

Figure 13-29 Shure SM81 unidirectional electret microphone. *(Courtesy Shure Brothers, Inc.)*

The Shure SM81 cardioid condenser microphone[14] shown in Fig. 13-29 uses an electret material as a means of establishing a bias voltage on the transducer. The backplate carries the electret material based upon the physical properties of halocarbon materials such as Teflon™ and Aclar, which are excellent electrets, and materials such as polypropylene and polyester terephthalate (Mylar™), which are more suitable for diaphragms.

The operation of the Shure SM-81 microphone is explained in section 13.13.3.3.

13.9 PRESSURE ZONE MICROPHONES (PZM)

One of the latest types of microphones is the *pressure zone microphone* (PZM). It has only been around since 1978 and, therefore, is in its infancy. Because little has been written about it, we will discuss the microphone plus its history and applications.

Sound is described as a series of contractions and rarefactions of the air. Without air there is no sound. In order for something to emit a sound, it must impart energy to the air as both kinetic and potential energy. The terms *compression* and *rarefaction* are somewhat misleading. When we think of the term *compression*, we think of air being compressed. Realistically speaking, if we impart a kinetic energy to this fluid media, which air really is, the air molecules that are already under atmospheric pressure are accelerated rather than compressed. What we are really doing is changing or varying the amount of acceleration or the velocity of the air molecular particles.

We all know that sound like other forms of energy reflects off certain types of surfaces and is absorbed by different types of surfaces. The various surfaces of a room create the characteristics that make that room sound like no other. So the walls, the number and curvature of surfaces, the absorptive resonators, the highly reflective surfaces, and even the high-frequency air absorption are the characteristics that impart the uniqueness to this sonic aspect of the room much the same way as fingerprints associate a uniqueness to an individual human being.

All electrical input transducers have to contend with these. Frequently, sonic characteristics of the room are desirable. Consider, for instance, the grandiosity of a large symphony hall. How would a brilliant piano concerto sound in the middle of a football field? Obviously, it would be very unnatural. When dealing with realism, we have to ask ourselves the questions as to which characteristics of the room are desirable and which are not desirable.

What makes the most pleasant rendition of reality? An oversimplification is that the larger, more ambient, more reverberant areas are more desirable for music reproduction, and we wish to capture as much of this as we can. We must, however, deal with the concept of direct versus reverberant sound to maintain the realistic articulation that we are trying to capture. Small rooms often have flutter phenomena and near reflections due to close proximity. But these same problems may also occur in a concert-type environment because of cancellations caused by near reflections, as shown in Fig. 13-30.

The net result can be the microphone converting a signal into electrical energy that is not an accurate blend of direct-to-reverberant sound, but an odd mixture of the direct sound, the reverberant field, and the particular frequency response that occurs at the transducer level. The net result is all the information going into the element with its various time delays (i.e., the comb filter effect). In standard type microphones, this is caused by the environment and the microphones themselves with their inherent built-in delays to enhance directional performance as well as the diffractions that occur around the proximity of the capsule. This imparts a voice to a particular microphone that is not seen using third-octave-band-type analysis.

What has been established is coloration to the original source material. These colorations can sometimes be highly effective and very pleasant.

Often when working a microphone with a single instrument, the interaction and coloration between the microphone and the instrument may be pleasing; however, when it comes to picking up a large body, for instance an orchestra, one should be aware of the potential benefits that the pressure zone phenomenon offers. In our con-

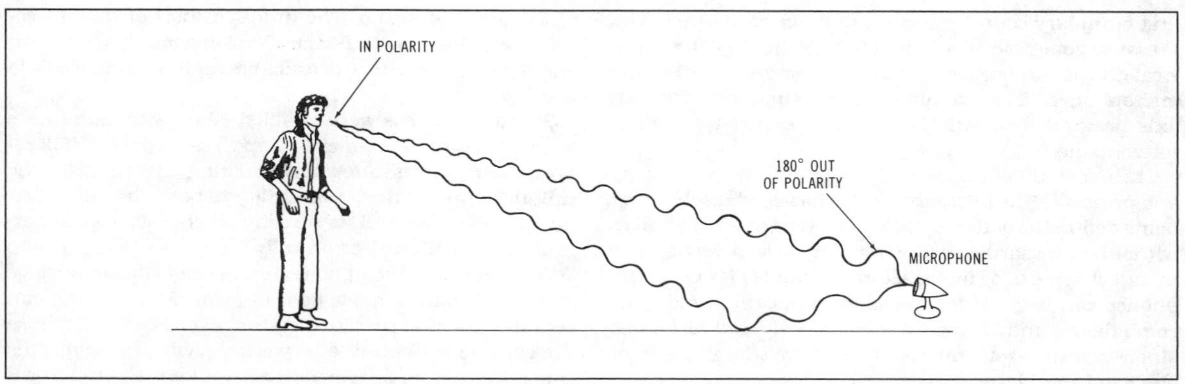

Figure 13-30 Effects of cancellations caused by near reflections (comb filters).

stant quest for ultimate perfection, we do not apologize for ultimately seeking more accurate transducers.

The pressure zone is the area where there is a coherent summation of all the information of the direct as well as reflective or delayed sound. The depth and the spatial square area of the pressure zone is involved with the waveform of the signal coming in and the longer wavelengths, that is, the low-frequency information, as a termination of boundary. The boundary is defined as the infinite boundary, which is that point where increasing the size of the area will not change the characteristic of the microphone. The infinite boundary theoretically imparts perfect low-frequency response to any capsule that would be capable of reproducing low frequencies. This is not desirable in any form of musical or voice-type recording or reinforcement; therefore, it is practical to utilize capsules that roll off between 20 and 40 Hz.

PZMs, as shown in Fig. 13-31, will be placed on a large boundary. The microphone capsule faces downward, which provides a number of advantages. First, it eliminates on-axis reinforcement that causes a peaking of the response of the sound based on the dimension of one wavelength with regard to the dimension of the capsule. Second, it gives the practical advantage of keeping the dust and dirt from falling down onto the microphone capsule diaphragm itself. It becomes obvious in choosing a capsule that the capsule must remain electroacoustically flat when loaded up against the boundary surface. Provided this capsule is inherently flat, the result of the overall pickup using the pressure zone technique is that of incredible accuracy.

In reviewing the results of the PZM on the infinite boundary, it is inherently flat both on-axis and off-axis and provides essentially an extra 6 dB of acoustic gain, making the microphone more efficient and giving the impression of adding directional characteristics. Frequently, PZMs are mistakenly called omnidirectional microphones; however, in reality, the microphone down to its lowest pressure-zone-loaded frequency is more

Figure 13-31 Crown PZMicrophone. *(Courtesy Crown International, Inc.)*

directional than a cardioid microphone. The PZM represents a hemispherical pattern having a Q of 2. This is dependent on boundary size, and the Q will vary with frequency as it does in most other areas of acoustics.

This is also the case with standard cardioid microphones. For instance, cardioid microphones may very well have a Q of 1.8 down to a frequency of 40 Hz. In which case the Q may go to 1.6 or 1.2 below 40 Hz. The directional characteristics of the standard cardioid microphone are permanent, they are not readily subject to variation. Any attempt to vary the characteristic can enhance the problem of mid- and high-frequency combing. This combing occurs from multiple entry into the microphone assembly itself as well as by diffraction around the capsule.

With the PZM, the boundary size and shape can be manipulated to establish different pickup patterns at different frequencies. PZMs represent a practical way to custom tailor the frequency response acoustically as well as pickup pattern and polar response for a particular application. The initial infinite boundary represents the theoretically perfect or textbook description of how PZMs operate. The PZM technique eliminates the comb filtering in the audible frequency range because the placement of the capsule into the pressure zone forces the primary and first boundary sound waves to reinforce each other. The pressure-zone placement also reduces the majority of the local diffraction properties that are common in free-field microphones. The technique also eliminates the on-axis peaking that can occur on a pressure-type omnimicrophone.

The net result of this is an enormous amount of clarity and presence. The microphone also has good reach, *reach* being defined as better articulation over greater distances without necessarily narrowing the pickup angle. The practical aspects of increased reach are (1) fewer microphones can be used for the same application, reducing comb filters, and (2) the increased clarity and reach of a single pressure-zone microphone allows a large group or choir to sound large.

13.9.1 History

The PZM is a new device with a unique history. The original rendition of this new technique involved the use of a modified ½-in. B & K instrument microphone. The technique of the Pressure Recording Process (PRP) was first demonstrated in February of 1978 by Ed Long and Ron Wickersham to the Syn-Aud-Con seminar in the San Francisco area. At that time the most impressive aspect of the demonstration was a somewhat startling realization that this was a new technique in theory and that in practice it represented a very apparent increase in the overall signal clarity.

Ken Wahrenbrock was at that demonstration and was so impressed that he further developed the concept using a small electret microphone capsule originally designed for high-quality miniature installations. Ken presented this prototype to Don Davis from Syn-Aud-Con when Don was first making Richard Heyser's time-delay spectrometry measurements. The TDS system enabled Wahrenbrock and Davis not only to hear but also to visualize the improvements that the PRP, or as it soon became known PZM, offered. Being able to measure with instruments what is heard is something that is always desirable, however, not always obtainable.

Wahrenbrock manufactured limited quantities of the PZMs, which were sold to graduates of the Syn-Aud-Con class for further experimentation. This became the beginning of one of the most unique aspects of any product development in the sound industry. The final stages of engineering of the product were done by its actual users, professional audio people.

In 1980 Crown International in Elkart, Indiana, purchased the world licensing rights to produce PZMs from Synergetic Audio Concepts. They made mechanical and electronic improvements to increase the versatility and sonic quality of the microphone further and renamed it the PZMicrophone. Meanwhile, Wahrenbrock continued research and development and maintained a strong communication with the newly formed PZM reader's group, called the *PZM Memo*. The unique aspect of this microphone continued with further development, by the Crown engineering department and the rapidly growing PZM user's group.

Standard models were established, new capsules were utilized, and development of special-purpose PZMicrophones and accessories began taking advantage of the unique aspect of the PZMs ability to both control its frequency response and its directional characteristics naturally rather than electronically.

The present PZMicrophones have a useful dynamic range of 130 dB, have a noise floor of below 20 dBa, and can respond to sound pressure levels above 150 dBa. Because the capsule is electret, a power supply is required. This can be either phantom derived or found through an external power supply. Fig. 13-32 shows various power supplies.

13.9.2 Applications

Because PZMicrophones are used in a different manner than standard microphones to accomplish the same goal, these differences allow the PZMicrophone to accomplish goals unobtainable with earlier microphone design. The applications of PZMicrophones will be discussed here rather than with other microphones.

As mentioned earlier, the microphone is not omnidirectional; in fact, it is more directional than a cardioid, since it is purely hemispherical when mounted on a properly sized boundary.

There are two different methods for controlling the directional pattern of the PZMicrophone.

The first method is by establishment of a second boundary where the nose of the PZMicrophone cantilever is abutted directly into the corner. This increases the directional characteristics of the microphone from a Q of two to a Q of four, or simply stated, one-quarter of the sphere, as shown in Fig. 13-33. This second boundary also provides several decibels of increased sensitivity of the microphone, thus, more directionality and increased acoustic gain.

Finally, a third boundary can be set in such that the microphone sits in a three-sided corner providing additional gain, as shown in Fig. 13-34. A very practical alternative to this setup would be to place the cantilever nose of the microphone into the natural corner of a large room. This offers an astounding increase in sensitivity and reduced room reverberation, making it most useful for picking up room conversations at meetings and around tables.

Once again we should be thinking of one-sixth-octave sizes with respect to usable directional frequencies if we are constructing our own boundary. A 2 × 2-ft size has a usable frequency response down to 80 Hz.

Many times an omnidirectional microphone is desirable for a speaking application in which case the boundary

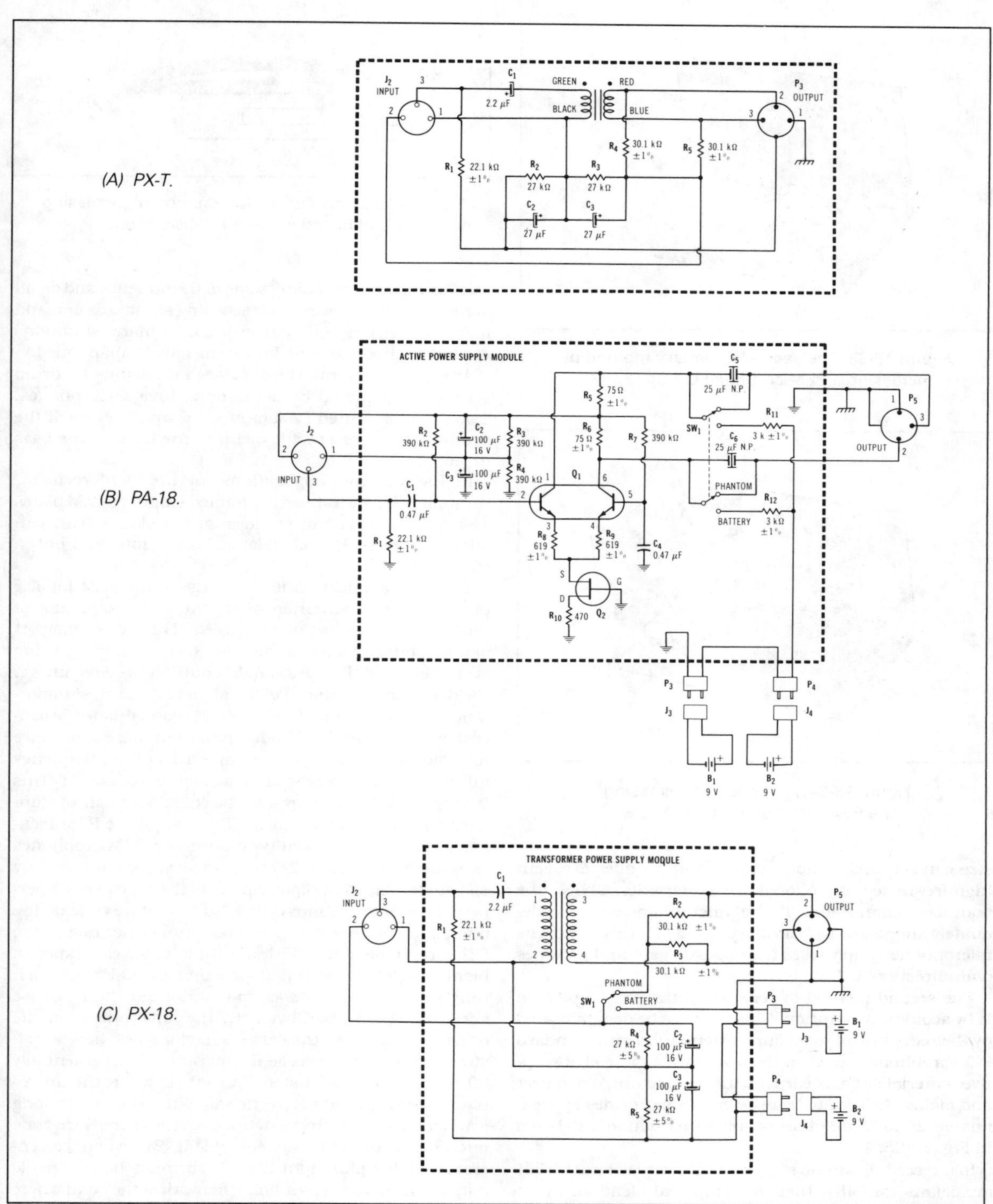

Figure 13-32 Crown PZMicrophone power supplies. *(Courtesy Crown International, Inc.)*

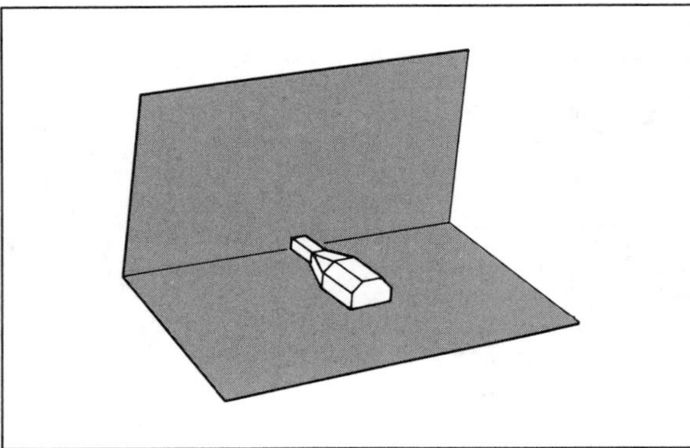

Figure 13-33 The second boundary method of increasing a PZMicrophone Q from 2 to 4.

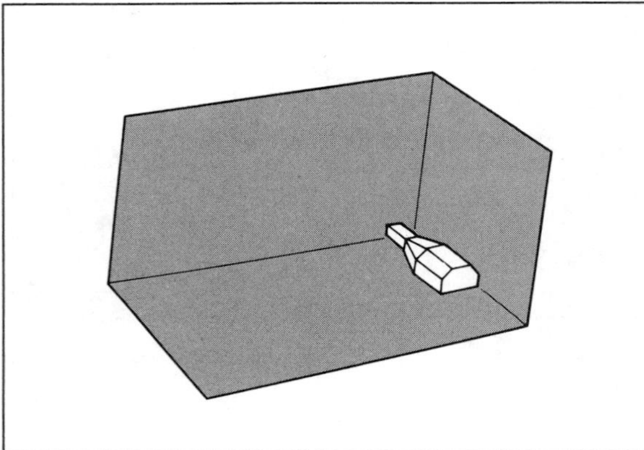

Figure 13-34 A method of increasing the PZMicrophone Q from 2 to 8.

size can be considerably smaller and yet offer excellent high-frequency directional characteristics above the boundary dimension. If the microphone is not adequately supported by boundary on any of the planes, the microphone simply loses the acoustic gain and becomes omnidirectional.

The second method of controlling the pickup pattern is by acoustic absorption. This can best be demonstrated by the reduction of rear sound attenuation on a standard PZMicrophone placed on the floor with a piece of absorptive material such as carpet with the nap out folded over and facing the area to be rejected. This provides approximately 20 to 25 dB of usable rear attenuation, as shown in Fig. 13-35.

In a recording studio situation, it is very desirable that musicians establish their own musical blend and that the recording engineer merely captures that blend. This, of course, necessitates working the microphone at a far-

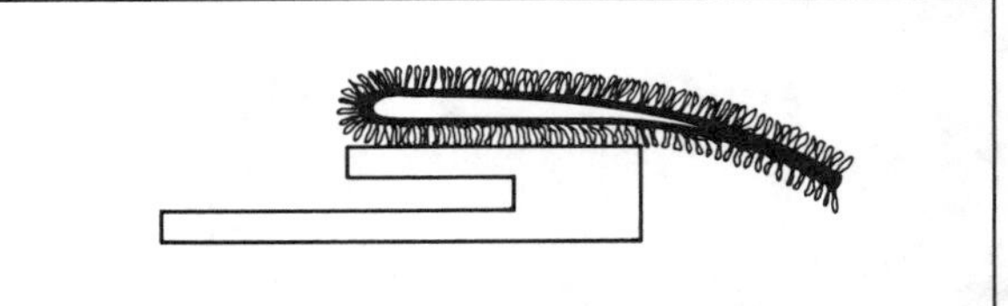

Figure 13-35 The absorption method of increasing Q and directivity of a PZMicrophone.

ther distance and reducing some of the presence and detail of the material. Present-day recording standards demand maximum detail and clarity; thus, in many situations the multimicrophone pickup technique is abandoned.

An excellent overall stereo image and detail of a drum set can be achieved by using only three microphones. Two stand-mounted PZMicrophones over the top of the drums and a third inside or up at the front of the bass drum.

In less complex applications for live reinforcement, drummers have strapped or chained standard PZM plates around their necks in the form of a necklace. This can offer a very usable, well-balanced drum mix with only a single microphone.

The next application is stereo using the PZM bipolar plate. Assume a situation where there is a large body of music to be recorded or reinforced. The stereo image is of utmost importance in this case; thus, multiple mic'ing is simply out of the question. In addition to stereo image, the detail and the clarity of the signal is of utmost importance because the material being recorded is for broadcast or for master disk production. Both these cases have to avoid out of phase or large amounts of low-frequency different signals in case of monaural reproduction. This is very nicely handled by a single coincident pair of standard free-field microphones. When using the PZM technique in a stereo modality, mount two PZMicrophones on either side of a 2 × 2-ft piece of plexiglass and slightly off center. The PZM bipolar plate is then suspended perpendicularly to the music body so that at no time do the music bodies see directly on-axis into either one of the PZMicrophone sides. With a 2-ft plate, we can expect a hemispherical pattern to approximately 80 Hz at which time the microphone goes monaural and the response shelves down 6 dB. Obviously, the microphone on the other side will offer the same behavior so we have a full-stereo sphere with excellent separation from essentially 80 Hz up and a 6-dB stepoff at 80 Hz when the microphone becomes omnidirectional. With respect to long wavelengths or low frequencies, both these pressure-zone microphone detectors are coincident. But when we generate our left-plus-right signal, running both capsule outputs into a voltage summing network at the point where we are out of boundary, both elements are essentially omni, coherent, low-frequency signals and, therefore, combine, providing 6 dB of gain. Thus, the net result is a flattening of the frequency response. The directional characteristics and somewhat desirable lack of coherency and isolation from left to right is precisely maintained at the critical imaging frequencies. Thus, the stereo bipolar plate is an almost perfect stereo sphere, offering many of the sonic advantages as to ambience and width of more widely spaced omnidirectional microphones and yet offering the technical advantages of the standard coherent pair mic'ing techniques.

This bipolar plate concept can be used with different boundary sizes for different mixing frequencies to establish low- or mid-frequency coherence, dependent on the engineer's choice of boundary size. For certain applications, such as pianos, drums, and other acoustical instruments, very usable stereo images can be obtained even from two PZM 6 × 5-in. plates mounted back to back.

13.9.3 Additional Microphone Techniques

A perfect stereo sphere is not desirable in certain applications. A varient of the original bipolar concept can be accomplished by mounting two PZMs on two 2 × 2-ft plates with a piano hinge on one end, as shown in Fig. 13-36. The PZM rear rejection, which essentially is lost to either side in the bipolar plate, can be reestablished by folding or angulating the two 2 × 2-ft plates in various angles for rear-frequency rejection. With this configuration, variable stereo separation can be adjusted, based on the angulation of the plates. As the angle approaches 180°, a number of things are expected to happen: (1) The image at most frequencies becomes monaural. (2) At higher frequencies, microphones remain temporarily spaced and combing, which occurs with any microphone pair at the mono mix or the left-plus-right signal, becomes a factor. Also the signal begins to see on axis directly at the plate, and the on-axis small boundary response peak begins to occur at wavelengths equal to the boundary size. Obviously, this can be either an asset or liability, depending upon how carefully the boundary size is thought out. By selecting different boundary sizes and angles, a natural acoustic form of equalization can be accomplished while at the same time adjusting the directional characteristic of a PZMicrophone.

The addition of two additional side wing boundaries can also be piano hinged to either side of the already hinged dual plates, as shown in Fig. 13-37. The microphone mounting position would be moved to the newly established corners of the side wings, which appear as a W. With this triply hinged four-plate system, additional mic'ing configurations can be simulated in that the angle and distance between the two PZMicrophone elements are adjustable by movement of the hinge surfaces. This system could facilitate an enormous amount of flexibility with respect to establishing your own recording standards.

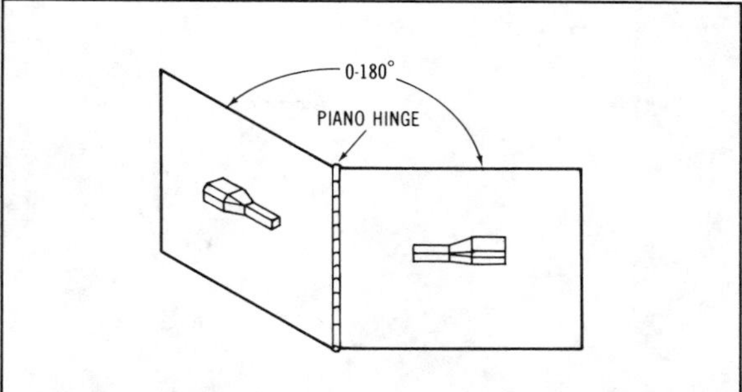

Figure 13-36 A method of varying the directivity of a bipolar PZMicrophone from coincident to monaural.

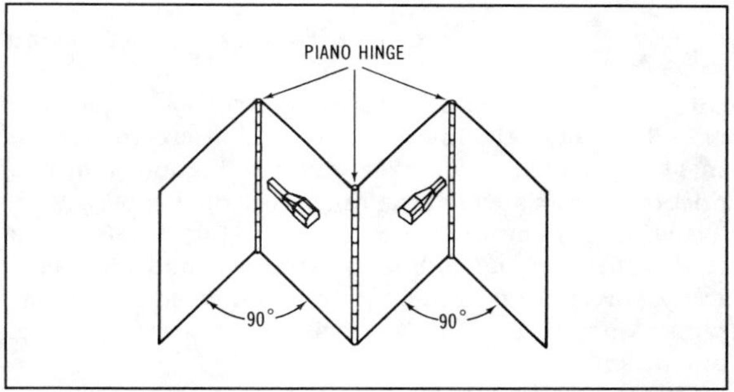

Figure 13-37 A "W" mounted PZMicrophone with capsule placement. Note the third capsule picks up the room ambience.

This system also offers the ability to place a third PZM element in the rear apex of the triangle, or point of the W, as a rear ambience transducer.

Needless to say, the pickup characteristics, frequency response, and imaging of this microphone array offer an enormous amount of flexibility. Yet with a basic understanding of what is happening with sound as it approaches boundaries and the pressure-zone phenomenon, the experienced engineer is offered flexibility heretofore unattainable.

13.10 WIRELESS COMMUNICATION SYSTEMS

Wireless communication systems is the term referred to wireless microphones (*radio microphones*) and a related concept, wireless intercoms. Because wireless microphones and intercoms share the same basic technology, many companies that manufacture one also manufac-

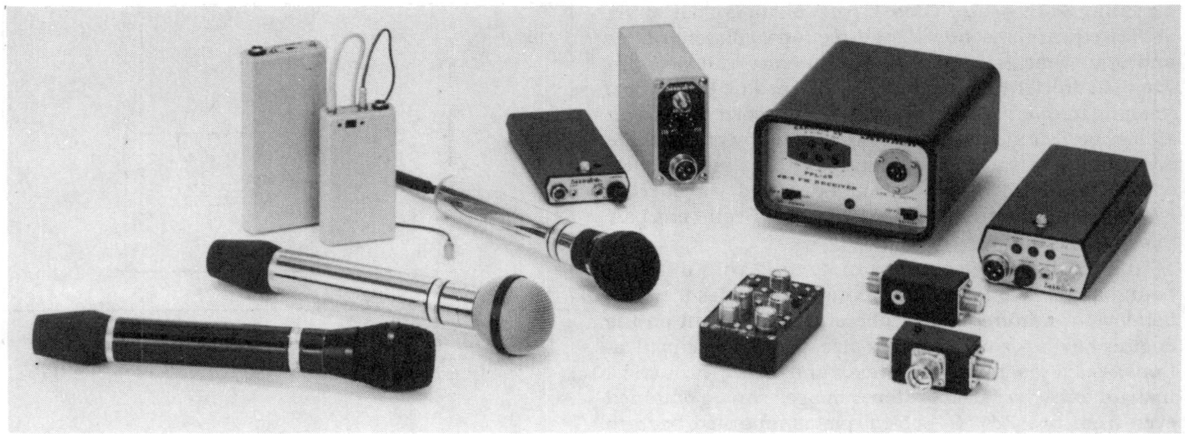

Figure 13-38 Swintek wireless microphone. *(Courtesy Swintek Enterprises, Inc.)*

ture the other. And, as it turns out, the same end user often buys both the microphones and intercoms for use in television and radio broadcast production, film production, and related entertainment-oriented applications.

A wireless microphone, as shown in Fig. 13-38, is one that on the sending end has a dynamic, condenser, electret, or pressure zone microphone connected to a preamplifier, compressor, and a small transmitter/modulator and antenna.

On the receiving end is an antenna, receiver/discriminator, expander, and preamplifier, which is connected to the audio equipment.

Most of us know how a standard intercom system operates: Each person has a headset and belt pack (or equivalent), all interconnected by wires. Wireless intercoms are essentially identical in operation, only they use no cable between operators. Instead, each belt pack includes a radio transmitter and receiver. The wireless intercom user typically wears a headset (a boom microphone with one or two earpieces) and can simultaneously transmit on one frequency and receive on another. The wireless intercom transmitter is virtually identical to a wireless microphone transmitter, but the receiver is miniaturized so that it, too, can be conveniently carried around and operated with minimum battery drain.

Wireless microphones are widely used today in television production. Hand-held models (integral microphone capsule and transmitter) are used by performers "on camera," where they not only free the performer to walk around and gesture spontaneously, they also avoid the need for stage personnel to feed wires around cameras, props, and so on. Lavalier models (small pocket-sized transmitters that work with lavalier or miniature "hidden" microphones) are used in game shows, soap operas, dance routines, and so on, where they eliminate the need for boom microphones and further avoid visual clutter. For location film production, as well as electronic news gathering (ENG), and electronic field production (EFP), wireless microphones make it possible to obtain usable "first take" sound tracks in situations where, previously, postproduction dialogue looping was necessary. The resultant savings in time and cost can really add up. In theatrical productions, wireless microphones free actors to speak and/or sing at less than operatic levels with a sound-reinforcement system supplementing lung power—and there is no visual distraction from boom microphones and no amplified foot or background noise from floor-mounted microphones and overhead microphones. In concerts, hand-held wireless microphones permit vocalists to gyrate and dance around without restriction, and without shock hazard even in the rain. Some lavalier models have high-impedance line inputs that accept electric guitar cords to create wireless guitars.

In all these applications where wireless microphones are used, in the studio or on location, a wireless intercom also is an invaluable communications aid between directors, stage managers, camera, lighting and sound crews, and security personnel. For cueing of talent and crews (or monitoring intercom conversations), economical receive-only units are available. In sports production, wireless intercoms are not only used by coaches, spotters, and players, but also by production crews and reporters. A major advantage is zero setup time. In critical stunt coordination, a wireless intercom can make the difference between a safe event or none at all.

13.11 CRITERIA FOR SELECTING A WIRELESS MICROPHONE OR INTERCOM

There are a number of criteria that must be considered in obtaining a wireless microphone or intercom system suitable for professional use. Ideally, such a system must work perfectly and reliably in a variety of tough environments with good intelligibility and must be usable near strong radio-frequency fields, lighting dimmers, and other sources of electromagnetic interference. This relates directly to the type of modulation (standard frequency modulation or narrow band frequency modulation), the operating frequency, high frequency (HF), very high frequency (VHF), ultrahigh frequency (UHF), the receiver selectivity, and so forth. The system should be very reliable and should be capable of operating at least five hours on one set of disposable batteries (or on one recharge if Ni-Cads are used).

Wireless microphones are licensed on several frequencies, the most common being:

VHF low band (AM and FM) 25 to 50 and 72 to 76 MHz

FM broadcast (FM) 88 to 108 MHz

VHF high band (FM) 150 to 216 MHz

VHF (FM) 450 to 488 and 902 to 952 MHz

The VHF low band is a favorite of low-cost systems; however, it is in the noisiest radio spectrum and, because of the length of the wavelength, requires a long antenna (5 ft). The VHF low band is also susceptible to "skip," which is signals from a long distance away bouncing off of the ionosphere back to earth, creating interference. Many VHF low-band systems are manufactured for use on the citizens band, which is very full and almost guaranteed to create noise interference and poor quality.

The FM broadcast band is another band used for low-cost systems. The advantage of using this band is that the system is compatible to FM stereo receivers and tuners; therefore, only the transmitter section must be purchased. This system is useful in remote areas where FM stations are few and far between; however, it is not reliable in areas such as New York City where the FM band is saturated.

The VHF high band is the most favorable for most applications. The one-quarter-wavelength antenna is only about 17 in. long and, therefore, requires little space. The VHF band has some penetration through buildings that can be advantageous and disadvantageous. It is advantageous in being able to communicate between rooms and around surfaces. It is disadvantageous in that transmission is not controlled (security), and outside noise sources can reach the receiver.

The UHF band equipment is similar to the VHF high band equipment except that the antennas are much shorter, the range is not as good, penetration through buildings is better, and there are fewer allocated frequency assignments.

The 130- to 230-MHz VHF high band is very low in noise and interference and allows good range at low power (up to 1000 ft line-of-sight at 50 mW radio-frequency power output). Most often the frequencies between 174 and 216 MHz are used corresponding to television channels 7 to 13. You'll have to select frequencies on inactive channels in a given geographical area. The VHF high band is free of citizens band and business radio interference, and any commercial broadcast stations that might cause interference are scheduled so you know where they are and can avoid them. Inherent immunity to noise is built in because FM modulation, not AM, is used. Better VHF high-band receivers will have adequate selectivity to reject nearby commercial television or FM broadcast signals. Naturally, if you're operating the microphone or intercom on unused television channel 7, you'll want protection against a local television station on channel 8. However you also should be concerned about the FM radio band from 88 to 108 MHz because of harmonics. If a multi-thousand-watt FM station is broadcasting near your 0.05-W (50 mW) radio microphone, even a well-suppressed second harmonic can have a radio frequency field strength comparable to the wireless microphone or intercom signal. Remember, the second harmonic of FM 88 is 176 MHz, right in the middle of television channel 7, and the second harmonic of FM 107 is 214 MHz, right in the middle of channel 13. Thus, if your VHF wireless system is to be utilized fully, especially with several microphones or intercoms on adjacent frequencies, the wireless receiver should have a very selective front end—either helical or crystal tuned—which can raise the cost compared to mid- or low-band systems. An added advantage of VHF high-band systems is that they are not as likely to interfere with video monitors or recorders as are lower frequency systems.

With wireless intercoms, where two-way communication is involved, some manufacturers utilize VHF high-band transmission at the base station, while the remotes broadcast on a lower frequency (near 27 MHz CB, or the 30 to 35 MHz and 72- to 76-MHz business bands). In split-band systems, there is the possibility that half the communications link will be more subject to noise and interference than the other half.

One television channel occupies a 6-MHz wide segment of the VHF band. Channel 7, for example, covers from 174 to 180 MHz. A wireless intercom occupies much less bandwidth, about 0.2 MHz (200 kHz). In fact, by Federal Communications Commission (FCC) Part 74 allocation, up to 24 discrete VHF high-band microphones and/or intercoms can be operated in the space of a single television channel. However, in order to use multiple systems on adjacent frequencies, the wireless microphone/intercom receivers must be very selective and have an excellent capture ratio. On a practical basis, this means using narrow-deviation FM (approximately 12-kHz modulation). Wide-deviation systems (75-kHz modulation or more) can easily cause interference on adjacent microphone/intercom frequencies; such systems also require wideband-width receivers that are more apt to be plagued by interference from adjacent frequencies. Receivers for wideband FM transmitters, or poorly designed narrowband FM receivers, are also subject to *desensing*. Desensing means the wireless microphone/intercom receiver is muted because another microphone, intercom, television station, or FM station (second harmonic) is transmitting in close proximity; this limits the effective range of the microphone or intercom.

With wireless microphones, check the capture ratio and muting specifications of the receiver. It should provide at least 40- to 50-dB signal to noise with a 10-μV signal, and 70- to 80-dB signal to noise with an 80-μV signal. With wireless intercoms, you can look to see whether a single antenna is used simultaneously for transmitting and receiving; such systems have antenna duplexers and are more likely to be immune to the desensing problem.

The maximum legal radio-frequency power output of a VHF high-band microphone or intercom transmitter is 50 mW; most deliver from 25 to 50 mW, at most a 3-dB difference. Up to 120 mW is permissible in the business band (for wireless intercoms) under FCC part 90.217, but even this represents less than 4 dB more than 50 mW. The FCC does not permit the use of high-gain transmitter antennas, and even if they did, such antennas are large and directional so they would not be practical for someone who is moving around. Incidentally, high-gain receiving antennas are also a bad idea because (1) the transmitter is constantly moving around with the performer, and (2) much of the received radio signal is actually caught "on the bounce" from walls, props, and so on. So even if you stood off stage and aimed a beam antenna at the performer, you'd probably be aiming at the wrong target. Diversity receiving antenna systems, where two or more antennas pick up and combine signals to feed the receiver, will reduce dropouts or fades for fixed receiver installations.

Given that you can't do much to boost the received signal level given the restrictions on antennas and transmitted power, what is the primary factor in increasing the usable distance of a wireless microphone or intercom system? Usable range relies heavily on receiver sensitivity and selectivity (i.e., capture ratio and signal-to-noise ratio) as well as on the audio dynamic range. Whether you get a greater signal-to-noise ratio in the radio frequency or the audio, it lets you communicate over greater distances. There are now a number of systems that are designed for improved audio signal-to-noise performance.

In the "old days" (pre 1980), most wireless microphones and intercoms used a simple compressor to avoid transmitter overmodulation. Today, many systems include compandor circuitry for 15 to 30 dB better audio signal to noise without changing the radio-frequency signal to noise. This is achieved by building a full-range compressor into the microphone or intercom transmitter, and then providing complementary expansion of the audio signal at the receiver—much like the encoder of a tape noise-reduction system. The compression keeps loud sounds from overmodulating the transmitter and keeps quiet sounds above the hiss and static. The expander restores the loud sounds after reception and further reduces any low-level hiss or static. Companding the audio signal can provide from 80 to 85 dB of dynamic range compared to the 50 or 60 dB of a straight noncompanded transmit/receive system using the same deviation.

No wireless microphone will provide flat response from 20 Hz to 20 kHz, nor is it really needed. Wireless or not, by the time the audience hears the broadcast, film, or concert, they are lucky to enjoy frequency response from 40 Hz to 15 kHz. Probably the best criteria for judging a hand-held wireless microphone system is to compare it to the microphone capsule's "naked" response. If the transmit/receive bandwidth basically includes the capsule's bandwidth, that is enough. Generally speaking, a good wireless microphone should sound just like the hard-wired microphone that used the same capsule (and most do). A lavalier wireless system should have the best bandwidth spec because almost any microphone may be plugged into it, and given the extra physical space available, it is easier for the manufacturer to do a better job with a lavalier. Still, no very high frequency high-band wireless system currently available can legally go much beyond 13 to 15 kHz at the top end due to FCC-mandated modulation limitations—not if it is to retain the important benefits of adjacent channel rejection so that several microphones can be used at one time, regardless of location. Wireless intercom systems, because they are primarily for speech communication, are less critical with regard to audio bandwidth; 300 Hz to 3 kHz is telephone quality, and 50 Hz to 8 kHz is excellent for an intercom.

Dynamic range is probably the most critical aspect of performance for natural sound. A good compandor system will provide 80 to 85 dB of dynamic range, assuming the microphone is adjusted to 100% modulation on the loudest sounds. If you leave a "margin of safety" by turning down the microphone modulation level, you sacrifice signal-to-noise; even if you allow extra headroom and assume a working signal-to-noise ratio of 75 dB, that is still about twice the dynamic range of a typical optical film sound track or television show. When wireless microphones were improved from the 50- to 60-dB state-of-the-art to today's 80 to 85 dB, some audio-mixing engineers found their job became more difficult. That is because there was no longer a compressor on each microphone, so they had to be careful to ensure that the console's gain structure was properly adjusted to avoid overdriving the microphone preamps. In fact, at least one manufacturer (Swintek) went back and put some compression in the wireless microphones—not adjusted to work on the majority of the program, but only to level the loudest signals that go beyond the radio link's 85-dB companded capability—primarily to make it easier for the engineer to avoid overdriving the console input.

When an electret condenser microphone is used, a major limitation in dynamic range can be the capsule itself, not the wireless system. Typically, an electret powered by a 1.5-V cell gives up at about 105-dB sound pressure level. Powered by a 9-V battery, the same microphone may be usable to 120-dB sound pressure level. Thus, the wireless microphone system ought to be able to provide a high enough bias voltage to ensure adequate dynamic range from the microphone capsule. The user should not expect a greater dynamic range spec from an electret condenser microphone. Although the condenser may be "hotter" in output level than a dynamic microphone, its background noise level is disproportionately higher, so the overall signal-to-noise spec may be lower. Practically speaking, though, dynamic microphones can be subject to more handling noise so their quieter capsules may not produce more usable dynamic range than a condenser microphone, which all seems to point to using the microphone whose sound you like. Do not try to base your decision solely on a printed specification, however honest it may be.

Wireless intercom systems do not need the same dynamic range as a microphone. They do not have to convey a "natural" musical performance. However, natural dynamics are less fatiguing than highly compressed audio, especially given a long work shift. So aside from greater range, there are other benefits to seeking good signal to noise in the intercom: 40 or 50 dB would be usable, and 60 or 70 dB is superb for an intercom. An exception might be in a very high noise industrial environment, where a compressed loud intercom is necessary to overcome background noise. Of course, a good intercom headset should double as a hearing protector and exclude much of the ambient noise.

Distortion is higher in a wireless system than in a hard-wired system—a radio link will never be as clean as the proverbial "straight piece of wire." Still, total harmonic distortion (THD) specs of less than 1% overall are commonly available in today's better wireless microphones. In these microphones, one of the largest contributors to harmonic distortion is the compandor, so you do trade some distortion to gain signal-to-noise ratio. The wireless intercom can tolerate more THD, but lower distortion can prevent fatigue and improve communication.

Two of the biggest problems with using wireless microphones are signal-to-noise ratio and dynamic range.

To overcome these problems, the signal is compressed at the transmitter and expanded at the receiver, as shown in Fig. 13-39. Fig. 13-40 graphically illustrates what this can accomplish with respect to improving the signal-to-noise ratio and reducing the susceptibility to low-level incidental FM modulation, such as buzz zones.

As the typical input level changes by a factor of 80 dB, the audio output to the modulator undergoes a contoured compression, whereby a change in input audio level is translated into a pseudologarithmic output. This increases the average modulation level, which reduces all forms of interference encountered in the transmission medium.

By employing standard narrow-band techniques at the

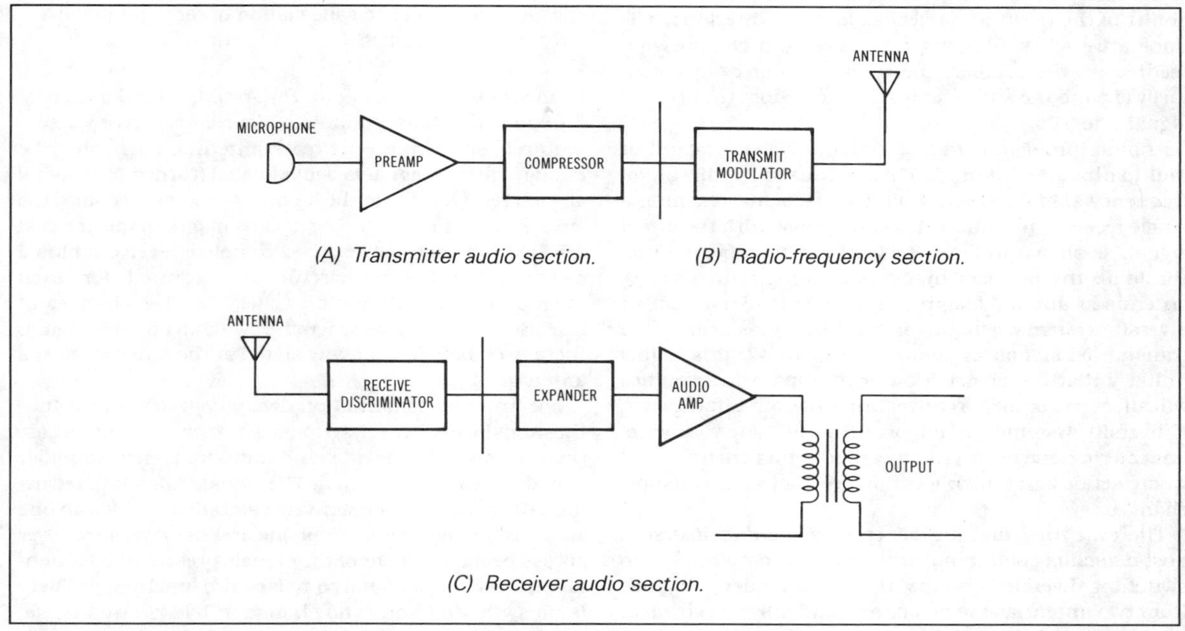

Figure 13-39 Wireless microphone transmitter section with built-in preamplifier, compresser, and transmitter, and the receive section with built-in discriminator expander.

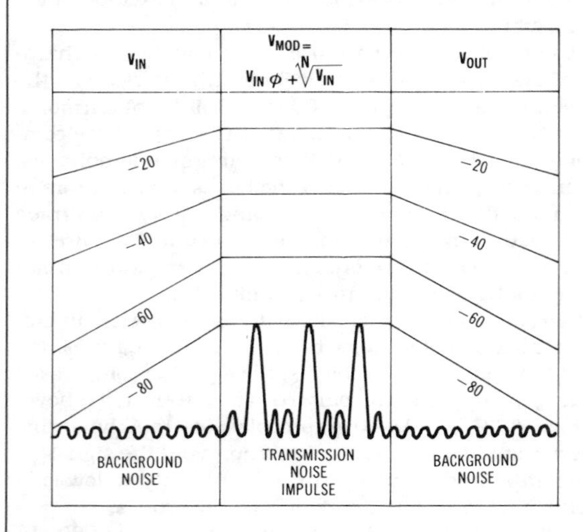

Figure 13-40 Compression and expansion of the audio signal. Note the −80-dB signal is not altered, and the −20-dB signal is altered significantly.

receiver, the recovered audio is virtually free of adjacent channel and spurious response interference. In addition, up to ten times the number of systems can be operated simultaneously without cross-channel interference. The ability of the receiver to reject all forms of interference is imperative when utilizing expansion and compression techniques. Remember, the receiver must complementarily expand the audio component to restore the original signal integrity.

Another problem is radio-frequency signal dropout or multipath cancellation.[10] This is caused by the radio-frequency signal reflecting off a surface and reaching a single receiver antenna 180° out-of-phase with the direct signal, as shown in Fig. 13-41. Although you can often eliminate the problem by experimenting with receiver antenna location, a foolproof approach is to use a space diversity system where two or more antennas pick up the transmitted signal, as shown in Fig. 13-42. It is highly unlikely that the obstruction or multipath interference will affect two or more receiver antennas simultaneously. A diversity system is an important addition to your wireless microphone receiver in any production environment where set design and/or location are subject to constant changes.

There are three diversity schemes: *switching diversity*, *post-detection combining*, and *antenna combination*. In switching diversity systems, the radio-frequency signals from two antennas are compared, and only the stronger one is selected. The problem here is that no benefit is derived from the signal at the other antenna, and if the stronger signal happens to be stronger due to an interference or noise component, that problem predominates.

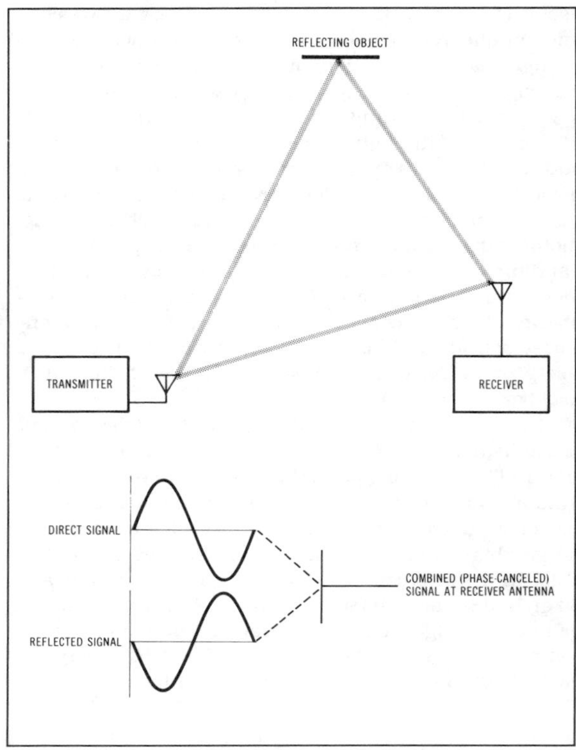

Figure 13-41 Phase cancellation of radio-frequency signals due to reflections.

In post-detection combining, two complete receivers are required, one connected to each antenna. Then, after the radio-frequency signal is demodulated (turned into audio) at each receiver, the audio signals are compared, and the stronger one is selected. The disadvantages to this method are (1) high cost because two complete receivers plus a comparator/switching circuit are required for each microphone and (2) audible "clicks" and/or changes in background noise level when the switching occurs. Again, there is no benefit from any signal at the other receiver's antenna.

The antenna combination diversity system overcomes these obstacles. This system uses two or more antennas, each connected to a wideband radio-frequency amplifier to boost the received signal. The signals from both receiving antennas are then actively combined and fed to one standard receiver per microphone. In this way, the receiver always gets the benefit of the signals present at all antennas, so a superior signal-to-noise ratio is achieved. There is no switching noise, no change in background noise, and best of all, you don't have to buy a receiver for each channel. It is often common to use a near antenna and a far antenna. The near antenna, which is the one near-

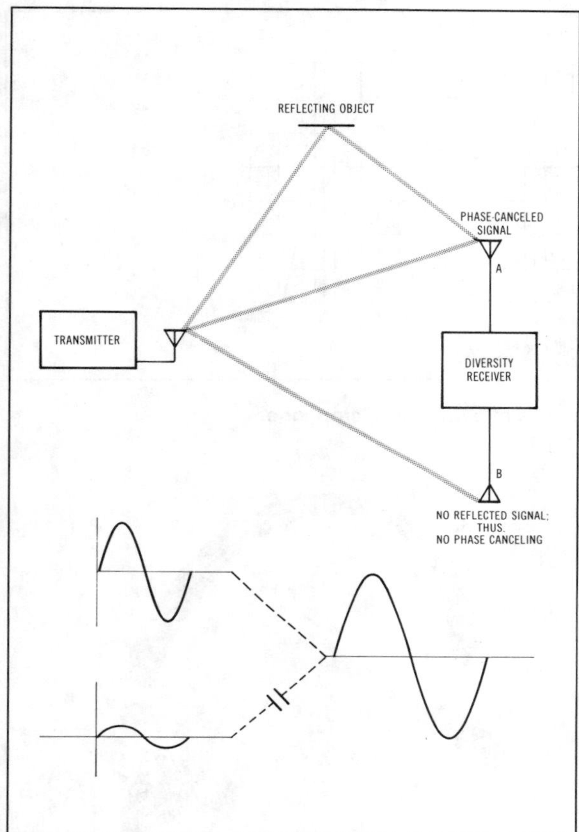

Figure 13-42 Diversity antenna system used to reduce multipath radio-frequency phase cancellation.

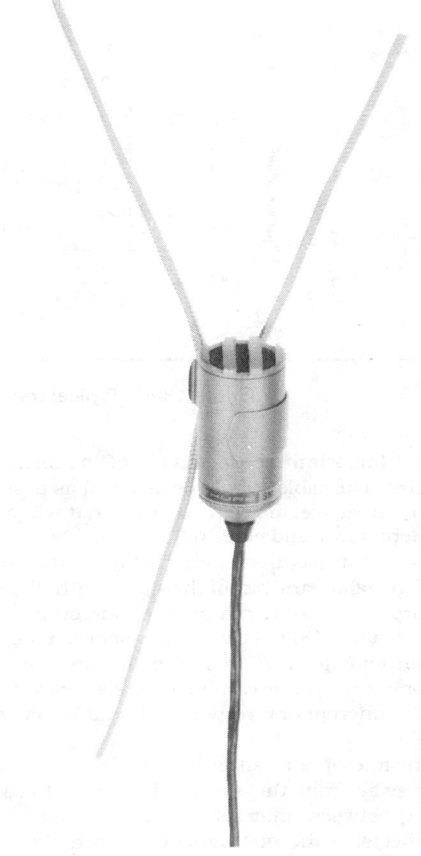

Figure 13-43 Shure SM11 dynamic omnidirectional lavalier microphone. *(Courtesy Shure Brothers, Inc.)*

est the transmitter, produces the majority of the signal most of the time; in fact, it may even be amplified with an in-line amplifier. The far-field antenna may be one or more antennas usually offset in elevation and position; therefore, the possibility of dropout is greatly reduced. Because the antennas are common to all receivers, many wireless microphones can be used at the same time on the same antenna system. This means that there are fewer antennas and a greater possibility of proper antenna placement.

13.12 MISCELLANEOUS MICROPHONES

13.12.1 Lavalier Microphones

Lavalier microphones are made either to wear on a lavalier around the neck or to clip onto a tie, shirt, or other piece of clothing, as shown in Fig. 13-43.

Lavalier microphones may be dynamic, condenser (capacitor), pressure-zone, electret, or even high-impedance ceramic. They have one thing in common, however; they are all omnidirectional. Because they are worn on the body in the vicinity of the chest cavity, the lavalier microphone response is "shaped" to reduce the boominess of the chest cavity and the loss of high-frequency response caused by being 90° off axis to the signal, as shown in Fig. 13-44.

Lavalier microphones are normally used to give the user freedom of movement. This causes problems associated with motion, for instance, noise being transmitted through the microphone cable. To reduce this noise, soft, flexible microphone cable with good fill to reduce wire movement should be used. The cable, or power supply for electret/condenser microphones, should be clipped to the user's belt or pants to reduce cable noise to only that created between the clip and the microphone. Clipping to the waist also has the advantage of acting as a strain relief when the cord is pulled or stepped on.

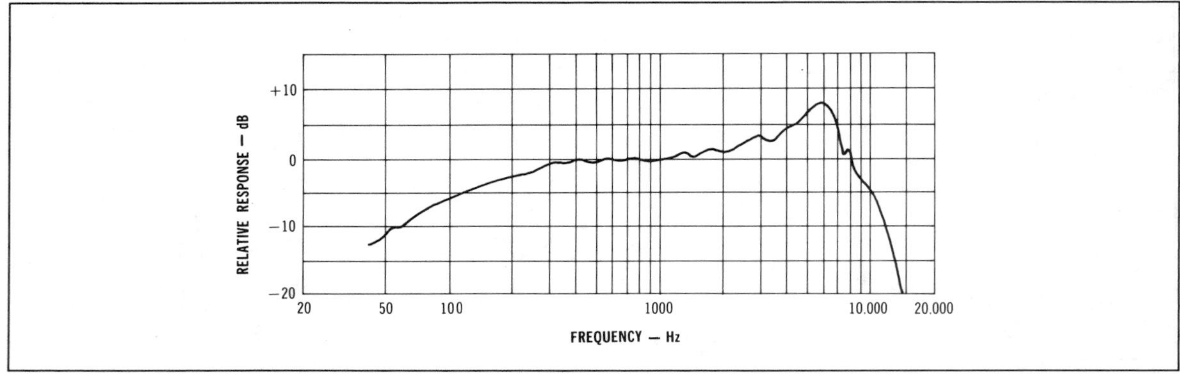

Figure 13-44 Typical frequency response of a lavalier microphone.

A second important characteristic of the microphone cable is size. The cable should be as small as possible to make it unobtrusive and light enough so it will not pull on the microphone and clothing.

Because the microphone is normally 10 in. from the mouth of the talker and out of the signal path, the microphone output is less than a microphone on a stand in front of the talker. Unless the torso is between the microphone and loudspeaker, this often means the lavalier microphone is the prime candidate for feedback. For this reason, the microphone response should be as smooth as possible.

As in any microphone situation, the farther the microphone is away from the source, the more freedom of movement between microphone and source without adverse effects. If the microphone is worn close to the neck for increased gain, the output level will be greatly affected by the raising and lowering and turning of the head (see section 13.15.1); therefore, it is most important that the microphone be worn chest high.

Lavalier microphones normally do not make good free-standing microphones because of their "shaping" and, therefore, should only be used as a lavalier microphone.

13.12.2 Head-Worn Microphones

Head-worn microphones such as the Shure Model SM10 shown in Fig. 13-45, are low-impedance, unidirectional, dynamic microphones, designed for sports and news announcing, for interviewing and intercommunications systems, and for special-event remote broadcasting. Head-worn microphones offer convenient, hands-free operation without user fatigue. As close-talking units, they may be used under noisy conditions without the losing or masking of voice signals. They are small, lightweight, rugged, and reliable units that normally mount to a cushioned headband. A pivot permits the microphone boom to be moved 20° in any direction, and the distance between the microphone and pivot to be changed 3½ in.

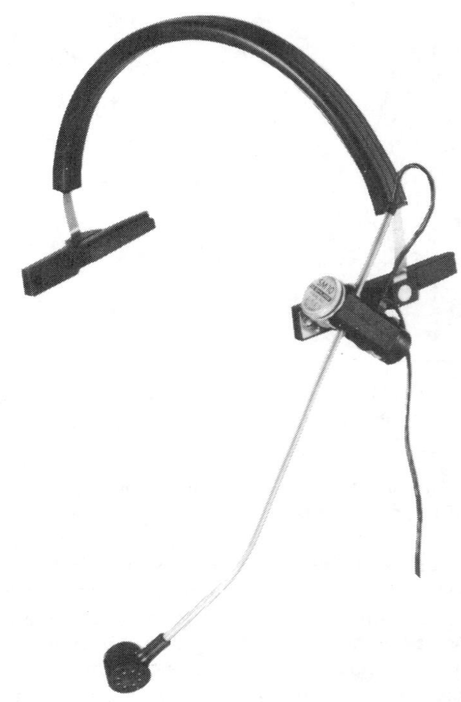

Figure 13-45 Shure SM10 dynamic unidirectional head-worn microphone. *(Courtesy Shure Brothers, Inc.)*

13.12.3 Base Station Power Microphones

Base station microphones are designed specifically for citizens band transceivers, amateur radio, and two-way radio applications. For clearer transmission and improved reliability, transistorized microphones can be used to

Figure 13-46 Shure 526T dynamic omnidirectional base station microphone. *(Courtesy Shure Brothers, Inc.)*

replace ceramic or dynamic, high- or low-impedance microphones supplied as original equipment.

The microphones shown in Fig. 13-46 are designed for base station operation with maximum versatility. They have a momentary or locking press-to-talk transmit/receive switch for ease of use, a modulation level volume control for the highest undistorted output with high- or low-impedance inputs, and a normal/vox selector switch for press-to-talk or vox-operated transceivers.

13.12.4 Throat Microphones

With *throat microphones* the diaphragm is actuated by being directly on contact with the external portions of the throat. Such microphones were widely used in aircraft for radio and internal intercommunication, or where the ambient noise level was high. These microphones are now obsolete.

To obtain the maximum intelligibility, the high frequencies are attenuated. The unit may be of the moving coil or button design.

13.12.5 Sound-Powered Microphones

Sound-powered microphones are constructed similarly to dynamic microphones with the exception that they generate considerably more output power and may be used without amplification over a considerable distance. They are frequently used in intercommunication systems. The frequency response is limited to the voice frequency range.

13.12.6 Differential Noise-Canceling Microphones

Differential noise-canceling microphones, as shown in Fig. 13-47, are essentially designed for use in automobiles, aircraft, boats, tanks, public-address systems, industrial plants, or for any service where the ambient noise level is 80 dB or greater and the microphone is hand held. Discrimination is afforded against all sounds originating more than ¼ in. from the front of the microphone. The noise-canceling characteristic is achieved through the use of a balanced port opening, which conducts the unwanted sound to the rear of the dynamic unit diaphragm and is out of phase with the sound arriving at the front of the microphone. The noise canceling is most effective for frequencies above 2000 Hz. Only the speech originating within ¼ in. of the aperture is fully reproduced. The average discrimination between speech and noise is 20 dB with a frequency response of 200 to 5000 Hz.

Figure 13-47 Shure 419 controlled magnetic noise-canceling microphone. *(Courtesy Shure Brothers, Inc.)*

13.12.7 Filter Microphones

Filter microphones are used to simulate a telephone conversation during a radio or television broadcast. A normal microphone is used with a telephone equalizer or filter that cuts off below 300 Hz and above 3500 Hz. The effect is telephone conversation.

13.12.8 Line-Level Microphones

Line-level microphones, such as the Shure SM-82, are hand-held self-contained microphones with their own line-level amplifier, peak limiter, and battery power supply. They are designed to provide a line-level output for use in a variety of broadcast situations, sound reinforcement, and recording applications where a line-level microphone with a built-in limiter is required. The microphone output is 0 dBm for a 94-dB sound pressure level. When the input reaches approximately 100-dB sound pressure level, the built-in limiter holds the output to about +6 dBm.

The line-level microphone can be used to up to 1 mi with unshielded cable and is capable of driving telephone lines.

13.12.9 Controlled-Reluctance Microphones

The *controlled-reluctance microphone* operates on the principle that an electrical current is induced in a coil, located in a changing magnetic field. A magnetic armature is attached to a diaphragm suspended inside a coil. The diaphragm, when disturbed by a sound wave, moves the armature and induces a corresponding varying voltage in the coil. High output with fairly good frequency response is typical of this type microphone.

13.13 PICKUP PATTERNS

Microphones are made with single- or multiple-pickup patterns and are named by the pickup pattern they employ. The pickup patterns and directional response characteristics of the various types of microphones are shown in Fig. 13-1.

13.13.1 Omnidirectional Microphones

The omnidirectional, or spherical, polar response of the pressure microphones is due to the fact that the diaphragm is only exposed to the acoustic wave on the front side. Therefore, no cancellations are produced by having sound waves hitting both the front and rear of the diaphragm at the same time.

Omnidirectional microphones become increasingly

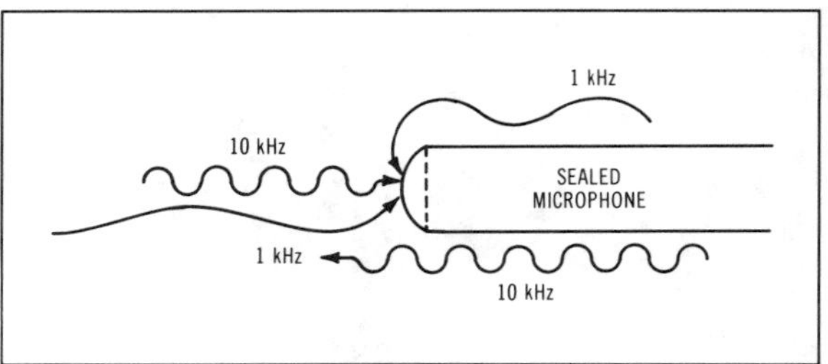

Figure 13-48 High-frequency directivity of an omnidirectional microphone.

directional as the diameter of the microphone reaches the wavelength of the frequency in question, as shown in Fig. 13-48; therefore, the microphone should have the smallest diameter possible if omnidirectional characteristics are required at high frequencies.[11] The characteristic that allows waves to bend around objects is known as diffraction. As the wavelength approaches the size of the object, the wave cannot bend sharply enough and, therefore, passes by the object. The various responses start to diverge at the frequency at which the diameter of the diaphragm of the microphone (D) is approximately one-tenth the wavelength (λ) of the sound ($D = \lambda/10$). Thus, the frequency (f) at which the variation begins is

$$f = v/10D \qquad (13\text{-}2)$$

where,
v is the velocity of sound in feet per second,
10D is the wavelength λ in feet.

For example, a ½-in. microphone will begin to vary from omnidirectional, though only slightly, at

$$f = 1130/[(10)(0.5/12)]$$
$$= 2712\,\text{Hz}$$

and will be down approximately 3 dB at 10,000 Hz.

Omnidirectional microphones are capable of having a very flat, smooth frequency response over the entire audio spectrum because only the front of the diaphragm is exposed to the source, eliminating phase cancellations found in unidirectional microphones.

For smoothness of response in omnidirectional microphones, the smaller they are, the better. The problem usually revolves around the smallest diaphragm possible versus the lowest noise level, or put another way, the smaller the diaphragm, the lower the microphone sensitivity, therefore, the poorer the signal-to-noise ratio.

Omnidirectional microphones have very little proximity effect. See section 13.13.3 for a discussion on proximity effect.

Because the pickup pattern is spherical, the random energy efficiency is 100%, and the ratio of front response to back or side is 1:1. This means signals from the sides or rear will have the same pickup sensitivity as from the front, giving a directivity index of 0 dB, which can be helpful in picking up conversations around a table or wanted room characteristics as recording a symphony. However, it can be detrimental when in a noisy environment.

Omnidirectional microphones are relatively free from mechanical shock because the output at all frequencies is high; therefore, the diaphragm can be stiff. This allows the diaphragm to follow the magnet or stationary system it operates against when subjected to mechanical motion.

13.13.2 Bidirectional Microphones

A *bidirectional microphone* is one that picks up from the front and back equally well with little or no pickup from the sides. The field pattern (Fig. 13-1) is called a *figure eight*.

Because the microphone discriminates between the front, back, and sides, random energy efficiency is 33%. In other words, background noise, if it is in a reverberant field, will be 67% lower than with an omnidirectional microphone. The front-to-back response will still remain one; however, the front-to-side response will approach infinity, producing a directivity index of 4.8, which can be extremely useful when picking up two conversations on opposite sides of a table. Because of the increased directional capabilities of the microphone, pickup distance is 1.7 times greater before feedback in the direct field than for an omnidirectional microphone. The included pickup cone angle shown in Fig. 13-49 for 6-dB attenuation on a perfect bidirectional microphone is 120° off the front of the microphone and 120° off the rear of the microphone. Because of diffraction, this angle varies with frequency, becoming narrower as the frequency increases.

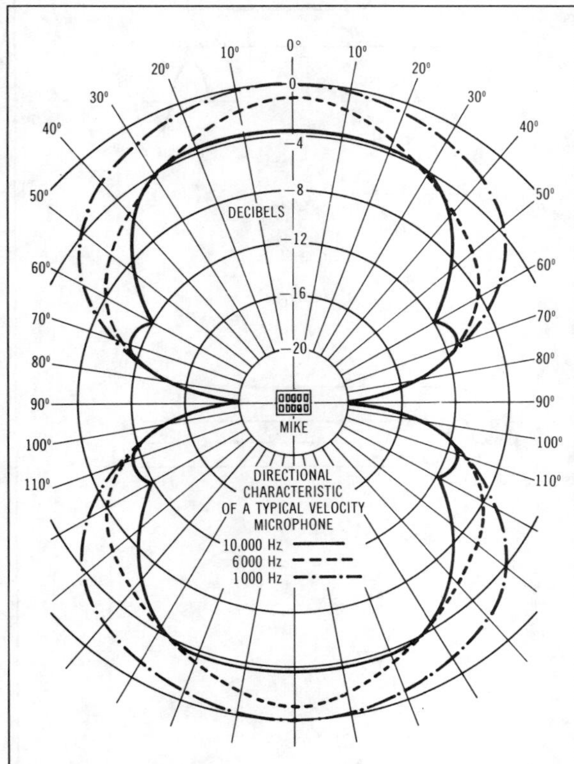

Figure 13-49 Polar pattern of a typical bidirectional ribbon velocity microphone showing the narrowing pattern at high frequencies.

13.13.3 Unidirectional Microphones

Unidirectional microphones have a greater sensitivity to sound pickup from the front than any other direction. The average unidirectional microphone has a front-to-back ratio of 20 to 30 dB; that is, it has 20 to 30 dB greater sensitivity to sound waves approaching from the front than from the rear.

Unidirectional microphones are usually listed as *cardioid* or *directional, super-cardioid* or *hyper-cardioid.* The pickup pattern is called *cardioid* because it is heart shaped, as shown in Fig. 13-1. Unidirectional microphones are the most commonly used microphones because they discriminate between signal and random unwanted noise. This has many advantages, namely:

1. Less background noise,
2. More gain before feedback when used in the direct field,
3. Discrimination between sound sources.

The cardioid pattern can be produced by one of two methods:

1. The first method combines the output of a pressure diaphragm and a pressure-gradient diaphragm, as shown in Fig. 13-50. Since the pressure-gradient diaphragm has a bidirectional pickup pattern and the pressure diaphragm has an omnidirectional pickup pattern, the wave hitting the front of the diaphragms adds, while the wave hitting the rear of the diaphragms cancels as the rear pickup pattern of the pressure gradient diaphragm is 180° out-of-phase with the rear pickup pattern of the pressure diaphragm. This method is expensive and seldom used for sound reinforcement or general-purpose microphones.
2. The second and most widely used method of producing a cardioid pattern is to use a single dia-

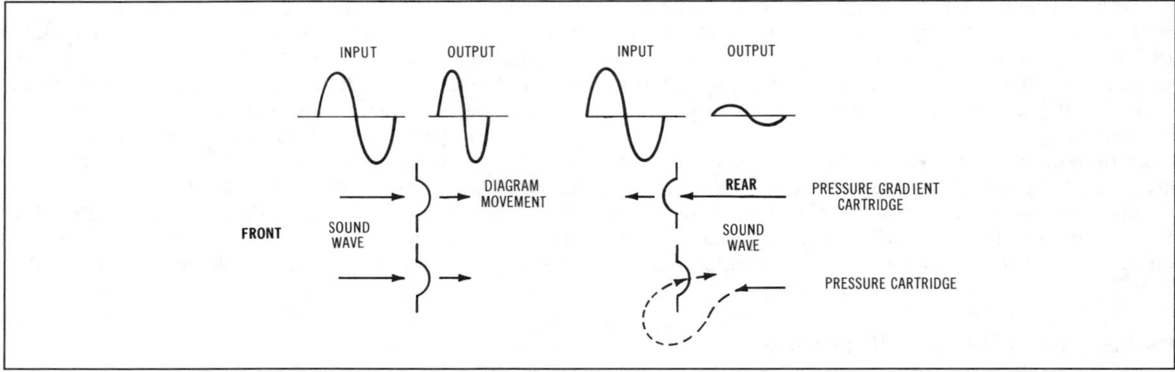

Figure 13-50 Two diaphragm cardioid microphone.

phragm and acoustically delay the wave reaching the rear of the diaphragm. When the wave is approaching from the front of the diaphragm, it first hits the front and then the rear of the diaphragm after traveling through the acoustical delay circuit, as shown in Fig. 13-51A. The pressure on the front of the diaphragm is at 0° while on the rear of the diaphragm it is some angle between 0° and 180°, as shown in Fig. 13-51B. If the rear pressure was at 0°, the output would be 0. It would be ideal if the rear pressure were at 180° so that it could add to the input, doubling the output.

The phase inversion is caused by the extra distance the wave has to travel to reach the back of the diaphragm. When the wave is coming from the rear of the microphone, it hits the front and back of the diaphragm at the same time and with the same polarity, therefore, canceling the output.

The frequency response of cardioid microphones is usually rougher than an omnidirectional microphone due to the acoustical impedance path and its effects on the front wave response. The front and rear responses of a cardioid microphone are not the same. Although the front pattern may be essentially flat over the audio spectrum, the back response usually increases at low and high frequencies, as shown in Fig. 13-52.

Discrimination between the front and back response varies between 15 and 30 dB in the mid frequencies and could be as little as 5 to 10 dB at the extreme ends, as shown in Fig. 13-52.

As the source is moved closer to the diaphragm, the low-frequency response increases due to the proximity effect shown in Fig. 13-53. The proximity effect[12] (i.e., the closer the source gets to the microphone, the more the low frequencies are enhanced) is created because the magnitude of the sound pressure on the front is appreciably greater than the sound pressure on the rear. In the vector diagram shown in Fig. 13-54A, it was assumed

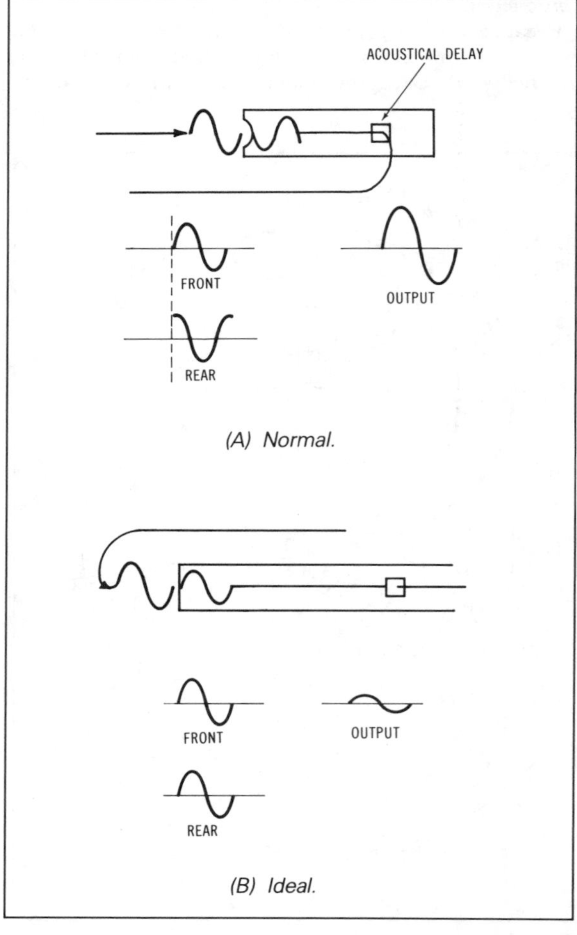

Figure 13-51 Cardioid microphone employing acoustical delay.

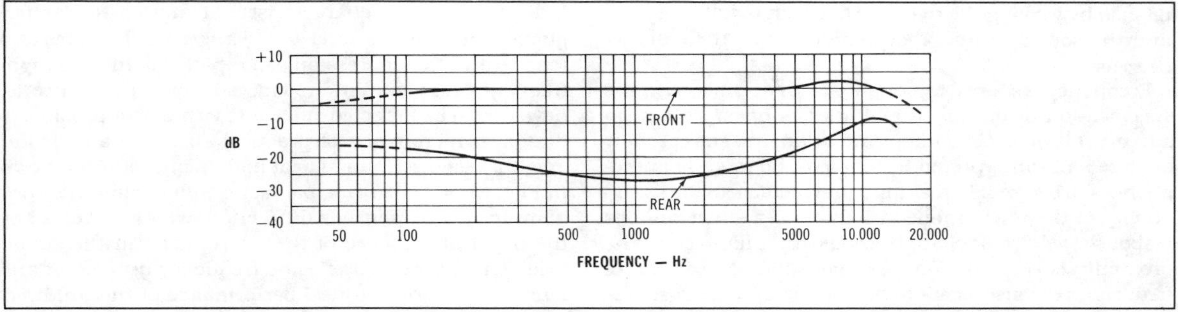

Figure 13-52 Frequency response of a typical cardioid microphone.

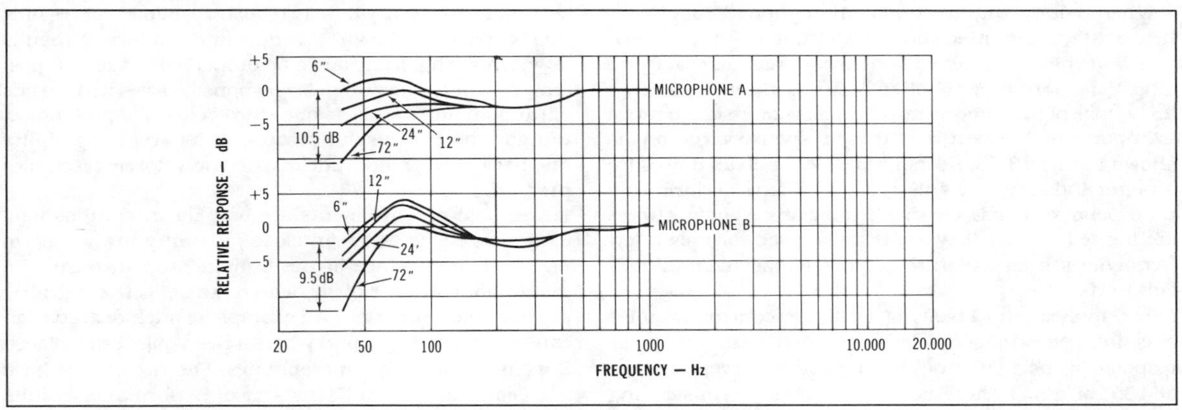

Figure 13-53 Proximity effect variations in response with distance between source and microphone for cardioid microphones. *(Courtesy Electro-Voice, Inc.)*

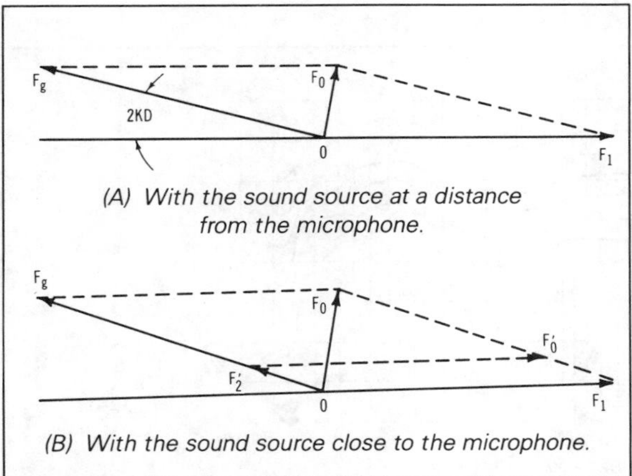

(A) With the sound source at a distance from the microphone.

(B) With the sound source close to the microphone.

Figure 13-54 Vector diagram of a unidirectional microphone. *(Courtesy Electro-Voice, Inc.)*

that the sound source was at a distance from the microphone. The angle 2KD is found from D, which is the acoustic distance from front to rear and $K = 2\pi/\lambda$. Fig. 13-54B shows the vector diagram when used close to the sound source and at a distance from the sound source. In both cases, it was assumed that the sound pressure at the front of the diaphragm was the same.

The force F_1 is on the front of the diaphragm in either case. The force F_2 is on the back when the microphone is used at a distance from the sound source, and F_O is the resultant. The force F_2' is due to a close sound source on the back of the diaphragm and is less because the difference in distance between the front and rear of the microphone. Laterally, the vector sum F_O' is considerably larger in magnitude than F_O. This increased force produces greater output from the microphone at the bass frequencies. This can be advantageous or disadvantageous. It is particularly useful when vocalists want to add low frequency to their voice or instrumentalist to add low frequencies to their instrument. This is accomplished by varying the distance between the microphone and the sound source, increasing bass as the distance decreases.

Frequency response is a quality of great concern in the specification of unidirectional microphones. This measurement is of obvious importance and must be carefully analyzed and interpreted in terms of the way the microphone is to be used. In making a judgment as to the sound quality of the microphone strictly from a single on-axis response, we are liable to overlook the influence of the proximity effect and off-axis response. A comparison of frequency response as a function of microphone-to-source distance will reveal that all unidirectional microphones experience a certain amount of proximity effect (bass boost as distance is decreased). In order to evaluate a microphone, this variation with distance is quite important.

When using a unidirectional microphone[13] in a handheld or stand-mounted configuration, it is quite conceivable that the performer will not always remain exactly on axis. Variations of ±45° often occur, and consequently a knowledge of the uniformity of response over such a range is important. The nature of these response variations is shown in Fig. 13-55. Response curves such as these give a better indication of this type of off-axis performance than polar response curves. The polar response curves are limited in that they are usually given for only a few frequencies from which the complete spectrum is difficult to visualize.

For applications involving feedback control or noise rejection, we are generally concerned with the polar response or particular off-axis response curves, such as at 135° or 180°. These curves can often be misleading due to the acoustic conditions and excitation signals used. Such measurements are usually made under anechoic conditions at various distances with sine-wave excitation. Looking solely at a rear response curve as a function of frequency is misleading since such a curve does not indicate the polar characteristic at any particular frequency, but only the level at one angle. Such curves also tend to give the impression of a rapidly fluctuating high-frequency discrimination. This sort of performance is, however, to be expected since it is virtually impossible to design a microphone of practical size with a constant angle of best discrimination at high frequencies, as shown in Fig. 13-56. The principal factor influencing this variation in rear response is diffraction, which is caused by the physical presence of the microphone in the sound field. This diffraction effect is frequency dependent and tends to disrupt the ideal performance of the unidirectional phase-shift elements. To properly represent this high-frequency off-axis performance, a polar response curve is of some value, but it, too, can be confusing at high frequencies. The reason for this confusion can be seen in Fig. 13-57, where two polar response curves only 20 Hz apart are shown. The question that arises then is how can such performance be properly analyzed? A possible solution is to run polar response curves with bands of random noise such as one-third octaves of pink noise. Random noise is useful because of its averaging ability and because its amplitude distribution closely resembles program material.

Anechoic measurements are only meaningful as long as no large objects are in close proximity to the microphone. The presence of the human head in front of a microphone will seriously degrade the effective high-frequency discrimination. An example of such degradation can be seen in Fig. 13-58 where a head object was placed 2 in. in front of the microphone. (The two curves have not been normalized.) This sort of performance results from the head as a reflector and is a common cause of feedback as one approaches a microphone. We should not consider this as a shortcoming of the microphone, but rather as an unavoidable result of the sound field in which it is being used. At 180°, for example, the microphone

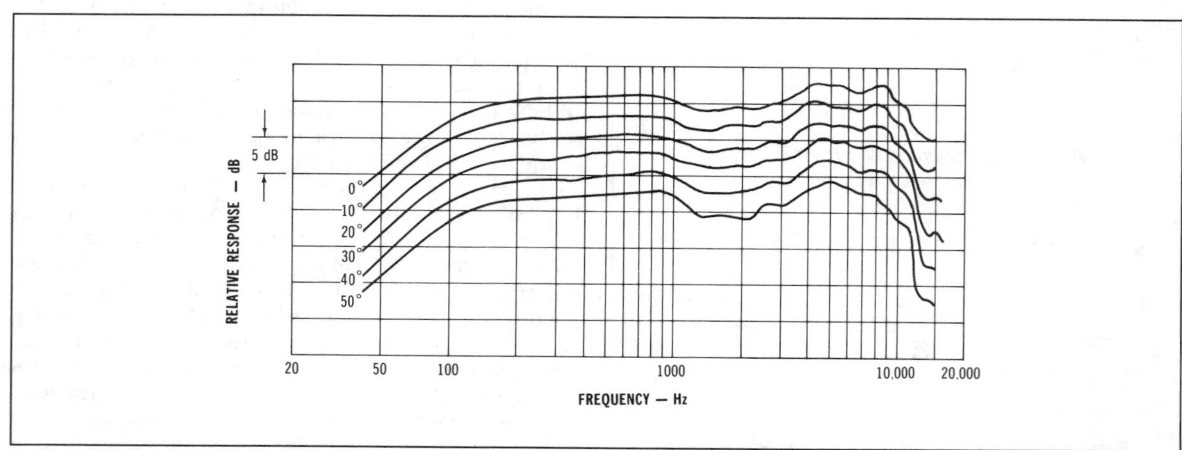

Figure 13-55 Variations in front response versus angular position. Note: curves have been displaced by 2.5 dB for comparison purposes.

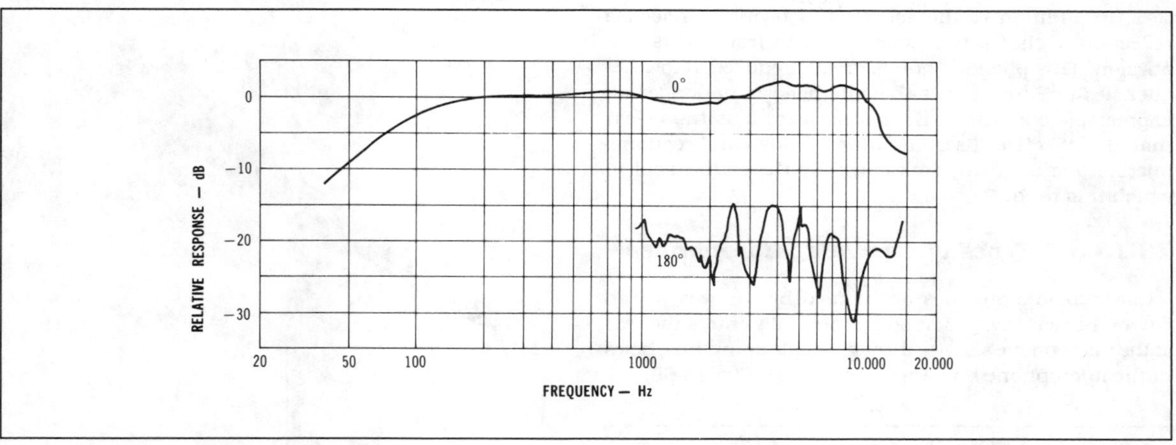

Figure 13-56 Typical fluctuations in high-frequency rear response for a cardioid microphone. *(Courtesy Shure Brothers, Inc.)*

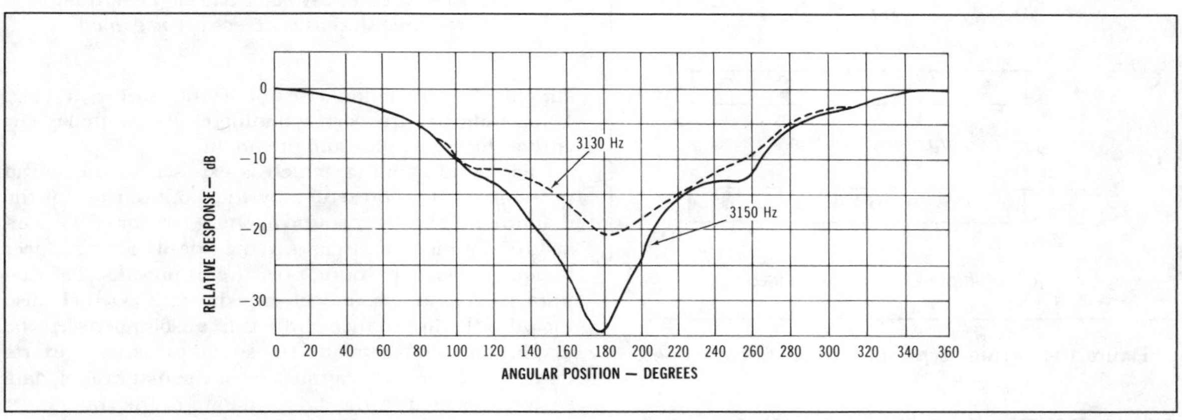

Figure 13-57 An example of rapid variations in high-frequency polar response for single-frequency excitation. *(Courtesy Shure Brothers, Inc.)*

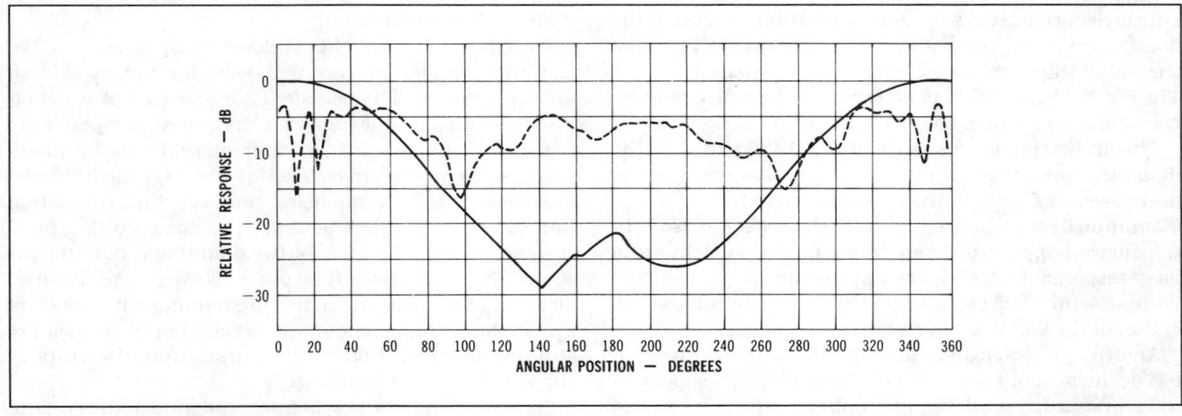

Figure 13-58 An example of a head obstacle on a polar response. *(Courtesy Shure Brothers, Inc.)*

sees, in addition to the source it is trying to reject, a reflection of that source some 2 in. in front of its diaphragm. This phenomenon is greatly reduced at low frequencies due to the fact that the head is no longer an appreciable obstacle to the sound field. It is thus clear that the effective discrimination of any unidirectional microphone is greatly influenced by the sound field in which it is used.

13.13.3.1 Types of Cardioid Microphones

Cardioid microphones are named by the way sound enters the rear cavity. The sound normally enters the rear of the microphone's cavity through single or multiple holes in the microphone housing, as shown in Fig. 13-59.

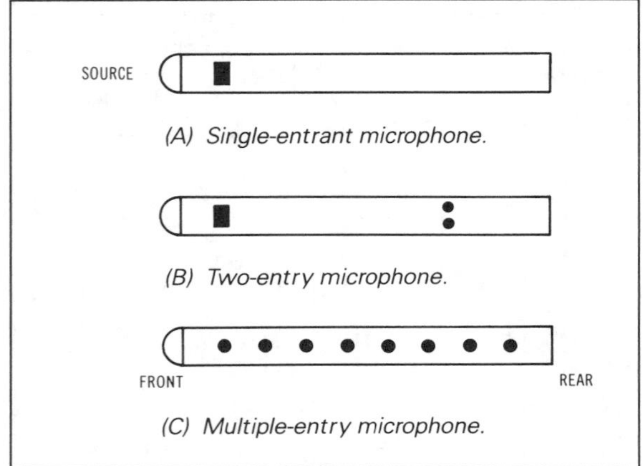

Figure 13-59 Three types of cardioid microphones.

13.13.3.2 Single-Entrant Cardioid Microphones

Single-entrant cardioid microphones have the rear entrance port located at one distance from the rear of the diaphragm. The port location is usually within 1½ in. of the diaphragm and can cause a large proximity effect. The Electro-Voice DS35 is an example of a single-entrant cardioid microphone, as shown in Fig. 13-60.

The low-frequency response of the DS35 varies as the distance from the sound source to the microphone decreases, as shown in the response curve in Fig. 13-61. Maximum bass response is produced in close-up use with the microphone 1½ in. from the sound source. Minimum bass response is experienced at distances greater than 24 in. Useful effects can be created by imaginative application of the variable low-frequency response.

Another single-entrant microphone is the Shure SM-81.[14] The acoustical system of the microphone operates as a first-order gradient microphone with two sound openings, as shown in Fig. 13-29. Fig. 13-62 shows a simplified cross-sectional view of the transducer, and Fig. 13-63 indicates the corresponding electrical analog circuit of the transducer and preamplifier.

Figure 13-60 Electro-Voice DS35 single-entrant microphone. *(Courtesy Electro-Voice, Inc.)*

One sound opening, which is exposed to the sound pressure p_1, is represented by the front surface of the diaphragm. The other sound opening, or rear entry, consists of a number of windows in the side of the transducer housing where the sound pressure p_2 prevails. The diaphragm has an acoustical impedance Z_o, which also includes the impedance of the thin air film between the diaphragm and backplate. The sound pressure p_2 exerts its influence on the rear surface of the diaphragm via a screen mounted in the side windows of the transducer housing, having a resistance R_1 and inertance L_1, through the cavity V_1 with compliance C_1. A second screen has a resistance R_2 and inertance L_2, through a second cavity V_2 with compliance C_2, and finally through the perforations in the backplate.

The combination of circuit elements L_1, R_1, C_1, L_2, R_2, C_2 forms a ladder network with lossy inertances, a *lossy ladder network*. The transfer characteristic of this network enforces a time delay on the pressure p_2 so as to impart directional (cardioid) characteristics to the microphone system, which is true for low and medium frequencies. At high frequencies, however, the attenuation caused by the network is large, and the resulting pressure arriving at the back of the diaphragm due to p_2 is small. The microphone then operates much like an omnidirectional system under the predominant influence of p_1. At these frequencies directional characteristics are attained by diffraction of the sound around a suitably shaped transducer housing.

Fig. 13-64 shows the schematic diagram of the system. A rotary low-frequency response shaping switch allows

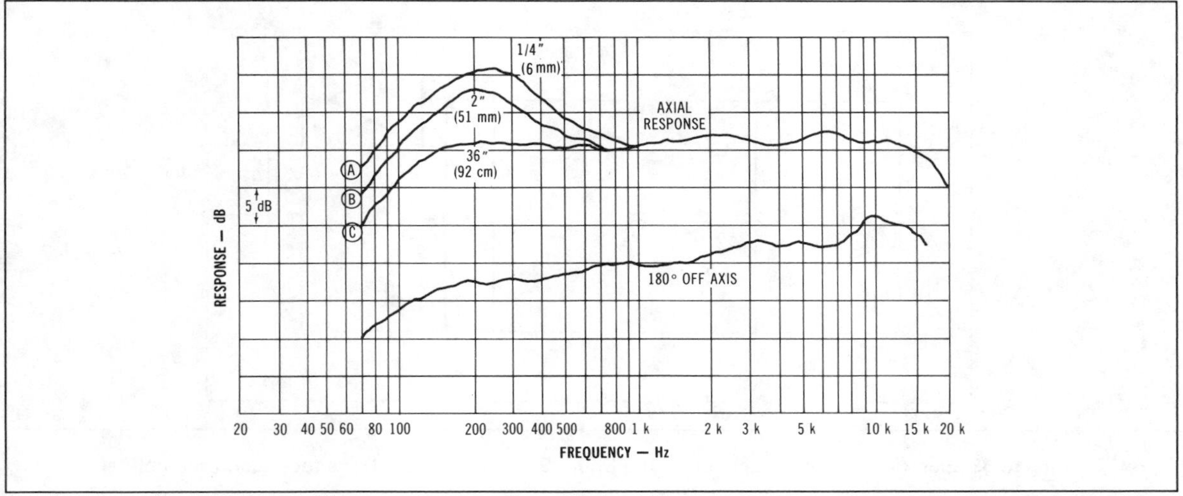

Figure 13-61 Frequency response versus distance for an Electro-Voice DS35 single-entrant cardioid microphone. *(Courtesy Electro-Voice, Inc.)*

the user to select between flat and a 6-dB/octave rolloff at 100 Hz or an 18-dB/octave cutoff at 80 Hz. The 100-Hz rolloff compensates for the proximity effect associated with a 15-cm (6-in.) source to microphone distance, while the 80-Hz cutoff significantly reduces most low-frequency disturbances with minimal effect on wide-range program material. In the flat position the microphone has a 6-dB/octave electronic infrasonic rolloff, which is 3-dB down at 10 Hz and is provided to reduce the effects of inaudible low-frequency disturbances on microphone preamplifier and tape recorder inputs. Attenuation is provided for operation at high sound pressure levels (to 145-dB SPL) by means of a rotary capacitive switch located between the transducer housing and the microphone handle. The microphone has an open-circuit voltage sensitivity of −45 dB re 1 V/Pa, an output impedance of 85 Ω, and it will operate with simplex power supplied from 12 to 48 V dc in accordance with DIN 45 596. The A-weighted self-noise of the microphone is a 60-dB sound pressure level as measured with a true rms voltmeter that results in a dynamic range of 119 dB between output clipping and the self-noise of the microphone. The overall distortion of the microphone is less than 0.5% at 250 Hz at a sound pressure level of 130-dB SPL while driving an 800-Ω load.

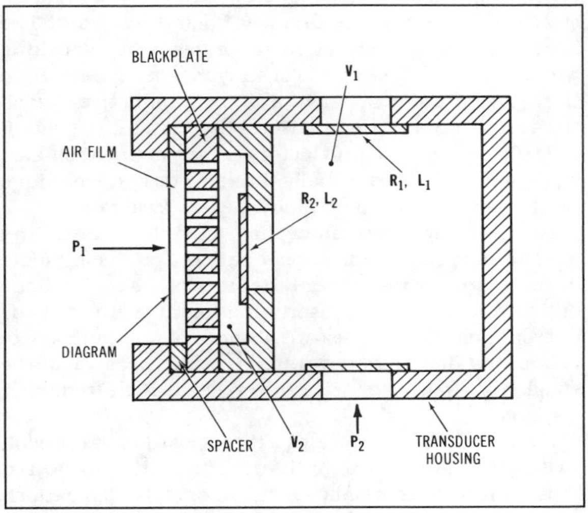

Figure 13-62 Simplified cross-sectional view of the Shure SM81 condenser transducer. *(Reference 13.)* *(Courtesy Shure Brothers, Inc.)*

13.13.3.3 Two-Entry Cardioid Microphones

The Shure SM53 and SM54 are examples of two-entry cardioid microphones.

The Shure SM-53 microphone is shown in Fig. 13-65. The low-frequency rear entry has a *d* (distance from center of diaphragm to the entry port) of about 4.75 in. and the high-frequency entry a *d* of about 1 in. with the transition in frequency occurring between 800 Hz and 1 kHz.[13] Each entry consists of several holes around the microphone case rather than a single hole.

This configuration is used for three reasons. By using a multiple arrangement of entry holes around the circumference of the microphone case into the low-frequency system, optimum front response and polar performance can be maintained, even though most of the

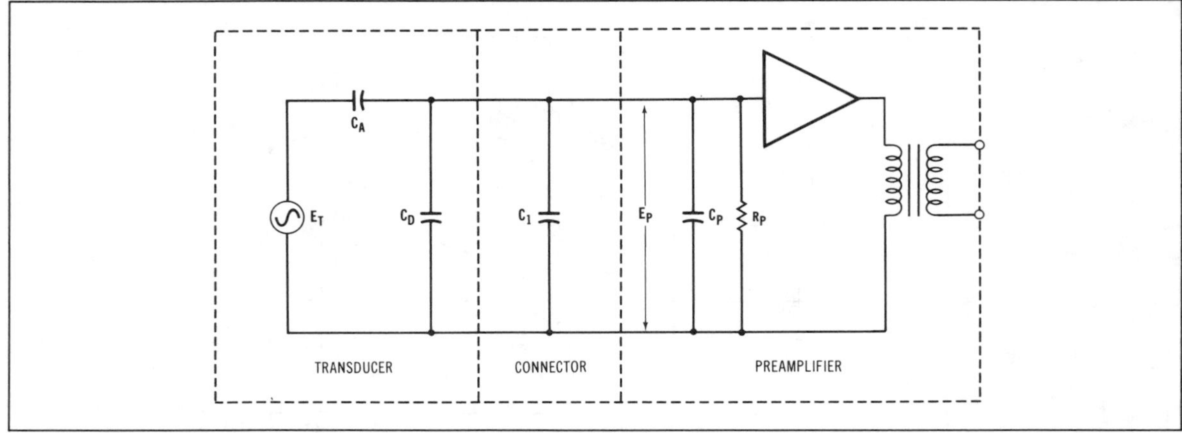

Figure 13-63 Electrical equivalent circuit of the Shure SM81 condenser transducer and preamplifier. *(Courtesy Shure Brothers, Inc.)*

entries may be accidentally covered when the microphone (Fig. 13-65) is hand held or stand mounted. The microphone has good proximity performance as a direct result of the low-frequency entry being as far as possible from the diaphragm as well as the high-frequency entry having very little proximity influence at low frequencies. Also, the two-entry configuration has a cardioid polar response pattern that provides a wide front working angle as well as excellent noise rejection and feedback control.

13.13.3.4 Multiple-Entry Cardioid Microphones

The Electro-Voice RE20 Continuously Variable-D microphone (Fig. 13-66) is an example of multiple-entry microphones. The multiple-entry microphones have many rear entrance ports. They are constructed as single ports, all at a different distance from the diaphragm, or as a single continuous opening port. Each entrance is tuned to a different band of frequencies, the ports closest to the diaphragm being tuned to the high frequencies, and the ports farthest from the diaphragm being tuned to the low frequency band. The greatest advantage of this arrangement is reduced-proximity effect because of the large distance between the source and the rear entry low frequencies; crossovers are not as sharp and can be more precise for the frequencies in question.

As in many cardioid microphones, the RE-20 has a low-frequency rolloff switch to reduce the proximity effect when close mic'ing. Fig. 13-67 shows the frequency response curves of the manufacturer with and without the low-frequency rolloff. Fig. 13-68 shows the wiring diagram of the RE-20. By moving the red wire to either the 250- or 50-Ω tap, the microphone output impedance can be changed. Note the "bass tilt" switch that, when open, reduces the series inductance and, therefore, the low-frequency response.

13.13.3.5 Two-Way Cardioid Dynamic Microphones

In a two-way microphone system, the total response range is divided between a high-frequency and a low-frequency transducer, each of which is optimally adjusted to its specific range similar to a two-way loudspeaker system. The two systems are connected by means of a crossover network.

The AKG D-222EG shown in Figs. 13-69 and 13-70 employs two coaxially mounted dynamic transducers: one designed for optimum performance at high frequencies, placed closest to the front grille and facing forward; the other designed for optimum performance at low frequencies, placed behind the first and facing rearward. The low-frequency transducer incorporates a hum-bucking winding to cancel the effects of stray magnetic fields. Both transducers are coupled to a 500-Hz inductive-capacitive-resistive crossover network that is electroacoustically phase corrected and factory preset for linear off-axis response. (This is essentially the same design technique used in a modern two-way loudspeaker system.)

The two-way microphone has a predominantly frequency-independent directional pattern, producing more linear frequency response at the sides of the microphone and far more constant discrimination at the rear of the microphone. There is also an absence of proximity effect at working distances down to 6 in. and, because of the small high-frequency transducer, good high-frequency response.

The D-222EB incorporates a three-position bass-rolloff switch that provides 6- or 12-dB attenuation at 50 Hz. This feature is especially useful in speech applications and in acoustically unfavorable environments with excessive low-frequency ambient noise, reverberation, or feedback.

Another interesting feature is that the transducer and

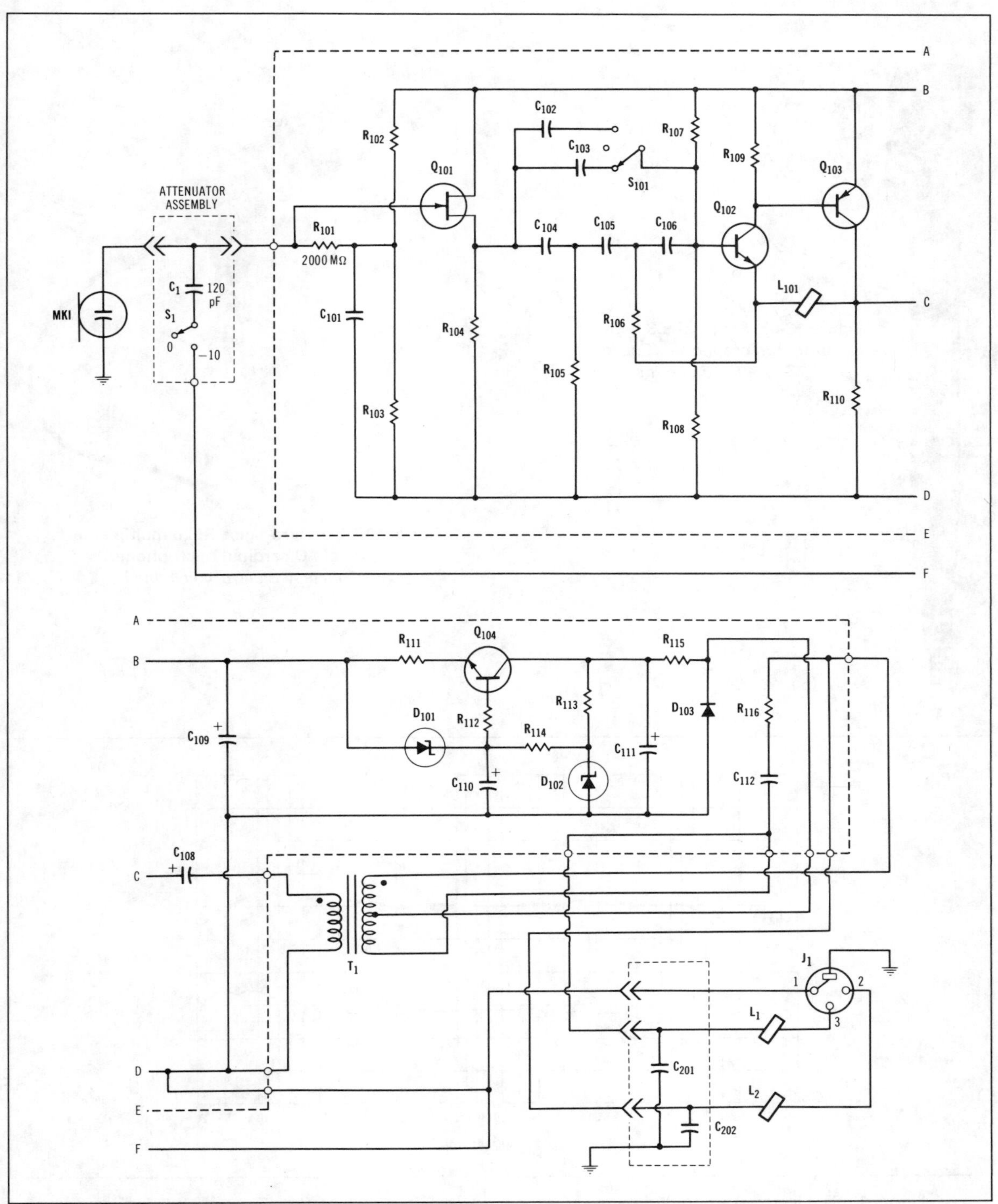

Figure 13-64 Shure SM81 condenser microphone schematic. *(Courtesy Shure Brothers, Inc.)*

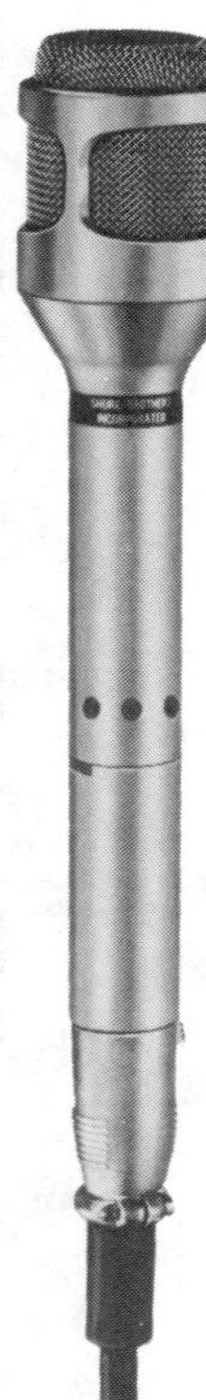

Figure 13-65 Shure SM53 two-entry cardioid microphone. *(Courtesy Shure Brothers, Inc.)*

Figure 13-66 Electro-Voice RE20 multiple-entry (variable-D cardioid microphone. *(Courtesy Electro-Voice, Inc.)*

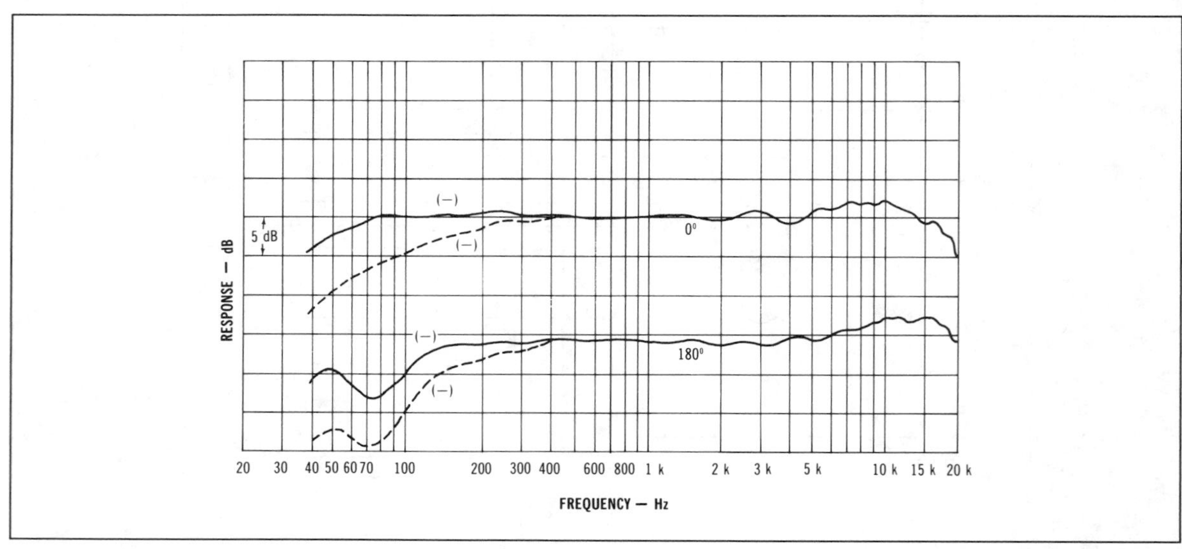

Figure 13-67 Electro-Voice RE20 frequency response on axis and 180° of axis. The solid line indicates a flat response; the dashed one indicates "bass tilt" on. *(Courtesy Electro-Voice, Inc.)*

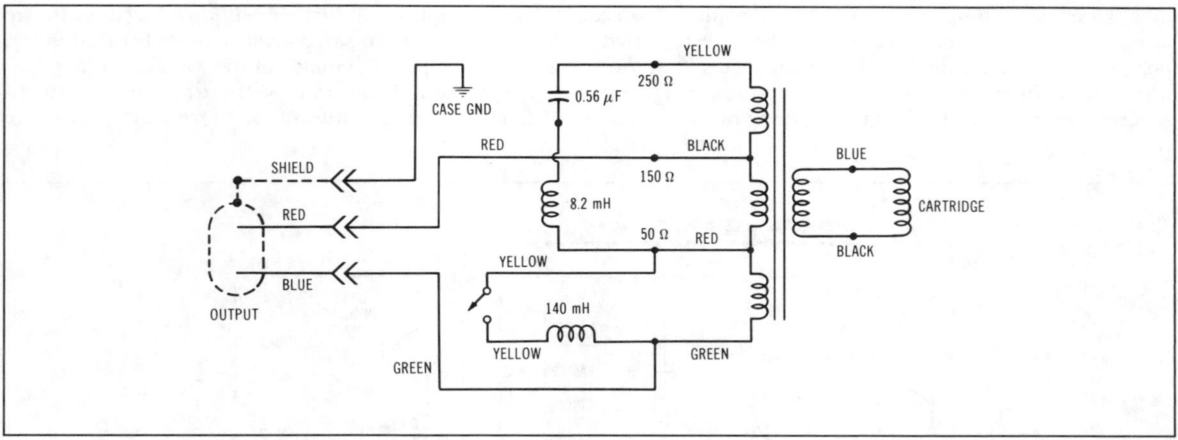

Figure 13-68 Electro-Voice RE20 cardioid microphone wiring diagram. Note "bass tilt" switch circuit and output impedance taps. *(Courtesy Electro-Voice, Inc.)*

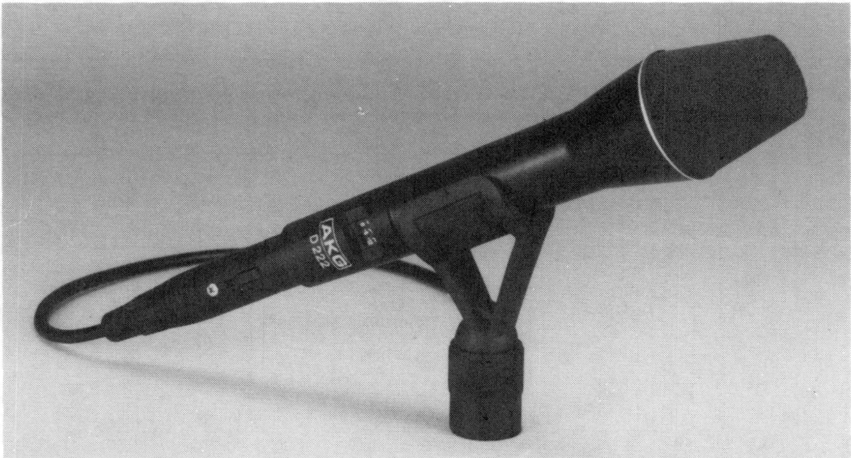

Figure 13-69 AKG D222EB two-way cardioid dynamic microphone. *(Courtesy AKG Acoustics, Inc.)*

crossover network are housed in a replaceable slide-in module that can be replaced simply by unscrewing the windscreen/pop filter of the microphone. The transducers are elastically suspended within the module, to reduce handling noise, mechanical shocks, and spurious vibrations.

13.13.3.6 Hand-Held Entertainer Microphones

The *hand-held entertainer microphone* is most often used by a performer on stage and, therefore, requires a special frequency response that will increase articulation and presence. The microphones are often subjected to rough handling, extreme shock, and vibration. For live performances, the proximity effect can be useful to produce a low "bass" sound. By using a low-frequency attenuator and a high-frequency boost, various responses can be produced, as shown in Fig. 13-71.

To overcome rough handling and handling noise, special construction techniques are used to reduce wind, pop noise, and mechanical noise and to ensure that the microphone will withstand sudden collisions with the floor. The AKG D-330BT dynamic cardioid microphone shown in Fig. 13-72 was designed for this use. Fig. 13-73 shows the design and construction of the microphone.

The microphone incorporates a sturdy three-layer windscreen/pop-filter assembly. The assembly consists of a shock-absorbing stainless-steel wire-mesh outer layer, a blast-diffusing fabric middle layer, reticulated polyurethane-foam inner layer (sandwiched together into a removable liner), plus a threaded retaining ring that secures the entire unit to the microphone housing.

The microphone is further reinforced against impact damage by a special safety-basket assembly that is contoured to support the inside of the windscreen/pop filter and to surround the front of the transducer system—thus also isolating all internal parts from head-on impact

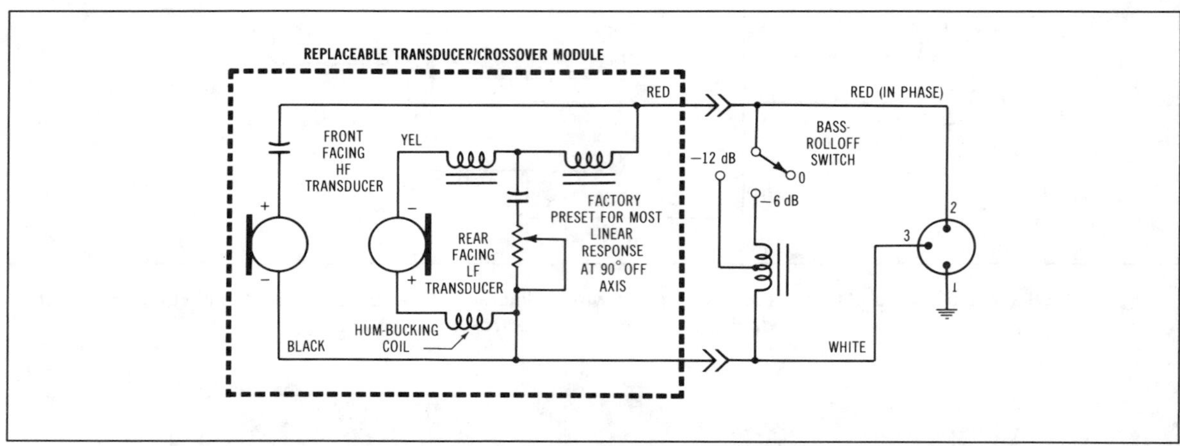

Figure 13-70 Schematic of an AKG D222EB two-way cardioid microphone. *(Courtesy AKG Acoustics, Inc.)*

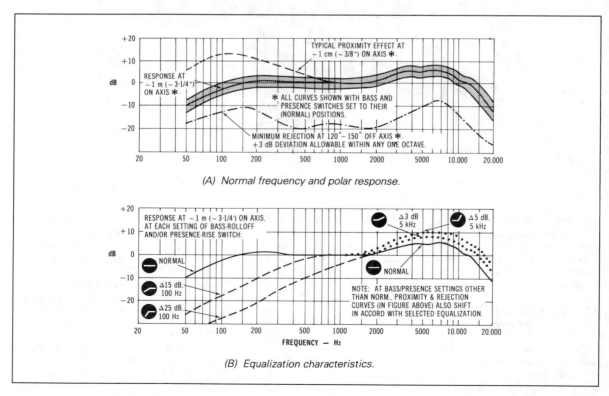

(A) Normal frequency and polar response.

(B) Equalization characteristics.

Figure 13-71 Frequency response curves of a cardioid hand-held microphone.

damage. As shown, the safety basket consists of a resilient dome-shaped ribbed cage joined to a reinforced open-framed casting. Fitted with a fine wire-mesh screen that coincides with side ports in the microphone housing, the casting also has indexing notches that align the entire rugged assembly with structural members in the microphone housing.

Next in line is the transducer system. The transducer system floats uniformly in all directions within the microphone housing for isolation from the effects of impact damage, handling noise, and spurious vibrations. This is achieved by two special ring-shaped elastomer suspensions, one near the front of the system and the other at the rear of the system. To combine the advantages of both hard- and soft-suspension designs, each of these ring suspensions has a dense, relatively hard body and a series of compliant, progressively compressible dome-shaped projections around its periphery, in effect forming a complex, highly damped, low-pass mechanical filter. Therefore, under normal handling conditions, the compliant domes effectively decouple the transducer system from mechanically and motionally induced vibration. Further, under extremely abusive conditions (dropping the microphone or subjecting it to lateral impact), the domes increasingly compress, in proportion to applied *g*-force, in a progressive braking action, ultimately allowing the harder body of each suspension to act as a bumper.

Note that the transducer system uses two generating elements, the main front-facing sound-pickup transducer plus a special rear-facing nonacoustic (sealed) noise-compensating transducer. Working together, these transducers further reduce the effects of mechanically

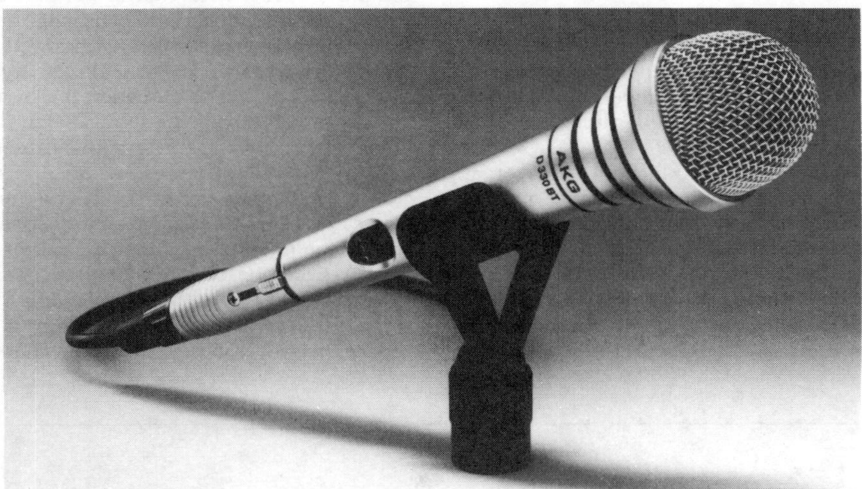

Figure 13-72 AKG D330BT hypercardioid hand-held microphone. *(Courtesy AKG Acoustics, Inc.)*

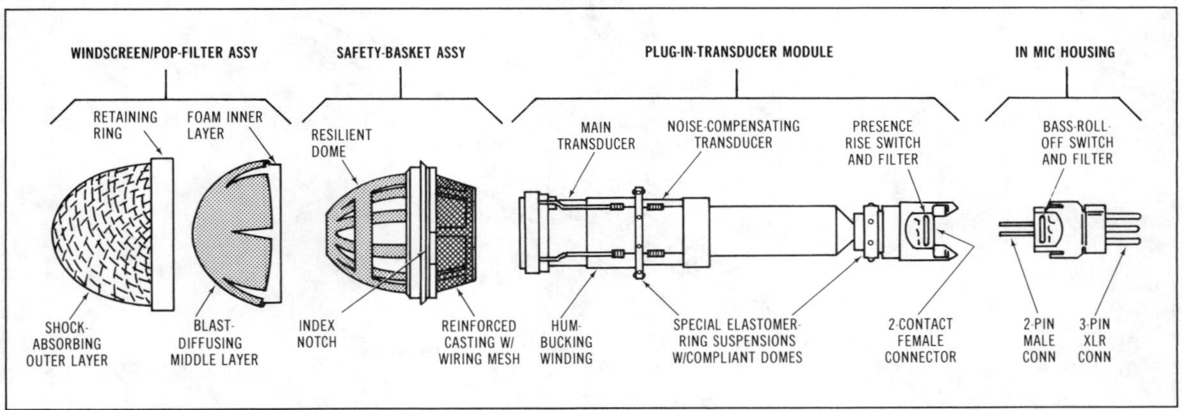

Figure 13-73 Construction of the AKG D330BT hand-held Microphone. *(Courtesy AKG Acoustics, Inc.)*

and motionally induced handling noise by an additional 30 dB at 100 Hz. The two carefully matched transducers are wired in parallel and electrically in phase, but because of their opposed orientation, they operate out-of-phase. Thus, any handling-noise signal generated by the main transducer is nulled by an equal but opposite handling-noise signal generated by the compensating transducer (which acts strictly as an electromechanical motion-sensing accelerometer). As still another precaution, the main transducer incorporates a hum-bucking winding to cancel the effects of electromagnetically induced noise from ever-present power and lighting cables as well as from dimmers, power switchboards, and the like.

This type of design is required for hand-held microphones and is not used for fixed or stand-mounted microphones since rugged design reduces overall response and quality.

13.13.3.7 Shotgun Microphones

A *cardioid in-line directional microphone* as described by Olson in 1938 is often called a *shotgun microphone* because of its physical shape and directional characteristics.

Two of the most important characteristics of any microphone are its sensitivity and directional qualities. Assuming a constant sound pressure source, increasing the distance of the microphone from the source requires an increase in the gain of the amplifying system after the microphone. This is accompanied by a decrease in signal-to-noise ratio and an increase in environmental noises, such as reverberation and background noise, to where the indirect sound may equal the direct sound. The wanted signal then deteriorates to where it is unusable. Distance limitations can be overcome by increasing the sensitivity of the microphone, and the effect of reverberation can be lessened by increasing the directivity of the pattern. The in-line microphone has these two desirable qualities.

The basic components of this type microphone are shown by the Electro-Voice CL42S condenser shotgun system in Fig. 13-74.[15] Line-tube (2) has a slot milled its entire length and a group of ports that act like a linear tapering acoustic resistance; they are equally sensitive to equal sound pressures and will cause equal voltage to be generated at the output of the transducer unit. Since the ports are acoustically connected to the transducer unit by the common tube, acoustic delays are introduced ahead of the transducer element. When placed in a plane-wave sound field, this equally sensitive line with variable delay produces wave interference in the common cavity at the front of the transducer unit. The magnitude of this interference will depend on the angle between the plane wave and the axis of the tube. The directivity of a line microphone is a function of frequency; the lower the frequency, the broader the polar pattern, as shown in Fig. 13-75. Large diaphragm and shock mount structures can be used because no baffle effects occur, the directivity being controlled by the openings in the in-line tube structure.

Because of the directional characteristics and sensitivity, in-line microphones may be operated from 2 to 4 ft farther from the sound source than the conventional microphone. A super directional in-line microphone used for picking up a group of persons in a crowd from the roof of a nearby building, following a horse around a race

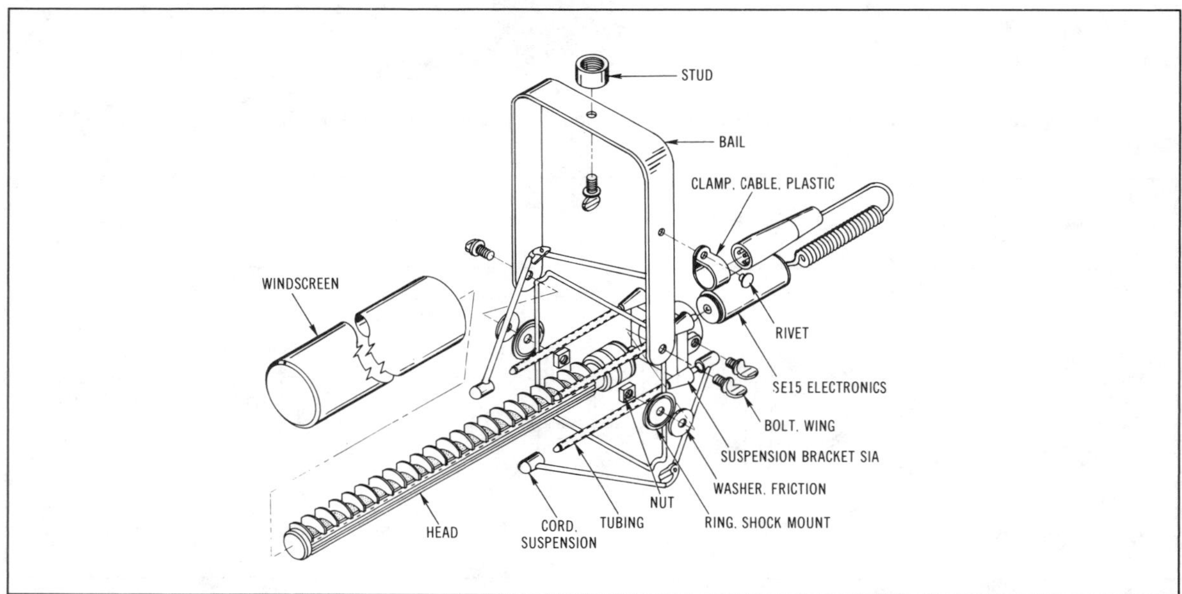

Figure 13-74 Assembly exploded view of an Electro-Voice CL42S shotgun microphone. *(Courtesy Electro-Voice, Inc.)*

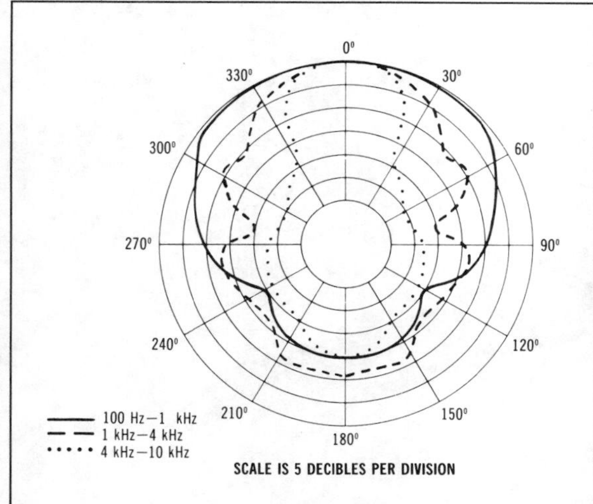

Figure 13-75 Polar response of the Electro-Voice CL42S shotgun microphone. *(Courtesy Electro-Voice, Inc.)*

track, picking up a band in a parade, and picking up other hard-to-get sounds from a distance is an enlarged microphone of the one previously discussed.

The in-line microphone has a directivity index ratio of 6:1 with an included pickup angle of 80°. The super in-line microphone has an included pickup angle of 40°, with a 30:1 directivity index ratio. The basic designs are the same except that the super in-line has a much sharper angle of pickup because of its longer in-line tube (86 in. versus 13 in.) with a greater number of in-line ports.

Whereas a cardioid microphone may be able to pick up satisfactorily at 3 ft, a cardioid in-line may reach 6 to 9 ft, and a super in-line may reach as far as 40 ft.

There are precautions that should be followed when using in-line microphones.[16] Because they obtain directivity by cancellation, frequency response and phase are not smooth. Also, since low frequencies become omnidirectional, the frequency response drops rapidly below 200 Hz to help control directivity.

When using the super in-line with the specified 40° conical pickup pattern, which is the starting point for cancellation, it should not be interpreted that no sound will be picked up outside this cone. As the microphone is rotated from an on-axis position to a 180° off-axis position, there will be a progressive drop in level. Sounds originating at angles of 90° to 180° off axis will cancel by 20 dB or more; however, the amount of cancellation depends on the level and distance of the microphone from the sound source. As an example, if an on-axis sound originated at a distance of 20 ft, a 90° to 180° off-axis sound occurring at the same distance and intensity will be reduced by 20 dB or more, providing none of the off-axis sound is reflected into the front of the microphone by walls, ceiling, and so on. On the other hand, should the off-axis sound originate at a distance of 2 ft and at the same sound pressure level as the sound at 20 ft on axis, it will be reproduced at the same level. The reason for this behavior is that the microphone is still cancelling the unwanted sound as much as 20 dB, but due to the difference in the distances of the two sounds, the off-axis sound is 20 dB louder than the axial sound. Therefore, they are reproduced at the same level. For a pickup in an area where random noise and reverberation is a problem, the microphone should be located with the back end to the source of unwanted sound and as far from the disturbances as possible.

If the microphone is being used inside a truck and pointing out a rear door, poor pickup may be experienced because all sounds, both wanted and unwanted, arrive at the microphone on-axis. Since the only entrance is through the truck door, no cancellation occurs because the truck walls inhibit the sound from entering the sides of the microphone. In this instance, the microphone will be operating as an omnidirectional microphone. Due to the reflected sound from the walls, the same condition will prevail in a room where the microphone is pointed through a window or when operating in a long hallway. For good pickup, the microphone should be operated in the open and not in closely confined quarters.

Because of the narrow included angle of the pickup, random noise is reduced considerably, and the distance to the sound source may be increased without a loss of presence. An in-line microphone cannot be compared to a zoom lens since the focus does not vary nor does it reach out to gather in the sound. What the narrow polar pattern and high rate of cancellation does is to reduce pickup of the random sound energy and to permit the raising of the amplifier gain following the microphone without seriously decreasing the signal-to-noise ratio.

Difficulties may also be encountered using this microphone on stage and picking out a talker in the audience, particularly where the voice is 75 to 100 ft away and fed back through a reinforcement system for the audience to hear. Under these circumstances, only about 30 to 50 ft is possible without acoustic feedback; even then, the system must be balanced very carefully.

13.13.3.8 Rifle Microphones

The *rifle microphone* consists of a microphone transducer with a series of tubes of varied length mounted in front of the transducer diaphragm, as shown in Fig. 13-76. The transducer may be either a capacitor or dynamic type. The tubes are cut in lengths from 2 to 60 in. and bound together. The bundling of the tubes in front of the transducer diaphragm creates a distributed sound entrance, and the omnidirectional transducer becomes highly directional.

Sound originating on the axis of the tubes first enters the longest tube and, as the wave front advances, enters successively shorter tubes in normal progression until the diaphragm is reached. Sounds reaching the diaphragm from the source travel the same distance, regardless of the tube entered; thus, all sounds arriving on-axis

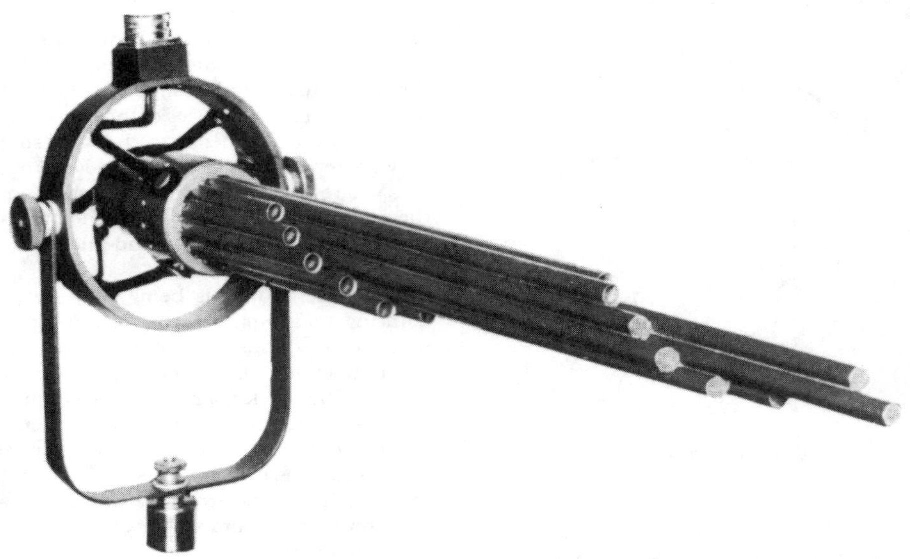

Figure 13-76 RCA rifle microphone. *(Courtesy of Radio Corporation of America)*

are in phase when they reach the diaphragm. However, sounds originating 90° off-axis enter all tubes simultaneously. A sound entering a longer tube may travel 18 in. to reach the diaphragm, while the same sound traveling through the shortest tube will travel only 3 in., with other differences for the varied length of tubing, thus causing an out-of-phase signal at the diaphragm. Under these conditions, a large portion of the sound originating at 90° is cancelled; from 180° an even greater phase difference occurs, and cancellation is increased considerably. The RCA MI-100006A varidirectional microphone shown in Fig. 13-76 consists of nineteen 5⁄16-in. plastic tubes, ranging from 3 to 18 in. in length. The tubes are bundled and mounted in front of an omnidirectional capacitor-microphone head.

13.13.3.9 Parabolic Microphones

Parabolic microphones use a parabolic reflector with a microphone to obtain a highly directional pickup response. The microphone diaphragm is mounted at the focal point of the reflector, as shown in Fig. 13-77. The microphone is focused by moving it in or out from the reflector for maximum pickup. This type concentrator is often used to pick up a horse race or a group of people in a crowd.

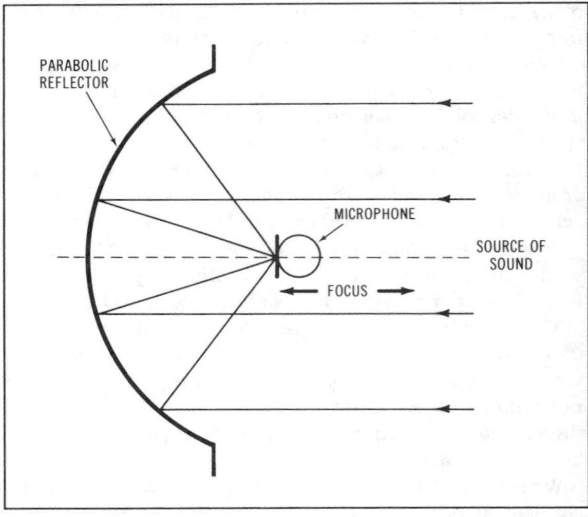

Figure 13-77 A parabolic bowl concentrator for directional microphone pickup.

The greatest gain in sound pressure is obtained when the reflector is large compared to the wavelength of the incident sound. With the microphone in focus, the gain is the greatest at the mid-frequency range. The loss of high frequencies may be improved somewhat by defocusing the microphone a slight amount, which also tends to broaden the sharp directional characteristics at the higher frequencies. A bowl 3 ft in diameter is practically nondirectional below 200 Hz, but it is very sharp at 8000 Hz, as shown in Fig. 13-78. For a diameter of 3 ft, the gain over the microphone without the bowl is about 10 dB, and for a 6-ft diameter, approximately 16 dB.

13.13.3.10 Zoom Microphones[17]

A *zoom microphone* is one that operates like and in conjunction with a zoom lens. This type microphone is

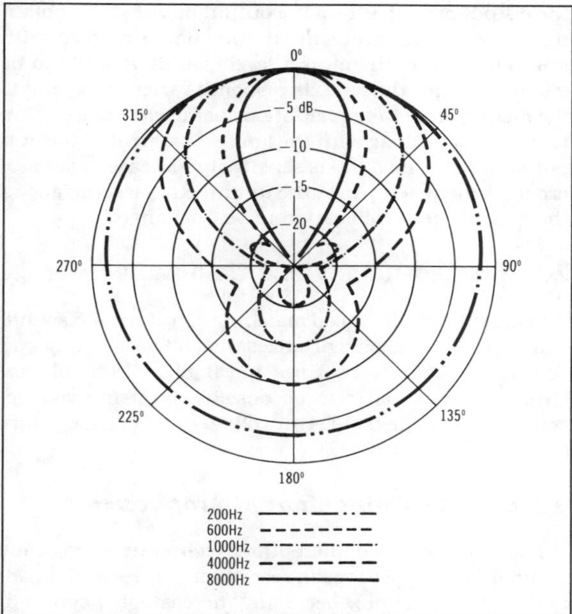

Figure 13-78 Polar pattern for a typical parabolic concentrator.

useful mainly with television and motion-picture operations.

The optical perception of distance to the object is simply determined by the shot angle of the picture. On the other hand, a sound image is perceived by the following factors:

1. Loudness,
2. Reverberation (ratio of direct sound to reflected sound),
3. Acquired response to sound,
4. Level and arriving time difference between the two ears.

Since most 8mm or video cameras have the sound recorded in monophonic, the factors 1, 2, and 3 can be skillfully combined to reproduce a natural sound image with respect to the perceived distance. The three factors, which must be taken into account in designing a *variable-directivity microphone*, are described in the following:

1. *Loudness*: Perceived loudness can be controlled by varying microphone sensitivity.
2. *Reverberation*: The representation of the distance is made by changing the ratio between direct and reverberant sound. This ratio is varied in accordance with the directivity change of the microphone. In a normal environment, we hear a combination of direct sound and its reflections. The nearer a listening point is to the source, the larger the ratio of direct sound to reflected sound. The farther the listening point is from the source, the smaller the ratio; therefore, use of a high-directivity microphone to keep direct sound greater than reflected sound permits the microphone to get apparently closer to the source by the decrease of the reflected sound level.

   For outdoor environments, use of directional microphones allows the ambient noise level to be changed for natural representation of distances.
3. *Acquired human response to sound*: Normally we can tell approximately how far a familiar object as a car or a person is by the sound generated by the objects because we acquire the response to sound through our daily experiences.

Distance Factor

The fact the microphone directivity determines the perceived distance can be explained from the viewpoint of the distance factor. Fig. 13-79 shows the sound pressure level at the position of an omnidirectional microphone versus the distance between the microphone and a sound source S, with ambient noise evenly distributed. Suppose the distance is 7 m and the ambient noise level is at 1. If the microphone is replaced by one that has a narrow directivity with the same on-axis sensitivity, less noise is picked up; thus, the observed noise level is lowered to 2. For an omnidirectional microphone, the same effect can be obtained at a distance of 2.3 m. From a different standpoint, the same signal-to-noise ratio as for an omnidirectional microphone at 6.3 m can be obtained at a distance of 20 m. The ratio of actual-to-observed distance is called the distance factor.

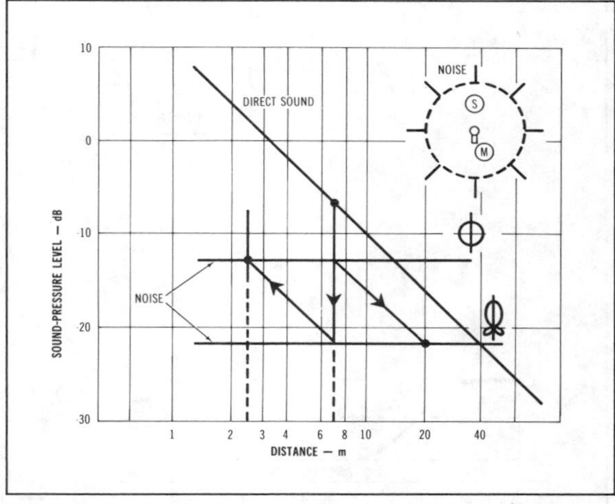

Figure 13-79 Relationship between sound pressure level and distance in an evenly distributed noise environment.

Operation of Zoom Microphones

By changing the sensitivity and the directivity of a microphone simultaneously, an acoustical "zoom" effect is realized, and more reality becomes possible in sound recording. Fig. 13-80 is the basic block diagram of a zoom microphone system. The system consists of three unidirectional microphone units (1 through 3) arranged on the same axis. The three units have the same characteristics, and unit 3 faces the opposite direction. The directivity can be varied from omnidirectional to second-order gradient unidirectional by varying the mixing ratio of the output of each unit and changing the equalization characteristic coordinatively. An omnidirectional pattern is obtained by simply combining the outputs of unit 2 and unit 3. In the process of directivity change from omnidirectional to unidirectional, the output of unit 3 is gradually faded out, while the output of unit 1 is kept off. Furthermore, the equalization characteristic is kept flat, because the on-axis frequency response does not change during this process. In the process of changing from unidirectional to second-order gradient unidirectional, the output of unit 3 is kept off. The second-order gradient unidirectional pattern can be obtained by subtracting the output of unit 1 from the output of unit 2. To obtain the second-order gradient unidirectional pattern with minimum error, the output level of unit 1 needs to be trimmed. Since the on-axis response varies according to the mixing ratio, the equalization characteristics also have to be adjusted along with the level adjustment of the output of unit 1. The on-axis sensitivity increase of second-order gradient setup over the unidirectional setup allows the gain of the amplification to be unchanged.

Zoom-Microphone Video Camera Linkage

In order to obtain a good matching of picture and sound, a mechanism that synchronizes the optical zooming and acoustical zooming becomes inevitable. Electrical synchronization would also be possible by using voltage-controlled amplifiers (VCA) or voltage-controlled resistors (VCR).

13.13.3.11 Coincident Microphones

The coincident two-microphone technique, a long-time standard among European record companies and broadcast networks, is now becoming increasingly popular in

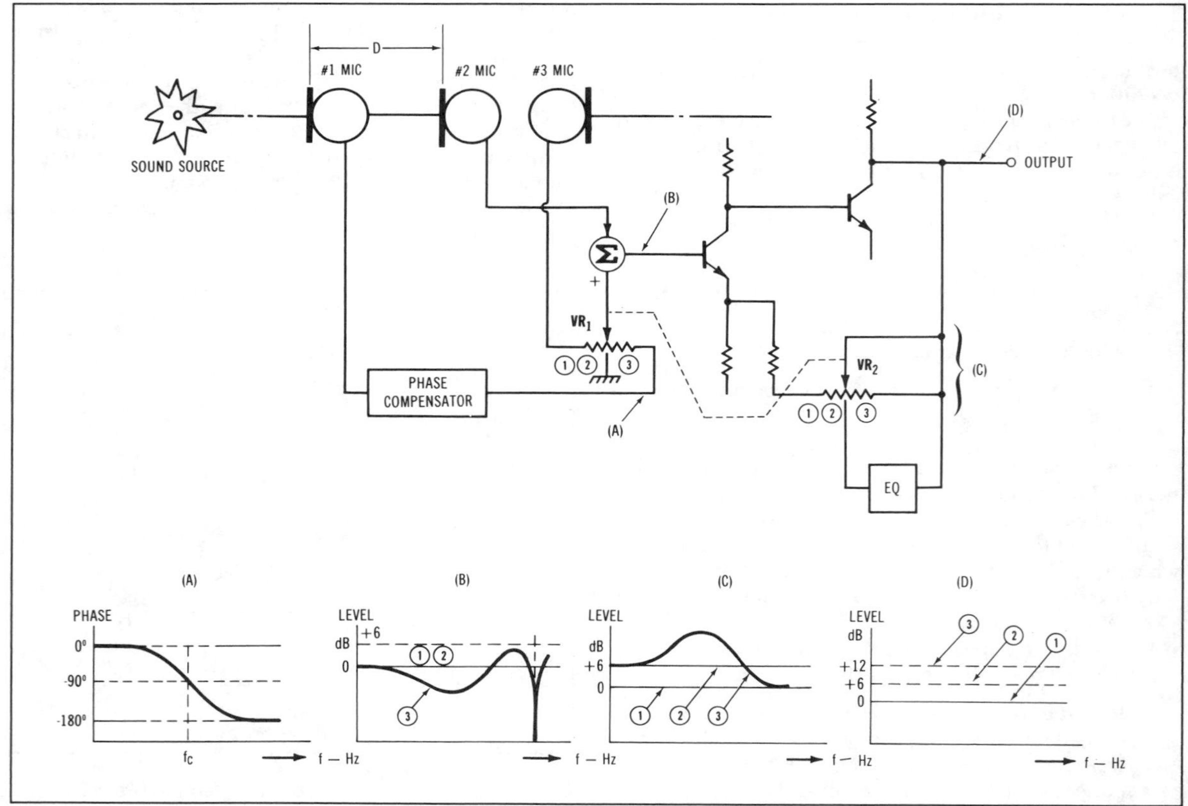

Figure 13-80 Configuration of the zoom microphone.

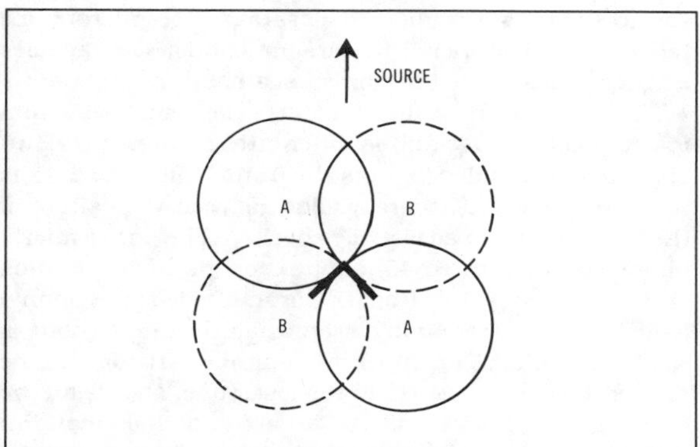

Figure 13-81 Coincident microphone technique using two bidirectional microphones.

the United States. Although originally intended for true "concert-hall-sound" reproduction of symphony orchestras, big bands, and vocal ensembles, mid-side (M-S) and XY techniques are now finding applications in studio rock sessions.

Coincident microphones are used for stereo recording.[18] The basic coincident technique was developed in the 1930s (along with the first stereo recordings) by English engineer Alan Blumlein. Blumlein used two figure-eight pattern ribbon microphones mounted so that their pattern lobes were at right angles (90°) to each other, as shown in Fig. 13-81. The stereo effect is produced primarily by the difference in amplitude generated in the two microphones by the sound source. A sound on the right generates a larger signal in microphone B than in microphone A. A sound directly in front produces an equal signal in both microphones, and a sound on the left produces a larger signal in microphone A than in microphone B. The same process takes place with spaced omnidirectional microphones, but because of the spacing, there is also a time delay between two signals (comb filter effect). It can also produce a loss in gain and unpleasant sound if the two channels are combined into a single monosignal. Since the coincident microphone has both its transducers mounted on the same vertical axis, the arrival time is identical in both channels, thus reducing this problem to a large degree.

Coincident Techniques

Modern coincident microphones often use cardioid or hyper-cardioid patterns.

These patterns work as well as the figure-eight pattern microphones in producing a stereo image, but they pick up less of the ambient hall sound.

Two variations on the basic coincident technique are the *M-S technique* and the *O.R.T.F. technique*. The M-S technique uses a forward-facing cardioid microphone and a side-facing, figure-eight microphone, as shown in Fig. 13-82. The microphone outputs form a signal matrix with the cardioid microphone supplying the sum L + R signal and the figure-eight microphone supplying the difference or L − R signal. These two signals are then added and subtracted electrically (either before or after recording) to produce pure left and right signals. This sum and difference technique can be used to produce signals that are electrically equivalent to the various XY patterns normally used in coincident recording.

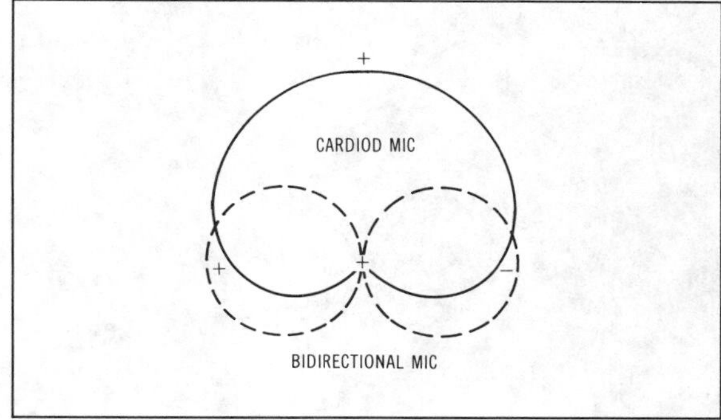

Figure 13-82 The M-S (mid-side) coincident microphone technique.

The advantage of this method is that the acoustic characteristics of the recordings can be controlled electrically without having to move the microphone physically. The amount of separation can be varied from pure mono to pure stereo, or somewhere in between. It also allows the amount of hall sound to be increased or decreased without changing the amount of presence (distance from the performers).

The initials O.R.T.F. stand for *Office de Radiodiffusion Television Francais*, the French government radio network that developed this technique. The O.R.T.F. method uses two cardioid microphones facing outward with an angle of 110° between them. Because of the spacing between the transducers, the O.R.T.F. method does not have the time-coherence properties of M-S mic'ing.

Probably the strongest virtue of the coincident microphone technique is its simplicity under actual working conditions. Just place the microphone in a central location that gives a good balance between the musicians and the acoustics of the hall. It is this simplicity that makes coincident microphones a favorite of broadcast engineers recording (or transmitting) live symphonic concerts.

Coincident-Stereophonic Microphone Design

Stereophonic microphones are essentially two matched diaphragm microphones in one housing that have been specially designed for use in M-S and XY "intensity" stereophony.

The AKG C422 shown in Fig. 13-83 is a studio condenser microphone that has been specially designed for

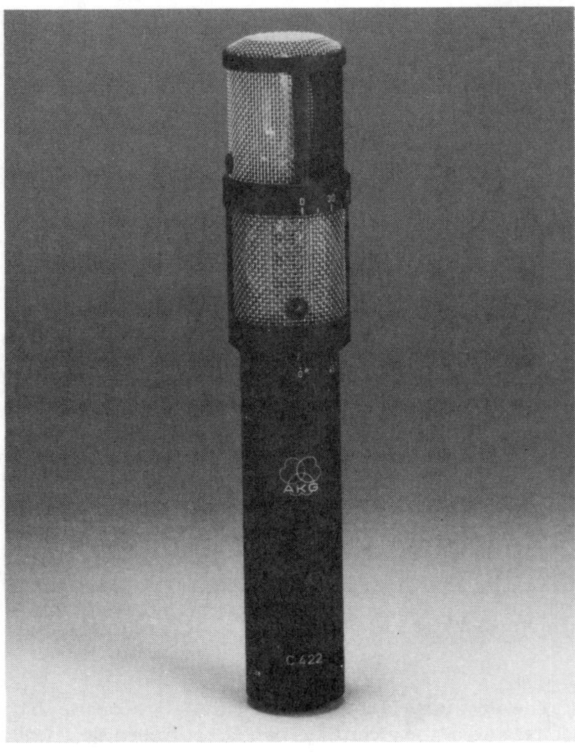

Figure 13-83 AKG C422 stereo coincident microphone. *(Courtesy AKG Acoustics, Inc.)*

sound studio and radio broadcasting. The microphone head holds two twin diaphragm condenser capsules elastically suspended to protect against handling noise.

The wire-mesh grille protects the capsules from mechanical damage and is differently colored at the two opposing grille sides (light is the front grille side; dark is the rear grille side), thereby allowing relative position of the two systems to be visually checked. The entire microphone can be rotated 45° about the axis to allow quick and exact changeover from 0° (for mid-side stereophony) to 45° (for XY stereophony) even when the microphone is rigidly mounted. The upper microphone cartridge can be rotated 180° with respect to the lower one. A scale on the housing adjustment ring and an arrow-shaped mark on the upper system allows the included angle to be exactly adjusted. In sound studio work and radio broadcasts, it is often necessary to recognize the respective positions of the two systems from great distances; therefore, two light-emitting diodes with a particularly narrow light-emitting angle are employed. One is mounted in the upper (rotatable) housing, and the other in the lower (nonrotatable) housing. To align the heads, simply have the units rotated until the light-emitting diode is brightest on the preferred axis.

Enclosed within the microphone shaft are two separate field-effect transistor preamplifiers, one for each channel. These are characterized by a particularly high input impedance, an extremely low internal noise, and a high crosstalk attenuation. The output level of both channels may be simultaneously lowered by 10 or 20 dB.

The C422 is connected to an S42E remote-control unit that allows any one of nine polar patterns to be selected

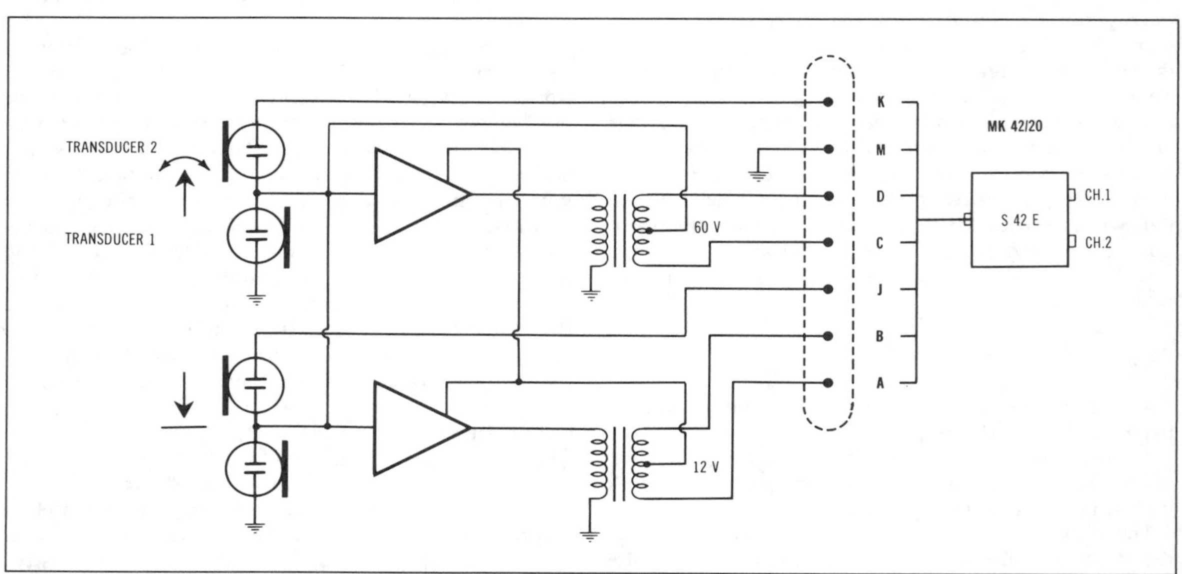

Figure 13-84 Schematic of the AKG C-422 coincident microphone. *(Courtesy AKG Acoustics, Inc.)*

for each channel. Because of noiseless selection, polar-pattern changeover is possible even during recording.

Each channel of the microphone incorporates two cardioid diaphragms facing 180° of each other (back to back), as shown in Fig. 13-84. Note the 12-V phantom power for the electronics and the 60-V phantom power for the lower transducer (1), insuring that transducer 1 is always biased on. This transducer has a positive output for a positive pressure. The second or upper transducer is connected to pin K, which through the S42E, has nine switchable voltages between 0 and 120 V. When the voltage at K is 60 V, the output of transducer 2 is 0 (60 V on either side of it), so the microphone output is cardioid.

When the voltage at K is 120 V, transducer 2 is biased with 60 V of an opposite polarity from transducer 1 so the output is 180° out of polarity, the mixed output being a figure-eight pattern.

When the voltage at K is 0 V, transducer 2 has a 60-V bias on it with the same polarity as transducer 1. Because the transducers face in opposite directions, when these two outputs are combined, an omnidirectional pattern is produced.

By varying the voltage on K between 0 and 120 V, various patterns between a figure-eight and an omnidirectional pattern can be produced.

13.13.3.12 Automatic Microphone Systems

There have been many new advances in automatic mixers where the microphone is normally off until gated on by a signal, hopefully, a wanted signal. Many operate on an increased level in one or more microphones with respect to the random background noise (see section 15.2.7).

The Shure *Automatic Microphone System (AMS)* turns microphones on and off (with automatic gating), greatly reducing the reverberant sound quality and feedback problems often associated with the use of multiple microphones. The special AMS microphones are gated on only by sounds arriving from the front within their acceptance angle of 120°. Other sounds outside the 120° angle, including background noise, will not gate the microphones on, regardless of level. In addition, the AMS adjusts gain automatically to prevent feedback as the number of "on" microphones increases.

The Shure Model AMS22 Low-Profile Condenser Microphone shown in Fig. 13-85 and the AMS26 Condenser Microphone shown in Fig. 13-86 are designed for use only with the Shure AMS. Unlike conventional microphones, these contain electronic circuitry and a novel transducer configuration to make them compatible with the Shure AMS mixers. These microphones should not be connected to standard simplex- (phantom-) or non-simplex-powered microphone inputs because they will not function properly.

AMS microphones, in conjunction with the special circuitry in the AMS mixers, uniquely discriminate between desired sounds that originate within their 120° front acceptance angle and all other sounds. Sounds from the front of a microphone are detected and cause it to be gated on, transmitting its signal to the mixer output. Sounds outside the acceptance angle will not gate the microphone on. When an AMS22 is gated on, it operates like a hemi- or half-cardioid microphone (because half the cardioid pattern "disappears" when the microphone is placed on a surface, as shown in Fig. 13-87). Each AMS microphone operates completely independently in analyzing its own sound field and deciding whether or not a sound source is within the front acceptance angle.

Figure 13-85 Shure Automatic Microphone System (AMS) model AMS22 low-profile microphone. *(Courtesy Shure Brothers, Inc.)*

Figure 13-86 Shure Automatic Microphone System (AMS) model AMS26 probe microphone. *(Courtesy Shure Brothers, Inc.)*

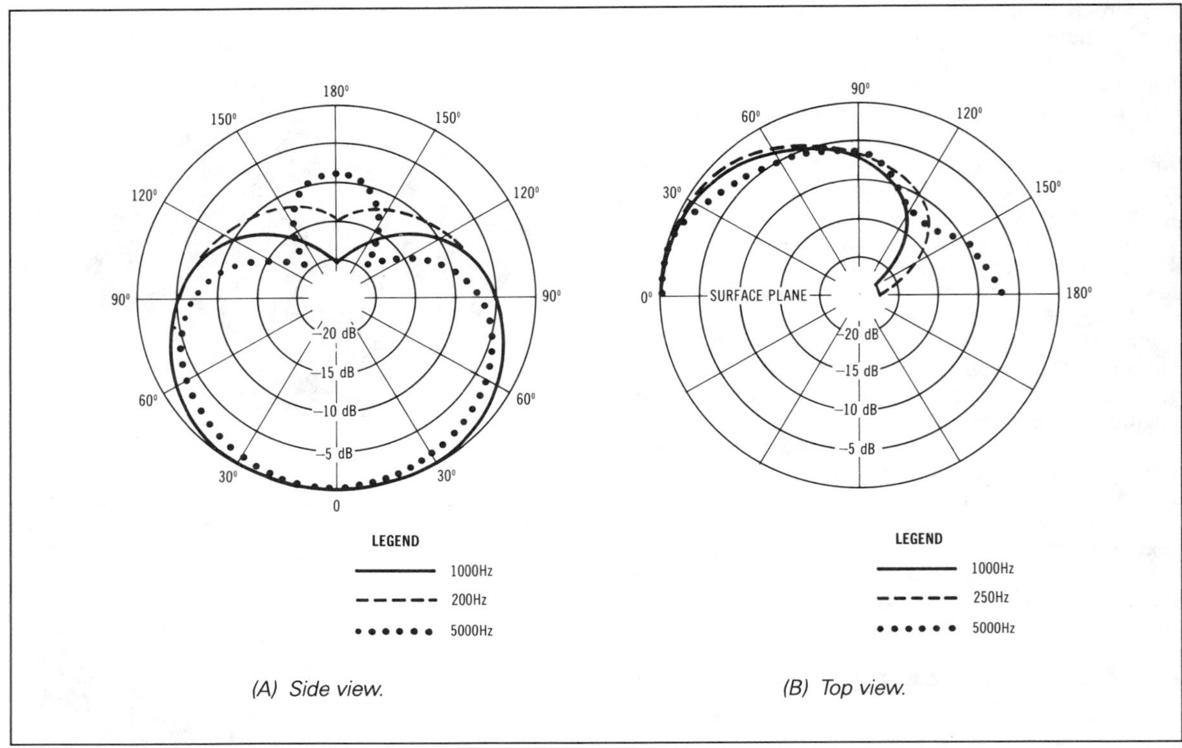

Figure 13-87 Hemi-cardioid polar pickup pattern for a Shure AMS surface microphone. *(Courtesy Shure Brothers, Inc.)*

Low-profile AMS22 microphones should be used on tables and desks while the AMS26 microphone is used on stands and goose necks. The microphone should be placed so that intended sources are within 60° of either side of the front of the microphone, that is, within 120° acceptance angle. Sources of undesired sound should be located outside the 120° acceptance angle. Each microphone should be at least 3 ft from the wall behind it, and items such as large ashtrays or briefcases should be at least 1 ft behind it. If the microphones are closer than that, reflections will reduce the front-to-back discrimination and, therefore, make the microphone act more like a conventional cardioid type.

13.13.3.13 Pressure-Gradient Condenser Microphones*

One of the most popular studio microphones is the Neumann U-87 multidirectional microphone shown in Fig. 13-88. This microphone is used for close mic'ing where high sound pressure levels are commonly encountered. The response below 30 Hz is rolled off to prevent low-frequency blocking and can be switched to 200 Hz to allow compensation for the bass rise common to all directional microphones at close range.

The U-87 microphone is a condenser microphone. The figure-eight characteristic is produced by means of two closely spaced or assembled cardioid characteristic capsules, whose principal axes are pointed in opposite directions and are electrically connected in antiphase.

These microphones are usually made with backplates equipped with holes, slots, and chambers forming delay elements whose perforations act as part friction resistances and part energy storage (acoustic inductances and capacitances) giving the backplate the character of an acoustic low-pass network. In the cutoff range of this low-pass network, above the transition frequency f_t, the membrane is impinged upon only from the front, and the microphone capsule changes to a pressure or interference transducer.

The output voltage e(t) of a condenser microphone using dc polarization is proportional to the applied dc voltage E_O and, for small displacement amplitudes of the diaphragm, to the relative variation in capacity $[c(t)]/C_O$ caused by the sound pressure:

$$e(t) = E_O[c(t)/C_O]$$

*Courtesy of Gotham Audio Corporation.

where,

c(t) is the variable component of capsule capacity,

C_0 is the capsule capacity in the absense of sound pressure,

t is the time.

The dependence of output voltage e(t) on E_0 is also utilized in some types of microphones, to control the directional characteristic. Two capsules with cardioid characteristics shown in Fig. 13-89 are placed back to back, or else they are assembled as a unit with a common backplate. The audio (ac) signals provided by the two diaphragms are connected in parallel through a capacitor C. The intensity and phase relationship of the outputs from the two capsule halves can be affected by varying the dc voltage applied to one of them (the left cartridge in Fig.

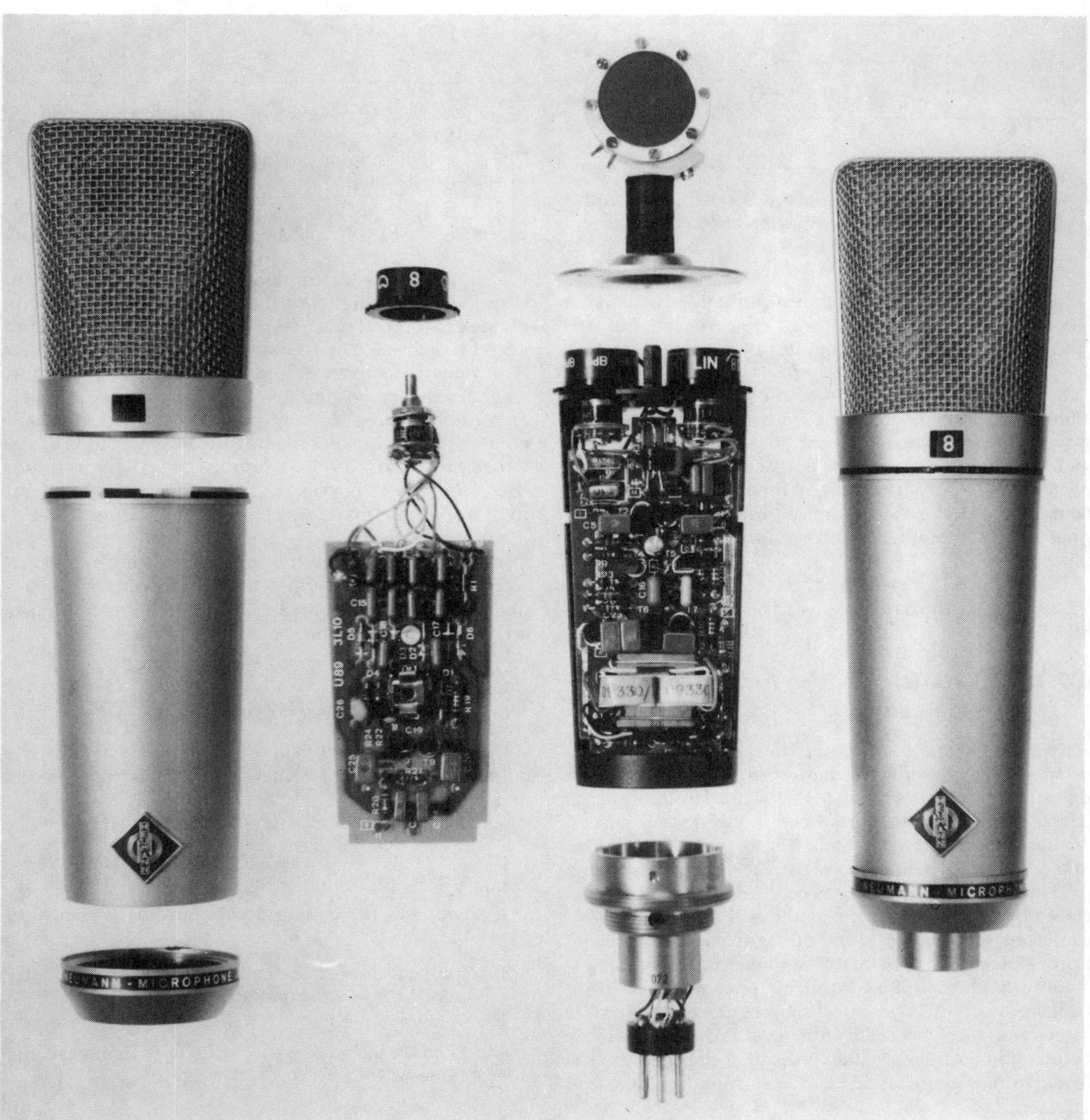

Figure 13-88 Neumann U-87 microphone. *(Courtesy Gotham Audio Corp.)*

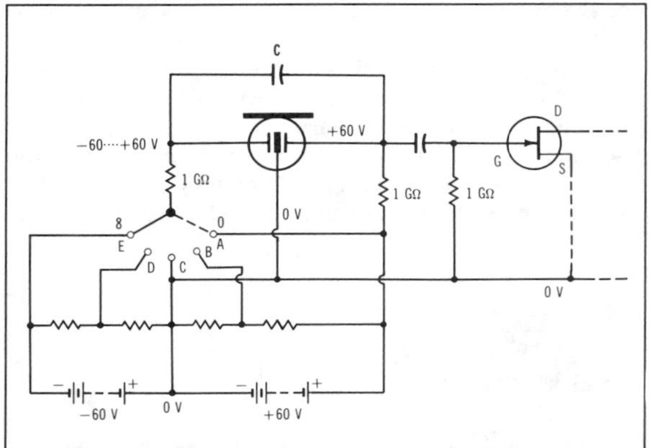

Figure 13-89 Circuit of a condenser microphone with electrically switchable direction characteristic. *(Courtesy Gotham Audio Corp.)*

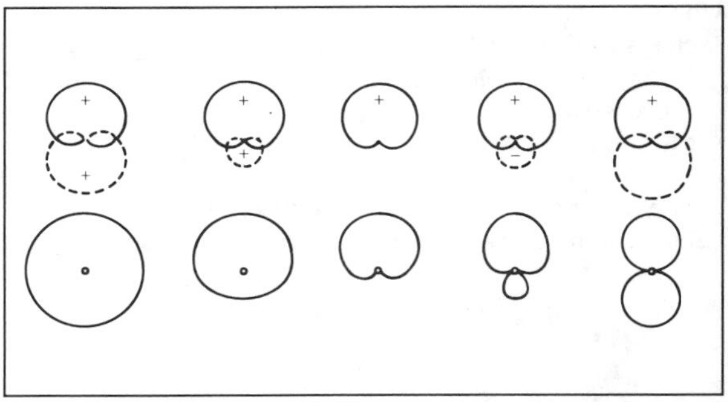

Figure 13-90 By using a microphone as shown in Fig. 13-89 and superimposing two cardioid patterns (top row), directional response patterns (bottom row) can be obtained. *(Courtesy Gotham Audio Corp.)*

13-89). This can be accomplished through a switch, or a potentiometer. The directional characteristic of the microphone may thus be changed by remote control via long extension cables.

If the switch in Fig. 13-89 is in its center position (c), then the left capsule-half does not contribute any voltage, and the microphone has the cardioid characteristic of the right capsule-half. In switch position *a*, the two ac voltages are in parallel, resulting in an omnidirectional pattern. In position *e* the two halves are connected in antiphase, and the result is a figure-eight directional response pattern.

The letters *a* to *e* given for the switch positions in Fig. 13-89 produce the patterns given the same letters in Fig. 13-90.

*13.13.3.14 Microphones for Binaural Recording**

Recordings made according to the binaural (head-oriented) stereophonic technique are generally processed using two channels with an artificial head (dummy head) that is equipped with microphones instead of the normal human hearing organs. Listening is with headphones and is not at all compatible with other playback systems unless special methods are used. The sound signal perceived by the left ear of the artificial head is fed only to the left ear of the listener, and the right ear of the artificial head is picked up only by the right ear of the listener.

All earlier binaural recording methods resulted in "in-head localization." The sound sources come from various directions, but they seem to be positioned along a line connecting both ears inside the head or closely above the head. In new artificial heads, the form of the head and especially the ear pinnae of a human are simulated more exactly.

Also an acoustic (frictional) resistance is inserted between the passage into the inner ear and the microphone capsule (pressure transducer), where the eardrum would be placed. This terminates the ear canal so that reflections are suppressed. Artificial heads of this type, when listened to with high-quality headphones, provide an audible impression that is virtually identical to that obtained by the listener holding his head still at the location of the dummy head. Recordings using dummy heads, therefore, have evoked an interest quite separate and distinct from those made only for loudspeaker playback.

Fig. 13-91 shows a disassembled dummy head made from a plastic material. It was designed for professional recordings and is equipped with two condenser microphones. In the upper angled sections the microphones are placed as well as the acoustic resistances.

*Courtesy of Gotham Audio Corporation.

13.14 MICROPHONE SENSITIVITY[19]

Microphone sensitivity is the measure of the electrical output of a microphone with respect to the acoustic sound pressure level input.

Sensitivity is measured in one of three methods:

1. Open-circuit voltage where 0 dB = 1 V/μbar,
2. Maximum power output where 0 dB = 1 mW/10 μbar,
3. Electronic Industries Association (EIA) sensitivity where 0 dB = EIA standard SE-105.

The common sound pressure levels used for measuring microphone sensitivity are:

94-dB SPL (10 dyn/cm^2 SPL) or 10 μbar,

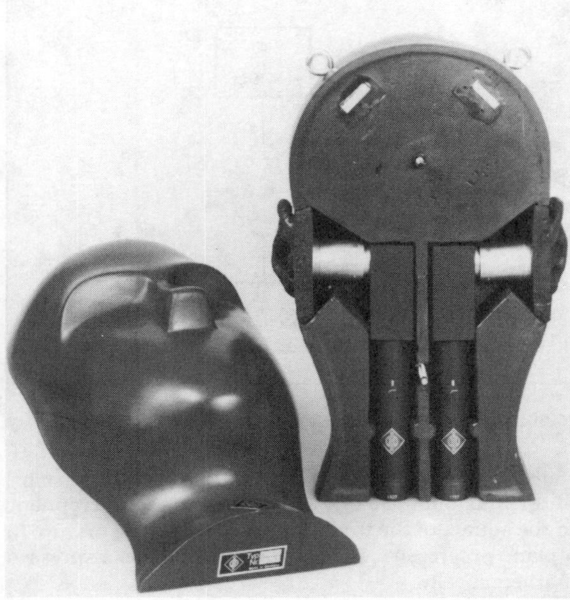

Figure 13-91 Neumann dummy head KU81. *(Courtesy Gotham Audio Corp.)*

74-dB SPL (1 dyn/cm^2 SPL) or 1 μbar,

0-dB SPL (0.0002 dyn/cm^2 SPL) or threshold of hearing.

94-dB SPL is recommended because 74-dB SPL is harder to use in field measurements because of its closeness to typical noise levels.

13.14.1 Open-Circuit Voltage Sensitivity

There are several good reasons for measuring the open-circuit voltage:

1. If the open-circuit voltage and the microphone impedance are known, the microphone performance can be calculated for any condition of loading.
2. It corresponds to an effective condition of use. A microphone should be connected to a high impedance to yield maximum signal-to-noise ratio.
3. When the microphone is connected to a high impedance compared to its own, variations in microphone impedance do not cause variations in response.

The open-circuit voltage sensitivity (S_v) can be calculated by exposing the microphone to a known sound pressure level, measuring the voltage output, and using the following formula:

$$S_v = 20 \log E_o - \text{dB SPL} + 74 \qquad (13\text{-}3)$$

where,

S_v is the open-circuit voltage sensitivity in decibels re 1 V for a 1 dyn/cm^2 SPL (74-dB SPL) acoustic input to the microphone,
E_o is the output of the microphone in volts,
dB SPL is the level of the actual acoustic input.

Setting up the microphone measurement system, as shown in Fig. 13-92, requires a random-noise generator, a microvoltmeter, a high-pass and a low-pass filter set, a power amplifier, and a test-loudspeaker in addition to the sound level meter (SLM). The SLM is placed a specific measuring distance (about 5 to 6 ft) in front of the loudspeaker. The system is adjusted until the SLM reads 94-dB SPL (a band of pink noise from 250 to 5000 Hz is excellent for this purpose). The microphone to be tested is now substituted for the SLM.

It is often necessary to know the voltage output of the microphone for various sound pressure levels to determine whether the microphone will overload the preamplifier circuit or the signal-to-noise ratio will be inadequate. To determine this, use the following formula:

$$E_o = 10^{(S_v + \text{dB SPL} - 74)/20} \qquad (13\text{-}4)$$

where,

E_o is the voltage output of microphone,
S_v is the open-circuit voltage sensitivity,
dB SPL is the sound pressure level at the microphone.

13.14.2 Maximum Power Output Sensitivity[19]

The *maximum power output sensitivity* form of specification gives the maximum power output in decibels available from the microphone for a given sound pressure and power reference. Such a specification can be calculated from the internal impedance and the open-circuit voltage of the microphone. This specification also indicates the ability of a microphone to convert sound energy into electrical power. The formula is

$$S_p = 10 \log[(V_O)^2/R_O] + 44\,\text{dB} \qquad (13\text{-}5)$$

where,

S_p is the power level microphone sensitivity in decibels,
V_O is the open-circuit voltage produced by a 1 μbar sound pressure,
R_O is the internal impedance of the microphone.

The form of this specification is similar to the voltage

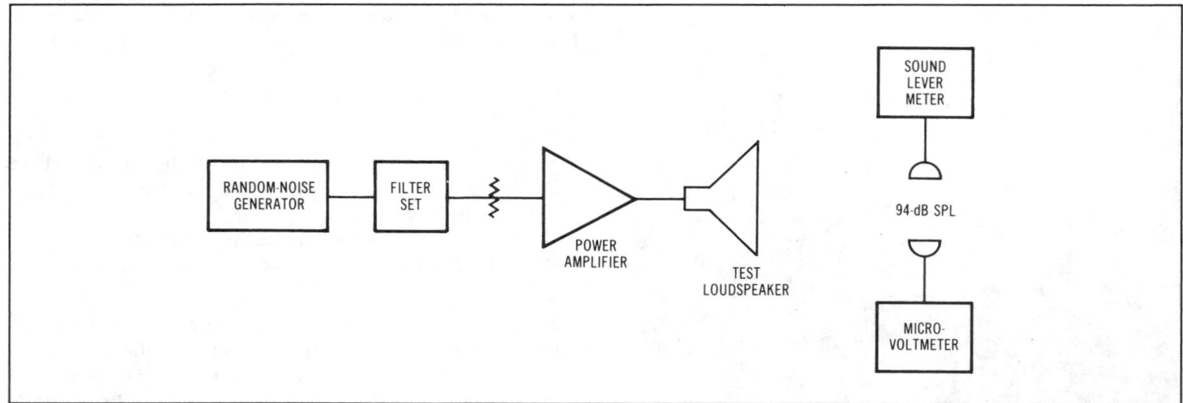

Figure 13-92 Method of determining open-circuit voltage sensitivity of a microphone. *(From Reference 18.)*

specification except that a power as opposed to a voltage reference is given with the sound pressure reference. A 1-mW power reference and a 10-μbar pressure reference are commonly used (as for the previous case). This form of microphone specification is quite meaningful because it takes into account both the voltage output and the internal impedance of the microphone.

S_p can also be calculated easily from the open-circuit voltage sensitivity with the formula:

$$S_p = S_v - 10 \log Z + 44\,\text{dB} \quad (13\text{-}6)$$

where,

S_p is the decibel rating for an acoustical input of 94-dB SPL (10 dyn/cm^2),

Z is the measured impedance of the microphone (the specifications of most manufacturers use the rated impedance).

The output level can also be determined directly from the open-circuit voltage with the formula:

$$S_p = 10 \log(E_o^2/0.001Z) - 6\,\text{dB} \quad (13\text{-}7)$$

where,

E_o is the open-circuit voltage,

Z is the microphone impedance.

Because the quantity 10 log (E^2/0.001Z) treats the open-circuit voltage as if it appears across a load, it is necessary to subtract 6 dB. (The reading is 6 dB higher than it would have been had a load been present.)

13.14.3 Electronic Industries Association (EIA) Output Sensitivity

The Electronic Industries Association (EIA) Standard SE-105, August 1949, defines the system rating (G_M) as the ratio (in decibels relative to 0.001 W/0.0002 dyn/cm^2) of the maximum electrical output from the microphone to the square of the undisturbed sound field pressure in a plane progressive wave at the microphone. Expressed mathematically,

$$G_M = (20 \log(E_o/P) - 10 \log Z_o) - 50\,\text{dB} \quad (13\text{-}8)$$

where,

E_o is the open-circuit voltage of the microphone,

P is the undisturbed sound field pressure in dyn/cm^2,

Z_o is the microphone rated output impedance in ohms.

For all practical purposes, the output level of the microphone can be obtained by adding to G_M the sound pressure level relative to 0.0002 dyn/cm^2.

Because G_M, S_V, and S_P are compatible, G_M can also be calculated with the formula:

$$G_M = S_v - 10 \log R_{MR} - 50\,\text{dB} \quad (13\text{-}9)$$

where,

G_M is the EIA rating,

R_{MR} is the EIA center value of the nominal impedance range.

Ranges (ohms)				*Values Used (ohms)*
20	–	80	=	38
80	–	300	=	150
300	–	1250	=	600
1250	–	4500	=	2400
4500	–	20,000	=	9600
20,000	–	70,000	=	40,000

The EIA rating can also be determined from the chart in Fig. 13-93.

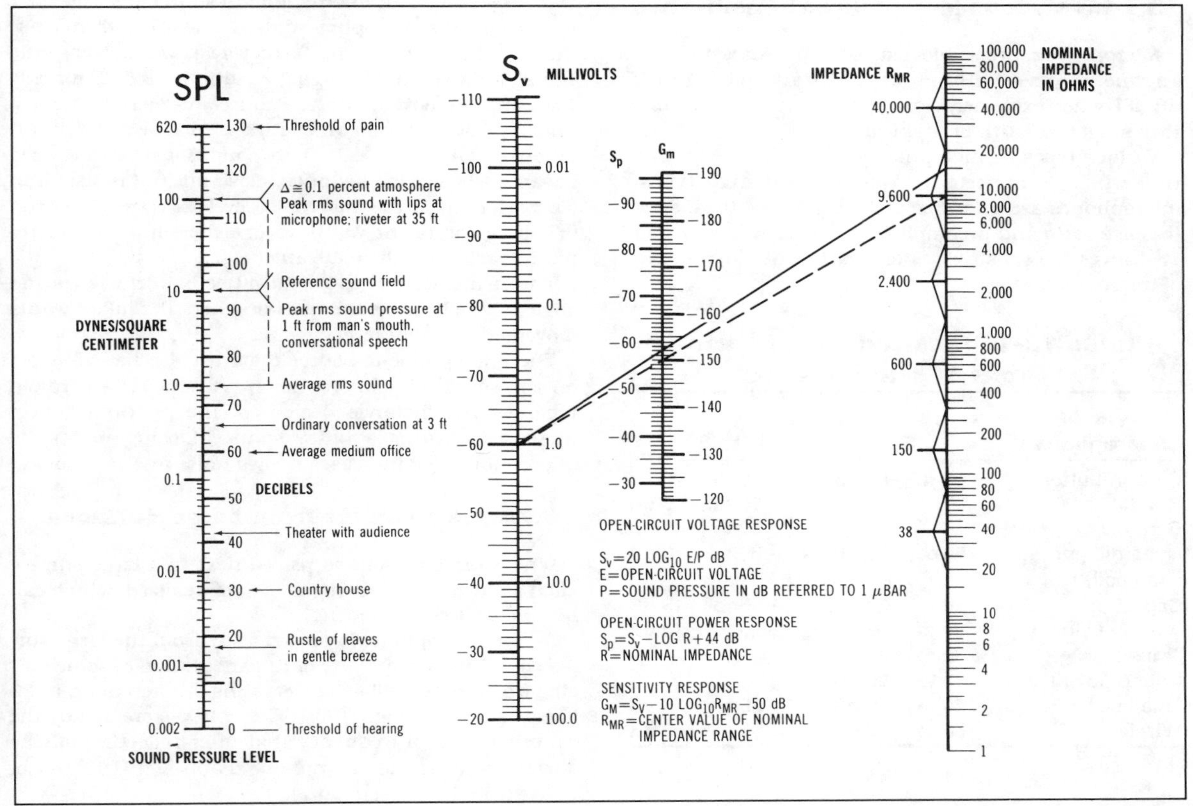

Figure 13-93 Microphone sensitivity conversion chart.

13.14.4 Microphone Thermal Noise

Just by having an impedance, a microphone generates thermal noise. Even without an acoustic signal, the microphone would still produce a minute output voltage. The thermal noise voltage (E_n) produced by the electrical resistance of a sound source is dependent on the frequency bandwidth under consideration, the magnitude of the resistance, and the temperature existing at the time of the measurement. This voltage is

$$E_n = 4ktR(bw) \tag{13-10}$$

where,
k is the Boltzmann's constant, which is 1.38×10^{-23} J/K,
t is the absolute temperature, 273° + room temperature, both in °C,
R is the resistance in ohms,
bw is the bandwidth in hertz.

To change this to dBv use the formula:

$$EIN_{dBv} = 20\log(E_n/0.775) \tag{13-11}$$

The thermal noise relative to 1 V is −198 dB for a 1-Hz bandwidth and 1-Ω impedance. Therefore,

$$TN/1\,V = -198\,dB + 10\log(bw) + 10\log Z \tag{13-12}$$

where,
TN/1 V is the thermal noise relative to 1 V,
bw is the bandwidth in hertz,
Z is the microphone impedance.

Thermal noise relative to 1 V can be converted to equivalent input noise (EIN) by the formula:

$$EIN_{dB} = -198\,dB + 10\log(bw) + 10\log Z - 6 - 20\log 0.775\,V \tag{13-13}$$

Since the EIN is in dBm and dBm is referenced to 600 Ω, the impedance Z is 600 Ω.

13.14.5 Various Microphone Sensitivities

Microphones are subjected to sound pressure levels anywhere from 40 dB SPL when distant mic'ing to 150 dB SPL when extremely close mic'ing (i.e., ¼ in. from the rock singer's mouth or inside a drum or horn).

Various types of microphones have different sensitivities, which is important to know if different types of microphones are intermixed since gain settings, signal-to-noise ratio and preamplifier overload will vary. Table 13-1 gives the sensitivities of a variety of different types of microphones.

Table 13-1. Sensitivities of Various Types of Microphones

Type of Microphone	S_p	S_v
Carbon-button	−60 to −50 dB	
Crystal		−50 to −40 dB
Ceramic		−50 to −40 dB
Dynamic (moving coil)	−60 to −52 dB	−85 to −70 dB
Capacitor	−60 to −37 dB	−85 to −45 dB
Ribbon-velocity	−60 to −50 dB	−85 to −70 dB
Transistor	−60 to −40 dB	
Sound power	−32 to −20 dB	
Line level	−40 to 0 dB	−20 to 0 dB
Wireless	−60 to 0 dB	−85 to 0 dB

13.15 MICROPHONE PRACTICES

13.15.1 Placement

Microphones are placed in various relationships to the sound source to obtain various sounds. Whatever position gives the desired effect that is wanted is the correct position. There are certain recommendations that should be followed to assure a good recording.

13.15.1.1 Microphone-to-Source Distance

Microphones are usually used in the direct field. Under this condition, inverse square-law attenuation prevails, meaning that each time the distance is doubled, the microphone output is reduced 6 dB. For instance, moving from a microphone to source distance of 1 to 2 in. has the same effect as moving from 6 to 12 in., 1 to 2 ft, or 5 to 10 ft.

Distance has many effects on the system. In a reinforcement system, doubling the distance reduces gain before feedback 6 dB; in all systems, it reduces the effect of microphone to source variations.

By using the inverse-square-law formula for attenuation,

$$\text{decibel attenuation} = 20\log(D_1/D_2) \qquad (13\text{-}14)$$

It can be seen, at a microphone-to-source distance of 1 in., moving the microphone only ½ in. closer will increase the signal 6 dB and ½ in. farther away will decrease the signal 3.5 dB for a total signal variation of 9.5 dB for only 1 in. of total movement! At a source-to-microphone distance of 1 ft, a movement of 1 in. will cause a signal variation of only 0.72 dB. Both conditions can be used advantageously; for instance, close mic'ing is useful in feedback prone areas, high noise level areas (rock groups), or where the talent wants to use the source to microphone variations to create an effect.

The farther distances are most useful in churches and so on where lecterns are used or where the talker wants movement without level change.

The microphone-to-source distance also has an effect on the sound of a microphone, particularly a cardioid type. As the distance decreases, the proximity effect increases creating a bassy sound. Closing in on the microphone also increases breath noise and pop noise.

13.15.1.2 Distance from Large Surfaces

When a microphone is placed next to a large surface such as the floor, 6 dB of gain can be realized, which can be a help when far mic'ing.

As the microphone is moved away from the large surface but still in proximity of it, cancellation of some specific frequencies will occur, creating a notch of up to 30 dB, as shown in Fig. 13-30. The notch is created by the cancellation of a frequency that after reflecting off the surface reaches the microphone diaphragm 180° out of phase from the direct sound.

The frequency of cancellation (f_c) can be calculated from the formula:

$$f_c = 1130(0.5)/(D_{r1} + D_{r2} - D_d) \qquad (13\text{-}15)$$

where,

1130 is the speed of sound in feet per second,
0.5 is the out-of-phase frequency ratio,
D_{r1} is the reflected path from the source to the surface,
D_{r2} is the reflected path from the surface to the microphone,
D_d is the direct path from the source to the microphone.

If the microphone were 10 ft from the source and both were 5 ft above the floor, the cancelled frequency would be

$$f_c = 1130(0.5)/(7.07 + 7.07 - 10)$$
$$= 136.47\,\text{Hz}$$

If the microphone were moved to 2 ft above the floor, the cancelled frequency would be 319.20 Hz. If the microphone were 6 in. from the floor, the cancelled frequency would be 1266.6 Hz. If the microphone were 1 in. from the floor, the cancelled frequency would be 7239.7 Hz.

13.15.1.3 Behind Objects

Sound, like light, does not go through solid or acoustically opaque objects. It does, however, go through objects of various density. The transmission loss or ability of sound to go through this type of material is frequency dependent; therefore, if an object of this type is placed between the sound source and the microphone, the pickup will be attenuated according to the transmission characteristics of the object.

Low-frequency sound will bend around small objects, which also affects the frequency response of the signal.

The normal effect of placing the microphone behind an object, therefore, is a reduction of level, a low-frequency boost, and a high-fequency rolloff.

13.15.1.4 Above the Source

When the microphone is placed above or to the side of a directional sound source (i.e., horn, trumpet, and so on), the frequency response will roll off at the high end because high frequencies are more directional than low frequencies. Therefore, less high-frequency sound pressure level will reach the microphone than low-frequency sound pressure level.

13.15.1.5 Direct versus Reverberant Field

Mic'ing in the reverberant field picks up the characteristic of the room because the microphone is picking up as much or more of the "room," as it is the direct sound. When mic'ing in the reverberant field, only two microphones are required for stereo since isolation of the individual sound sources is impossible. When in the reverberant field, a directional microphone will lose its directivity; therefore, it is advantageous to use an omnidirectional microphone that has smoother frequency response. To mic sources individually, you must be in the direct field and usually very close to the source to eliminate cross feed.

13.15.2 Grounding

The grounding of microphones and their interconnecting cables is of extreme importance since any hum or noise picked up by the cables will be amplified along with the audio signal. Professional systems generally use the method shown in Fig. 13-94. Here the signal is passed through a two-conductor cable to the balanced input of a preamplifier. The cable shield is connected to pin number 1, and the audio signal is carried by the two conductors and pins 2 and 3. The actual physical ground is connected at the preamplifier chassis only and carried to the microphone case. In no instance is a second ground ever connected to the far end of the cable, because this will cause the flow of ground currents between two points of grounding.

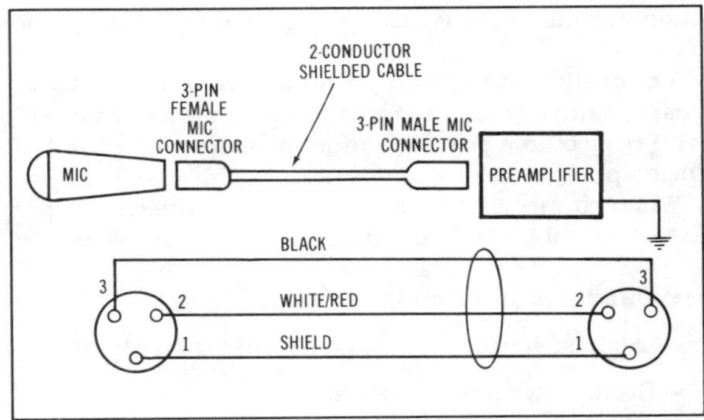

Figure 13-94 Typical low-impedance microphone to preamplifier wiring.

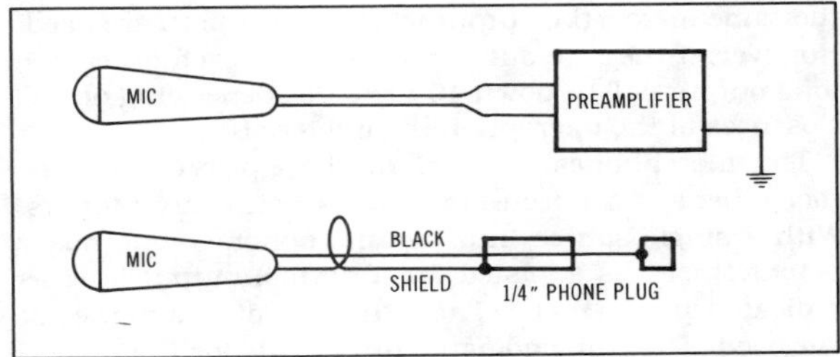

Figure 13-95 Typical semiprofessional, hi-fi microphone to preamplifier wiring.

In systems designed for semiprofessional and home use, the method in Fig. 13-95 is used. Note that one side of the audio signal is carried over the cable shield to a pin-type connector. The bodies of both the male and female connector are grounded: the female to the amplifier case and the male to the cable shield. The microphone end is connected in a similar manner; here again the physical ground is connected only at the preamplifier chassis.

13.15.3 Polarity

Microphone polarity, or phase as it is often called in error, is important especially when multiple microphones are used. Here they add to each other rather than have cancelling effects. If multiple microphones are used and one is out of polarity, it will cause comb filters, reducing quality and stereo enhancement. The EIA standard RS.221.A, October 1979, defines polarity as "Polarity of a microphone or a microphone transducer element refers to in-phase or out-of-phase condition of voltage developed at its terminals with respect to the sound pressure of a sound wave causing the voltage."

"Note: Exact in-phase relationship can be taken to mean that the voltage is coincident with the phase of the sound pressure wave causing the voltage. In practical microphones, this perfect relationship may not always be obtainable."

The positive or in-phase terminal is that terminal that has a positive potential and a phase angle less than 90° with respect to a positive sound pressure at the front of the diaphragm.

When connected to a *three-pin XLR connector* as per EIA standard RS-297, the polarity shall be as follows:

- Out-of-phase, terminal 3 (black)
- In-phase, terminal 2 (red—or other than black)
- Ground, terminal 1, (shield)

A simple method of determining microphone polarity is as follows:

If two microphones have the same frequency response and sensitivity and are placed next to each other and into the same mixer, the output will double if both are used. However, if they are out of polarity with each other, the total output will be down 40 to 50 dB, depending on the closeness of the microphone characteristics.

The microphones to be polarized are placed alongside each other and connected to their respective mixer inputs. With a single source into the microphones, one mixer potentiometer is adjusted for a normal output level as indicated on a vu meter. The setting is noted, and the pot is closed. The same adjustment is made for the second microphone, and the setting of that pot is noted. Now both pots are opened to these settings. If the microphones are out of polarity, the quality of reproduction will be distorted, and there will be a distinct drop in level. Reversing the electrical connections to one microphone will bring them into polarity.

If the microphone is of the bidirectional type, it may be turned 180° to bring it into polarity and later corrected electrically. If the microphones are of the directional type, only the output or cable connections can be reversed. After polarizing a bidirectional microphone, the rear should be marked with a white stripe for future reference.

13.15.4 Balanced or Unbalanced

Microphones can be connected either *balanced* or *unbalanced*. All professional installations use a balanced system for the following reasons:

1. Reduced pickup of hum,
2. Reduced pickup of electrical noise and transients,
3. Reduced pickup of electrical signals from adjacent wires.

These reductions are realized because the two signal conductors shown in Fig. 13-96 pick up the same stray signal with equal intensity and polarity; therefore, the noise is impressed evenly on each end of the transformer primary, eliminating a potential across the transformer

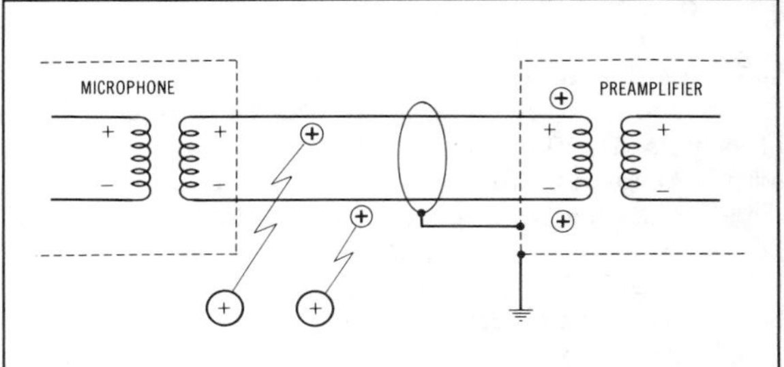

Figure 13-96 Noice cancellation on balanced, shielded microphone cables.

and cancelling any input noise. Because the balanced wires are in a shielded cable, the signal to each conductor is also greatly reduced.

When installing microphones into an unbalanced system, any noise that gets to the inner unbalanced conductor is not cancelled by the noise in the shield; therefore, the noise is transmitted into the preamplifier.

Balanced low-impedance microphone lines can be as long as 500 ft but unbalanced microphone lines should never exceed 15 ft.

13.15.5 Impedance

Most professional microphones are low impedance; that is, their impedance is approximately 200 Ω, and they are designed to work into a load of 2000 Ω. High-impedance microphones are 50,000 Ω and are designed to work into a very high impedance of 1 to 10 MΩ. The low-impedance microphone has the following advantages:

1. Less susceptible to noise. A noise source of relatively high impedance cannot "drive" into a source of relatively low impedance (i.e., the microphone cable).
2. Capable of being connected to long microphone lines.

All microphone cable has inductance and capacitance. The capacitance is often about 40 pF (40×10^{-12}) per foot. If a cable is 100 ft long, the capacitance would be (40×10^{-12}) × 100 ft or 4×10^{-9} F. This is equivalent to a 3978.9-Ω impedance at 10,000 Hz as calculated from the formula:

$$X_c = 1/2\pi fC \quad (4\text{-}16)$$

This has little effect on a microphone with an impedance of 200 Ω.

$$Z_T = (X_c Z_m)/(X_c + Z_m) \quad (4\text{-}17)$$

For a microphone impedance of 200 Ω, the total impedance Z_T = 190 Ω or less than 0.5 dB.

If this same cable were used with a high-impedance microphone of 50,000 Ω, 10,000 Hz would be down more than 20 dB.

Making the load impedance equal to the microphone impedance will reduce the microphone sensitivity 6 dB, which reduces the overall signal-to-noise ratio by 6 dB. For the best signal-to-noise ratio, the input impedance of low-impedance microphone preamplifiers is always 2000 Ω or greater.

If the load impedance is reduced to less than the microphone impedance, or the load impedance is not resistive, the microphone frequency response and output voltage will be affected.

Loading a high-impedance or ceramic microphone from 10 MΩ to 100 kΩ reduces the output at 100 Hz by 27 dB.

13.16 MICROPHONE ACCESSORIES

13.16.1 Windscreens and Pop Filters

A *windscreen* is a device placed over the exterior of a microphone for the purpose of reducing the effects of wind noise when recording out of doors or when panning or gunning a microphone. The screen shown in Fig. 13-97 may consist of a wire frame covered with silk or may be a special polyurethane foam type, as shown in Fig. 13-98. Most microphones made today have an integral windscreen/pop filter built in. In very windy conditions, these may not be enough; therefore, an external windscreen must be used.

With a properly designed windscreen, a reduction of 20 to 30 dB in wind noise can be expected, depending on the sound pressure level at the time, wind velocity, and the frequency of the sound pickup. Windscreens may be used with any type microphone, and they vary in their size and shape. Two types of wind screens by Shure employing a special type polyurethane foam are shown in Fig. 13-98. This material has no affect on the high-frequency response of the microphone because of its porous nature. Standard Styrofoam® is not satisfactory for windscreen construction because of its homogenous nature.

Figure 13-98 Polyurethane windscreens by Shure Brothers. *(Courtesy Shure Brothers, Inc.)*

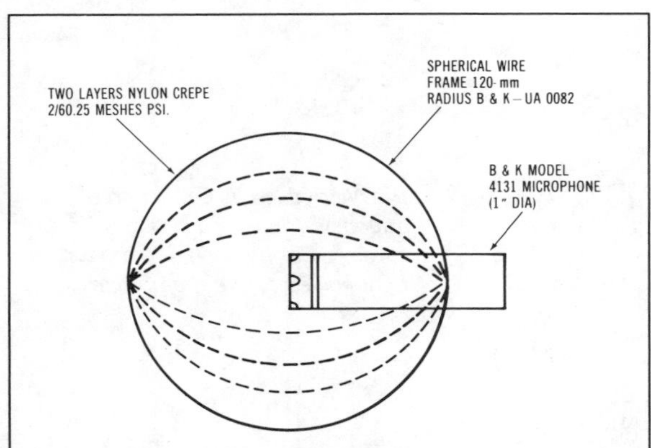

Figure 13-97 Typical silk-covered wind screen and microphone. *(Courtesy B and K Technical Review)*

A cross-sectional view of a typical windscreen employing a wire frame covered with nylon crepe for mounting on a 1-in.-diameter microphone is shown in Fig. 13-97. The effectiveness of this screen as measured by Dr. V. Brüel of Brüel and Kjaer is given in Fig. 13-99.

Pop protection is best appreciated when close-talking where explosive breath sounds are particularly bothersome. These explosive breath sounds are commonly produced when saying words involving P and T sounds. The term "explosive breath sound" is somewhat of a misnomer since these sounds are normally inaudible to a listener.[13]

The electrical output from the microphone is actually the transient microphone response to this low-velocity, high-pressure, pulse-type wave front. The P and T sounds are projected in different directions and can be shown by saying the words P and T while holding your hand about 3 in. in front of your mouth. Note that the T sound is felt at a considerable distance below the P sound.

For most microphones, pop output varies with distance between the source and microphone reaching a peak at about 3 in. Also the worst angle of incidence for most microphones is about 45° to the microphone and for a glancing contact just at the edge of the microphone along a path parallel to the longitudinal axis.

Pop filters can be as simple as two wire-mesh screens treated with flocking material to create an acoustic resistance.

13.16.2 Shock Mounts

Shock mounts are used to eliminate noise from being transmitted to the microphone, usually from the floor or table. Shock mounts may be the type shown in Fig. 13-100. This microphone shock mount, a Shure A53M, mounts on a standard ⅝-in.-27 thread and reduces mechanical and vibration noises by more than 20 dB. Because of its design, this shock mount can be used on a floor or table stand, hung from a boom, or used as a low-profile stand to place the microphone cartridge close to a surface such as a floor.

Shock mounts are designed to resonate at a frequency at least 2½ times lower than the lowest frequency of the microphone.[20] The goal is simple but there are practical limitations. The resonant frequency (f_n) of a mechanical system can be computed from the equation:

$$f_n = (1/2\pi)\sqrt{(Kg/w)} \qquad (4\text{-}18)$$

where,

K is the spring rate of the isolator,
g is the acceleration due to gravity,
w is the load.

A microphone shock-mount load is pretty much determined by the weight of the microphone. To obtain a low-resonant frequency, the spring rate or stiffness must be as low as possible; however, it must be able to support the microphone without too much sag and be effective in any position the microphone may be used.

Curve A in Fig. 13-101 is the output signal of the microphone when vibrated axially without a shock mount. Curve B shows the output of the same microphone when vibrated at the same acceleration in the rubber-band-type development model. The resonance is about 20 Hz and could be adjusted by modifying the thickness of the rubber strands. The additional resonances at around 180 and 250 Hz, which are caused by frame-member vibration, are not easily subdued and require further work to rigi-

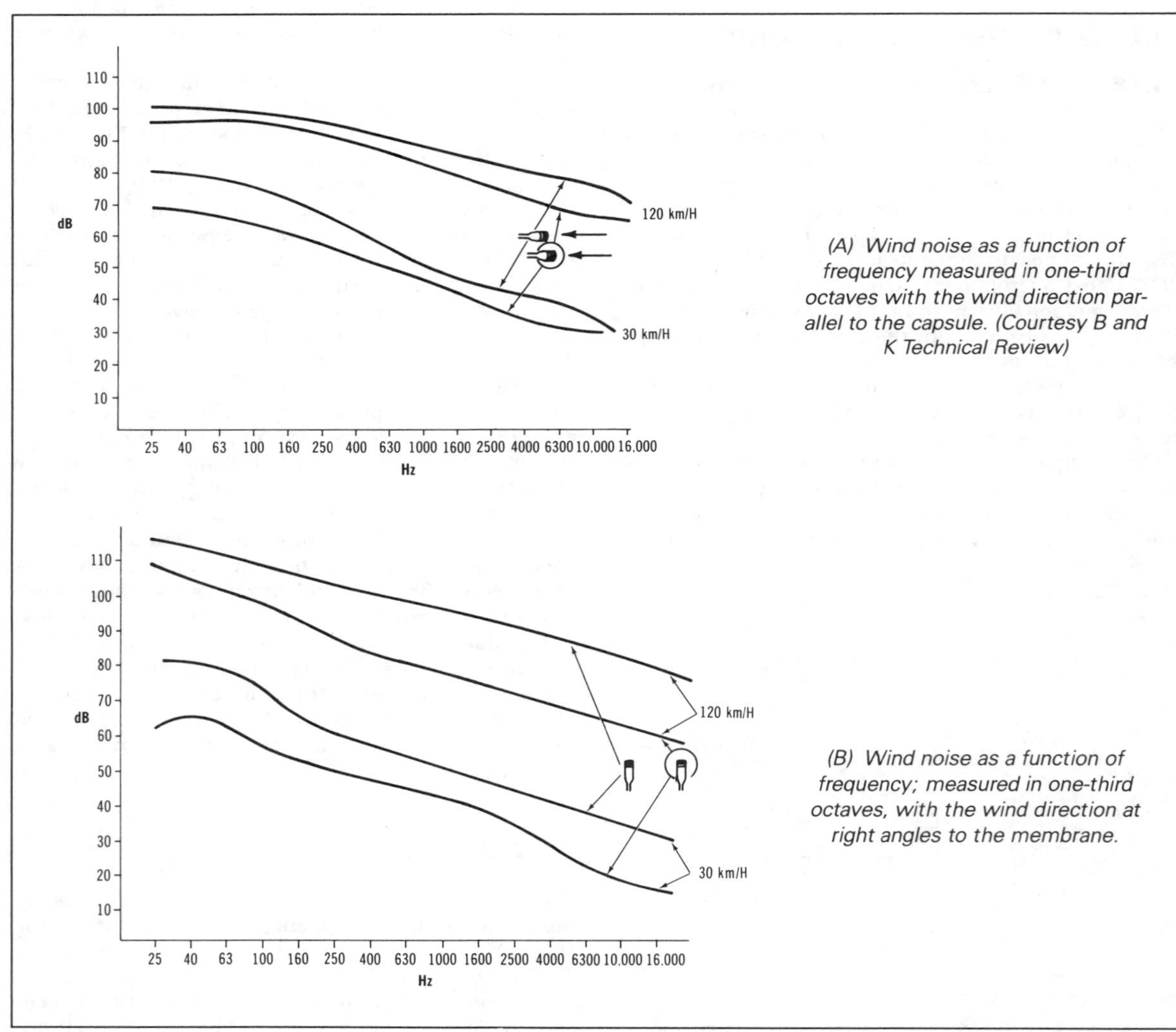

(A) Wind noise as a function of frequency measured in one-third octaves with the wind direction parallel to the capsule. (Courtesy B and K Technical Review)

(B) Wind noise as a function of frequency; measured in one-third octaves, with the wind direction at right angles to the membrane.

Figure 13-99 The effectiveness of

dize the framework. Fig. 13-101C shows the microphone output when vibrated in the Shure A53B/M shock mount. The resonant frequency is about 10 Hz, which means the shock mount should be effective down to 25 Hz if we apply the 2½-to-1 rule of thumb.

Boom noise is created by racking the boom in and out. The greatest amplitude of vibration happens in the axis parallel to the boom extension. The vibration level is in the order of 10^{-3}g, where 10^{-3}g is approximately equal to the output from a sound pressure of 0.1 μbar or the level of conversational voice at 6 ft. To eliminate boom noise, microphone hangers are used. These differ from shock mounts in that the mounts are under tension rather than compression.

Each type of microphone as a rule requires an individually designed hanger because of the microphone body contour and weight. However, all the microphone hangers have one thing in common, the microphone is supported by a metal holder that is in turn supported by some type of rubber mounting. The hanger in Fig. 13-102 is made by AKG and consists of a metal ring with rubber bands, forming a spider, holding the microphone clamp. The shock mount uses rubber in tension for the isolation qualities.

13.16.3 Stands and Booms

Microphones are mounted on microphone floor stands or table stands to place the microphone in front of the

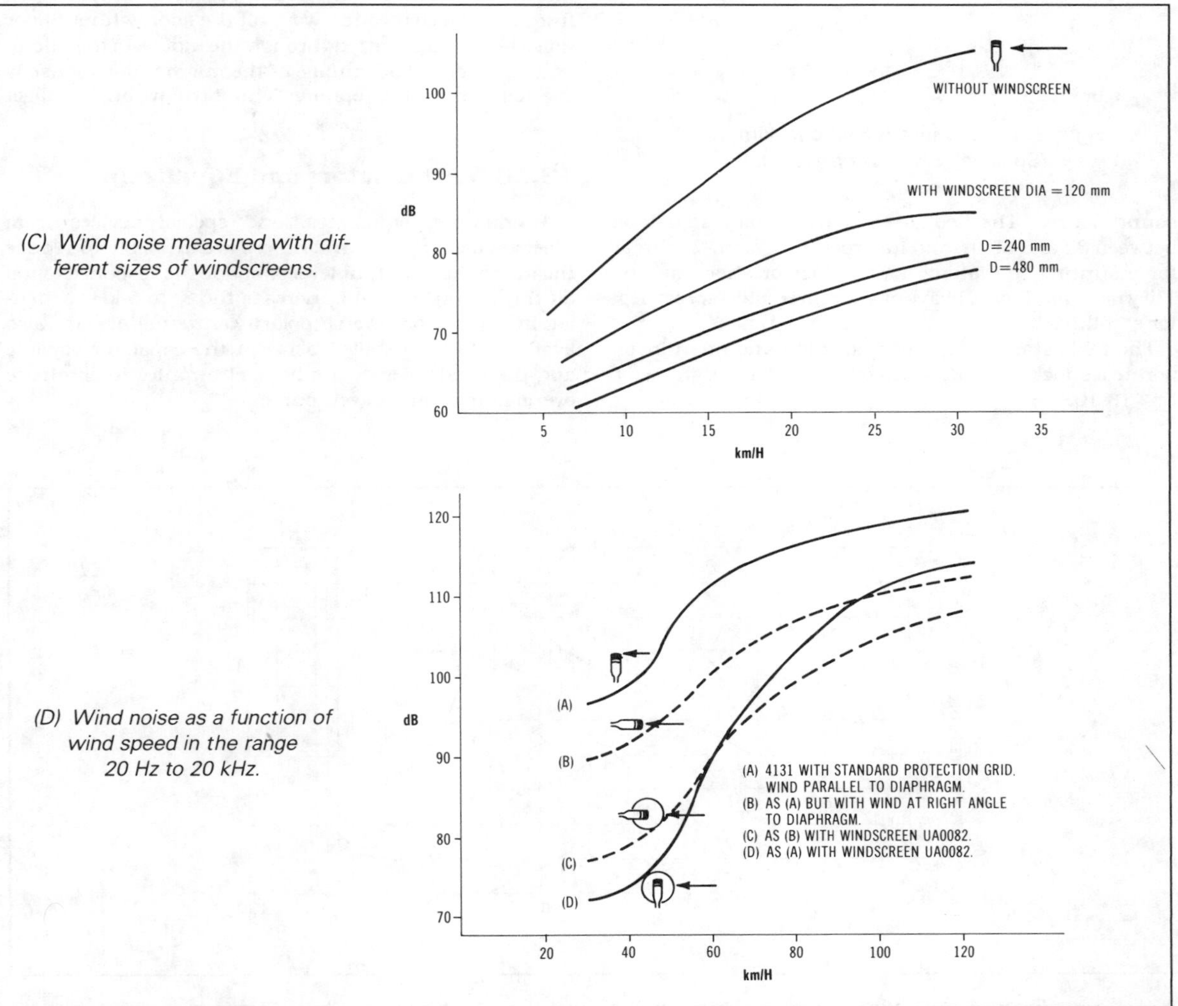

(C) Wind noise measured with different sizes of windscreens.

(D) Wind noise as a function of wind speed in the range 20 Hz to 20 kHz.

the windscreen shown in Fig. 13-97.

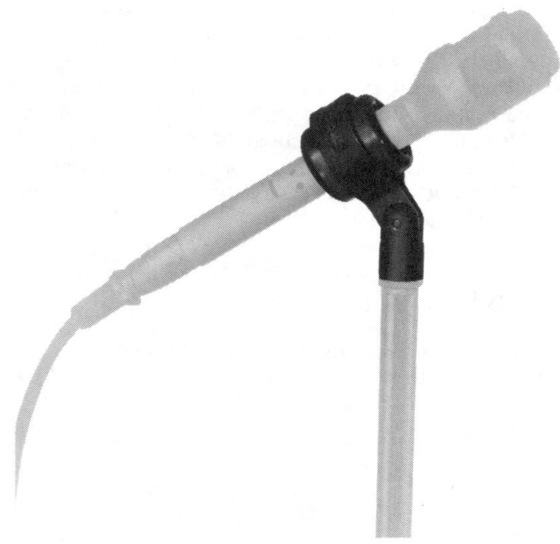

Figure 13-100 Shure A-53M shock mount. *(Courtesy Shure Brothers, Inc.)*

sound source. The floor stands are usually adjustable between 32 and 65 in. and incorporate a 5⁄8-in.-27 thread for mounting the microphone holder or shock mount. They normally have a heavy base or three wide-spread legs for stability.

The table stands are 6 to 8 in. high and often incorporate a shock mount and an on-off switch, as shown in Fig. 13-103.

Small booms are normally used to put the microphone in a place where it is difficult to reach with a floor stand. They are also useful when mic'ing from above the source. These stands are often on wheels and adjustable from 60 to 90 in. vertically and 90 to 110 in. horizontally, as shown in Fig. 13-104.

Large booms, as used in television and motion-picture sound stages, are motorized and often include a stage for the microphone sound person.

13.16.4 Microphone Mouse

Microphones can also be mounted in a foam "mic mouse," such as the Electro-Voice 411 shown in Fig. 13-105. The microphone mouse holds the microphone a minimum distance off the floor to allow for increased gain from the reflected sound wave off the floor, without floor noise being transmitted through the mouse to the microphone. A second advantage of the microphone mouse is the fact that the microphone is unobtrusive on the stage.

13.16.5 Attenuators and Equalizers

Attenuators, equalizers, and special devices from Electro-Voice, Shure, and others are available to reduce the microphone output level or shape the response to roll off the low or high end, increase the 3- to 5-kHz articulation region, or reverse polarity. Attenuators are also available to be installed between the capacitor capsule and the condenser microphone electronics to eliminate overload from high-level sources.

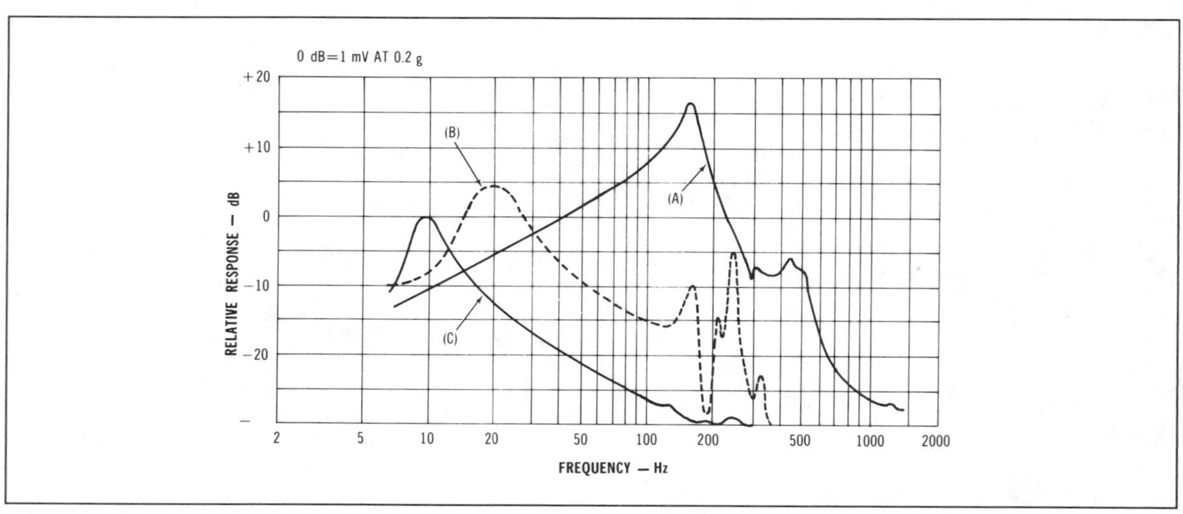

Figure 13-101 Vibration isolation of various shock mounts. *(Courtesy Shure Brothers, Inc.)*

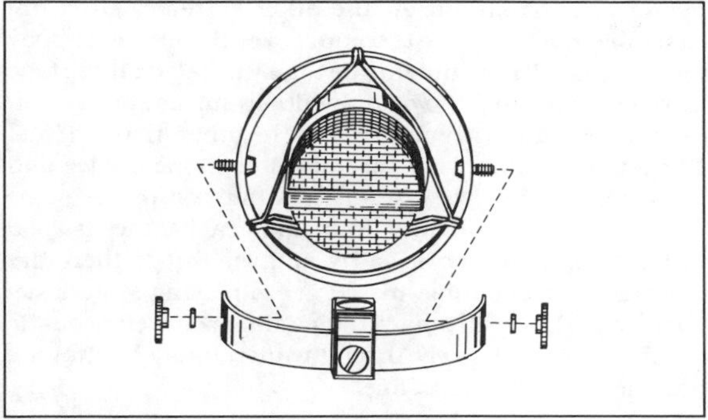

Figure 13-102 AKG boom hanger rubber-band type shock mount. *(Courtesy AKG Acoustics, Inc.)*

Figure 13-103 Electro-Voice table microphone stand with push-to-talk switch. *(Courtesy Electro-Voice, Inc.)*

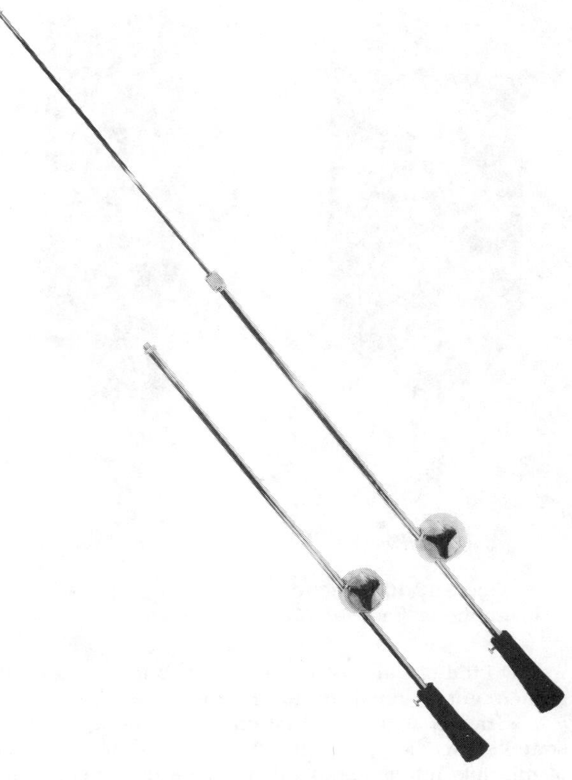

Figure 13-104 Atlas BB-44 microphone boom. *(Courtesy Atlas Sound)*

13.17 MICROPHONE TECHNIQUES

The quality of the reproduction can be greatly influenced by the position of a microphone in relation to the sound source. When only one microphone and one sound source are involved, this positioning is fairly straightforward: the closer the microphone, the more the direct sound will dominate over the reverberant sound. Except in an anechoic chamber, there will always be a certain amount of reflected sound present in the microphone output. This results from sound bouncing off boundaries such as the floor, ceiling, walls, and objects of significant proportions located in the area of the microphone. At a certain distance from the sound source, the amount of reflected sound will exceed the amount of the direct sound. The microphone is then said to be in the reverberant, or far, field. The effect is to make the acoustic environment (usually a room) more evident to the listener than would be the case with close mic'ing (microphone in the near field).

The proper position of the microphone depends on the effect desired. Close mic'ing produces a highly present, up-front sound, with little of the acoustic environment evident, whereas distant mic'ing produces a more spacious sound with the room characteristics becoming very obvious. A close microphone position may not accurately reproduce the sound of the source, and equalization may be required to achieve a sound similar to the natural sound. If the room acoustics are not suited to the sound reproduction desired, a distant microphone position may produce an unpleasant or unintelligible result. The correct choice requires the engineer to choose the appropriate microphone position for the sound desired. A microphone placed an inch from a snare drum will produce an up-front, bigger-than-life sound, which could be appropriate for a modern rock recording but might be totally inappropriate for a jazz or big band recording. Distant mic'ing of the snare drum *could* produce a powerful effect,

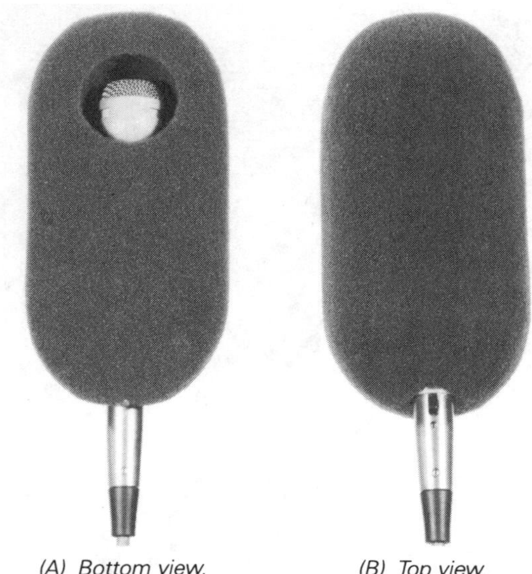

(A) Bottom view. (B) Top view.

Figure 13-105 Electro-Voice 411 stage-mount microphone "mouse." *(Courtesy Electro-Voice, Inc.)*

in any kind of music, since the contribution of a good room might be important to the music.

It is rare that there is just one microphone and one sound source. Modern recording often requires the use of multiple microphones. Microphone placement then becomes more complicated, because as the microphone is moved farther from its intended source, more of the other sources will be picked up as well. No instrument is a point source, and there are different characteristic sounds emanating from various places on the instrument (i.e., a flute has vastly different sounds coming from the open end, the body of the flute, or the mouthpiece). Most instruments have complex directional characteristics, which vary from note to note. Even instruments of the same make and model can sound quite different from one another.

Whenever there is more than one microphone receiving sound from a single source, a problem of time and phase differences can become audible. This problem can have a major effect on the frequency response, presence, and clarity of the recording. The result for spaced microphones can be a comb filter effect, which will tend to reduce presence, upset the natural balance of various notes and overtones, and disturb localization of the source. In an extreme case, certain notes may be attenuated to inaudibility. In practice, the contribution of room reflections, pickup by other microphones, and intrinsic instrument imbalances may mask many of these effects.

Multitrack recording generally requires the engineer to isolate instruments so that only the intended source is recorded on each track. Sometimes this is simple because the track is being overdubbed and only that one instrument is in the studio. At the other extreme, an entire ensemble may be playing at once, yet the situation may require that all instruments be totally isolated on the tape tracks so that they can be individually mixed, processed, or even replaced with no effect on the other instruments. The latter requires very careful microphone choice and placement and/or the use of isolation booths for some troublesome instruments. If the musical balance is good in the room, the job is fairly simple. But if there are obviously incompatible instruments playing simultaneously (e.g., heavy drums versus a finger-picked acoustic guitar), isolation solely through microphone technique becomes next to impossible.

13.17.1 Stereo Mic'ing Techniques

Modern recording practice often employs multiple microphones, each feeding a separate track of a multitrack tape machine. Sound reinforcement practice usually requires good isolation of the various sound sources. In either case, the end result is a composite of a number of monaural sources, which are often placed in the stereo image with pan pots. This practice is not the same as true stereo recording, which can provide a sense of depth and realism unachievable with panned mono sources. It requires greater effort for superior results; a good acoustic environment is essential.

There are a number of stereophonic recording techniques available to the engineer. The simplest requires two microphones, often omnidirectional types, spaced apart by a distance ranging from several feet to more than 30 ft (Fig. 13-106). The spacing depends on the size of the sound source, the size of the room, and the effect desired. A broad source like an orchestra will require a

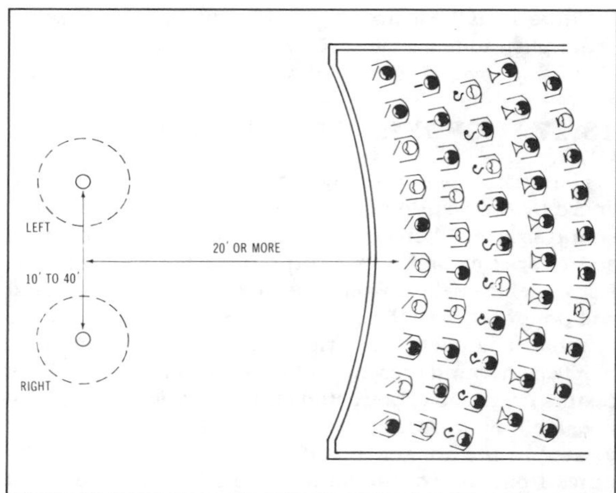

Figure 13-106 Spaced omnidirectional microphones for stereo recording.

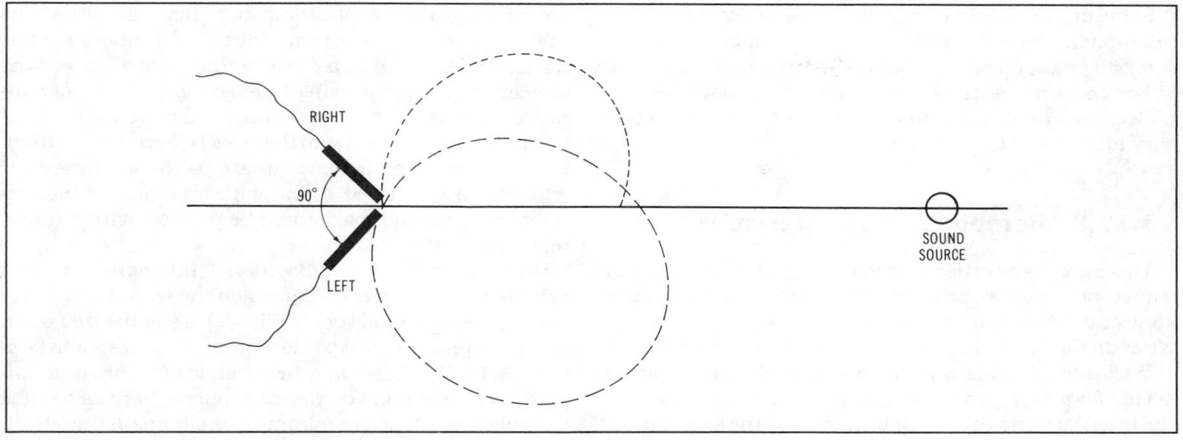

Figure 13-107 Coincident stereo microphones.

wider spacing than a small source such as a single voice or instrument. If the microphones are too far apart, a "hole in the middle" of the stereo image will result, since the sound produced in the center of the stage will be too far from either microphone. When placed too closely together, a mono result will be obtained. When the spacing is comparable to the wavelength of the sound, phase cancellations may result, which will destroy the monaural compatibility of the recording. The best spacing seems to be from 10 to 40 ft. Experimentation is necessary since every situation will be different. Needless to say, good monitoring is required; stereo headphones will not generally reveal defects evident on good monitor loudspeakers. A method of summing the two channels to mono is essential for testing compatibility.

Variations on the spaced microphone technique involve using bi- or unidirectional microphones, which may be helpful when the room characteristics are not perfect for the material being performed; additional microphones in the center, fed to both left and right channels ("fill" microphones); and combinations of spaced mic'ing and other techniques.

A highly versatile stereo pickup is the *coincident microphone technique* (Fig. 13-107). Coincident means that sound reaches both microphones at the same time, implying that they are at the same point in space. In practice, the two microphones cannot occupy the same point, but they are placed as closely together as possible. There are special-purpose stereo microphones available that combine the two microphones in one case. (See section 13.13.3.11.) Since they are essentially at the same point, there can be no time differences between arrival of any sound from any direction; thus no cancellation can occur. It might first appear that there could be no stereophonic result from this configuration, but there is. The two microphones are usually unidirectional and oriented at 90° to one another. The combination is then aimed at the sound source, each microphone 45° to a line through the source. Stereo results from intensity differences—the left microphone (which is to the right of the pair) will receive sounds from the left-hand part of the stage with greater volume than it will receive from the right-hand side of the stage.

The stereo result, although often not as spectacular as that obtained from spaced microphones, is fully mono compatible, and it most accurately reproduces the sound of the acoustic environment. It is quite foolproof and quick to set up.

Variations of the coincident technique include changing the angle between the microphone (some stereo microphones are adjustable); using bidirectional microphones, which results in more reverberant sound; using combinations of uni- and bidirectional microphones; and using "matrix" systems, which electrically provide sum and difference signals from the left and right channels (these can be manipulated later for the desired effect).

13.17.2 Microphone Choice

Every microphone type has certain characteristics. These characteristics must be taken into account when choosing a microphone for a specific application. Some of the factors to be considered are general type (condenser, moving coil dynamic, ribbon); directional pattern (omni-, bi-, or unidirectional); and specific microphone traits (bright, bassy, dull, presence peak, and so on).

Also, the susceptibility of the microphone to overload or its tendency to overload the associated preamplifier must be considered. The off-axis frequency response can have a large effect on the sound of a microphone in a particular application. Certain microphones may exhibit unusual traits that may make them more, or less, suitable for a certain application. For example, the design of the grille may have a major effect on the sound of a microphone when recording closely mic'ed vocals.

Some of these characteristics can be inferred from the microphone specifications (i.e., frequency response, overload point, directional pattern—both on and off axis). Other characteristics are not as easy to measure or visualize, and experience and experimentation are necessary to make an intelligent choice.

13.17.3 Microphone Characteristics

There are many criteria used to judge the suitability of a microphone for a particular application; some are quite subjective. Frequency response is one obvious characteristic; distortion is another. The ability of a microphone to accurately translate waveforms into electrical signals is vital for good reproduction. Generally, the less massive the internal parts that must be moved by the sound pressure, the more accurate the reproduction, especially the reproduction of waveforms with steep leading edges and/or rapid level changes (e.g., percussive sounds). The condenser microphone has the lowest mass (only a thin plastic diaphragm with a very thin coating of metal must be moved by the sound pressure). The diaphragm and coil in the dynamic microphone have considerably more mass than the condenser diaphragm. The ribbon in a ribbon microphone has relatively low mass; it is somewhere in between the condenser and the dynamic microphone.

It would seem that the condenser microphone would always be the best choice, but other factors must be considered. Condenser microphones are generally less rugged than dynamic ones, and since they are usually more expensive, the decision to place a valuable microphone in a position where it could be hit or knocked over must be weighed against the possible benefit of improved sound. Also, condenser microphones contain internal active electronics, which can be overloaded by high sound levels. Many condenser microphones contain switchable or insertible pads, but long before the overload distortion becomes apparent, clipping of the transient peaks may muddy the sound in a subtle way.

Ribbon microphones are somewhat fragile. They can be especially vulnerable to blasts of air that can occur when closely mic'ing vocals, inside a bass drum, or even when a door is slammed in an airtight studio.

In each type of microphone, there are many other factors that can affect the "sound." The design of the mounting for the microphone components, the internal obstacles in the sound path, and the effect of the body of the microphone, all can have a major effect on the ultimate sound reproduction.

13.17.4 Directional Pattern

It might at first seem that the unidirectional microphone (see section 13.13.3) would be the universal choice for all applications, since picking up the intended source is the goal. It is true that unidirectional microphones have the greatest application, but there are situations that require the use of omnidirectional microphones, which are designed to pick up sound from all directions as nearly equally as possible (see section 13.13.1), or bidirectional microphones, which are sensitive to the front and back, but insensitive to the sides (see section 13.13.2). But it is possible, in some situations, to obtain greater rejection of unwanted sound with an omni- or bidirectional microphone than would be possible with a unidirectional pattern.

Unidirectional and bidirectional microphones often exhibit a proximity effect, in which the response to lower frequencies (generally below 150 Hz) is emphasized when the microphone is placed close to the sound source (section 13.13.3). "Close" may be a couple of inches or a couple of feet, depending on the microphone. Various designs have been developed to minimize or eliminate this effect. A switchable high-pass filter may be included on the microphone to roll off the bass in close mic'ing positions. Proximity effect must be considered when choosing and placing a microphone. Sometimes the effect can be used to advantage (i.e., when additional bass response is desirable, perhaps on a snare drum or on certain vocals). But often the proximity effect emphasizes the (unrelated) tendency of some sound sources to sound more bassy when close mic'ed.

Directional microphones do not always have the same frequency response off axis as they do on axis. This can cause increased apparent sound leakage from other sources, tonal aberrations of the reproduced sound, or unexpected phase cancellations. For example, many directional microphones exhibit less directionality at both higher frequencies and lower frequencies. If such a microphone were used to close microphone a snare drum, the amount of pickup of the nearby bass drum and cymbals might be excessive.

13.17.5 Specific Mic'ing Techniques

There are probably as many methods of using microphones as there are engineers. Contrary to popular opinion, there does not seem to be any special microphone or magical technique for recording any particular sound. What is right is what sounds best. The following discussion is merely a review of some common techniques widely employed and likely to work well in many circumstances.

13.17.5.1 Musicians

The first requirement for obtaining a good sound from any instrument is a superior player. An experienced studio musician can make almost any studio or engineer sound good. Unfortunately, the engineer usually has very little to say about the musicians who are hired for the session. When inexperienced players record, they may often expect to be made to sound like whoever their idols may be. They probably don't want to know that their idol spent the last ten years or more learning how to use the studio, and they may be likely to blame the engineer for their inability to play properly for recording. There isn't much that can be done in such a circumstance.

13.17.5.2 Drums

Studios involved in music recording today are more often judged by their drum sound than by anything else. It is true that much contemporary music relies heavily on drums and that getting the best possible sound is a goal worth pursuing. There are any number of ways to record drums, but the most commonly used technique today utilizes close mic'ing.

Just as the musician is a vital element in obtaining a good sound, the drums themselves must be in good condition and properly tuned to obtain their best sound. The type of drum head used will have a major effect on the sound.

Mic'ing Each Drum

A mic'ing arrangement that is almost standardized today requires the use of one microphone on each drum (Fig. 13-108). In addition, one or more microphones may be suspended over the drum set to pick up either an overall sound or primarily cymbals. How closely each microphone is placed depends on several factors: how "tight" a sound is required, which in turn is related to the relative liveness and character of the room; what isolation problems might exist, in terms of various drums leaking into other drum microphones and leakage from other instruments in the room; how dangerous it may be to place an expensive and fragile microphone in a position of possible destruction by an overly enthusiastic or inaccurate drummer; and whether the microphone and/or console can take the level produced without distortion.

Above versus Underneath Mic'ing

Individual drums can be mic'd either from above or below (Fig. 13-109). The two positions will usually have vastly different sounds. If the sound is appropriate, the underneath position may be preferable if isolation is a problem.

When mic'ed from above, microphones are commonly positioned at an angle to the drum head and near the edge of the drum. Seemingly minor changes in position can have a major effect on the sound, especially with some microphones.

Bass Drum

For recording, bass drums usually have only the beaten head, which is not to say that bass drums with both heads cannot be recorded, however. For some music, the use of both heads is preferable. In the single-head configuration, the usual microphone placement is within the shell

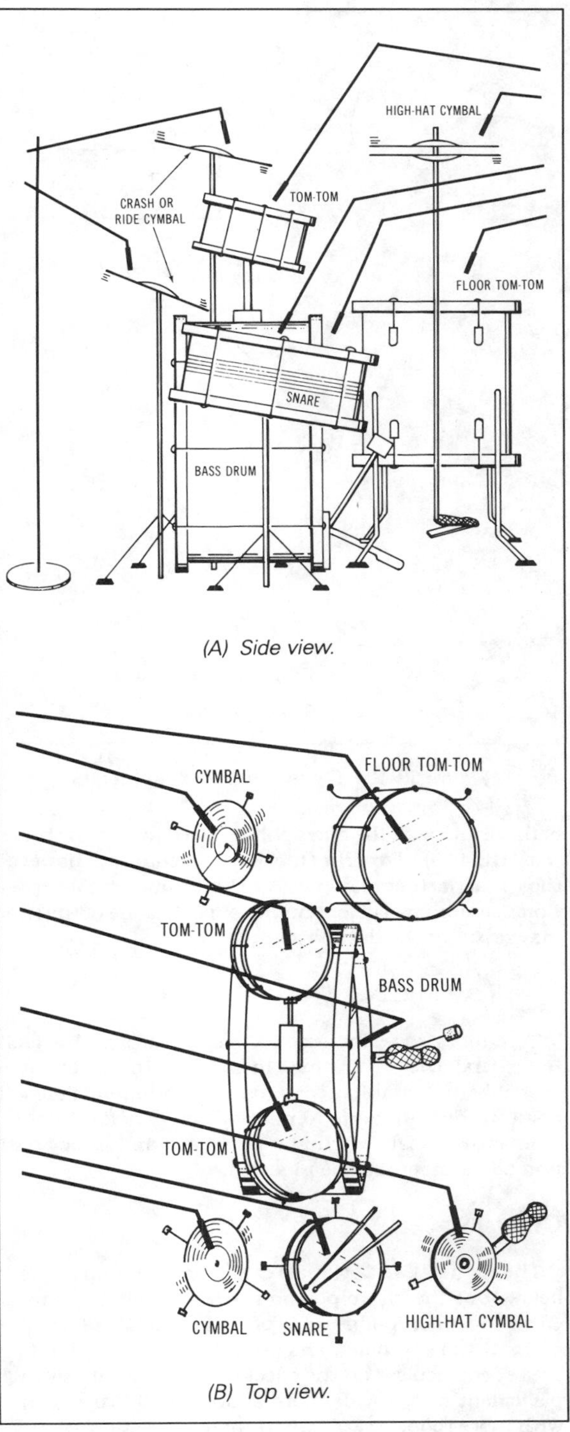

Figure 13-108 Close drum mic'ing.

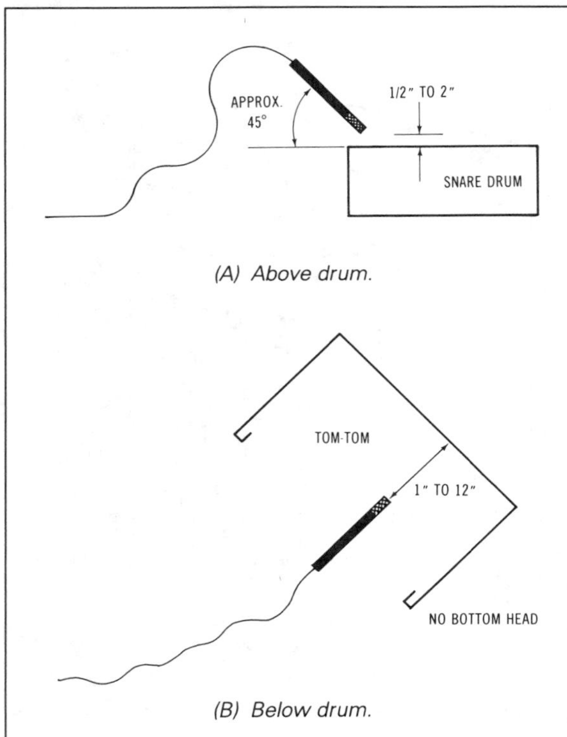

Figure 13-109 Close drum mic'ing (detail).

of the drum, with the microphone aimed toward the beater (Fig. 13-110). Experimentation is required, however. Closer or farther distances, off-axis microphone positions, or even placement on the opposite side of the head may result in the desired sound.

Tom-Tom Mic'ing

Tom-toms, too, often use only the top head. This facilitates underneath mic'ing. In mic'ing any drum, it is probable that simultaneous top and bottom mic'ing will result in difficulty due to phase discrepancies. The use of phase-reversal switches at the board and minor position adjustment may be required.

Cymbals

The high hat and cymbals can be mic'ed from above or below, but the above position is more commonly used. Overhead microphones are often positioned above the entire drum set, usually as a stereo pair. How high they are set will depend on the effect desired; a relatively high placement will provide more of an overall drum sound, with more room reverberation than a closer position.

It is not unusual to pick up sufficient cymbals, or even excessive cymbals, from just the other drum microphones without the overhead mics even being on. The amount of cymbal leakage will be determined mostly by the drummer's technique and balance, with the room characteristics also being a factor.

Other Drum Mic'ing Techniques

Close mic'ing every drum is only one method. Another is to use relatively distant microphones to pick up an overall drum sound (Fig. 13-111). This, of course, results in much more room sound and possible leakage from other instruments. It also requires that the drummer play all the drums, and particularly the cymbals, in the proper balance. The engineer has much less control of the sound. This approach will not be successful in poor rooms, nor with drummers who do not correctly balance their various drums and cymbals. But in a good room, with a good drummer, the sound can be quite natural and often very powerful, too. A common technique is to use two overhead microphones, placed in such a way as to capture the natural sound and balance of the drum set. Some experimentation will be required to find the proper placement. Usually a separate bass drum microphone is used as well, to give the bass drum better definition and more "punch."

13.17.5.3 Piano

Pianos are often recorded in stereo and can add "width" and a greater sense of space if done properly. Multiple microphones spread all over the sounding board may seem like an ideal way to pick up the full piano sound, but this procedure can lead to a very artificial and distant sound when heard in mono.

First, be certain that a stereo piano is really desirable. In multitrack recording, are there sufficient tracks available? And is the piano sound required to be so big? A mono piano can often have more "punch" and might be a better choice.

For a mono track, one microphone is usually all that is needed. For stereo, a pair of adjacent directional microphones will probably suffice. In mic'ing either a grand or upright piano, keep in mind that the sounding board and not the hammers and strings is the source of most of the sound. With a good piano, there may be surprisingly little difference in the sound picked up from various areas of the sounding board. A commonly mic'ed point is where the bass and treble strings cross (Fig. 13-112). Variations such as mic'ing from beneath (or in the case of an upright, in back of) the sounding board, inserting microphones into the circular holes in the harp, or using various types of piano pickups can all be tried. Each piano is different, and each player will also have a large effect on the sound, so a variety of techniques should be tried.

The PZMicrophones are often used in recording piano. They can be placed on the inside of the piano lid, and the lid closed for improved isolation.

As in all percussive instruments, the peak level produced by a piano can be far greater than the level shown on the volume unit (VU) meter. Peaks 20 dB above the

ALTERNATE
POSITION
2" TO 3'

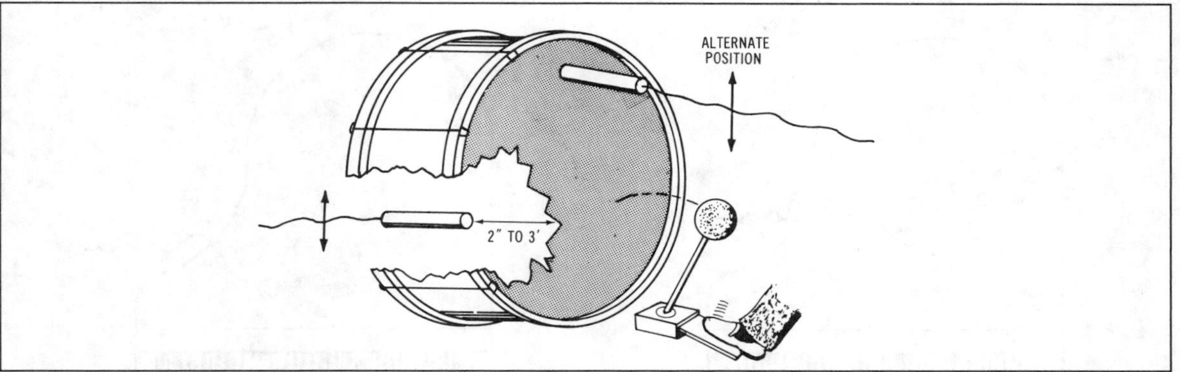

Figure 13-110 Bass drum mic'ing.

(A) Coincident microphones.

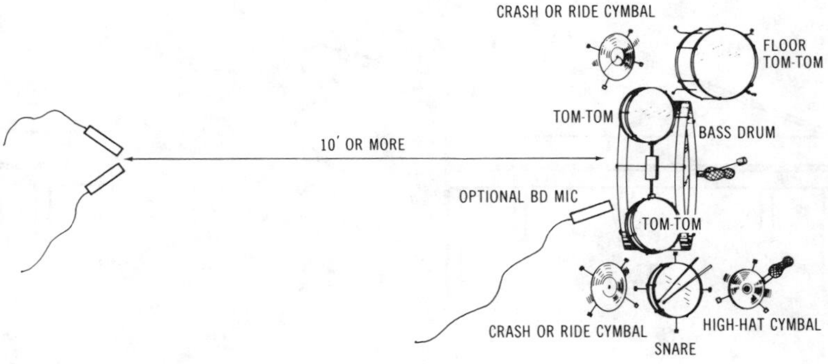

CRASH OR RIDE CYMBAL
FLOOR
TOM-TOM
TOM-TOM
BASS DRUM
10' OR MORE
OPTIONAL BD MIC
TOM-TOM
CRASH OR RIDE CYMBAL
HIGH-HAT CYMBAL
SNARE

(B) Overhead spaced microphones.

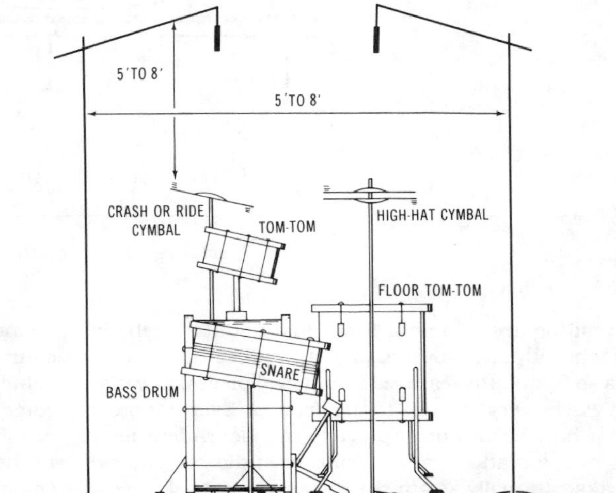

5'TO 8'
5'TO 8'
CRASH OR RIDE
CYMBAL
TOM-TOM
HIGH-HAT CYMBAL
FLOOR TOM-TOM
SNARE
BASS DRUM

Figure 13-111 Distant drum mic'ing.

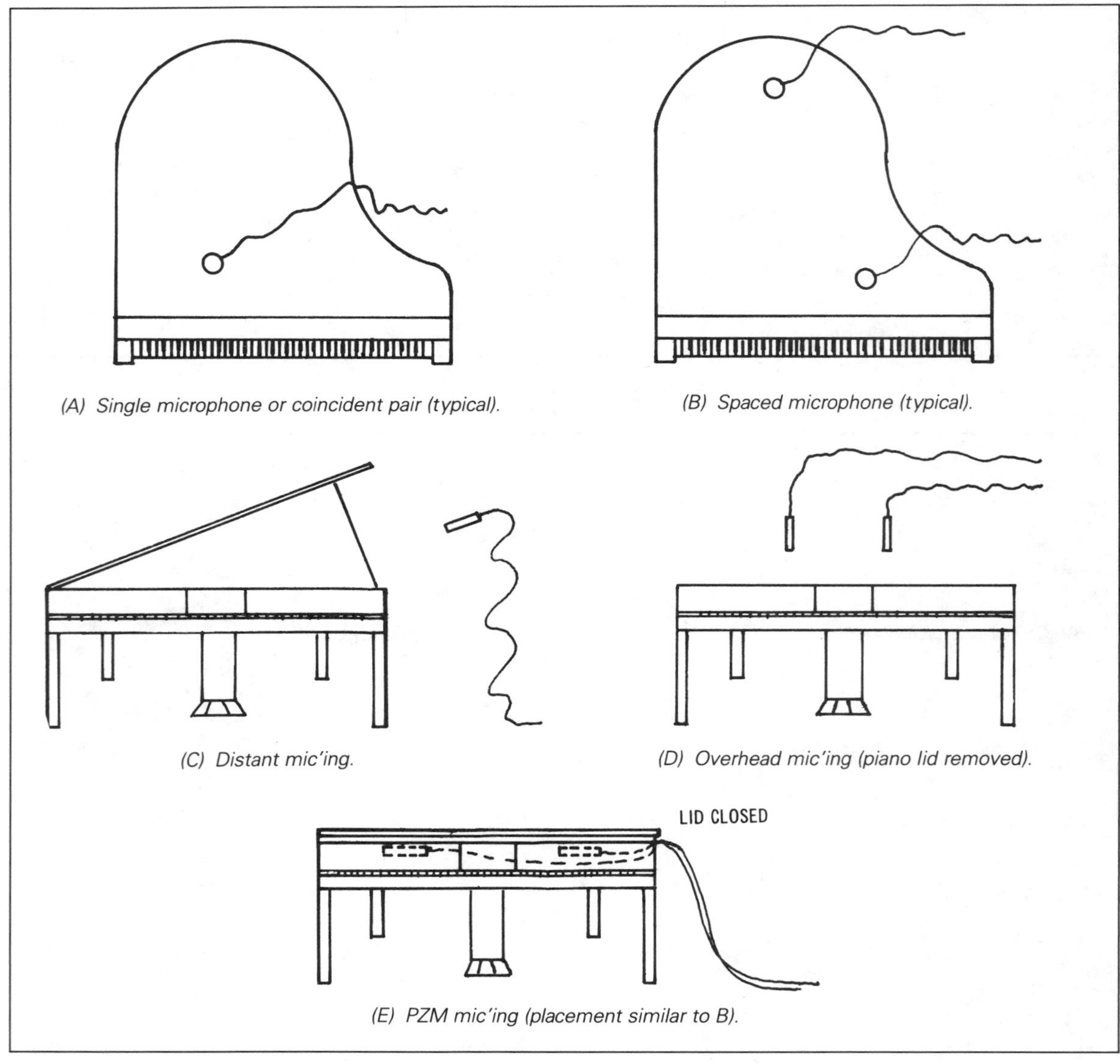

Figure 13-112 Piano mic'ing

meter reading are common. Since just about everybody knows what a piano sounds like, and since the instrument is so frequently featured in musical pieces, any distortion will be very obvious to the listener. Even a distortion that only occurs on the peaks can be evident as a dulling of the piano attack, a kind of audio blurriness. The peaks can really strain the dynamic range of microphones, preamps, and tape. If condenser microphones are used, be sure the pads are switched on even if the level seems moderate. Also, some engineers routinely record piano at a somewhat lower than normal level to avoid tape saturation.

Obtaining satisfactory isolation while still getting a good sound can be a problem with the piano. Isolation can be achieved with a booth, of course, but careful mic'ing and some baffling can often work almost as well. One technique used in many studios is to place the microphone in the piano and then close the lid as much as possible. Often the "short stick" position of the lid works well. Then carpeting or other dense, heavy, absorbent material is draped over the piano. With a good arrangement of other instruments, and reasonably balanced volumes, very little leakage should exist. Another technique requires that microphones be mounted inside the piano, usually suspended from the lid, in such a way that the lid can be completely closed. The PZM type of microphone is particularly well suited for this approach.

Of course, a much better sound is obtained with the lid open and with perhaps a little more distance between the sounding board and the microphones. Sometimes removing the lid and suspending the microphones above the piano work well. (Most pianos have pins in the hinges that can be easily removed for this purpose.) Fairly distant mic'ing may sound good too.

13.17.5.4 Vocals

A single vocal, either speaking or singing, is usually recorded with one microphone placed within 2 ft of the mouth. For popular music, it is common to have the singer very close to the microphone; in a recording of a classical singing voice, a greater distance is appropriate, even up to several feet may be used if the room acoustics permit. Speakers at a lectern usually are about a foot or two from the microphone.

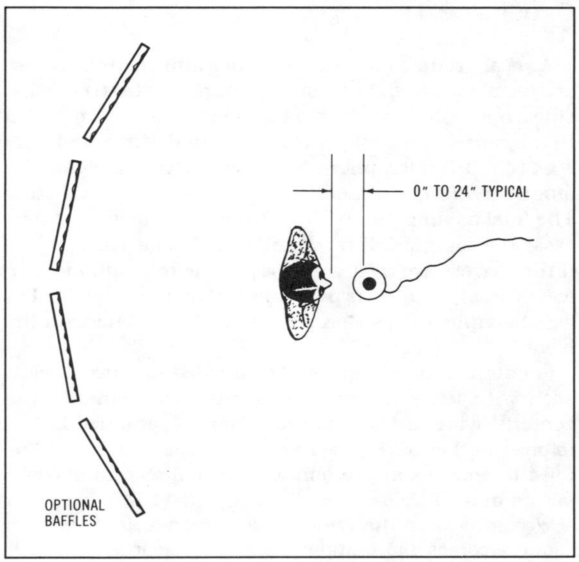

Figure 13-113 Vocal mic'ing.

SINGERS

Although vocals could be recorded in stereo, with any of the techniques previously described, it is customary to record the voice in mono. It is basically a point source, with little directional information. In a superior acoustic environment, such as a good concert hall, natural reverberation may be mixed in with additional microphones. But most often artificial reverb is added. It can be stereo and add considerable depth and width to the voice.

Condenser microphones, placed very close to the mouth, are the usual choice in the studio. A pop filter will be necessary for all but the most careful singers. This prevents explosive sounds from being produced when the vocalist sings a word containing p's or other hard consonant sounds (see section 13.16.1). It is important to remember that the output level of the microphone will adhere to the inverse-square law, which states that if the distance from the source to the microphone is doubled, the level will be reduced to one-quarter (see section 13.15.1.1). Experienced vocalists are well aware of this phenomenon and may even use it to obtain certain effects. The inexperienced or inattentive singer will probably require electronic processing (i.e., limiting) to obtain a satisfactory performance. This problem is further complicated by the trend toward mixing vocals quite low in the musical track and relying on processing to maintain intelligibility.

In the studio, it is often necessary to provide an acoustic environment less reverberant than normal for the recording of vocals. Cutting down on reverberation could be accomplished with a separate vocal booth with highly sound-absorbent surfaces, or it can be obtained by placing absorbent baffles around the singer and microphone in the studio (Fig. 13-113). On the other hand, it may sometimes be necessary to emphasize the reverberation for a special effect by distant mic'ing or by mixing in another microphone placed some distance away.

Proximity effect can be a problem with vocals. Many microphones have provision for a bass rolloff, which can be used to correct this deficiency. This approach is often superior to using equalization in the control room, especially if a limiter is used before the equalizer (the limiter would respond to the emphasized bass and thus not accurately track the vocal intensity). Some singers prefer the effect obtained from proximity, using the bass boost in their performance to emphasize certain words or phrases.

In a live performance, large studio condenser microphones would be inappropriate. With their suspensions and pop filters and the large microphone stand required, they would obscure the singer's face. What is needed is a relatively small, rugged microphone that can be hand held if desired. Although there are a number of condenser microphones that can be used this way, the usual choice is a compact dynamic microphone with built-in pop filters, integral shock mounting, and switchable bass rolloff (see section 13.13.3.6).

Good directionality is required of a live performance microphone. The usual practice of providing the singer with a stage monitor loudspeaker, usually placed within a few feet of the microphone, requires good rejection of sound from off axis to minimize the possibility of feedback and reduce the degradation of the sound from the vocal microphone picking up the monitor's reproduction of the other instruments and voices. Some microphones designed for live work have their direction of minimum sensitivity oriented toward the direction where the most unwanted sound would come from (i.e., not directly off the back of the microphone, but at some intermediate angle).

Group Vocals

A vocal group could consist of two singers or a chorus of several hundred. For a small group (less than eight), a single microphone with an omnidirectional pattern placed in the center of a circle of vocalists often works well (Fig. 13-114). This microphone arrangement requires that the singers achieve a proper balance of voices in the studio. The final balance can be "fine tuned" by having the necessary voices move closer or farther from the microphone. If the singers are relatively close to the microphone (two feet or less), then their positions become more critical. A small change in position can have a major effect on the blend.

For stereo, the group could be divided into two circles, each with its own omnidirectional microphone in the center. Two bidirectional microphones, oriented at 90° to one another and placed one above the other, could be used to obtain a stereo omnidirectional recording when placed in the circle of vocalists (Fig. 13-115).

Whenever omnidirectional microphones are used, the room becomes more apparent in the recording than it would with unidirectional microphones. This effect must be considered when recording group vocals in this manner.

If greater presence is required (or less room sound) or if the balance must be controlled by the engineer for some reason, individual microphones could be used for each singer; however, this method has obvious practical limitations if the group is large. It also requires more set-up and balancing time, puts a musical burden on the recording personnel, and might have a disappointing result if lack of isolation creates phase problems when mixing the multiple microphones.

For really large groups, techniques similar to those described for string sections might be employed.

Typically, group vocals will be recorded as an overdub on a previously recorded musical track, requiring the vocalists to wear headphones. With a number of singers wearing headphones (which could be turned up quite loud)

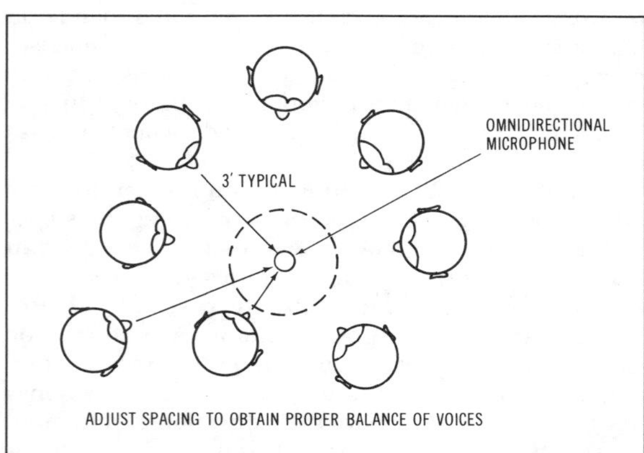

Figure 13-114 Group vocals mic'ing (monaural).

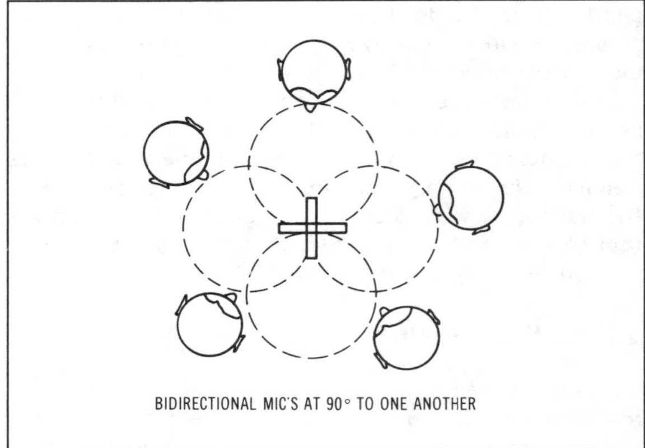

Figure 13-115 Group vocals mic'ing (stereo).

standing next to an omnidirectional microphone, a significant amount of leakage from the headphone mix is possible. This leakage from the headphone mix can become even more of a problem if one or more of the singers prefer to remove one side of the headphones from his or her ear in order to better hear their own voice and/or the blend of the other voices. Background vocals are often by nature relatively quiet parts requiring higher than normal gain on the microphone channel. All these factors can combine to degrade the entire recording seriously.

Solutions might be to use as low a headphone level as possible, have the singers sing as loudly as is appropriate for the part, turn the microphone off when the vocalists are not singing, or use a noise gate to do this automatically. In a really severe situation, the solution might be to use individual directional microphones.

13.17.5.5 Lectern Microphones

For redundancy, two or more microphones are often provided on a lectern. Only one should be active at a time, or phase cancellations can result. Often two microphones are arranged on opposite sides of the lectern, angled in toward the talker. The goal is satisfactory pickup as the speaker moves from side to side. This arrangement can

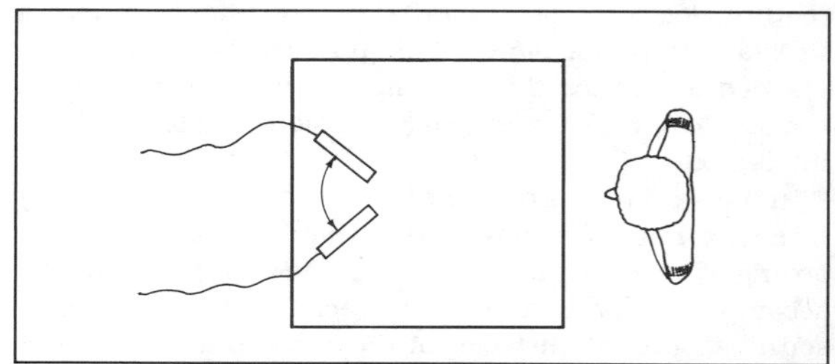

Figure 13-116 Lectern microphones for increased coverage pattern.

cause serious phase cancellation problems because of the spacing (usually a couple of feet) resulting in feedback problems since the normal frequency response has been disturbed through the comb filter effect. A better arrangement places the two microphones in the coincident configuration—as close together as possible and angled toward opposite sides of the lectern (Fig. 13-116). The outputs can be summed with no phase problems. The angle between the microphones may be changed from the normal 90° if necessary to obtain proper coverage.

13.17.5.6 Strings

Although strings could be close mic'ed, this approach usually results in an unnatural sound. Distant mic'ing is more appropriate but puts a greater demand on the room acoustics. Obtaining a good string sound really requires a good room of considerable size.

A string quartet might sound fine recorded in a relatively small studio (2200 ft^3), but a large string section needs more volume. Not only will a larger room accommodate more players, but the microphone placement will also be simpler and the results will be closer to the actual sound of the section.

Each instrument could have a microphone, and this would give the mixer complete control of the balance of all the strings. But unless a great deal of time is available to obtain the proper balance, this approach is not cost effective when recording highly paid musicians. It does not guarantee the best results, either.

At the opposite extreme, a single microphone, placed at a point determined to provide the best overall balance and sound, could be a simple and quick way to get good results (Fig. 13-117). This placement works well if the engineer is familiar with the room and can rapidly duplicate a setup that has been successful in the past. A coincident pair can provide the same sound if stereo is required.

Another technique is to mic the ensemble in sections (Fig. 13-118), providing, for example, a single microphone for the first violins, another for the second violins, another for the violas, and so on. Cello and double bass often have microphones to pick them up individually in this type of setup.

It is also possible to set up microphones above each row of players, or above each two rows. This method is often used in conjunction with the single overall microphone.

In a practice session (see Fig. 13-119), the setup is often a composite of all of these techniques: a single coincident pair at a distant point (perhaps 15 to 20 ft from the first row, and up as high as practical in the room); a set of microphones over each section (one microphone for every two players, up above the space required for their bows and slightly in front of the instrument); and individual microphones for the cellos and basses (a foot or two in front of the instrument, opposite the F holes). At the start of the session, the overall microphone would first be monitored to determine what, if any, balance problems exist. If time permits, the overall microphone position might be changed to obtain a better balance. If the desired balance cannot be obtained with the single microphone, the necessary individual section microphones may be brought into the mix. In many practically sized rooms, it is not possible to obtain a good balance of the near strings (usu-

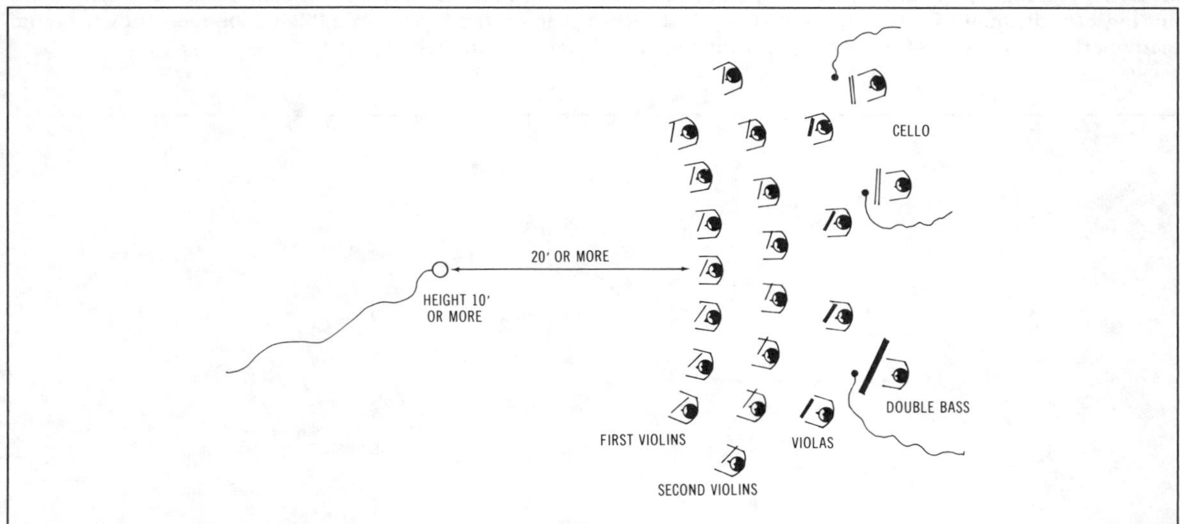

Figure 13-117 Single microphone (or coincident stereo) for string section recording. (Optional microphones are shown for cello and double bass.)

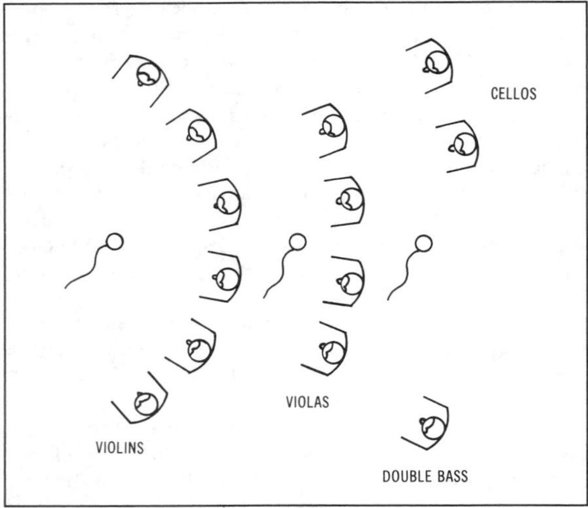

Figure 13-118 String mic'ing by section.

ally violins) and the far strings (cello and bass). Careful use of the section microphones can correct this.

Since good high-frequency and transient response is required to reproduce the string section sound, condenser microphones are the most frequent types used for string recording.

13.17.5.7 Horns

In the recording world, "horns" are any brass instrument: trumpets, trombones, saxophones, and so on. Modern recording of popular music usually requires close mic'ing of individual instruments (Fig. 13-120). Since many horns are capable of producing very high sound-pressure levels (as high as 130 dB), it is important to choose microphones that will not be overloaded by this close placement. Also, pads may be required to prevent overloading the mixer preamplifier or saturating an input transformer.

Condenser microphones are often used to pick up horns, but ribbon and dynamic types may also give good results.

It is important to remember that the sound produced by these instruments does not come entirely from the bell; this is particularly true of saxophones. Although the instrument output may be loudest at the bell, the contribution of the various other parts of the horn cannot be ignored. The microphone position is often a compromise between the presence of very close placement, the better tonality of a slightly greater microphone distance, the leakage from other instruments as the microphone distance is increased, and the degree of room contribution desired in the finished recording. Depending on the effect desired, 6 in. to a couple of feet may be appropriate.

13.17.5.8 Woodwinds

Instruments like the oboe, flute, bassoon, clarinet, and their variations cannot generally have microphones placed too closely and still retain their character. In popular music they are often mic'ed individually at a distance of one to several feet, which is generally not far enough to provide a true sound, but the result is often acceptable—or even desirable—for compatibility with other instruments in the song.

Condenser or ribbon microphones are the usual choice. Most woodwinds tend to sound most natural when mic'ed from about 3 ft away, with the microphone directed toward the middle of the instrument, or perhaps pointing slightly toward the bell or end of the instrument. Low placement, even on the floor with a PZMicrophone, tends to sound better than high placement.

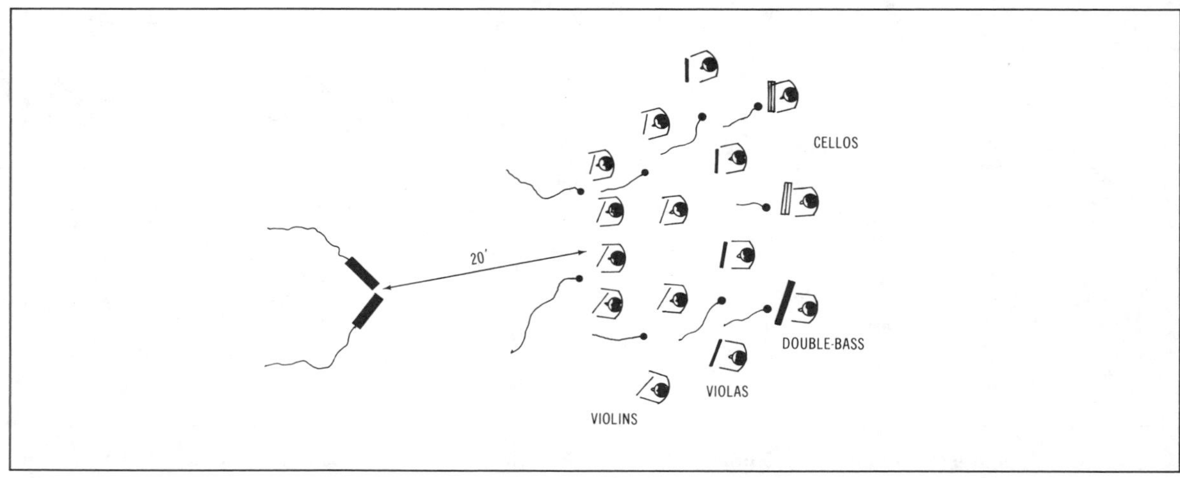

Figure 13-119 String mic'ing typical composite technique.

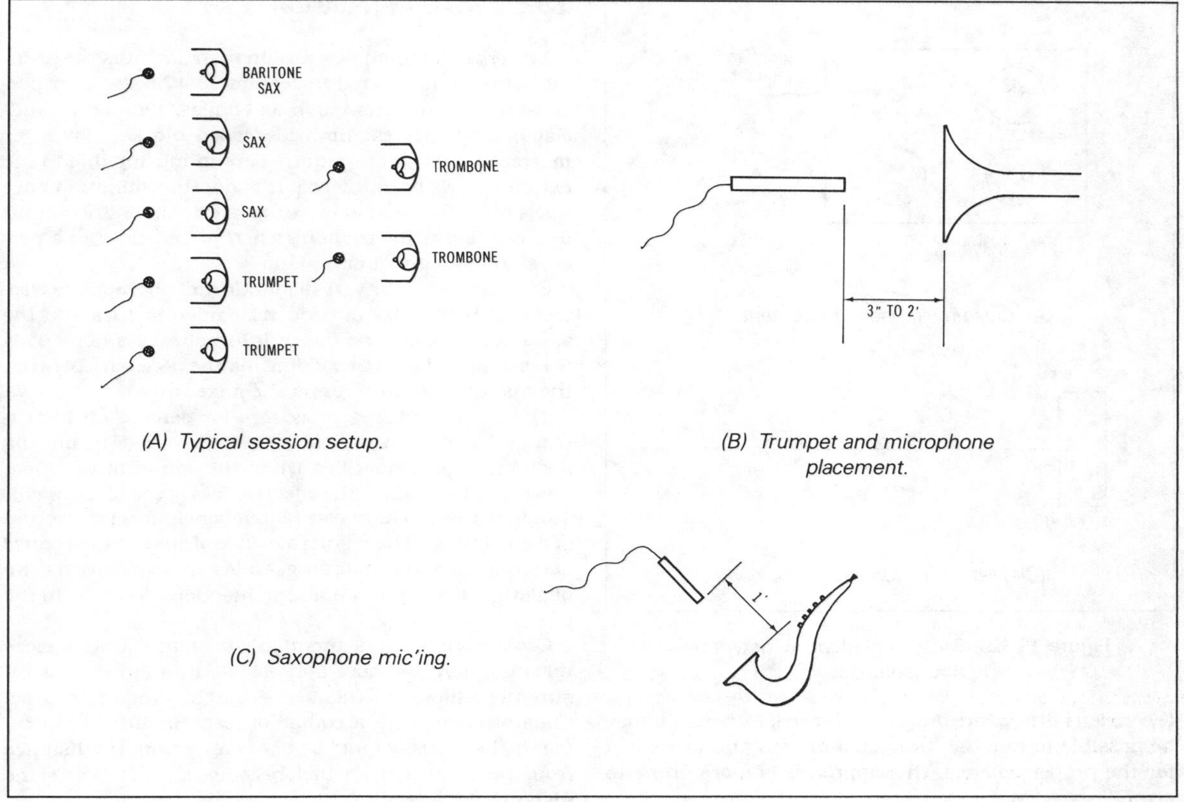

(A) Typical session setup.

(B) Trumpet and microphone placement.

(C) Saxophone mic'ing.

Figure 13-120 Horn and microphone placement.

For classical recording, a more distant pickup is necessary. A woodwind ensemble might be successfully recorded using the techniques described previously for string sections.

13.17.5.9 Electric Instruments

In this category are all instruments designed to be reproduced through amplifiers and loudspeakers. Electric guitar; electric bass; various synthesizer, organ, and other electronic keyboards; and acoustic instruments with attached microphones or pickups designed for amplification all fall into this category.

Generally, these instruments require microphone placement with the associated amplifier/loudspeaker combination. However, another technique is possible and in many cases preferable, that is, the direct recording of the instrument. Since most of these instruments produce a microphone level, high-impedance unbalanced output, all that is required in most cases is a high-quality transformer, providing the match between the instrument and the low-impedance, balanced inputs of most mixers. Various "direct boxes" are available, some with active electronics to provide the required impedance transformation. Almost all provide an output to drive the instrument amplifier as well as the mixer, and most have a ground switch to select the grounding configuration with the least noise.

In many situations, the instrument and its amplifier constitute a system. The amplifier, which may contain loudspeakers or may be connected to a separate loudspeaker system, may have a major effect on the sound of the instrument. Taking a direct feed may result in a totally unnatural sound.

Mic'ing the instrument amplifier may seem simple, but often the cabinet contains several loudspeakers. These may be identical loudspeakers or separate drivers for various frequency ranges. A single close microphone may not provide the proper balance. Even in systems with identical loudspeakers, careless microphone placement may result in phase discrepancies producing a distant and/or colored sound. Two solutions are practicable: either we can give the microphone a more distant placement, far enough to be equidistant from all the loudspeakers, or we can position it very close, to pick up only one loudspeaker (Fig. 13-121).

Systems with multiple drivers for different frequency ranges will have to be mic'ed from far enough away that

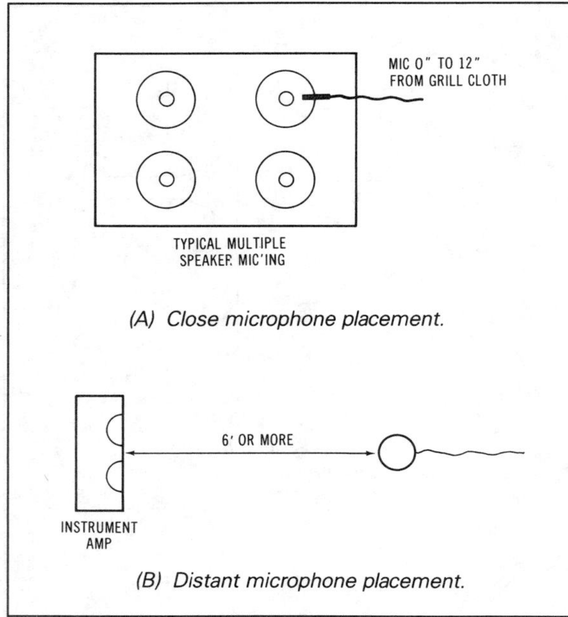

(A) Close microphone placement.

(B) Distant microphone placement.

Figure 13-121 Mic'ing of electric instrument loudspeakers.

the various drivers are properly balanced. Although it may be possible to mic the individual drivers and mix them for the proper balance, this approach is more prone to error.

Distant mic'ing is often desired, especially for electric guitar. Naturally, the character of the room must be appropriate.

Often a combination of the direct and mic'ed sound is used. This combination can be effective, but the phase relationship between the two sources will be arbitrary, which can cause severe coloration of the sound. The tonal balance will change unpredictably as the ratio of direct and mic'ed sound changes. This change usually precludes any gain riding of the individual inputs. A phase reversal switch can sometimes be used to optimize the gross phasing between the two inputs.

Instruments like synthesizers or other electronic keyboards generally should be recorded directly. The sound of these instruments is usually not augmented by the addition of a musical instrument amplifier. There are exceptions, however, and the choice of technique depends on the effect desired—perhaps the limited frequency response and soft distortion of a tube-type amplifier is appropriate.

13.17.5.10 Percussion

The most common percussion instrument is the drum kit, which was covered in section 13.17.5.2. Other percussion instruments, such as congas, tympani, handclaps, tambourines, timbales, wood blocks, claves, or morracas, and so on, require care in mic'ing due to the extreme levels encountered. It is not uncommon to have levels of + 10 dBm and more (open circuit) on the output of a condenser microphone when placed close to a percussion instrument or a piano.

Such levels can be very demanding of microphone electronics, in the case of condenser microphones and the associated mixer. The use of internal microphone pads is essential. Additional padding may be necessary between the microphone output and the mixer input.

The correct mic'ing procedure for percussion instruments depends on the effect desired. A distant mic'ing position is often justified when the sound of the room reverberation adds to the effectiveness of the instrument. Tambourine and handclaps often benefit from the sound of a good room. The resultant sense of space can produce better depth in the recording, and/or the explosive nature of a large, live room can add tremendous "punch" to the part.

On the other hand, the highly present sound of close mic'ing might be more appropriate in another musical situation. Close, in this sense, might range from fractions of an inch to a couple of feet. Hand-held instruments, like claves, must be played at a uniform distance from the microphone, which becomes more critical as the distance decreases.

13.17.6 Conclusion

It is important to remember that there is never only one way to position microphones. The techniques presented here are representative of the methods widely used in the recording and sound-reinforcement industries, but such practices have evolved over many years. Some are traditional; however, there may be better ways. Using the procedures outlined will result in reasonably accurate reproduction, or "commercial" reproduction as it applies to mainstream music recording. Since sound reproduction can be a creative endeavor, experimentation may yield new techniques. The exact reproduction of the original sound may not be the goal. Perhaps the engineer is attempting to obtain a previously unheard sound or effect. When the luxury of experimentation is available, the engineer may well use the time to pioneer new techniques that can supplement or even replace existing procedures.

REFERENCES

1. H. Tremaine, *Audio Cyclopedia*, Indianapolis: Howard W. Sams & Co., Inc., 1969, pp. 148–150.
2. Ibid., pp. 150–151, 152.
3. *Altec Lansing Technical Letter*, 148, Altec Lansing Corp. Oklahoma City, OK
4. Tremaine, *Audio Cyclopedia*, pp. 152–153.
5. *Altec Lansing Technical Letter*, 148. Altec Lansing Corp. Oklahoma City, OK
6. A. P. G. Peterson and E. E. Gross, Jr., *Handbook of Noise Measurements*, General Radio Co., p. 33.
7. R. S. Burwen, "A Low Noise High-Output Capacitor Microphone System," *Journal of the AES*, vol. 25, no. 5, May 1977. (Parts copied with permission.)
8. "C460B—A New Microphone Preamplifier for the Existing Condenser Microphone Module System," AKG Acoustics, Inc. (Parts copied with permission.)
9. Tremaine, *Audio Cyclopedia*, pp. 179–186.
10. K. M. Bourne, "Professional Wireless Microphones Simplify Sound System Design," *dB The Sound System Engineering Magazine*, February 1982.
11. *Synergetic Audio Concepts Newsletter*, vol. 5, no. 4, p. 8.
12. A. M. Wiggins, "Unidirectional Microphone Utilizing a Variable Distance between the Front and Back of the Diaphragm," *Journal of the ASA*, vol. 26, no. 5, September 1954. (Parts copied with permission.)
13. R. Schulein, Shure Brothers, Inc., "Development Consideration of a Versatile Professional Unidirectional Microphone," *Journal of the AES*, vol. 18, no. 1, p. 44, February 1970. (Parts copied with permission.)
14. W. R. Bevan; R. B. Schulein; and C. E. Seeler, Shure Brothers, Inc., "Design of a Studio-Quality Condenser Microphone Using Electret Technology," *Journal of the AES*, vol. 26, no. 12, p. 947, December 1978.
15. "Unidirectional Microphone," US Patent Office no. 3,095,484, June 25, 1963.
16. Tremaine, *Audio Cyclopedia*, pp. 201–203, 205–208.
17. Y. Ishigaki, M. Yamamoto, K. Totsuka, and N. Miyaji, Victor Company of Japan, Ltd., "Zoom Microphone," AES preprint 1718 (A-7). (Parts copied with permission.)
18. C. P. Repka, "A Guide to Coincident Mikes," *Audio Magazine*, November 1978.
19. D. Davis and Carolyn Davis, *Sound System Engineering*, Indianapolis: Howard W. Sams & Co., Inc., 1975.
20. G. W. Plice, "Microphone Accessory Shock Mount for Stand or Boom Use," *Journal of the AES*, vol. 19, no. 2, February 1971. (Parts copied with permission.)

ADDITIONAL BIBLIOGRAPHY

J. Eargle, *The Microphone Handbook*, Elar Publishing Co., Inc.

Microphones, New York: AES, 1979.

CHAPTER **14**

Loudspeakers, Enclosures, and Headphones

by Clifford A. Henricksen

14.1 INTRODUCTION

This chapter is intended either for end users of loudspeaker components or complete systems or for those merely fascinated with them. It is an updated historical statement of loudspeaker art as well as practical loudspeaker use. End-use design activities, such as for boxes, passive crossovers, and horns, are covered so that original systems work may be encouraged.

14.2 LOUDSPEAKER MEASUREMENTS AND STANDARDS

Loudspeaker characteristics are probably exaggerated more than any other part of a sound system. If specifications by some manufacturers are believed, all loudspeakers have perfect response, sensitivity, and directivity, yet every loudspeaker sounds different.

Loudspeakers all have measurable performance and may be evaluated by frequency-response curves. However, the lack of a standard method of producing such a curve necessitates exclusion of any such curves herein because they would just confuse the reader. Some loudspeakers are advertised with curves, which may bear little resemblance either to those curves used by in-house engineers to evaluate the product or to those curves obtained by trying to duplicate the results by another method or test. This "marketing curve" looms as an evil specter to many acoustic engineers, and industry-wide jokes abound about the "finger on the recording pen" similar to the stories about the butcher with his "thumb on the scale." Curves are not the sole criteria for judging performance of a loudspeaker. Factors such as distortion, directivity response, efficiency or sensitivity, smoothness of response, and phase response all enter into measurable factors contributing to "good sound." Some users or evaluators of sound equipment are actually capable of making judgments merely by listening to the sound quality of a loudspeaker with music or voice signals being the input. Others are content to read and believe specs and will design systems around these components. Other factors also enter into the choice and/or purchase of loudspeakers. These include reliability, power handling, ease of use, compatibility with existing equipment, appearance, price, blind dedication to a certain manufacturer, peer pressure, and countless others that are more-or-less rational. This chapter on loudspeakers will help clear some of these misconceptions.

This chapter is dedicated to Dr. Harry F. Olson, a genuine pioneer in acoustics and electronic sound recording whose work has influenced literally every inclusion herein. Dr. Olson was a staff vice-president for the Acoustical and Electromechanical Research Division of RCA and was associated with that company from 1928 to the time of his death—April 1, 1982. His combined love of music and technology shines brightly in his works, and he was awarded many high honors in his field from such organizations as Audio Engineering Society (AES), Acoustical Society of America (ASA), Society of Motion Picture and Television Engineers (SMPTE), Institute of Electrical and Electronic Engineers (IEEE), and American Physical Society. He was also elected to the National Academy of Sciences in 1959. Dr. Olson was a prolific writer and lecturer in his field, having authored more than 130 articles and professional papers and three important and well-known acoustics texts (referenced herein), which are considered "classics" to those who own and use them in their work. Dr. Olson was a great American and, personally, a joy to have met and spoken with on several brief occasions.

14.2.1 Measurement Environments

Frequency-response measurements (and some distortion measurements) are all subject to the acoustic environment. Loudspeakers are measured in perfectly dead anechoic chambers (rarely), semianechoic chambers (most "anechoic" chambers are semianechoic.), real rooms, studio control rooms, outside (flush with the ground in a pit, "half space"), and reflective reverberation chambers. The latter method is claimed to show the true "power response" of a loudspeaker, since a highly reverberant environment such as this negates directivity changes, which in some instances help on-axis response tremendously by converting the direct sound to omnidirectional reverberated sound. These rooms are built to have the most rigid, glossy, and smooth walls possible, as opposed to anechoic rooms, which are lined with massive amounts of absorbing (fiberglass) wedges.

Some loudspeakers (normally compression drivers) are measured on plane-wave tubes, which are rigid tubes normally the same diameter as the driver's exit hole and lined with absorbing material designed to absorb fully the driver's sound output. A microphone is placed in a hole in the wall of the tube for measurement. The plane-wave tube is probably the most controllable test "chamber" the loudspeaker tester can use.

14.2.2 Test Equipment

All measurement "environments" certainly can affect the outcome of a response measurement, including the measuring apparatus. Chart recorders may be run slowly (a slow frequency sweep) with a very fast relative vertical dB_{SPL} pen speed with a high-resolution vertical scale (dB/in.), resulting in a high-resolution response curve, and excellent loudspeakers will still draw smooth curves under these conditions in an anechoic room. Conversely, if the vertical scale is compressed, the pen will run very slowly, and the frequency swept very quickly. A straight line (flat response) may be drawn independently of the actual response of the loudspeaker being measured. Slightly less severe than this lies the "marketing-curve" region. The true curve of any device will be that which does not change as the frequency is swept slower and slower. Some chart recorders use FM techniques (warble) to "average out" curves, which is sometimes helpful in discouraging measurement of reflections and standing waves when measuring response in a nonanechoic situation such as a room. Lastly, flat, pink noise is used as a source, and a real-time spectrum analyzer is used to measure response. This method is normally not used for loudspeaker evaluation and development but rather is used for balancing or equalizing a system in a room. Pink-noise response is by far the least-resolution response measurement method, except, of course, for the real-response-independent marketing curve. The output is usually documented as a bar graph corresponding to levels in various one-third-octave bands and is sometimes used to show the average response in advertisements.

Figs. 14-1 through 14-4, originally printed on 8 × 10-in. graph paper, will illustrate the "curve-manipulation" ability of a chart recorder. A small three-way loudspeaker system was measured four times at approximately 1 m from the loudspeaker in a relatively "dead" room, without changing anything except recorder writing speed and warble. Fig. 14-1 uses a very slow sine sweep and 5-dB/in. vertical scale. Fig. 14-2 uses the same frequency sweep rate, but the scale is "compressed" or changed to 10 dB/in. Fig. 14-3 is as Fig. 14-2 only the fastest frequency sweep was used. Last, Fig. 14-4 is as Fig. 14-3 except a one-half-octave, 5-Hz warble was used to modulate the input to the loudspeaker. Fig. 14-1 "looks bad" and Fig. 14-4 "looks great," but they are from the same loudspeaker. Fig. 14-4 is as useful as Fig. 14-1 to a loudspeaker; for different reasons, however, Fig. 14-4 approaches the marketing curve. Some chart recorders can compress the scale from 25 dB in 100 mm to 50 dB and 75 dB in 50 mm. Also, the vertical and horizontal writing speeds can be adjusted easily to give the loudspeaker an independent curve. These systems can also be adjusted to give a curve with the resolution of Fig. 14-1. The main problem is that the average user of audio equipment will not know how to interpret a curve. It is a problem, and it certainly is, only the tip of the iceberg when it comes to trying to measure good sound. For these reasons and others, frequency-response curves will not be presented in this chapter.

14.2.3 Measurement Standards

In an effort to standardize loudspeaker measurement techniques, the Audio Engineering Society (AES), designated as secretariat for all audio standards work by the

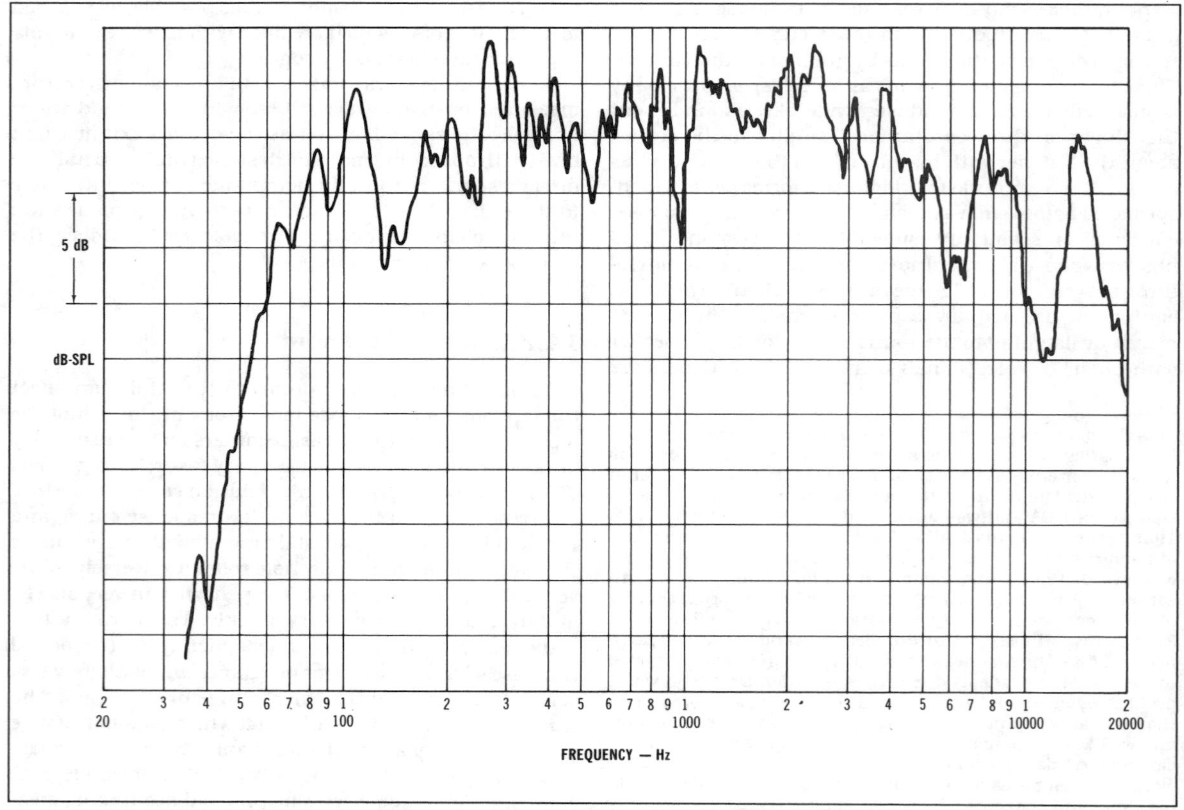

Figure 14-1 Slow sine-wave sweep with high dB_{SPL} resolution (5 dB/div) (Engineering Curve).

American National Standards Institute (ANSI), has organized a working group to compile a complete recommended practice for loudspeaker measurement and specification. This document represents a concensus or agreement on the part of the committee from around the world that the recommended practice is the best possible (i.e., the state of the art). Committee members represent users, manufacturers, consultants, and academics from the U.S. and abroad. The following is a synopsis of the proposed standard.

I. General Overview

The document is a draft recommended practice for describing and specifying loudspeaker components used in professional audio and sound-reinforcement systems. These components include high-frequency drivers and low-frequency enclosures. For drivers, specifications are given for describing directional characteristics and additional pertinent performance data. For all components, specifications are given for describing necessary physical and mechanical characteristics, such as hardware, mounting data, size, and weight. Appendices supporting the text give guidelines for making proper free-field measurements, guidelines for sizing baffles for low-frequency driver measurements, a method for producing the specified noise signal used in power testing, and a summary of required information.

II. Specific Provisions

1. General
   a. SI units to be used exclusively
   b. Response measurements to be made in the free field

The Audio Engineering Society (AES) recommends a measurement distance at least four times the largest dimension of the effective radiating surface or two times the square of the largest dimension of the radiator divided by the shortest wavelength to be measured. Actual measurement distances must be specified by the manufacturer of the device being measured as well as the location of the *acoustic center.*

The acoustic center is usually a source of confusion for many persons. The acoustic center of any acoustic source is the point in space that the sound appears to be radiating from. In the free field, a loudspeaker "looks like" a point source, and the position of that apparent point source is the acoustic center, which is not the "time center" of the loudspeaker, such as those points used for phase alignment of loudspeaker components. These "time" points depend on the dynamic or reactive behavior of the loudspeaker. The acoustic center is the result of a radiation phenomenon and is not time dependent. It is, however, frequency dependent. For instance, a loudspeaker horn may have a low-frequency acoustic center in front of the horn mouth, and as frequency increases, the

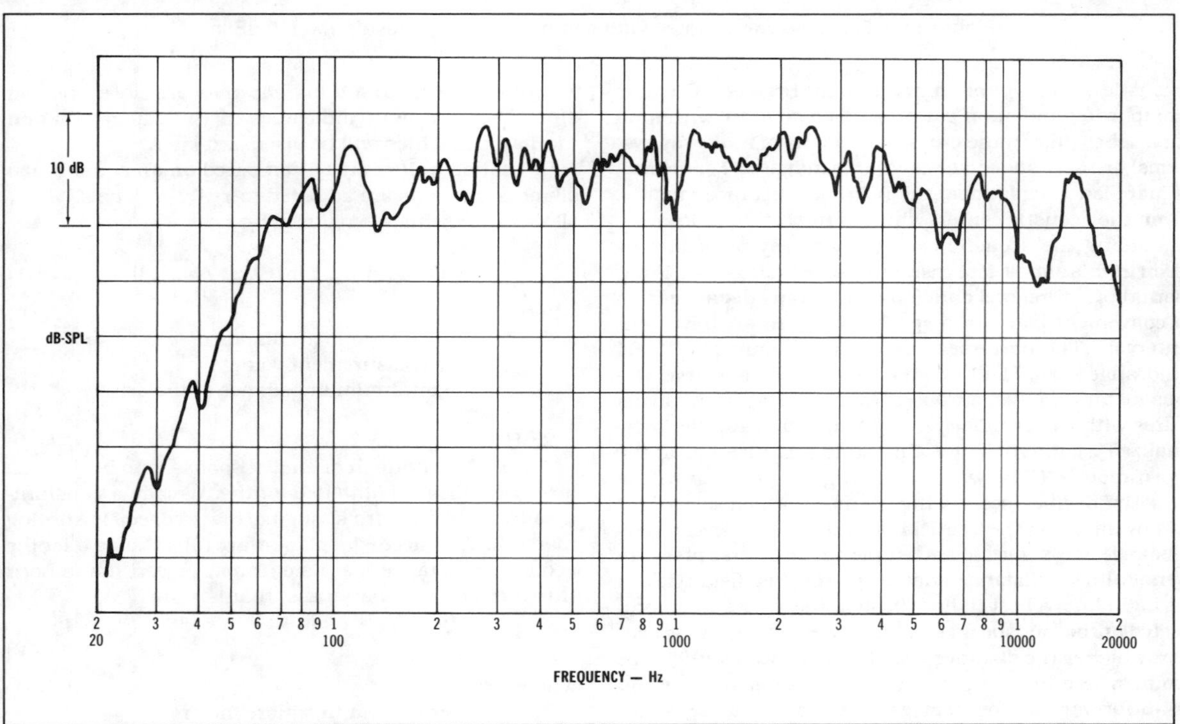

Figure 14-2 Slow sine-wave sweep with compressed dB_{SPL} resolution (10 dB/in).

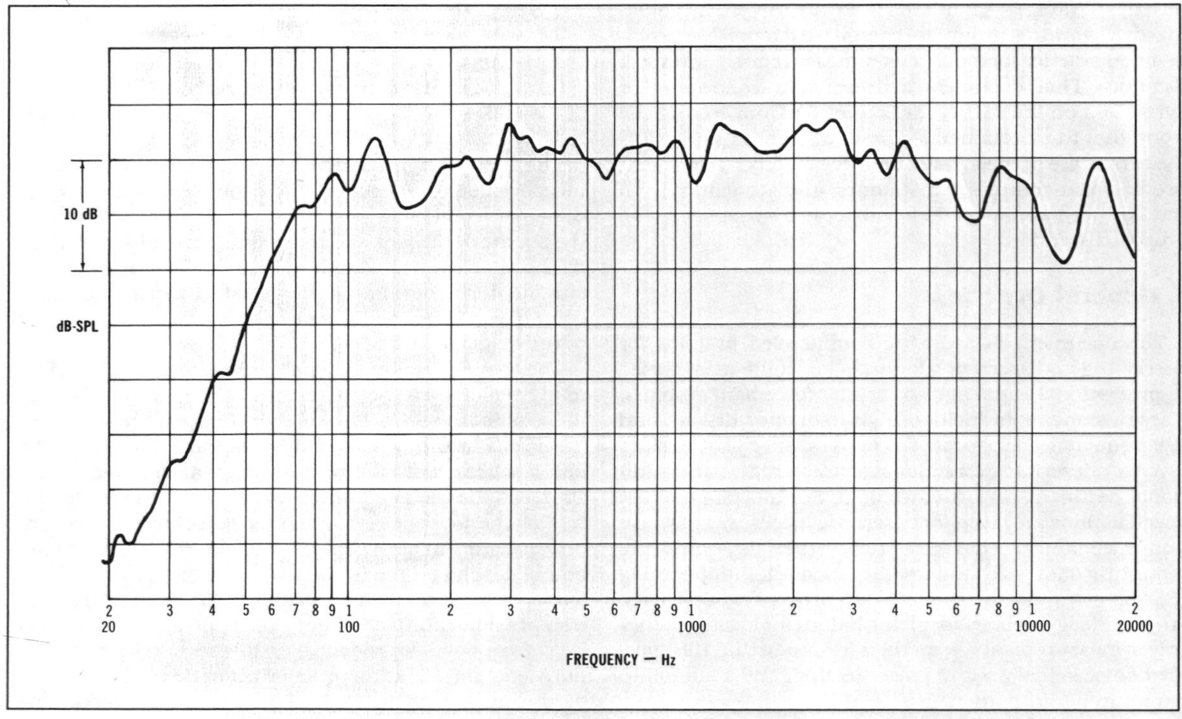

Figure 14-3 Fast sine-wave sweep with compressed dB_{SPL} resolution (10 dB/in).

acoustic center typically moves into the horn bell. On more complicated radiation patterns, such as those with multiple lobes (like in the crossover regions of multiway systems), the acoustic center may be meaningless. For inverse-square-law calculations, the reference distance must be from the acoustic center, which is important to know.

Finding the acoustic center is an easy procedure as seen in this simple test case with some typical data. First, sound pressure level data (on-axis) versus distance from a convenient place on a speaker is taken at convenient intervals. The horn measured is a Community PC1564 midrange horn. Fig. 14-5 shows sound pressure level versus distance, taken outdoors, away from adjacent structures with the horn facing upwards. The data was "normalized" so that 0 dB was the sound pressure level at the horn mouth. (This was done using a Fluke vom with a "relative decibel" scale, which can be normalized to 0 dB at any input.) In the free field, sound pressure level versus distance obeys inverse-square power, or inverse pressure versus linear distance should, in the free field, yield a straight line. A best-fit line through these data when projected at the loudspeaker will thus yield the acoustic center, which is the distance from the loudspeaker reference point where inverse pressure is zero, as shown in Fig. 14-6 for various frequencies. Note the acoustic center moving into the bell of the horn as frequency goes up.

Acoustic center and *apparent apex* are closely related since they are both indicators of the same radiation mechanism, which will be discussed later.

So that all units may be compared on an equal basis, all measurements are adjusted to *1-W 1-m levels*. Thus, all measurements are reduced by

$$20 \log[(d_{meas}/1\text{ m})(V_{meas}/\sqrt{Z_{min}})] \qquad (14\text{-}1)$$

where,

d_{meas} is the measurement distance,
V_{meas} is the measurement voltage,
Z_{min} is the minimum impedance of the driver.

2. High frequency

a. *Amplitude frequency response* is to be done on a device called a *plane-wave tube*, usually a constant-area tube stuffed with a long narrow wedge of absorbing material. The successful plane-wave tube should offer the acoustic resistance R at its entrance or *port* that a horn throat offers in its bandpass, that is,

$$R = p_o c/S_T \qquad (14\text{-}2)$$

where,

S_T is the throat area in square meters,
$p_o c$ equals 407 mks rayls.

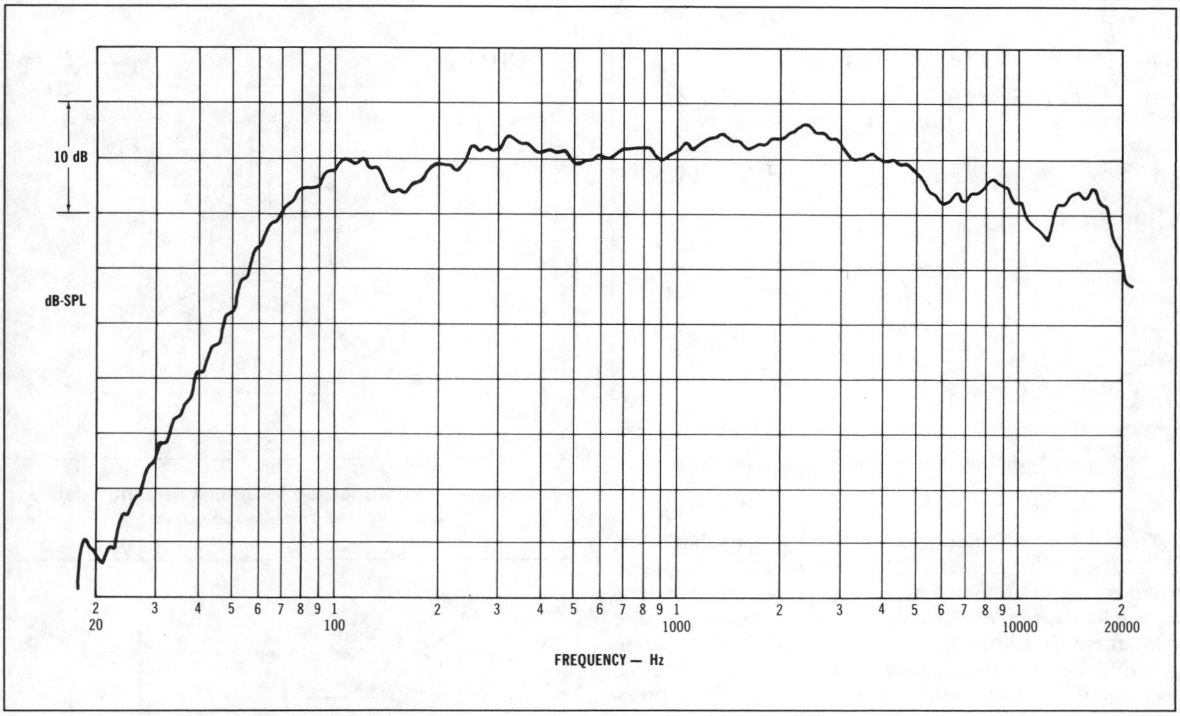

Figure 14-4 Fast sine-wave sweep with warble tone.

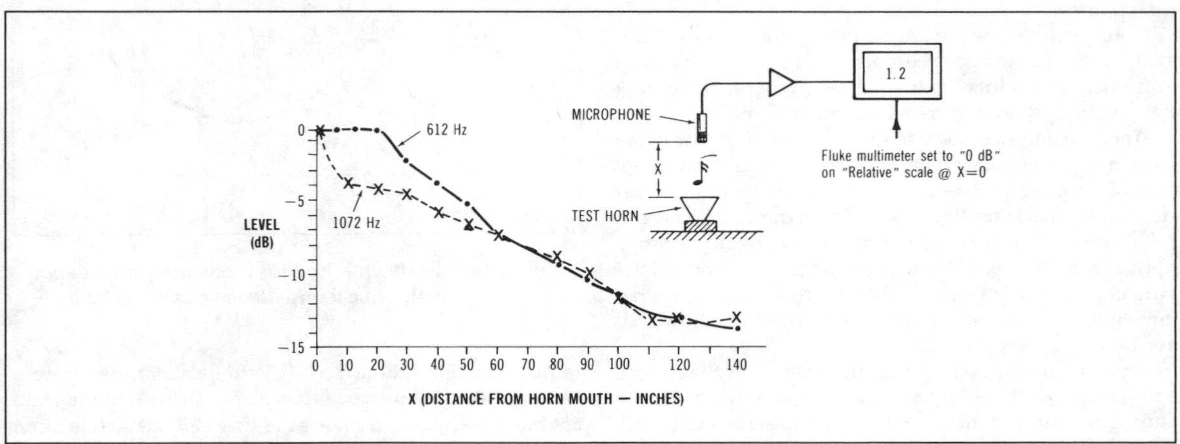

Figure 14-5 Relative level versus distance for horn at two frequencies *(measured by Wiggins and Henricksen).*

Plane-wave tubes are sometimes clear plastic so that the installation of the absorbing wedge can be visually inspected. The tube has to be λ/4 long; thus, a 25-in. long tube will be good to about 135 Hz. The first radial mode of air vibration in the tube is known to be

$$1.22\,(c/d) \qquad (14\text{-}3)$$

where,

c is the speed of sound in air,
d is the tube diameter.

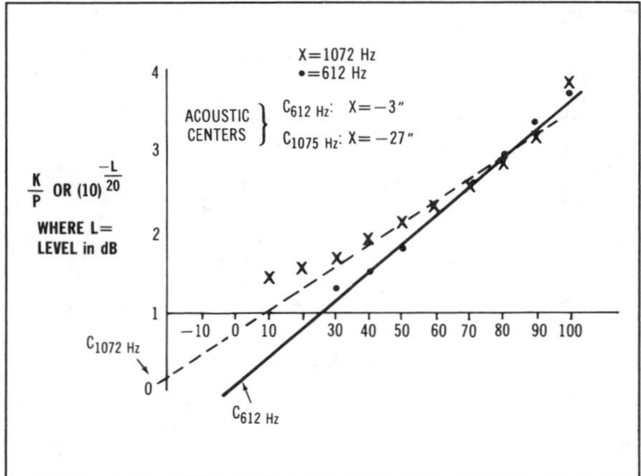

Figure 14-6 K/P plot to find acoustic centers.

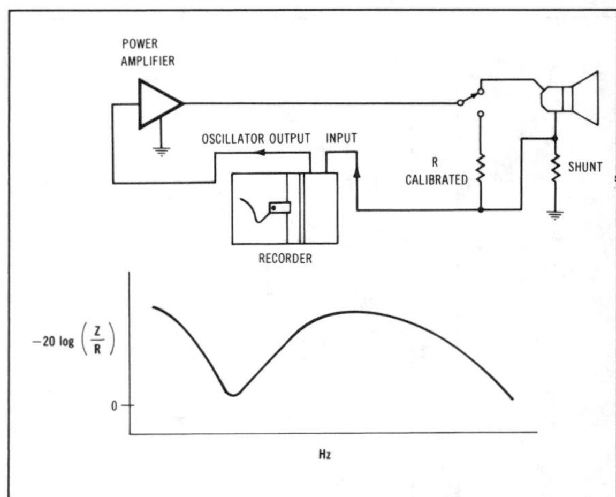

Figure 14-7 Shunt method for measuring impedance with typical impedance curve.

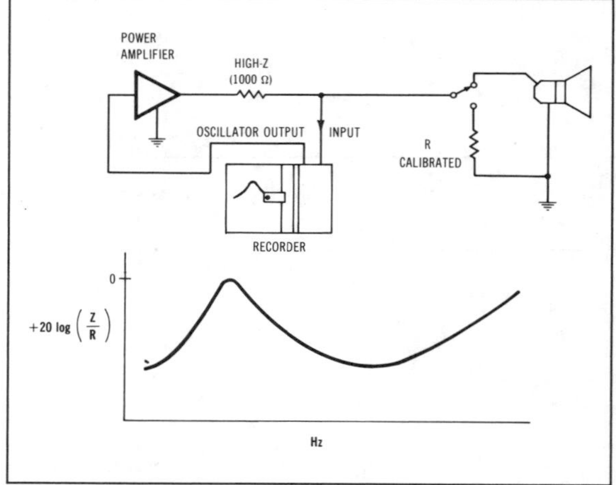

Figure 14-8 Series method for measuring impedance with typical impedance curve.

Thus, a 1-in. diameter tube will only be usable below 16.4 kHz; a 4-in. diameter tube, below 4.1 kHz. However, there is still much to be learned and presented on how to construct, design, and use tubes. Some tubes are smaller in diameter than the driver throat so that high frequencies may be inspected. These tubes employ exponential connectors for the area-reducing transition. Other problems can crop up that give unexpected results. For example, axial, radial, and angular placement of the measurement microphone has been shown to give wide variations in response.

b. *Impedance measurements*—For all loudspeakers, impedance sweeps are important since they indicate minimum impedance, principal resonances, regions of high relative diaphragm displacement, and tuned (or untuned) resonances. These sweeps are run in the same manner as frequency response, and there are two usual ways of doing this. First, a shunt can be used in series with the loudspeaker in question, and the voltage across the shunt is fed to the recorder as a constant voltage input signal is swept. High impedance will show a lowering of measured shunt voltage (current), and a reverse impedance curve will result. This curve is shown in Fig. 14-7.

A more common way to measure impedance response is to put a high impedance (1 to 2 kΩ) in series with the loudspeaker and to measure the voltage across the loudspeaker. The relatively high-value resistor ensures constant current to the circuit. Thus, frequency-varying voltage across the loudspeaker will directly reflect impedance change ($Z = E/I_{constant}$), as shown in Fig. 14-8.

In both cases, a known value dc resistance is inserted in place of the loudspeaker so that a reference calibration can be made for the test.

c. *Minimum impedance*—a term originally called *nominal impedance*, has been replaced with minimum impedance. For example, 8-Ω loudspeakers may have a minimum impedance of as low as 5½ Ω; 16-Ω loudspeakers have been known to be as low as 12 Ω, which is often very misleading. In the design of large sound systems, a 4-Ω discrepancy such as this could easily cause unknowingly designed-in amplifier overload.

Every magnetic loudspeaker reaches its minimum or *trough* impedance toward the top end of its useful working range in approximately a one-octave region just before the impedance begins to rise due to voice-coil inductance. This region is where the loudspeaker will draw the most current, and its value *must* be known to the user.

This value is thus specified directly, without reference to "rated" or "nominal" impedance.

d. *Plotting scales*—The aspect ratio of various impedance and frequency-response data plots are set so that all may be compared on an equal visual basis. The art of scanning a frequency response plot is very dependent on this.

e. *Power-handling measurements*—Power level (watts) is specified to be used on minimum impedance (V^2/Z_{min}), and a preselected one-decade band of filtered and clipped pink noise is used to test the loudspeaker. The rated power of the device means it can take a power level for two hours, without damage or irreversible performance change. This time duration was chosen for three reasons. First, it has been determined that two hours is a typical time period for most loudspeakers to reach "thermal equilibrium" with the ambient air. Second, it is about the extent of most one-time uses of a "pro" loudspeaker (e.g., one "show"). Third, it's a test that can be easily repeated by a user or evaluator in the field.

Loading the driver with a "constant- or expanding-area acoustical load whose initial area is no smaller than that of the driver throat" is left up to the manufacturer. Plane-wave tubes are bad choices for power testing since the absorbing material could easily catch fire or at least degrade, due to almost total absorption of the driver's output into the tube, which could be in the tens of acoustical watts or more, with almost no heat transfer mechanism present. The best choice is a horn of the manufacturer's choice, operating in a suitable sound-absorbing room. The acoustical leakage problem is basically a low-end impedance problem that affects diaphragm excursion directly. Therefore, any mechanical load on the diaphragm that has the same absolute value of impedance as a "suitable" horn will produce the same diaphragm excursion. Anything that can be attached to the driver's throat and produce the same impedance response (at the driver terminals) as the right horn will work.

The noise signal is a decade of 6-dB peak-to-average (clipped) pink noise, and the decade is user selected. Since the class of equipment covered includes 30-in. subwoofers, all kinds of compression drivers, and endless varieties of ultrahigh-frequency devices with recommended low-frequency limits from 15 Hz to 7 kHz, the sliding decade is a natural. The manufacturer should specify several decade bands of noise so that the trade-off between low-frequency excursion/mechanical power limit and high-frequency thermal power limit, and accelerated fatigue may be demonstrated. Although the sliding decade invites "interpretation," there is no better way to do this, given the enormous range and variety of products covered.

3. High-frequency horns

a. *Frequency response and polar data*—Frequency response is measured on axis with off-axis curves (every 15°) being provided in both vertical and horizontal directions. Polar curves are the usual one-third-octave variety in both horizontal and vertical directions. The point of rotation for these measurements is usually the geometric apex of the sides, the driver mounting flange, or thereabouts. On exponential horns, the vertical apparent apex varies with frequency and for most frequencies is near the mouth. Fig. 14-9 shows some typical points of rotation. Ureda[1] suggests a test for apparent apex. The loudspeaker under question is measured for −6-dB polar response angle at a variety of measurement locations. A best-fit line through these data projected to the horn will determine the apparent apex at that frequency. Note that this apparent apex is very similar to acoustic center discussed earlier. It appears that acoustic center is sort of the averaged apparent apex in the same way that total *directivity index (DI)* is the averaged vertical and horizontal DI. Now, all this discussion of rotation point is moot when you can do angular measurements at a large distance compared to the dimensions of the horn. However, in most test facilities, this is not possible, and the precautions and test practices described here must be carefully adhered to for meaningful and accurate data gathering.

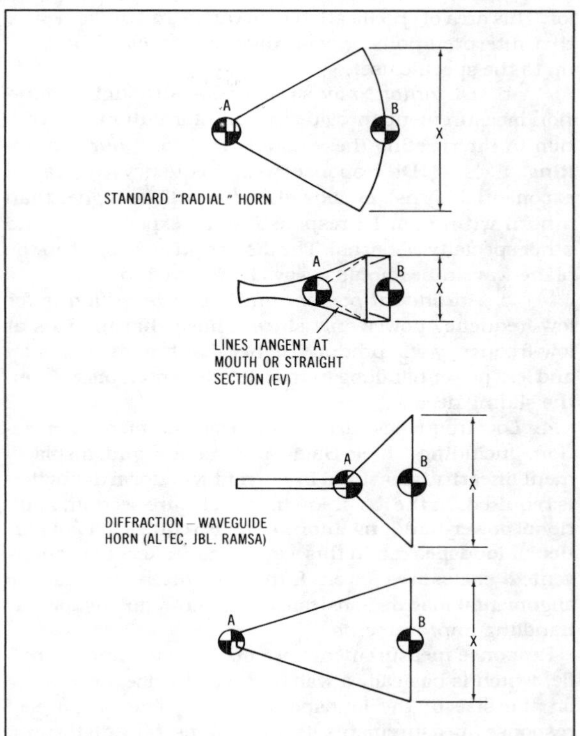

Figure 14-9 Suggested points of rotation for two common horn shapes. Use "A" if $X > \lambda$. Use "B" if $X < 2\lambda$.

Note that for this section, DI and Q data are not asked

for. This area of specification is so varied and under debate that interpretations of polar data were decided best left up to the specific user.

b. *Distortion measurements*—Although distortion measurements provide useful information, the caution in interpreting these data is that for a horn exhibiting a rising DI response with frequency (typical of exponential horns), on-axis distortion will be higher than a horn with a flat DI response (some exponentials and other specialty DI horns). The distortion measured on the plane-wave tube should always be referred to first.

c. *Additional power-handling information* is for low-frequency power only since a horn that unloads at low-frequency will produce higher diaphragm excursion and less power handling in that decade. Enter, once again, the sliding decade.

4. Low-frequency drivers—Normal woofer information, including Thiele-Small parameters and displacement linearity, measured by current waveform distortion is required. In the low-frequency enclosure section, additional power-handling information is requested for a particular loudspeaker. In this way, loudspeakers in properly vented enclosures (even fifth- and sixth-order active alignments) may demonstrate excursion-reducing, power-handling improvements.

Response measurements are made on a standard baffle, which is basically a wall of a certain size, depending on the size of the loudspeaker used. The purpose of response measurements is to demonstrate distortion, high-frequency response, smoothness of response, and angular or off-axis response measurements, not to demonstrate which has more bass.

14.3 ELECTROMAGNETIC MOTORS

By far, the most widely used type of drive mechanism for loudspeakers (and almost any other form of electrical-to-mechanical transduction) is the electrical conductor in a constant magnetic field, shown in Fig. 14-10. The force on the conductor is found by the following:

$$F = BLI \tag{14-4}$$

where,

F is the total force on the conductor in newtons,
B is the flux density in tesla or gauss/10^4,
L is the conductor length in field B in meters,
I is the current in amperes.

The *flux field* (lines of force per unit area) is usually produced by some kind of magnetic source, a permanent magnet or electromagnet, connected to a magnetic circuit. This circuit is usually machined mild steel, and its purpose is to focus the magnetic energy in the area of the conductor or voice coil. (A magnet without its corresponding circuit would be useless because the field surrounding it would be "everywhere" at low-flux density as opposed to being "focused" into high-flux density in a useful area.) The area where the intense magnetic field is focused is called the *air gap*, which can take on many manifestations. The magnetic conducting circuit is designed, usually, to be as small as possible for a given amount of magnetic gap energy required, involving a choice of both materials and design, the latter being a choice of material properties and ease of fabrication. Fig.

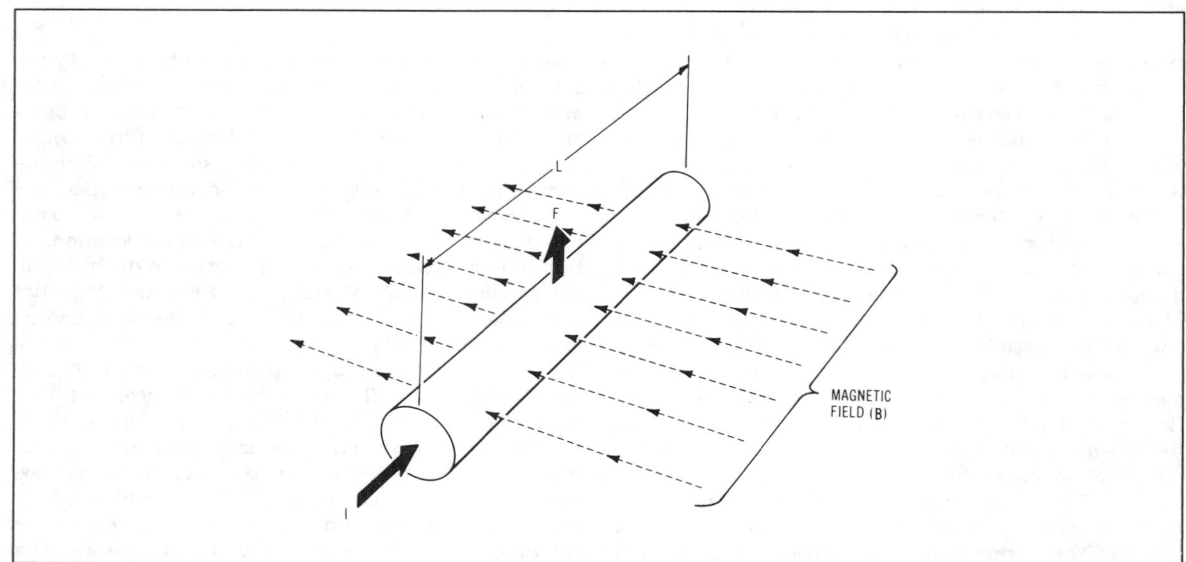

Figure 14-10 Conductor in a magnetic field (B).

14-11 shows the flux density versus magnetization force (equivalent to electrical current versus applied voltage) for various materials. Most loudspeakers require flux densities of between 11,000 and 13,000 G (woofers), and 18,000 or 19,000 G (compression drivers). On the chart, suitable materials are various steels, cast iron, pure iron, and a few special materials such as Permendur and Supermendur. Permendur is special material that looks great on paper; however, cutting it with carbide is the equivalent of cutting aluminum with an aluminum tool: it is virtually impossible to cut. Supermendur is basically the same material, which is held in a strong magnetic field while it is annealed, an expensive and difficult material. Pure iron is also good, but cutting it with standard machine tools is like cutting clay or putty. Little energy is required, but it flows instead of cuts and is, therefore, difficult to machine accurately or cleanly. Aluminum and brass are easy to cut, but they are not on the chart because they cannot be magnetized. We are really left with mild steel and cast iron as choices, the latter being useful to about 8000 G. Low-carbon steel (1002, 1008, 1010, and so on) is a better choice than "normal steel" (1020), but it also has problems. The lower the percent carbon, the more its tendency to cut like pure iron, and the harder it is to find in stock, much less be assured of correct metallurgical consistency. The manufacturer of loudspeakers, beaten back by suppliers who really don't want to stock low-carbon steel, and machinists who don't want to deal with steel having bad machinability usually ends up making machined magnetic circuit parts of steel, usually hot rolled. Some manufacturers have been very successful with very low-carbon steel magnetic circuits, due to the relative ductility of low-carbon steel. Forgings and even pressed, coined, and sintered pure iron powder circuits have met with great success in mass production items. Most high-flux density structures today, however, still use steel.

Magnetic sources are either permanent magnets or electromagnets, the latter being popular in the 1930s and 1940s, the former being used today.

Permanent magnets for loudspeakers are one of three available materials; alnico V, *ceramic* (aka *ferrite*, mud, and so on), and *rare earth* or samarium cobalt, the latter being the most expensive but, interestingly enough, having names with the most marketing appeal. Alnico, once a very popular material (1940s through 1960s), is a metallurgical alloy made in a foundry, and its principal ingredient, cobalt, has become extremely expensive and hard to get as of the late 1970s. Ferrite magnets (from barium ferrite) are true ceramics, being made from a mudlike water slurry that is pressed, baked, and finally ground to produce a finished, true ceramic product. These are currently the standard magnets used in virtually all but a few loudspeakers today. Samarium cobalt is also a baked ceramic. Though expensive (much too expensive for a conventional cone loudspeaker), these have the advantage of very small size and light weight. They are typically used in small tweeters and lightweight headphones and magnetic phono cartridges, as discussed in Chapter 24.

Fig. 14-12 shows relative "magnetization curves" for these materials. The permanent magnetic behavior of any material is described by two properties: its magnetic force-per-unit-length-of-magnet, H_c or coercive force, and its operating flux density, B_g. H_c and B_g are equivalent to voltage gradient and current density. Their product is referred to as "magnetizing energy" or $H_c \times B_g$. The larger $H_c \times B_g$ is, the smaller the volume of magnet used to fill a given air-gap volume with any flux density. The *operating point* of a magnet is determined by a choice of H_c and B_g where $H_c \times B_g$ is a maximum. This produces the smallest volume, which is, thus, the most economical magnet for a given air-gap requirement, an optimum design. In comparing the three materials, alnico has the lowest coercive force, ceramic the next highest, and rare earth the highest. Therefore, for the same total magnetic force, the alnico magnet would be the longest, ceramic shorter, and rare earth the shortest. In general, magnetic force is linear with gap width; if the gap width is doubled, the magnetic force or magnet thickness must be doubled. In terms of the operating flux density through the magnet, alnico is highest, rare earth next highest, and ceramic the lowest. Therefore, if a loudspeaker designer wanted to design three different magnet structures to do the same job using the three different magnetic materials, they would look similar to those shown in Fig. 14-13. For the same air gap, the total number of magnetic lines (like fluid flow, gallons per second) is a constant, so flux density in the magnet is varied by magnet area similar to a change in orifice size in fluid flow. The alnico magnet would be long, per the previous discussion and relatively small in cross-sectional area, needing a relatively high-flux density through its magnetic circuit. The ceramic is the reverse, having more of a pancake appearance. The rare earth magnet is the most compact overall due to its properties; however, this magnet would also be vastly more expensive. If the loudspeaker designer wanted to increase the gap length, this would require a corresponding increase in magnet length in all cases, since the magnetic voltage or force required for an air gap increases linearly with length. If the gap flux density were to be increased, in all cases the magnet areas would have to be larger. Therefore, as the gap energy ($L_g \times B_g$) is increased, the magnet volume, and the volume of the magnetic circuit (and, therefore, the total magnet structure weight) would go up. Since motor strength depends on air-gap volume available to the conductor, there is a direct correlation between loudspeaker weight and motor strength, assuming good magnet design practice.

As gap flux densities approach and exceed 13,000 to 15,000 G in steel, extraordinary (nonlinear) amounts of magnetic force are needed, Fig. 14-11. Also, as 18,000 G is approached in the gap, the material (steel) starts to look similar to air, and the field becomes divergent. This

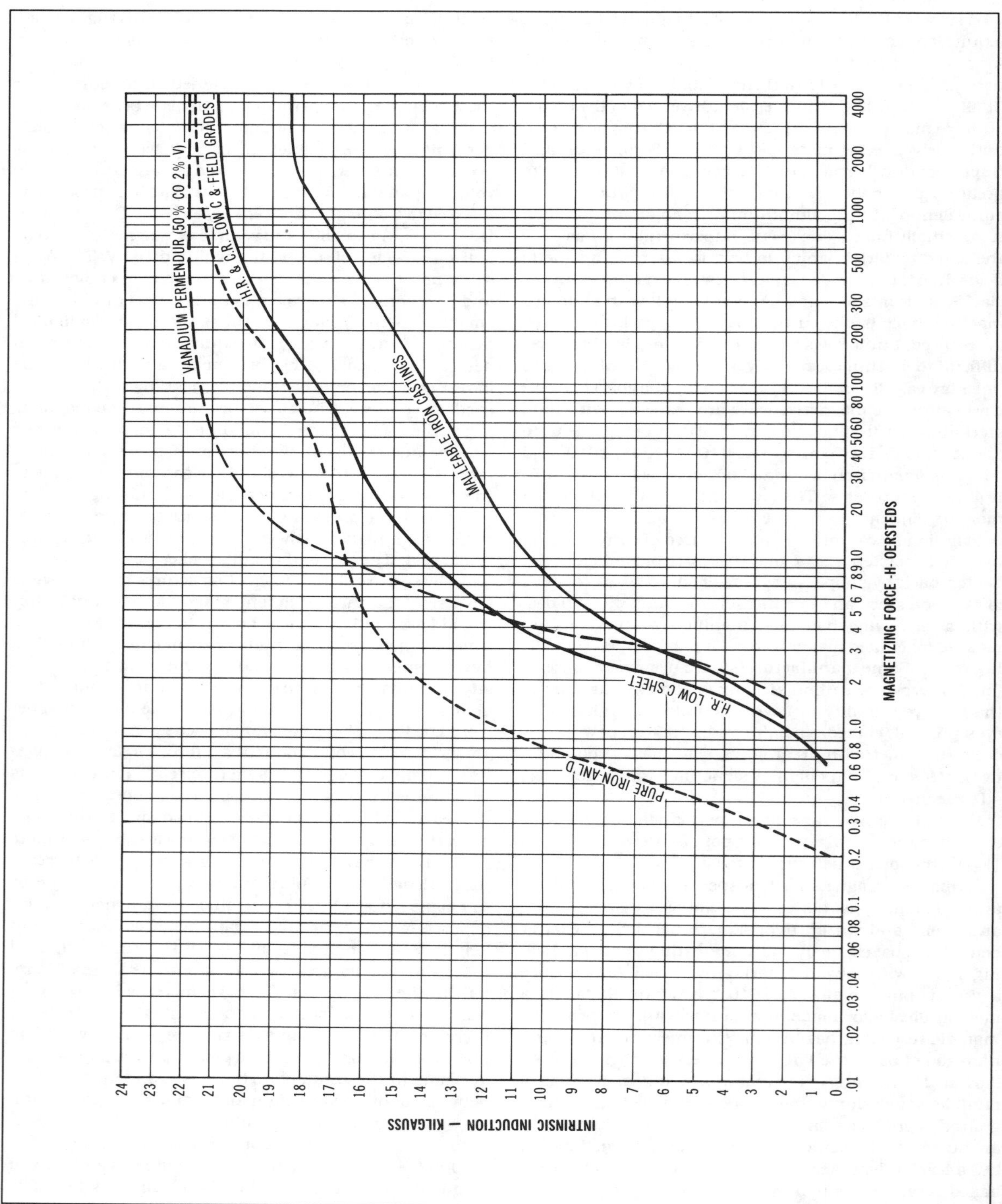

Figure 14-11 Magnetization curves for various materials.

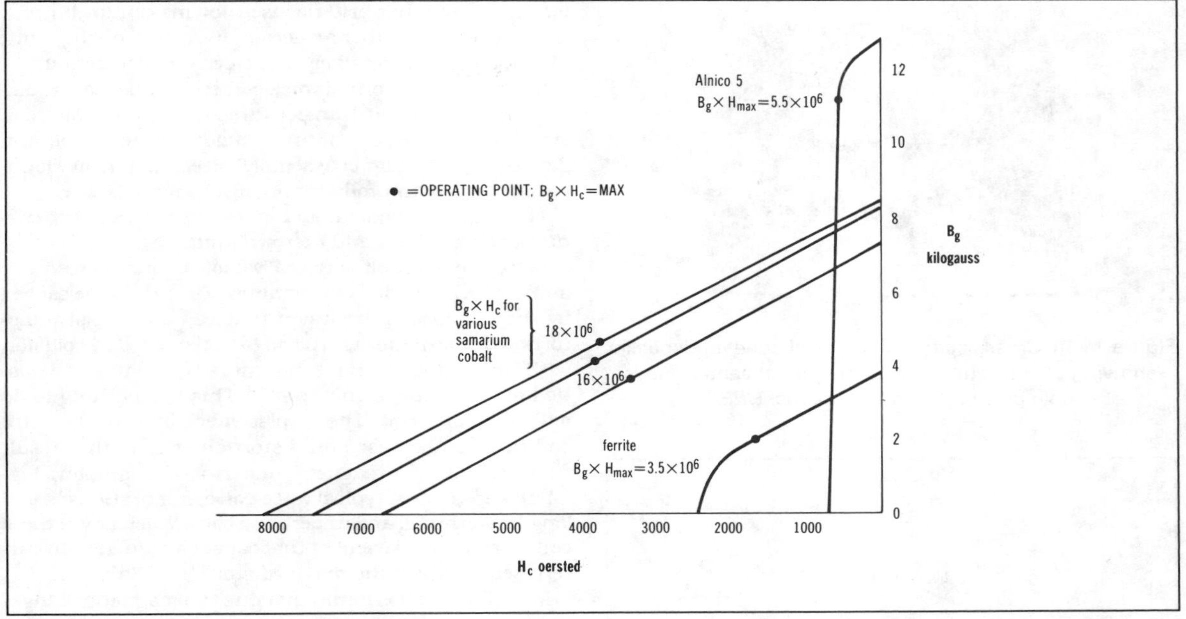

Figure 14-12 Magnetization curves for various permanent magnetic materials suitable for loudspeakers.

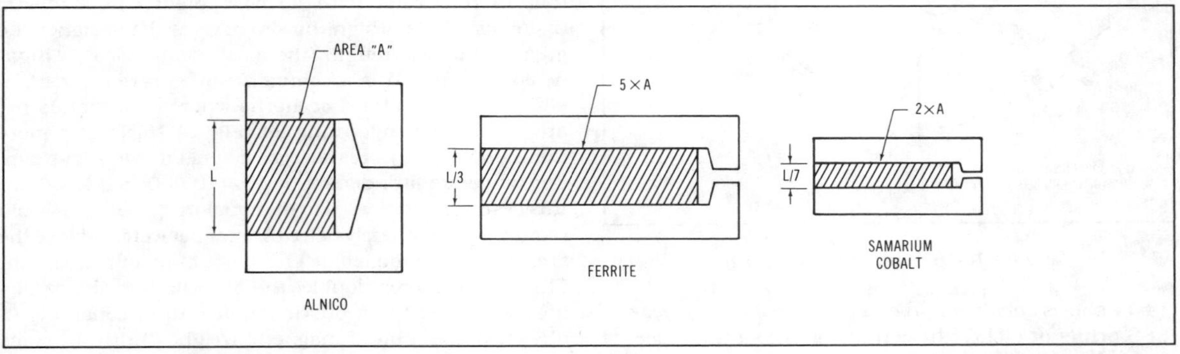

Figure 14-13 Three equivalent magnetic structures using alnico, ferrite, and samarium cobalt. All air gaps are the same.

is known as leakage and makes the gap area look much larger at high flux levels than that of the geometric gap. This increases the required magnet area to operate properly. This whole phenomenon on nonlinear magnetic force and leakage is known as *saturation*. As loudspeaker performance is pushed to the limits, magnetic assemblies get large and very expensive due to saturation of the magnetic circuit materials. Small changes in performance are met with much larger product costs; great loudspeakers are often vastly more expensive than good loudspeakers.

14.3.1 Motor Configuration

The most common way to couple the conductor to the diaphragm is via the cylindrical voice coil, which is used on all magnetic cone loudspeakers and compression drivers. The coil, made of round or rectangular wire (edge-wound) is wound onto (or vice versa) a cylinder, called the voice coil former or support. These are made of paper, plastic ("Kapton" polymer, Mylar™, and so on), or aluminum, which is then bonded to the diaphragm. Fig.

Figure 14-14 Cross section of a typical cone loudspeaker showing construction (alnico magnet at center under pole piece). *(Courtesy JBL Inc./UREI)*

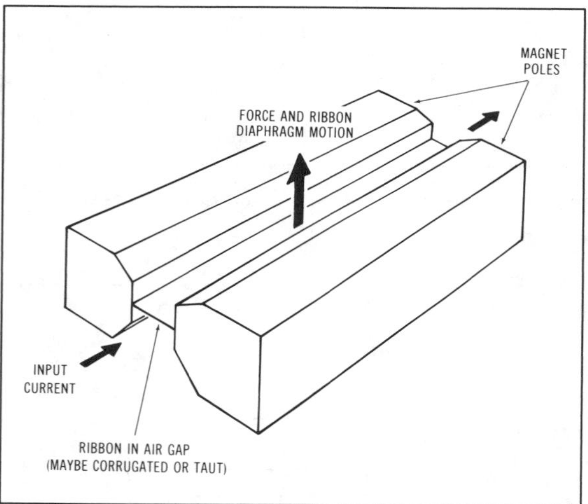

Figure 14-15 Ribbon loudspeaker.

14-14 shows construction of a typical cone loudspeaker. ESS prints or etches the conductor onto a thin sheet of Mylar™ (0.0005 in.), then folds it to produce a pleated diaphragm that is forced in the magnetic field. Magneplanar® adheres continuous lengths of wire to a large panel of Mylar™, which is operated over a large field of charged bar magnets. The Mitsubishi leaf tweeter is similar, etching a conductor field on Mylar™. They all end up being identical in principle to Fig. 14-10 and will be discussed more thoroughly later in this text. The ribbon loudspeaker (Fig. 14-15) is a special case in that the voice coil is both the conductor and the diaphragm itself.

14.3.2 Output Limitations[2]

The maximum output capability of any electromagnetic loudspeaker is a matter of displacement, heat transfer, and any other criteria used for maximum output, which is usually either an acceptable sound quality limit (distortion), or more likely, loudspeaker destruction.

In the case of a normal voice-coil-type loudspeaker, displacement and heat transfer directly relate to voice coil size, voice coil length, former length and material, and gap (therefore, magnet assembly) size. A big, heavy loudspeaker will both produce and absorb more power.

There are two major limitations on any magnetic driver—*displacement limit* and *thermal limit.*

Displacement limit is typically a low-frequency restraint and can be a function of two things. First, it can be caused by the diaphragm excursion that causes excessive distortion or the diaphragm parts to be damaged by collision with the magnet or frame, fatigue, or exceeding the elastic limit of suspension parts.[3–6] This has nothing to do with the voice coil. The displacement limit of the voice coil can also be based on distortion criteria that result from exceeding a magnetic linearity of the motor. Fig. 14-16 shows three typical voice-coil configurations: equal length, overhung, and underhung coils. When any of these coils reach a displacement that causes a reduction in current sensitivity of the motor, distortion will result.

Mark Gander has found that due to a magnetic "fringe" or leakage field at the pole tips, an excursion of 15% further than the gap length is a reasonable distortion limit since it will give approximately 3% harmonic distortion at low frequencies.[7, 8] Clearly, the equal-length voice coil (Fig. 14-16C) would have the most potential for magnetic distortion. This design, however, gives the designer the greatest motor strength (the most conductor in a high-density field) and is a common configuration for high-efficiency drivers used on horns where excursion is relatively low. The underhung coil (Fig. 14-16B) allows more excursion but requires a larger magnet due to a long gap. For moderate-flux density levels (10,000 to 14,000 G), this design, as compared to the equal-length design, would require approximately twice the magnet weight (twice the area and the same length) for a doubling of gap length. This approximately doubles the excursion capability, giving four times the acoustic power output capability (6 dB) for a doubling of magnetic weight (3 dB). In some cases this is worth it. The overhung coil (Fig. 14-16A) is capable of the highest magnetic linearity without a big change in magnet. It is commonly seen on woofers used for direct radiation, requiring higher excursions. The major disadvantage here is that the coil that is not in the gap is essentially not used for transduction. The extra coil length adds both mass and dc resistance, which reduces sensitivity and raises total Q. However, there are many examples of successful and good-sounding commercial woofers using overhung coils. The designer has to take all these things into consideration and can certainly design a woofer with good low end and excursion (therefore, low-frequency output) using an overhung coil.

Thermal limit of a magnetic loudspeaker motor is a function of two things: thermal limit of materials used and heat transfer from the coil assembly.[9] Most adhesives

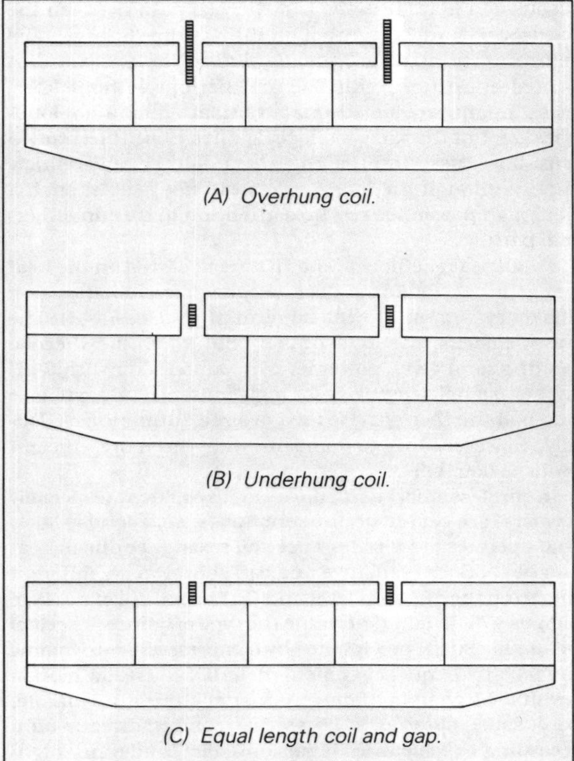

(A) Overhung coil.
(B) Underhung coil.
(C) Equal length coil and gap.

Figure 14-16 Three basic voice coil/magnetic gap configurations.

used in the loudspeaker industry have an upper limit between 250 and 350°F. Some epoxies go higher but may become difficult to work with due to the exotic curing required. Insulation on wire may be as high as 425°F, and anodized aluminum wire has the melting point of aluminum as a limit that is sometimes reached in practice. Voice coils operated at high temperatures will have higher resistance at speed, and a 1°C rise will produce approximately a 0.4% rise in dc resistance in both copper and aluminum. Therefore, operating a voice coil 100°C above ambient (127°C or 261°F) will raise the voice coil to 40% above its ambient value. The following equation will give voice coil resistance at any temperature in degrees Celsius:

$$R_T = R_O + 0.004(T - T_O) \qquad (14\text{-}5)$$

where,

R_T is the resistance at temperature T in ohms,
R_O is the resistance at ambient temperature T_O in ohms,
T and T_O are converted from degrees Fahrenheit to degrees Celsius by using 5(°F − 32)/9.

Heat transfer *from* the coil determines coil temperature T, and the ability of a loudspeaker mechanism to do this is its thermal resistance, measured in degrees Celsius per watt. Therefore, as power is doubled, final temperature rise is doubled, which is an important point. Heat transfer in any loudspeaker is primarily a function of the air-gap design and voice-coil design and the ability of the loudspeaker frame and magnet to dissipate heat to the surrounding or ambient air. Referring to Fig. 14-17, the thermal rise of any stationary voice coil in any air gap is found by the following:

$$(T - T_s) = QL/A_TK \qquad (14\text{-}6)$$

where

T_s is the temperature of structure (magnet) in degrees Celsius,
Q is the electrical heating power (I^2R) in watts,
L is the effective air-gap length or $(L_1L_2)/(L_1 + L_2)$ in inches,
A_T is the total gap area in square inches exposed to the voice coil,
K is the conductivity of air or 7×10^{-4} W/in.°C.

As the air gap length is decreased and the area increased, heat transfer increases. Making the voice coil former or support out of aluminum will increase the effective heat transfer area as it spreads the heat out; the thicker the aluminum, the more the thermal spreading. Therefore, the effective heat transfer area is higher. A general statement of truth is that voice coils wound on aluminum formers with large diameters in magnets with large gap areas and very tight coil-to-gap tolerances are capable of handling high electrical power due to good heat transfer in the air gap. In other words, big, expensive, accurately made loudspeakers handle more thermal power. The reverse is also true. As the loudspeaker moves, it may be able to pump or scrub the air in the gap to improve heat transfer many times over. The clever designer may be able to improve this quality. Also, of the three voice coil types shown in Fig. 14-16, the underhung and equal length

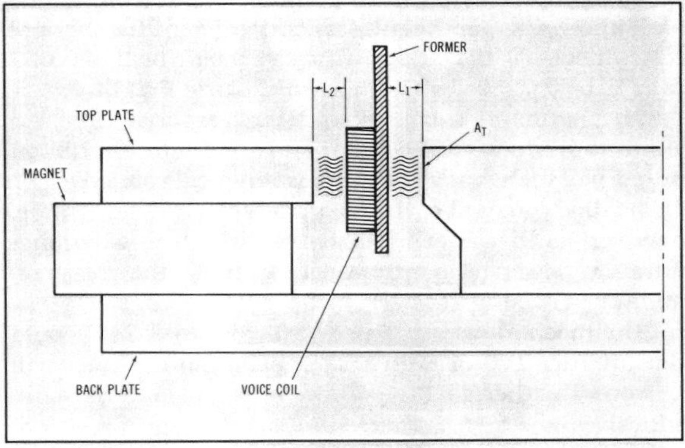

Figure 14-17 Heat conduction in magnetic loudspeakers.

would have the best heat transfer if the coils were the same height. The overhung coil would only conduct heat well in the gap region, while the coil ends remaining out of the gap would be likely to bake at high power because of relatively poor heat transfer. This is indeed a common failure mode of overhung voice coils. Typical thermal behavior for most coils is on the order of 0.5 to 3°C/W input.

Lastly, a heat-conducting magnetic liquid may be used to improve heat transfer. Known as *Ferrofluids*, these special magnetic fluids will be retained in a magnetic air gap due to magnetic force. Their thermal conductivity is seven to ten times higher than that of air and can substantially improve heat transfer. They should, however, be used with caution since indiscriminate use may degrade the performance of a loudspeaker due to mechanical damping and added mass. They also may soak into fibrous (paper) diaphragm materials and be permanently attached to the diaphragm. Generally, Ferrofluids should be designed into a loudspeaker, not added on, although this may be done with success depending on the particular loudspeaker design. Some loudspeakers are advertised to be "liquid cooled"; Ferrofluids are in the gap.

Thermal rise in voice coils is not instantaneous and is, in fact, directly related to mass M. As one might suspect, light voice coils have short thermal rise times, and vice versa. The thermal rise-time constant of any loudspeaker coil is found by Eq. 14-7 and is the time required for the coil to reach 63% of its final value, the rise being exponential with time:

$$t = MC(\Delta T/Q) \qquad (14\text{-}7)$$
$$= MC(L/A_TK)$$

where,

t is the time constant in seconds,

C is the specific heat of voice-coil material in joules per gram in degrees Celsius,

$\Delta T/Q$ is the thermal resistance in degrees Celsius per watt.

For example, a typical copper woofer voice coil weighs 24 g and has a gap heat transfer coefficient (or thermal resistance) of 1°C/W. Copper has a specific heat of 0.092 cal/g°C or 0.0220 J/g°C. Therefore, using Eq. 14-7, t = 0.528 s, which is a typical voice-coil response time. An aluminum coil would be faster and an aluminum ribbon might be much faster, but this is a typical value.

The time constant of the magnetic structure and frame, however, is in the order of hours, which is why long-duration power tests are needed. Initially, the voice coil might be cruising at 280°F, but over the course of 2 h or so, the mechanical structure (typical 1 to 3°C/W) could rise another 100 or even 150°C, bringing the voice coil well over the thermal limit of its composite materials and adhesives.

The heat transfer from the frame and magnet bears discussion here. It is the last thermal path between the loudspeaker and air. Although the rise time is large, final temperature may vary greatly due to the enclosure. A vented enclosure, vents top and bottom without fiberglass, might provide adequate ventilation for a hot loudspeaker. Put the same loudspeaker in a closed box stuffed with fiberglass, and the final rise might be surprisingly high. Although the loudspeaker will not melt in such a box, high power use requires attention to this final thermal path.

Loudspeaker efficiency has a direct bearing on the heat power input, Q. For a given output power, loudspeaker efficiency determines the amount of this loss (I^2R). The more efficient the loudspeaker, the lower the thermal heating for a given power level; a loudspeaker with 3-dB higher overall sensitivity for a given impedance will give one-half the thermal rise for a desired output level. (Usually, however, this just means that the more efficient loudspeaker will be driven harder.)

In professional use, most loudspeakers (especially woofers) are beaten on unmercifully; also, a loudspeaker that operates at twice its voice coil resistance due to heat can be 6-dB less sensitive and can sound vastly different due to change in both level and Q. The nature of musical signals will usually determine the type of failure. Thermal failure is usually precipitated by compressed (low dynamic range) high-frequency content material, where low motion results. Mechanical failure is usually due to dynamic, percussive material, such as that coming directly off a recording console with drums on "solo," and other high-fidelity signals that do not limit dynamic range. Most rock-and-roll commercial pressings and complex legato orchestral recordings using strings will give thermal failure, the former because of imposed limiting, the latter due to inherently limited dynamic range. Direct-to-disk recordings are usually more of a mechanical rather than thermal punishment.

14.3.3 Mobility Modeling[10]

The fundamental way an electromagnetic driver operates is that current through the voice coil results in a force. This force necessitates the use of a mobility analysis where electrical current transforms to mechanical force; conversely, electrical voltage transforms to mechanical velocity. Current (I) passed through a conductor of length (L) in a magnetic field (B) will cause a force (F) on the conductor, which is normal to that conductor according to the relationship of eq. 14-4.

The model of this equation is a transformer, shown in Fig. 14-18. Current transforms to force, and voltage transforms to velocity by

$$v = E/BL \qquad (14\text{-}8)$$

Therefore, if there is a mechanical impedance (Z_{mech})

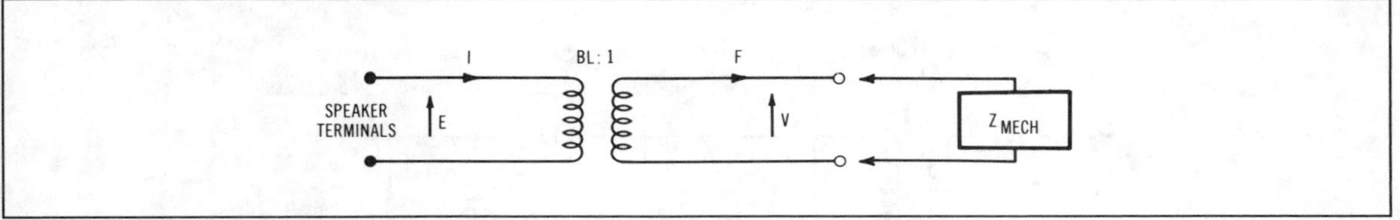

Figure 14-18 Mobility model of electromagnetic transduction.

of any kind connected to the conductor or voice coil, an electrically referred impedance (Z_e) will be seen on the electrical size according to the relationship

$$Z_e = B^2L^2Z_{mech} \qquad (14\text{-}9)$$

However, the nature of Z_{mech} is such that force corresponds to current and velocity, to voltage, which necessitates a sort of inverse analysis, called *mobility*, to properly define Z_{mech}.

14.3.3.1 Mobility Resistor

A dashpot or any Newtonian mechanical resistance is a resistor, as is anything that has a force (F) proportional to velocity (v) or flow. The resistor is the only linear component that dissipates real energy or real power. The normal relationship between the mobility resistor results from the normal mechanical relationship

$$F = vR_m \qquad (14\text{-}10)$$

$$= (dx/dt)R_m$$

where,
R_m is the mechanical resistance,
dx/dt is the change in displacement with respect to time.

14.3.3.2 Mobility Mass

A mechanical mass exerts a force proportional to the rate of change of velocity

$$F = M(dv/dt) \qquad (14\text{-}11)$$

$$= M(j\omega v)$$

where,
$\omega = 2\pi f$.

Therefore, the mobility mass is governed by the relationship

$$v = F(1/j\omega M) \qquad (14\text{-}12)$$

or,

$$X_{mass} = v/F$$

$$= B^2L^2/j\omega M$$

Therefore, the mechanical mass transforms to a mobility electrical equivalent capacitor

$$C_m = M/B^2L^2 \qquad (14\text{-}13)$$

14.3.3.3 Mobility Compliance

A mechanical spring exerts a force proportional to displacement according to

$$F = K \qquad (14\text{-}14)$$

$$= (1/C)$$

where,
K is the spring rate,
C is the compliance or 1/K.

Therefore, the mobility compliance relationship is

$$X_c = vdt \qquad (14\text{-}15)$$

$$= FC$$

or,

$$v = j\omega CF$$

Therefore,

$$X_c = v/F$$

$$= j\omega C$$

The mechanical compliance transforms to a mobility electrical equivalent inductor

$$L_c = B^2L^2C \qquad (14\text{-}16)$$

Using these transformed modeling techniques, one can model a loudspeaker so that a better understanding can be made of its operation, through analytic relationships derived from the equivalent circuit. As an example, Figs. 14-19 and 14-20 show models of a direct-radiator and a compression-driven loudspeaker, respectively.

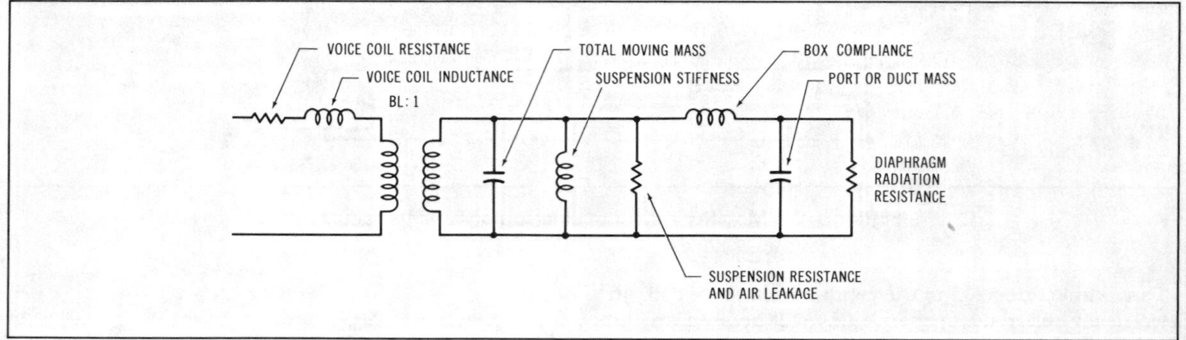

Figure 14-19 Mobility model of a direct-radiator loudspeaker in a vented box.

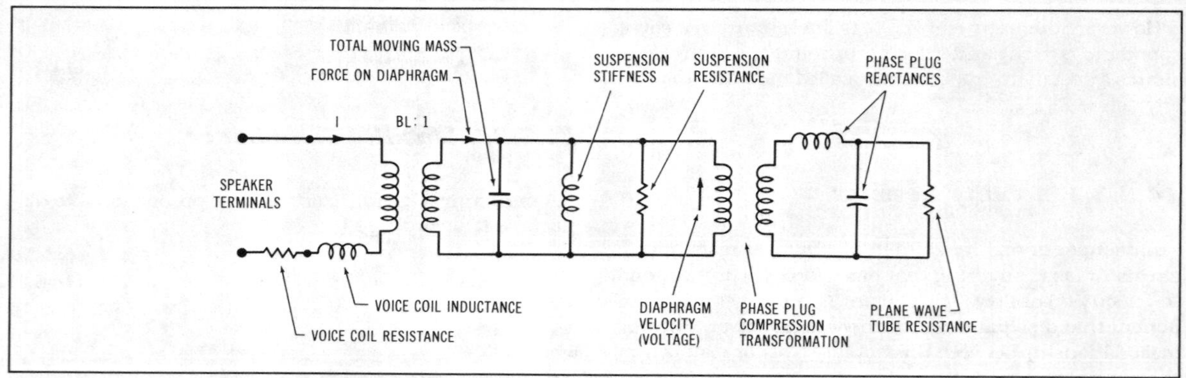

Figure 14-20 Mobility model of compression driver in a plane wave tube.

14.4 DIRECT RADIATION OF SOUND[11,12]

In order to make sound, we have to make air move. To the loudspeaker engineer, the invention of the wheel and the taming of fire is secondary to the invention of the diaphragm or piston, the classic mover of air. Since the first loudspeaker sounded its note, we have strived to create the perfectly rigid, lightweight piston and incorporate it into a loudspeaker system, with a few exceptions.

Direct sound radiation from a piston in space, a baffle, or a box can be understood by analyzing two distinct but directly related quantities, *acoustic radiation resistance* and *directivity*.

Acoustic radiation resistance is the measurement of the capacity or ability of an acoustic radiator to convert piston motion into real sound power, measured in acoustic watts. It is the ratio of pressure (psi) to volume velocity in cubic inches per second (in.^{3}/s) of the piston. At high frequencies, all pistons have the same ability to produce real acoustic power per unit of surface area. However, as the size of the wavelength of sound being produced approaches the size of the piston, the radiation resistance begins to unload or decrease at the rate of 12 dB/octave or the square of the decreasing frequency. This is shown in Fig. 14-21. As an example, a 13.5-in. piston (15-in. loudspeaker) will begin to unload at around 500 Hz. For low-frequency loudspeakers (woofers), a flat response below 500 Hz is normally seen, which is due to the fact that the mass reactance of the loudspeaker is also changing (lowering) with frequency, allowing the motion of the loudspeaker to increase with decreasing frequency, which is the so-called mass-controlled region of a normal operation of a woofer. Due to this phenomenon, the mass of the loudspeaker actually is a major determinant of the loudspeaker's flat or asymptotic sensitivity or efficiency, as will be seen in the low-frequency performance section.

14.4.1 Radiation of a Piston in a Flat Baffle

A piston in an infinite wall is the most common model of a loudspeaker and the one most commonly used for loudspeaker analysis. It turns out to be the least common

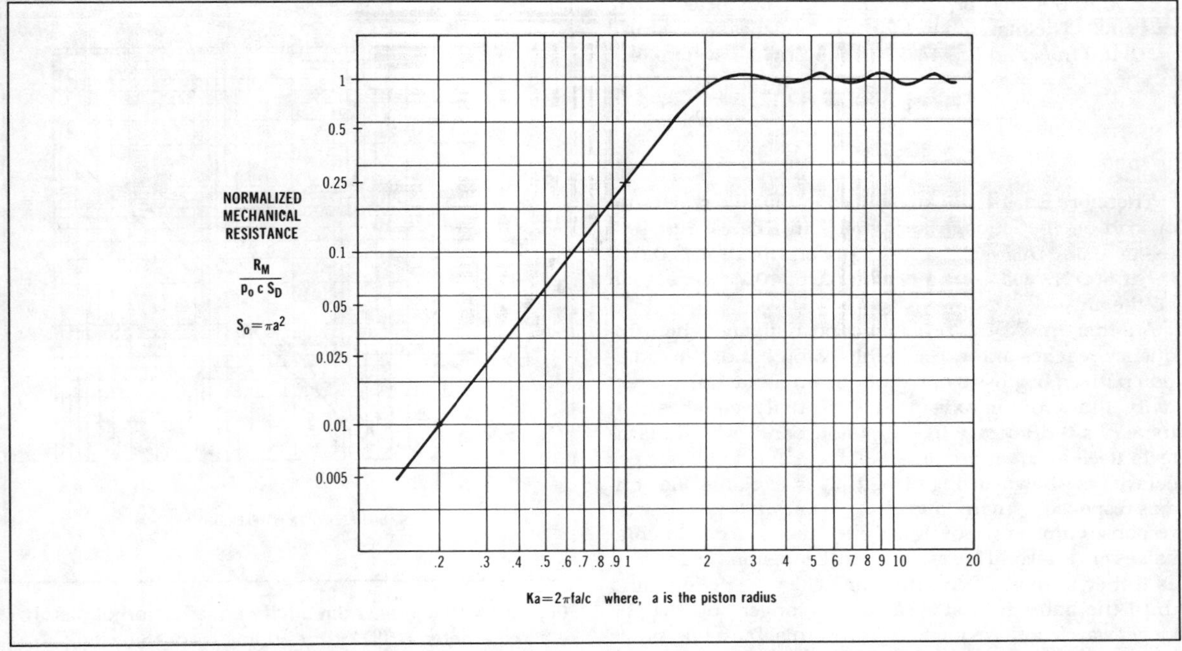

Figure 14-21 Radiation resistance of a piston in an infinite baffle.

practical manifestation of a loudspeaker in a room, save for flush-mount studio and custom hi-fi systems. However, due to its relatively well-behaved mathematical description, the piston in an infinite wall is used so that relative analytic comparisons can be made. (Interestingly, it is the best way to get good bass; smooth, wide-band response; and best stereo image.)

A piston in an infinite baffle will develop an acoustic load depending on its size relative to the frequency of interest. When the circumference of a piston is equal in size to one wavelength of sound, a constant acoustic load versus frequency will be seen on the diaphragm at all frequencies above this transition frequency. This high-frequency band is commonly known as the piston band of the loudspeaker and is found by the following equation:

$$f_{pb} = c/\pi D_p \tag{14-17}$$

where,

f_{pb} is the lowest piston band cutoff frequency in hertz,
c is the speed of sound in meters per second,
D_p is the piston diameter in meters.

Below the piston band, the acoustical or mechanical resistive load on the diaphragm will fall at a rate of 12 dB/octave. The actual value of the acoustical load in the piston band is found by the following equation:

$$R_D = \rho_o c S_D \tag{14-18}$$
$$= F_D/V_D$$

where,

R_D equals piston band diaphragm resistance in newton seconds per meter,
$\rho_o c$ is 407 mks rayls,
S_D is the diaphragm area in square meters,
F_D is the force on the diaphragm in newtons,
V_D is the diaphragm velocity in meters per second.

For example, a 1-m^2 diaphragm will exert 1 N (about 0.225 lb) of force when vibrated at a velocity of 1 m/s at any frequency in the piston band. The velocity of a loudspeaker, or any other device under sinusoidal vibration, is found by the following equation:

$$v = 2\pi f X \tag{14-19}$$

where,

v is the velocity in meters per second,
f is the frequency in hertz,
X is the displacement in meters.

For example, a 0.1-m^2 piston (155 in.^{2}; a 14-in. diameter piston) vibrating at 600 Hz at ±0.010 in. or 0.000254 m will produce peak velocities, computed via Eq. 14-19, of

2π 600 (0.000254) or approximately 1 m/s peak (0.707 m/s rms). The piston band for this loudspeaker, using c = 13450 in./s and Eq. 14-17 in the English system is

$$f_{pb} = 13{,}450/\pi(14)$$
$$= 306\ \text{Hz}$$

Therefore Eq. 14-18 can be used to find the resistance or load on the loudspeaker, which in this case is 40.7 N•s/m. Using this value, a 14-in. piston vibrating at 0.010 in. at 600 Hz will exert a peak force of 40.7 N or 9.16 lb on the air.

Another interesting phenomenon happens when frequency reaches and exceeds the piston band; the radiation pattern begins to narrow or beam. In fact, the directivity index or on-axis gain (directivity equalization) increases 6 dB/octave in the piston band, which manifests itself as an approximate halving of beam angle per octave, as shown in Fig. 14-22. This explains "flat on-axis response" of many loudspeakers known to have power-response cutoff at relatively low frequencies. When in finite baffles or real-world boxes, loudspeaker pistons will appear as if they were in an infinite wall below the piston band until the baffle frontal area can no longer support the longer wavelength frequencies. Below this, the baffle moves out of its piston band, and the acoustic radiation makes a transition from half-space to full-space and is subject to room boundaries. The chart in Fig. 14-23 shows how these frequency-size relationships behave for common piston and baffle sizes.

Note that we have not discussed whether the piston is flat, concave, convex, domed, coned, or any other geometry. The fact is that for most of the range of any loudspeaker, its geometry has little effect on dispersion or directivity, its projected area or perimeter being the major factor. Here are several items of evidence to support this.

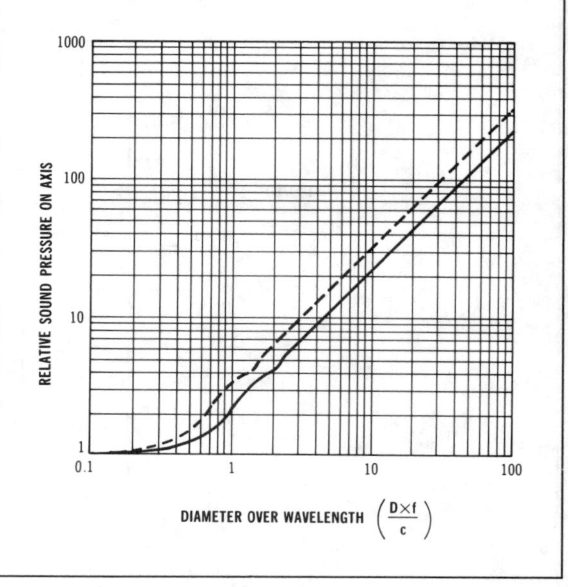

Figure 14-22 On-axis directivity equalization of piston; diameter = "D." (Dotted line is for thin ring of same diameter as piston.)

Domes and other convex or concave radiators[13] have shape effects on directivity only at very high frequencies compared to their size.[14] The elegant (and accurate) work of James Kates shows that for Ka = $2\pi a/\lambda$, or piston circumference-to-wavelength ratio, in the normal operating region of domes, the effect of dome height has little bearing on directivity. Fig. 14-24 shows relative DI versus frequency; Fig. 14-25 shows ±45° (90°) response for domes of various aspect ratios. Below Ka = 4, there is virtually

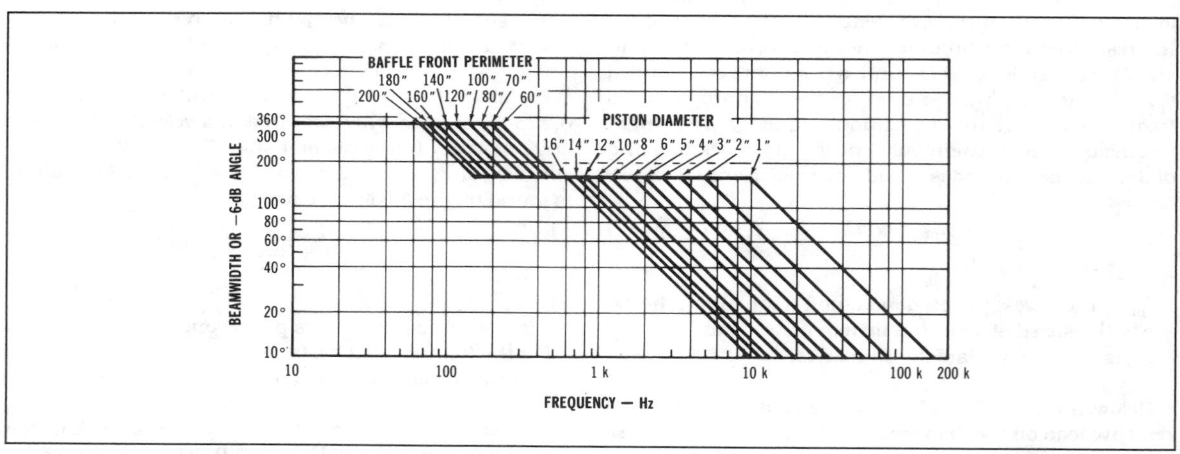

Figure 14-23 Chart for predicting −6-dB angle (beam width) response for piston-and-box systems. *(Courtesy Altec Lansing Corp.)*

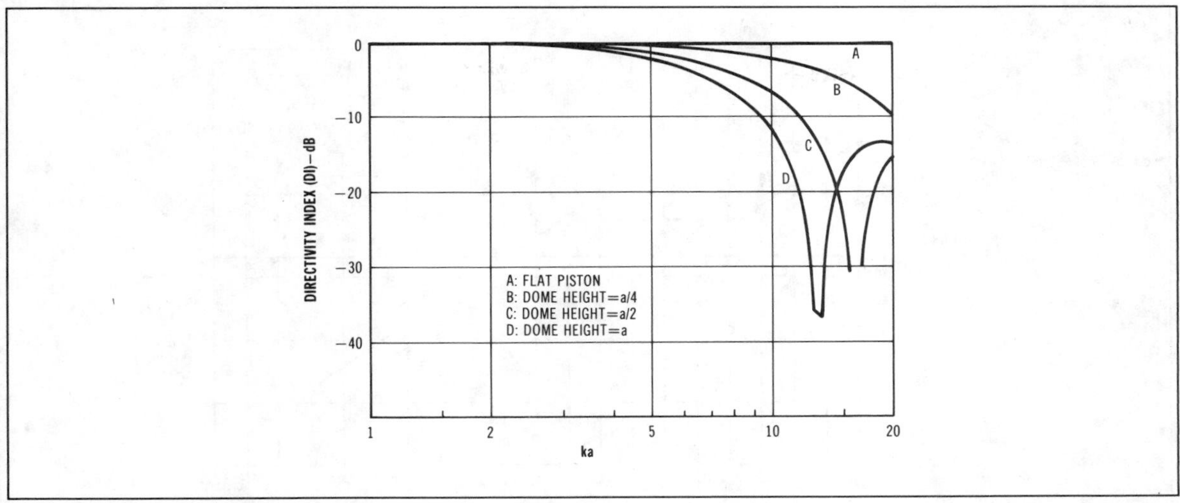

Figure 14-24 Relative on-axis response from various pistons of radius "a." A: Flat piston, B: Dome height = a/4, C: Dome height = a/2, F: Dome height = a.

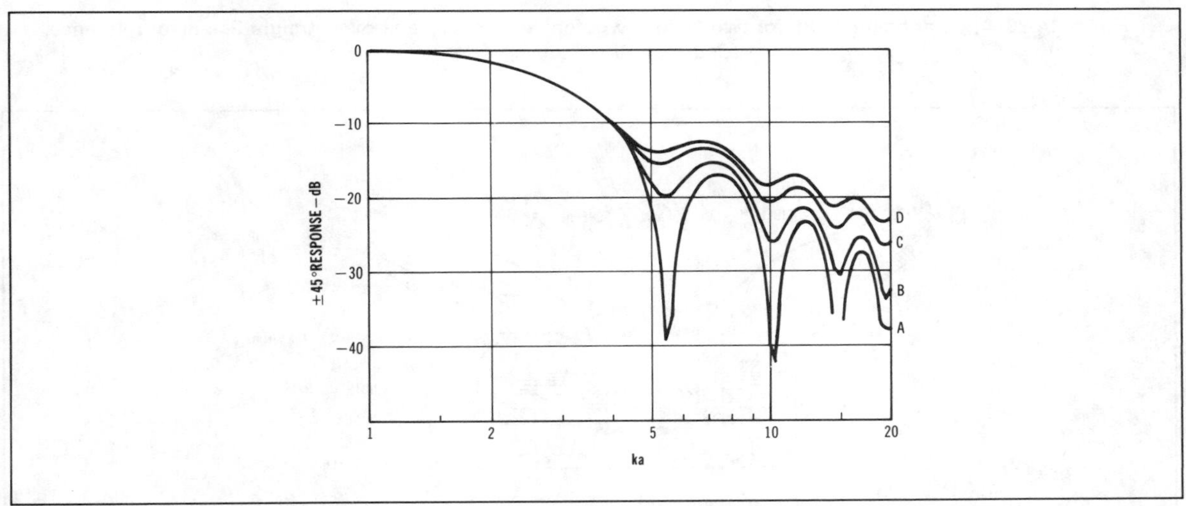

Figure 14-25 Relative 45° off-axis response curves for flat-on-axis response from various diaphragms of radius "a." A: Flat piston, B: Dome height = a/4, C: Dome height = a/2, D: Dome height = a.

no difference. This corresponds, for example, to a frequency of 17.1 kHz for a 1-in. diameter dome, certainly near the top extreme of the normal operating range of such a direct-radiating loudspeaker. The convex argument also holds true for convex cones. Often the subject of debate, shallow or deep cones have practically no effect in normal range, and all appear as a flat piston would, with regards to directivity. Fig. 14-26 illustrates this. The JBL cone is very shallow and flat; in contrast the Altec is relatively deep. Notice the similarity in beam-width responses.

14.4.2 Electromagnetic Drivers

Fig. 14-27 shows a *very* typical generic cone driver employing a ferrite or ceramic magnet. The magnet structure is typically held together with an adhesive only; usually an anaerobic as manufactured by Loc-Tite. Sometimes, a "pro" loudspeaker will have to be made more rugged by bolting through the magnet. In this case, stainless steel or brass screws must be used, so as not to magnetically short the top plate to the back plate. A rear cover may or may not be used; however, the ferrite mag-

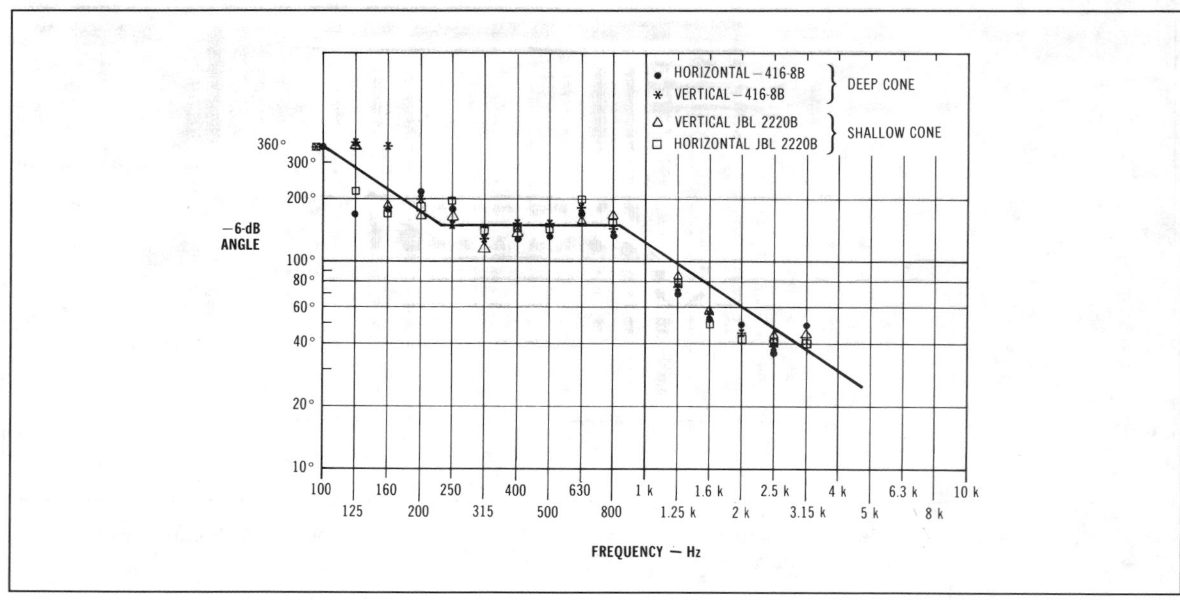

Figure 14-26 Angular beam width for two 15-inch woofers in an enclosed box—straight line is for reference. *(Courtesy Altec Lansing Corp.)*

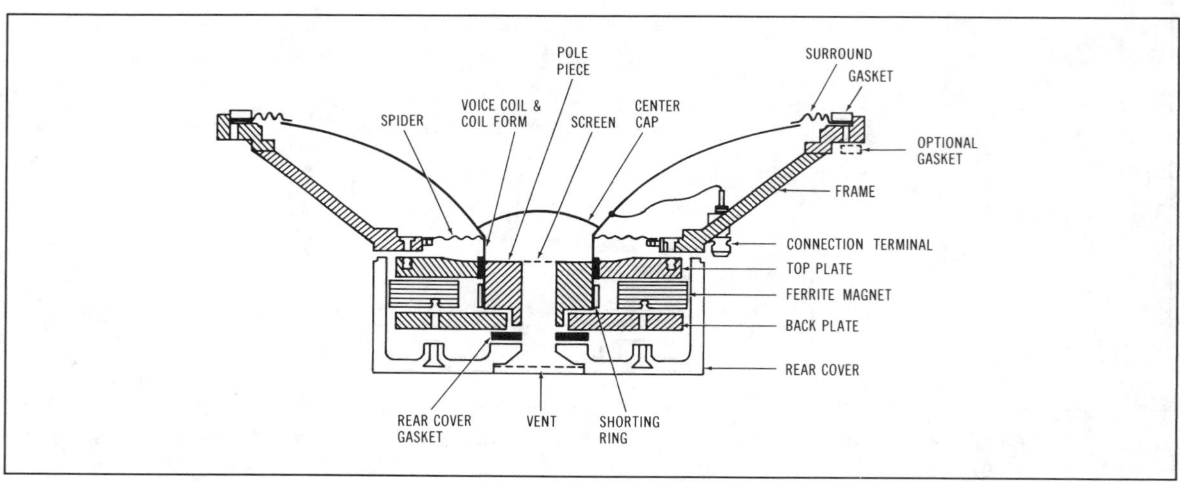

Figure 14-27 Typical woofer parts identification. *(Courtesy Yamaha International Corp.)*

net is usually protected by something. One such protection method is a rubber boot that fits over the magnet outside diameter. The ferrite magnet chips easily, and these flakes become a real threat to the loudspeaker since they can work their way into the air gap easily. Also, the ferrite magnet is not particularly attractive, and an expensive product usually necessitates a cosmetic cover-up for higher perceived value. The vent through the pole piece is typical and is necessary to avoid causing a stiff air cavity under the center cap or dust cover.

14.4.2.1 Diaphragm Types

The most common direct-radiation device in the world today is the *cylindrical voice coil-driven paper cone.* The cheapest cone to make is the *folded cone,* which is cut from a sheet of paper and bonded with a strong adhesive. A more expensive and difficult-to-make cone is the *molded-paper cone.* These are one piece molded by straining paper pulp through a strainer-mold in the shape of the desired end product. The formed slurry is then pressed and baked to remove residual moisture, bearing a one-piece cone, free of joints. Various ribs and concentric rings are sometimes molded into the cone, and the cones can be had with straight and curved sides of varying depth. These

Figure 14-28 Loudspeaker incorporating a whizzer cone.

are available from suppliers of cones. It is interesting that the loudspeaker industry is supplied with cones, spiders, and domes from a few specialty manufacturers of these items. A rare manufacturer makes its own cone and suspension parts. Cones are available as "styles" with varying weights of paper and generally unknown mechanical properties. Debates often crop up between cone and loudspeaker engineers over the various merits of one over the other when, in fact, little is really known about how their (exceedingly complex) mechanical behavior contributes to sound. Comparative A to B listening usually determines which sounds better, rather than an engineering analysis/prediction of breakup behavior.

The principle of a rigid piston has not always been adhered to for a loudspeaker diaphragm. Two examples involving a controlled breakup are shown in Figs. 14-28 and 14-29. The whizzer cone in Fig. 14-28 is intended to radiate high frequencies as the larger cone decouples, a concept of getting better high frequency by adding mass. The Biflex principle, as popularized by Altec in the 1950s, is shown in Fig. 14-29.[15] The inner cone is compliantly attached at A to the large outer cone in hopes of decoupling the outer cone at high frequencies. Damping dope is applied to the coupling connection in an attempt to smooth the decoupling transition frequency response. Neither are very popular today, and it is generally accepted today that these are not good approaches to pure sound.

Recently, a veritable cornucopia[16] of new materials have been successfully introduced into new cone low-frequency and medium-frequency loudspeakers.[17] A variety of plastics have been used, the most popular being polypropylene and bextrene. The KEF Company (U.K.) introduced an aluminum-skinned foamcore sandwich cone, which as a composite has a very high stiffness-to-weight ratio.[18–20] Mitsubishi Electric (Japan) introduced a studio monitor, which used cone woofers elegantly fabricated from a honeycomb-core, carbon-fiber skin composite, claimed (rightfully so) to have extremely high stiffness-to-weight ratio.

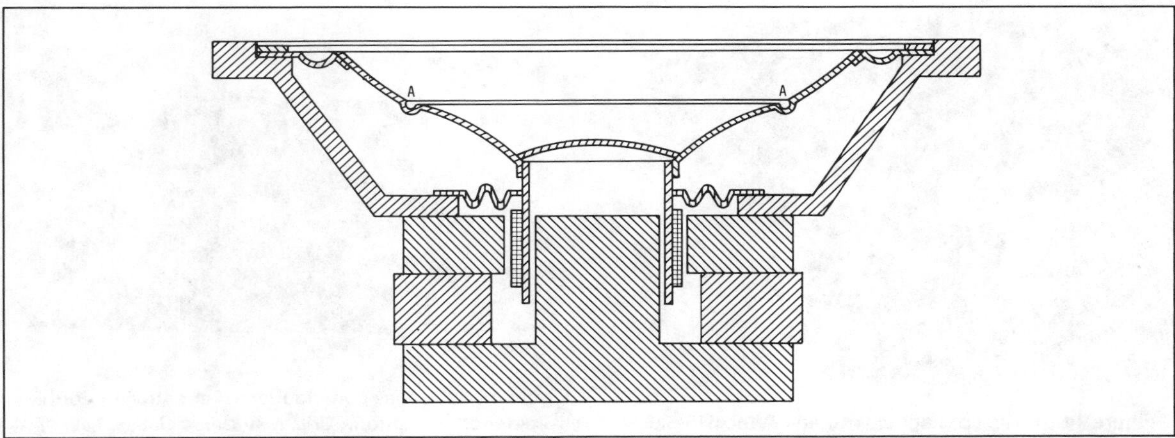

Figure 14-29 Loudspeaker illustrating decoupling center cone. *(From US Patent 4, 146, 756)*

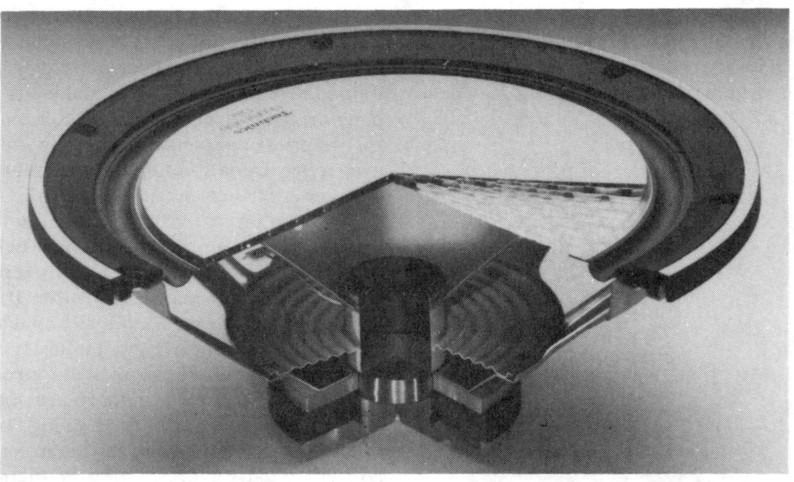

Figure 14-30 Cutaway view of flat-plate honeycomb disk Matsushita woofer (Technics SB-X700 system). Note "drive cone" connecting coil former to nodal portion of disk. *(Courtesy Panasonic International Corp.)*

One of the more exciting advances in low-frequency and general diaphragm design to date has been made by Sony[21] and Matsushita (Japan), which developed a series of flat-plate direct radiators. The diaphragm (Fig. 14-30) is made from aluminum honeycomb and is driven at selected modal points to avoid major breakup nodes. Celestion, KEF, and ESS have also used flat-plate passive radiator diaphragms in several systems.

In an alnico loudspeaker, such as the Altec model 515 (Fig. 14-31) the magnet is directly under the pole piece (as opposed to being between the top and back plates), and the outside diameter of the magnet structure is a cast iron return from the bottom of the magnet to the top plate. The structure is easy to make very attractive via painting and plating, the plated top plate being visible on the 515 as a lighter-colored ring between the return and basket or frame, which is painted cast aluminum. Venting here is accomplished via a hole covered with open wire mesh in the center dome, clearly visible. Other methods use a uniformly porous dome with no magnet vent.

Still another method of venting is shown in Fig. 14-32, this being a Gauss design using vent holes in the former itself, a very common practice. The suspension of the loudspeaker (the guidance system of the cone and voice coil) is the combination of the surround, connecting the cone or diaphragm to the frame at its outside diameter, and the spider, which usually connects the cone to the frame at the voice coil former-to-cone joint. The spider is the main centering member, and the surround assures straight-line motion. Gap clearances are as small as 0.007 in. up to 0.015 in. or greater (radial clearance) so assembly is critical.

Most woofers are made by pre-assembling the cone, surround, leads, voice coil, former, and spider in an accu-

Figure 14-31 Alnico magnet woofer—Altec 515-8LF. *(Courtesy Altec Lansing Corp.)*

Figure 14-32 Gauss cone loudspeaker showing double-spider construction. *(Courtesy Cetec Gauss, Div. of Cetec Corp.)*

rate assembly fixture; this is also what a recone kit consists of. This assembly is dropped into place with adhesives applied to the frame at the surround and spider seating surfaces. Fiberboard shims ½-in. wide or so, several inches long, and slightly thinner than the gap clearances between the pole and voice coil former outside diameter, are then inserted between the pole and voice coil, and the surround and spider are allowed to bond as the adhesive sets up. This is usually an air-dry process. Once the assembly is sufficiently bonded, the shims are withdrawn, and the center cap and gasket are bonded on to complete the assembly. On some loudspeakers, a *viscoelastic* (never-drying) dope is applied to the surround (sometimes even to parts of the cone) for breakup control. The magnet is then charged to complete the assembly. Spiders are usually made of a heat-formed open-weave, resin-impregnated cloth formed into convolutions. The open material is another form of venting, since the air beneath the spiders can be trapped causing operational problems. This also tends to dampen the spider, reducing frequency-variant vibrational energy, which is directly transmitted to the drive point of the cone by this member. An early method of making porous spiders was to die-cut them from solid phenolic-impregnated linen sheet stock.

14.4.2.2 Suspension Methods

Surrounds are made to be nonresonant, although they are also made to be nonporous for obvious reasons. Some surrounds are made of foam in a half-roll. This method is not very popular due to age and environmental cracking of most foams suitable for surrounds. The most popular and successful surround construction is heat-formed open-weave resin-impregnated linen formed into convolutions and sealed with damping dope. This seems to be the best method for reduction of rim resonances common to undamped convoluted surrounds. Ancient speakers with surrounds made this way are still operating successfully today.

Loudspeaker leads are usually a woven cotton-and-ribbon conductor tinsel or just loosely woven multistrand wire, which is soldered to coil leads and glued to the cone as a method of mechanical termination. The leads are a common failure point at high power, and great attention to this is sometimes necessary for a successful product. Also, their own resonances can adversely affect the response, and damping dope is sometimes used to control this. The leads normally hang loosely in an arc so that at full diaphragm excursion, they do not stretch taut and rip out of the terminals or the cone.

The Gauss 15-in. woofer shown in Fig. 14-32 is additionally noteworthy. Two features are unique. First and most obvious is the patented double-spider suspension configuration, which provides a very stable, linear motion of the cone assembly. This design allows very long low-frequency excursions and thus the very high power ratings the Gauss drivers are famous for. The other feature, which is used in many high-powered designs, is the magnet-mounted aluminum heat sink. This heat sink aids natural convention heat transfer from the magnet structure, which is where most of the voice coil heating is sinked via the air gap.

Another unique suspension method, intended for high excursions, is the Cerwin-Vega stroker.[22] Fig. 14-33 shows the patent drawings for this loudspeaker. The central spider acts as a tandem suspension in concert with the lower normal spider and guides the cone with the same effectiveness that the Gauss double spider does. One difference is that on the Cerwin-Vega design, the mechanical connection to the cone will definitely *change* the vibra-

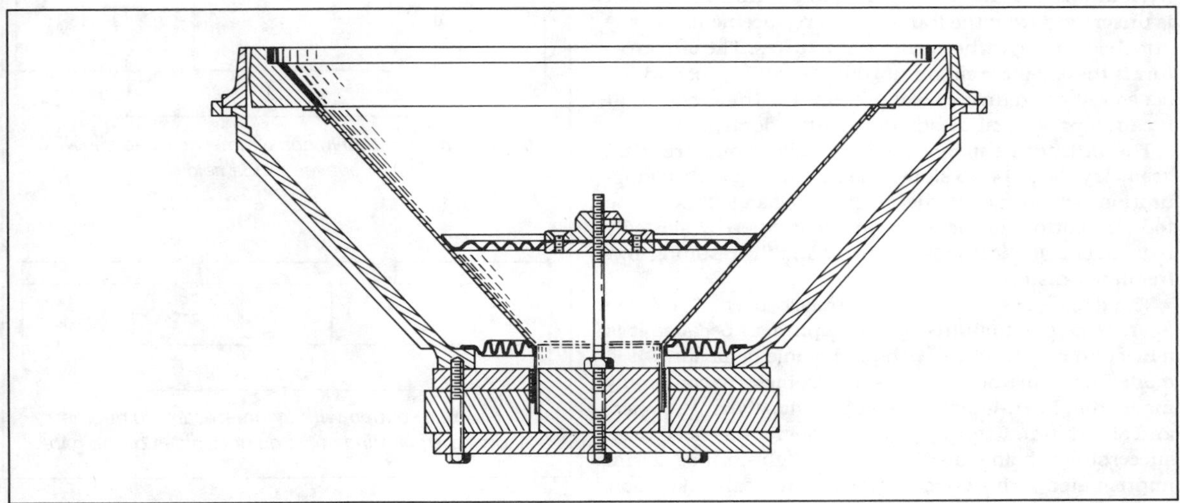

Figure 14-33 Stroker cross section. *(Courtesy Cerwin Vega, Inc.)*

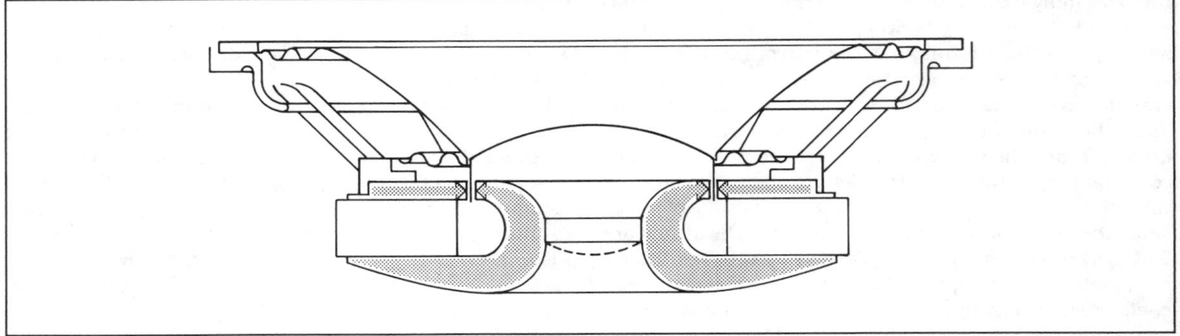

Figure 14-34 Peavey focused-field geometry magnet structure with one-piece backplate/pole piece forging. *(Courtesy Peavey Electronic Corp.)*

tional behavior (breakup) of the loudspeaker cone at high frequencies, whereas the Gauss design will transmit its vibrational energy to the voice-coil former. (Note the word "change." Breakup in paper cones is usually a matter of change, not better or worst. It's more like "choose your poison.")

14.4.2.3 Mechanical Construction

The Peavey Black Widow bass drivers are unique for several reasons. First, they have a very streamlined magnet structure, which they call "focused-field geometry" (Fig. 14-34). It is a very attractive and sensible-appearing magnetic circuit that has flowing lines, as you would expect would make water flow better if it were a fluid flow channel. This is actually a sensible approach, since laminar flow and magnetic field equations are identical. The other feature of the Peavy driver is its unique field replaceability, a unique feature for a low-frequency unit. The basket is unscrewed from the frame, and a replacement is easily attached on site without shims or fixtures. The other feature is the one-piece aluminum dust cap and former, which act as a shorted turn in real use, but the trade-off is that it can improve heat dissipation via the dome.

The JBL ferrite-magnet drivers have symmetric field geometry.[7] Fig. 14-35 shows the unique top plate configuration, which makes the magnetic leakage flux at the top and bottom of the gap symmetric, thereby allegedly reducing magnetic drive asymmetry and the resulting low-frequency distortion.

The dome direct radiator is popularly used. The dome is an attractive high-frequency diaphragm because it is a mechanical structure with predictable behavior if it is made from a predictable material. Domes are commonly made from linen-impregnated phenolic, Mylar™, paper, and aluminum. Recently, the "soft dome" has been used successfully, being made out of a light-formed scrim impregnated with a viscoelastic filler. You can poke a soft dome tweeter with your finger, and it will literally bounce back into shape without damage. It is believed that at high frequencies, the very lossy dome decouples mechanically, leaving high frequencies to be radiated by the mechanical structure adjacent to the voice coil and by the voice coil itself. In 1980, JBL introduced a hi-fi dome tweeter made from phenolic with aluminum-deposited skins. This construction is claimed to raise the stiffness-to-weight ratio of the base material. The highest stiffness-to-weight-ratio domes used today are made of beryllium by such companies as Yamaha and Pioneer.

Several flexible diaphragms have been used on magnetic drivers, all sharing the same basic construction, etched aluminum conductors on Mylar™ film. These are operated in various magnetic field configurations to pro-

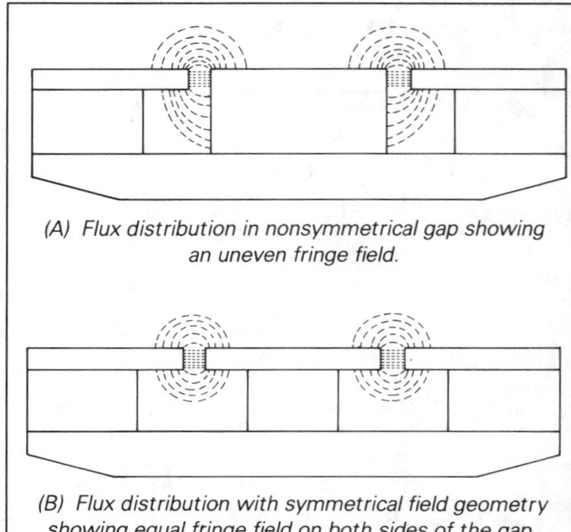

(A) Flux distribution in nonsymmetrical gap showing an uneven fringe field.

(B) Flux distribution with symmetrical field geometry showing equal fringe field on both sides of the gap.

Figure 14-35 JBL symmetric field geometry versus asymmetric design. *(Courtesy JBL Inc./UREI).*

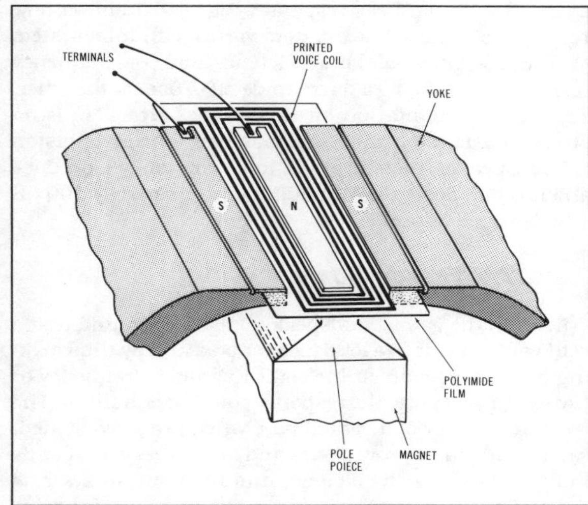

Figure 14-36 Technics Leaf Tweeter diaphragm detail. *(Courtesy Panasonic Industrial Corp.)*

duce sound. One of the earliest of these is the Magneplanar® loudspeaker, which consisted of an entire field of magnets over which the diaphragm-conductor was mounted. The Magneplanars are available as large sound panels, which are erected as one would erect room dividers. The Heil high-frequency driver, used exclusively in systems manufactured by ESS, used direct radiators similar to Magneplanar® in that the voice coil was printed on Mylar™. The ESS-Heil unit, however, was corrugated, and the sound was produced by these vertical pleats moving open and closed, thereby squeezing air into radiated sound.[23] A remarkable extension of this was used also by ESS in the "Transar" system, which used hollow spheres modulated by electromagnetically driven rods. Mitsubishi Electric (Japan) developed a printed-conductor high-frequency device called the leaf tweeter, as shown in Fig. 14-36. Last, the ribbon loudspeaker is the simplest and has excellent potential for good high-frequency response due to the fact that the diaphragm is the conductor. No extra diaphragm structure is used on the ribbon.

There are certainly other variations on these themes, but this discussion should be a reasonable indication of what is possible and what has been done successfully.

14.4.2.4 Low-Frequency Performance of Magnetic Drivers[24–26]

A piston vibrating in space (in air) will begin to produce usable sound as its circumference becomes larger than the wavelength of sound being produced. At lower frequencies, front and back air in motion will merely pump back and forth around the cone and cancel each other. The diaphragm could be mounted in a large wall, as an attempt to separate the front and back air motion. This is affectionately known as the baffle. For proper baffling to, say, 40 Hz, the wall would have to be greater than 7 ft or so on a side to prevent front and back radiation from the diaphragm from exchanging or canceling. This isn't a great solution, due to size. So in our typical search for solutions, we have invented the enclosure or the box.

14.4.2.5 Enclosures

The closed box, or infinite baffle, does what a finite wall does, only smaller—it's something for nothing, almost. If the box is small enough, it will produce two results that the giant wall won't. First, its frontal area is lower than that of the giant wall so it will go from half-space to full-space at a higher frequency, usually in the middle of the bass region (80 to 150 Hz). (See Fig. 14-23.) The second effect is that the enclosed air acts as a spring on the diaphragm, making the resonance frequency of the loudspeaker increase. This may or may not be desirable, but it's at least a calculatable effect.

14.4.2.6 Closed-Box Systems[27–29]

The frequency response of a loudspeaker in a closed box is a simple matter. The response will be flat to near its resonance frequency (in-box) if the Q is 0.7 or so. If the Q is higher, it will bump and tend to ring at resonance, and if it is lower, the response will sag. For a simple second-order [resistance-inductance-capacitance (RLC) or mass-spring-dashpot] system, Q is the ratio of reactive energy to resistive (damping) energy and is calculated by the following equation:

$$Q = 2\pi f_0 M_T / R_T \qquad (14\text{-}20)$$

where,

f_0 is the system resonance frequency $[(1/2\pi)\sqrt{K_T/M_T}$ in hertz,
M_T is the total system mass in kilograms,
R_T is the total system damping resistance in newton seconds per meter.

The effect of the air volume on the diaphragm can be found by the following:

$$K_A = P_o c^2 S_D{}^2 / V_B \qquad (14\text{-}21)$$

where,

K_A is the air spring constant in newtons per meter,
$P_o c^2$ is 1.4×10^5 mks,
S_D is the diaphragm area in square meters,
V_B is the box volume in cubed meters.

Since the loudspeaker suspension acts in conjunction with the air spring, the spring constants are merely additive, this is,

$$K_T = K_A + K_s \qquad (14\text{-}22)$$

where,

K_T is the total system spring rate in newtons per meter,

K_s is the loudspeaker suspension spring constant in newtons per meter.

Total system damping is the result of mechanical losses and *electrodynamic drag*, which is the major damping mechanism on most loudspeakers. This is found as follows:

$$R_T = R_m + R_{em} \quad (14\text{-}23)$$

where,

R_m is the total mechanical drag (force/velocity) in newton seconds per meter,

R_{em} is the electrodynamic drag, so that

$$R_{em} = (BL)^2/Re$$

where,

BL is the product of flux density and length L (meters) of conductor in field B (tesla). This is also the amount of force available (newtons) per input ampere.

There are two extremes of closed-box systems. One is where the free-air Q is 0.7, and the box is large enough so the in-box resonance and final Q is essentially the same as in free air. This is the true infinite baffle. The other extreme is where the loudspeaker suspension stiffness is negligible, in effect, to the in-box air stiffness. It produces a very low-Q woofer with an extremely loose, floppy suspension when mounted in the proper box. This is called an *acoustic suspension design*, and final system Q is, again, 0.7 for flat bass response. Fig. 14-37 shows how response of a closed-box system varies with total system Q. The designer balances efficiency and low-frequency response, there being a direct trade-off of one for the other. The ultimate limitation on closed-box output is piston size and excursion. A 10-in. diameter (effective) piston (12-in. speaker) moving at 0.1-in. excursion will produce about 0.045 acoustic W at 50 Hz (approximately 100 dB at 4 ft in half-space).

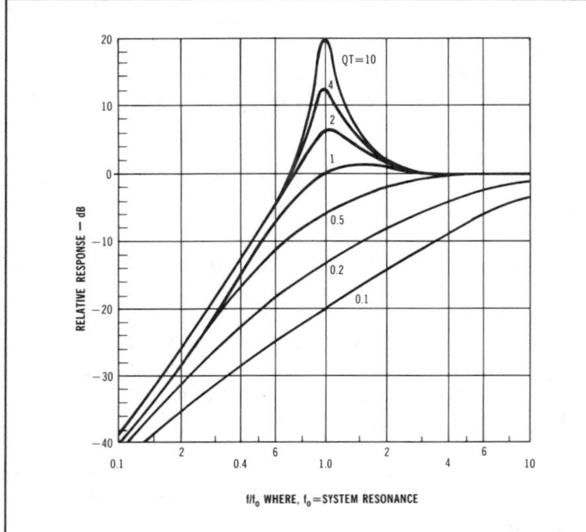

Figure 14-37 Response of closed-box system versus Q and normalized frequency relative to system resonance.

14.4.2.7 Vented Boxes[30]

Early in the game, loudspeaker engineers found that a vent could be put in a loudspeaker box, and by thus making the box resonate at the right Helmholtz frequency or tuned musical note, the response could be enhanced. The resonant energy of a vented box, when properly aligned, can give much improved bass and is used very frequently in many larger high-efficiency and high-output systems today. The box resonance is usually responsible for delivering the lower octave or so of performance in a typical vented system. Because of this, diaphragm motion in this region is greatly reduced over a closed-box design due to the box pumping air (not the loudspeaker), and higher outputs are possible than with an equivalent closed-box system.

There are two drawbacks for vented-box designs. First of all, a closed box rolls off a 12 dB/octave; a vented box rolls off at 24 dB/octave. Second, due to the resonance of the box, the lower octave of sound (or whatever is contributed by the resonating box) is as much as 180° out of phase at resonance. The drawback here is sound purity with respect to phase and transient response. A closed-box system is inherently "purer"; however, many more vented boxes are used, especially in professional applications, than closed boxes. The illusion of "pure" bass given by the vented box is apparently pretty convincing as evidenced by its popularity.

Early work by Olson, Beranek, Novak, and others led to the work of Benson and later, Thiele and Small, two engineering types in Australia (Thiele a broadcast engineer, Small an electrical engineering professor) who published a large volume of work in the *Journal of the Audio Engineering Society* on vented boxes. Thiele and Small were able to "crank through the math" and organize driver, box, and system parameters so that a systematic, unified approach to vented boxes could be made. They coined the word "alignment" for categorizing various types of ventings, based on Q and modern filter theory.

14.4.2.8 Design of Vented Boxes Using Thiele-Small Parameters[31–35]

A vented box (without a loudspeaker installed) is a second-order acoustic filter and behaves identically to boost sections of many popular graphic and parametric equalizers. If we somehow introduce acoustic power into the box, we will get a peak in output from the vent at the box resonance frequency, henceforth known as f_B.

If the box is heavily damped (which can be accomplished by lots of fiberglass stuffing, a resistive cloth stretched over the vent, and so on), the box as a filter will be low Q and deliver a relatively low level but wideband peak in output, centered at f_B. If the box has very little damping of its resonance, it will be high Q and deliver a relatively high level but narrow-band peak in output, centered at f_B. Thus, it will tend to be peaky and to ring at f_B after the input signal is removed.

Q is the ratio of reactive energy to resistive or damping energy. As a reference, any second-order system such as a damped vented box or a resistance-inductance-capacitance equalizer filter with a Q of 0.707 will be critically damped and have good transient response. Higher Q systems tend to ring and be boomy and low-Q systems will be well damped and sound tight. Like filters and boxes, loudspeaker Q will tell how well damped the free-air resonance (f_S) of the cone and suspension is. When a loudspeaker is placed in a vented box, it will damp the resonant air in the box, via its diaphragm, according to the area of the diaphragm and strength of its motor. Generally, high-frequency loudspeakers will provide the highest (low-Q) damping of a box.

A vented box can enhance the response of a loudspeaker by acting as a low-frequency equalizer. However, an active equalizer is completely isolated from the loudspeaker, whereas the box is directly connected to the loudspeaker. It probably seems easier to connect up an equalizer than to build a box, until you consider this: when the box is working at or near its resonant frequency, the box is doing all the work. This means that the loudspeaker is barely moving. To boost the low end of a closed-box system by 6 dB with an active equalizer requires a doubling of cone displacement.

Because of the direct connection of the loudspeaker to the box, we have to consider the relative physical and electrical parameters of the box and the loudspeaker to be able to design the box. The now famous work of Thiele and Small makes this a much simplified task. An electrical mobility circuit analysis of a loudspeaker in a vented box shows that the (second-order) vented box and the (second-order) loudspeaker could be combined and modeled as a fourth-order high-pass filter. When they applied modern filter theory to this electrical model, they were able to simplify and organize the box and loudspeaker parameters into easy-to-use dimensionless parameters, which will be discussed. They were also able to characterize the shape of the responses from high-Q (Chebychev) responses, with ripple or bumps near the low end, to maximally flat response (Butterworth) to more gradual rolloff, lower Q responses (QB_3 or quasi-third-order Butterworth) shown in Fig. 14-38. This new system for loudspeaker and box design allows the designer to optimally tailor a box to a loudspeaker in a variety of alignments of box tuning and box sizes relative to the loudspeaker parameters.

Loudspeakers are partially characterized by their total

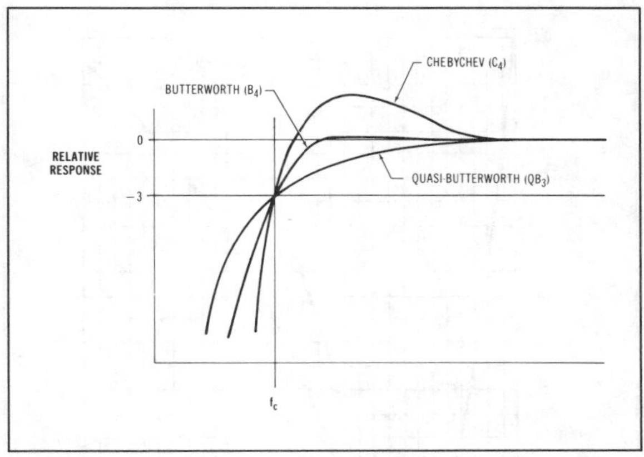

Figure 14-38 Comparison of three response shapes, all having the same cutoff frequency, f3.

Q or relative damping. High-Q loudspeakers have relatively large amounts of reactive energy and need relatively large boxes (which have large amounts of reactive energy) to effect or enhance (or make proper) their response, the reverse being true for low-Q loudspeakers. High-Q loudspeakers tend to have heavy moving mass and stiff suspensions and/or relatively small (magnet-and-voice coil) motors. Low-Q loudspeakers have light cones, soft suspensions, and magnetically strong motors.

To design a proper box, we need to know the following loudspeaker parameters:

Q_T—total loudspeaker Q,

F_S—free-air cone resonance of the loudspeaker,

V_{AS}—equivalent volume compliance of the suspension of the loudspeaker.

With the alignment chart (Fig. 14-39) and the previously mentioned loudspeaker parameters, we simply look up a loudspeaker alignment and write it down. Basically, that is all there is to it.

Most manufacturers will give you f_S, Q, and V_{AS} per the new Audio Engineering Society (AES) draft recommended practice on loudspeaker specifications.

V_{AS} is the box volume that produces the same stiffness on the loudspeaker cone as the suspension of the loudspeaker. With this information, go to the alignment chart and select the alignment parameters—S, f_B/f_S, and f_c/f_S.

S, or the compliance ratio, is the ratio of the optimum box volume (V_B) to the equivalent volume compliance, (V_{AS}) of the loudspeaker.

Multiply S by V_{AS} to find the box size required. Multiply f_B/f_S by f_S to find the box resonance frequency needed; use Fig. 14-40 to find the proper vent to tune the box to the right f_c. Multiply f_c/f_S by f_S to find what the f_c (−3 dB or cutoff) frequency is for the design.

The previous design exercise is for a flat response. You may want a bump in the response before the low-frequency

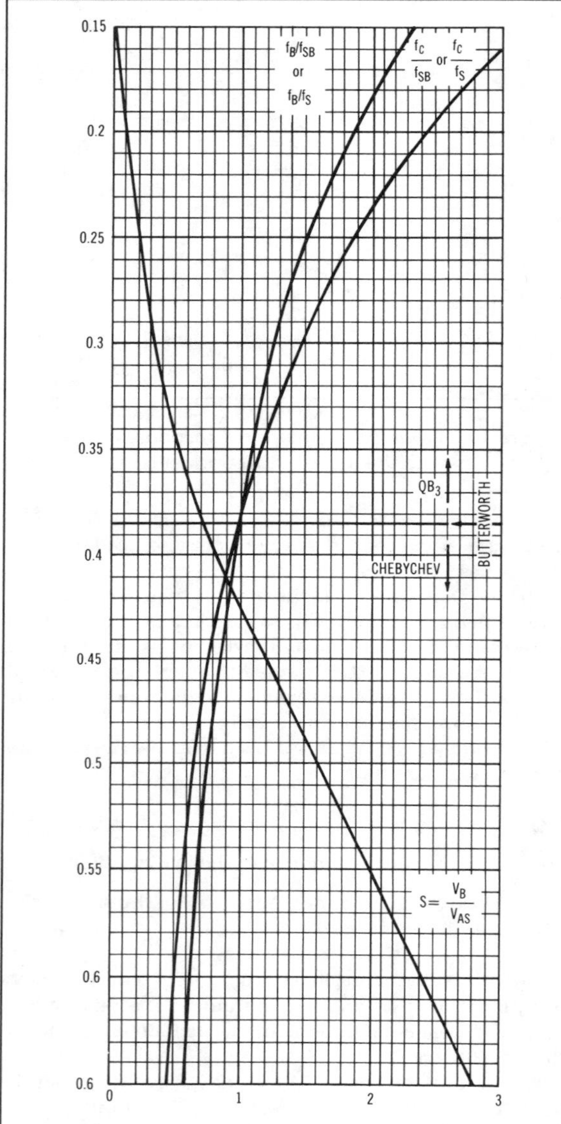

Figure 14-39 Thiele-Small alignment chart.

rolloff begins. Fig. 14-41 is a flowchart and computation method for general box design developed by Don Keele, which allows you to compute the bump. It also includes a design chart for sixth-order actively augmented low-frequency design.

When attempting to deliver very high low-frequency power, there might not be enough air in the vent; therefore, the solution might be the ducted port. If we make the port longer and larger in area, we can produce the same f_B, only with increased air volume capability. When the hole-in-baffle vents are less than 15 in.^{2}, we might consider a ducted port. This will also reduce the possibility of turbulent whistling (thus distortion) of the vent and a restrictive effect, which can produce unwanted box damping and consequently lowering of the system Q.

14.4.2.9 Duct Design

Although ducts are a bit harder to fabricate than vents, their design is relatively simple. Once we know the vent area (S_V), that we need for our alignment and its length (usually the baffle thickness l_V), we can choose the duct area (S_D) needed. As a rule of thumb, the duct should contain enough air volume to accommodate the total (peak-to-peak) volume displacement of the loudspeaker at the power level we want to operate. Then, with Eq. 14-24 solve for duct length. The constant 0.91 was derived from actual measurement of real vents

$$L_D = (S_D/S_V)(l_V + 0.91 \times \sqrt{S_V}) - 0.91\sqrt{SD} \quad (14\text{-}24)$$

The duct can be square, round, or rectangular, just stay away from something that looks too thin. This will add resistance to the box and lower the Q of the box.

Example and discussion—A 9.6-in.^{2} vent in a ¾-in. baffle will tune a 4-ft^3 box to 43 Hz. We would like a 25-in.^{2} duct to do the same. Using Eq. 14-22,

$$L_D = (25/9.6)(0.75 + 0.91\sqrt{9.6}) - 0.91\sqrt{25}$$
$$= 4.75 \text{ in.}$$

Note that the duct volume will be about 119 in.^{3} A 15-in. loudspeaker displacing ±⅜ in. would be displacing around 106 in.^{3}, peak to peak. (This loudspeaker would be rather loud.) Therefore, it's probably a good vent for a high-power 15-in. loudspeaker, certainly more so for a 12-in. one. Note also that the vent will change the 4-ft^3 volume by about 170 in.^{3}, if it is made of ½-in. ply. This changes the volume by about 10% and raises the theoretical tuning by about 4.7%. You might want to make the box a little bigger (or the vent a little smaller in area) to compensate, but the change probably will not be audible.

14.4.2.10 Box Construction and Design

Make the box out of 12-in. thick lead with no leaks. If you must make a box of wood, approximate the lead box by bracing the box sturdily so only the air (and not the box) moves. If the box vibrates "at speed," the wood structure is absorbing power that would otherwise be sound. The same is true of leaks. A leak will act like a (power-robbing) resistor.

Box Bracing

There are many ways to brace boxes; however, the best way (for the stiffest panel) is to place a brace (say 1 × 4

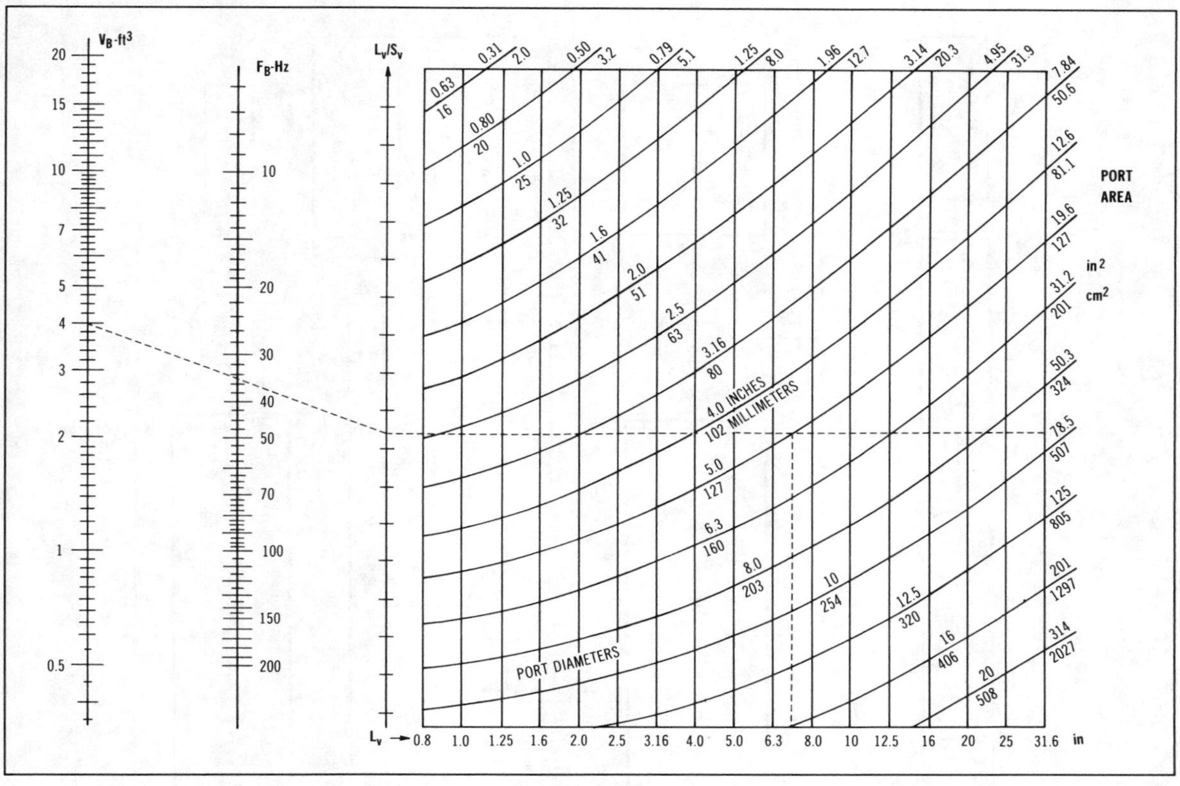

Figure 14-40 Box venting nomograph. *(Courtesy JBL Inc./UREI)*

in.) at the center and across the longest dimension of the panel. (Note: Not on a diagonal.)

Box Modes

Loudspeaker boxes (and rooms) will develop internal vibrational modes due to their size. These air resonances are set up because the parallel walls of the box are hard surfaces and start at the first half-wavelength. These frequencies (f_b) are found as follows:

$$f_b = 6725/X \tag{14-25}$$

where,

f_b is in hertz,
X is the box internal dimension in inches.

For example, the first modes of internal air resonance of a box measuring 32 × 24 × 18 in. inside are 210, 280, and 374 Hz, respectively. Above these frequencies, cross-coupled modes take place as do higher order cross modes. The general equation for the modes (f_n) in a box is as follows:

$$f_n = 6725\sqrt{(n_x/l_x)^2 + (n_y/l_y)^2 + (n_z/l_z)^2} \tag{14-26}$$

where,

x y and z are the three box dimensions in inches,
l is the specific cross dimension of the box in inches,
n is the order of resonance (n = 1, 2, 3, . . .).

Cross-coupled modes are not common (N_x, N_y, and $N_z > 0$), and the simple cross-modes, where two n's are zero, simplify to the previous equation. To reduce box modes, fiberglass padding is often used to line box walls.

Installing fiberglass in an enclosure reduces box modes.[36, 37] If we put too much in, we can actually add air mass to the cone and damp the box resonance, ruining the alignment. Stuff the box with fiberglass, and the resonance of the box will not work at all; it can even reduce efficiency. When building a sub-bass enclosure to cross over at 150 Hz or lower, no fiberglass will be necessary at all. At worst, line one side, the back, and the top or bottom. When it comes down to it, use your ears.

14.4.2.11 Measurement of Thiele-Small Parameters[38–40]

Thiele-Small parameters can be measured if they're not given by the manufacturer.

The most accurate way of determining f_S is by obser-

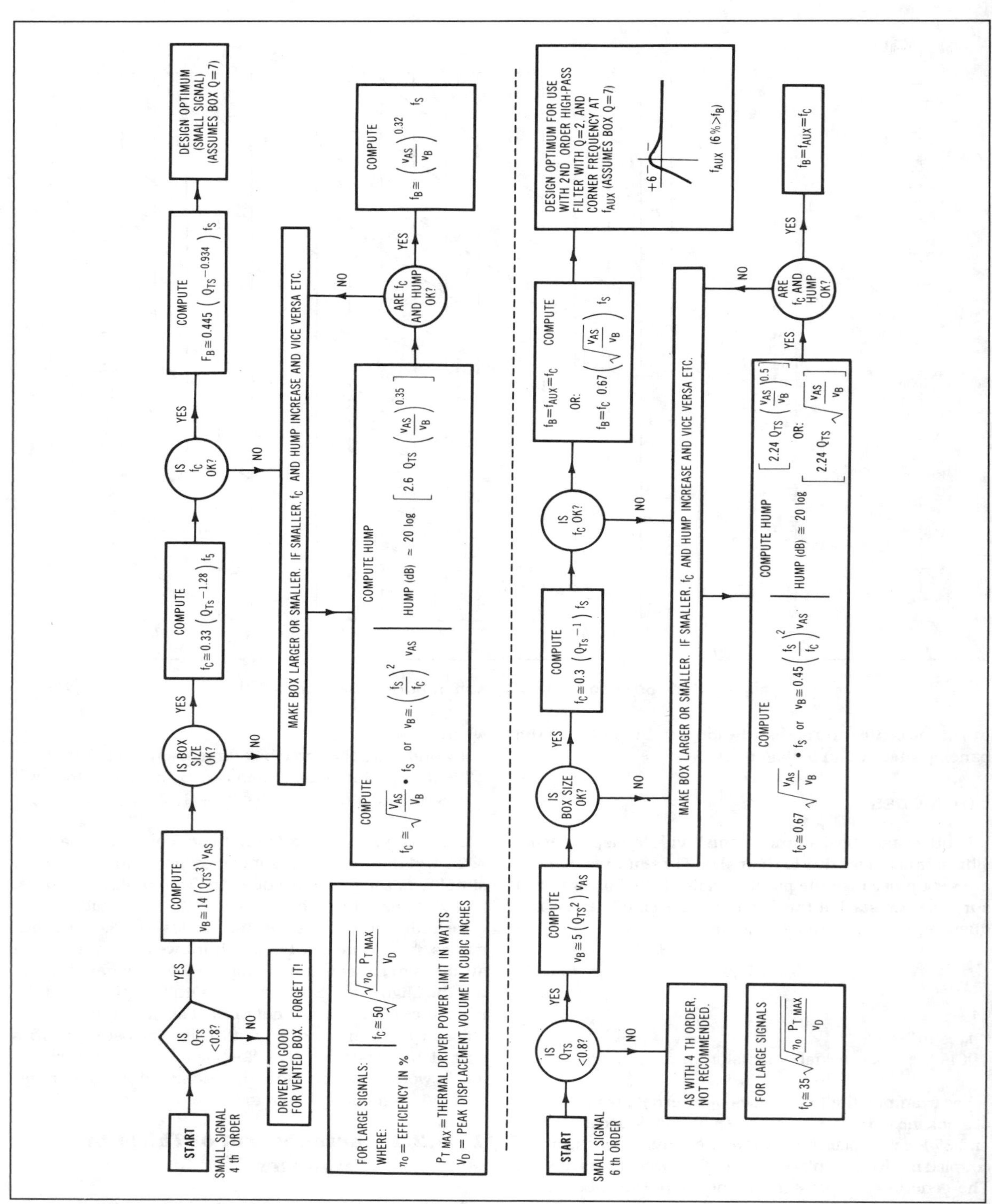

Figure 14-41 Computer program for venting box design. *(Courtesy Don Keele)*

vation of a Lissajous pattern on an oscilloscope of voltage versus current (via a current probe and not a sampling resistor) with the speaker in free air. When the pattern is a diagonal line, zero phase and thus true free-air resonance is attained.

V_{AS} is found in three steps, with the loudspeaker in free air, as follows:

1. Find total moving mass (M_S) by attaching an extra mass (M_X) to the cone (as close to the voice coil as possible) and observing the new resonant frequency, f_{SX}. M_X can be "mortile" putty or some such substance; measure M_X accurately. The total mass can then be found by the equation

$$M_S = M_X/[(f_S/f_{SX})^2 - 1] \quad (14\text{-}27)$$

2. The suspension stiffness (S_1, in mks units) can then be found, knowing the resonance and mass, by the equation

$$S_1 = (2\pi f_S)2M_S \quad (14\text{-}28)$$

where,
M_S is in kilograms,
S_1 is in newtons per meter.

3. Knowing the effective diaphragm area of the loudspeaker, S_D, you can find V_{AS} by the equation

$$V_{AS} = KS_D^2/S_1 \quad (14\text{-}29)$$

where,
K is a constant.

If S_D is in square inches and S_1 is in newtons per meter, V_{AS} can be found in cubic feet if K is 2.09.

Q_T is total Q. This is found in four steps.

1. K_{nq} is the ratio of total Q (Q_T) to electrical Q (Q_e) and is an indication of how much mechanical resistance there is in the suspension. Therefore, if there is no suspension loss, Q_e and Q_T will be equal and K_{nq} will be numerically one. The smaller K_{nq} is, the more suspension loss there is. K_{nq} is found as follows:

$$K_{nq} = 1 - R_e/Z_S \quad (14\text{-}30)$$

where,
R_e is the voice coil resistance in ohms,
Z_S is the free-air impedance of the speaker at f_S in ohms.

2. BL product is the quantity that is a description of the motor strength (how the loudspeaker transforms current to force) of a loudspeaker and is theoretically equal to the product of the flux density and total length of wire in the gap. Realistically, flux fields vary in intensity and things generally change as the voice coil goes in and out of the gap; so if you want a real BL product, you have to go to the source. Fortunately, the same BL product that transforms current to force also transforms velocity to voltage. Therefore, if we know the velocity (by knowing displacement, X, and frequency) of the voice coil in a gap and measure the open circuit voice coil voltage at the loudspeaker terminals (E_O), we can easily find the BL product by the equation.

$$BL = E_O(\text{rms})/2\pi fX(\text{rms}) \quad (14\text{-}31)$$

We can measure BL product as follows: with a driver loudspeaker connected to the test unit via the air in an appropriately sized tube, we supply a signal to the driver, measure the displacement of the test unit with an accurate displacement probe, and measure the open circuit voltage of the test unit. This yields an accurate real-world BL product measured directly and in use.

We can also find BL product, using step 1, by placing a weight (nonmagnetic) on the loudspeaker cone (cone facing upward) and running dc into the coil. If I_m is the dc current needed to return the cone to its rest position before the mass was added, then

$$BL = M_A/I_m \text{ tesla-meters or newtons per ampere} \quad (14\text{-}32)$$

where,
M_A is the added weight in kilograms.

Obviously, an accurate method of determining rest position is needed here. An electrical contact will work well. Also, M_A must be carefully positioned in the cone so as not to permanently deform or damage it.

3. Electrical Q_e is found by

$$Q_e = 2\pi f_S M_S R_e/(BL)^2 \quad (14\text{-}33)$$

4. The total Q_T is found by

$$Q_T = K_{nq} Q_e \quad (14\text{-}34)$$

We know from actual measurement that when taking a loudspeaker from free air and putting it in a box, the air mass attached to the cone changes. In most cases, putting the loudspeaker in a box increases the total mass M_S. From a study of many loudspeakers in boxes, a good model of the loudspeakers in boxes, and a good model of the loudspeaker air loads, we derived the following semiempirical equations for the added mass (M_B) in a box whose depth is L_B, in inches.

For a 15-in. loudspeaker,

$$M_B = 1.52L_B - 15.75\,(\text{grams}) \quad (14\text{-}35)$$

For a 12-in. loudspeaker,

$$M_B = 0.993L_B - 8.3\,(\text{grams}) \quad (14\text{-}36)$$

The change in mass caused by placing a loudspeaker in a box results in a change in free-air resonance and total Q. The total moving mass in a box (M_{SB}) is equal to M_S plus M_B. Our parameter chart will include M_S, and we can find the new parameters as follows:

$$f_{SB} = f_S \sqrt{M_S/(M_S + M_B)} \quad (14\text{-}37)$$

$$Q_{TB} = Q_T(f_S/f_{SB}) \quad (14\text{-}38)$$

Altec recommends use of f_{SB} and Q_{TB} in place of f_S and Q_T for a more accurate alignment, if you know the depth of the box. Note that V_{AS} should not change.

For example, an Altec 414-8C 12-in. woofer has a Q_T of 0.305, a V_{AS} of 14.13 ft^3, and an f_S of 34.23 Hz. If we put it in a box whose depth is 15 to 16 in. the extra mass, by Eq. 14-36, it will be 7.8 g. This makes the total moving mass (36.25 + 7.3) or 43.55 g.

The new free-air resonance or free-box resonance, f_{SB} will be

$$f_{SB} = 34.23\sqrt{36.25/43.55}$$
$$= 31.22\,\text{Hz}$$

The new effective Q_T in the box will be

$$Q_{TB} = 0.305\,(34.23/31.22)$$
$$= 0.334$$

On the alignment chart for $Q_{TB} = 0.334$ we find $f/f_{SB} = 1.14$, $f_c/f_{SB} = 1.27$, and $V_B/V_{AS} = 0.45$. From this we should, for an optimum alignment, put the 414 in a box

$$V_B = 0.45\,(14.13)$$
$$= 6.36\,\text{ft}^3$$

We should expect a low end of

$$f_c = 1.27\,(34.23)$$
$$= 43\,\text{Hz}$$

14.4.2.12 Active Vented Systems

More efficient loudspeakers may be used to produce extended low-frequency response when used with active equalization, typically first- and second-order high pass. The second-order high pass is most attractive for this in that a Chebychev-type filter may be used with a bump hitting the system near box resonance. This has excellent advantages with regard to cone excursion. Fig. 14-42 shows relative cone excursion for various (optimally flat) Butterworth response characteristics. B5 and B6 are the first- and second-order active high-pass systems. Electro-Voice has engineered and marketed their Interface A System since 1973 using this principle.

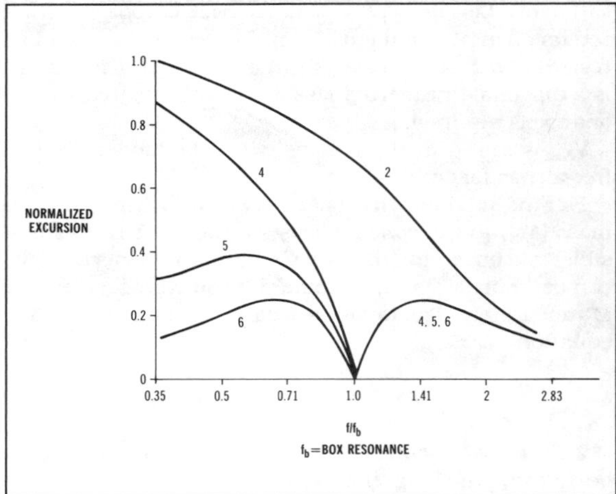

Figure 14-42 Cone excursion for various optimally flat Butterworth response characteristics.

14.4.2.13 High-Frequency Response of Direct Radiators

High-frequency power response of direct-radiator loudspeakers is limited by two mechanisms: mass and inductance, both of which are inherent and unavoidable. Loudspeakers with strong moving structures (diaphragms) and large voice coils can take a lot of mechanical and electrical power. As a result, they also have lots of mass and inductance, giving them relatively low high-frequency cutoffs. Light-diaphragm loudspeakers with light voice coils have better high-frequency response, better sensitivity, and transient behavior (although may be more prone to breakup due to lower diaphragm rigidity). Due to this, they handle less mechanical and electrical power. A comparison of two popular competing 15-in. woofers used in sound-reinforcement shows one to handle 150 W and the other to handle 300 W. However, the former is 3 dB more sensitive and has more relative high end than the latter across its intended frequency range. One sells well because of its sensitivity and "sound," and the other sells well because of its ruggedness even though twice the power is needed for a given sound pressure level. How you get there is a matter of choice. The balance of all these parameters is the crux of the art.

The cutoff frequency in most direct-radiator loudspeakers is primarily determined by the mass of the loudspeaker, the inductance becoming interactive at higher frequencies. This mass break frequency (f_m) is found as follows:

$$f_m = (1/2\pi M_T)[(BL)^2/(R_{vc}) + 2\rho_o cS_D] \quad (14\text{-}39)$$

where,

M_T is the total moving mass in kilograms,

B is the flux density in tesla (gauss/10^4),
L is the voice coil length in gap meters,
R_{vc} is the voice coil resistance in ohms,
$\rho_o c$ equals 407 mks rayls,
S_D is the diaphragm area in square meters.

For instance, a 15-in. woofer has a total mass of 70 g (0.07 kg), a BL product of 16 Tm, a dc resistance of 5.6 Ω, and an effective diaphragm area of 130 in.^{2} (0.084 m^2). Using Eq. 14-39,

$$f_m = [1/(2\pi 0.07)][(16^2/5.6) + (2(407)0.084)]$$
$$= 259\,\text{Hz}$$

This particular loudspeaker is measured on axis, and its response is flat to 1200 Hz. The discrepancy is due to on-axis high-frequency beaming (directivity equalization), as discussed earlier.

14.4.3 Electrostatic Loudspeakers

An *electrostatic loudspeaker* is an acoustic transducer consisting of two pieces of metallic foil separated by a sheet of dielectric. A polarizing voltage is applied to the foils to maintain a steady attraction between them. Audio-frequency voltages are superimposed on the polarizing voltage and may either add to or subtract from the polarizing voltage, thus causing the foils to move in accordance with the waveforms of the applied audio-frequency voltage. The movement of the foil generates sound waves.

It is claimed by the designers of electrostatic loudspeakers that certain basic disadvantages of the cone-type loudspeakers, particularly with respect to the propagation of acoustic energy at the high frequencies, are overcome because cone-type loudspeakers driven by a voice coil attached to the center of the diaphragm fail to act as a piston at the middle and high frequencies. Because of this breakup at the higher frequencies, the voice coil does not control the diaphragm motion, and the result is a lack of correspondence between the electrical input and the acoustic output.

One of the advantages claimed for the electrostatic loudspeaker is that it has a diaphragm that is driven equally at all points of its surface. Breakup is eliminated, and harmonic distortion and phase differences are reduced. Because of the design, the diaphragm can be made essentially massless (or extremely low) compared to the air load on the diaphragm. This permits the loudspeaker to have a good high-frequency and transient response.

As a rule, electrostatic loudspeakers are made to operate as push-pull transducers, because they are essentially linear in operation and free from waveform distortion, producing neither even nor odd harmonics. Electrostatic loudspeakers may be constructed in several different ways. Two of the most important are:

1. Stretching the diaphragm between supports around its periphery and leaving an air gap between the diaphragm and the two electrodes (Fig. 14-43).
2. Using an inert diaphragm that is supported by a large multiplicity of tiny elements disposed across the entire surfaces of the two electrodes. These elements act as spacers to hold the diaphragm in the center between the electrodes (Fig. 14-44).

In this latter type of loudspeaker, the diaphragm is a thin sheet of plastic on which has been deposited a very thin layer of conductive material. It is supported by a

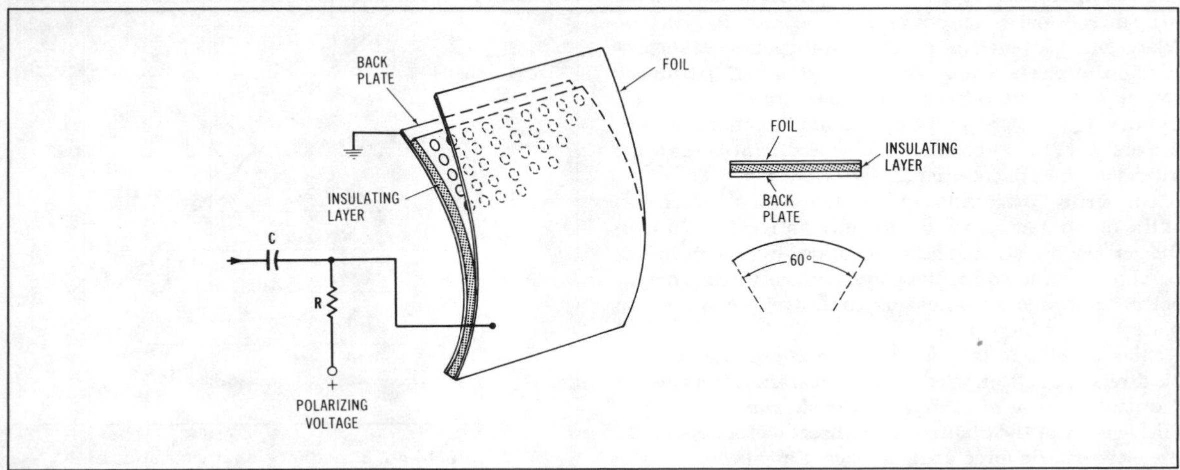

Figure 14-43 Electrostatic- or capacitor-type loudspeaker.

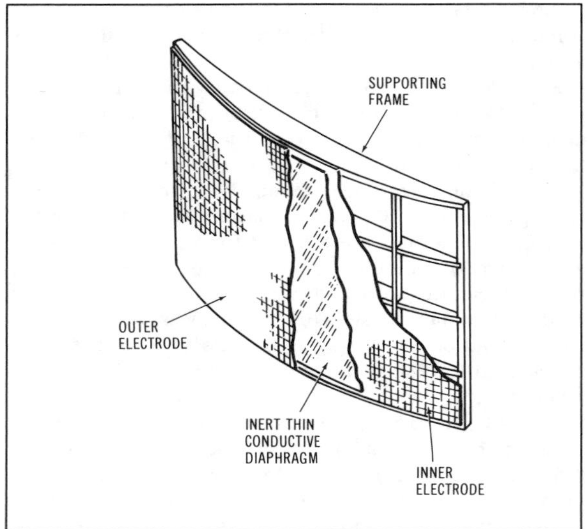

Figure 14-44 Cutaway view showing the internal construction of an electrostatic loudspeaker.

multiplicity of small elastic elements that hold the diaphragm but permit it to follow the audio-signal waveforms. The electrodes on each side of the diaphragm are acoustically transparent to avoid pressure effects from the trapped air as well as to permit the acoustic energy to move away from the diaphragm. This type of construction permits the diaphragm to be made almost any size required. The performance-per-unit area is the same for any area of the diaphragm.

The actual loudspeaker is a plane surface curved in the horizontal plane, a section of a cylinder. A surface that is large with respect to the wavelength becomes increasingly directional as a propagator at the high frequencies. A large surface, such as an electrostatic loudspeaker diaphragm, projects a large portion of this high-frequency energy outward at right angles to the plane of the surface. By curving the plane in the horizontal direction, an even dispersion of high frequencies may be obtained over some intended angle of coverage.

The vertical pattern is equal to the vertical dimension of the diaphragm, since the diaphragm is a flat plane in the vertical direction. Thus, by controlling the radius of curvature in the horizontal plane and the vertical height of the diaphragm, it is possible to control the dispersion pattern over a large area.

Since an electrostatic loudspeaker is designed to couple directly, in effect, with the air resistance, the mass of the diaphragm, as mentioned previously, can be neglected. The velocity of the diaphragm is directly proportional to the electrostatic force applied, except as affected by the stiffness of the diaphragm suspension. Measurements indicate that for a constant voltage applied to the electrodes, the acoustic response is uniform (flat) to well beyond the range of human hearing. A slight rise in the impedance curve is observed around 35 kHz, as shown in Fig. 14-45.

The frequency response at the low-frequency end is limited by the maximum linear amplitude of the diaphragm motion as determined by the spacing and the stiffness of the suspension. The power input to the loudspeaker must be increased to overcome this and to maintain sound pressure at low frequencies with a diaphragm area large enough to move an adequate volume of air for this purpose.

The maximum power output from an electrostatic loudspeaker of a given diaphragm area is determined by the strength of the electrostatic field that can be produced between the diaphragm and the electrodes. Therefore, a dc polarizing voltage is applied to the plates. The electrostatic field is the sum of the field produced by the polarizing voltage and the peak signal voltage superimposed on the polarizing field. Polarizing voltages of 1000 to 2000 V dc are common. A second function of the polarizing voltage is the prevention of frequency doubling. If a polarizing voltage is not employed, when a frequency of, for example, 2000 Hz is applied to the loudspeaker, the results could be a distorted 4000 Hz. If a sine-wave signal is applied to the plates without a polarizing voltage, as the difference of potential increases toward the peak of the sine wave, the movable plate is attracted to the fixed plate. With the decreasing potential on the downward side of the sine wave, the electrostatic force between the plates decreases, the movable plate returns to its original position, and the sine-wave voltage is zero.

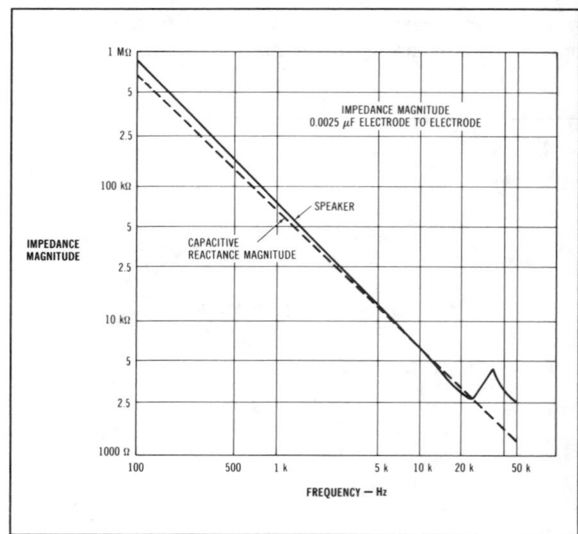

Figure 14-45 Impedance characteristics of an electrostatic loudspeaker. *(Courtesy Pickering and Co., Inc.)*

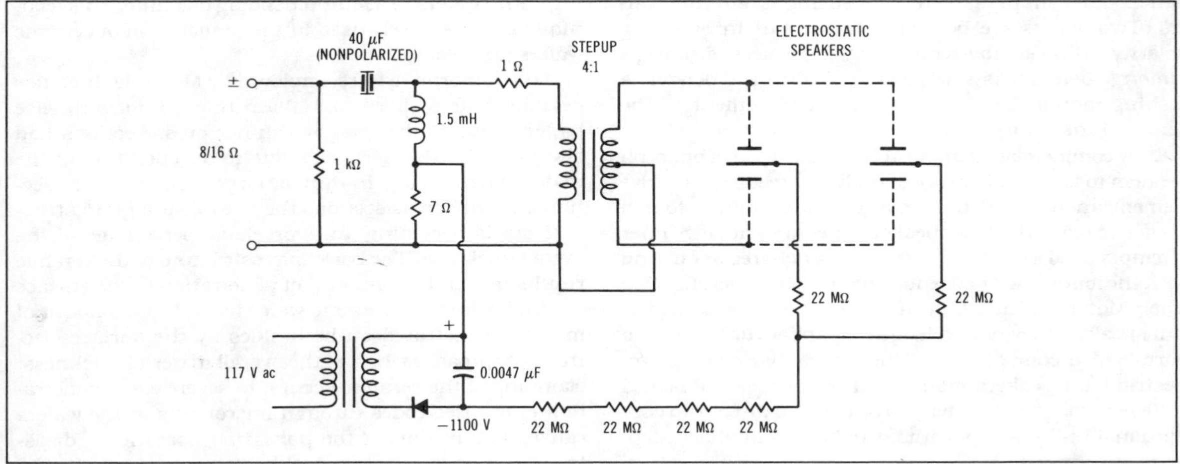

Figure 14-46 Typical coupling circuit and high-voltage power supply for electrostatic loudspeakers.

This motion of the movable plate has produced a single air motion for the positive half of the sine wave.

On the negative half of the cycle, the voltage rises to a peak again and applies a voltage of opposite polarity to the plates. The plates are again attracted to each other. The movable plate goes through the same action and eventually returns to the zero position. Thus, two pulses, both moving in the same direction, have been obtained for a single cycle of the applied sine wave—frequency doubling. With the polarizing voltage applied, a steady electrostatic force is created between the plates, and the movable plate is slightly attracted toward the fixed plate.

Applying a sine wave (plus), the movable plate is attracted to the fixed plate beyond its position fixed by the polarizing voltage. Upon reversal of the sine wave, the electrostatic force between the plates is reduced, and the movable plate returns to its zero position. On the next half of the cycle (negative), the polarizing voltage is reduced because the sine wave is of opposite polarity, and the attracting force is decreased below the polarizing voltage value. Therefore, the plate moves away from the fixed plate, completing the cycle. In this manner, frequency doubling has been eliminated, and the loudspeaker produces a sine wave similar to the conventional piston-type loudspeaker. By connecting the plates for push-pull operation, as shown in Fig. 14-46, the signal is split between the two sides of the loudspeaker, and distortion is further reduced.

An electrostatic loudspeaker is nothing more than a capacitor; the internal-capacitance is in the order of 0.0025 μF from electrode to electrode. Thus, the impedance presented by the loudspeaker to the output of the amplifier falls off at a constant rate of 6 dB/octave as the frequency is increased. This precludes the possibility of maintaining a constant voltage at the loudspeaker input for high volume levels when using a conventional amplifier. If the matching transformer is designed for the most efficient transfer of power at the high frequencies, insufficient signal voltage will be available at the middle frequencies.

14.4.4 Piezoelectric Loudspeakers

Piezoelectricity or pressure electricity was discovered in the 1880s by the Curies and is today a feasible and common motor drive mechanism for loudspeakers. The mechanism is simply that, in a piezoelectric material, a voltage applied to the material will result in mechanical strain or deflection of the material (the reverse is also true, and piezoelectrics can also be used in microphones). This is attractive for direct-drive units such as ultrasonic devices. For loudspeakers, however, some means must be applied to amplify the inherently low excursion mechanically so that a loudspeaker diaphragm may be driven properly.

Probably the largest of any piezo loudspeaker company in the U.S. market is Motorola, Inc., who manufacture the bulk of these kinds of devices, which is largely due to the efforts of John Bost, chief engineer of Motorola's Piezo Ceramics' group. Motorola's piezo drivers are both cone direct-radiator devices and cone compression drivers.

One of the earliest discovered and studied piezoelectric substances is *Rochelle salt*. Although Rochelle salt is still widely used, it suffers from poor mechanical strength, low-temperature breakdown (55°C), and extreme sensitivity to humidity. Barium titanate is the first piezoceramic to be developed. Although it is not as electrically sensitive, it is still widely used, exhibiting many superior characteristics over Rochelle salt. The most widely used piezo material today is lead-zirconate-titanate, developed first in Japan in the 1950s. This material (PZT) is now highly refined and exhibits the best properties of any piezo material for loudspeaker use.

In order to get the required motion out of PZT, the material is formed by baking a ceramic slurry or clay into bars about 1 in. in diameter and slicing it into thin wafers. Two wafers are bonded together but in opposing polarity, with electrodes on their flat surfaces, forming a *bimorph bender.* As voltage is applied to the bender, a dishing motion results in greater displacement at the center of the bender/disk.

Early commercial attempts at the application of bimorph benders to loudspeaker cones involved a rectangular drive element anchored at three corners, allowing the fourth corner to drive the loudspeaker cone fore and aft. Other attempts used a cantilever structure anchored at one end with the loudspeaker cone mounted at the other. In 1965 when Motorola, Inc., first manufactured a piezoelectric loudspeaker, they used a length expander tube driving a horn-loaded cone directly. This device, like most piezoelectric loudspeakers made until that time, still lacked sufficient voltage sensitivity to be coupled directly to conventional hi-fi systems without using an auxiliary step-up transformer.

The development of the circular bimorph using a corrugated centervane represented the next step forward in piezo loudspeaker technology. The action of the two disks working against each other, one expanding while the other contracts, functions as a mechanical transformer, giving impedance reductions of about 20:1. The basic operation is as follows: The driver dishes in and out; it pumps the cone fore and aft or, in the case of the horn, into a compression chamber that is then coupled to the throat of a horn via a slot and flared rib construction. The driver is allowed to hang free in space, working against its own momentum to pump the cone. This is Motorola's "inertial drive" principle.

Further advancements in the state of the piezoelectric art came from Tamura and co-workers in their excellent work on piezoelectric high-polymer films. This concept of a diaphragm possessing piezoelectric properties and thus coupling directly to the air without the use of any separate motor structure represents a substantial advancement toward the ideal acoustic transducer.

The PZT circular bimorph is designed to operate above its fundamental resonance, where the output is mass-controlled. However, its impedance is falling at the same rate (looking like a capacitor) so its response is relatively flat over a high-frequency range. The low-frequency cutoff varies directly with the thickness and inversely with the diameter of the driver. It is apparent then that a lower frequency loudspeaker is going to need a larger, thinner bimorph driver. Today there exist two methods of producing thin PZT wafers. One method, which is used largely in the manufacture of ceramic pickup cartridges, involves processing and firing the ceramic in thin sheets directly. Individual wafers then can be ground out by machining techniques. The problem encountered here is primarily one of holding the thickness tolerances and wafer thinness required of the manufacture of a quality loudspeaker. The second problem is the cost of coring out individual wafers from large sheets. The second process involves casting and firing material in rod form and slicing it into wafers in a multiple slicing machine. This technique is more widely used in the preparation of ceramic wafers and disks.

Many bimorph drivers employed by Motorola, Inc., use ceramic wafers sliced to 140-μm thick. Efforts to slice larger-diameter material or thinner cross sections had always met with poor yields due to degeneration of the material parameters in thin- or large-diameter cross sections. In thin cross sections the 8- to 16-μm grain structure starts becoming an appreciable percentage of the overall thickness. The basic microstructure of the ceramic results in a certain amount of penetration of the surface electrodes into the ceramic wafer itself. If the amount of material penetrated on both sides by the surface electrodes approaches 10% of the overall material thickness, clamping of the ceramic occurs. In severe cases penetration of the electrodes through microfaults in the wafers causes failure during the polarizing operations, disastrously affecting factory yields. Improvements in the processing of the powders prior to and during the firing operation in conjunction with some basic material mix improvements have resulted in yield improvements that have allowed production of larger-diameter, thinner wafers.

Another problem area investigated in the development of the PZT loudspeaker was in the power-handling capability of the driver. The theoretical failure mode of a piezoelectric tweeter is the depoling of the driver through excessive drive level and/or high temperature. The Curie point (depoling temperature) of the PZT used here is above 140°C, and the depoling voltage is 10 V/25-μm thickness, or about 35 V rms for the basic driver. These numbers describe a fairly impressive power-handling capability, but unfortunately one that is reached only in theory. In reality, under continuous high drive levels, the excessive mechanical stress on the surface of the ceramic wafers generates cracks in the microstructure that eventually permeate through the entire wafer. This is especially severe around the area where the solder connections are made to the wafers since this operation tends to prestress the material at this point. The net result is that the 35-V maximum drive level is reduced to being an intermittent specification only, with the continuous drive level recommended at a 15-V maximum up to 20 kHz. For use above that frequency, it has been recommended that the level be reduced further through the addition of a series attenuation resistor so as to safeguard the ceramic element from absorbing excessive high-frequency power. Here again, when using larger, thinner ceramic, these problems are further aggravated, using this ceramic is an area for future development.

Two examples of this relatively restricted area of the loudspeaker art are presented. Probably the most shining success in airborne sound transducers is the Motorola, Inc., KSN 1001A ultrahigh-frequency driver/horn combination. This unit has been used everywhere in all kinds of systems for just about every use. Today it is an industry standard for getting lots of usable upper-octave performance for relatively low cost. Motorola, Inc., recommends using the device across the line without a crossover, due to the inherent self-crossing nature of the device; it "looks" like a capacitor for most of its range. However, better use of the device is with a real crossover network. By restricting the low end of the device, a scratchy sound quality can be avoided and good-sounding results obtained. Fig. 14-47 shows the KSN 1001A, and Fig. 14-48 shows possible crossover circuits for use with this driver. Although Motorola manufactures a wide variety of other piezo-driven loudspeakers, the one illustrated here is certainly the most widely used.

A true optimum use of piezo drive is for underwater use, due to the excellent impedance match of the piezo material to water via a waterproof barrier. Lubell Labs manufactures the underwater or pool loudspeaker shown in Fig. 14-49. Although pool loudspeakers using standard electromagnetic drivers are also available, the piezo is actually more efficient or sensitive due to its mechanical impedance match to water. The loudspeaker is fixed to the side of the pool and merely driven like a normal loudspeaker. Lubell Labs also makes high-power arrays of these and a portable swim coach system with a noise cancelling microphone for underwater communications in various pool athletic events. (Listening to music underwater is a very nice experience.)

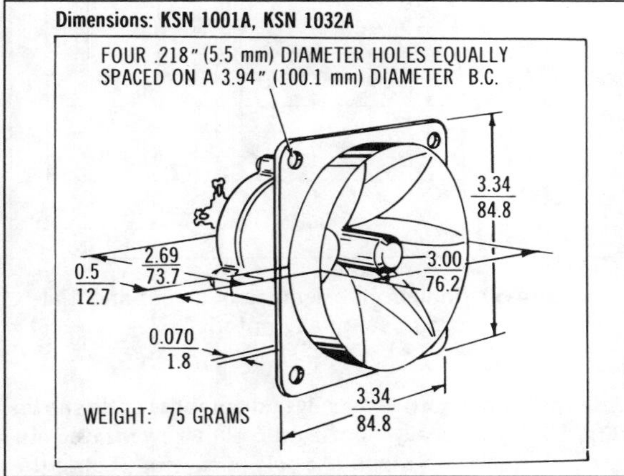

Figure 14-47 Motorola KSN 1001A piezoelectric ultrahigh-frequency driver/horn. *(Courtesy Motorola, Inc.)*

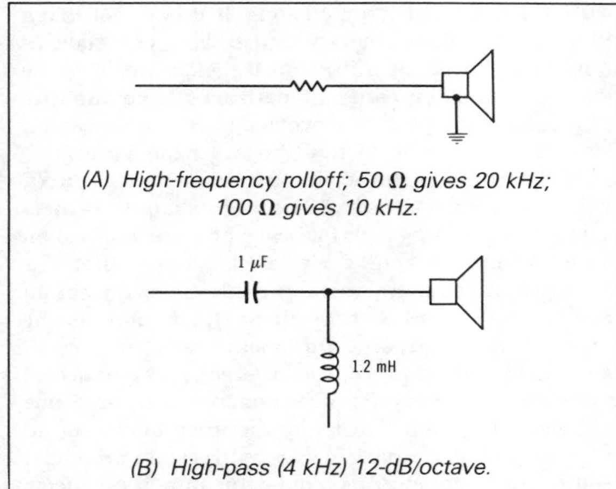

(A) High-frequency rolloff; 50 Ω gives 20 kHz; 100 Ω gives 10 kHz.

(B) High-pass (4 kHz) 12-dB/octave.

Figure 14-48 Crossovers for Motorola piezoelectric ultrahigh-frequency drivers.

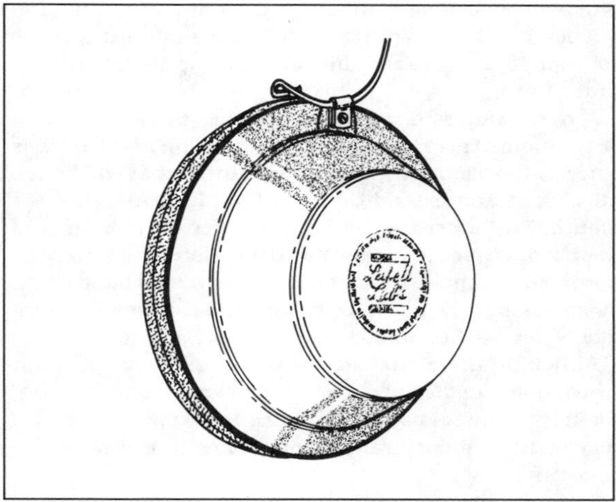

Figure 14-49 Lubell Labs underwater piezoelectric loudspeaker. *(Courtesy Lubell Laboratories, Inc.)*

14.5 INDIRECT SOUND RADIATION—COMPRESSION DRIVERS ON HORNS[36, 41]

14.5.1 Low-Frequency Cutoff

Small, lightweight diaphragms in high-flux density fields will have good high-frequency response; however, their size (i.e., high piston band cutoff frequencies) restricts them from producing very low frequencies, and their inherently small excursion is a severe restriction on development of low-frequency power. For example, a 4-in. diameter aluminum dome in an 18-kG field represents a typical state-of-the-art compression driver diaphragm. It will begin a high-frequency power response rolloff or cutoff in the area of 4 to 5 kHz.

As a direct radiator, this will be somewhat lower, about 3 to 4 kHz. Using Eq. 14-17, we see that the low end of the piston range for this loudspeaker is about 1 kHz. Practically, the limit is about a one-octave bandwidth if the piston were to be used as a direct radiator. The 4-in. piston is relatively large and 2 or 1.75-in. pistons are much more common in the real world, with high-frequency cutoffs in approximately the same range. The solution to this very real dilemma is compression loading into a horn.

A horn couples or connects a small (throat) area to a large (mouth) area. If the rate of expansion of the horn is correct, the acoustic impedance at the throat will be relatively flat and extend down to the piston band of the mouth. The larger the mouth, the lower the frequency of the horn, given the proper flare (therefore, the larger the horn). For example, a 1-in. piston has a piston band cutoff of approximately 4 kHz, but 1-in. throat horns are commonly used to 500 and even 300 Hz.

Although there are still low-frequency power limit restrictions on displacement for a given diaphragm size, the horn allows small diaphragms to be operated over a very wide frequency range, sometimes in excess of five octaves!

The mouth size and flare rate of a horn determines its low-frequency limit, the throat size being a matter of design choice. The most common horn expansion is the exponential, and it is the easiest to deal with mathematically, since a properly designed exponential horn *will* work without a doubt if it is designed properly. The most common method is to design the mouth size using Eq. 14-17 and to design the flare according to Eq. 14-40 as follows:

$$A(x) = A_0 e^{(4\pi f_c X/c)} \qquad (14\text{-}40)$$

where,

$A(x)$ is the area at distance x in square inches,
A_0 is the area at $x = 0$ (throat area),
f_c is the cutoff frequency in hertz,
X is the distance along a streamline or path of the horn in inches,
c is the speed of sound in air in inches per second.

Fig. 14-50 shows radiation resistance versus frequency of an exponential horn. Note that at cutoff frequency f_c, the horn is (theoretically) not working. For instance, a horn loading to 300 Hz would have a mouth area of 0.1 m^2 or 155 $in.^2$ From Fig. 14-50, the flare of the horn should be from approximately 200 Hz if we expect good loading to 300 Hz. The length of the horn is found from Eq. 14-38, which can be rewritten as follows:

$$L = \ln(A_m/A_0)/(4\pi f_c/c) \qquad (14\text{-}41)$$

where,

L is the horn length in inches,
A_m is the mouth area.

Solving for the length of a 300-Hz horn,

$$L = \ln(155/0.785)/(4\pi 200/13{,}450)$$
$$= 28.28$$

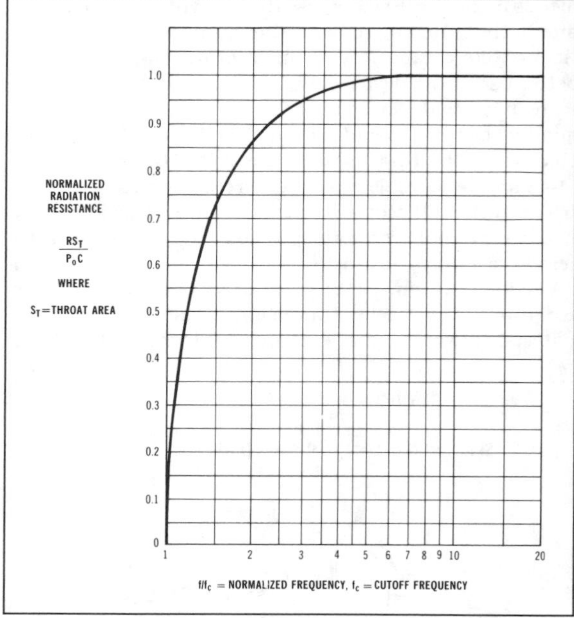

Figure 14-50 Radiation resistance of an exponential horn (ideal or asymptotic).

An exponential horn is usually laid out radially, as shown in Fig. 14-51. Typically a horizontal plan view is layed out first, the intended horizontal angle of coverage being the usual first design choice. Then the height H(x) is plotted versus x by dividing A(x) by the arc length of A(x). Straight horns are harder to design since the actual area of expansion of the sound wave in the horn A(x) has two arc lengths, as shown in Fig. 14-52, and is not just the product of horizontal and vertical dimensions. If this is not taken into account, a faster-than-designed flare, especially at the mouth, will result. Although the sides are flat, the wave expands along constant path length streamlines (quasi-radial). The greatest area of the wave is at the center.

Many acoustic texts say that the larger the mouth (for a given flare) the smoother the impedance near cutoff, per this excerpt from Olson, "The infinite mouth is theorized as the best thing to do for best smoothness of acoustic impedance." Recently, Keele has found that the impedance will actually reach an optimum or minimum passband ripple and then begin to ripple more as the horn is lengthened and the mouth size increased. According to Keele, this is due to low-frequency re-reflected waves back into the mouth due to nonoptimum size. Some horn designers claim that larger-mouthed horns sound better, which is certainly in evidence in certain products. Possibly, the larger mouths reduce the diffraction effects present around smaller-mouthed horns. It is well known that horns all have smoother response when put in flat

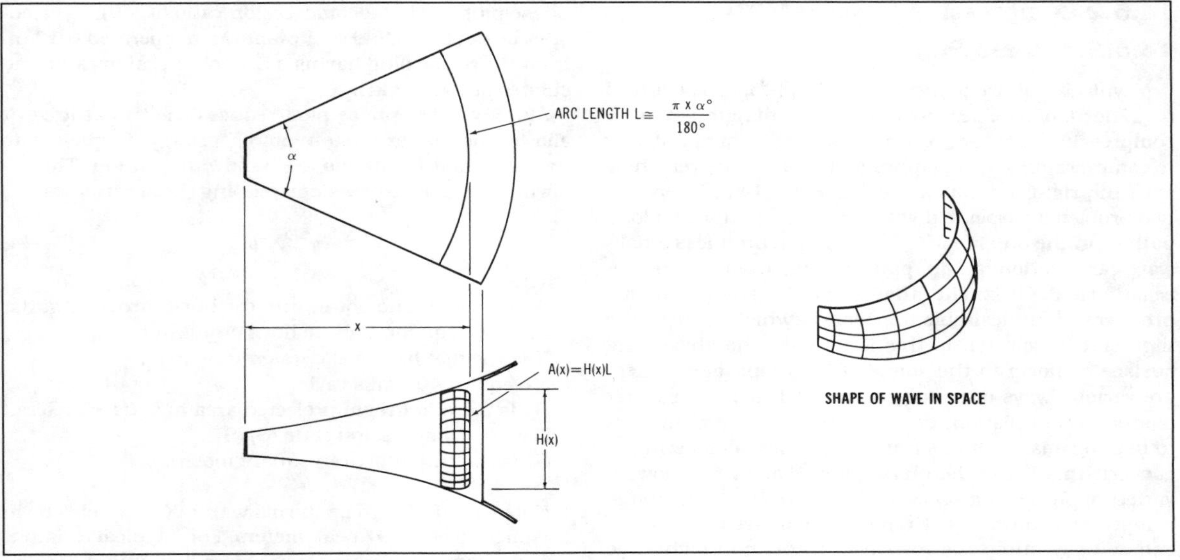

Figure 14-51 Layout of an exponential horn.

baffles larger than the mouth. The stipulation of good sound in horns is a trade-off, which certainly should be made but which rarely is. Hyperbolic horns are also useful, and a complete range of horn types is possible by varying a T parameter. Hyperbolics have a much more abrupt cutoff than exponentials and may be operated, theoretically at least, much closer to their cutoffs than exponentials. A famous hybrid, the Jensen Hypex, uses T = 0.6. Nevertheless, the following is the equation for the general family of hyperbolics:

$$A(x) = A_0[(1 + T/2)e^{(2\pi f_c/c)X} + (1 - T/2)e^{(-2\pi f_c/c)X}]^2 \qquad (14\text{-}42)$$

Note that if T = 0, the expansion becomes

$$A(x) = A_0[\cosh(2\pi f_c X/c)]^2$$

and if T = 1, the expansion becomes pure exponential, the same equation as Eq. 14-40.

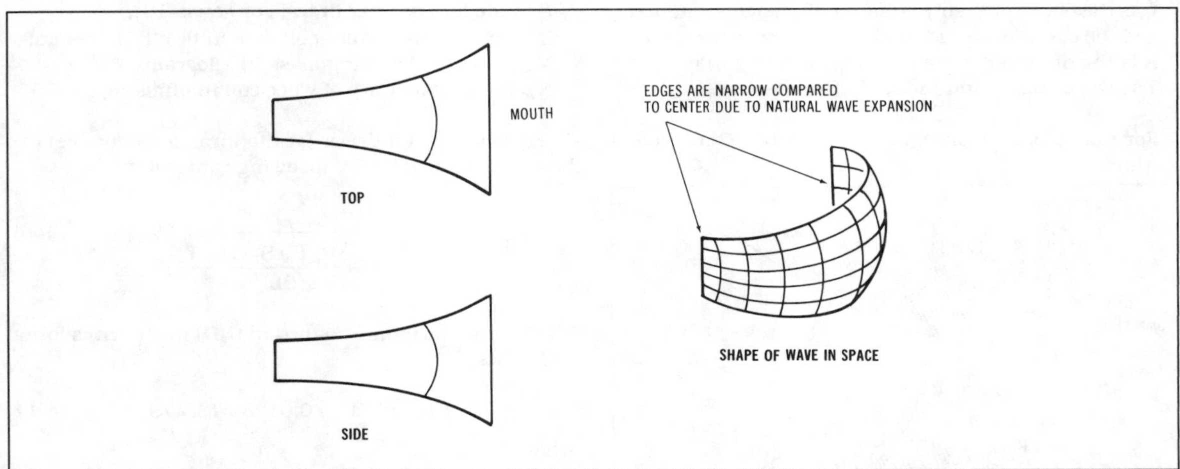

Figure 14-52 Waveform propagation in a straight horn.

14.5.2 Compression Loading[43–47]

14.5.2.1 Phase Plugs

A typical high-frequency driver diaphragm is coupled to a horn of smaller area than the diaphragm by a compression chamber or phase plug. The simplest way to compression load a diaphragm is to place it over a hole with the right area, as shown in Fig. 14-53. There are two problems associated with this. One is that the long path from the outside of the diaphragm produces a half-wave cancellation: a 1-in. path difference will give a cancellation at 6.7 kHz. The other is that the large air volume produces an undesirable impedance, which reduces the high end. A solution to this is to make the phase-plug surface conform to the shape of the diaphragm. There are various ways of making small path lengths so that passband cancellations do not occur, but they all amount to making a large number of air channels all meeting in concert, this being the phase plug. Fig. 14-54 shows a variety of phase plug styles in popular use.[48–52] For large compression ratios (10:1 typical) the quarter-wave path can actually bump the response, a common technique used by designers to extend the response of a driver. Unfortunately, this requires moving the diaphragm close to the phase plug, and it restricts the excursion, thus lowering the low-frequency power capability of the driver. As can be seen, this is the first of many conflicting parameters that have basically boxed modern compression drivers into a typical size and format. Independent of the bumping, the impedance of the air cavity as it relates to the resistance impedance of the horn (at the throat) is an important factor in driver design. The break frequency caused by the air cavity is found by

$$f_p = c/2\pi hT \qquad (14\text{-}43)$$

where,

f_p is the phase plug air volume cutoff frequency in hertz,
c is the speed of sound in air in meters per second,
h is the diaphragm-to-phase plug spacing in meters,
T is the compression ratio, (S_D/S_T).

For example, a diaphragm is operated 0.02 in. from a phase plug having a compression ratio of 10:1; f_p calculates out to be 10.7 kHz. A diaphragm, operated 0.10 in. from the phase plug having a 5:1 compression ratio, calculates out at 4.3 kHz.

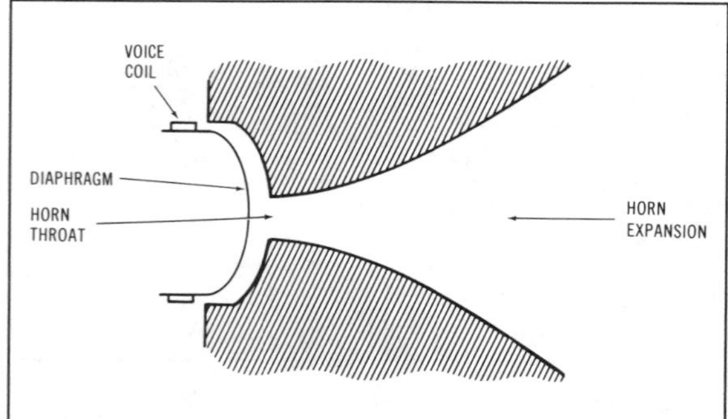

Figure 14-53 Simple compression loading.

Although this phase plug reduces the throat area, it allows the per-excursion power at any frequency to increase, and it extends the bandwidth on top. The following are good expressions relating these variables:

$$W = 4\pi^2 f^2 X^2 \rho_o c S_D T \qquad (14\text{-}44)$$

where,

W is the acoustic power into the horn throat in watts,
f is the frequency, above horn cutoff in hertz,
X is the diaphragm excursion in meters,
$\rho_o c$ equals 407 mks rayls,
S_D is the diaphragm projected area in square meters,
T is the compression ratio (S_D/S_T),
S_T is the throat area in square meters.

Note that if W is to be in rms watts, X must also be in rms meters or 0.707 peak meters. For a typical example, a 4-in. diameter compression driver diaphragm (0.0081 m^2) moves 0.010 in. at 500 Hz. The compression ratio is 10:1. The acoustic power on a well-loaded horn is

$$W = 4\pi^2 500^2 [0.01(0.0254)(0.707)]^2 (407)(0.0081)(10)$$
$$= 10.49 \text{ acoustic W}$$

The high-frequency response cutoff, due to mass only, of any high-frequency driver can be approximated by

$$f_m = \left(\frac{(BL)^2}{2\pi M_T}\right)\left(\frac{1}{R_{VC}} + \frac{P_o c S_D(1+T)}{(BL)^2}\right) \qquad (14\text{-}45)$$

where,

f_m is the mass-controlled high-frequency rolloff,
B is the flux density in tesla or gauss/10^4,
L is the length of voice coil wire in field B in meters,
M_T is the total moving mass in kilograms,
R_{vc} is the resistance of voice coil in ohms.

The efficiency of a driver (at diaphragm resonance) can be approximated by the following expression:

$$n = \frac{1}{\left(\frac{1 + R_{vc} P_o c S_D(1+T)}{(BL)^2}\right)} \% \qquad (14\text{-}46)$$

The second harmonic distortion (HD) in a horn is found as follows:

$$\text{Second HD} = 0.0173(f/f_c)(W/S_T) \qquad (14\text{-}17)$$

where,

f is the frequency of interest,
f_c is the cutoff frequency of the horn,
W is the acoustic power into the horn in watts,
S_T is the throat area in square meters.

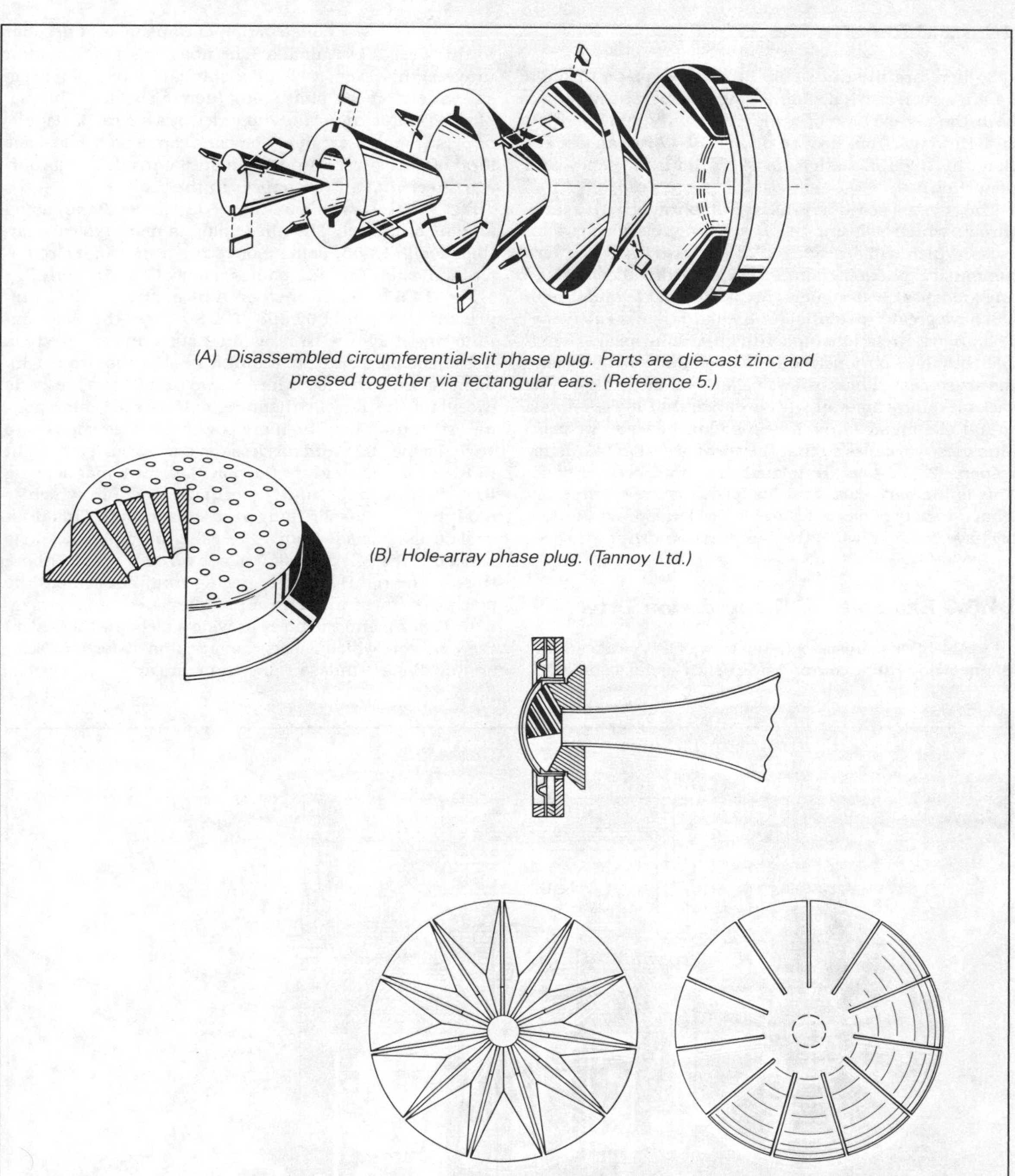

(A) Disassembled circumferential-slit phase plug. Parts are die-cast zinc and pressed together via rectangular ears. (Reference 5.)

(B) Hole-array phase plug. (Tannoy Ltd.)

(C) Radial phase plug, Altec "Tangerine" one-piece cast plastic—after Henricksen. (Courtesy Altec Lansing Corp.)

Figure 14-54 A variety of phase plug styles.

14.5.2.2 Relative Merits

So here are the trade-offs: From Eqs. 14-43 through 14-45, we can see that a high compression ratio improves both the per-excursion output capability and the high end. However, from Eqs. 14-46 and 14-47 we can also see that this type of design degrades both efficiency and distortion.

The obvious solution is a large diaphragm with a large throat, which will improve everything, except for total mass, which will degrade top end. It also leads to a very nonmusical phenomenon, which is the dread nemesis to any loudspeaker designer—breakup. A large diaphragm will have greater potential for breakup than a small one. The analytic relationships guide the loudspeaker engineer, but these obviously contradictory trade-offs are where the art comes in: how can we balance all these tug-of-war variables and come up with a device that makes music sound like music? To a lesser extent, how can we combine these variables so that they produce a flat frequency response? The two are related, but not necessarily so. This is the hard part, and the following are examples of what a variety of clever fellows in the loudspeaker industry have come up with, the compression-driver art.

14.5.3 Examples of Compression Drivers

Fig. 14-55 is a cross-sectional view of a typical ceramic magnet wide-range compression driver using a dome diaphragm. The case construction is unusual and peculiar to this design by Yamaha. The phase plug is also a bit unusual; however, it is still a standard circumferential-slit variety on the phase plug (dome) surface. The diaphragm is aluminum and supported by a typical Bakelite™ or plastic support frame. The back cap usually has some kind of acoustical absorbing material inside to discourage interfering air resonances in the cap.

Fig. 14-56 shows a 2-in. throat JBL driver (2440) using an alnico magnet. The phase plug is more typical than that in Fig. 14-55, using more straight-through circumferential slits. The JBL plug is made of cast Bakelite™.

Fig. 14-57 shows another Alnico driver, the omnipresent 1-in. Altec 802/808. The 802 uses the all-aluminum diaphragm with tangential surround coupled via the phase plug and expanding throat section to a 1-in. diameter exit. The 808 is identical to the 802 in all respects except for the (retrofit) diaphragm. It uses a Kapton polymer surround, handles more power (40 W as opposed to 15 W for the 802), and has less top end. From left to right in the exploded view are the pot, the alnico magnet slug that fits under the (next item) pole piece, in which is mounted a radial-slit "tangerine" phase plug. This unusual design is made from a glass fiber-filled plastic and is bonded to the pole piece; its color is a bright orange. Above this (to the right) is the centering ring that centers the pole piece in the air gap via the top plate. It is nonmagnetic (brass), and the holes provide a mechanical load on the voice coil, which affects response and distortion. Next, are the diaphragm assembly and rear cap.

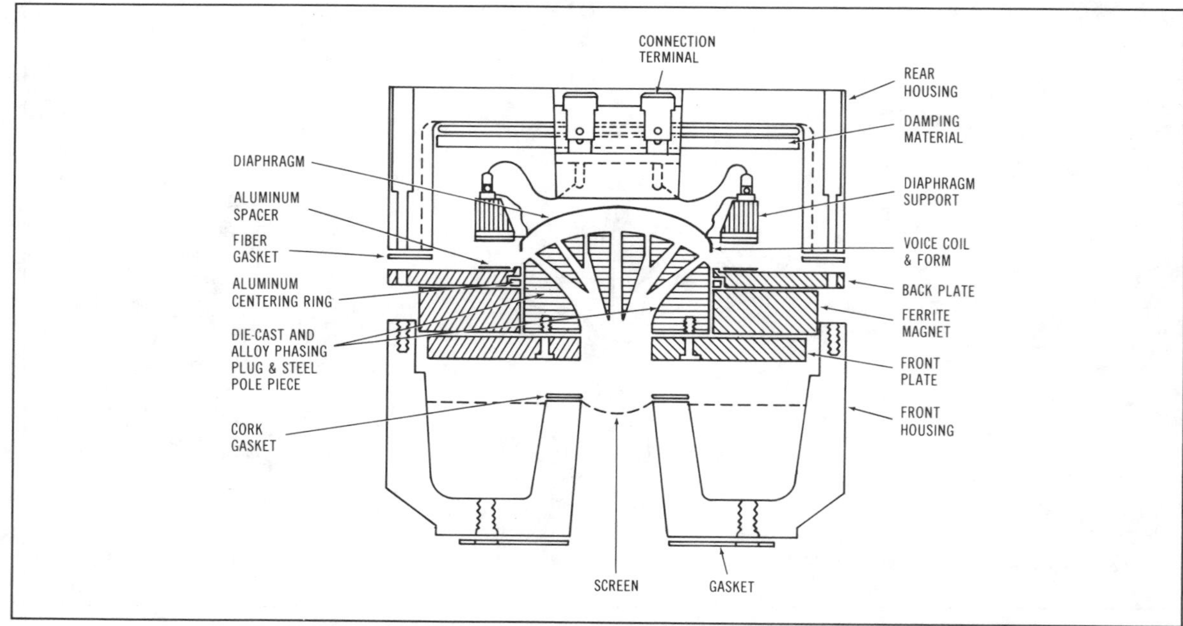

Figure 14-55 Typical ceramic-magnet compression driver. *(Courtesy Yamaha International Corp.)*

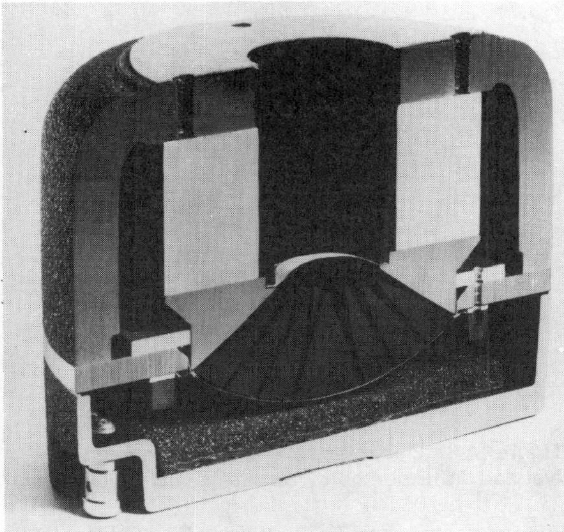

Figure 14-56 JBL 2440 2-in. throat alnico compression driver. *(Courtesy JBL Inc./UREI)*

Figure 14-57 Altec 802/808 alnico 1-in. throat compression driver with "Tangerine" radial phase plug. *(Courtesy Altec Lansing Corp.)*

These three are about the extent of normal dome diaphragm compression-driver design, in concept and practical manifestation.

Semi-infinite variations exist in the art including an endless variety of suspension shapes and materials. Domes are made from aluminum, titanium, and, in one case, beryllium (TAD).[53] Yamaha International Corp. makes its suspension out of stamped beryllium-copper cantilever fingers, Emilar makes its out of cast RTV rubber, and JBL and Ramsa stiffen their suspensions with rhombic and diamond patterns, respectively, for better high end.[54] One exception to the format norm is the Cetec-Gauss Big Tweet. This driver compresses the sound into a phase plug on the convex side of a dome and expands into two concentric horns from two concentric slits making up the phase plug. This driver is intended for very high-frequency use.

Midrange drivers are beginning to emerge as demand for more power and less distortion becomes stronger. Midrange drivers are intended for 300 to 3000 Hz and often use a phenolic dome into a relatively simple phase plug, due to the relatively restricted bandwidth. (Bandwidth reduction allows the designer to optimize other parameters.)

The Community Light & Sound, Inc., M4 driver as shown in Figs. 14-58 and 14-59 is intended for the 200- to 2000-Hz decade and is a rather impressive (and expensive) driver, using a 9.6-in. outside diameter 1.2-in. thick ceramic slug.[55] The diaphragm is about 7 in. in diameter, employs a special shape designed to push the first mode of breakup above the passband, and is fabricated from aluminum skins and a light, stiff foam core, about 0.090 in. thick. The upper and lower suspensions are heat-formed Mylar™, using a special ribbed design to prevent

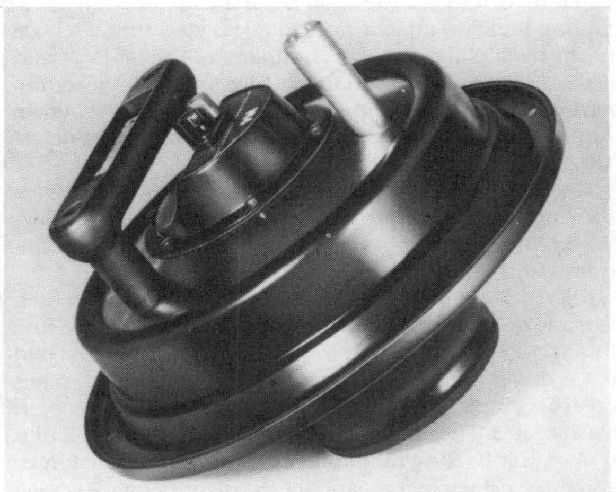

Figure 14-58 Community M4 4-in. throat midrange driver. *(Courtesy Community Light & Sound, Inc.)*

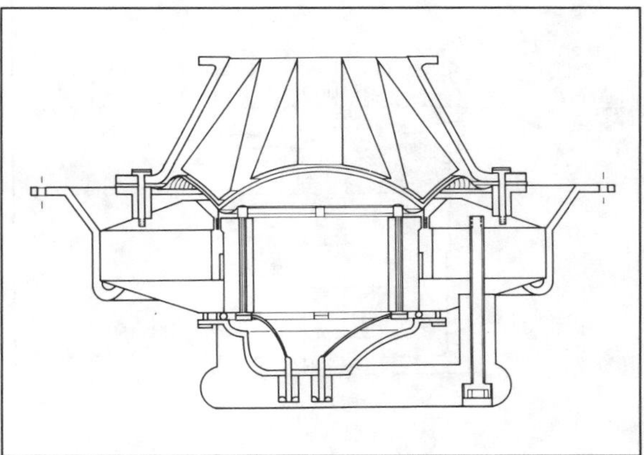

Figure 14-59 Community M4 cross-section view. *(Courtesy Community Light & Sound, Inc.)*

breakup. The M4 is unusual in that its diaphragm is centered by the lower suspension on the inside of the voice coil. The leads attach to two of the four hold-down bolts, which conduct the input signal via the connectors on the back cap. Also unusual on the M4 is the practice of bonding the voice coil former to the outside diameter of the voice coil. The phase plug is a usual circumferential-slit configuration, driving off the back side of the diaphragm. It has a 5:1 compression ratio leading to a 4-in. diameter throat, this being a balance giving low distortion, good low-frequency pumping capability (100 acoustic watts at 250 Hz at 0.050-in. deflection). It also has good directivity control. The magnet is potted in the laminated fiberglass magnet cover/flange mount, thereby getting around many of the typical ceramic magnet problems discussed earlier. The driver mounts sturdily into a cup attached to the throat of the mating horn. Cast aluminum handles, attached via stainless steel through bolts to the back plate, facilitate handling of the 38-lb driver, act as a temporary stand for the driver and horn combination, protect the terminals when the driver is set down this way, and act as anchor points for hanging the driver and horn.

Another type of diaphragm popularized by JBL Inc. is the ring radiator. The 075 Bullet is intended for use above 7 kHz, and the diaphragm is a V-shaped ring of aluminum attached to a usual coil and former.

Fig. 14-60 shows a ceramic version of the ring, which is made by Yamaha. The phase plug is a simple slit ending in a large enough mouth to project the desired low end of the driver. The rear housing of the Yamaha merely takes up space, probably a market driven design for a pleasant aspect ratio. The suspension is the diaphragm itself, and it is very stiff. Ring radiators are typically operated in or above the principle resonance of the diaphragm assembly.

Several other high-frequency compression drivers are worth mentioning here. The T-35, from Electro-Voice (Fig. 14-61) uses a small phenolic diaphragm driving a vertical diffraction horn via a simple 1-slit phase plug. The EVST350B is similar to the T-35 but drives a wide-angle 120° horn and offers better off-axis response.

Figure 14-61 Electro-Voice T-35 very high frequency driver and diffraction horn. *(Courtesy Electro-Voice, Inc.)*

The Technics EAS-10TH1000 "leaf tweeter" very high-frequency device is shown in Fig. 14-62. Its low-mass Mylar™ and aluminum diaphragm gives it an almost unbelievable response (on-axis) to over 150 kHz!

Last, but not least is the PA Driver or screw-on driver, such as the University 7110XC (explosion proof) shown in Fig. 14-63. This type unit is used extensively in public address systems. Their throats are usually ¾-in. diameter, and they have a 1⅜ in. × 16 thread for horn mount. Their diaphragms are usually phenolic resin-impregnated domes with integral convoluted suspensions. Voice coils are usually round copper wire, and some are capable of handling up to 100 W.

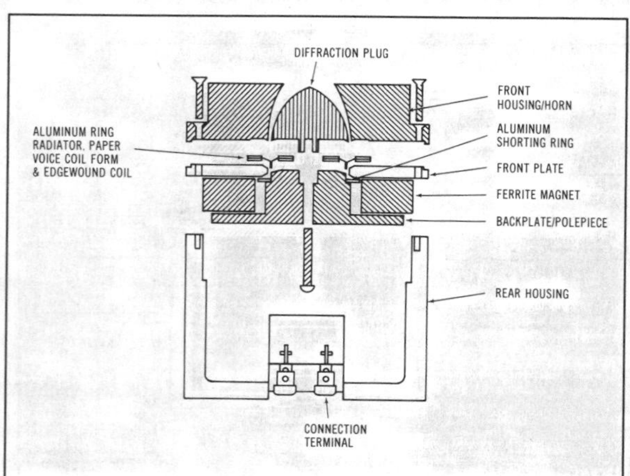

Figure 14-60 Yamaha ceramic-magnet ring radiator cross section. *(Courtesy Yamaha International Corp.)*

Figure 14-62 Technics EAS-10TH1000 "Leaf Tweeter." *(Courtesy Panasonic International Corp.)*

Figure 14-63 University 7110XC ¾-in. throat explosion proof PA driver. *(Courtesy Altec Lansing Corp.)*

Figure 14-64 Altec Lansing 311-60 cast aluminum sectoral (radial) horn with sound-deadening material. *(Courtesy Altec Lansing Corp.)*

14.6 STRAIGHT HORNS[42, 56]

Straight horns are the simplest horns to build since their sides are straight or two dimensional; their sides may be fabricated from bent sheets of a suitable material. Straight horns can be designed so that all their sides are curved. Particular sides may be made straight for reasons of directivity control, but as long as the correct expansion is maintained, the desired low-frequency performance will be maintained. Certainly, for a given area expansion, an endless series of straight horns may be designed. All have the same low-frequency impedance response, but they all also have vastly differing on- and off-axis response and directivity performance.

14.7 RADIAL HORNS[57]

Radial horns are allegedly designed to allow a natural radial expansion of the sound wave from the driver, while maintaining a correct expansion rate for desired low-frequency response. Typically, a radial horn design has straight horizontal sides, which act as horizontal wave guides, and radially curved top and bottom walls, which serve to maintain a proper area expansion. A radial horn is usually designed by first laying out the sides to the desired angle of coverage. Then, given the area expansion desired, the top and bottom surfaces are derived mathematically. The most popular materials used in making radial horns are cast aluminum, molded plastic, and laminated glass fiber and polyester resin.

Radial horns usually have well-behaved horizontal directivity due to the straight sides. Conical radial horns will have excellent vertical directivity control also, but they are not usually used, due to poor low-frequency loading. Exponential and hyperbolic horns have sides that form narrow guiding angles at the throat and wide guiding angles at the mouth, thereby causing low frequencies to be wide and high frequencies to be narrow. This is very typical vertical directivity behavior for an exponential horn.

Fig. 14-64 is an Altec 311-60; it has a 60° horizontal coverage radial intended for use above 300 Hz, using a 1.4-in. throat diameter driver. This horn is solid cast aluminum spray coated with a sound-deadening material and finished in gray paint. Altec is well known for this "sectoral" design, which places vertical vanes at the mouth of the horn, allegedly for improvement of directivity in some range of the operation of the horn. The 511B and 811B are two other famous Altec "sectorals," which are widely used in virtually every Altec product that incorporates one of their 1-in. exit drivers. These are used bare without a sound deadener.

Fig. 14-65 shows a recent design practice, the flat-front radial, in this case the SQ 90 high-frequency horn, of Community Light & Sound, Inc. The flat-front design is an obvious advantage in mounting on flat baffles.

A special case of radial horn is the diffraction horn. This type of horn is designed to have a very small vertical

Figure 14-65 Community SQ 90 flat-front radial horn. *(Courtesy Community Light & Sound)*

Figure 14-66 JBL 2397 diffraction horn ("Smith" horn). Note the wooden bell and the cast-iron throat hybrid construction. *(Courtesy JBL Inc./UREI)*

Figure 14-67 Altec Lansing 1.4-in. throat, all soldered and coated steel multicell horn family showing throat "plumbing" fixtures. *(Courtesy Altec Lansing Corp.)*

mouth size, thus making the vertical angle very large for most frequencies, approaching 90° when a wavelength reaches the vertical mouth height. Fig. 14-66 shows a popular diffraction horn, this one being fabricated from wood. Another advantage of a diffraction horn is that the small vertical mouth size will not support a midrange horizontal beaming diffraction phenomenon common to horns with large vertical dimensions.

14.8 MULTICELL HORNS

Multicell horns were the original directivity control horns. They used a very straightforward approach: as many small horns as needed are pointed where the sound should go. These are then connected to a common manifold so that one driver can power them all at once.

Multicells have been used since the late 1930s, and they exhibit very desirable directivity characteristics. They were originally made of sheet metal soldered together and either filled on the outside with sand or covered with a mechanical damping material such as Soundcoat or Aquaplas. Recently, all-fiberglass multicells have been successfully used and accepted. Fig. 14-67 shows a series of metal multicells.

Multicells have a few problems associated with them. First, they are complicated, difficult to fabricate correctly, and, consequently, expensive to the end user. Second, multicells typically exhibit high-frequency (above 6 kHz or so) fingering, where the individual cells decouple from the cell cluster and become more and more individual narrow beams as frequencies increase. This is said to give less-than-desirable distribution patterns for hi-fi, extended-range systems. Lastly, most multicells suffer from midrange beaming in both vertical and horizontal directions, which is thought to be the result of diffraction phenomena around the horn mouth perimeter.

In spite of these problems, the multicell is still an excellent horn choice for many applications. Most are designed with exponential cells and exhibit excellent low-frequency loading. Many multicells sound good, which is not always true for single-celled horns. This old-but-dependable design is still with us for many good reasons.

14.9 FIRST SINGLE-CELL DIRECTIVITY-CONTROL HORN

In May of 1975, Electro-Voice introduced the world's first constant-beamwidth single-celled horn family, engineered by Don Keele as a result of suggestions made by Ray Newman and John Gilliom. These horns (molded from white fiberglass) used a remarkable new concept: a hyperbolic throat section coupled to a conical radial bell section, as shown in Fig. 14-68. This hybrid horn had good low-frequency loading as well as constant angular beamwidth in both vertical and horizontal directions over a wide frequency range, and it set the small community of horn designers across the country literally buzzing. Keele presented an accompanying AES paper ("What's So Sacred About Exponential Horns")[58], which generously discussed all the relationships between mouth size, frequency, and maintenance of coverage angle. Electro-Voice also added another engineering advance with these new horns: a horn mouth wall construction for correcting midrange beaming. They simply expanded the horn walls at a greater angle than the waveguide angle. These flanges worked, and the world's first flat curve of both vertical and horizontal beamwidth versus frequency was obtained.

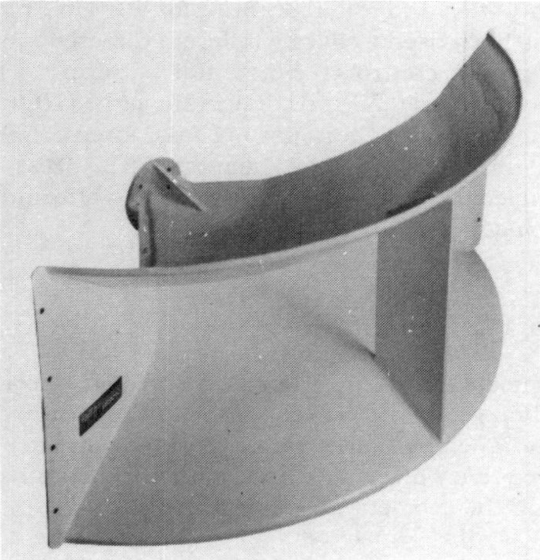

Figure 14-68 Electro-Voice HR9040 constant directivity horn. *(Courtesy Electro-Voice, Inc.)*

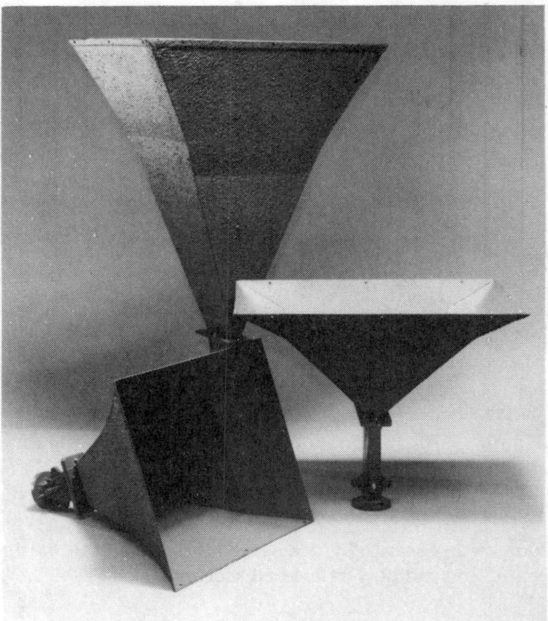

Figure 14-69 Altec Lansing Manta-Ray horn family, cast aluminum throat and soldered, coated bell construction. *(Courtesy Altec Lansing Corp.)*

14.10 HORIZONTAL DIFFRACTION HORNS

Keele's paper provided the groundwork for all future directivity-control work. Using these principles, it was deduced (by the author, then an acoustics engineer at Altec Lansing) that for a normal radial-horn layout such as the Electro-Voice, the vertical mouth dimension was necessarily smaller than the horizontal dimension (by approximately the ratio of horizontal and vertical intended coverage angles).

A way to make the vertical mouth size larger, independent of the horizontal dimension was found, leading to the unique *Manta-Ray* geometry (Fig. 14-69). It's basically a vertical narrow-angle diffraction horn, filling into a conical waveguide by diffraction, due to the narrow width of the vertical tail slit. This new horn geometry became the father for many new designs to follow. Originally conceived as a radial bell design, the Manta-Ray quickly got planar sides as a suggestion by Mark Ureda. Besides easing construction, the planar sides seemed to reduce side polar widening, which plagued some early prototypes. Ureda continued Manta-Ray development work and did the final product design, bristling with the trademark features of Altec Lansing, a cast aluminum throat and a sheet-metal bell covered with sound-damping material and painted gray. The sheet-metal bell works well; it's very neutral (doesn't ring) and is weatherproof. Performance is also good, with flat directivity or coverage angles and an improvement in vertical-directivity control over the Electro-Voice design. The only drawback was that the conical Manta-Ray expansions didn't quite give the loading afforded by the Electro-Voice design, but it was well within what Altec needed for two-way systems (800 Hz). The Manta-Ray also used Keele's flanges to discourage midrange beaming.

14.11 BIRADIAL HORNS

Keele, by this time, had settled into the engineering department at JBL, which also needed a constant-directivity horn concept. He took the Manta-Ray concept and his own work a step further. A problem with discrete flanges is that the abrupt change in angle can cause diffraction disturbances in the response. The biradial uses continuously varying flanges in both directions, ending in a continuous horn. The vertical diffraction concept was used, except that an exponential expansion was fitted into the design, and a vertical and horizontal radial bell (thus biradial) was used. The biradials shown in Fig. 14-70 have both good directivity control and low frequency loading. They are fabricated from cast aluminum (throat section) and molded fiberglass (bell section) and fit 2-in. exit drivers.

14.12 TWIN BESSEL HORNS

Shortly after the debut of the Manta-Rays, Ramsa ("Pro" Division of Panasonic) introduced a horn that apparently mathematically fits a dual series Bessel expansion. The

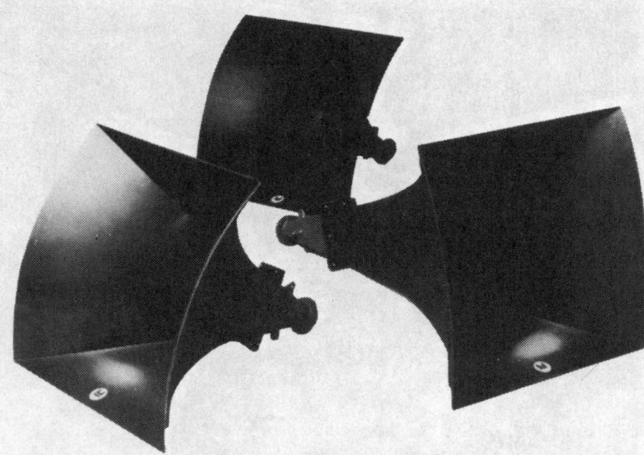

Figure 14-70 JBL biradial horn family cast aluminum throat and fiberglass bell construction. *(Courtesy JBL Inc./UREI)*

geometry is essentially the same as the original Manta-Rays, using radial, vertical bell sections.

14.13 VOICE WARNING HORNS

Fig. 14-71 shows another horizontal-diffraction waveguide horn, designed by Bruce Howze of Community Light & Sound, Inc., and originally built for Whelen Engineering. The horn used a slightly different directivity-control philosophy; a controlled horizontal pattern (45°), and minimum vertical pattern, due to the large (70-in.) vertical dimension. The horn uses 16 Atlas siren drivers and the system, at 1600-W input, generates 127 dB at 100 ft. Its intended use is similar to a searchlight—aim and shoot via a remote rotor.

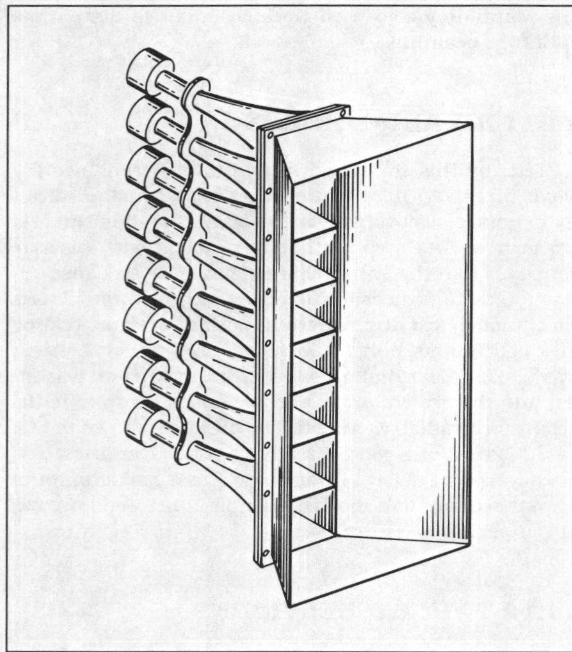

Figure 14-71 Whelen Engineering horizontal diffraction horn with multiple drivers. *(Courtesy Whelen Engineering Co., Inc.)*

14.14 PC HORNS

A complete series of new horns, based on the horizontal diffraction geometry, was developed at Community Light & Sound, Inc., by Howze, using a central vane to control high-frequency directivity and fit an exponential expansion into the geometry, as shown in Fig. 14-72.

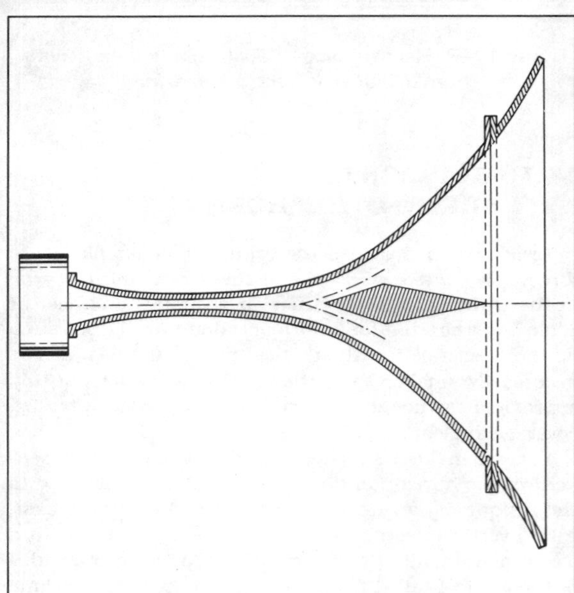

Figure 14-72 Community "PC" horn layout showing central vane. *(Courtesy Community Light & Sound, Inc.)*

14.15 ACOUSTIC LENSES

Although an *acoustic lens* is not a directivity control or constant angular beam device, it is a directivity alteration device. Acoustic lenses are generally used to widen directivity patterns at the mouths of horns; however, they could be used to narrow them. An acoustic lens depends on the refraction of sound. By passing sound through a volume that has a different apparent density from air, the speed of sound through that volume will change relative to that in air. Typically, lenses are set up so that the speed of sound is reduced or slowed down, by making a mechanical obstacle array appear in the path of the sound.

Figure 14-73 JBL studio monitor employing slant-plate type acoustic lens on a high-frequency component. *(Courtesy JBL Inc./UREI)*

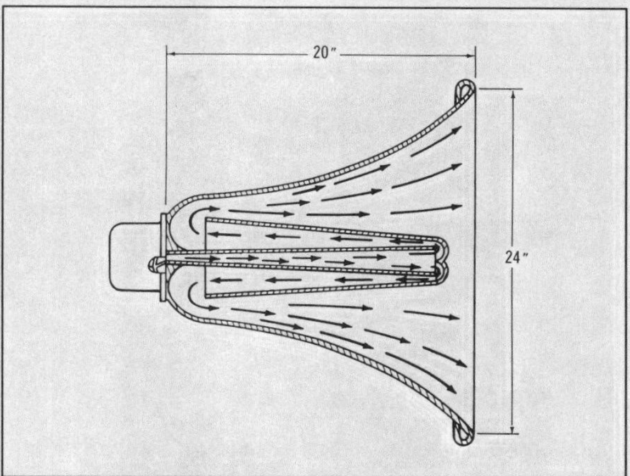

Figure 14-74 Cross-sectional drawing of an exponential folded horn.

This could be done by a variety of methods but is normally done by a path-length refractor, such as the slant-plate lens assembly shown mounted on a JBL studio monitor in Fig. 14-73. Note that the device has concave openings in the plate array. As the wave leaves the horn and progresses through the lens plate array, the center of the wave reaches the air on the outside first. Therefore, it speeds up first. The outer portions of the wave traveling through the thicker portions of the lens have a longer distance to travel at lower wave velocity; therefore, they are delayed in time relative to the center. The net effect is making the wave more convex and widening the polar pattern in the horizontal direction. Of interest is the fact that the vertical pattern is unaltered. Also, studies have shown that a severe reflected wave occurs in a lens, causing potential "funny sounds." Lastly, lenses obey similar laws to those for any directivity-controlling device. They have to be large in order to be of any influence on low frequencies.

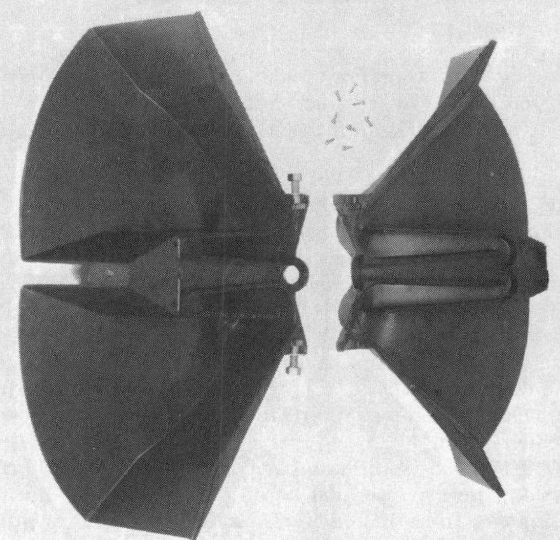

Figure 14-75 University Cobraflex horn—disassembled. *(Courtesy Altec Lansing Corp.)*

14.16 FOLDED AND BASS HORNS

Horns designed to go low in frequency, especially those that have small throat areas, can be folded to make compact products. These are usually bass horns or certain public address horns intended for speech or background music, down to 200 or 150 Hz, using screw-on drivers. The purity of the music signal from a folded horn is often a subject of debate; however, many commercially successful designs of both types have enjoyed good market acceptance.

Fig. 14-74 shows a University Sound *GH (for Giant Horn)* directional trumpet cross section and how the area expands by making two 180° turns. The GH (and a whole family of these) are made of spun aluminum and are still used; the design has been around since the 1940s. Another interesting University folded public address horn design is the cast zinc Cobraflex shown disassembled in Fig. 14-75. This horn expands into a double mouth and affords better directional control, especially in the horizontal plane over a design such as the GH.

The most famous folded bass horn ever is the Klipschorn shown in Fig. 14-76. It was cleverly named for its inventor, Paul Klipsch, one of the pioneers in horn loudspeaker design. The Klipschorn uses a single, high-efficiency 15-in. loudspeaker folded into a relatively compact, sturdily braced package. The Klipschorn is designed to be situated in a corner of the room since the mouth of the horn exists at the sides of the cabinet. This is inherent in the design of the cabinet, making it somewhat dependent on the room. Klipsch also recommends a "false

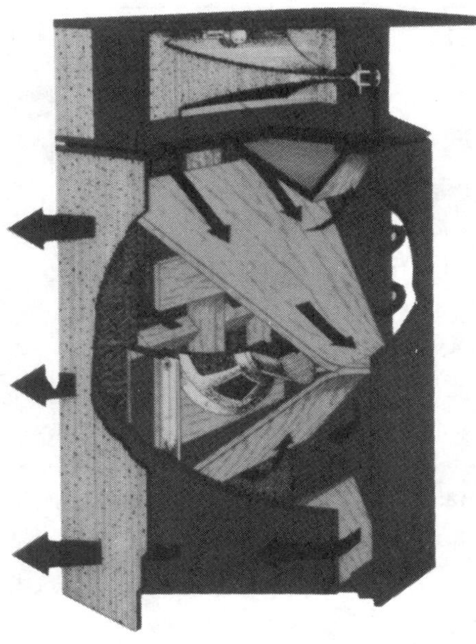

Figure 14-76 Klipschorn folded corner bass horn—rear cutaway view with high-frequency components. *(Courtesy Klipsch & Associates, Inc.)*

corner," which can be set up to simulate corner loading and to allow more flexible speaker placement.

The Cerwin-Vega E horn, so called due to its importance in the "Earthquake" low-frequency theater system, is another form of folded bass horn. A Cerwin-Vega 18-in. low-frequency driver sits between the upper and lower mouths and faces to the rear in a compression chamber. The E horn makes one 180° fold, opening to the double mouths, and is intended for use with additional mouth extensions and in multiples for mutual low-frequency coupling.

The W horn is still another famous folded bass horn design, the most popular being the RCA theater horn, using two 15-in. RCA drivers. Many of these horns still exist and are used by many public address rental companies for concert work. The W uses front-facing drivers, and the horn flare is designed as a W-shaped double fold, expanding to twin mouths.

Lastly, the Altec cast aluminum 31A uses a single 90° fold for two reasons. One is that it allows a short front-to-back dimension as per all folded horns. Second, and more important, is that the driver is mounted facing down, making it rain- and dust-resistant. This horn uses a 120° mouth and is used above 500 Hz for a wide variety of applications including voice only.

The simplest and thus purest bass horn is the straight horn. For very low frequencies, this kind of horn must be large. The dual 15-in. driver Altec 815 shown in Fig. 14-77 is an example; it is made exclusively from wood and is usable to about 65 Hz. Note that the horn throat

Figure 14-77 Altec Lansing 815 straight bass horn. *(Courtesy Altec Lansing Corp.)*

is much larger than the combined driver area. This is a typical practice for wood horns and is said to have little effect on response at the low frequencies where the horn works. A disadvantage of this design is the parallel top and bottom sides, which will produce a null at a half-wavelength frequency, in this case approximately 200 Hz.

The Community Light & Sound, Inc., Leviathan shown in Fig. 14-78 is another straight bass horn. The horn comes in three sections, as shown, and is made exclusively from laminated fiberglass and polyester resin. The collapsible design is intended for portable touring use, is relatively lightweight, and with the mouth extension is usable to just below 50 Hz. This is probably the largest straight bass horn ever produced. Of interest is the throat detailing and general nonparallel sides design made possible due to molded construction. The throat area matches the driver area exactly, and this horn is considered by many to be the ultimate in terms of transient accuracy when used with high-quality efficient drivers.

The vented bass horn is a practical compromise. Although it makes a sacrifice of straight-horn purity and "shock," it does this for more low-frequency bandwidth and compact size. Altec makes a complete assortment of these cabinets, the most well known being the various Voice-of-the-Theater horns, the 210, which is shown in Fig. 14-79, is the granddaddy of them all. Although not a real low-frequency shaker, the 210 illustrates the vented horn design. Mid-bass frequencies up to crossover (500 Hz) are projected by the bass horn via the dual 15-in. drivers. Low-end bass is generated by resonating the rear volume of the enclosure via the ports shown at the bottom, i.e., bass reflex. Wings on either side of the enclo-

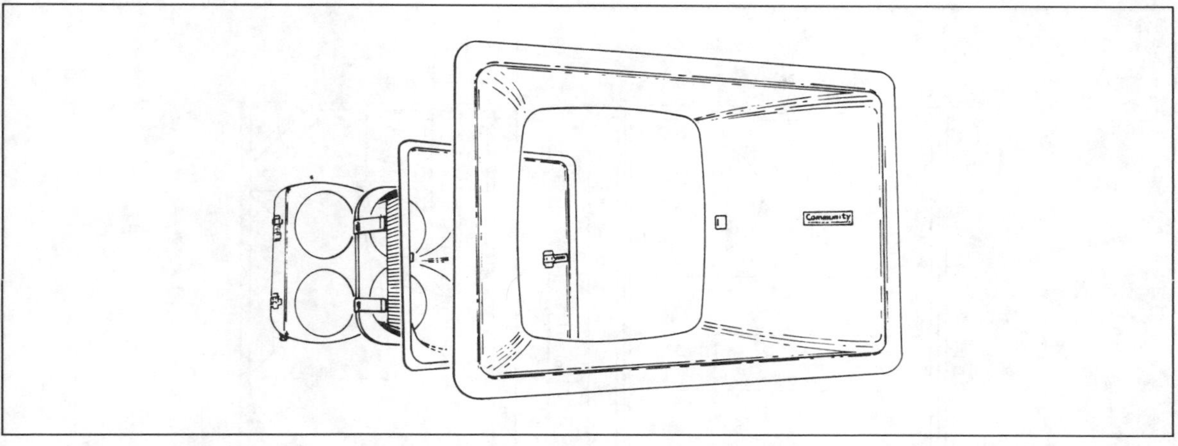

Figure 14-78 Community Leviathan portable straight bass horn. *(Courtesy Community Light & Sound, Inc.)*

Figure 14-79 Altec Lansing 210 vented bass horn for theater use. *(Courtesy Altec Lansing Corp.)*

Figure 14-80 Altec Lansing 816A vented bass horn. *(Courtesy Altec Lansing Corp.)*

sure are used to aid low-frequency projection. The enclosure is 84 in. high, 82 in. wide with wings, 39½ in. deep, and weighs 433 lb less loudspeakers.

Probably the best-compromise design from Altec Lansing is the model 816, which is shown in Fig. 14-80. It is a compact, single 15-in. cabinet measuring 22 in. high, 30 in. wide, and 26 in. deep, and is usable to 50 Hz. The 816 is very popular for this reason and finds many uses, from fixed installations to tour sound.

Another "ultimate" from Community Light & Sound, Inc., is the Boxer bass horn, which uses a 48-Hz flare, a double 15-in. driver, a bass horn, and a large vented enclosure. The Boxer is usable to about 30 Hz and is so named because the box is made to specification by the dealer. Community supplies the plans and horn flare, which is a molded single-piece from fiberglass and polyester resin.

Fig. 14-81 shows one last example of the bass horn art, the JBL scoop, which is available for one or two 15-in. drivers. This is an interesting design since it uses both direct radiation from the low-frequency driver for mid bass to crossover and a rear-vented enclosure for the low frequencies. The rear vent expands into the bass horn shown below the driver cutout. This design has been used widely for sound reinforcement, especially entertainment systems.

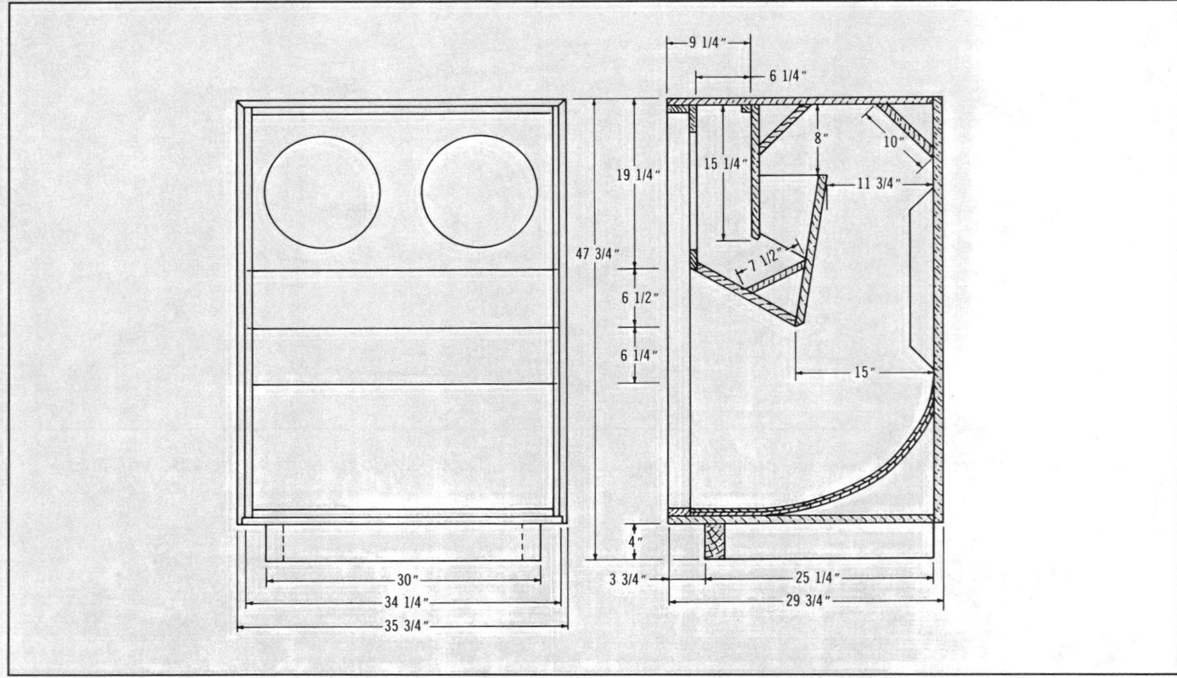

Figure 14-81 JBL "Scoop" rear loaded bass horn. *(Courtesy JBL Inc./UREI)*

14.17 LOUDSPEAKER SYSTEMS[59–62]

Systems are usually assemblages of loudspeaker components with crossovers and/or amplifiers and other electronic signal-processing equipment. The complete system is normally intended for full-range flat reproduction of music, speech, and signals from below 80 Hz to over 15 kHz. Some components discussed previously are capable of reproducing below 25 Hz to over 100 kHz; however, the integration of any of these components into a system that "sounds like real music" is not easily accomplished.

The designer must know what music sounds like, something not gained by reading any of the over 100 references cited for this portion of the book. Second, continuous listening experience in sound is needed.

A professional acoustic engineer may be able to get a loudspeaker to be flat at a point in space in an anechoic chamber, but it won't necessarily be suitable for reproduction of anything but a kazoo band. The systems' designers who are very successful at their craft can get so involved with the sound that they lose sight of the music, which was probably the main reason they got into it in the first place. More perplexing, many musicians, especially "studio cats," listen to the music only and never listen to the sound. (It is a fact that great music will transcend just about any sound-reinforcement system's faults.) Many musicians would make terrible sound systems' designers for these reasons.

Probably the best advice for most buyers and end-users of systems is to purchase a complete system that sounds good. Usually, a lot of trial-and-error tweaking and engineering has gòne into a good system, and the average person would have to try very hard (with much more limited resources) to do better. If someone wanted to do much better, the only way to do it is with an active system involving bi-, tri- or quad-amplifying.

14.17.1 Systems: Integration of Components

When a system is designed or assembled, various components must be integrated or made compatible with one another. The following are some of the requirements necessary for a successful system.

14.17.1.1 On-Axis Frequency Response

On-axis frequency response must be flat or at least smooth. There is varying opinion as to where the flat region is, but most system's aficionados will agree that a smooth, flat response from as low as possible (at least 40 Hz) to at least 5 kHz is important. Above this, opinion varies; some prefer a gradual rolloff above 5 kHz to − 10 dB at 16 kHz, while others prefer a system flat to at least 10 kHz. In many cases smoothness of response is as important to musical sound as is the response itself. Smoothness is an indication of good, nonreflective, nonrefractive breakup-free sound radiation.

14.17.1.2 Horizontal Off-Axis Response

Horizontal off-axis response is as important as on-axis response. A system with smooth, dip-free, off-axis response to at least ±45° off-axis will have a smooth, even power response. This is seen in similar, parallel curves at various off-axis angles. When listening to a system in semireverberant rooms (such as most studio control rooms and living rooms), you will hear or perceive the power response of the system more than you will the on-axis response. A flat on-axis response accompanied by a wavy, overlapping off-axis curve family will probably sound "funny" and should be avoided.

14.17.1.3 Vertical Off-Axis Response

Vertical off-axis response should be inspected, but it is not necessarily a strong contributor to good sound in a given plane. At crossover, two components will not necessarily be radiating equal amounts of acoustical energy. These components will have to be physically separated by some distance, and simple path-length geometry will tell how much attenuation due to phase cancellation will occur at some off-axis angle. (This, of course, depends on the relative phase of these components at crossover—a much more complicated matter.) The exception to this problem is the concentric coaxial two-way system, such as those illustrated in section 14.17.5.

14.17.1.4 Time or Phase Alignment

Various components in a system producing complex transient musical signals must assemble the various frequency ranges of these signals acoustically at the listening position. If the physical position of these components causes different relative arrival times of these various signal bands, a "funny sound" can result. A recent attention to this problem has brought out a whole variety of schemes for making coherent arrival times possible in multiway systems. These range from passive time-delay networks to active ones to actual physical design of all components to be compatible in this regard. There seems to be a consensus that to do the latter, lining up voice coils relative to the listening position is the way to do it. Note that as the listener is more off-axis vertically, time coherency goes more out of sync. On good recordings of the human speaking voice, the in-sync condition is said to make a remarkable difference in naturalness. The listener can clearly hear the time synchronization lock in as relative time or phase is varied.

14.17.1.5 Power Handling

A system that exhibits power compression at moderate sound pressure levels is not as much of a problem as one that audibly complains as it is hit with dynamic musical signals. A system that is destroyed by music is of no musical value; *power handling* is a musical virtue.

14.17.1.6 Sensitivity and Efficiency

Power and sound pressure level requirements for listening are the old argument of big versus little loudspeakers.

First of all, big loudspeakers are efficient, typically, producing 95 to 100 dB/1W/1m; little loudspeakers are inefficient, for the same approximate power response bandwidth, and produce in the order of 82 to 90 dB/1W/1m. Big loudspeakers, like studio monitors, are typically more than 10 dB more efficient or sensitive than small ones.

Listening for hi-fi pleasure at 3 m. from the loudspeakers loses about 10 dB (re 1 m), and a 90-dB level is certainly a typical and pleasurable one if the music comes out clean; 100 dB is more typical of studio control room levels, which is often exceeded. On top of this, peak-to-average levels of 15 to 20 dB are realistically available from a tape master, direct-to-disk or digital source. Real life is this way, especially the spectacular and aggressive music that is enjoyed by and produced for the American public.

One watt into an 85 dB/1W/1m will give about 75 dB at 3 m. To listen at 90 dB, we need +15 dB or 32 W average and +20 dB more, or 3200 W, to handle large peaks. It will not work. To listen at 80 dB and expect a peak-to-average of 15 dB means we need a 3.2-W average and a 420-W total to handle peaks. The amplifier is still enormous and expensive and may damage the loudspeakers. The fact is that many so-called hi-fi loudspeakers are really misnamed because they cannot handle realistic swings in pressure, only reproduce on-axis (not power) response approaching hi-fi with a 1-W input.

A look at larger loudspeaker systems, such as recording monitors, shows that average sensitivities range from 96 to 100 dB/1W/1m. At 98 dB/1W/1m we have 88 dB available at 3 m and need +2 dB or 1.6 W to listen at 90 dB, 160 W (+20 dB) to handle peaks. This is definitely a real-world practicality. However, as 100-dB levels are reached, 1600 W is required for 20-dB peaks. Most large power amplifiers are limited to 200 to 400 W per side in stereo; 1600 W may be approached by bridging an amplifier, but the loudspeaker may be damaged. For 100-dB listening levels, a 15-dB peak to average will be handled by a 500-W amplifier, something more realizable.

A last comment and conclusion here is that the illusion of high-fidelity listening requires at least two items discussed here: response and dynamic range capability, which includes noncompliant, low-distortion peak response. On small loudspeakers, you just have to go slower. The right big system is usually a "forever" transition for the true high-fidelity listener.

14.17.2 Passive Systems[63–72]

A *passive system* is one that has no external power source. It is usually an assembly of two or more selected components and a passive crossover network. The crossover is an electrical filter network that assigns the desired band of frequencies to the proper component. Crossovers and other filters vary in shape of response in the region of crossover, or a −3-dB region, and in rate of response rolloff or cutoff. Final response rolloff rates occur in multiples of 6 dB/octave, according to the order of the filter: an nth order filter has a final rolloff rate of n × 6 dB/octave. Therefore, a 12 dB/octave crossover is a second-order filter. Response shape at crossover is important for two reasons. One is that response shape affects how adjacent filter sections combine at crossover and produce final response through the crossover. The other is that response shape is an indication of how much reactive energy is resonating in the various reactive elements in the crossover region. For example, a Bessel filter (any order) is very gradual in slope and reaches its final rolloff well above or below crossover. Bessel filters offer a very gradual electrical phase change through crossover and are also used for passive time-delay networks. This is due to most reactive attenuation taking place well above crossover.

Chebychev filters bump and dip before the crossover region and are usually designed with 1-, 2-, or 3-dB ripple. These types offer rapid response/bump and then roll off near crossover, but only at the expense of transient response and distortion at crossover. (Chebychev's ring, the more ripple in the passband, the more the ringing.)

The best choice of filter type for crossovers is probably the Butterworth. These are called "maximally flat" filters and are as flat as possible in response, without bumping, before reaching crossover. Their damping, though not as high as a Bessel, is a good balance, and they offer excellent combining shapes.

The following is a design chart for Butterworth-shaped crossovers. For design of bandpass elements, high- and low-pass filters may be combined, so long as a one decade or so frequency range is maintained. If the bandwidth is smaller, interaction between the two sections will result, causing unpredicted response variation and ringing.

14.17.2.1 Low-Pass Butterworth Filters

Fig. 14-82 shows first-, second-, third-, fourth-, fifth-, and sixth-order circuits for low pass. Fig. 14-83 shows first-, second-, third-, fourth-, fifth-, and sixth-order circuits for high pass. The following is a list of constants and equations for the design of these filter networks.

order n	K_{L1}	K_{C1}	K_{L2}
1	1.0		
2	0.7071	1.414	
3	0.500	1.333	1.500
4	0.3827	1.082	1.577
5	0.3090	0.8944	1.382
6	0.2588	0.7579	1.202

order n	K_{C2}	K_{L3}	K_{C3}
1			
2			
3			
4	1.531		
5	1.694	1.545	
6	1.553	1.759	1.533

$$L_n = K_{Ln}R_L/2\pi f_c \tag{14-48}$$

$$C_n = K_{Cn}/2\,\pi f_c R_L \tag{14-49}$$

where,
L_n is the inductance in henrys,
C_n is the capacitance in farads,
n is the integer value; 1, 2, 3, ...
R_L is the load dc resistance in ohms,
f_c is the crossover frequency, −3dB, in hertz.

14.17.2.2 High-Pass Butterworth Filters

$$C_n = \frac{1/K_{Ln}}{2\pi f_c R_2} \tag{14-50}$$

$$L_n = \frac{(1/K_{Cn})R_L}{2\pi f_c} \tag{14-51}$$

Bessel Second Order

There are many (seemingly endless) opinions of how crossovers should be designed. Recent work on this subject was enormous when this book was printed; consequently, much has not been included due to time constraints. However, as an alternate example, the second-order Bessel filter characteristic is discussed here. Eugene Patronis (professor of physics, Georgia Institute of Technology) recommends against higher-than-third-order Butterworth filters due to the onset of audible ringing. He recommends the use of a second-order Bessel and compares this to the second-order Butterworth. Fig. 14-84 shows the shape of the two (low-pass) response curves. Note that the final slopes are the same. The Butterworth is quicker in response, but the Bessel has a much

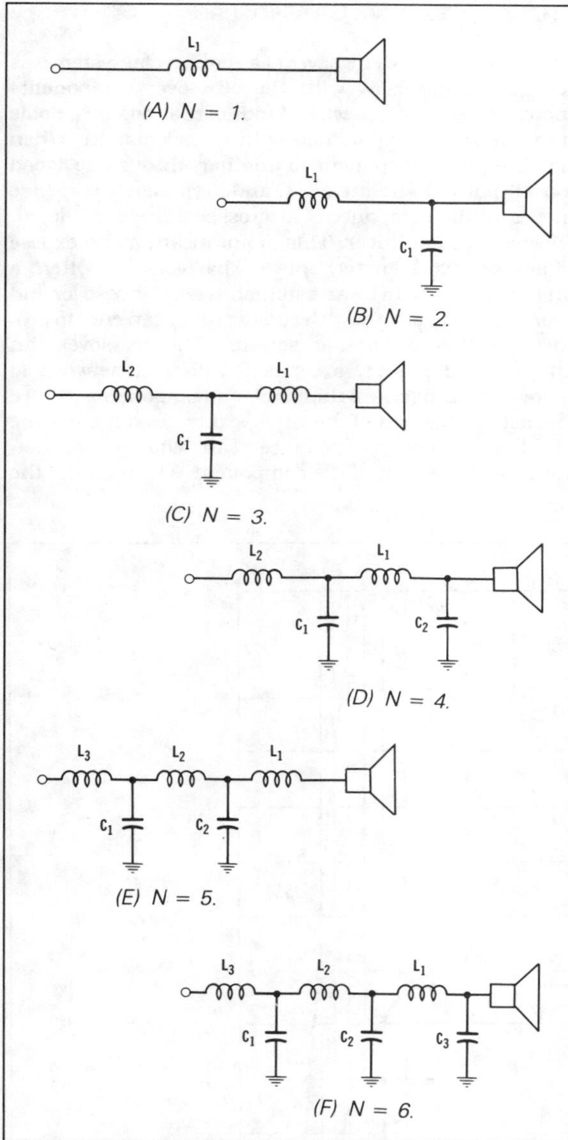

Figure 14-82 Low-pass circuits for N = 1 through N = 6.

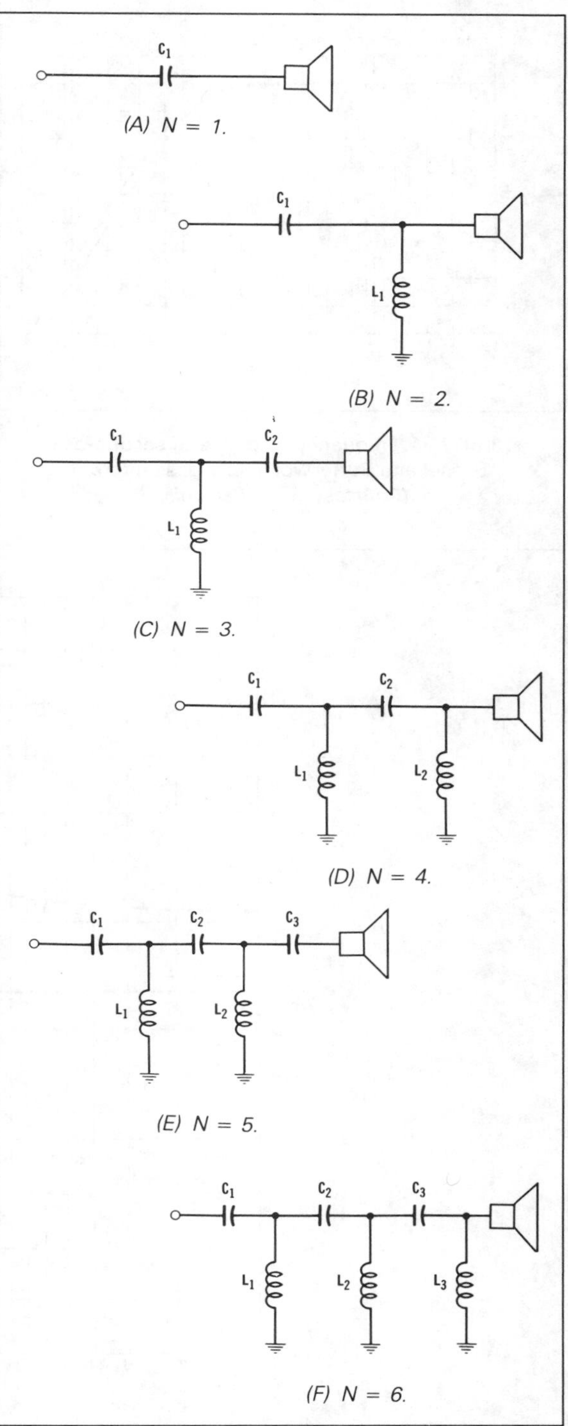

Figure 14-83 High-pass circuits for N = 1 through N = 6.

more well-behaved group delay characteristic, which is shown in Fig. 14-85. This is the same as phase response. The following are the constants for the second-order Bessel; $K_{L1} = 1.362$ and $K_{C1} = 0.454$. Use these in place of K_{L1} and K_{C1} for the second-order Butterworth, which are 0.7071 and 1.414, respectively. The inductor is larger (thus the rolloff starts a little sooner), and the capacitor is smaller (thus the Q of the filter is lower) and the phase, or group delay or transient response is better (less ringing). High-pass design follows suit as discussed.

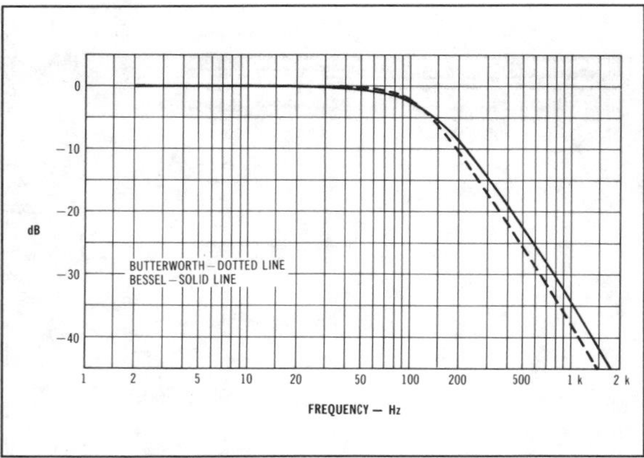

Figure 14-84 Frequency response of second-order Bessel and Butterworth low-pass filters. *(Courtesy Gene Patronis)*

Empirical Passive Crossovers

Often the passive crossover of a commercial system was designed empirically, with the crossover components approximated by the previous kinds of relationships. Some are even done from scratch with no calculation. When matching one component to another, things like "good sound" power handling, cost, and asymmetric response shapes of the components at crossover are considered. The world is not linear. This is not meant as an exposé by any means. It merely shows what goes on. Often, a single capacitor can be an astonishing hi-fi crossover and a complicated network with equalization, can end up producing rather unfamiliar sounds. The crossover can employ, for instance, a series RC parallel network to depress midrange, and the crossover components will see this network as part of the loudspeaker. Its values will be based on the series impedance of the equalization network as well as that of the component. The point is, the

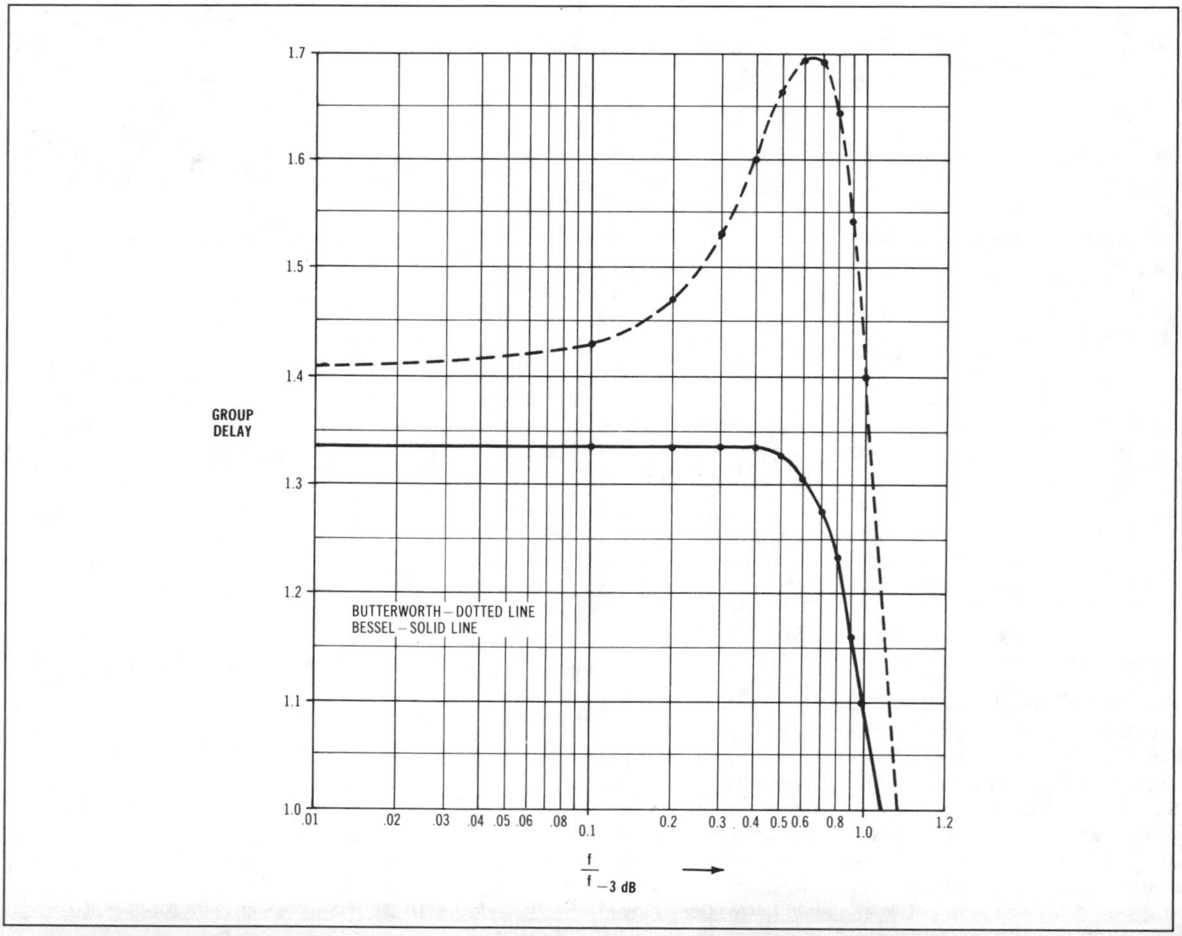

Figure 14-85 Group delay of Butterworth and Bessel filters *(Courtesy Gene Patronis)*

seemingly hard-and-fast relationships presented previously often quickly go by the wayside when trying to make it work. This is where the art comes in and the technology leaves; music, feel, and personal taste take over. Each product on the market is a personal statement of opinion on how music should sound. It's an amazing business.

14.17.2.3 Example of the Butterworth Crossover Design

A three-way system is to be constructed. It consists of a 15-in. direct-radiator woofer in a box, a theater-type compression driver on a multicellular horn for midrange and most highs, and a beryllium-dome direct-radiator super-tweeter for the top one and one-half octaves. Crossover frequencies are 630 Hz and 8 kHz; sensitivities for low, mid, and high are 96, 108, and 96 dB/1 W/1 m. All components are 8 Ω, with a dc resistance of 5.6 Ω. The theater driver, because of its 12-dB sensitivity over the other components, will be operated on the other side of an 8-Ω attenuator (i.e., the crossover will see 8 Ω for the midrange). An 18-dB/octave crossover is chosen for all components.

The low pass for the woofer is first. From our chart,

$$L_1 = 0.5(5.6)/2\pi 630$$
$$= 0.00071\,H(0.7mH)$$
$$C_1 = 1.333/2\pi 630(5.6)$$
$$= 6 \times 10^{-5}F(60\,\mu F)$$
$$L_2 = 1.5(5.6)/2\pi 630$$
$$= 2.12\,mH$$

Midrange high pass (630 Hz) is

$$C_1 = (1/0.5)/2\pi 630(8)$$
$$= 63\,\mu F$$
$$L_1 = (1/1.333)8/2\pi 630$$
$$= 1.51\,mH$$
$$C_2 = (1/1.500)/2\pi 630(8)$$
$$= 21\,\mu F$$

Midrange low pass (8000 Hz) is

$$L_1 = 0.5(8)/2\pi 8000$$
$$= 0.08\,mH$$
$$C_1 = 1.333/2\pi 8000(8)$$
$$= 3.32\,\mu F$$
$$L_2 = 1.5(8)/2\pi 8000$$
$$= 0.24\,mH$$

High-frequency high pass (8000 Hz) is

$$C_1 = (1/0.5)/2\pi 8000(5.6)$$
$$= 7.1\,\mu F$$
$$L_1 = (1/1.333)5.6/2\pi 8000$$
$$= 0.15\,mH$$
$$C_2 = (1/1.5)/2\pi 8000(5.6)$$
$$= 2.37\,\mu F$$

The final circuit is shown in Fig. 14-86.

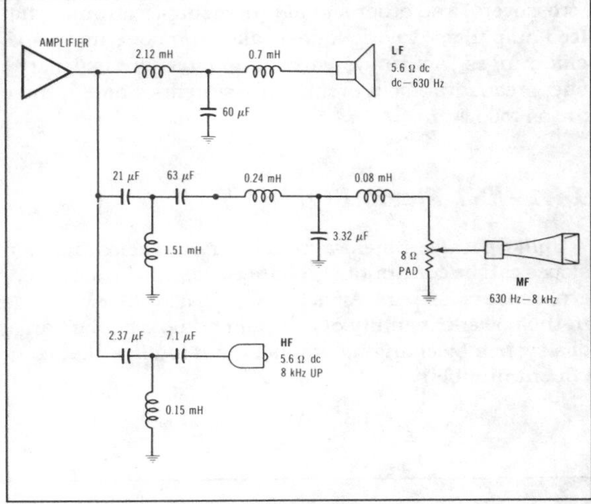

Figure 14-86 Final three-way Butterworth crossover.

14.17.2.4 Selection of Components for Passive Crossovers

Capacitors normally used vary. The best sounding and the most expensive are the Mylar™ and polypropylene high-voltage variety for small values (ganged in parallel to about 10 μF) and oil-filled (high-voltage, motor-run) capacitors for large values. Motor start, nonpolarized electrolytics and series plus-to-plus electrolytics do not sound as good (when used in series as a component as in the high-pass filters), although paralleling them with a small high-quality shunting capacitor (e.g., a 1- or 2- μF Mylar™) can improve the quality of sound. For low-pass filters, any type of capacitor can be used; however, the choice of inductor is more critical since it is the series element. The best-sounding inductors (low distortion) are air core; however, they tend to have higher dc resistance than iron-core varieties, since inductance is lower per turn.

Air-core inductors should be tightly wound and are preferably potted in an epoxy or polyester resin to eliminate sometimes audible distortion caused by inter-winding looseness and resulting mechanical motion. Those who wish to wind their own coils should make the final coil the aspect ratio of an approximate cube. The chart in Fig. 14-87 will show approximately how many turns are required to produce various values of inductance. The heavier the wire, the better; however, this means less inductance per turn—a heavier coil. Number 16 wire is a good start for most woofer coils, and number 18 is good for midrange and high frequency due to their inherently higher damping.

14.17.3 Active Systems

Active systems typically employ line-level filter sections (crossovers) and other signal-processing electronics that feed amplifiers driving loudspeaker components in specific ranges. Active systems, although more expensive, offer great advantages over passive systems. Some of these are as follows.

14.17.3.1 Flexibility

Unlike passive systems, crossover frequencies and even slopes can be continuously changed easily on many modern, active crossovers. An active system allows easy change in the power capability of a system or a particular range of a system by changing amplifier and loudspeaker component numbers.

14.17.3.2 Control

Crossovers may be located close to other control electronics (such as preamplifiers and mixers) so that system balance can be made. (Crossover frequency and level is as easily controlled as any other line-level system change.) Also, additional line-level signal processors (such as time delay, equalization, and compression) may be used in any frequency range desired. This is not possible with a passive system.

14.17.3.3 Isolation and Impedance Independence

A passive crossover is designed around components with specific impedances. If these impedances change, crossover frequencies as well as filter Q and thus response shape and damping will change. A 16-Ω component added to an 8-Ω crossover may result in a system with poor frequency response and ringing transient behavior. In an active system, the impedance variation of the loudspeaker component is not felt upstream by the crossover. Typical loudspeaker components vary widely in impedance across their intended band of use, and a passive crossover is designed, normally, for the minimum of the loudspeaker or even dc impedance. The active system is not affected by loudspeaker impedance changes as long as the amplifier has good damping. Moreover, as more components are connected to the amplifier in an active

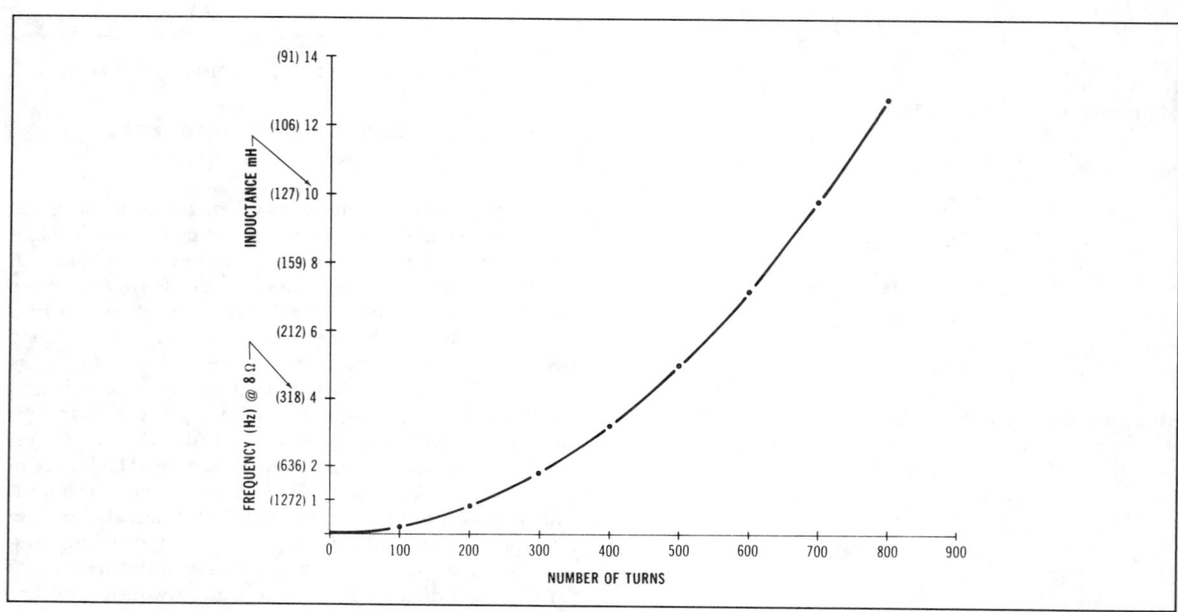

Figure 14-87 Approximate inductance for air-core inductors. $L = 2 \times 10^{-8} N$ for 1-in. outside diameter × 2-in. long core, number 16 wire.

system for increased output, crossover frequencies do not change. The complete opposite occurs with a passive crossover. Lastly, and of great importance, is the fact that no passive series components are introduced in the active system. The purist appreciates this fact; there is less complication, no series components, better sound. This is probably most important for bass. Those who have heard the difference between 30 ft of number 10 cable and 4 ft of the same on the transient bass accuracy and detail appreciate the need for maintenance of a high damping factor. A typical passive crossover necessarily inserts at least one if not several large inductors in series with the low-frequency device. The lower the low-frequency/mid-frequency or low-frequency/high-frequency crossover and the higher the rolloff slope (decibels per octave), the longer the wire used in the inductors; therefore, the worse the damping factor for the woofer. Heavier wire improves this; however, the highest quality low-frequency inductors are number 16 wire air core and are expensive. The active system makes a direct connection between the amplifiers and the loudspeaker components, and the smart, active system designer places the amplifiers as close to the components as possible.

14.17.4 Sound Reinforcement

Sound-reinforcement systems are generally complete systems intended for music, voice, or other signals. They can be used as sole sources or to augment portions of an audio presentation, such as voice only in the presence of amplified instruments or drums. There are two distinct categories of systems for two distinct purposes: "house" systems for the listeners and "stage" systems or "stage monitors" for the musicians or performers.

14.17.4.1 Low-Distortion Loudspeaker Design

Most sound systems, especially those used for musical sound reinforcement, are normally designed with respect to the bulk specifications of system parts. These are supplied by their respective manufacturers in the form of response, distortion, impedance, and so on.

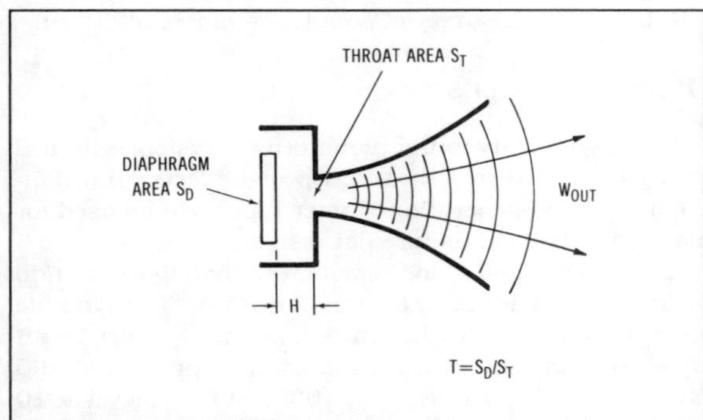

Figure 14-88 A diaphragm driving a horn via a compression chamber.

Another way to look at system design is by using predictable behavior of two simple loudspeaker mechanisms. These are volume displacement-limited low-frequency peak power capability and throat distortion. Using these, we can choose the number of components and number of frequency bands, including their crossover frequencies.

The following are some simple relationships describing these mechanisms.

Diaphragm Driving a Horn via a Compression Chamber

Referring to Fig. 14-88,

$$W_{out}\,(peak) = 0.00472\,(f^2 X_{max}{}^2\, S_D T N)\ (acoustic\ watts) \tag{14-52}$$

where,

f is the frequency of interest in hertz,
X_{max} is the diaphragm throw in inches,
S_D is the throat area in in.^{2},
T is the compression ratio,
N is the number of drivers in a cluster.

Given a peak output power and driver parameters, we can solve for f_c, at the required cutoff (−3 dB). This will prevent diaphragm bottoming onto the phase plug by a factor of 1.4:

$$fc = (14.6/X_{max})\sqrt{W_{out}\,(peak)/NS_D T}\quad Hz \tag{14-53}$$

Consequently, the number of drivers required for a given crossover frequency can be also found by solving for N;

$$N = W_{out}\,(peak)/0.00472\, f^2\, X_{max}{}^2 S_D T \tag{14-54}$$

Second Harmonic Distortion (2HD)

So-called "throat distortion" is a function of various driver parameters, including f_{pg}, which is the flare rate of the phase plug of the driver. Second harmonic distortion is found as follows:

$$2HD = (0.4f/f_{pg})\sqrt{W_{out}(avg)/S_T N} \tag{14-55}$$

This is basically the same equation as equation 9.33, pg. 275 of *Acoustics* by Leo Beranek (McGraw-Hill)[73], only an empirical constant of 0.4 is used, as per direct measurements on axis of normal exponential horns. Constant-directivity or directivity-control horns should probably use a lower value, say 0.2 or so. Because of beaming or directivity index (DI) increasing with frequency increase, it is not unusual for exponential horns to have high-frequency DI increases in the order of 3 dB/octave or greater. Therefore, a 5-kHz sine wave that generates 5% harmonic distortion in the horn could easily net 10% distortion or more *on axis*, as the second harmonic (10 kHz) is amplified by the DI rise. This directivity equalization helps draw smooth on-axis curves, but it also does the reverse to on-axis distortion. The frequency f_{pg} has been used in place of Beranek's (Thuras et al.'s) cutoff frequency f_c. This is, of course, the cutoff frequency of the exponential horn connected to the driver. Most drivers have an exponentially expanding air channel or channels in them, called the phase plug and throat. A horn of much greater cutoff (fast flare) than f_{pg} is sometimes connected to the driver, which may reduce the distortion at lower frequencies. However, at high frequencies, this is probably a good number to use. Lastly, this is an excellent relative equation for comparing various system designs.

The total throat area NS_D required for a tolerable distortion ceiling is found by rewriting Eq. 14-55 in terms of NS_T:

$$\text{total throat area} = NS_T$$

$$= (0.16\,W_{out}(\text{avg})/S_T)\left(\frac{f/f_{pg}}{2\,HD}\right)^2 \text{in.}^2 \qquad (14\text{-}56)$$

where,

S_T is the throat area in in.^{2}

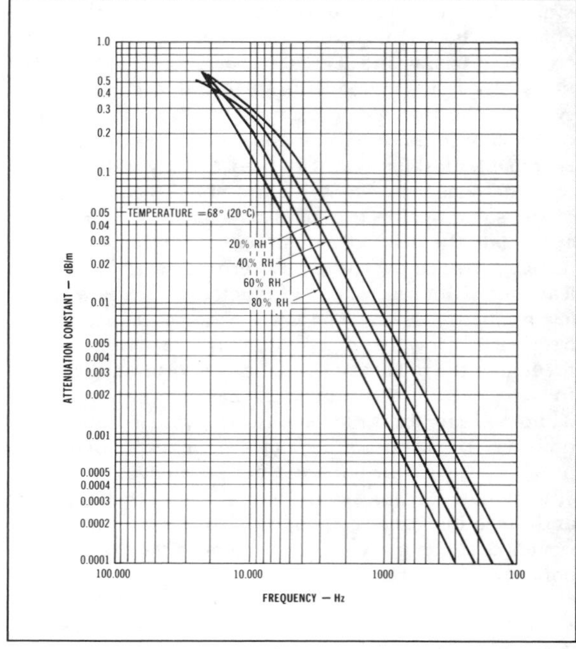

Figure 14-89 Effects of air absorption on high-frequency response. *(Courtesy Synergetic Audio Concepts)*

Air Absorption of Sound and Distortion

Long-distance throw of sound, especially at high frequencies, can become a major distortion-producing mechanism at high or even moderate levels to the listener. The extra gain required at the driver to compensate for high-frequency loss results in much higher distortion than normal. For example, a throw of 30 m at 10,000 Hz requires between 4.5 dB (80% humidity) and 9 dB (20% humidity) more gain due to air absorption. Referring to Eq. 14-55, we find that this increase in power level at the throat of the driver results in between 2.25 and 4.5 dB more distortion (a factor of 1.7 and 2.8 times higher distortion, respectively). The air absorption curve in Fig. 14-89 should be consulted for calculations of this nature.

Using These Equations to Design a System

a. Determine the average/continuous and peak levels of acoustical power required in watts, W_{out} versus frequency. This assumes that power is converted into sound pressure level at the listening position with directivity (i.e., further areas are covered with higher-directivity horns). This results in the good design practice of all drivers in the cluster operating at the same power level.

b. Determine the maximum tolerable distortion versus frequency at the maximum (avg) power level.

c. Choose a driver for this high-frequency range. Using Eq. 14-56 and the highest frequency of interest, determine the total throat area required from W_{out} and driver parameters.

d. Choose the number of drivers required by dividing NS_T by S_T for the individual driver.

e. If N is acceptable, proceed. If not, relax the power output, raise the distortion limit, or choose a new driver.

f. Using Eq. 14-53, find the cutoff frequency of the cluster, based on peak power, limited by X_{max}.

g. Choose the next driver down. If f_c is higher than the power response rolloff of the next component down, determine if this hole in the power response is acceptable. If so, proceed. If not, choose more drivers and reiterate.

h. Repeat a through g until the system is complete.

Table 14-1 is a survey of popular commercial drivers.

Design Examples

a. A high-quality sound-reinforcement system is needed for a small, 500-seat theater. Special effects and high-quality second-generation master tapes will be used for playback. This will require flat response from 50 Hz to 5 kHz with a gradual rolloff to not more than 6 dB down to 10 kHz as determined by the music director. The dynamic or peak-to-average level of the signals is typically 16 dB (40X) and an average-continuous listening level of 100 dB is required at the seats. A 10% distortion level at 10 kHz and 5% at 600 Hz is not to be exceeded at the maximum sound pressure level. From geometric calculations

Table 14-1. Output Distortion of Various Commercial Drivers on Exponential Horns

Driver	f_{pg}	S_D, in.^{2}	S_T, in.^{2}	X_{max}in.	2HD 2 kHz	2HD 5 kHz	2HD 8 kHz	W_{out}
TAD 2001	350	3.1	0.39	0.018	2.2	4.5	7.1	0.25
Altec 288	225	6.3	0.63	0.025	2.2	4.5	5.0	0.25
JBL 2440,1	225	12.5	1.25	0.025	2.0	4.5	6.3	0.25
TAD 4001	225	12.5	1.25	0.025	1.8	4.5	7.1	0.25
					2HD 200 Hz	**2HD 500 Hz**	**2HD 800 Hz**	W_{out}
CL & S M4	150	40.0	0.08	0.10	0.1*	0.1*	0.1*	0.25
					0.25*	0.63*	2.0*	3.00

*Plane Wave Tube (PWT) Measurement

of the room, it is determined that 2.5 acoustic watts average (100-W peak) is needed across the flat portion of the band and 0.6 W is required at 10 kHz. Using Eq. 14-56, and a JBL 2441 driver;

$$NS_T = 0.16(0.6)[(10{,}000/225)/10\%]^2$$
$$= 1.9$$

This driver has 1.26 in.^{2} of (real) throat area, and thus two are chosen to exceed 1.9 in.^{2} as required. This works out well for coverage also. Now, using Eq. 14-53,

$$f_c = (14.6/0.025)\sqrt{100/2(12.5)(10)}$$
$$= 370\,\text{Hz}$$

The crossover frequency is chosen at 500 Hz, due to available horns, and a classic two-way system is set up. Since 600 Hz will be mostly handled by the high-frequency driver, the low-distortion spec is guaranteed. As a check, using Eq. 14-55,

$$2HD = 0.4(600/255)\sqrt{2.5/(1.25(2)}$$
$$= 1\%$$

We choose a pair of 15-in. (140 in.^{2}) drivers in bass horns, each having a 140-in.^{2} throat, for use below 500 Hz. To check if this is all right at 50 Hz, use Eq. 14-54

$$N = 100/0.00472(50)^2(0.025)^2(140)(1)$$
$$= 0.97\ \text{low-frequency drivers}$$

b. Another example is a 5000-seat theater. This requires a 25-acoustic-W average (1000-W peak) and a 6-W average at 10,000 Hz. Using Eq. 14-56 and the same drivers,

$$NS_T = 0.16(6)[(10{,}000/225)/10]^2$$
$$= 19\ \text{in.}^2$$

Thus, we need 15 drivers having 1.25 in.^{2} of throat area. The theater owner says he only wants six drivers because of expense and because the cluster will be too complicated. This raises the 2HD to 16% at 10 kHz at a 6-average/continuous-acoustic-W total. Using Eq. 14-53,

$$f_c = (14.6/0.025)\sqrt{1000/10(12.5)(6)}$$
$$= 674\,\text{Hz}$$

Of the 15-in. drivers surveyed, none have flat power response much above 250 Hz. The environment is much more reverberent than the 500-seater, making this over-one-octave hole unacceptable to the system designer. A Community Light & Sound, Inc., M4 midrange driver is chosen and crossed over at 1000 Hz on top, making it much easier on the high-frequency units. Using Eq. 14-55,

$$2HD = [0.4(1000)/150]\sqrt{25/8(1)}$$
$$= 4.7\%\ \text{for 1 M4 driver}$$

Using Eq. 14-53,

$$f_c = (14.6/0.10)\sqrt{1000/(1)(40)(5)}$$
$$= 326\,\text{Hz}$$

We want the crossover frequency lower, so two M4 drivers are chosen, bringing the cutoff to 230 Hz, which is acceptable with respect to the power response of the woofers. This selection brings the distortion at 1000-Hz crossover to 3.3% at 25 acoustic watts out of the system. For the low-frequency section, using 15-in. drivers and Eq. 14-54

$$N = 1000/0.00472(50)^2(0.25)^2\,140(T = 1)$$
$$= 9.7\ \text{low-frequency drivers}$$

Special Considerations and Limitations Herein

Vented boxes are not covered by equations herein; they relate to drivers in horns. The spectral distribution of the music signals presented will have to be considered. Speech may have much more level centered around 500 Hz than wide-range musical material; commercial pop recordings may have 6-dB peak-to-average levels, whereas direct-to-disk and master tape recordings may approach 20 dB.

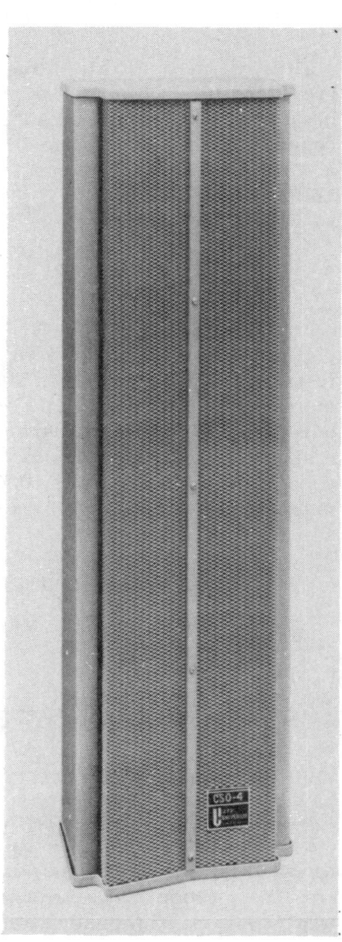

(A) University Sound CSO-4 phase-aligned column loudspeaker. (Courtesy Altec Lansing Corp.)

(B) University Sound CS-2 Uni-line sound column loudspeaker (Courtesy Altec Lansing Corp.)

Figure 14-90 Two column loudspeakers.

However, at the least, these methods presented will provide accurate and fair comparisons of a variety of system designs for a given application. Lastly, clusters are sometimes operated with some drivers at higher levels than others. Good directivity control and cluster design should assure that all drivers operate close to the same levels, but this is not always the case. If not, the relationships presented may still be used to evaluate the capabilities of the system by showing how the hotter run components will limit the maximum output of the system.

14.17.4.2 House Systems

Column loudspeakers were one of the first successful vocal systems, becoming very popular in the late 1950s. Fig. 14-90A shows a typical column loudspeaker, University Sound CSO-4, consisting of four 8-in. cone loudspeakers, intended for speech reinforcement in moderate power applications. The concept is simple: a vertical line array of small (typically 8-in.) loudspeakers gives a wide horizontal and a tight vertical pattern. Unfortunately, the pattern is frequency-dependent, and as the frequency lowers, the dispersion increases to a point where the dispersion is omnidirectional. At the upper frequencies, the loudspeaker begins to beam, and comb filters develop. Multiple drivers give improved power handling and a relatively lightweight unit can be made relatively inexpensively.

Probably the most successful column loudspeaker system design was the Shure Vocal Master. As a voice only system, the Vocal Master literally became a standard fixture in lounges and bars across the country. It had a clear, intelligible midrange and was perfect for vocal reinforcement to be heard over standard instrument amplifiers and drums.

Electro-Voice has been an active advocate and practitioner of line-array loudspeakers. Unique to this manufacturer are a pair of focused line-array loudspeakers, the LR-4A and the LR-4B, a recent successor to the 4A, shown with the grille removed in Fig. 14-91. The nonparallel loudspeaker alignment of the LR-4B is said to correct some phase-canceling problems associated with column loudspeakers.

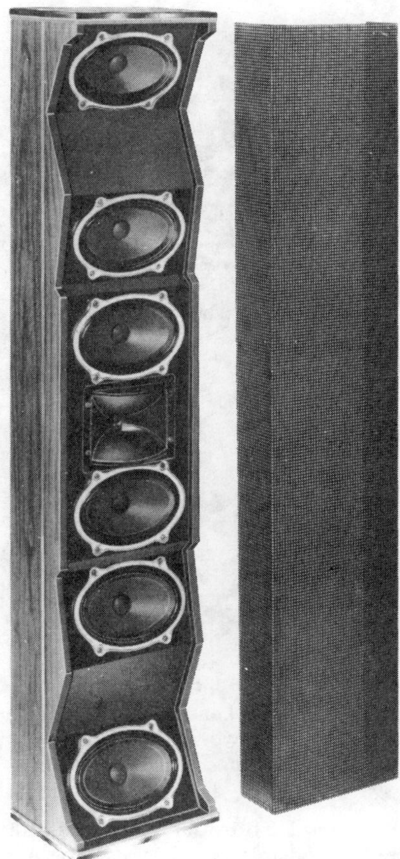

Figure 14-91 Electro-Voice LR-4B phase-aligned column loudspeaker. *(Courtesy Electro-Voice, Inc.)*

Another small, portable, multidriver system is the Bose Corp. pro line, consisting of eight small (4-in.) drivers in a small box, as shown in Fig. 14-92. This is literally a strange turn-around, since the Bose public address system evolved from the direct-reflecting concept, which had astounding marketing success in consumer hi-fi. In the original Bose format, the eight speakers faced into corners of the room and a single ninth speaker direct radiated at the listener; the reinforcement Bose dropped the ninth speaker and turned the loudspeaker 180°. The loudspeaker by itself has poor low- and high-frequency response; therefore, it comes with an active equalizer to boost the appropriate frequencies.

Figure 14-92 Bose Pro-Public Address loudspeaker with equalizer. *(Courtesy Bose Corp.)*

Interestingly, all these successful designs had clear efficient midrange, thus excellent vocal reproducibility.

In the 1960s, more power was needed as rock-and-roll music got louder and more instruments were amplified by the sound system, including drums. Groups started using the Altec Lansing A-7 shown in Fig. 14-93, which

Figure 14-93 Altec Lansing A-7-800 theater/ entertainment two-way loudspeaker. *(Courtesy Altec Lansing Corp.)*

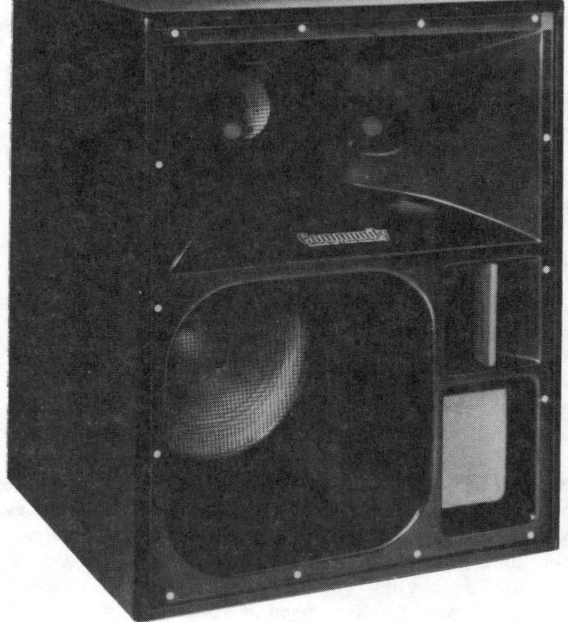

Figure 14-94 Community RS-440 four-way high-power portable loudspeaker system. *(Courtesy Community Light & Sound, Inc.)*

became a standard fixture for years and still is used extensively for moderate power levels. The A-7 became well known from its use in theater applications where its superb vocal intelligibility was required.

As power levels increase, a two-way concept becomes inadequate for power output and distortion reasons, and three- and four-way systems become necessary.

Fig. 14-94 shows a four-way system, Community Light & Sound, Inc., Model RS-440, which employs a novel all-fiberglass face plate mounted on a wooden box. All the horns, including an exponential bass coupler, are lined up using time-delay measurement techniques (TDS/TEF) so that all frequencies arrive in time synchronization. This unit employs a 15-in. woofer, 4-in. throat compression-loaded 6½-in. midrange unit (for lower mid-frequency distortion and power), a 1-in. compression driver and two specially configured piezoelectric drivers with a sensitivity-boosting bandpass circuit. Crossover frequencies are 300 Hz, 1200 Hz, and 10 kHz, with a claimed response of 45 to 20 kHz and sensitivity of 100 dB/1 W/1 m.

Peavey has engineered a large four-way all-horn system shown in Fig. 14-95, which uses a large mid-bass horn for low midrange (100 to 1000 Hz), driven by a sensitive, high-powered 12-in. loudspeaker compression loaded by a circumferential-slit phase plug. The rest of the system uses standard components, but the midrange is a recent innovation for higher vocal clarity and low distortion not possible with a two-way system. Although this is a small overview, it illustrates typical examples of most types of reinforcement systems. The actual numbers of products and manufacturers is staggering.

14.17.4.3 Stage Systems

As late as the mid 1960s, musicians and especially singers used to perform without stage monitors, depending on diffracted sound from the house system for hearing themselves. Many singers went hoarse and sang out of tune as a result. The stage monitor changed it all and resulted in the emergence of a diabolic and ever-maddening new position in pro audio: the monitor mixer.

Musicians and performers who can hear themselves loudly and clearly can play better and enjoy playing more. It is common to have eight or more separate monitor mixes (therefore, separate amplifier and equalization systems) for a large-scale performance. Monitors are usually high-output systems, which are sometimes necessary for raising monitored signals above stage sound pressure levels. This is particularly demanding on monitor systems for

Figure 14-95 Peavey four-way all horn portable concert system. *(Courtesy Peavey Electronic Corp.)*

Figure 14-96 Altec "Stanley-Screamer" SS-2050 wide-angle stage monitor. *(Courtesy Altec Lansing Corp.)*

loud all-guitar Marshall-Stack rock-and-roll bands. There is a variety of types of monitor techniques or "styles" in use.

The first and most typical is the large, wide-angle floor monitor, Fig. 14-96 manufactured and designed for Altec by Stanal Sound (Kearney, Nebraska) under the trademark Stanley Screamers.™ It uses a pair of 15-in. bass drivers and a wide-angle (120°) horn and compression driver. The wide angle of coverage allows the performer to move around and still hear the monitor output. It can also be used singularly for a group of singers or a horn section, making it economical regarding stage space.

The "spot" floor monitor is used for more stationary or localized monitoring and has a much narrower coverage angle. The Community Light & Sound, Inc., NC-12 two-way monitor is such a system, which is all fiberglass in construction and intended for a 12-in. low-frequency driver and a 1-in. flange-mount or ¾-in. screw-in high-frequency driver. Crossover is recommended at 1500 Hz, and the horn provides a very tight high-frequency coverage pattern. The John Meyer Model system is similar, only it uses a narrow-angle conical horn on a larger-throat driver. The Meyer system consists of both a loudspeaker box and an electronics package containing power amplifiers, an electronic crossover, compression, time-and-amplitude equalization, and a level-sensitive automatic bandpass circuit. Normally, the system operates full range, but when the level rises due to the signal being monitored (i.e., being on a vocal), the low frequency and high frequency reduces, bringing the monitored signal "out" more than in a normal gain change. The effect is better vocal intelligibility (more midrange), especially for very high stage sound pressure levels, the intended use of this rather expensive but very effective system.

An alternative to the floor monitors is the near-field monitor, such as the Galaxy Audio Hot Spot.™ This approach is to bring a small relatively low-powered loudspeaker system close to the performer, thereby letting the inverse-square law save money (less expensive loudspeaker and amps). This is a very acceptable solution for many applications.

The logical extension of the near-field stage monitor is the headphone. Many headphones are available (section 14.18), but a particular device, the Shure SM-14 (Fig. 14-97) is a high-level dual headphone-and-microphone headset, which is intended for and is apparently successfully used by drummer/vocalists. The relatively cosmetic appearance of the SM-14A makes it more attractive to a performer not wanting to appear to be wearing headphones, and the monitoring approach of putting the signal right in the ears is certainly the most direct.

14.17.5 Studio Monitor Systems

A studio monitor should be many things. First, it should be a high-fidelity reference; the widest bandwidth, highest dynamic range, lowest distortion, most musical-

Figure 14-97 Shure professional headphone/microphone set SM14A. *(Courtesy Shure Brothers, Inc.)*

sounding device possible. The latter is an impassioned subject of great diversity. It should also be a test device for the commercial product produced in studios—commercial musical art. Therefore, studio monitors range from $6000 four-way quad-amped behemoths to bookshelf loudspeakers (representing home loudspeakers) to small 4-in. loudspeakers and table radios hard-wired to the consoles. Some studios even broadcast recently mixed music to the artists and/or producers in their cars, listening to their latest would-be hit in the studio lot.

One opinion popular among recording engineers is that if a system is really correct, good recordings monitored on *it* will sound good anywhere, even on bad loudspeakers. Another opinion is that an engineer or producer "adopts" a certain loudspeaker, which he or she learns to use, in spite of possible shortcomings. The personal monitor is the acoustic translator between the sound of the microphones, the console and tape, and the actual recording. Many successful engineer/producers use the same loudspeaker system all the time because they have learned how to translate the sound out of the loudspeaker into the groove on the vinyl, which will be a "hit sound" on all loudspeakers. Some producers will even bring their own loudspeaker system into a strange studio. Aside from being a translating device, a big accurate hi-fi monitor system (delivering noiseless, flat power response, low-distortion, accurate stereo image, impact, and high peak output) acts as a magnifying glass—a scrutinizer. When recording and monitoring specific instruments, the big monitor system may be turned up to high levels, making the instrument(s) under scrutiny many times larger than life. This way, small details may be heard very clearly, and small faults, easily corrected. If this detailing is done to all instruments being recorded, a superior multitrack recording can be made. On a small low-powered system, this kind of attention to sonic detail is not possible, which is the major advantage of a large, high-quality monitor system. Music from large loudspeakers can hurt and even damage the listener; they can also be the ultimate listening pleasure. The latter is the reason for music (from loudspeakers or other musical instruments).

A common format for studio loudspeakers is the coaxial, which consists of an up-the-center compression driver and horn combination for high frequency and a coaxial low-frequency driver, all built on the same structure. One of the favorite coaxial monitors in recording history, and certainly a unique system, is the Altec Lansing 604, as shown in Fig. 14-98. The 604 is unique in that it uses two separate magnet structures and diaphragms on a single frame; it is actually a two-way concentric system with the high-frequency horn up the middle. The 604 works best in a 9-ft^3 enclosure vented at about 38 Hz, as in Altec's model 620 enclosure. The sound of the 604 is very specific—an opinion as valid as any. However, its geometry yields a great and unique advantage; the point source quality gives probably the best stereo image available. A similar coaxial loudspeaker, which is popular in the U.K. is the Tannoy monitor. The Tannoy exhibits

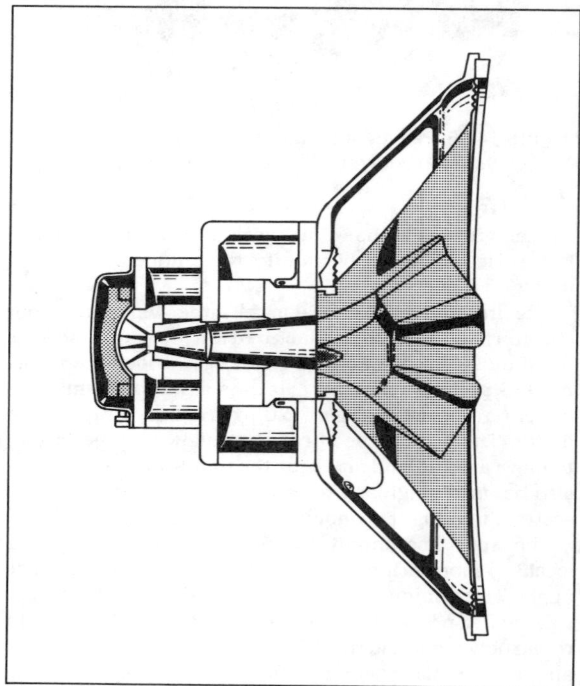

Figure 14-98 Cutaway showing the internal construction of an Altec Lansing 604E coaxial loudspeaker. *(Courtesy Altec Lansing Corp.)*

similar image localization properties as the 604, but it is unique in that it actually uses the low-frequency cone as the bell of the high-frequency cone. Great debates abound on whether or not the low-frequency modulated hornbell gives distortion, but that is another opinion on sound. Its proponents have accepted it and use it successfully in making commercial products. The Tannoy is interesting in that it uses a circular-hole matrix phasing plug for the high-frequency section.

The 604 has been used by many other loudspeaker companies as the loudspeaker for their system.

Audio-Techniques marketed a Big Red series, using a stock 604 but supplying a special crossover that used air core inductors, allegedly better-sounding capacitors, different crossover points, and passive equalization.

The most successful version of the 604, however, resulted from the collaboration of Bill Putnam and Ed Long, both long-time audio pioneers and mutual friends. Ed Long developed the concept of Time Align™, where the signal to the woofer is delayed (in the crossover network) in time so that at crossover acoustic signals from the low frequency and the high frequency arrived at the listener in phase and in time synchronization. Bill Putnam licensed the Time Align™ method from Long, and it was applied to the 604 for UREI. Putnam, assisted by and in real collaboration with his son Bill, Jr., developed three models shown in Fig. 14-99. The loudspeakers were tested and measured in the air on a tower lift facility. The UREI monitors used a stock Alnico 604, a newly developed horn with improvements for reducing distortion and horn shadow (called a diffraction buffer), a Time Align™ crossover with equalization and superb quality control testing. The two larger monitors used one and two additional 15-in. woofers for more low-frequency power (biampable), needed in larger control rooms. The foam horn lips as well as acoustic filtering slots in the horn bell were

Figure 14-99 UREI time align coaxial studio monitor systems from the "A" series. *(Courtesy JBL Inc./UREI)*

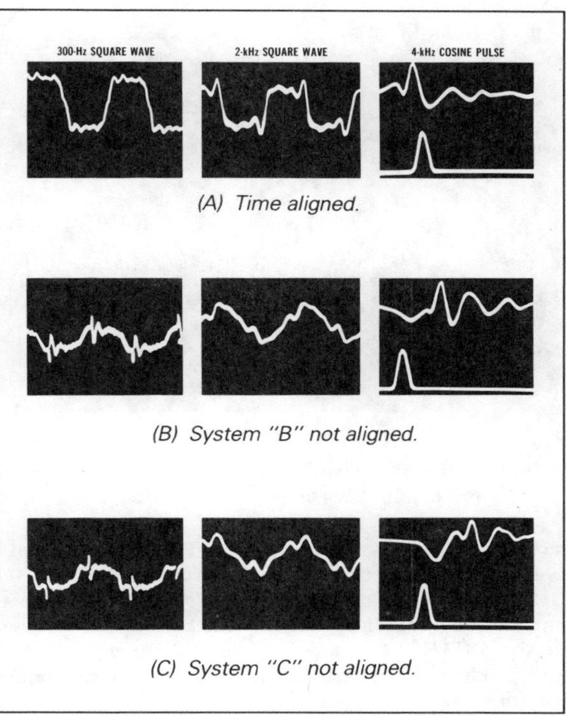

Figure 14-100 Transient behavior of three 604 series duplex loudspeaker systems.

recent innovations to improve the high-frequency/low-frequency interface, including a shadow effect caused by the horn on the directivity pattern of the low-frequency speaker in the crossover region. Fig. 14-100 shows the output of these new monitors (Fig. 14-100A) compared to two other popular studio monitors (Figs. 14-100B and C).

Another successful (popular) expensive monitor is a series designed initially by Tom Hidley and presently under continuous development by Westlake Audio. The large Westlake monitor, currently the model TM-3F, is somewhat of a bridge between off-the-shelf systems like Altec/UREI/JBL and a full custom system. These were three way and are now four way, using a pair of vented 15-in. low-frequency drivers, a 2-in. mid-frequency compression driver (JBL) on a wooden radial diffraction horn a special 10-in. low-mid unit of their own design and a 1-in. compression driver on a diffraction horn for high-frequency, as shown in Fig. 14-101 without a grille, which covers the three cone units. In contrast to most other available monitors, the Westlake units are typically sold with oiled walnut finishes, sculptured wood parts, and matching grille materials.

In the mid 1970s Teac introduced the 80-8 ½-in. eight-track recorder for semi-pro or demo studios. This started a revolution all over the country, as countless ½-in. eight-

Figure 14-101 Westlake TM-3F studio monitor (grille removed). *(Courtesy Westlake Audio)*

track studios sprang up everywhere. Probably the most popular monitor used in these studios was the JBL 4311/4312 shown in Fig. 14-102, which also sold well in the consumer market. Many large commercial studios today use the 4311/4312 as a reference, and there are engineers/producers who use it as well as their personal monitor.

The most successful small monitor is the Auratone cube shown in Fig. 14-103. Basically a 4-in. extended midrange speaker, most commercial recording facilities have a pair of these perched above the meter panel on the console. After hours of mixing at 110 dB plus flat from 30 to 16 Hz, engineers and producers often switch these on for

Figure 14-102 JBL 4312 compact studio monitor (successor to 4311). *(Courtesy JBL Inc./UREI)*

Figure 14-103 Auratone "cube" studio monitor. *(Courtesy Auratone Corp.)*

a combination of concussion-relief and change of reference. The sound from the small loudspeaker is an indication of what the product will sound like in cars, small table radios, and portable cassette recorders. It is also a better focus on the information band of music (200 Hz to 5 kHz), which sometimes gets lost with loud large-system listening. Often, major portions of recording projects are mixed over these loudspeakers, basically a world-standard reference that uses a folded paper cone: it is the sound that matters.

14.17.6 Custom Systems

There are studios and engineers who are knowledgable enough (or dissatisfied enough with what is available off the shelf) to design their own systems. Custom systems are usually bi-, tri-, or quad-amped. Components are carefully listened to in their intended passband and selected on that basis. This includes drivers, horns, crossover networks, and even amplifiers. Discriminating listeners can select certain amplifiers for low-frequency use and others for highs and mids. This is a growing trend among privately owned studios, where the studio is a very personal statement of opinion on the recording. It is from this kind of activity that future advances in studio monitor loudspeaker and monitor facility design will probably be made. Fig. 14-104 shows a custom monitoring system used in monitoring record releases and masters. At this writing, the system is quad-amped, with crossovers at 300, 1200, and 7000 Hz. The low-frequency units are JBL 2234, mid-frequency is Community M4, high frequency is TAD4001, and ultrahigh frequency is Pioneer PT150. The latter two are beryllium-diaphragm units, the mid frequency has aluminum-foam sandwich diaphragms, and the low frequency has standard cone drivers. The low-frequency enclosures are 12 ft^3 tuned to 34 Hz and are 1½-in. thick double-laminated plywood, sturdily braced. The horns are by Community and are specially rigid-urethane-foamed into fiberglass-reinforced high-density ¾-in. thick particleboard shells. Amplification is all by Crown Int'l, as follows: low-fre-

Figure 14-104 Custom four-way system. *(Courtesy Mike Pappas/Sounds Wonderful Records)*

quency, Delta-Omega 2000; mid frequency, PSA-2; high frequency, PSA-2; and very high frequency, PL2. Crossovers are VFX-2As. This represents enormous attention to sonic detail as well as dynamic range capability.

14.17.7 Consumer Hi-Fi

This class of sound equipment is specifically intended for home use. Because many of these mass-appeal products must often excite consumer lust in hi-fi buyers to make a sale, home hi-fi products are often found with the most creative and alluring trademarks, aesthetic treatments, and identifying logos. This class of product, especially mid-priced models that are designed to attract the majority of the market, tend to have the most flagrant claims to "wowie-zowie" performance of any class of sound equipment. Since many of the buyers consider loudspeakers the product of a magical art, sometimes hilarious advertising schemes are used to make the products seem desirable.

Consumer high-fidelity loudspeakers tend to be lower in power-handling capacity and lower in sensitivity than pro loudspeakers, although some hi-fi loudspeakers are actually just cosmetically more attractive repackagings of pro components. It seems that the prime selling item or feature of most home systems is the high-frequency reproduction mechanism. Many of these are extremely wide in bandwidth but cannot produce as much peak high-frequency output as pro high-frequency devices. Thus, most commercial home hi-fi systems are usually played at lower sound pressure levels than in pro listening situations.

The following is a series of examples of successful or noteworthy home hi-fi art.

The bookshelf loudspeaker really turned consumer hi-fi around, and the three-way AR-3 and AR-3a, were probably most responsible for this. Manufactured by Acoustic Research (AR), originally of Cambridge, Massachusetts, the AR speakers popularized the acoustic suspension method of making bass, which used a very loosely suspended 12-in. woofer in a small box to produce excellent bass response. AR provided an unusually complete technical description, complete with curves of the AR-3, which measured a very even on-axis (and off-axis) response, via its dome mid- and high-frequency drivers. The AR-3 was a highly damped loudspeaker throughout. It is low in sensitivity (less than 90 dB/1 w/1 m), therefore, it is low in dynamic range. It became the unofficial producer of the "Boston Sound" due to its design philosophy, as did others like it from companies like Allison Acoustics and KLH. The AR3 was an extremely influential and successful loudspeaker. No longer made, the AR3 was replaced by the AR-50 shown in Fig. 14-105 and is very typical of most direct-radiator three-ways on the market today.

In direct opposition to this design philosophy are the West Coast Sound companies, who sold more expensive, more efficient, higher-powered systems. Altec Lansing using components developed in its motion picture theater systems (Voice of the Theater) steadfastly defended the efficient two-way system using lightweight coned woofers with strong drive motors and horns on compression drivers for high frequencies. These systems were and are large floor-standing devices, usually with carved, ornate grilles, and deluxe woodwork. Probably the best-sounding two-way loudspeaker, the Altec Model 19, which is shown in Fig. 14-106, is considered by many to be the classic two-way system. The 19 uses a 15-in. woofer and a 1-in. exit compression driver on the sectoral horn of the Altec 811B. The compression driver in the Model 19 debuted the new tangerine radial-slit phase plug.

The Bose 902 is the result of a study of orchestral music played in various halls. Dr. Amar Bose determined that 11% of all symphonic music is direct, the rest being reflected. This conveniently allows nine loudspeakers to be placed in the box, eight facing the rear and one facing

Figure 14-105 Acoustic Research AR50 three-way bookshelf loudspeaker. *(Courtesy Teledyne Acoustic Research)*

Figure 14-106 Altec Lansing model 19 two-way floor-standing loudspeaker system (grilles removed). *(Courtesy Altec Lansing Corp.)*

forward. The loudspeaker depends on reflections of the wall it is placed against and is, therefore, dependent on the absorbing/reflecting characteristics of that wall. The Bose comes with an active equalizer that is needed to flatten the loudspeaker's response by boosting the low-frequency and high-frequency ranges.

Like the AR3, most common hi-fi products rely on direct radiation of sound and a semi-endless assortment of attempts to make effective sound radiation mechanisms have been made available. The Yamaha NS-1000 system uses vapor-deposited beryllium domes for high frequency and mid frequency.[74] Other manufacturers have made domes of titanium and boronized titanium. The Sony Esprit shown in Fig. 14-107 uses flat, square plates made of an advanced honeycomb composite. The low-frequency unit uses four voice coils, and the high-frequency unit uses one, driving the extremely high stiffness-to-weight ratio plates at nodal points so that breakup is discouraged in the individual passband of the driver. Similar to the Esprit, Technics (Panasonic) manufactures flat circular plate systems; all components are made of honeycomb construction. The Technics drivers also employ a nodal drive system to encourage higher-mode breakup behavior.

Sacramento-based ESS has built an entire product line around Dr. Oskar Heil's "Air Motion Transformer." This drive method uses pleated Mylar™ with printed conductors to squeeze air into motion via its accordion-type bellows motion. The two-way AMT-1B uses a standard 12-in. low-frequency driver with a passive radiator at the rear crossed over at 800 Hz to the Heil Tweeter. The ESS Transar-ATD uses two Heil-type components per loudspeaker. A normal AMT high-frequency device sits above a vertical array of compliant polymeric membranes, all driven by vertical carbon fiber rods connected to electro-

Figure 14-107 Sony Esprit two-way system with square flat-plate aluminum honeycomb diaphragms. *(Courtesy Sony Corporation of America)*

dynamic drivers at the base. This entire array is open on both sides and radiates in a horizontal bipolar pattern by nature. Low frequencies are reproduced by a single subwoofer, and a crossover is supplied with the stereo pair.

The Ohm Walsh-2 uses a single, inverted vertical cone Walsh full-range driver at the top of the unit. A vented enclosure develops bass, and the rest of the range is direct-radiated off the back of the cone in an omnidirectional pattern.

14.17.8 Guitar Amplifiers

Modern musicians depend heavily on electronics for their "sound." This has never been a truer statement than for the electric guitarist, a musician whose instrument is literally both the guitar and the amplification system. Electric guitarists constantly spend a significant portion of their musical activity time on improving their instrument. They are frequently in music stores, pawn shops, or the car running down for sale ads, trying new and, more so, vintage guitars. The same is true for amplifiers. Loudspeakers are replaced; pickups are added, subtracted, wired out-of-polarity; and capacitors in tone controls are changed. Since the early days of electric guitar amps, little has changed in concept, except for solid-state amplifiers. The typical guitar amp has an input stage or a series of them mixed together (channels). Each channel has equalization, variable gain, and often "effects" that include vibrato, reverberation (from springs), and, recently, harmonic distortion control, chorus, digital delay, remote channel selection, and others. This front end drives a monophonic power amplifier that supplies power to the loudspeakers. There are usually only two forms of physical arrangements of these. One, the self-contained amp contains all components (electronics and loudspeakers) in one housing with a carrying handle and sometimes casters on the base for ease of moving. Often, the loudspeakers are housed in an open-back cabinet. For electric guitar, this is usually sufficient baffling for low frequencies (175 Hz or so). Closed-back cabinets are also used; the open-back version is usually a necessity for tube amps, since the tubes, usually upside down at the top of the amp, need open-air ventilation. Therefore, most closed-back self-contained amps are driven with solid-state electronics, although many self-contained amps are nonetheless open-back designs, merely because many guitarists prefer that sound. The second form a guitar amp can take is separate packages for the amplifier (called the head) and the loudspeakers (called bottoms). This separated arrangement is typically used for larger systems, for ease of moving. Bottoms are almost always closed or vented boxes. Heads are higher powered and less of a compromise is made on ventilation than in the self-contained amp.

Interestingly enough, as modern solid-state amplifiers reach new levels of harmonic and transient purity, many modern guitarists still prefer the "warm" sound of vacuum tubes; the 12AX7 (7025) for preamp and the 6L6 and 6550 for power amps are the most popular. This preference is clear from merely observing the popular selling amplifiers in use.

The king of the modern electric guitarists is, of course, the concert guitarist—the recording and performing artist. Modern sound-reinforcement techniques allow small amplifiers, even direct-feed techniques, to be used on stage. Nevertheless, many guitar players still prefer to get their stage sound from their amplifier.

Certainly, the world's most commercially successful musical heros are the rock-and-roll guitarists, and of the large amplifiers available, the Marshall 100 double stack (Fig. 14-108) is the rock-and-roll concert guitarist's standard item. These acoustic battleships contain a one-channel 100-W all-tube head (no reverb or effects) and two closed-back bottoms, each housing four Celestion 12-in. loudspeakers, crafted especially for electric guitar use. It is really a one-guitar, one-sound amp. Marshalls are normally used at full output (all knobs on "10"), either singularly or in multiples, giving the concert-guitarist a rather awesome sound and output. The full output is not clean. Marshalls in concert are operated at hard, full amplifier clipping, giving a very distinctive harmonic overload desired by the modern electric guitarist (and

Figure 14-108 Marshall "4 × 12" 100-W "Stack" using Celestion 12-in. loudspeakers. *(Courtesy Marshall Amplifiers)*

much more than a 100-W output). Marshall heads do not clip into square waves like a conventional amplifier, and it is this nonlinearity that gives it its distinctive sound. Marshall also makes smaller amps for reasonable levels in more normal situations like night-club performing. These include smaller stacks and a self-contained open-back model with the controlled-distortion sound of the biggies.

Probably the most successful self-contained guitar amplifier made is the all-tube Fender Twin-Reverb, designed by Leo Fender, thought by many to be the commercial father of the modern electric guitar. There are hundreds of amps like the Twin, but its success and acceptance makes it a standard. Twins sound good both clean and at full clip, which makes them very versatile. They have two channels; one "dry" with equalization and one with switchable reverb and vibrato. A 90-W power amplifier drives two stock or special 12-in. loudspeakers, housed in an open-back cabinet.

The Mesa Boogie® (Fig. 14-109) is a notable exception to the Twin. This popular pro amplifier was designed as the highest output amp possible within a single 12-in. loudspeaker with a self-contained format. The Boogie® contains a lot of now-copied advances, such as XLR (Cannon) outputs for studio recording and advanced equalization. The Boogie® is a smaller package than the twin, loud enough for stage use and compact enough to carry into the studio.

The Pignose started a revolution in small practice amplifiers. Battery-powered, the Pignose has clean, hum-free electronics (via battery power supply) and can be put into a napsack. They can be operated at full clip for an enjoyable distortion sound, or clean at lower levels. Pignoses are ideal recording amplifiers, because they do not hum.

Figure 14-109 Mesa Boogie Professional guitarists amplifier. *(Courtesy Mesa Engineering)*

The ultimate personal guitar amplifier was innovated by Tom Scholz ("Boston" guitarist/composer) for his company, Scholz Research, under the name Rockman, an obvious pun on the Sony Walkman. The Rockman contains front-end electronics with various effects like chorus and a specific distortion, which is claimed to give a desirable concert sound in the lightweight headphones. A line-level output allows the owner to record directly. Many headphone-type systems have been made available to the guitarist, but none are so specifically aimed at the electric guitarist as this.

14.17.9 Bass Amplifiers

Low E, the lowest note on the modern electric bass guitar, has a fundamental frequency of about 42 Hz. Therefore, bass amplifiers need to produce lower frequencies than guitar amplifiers, even though they are typically identical in concept and construction. There are three basic types of bass amplifiers used today; the self-contained amp, the separate head-and-bottom closed- or vented-box amp, and the separate head-and-bottom folded bass horn amp. These are typified, respectively, by the Ampeg B-15N, considered a classic by many electric bassists, especially studio types (50 W); the Ampeg SVT double (300 W) with eight 10-in. loudspeakers per cabinet; and the Acoustic 370 with one 18-in. loudspeaker driving a folded bass horn.

14.17.10 Keyboard Amplifiers

Keyboard players typically use clean, relatively flat systems without much of the passionate embraces that guitar players give their amplifiers. Often, keyboard players rely on a stage monitor and house system for their sound. One outstanding exception is the organist who uses a Leslie loudspeaker.

14.17.11 Leslie Loudspeakers[75]

First and foremost, the Leslie Rotating Loudspeaker is designed as a sound modification device. It is not a hi-fi speaker, but rather a part of a musical instrument. The Leslie Speaker System, named after its inventor, Don Leslie, operates on a simple principle. A directional sound source is rotated at constant (or variable) speed around a fixed pivot point. At a listening point some distance from this whirling affair, three things happen. First, because the source is directional, the intensity of the sound will be at a maximum when it points at the listener (or microphone). The sound intensity will increase as the rotating source approaches dead center and decrease as it rotates past this point. The resultant effect is called amplitude modulation (AM), which is a feature on any guitar amp with a vibrato or tremolo feature. By moving closer to the rotating speaker, the inverse-square law will increase the modulation effect.

However, the Leslie can also be used to create frequency modulation (FM). As the source rotates toward the listener, its relative velocity will increase the pitch of any tone it produces; as it rotates away, the pitch will be lowered. This is the same Doppler effect that causes a train whistle to rise and then fall in pitch as the train approaches and then passes.

Lastly, if you are listening in a room with any significant reverberation, a complete spatial modulation of the sound will happen, because sound is "shot" all around and goes through multiple reflections.

A practical and commercial manifestation of the Leslie principle may take on many forms. Indeed, the manufacturer of Leslie Loudspeakers, Electro Music, Inc., a division of Hammond Organ, produces a wide variety. These include models with reverberation, triple channels, and rotating cone loudspeakers. The Leslie Models 145, 147, and 122 share the same basic insides: a 40-W monophonic tube amplifier, an 800-Hz 16-Ω passive crossover, a rotating treble horn, and a rotating bass loudspeaker. Both rotating loudspeakers are available with slow and fast ac induction motors.

Furthermore, these Leslie models are similar in that they all have components mounted in a three-compartment cabinet. The top compartment houses the rotating high-frequency horn, the middle box the high- and low-frequency drivers and crossover (and which also acts as a vented box for the low-frequency driver), and the bottom compartment the low-frequency rotor and amplifier. Louvres located in the top and bottom compartments let out treble and bass sound, respectively. All the previously listed loudspeaker systems are virtually identical in terms of their use and sound quality. (The larger Models 147 and 122 allegedly have a better low end.) Both high- and low-frequency loudspeakers operate on the same principle: a stationary driver (loudspeaker) and a rotating acoustic projector.

14.17.11.1 Treble Rotor

The Leslie's high-frequency unit is largely responsible for the Leslie Sound. Some organists actually find that the bass rotor's slower response to speed changes is distracting and will actually disconnect the bass rotor drive—especially when playing a bass line. The treble unit consists of a stationary ¾-in. throat Jensen compression driver, connected to a vertical tube that acts as a thrust bearing. A twin-bell, molded black Bakelite™ horn, which starts vertically but flares horizontally, sits on this bearing/tube and rotates via a two-speed ac induction motor fitted with three (selectable) drive pulleys. This motor drives the treble horn at fast or slow speeds via a drive belt and belt tension spring. Direct current is sometimes applied to the fast motor so that it will slow down more quickly; this is called a dc brake. The treble horn actually looks like two horn assemblies; in fact, only one is operable as a horn. The other side, a "dummy" acts as a counterweight or dynamic balancer, providing symmetric air drag at high speed. The resulting structure rotates smoothly and without eccentric wobble forces.

At the mouth of the horn is a diffuser cone, which is supposed to widen the dispersion of the horn and make a more musically pleasing tone. Actually, it does work, and the results are dramatic. If the deflector is taken off, the directivity behavior is typical of a beamy straight horn, with a lot of sound concentrated on axis, and very little sound, off axis. With the diffuser on, the directivity behavior is almost omnidirectional, with a lot of multiple polar lobing. As the horn revolves, the sound will actually rise and fall a number of times, giving it an even more characteristic sound.

In real life, the horn is mounted in a louvered wooden box, which means that the picture changes somewhat with resulting internal reflections. The diffuser cone does another important thing: it shifts the apparent sound source position on the horn. With the cone in, more of the entire range of the horn will appear to come from the mouth of the horn; with it out, however, while lower frequencies still appear to come from the mouth, higher and higher frequencies will appear to come from progressively further down the throat. They, therefore, appear to be rotating at a smaller radius, which results in less frequency modulation (FM) effect. (If the directional sound source was rotating at dead center, there would be no FM effect at all.) So here we are faced with a choice: leave the deflectors in place and the result will be maximum frequency modulation, because of the very wide directional characteristics of the horn, or take the deflectors out and the FM will be lost, but you obtain very strong AM (especially at higher frequencies) due to the very narrow beam width of the naked horn.

14.17.11.2 Bass Rotor

In the lower compartment of the Leslie box is a rotating wooden drum mounted on a vertical shaft and covered with a black scrim cloth, which provides lower aerodynamic drag on the drum at fast speed. At the drum's center is a cylinder fitted with a "scoop" that, as in the treble unit, starts vertically (the bass driver faces downward into its entrance) and projects sound horizontally. The drum assembly is driven with a two-speed motor and ends up at approximately the same rotational speed as the treble unit. The only difference is that the inertia of the drum makes it approach final speed over a much longer time period. A dc braking voltage can also be applied to the fast motor to slow down the speed more quickly when switching from fast to slow.

The bass rotor appears to work as an amplitude modulation device, and only for the upper two octaves or so of the bass section (200 to 800 Hz). Frequencies lower than 200 Hz are probably unaffected by a scoop of this size, since 200 Hz has a wavelength of approximately 5.5 ft. There may be some frequency modulation effect near the 800-Hz crossover point, but it is almost all AM. The result is a low-frequency throb, which is very pleasant and especially powerful and beautiful when used in slow or chorus mode.

14.17.11.3 Complete Leslie System

With all these rotating components installed in the box, the Leslie system works as follows: an electrical signal is sent into the Leslie amplifier driving a 12-dB/octave, 16-Ω crossover, which feeds the 16-Ω bass and treble drivers with the appropriate frequency bands. Input signals, motor controls, and ac line voltage (115 V, 60 Hz) are connected to the unit via special cable plugs and sockets.

The amplifier chassis contains a 40-W amplifier fitted with 6550 tubes for instruments and motor control circuitry. Each rotor is actually driven by two separate motors (fast and slow) mounted in one package. Therefore, there are a total of four rotor motors and four pairs of wires, which all plug into the amplifier chassis.

14.17.12 Automotive Sound Systems

Automotive sound systems grew out of a natural desire on the part of the American public to make their beloved automobile a more hospitable and entertaining environment. Since the 1940s, many passenger cars have come with a radio and a small, limited-range loudspeaker mounted in the dash. Music lovers and broadcast art advanced in taste and technique, respectively; better loudspeakers, better radios (including FM), and stereo sound found their way into the passenger compartment. Gradually, cassette and eight-track tape players for the auto became available. Today, car stereo is literally as elaborate as one can afford. For instance, 2000-watts triamplified systems are manufactured by Audiomobile using procomponents, and it is capable of 130 dB with low distortion. In Detroit, General Motors Corp. has collaborated with the Framingham, Massachusetts, loudspeaker giant Bose to design the loudspeaker system and the acoustic environment of the car interior together for better sound. The true audiophile can literally spend as much money on a car system as on a home system.

The automotive environment presents a unique series of challenges to the loudspeaker designer. First of all, any loudspeaker must be either a 6 × 9-in. oval frame design to fit existing holes in cars or some other small format. They all must be very shallow, since custom mounting in car doors is a usual mounting site. Unlike most home loudspeakers, car loudspeakers must be much more resistant to the elements, especially direct sunlight, moisture, heat, and air pollution. The luxury of a closed or vented box is not possible for the add-on or stock car loudspeaker. Consequently, the loudspeakers must be designed as high-Q infinite baffle devices, the enclosure being the car trunk, the inside of the underside of a dashboard, or the air volume between the car door exterior and the interior wall, usually vinyl padding over fiberboard. Most sound radiation is indirectly reflected off windows, so stereo imaging and smooth sound are almost impossible.

A large variety of booster amplifiers are available, many with one-octave equalizers for a better sound balance. A last ultimate restriction on auto sound is the power source: a 12-V battery and alternator. As a single-ended amplifier power supply, the maximum peak output is 6 V, which amounts to a peak output of 4.5 W or a little over 3 W rms into 8 Ω.

Certain bridging amplifiers can provide 12-V peaks or 12.7 W rms into 8 Ω. There are two ways to get more power. One is a low-impedance loudspeaker (i.e., 2 Ω), which could draw four times more current (thus power) from any amplifier. The other way, which is extremely expensive, is to chop the 12 V dc into ac, step it up via a transformer, and rectify to a higher voltage dc. This way, the power available is unlimited, given that unlimited power is available from the battery of the car. A current source capable of starting a car certainly has great potential for low-frequency punch.

The loudspeaker that started it all for car stereo is the Jensen J1065 6 × 9-in. Triax (Fig. 14-110). The oval loudspeaker format is unique to auto sound and is a design intended to get a lot of cone area into narrow places such as dashboards and rear decks. Today, the 6 × 9-in. oval is a standard, and Jensen made this true, three-way system available as an add-on.

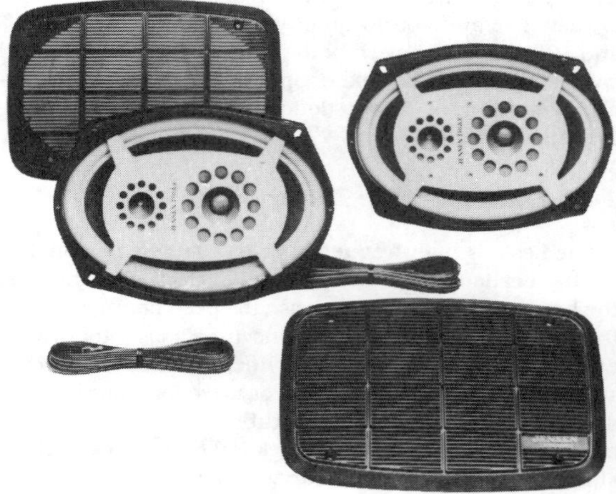

Figure 14-110 Jensen Triax full-range 6- × 9-in. automotive loudspeaker. *(Courtesy Jensen Sound Laboratories, An Esmark Co.)*

14.18 HEADPHONES

Headphones offer the possibility of the ultimate private listening experience. Their small transducers can reproduce extremely low-frequency tones when connected almost directly to the ear, and their small size contributes to good high-frequency response. As a tool for the professional recording artist or engineer, headphones are the perfect in-studio (as opposed to in-control-room) monitor. They allow the performer to hear everything wanted at any sound level without any of this information leaking onto the instrument's recording. The bleed-free overdub would be impossible without the use of headphones. For live monitoring, headphones are sometimes used mostly by drummers who are not the artist. This is because of appearance; the sensitive artist would certainly appear quite removed from the audience, sitting on a stool, guitar in hand, with a pair of headphones on.

Another drawback that headphones inherently present, which is the main reason they aren't used in live and control room monitoring, is their privacy or confinement of sound to the listener's ear only, which has several manifestations. First, headphones do not allow immediate communication with adjacent personnel, and there is no way around this. (For overdubs, communication is usually limited to one performer via talk-back mics in the control room.) Second, headphones remove any information about the listening environment, including expected diffraction effects of the head, which removes the listener from the real world. Third, headphones do not allow listeners to feel low frequencies (below 150 Hz) via their body as a loudspeaker system, especially as a robust one does and as real life does. Hearing low frequencies at the ears only is a step back from real life.

Despite the natural drawbacks of headphones, the privacy (therefore, low acoustic leakage), extreme bandwidth, and dynamic range possible at the ear make the headphone a vital professional tool and a relatively low-cost, super-fidelity personal listening system.

Headphones were made popular in the U.S., largely by the efforts of the Koss Corp., which sold their model K0727 in large quantities. This unit was for many years a standard hi-fi item as well as being used in studios. It was an all dynamic 8-Ω unit and was the mother headphone system in many respects. AKG, at the same time, introduced their model, intended for studio use only. Its 600-Ω impedance made it well-suited for distributed multiunit systems, and the all-dynamic design reproduced good sound. These two early examples are typical of soft cushions that actually fit over the ear. The sealed air volume is extremely small and close to dc performance is possible (much more so than in a loudspeaker, where dc response requires enormous diaphragm area and excursion to pressurize any room). Later, Koss introduced the PRO-4 all-dynamic headphone series that was extremely popular due to great improvements in bandwidth and other sonic qualities over the K0727. Fig. 14-111 shows a recent version of this model.

Figure 14-111 Koss PRO-4X dynamic pressure-type headphone. *(Courtesy Koss Corp.)*

Figure 14-112 Sennheiser MD-414 high-velocity headphones. *(Courtesy Sennheiser Electronic Corp.)*

Superex engineered a pressure unit that was two-way, using a dynamic low-frequency unit, crossover, and piezoelectric high-frequency unit. This model, the Superex ST Pro-BV, is similar to a two-way loudspeaker system, even using a vented headphone cavity.

Lastly, Koss introduced the ESP-9 all-electrostatic pressure phone. This is thought by many to be the ultimate in headphone engineering with its clear, low-distortion sound. The ESP-9 is supplied with its own power supply and impedance-matching electronics.

Another type of headphone design is the high-velocity phone. This design sits on (not over) the ear on a soft, acoustically transparent pad. Because the coupling between the ear and the driver is not as direct as in the pressure-type, air must be pumped at a higher velocity at the ear to produce more bass, similar to proximity effect in microphones. Sennheiser was a major force behind the popularity of velocity phones, with their model MD-414 shown in Fig. 14-112. The advantages of these designs are that the design is inherently lightweight and that the real world is allowed to "come in," due to much less acoustical isolation of the ears.

In the 1980s, Sony introduced the Walkman personal radio and/or cassette player and started a revolution in small, portable personal systems. Part of its success is due to the superb-sounding lightweight headphones that accompanied the package. Before too long almost every major manufacturer of headphones had similar units for sale. These units employ samarium-cobalt magnets. Although these are expensive (per gram), they offer enormous magnetic energy in a small package. These phones sit on small foam pads over the ear and are ideal for the intended use.

REFERENCES

1. *Synergetic Audio Concepts Technical Topics*, vol. 11, no. 2.
2. R. M. Mitchell, "Transient Performance of Loudspeaker Dividing Networks," *Audio*, January 1964.
3. H. F. Olson, "The Action of a Direct Radiator Loudspeaker with a Non-Linear Cone Suspension System," *Journal of the ASA*, vol. 16, no. 1, pp. 1–4, July 1944.
4. T. H. Wiik, "Transient Distortion Caused by Nonlinearities in Driving Force and Suspension of a Loudspeaker," presented at the 56th convention of the AES, Paris, March 1977, preprint 1205 (C-6).
5. J. R. Gilliom, "Distortion in Dynamic Loudspeakers Due to Modulation of the Permanent Field," presented at the 42nd convention of the AES, Los Angeles, May 1972, Paper L-10.
6. J. R. Gilliom, "Design Problems of High Level Cone Loudspeakers," *Journal of the AES*, vol. 25, no. 5, pp. 294–299, May 1977.
7. M. Gander, "Moving-Coil Loudspeaker Topology as an Indicator of Linear Excursion Capability," AES preprint 1554 (A-4).
8. W. J. Cunningham, "Non-Linear Distortion in Dynamic Loudspeaker Due to Magnetic Effects," *Journal of the ASA*, vol. 21, no. 3, pp. 202–207, May 1949.
9. C. A. Henricksen, "Heat Transfer Mechanisms in Moving Coil Loudspeakers," AES preprint 1247 (K-2).
10. B. N. Locanthi, "Application of Electric Circuit Analogies to Loudspeaker Design Problems," *Journal of the AES*, vol. 19, no. 9, October 1971.
11. R. H. Small, "Direct-Radiator Loudspeaker System Analysis," *Journal of the AES*, vol. 20, no. 5, pp. 383–395, June 1972.
12. C. A. Henricksen, "Directivity Response of Single Direct-Radiator Loudspeakers in Enclosures," *Altec Technical Letter*, No. 227. Altec Lansing Corp. Oklahoma City, OK
13. J. M. Kates, "Radiation from a Dome," *Journal of the AES*, vol. 24, no. 9, November 1976.
14. H. Suzuki and J. Tichy, "Diffraction of Sound by a Convex or a Concave Dome in an Infinite Baffle," *Journal of the ASA*, preprint 0 (5), November 1981.
15. J. M. Kates, "Analysis of Decoupled-Cone Loudspeakers," *Journal of the AES*, vol. 25, no. 1/2, January/February 1977.
16. O. Heil, "Movable Diaphragm Method Flexible Hinge Diaphragm Surround and Electro-Acoustic Transducer with Folded Diaphragm with Intermediate Flexible Portions," US Patent 4,056,697, November 1, 1977. (ESS "Air Motion Transformer").
17. C. A. Henricksen, "Phase Plug Modeling and Analysis: Radial Versus Circumferential Types," presented at the 59th Convention of the AES, preprint 1328 (F-5).
18. D. A. Barlow, G. D. Galletly, and J. Mistry, "The Resonances of Loudspeaker Diaphragms," AES preprint 1590 (D4).
19. D. A. Barlow, "The Development of a Sandwich-Construction Loudspeaker System," *Journal of the AES*, vol. 18, no. 3, June 1970.

20. B. Howze, "Directional Loudspeaker," US Patent 4,344,50 August 17, 1982.

21. D. A. Barlow, "Diaphragm for Electro Acoustic Transducer," US Patent 3,111,187, November 10, 1963, (foam-aluminum sandwich diaphragm).

22. D. B. Keele, Jr., "Horn Loudspeaker," US Patent 4,071,112, January 31, 1978.

23. A. Matsuda et al., "Peripherally Reinforced Laminated Loudspeaker Diaphragm," US Patent 4,198,550, April 1980. (Sony "Esprit" square honeycomb diaphragm).

24. A. Badmaieff and D. Davis *How to Build Speaker Enclosures*, Indianapolis: Howard W. Sams & Co., 1966.

25. K. O. Johnson, "Single-Ended Wide-Range Electrostatic Tweeters with High Efficiency and Improved Dynamic Range," *Journal of the AES*, July 1964.

26. A. H. Benade, "Fundamentals of Musical Acoustics," Oxford University Press, 1976.

27. R. H. Small, "Closed Box Loudspeaker Systems; Part I: Analysis," *Journal of the AES*, vol. 20, no. 10, pp. 798–808, December 1972.

28. H. F. Olson, "Analysis of the Effects of Nonlinear Elements Upon the Performance of a Back-Enclosed, Direct Radiator Loudspeaker Mechanism," *Journal of the AES*, vol. 10, no. 2, pp. 156–162, April 1962.

29. E. M. Villchur, "Problems of Bass Reproduction," *Journal of the AES*, vol. 5, no. 3, july 1957.

30. J. E. Benson, "An Introduction to the Design of Filtered Loudspeaker Systems," *Journal of the AES*, vol. 23, no. 7, September 1975.

31. A. N. Theile, "Loudspeakers in Vented Boxes: Part I & II," *Journal of the AES*, vol. 19, no. 5 & 6, May & June 1971.

32. R. H. Small, "Vented-Box Loudspeaker Systems Part I, II, III & IV," *Journal of the AES*, vol. 21, no. 5, 6, 7, and 8; June, July, August, and September 1973.

33. D. B. Keele, "Vented Box Design Using a Pocket Calculator," February 1976.

34. J. F. Novak, "Performance of Enclosures for Low Resonance High Compliance Loudspeakers," *Journal of the AES*, vol. 7, no. 1, January 1959.

35. C. A. Henricksen, "Vented Box Design Method for Altec Low-Frequency Loudspeakers," Altec Technical Letter 245. Altec Lansing Corp. Oklahoma City, OK

36. D. J. Plach, "Design Factors in Horn-Type Speakers," *Journal of the AES*, vol. 1, no. 3, October 1953.

37. "Noise Control Manual," Publication 5-BMG-8277-B, Toledo, Ohio: Owens-Corning Fiberglas Corp.

38. J. Christophorou, "Low-Frequency Loudspeaker Measurements with an Accelerometer," presented at the 62nd convention of the AES, Brussels, March 1979, preprint 1444 (D-6).

39. D. B. Keele, Jr., "Low-Frequency Loudspeaker Assessment by Nearfield Sound-Pressure Measurements," *Journal of the AES*, vol. 22, no. 3, pp. 154–162, April 1974.

40. J. R. Ashley and M. D. Swam, "Experimental Determination of Low-Frequency Loudspeaker Parameters," *Journal of the AES*, vol. 17, no. 5, October 1969.

41. J. Hilliard, "Historical Review of Horns Used for Audience Type Sound Reproduction," *Journal of the ASA*, vol. 59, no. 1, p. 1, January 1976.

42. D. B. Keele, Jr., "Optimum Horn Mouth Size," AES reprint 933 (B7).

43. C. A. Henricksen, "Ultimate Performance of Wide-Range High-Frequency Compression Drivers," AES preprint 1126 (M-3).

44. C. A. Henricksen, "Phase Plug Modeling and Analysis: Radial versus Circumferential Types," AES preprint 1328 (F-S).

45. F. M. Murray, "An Application of Bob Smith's Phasing Plug," AES preprint 1384 (K-4).

46. E. C. Wente and A. L. Thuras, "A High Efficiency Receiver for a Horn Type Loudspeaker of Large Power Capacity," reprinted from the *BSTJ*, January 1928, by the *Journal of the AES*, vol. 26, pp. 139–144.

47. B. H. Smith, "An Investigation of the Air Chamber of Horn Type Loudspeakers," *Journal of the ASA*.

48. E. J. Czerwinski, "Adjustable Dual Spider for a Loudspeaker," US Patent 4,239,943, December 16, 1980.

49. J. F. Blackburn, "Loudspeaker," US Patent 2,183,528, December 19, 1939 (radial phase plug).

50. S. E. Levy, "Driver Unit for Loudspeakers," US Patent 2,858,37 October 28, 1958 (phase plug).

51. E. C. Wente, "Sound Translating Device," US Patent 2,037,187, April 14, 1936. (phase plug).

52. C. A. Henricksen, "Acoustical Transformer for Horn-Type Loudspeaker," US Patent 4,050,541, September 27, 1977. ("Tangerine" phase plug).

53. S. Kinoshita, T. Yoshimi, H. Hamada, and B. Locanthi, "Design of a 48mm Beryllium Diaphragm Compression Driver," AES preprint 1364 (D-9).

54. F. M. Murray and H. Durbin, "Three Dimensional Diaphragm Suspensions for Compression Drivers," *Journal of the AES*, vol. 28. no. 10, October 1980.

55. B. Howze and C. Henricksen, "A High-Efficiency One-Decade Midrange Loudspeaker," AES preprint 1848, 70th Convention, October 1981.

56. C. R. Hanna and J. Slepian, "The Functions and Design of Horns for Loudspeakers," reprinted in the *Journal of the AES*, vol. 25, no. 9, pp. 573–585, September 1977.

57. C. A. Henricksen and M. S. Ureda, "Loudspeaker Horn," US Patent 4,187,926, February 12, 1980.

58. D. B. Keele, Jr., "What's So Sacred about Exponential Horns?" AES preprint 1038 (F-3).

59. S. Ishii and K. Takahashi, "Design of Linear Phase Multi-Way Loudspeaker System," AES 52nd Convention, October 1975, preprint 1059.

60. E. M. Long, "Design Parameters of a Dual Woofer Loudspeaker System," *Journal of the AES*, vol. 17, no. 5, p. 515, October 1969.

61. R. Heyser, "Loudspeaker Phase Characteristics and Time Delay Distortion, Part 1," *Journal of the AES*, vol. 17, no. 1, p. 30, January 1969.

62. R. Heyser, "Loudspeaker Phase Characteristics and Time Delay Distortion, Part 2, *Journal of the AES*, vol. 17, no. 2, p. 130, April 1969.

63. J. King, "The Use of Magnetic Fluids in Loudspeaker Design," AES preprint 1246 (K-1).

64. E. M. Long, "Crossover Network Design," *Audio*, vol. 56, no. 3, p. 34, March 1972.

65. E. M. Long, "A Time-Align Technique for Loudspeaker System Design," AES preprint 1131 (M-8).

66 R. H. Small, "Constant-Voltage Crossover Network Design," *Journal of the AES*, vol. 19, no. 1, January 1971.

67. R. H. Small, "Phase and Delay Distortion in Multiple-Driver Loudspeaker Systems," *Journal of the AES*, vol. 19, no. 1, January 1971.

68. J. R. Ashley and A. L. Kaminsky, "Active and Passive Filters as Loudspeaker Crossover Networks," *Journal of the AES*, vol. 19, no. 6, June 1971.

69. G. L. Augsburger, "Electrical versus Acoustical Parameters in the Design of Loudspeaker Crossover Networks," *Journal of the AES*, vol. 19, no. 6, June 1971.

70. P. B. Williams and J. F. Novak, "Polystyrene Foam Loudspeaker Cones," *Audio*, May 1960.

71. J. F. Novak, "Performance of Series-Parallel Speaker Arrays," *Audio*, September 1961.

72. P. W. Klipsch, "A Low-Frequency Horn of Small Dimensions," *Journal of the ASA*, October 1941.

73. L. L. Beranek, *Acoustics*, New York: McGraw-Hill, 1954.

74. Y. Yuasa and S. Greenberg, "The Beryllium Dome Diaphragm—Its Use, Manufacture, and Importance in Loudspeaker Systems," AES Preprint 1087 (L-6).

75. C. A. Henricksen, "Unearthing the Mysteries of the Leslie," *Recording Engineer/Producer*, vol. 12, no. 2, October 1980.

ADDITIONAL BIBLIOGRAPHY

R. F. Allison, "The Sound Field in Home Listening Rooms," *Journal of the AES*, vol. 24, no. 1/2, January/February 1976.

R. F. Allison, "The Influence of Room Boundaries on Loudspeaker Power Output," *Journal of the AES*, vol. 22, no. 5, June 1974.

G. L. Augsburger, "The Acoustic Lens," *Electronic World*, January 1962.

J. L. Bernstein, *Audio Systems*, New York: John Wiley & Sons, 1966.

L. J. S. Bradbury, "The Use of Fibrous Materials in Loudspeaker Enclosures," *Journal of the AES*, vol. 24, no. 6, April 1976.

R. G. Brown, *Lines, Waves, and Antennas*, New York: The Ronald Press Co., 1961.

W. E. Cock and F. K. Harvey, "Reflecting Sound Waves," *Journal of the ASA*, September 1949.

A. B. Cohen, *Hi-Fi Loudspeakers and Enclosures*, New York: Hayden Book Co., 1968.

E. J. Czerwinski and M. D. Buck, "A Compact, High Performance Cinema Loudspeaker for Dialogue, Music, and Effects," AES preprint 1853 (D-7).

E. Geddis, "Acoustic Lens, Their Design and Application," AES preprint 1401 (G-5).

C. A. Henricksen, "Engineering Justifications for Selected Portions of the AES Recommended Practice on Specification of Loudspeakers Components," AES preprint 1932 (G-10).

C. A. Henricksen and M. Ureda, "The Manta-Ray Horns," *Journal of the AES*, vol. 26, no. 9, September 1978.

J. K. Hilliard, "High-Power, Low-Frequency Loudspeakers," *Journal of the AES*, July 1965.

I. Imoto, M. Iwahara, and H. Onoye, "Technique for Observing Loudspeaker Wave-Front Propagation," *Journal of the AES*, vol. 24, no. 1/2, January/February 1976.

A. A. Janszen, "An Electrostatic Loudspeaker Development," *Journal of the AES*, vol. 3, no. 2, April 1955.

D. B. Keele, Jr., "Low-Frequency Horn Design Using Thiele/Small Driver Parameters," presented at the 57th convention of the AES, preprint no. 1250 (K-7), May 1977.

L. E. Kinsler and A. R. Frey, *Fundamentals of Acoustics*, New York: John Wiley & Sons, 1962.

P. W. Klipsch, "Loudspeaker Horn," US Patent 2,537,141, January 9, 1951.

P. W. Klipsch, "Modulation Distortion in Loudspeakers," *Journal of the AES*, vol. 17, no. 2, April 1969. (See Parts II and III, *Journal of the AES*, vol. 18, no. 1, February 1970, *Journal of the AES*, vol. 20, no. 10, December 1972.)

P. W. Klipsch, "Modulation Distortion in Loudspeakers, Part II," *Journal of the AES*, vol. 18, no. 1, February 1970.

J. B. Lansing and J. K. Hilliard, "An Improved Loudspeaker System for Theaters," *Journal of the SMPTE*, November 1945.

S. H. Linkwitz, "Active Crossover Networks for Non-Coincident Drivers," *Journal of the AES*, vol. 24, no. 1, p. 2, January/February 1976.

Massa, "Acoustic Design Charts," Philadelphia: The Blakiston Company, 1942.

N. W. McLachlan, *Loudspeakers; Theory, Performances Testing, and Design*, Corrected Edition, New York: Dover Publications, 1960.

P. M. Morse, *Vibration and Sound*, New York: McGraw-Hill, 1948.

J. Nakazono, et al., "Coaxial Flat-Plane Loudspeaker with Polymer-Graphite Honeycomb Sandwich Plate Diaphragm," AES preprint 1662 (J-6).

H. F. Olson, *Acoustical Engineering*, Princeton: Van Nostrand, 1976.

R. J. Newman, "Loudspeaker System Design Utilizing a Sixth-Order Butterworth Response Characteristic, *Journal of the AES*, July-August 1973.

H. F. Olson, "Music, Physics, and Engineering," New York: Dover Publications.

H. W. Schafft, "Acoustic Horn," US Patent 3,852,529, December 3, 1974. (Piezo driver).

H. Schafft, "A New Piezoelectric Direct Radiating Tweeter," presented at the 42nd convention of the Audio Engineering Society, Los Angeles, May 1972.

H. M. Tremaine, *Passive Audio Network Design*, Indianapolis: Howard W. Sams & Co., 1964.

P. B. Williams and J. Novak, "Improvement in Air Suspension Speaker Enclosure with Tube Venting," *Audio*, November 1958.

A. Wood, *Acoustics*, New York: Dover Publications, Inc., 1966.

PART 4

Audio Electronic Circuits and Equipment

CHAPTER **15**

Amplifiers

by Gene Patronis and Mahlon Burkhard*

*Sections 15.1 and 15.3 by Gene Patronis; Section 15.2 by Mahlon Burkhard

15.1 AMPLIFIER DESIGN

15.1.1 The Necessity for Amplifiers

The necessity for amplification becomes apparent from an analysis of the unlikely arrangement depicted in Fig. 15-1, wherein a dynamic microphone is connected directly to a loudspeaker.

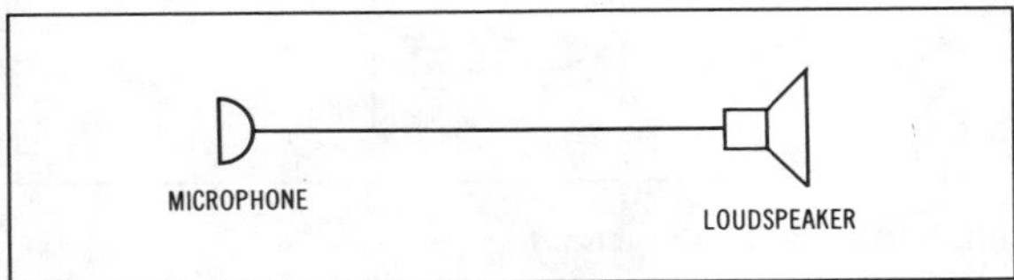

Figure 15-1 The impossible sound reinforcement system.

The microphone typically, with moderate excitation, would generate an open-circuit voltage of 10 mV and possess an internal impedance of 200 Ω. The loudspeaker typically would have an impedance of 8 Ω and an efficiency of 10%. The electrical power delivered to the loudspeaker, assuming that the microphone and loudspeaker impedances are predominantly resistive, would be 1.8×10^{-8} W, although the acoustical output of the loudspeaker would only be 1.8×10^{-9} W. Even if a matching transformer is interposed between the microphone and the loudspeaker, the improvement is hardly significant. The acoustical output in this event becomes only 1.25×10^{-8} W, which is several orders of magnitude below the acoustical power requirements of most applications.

15.1.2 Types and Descriptions of Amplifiers

The initial description for an amplifier is based on the nature of the active elements involved such as a vacuum tube, a bipolar transistor, a field-effect transistor, an integrated circuit, a magnetic field, or a mixture of two or more of these technologies in which case it is called a *hybrid*. The second descriptor is associated with the principal quantity being amplified and is associated indirectly with the input-output relationships exhibited by the amplifier.

For example, a voltage amplifier is excited at its input by a signal in the form of a voltage and responds by producing a related voltage at its output. In this instance, it is desirable that the input impedance of a voltage amplifier be large compared with the impedance of the signal source and that the output impedance of the amplifier be small compared with the load impedance connected at its output. As a result, the signal source impresses a maximum voltage across the input of the amplifier, and the amplifier subsequently produces a maximum voltage across its associated load.

A current amplifier is excited at its input by a signal in the form of a current and responds by producing a related current in its associated load. Current amplifiers have low input impedances and high output impedances.

A transconductance amplifier is excited at its input by a voltage and responds by producing a related current in its associated load. Transconductance amplifiers have high input impedances and high output impedances.

Transresistance amplifiers are excited at the input by a signal current and respond by producing a related voltage at the output. A transresistance amplifier has a low input impedance as well as a low output impedance.

Another useful amplifier descriptor is the functional relationship, in a mathematical sense, that exists between the input and output signals. For example, in linear amplifiers, the output signal is a linear function of the input signal, whereas in logarithmic amplifiers, the output signal is proportional to the logarithm of the input signal. The majority of the amplifiers employed in audio are linear, but a significant number of logarithmic or other special-function amplifiers find use in signal-processing applications.

Additional descriptions are associated with the physical location of an amplifier in the overall amplification chain. For example, a preamplifier is usually placed immediately after a transducer where the signal levels are quite low and noise characteristics are of considerable importance. Certain preamplifiers will incorporate special equalization circuitry; for instance, a phono preamplifier provides the required Record Industries Association of America (RIAA) playback characteristic.

Preamplifiers are followed by mixing amplifiers that can combine and individually control the signals from several different sources. Although there may exist several other intermediate steps, the power amplifier is the last step.

Power amplifiers in audio work have the input-output impedance characteristics of a voltage amplifier along with the ability to deliver large amounts of electrical power. Fig. 15-2 and Table 15-1 illustrate a typical arrangement in a reinforcement chain.

The final descriptor to be discussed concerns amplifier terminal connections. Amplifiers are essentially two-port devices (i.e., they are constituted with a pair of input terminals and a pair of output terminals, as indicated in Fig. 15-3).

If neither of the input terminals is connected directly to ground and if both of the input terminals are electrically symmetric with respect to ground, the input is said to be balanced. If one of the input terminals is connected to ground, the input is unbalanced and is described as being single ended. Similar statements are applicable to the output pair of terminals. All possible combinations are encountered in practice. The input may be balanced while the output is unbalanced, or the input may be unbalanced while the output is balanced; both in and out may be balanced, or both in and out may be unbalanced. The balanced configuration is preferable when dealing with long lines and low signal levels or where ground isolation is required. This preference is based on

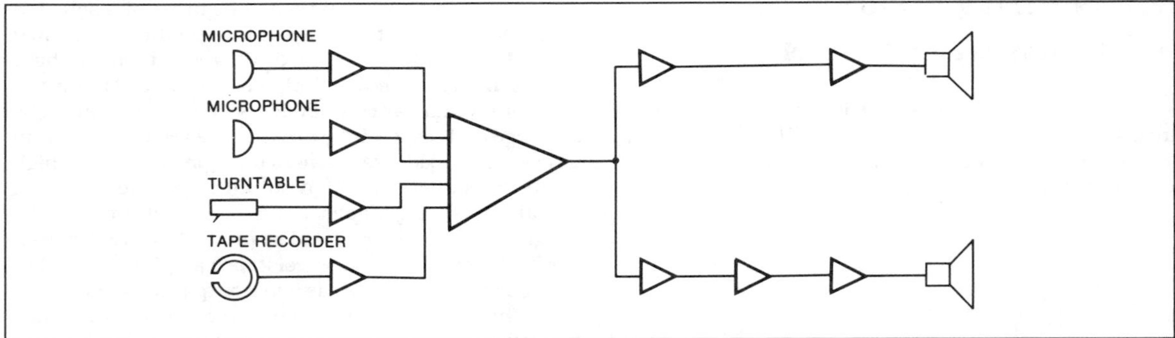

Figure 15-2 A typical reinforcement and reproduction chain.

Table 15-1. Signal Chain Partitioning

Microphone	Preamplifier		One-Third Octave Equalizer		Power Amplifier	Prompt Loudspeaker
Microphone	Preamplifier	Mixer				
Phono	Preamplifier/Eq					
Tape	Preamplifier/Eq		One-Third Octave Equalizer	Signal Delay	Power Amplifier	Delayed Loudspeaker

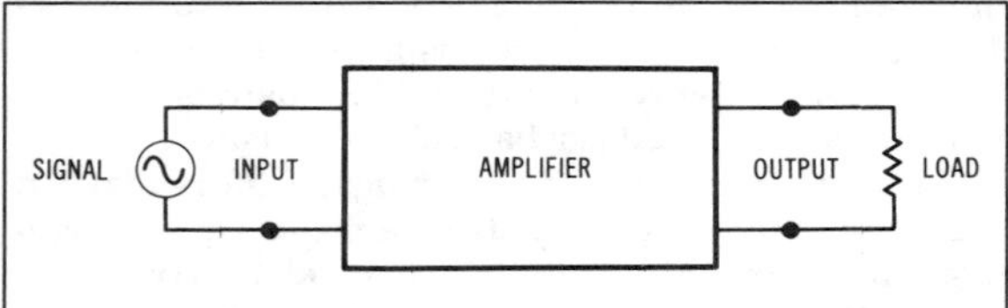

Figure 15-3 An amplifier as a two port device.

the common-mode rejection properties of the balanced arrangement. For example, consider the signal leads in Fig. 15-3 to be a long twisted pair contained within an electrostatic shield with the shield grounded. The electrostatic shield offers no noise immunity from external time-varying magnetic fields. When such varying magnetic fields exist, a noise signal will be induced between each of the signal conductors and ground. The amplifier, however, amplifies the difference that appears between its input terminals; hence, any common signal between the input terminals and ground is rejected.

15.1.3 Amplifier Transfer Function

The relationship that exists in the steady state between the output signal and the input signal of a two-port device such as an amplifier or filter is called the *transfer function*. The transfer function has a magnitude and an angle with each being dependent on the steady-state signal frequency. Mathematically, the transfer function is expressed concisely in the form of a complex function that has both real and imaginary parts. The magnitude of the transfer function at any particular frequency is the square root of the sum of the squares of the real and imaginary parts and physically corresponds to the ratio of the output signal amplitude to the input signal amplitude. The angle of the transfer function at any particular frequency is the angle whose tangent is the ratio of the imaginary and real parts and physically corresponds to the phase difference between the output signal and the input signal. These ideas are best expressed by a simple example. Consider a dc-coupled voltage amplifier that offers an amplification of 10 volts per volt at dc or zero frequency and an amplification of $10/\sqrt{2}$ volts per volt at a frequency f_0 while having introduced a phase shift of $-\pi/4$ radian or $-45°$. Upon denoting the transfer function by the symbol A and the independent frequency variable by the symbol f, the following statements can be made:

$$A = \underbrace{\left[\frac{10}{[1 + (f/f_0)^2]}\right]}_{\text{Real Part}} - \underbrace{\left[\frac{j10(f/f_0)}{1 + (f/f_0)^2}\right]}_{\text{Imaginary Part}} \qquad (15\text{-}1)$$

or more compactly

$$A = G\epsilon^{j\theta} \qquad (15\text{-}2)$$

where,

G is the magnitude of the transfer function or gain function,

ϵ is the base of the natural logarithm,

ϕ is the angle of the transfer function or phase function, the angle whose tangent is the imaginary part divided by the real part of Eq. 15-1.

G is the square root of the sum of the squares of the real and imaginary parts of Eq. 15-1.

j is -1

$$G = \frac{10}{\sqrt{1 + (f/f_o)^2}} \qquad (15\text{-}3)$$

$$\phi = \tan^{-1}(-f/f_o) \qquad (15\text{-}4)$$

An elegant form in which to express Eq. 15-1 is obtained by letting $S = j\omega$ with $\omega = 2\pi f$ and $\omega_o = 2\pi f_o$. Eq. 15-1 after substitution and simplification becomes

$$A = \frac{10\omega_o}{S + \omega_o} \qquad (15\text{-}5)$$

Eq. 15-5 is the statement of Eq. 15-1 in the language of the Laplace transform, which is really the basis for transfer function analysis. It is worthwhile at this point to note that Eqs. 15-1, 15-2, and 15-5 are alternative ways of expressing the transfer function of the simple amplifier under discussion. The form in Eq. 15-5 is that which is used most often in practice because of its simplicity.

If S were allowed to assume any possible value whether it be real, imaginary, or complex, such that all points in a two-dimensional complex plane were accessible, there would be only one value of S in Eq. 15-5 for which the denominator would become zero, and A would become infinite. That value of S is when $S = -\omega_o$. It is said then that Eq. 15-5 has a single pole located at $S = -\omega_o$. The pole order of a transfer function is determined by the power of S appearing in the denominator. A two-pole amplifier would have an S^2, a three pole an S^3, and so on, appearing in the denominator of the transfer function. In the steady state as opposed to transient state, recall that S is restricted to the values $S = j\omega$, and the only accessible points lie on the positive imaginary axis because the physical frequency values must be positive. In the steady state even though the value of S never coincides with the location of our example pole, the pole location nevertheless influences the operation of the amplifier. Changing the pole location in effect changes the value of ω_o and, hence, changes the value of the transfer function at all frequencies other than zero frequency.

A further study of the Laplace transform and the inverse Laplace transform indicates that the transfer function is a description also of the impulse response of the device in the complex frequency plane, and the inverse Laplace transform of the transfer function is the description of the response of the device to an impulse described in the time domain (i.e., it is the transient response of the device to an impulse expressed as a function of time). An important consequence of this is that in order for a device to exhibit a transient response that decays with increasing time, all the poles of the transfer function of the device must have negative real parts. The amplifier under discussion satisfies this criterion with a pole at $-\omega_o$; hence, its transient response decays with time, which allows the amplifier to exhibit a stable, steady-state response. If this were not true, the device would not be useful as an amplifier.

The information contained in the transfer function of the amplifier may be depicted in a variety of ways. The two most popular ways are the *Bode* and *Nyquist diagrams*. The Bode diagram displays Eqs. 15-3 and 15-4 in the form of a graph of 20 dB log G plotted versus log ω and a graph of ϕ plotted versus log ω. Fig. 15-4 is the Bode diagram for the amplifier of the example.

An examination of the Bode diagram in Fig. 15-4 leads to the conclusion that this amplifier is in essence a low-pass filter having a reference gain of 20 dB, a single pole, and a half power point at $\omega = \omega_o$. The pole order is deduced from the fact that even though the response is low pass in nature, its asymptotic slope is -20 dB/decade or equivalently -6 dB/octave. A two-pole low pass would produce -12 dB/octave; a three-pole, -18 dB/octave; and so on in the asymptotic slope.

This same information is displayed in a different form by means of a Nyquist diagram. A Nyquist diagram is a graph in the complex plane of Eq. 15-1 plotted under the condition that ω is allowed to take on all values from zero to infinity. Fig. 15-5 is the Nyquist diagram for the amplifier of the example.

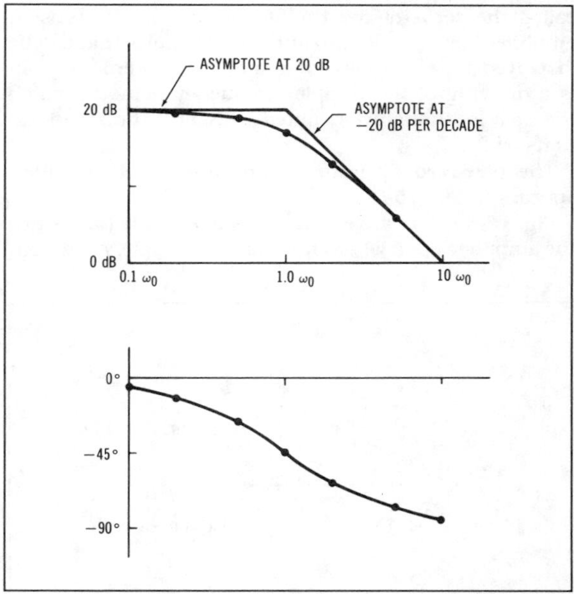

Figure 15-4 Gain and phase graphs for the example amplifier.

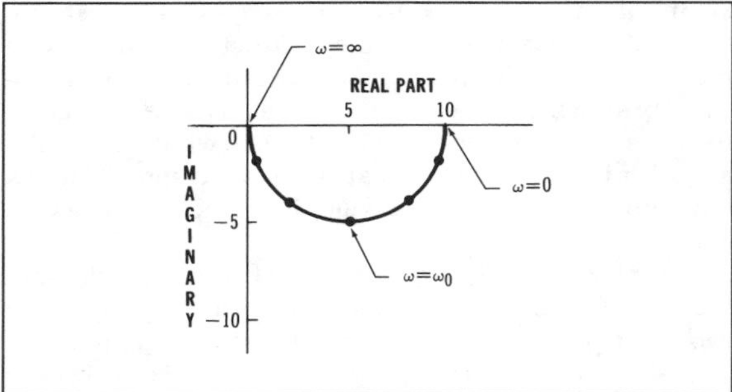

Figure 15-5 Nyquist diagram for the example amplifier.

A second example will serve to explore further the properties of transfer functions. Consider that the amplifier of the previous example had an input resistance of amount R. The input circuit is now to be modified by connecting a capacitor of size C in series with this input resistance to form a simple ac-coupled amplifier. Upon denoting $\omega_o' = 1/RC$ the transfer function for this new amplifier is given by

$$A = \frac{10S\,\omega_o}{(S + \omega_o')(S + \omega_o)} \qquad (15\text{-}6)$$

Eq. 15-6 indicates that the amplifier now has two poles, the original one at $S = -\omega_o$ and a new one located at $S = -\omega_o'$. In addition, an examination of the numerator of the transfer function indicates that there is now a value of S for which the numerator becomes zero namely at $S = 0$. Values of S that make the numerator zero are called the zeros of the transfer function. The present amplifier has a single zero and a pair of poles that can be displayed in a pole-zero diagram. A pole-zero diagram is a drawing of the complex frequency plane in which the pole locations are denoted by X and the zero locations by O.

The pole-zero diagram for the ac-coupled amplifier appears in Fig. 15-6.

Fig. 15-6 is a relatively simple pole-zero diagram since the amplifier upon which it is based is simple. A few conclusions based upon more general amplifiers are worth noting. Real poles may be singular while complex poles always appear as conjugate pairs. The poles for amplifiers that exhibit stable, steady-state behavior may be real or complex but must have negative real parts. The zeros may appear anywhere in the S plane but any zeros with positive real parts are associated with nonminimum phase behavior.

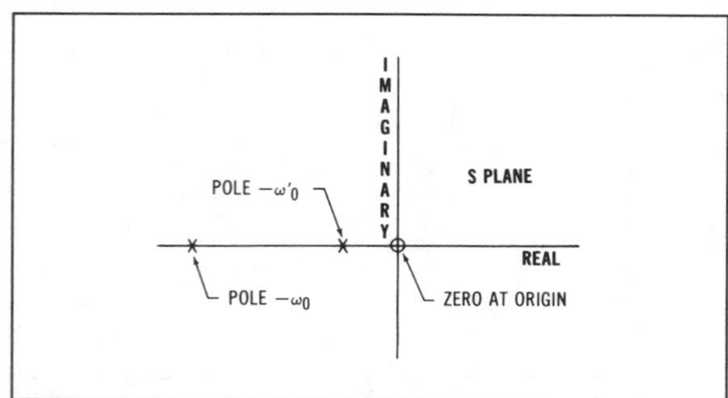

Figure 15-6 Pole-zero diagram.

The Bode diagram for this example is arrived at by the following steps. First, reform Eq. 15-6:

$$A = \left(\frac{S}{S + \omega_o'}\right)\left(\frac{10\omega_o}{S + \omega_o}\right)$$

Substitute for ω_o in terms of ω_o by examining the pole-zero diagram, $\omega_o' = 1/4\ \omega_o$

$$A = \left(\frac{S}{S + \omega_o/4}\right)\left(\frac{10\,\omega_o}{S + \omega_o}\right)$$

Substitute $S = j\omega$ and find the absolute magnitude of the resulting expression to obtain the gain function as indicated here:

$$G = |A|$$

$$= \left(\frac{\omega}{\sqrt{\omega^2 + \omega_o^2/16}}\right)\left(\frac{10\omega_o}{\sqrt{\omega^2 + \omega_o^2}}\right)$$

$$= \left(\frac{\omega/\omega_o}{\sqrt{\omega^2/\omega_o^2 + (1/16)}}\right)\left(\frac{10}{\sqrt{\omega^2/\omega_o^2 + 1}}\right)$$

Make a graph of 20 dB log G versus log ω/ω_o. This graph appears in Fig. 15-7. Next determine the phase function ϕ:

$$A = \left(\frac{S}{S + \omega_o/4}\right)\left(\frac{10\omega_o}{S + \omega_o}\right)$$

$$= \left(\frac{j\omega}{j\omega + \omega_o/4}\right)\left(\frac{10\omega_o}{j\omega + \omega_o}\right)$$

The angle of the first factor is $90° - \tan^{-1}(4\omega/\omega_o)$, while the angle of the second factor is $-\tan^{-1}(\omega/\omega_o)$; therefore, the total phase shift is

$$\phi = 90° - \tan^{-1}(4\omega/\omega_o) - \tan^{-1}(\omega/\omega_o)$$

Make a graph of ϕ versus log (ω/ω_o) in order to complete the Bode diagram. This graph also appears in Fig. 15-7.

15.1.4 Feedback Theory

Fig. 15-8 represents a generalized feedback loop based on a voltage amplifier. In the absence of feedback with the loop open, the amplifier has a transfer function A.

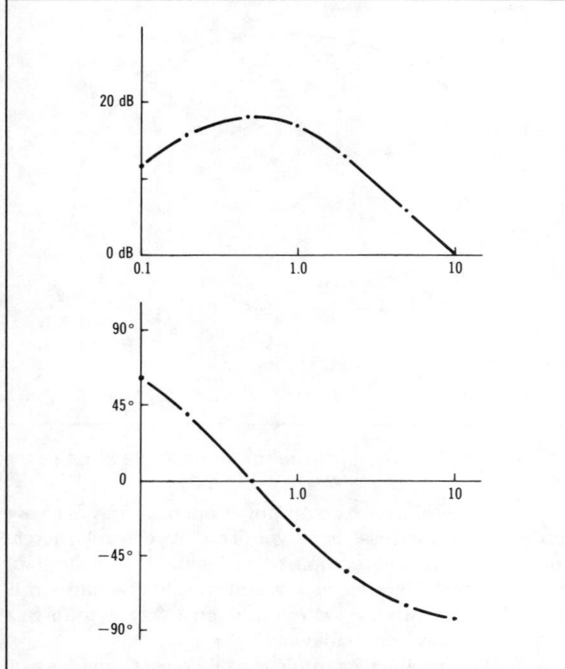

Figure 15-7 Bode diagram for simple ac amplifier.

The feedback path has a transfer function B, the input signal from the outside world is V_{in}, and the signal supplied as an output is V_O. When the loop is closed, the input signal is combined with the feedback signal in the indicated junction to form an error signal V_e. The process that occurs in the junction may be either addition or subtraction depending upon the nature of A, B, and the type of feedback (positive or negative) desired. In any event the signal actually supplied to the amplifier when the loop is closed is V_e.

The system contained within the dotted enclosure of

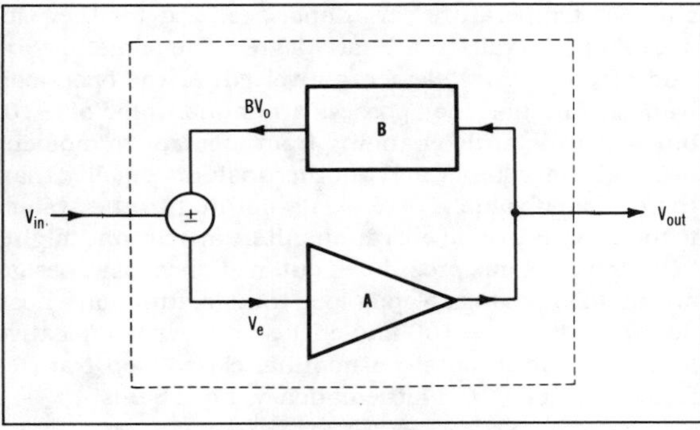

Figure 15-8 Generalized feedback loop.

Fig. 15-8 has a rather different transfer function from that of the amplifier operated under open-loop conditions. The closed-loop transfer function denoted by A′ is derived as follows:

$$V_e = V_{in} + BV_O \tag{15-7}$$

$$V_O = AV_e = AV_{in} + ABV_O \tag{15-8}$$

$$A' = V_O/V_{in} = A/(1 - AB) \tag{15-9}$$

A and B, in general, are complex functions of the steady-state frequency of operation. The absolute magnitude of the denominator of Eq. 15-9 is called the gain reduction factor. The feedback is called negative when

$$|1 - AB| > 1 \tag{15-10}$$

and is positive when

$$|1 - AB| < 1 \tag{15-11}$$

The nature of the feedback is best explored by studying the quantity AB as a function of the frequency as displayed in a Nyquist diagram. The quantity AB is called the loop gain of the hypothetical amplifier. Included in the diagram is a circle of unit radius centered on the point 1,j0.

The perimeter of the unit circle divides the plane into two regions. For all the points outside the circle $|1 - AB| > 1$, the feedback is negative, whereas for any point on the curve within the unit circle $|1 - AB| < 1$, the feedback is positive. The hypothetical amplifier for which Fig. 15-9 was drawn thus has negative feedback at low frequencies but exhibits positive feedback over a range of high frequencies. Note that AB is negative and real, and has its maximum absolute value at $\omega = 0$. This is characteristic of a dc-coupled amplifier having a loop gain transfer function that has poles but no zeros. Furthermore, AB resides in the second quadrant until ω exceeds ω_1; for $\omega_1 < \omega < \omega_2$, AB is in the first quadrant, but the feedback is still negative. Whenever the frequency is such that $\omega > \omega_2$, AB falls within the unit circle, and the feedback becomes positive. This region must be handled with extreme care.

As will presently be discussed in detail, negative feedback is a stabilizing influence on amplifier performance, but positive feedback is a destabilizing influence and can, in fact, lead to an uncontrolled oscillatory condition. The final conclusion to be drawn from Fig. 15-9 is that for $\omega > \omega_3$, AB is in the fourth quadrant and finally approaches zero as the operating frequency becomes very large. As ω is allowed to vary from zero to infinity, the angle associated with AB undergoes a change of −270°, which is characteristic of a transfer function. In the absence of

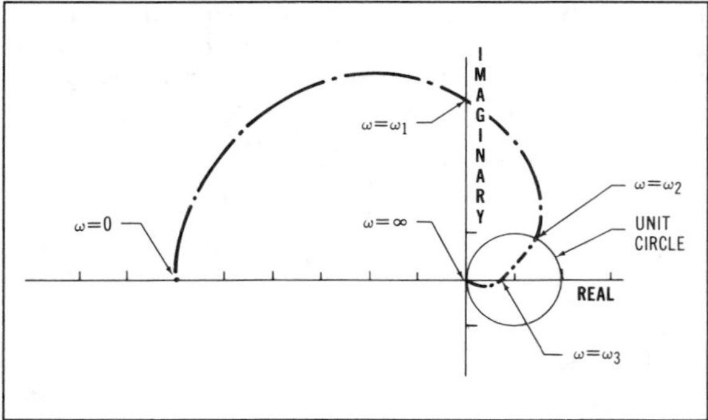

Figure 15-9 Nyquist diagram for loop gain.

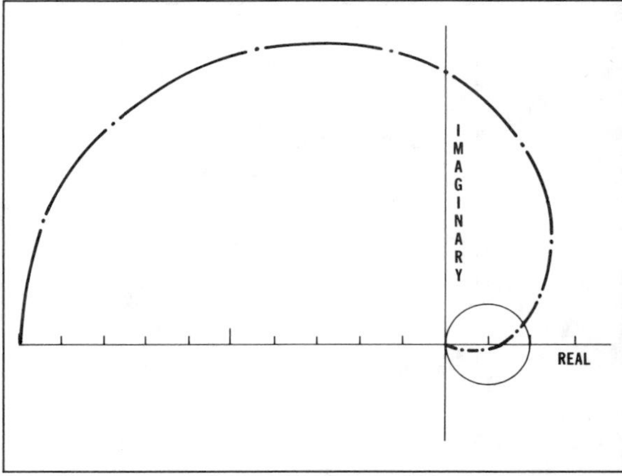

Figure 15-10 Nyquist curve for an unstable amplifier.

zeros, it possesses three poles. If AB for the hypothetical amplifier had possessed just a single pole, the entire Nyquist diagram would have been restricted to the second quadrant, and the feedback would have been negative for all frequencies. On the other hand, if AB had possessed just two poles, the Nyquist diagram would enter the first quadrant at high frequencies but would approach zero without ever crossing the real axis. The feedback would be positive at high frequencies but not to an excessive degree. The critical point to be avoided for stable operation is the point 1,j0 on the positive real axis. If the Nyquist curve passes through this point under any condition, the loop gain becomes one with an angle of zero. As a consequence, $|1 - AB|$ becomes zero, and A′ becomes infinite. Physically this implies that the amplifier will produce an output even in the absence of an input signal from the outside world. That is, what was intended to be an amplifier has become an oscillator. The type of Nyquist diagram that is to be avoided is any one that even just encircles the critical point such as displayed in Fig. 15-10. Fig. 15-10 was obtained by a modification of the amplifier described by Fig. 15-9. This modification amounted to changing AB at zero frequency from its former value of −6 to a new value of −10 with all other factors remaining the same.

Unlike Fig. 15-9, Fig. 15-10 is the Nyquist curve for an unstable amplifier. The curve does not pass through the critical point, but it does encircle the critical point. Consider for the moment that the amplifier is initially off. Under such a circumstance, A is zero; consequently, AB is also zero. Under these conditions, the Nyquist curve is collapsed into a single point at the origin. Following turnon, there is a period of time in which A and AB are growing toward their final values. In this interval, the Nyquist curve is in effect growing outward from the origin. At some instant during this growth period, the Nyquist curve will intersect the critical point 1,j0, and the amplifier will break into oscillation. Precaution must be taken, therefore, when dealing with feedback loops in which the loop gain transfer function has three or more poles.

It was mentioned earlier that negative feedback can be a stabilizing influence on amplifier operation. A negative feedback loop is in essence a type of quality control wherein the system output is compared with what it is desired for it to be. Any difference as a result of this comparison is injected back into the system in such a way as to force a correction of system behavior.

A highly simplified example is as follows. Consider a dc voltage amplifier for which it is desired that the voltage gain be −10, that is an output voltage ten times as large as the input signal but with the opposite polarity. One might proceed on good faith and employ the latest electronic design techniques, consult manufacturers' specifications on the best available active devices, design, and finally construct an amplifier that, according to the best available information, possesses an open-loop transfer function at low frequencies of −10. In fact, to be on the safe side, we may follow the same procedure yielding a value of −20 and precede the device by an adjustable attenuator set at an absolute value of 1/2 or whatever is required to obtain an overall transfer function of −10 when the system is first tested. Unfortunately, the active devices employed are at the mercy of the operating voltages supplied to them (line voltage variations, and so on), ambient temperature variations, age, and weather elements in general. To a lesser degree, the same may be said of the passive elements involved. A, the open-loop transfer function may possess a nominal value of −10, but it is constantly changing from moment to moment being at times larger and at other instants smaller than the intended value. There exists nothing in the system to monitor its overall operation. Alternatively, one might, following the same procedures outlined previously, design an amplifier having an open-loop transfer function whose nominal value is −100 and enclose this with a negative feedback loop to obtain a nominal closed-loop transfer function A′ of −10. Mathematically, Eq. 15-9 is

$$A' = A/(1 - AB)$$

By substituting nominal values, we can solve for B:

$$-10 = -100/(1 + 100B)$$
$$1 + 100B = 10$$
$$100B = 9$$
$$B = 9/100$$

B is found to require the properties of a simple attenuator or voltage divider. The next step would be to construct this divider from precision resistors possessing very small voltage and temperature coefficients of resistance. The feedback loop is then closed making use of this stable attenuator. The resulting system has a nominal closed-loop transfer function $A' = -10$, a nominal loop gain $AB = -9$, and a nominal gain reduction factor of 10. What has been accomplished? Suppose that the original open-loop amplifier whose nominal transfer function was -10 had variations or changes in A, which were about $\pm 20\%$, and the new amplifier that was constructed employing the same technology has similar variations under open-loop conditions. Now compare the ratio of the variations to the nominal values with and without feedback.

That is, $\Delta A/A$ is to be compared with $\Delta A'/A'$. Knowing that $A' = A/(1 - AB)$ and employing the techniques of differential calculus, we find that

$$\Delta A' = \Delta A/(1 - AB)^2$$

consequently,

$$\Delta A'/A' = \frac{\Delta A/(1 - AB)^2}{A/(1 - AB)}$$
$$= \left(\frac{\Delta A}{A}\right)\left(\frac{1}{1 - AB}\right)$$
$$= (\pm 20\%)(1/10)$$
$$= \pm 2\%$$

The application of negative feedback has produced a system that has a nominal transfer function of -10 with a variation of $\pm 2\%$, whereas previously in the absence of feedback, there existed a system having a nominal transfer function of -10 with a variation of $\pm 20\%$ under the same conditions. The price paid for this improvement amounted to trading off a higher open-loop gain for the sake of a more stable value of gain.

Negative feedback affects many amplifier properties other than gain stability. Negative feedback increases amplifier bandwidth, reduces most but not all forms of distortion, modifies amplifier input and output impedances, and can be beneficially employed in shaping frequency-response characteristics. Examples of these features are given in the next section.

Negative feedback is not, however, a panacea. It cannot turn a bad amplifier into a good one. However, it may make a good amplifier into a better one. Always remember that the derivations and conclusions obtained previously are based on linear or nearly linear operating conditions of the active devices. Negative feedback loops lose control under clipping conditions, and recovery from such conditions may be poorer with negative feedback than without it.

15.1.5 Operational Amplifiers

Operational amplifiers derive the name as a result of their first employment in analog computing systems. In this role, with suitable feedback, they were employed to accomplish the mathematical operations of addition, subtraction, integration, and differentiation. In their current form of integrated circuits, operational amplifiers have become the fundamental building blocks of electronic analog circuits with notable uses in power supply regulation, voltage and current amplification, and active filters, as well as other forms of signal processors.

Operational amplifiers are dc-coupled voltage amplifiers possessing, under open-loop conditions, very high gain, wide bandwidth, high input impedance, low output impedance, balanced or difference inputs accompanied usually by a single-ended output, and provisions for accomplishing a dc voltage balance at the output.

Fig. 15-11 displays the configurations commonly employed for operational amplifiers where signal inversion (polarity change) is required or desirable. In each instance the open-loop transfer function A is negative and real at low frequencies.

In Figs. 5-11A through 5-11D expressions are given for the respective closed-loop transfer functions A′. These expressions are valid without correction provided that the input impedance of the operational amplifier under open-loop conditions is much larger than the impedances used in structuring the loop and that the output impedance of the operational amplifier under open-loop conditions is much smaller than any of the impedances used in structuring the loop. These requirements are easily met in practice since input impedances of commercial devices range upward from several megohms and the output impedances range downward from several tens of ohms throughout the audio frequency range. The approximate values given for V_O/V_I are valid if, in addition to the requirements stated, the magnitude of A is large throughout the frequency range being employed. Fig. 5-11A is an inverting voltage amplifier having an unbalanced input as well as output. Fig. 5-11B is an inverting voltage amplifier with a balanced input. Fig. 5-11C unbalanced and Fig. 5-11D balanced are examples of more versatile configurations. The impedances Z_1 and Z_2 can be any two-terminal configuration of impedance elements. These circuits find applications as low-pass filters or integrators, high-pass filters or differentiators, phase compensators, shelving filters, and tone control, among a myriad of other possibilities. Fig. 15-11E is a combining amplifier that combines or adds signals from several

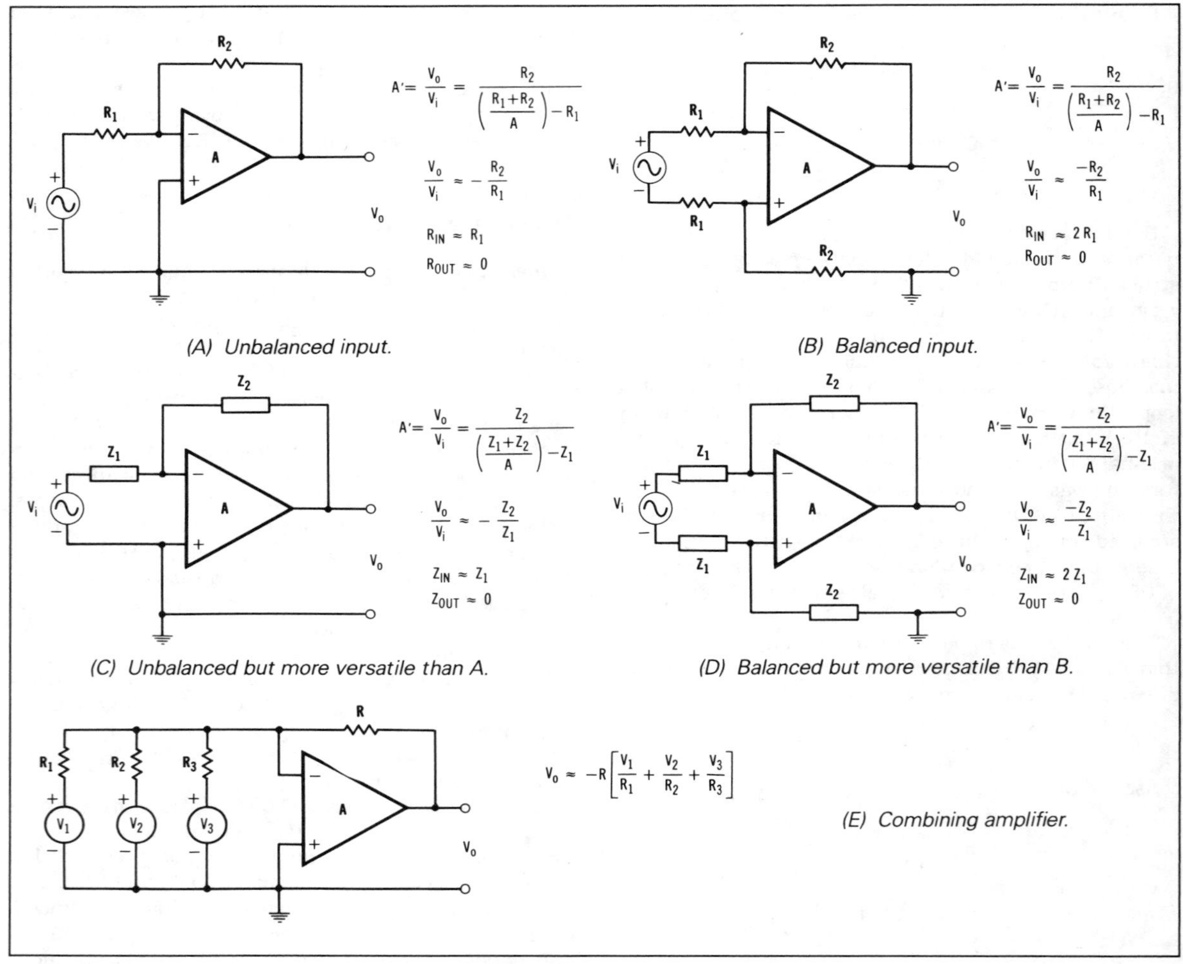

Figure 15-11 Inverting operational amplifier circuits.

sources with different weighting or gain factors for each signal.

Fig. 15-12A is an example of a noninverting voltage amplifier, and Fig. 15-12B is a noninverting unity gain voltage follower, which is often employed as a buffer because of its extremely high input impedance and exceptionally low output impedance. In each instance the open-loop transfer function A is positive and real at low frequencies.

Most of the wideband low-noise operational amplifiers currently available for audio applications are internally structured so as to exhibit dominant pole characteristics. This means that the open-loop transfer function of such an amplifier exhibits the behavior of a single-pole amplifier over the frequency range for which it is useful. Such an amplifier is easily employed in the majority of feedback arrangements without fear of violating the conditions necessary for stability. Fig. 15-13 is a Bode diagram typical of such amplifiers both when operated open loop as well as when operated with a closed-loop noninverting voltage gain of 20 dB.

An examination of Fig. 15-13 reveals that under open-loop conditions this amplifier exhibits a gain of 90 dB or $\sqrt{10} \times 10^4$ volts per volt at dc with the gain being down by 3 dB at a frequency of $\sqrt{10} \times 10^2$ Hz attended by a phase shift of $-45°$. The bandwidth of this amplifier is then $\sqrt{10} \times 10^2$ Hz, and the product of the gain at dc with the bandwidth or the gain bandwidth product is 10^7-Hz volts per volt. The loop is closed in this example by requiring that R_2 in Fig. 15-12A be nine times the value of R_1. The second set of curves in Fig. 15-13 describes the performance under this closed-loop condition. The curves reveal that the gain at dc is now 20 dB or 10 volts per volt and that the bandwidth has now become 10^6 Hz. The gain bandwidth product is still 10^7-Hz volts per volt. The bandwidth has been increased by exactly the same

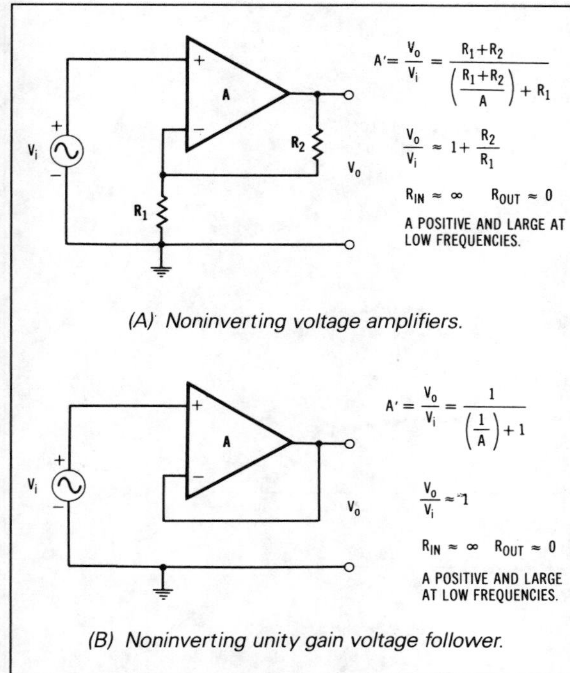

(A) Noninverting voltage amplifiers.

(B) Noninverting unity gain voltage follower.

Figure 15-12 Noninverting voltage amplifiers.

factor that the gain was reduced. This behavior is characteristic of dominant pole amplifiers. The application of feedback has yielded another important benefit. The open-loop amplifier not only had a nonflat amplitude response throughout most of the audio spectrum, it suffered from phase or group delay distortion above a few hertz as well. The amplifier with feedback has a linear phase behavior from dc to beyond 10^4 Hz and, hence, does not introduce any group delay distortion in this frequency range.

15.1.6 Active Filters Employing Operational Amplifiers

Filter technology has a long, time-honored history that actually predates electronics by several decades. In fact if Lord Kelvin (William Thomson) had not discovered the physical and mathematical properties of the so-called wave filters in the middle of the 1800s, submarine telegraphic cable communications and later long-distance telephone communications would have been delayed until well into the 20th century.

Despite the voluminous literature and interest in this subject, what will be touched on here is just a few of the filter types that have proven to be of paramount importance in modern audio applications and more particularly those that are readily implemented by means of active circuitry. Even though the emphasis will be on active circuitry, a cursory examination of some simple passive structures is of value.

Fig. 15-14 displays a few passive filter structures along with their associated transfer functions. Note that in each instance the filter transfer functions involve a polynomial in S appearing in the denominator. The characteristics of the various filters are associated with the structure of these polynomials. With the possible exception of anti-aliasing use, the filters employed in audio work are restricted to pole orders of three or less in order to maintain good transient response. A pole order of three corresponds to an asymptotic slope rate of −18-dB/octave in the filter stop band. The most popular polynomials for audio applications are the Butterworth with maximally flat amplitude response and the Bessel with linear phase response (maximally flat group delay). The Butterworth polynomials through third order are

1. $S + \omega_O$
2. $S^2 + \sqrt{2}\,S\,\omega_O + \omega_O{}^2$
3. $(S + \omega_O)(S^2 + S\,\omega_O + \omega_O{}^2) = S^3 + 2S^2\,\omega_O + 2S\,\omega_O{}^2 + \omega_O{}^3$

These are often written in a normalized form such as

1. $(S/\omega_O) + 1$
2. $(S^2/\omega_O{}^2) + (\sqrt{2}\,S/\omega_O) + 1$
3. $(S^3/\omega_O{}^3) + (2S^2/\omega_O{}^2) + (2S/\omega_O) + 1$

In the Butterworth polynomials, $\omega_O = 2\pi f_O$, where f_O is the frequency at which the response is 3 dB down. The Butterworth polynomials yield excellent amplitude response characteristics, although their phase and group delay characteristics are far from being ideal. Their use in constant resistance crossover networks is almost universal.

The Bessel polynomials in normalized form are

1. $(S/\omega_O) + 1$
2. $(S^2/3\,\omega_O{}^2) + (S/\omega_O) + 1$
3. $(S^3/15\,\omega_O{}^3) + (2S^2/5\,\omega_O{}^2) + 1$

Here, ω_O has the significance that the group delay at zero frequency is just the reciprocal of ω_O. The group delay for any filter at any frequency is given by the negative of the first derivative of phase response with respect to ω:

$$T_g = -d\phi/d\omega \qquad (15\text{-}12)$$

For a system to not introduce any phase distortion, it is necessary that ϕ be either independent of frequency or of the form

$$\phi = -k\,\omega + \text{constant} \qquad (15\text{-}13)$$

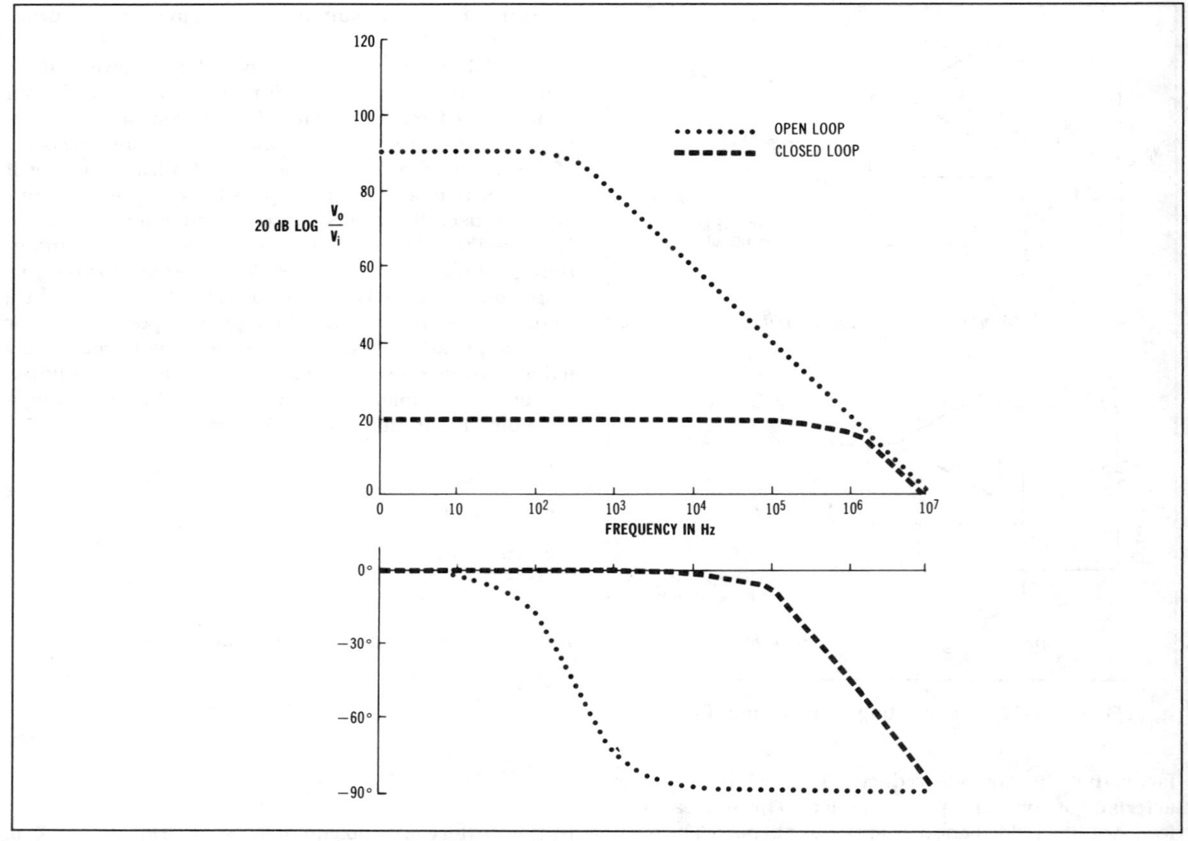

Figure 15-13 Bode diagram for a dominant pole amplifier.

In the first instance $T_g = 0$, and for Eq. 15-13 $T_g = k$, where k is a constant. Bessel filters are nearly ideal in this respect since their group delays are constant or nearly so throughout their passbands. Unfortunately, the amplitude response of Bessel filters for orders higher than one, though without ripples, is not as flat as the corresponding Butterworth filter. The first-order Bessel and Butterworth filters are identical.

Operational amplifiers make significant contributions in the area of active filter implementation. The following examples, though by no means exhaustive, will serve as an introduction to this important subject.

The circuit of Fig. 15-15 simulates a physical inductor. A physical inductor at low frequencies, where interturn capacitance is not of importance, can be thought of as a pure resistance in series with a pure self-inductance. As such, a physical inductor has an impedance Z that has both a real and an imaginary part.

A physical inductor also has a quality factor or Q. These properties are summarized by the following equations:

$$Z = R + j\omega L \quad (15\text{-}14)$$

$$Q = \omega L / R \quad (15\text{-}15)$$

Third-order or higher filters are readily obtained by cascading two or more sections of the examples displayed in Fig. 15-16.

The transfer functions of the various filters appear in Table 15-2.

This discussion of active filters employing operational amplifiers will now be concluded by exploring two design examples.

Example 1. Third-order Butterworth low pass has a corner frequency f_O of 500 Hz and unity gain.

This filter can be implemented by cascading a first-order section followed by a second-order section. The required overall transfer function is

$$\frac{V_O}{V_{in}} = \left(\frac{\omega_O}{S + \omega_O}\right)\left(\frac{\omega_O{}^2}{S^2 + S\omega_O + \omega_O{}^2}\right) \quad (15\text{-}16)$$

Taking Fig. 15-16A for the first-order section along with its transfer function leads to the identification

$$\omega_O/(S + \omega_O) = (1/RC)/[S + (1/RC)] \quad (15\text{-}17)$$

from which it is found that

$$A = \frac{1/RC}{S + \left(\frac{1}{RC}\right)} = \frac{\omega_0}{S+\omega_0}$$

$$A = \frac{R/L}{S+(R/L)} = \frac{\omega_0}{S+\omega_0}$$

(A) Single-pole low pass.

$$A = \frac{S}{S+(R/L)} = \frac{S}{S+\omega_0}$$

$$A = \frac{S}{S+(1/RC)} = \frac{S}{S+\omega_0}$$

(B) Single-pole high pass

$$A = \frac{1/LC}{S^2 + \left(\frac{S}{RC}\right) + \left(\frac{1}{LC}\right)} = \frac{\omega_0^2}{S^2 + \left(\frac{S\omega_0}{R\sqrt{C/L}}\right) + \omega_0^2}$$

(C) Two-pole low pass.

$$A = \frac{S^2}{S^2 + \left(\frac{S}{RC}\right) + \left(\frac{1}{LC}\right)} = \frac{S^2}{S^2 + \left(\frac{S\omega_0}{R\sqrt{C/L}}\right) + \omega_0^2}$$

(D) Two-pole high pass.

$$A = \frac{\frac{RS}{L}}{S^2 + \left(\frac{RS}{L}\right) + \left(\frac{1}{LC}\right)} = \frac{\frac{R\omega_0 S}{\sqrt{L/C}}}{S^2 + \frac{R\omega_0 S}{\sqrt{L/C}} + \omega_0^2}$$

(E) Two-pole bandpass.

$$A = \frac{S^2 + \frac{1}{L/C}}{S^2 + \left(\frac{RS}{L}\right) + \left(\frac{1}{LC}\right)} = \frac{S^2 + \omega_0^2}{S^2 + \frac{R\omega_0 S}{\sqrt{L/C}} + \omega_0^2}$$

(F) Two-pole band reject.

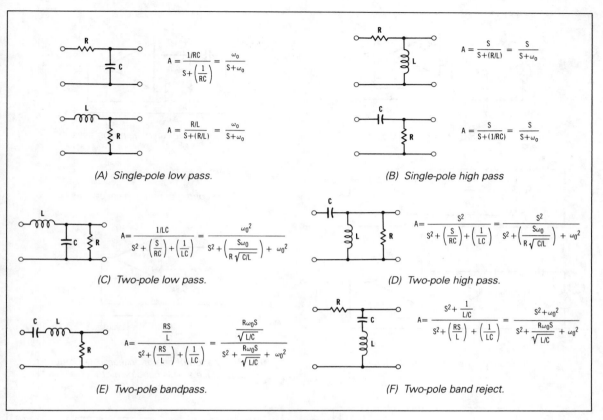

Figure 15-14 Passive filter structures.

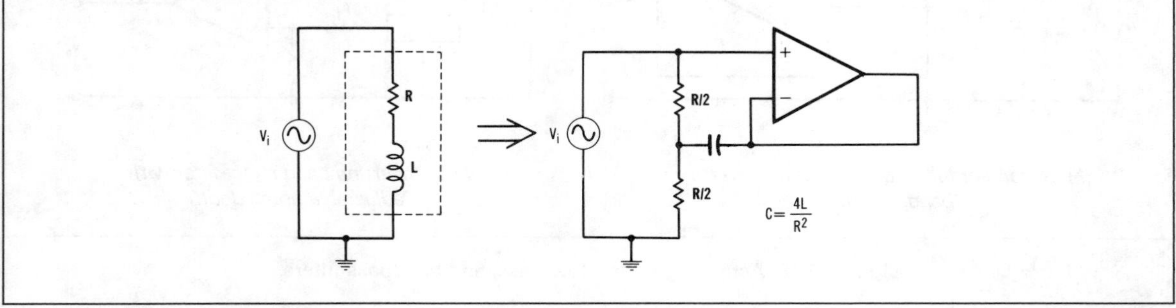

Figure 15-15 The resistor, capacitor, operational amplifier combination presents the signal source with the same impedance at all frequencies as does the physical inductor in the dotted enclosure. The two circuits are equivalent.

$$\omega_0 = 1/RC = 2\pi f_0 \qquad (15\text{-}18)$$
$$= 2\pi 500\,\text{Hz}$$

By choosing for C a value of 0.02 μF, Eq. 15-18 yields a value for R of 15.9 kΩ.

Taking Fig. 15-16C for the second-order section along with its transfer function leads to the identification

$$\frac{\omega_0}{S^2 + S\omega_0 + \omega_0^2} = \frac{1/R_1R_2C_1C_2}{S^2 + \left(\frac{R_1C_2 + R_2C_2}{R_1R_2C_1C_2}\right)S + \left(\frac{1}{R_1R_2C_1C_2}\right)} \qquad (15\text{-}19)$$

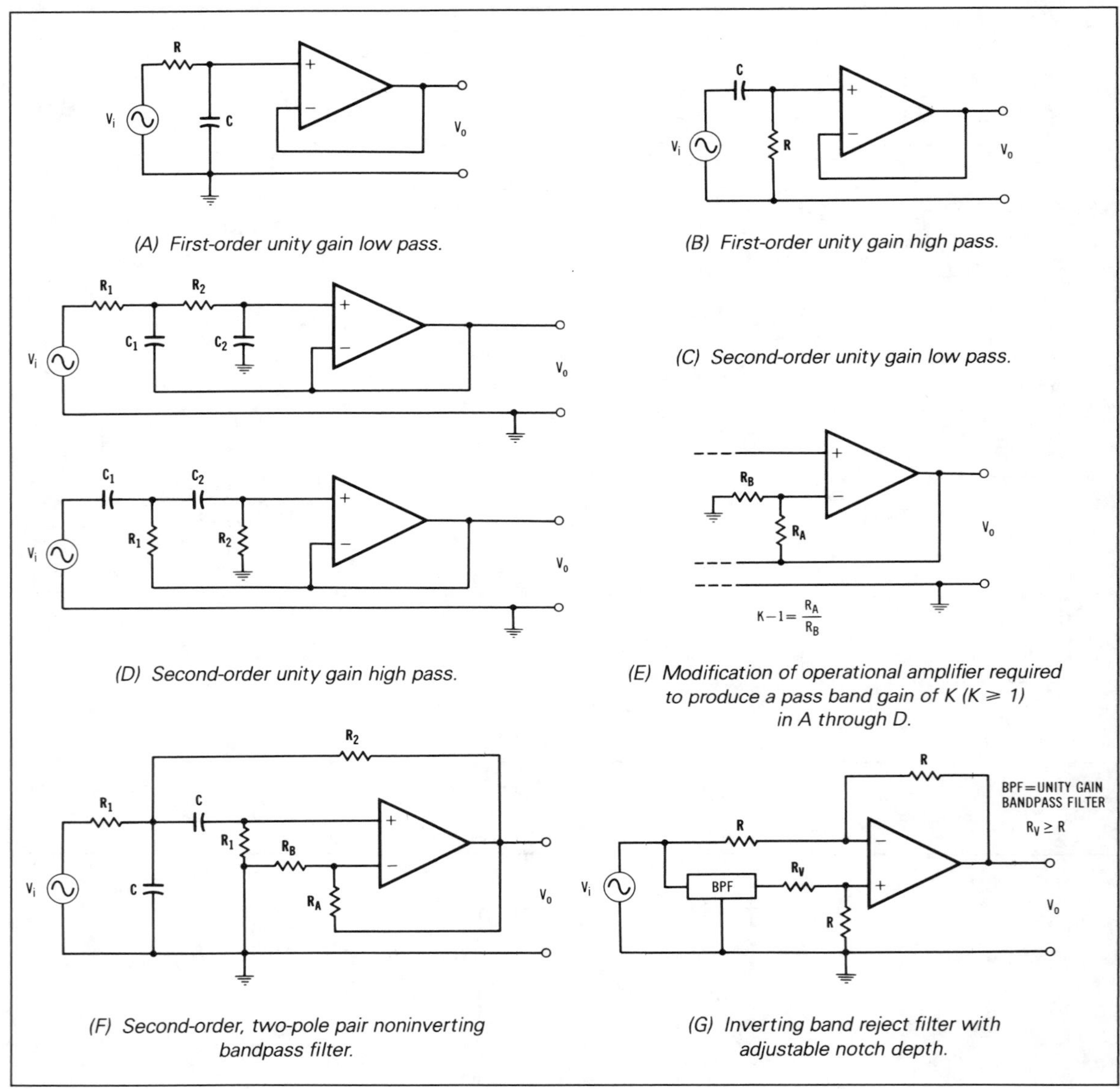

(A) First-order unity gain low pass.

(B) First-order unity gain high pass.

(C) Second-order unity gain low pass.

(D) Second-order unity gain high pass.

(E) Modification of operational amplifier required to produce a pass band gain of K (K ≥ 1) in A through D.

(F) Second-order, two-pole pair noninverting bandpass filter.

(G) Inverting band reject filter with adjustable notch depth.

Figure 15-16 Active high-pass, low-pass, and bandpass filters.

$$\omega_o = 1/\sqrt{R_1R_2C_1C_2} \qquad (15\text{-}20)$$

$$= 2\pi 500\,\text{Hz}$$

and

$$1/\sqrt{R_1R_2C_1C_2} = (R_1C_2 + R_2C_2)/(R_1R_2C_1C_2) \qquad (15\text{-}21)$$

Upon choosing $R_1 = R_2$, Eq. 15-21 dictates that $C_1 = 4C_2$. If C_1 is chosen to be 0.02 μF, then C_2 becomes 0.005 μF and Eq. 15-20 then requires that R_1 be 10 kΩ. The reasonableness of these values allows the design to be concluded with the circuit of Fig. 15-17.

Example 2. Second-order Bessel low pass has a zero-frequency group delay of 500 μs.

The required transfer function is

$$V_o/V_{in} = 3\,\omega_o{}^2/(S^2 + 3\,\omega_oS + 3\,\omega_o{}^2) \qquad (15\text{-}22)$$

with $\omega_o = 1/500$ μs. Taking Fig. 15-16C along with its transfer function leads to the identification

Table 15-2. Transfer Functions of Various Circuits of Fig. 15-16

Fig.	K	Transfer Function
15-16A	= 1	$\frac{V_o}{V_i} = \frac{\frac{1}{RC}}{S + \frac{1}{RC}}$
15-16B	= 1	$\frac{V_o}{V_i} = \frac{S}{S + \frac{1}{RC}}$
15-16C	= 1	$\frac{V_o}{V_i} = \frac{\frac{1}{R_1R_2C_1C_2}}{S^2 + \left(\frac{R_1C_2 + R_2C_2}{R_1R_2C_1C_2}\right)S + \frac{1}{R_1R_2C_1C_2}}$
15-16D	= 1	$\frac{V_o}{V_i} = \frac{S^2}{S^2 + \left(\frac{R_1C_2 + R_1C_1}{R_1R_2C_1C_2}\right)S + \frac{1}{R_1R_2C_1C_2}}$
15-16A	⩾ 1	$\frac{V_o}{V_i} = \frac{K\left(\frac{1}{RC}\right)}{S + \frac{1}{RC}}$
15-16B	⩾ 1	$\frac{V_o}{V_i} = \frac{KS}{S + \frac{1}{RC}}$
15-16C	⩾ 1	$\frac{V_o}{V_i} = \frac{K\left(\frac{1}{R_1R_2C_1C_2}\right)}{S^2 + \left[\frac{R_1C_2 + R_2C_2 + (1-K)R_1C_1}{R_1R_2C_1C_2}\right]S + \frac{1}{R_1R_2C_1C_2}}$
15-16D	⩾ 1	$\frac{V_o}{V_i} = \frac{KS^2}{S^2 + \left[\frac{R_1C_2 + R_1C_1 + (1-K)R_2C_2}{R_1R_2C_1C_2}\right]S + \frac{1}{R_1R_2C_1C_2}}$
15-16F	⩾ 1	$\frac{V_o}{V_i} = \frac{\frac{KS}{R_1C}}{S^2 + \left[\frac{3R_1R_2C + (1-K)R_1^2C}{R_1^2R_2C^2}\right]S + \frac{R_1 + R_2}{R_1^2R_2C^2}}$

or,

$$\frac{V_o}{V_i} = \frac{\left(\frac{A_o}{Q}\right)\omega_0 S}{S^2 + \left(\frac{\omega_0}{Q}\right)S + \omega_0{}^2}$$

where,

A_o is the gain at pass band center

$$A_o = \frac{R_2}{\frac{1}{K}(3R_2 + R_1 - KR_1)}$$

(continued on next page)

Table 15-2.-Cont. Transfer Functions of Various Circuits of Fig. 15-16

Fig.	K	Transfer Function
		Q is the quality factor $Q = \dfrac{R_2\sqrt{1 + \dfrac{R_1}{R_2}}}{3R_2 + R_1 - KR_1}$ ω_o is the resonant angular frequency $\omega_o = \dfrac{\sqrt{1 + \dfrac{R_1}{R_2}}}{R_1C}$
15-16G		$\dfrac{V_o}{V_i} = -\left[\dfrac{S^2 + \left(\dfrac{R_v - R}{R_v + R}\right)\left(\dfrac{\omega_o}{Q}\right)S + \omega_o^2}{S^2 + \left(\dfrac{\omega_o}{Q}\right)S + \omega_o^2}\right]$

$$3\,\omega_o^2/(S^2 + 3\,\omega_oS + 3\,\omega_o^2) = \frac{1/R_1R_2C_1C_2}{S^2 + \left(\dfrac{R_1C_2 + R_2C_2}{R_1R_2C_1C_2}\right)S + \left(\dfrac{1}{R_1R_2C_1C_2}\right)} \tag{15-23}$$

from which it is found that

$$\omega_o = 1\sqrt{(3R_1R_2C_1C_2)} \tag{15-24}$$

and

$$\frac{3}{\sqrt{3R_1R_2C_1C_2}} = \frac{R_1C_2 + R_2C_2}{R_1R_2C_1C_2} \tag{15-25}$$

Upon choosing $R_1 = R_2$, Eq. 15-25 requires that:

$$C_1 = (4/3)C_2 \tag{15-26}$$

Substitution into Eq. 15-24 while invoking the necessary value of ω_o leads to

$$2000\ \text{rad/s} = 1\sqrt{3R_1^2(4/3)C_2^2}$$
$$= 1/2R_1C_2$$

or

$$R_1C_2 = \text{group delay}/2$$
$$= 250 \times 10^{-6}\ \text{s} \tag{15-27}$$

If C_2 is taken to be 0.05 μF, then Eq. 15-27 requires R_1 and, hence, R_2 to be 5 kΩ. Eq. 15-26 would then require

$$C_1 = (4/3)C_2$$
$$= (4/3) \times (5 \times 10^{-8}\ \text{F})$$
$$= 0.066\ \mu\text{F}$$

which is quite close to a readily available value of 0.068 μF. These are all reasonable values; hence, the example is concluded with the circuit of Fig. 15-18.

In fairness it is necessary to state that the solutions given to the two examples are not unique. In fact, even more elegant solutions than the ones given are possible though not quite as straightforward. These more elegant ones will no doubt occur to the reader after further study.

15.2 PREAMPLIFIERS

Preamplifiers provide the interface between low-level signals from microphones, phono pickups, and so on, and the various signal-processing equipment in a sound system or a studio. Typical signal levels will be in the range of 10 to 100 μV, although most signal-processing equipment is designed to operate with volts of signal amplitude. Preamplifiers must, therefore, provide stable gain for small signals with low input noise, provide little or no sensitivity to induced noise and hum on input cables

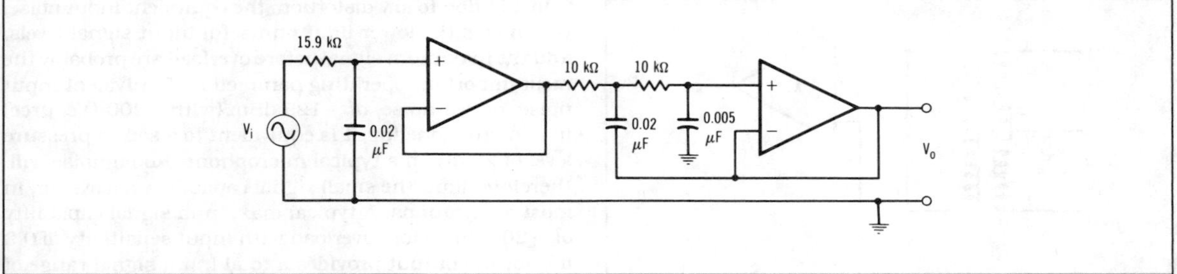

Figure 15-17 Third-order unity gain Butterworth low-pass filter with f_o = 500 Hz.

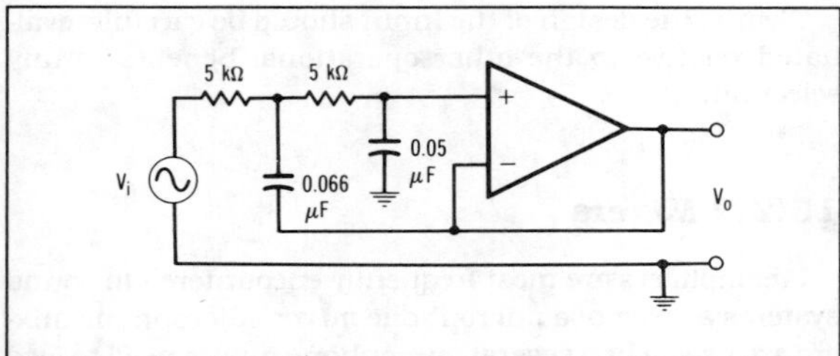

Figure 15-18 Second-order unity gain Bessel low-pass with a zero frequency group delay of 500 μs.

and terminals, and at the same time not provide distortion of large amplitude signals.

15.2.1 General Requirements

The most critical parameters of preamplifier and microphone mixer design and use relate to the equivalent input noise; the avoidance of noise pickup and interference and its handling (i.e. rejection of common-mode signals and distortion).

Input noise due to external sources, such as pickup on signal leads and on the transducers, is largely the responsibility of the system installer. Attention to grounds to avoid ground loops, shielded twisted-pair cables, and other good installation practices should be followed. On the other hand, the preamplifier itself should be designed adequately with low noise and good signal-handling capability in its input stages so that the full range of expected input signal amplitudes can be accommodated.

Common-mode signals can be troublesome in preamplifiers. Common-mode signals are those that appear on both terminals of the amplifier at the same time. They are frequently caused by induced pickup in long cable runs or by inadvertent connections between power lines and ground. As can be seen from the diagram in Fig. 15-19, they cause no amplifiable input if the input terminals are symmetrical to ground or common, unless they exceed the signal-handling limits of the input stage.

Common-mode rejection ratio is a common measure of the ability of a balanced input amplifier to avoid amplifying common-mode signals. Common-mode rejection ratio (CMRR) is the ratio of the differential voltage gain to the common-mode voltage gain and is generally expressed in decibels:

$$\text{CMRR} = 20 \log (A_D / A_{CM})$$

where,

A_D is the differential voltage gain,

A_{CM} is the common-mode voltage gain.

CMRR is a function of frequency and also the imped-

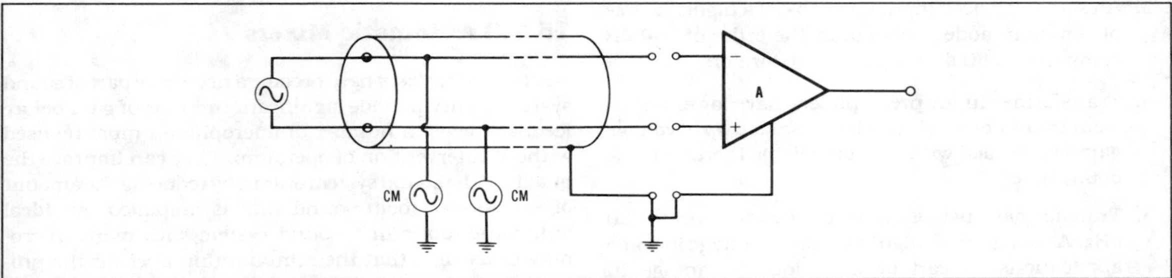

Figure 15-19 Typical microphone cable connection to a balanced input amplifier, showing common-mode (CM) signal source.

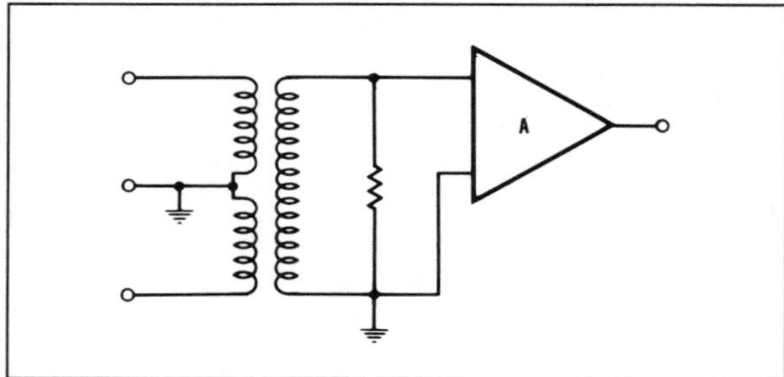

Figure 15-20 Amplifier with balanced transformer input.

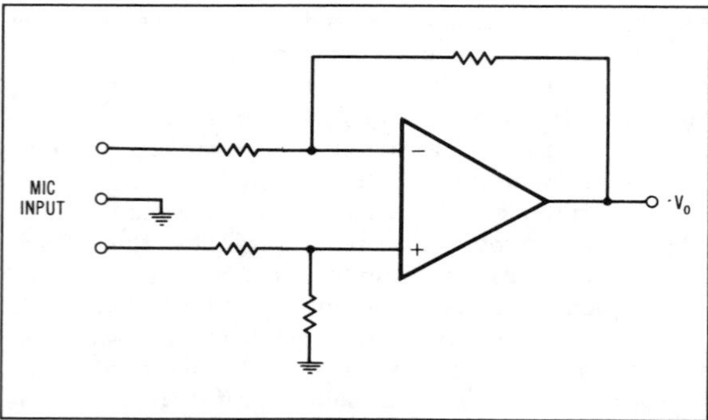

Figure 15-21 Amplifier with active balanced input.

ance balance between the two input terminals of the amplifier.

Either balanced transformer inputs with single-ended secondary as in Fig. 15-20, or active balanced input amplifiers as in Fig. 15-21, will be found. The relative merits of transformer and active balanced inputs are:

1. Both give better balance of input terminal impedances and sensitivities than is likely to be provided in the manufacture of twisted-pair cables.
2. Transformer inputs are more tolerant of large common-mode over voltage signals than are the active balanced inputs.
3. An active balanced input is capable of a higher degree of common-mode rejection, in the order of 100 dB compared to 60 dB for good transformers.
4. Transformer input preamplifiers have lower equivalent input noise voltages because step up of voltage gain is provided without appreciable thermal noise being added.
5. Transformers usually have bandwidths under 20 kHz. Although this might be a disadvantage in some applications, it can be a decided advantage in reduction of radio-frequency interference.
6. Transformers tend to introduce more distortion.

In addition to low distortion, the equivalent input noise, which sets the lower limit on useful input signal levels, and the maximum signal before overload are probably the most important operating parameters. Equivalent input noise, or self-noise, of −125 dBm (with a 200-Ω source) in a microphone input is equivalent to a sound pressure level of 26 dB on a typical microphone. Room noise will, therefore, limit the small signal capability of a system in most applications. A typical maximum signal capability of −20 dBm before overload with input sensitivity of 0.3 mV for full output provides a total input signal range of 105 dB. Input sensitivity or gain controls then set the signal level at the best combination for the room or background noise and expected peak signal amplitudes.

Clearly, the design of the input should be carefully evaluated relative to the other operational benefits in any selection.

15.2.2 Mixers

Preamplifiers are most frequently encountered in sound systems as part of a microphone *mixer*. Microphone mixers are used when several microphone inputs need to feed a common sound distribution system, such as an equalizer, power amplifier, and one or more loudspeakers. In the typical microphone mixer shown in Fig. 15-22, each microphone line is connected to its own preamplifier. There may be tone controls on each input channel. The outputs of the preamplifiers are fed to a main mixing bus. A master summing amplifier, possibly more spectrum shaping, and an output level control provide a single output for the rest of the system. Auxiliary inputs and outputs take care of line level connections to tape recorders, projectors, reverberators, and other special equipment.

The channel level or sensitivity control is used to adjust the gain for each microphone input to obtain uniform levels among all the microphones. It can be used to compensate for microphone sensitivities when several microphone types are used in one system. The master level affects the overall output level and may be a convenient point in the system to adjust loudspeaker output levels if needed.

15.2.3 Automatic Mixers

Automatic mixers have become a necessary part of sound systems. They provide significant increase of gain before feedback when a number of microphones must be used without intervention of operators. They can improve the quality of the sound system output by reducing the amount of extraneous room sound that is amplified. An ideal automatic mixer in a sound system with many microphones assures that the minimum number for the program being amplified is given access to the system; all others are temporarily "removed." In addition, it automatically adjusts system gain to compensate for program

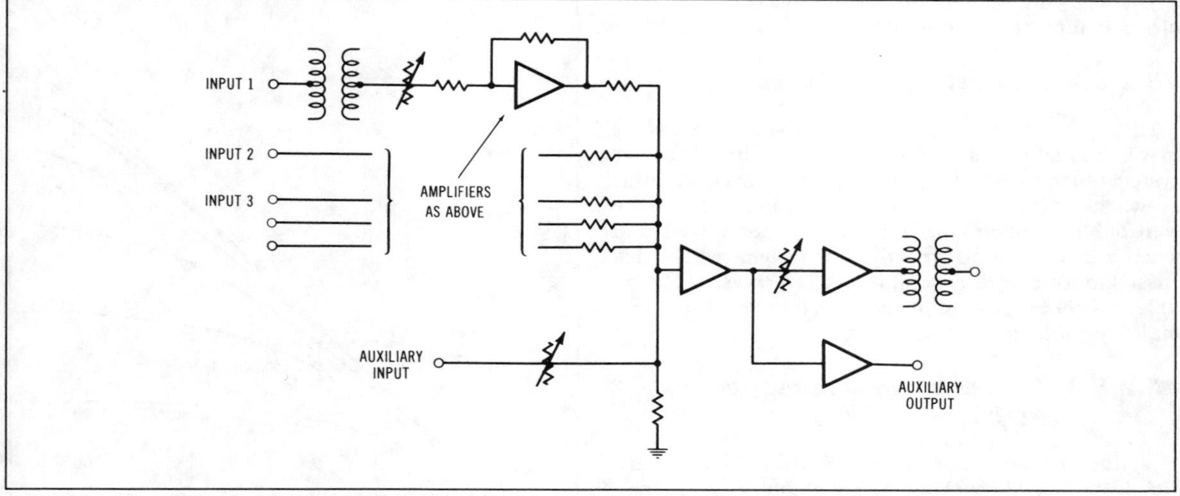

Figure 15-22 Simplified diagram of a microphone mixer.

level variations and to produce more uniform listening sound levels. Thus, an automatic mixer provides for essentially every control that might be produced manually otherwise.

15.2.3.1 Why Automatic Mixers?

As shown in Fig. 15-22, a conventional microphone mixer in a sound system amplifies the signal from each microphone and adds these amplified signals together to produce a single output that feeds a power amplifier and then one or more loudspeakers. Each doubling of the number of microphones feeding into a sound system reduces the available gain before feedback by 3 dB. A large system easily becomes ineffective if an operator is not present to operate faders and switch unused microphone channels out of the system. Since acoustic gain is often only marginal because of architectural or other room features, an automatic mixer may be the only way to get adequately high program sound levels in an audience area with unattended systems.

The following are some automatic microphone mixer selection and design objectives found in various available automatic mixers:

- It keeps the sound system gain below the threshold of feedback instability.
- It requires no operator or technician at the controls.
- It does not introduce spurious and undesirable noises and distortions of the program while it is operating.
- It can be installed as easily as a conventional mixer.
- It controls on the desired program input and is relatively unaffected by other inputs.
- It responds fast enough that no audible loss of portions of signals occurs.
- It allows more than one signal on the system if required by the program content while still maintaining control over the gain.
- It adjusts the system gain to compensate for a range of signal (talker) input levels.
- It provides system status outputs for peripheral equipment control.

The mixer operation should allow relatively easy access to the system. We want a bona fide signal to have immediate access to the system, which may not always happen if the access is made too difficult. Little is lost through random false gating by remote microphones, since those signals are surely a number of decibels lower in level than the desired signal. The automatic mixer is doing its job if the talker or talkers are heard on the system output when they say something, and the sound system remains stable!

Automatic mixers cannot improve the "reach" of microphones. Their benefit comes from limiting the number of microphones feeding signals into the mixer and, if available, automatically adjusting the mixer gain to compensate for changes in the input signal level. As a result, there may be an apparent increase of critical distance in a multiple microphone system. This is because of the elimination of room sound pickup that would otherwise be amplified in channels connected to more remote microphones.

The following sections review approaches and examples of equipment for automatic mixing.

15.2.3.2 Automatic Mixer Types

The *automatic microphone mixers* to be considered here may be thought of as *signal responding*, which excludes systems such as the floor pad switch that turns a channel on when someone is standing on it. Signal responsive control offers much more versatility to the installation when it is performing properly. The systems will be discussed in functional groupings of *fixed threshold, variable threshold, gain sharing, direction sensitive,* and *multi-variable dependent.*

15.2.3.3 Number of Open Microphones (NOM) Attenuation

Number of open microphones (NOM) attenuation is a simple method of ensuring system stability by automatically reducing the system gain in proportion to the number of microphones in the system. The attenuation A in decibels should vary as

$$A = 10 \log N \qquad (15\text{-}28)$$

where,
N is the number of microphones.

This attenuation cancels the growth of closed-loop gain with this number of microphones in a conventional system. While NOM attenuation can maintain a stable gain system, it does not by itself take advantage of the gain available through restricting the number of on microphones in a many-microphone installation.

15.2.3.4 Channel-Off Attenuation

Most automatic mixers use some form of channel gating to minimize the number of open microphone channels. The audibility of the gain change during gating decreases as the size of the change decreases. But more channel-off attenuation is required for gain stability as the number of microphones in the system increases. Adjustment of channel-off attenuation may be available to the installer. The amount of gain increase is related to the attenuation and the number of microphones by the following equation:

$$\Delta G = 10 \log \frac{N}{1 + (N - 1)\, 10^{A/10}} \qquad (15\text{-}29)$$

where,
ΔG is the gain improvement in decibels when the system has only one microphone gated on,
N is the number of microphones,
A is the channel-off attenuation (all channels equal) in decibels.

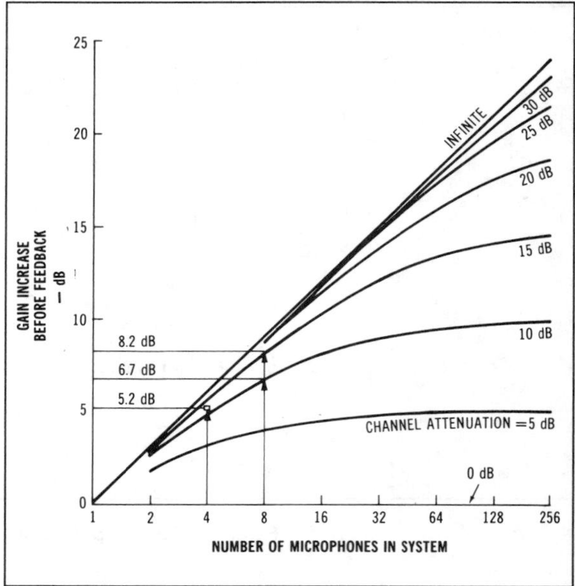

Figure 15-23 Gain improvement with different channel-off attenuations in a mixer that has a number of microphones and only one channel on.

Fig. 15-23 shows the relationship in graphical form. Note that the asymptotic maximum value of gain improvement is with infinite attenuation (i.e., all but one channel turned off). The arrows on the figure show possible gain improvements for an eight-channel mixer with 10- and 15-dB channel-off attenuations. The four-microphone example is for a mixer discussed in section 15.2.8. It is evident that channel-off attenuation greater than 30 dB offers little improvement for systems with up to 256 microphones.

15.2.4 Fixed-Threshold Automatic Mixers

A detector in the microphone channel amplifier circuit switches the amplifier on when a signal is present and off again when the signal ceases. To turn on, the signal must be larger than a threshold preset for the channel at the time of installation. This method has several shortcomings. First, there is the dilemma of where to set the threshold for determining whether a signal is present. If it is set to a low level, it will easily respond falsely to room noise and be triggered on by reverberation and room-reflected sound. On the other hand, if the threshold is set high to avoid false turn on with room noise, the risk of signal chopping and clipping and signal drop-out is high. The threshold should be high enough to avoid turnon with adventitious noises but low enough to turn on with program signals; these are frequently contradictory requirements, and compromise is not satisfactory. A more serious problem though is that any number of the microphone channels may turn on unless a first-on inhibiting circuit that permits only one channel to be on at a time is added. One-on-at-a-time operation is unacceptable in a conversational dialog situation because a hold-on needed to cover pauses will keep the second talker off. Without inhibiting, the 3-dB decrease of gain margin for each doubling of the number of on channels occurs. The deficiencies of performance may be compensated to some extent by adding a number of open microphones attenuator to the mixer output.

15.2.5 Variable-Threshold Automatic Mixers

One attempt at overcoming the defects of an internal fixed reference has been to set the reference threshold as the signal from a remote microphone in the environment that is not expected to produce program input. The remote microphone is presumed to provide a reference that depends on variations in room noise or reverberation. Any channel input must then exceed this level by some preset amount before it is given access to the system. In such systems it is assumed that the desired signal will be larger than the reference as in the fixed-threshold system. This may not be true especially when the sample at a single randomly selected microphone location does not represent the ambient sound in the vicinity of a microphone that is supposed to have program input. There would most likely be a form of NOM attenuation of the output signal to compensate for increases in the number of active channels.

An alternative source of reference threshold may be derived from the sum of the outputs of all the microphones in the system. This is the basis of a system described by Dugan.[1]

The JBL model 7510 used such a variable threshold to override a fixed threshold on the assumption that if a disturbance was sensed similarly at several microphone channels, a channel should not be turned on, but the overall system threshold should be raised instead. A talker must then be loud enough at the microphone to override the new raised threshold. Both the fixed threshold and the contribution of the background threshold reference would be set by the installer. Release time, off attenuation (0 to 26 dB) and gain were included in the total of five set-up adjustments to be made on each channel. A NOM attenuation of 0 to 13.8 dB was automatically applied in the output, as would be required for the total of 24 possible inputs.

15.2.6 Gain-Sharing Automatic Mixers

A gain-sharing automatic microphone mixer works from the premise that the sum of the signal inputs from all microphones in the system must be below some maximum value that avoids feedback oscillation. The safe system gain is set relative to the sum of all microphone signals in the system. If one microphone has more signal than the average of all signals, then that microphone channel is given more gain and all the other channels less gain roughly in proportion to the relative increase of signal level.

In such a system[2], a 3-dB level increase at one microphone causes that channel gain to go up by 3 dB, while the gain of the other channels decreases by 3 dB. Speech from two persons talking into separate microphones with levels differing by 3 dB, both appreciably above the background level, would appear at the output of the system with a 6-dB difference. In other words, the signal from a microphone with the highest output is given the most gain, and a signal from a microphone with the smallest output is given the least gain. A NOM attenuator is not needed in the output stage. Theoretically, the system is configured so that the total gain is constant at a level that safely avoids feedback oscillation.

This mixer, marketed by Altec Leasing, uses proportional control based on average signal amplitudes. The mixer, Models 1674 and 1678, may be used with any microphone. To install one in a sound system, the master level control is first set about midrange. This allows maximum flexibility in setting individual channel mix controls. Gain for each channel is set while all other channels are in their off condition or disconnected. Individual channels have switch-selectable high-pass filters and an auto/direct mode switch accessible internally. An auto/manual switch converts the whole mixer from one mode to the other. One channel may be set as a priority channel so that all others are off when it is active. Up to 40 inputs are possible by linking the chassis.

15.2.7 Direction-Dependent Automatic Mixers

A *direction-sensitive automatic mixer* responds to signals having acceptable levels within a predefined space in front of a microphone. Making the decision as to whether a channel should be on depends on the relative signal levels at two back-to-back cardioid microphones, the Shure AMS (automatic microphone system) responds in part to the location of the sound source. This mixer works only with its own microphones, which are described in section 13.13.3.12 and Figs. 13-85 through 13-87. When a channel is on, the front microphone signal is transmitted to the mix bus and the sound pickup is that of a cardioid microphone. Off attenuation may be set to the same value for all channels by the installer over the range between completely off and 8.5 dB (for one chassis). This mixer functions like a variable-threshold system with its threshold a fixed amount above the background, but with the threshold parameter being a function of the source location around its microphone.

Any channel may turn on when the signal level from the front of its microphone is 9.54 dB above the level from the rear. Effectively, a signal-to-noise ratio of 5 to 7 dB is required for a channel to turn on. Of course, a weaker signal source will not activate the channel. The level difference of 9.54 dB is derived from the criterion that a cardioid microphone response at 60° off axis is typically one-third of its on-axis response. The acceptance angle of the mixer channel is, thus, 120° but the acceptance angle narrows as the source decreases in output level or moves away from the microphone. Sources outside of the acceptance angle are also automatically cut off.

The automatic channel selection process responds over a level range of 60 dB. Input levels larger than 45 dBa are required for a channel to gate on, although levels greater than 110 dBa will cause a channel to gate off incorrectly.

The eight-channel version of the mixer is shown in Fig. 15-24. There is also a four-channel model. It has front-panel microphone channel gain controls and a master control that operate as in conventional mixers. Light-emitting diodes indicate the status of the various channels and the output. Status logic outputs and inputs permit control of external equipment from the mixer and external override for control of access, cough control, and so on. An accessory interface provides television camera control.

The equivalent of NOM attenuation of the master output level is provided by controlled impedance loading of the mix bus in proportion to the number of active channels. Up to 200 channels may be installed in one system by linking 25 eight-channel chassis.

For compatibility of the AMS microphones with conventional three-wire cabies and connectors while keeping the two microphone signals separated until they can be processed in the mixer, single-ended unbalanced connections are used. This approach is more susceptible to induced hum and noise pickup than a well-balanced cable; the use of current source preamplifiers in the microphone and low impedance at the mixer is intended to minimize the effect.

It is recommended that as few microphones as necessary be used in an AMS installation and that each be placed closed to its source. Each microphone should be at least 3 ft from the wall behind it and at least 1 ft from objects behind it such as books, large ashtrays, or briefcases.

15.2.8 Multivariable Dependent Automatic Mixers

Amplitude at each input is one set of signal variables to consider, the relative timing of signals at each input is another set of variables, and the processing defects that may be audible represent a third set of variables against which the effectiveness of the processing is judged. The automatic mixer methods described so far essentially react to average signal amplitude. A multivariable dependent system develops its gain and channel access controls from both signal amplitude and the time sequence or history of the signals. As a result system gain stability can be maintained with less attenuation of signals when several channels are on.

The description of one scheme[3] for accomplishing this performance follows: The instantaneous positive-going signal amplitudes of all channels are simultaneously compared to a reference voltage that decays 80 dB in 10 ms or less from a high value to a low value near the noise voltage of the input amplifier. All channels are initially held in their low gain or off condition. The first channel indicating an instantaneous amplitude equal to the instantaneous value of the sweeping reference is given on status, and others remain off. When an amplitude match occurs, the sweep is restarted at its high value for a new search. If an amplitude match is not found, the sweep progresses the full 80 dB in 10 ms. Since a signal

Figure 15-24 Shure eight-channel model AMS8000 mixer. *(Courtesy Shure Brothers, Inc.)*

on any input will produce an amplitude match early in the sweep, the average access time is only 3 or 4 ms, and the frequency of the scans will be correspondingly increased. The on status is maintained for 200 ms. If on the second sweep the same channel still has the largest signal, its on status is renewed for a new 200-ms interval. If on a future sweep of the reference another channel has the higher amplitude, it is turned on for 200 ms, and the first one times out and turns off if not reactivated within 200 ms on an intermediate or future sweep. This rapid response enables dialog to be conducted, and, furthermore, the sampling scheme permits weaker sources relatively easy access. Since the on gain of all channels is the same, any signal source on an active channel has the same gain, and the relative levels of different talkers is preserved in the sound system output.

When several different people vie for access to the system, the probability of all of them obtaining access decreases in proportion to the number. This effectively limits the maximum number of channels that can be on at any given time. For example, probability analysis shows that ten equally loud talkers will each still be on 88% of the time. Since more than three or four persons talking at the same time is not very intelligible, this is of little consequence.

One of the results of this time sharing of access is that a total NOM attenuation of only 6.3 dB is needed for any number of active microphones. Without time sharing, a NOM attenuation of 10 dB is required for the ten-microphone example to ensure gain stability. The mixer designers have considerable latitude in selecting this and other parameters through a variable called the *access ratio*. The access ratio is approximately the ratio of the allotted channel on time to the time to make a channel on decision. Access ratio can be used to control the number of channels that are on the system at one time, for example.

Control of missed signal segments—chopping, upcutting, and so on—is possible with the access ratio also. The effect is analogous to dropouts in audio magnetic tape, for which 0.3% is the just audible rate for speech of a single talker. The likelihood of a dropout due to the time-sharing properties of this type mixer is less than 0.0003% with two active microphones and an access ratio of 20. Dropout rate reaches 0.3% with four active microphones and an access ratio of 20, but the speech of four or more simultaneous talkers would mask these anomalous effects.

The manufacturer of an automatic mixer with this sensing method, Industrial Research Products, Inc., calls it Dynamic Threshold Sensing (DTS), which is used in its Voice-Matic™ Models DE-4013 and DE-4014 mixers, as shown in Figs. 15-25 and 15-26. As in conventional mixers, both models have gain or sensitivity controls for each input channel and a master gain control on the mixed signal. A light-emitting diode indicates when a particular channel is feeding to the mix. Also, both models may be operated either as standard or automatic mixers by setting the *Standard Voice-Matic™* mode switch. They accept signal input from any conventional microphone and a wide range of sensitivities.

With a typical dynamic microphone sensitivity, −55 dBm for 10-μbar sound pressure level, the self-noise is equivalent to a 22-dB sound pressure level. With the large 80-dB range of sensing, the minimum signal level for triggering on is less than 35 dBa. The signal maximum is greater than 130-dB sound pressure level. DTS permits channel activation with signals as poor as 10 dB below the noise in the vicinity.

The model DE-4014 is a four-microphone and one-auxiliary-input mixer. Its channel off attenuation is fixed at 12 dB, and the NOM attenuation maximum is 6 dB. As discussed previously, these represent the optimum values for a four-input system. A 5-dB improvement of gain margin compared to a standard four-input mixer is assured.

The model DE-4013 automatic mixer has no limit on the number of microphones that may be used by linking the chassis together. Each chassis holds up to 6 dual-input modules for a total of 12 inputs. The power supply and the output are also independent modules. The NOM attenuator in the output never needs to exceed 6.3 dB

Figure 15-25 Voice-Matic™ model DE-4013 modular mixer. *(Courtesy Industrial Research Products, Subsidiary of Knowles Electronics, Inc.)*

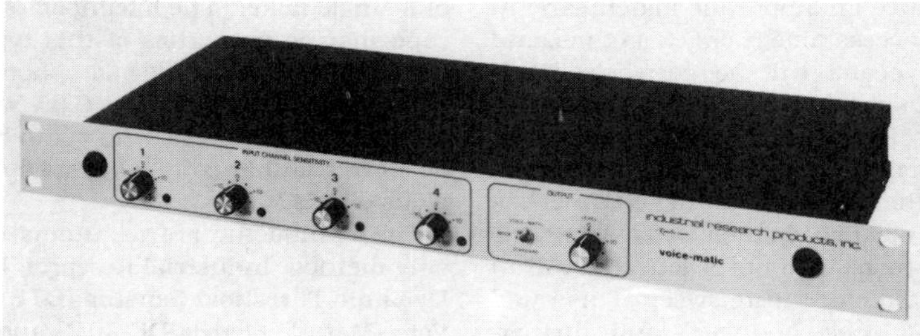

Figure 15-26 Voice-Matic™ model DE-4014 four-channel mixer. *(Courtesy Industrial Research Products, Subsidiary of Knowles Electronics, Inc.)*

because of the DTS system. In addition to the channel sensitivity, there is a channel off attenuation control that would be set between 0 and 40 dB on installation according to the number of microphones in the system, as described in section 15.2.3.4. A direct/auto switch in each input channel can convert that channel from automatic to direct nonautomatic feed to the main mix bus. Any channel may be reprogrammed for high-level signal input, bridging impedances and high-pass filter frequency. Any channel may be internally programmed for "chairman override" when a set of external switch contacts is closed. Options include channel status signals and individual channel preamplified signal outputs. This mixer also accepts an automatic gain control module that is described in section 15.2.9. The status output may be used in a remote indicator panel or, more typically, as a logic control to select speakers that are to receive particular program inputs or to select television camera coverage of conference participants automatically according to which one is talking. Individual channel amplified outputs may be fed, for example, to a multiple-channel tape recorder to record the proceedings of a court or council meeting.

These mixers are set up like a standard mixer. Each input sensitivity control is usually adjusted so that sound pressure level of around 75 dBa will be in the middle of the 80-dB DTS sweep. It is convenient to think of the input sensitivity control as a part of the microphone rather than the mixer. Although this means more gain for low-sensitivity and less for high-sensitivity microphones, the output voltage from the mixer will be about the same. The master output gain is then adjusted as required for following equipment.

15.2.9 Automatic Gain Control

Automatic gain or *output level control* pretty well covers the remaining function that an operator performs in a manned sound system. An operator rides master gain to bring up weak signals, or cut back too-loud signals and tries to do this without destroying the inherent dynamic range of the particular input while trying to keep the system out of oscillation.

An automatic gain control works in an automatic mixer if it is installed so that it can only reduce gain should the input signal level increase. The gain required to bring the lowest level source up to desired listening levels should be the most gain that can be applied. The only control that does not risk unintentional howlback oscillation in a sound system decreases the gain for louder signals. A secondary benefit of automatic output level control used in this way is reduced frequency-response distortion due to excessive room amplification of high-level signal peaks. A third benefit is howlback protection against such things as a hand over a microphone and hand or body movement near a microphone.

The Level-Matic™ output module shown in Fig. 15-27 provides optional automatic output level control in the model DE-4013 automatic mixer from Industrial Research Products, Inc. It automatically adjusts the master gain to maintain a uniform output signal level for an input signal variation of as much as 10 dB. A loud talker causes the gain to decrease. If he stops talking, the gain holds as established by his average talking level. If a quiet talker then begins to use the system, the gain increases to a new value set by his average speaking level. Gain control voltages are based on loudness versus frequency and loudness versus time response of the ear. Two control voltages are created, one establishes a quasi-stationary control voltage, and the other voltage follows the signal peaks. At any instant, a voltage-controlled attenuation is controlled by one, but not both, of these voltages. Gain corrections are made at a constant decibels per second slew rate to minimize gain "hunting." The gain holds at its last value if there is no signal.

There is a relative-gain light-emitting diode indicator that is helpful in initial set up. The maximum permissible system gain is set for the quietest expected input. Other controls are a Voice-Matic™/Standard switch, a master level, a Level-Matic™ bypass switch, and a threshold control that is adjusted so that the light-emitting diode indicator just moves occasionally when the quiet signal is applied.

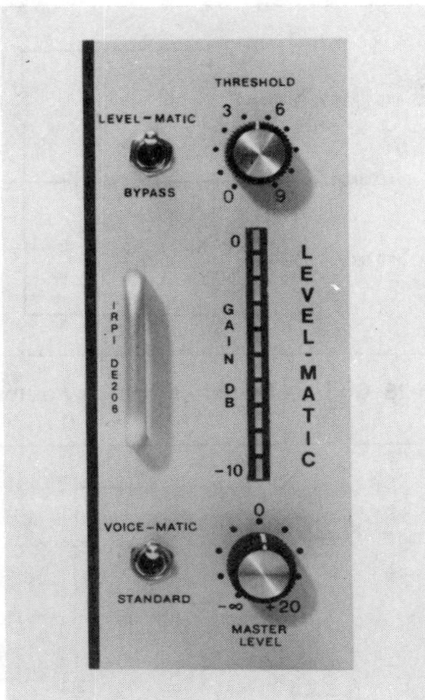

Figure 15-27 Level-Matic™ automatic output level and gain control module, DE-206, for optional use in the model DE-4013 Voice-Matic™ mixer.

15.3 POWER AMPLIFIERS

Power amplifiers for professional applications, unlike those intended for home entertainment use, must usually be capable of providing a multiplicity of voltage values at their output terminals. Furthermore, for reasons of safety and to avoid inadvertent mishaps in wiring or handling, it is often required that neither side of the output distribution lines be referenced to ground except in a balanced way through a high impedance to provide a static discharge path. These requirements are usually met by feeding the distribution lines from an isolated transformer secondary even though the transformer itself presents a source of distortion and bandwidth limitation.

Power amplifiers, when operated within their inherent limitations, are essentially constant voltage sources. The sinusoidal rms voltages at the output terminals at a rated power (that are required in professional applications) are commonly voice coil values, 25, 70.7, or, in recent times, 200 V. The loudspeakers or other loads are, in the case of 25-, 70.7-, or 200-V lines, fed from the secondary of a transformer that has several primary taps for determining the actual average sinusoidal power supplied to an individual device. When feeding several devices from a common constant voltage distribution line, it is only necessary to ensure that the sum of the power taps to the individual devices does not exceed the output capability of the driving amplifier (see section 10.4.6.9). High values, such as 70.7 or 200 V, for the constant voltage distribution system will minimize the I^2R loss in the distribution lines themselves. It is an absolute necessity, however, that the transformer at the amplifier, when such is employed, and the step-down transformers at the individual load devices be of high quality. Poor-quality transformers with either high insertion losses and/or poor impedance characteristics will completely defeat the advantages offered by the constant voltage distribution technique.

Many of the present-day power amplifiers intended for professional use are produced in two channel versions even when the ultimate employment is to be with monaural program material. When preceded by active or passive crossover networks, such amplifiers can provide biamplification by devoting each amplifier channel to a separate part of the audio spectrum. This technique when properly employed may offer level adjustment, distortion, and loudspeaker damping advantages over the full spectrum approach employing an individual amplifying channel. Additionally, such amplifiers may be employed with a balanced-bridge output driven by both channels that doubles the output voltage swing but requires a load impedance that is twice as large as a single channel alone. This technique can drive a 70.7-V or even higher voltage balanced distribution line without a transformer at the amplifier, but the ground isolation previously mentioned is lost in the process. This may furnish the user with a difficult choice.

Audio power amplifiers are designed in reverse, which means that the output stage is designed first followed by the design of the output driver stage, which in turn is followed by the required intermediate stage or stages and then finally the input stage. Depending upon the power, distortion, and efficiency requirements, the class of operation of the output device or devices has traditionally been restricted to A, AB, B, or more recently D. The most recent developments have widened the choice somewhat in that some current designs involve changing the supply voltage to the output stage under dynamic conditions. It appears that we may look forward to an entire alphabet of classes of operation. When a single device is employed in the output stage, Class-A operation, in which current exists in the active device throughout a complete cycle of signal swing, is the only acceptable class of operation. Class A is inherently the most linear class of operation. If pairs of output devices are employed in push-pull in the output stage, then Classes A, B, AB, and AB plus B (at least two pairs of devices) are distinct possibilities. Other than A, the other classes are in general more efficient but inherently are not as linear as Class A. In Class B operation each member of a push-pull pair is active over only one half of a complete sinusoidal signal cycle. Class AB is intermediate in this regard between A and B. In AB plus B a pair of devices operates push-pull in Class AB while a second pair of devices in push-pull operates nearly in Class B. Class D is the designation given to the mode of operation wherein the output devices are operated in a switching mode. This means that the output devices are conducting as heavily as possible or not at all. This mode of operation offers efficiencies bordering on 90% but introduces a host of other problems with regard to radio-frequency interference as well as requiring specialized active devices, drive circuitry, and design techniques. The advent of bipolar complementary symmetry transistors introduced, for the first time, the possibilities of many new circuit topologies in power amplifier design, and the recent development of complementary symmetry power field-effect transistors has opened up even more exciting avenues for truly superb amplifier developments.

Fig. 15-28 is a rather basic complementary symmetry bipolar transistor output stage for operation in Classes A, AB, and B. The class of operation is dictated by the details of the biasing and drive arrangements.

The currents in Q_1 and Q_2 are equal at quiescence, and there is no current in the load. If the bases of Q_1 and Q_2 are driven with a positive-going signal, Q_1 conducts more heavily while the current in Q_2 decreases, thus producing a net current in the load directed from left to right such that the left end of the load assumes a positive voltage relative to ground. On the other hand, if the bases of Q_1 and Q_2 are driven with a negative-going signal, Q_1 conducts less heavily while Q_2 conducts more. This produces a net current in the load directed from right to left such that the left end of the load assumes a negative voltage relative to ground. The load in effect is connected in the emitter circuits of both transistors, which consequently operate as common-collector transistors. As is well known, the voltage gain of a common-collector amplifier is slightly less than one and without polarity inversion; hence, the driving circuitry must be able to produce a signal swing in excess of the swing to be expected across the load.

Fig. 15-29 represents a circuit configuration that is superficially similar to Fig. 15-28 but is drastically different in its operation. The currents in Q_1 and Q_2 are again equal at quiescence, and there is no current in the load. When the bases of Q_1 and Q_2 are driven with a positive-going signal, Q_1 conducts more heavily while the current in Q_2 decreases. This produces a net current in the load directed from left to right such that the right end of the load assumes a negative voltage relative to ground. On the other hand, if the bases of Q_1 and Q_2 are driven with a negative-going signal, Q_1 conducts less heavily while Q_2 conducts more. This produces a net current in the load directed from right to left such that the right end of the load assumes a positive voltage relative to ground. The load now in contrast to Fig. 15-28 has been shifted from the transistor emitters to the transistor collectors. Instead of dealing with a common-collector stage as in Fig. 15-28, the circuit of Fig. 15-29 is that of a common-emitter amplifier. That is, the load is really in the collector circuits of the transistors. Such a stage produces an output signal swing that is inverted in polarity and possibly of much larger amplitude than the input signal swing. The drive requirements of such a stage are greatly relaxed as compared with those of the circuit of Fig. 15-28. In fact, if power field-effect transistors (FETs) are employed instead of bipolar transistors in the circuit of Fig. 15-29, it is possible to produce a high-power, high-voltage output stage that can be easily driven by a single, low-power

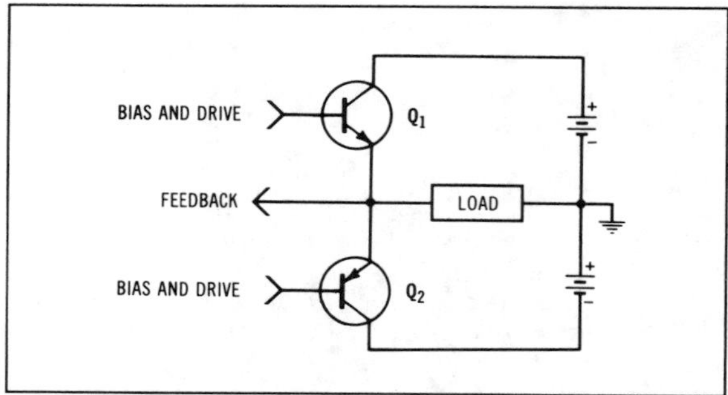

Figure 15-28 Complementary symmetry output stage.

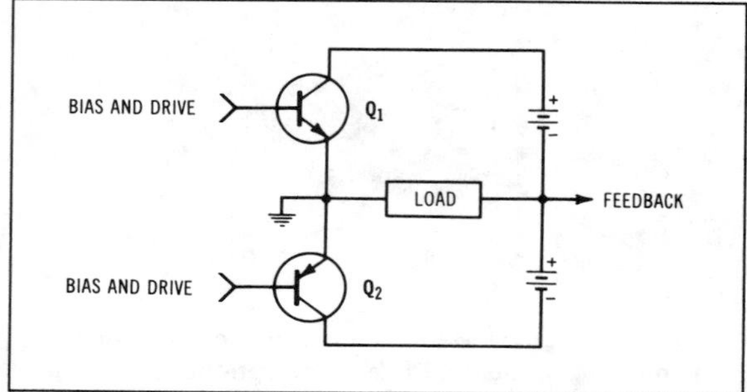

Figure 15-29 Common-emitter complementary symmetry output.

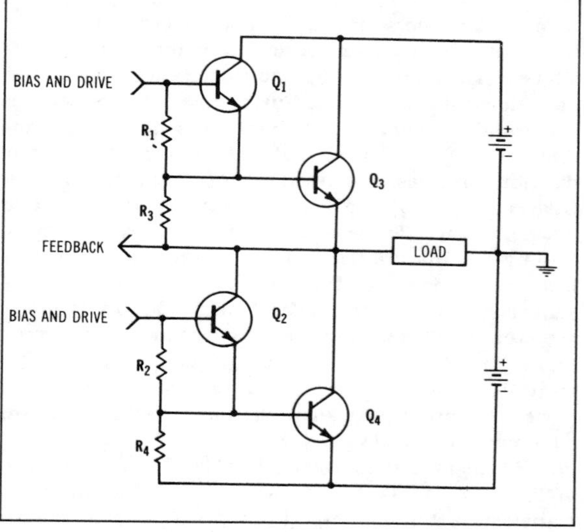

Figure 15-30 Totem pole with AB plus B.

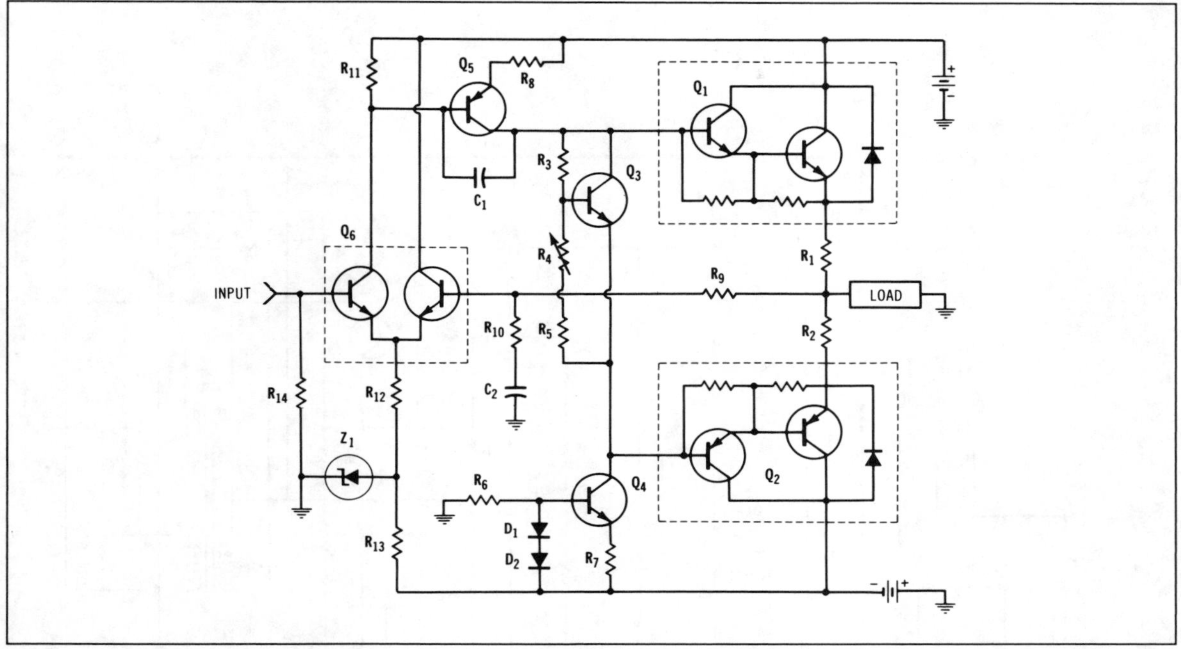

Figure 15-31 Complete power amplifier.

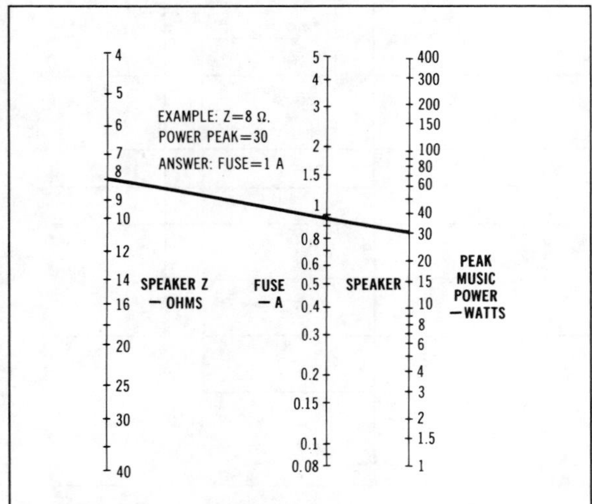

Figure 15-32 Short-circuit protector for the amplifier of Fig. 15-31.

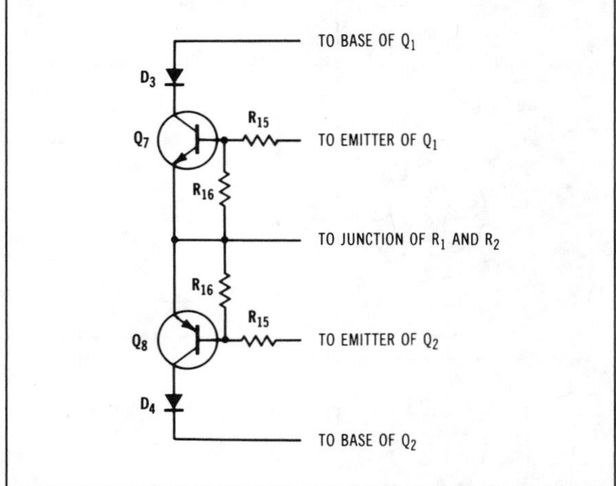

Figure 15-33 Fuse selector nomograph for loudspeaker protection. *(Courtesy Crown International, Inc.)*

operational amplifier. This is made possible because a field-effect transistor is a voltage-controlled device having a high input impedance, whereas a bipolar transistor is a current-controlled device with an inherently low input impedance in the common-emitter configuration.

Fig. 15-30 is a totem-pole configuration that has been supplemented by an additional pair of transistors to produce the AB plus B mode of operation. The totem-pole configuration became popular before the advent of high-power complementary symmetry pairs and is still employed where it is desirable to use only a single type of power transistor. This configuration must be driven by a circuit that furnishes two drive signals of opposite polarity. The resistors R_1 and R_2 are typically a few hundred ohms, while the resistors R_3 and R_4 are of the order of an ohm. At quiescence neither Q_3 or Q_4 are conducting, the emitter currents of Q_1 and Q_2 are equal in the range of 50 to

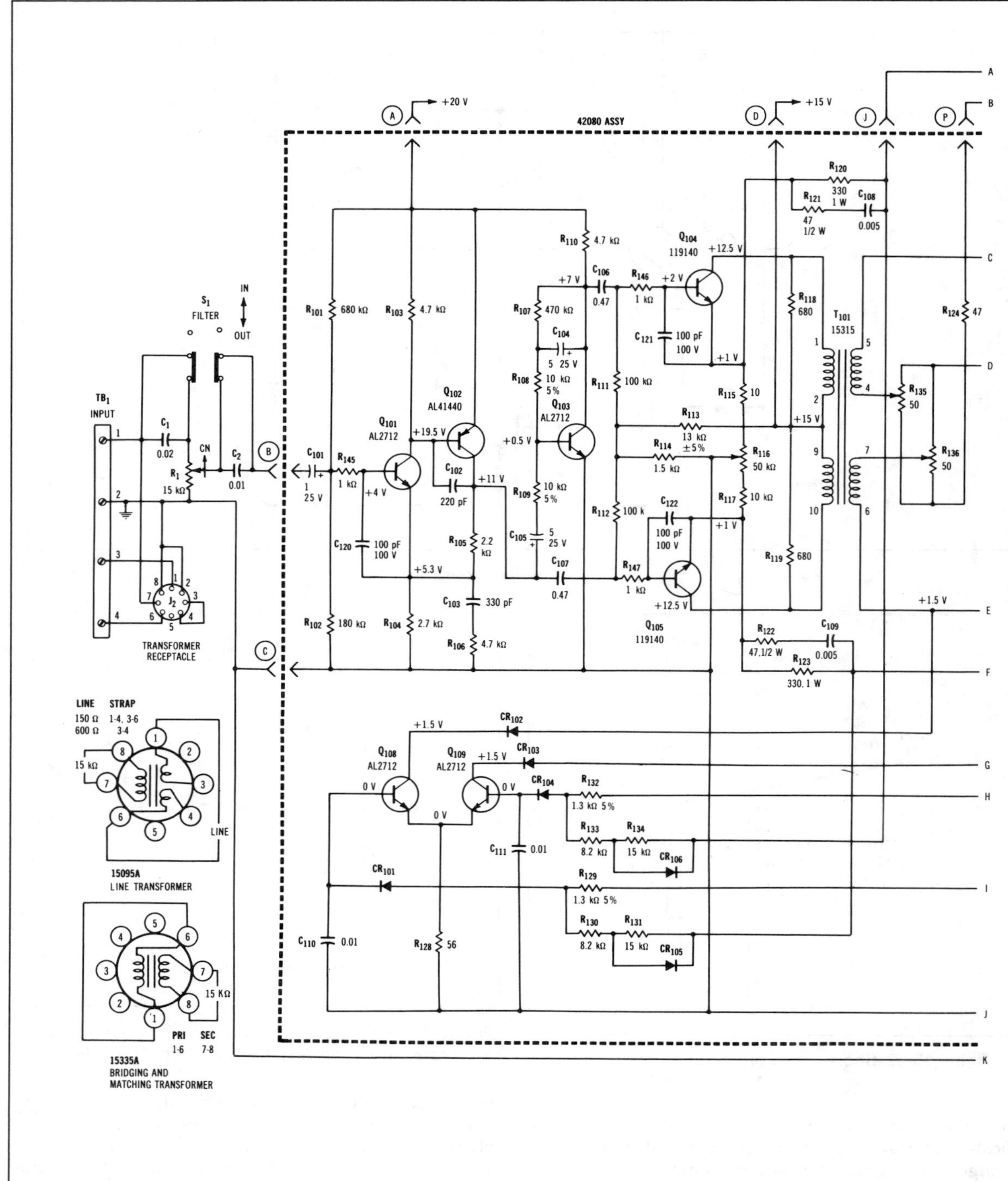

Figure 15-34 Schematic of an Altec Lansing 1590C power

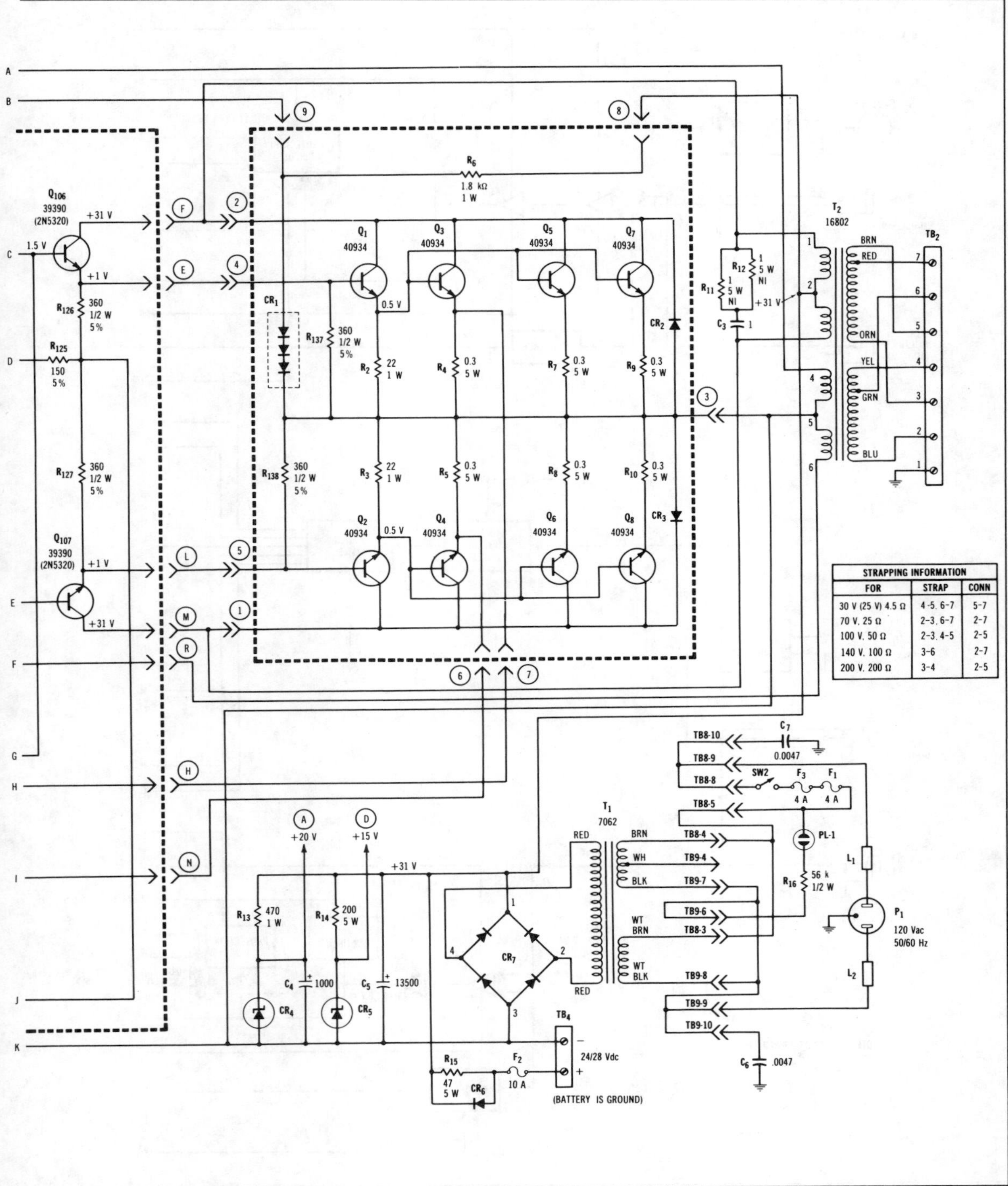

amplifier with short-circuit protection. *(Courtesy Altec Lansing Corp.)*

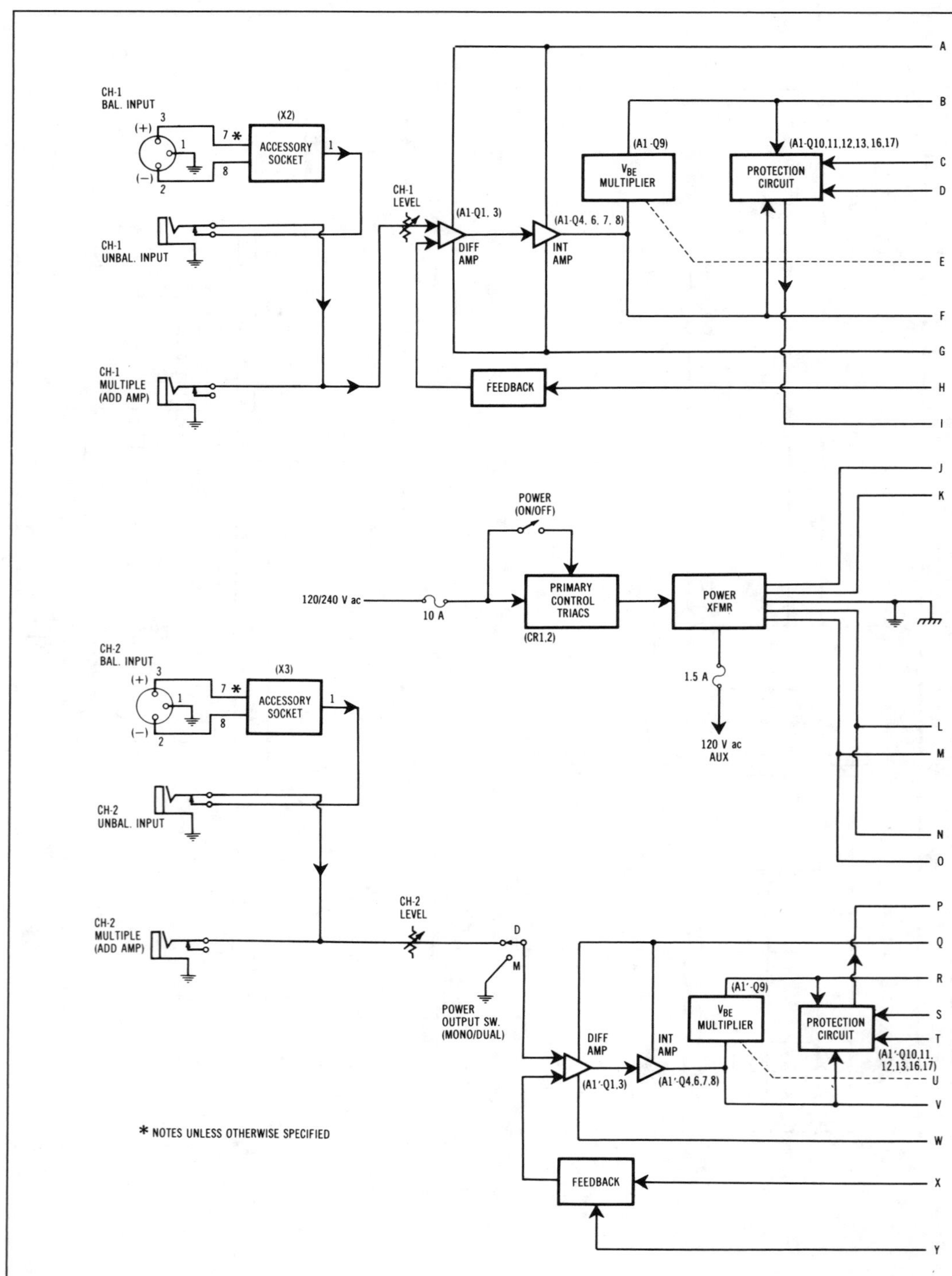

Figure 15-35 Block diagram of the Altec Lansing 9440A

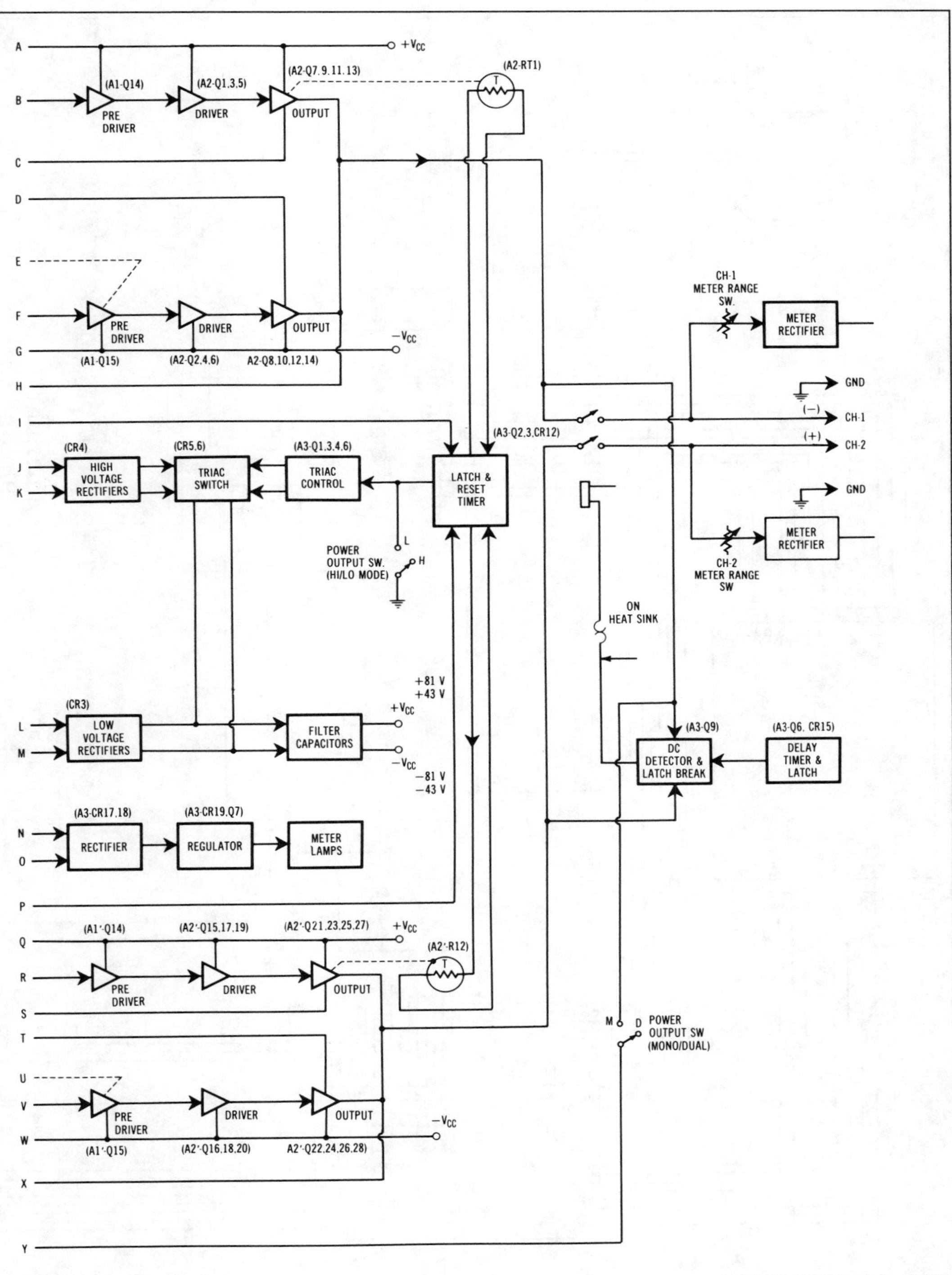

power amplifier. *(Courtesy Altec Lansing Corp.)*

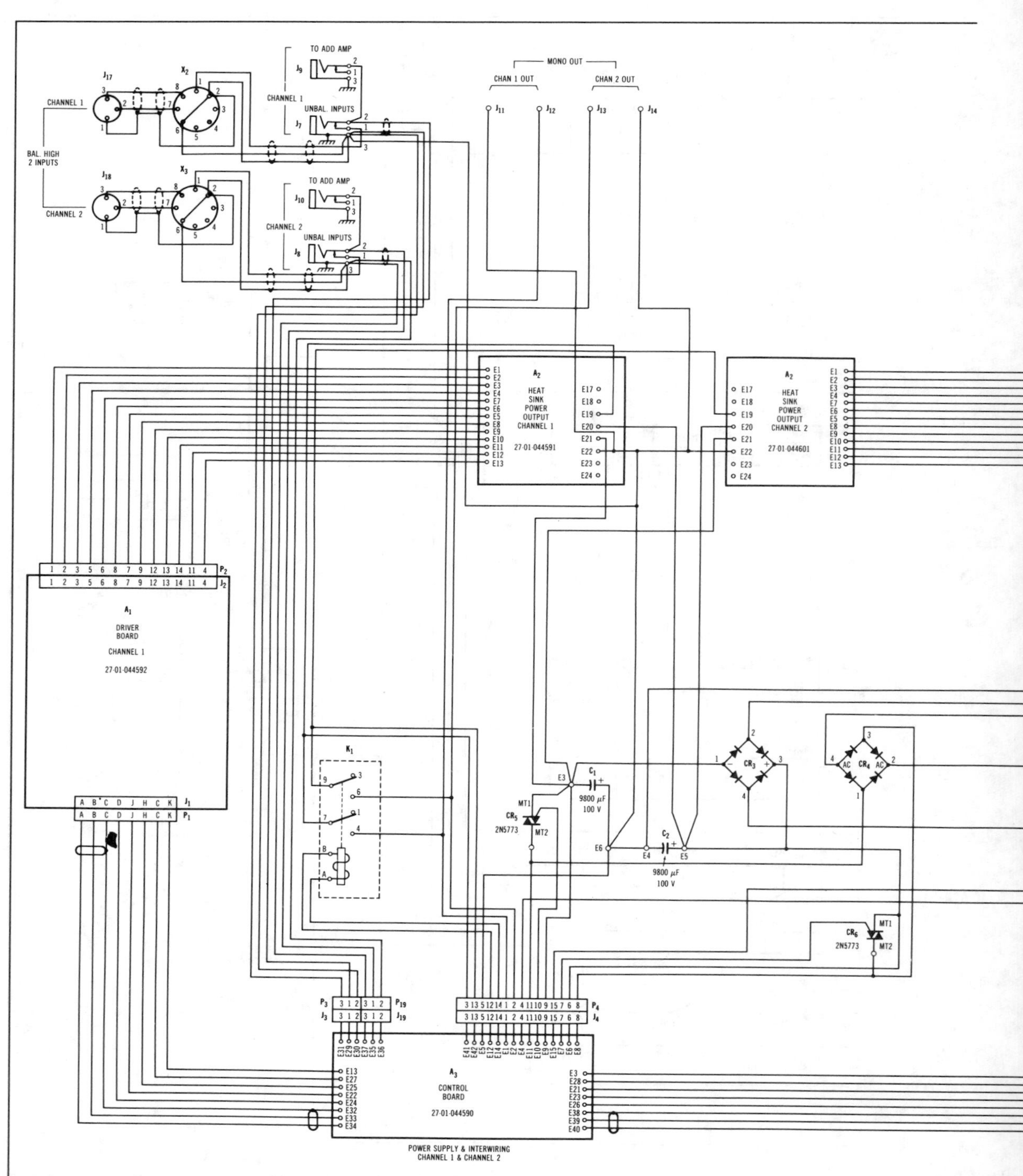

Figure 15-36 Schematic of the Altec Lansing 9440A power amplifier power supply

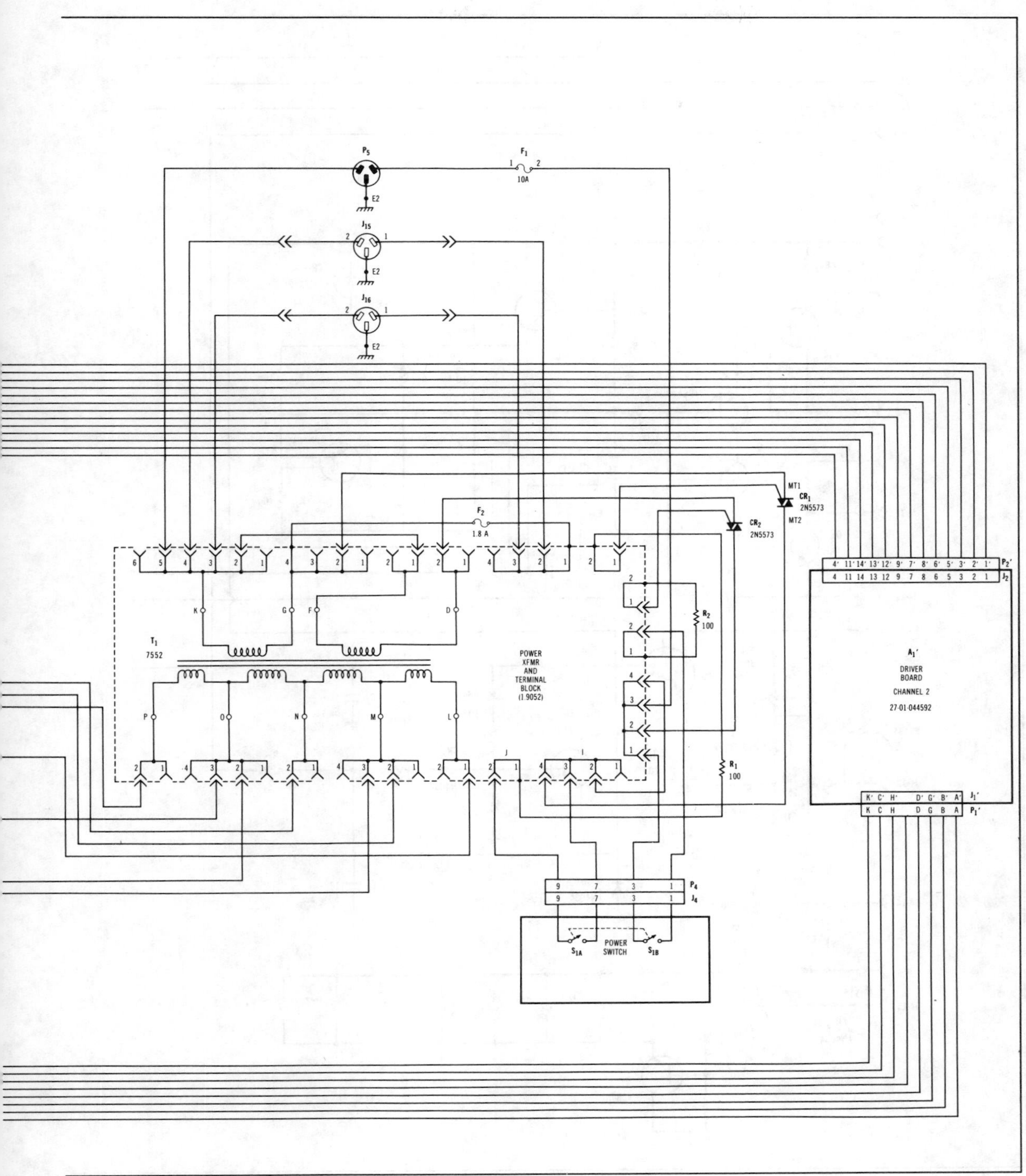

and interwiring (channel 1 and channel 2). *(Courtesy Altec Lansing Corp.)*

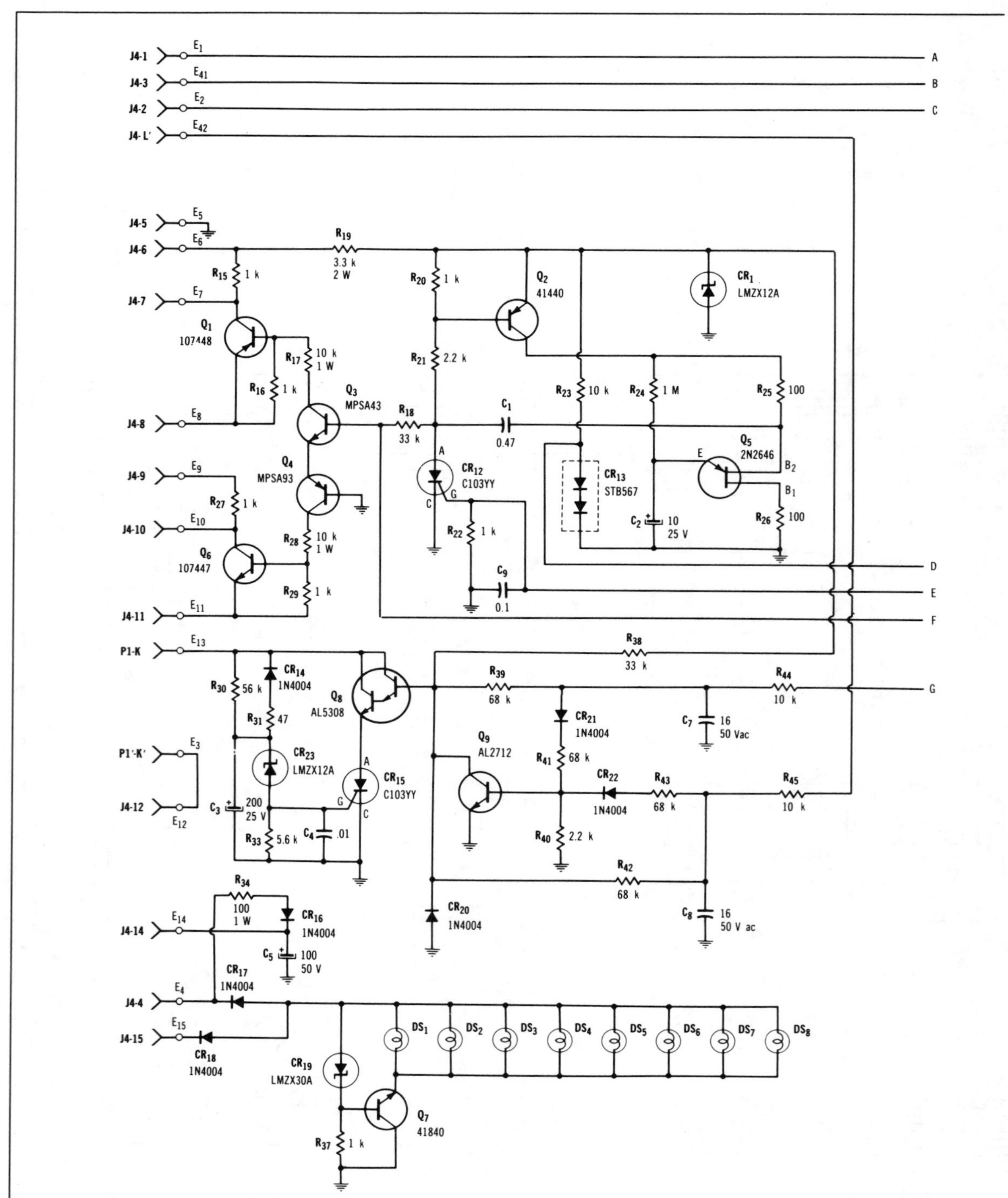

Figure 15-37 Schematic of the Altec Lansing 9440A power amplifier control

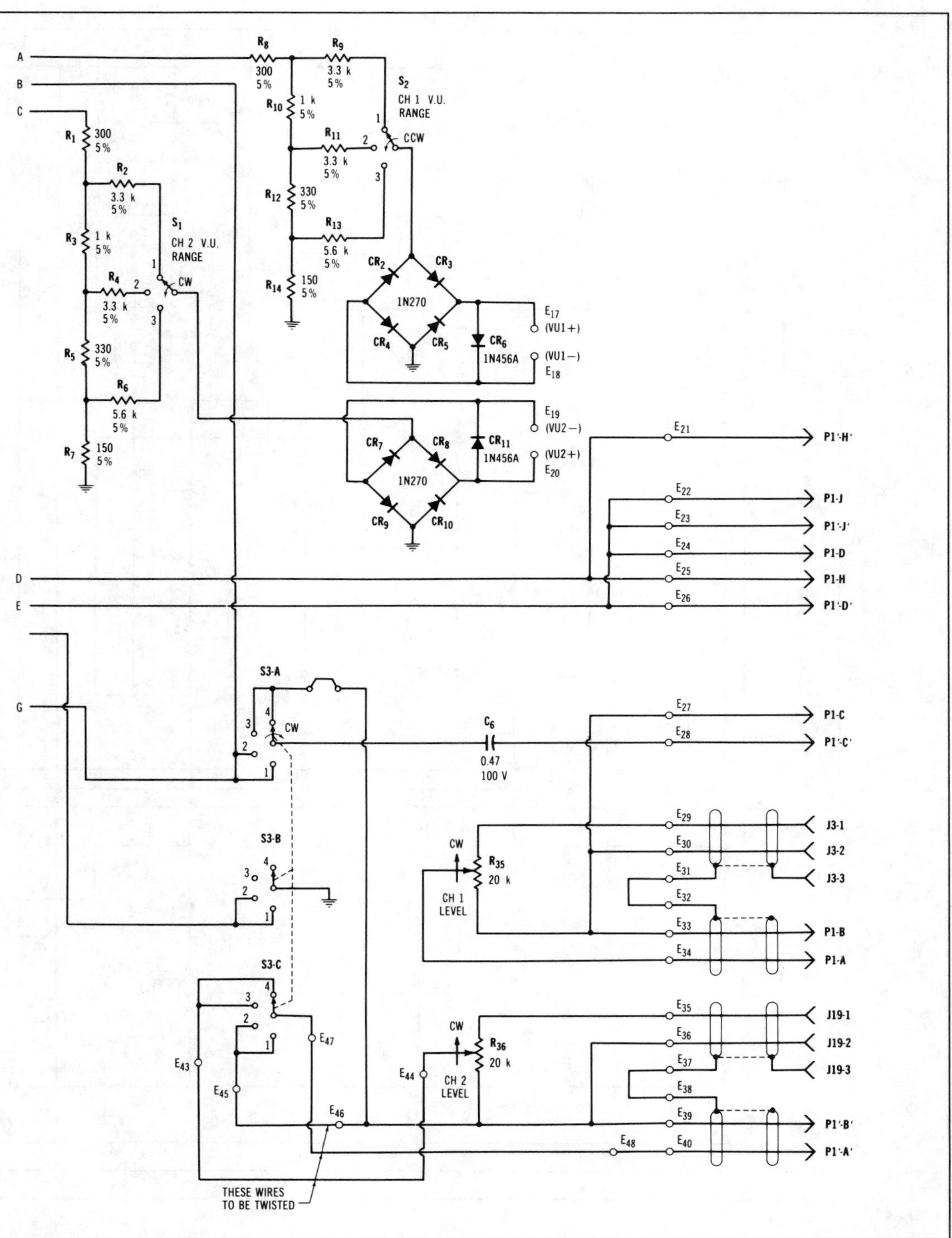

board (channel 1 and channel 2). *(Courtesy Altec Lansing Corp.)*

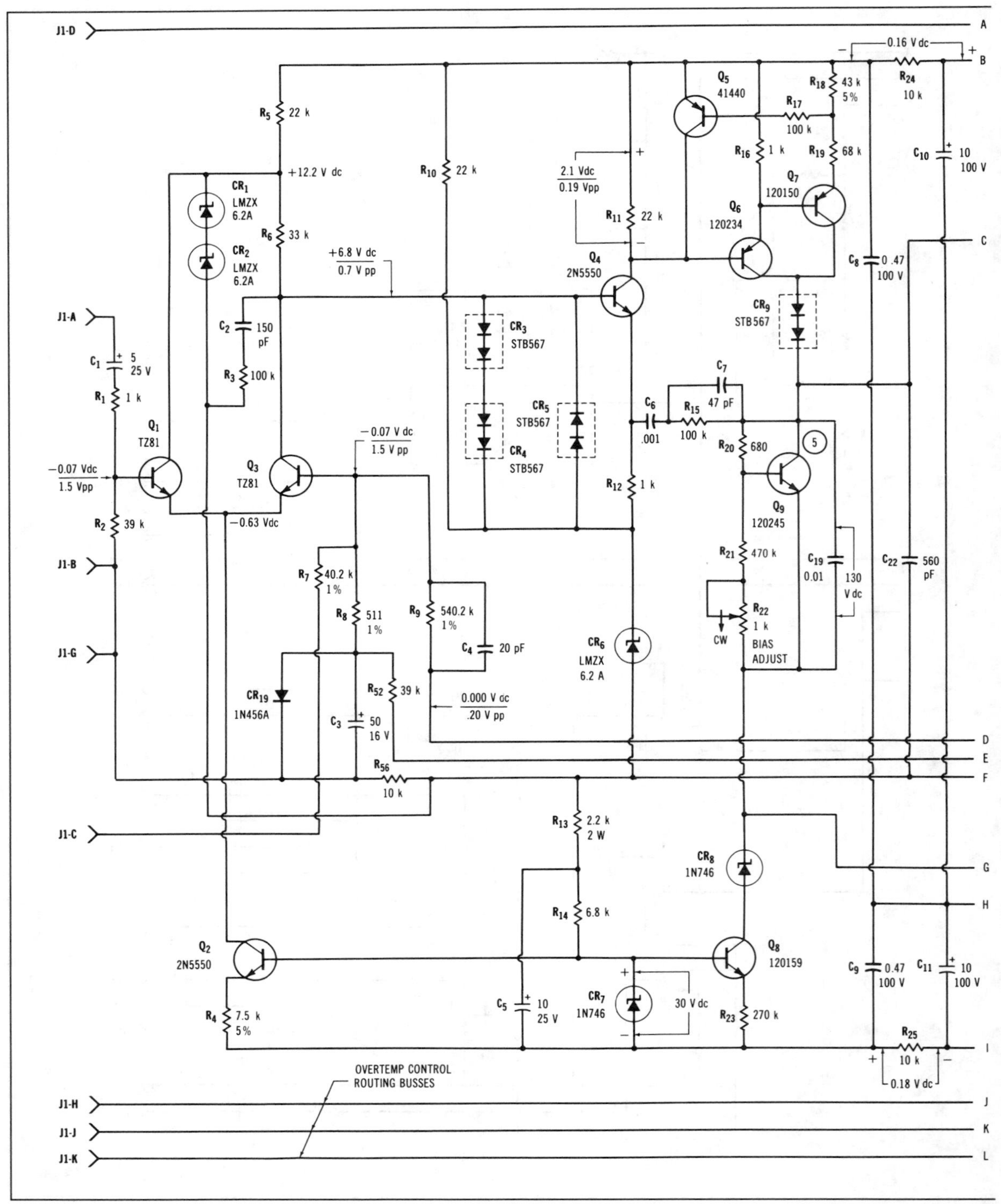

Figure 15-38 Schematic of the Altec Lansing 9440A power amplifier

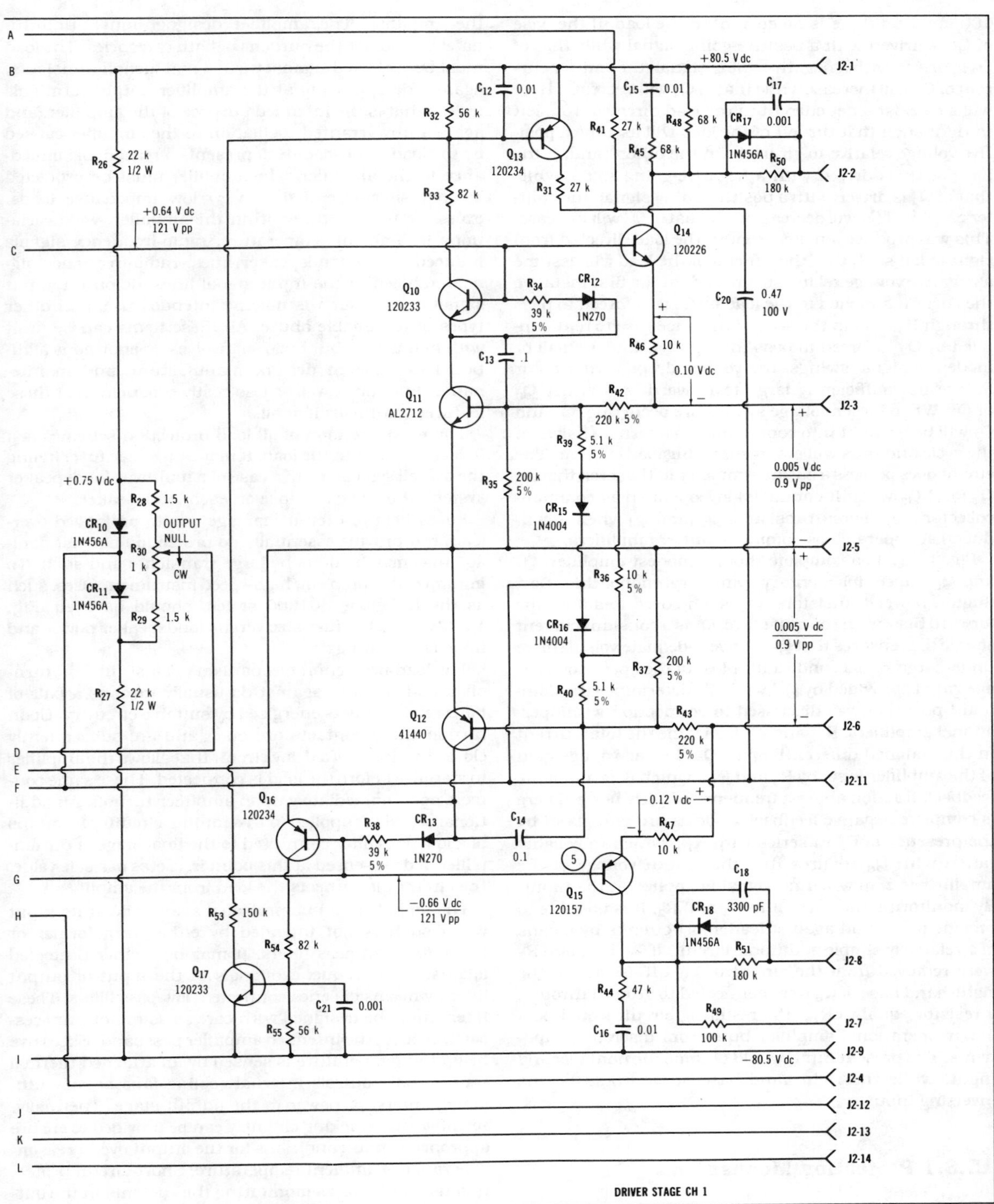

driver stage (channel 1). *(Courtesy Altec Lansing Corp.)*

100 mA, and there is no current in the load. If the base of Q_1 is driven with a positive-going signal while that of Q_2 is driven with a negative-going signal, the emitter current of Q_1 will increase while that of Q_2 will decrease. Here will also exist a net current in the load directed from left to right such that the left of the load will assume a positive voltage relative to ground. On the other hand, if the base of Q_1 is driven with a negative-going signal while that of Q_2 is driven with a positive-going signal, the emitter current of Q_1 will decrease while that of Q_2 will increase. This will produce a net current in the load directed from right to left such that the left end of the load will assume a negative voltage relative to ground. In the first instance the current supplied to the load by Q_1 was forced to pass through R_3, and in the second instance the current supplied by Q_2 is forced to pass through R_4. Under small or moderate signal swings, the voltage drops across R_3 or R_4 are not sufficiently large to forward bias either Q_3 or Q_4. When larger voltage swings are occurring, Q_3 and Q_4 will be brought into conduction on alternate halves of the cycle and thus will aid in supplying load current. The circuit does possess a basic asymmetry in that even though Q_1 (and Q_3 when it conducts) are operated as common-collector amplifiers, transistors Q_2 (and Q_4 when it conducts) are operated as common-emitter amplifiers.

Fig. 15-31 is a complete though modest amplifier. Q_1 and Q_2 are complementary symmetry, monolithic, Darlington power transistors. Q_3 is employed to adjust the forward bias on the output stage. Q_4 is a constant current source that ensures that Q_2 receives adequate voltage drive under large signal conditions. Most of the open-loop voltage gain is provided by Q_5, while C_1 determines the dominant pole that was discussed in connection with operational amplifiers. R_{12} and Z_1 determine the total current in the matched differential pair Q_6. The ac voltage gain of the amplifier is set by R_9 and R_{10}, which determine the feedback fraction above a frequency of a few hertz. There is complete negative feedback at dc as brought about by the presence of C_2 in series with R_{10}, which in collaboration with Q_6 ensures that the output voltage of the amplifier is zero when no signal is applied at the input. By monitoring the current in R_1 and R_2, it is possible to provide protection against load short circuits by means of a relatively simple additional circuit. If C_2, R_{10}, and R_9 were removed from the circuit of Fig. 15-31 and if the right-hand base of Q_6 were connected to ground through a resistor equal to R_{14}, the resulting circuit would be a power operational amplifier built from discrete components. The present input would become the noninverting input, while the right-hand base of Q_6 would be the inverting input.

15.3.1 Protection Mechanisms

Power amplifier protection mechanisms fall roughly into two categories: the protection of the amplifier against faults in the load and protection of the load against faults in the amplifier. The amplifier designer must, unfortunately, shoulder the burdens of both categories. The load must be protected against turnon and turnoff transients, against dc appearing at the amplifier output terminals unless that is the intended purpose of the amplifier, and against unwarranted oscillation in the amplifier caused by the load if the load itself presents a reasonable impedance to the amplifier. The amplifier must be protected against short-circuited or very low impedance loads, excessive temperature within the amplifier, wide variations in ambient temperature, radio-frequency signals induced in the loudspeaker lines, radio-frequency signals induced in the input signal lines, dc on the input signal lines if such is not the intended use, and other types of reasonable abuse. All these items can be dealt with in practice, but to do so involves an enormous additional expense in design, manufacture, and maintenance. Inferior as well as less costly products treat these features minimally if at all.

The most common of all load-protection schemes is a fuse in series with the load. It may be a single fuse, fusing the overall system, or in a case of a multiway loudspeaker system, it may be one fuse on each loudspeaker.

Fuses help to prevent damage due to prolonged overload, but provide essentially no protection against damage that may be done by large transients and such. To minimize this problem, high-speed instrument fuses, such as the Littlefuse 361000 series, should be used. Fig. 15-32 shows the fuse size versus loudspeaker power and impedance ratings.

The load-protection mechanism against turnon, turnoff transients and against dc usually involves a pair of hard relay contacts energized by suitable circuitry. Upon turnon these contacts are open and are subsequently closed by means of a delay circuit that allows the amplifier to stabilize before the load is connected. These same contacts open immediately upon amplifier turnoff. An additional signal is supplied to this muting circuitry by means of a low-pass filter connected to the final stage of the amplifier. If dc is sensed at this point in excess of a safe value, the circuit disconnects the load from the amplifier.

The amplifier can be protected against dc at its input when such is not intended by either transformer or capacitor high-pass filters. It may be further protected against radio-frequency signals at the input or output lines by means of series-connected, low-pass filters. These filters must be designed with care so as to not unnecessarily restrict the intended amplifier passband. Excessive heat-sink temperature is sensed by an attached thermal sensor that controls internal cooling fans or may ultimately interrupt power to the output stage. Thermally, sensitive bias-tracking circuitry can be provided to ensure appropriate bias conditions for the output over a reasonable range of ambient temperature. Short-circuit protection usually involves monitoring the currents in the output devices and restricting the drive applied to the output stage whenever excessive current is detected with long-term protection still being provided by the thermal mech-

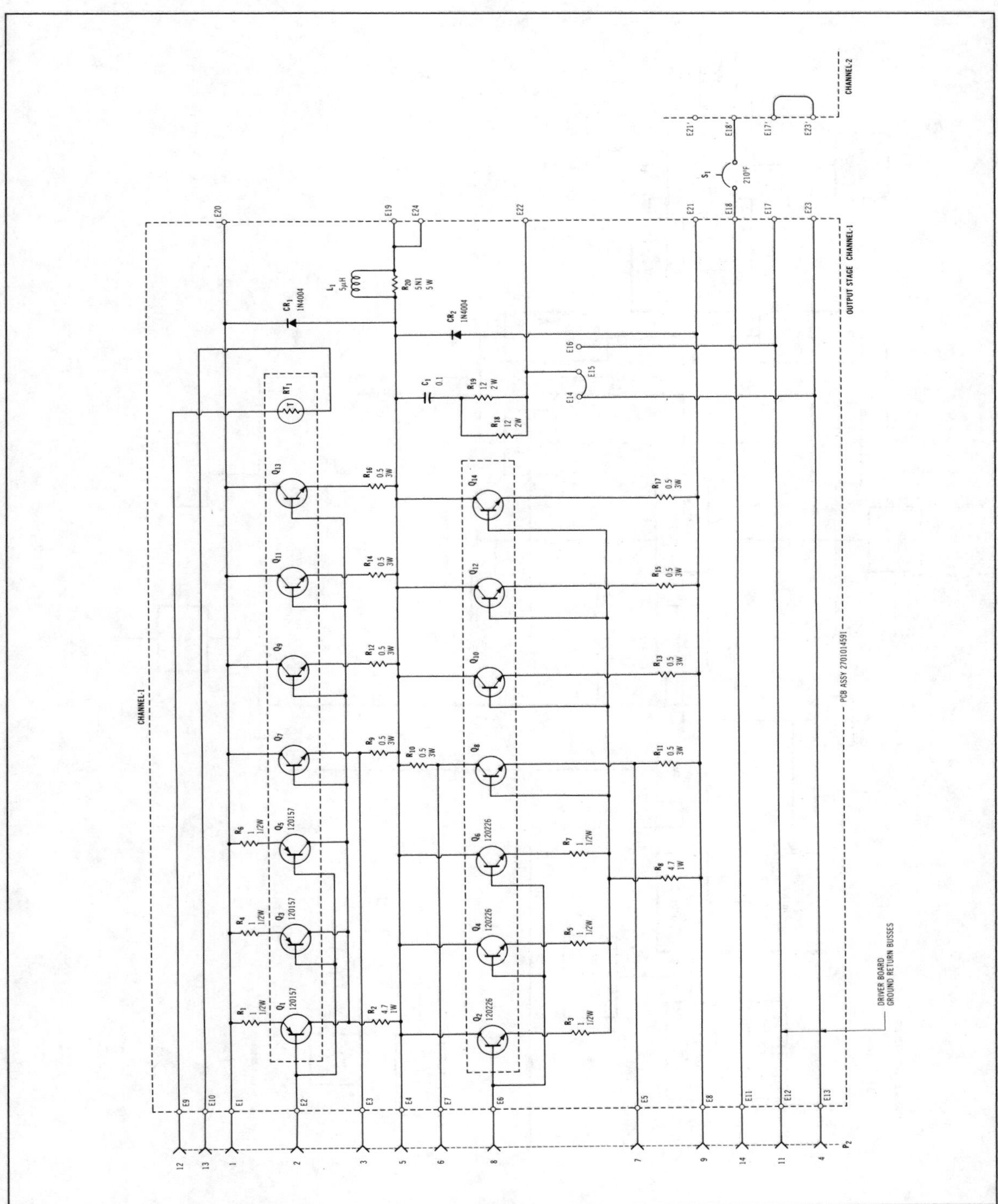

Figure 15-39 Schematic of the Altec Lansing 9440A power amplifier output stage (channel 1). *(Courtesy Altec Lansing Corp.)*

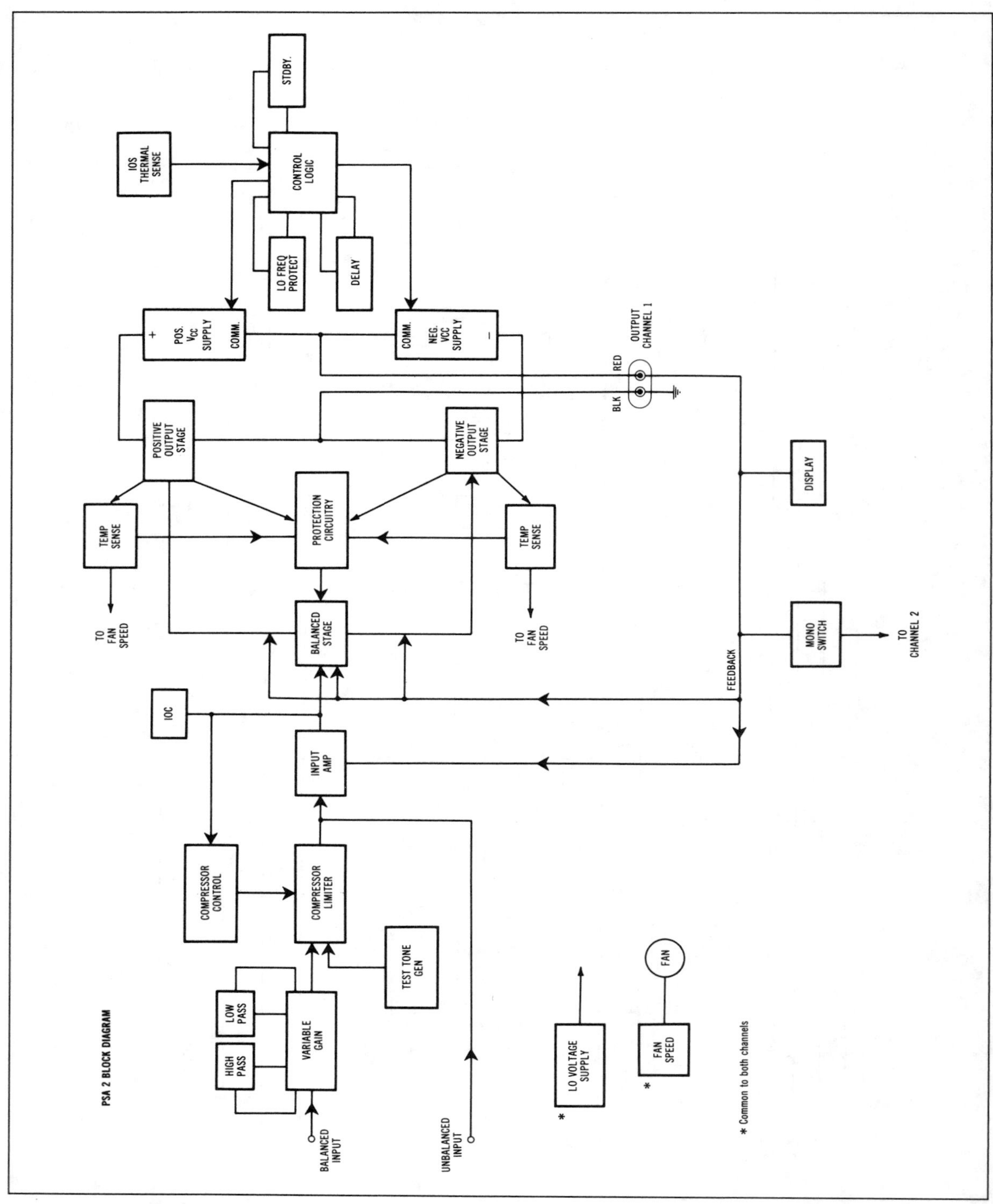

Figure 15-40 Block diagram of the Crown PSA-2 professional self-analyzing amplifier. *(Courtesy Crown International, Inc.)*

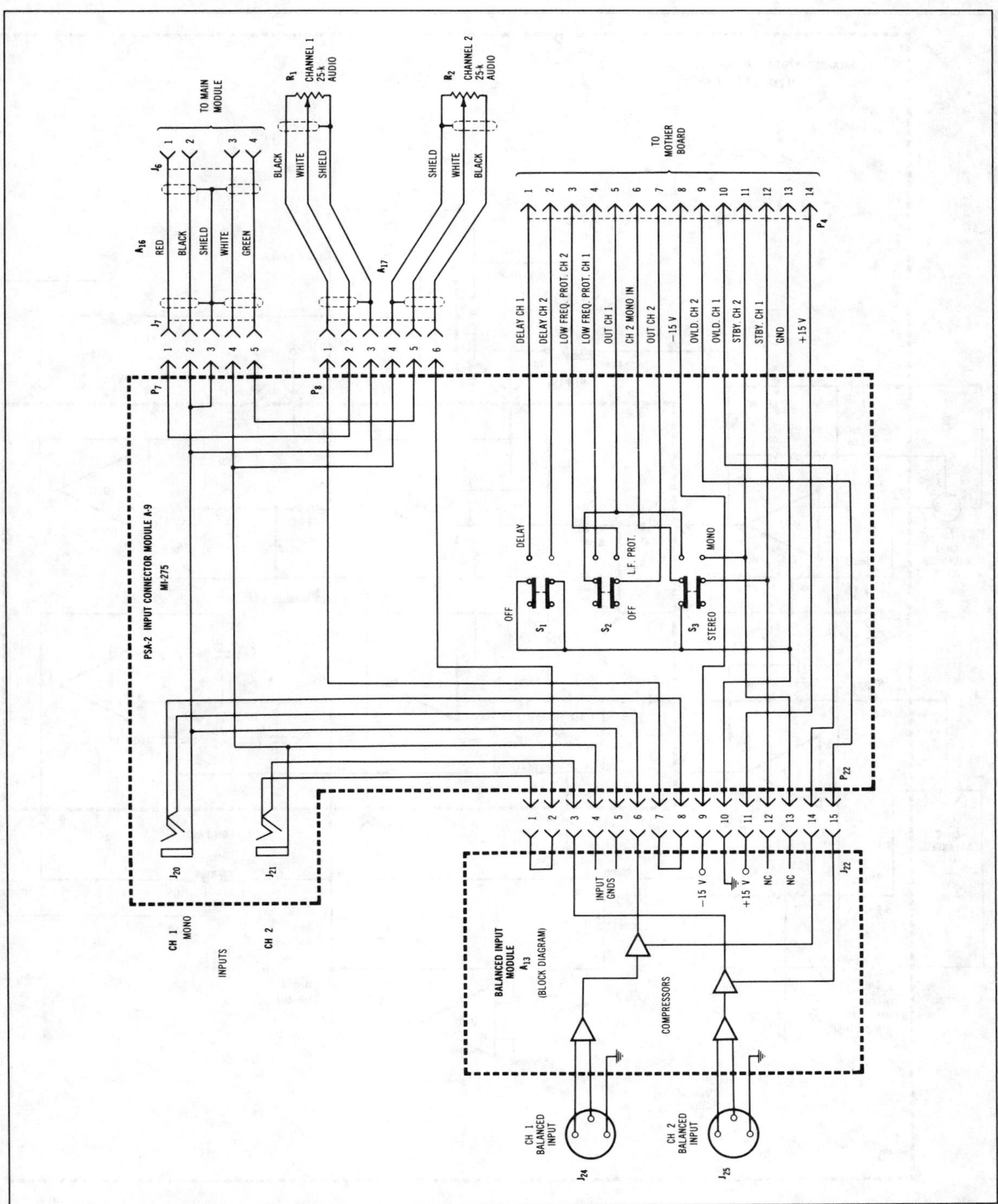

Figure 15-41 Schematic of the input connector module for the Crown PSA-2 amplifier. *(Courtesy Crown International, Inc.)*

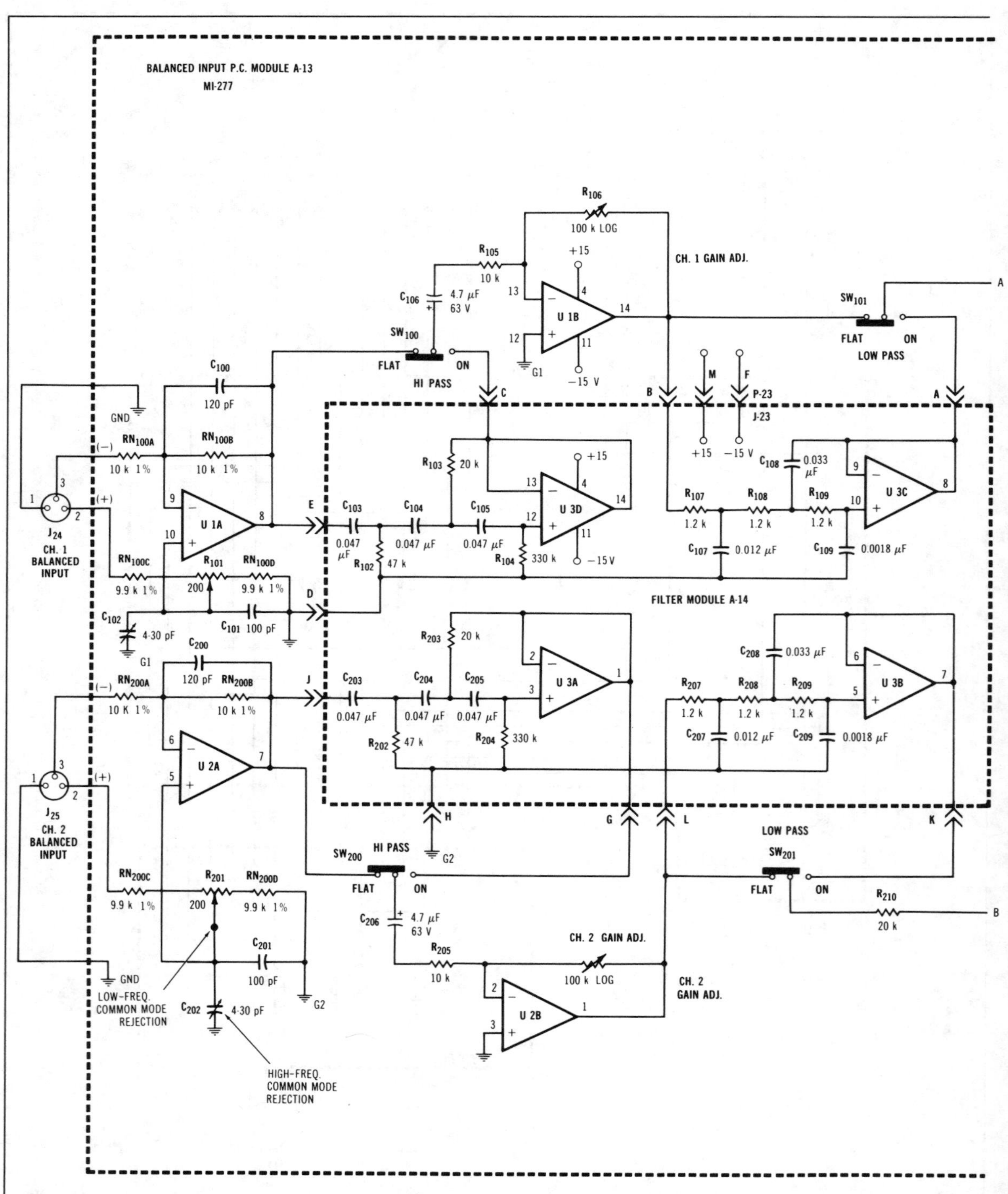

Figure 15-42 Schematic of the balanced input P. C. module for

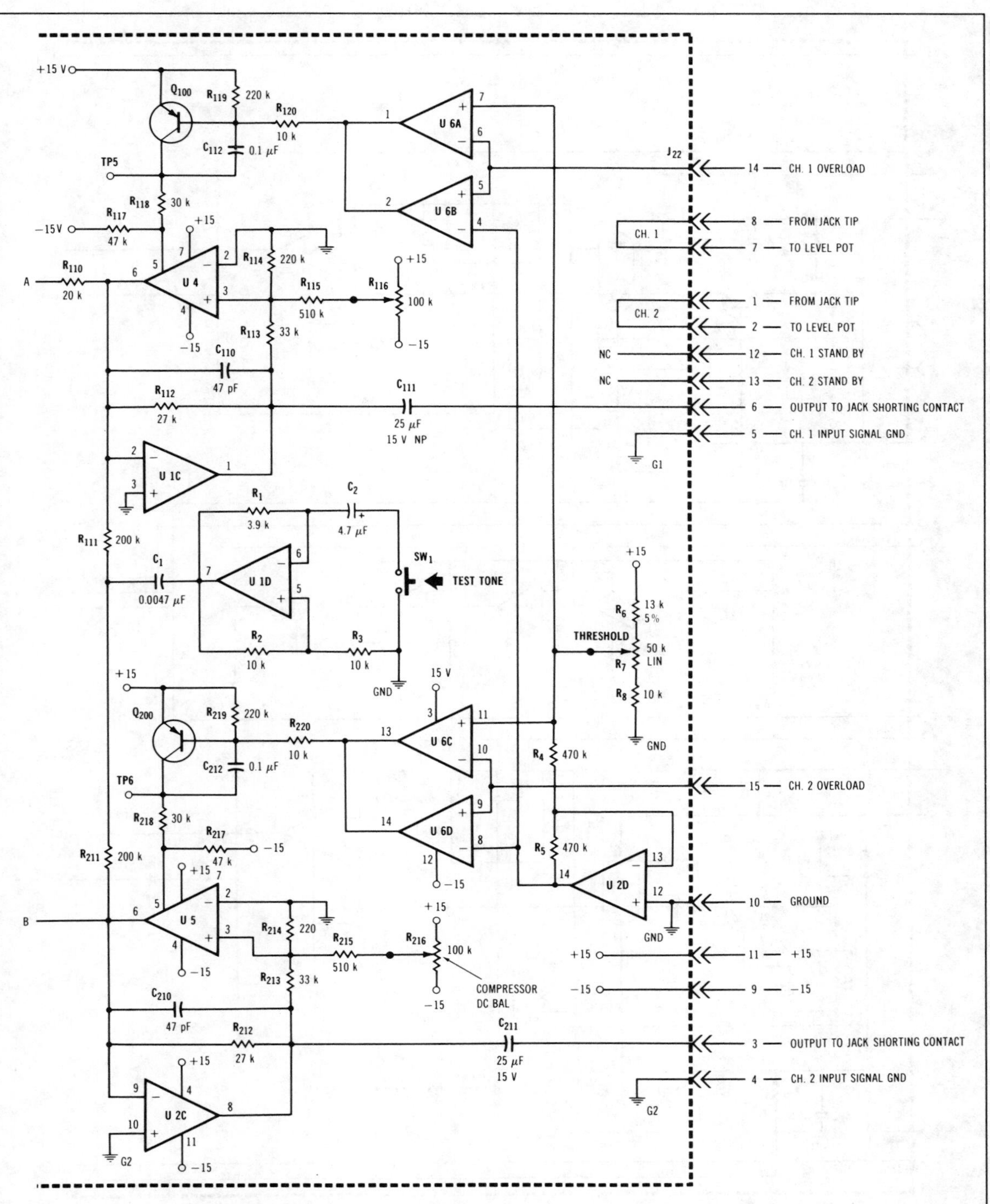

the Crown PSA-2 amplifier. *(Courtesy Crown International, Inc.)*

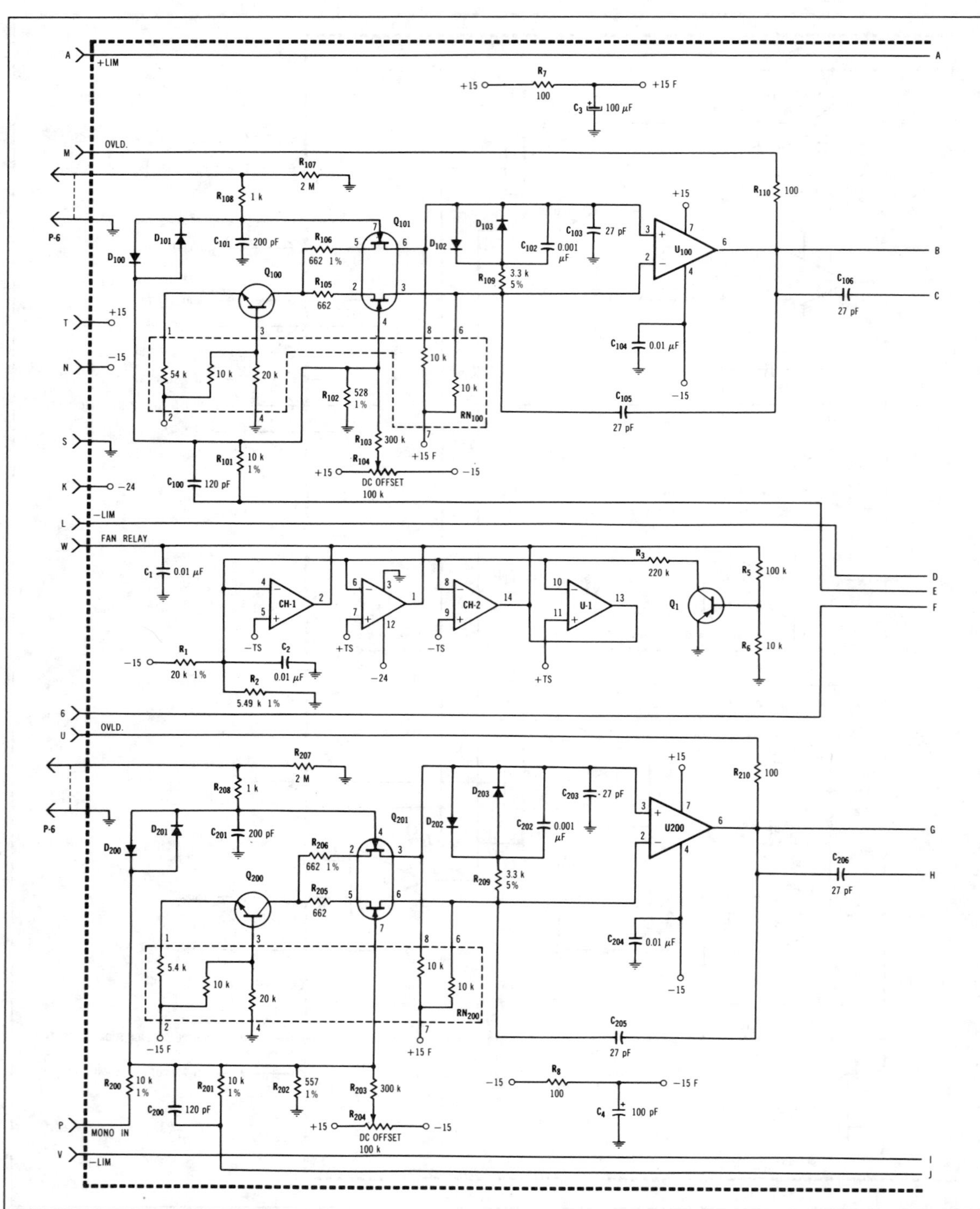

Figure 15-43 Schematic of the main module for the Crown

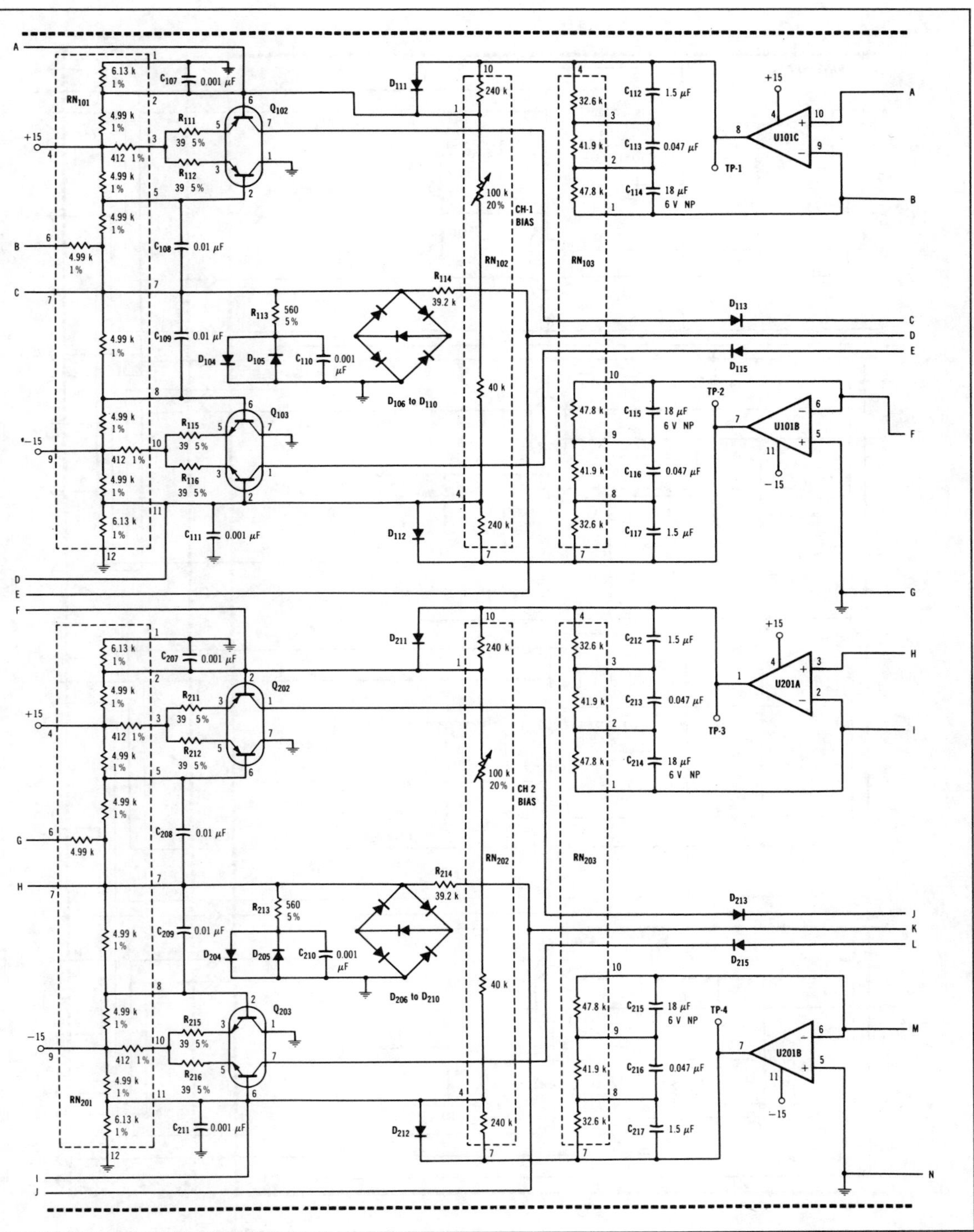

PSA-2 amplifier. *(Courtesy Crown International, Inc.)*

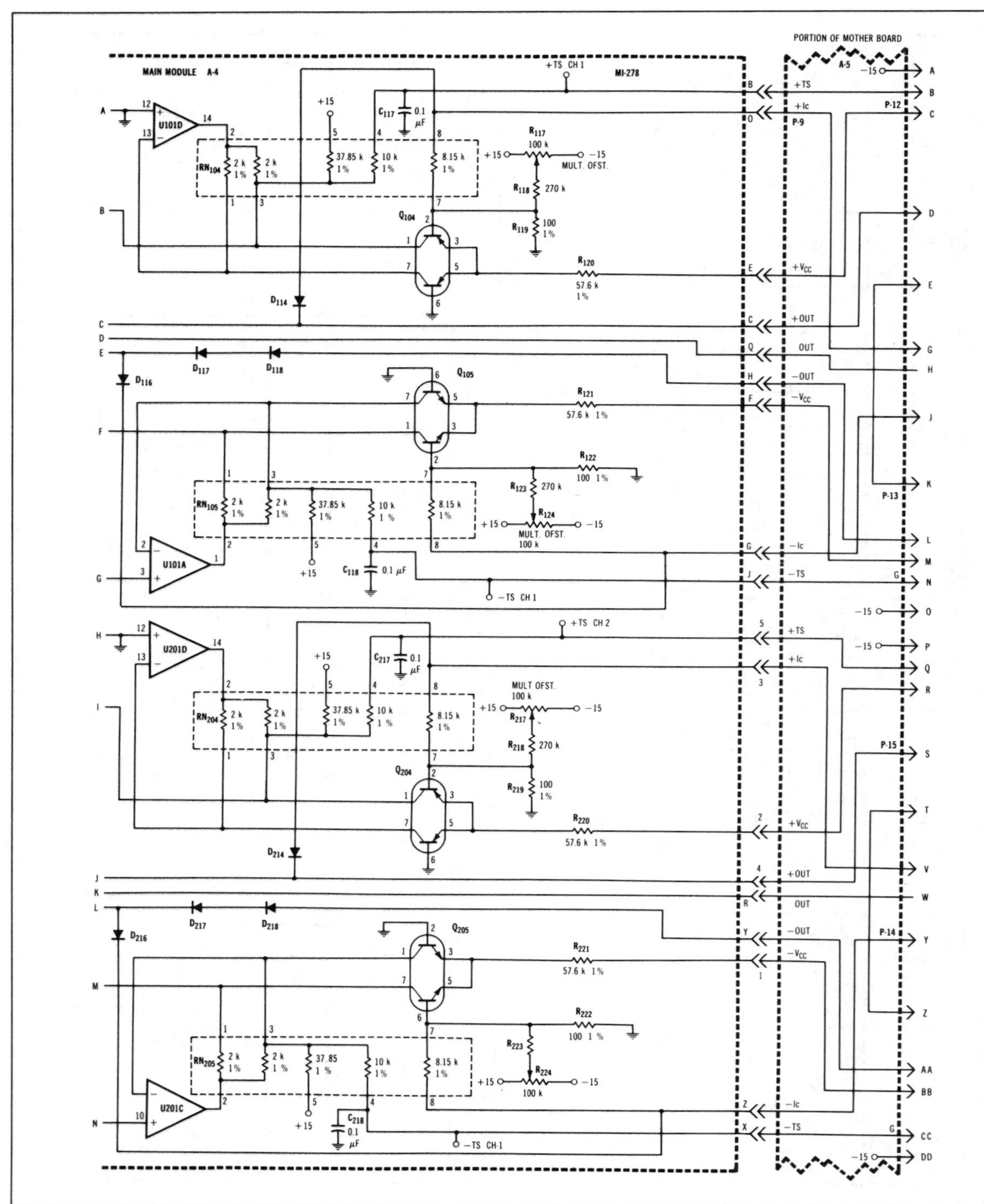

Figure 15-43-Cont. Schematic of the main module for the

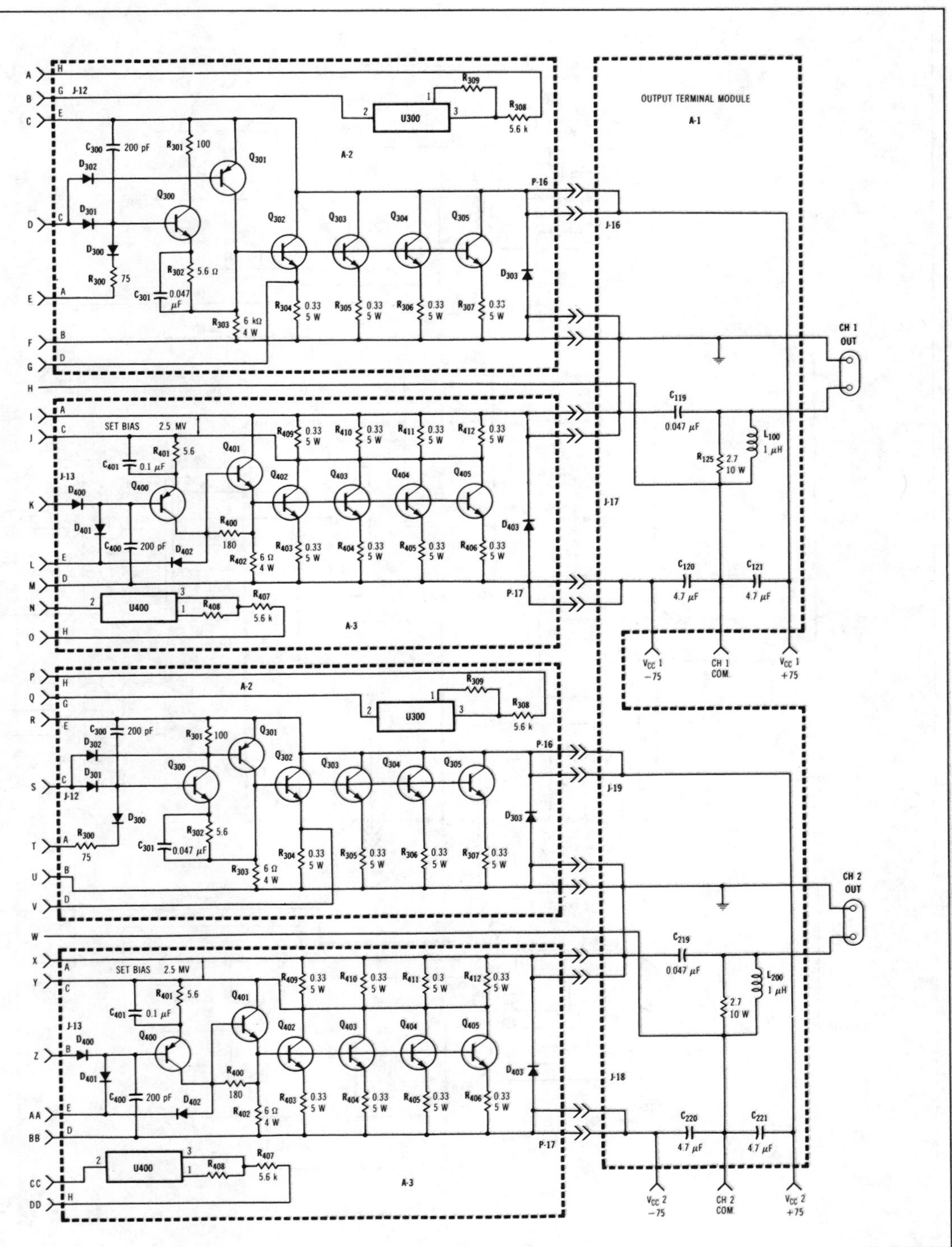

Crown International PSA-2 amplifier. *(Courtesy Crown International, Inc.)*

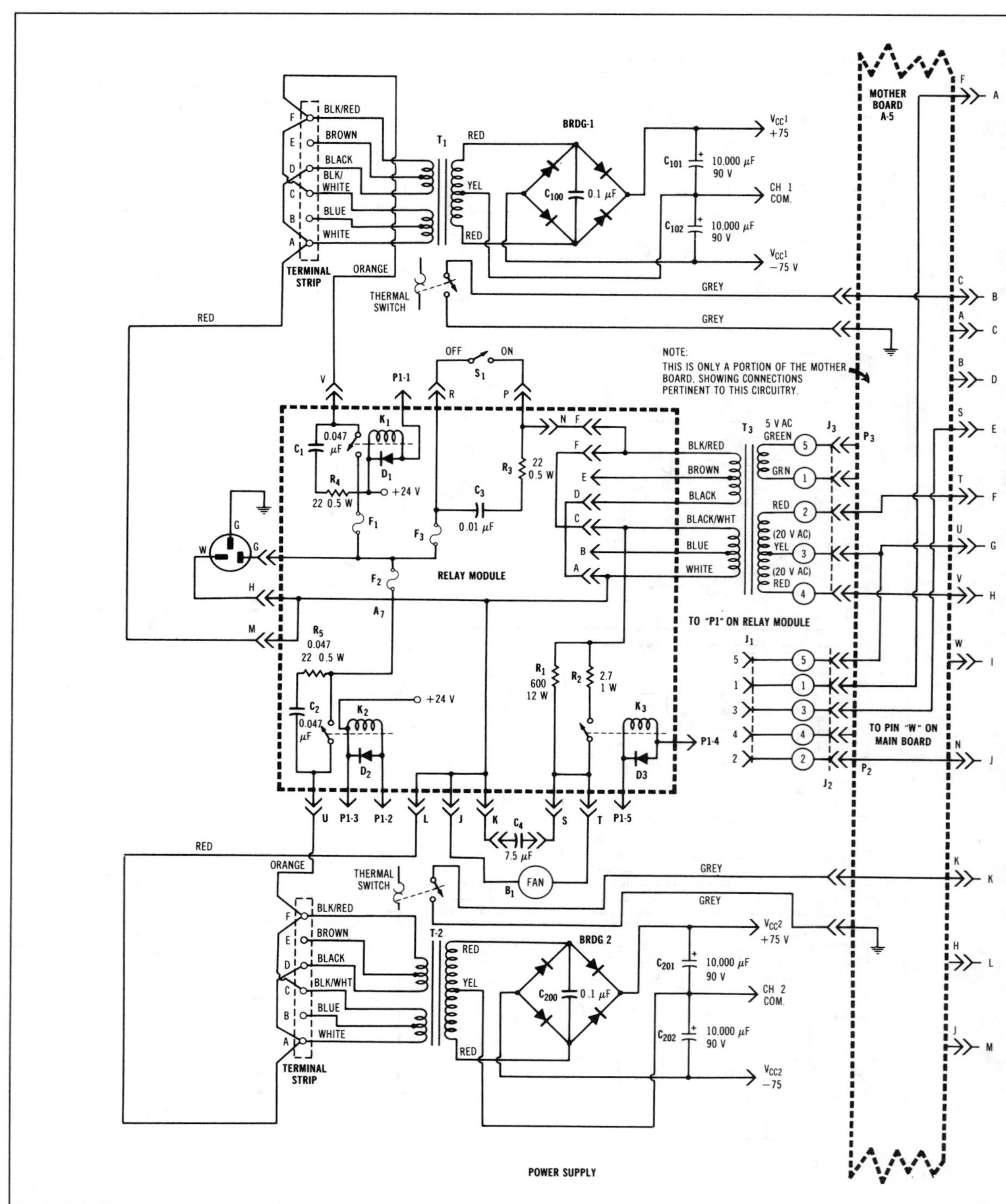

Figure 15-44 Schematic of the power supply circuit for the

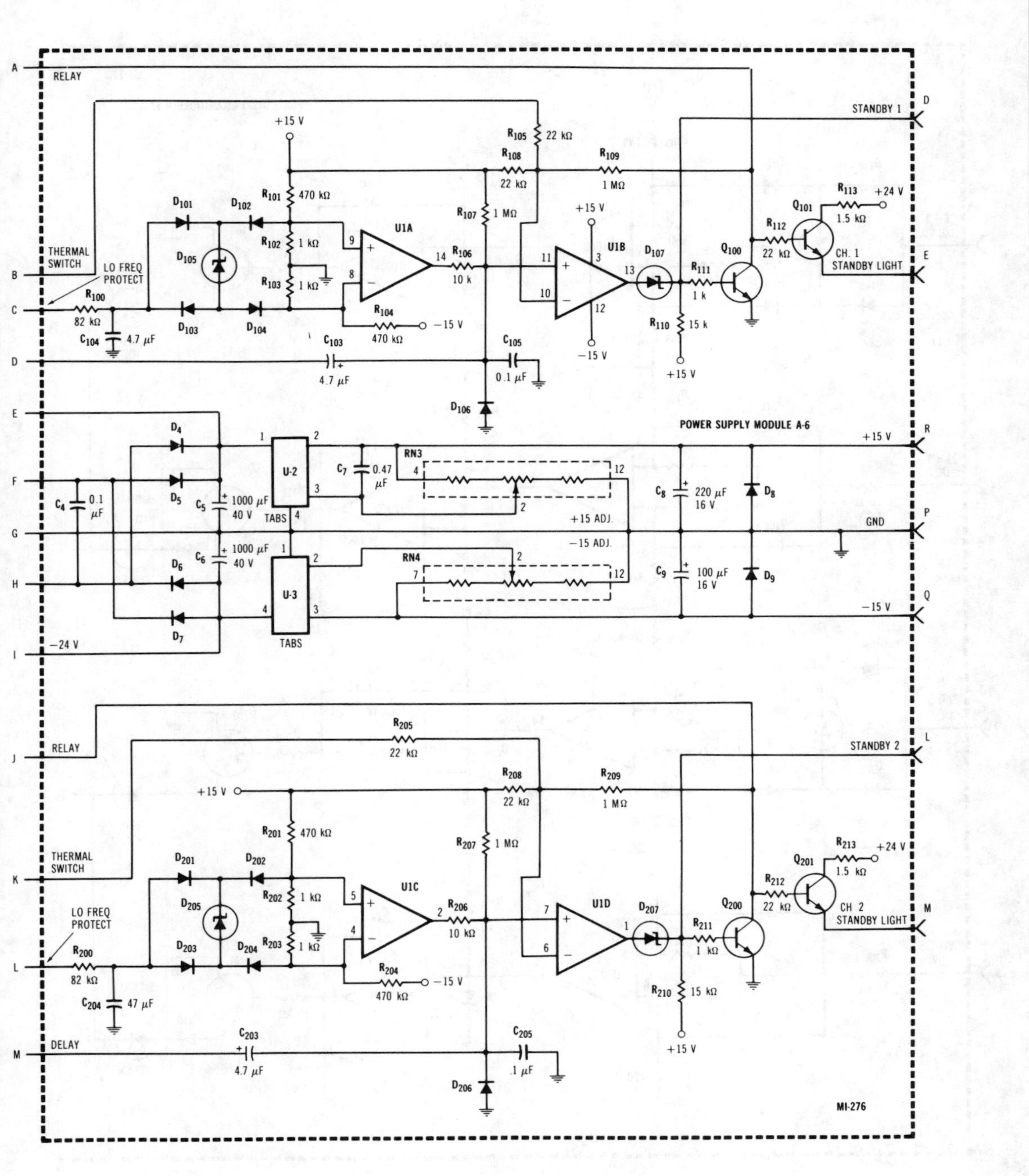

Crown PSA-2 amplifier. *(Courtesy Crown International, Inc.)*

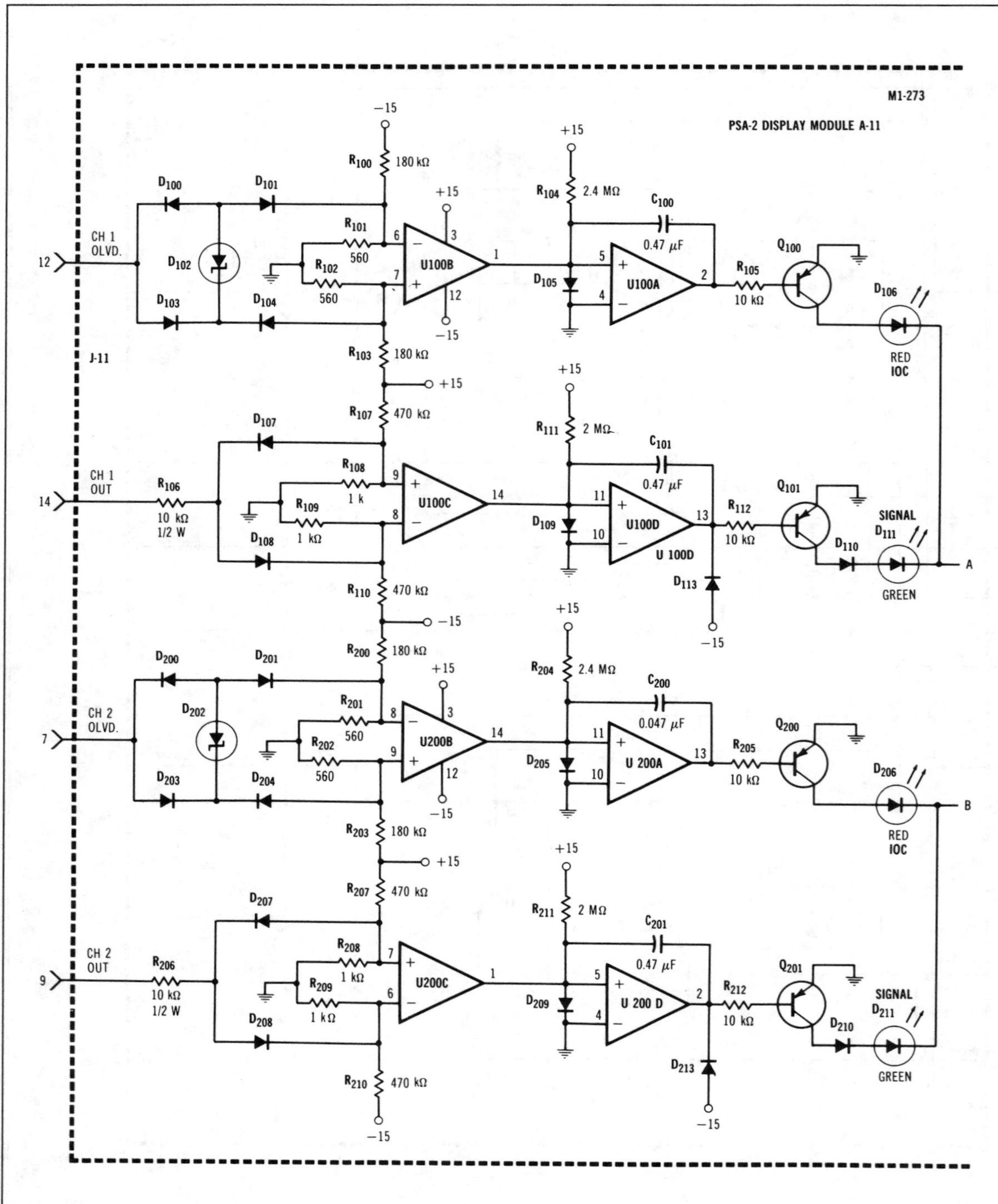

Figure 15-45 Schematic of the display and muting modules for

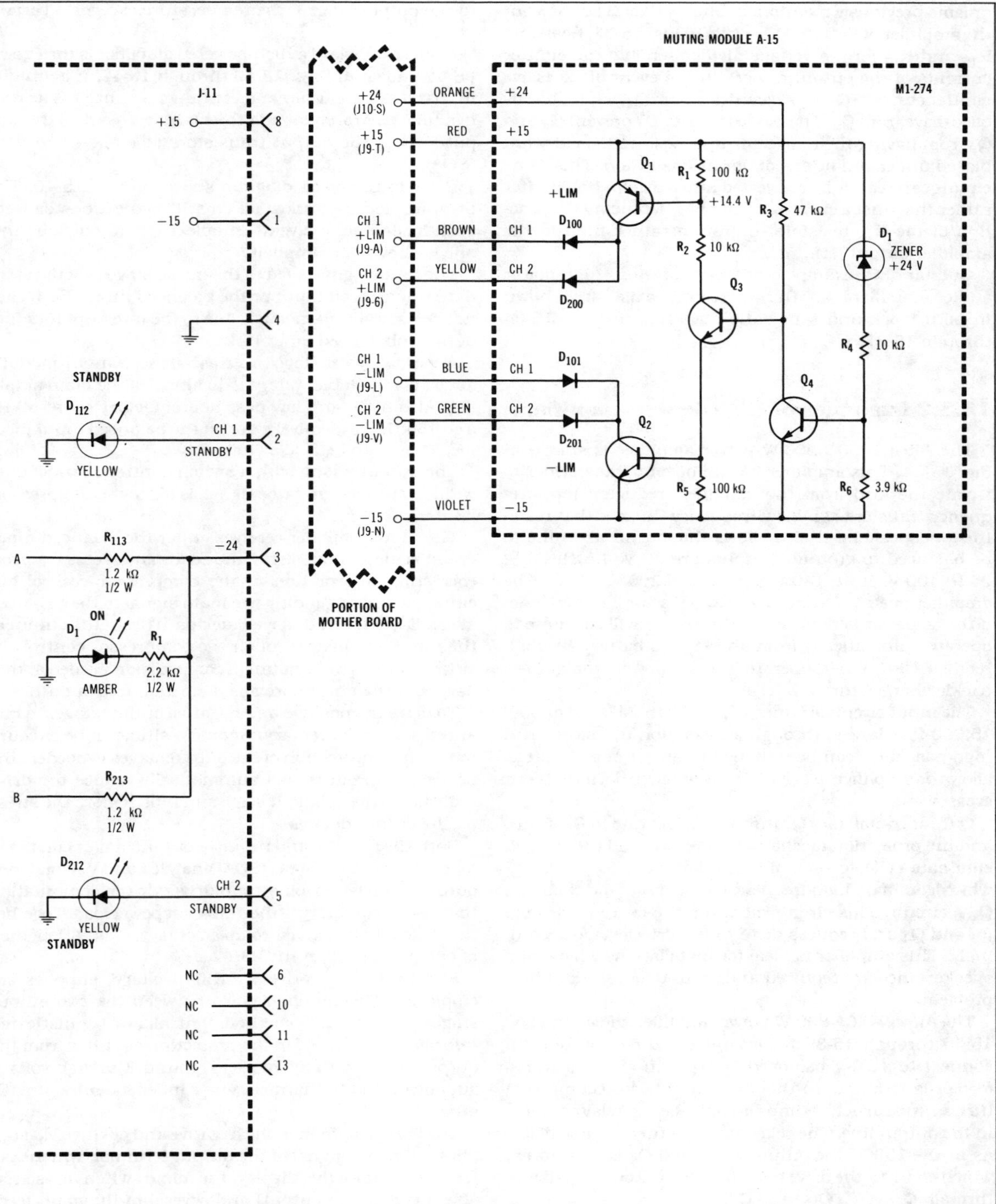

the Crown PSA-2 amplifier. *(Courtesy Crown International, Inc.)*

anisms previously mentioned. Such a circuit suitable for the amplifier of Fig. 15-31 is given in Fig. 15-33. Resistors R_{15} and R_{16} form a voltage divider sensing the emitter currents of the output devices in the event of excessive emitter current; Q_7 robs base drive from Q_1, while Q_8 robs base drive from Q_2. The diodes D_3 and D_4 prevent Q_7 and Q_8 from having their collector-to-base junctions forward biased under conditions of normal operation. This same circuit can readily be converted into a dissipation limiter rather than just a current limiter by referencing the junction of the R_{16} resistors to ground rather than to the amplifier output terminal.

Outstanding examples of well-protected, high-power audio amplifiers as they currently exist are shown in both block and schematic diagrams in Figs. 15-34 through 15-37.

15.3.2 Examples of High-Power Amplifiers

The Altec 1590C 200-W power amplifier is shown in Fig. 15-34. This amplifier has an output transformer to isolate the load from the amplifier, reducing high-frequency transients and low-frequency thumps that reach the loudspeakers. It also allows the loudspeaker line to be balanced to ground. Outputs are 30 V, 4.5 Ω; 70 V, 25 Ω; 100 V, 50 Ω; 140 V, 100 Ω; and 200 V, 200 Ω. The amplifier operates from 110 or 220 V ac or 24 to 28 V dc. If the ac power is removed, the amplifier will continue to operate automatically from an external battery through rectifier CR6. When operating on ac power, the battery trickle charges through R_{15}.

The input circuit is either 15,000 Ω unbalanced or 600/15,000 Ω balanced through an isolation transformer. A high-pass filter can be switched in or out of a circuit to allow the amplifier to drive high-frequency horns without crossovers.

Output transistors Q_1 through Q_8 operate in Class AB, and the protection mechanisms are CR_2 and CR_3, which eliminate collector-to-emitter spikes; R_{11}, R_{12}, and C_3, which eliminate high-frequency oscillation; and the Q_{108}, Q_{109} circuit. This circuit monitors the current through Q_3 and Q_4 and reduces drive to the driver stage accordingly. This amplifier is ideal for installations where long speaker lines are required and ground loops might be a problem.

The Altec 9440A 800-W power amplifier shown in Figs. 15-35 through 15-39 incorporates a direct output. To connect to a 70-V balanced system, an external transformer is required. In this type circuit, protection from turnon and turnoff thumps is controlled by relay contacts in the output line. The relay has a 4-s turnon time delay. As in the 1590C the output of Q_7 and Q_8 is monitored, which controls the drive current of the output transistors through Q_{10}, Q_{11}, Q_{12}, and Q_{15}.

A thermistor is mounted on the heat sinks to monitor the transistor temperature and to reduce the high voltage to the output stage if the temperature exceeds a certain value.

A final example of a high-powered amplifier is the Crown PSA-2 shown in Figs. 13-40 through 13-42. It is unique in that it automatically and continuously analyzes its own dynamic environment and thus is able to control the output level to the output transistors *safe operating area (SOA)*.

Refer to the block diagram shown in Fig. 15-40. The diagram does not show all circuit connections or feedback loops due to circuit complexity, and only channel one is shown for simplicity.

The input signal is fed to the initial stages via the standard unbalanced input or the balanced input. Both cannot be used simultaneously due to the interrupt function of the unbalanced input jacks.

A variable-gain stage, on the balanced input module, adds an adjustable voltage gain ahead of the main amplifier. Also high- and low-pass filters, factory set at 50 Hz and 15 kHz, respectively, are on the balanced input module. These can be field switched.

The output, along with a switch-controlled widebandwidth test-tone generator signal, is fed to the compressor-limiter circuitry.

The input amplifier receives either the balanced input or unbalanced input signal and sends any necessary error-correcting information to the compressor control circuitry as well as sending the main signal to the balanced stage. Essentially, this feedback path (from the output of the input amplifier through the compressor control circuitry) adjusts the amount of compression needed at that particular instant to provide distortion-free output.

To drive the positive and negative output stages, a balanced stage is necessary. Should a situation be encountered where protection of the output stages is needed, the protection circuitry will automatically reduce the drive available to the balanced stage and thus remove the stress on the output devices.

Both the positive and negative output stages consist of four safe operating areas (SOA) analyzed and V_{BE} matched output transistors plus a predriver/driver combination that also aid in carrying the quiescent power load. Together they help form the quasi-complementary, Class AB method of operation used in the PSA-2.

Positive and negative V_{cc} (high-voltage) supplies are employed. The common point between the two output stages is ground, a method that allows sophisticated information to be fed to the protection circuitry from the output stages with reference to ground. The high-voltage supplies of both channels work independently of each other.

The point common to the negative and positive V_{cc} supplies is the hot signal of the output terminal, which also feeds the front panel display, the mono switch (for selectable stereo-mono output) and several of the main feedback paths.

The control logic is responsible for the action of the low-frequency protection, delay, standby, and thermal protection of the unit. When signaled by the low-frequency protection, standby, and/or delay feature, the control logic will remove the power from the V_{cc} supplies. In the case of low-frequency protection, when the output has subsided it will place the high-voltage supplies back into operation from standby or cycle through the same procedure, depending upon the existence of the problem. Thermal protection may involve the same procedure as mentioned previously but only in extreme cases. A thermal switch imbedded in the windings of the high- voltage transformer will activate the control logic when potentially damaging current demands are being placed on it.

The low-voltage supply drives all low-power signal-path circuitry including the control logic, display, and fan-speed logic. At an internal temperature of 47°C, the unit will automatically shift to high fan speed operation for additional cooling.

REFERENCES

1. D. Dugan, U.S. Patent 3,814,856.
2. D. Dugan, U.S. Patent 3,992,584.
3. R. W. Peters, U.S. Patent 4,149,032.

CHAPTER **16**

Attenuators

by Glen Ballou

An *attenuator* or pad is an arrangement of noninductive resistors in an electrical circuit used to reduce the level of an audio or radio-frequency signal without introducing appreciable distortion. Attenuators may be fixed or variable and are often designed to reduce the signal in a logarithmic manner.

Attenuator networks have been in use since the inception of the telephone for controlling sound levels and the matching of impedances. Many of the present-day configurations are the work of Otto J. Zobel, W. H. Bode, R. L. Diezold, Sallie Pero Mead, and T. E. Shay, all of the Bell Telephone Laboratories. Also, tables of constants developed by P. K. McElroy (also of Bell Telephone Laborratories) for various values of expression and substitution in equations have long been a time-saver for the design engineer.

Attenuators and pads may be unbalanced or balanced. In an unbalanced attenuator, the resistive elements are on one side of the line only (Fig. 16-1) while in the balanced configuration, the resistive elements are located on both sides of the line (Fig. 16-2).

An unbalanced pad should be grounded to prevent leakage at the higher frequencies. The line without the resistor elements, called the *common*, is the only line that should be grounded.

A balanced attenuator should be grounded at a center point created by a balancing shunt resistance.

Balanced and unbalanced configurations cannot be directly connected; however, they may be connected by the use of an isolation transformer (Fig. 16-3). If the networks are not separated electrically, severe instability and leakage at the high frequencies can result, as illustrated in Fig. 16-4. If the networks are connected without the transformer, half of the balanced circuit will be shorted to the ground, as indicated by the broken line. The transformer will permit the transfer of the audio signal inductively while separating the grounds of the two networks. Even if the balanced network is not grounded, it should be isolated by a transformer. Transformers are usually designed for a 1:1 impedance ratio; however, they may have taps for other impedance ratios.

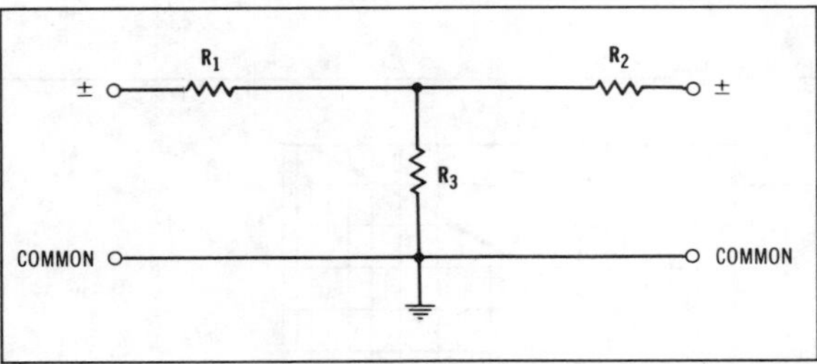

Figure 16-1 An unbalanced T-type attenuator.

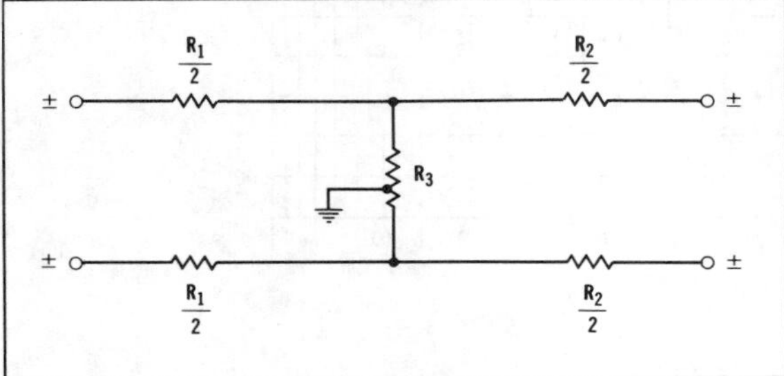

Figure 16-2 A balanced-T-type attenuator.

The term *loss* is constantly used in attenuator and pad design. Loss is a decrease in the power, voltage, or current at the output of a device compared to the power, voltage, or current at the input of the device. The loss in decibels may be calculated by means of one of the following equations:

$$dB_{loss} = 10 \log P_1/P_2 \tag{16-1}$$

or,

$$dB_{loss} = 20 \log V_1/V_2 \tag{16-2}$$

or,

$$dB_{loss} = 20 \log I_1/I_2 \tag{16-3}$$

where,

P_1 is the power at the input,
P_2 is the power at the output,
V_1 is the voltage at the input,
V_2 is the voltage at the output,
I_1 is the current at the input,
I_2 is the current at the output.

The *insertion loss* is created by the insertion of a device in an electrical circuit. The resulting loss is generally expressed in decibels.

A *minimum-loss pad* is designed to match circuits of unequal impedance with a minimum loss in the matching network. This minimum loss is dependent on the ratio of the terminating impedances.

The minimum loss for attenuators of unequal impedance may be read from the graph of Fig. 16-5.

The graph is entered at the bottom at the desired impedance ratio, then followed vertically until it intersects the diagonal line. The minimum loss in decibels is then read at the left margin. As an example, assume an impedance of 600 Ω is to be matched to an impedance of 150 Ω; this is an impedance ratio of four. For this ratio, the graph indicates a minimum loss of 11.5 dB. This is the lowest value for which a passive attenuator can be designed. In actual practice the network would be designed for a loss of 12 to 15 dB.

An *impedance-matching network* is a noninductive, resistive network designed for insertion between two or more circuits of equal or unequal impedance. When prop-

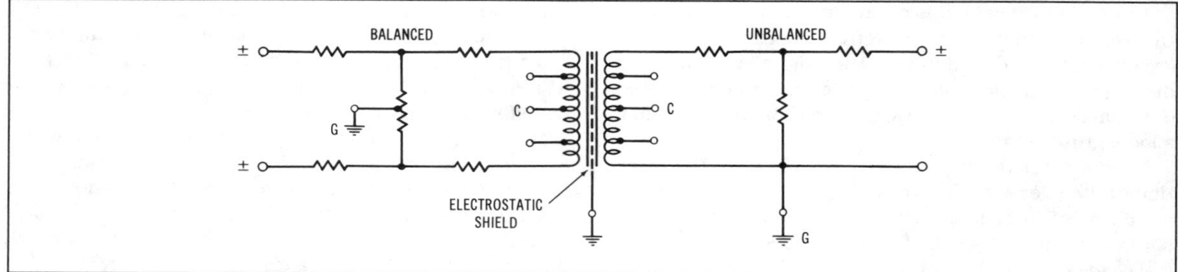

Figure 16-3 Method of connecting balanced and unbalanced networks through a transformer.

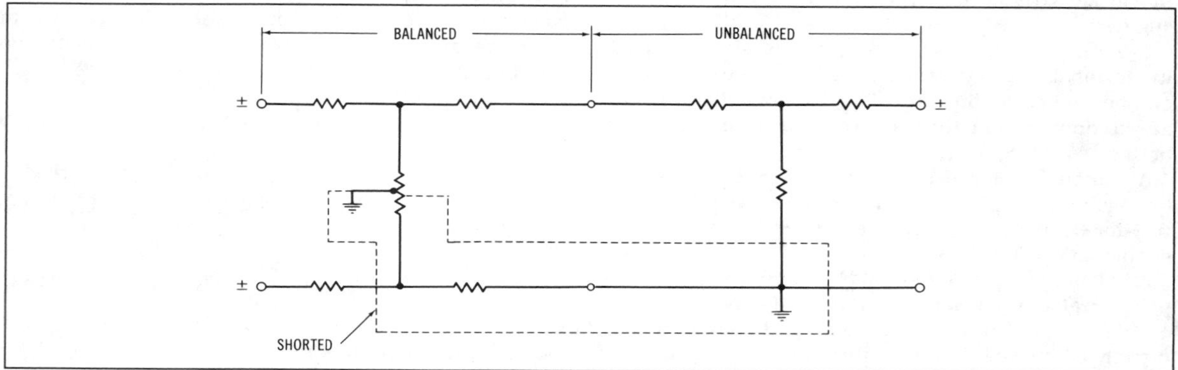

Figure 16-4 Two networks, one balanced and one unbalanced, connected incorrectly.

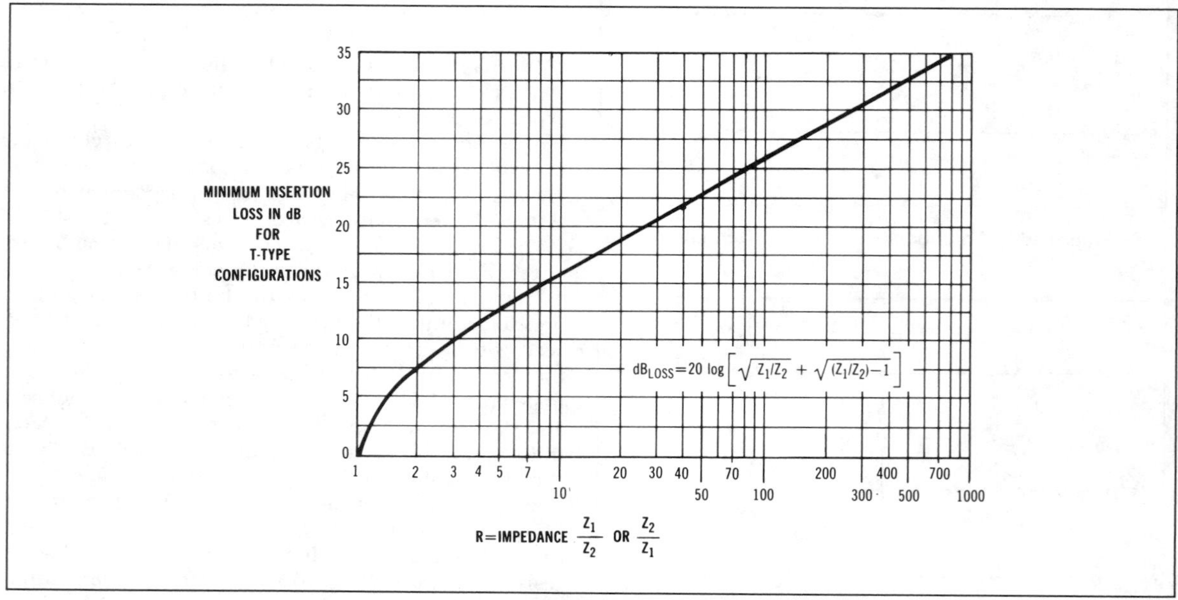

Figure 16-5 Minimum-loss graph for networks of unequal impedance.

erly designed, the network reflects the correct impedance to each branch of the circuit. A noninductive resistor is a resistor having little or no self-inductance.

If two resistive networks are mismatched, generally the frequency characteristics are not affected, only a loss in level occurs. If the impedance mismatch ratio is known, the loss in level may be directly read from the graph in Fig. 16-5 or with the formula

$$dB = 10\log[(Z_1 + Z_2)^2/(4Z_1Z_2)] \qquad (16\text{-}4)$$

The equation used for designing a minimum-loss attenuator when only the larger impedance Z_1 is to be matched is

$$R_1 = Z_1 - Z_2 \qquad (16\text{-}5)$$

Only a series resistor R is used, (Fig. 16-6).

If the smaller impedance is to be matched, the following formula is used:

$$R = Z_1 Z_2/(Z_1 - Z_2) \qquad (16\text{-}6)$$

The resistor is shunted across the line as in Fig. 16-7.

To simplify the design of complex attenuators, a K value is used in the formula. K is the ratio of current, voltage, or power corresponding to a given value of attenuation expressed in decibels. The formula for K is

$$K = 10^{dB/20} \qquad (16\text{-}7)$$

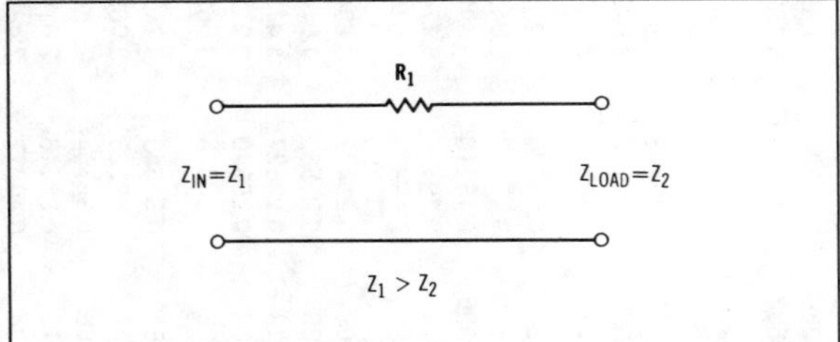

Figure 16-6 Impedance matching a low-impedance load to a high-impedance source.

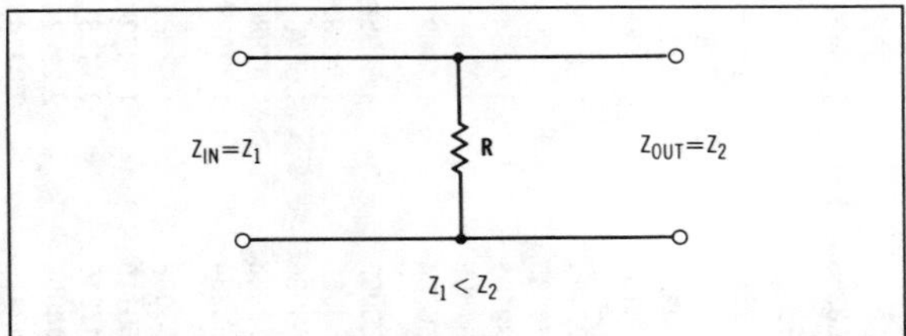

Figure 16-7 Impedance matching a high-impedance load to a low-impedance source.

To simplify the calculation of attenuator networks, the values of the most frequently used expressions as tabulated by P. K. McElroy are given in Table 16-1. The various values of the expressions are substituted in the equations, saving much time.

It is not good practice to build pads with over 40-dB loss, unless special precautions are taken to reduce the distributed capacity and leakage between the input and output sections. It is more practical to build two or more pads of lower loss and connect them in tandem. The total loss is the sum of the individual losses, assuming that all impedance matches are satisfied between sections.

When installing attenuators, the input and output circuits must be separated from each other and well shielded and grounded to prevent leakage at the higher frequencies. As an example, an attenuator of a 40-dB loss has a signal voltage reduction of 100:1 between the input and output terminals. Therefore, if coupling between the input and output circuits is permitted, serious leakage can occur at frequencies above 1000 Hz.

The resistance of an attenuator can be measured with an ohmmeter by terminating the output with a resistance equal to the terminating impedance and measuring the input resistance. The resistance as measured by the ohmmeter should equal the impedance of the pad. If the attenuator is variable, the dc resistance should be the same for all steps.

If the impedance of an attenuator is not known, its value can be determined by first measuring the resistance looking into one end with the far end open and then shorted. The impedance (Z) is the geometric mean of the two readings:

$$Z = \sqrt{Z_1 Z_2} \qquad (16\text{-}8)$$

where,

Z_1 is the resistance measured with the far end open,
Z_2 is the resistance measured with the far end shorted.

This measurement will hold true only for pads designed to be operated between equal terminations. If the dc resistance of the two ends differs, the pad is designed to be operated between unequal impedances.

If an attenuator is to be converted to a different impedance, the new resistors can be calculated with the following formula:

$$R_x = K(R) \qquad (16\text{-}9)$$

$$K = Z_x/Z \qquad (16\text{-}10)$$

where,

Z_x is the new impedance,
Z is the known impedance,
K is the multiplying factor,
R is the known value of resistance,
R_x is the new value of resistance.

Any balanced or unbalanced attenuator may be directly

Table 16-1. "K" Factors for Calculating Attenuator Loss Values

n(dB)	$r = \frac{1}{K}$	K	K^2	$\frac{K-1}{K+1}$	$\frac{K+1}{K-1}$	$\frac{K}{K^2-1}$	$\frac{K^2-1}{K} = K - r$	$\frac{K^2+1}{K^2-1}$	$\frac{K-1}{K} = 1 - r$	$\frac{K}{K-1} = \frac{1}{1-r}$	$\frac{1}{K-1}$	n(dB)
0.05	0.994260	1.0057731	1.011579	0.0028783	347.43	86.8618	0.011513	173.73	0.0057395	174.22	173.22	0.05
0.1	0.98855	1.011579	1.023292	0.0057562	173.73	43.4303	0.023029	86.866	1.011448	87.363	86.363	0.1
0.2	0.97724	1.023292	1.047128	0.011512	86.866	21.713	0.046052	43.437	0.022762	33.933	32.933	0.2
0.3	0.96605	1.035143	1.071520	0.017268	57.911	14.473	0.069093	28.965	0.033949	19.455	18.455	0.3
0.4	0.95499	1.047128	1.096477	0.023022	43.437	10.854	0.092138	21.730	0.045007	22.219	21.219	0.4
0.5	0.94406	1.059254	1.12202	0.028774	34.754	8.6810	0.11519	17.391	0.055939	17.877	16.877	0.5
0.6	0.93325	1.071520	1.14815	0.034525	28.965	7.2327	0.13827	14.499	0.066746	14.982	13.982	0.6
0.7	0.92257	1.083928	1.17490	0.040274	24.830	6.1974	0.16136	12.435	0.077428	12.915	11.915	0.7
0.8	0.91201	1.096477	1.20227	0.046019	21.730	5.4209	0.18447	10.888	0.087988	11.365	10.365	0.8
0.9	0.90157	1.10917	1.23027	0.051763	19.319	4.8168	0.20760	9.6853	0.098429	10.160	9.1600	0.9
1.0	0.89125	1.12202	1.25893	0.057502	17.391	4.3335	0.23077	8.7237	0.10875	9.1954	8.1954	1.0
1.1	0.88105	1.13501	1.28825	0.063237	15.814	3.9376	0.25396	7.9384	0.11895	8.4069	7.4069	1.1
1.2	0.87096	1.14815	1.31826	0.068968	14.499	3.6076	0.27719	7.2842	0.12904	7.7499	6.7499	1.2
1.3	0.86099	1.16145	1.34896	0.074695	13.388	3.3283	0.30046	6.7313	0.13901	7.1939	6.1939	1.3
1.4	0.85114	1.17490	1.38038	0.080418	12.435	3.0888	0.32376	6.2579	0.14886	6.7176	5.7176	1.4
1.5	0.84139	1.18850	1.41254	0.086132	11.610	2.8809	0.34711	5.8480	0.15861	6.3050	5.3050	1.5
1.6	0.83176	1.20227	1.44544	0.091846	10.888	2.6991	0.37051	5.4899	0.16824	5.9439	4.9439	1.6
1.7	0.82224	1.21618	1.47911	0.097551	10.251	2.5384	0.39394	5.1744	0.17776	5.6258	4.6258	1.7
1.8	0.81283	1.23027	1.51356	0.103249	9.6853	2.3956	0.41744	4.8944	0.18717	5.3427	4.3427	1.8
1.9	0.80353	1.24452	1.54882	0.108939	9.1794	2.2676	0.44099	4.6442	0.19647	5.0897	4.0897	1.9
2.0	0.79433	1.25893	1.58489	0.11463	8.7241	2.1523	0.46460	4.4195	0.20567	4.8620	3.8620	2.0
2.2	0.77625	1.28825	1.65959	0.12597	7.9384	1.9531	0.51200	4.0322	0.22375	4.4692	3.4692	2.2
2.4	0.75858	1.31826	1.73780	0.13728	7.2842	1.7867	0.55968	3.7108	0.24142	4.1421	3.1421	2.4
2.5	0.74989	1.33352	1.77828	0.14293	6.9966	1.7133	0.58363	3.5698	0.25011	3.9983	2.9983	2.5
2.6	0.74131	1.34896	1.81970	0.14856	6.7313	1.6457	0.60765	3.4399	0.25829	3.8657	2.8657	2.6
2.8	0.72444	1.38038	1.90546	0.15980	6.2579	1.5245	0.65594	3.2088	0.27556	3.6289	2.6289	2.8
3.0	0.70795	1.41254	1.99526	0.17100	5.8480	1.4192	0.70459	3.0095	0.29205	3.4240	2.4240	3.0
3.2	0.69183	1.44544	2.08930	0.18215	5.4899	1.3269	0.75361	2.8360	0.30817	3.2450	2.2450	3.2
3.4	0.67608	1.47911	2.18776	0.19326	5.1744	1.2453	0.80302	2.6838	0.32392	3.0872	2.0872	3.4
3.5	0.66834	1.49623	2.2387	0.19879	5.0304	1.2079	0.82789	2.6147	0.33166	3.0152	2.0152	3.5
3.6	0.66069	1.51356	2.2909	0.20432	4.8944	1.1725	0.85289	2.5493	0.33931	2.9472	1.9472	3.6
3.8	0.64565	1.54882	2.3988	0.21532	4.6442	1.1072	0.90314	2.4298	0.35435	2.8221	1.8221	3.8
4.0	0.63096	1.58489	2.5119	0.22627	4.4194	1.0483	0.95393	2.3229	0.36904	2.7097	1.7097	4.0
4.5	0.59566	1.67880	2.8184	0.25340	3.9464	0.92323	1.08314	2.0999	0.40434	2.4732	1.4732	4.5
5.0	0.56234	1.77828	3.1623	0.28013	3.5698	0.82241	1.21594	1.9249	0.43766	2.2849	1.2849	5.0
5.5	0.53088	1.88365	3.5481	0.30643	3.2633	0.73922	1.35277	1.7849	0.46912	2.1317	1.1317	5.5
6.0	0.50119	1.99526	3.9811	0.33228	3.0095	0.66932	1.49407	1.6709	0.49881	2.0048	1.0048	6.0
6.5	0.47315	2.1135	4.4668	0.35764	2.7961	0.60964	1.6403	1.5769	0.52685	1.89807	0.89807	6.5
7.0	0.44668	2.2387	5.0119	0.38246	2.6146	0.55801	1.7920	1.4985	0.55332	1.80730	0.80730	7.0
7.5	0.42170	2.3714	5.6234	0.40677	2.4854	0.51291	1.9497	1.4326	0.57830	1.72918	0.72918	7.5

8.0	0.39811	2.5119	6.3096	0.43051	2.3228	0.47309	2.1138	1.3767	0.60180	1.66142	0.66142	8.0
8.5	0.37584	2.6607	7.0795	0.45366	2.2043	0.43765	2.2849	1.3290	0.62416	1.60216	0.60216	8.5
9.0	0.35481	2.8184	7.9433	0.47622	2.0999	0.40592	2.4636	1.2880	0.64519	1.54993	0.54993	9.0
9.5	0.33497	2.9854	8.9125	0.49817	2.0074	0.37730	2.6504	1.2528	0.66503	1.50368	0.50368	9.5
10.0	0.31623	3.1623	10.000	0.51950	1.9249	0.35137	2.8561	1.2222	0.68377	1.46247	0.46247	10.0
10.5	0.29854	3.3497	11.220	0.54020	1.8512	0.32775	3.0512	1.1957	0.70146	1.42559	0.42559	10.5
11.0	0.28184	3.5481	12.589	0.56026	1.7849	0.30616	3.2663	1.1726	0.71816	1.39245	0.39245	11.0
11.5	0.26607	3.7584	14.125	0.57969	1.7251	0.28635	3.4923	1.1524	0.73393	1.36253	0.36253	11.5
12.0	0.25119	3.9811	15.849	0.59848	1.6709	0.26811	3.7299	1.1347	0.74881	1.33545	0.33545	12.0
12.5	0.23714	4.2170	17.783	0.61664	1.6217	0.25127	3.9799	1.1192	0.76286	1.31085	0.31085	12.5
13.0	0.22387	4.4668	19.953	0.63416	1.5769	0.23568	4.2429	1.1055	0.77613	1.28845	0.28845	13.0
13.5	0.21135	4.7315	22.387	0.65105	1.5360	0.22123	4.5202	1.0935	0.78865	1.26799	0.26799	13.5
14.0	0.19953	5.0119	25.119	0.66733	1.4985	0.20780	4.8124	1.0829	0.80047	1.24926	0.24926	14.0
14.5	0.18836	5.3088	28.184	0.68298	1.4642	0.19529	5.1204	1.0736	0.81164	1.23208	0.23208	14.5
15.0	0.17783	5.6234	31.623	0.69804	1.4326	0.18363	5.4456	1.0653	0.82217	1.21629	0.21629	15.0
15.5	0.16788	5.9566	35.481	0.71250	1.4035	0.17275	5.7887	1.0580	0.83212	1.20175	0.20175	15.5
16.0	0.15849	6.3096	39.811	0.72639	1.3767	0.16257	6.1511	1.0515	0.84151	1.18834	0.18834	16.0
16.5	0.14962	6.6834	44.668	0.73970	1.3519	0.15305	6.5338	1.0458	0.85038	1.17595	0.17595	16.5
17.0	0.14125	7.0795	50.119	0.75246	1.3290	0.14413	6.9382	1.04071	0.85875	1.16449	0.16449	17.0
17.5	0.13335	7.4989	56.234	0.76468	1.3077	0.13577	7.3655	1.03621	0.86665	1.15387	0.15387	17.5
18.0	0.12589	7.9433	63.096	0.77637	1.2880	0.12792	7.8174	1.03220	0.87411	1.14402	0.14402	18.0
18.5	0.118850	8.4139	70.795	0.78755	1.2698	0.12055	8.2950	1.02866	0.88115	1.13488	0.13488	18.5
19.0	0.112202	8.9125	79.433	0.79823	1.2528	0.11363	8.8003	1.02550	0.88780	1.12638	0.12638	19.0
19.5	0.105925	9.4406	89.125	0.80844	1.2369	0.10713	9.3347	1.02269	0.89407	1.11847	0.11847	19.5
20.0	0.100000	10.0000	100.000	0.81818	1.2222	0.10101	9.9000	1.02020	0.90000	1.11111	0.11111	20.0
20.5	0.094406	10.5925	112.202	0.82747	1.2085	0.095255	10.498	1.01799	0.90559	1.10425	0.10425	20.5
21.0	0.089125	11.2022	125.893	0.83634	1.1957	0.089841	11.131	1.01601	0.91087	1.09785	0.097815	21.0
21.5	0.084139	11.8850	141.254	0.84478	1.1837	0.084739	11.801	1.01426	0.91586	1.09187	0.091870	21.5
22.0	0.079433	12.589	158.49	0.85282	1.1726	0.079935	12.510	1.01270	0.92057	1.08629	0.086291	22.0
22.5	0.074989	13.335	177.83	0.86048	1.1621	0.075411	13.260	1.01126	0.92501	1.08107	0.081070	22.5
23.0	0.070795	14.125	199.53	0.86777	1.1524	0.071148	14.054	1.01007	0.92921	1.07619	0.076190	23.0
23.5	0.066834	14.962	223.87	0.87470	1.1432	0.067133	14.895	1.00897	0.93317	1.07162	0.071623	23.5
24.0	0.063096	15.849	251.19	0.88130	1.1347	0.063348	15.786	1.00799	0.93690	1.06734	0.067345	24.0
24.5	0.059566	16.788	281.84	0.88756	1.1267	0.059778	16.728	1.00712	0.94043	1.06334	0.063339	24.5
25.0	0.056234	17.783	316.23	0.89352	1.1192	0.056413	17.727	1.00634	0.94377	1.05985	0.059584	25.0
25.5	0.053088	18.836	354.81	0.89917	1.1121	0.053238	18.783	1.00565	0.94691	1.05607	0.056066	25.5
26.0	0.050119	19.953	398.11	0.90455	1.1055	0.050246	19.903	1.00504	0.94988	1.05276	0.052762	26.0
26.5	0.047315	21.135	446.68	0.90965	1.0993	0.047422	21.088	1.00449	0.95268	1.04966	0.049665	26.5
27.0	0.044668	22.387	501.19	0.91448	1.0935	0.044757	22.342	1.00400	0.95533	1.04676	0.046757	27.0
27.5	0.042170	23.714	562.34	0.91907	1.0881	0.042245	23.672	1.00356	0.95783	1.04403	0.044026	27.5
28.0	0.039811	25.119	630.96	0.92343	1.0829	0.039874	25.079	1.00317	0.96019	1.04146	0.041461	28.0
28.5	0.037584	26.607	707.95	0.92755	1.0781	0.037636	26.569	1.00283	0.96242	1.03905	0.039052	28.5
29.0	0.035481	28.184	794.33	0.93147	1.0736	0.035526	28.149	1.00252	0.96452	1.03679	0.036786	29.0
29.5	0.033497	29.854	891.25	0.93518	1.0693	0.033534	29.821	1.00225	0.96650	1.03466	0.034657	29.5
30.0	0.031623	31.623	1,000.0	0.93869	1.0653	0.031655	31.591	1.00200	0.96836	1.03266	0.032655	30.0
31.0	0.028184	35.481	1,258.9	0.94518	1.0580	0.028207	35.453	1.00159	0.97182	1.02900	0.029001	31.0

Table 16-1—cont. "K" Factors for Calculating Attenuator Loss Values

n(dB)	$r = \frac{1}{K}$	K	K^2	$\frac{K-1}{K+1}$	$\frac{K+1}{K-1}$	$\frac{K}{K^2-1}$	$\frac{K^2-1}{K} = K - r$	$\frac{K^2+1}{K^2-1}$	$\frac{K-1}{K} = 1 - r$	$\frac{K}{K-1} = \frac{1}{1-r}$	$\frac{1}{K-1}$	n(dB)
31.5	0.026607	37.584	1,412.5	0.94817	1.0547	0.026627	37.558	1.00142	0.97339	1.02733	0.027334	31.5
32.0	0.025119	39.811	1,584.9	0.95099	1.0515	0.025135	39.786	1.00126	0.97488	1.02577	0.025766	32.0
33.0	0.022387	44.668	1,995.3	0.95621	1.0458	0.022398	44.646	1.00100	0.97761	1.02290	0.022900	33.0
34.0	0.019953	50.119	2,511.9	0.96088	1.04072	0.019961	50.099	1.00080	0.98005	1.02036	0.020359	34.0
34.5	0.018836	53.088	2,818.4	0.96302	1.03840	0.018843	53.069	1.00071	0.98116	1.01920	0.019198	34.5
35.0	0.017783	56.234	3,162.3	0.96506	1.03621	0.017788	56.216	1.00063	0.98222	1.01810	0.018105	35.0
36.0	0.015849	63.096	3,981.1	0.96880	1.03221	0.015853	63.080	1.00050	0.98415	1.01610	0.016104	36.0
37.0	0.014125	70.795	5,011.9	0.97214	1.02866	0.014128	70.781	1.00040	0.98588	1.01433	0.014328	37.0
37.5	0.013335	74.989	5,623.4	0.97368	1.02703	0.013338	74.976	1.00036	0.98666	1.01352	0.013516	37.5
38.0	0.012589	79.433	6,309.6	0.97513	1.02550	0.012591	79.420	1.00032	0.98741	1.01275	0.012750	38.0
39.0	0.0112202	89.125	7,943.3	0.97781	1.02270	0.0112216	89.114	1.00025	0.98878	1.01135	0.011348	39.0
40.0	0.0100000	100.000	10,000.	0.98020	1.02020	0.0100010	99.990	1.00020	0.99000	1.01010	0.010101	40.0
40.5	0.0094406	105.925	11,220.	0.98130	1.01906	0.0094414	105.916	1.00018	0.99056	1.00953	0.0095306	40.5
41.0	0.0089125	112.202	12,589.	0.98233	0.01799	0.0089134	112.193	1.00016	0.99109	1.00899	0.0089926	41.0
42.0	0.0079433	125.89	15,849.	0.98424	1.01601	0.0079436	125.88	1.00013	0.99206	1.00801	0.0080070	42.0
43.0	0.0070795	141.25	19,953.	0.98594	1.01426	0.0070795	141.24	1.00010	0.99292	1.00713	0.0071301	43.0
43.5	0.0066834	149.62	22,387.	0.98672	1.01346	0.0066834	149.61	1.00009	0.99332	1.00673	0.0067286	43.5
44.0	0.0063096	158.49	25,119.	0.98746	1.01270	0.0063096	158.49	1.00008	0.99369	1.00635	0.0063496	44.0
45.0	0.0056234	177.83	31,623.	0.98887	1.01131	0.0056234	177.83	1.00006	0.99438	1.00566	0.0056551	45.0
46.0	0.0050119	199.53	39,811.	0.99003	1.01007	0.0050119	199.53	1.00005	0.99499	1.00504	0.0050370	46.0
46.5	0.0047315	211.35	44,668.	0.99058	1.00951	0.0047315	211.35	1.000045	0.99527	1.00475	0.0047540	46.5
47.0	0.0044668	223.87	50,119.	0.99111	1.00897	0.0044668	223.87	1.000040	0.99553	1.00449	0.0044869	47.0
48.0	0.0039811	251.19	63,096.	0.99207	1.00799	0.0039811	251.19	1.000032	0.99602	1.00400	0.0039970	48.0
49.0	0.0035481	281.84	79,433.	0.99293	1.00712	0.0035481	281.84	1.000025	0.99645	1.00356	0.0035607	49.0
50.0	0.0031623	316.23	100,000.	0.99370	1.00634	0.0031623	316.23	1.000020	0.99684	1.00317	0.0031723	50.0
51.0	0.0028184	354.81	125,890.	0.99438	1.00565	0.0028184	354.81	1.000016	0.99718	1.00283	0.0028264	51.0
52.0	0.0025119	398.11	158,490.	0.99499	1.00504	0.0025119	398.11	1.000013	0.99749	1.00252	0.0025182	52.0
54.0	0.0019953	501.19	251,190.	0.99602	1.00400	0.0019953	501.19	1.000008	0.99801	1.00200	0.0019992	54.0
55.0	0.0017783	564.34	316,230.	0.99645	1.00356	0.0017783	562.34	1.000006	0.99822	1.00178	0.0017815	55.0
56.0	0.0015849	630.96	398,110.	0.99684	1.00317	0.0015849	630.96	1.000005	0.99842	1.00159	0.0015874	56.0
57.0	0.0014125	707.95	501,190.	0.99718	1.00283	0.0014125	707.95	1.000004	0.99859	1.00141	0.0014145	57.0
58.0	0.0012589	794.33	630,960.	0.99749	1.00252	0.0012589	794.33	1.000003	0.99874	1.00126	0.0012605	58.0
60.0	0.0010000	1,000.0	10^6	0.99800	1.00200	0.0010000	1,000.0	1.000002	0.99900	1.00100	0.0010010	60.0
65.0	0.00056234	1,778.3	3.1623×10^6	0.99888	1.00112	0.00056234	1,778.3	1.000001	0.99944	1.00056	0.00056265	65.0
70.0	0.00031623	3,162.3	10^7	0.99937	1.00063	0.00031623	3,162.3	1.000000	0.99968	1.00032	0.00031633	70.0
75.0	0.00017783	5,623.4	3.1623×10^7	0.99964	1.00036	0.00017783	5,623.4	1.000000	0.99982	1.00018	0.00017786	75.0
80.0	0.00010000	10,000.	10^8	0.99980	1.00020	0.00010000	10,000.	1.000000	0.99990	1.00010	0.00010001	80.0
85.0	0.000056234	17,783.	3.1623×10^8	0.99989	1.00011	0.000056234	17,783.	1.000000	0.99994	1.00006	0.000056237	85.0
90.0	0.000031632	31,623.	10^9	0.99994	1.00006	0.000031623	31,623.	1.000000	0.99997	1.00003	0.000031624	90.0
95.0	0.000017783	56,234.	3.1623×10^9	0.99996	1.00004	0.000017783	56,234.	1.000000	0.99998	1.00002	0.000017783	95.0
100.0	0.000010000	10^5	10^{10}	0.99998	1.00002	0.000010000	10^5	1.000000	0.99999	1.00001	0.000010000	100.0

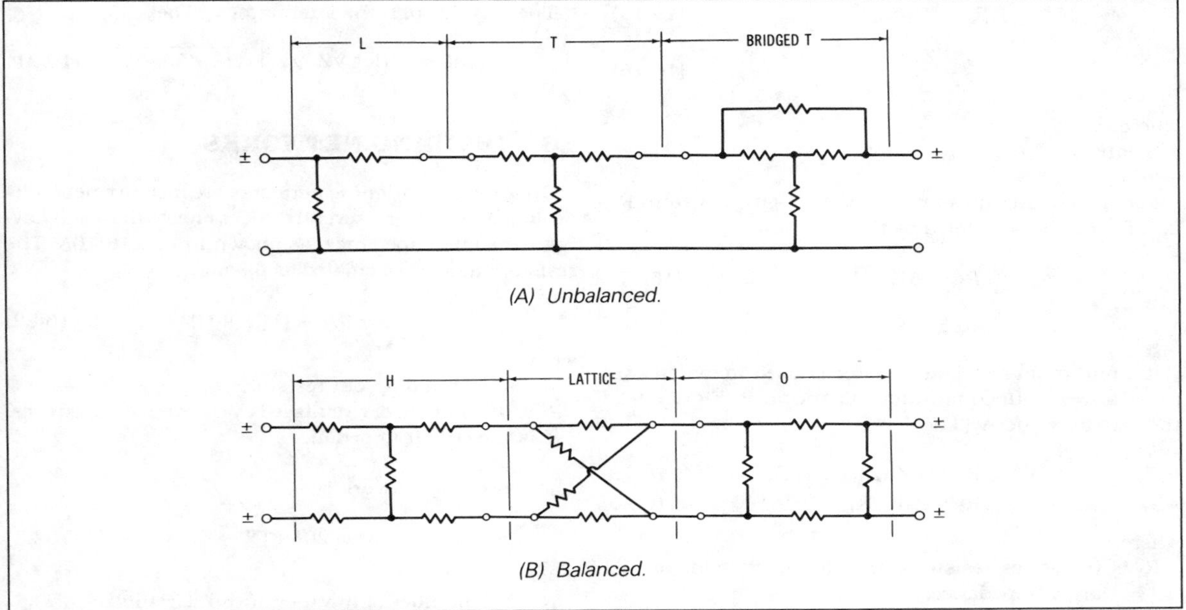

(A) Unbalanced.

(B) Balanced.

Figure 16-8 Attenuators connected in tandem.

connected to another, provided that the impedance match is satisfied and the configurations are of such nature that they will not cause an unbalanced condition. Fig. 16-8A shows how an L, a bridged-T, and a plain-T pad may be connected in tandem. Fig. 16-8B shows the method of connecting balanced attenuator configurations in tandem.

16.1 L PADS

L pads are the simplest form of attenuator and consist of two resistive elements connected in the form of an L, as shown in Fig. 16-9. This pad does not reflect the same impedance in both directions. An impedance match is afforded only in the direction of the arrow shown in the figures. If an L-type network is employed in a circuit that is sensitive to impedance match, the circuit characteristics may be affected. An L-type network should not be used, except where a minimum loss is required and a network of the T configuration will not serve because its minimum loss is too high.

For unequal impedances, the impedance match may be in the direction of the larger or the smaller impedance but not both.

The arrows in Fig. 16-9 indicate the direction of impedance match. If the network is designed to match the impedance in the direction of the series arm, the mismatch is toward the shunt arm. The mismatch increases with the increase of loss. At high values of attenuation, the value of the shunt resistor may become a fraction of an ohm, which can have a serious effect on the circuit to which it is connected.

The configuration for an L-type network operating between impedances of unequal value, Z_1 and Z_2, is shown in Fig. 16-9A. The impedance match is toward the larger of the two impedances, Z_1, and the values of the resistors are

$$R_1 = \frac{Z_1}{S}\left(\frac{KS - 1}{K}\right) \tag{16-11}$$

$$R_2 = \frac{Z_1}{S}\left(\frac{1}{K - S}\right) \tag{16-12}$$

where,

S equals $\sqrt{Z_1/Z_2}$

For a condition where the impedances are equal and the impedance match is in the direction of the arrows, as shown in Fig. 16-9B, the values of the resistors may be calculated by the equation

$$R_1 = Z[(K - 1)/K] \tag{16-13}$$

$$R_2 = Z[1/(K - 1)] \tag{16-14}$$

For a condition in which the impedances are unequal and the impedance match is toward the smaller of the two impedances, as shown in Fig. 16-9C, the values of the resistors are determined by the equation

$$R_1 = (Z_1/S)(K - S) \quad (16\text{-}15)$$

$$R_2 = \frac{Z_1}{S}\left(\frac{K}{KS - 1}\right) \quad (16\text{-}16)$$

where,
S equals $\sqrt{Z_1/Z_2}$.

For the conditions shown in Fig. 16-9D, resistors R_1 and R_2 may be calculated by the equation

$$R_1 = Z(K - 1) \quad (16\text{-}17)$$

$$R_2 = Z[K/(K - 1)] \quad (16\text{-}18)$$

If a minimum-loss L attenuator is used to match two impedances of unequal value, as shown in Fig. 16-9A, the resistor values will be

$$R_1 = \sqrt{Z_1(Z_1 - Z_2)} \quad (16\text{-}19)$$

$$R_2 = Z_1Z_2/R_1 \quad (16\text{-}20)$$

where,
R_1 is the series resistor connected in the side of the larger impedance,
R_2 is the shunt resistor.

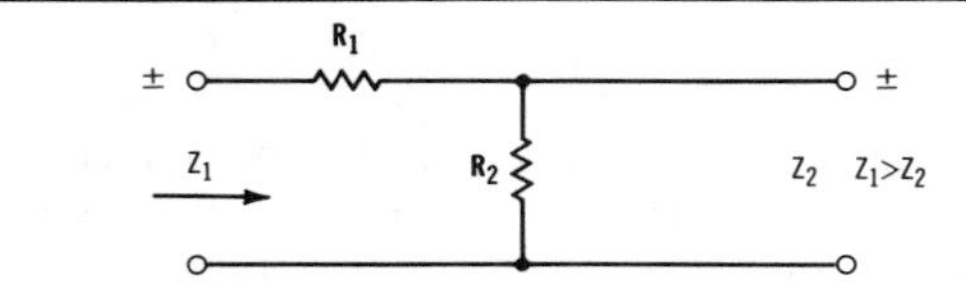

(A) Between impedances of unequal value.

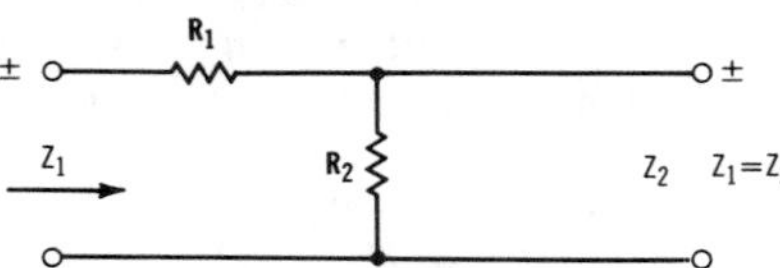

(B) Between impedances of equal value.

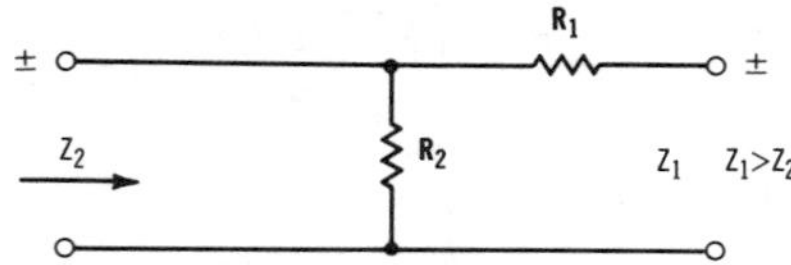

(C) Impedances unequal and impedance match is toward the smaller of the two.

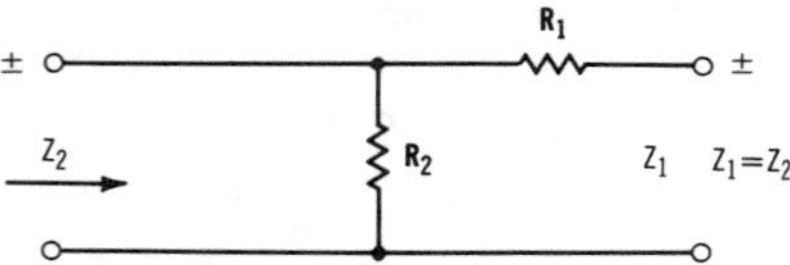

(D) Between impedances of equal value in the direction of the shunt arm.

Figure 16-9 Configurations of L-type networks.

The loss through the attenuator will be

$$dB = 20 \log \sqrt{Z_1/Z_2} + \sqrt{(Z_1/Z_2) - 1} \quad (16\text{-}21)$$

16.2 DIVIDING NETWORKS

Dividing or *combining networks* are resistive networks designed to combine several devices or circuits, each having the same impedance, as shown in Fig. 16-10A. The resistors may be calculated as follows:

$$R_B = [(N - 1)/(N + 1)]Z \quad (16\text{-}22)$$

where,
R_B is the building-out resistor,
N is the number of circuits fed by the source impedance,
Z is the circuit impedance.

The loss of the network is

$$dB = 20 \log (N - 1) \quad (16\text{-}23)$$

where,
N is the number of input or output circuits.

Unused circuits of a dividing or combining network must be terminated in a resistive load equal to the normal load impedance.

This same circuit can be reversed and used as a combining network.

Combining or branching networks may also be designed as a series configuration, as shown in Fig. 16-10B. For equal impedances the equation is

$$R_1 = [(N + 1)/(N - 1)]Z \quad (16\text{-}24)$$

where,
R_1 is the terminating resistor,
N is the number of branch circuits.

The insertion loss may be calculated

$$dB = 20 \log (N) \quad (16\text{-}25)$$

where,
N is the number of branch circuits.

A series configuration can only be used in an ungrounded circuit. The insertion loss of a combining network may be avoided by the use of an active combining network.

16.3 T ATTENUATORS

A T-type attenuator is a network consisting of three resistors connected in the form of a T as shown in Fig. 16-1. The network may be designed to supply an impedance match between circuits of equal or unequal impedance. When designed for use between circuits of unequal impedance, it is often referred to as a *taper pad*.

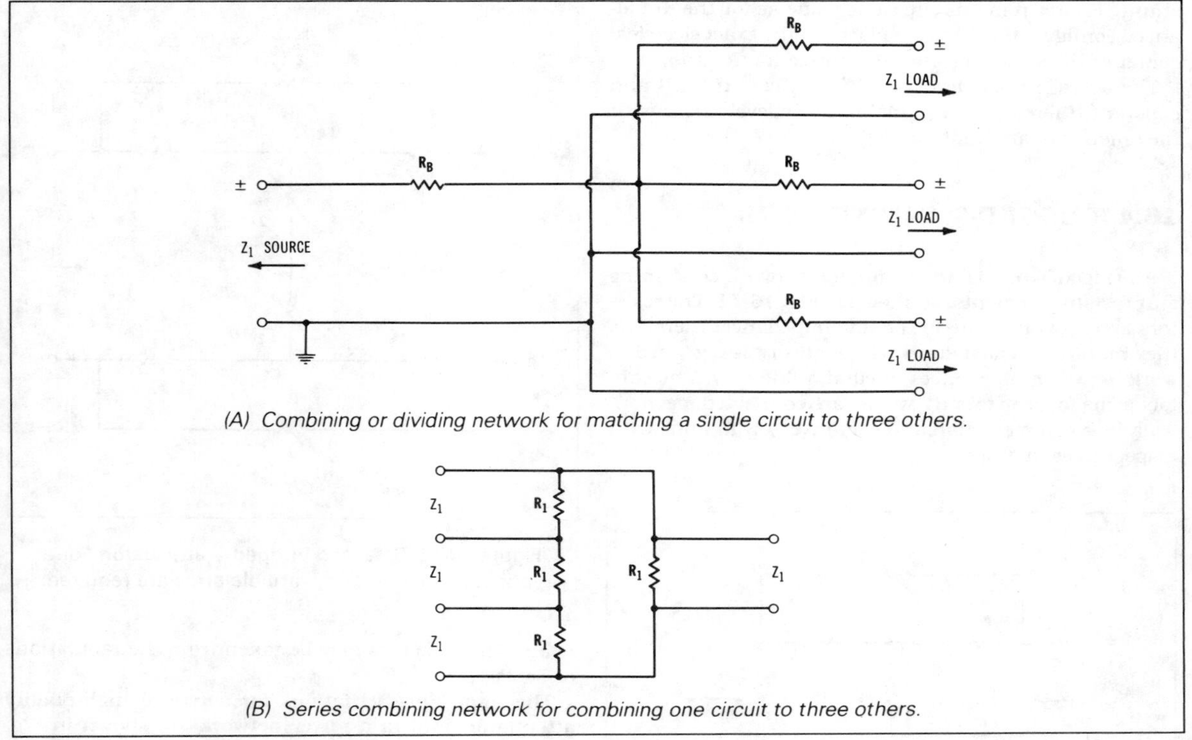

(A) Combining or dividing network for matching a single circuit to three others.

(B) Series combining network for combining one circuit to three others.

Figure 16-10 Two configurations for designing combining or branching networks.

If a T pad is to work between equal impedances, the resistor values will be

$$R_1 = R_2 = [(K - 1)/(K + 1)]Z \quad (16\text{-}26)$$

$$R_3 = [K/(K^2 - 1)]2Z \quad (16\text{-}27)$$

where,

Z is the input and output impedance,
R_1 and R_2 are the series resistors,
R_3 is the shunt arm or resistor.

A T-type attenuator may be designed for any value of loss if designed to operate between equal impedances. The numerical value of the foregoing expressions may be obtained from Table 16-1.

The resistors for a T pad of unequal impedances are calculated with the following equations:

$$R_1 = Z_1\left(\frac{K^2 + 1}{K^2 - 1}\right) - 2\sqrt{Z_1Z_2}\left(\frac{K}{K^2 - 1}\right) \quad (16\text{-}28)$$

$$R_2 = Z_2\left(\frac{K^2 + 1}{K^2 - 1}\right) - 2\sqrt{Z_1Z_2}\left(\frac{K}{K^2 - 1}\right) \quad (16\text{-}29)$$

$$R_3 = 2\sqrt{Z_1Z_2}\left(\frac{K}{K^2 - 1}\right) \quad (16\text{-}30)$$

where,

Z_1 is the larger of the two impedances.

The numerical values for these expressions may be taken from Table 16-1. Thus, for a network to match 600 Ω to a circuit of 250 Ω with a loss of 20 dB, the resistor values are

$$R_1 = 600(1.0202) - 2(\sqrt{150{,}000})(0.10101)$$
$$= 612.1 - 2(387.3)(0.10101)$$
$$= 533.88\ \Omega$$

$$R_2 = 250(1.0202) - 2(\sqrt{150{,}000})(0.10101)$$
$$= 255.05 - 2(387.3)(0.10101)$$
$$= 176.81\ \Omega$$

$$R_3 = 2(\sqrt{150{,}000})(0.10101)$$
$$= 2(387.3)(0.10101)$$
$$= 78.7\ \Omega$$

A balanced-T pad is called an H pad. The pad is first calculated as an unbalanced-T configuration. The series resistance elements are then divided, and half are connected in each side of the line, as shown in Fig. 16-2. The shunt resistor remains the same value as for the unbalanced configuration. A tap is placed at the exact electrical center of the shunt resistor for connection to ground.

The average noise level for a T pad is −100 dB and constant; therefore, the signal-to-noise level varies with the amount of attenuation.

16.4 BRIDGED-T ATTENUATORS

A bridged-T pad is an attenuator network containing four resistive elements, as shown in Fig. 16-11. The resistors are equal in value to the line impedance; therefore, they require no calculation. This network is designed to work between impedances of equal value only. The contact arms for resistors R_5 and R_6 are connected mechanically by a common shaft and vary inversely in value with respect to each other.

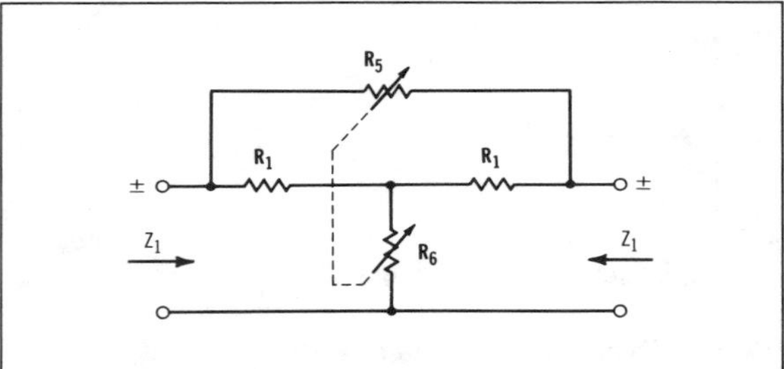

Figure 16-11 A bridged-T attenuator. For variable pads, the arms R_5 and R_6 are variable.

A balanced bridged-T attenuator is a configuration similar to the unbalanced bridged-T attenuator, except the resistor elements are divided and placed in each side of the line as shown in Fig. 16-12. The principal objection to the use of this configuration, if made variable, is that the shunt resistor R_6 must be divided into two separate arms to provide a ground connection at the exact electrical center. However, if the circuit feeding or terminating the attenuator is balanced to the ground, the ground connection at the attenuator center will not be required.

The resistor values are calculated with the following formulas:

$$R_1 = Z \tag{16-31}$$

$$R_5 = (K - 1)Z \tag{16-32}$$

$$R_6 = [1/(K - 1)]Z \tag{16-33}$$

where,

Z is the line impedance,
R_5 is the bridging resistor,
R_6 is the shunt resistor.

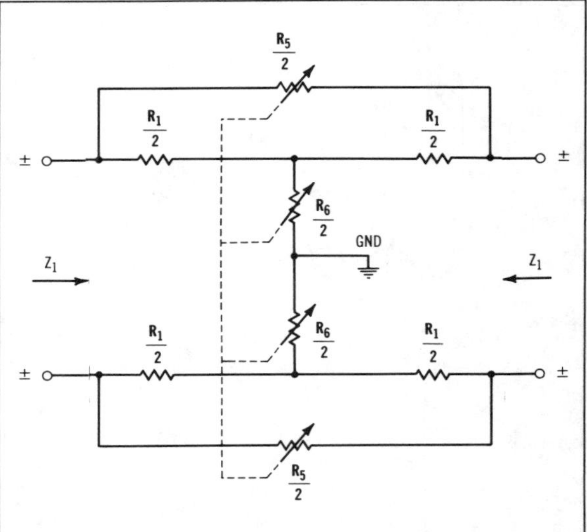

Figure 16-12 Balanced bridged-T attenuator. For a variable configuration, variable arms are required.

Again, the K factors may be taken from the tabulations of Table 16-1.

The impedance variations for a typical high-quality attenuator used in a mixer network are shown in Fig. 16-13. The greatest impedance variation occurs as the attenuator arm approaches zero attenuation and amounts to about 80 Ω. This impedance variation is not too serious, since the mixer-combining network with its building-out resistors isolates this variation to a great extent from associated attenuators.

16.5 PI ATTENUATORS

A pi (or delta) attenuator is a resistive network resembling the Greek letter pi, or delta, as shown in Fig. 16-14. Such networks may be used between impedances of equal or unequal values.

For networks operating between impedances of equal value,

$$R_1 = Z[(K + 1)/(K - 1)] \tag{16-34}$$

$$R_2 = \left(\frac{Z}{2}\right)\left(\frac{K^2 - 1}{K}\right) \tag{16-35}$$

where,

R_1 is the input and output resistor,
R_2 is the series resistor,
Z is the input and output impedance.

When the impedances are unequal values, the resistors are calculated with the following equations:

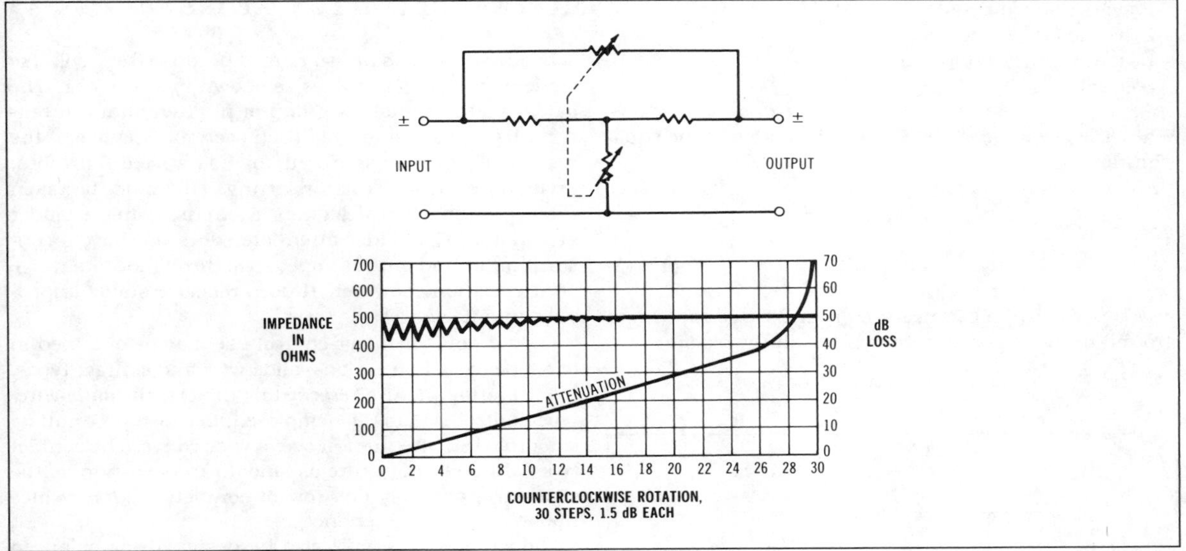

Figure 16-13 Impedance characteristics for a high-quality variable bridged-T attenuator.

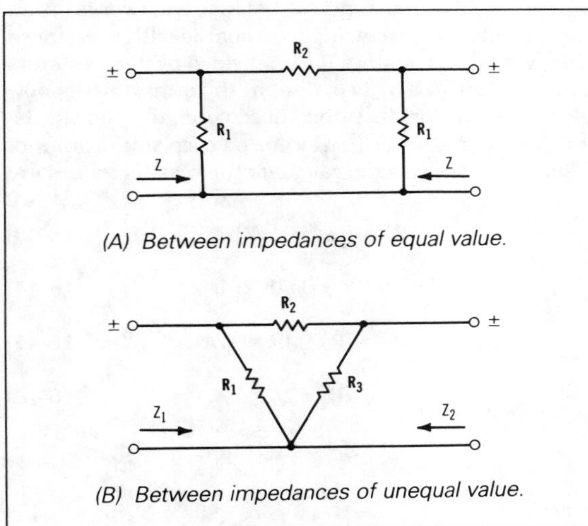

Figure 16-14 Pi-type or delta-type attenuator.

$$R_1 = Z_1\left(\frac{K^2 - 1}{K^2 - 2KS + 1}\right) \quad (16\text{-}36)$$

$$R_2 = \left(\frac{\sqrt{Z_1/Z_2}}{2}\right)\left(\frac{K^2 - 1}{K}\right) \quad (16\text{-}37)$$

$$R_3 = Z_2\left(\frac{K^2 - 1}{K^2 - 2(K/S) + 1}\right) \quad (16\text{-}38)$$

where,

R_1 and R_3 are shunt resistors,
R_2 is the series resistor,
Z_1 is the input impedance,
Z_2 is the output impedance,
S is Z_1/Z_2.

To simplify the calculations, the values of the factors may be selected from Table 16-1.

An O attenuator is a balanced pi attenuator configuration. The circuit element values may be obtained by first calculating for a pi-type configuration, then dividing the series resistor and placing half in each side of the line as shown in Fig. 16-15. The shunt resistors remain the same value.

16.6 U ATTENUATORS

U attenuators (Fig. 16-16) may be of a symmetrical or balanced-type configuration and are useful for matching a high impedance to a low impedance. The impedance match is of first importance, the loss being secondary. For a symmetrical configuration to work between unequal impedances when the impedance match of Z_1 is important, the resistors may be calculated as follows:

$$R_1 = (Z_1/2S)[(KS - 1)/K] \quad (16\text{-}39)$$

$$R_2 = (Z_1/S)[1/(K - S)] \quad (16\text{-}40)$$

where,

R_1 is the series resistor,

R_2 is the shunt resistor,
Z_1 is the larger impedance,
Z_2 is the smaller impedance,
S equals $\sqrt{Z_1/Z_2}$.

When the low impedance, Z_2, is to be matched the equations are

$$R_1 = (Z_1/2S)(K - S) \quad (16\text{-}41)$$

$$R_2 = (Z_1/S)[K/(KS - 1)] \quad (16\text{-}42)$$

Any U pad may be balanced to ground by connecting a ground to the electrical center of the shunt resistor.

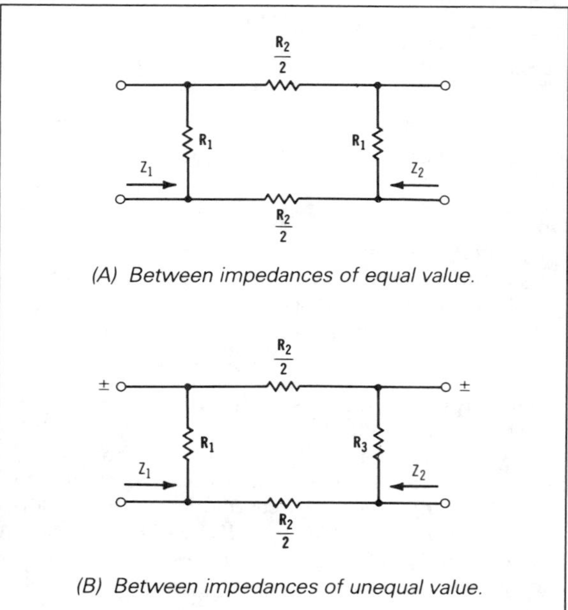

(A) Between impedances of equal value.

(B) Between impedances of unequal value.

Figure 16-15 Balanced pi-type or O-type attenuator.

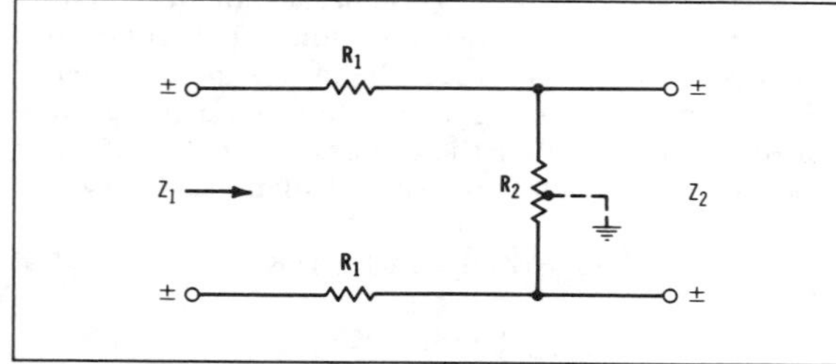

Figure 16-16 A U-pad configuration for operation between impedances of unequal value.

16.7 LADDER ATTENUATORS

Ladder-type pads are so named because they look like ladders lying on their sides as shown in Fig. 16-17. The ladder pad is actually a group of pi attenuators in tandem, R_2 being common to each section. Because of the resistor R_4, this type attenuator has a fixed 6-dB loss, exclusive of the attenuator setting. This must be taken into account when designing a circuit using a ladder attenuator. The ladder attenuator does not have a constant input and output impedance throughout its range of attenuation; however, it does reflect a stable impedance into its source.

Ladder pots for mixer-control use may be obtained in two types of construction—slide-wire and contact types.

For motion-picture rerecording mixers, the slide-wire-type control is generally employed, because it permits a smooth, even attenuation over a wide range. The contact type, although not quite as smooth in operation as the slide-wire, has only one row of contacts, which reduce the noise and maintenance.

Ladder networks may also be designed for balanced operation. This is accomplished by connecting two unbalanced networks side by side, as shown in Fig. 16-18. However, the circuit elements are not divided in the same manner as for other types of balanced networks. If an unbalanced ladder network is compared with a balanced ladder network, resistors R_1 are divided by two, resistors R_4 are also divided by two, and, at the output, R_2 is now *twice* the value for the unbalanced configuration. Resistor R_3 remains at its original value on each side of ground.

The equations used to calculate the resistor values are

$$R_1 = [(K^2 - 1)/2K]Z \quad (16\text{-}43)$$

$$R_2 = [(K + 1)/(K - 1)]Z \quad (16\text{-}44)$$

$$R_3 = (R_2Z)/(R_2 + Z) \quad (16\text{-}45)$$

$$R_4 = Z/2 \quad (16\text{-}46)$$

$$Z_{in} = Z_{out}$$

where,
R_1 is the series resistance,
R_2 is the shunt resistance,
R_3 is the input shunt resistor,
R_4 is the series resistance in the contact arm circuit.

The value of K is dependent on the loss per step—not the total loss.

The noise level for a ladder attenuator is in the order of −120 dB, and as the attenuation increases, the signal-to-noise ratio increases. This type attenuator will show impedance variations at both the input and output and between steps. However, when used in a combining network with the proper building-out resistors, these

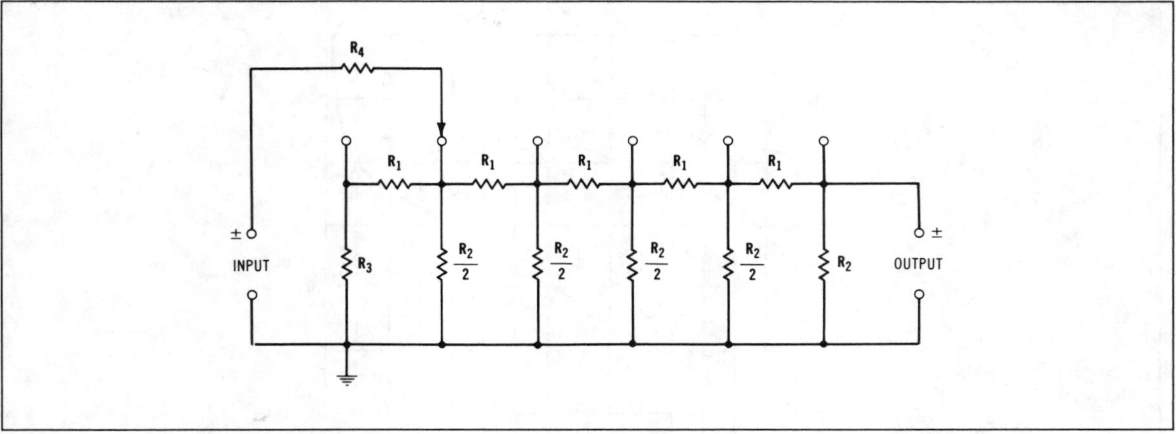

Figure 16-17 Unbalanced ladder attenuator with five fixed steps of loss.

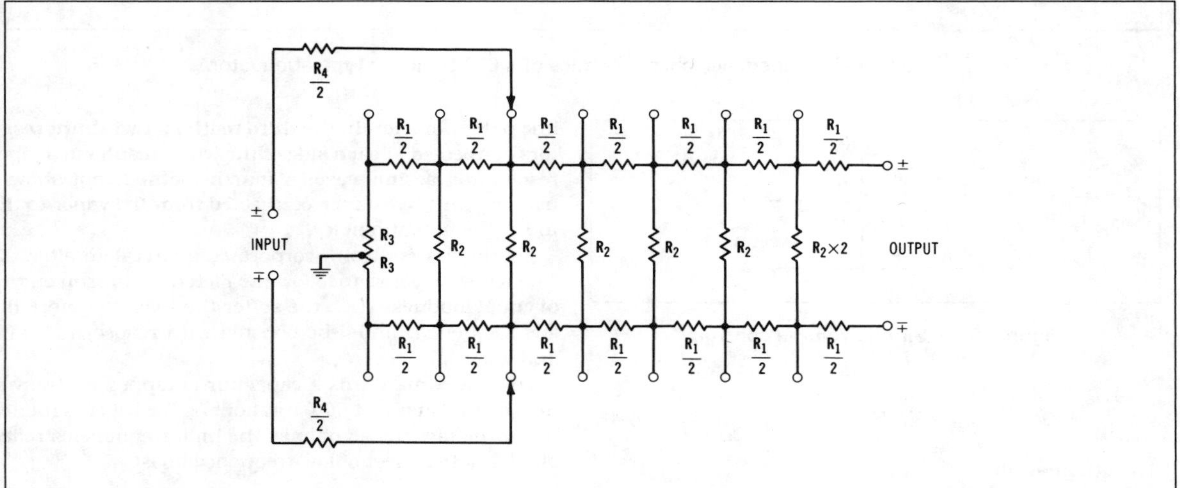

Figure 16-18 Balanced ladder attenuator.

variations are of little consequence. A typical impedance curve is shown in Fig. 16-19.

16.8 SIMPLE VOLUME AND LOUDNESS CONTROLS

A simple volume control consists of a potentiometer with the two ends connected to the source and the wiper, and one end connected to the load, as shown in Fig. 16-20. The volume control should be a high impedance with respect to the source so it will not load it, and the load impedance should be high enough so as not to affect the control.

The output voltage is calculated with the following equation:

$$V_{out} = \left(\frac{\dfrac{R_1 Z_2}{R_2 + Z_2}}{R_1 + \dfrac{R_2 Z_2}{R_2 + Z_2}} \right) \tag{16-47}$$

where,

R_1 is the upper section of control,
R_2 is the lower section of control.

If the load impedance is high compared to R_2, the equation is simplified to

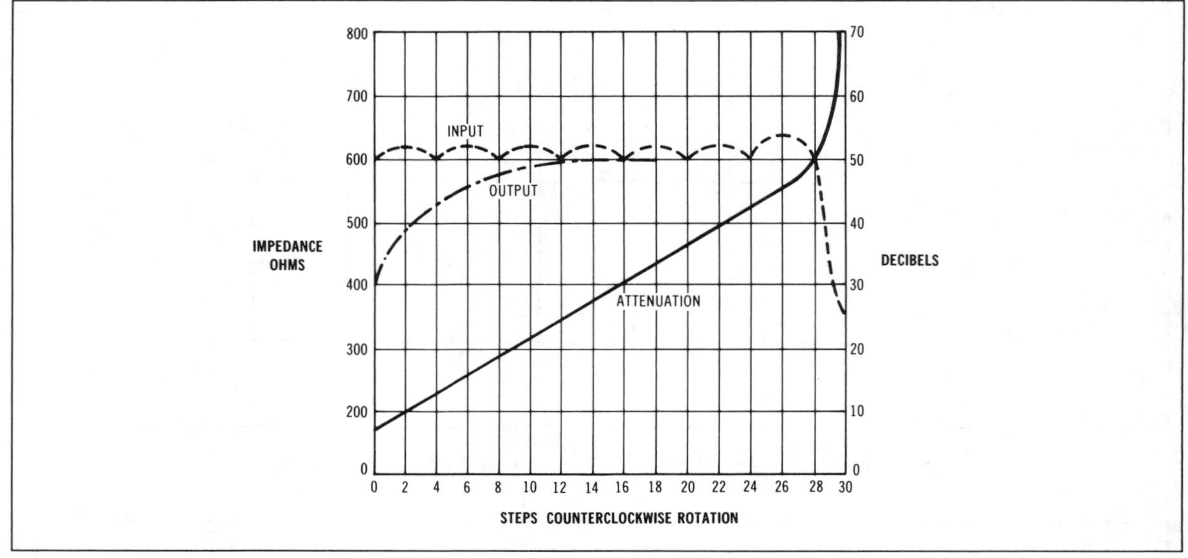

Figure 16-19 Impedance characteristics of a 600-Ω ladder-type attenuator.

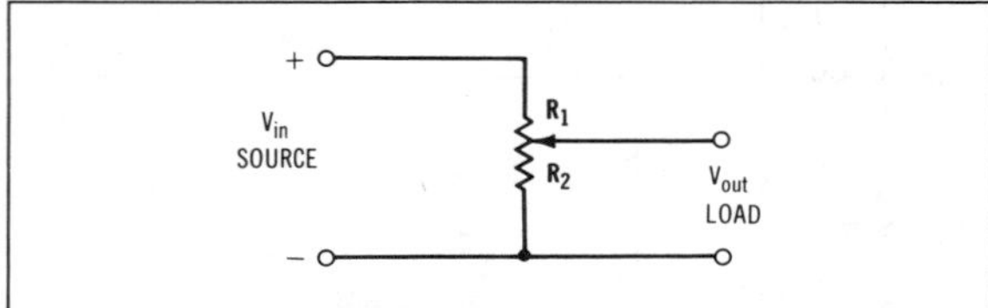

Figure 16-20 Simple volume control.

$$V_{out} = V_{in}[R_2/(R_1 + R_2)] \tag{16-48}$$

The attenuation is

$$dB = 10 \log 4 \left[\frac{\left(R_1 + \dfrac{R_2 Z_2}{R_2 + Z_2} \right)^2}{Z_1 Z_2} \right] \tag{16-49}$$

Normally, volume controls have a logarithmic taper, so the first 50% of the pot only represents a change of 7 to 8%, following the sensitivity of the ear.

If a special taper is required, a linear pot can be altered to change its characteristics by the shunting of a fixed resistance from one end of the resistance to the wiper. Three methods of shunting a straight-line potentiometer are shown in Fig. 16-21. In the first method, the shunt resistor is connected from the wiper to the ground. With the correct value shunt resistance, the potentiometer will have a taper relative to the angular rotation, as shown below the schematic diagram. The second method makes use of a second potentiometer ganged with the straight-line potentiometer. In the third method, two shunt resistors connected at each side of the wiper results in a taper resembling a sine wave. A fourth method, not shown, uses a shunt resistance connected from the wiper to the top of the potentiometer.

A loudness control incorporates a circuit to alter the frequency response to follow the Fletcher-Munson curves of equal loudness (i.e., the softer the level, the more the low frequencies must be boosted with respect to 1 kHz and above).

To approximate this a capacitor is tapped off the volume control at about 50% rotation. As the wiper is rotated below the tap, the signal has the high frequencies rolled off giving the effect of low-frequency boost.

16.9 LIGHT-DEPENDENT ATTENUATORS

In a light-dependent attenuator the attenuation is controlled by varying the intensity of a light source on a *light-dependent resistor (LDR)* (cadmium sulfide cell). Light-sensitive attenuators eliminate problems with noisy potentiometers as the potentiometers operate the lamp circuit. This type of circuit is also very useful for remote control as the remote control line carries lamp control voltage.

A simple volume control can be seen in Fig. 16-22. R and LDR form an attenuator. When the light source is bright, the resistance of the LDR is low; therefore, most of the signal is dropped across R. When the light intensity is decreased, the resistance of LDR increases, and more signal appears across the LDR. This circuit has constantly varying impedances.

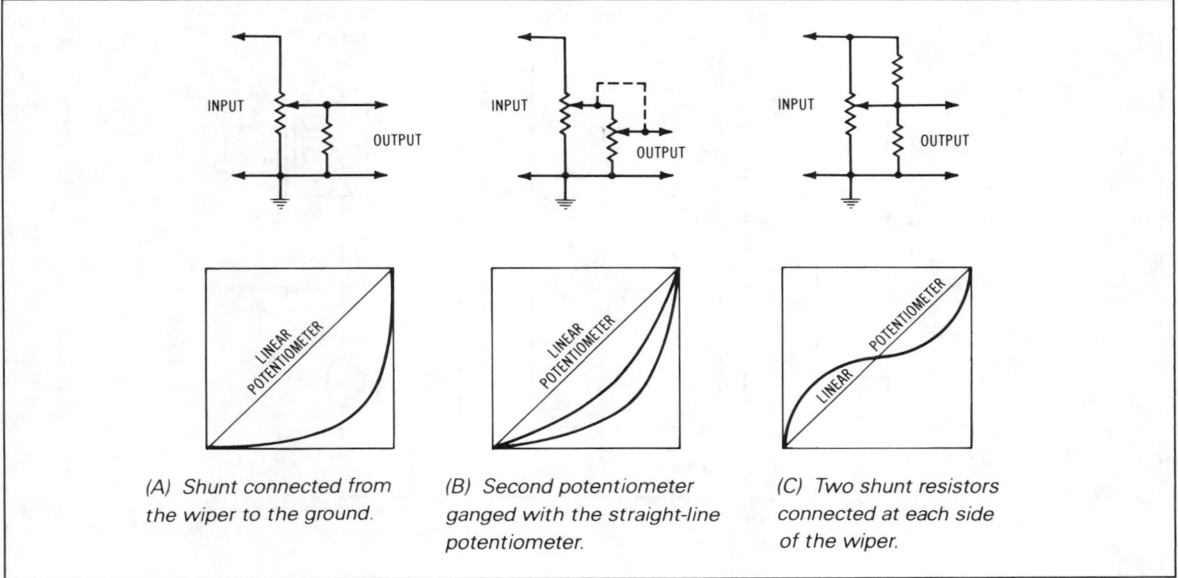

(A) Shunt connected from the wiper to the ground.

(B) Second potentiometer ganged with the straight-line potentiometer.

(C) Two shunt resistors connected at each side of the wiper.

Figure 16-21 Method of varying the response of a plain potentiometer.

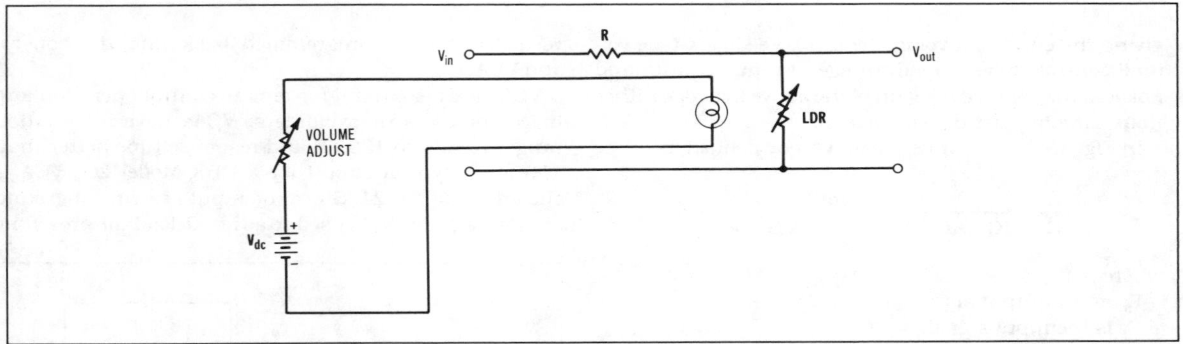

Figure 16-22 Volume control using a light-dependent resistor.

A constant-impedance attenuator would require more LDRs and light sources to approximate a constant-impedance type of attenuator.

The advantages of a light-dependent attenuator are:

1. No wiper noise,
2. Easy to connect one control to many attenuators,
3. Controls can be remoted from the attenuator.

The disadvantages are:

1. Lamp burnout or aging,
2. Slow response time.

16.10 FEEDBACK-TYPE VOLUME CONTROL

In a feedback-type volume control, attenuation is controlled by the amount of feedback in the circuit. Gain of a closed-loop circuit is

$$A_c = A_o/(1 + \beta A_o) \qquad (16\text{-}50)$$

where,

A_c is the closed-loop gain,
A_o is the open-loop gain,
β is the feedback factor.

By varying β, the amplifier gain can be changed, hence,

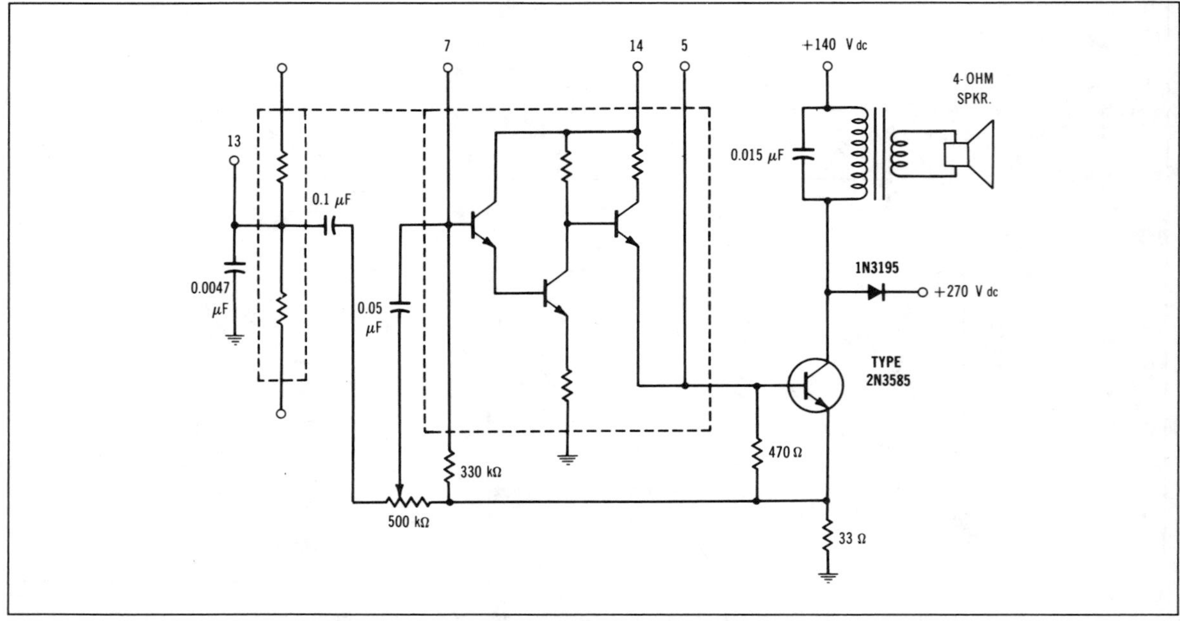

Figure 16-23 Feedback-type volume control. *(Courtesy Radio Corporation of America)*

giving the effect of a volume control. Feedback-type volume controls have the advantage of reduced hum and noise as they reduce the gain of the active network rather than reducing just the signal level.

In Fig. 16-23, the system gain can be defined as

$$\frac{E_o}{E_s} = \frac{G_s(1 - gm/G_f)}{(G_s + G_I)(1 + G_L/G_f) + G_m + G_L}$$

where,

E_o is the output signal,

E_s is the input signal,

G_s, G_f, G_I, G_L are the conductances of the source, feedback, input, and load resistance.

At maximum gain, the expression reduces to

$$E_o/E_s = (R_L - gmR_fR_L)/(R_L + R_f)$$

A feedback volume control using an RCA CA3042 integrated-circuit unit is shown in Fig. 16-23.

16.11 VOLTAGE-CONTROLLED AMPLIFIERS

A voltage-controlled amplifier is used as an attenuator by varying a dc control voltage. *Voltage-controlled amplifiers (VCA)* are often used for automatic mixing since the control voltage can be stored in analog form or in digital form. Upon command through a digital-to-analog converter, it can be programmed back into the console and VCA.

VCAs are also useful for remote-control operation and in compressors or expanders. VCAs have attenuation ranges from 0 to 130 dB and response time better than 100 μs. A typical circuit for a DBX Model 202 VCA is shown in Fig. 16-24. Since the input is a virtual-ground summing point, R_1 is used so as not to load the preceding

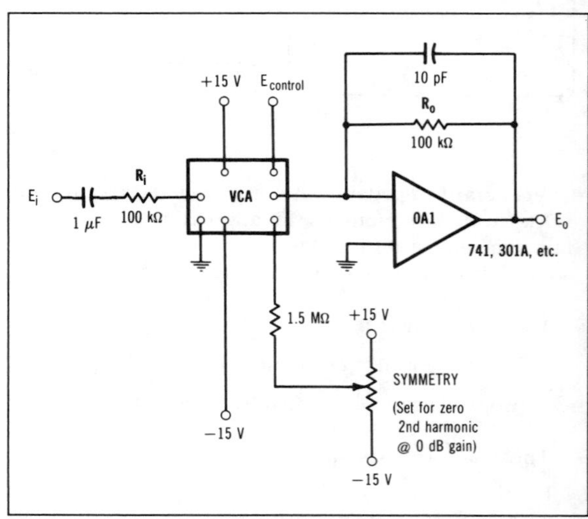

Figure 16-24 Voltage-controlled amplifier volume control.

circuit. The output circuit must feed a virtual ground so an operational amplifier current-to-voltage converter (any operational amplifier with a resistor from output to inverting input and with the noninverting input grounded) must be used. The DBX 202 can be used with a linear taper potentiometer to give a linear decibel control characteristic.

16.12 FIELD-EFFECT TRANSISTOR ATTENUATORS

An *FET attenuator* is one where an FET (field-effect transistor) is used to control gain. Field-effect transistors have characteristics much like a tube, that is, high input impedance and moderate output impedance. In its simplest form, the FET is used as the lower leg of a voltage divider, as shown in Fig. 16-25A.

The voltage out is

$$V_{out} = V_{in}\, r_{DS}\,(on) + V_{out}\,(max)$$

$$= V_{in}/[R + r_{DS}\,(on)]$$

where,

r_{DS} is the resistance of the source to drain.

To improve distortion and linearity, feedback is required around the FET, as shown in Fig. 16-25B.

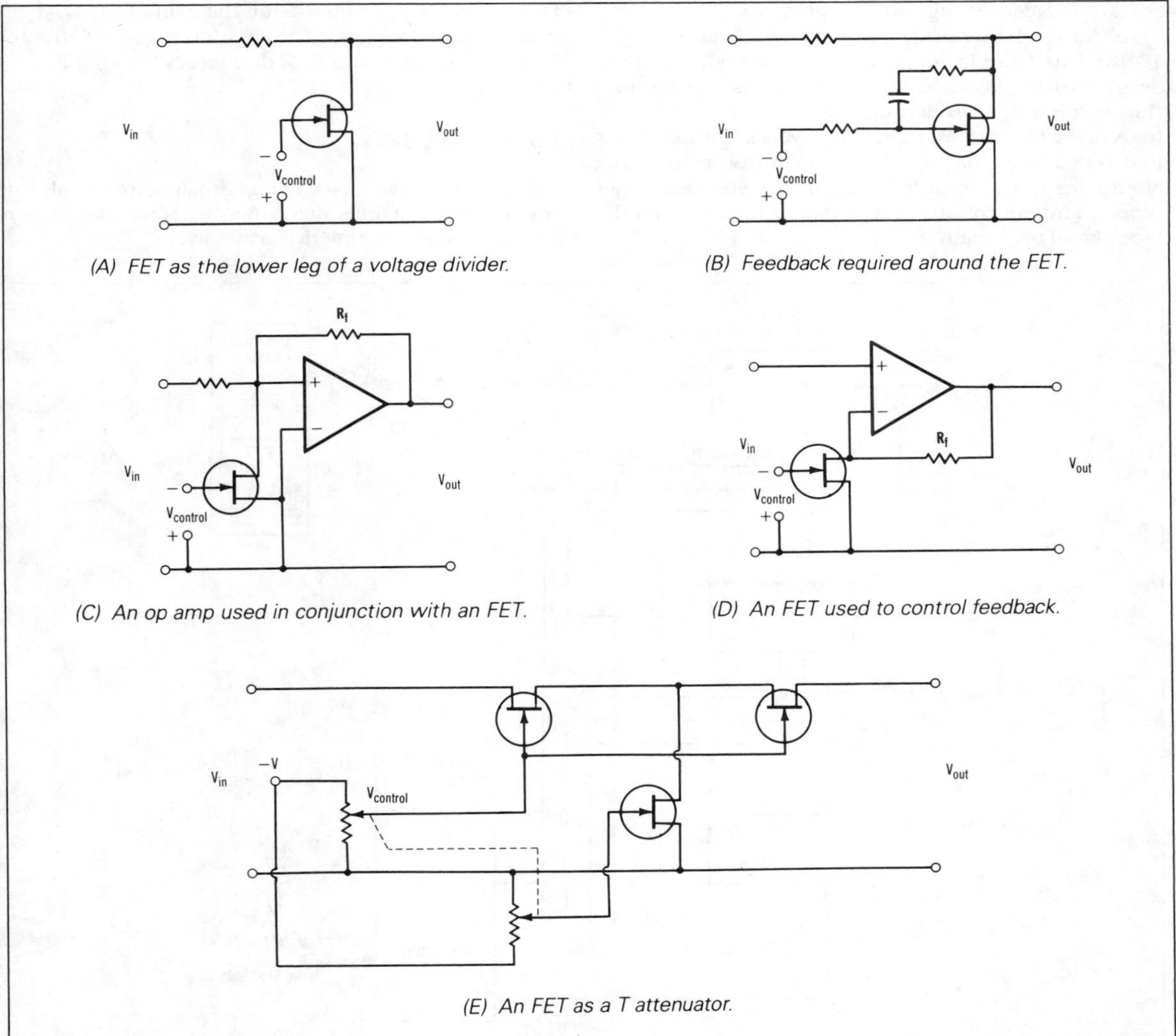

(A) FET as the lower leg of a voltage divider.

(B) Feedback required around the FET.

(C) An op amp used in conjunction with an FET.

(D) An FET used to control feedback.

(E) An FET as a T attenuator.

Figure 16-25 FET attenuators.

If a low-output impedance is required, an op amp can be used in conjunction with the FET (Fig. 16-25C). In this circuit, the op-amp is used to match impedances. The FET can also be used to control feedback (Fig. 16-25D). The gain in this circuit is $AV = 1 + R_F/r_{DS}$. When r_{DS} is minimum, gain is maximum as most of the feedback is shorted to ground.

The FET can also be used as a T attenuator. This provides optimum dynamic linear range attenuation and tends to hold the impedances more even (Fig. 16-25E).

16.13 AUTOMATED FADERS

In an *automated fader*, the fade control can be programmed into a date storage device (tape) and used to adjust the fader settings during mixdown.

The method operates in the following manner (Fig. 16-26). The fader is adjusted manually, and, when the desired setting is made, a write voltage is injected into the programmer (encoder) that supplies data to the data track of the tape recorder. During playback, the data track is decoded and, through the read control, adjusts the attenuator to the recorded level. If the mixdown is not proper, any control can be adjusted or updated and the tape played over again.

16.14 AUTOMATIC ATTENUATORS

In an *automatic attenuator*, the attenuation varies automatically between two points, usually off and a prescribed setting. Automatic attenuators are often voice operated but can be manually operated. They are used to automatically turn off unused inputs, as a "Ducker" and gating.

A Shure Model M625 Voicegate is an automatic attenuator. The circuit is illustrated in Fig. 16-27 (pages 566 and 567) and operates in the following manner. The audio signal arrives through the microphone connector J_1, through Q_{101} and Q_{102}, and out the microphone connector J_2. R_{106}–R_{108} sets the gain of the off threshold.

The signal also goes to an amplifier-filter consisting of Q_{103}–Q_{112}. The filtered signal is then rectified by D_{102}. This turns on Q_{116}, increasing the gain of the Q_{101} circuit, passing the signal. The circuit remains on after the signal has ceased until C_{122} discharges through R_{3B}.

16.15 MIXERS

A *mixer* is a device used to mix two or more signals into one composite signal. Mixers may be adjustable or nonadjustable and either active or passive.

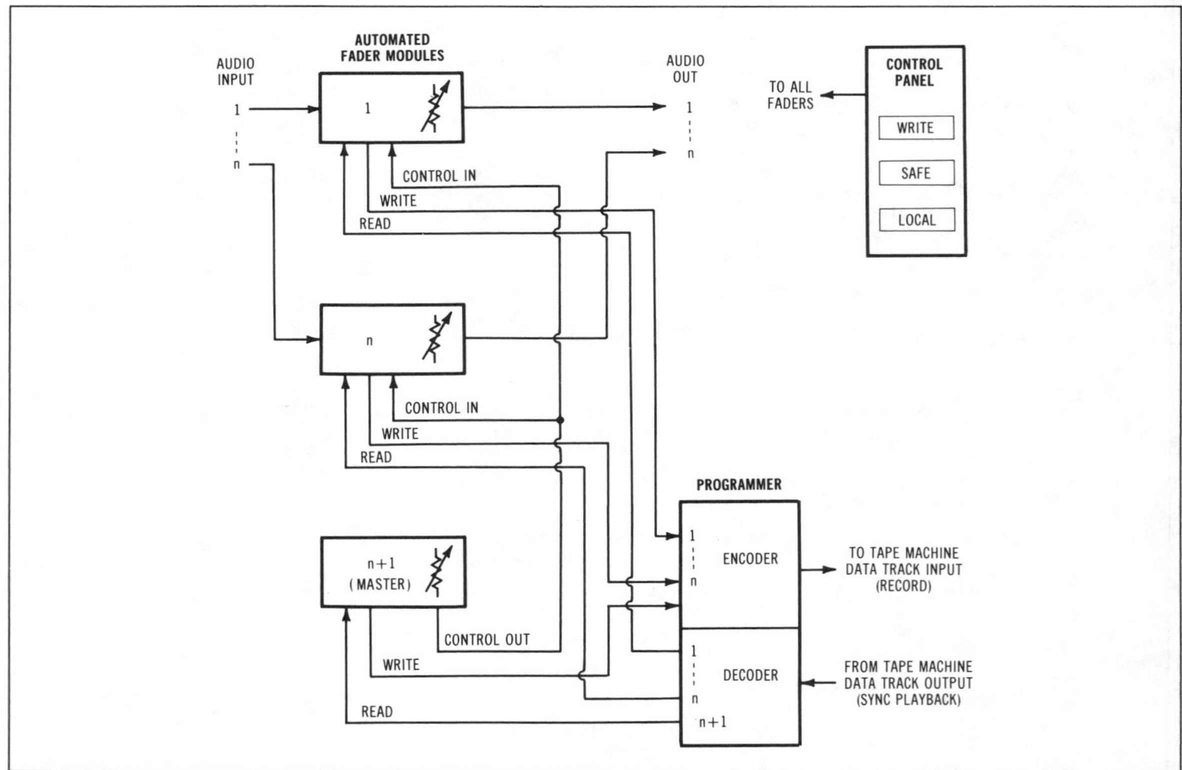

Figure 16-26 Functional block diagram of an automated fader.

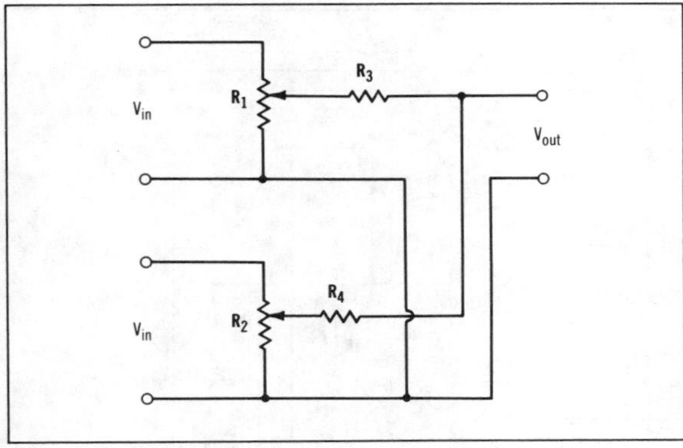

Figure 16-28 Passive mixer circuit.

A *passive* mixer uses only passive devices (i.e., resistors and potentiometers), as shown in Fig. 16-28.

The main disadvantage of passive mixing is that an amplifier is required after mixing to boost the gain back to the level at the input of the mixer. As the attenuator controls are lowered, the signal on the mixing bus is reduced; however, the mixing bus noise remains the same, so the signal-to-noise ratio is reduced.

In Fig. 16-29A the input of −125 dBm is not attenuated; therefore, the signal out of the booster amplifier is −73 dBm, while the noise is −92 dBm. Thus, the signal is 19 dB above the noise.

In Fig. 16-29B the input of −125 dBm is attenuated 20 dB in the mixer so the signal out of the booster amplifier is −93 dBm, while the noise remained −92 dBm. Thus, the signal is 1 dBm less than the noise.

An active mixer is one that uses operational amplifiers or some other active device along with resistors and/or potentiometers to control gain or attenuation.

A unity-gain current-summing amplifier using an op amp is a standard active mixer. The mixer is usually designed for an input impedance of about 5 kΩ to 10 kΩ, an output impedance of less than 200 Ω and a gain of 0 to 50. A typical active mixer is shown in Fig. 16-30.

In unity-gain current-summing amplifiers feedback to the minus or inverting input presents an extremely low apparent input impedance or virtual ground on the inverting input.

The positive input is also essentially ground since the current through R_N will only produce about a half millivolt. While the positive input can be grounded, it is better to make the R_N a value about the same as the parallel combination of $R_1 + R_2 + R_F$ to reduce offset voltage.

Any small, positive-going input applied to the left end of R_1 is amplified by the high-gain op amp and drives the output negative since the input signal is on the inverting

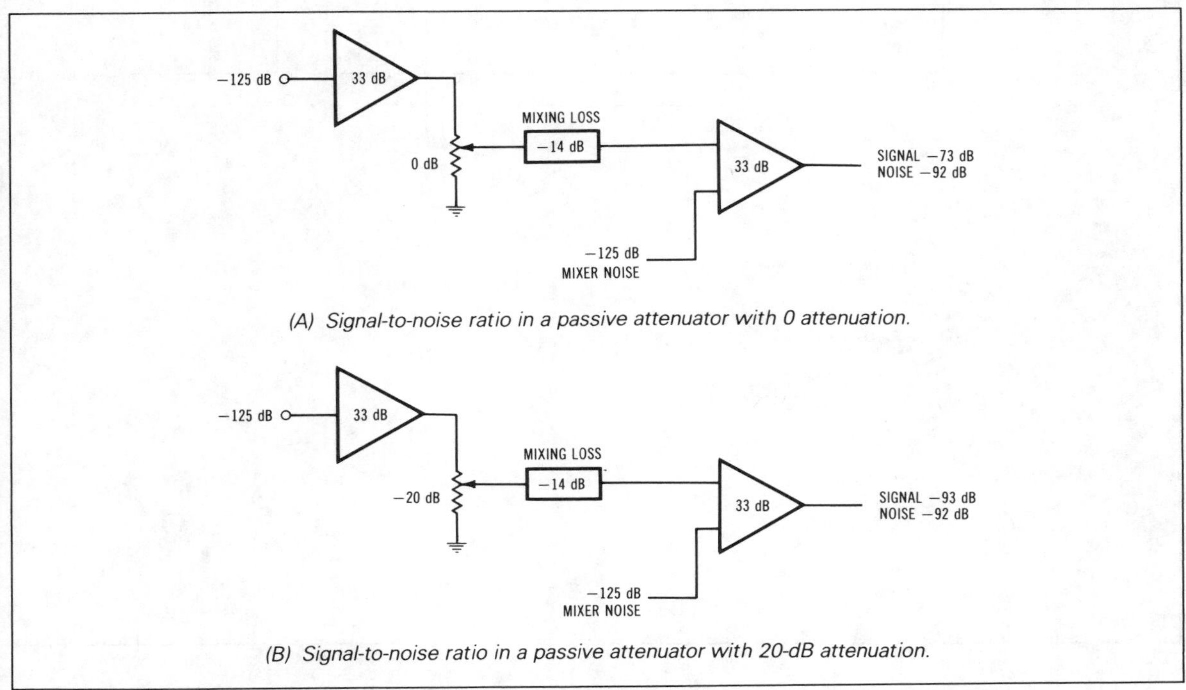

(A) Signal-to-noise ratio in a passive attenuator with 0 attenuation.

(B) Signal-to-noise ratio in a passive attenuator with 20-dB attenuation.

Figure 16-29 Passive-type mixer.

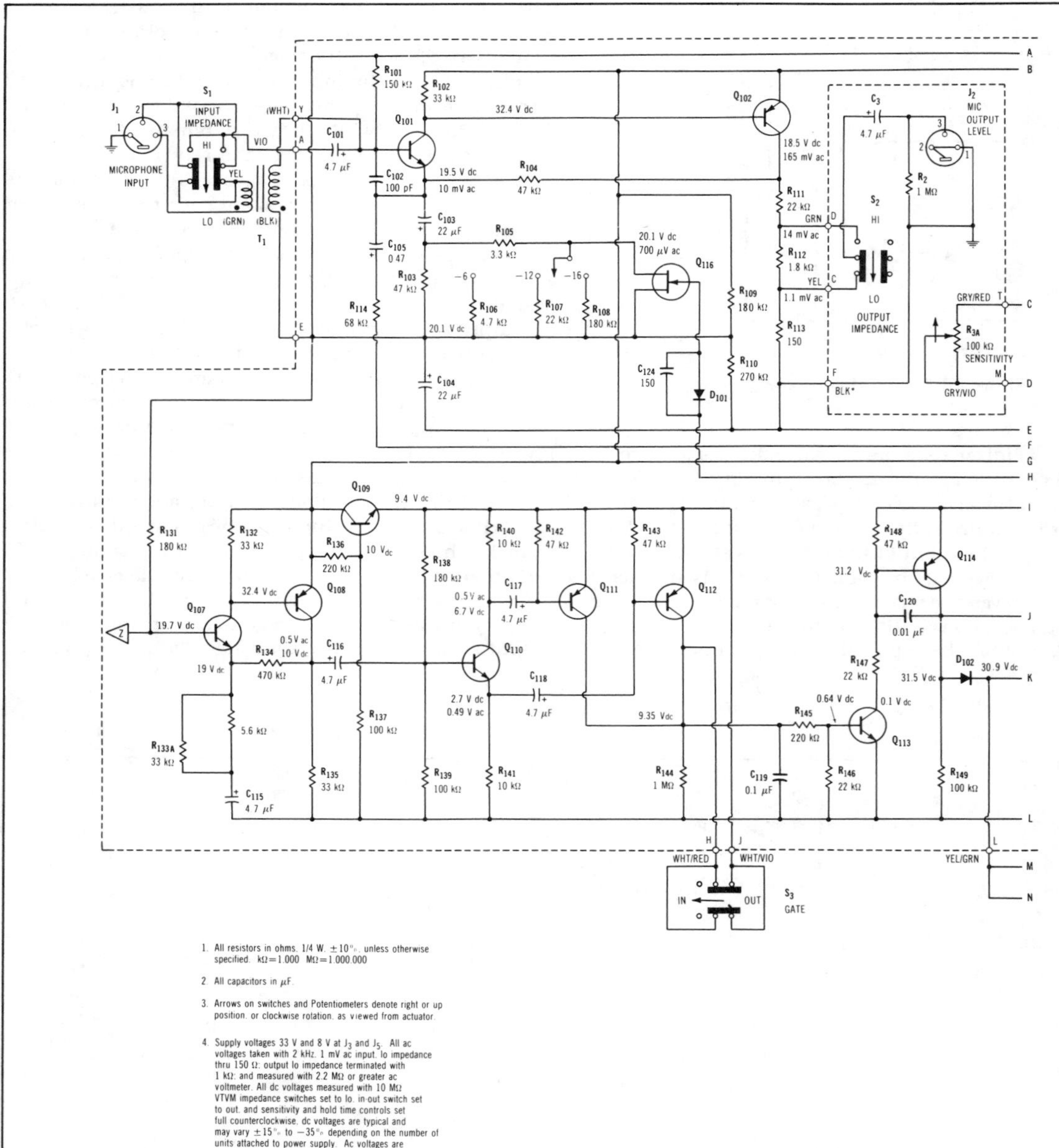

1. All resistors in ohms. 1/4 W. ±10%, unless otherwise specified. kΩ=1.000 MΩ=1.000.000

2. All capacitors in μF.

3. Arrows on switches and Potentiometers denote right or up position, or clockwise rotation, as viewed from actuator.

4. Supply voltages 33 V and 8 V at J_3 and J_5. All ac voltages taken with 2 kHz, 1 mV ac input, lo impedance thru 150 Ω; output lo impedance terminated with 1 kΩ; and measured with 2.2 MΩ or greater ac voltmeter. All dc voltages measured with 10 MΩ VTVM impedance switches set to lo, in-out switch set to out, and sensitivity and hold time controls set full counterclockwise. dc voltages are typical and may vary ±15% to −35% depending on the number of units attached to power supply. Ac voltages are typical and may vary ±15%.

5. Wires are No. 24 AWG except: * No. 20 AWG ( ) integral component lead.

Figure 16-27 Shure model M625 Voicegate automatic

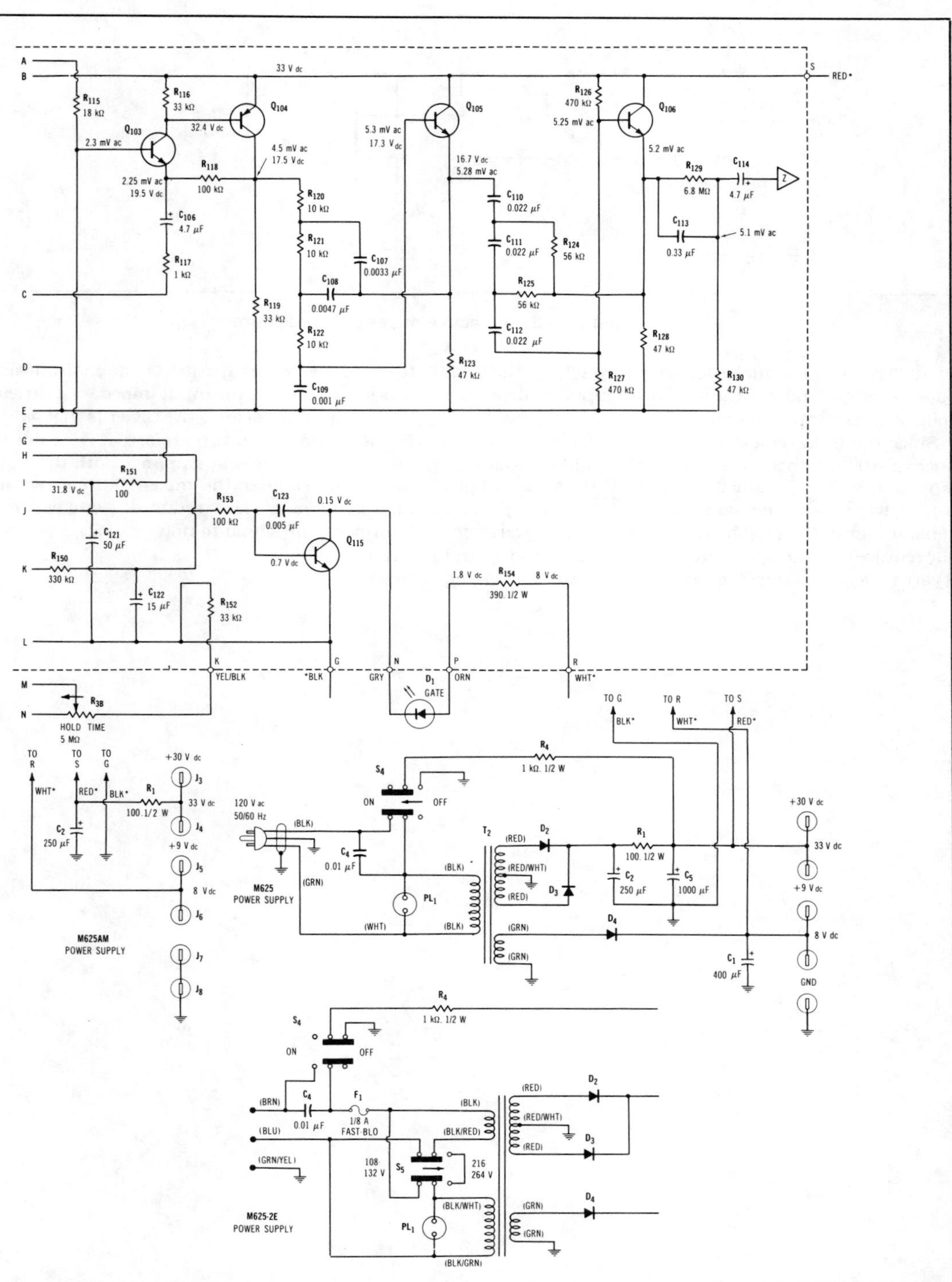

attenuator. *(Courtesy Shure Brothers, Inc.)*

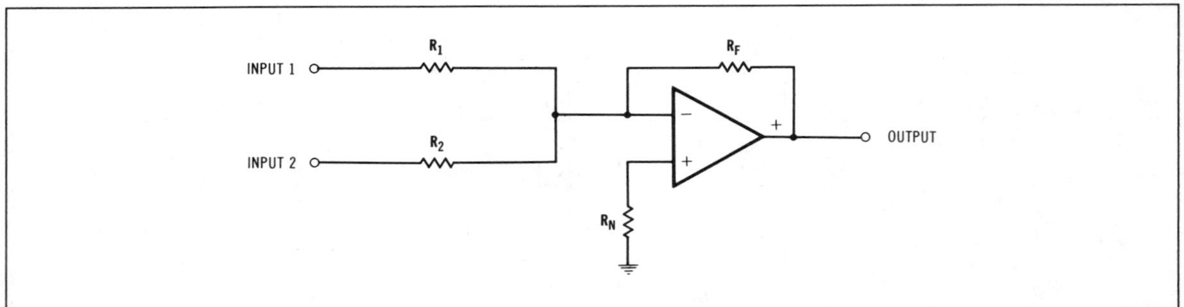

Figure 16-30 An active mixer block diagram.

input. The output signal is fed back through R_F, the feedback resistor, and continuously attempts to drive the voltage on the input to ground.

Since the input is a virtual ground, the input impedances are determined by R_1 and R_2. The gain of the circuit is gain 1 = R_F/R_1, gain 2 = R_F/R_2. If the gain of both inputs were to be the same, R_1 and R_2 would remain constant, and R_F would be varied. Mixers, however, usually require separate gain control for each input so R_1 and R_2 are varied to change the gain of the system. Increasing R_1 or R_2 decreases the gain. The main disadvantage of this system is that the input impedance varies with gain.

The advantage of an active mixer is that gain is included in the mixing circuit; therefore, it does not need a gain makeup amplifier that amplifies both the signal and the mixing noise after the mixer. With active mixing, the mixing noise is also reduced along with the signal, improving the signal-to-noise ratio, particularly at lower levels.

CHAPTER **17**

Filters and Equalizers

by Glen Ballou

17.1 FILTER AND EQUALIZER DEFINITIONS

A *filter* is a device or network that favors certain frequencies at the expense of others. Filters can either pass or reject bands of frequencies (bandpass or band reject) or can pass only high frequencies or low frequencies (high pass or low pass), as shown in Fig. 17-1.

An *equalizer* is a device consisting of reactive elements that may be connected into an electrical circuit for the purpose of altering the frequency characteristics of that circuit either up or down.

With the advent of the transistor, and more importantly the integrated circuit, active equalizers have become increasingly popular. They have the advantages of smaller size, and lack of large, hum-sensitive coils. They are usually indifferent to impedance match and have gain restoration. However, they also have disadvantages; namely, they require a power supply, have more components to fail, have more noise (usually high-frequency hiss), and have smaller dynamic range.

Figure 17-1 Types of pass filters.

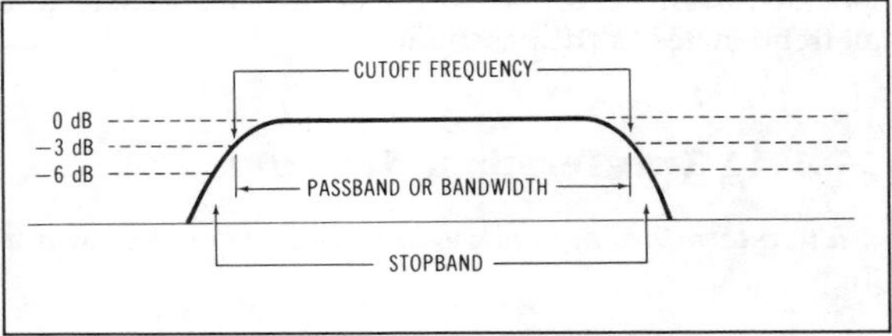

Figure 17-2 Passband and stopbands of a pass filter.

17.1.1 Passband

Passband is the portion of the frequency spectrum that the filter passes with less than 3-dB attenuation, as shown in Fig. 17-2.

17.1.2 Bandwidth

Bandwidth is the difference between the upper and lower points where the filter response falls to 3 dB below its peak value on the way out of the passband, as shown in Fig. 17-2.

17.1.3 Stopband

That part of the frequency spectrum that is subjected to specified attenuation of signal strength by a filter is the *stopband*, as shown in Fig. 17-2.

17.1.4 Cutoff Frequency

The *cutoff frequency* is the frequency where the filter response drops 3 dB, as shown in Fig. 17-2.

17.1.5 Center Frequency

The *center frequency* of the passband of any type filter or combination of filters is the geometric mean of the lowest and highest frequency of the passband. A typical example would be a recording channel employing a 40-Hz high-pass filter and a 20-kHz low-pass filter. The geometric mean, or center frequency (f_m), is

$$\begin{aligned} f_m &= \sqrt{f_1 f_2} \\ &= \sqrt{40(20{,}000)} \qquad (17\text{-}1) \\ &= 894.4\,\text{Hz} \end{aligned}$$

where,

f_1 is the cutoff frequency of the high-pass filter,
f_2 is the cutoff frequency of the low-pass filter.

17.1.6 Geometric Symmetry

A response showing mirror-image symmetry about the center frequency when the frequency is plotted on a log scale is the *geometric symmetry*. This is the natural response of many electrical circuits.

17.1.7 Arithmetic Symmetry

Arithmetic symmetry is a response showing mirror-image symmetry about the center frequency when frequency is displayed on an arithmetic scale. Constant envelope delay in bandpass filters is usually accompanied by arithmetic symmetry in phase and amplitude responses.

17.1.8 Phase Angle

The *phase angle* for a periodic waveform is obtained by multiplying the phase by 2π if the angle is to be expressed in radians, or by 360° if the angle is to be expressed in degrees.

17.1.9 Phase Shift

The *phase shift* is the change of signal phase as the signal passes through a filter.

17.1.10 Envelope Delay

The propagation time delay of the envelope of an amplitude-modulated signal as it passes through a filter is the *envelope delay*, sometimes called *time delay* or *group delay*. Envelope delay is proportional to the slope of the phase shift response versus the frequency curve. Envelope distortion occurs when the delay is not constant in all frequencies in the passband.

17.1.11 Two-Terminal Networks

A *two-terminal network* is a configuration as shown in Fig. 17-3A.

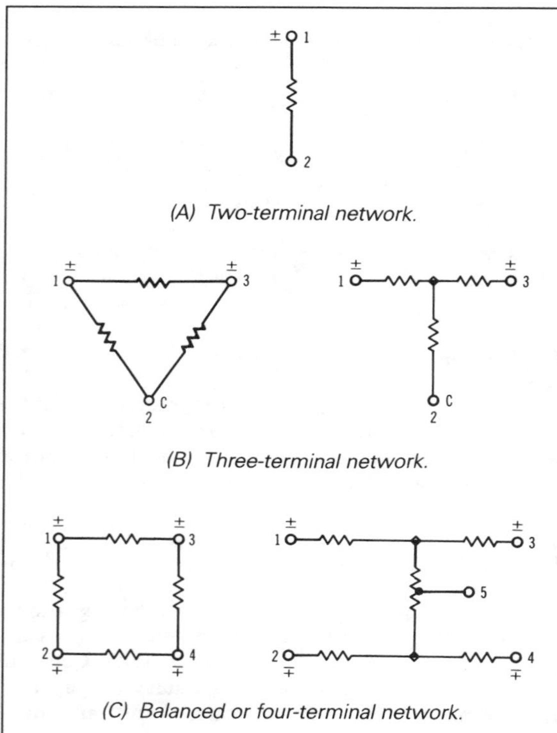

(A) Two-terminal network.
(B) Three-terminal network.
(C) Balanced or four-terminal network.

Figure 17-3 Various types of networks.

17.1.12 Three-Terminal Networks

A *three-terminal network* is an unbalanced configuration with one terminal common to both the input and output, as shown in Fig. 17-3B.

17.1.13 Four-Terminal Networks

A *four-terminal network* is a balanced configuration as shown in Fig. 17-3C.

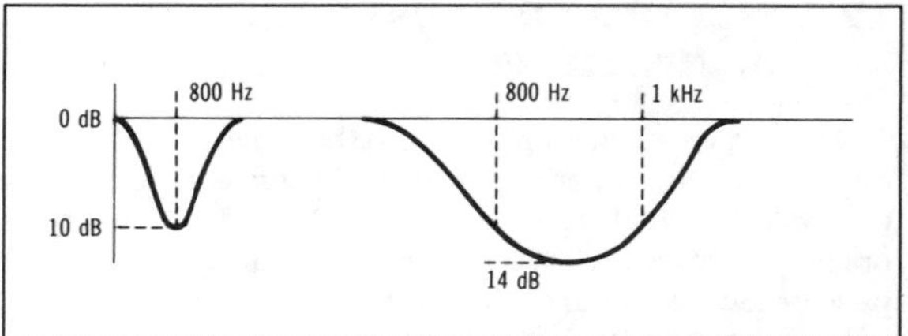

Figure 17-4 Combining filter response.

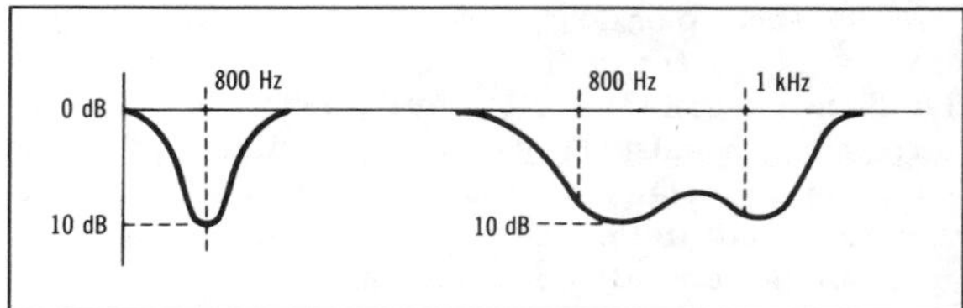

Figure 17-5 Noncombining filter response.

17.1.14 Combining Filters[1]

A *combining filter* is a filter that will combine with another filter, the total response being a combination of the two filters. For example, if an 800-Hz one-third-octave filter was combined with a 1-kHz one-third-octave filter, the total effect would be the sum of both filters. With combining filters, we can shift the maximum attenuation frequency between the two filters by varying the amount of attenuation given to each filter, as shown in Fig. 17-4.

17.1.15 Noncombining Filters[1]

A *noncombining filter* is one that will not combine with a filter of a frequency above or below it (Fig. 17-5). *Noncombining filters* will always produce ripple in the output.

17.1.16 Transient Filter Responses[2]

The ability of a filter to follow transients is the *transient filter response*. *Narrow Q filters*, when subjected to transients, ring because it takes a certain time for the inductor-capacitor network to change upon application of a signal and a certain time for them to discharge after the signal is removed. Ringing appears as a damped tail on a signal after it has been removed (Fig. 17-6).

17.1.17 Normalizing[2]

Adjusting filter component values to a convenient frequency and impedance level is called *normalizing*. For analyzing, the frequency is usually normalized to 1 rad/s, and the impedance, to 1 Ω. For designing practical audio circuits, the filter is normalized to 1 kHz and 10 kΩ.

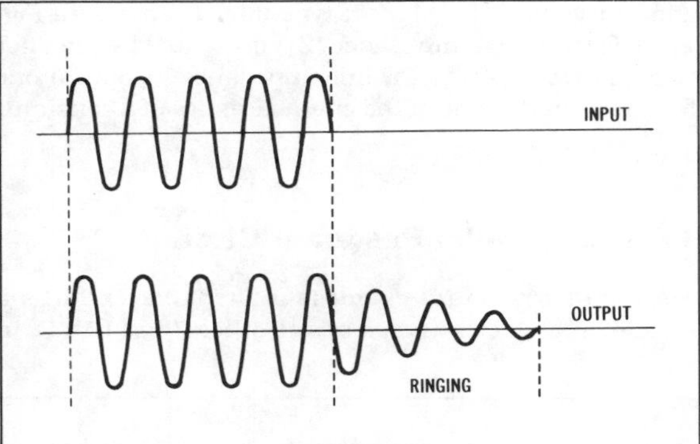

Figure 17-6 Effect of ringing on a filter.

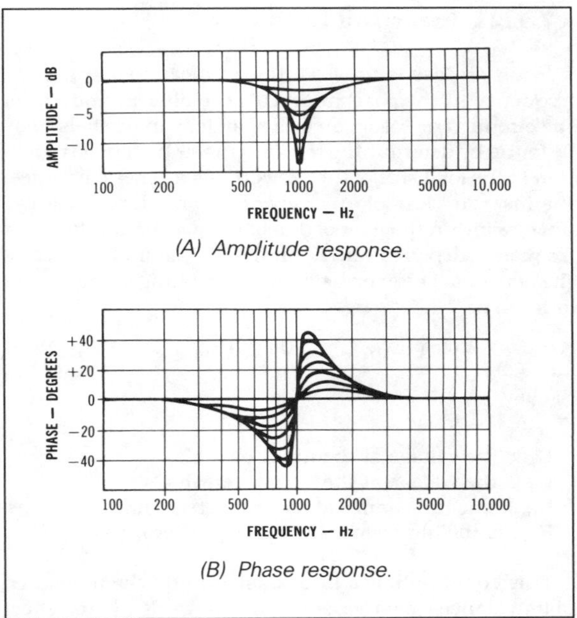

(A) Amplitude response.

(B) Phase response.

Figure 17-7 Minimum-phase-shift filter characteristics.

17.1.18 Scaling[2]

Scaling is denormalizing a filter by changing its frequency or impedance level by varying resistors and capacitors by the desired ratios. Frequency is changed inversely by multiplying all frequency-determining capacitors or resistors by the desired ratio, and the impedance is changed by multiplying all resistors or dividing all capacitors by the desired factor.

17.1.19 Minimum-Phase Filter[1]

A *minimum-phase filter* is one that produces minimum phase shift while retaining the proper amplitude change. Fig. 17-7 shows the amplitude and phase response of a minimum-phase bridged-T filter.

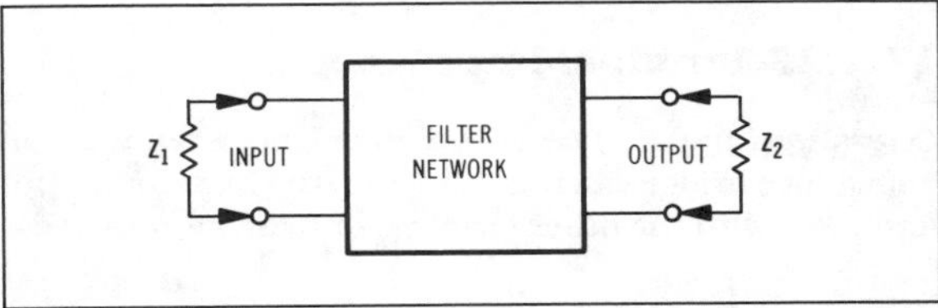

Figure 17-8 Filter network terminated in its image impedances.

17.1.20 Image Impedance[3]

The *image impedance* of a filter is presented by a group of curves, each curve having a different impedance characteristic, depending on the character of the configuration. The image impedance consists of two impedances, not necessarily alike, that will simultaneously terminate the network at its two ends, thereby avoiding internal reflection losses. Avoiding these losses occurs when the image impedance is equal to the impedance looking into the filter network. When the image impedances are equal in value (input and output), the filter is symmetrical and is equal to Z_O the characteristic impedance of the network.

The term *impedance* can best be explained by means of Fig. 17-8. The image impedances are equal to Z_1 and Z_2 if the termination impedances are of such value that, with Z_1 disconnected, the impedance looking into the input of the filter equals Z_2. With Z_1 connected and Z_2 disconnected, the impedance looking into the output terminals equals Z_1. Thus, the term *image impedance* may be explained as follows: looking into the input terminals, Z_1 sees its image, and looking back into the network, Z_2 sees its image. In this condition a filter network is said to be terminated in its image impedance. Mathematically the image impedance is

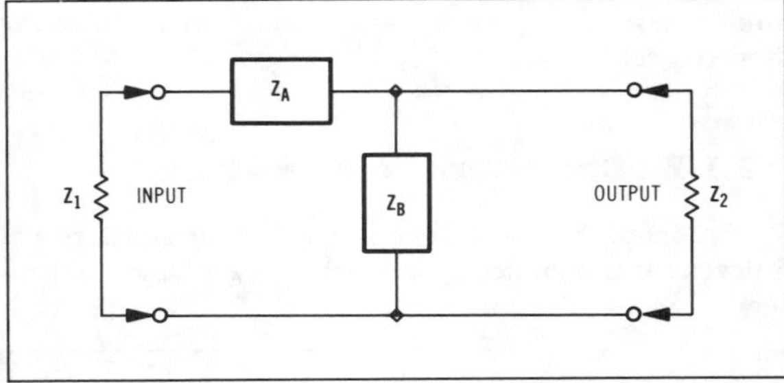

Figure 17-9 Elementary filter network terminated in its image impedances.

$$Z_{in} = Z_A + [(Z_B Z_2)/(Z_B + Z_2)] \qquad (17\text{-}2)$$

$$Z_{out} = [(Z_A + Z_1)Z_B]/(Z_A + Z_1 + Z_B)$$

where,

Z_1, Z_2, Z_A, and Z_B are shown in Fig. 17-9.

17.1.21 Insertion Loss

Insertion loss is the loss in level measured at a given frequency in the passband, with the filter in and out of the circuit. The insertion loss of a filter (in decibels) may be found by determining the amount of the voltage reduction at the load side of the network. As a general practice, the insertion loss of any network is measured at a frequency within the flat portion of the passband; the exact frequency depends on the individual characteristics of the network. The expression for calculating the insertion loss (IL) is

$$IL = 20 \log (E_1/E_2) - 20 \log [(R_{in} + R_{out})/(R_{out})] \quad (17\text{-}3)$$

where,
E_1 is the voltage at the input terminal,
E_2 is the voltage at the output terminals,
R_{in} is the impedance at the input terminal,
R_{out} is the impedance at the output terminal.

This equation takes into consideration the mismatch of impedances at either end of the network and the effect of series and shunt reactances in the network.

17.1.22 Terminal Impedance

Terminal impedance is the impedance seen with an impedance bridge when looking into the input or output terminals with the other terminal properly terminated.

17.1.23 Constant Impedance

Any device that maintains a fixed terminal impedance under normal operating conditions has constant impedance.

17.1.24 Characteristic Impedance

Characteristic impedance is the design impedance of a device, as designated by the symbol R_0. A typical impedance curve for a constant-k type filter is shown in Fig. 17-10. The actual impedance (Z_1) presented by the filter to the line is equal to the line impedance R_0 only at one frequency and is one of the characteristics of a constant-k filter.

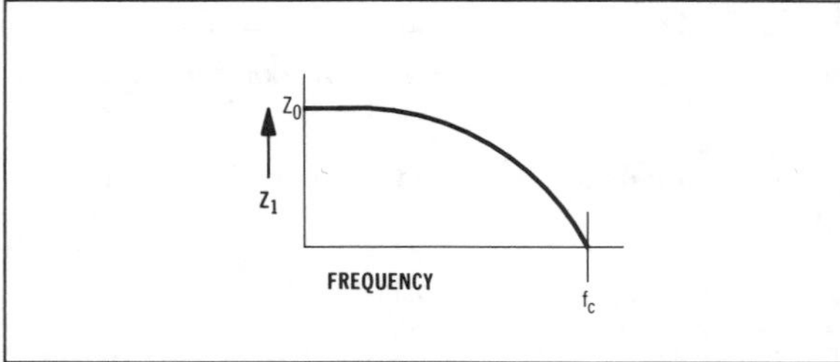

Figure 17-10 Impedance characteristic of a constant-k filter.

17.1.25 Parallel Resonant Circuits

A *parallel resonant circuit* is a filter that excludes a band of frequencies and passes all others (Fig. 17-11). In a parallel resonant circuit, the impedance reaches a maximum at the resonant frequency. The impedance of a parallel resonant circuit is determined by the equation

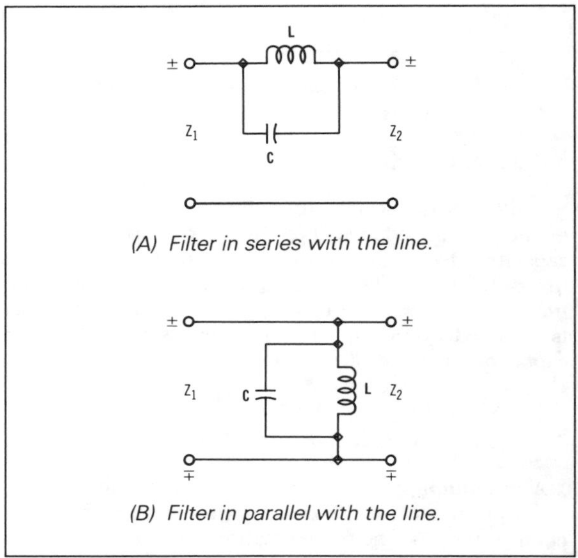

Figure 17-11 Parallel-resonant equalizer circuits.

$$Z = QL \quad (17\text{-}4)$$

where,
Z is the impedance,
Q equals X_L/R,
L is the inductance,
R is the dc resistance of the coil.

17.1.26 Series Resonant Circuits

A *series resonant circuit* is a filter circuit that passes a given band of frequencies and excludes all others (Fig. 17-12). The impedance is at a minimum at the resonant frequency:

$$Z = R \quad (17\text{-}5)$$

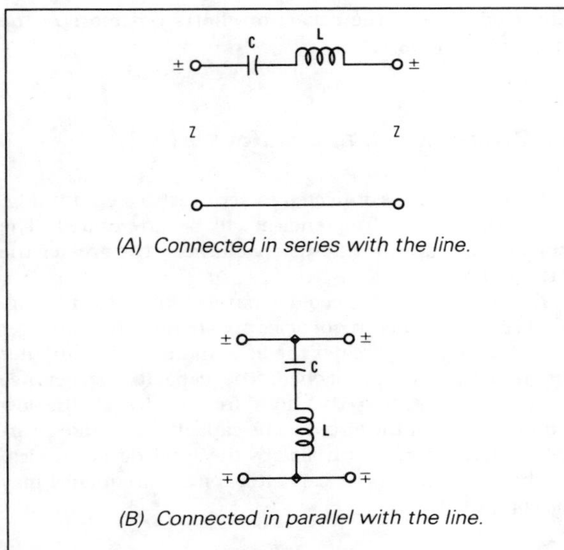

(A) Connected in series with the line.

(B) Connected in parallel with the line.

Figure 17-12 Series-resonant equalizer circuits.

where,
Z is the impedance,
R is the ac resistance of the coil.

17.1.27 LC Ratios

The *LC ratio* is the ratio of inductance to capacitance in a resonant circuit. The frequency of resonance may be calculated for either a series or parallel circuit by the equation:

$$f_r = 159/\sqrt{LC} \quad (17\text{-}6)$$

where,
f_r is the frequency of resonance,
159 is the constant,
L is the inductance in henrys,
C is the capacitance in microfarads.

Only one value of L times C will resonate to a given frequency. The intended use of the circuit will determine the LC ratio. For a series resonant circuit, the LC ratio is made high. Reducing the LC ratio reduces the steepness of the resonant curve and the selectivity.

The LC ratio affects a parallel resonant circuit in a manner opposite to the series resonant circuit. As the LC ratio is increased, the selectivity of a parallel resonant circuit is decreased.

Referring to the graph in Fig. 17-13, as the frequency is increased, the capacitive reactance (X_C) decreases, while the inductive reactance (X_L) increases. At the resonant frequency, the circuit acts as a resistance. Below the resonant frequency, it acts as a capacitor and the current leads the voltage. Above the resonant frequency, the circuit acts as an inductance, and the current lags the voltage.

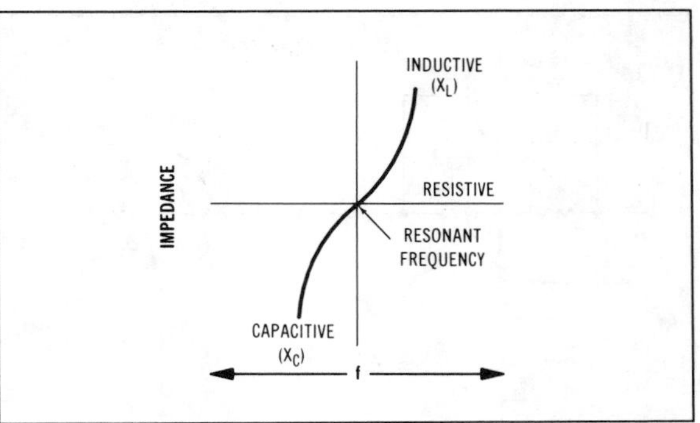

Figure 17-13 Characteristics of a resonant circuit consisting of inductance and capacitance.

17.1.28 Critical Bandwidth[1]

The *critical bandwidth* is that bandwidth within which the human ear cannot detect spectrum shape when listening to complex sounds. Fortunately, it is also the smallest bandwidth that does not produce ringing. When using a narrow band filter (notch filter), ringing does occur, particularly if the filter is deep (more than 5 dB). Most room equalization can be accomplished with one-third octave filters. Occasionally a notch filter is required to remove a resonance that cannot be removed acoustically. Complete room equalization is discussed in Chapter 26.

17.1.29 Constant Impedance Equalizer

A configuration using a constant resistance or impedance pad in conjunction with reactive elements is a *constant-impedance equalizer.* The reactive elements in the shunt and series arms have an inverse relationship; therefore, the impedance at either the input or output is essentially constant.

17.1.30 Constant-Loss Equalizers

A *constant-loss equalizer* has a constant insertion loss regardless of the amount of equalization. Variable equalizers, unless specially designed, have a variable amount of attenuation. To overcome this difficulty, equalizers have been designed that will present a constant loss for any setting of their equalization. Such equalizers employ two attenuator potentiometers connected mechanically in such a manner that, as the loss of one potentiometer is increased, the other is reduced in a like amount. Therefore, the loss in the circuit remains constant, only the

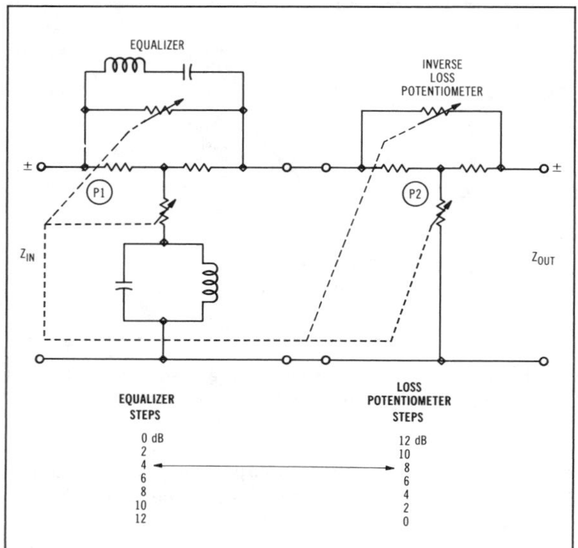

Figure 17-14 A bridged-T constant-loss equalizer.

amount of equalization is changed. This equalizer is often erroneously referred to as a constant-gain equalizer. A diagram of a constant-loss equalizer is shown in Fig. 17-14. The loss of the two potentiometers P1 and P2 always remains the same—for this example, 12 dB. Therefore, the insertion loss is 12 dB.

17.2 PASSIVE FILTERS

Passive filters never have an output equal to or greater than the input since the filter always has insertion loss. Therefore, a boost filter has a built-in attenuation for all frequencies except those boosted, the effect being a boost. To have the same base level at the output of the filter as at the input, an amplifier must be used with gain makeup equal to the boost.

Source and load impedance has a large effect on filter response. It can change the attenuation rate and/or often creates a peak in the signal just before the cutoff frequency. Fig. 17-15 shows various types of filters and the effects of improper source and load impedances. Note that the bridged-T filter is not affected by impedance mismatch due to the resistors in the filter. These resistors do create insertion loss in the filter.

17.2.1 Tone Control

A simple form of filter is the *tone control* as used on portable radios. The control only attenuates the high frequency (Fig. 17-16). As the tone control resistance approaches zero, the capacitor shorts out more of the high frequencies.

17.2.2 Simple L and C Networks

If a capacitor is connected in series with a circuit (Fig. 17-17A), the low frequencies will be attenuated. The smaller the capacitor (less capacitance), the greater the attenuation.

If a capacitor is connected in parallel with a circuit (Fig. 17-17B), the higher frequencies are attenuated. The larger the capacitor, the greater the attenuation. As the higher frequencies are approached, the capacitive reactance decreases, shunting the high frequencies to the low potential side of the circuit. The capacitor acts like a variable short circuit, controlled by the applied frequencies.

The reactance of the capacitor for any frequency may be computed:

$$X_c = 10^6/2\pi fC \qquad (17\text{-}7)$$

where,

X_c is the capacitive reactance in ohms,
f is the frequency in hertz,
C is the capacitance in microfarads.

At a frequency where the capacitive reactance equals the circuit impedance, the response is down 3 dB.

When the capacitive reactance is one-tenth of its original value and the impedance of the circuit is ten times the reactance of the capacitor, the change with frequency becomes negligible. To evaluate the change with frequency, it is necessary to refer to a reference frequency, generally 1000 Hz.

If the impedance of the circuit is known and the −3-dB frequency is known, the capacitor can be calculated as follows:

$$C = 10^6/2\pi fZ \qquad (17\text{-}8)$$

where,

C is in microfarads,
f is the −3-dB frequency,
Z is the circuit impedance.

If an inductance is connected in parallel with the circuit, a constant voltage is applied to the input, and the frequency is varied, the voltage at the output will increase with frequency, because of the increase in the inductive reactance of the coil (Fig. 17-18A). The circuit impedance will vary with frequency.

If an inductance is connected in series with a circuit (Fig. 17-18B), as the frequency is increased, the inductive reactance increases, attenuating the higher frequencies.

The inductance reactance for any frequency may be computed:

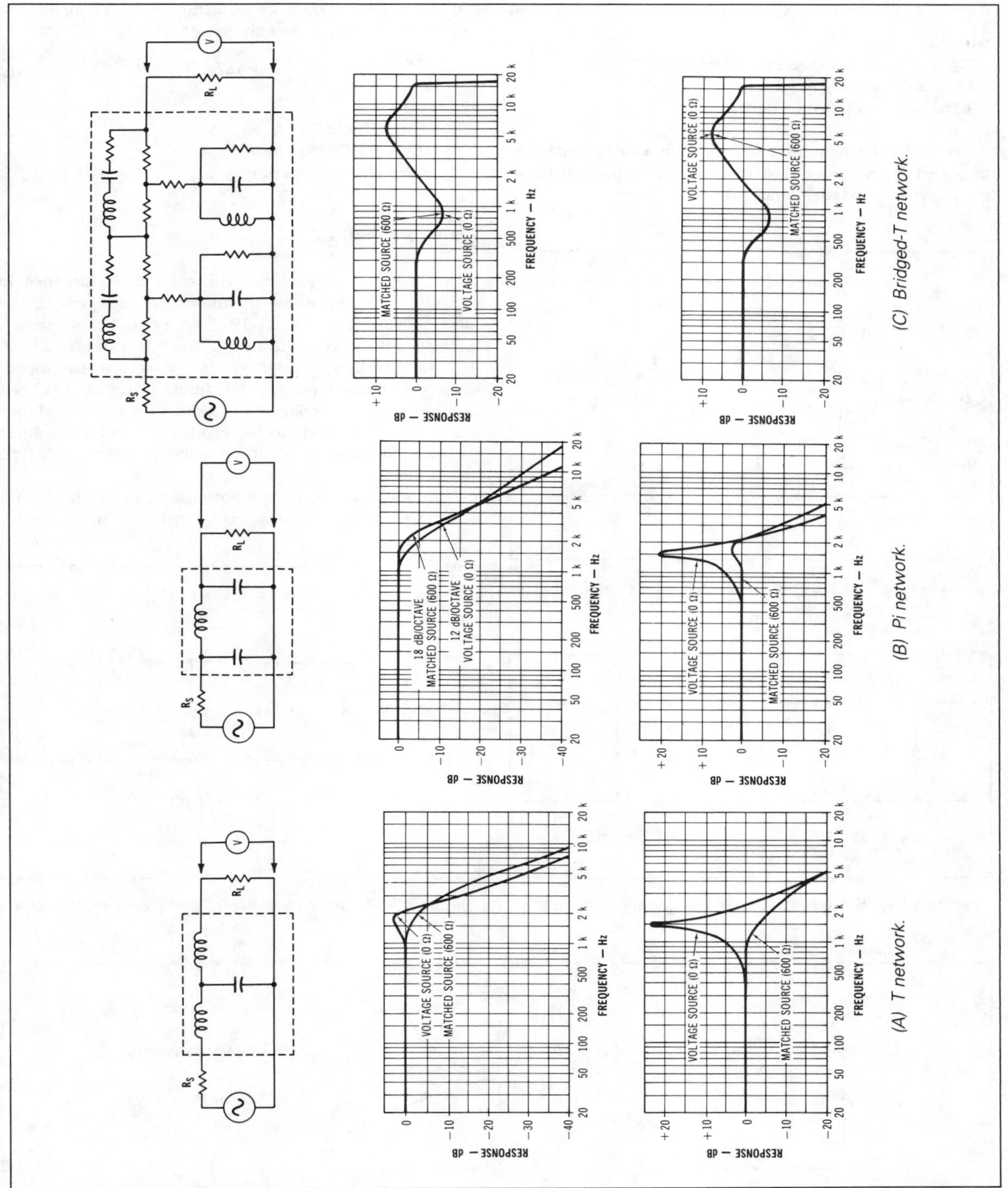

Figure 17-15 Effects of termination impedance on various filter sections.
(From Sound System Engineering, Reference 1)

$$X_L = 2\pi f L \qquad (17\text{-}9)$$

where,

X_L is the inductive reactance in ohms,
f is the frequency in hertz,
L is the inductance in henrys.

The inductive reactance of the coil may be looked upon as a series resistance that varies with frequency; thus, the circuit impedance changes with frequency.

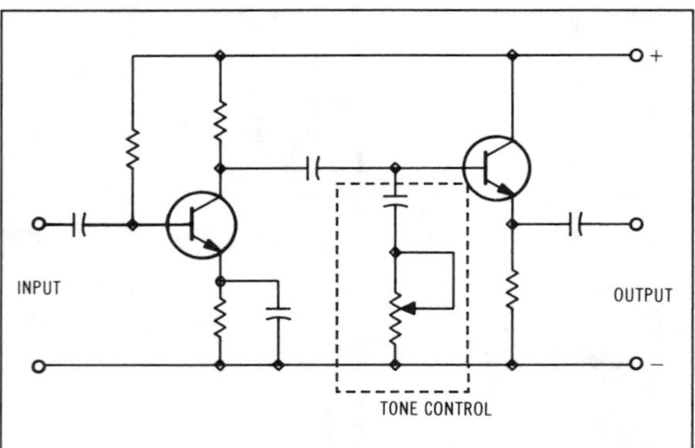

Figure 17-16 Simple low-pass tone control.

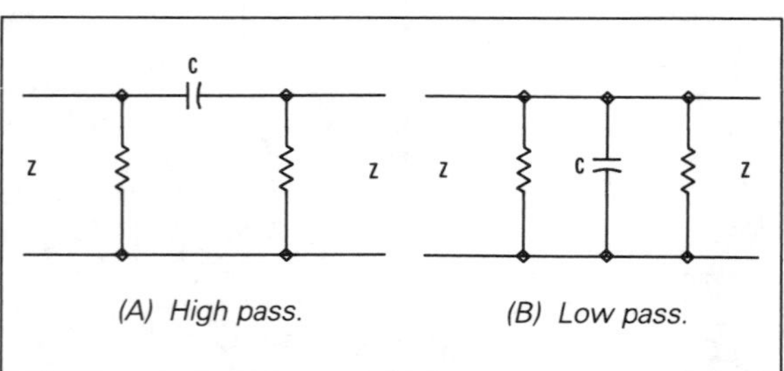

Figure 17-17 Simple equalizers using only a capacitor.

If the circuit impedance and the −3-dB frequency are known, the inductance can be calculated as follows:

$$L = 2\pi f Z_O \qquad (17\text{-}10)$$

where,

L is the inductance in henrys,
f is the −3-dB frequency,
Z_O is the circuit impedance.

17.2.3 L Filters[3]

In L filters or equalizers the ratio of inductance to capacitance determines the amount of damping in the filter, as shown in Fig. 17-19. L-type equalizers consist, basically, of two configurations, as shown in Fig. 17-20. Although the L-type equalizer presents a constant impedance only in one direction (terminals 1 and 2), it is used in many applications where the circuit is not impedance sensitive. The impedance at terminals 3 and 4 is subject to wide variations in impedance similar to L-type attenuators.

The design of an L-type equalizer is started by first selecting a design point called f_a, which is the frequency

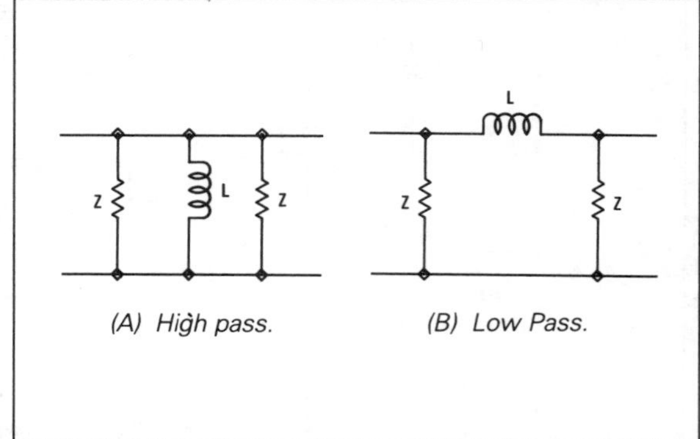

Figure 17-18 Simple equalizers using only an inductor.

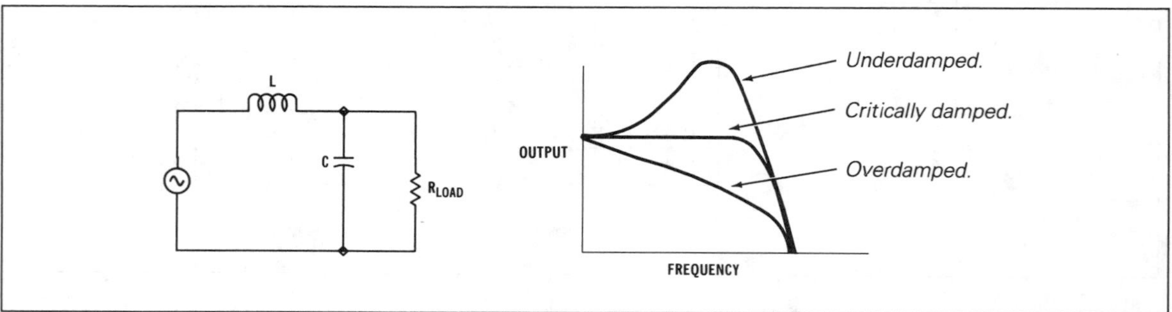

Figure 17-19 Effect of inductance and capacitance on damping.

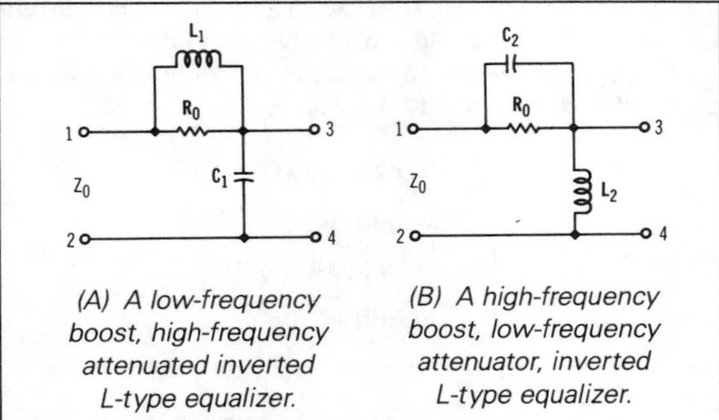

(A) A low-frequency boost, high-frequency attenuated inverted L-type equalizer.

(B) A high-frequency boost, low-frequency attenuator, inverted L-type equalizer.

Figure 17-20 Two configurations of L-type equalizers.

of 3-dB insertion loss. The frequency f_a is where both the reactive elements L and C have the same reactance and equal the line impedance Z. Knowing the 3-dB insertion-loss frequency, the frequency response for a given value of f_a may be plotted by the aid of the graphs in Fig. 17-21.

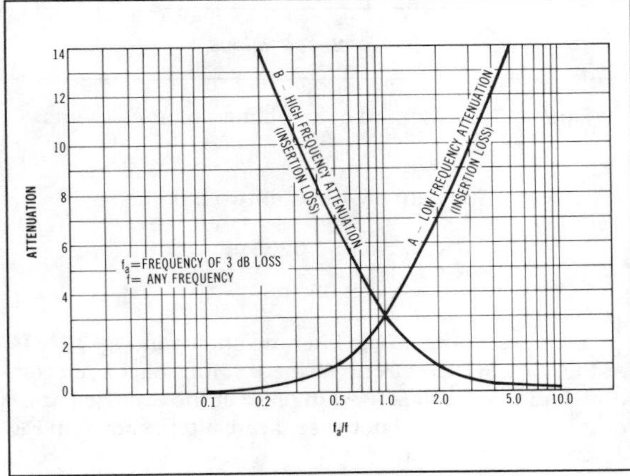

Figure 17-21 Design graph for attenuation of an L-type equalizer.

Assume, for a given frequency response, that f_a is equal to 2000 Hz. Referring to curve A of Fig. 17-21, frequency f_a is represented by the 1.0 at the bottom of the graph. This point represents the 3-dB insertion loss point. Therefore, 2000 Hz will be down 3 dB. The 2.0 on the chart will then represent 4000 Hz, and 4.0 will represent 8000 Hz. Position 0.5 represents 1000 Hz, and 0.25 represents 500 Hz. The response at any other frequency may be calculated by dividing f_a by f, f being any frequency. The loss for each frequency of interest is obtained by entering the graph at the bottom and following the frequency line to where it intersects the curved line, then reading the loss from the right- or left-hand side of the graph. After the response has been plotted, the values of inductance and capacity are calculated:

$$L_1 \text{ or } L_2 = Z_O/2\pi f_a \qquad (17\text{-}11)$$

$$C_1 \text{ or } C_2 = 1/2\pi f_a Z_O \qquad (17\text{-}12)$$

where,
Z_O is the circuit impedance,
f_a is the frequency of a 3-dB insertion loss.

The insertion loss for curve A for any frequency may be calculated using

$$IL_{dB} = 10\log[1 + (f/f_a)^2] \qquad (17\text{-}13)$$

or for curve B

$$IL_{dB} = 10\log[1 + (f_a/f)^2] \qquad (17\text{-}14)$$

where,
f_a is the frequency of a 3-dB insertion loss,
f is any frequency.

Curve A is used when designing an equalizer for increasing the low-frequency response or attenuating the high frequencies (low pass). Curve B is used when designing an equalizer for increasing the high-frequency response and attenuating the low frequencies (high pass).

17.2.4 Constant-K Filters[3]

A constant-k filter is a filter in which a constant term k is used. This term is sometimes misconstrued as meaning that the impedance of the filter is constant; however, this is not the case. The impedance of a constant-k filter is equal to the line impedance at only one frequency and presents a mismatch at all other frequencies.

To design a constant-k filter, the following information is required:

Line impedance,

Filter type (low pass, high pass, and so on),

Tolerance mismatch for Z_O.

The line impedance (Z_O) is the impedance of the circuit in which the filter is to operate. If the value of the inductance has been calculated for a pi section, the value is divided by two when used in the L or T sections. However, in the pi section, the value of the inductance remains unchanged. The calculated value of the capacitor for a T section is divided by two for the L and pi sections.

17.2.4.1 Low-Pass Filters[3]

The basic designs for constant-k low-pass filter sections are shown in Fig. 17-22. A T-type network has an inductance (L_n) in series with the line and a capacitance (C_2) in shunt with the line. Operation of the network may be visualized by consideration of the properties of inductive and capacitive reactance.

Inductive reactance varies directly with frequency. Since an inductive reactance is connected in series with the line, it offers an increasing opposition to transmission as the frequency is increased. The capacity in shunt with the line presents a capacitive reactance that decreases with frequency. As the frequency is increased, this capacitive reactance becomes more effective in shunting the audio signal, thereby reducing the transmission through

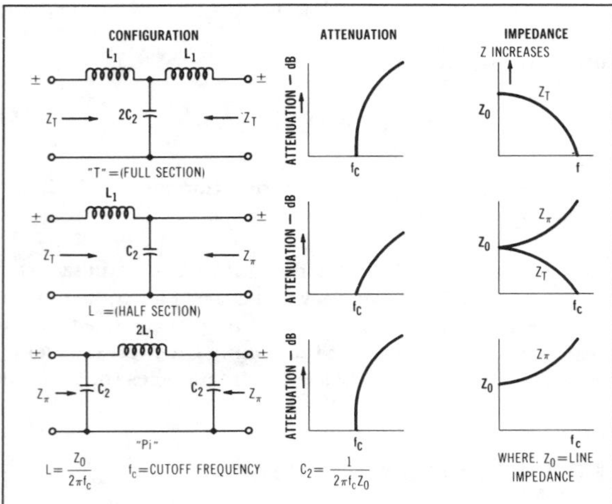

Figure 17-22 Configuration and frequency characteristics of a constant-k low-pass filter.

the filter. The combination of the inductive and capacitive reactance produces a net attenuation characteristic beginning at the cutoff frequency. The impedance presented by a T network to the transmission line is designated Z_1. This impedance is equal to the line impedance at zero frequency only and decreases progressively through the passband. This may be seen by referring to the impedance curve for a T section (Fig. 17-22).

An L-type network may be thought of as one-half of a T section or one-half of a pi section. An L section, also called a half-section, has an attenuation characteristic that is half as much as the attenuation of a full section (T or pi). The impedance of an L filter is designated Z_1 and $Z_{1'}$ because the impedance of the filter at one set of terminals differs from the impedance at the other.

The attenuation characteristics of a pi section can be made identical to those of a T section, as indicated by the attenuation curves. The impedance of the pi section is designated Z_π for both ends. A constant-k pi section presents at impedance to the line that equals the line impedance at zero frequency and increases as the frequency increases within the passband. To design a constant-k, 10-kHz, 600-Ω low-pass filter with at least 40 dB of attenuation at 20 kHz would require two T sections of 23 dB each. The first step is to calculate the values of L and C using Eqs. 17-11 and 17-12:

$$L = 600/2\pi\,10{,}000$$
$$= 0.0095\,\text{H}$$
$$C = 1/(2\pi\,10{,}000(600)$$
$$0.0265\,\mu\text{F}$$

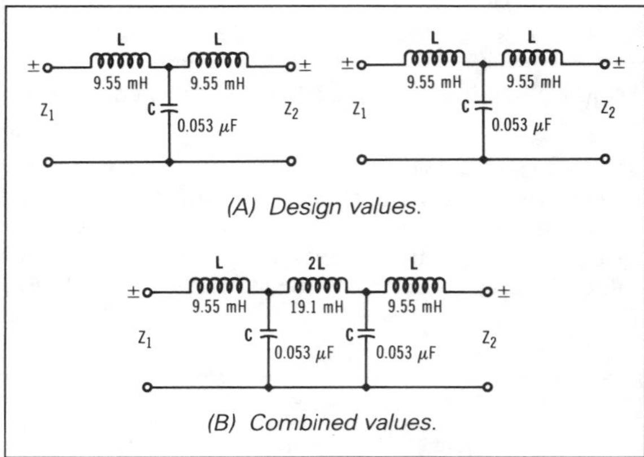

Figure 17-23 Method of combining filter elements.

However, C is actually the C of two L filters so

$$C = (2)0.0265\,\mu\text{F}$$
$$= 0.053\,\mu\text{F}$$

The two sections of the filter are shown in Fig. 17-23A. At Fig. 17-23B, the circuit element values have been combined, and one coil is used in place of the two used at the output and the input of the separate filters shown in Fig. 17-23A.

17.2.4.2 High-Pass Filters[3]

The basic designs for constant-k high-pass filter sections are shown in Fig. 17-24. The positions of the inductance and capacity are inverse to those of the low-pass filter. The design equations are

$$C_1 = 1/2\pi f_c Z_O \qquad (17\text{-}15)$$

$$L_2 = Z_O/2\pi f_c \qquad (17\text{-}16)$$

where,

f_c is the cutoff frequency,

Z_O is the line impedance.

A full section will provide approximately 23 dB of attenuation one octave removed from f_c. A half-section or L

CONSTANT-K HIGH-PASS FILTERS		
CONFIGURATION	ATTENUATION	IMPEDANCE
$\pm$ C_1 C_1 $\pm$ $Z_T \rightarrow$ $2L_2$ $\leftarrow Z_T$ "T" (FULL SECTION)	ATT $\rightarrow$ dB f_c	Z_0 Z_T f_c
$\pm$ C_1 $\pm$ $Z_T \rightarrow$ L_2 $\leftarrow Z_\pi$ "L" (HALF SECTION)	ATT $\rightarrow$ dB f_c	Z_0 Z_π Z_T f_c
$\pm$ $2C_1$ $\pm$ $Z_\pi \rightarrow$ L_2 L_2 $\leftarrow Z_\pi$ "Pi"	ATT $\rightarrow$ dB f_c	Z_0 Z_π f_c
$L_2 = \frac{Z_0}{2\pi f_c}$	$C_1 = \frac{1}{2\pi f_c Z_0}$	WHERE Z_0=LINE IMPEDANCE

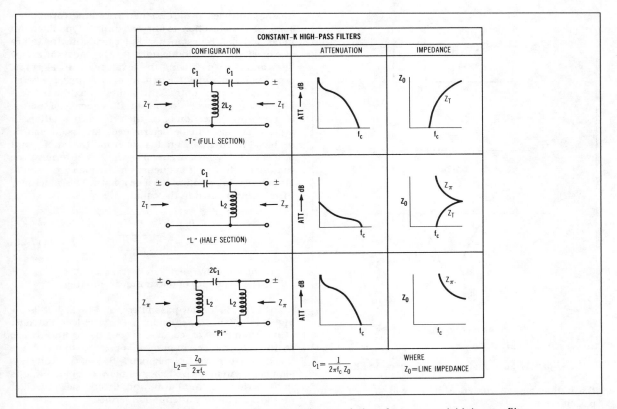

Figure 17-24 Configurations and frequency characteristics of a constant-k high-pass filter.

configuration will provide one-half the attenuation of a full section at any frequency. The various sections may be connected in tandem to form a composite filter; however, the impedance match must be made so that each section is properly terminated. The procedure for designing and combining high-pass, constant-k filters is the same as that described for the low-pass filter.

17.2.4.3 Bandpass Filters[3]

The configuration for a bandpass filter is shown in Fig. 17-25. The equations are

$$L_1 = Z_O/2\pi(f_2 - f_1) \quad (17\text{-}17)$$

$$L_2 = (f_2 - f_1)Z_O/2\pi f_1 f_2 \quad (17\text{-}18)$$

$$C_1 = (f_2 - f_1)/2\pi f_1 f_2 Z_O \quad (17\text{-}19)$$

$$C_2 = 1/2\pi(f_2 - f_1)Z_O \quad (17\text{-}20)$$

where,

f_1 is the lower cutoff frequency,
f_2 is the upper cutoff frequency,
Z_O is the line impedance.

These filters utilize resonant circuit arms, both in series and in shunt with the line. The frequency f_m is the frequency in the center of the passband and $f_{1\infty}$ and $f_{2\infty}$ are

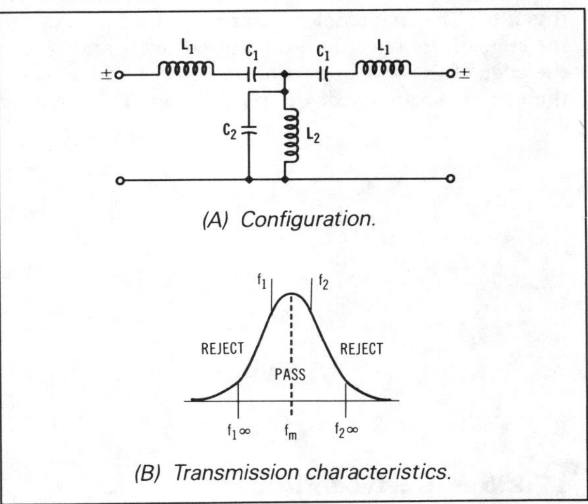

(A) Configuration.

(B) Transmission characteristics.

Figure 17-25 Constant-k bandpass filter.

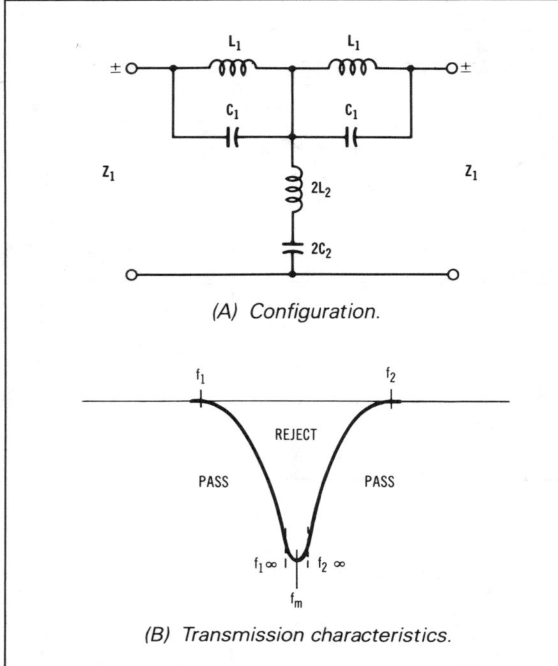

(A) Configuration.

(B) Transmission characteristics.

Figure 17-26 Constant-k band-rejection filter.

the frequencies at the edge of the widest part of the passband.

17.2.4.4 Band-Rejection Filters[3]

The configuration for a *band-rejection* or *band-elimination filter* is shown in Fig. 17-26. Note that the configuration is reversed from that of the bandpass filter. For this filter, the frequencies $f_{1\infty}$ and $f_{2\infty}$ are frequencies at the edge of the reject band. Frequencies f_1 and f_2 are at the edge of the widest part of the reject band, and f_m is the center frequency of the reject band. The equations are

$$L_1 = (f_2 - f_1)Z_O/2\pi f_2 f_1 \tag{17-21}$$

$$C_1 = 1/2\pi(f_2 - f_1)Z_O \tag{17-22}$$

$$L_2 = Z_O/2\pi(f_2 - f_1) \tag{17-23}$$

$$C_2 = (f_2 - f_1)/2\pi f_1 f_2 Z_O \tag{17-24}$$

$$f_m = \sqrt{f_1 f_2} \tag{17-25}$$

$$Z_O = \sqrt{L_1}/C_1 = \sqrt{L_2}/C_1 \tag{17-26}$$

17.2.5 M-Derived Filters[3]

An *m-derived filter* is so designed that either the impedance or the attenuation characteristic, but not both, may be controlled by the designer. This design overcomes some of the objection to the constant-k type filter. An m-derived filter is designed by first calculating the values of capacitance and inductance for the constant-k type filter and then modifying these values by an algebraic expression containing the term m; m is a number between zero and one and controls the point of maximum attenuation with reference to the cutoff frequency of a filter. By the proper selection of m, the rate of attenuation for a given section can be determined; that is, it can be designed to attenuate gradually beyond the cutoff point or it can be designed to cut off sharply. To determine the value of m, the cutoff frequency and frequency of infinite attenuation (maximum) must be known. The values may then be substituted in the equation:

$$m = \sqrt{1 - (f_c/f_\infty)^2} \tag{17-27}$$

$$m = \sqrt{1 - (f_\infty/f_c)} \tag{17-28}$$

where,

f_c is the cutoff frequency in hertz,

f_∞ is the frequency of maximum attenuation.

Eq. 17-27 is for low-pass filters, and Eq. 17-28 is for high-pass filters. The constant m is always less than one.

In certain types of sections, m governs the impedance. By the proper selection of m, it is possible to match the line impedance over approximately 85% of the transmission band. An m-derived filter employs resonant circuits in the series and shunt arms and, theoretically, the filter presents an infinite attenuation termed f_∞.

The term m may be used to control the spacing between the frequency of cutoff and that of attenuation. Fig. 17-27 shows the effect on the impedance for different

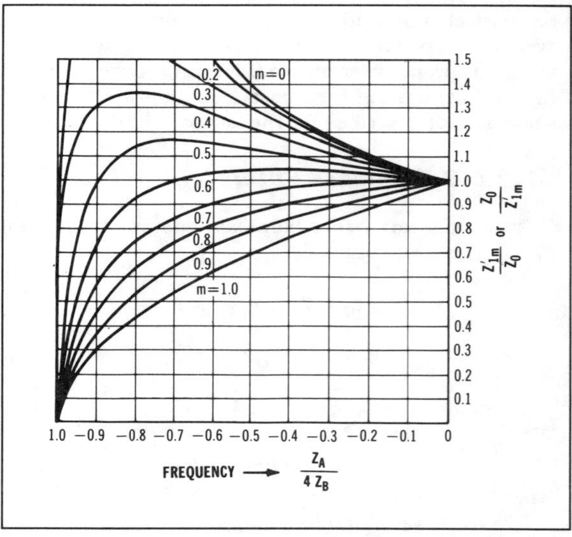

Figure 17-27 Impedance characteristics of m-derived filters for different values of m.

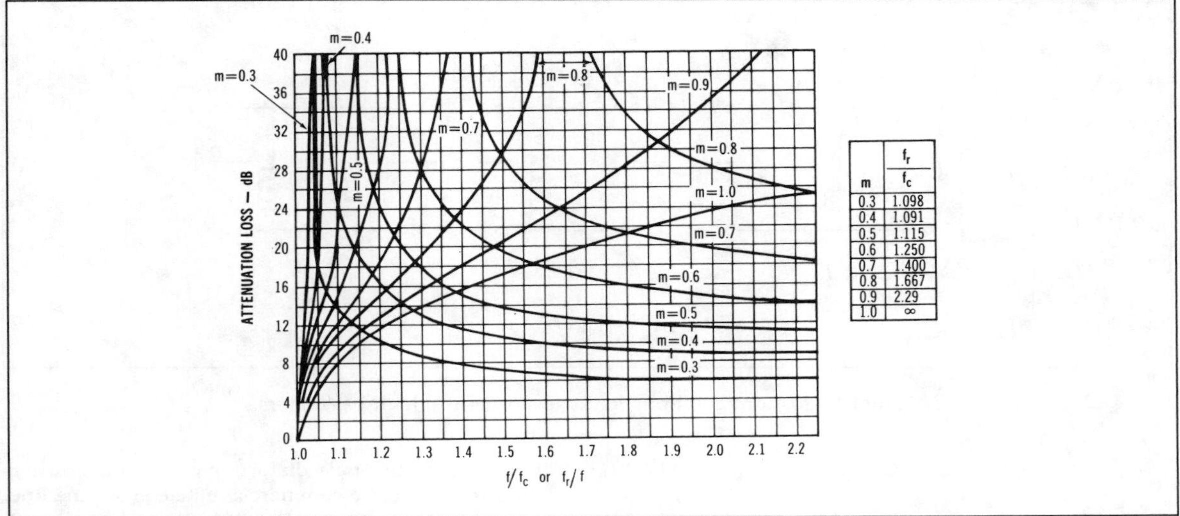

m	f_r/f_c
0.3	1.098
0.4	1.091
0.5	1.115
0.6	1.250
0.7	1.400
0.8	1.667
0.9	2.29
1.0	∞

Figure 17-28 Attenuation characteristics of m-derived filter sections.

values of m between zero and one. The best impedance match is obtained when m equals 0.60. This is the value generally used for audio-frequency filters. Attenuation characteristics for different values of m are shown in Fig. 17-28. Note from this family of curves that the attenuation rises to a maximum and then decreases due to the resonant circuit incorporated in the m-derived filter. The graph may be used for either low- or high-pass filters.

17.2.5.1 Series M-Derived Low-Pass Filters[3]

The series m-derived low-pass filters are shown in Fig. 17-29. The constant-K values of L_1 and C_2 are found with Eqs. 17-11 and 17-12. The m-derived values are found with the following equations:

$$L_1 = mL_{1(k)} \tag{17-29}$$

$$L_2 = [(1 - m^2)/4m]L_{1(k)} \tag{17-30}$$

$$C_2 = mC_{2(k)} \tag{17-31}$$

17.2.5.2 Series M-Derived High-Pass Filters[3]

The series m-derived high-pass filters are shown in Fig. 17-30. The constant-k values for C_1 and L_2 are found with Eqs. 17-15 and 17-16. The m-derived values are found with the following equations:

$$L_2 = L_{2(K)}/m \tag{17-32}$$

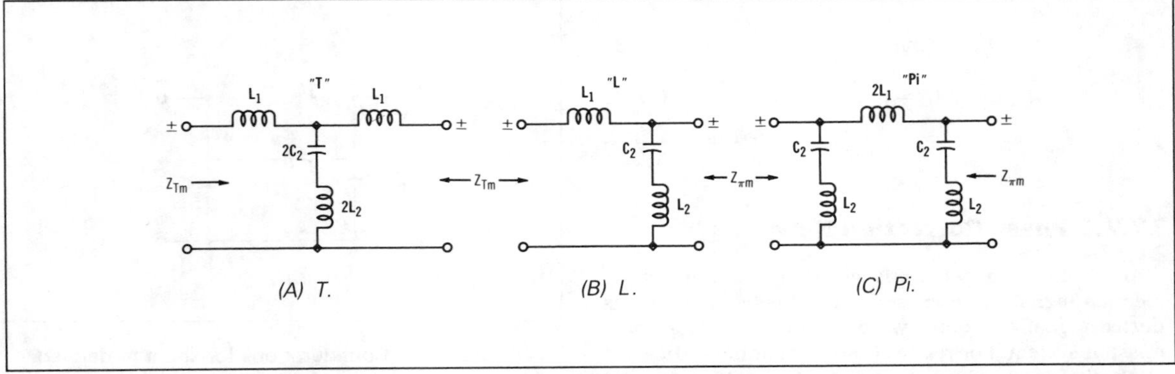

Figure 17-29 Configurations for series m-derived low-pass filters.

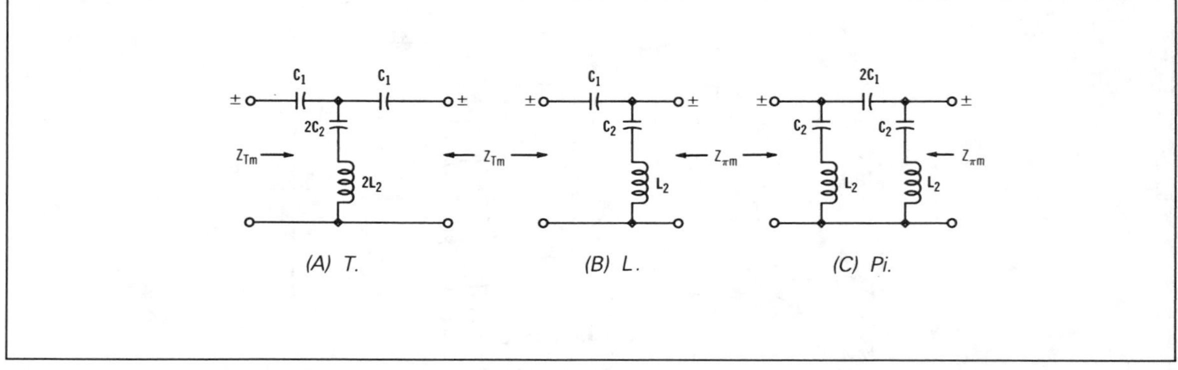

Figure 17-30 Configurations for series m-derived high-pass filters.

$$C_1 = C_{1(K)}/m \quad (17\text{-}33)$$

$$C_2 = [4m/(1 - m^2)]C_{1(K)} \quad (17\text{-}34)$$

17.2.5.3 Shunt M-Derived Low-Pass Filters[3]

These filters are shown in Fig. 17-31. The constant-k values for L_1 and C_2 are found with Eqs. 17-11 and 17-12. The m-adjusted values are found with the following equations:

$$L_1 = mL_{1(K)} \quad (17\text{-}35)$$

$$C_1 = [(1 - m^2)/4m]C_{2(K)} \quad (17\text{-}36)$$

$$C_2 = mC_{2(K)} \quad (17\text{-}37)$$

17.2.5.4 Shunt M-Derived High-Pass Filters[3]

Shunt m-derived high-pass filters are shown in Fig. 17-32. Eqs. 17-15 and 17-16 are used for determining the constant-k values, and the following equations are used for the m-derived values:

$$L_1 = [4m/(1 - m^2)]L_{2(K)} \quad (17\text{-}38)$$

$$L_2 = L_{2(K)}/m \quad (17\text{-}39)$$

$$C_1 = C_{1(K)}/m \quad (17\text{-}40)$$

17.2.6 Phase Correction Networks[3]

An ideal transmission line would be one in which the received signal represents a faithful copy of the transmitted signal—in other words, a distortionless transmission system. For relatively short distances, the effect of phase distortion is not appreciable. For long-distance transmissions, the phase distortion can become serious enough to impair the commercial efficiency of the line. The correction of frequency distortion by the use of equalizers is not enough because as the equalization is

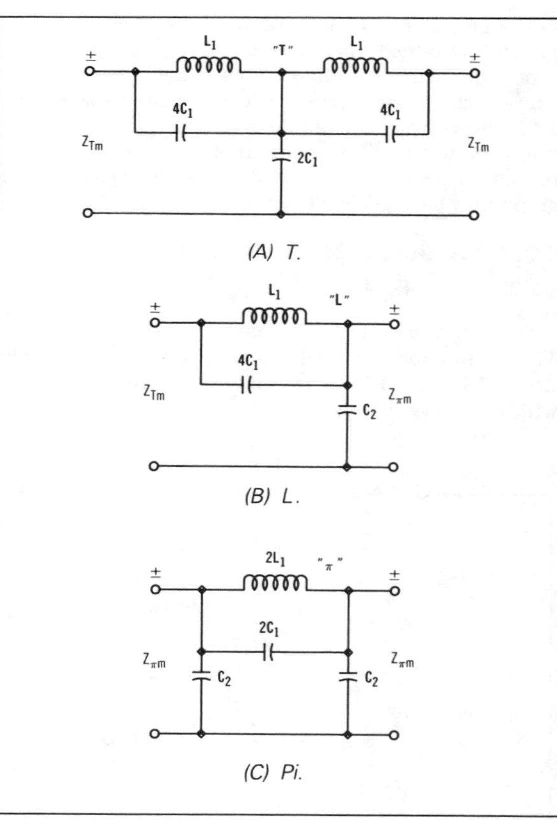

Figure 17-31 Configurations for shunt m-derived low-pass filters.

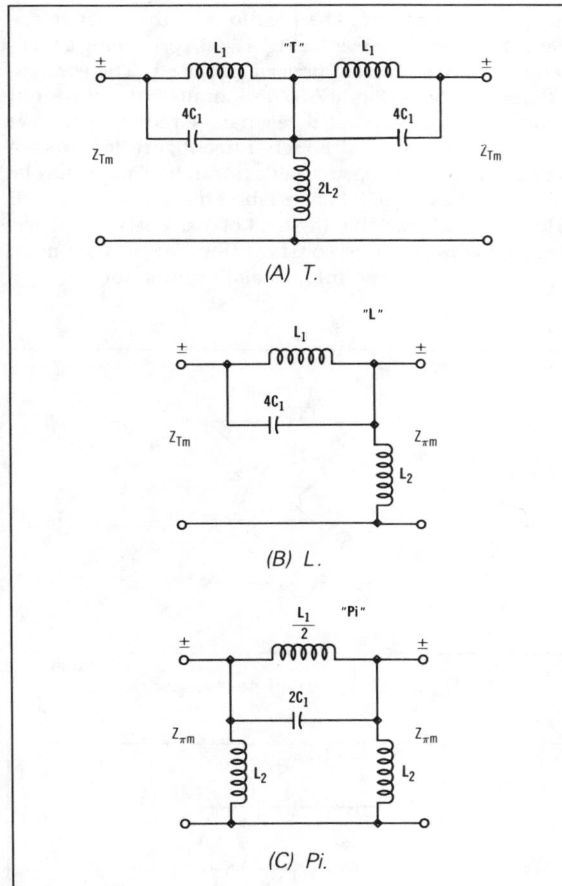

Figure 17-32 Configurations for shunt m-derived high-pass filters.

increased, the phase distortion is also increased. For high-quality transmissions, the phase distortion must be reduced to a negligible amount.

Distortion due to frequency variations and phase differences between the signals at the sending and receiving ends of the line gives rise to transient effects. The signal, after arriving at the far end of the line, requires an appreciable time, which varies with frequency, to build up and may at times never build up to anything resembling the transmitted signal. To correct for these difficiencies, filter networks, termed phase-correction or all-pass filters, are used. Such networks have zero attenuation for all frequencies within their design range. They are used as phase-correction equalizers to induce a signal delay for a given group of frequencies.

When a complex waveform, consisting of many frequencies, is applied to a long transmission line, each frequency will be delayed a different length of time in its transmission. The delay time increases with the length of the line and the frequency. The actual signal delay is not important, but the relative signal delay between the frequencies is important. The difference in phase between the signal at the sending and at the receiving end of the line can be expressed in terms of time through the line

$$\text{phase shift} = \gamma\omega + n\pi \text{ radians} \qquad (17\text{-}41)$$

where,

γ is the signal delay of the network,

ω is equal to $2\pi f$,

n is an integer.

For a network to have zero phase shift, the signal delay must remain constant for all frequencies, or the curve of the phase shift, as a function of frequency, must be a straight line. The low frequencies are delayed by the presence of series capacitance and shunt inductions, the delay increasing with the value of the circuit constants. High frequencies are delayed by the presence of series inductance and shunt capacitance, the delay increasing with the increase of these values.

All-pass networks are developed by the use of lattice networks, in which the reactances Z_A and Z_B are reciprocal with respect to image impedances Z_O. This results in a passband in which the attenuation is zero, and the image impedance is a constant impedance for all frequencies.

The phase-shift characteristics for two different types of networks are given in Fig. 17-33. Fig. 17-33A indicates the phase-shift characteristic when the inductance-capacitance ratio is large, and Fig. 17-33B indicates the phase-shift characteristic when the inductance-capacitance ratio is small. Fig. 17-34 is an all-pass network. The equations used in the design of all-pass networks are as follows:

$$\begin{aligned}
f_c &= \frac{1}{2\pi\sqrt{L_K C_K}} \\
Z_O &= \sqrt{L_K C_K} \\
L_K &= Z_O/2\pi f_c \\
L_1 &= (m/2)L_K \\
L_2 &= (1/2m)L_K \\
C_K &= 1/2\pi f_c Z_O \\
C_r &= (m/2)C_K \\
\text{time} &= \left[\frac{2m}{\sqrt{1-(f/f_c)^2}}\right][1-(1-m^2)(f/f_2)^2]
\end{aligned} \qquad (17\text{-}42)$$

17.2.7 T and Bridged-T Equalizers[1, 3]

For constant-impedance equalizers, a T-type equalizer is often used (Fig. 17-35).

The four basic bridged-T equalizers are shown in Figs. 17-36 and 17-37, with their frequency characteristics depicted with their configurations. The configuration in Fig. 17-36B is a low-frequency shelf-type suppressor equalizer employing only two reactive elements: a capacitor and an inductor. The positions of the reactive elements have been reversed in Fig. 17-36A producing a high-frequency shelf-type suppressor equalizer. The configurations shown in Fig. 17-37 are similar in nature but employ series and parallel resonant circuits to achieve their characteristics. Although the configurations shown are designed for bridged-T pads, straight-T pads may be substituted if desired. For variable equalization, a 20-dB bridged-T pad, variable in steps of 1 dB, is used. Since these equalizers are of constant impedance, they must be operated from, and into, a solid termination.

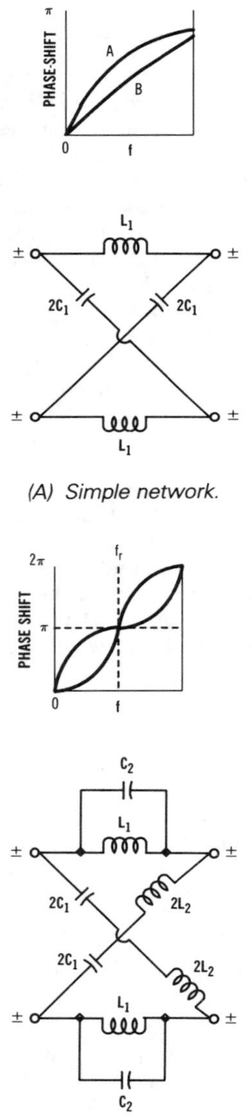

(A) Simple network.

(B) Complex network.

Figure 17-33 Phase shift characteristics for two different types of networks.

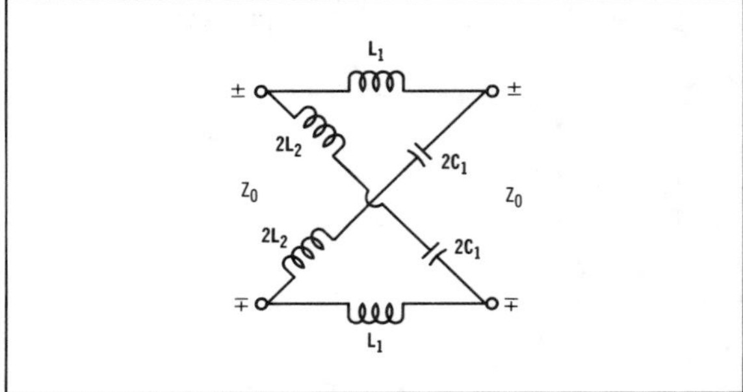

Figure 17-34 An all-pass network.

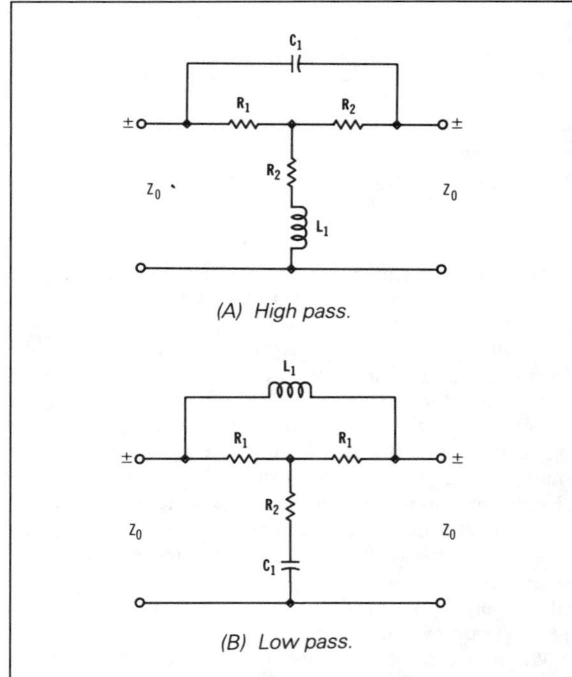

(A) High pass.

(B) Low pass.

Figure 17-35 Constant-resistance or impedance equalizers.

The reactive elements control the loss as a function of frequency. In the design of a resistive bridged-T pad (Fig. 16-11) the resistors R_1 are equal in value to the circuit impedance. Resistors R_5 and R_6 vary inversely to each other, to obtain different values of loss. For a condition of zero loss, R_5 is zero, and R_6 is infinite resistance. If reactive elements are connected in parallel and in series with R_5 and R_6, and R_5 and R_6 are selected for a given pad loss, the reactive elements may be employed to control the pad loss as a function of the applied frequencies.

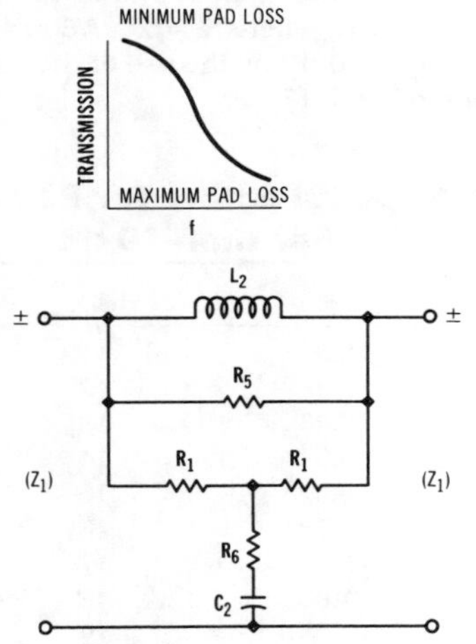

(A) High-frequency shelf-type equalizer.

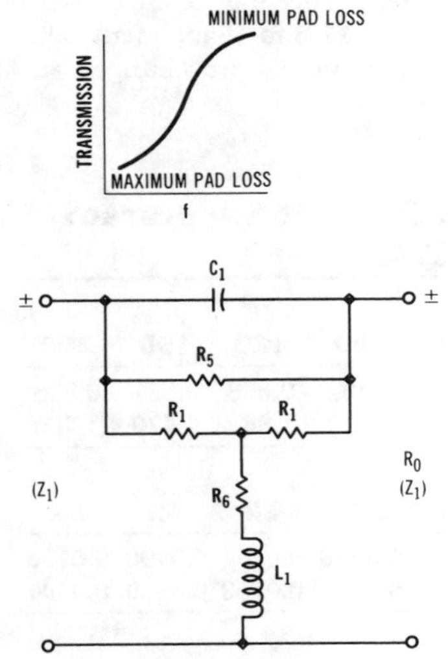

(B) Low-frequency shelf-type equalizer.

Figure 17-36 Shelf-type equalizer.

The configuration shown in Fig. 17-36B is a low-frequency equalizer. At low frequencies, C_1 has a high reactance, and L_1 has a low reactance. Under these conditions, the pad loss is approximately normal.

As the frequency is increased, the reactance of C_1 decreases, and the reactance of L_1 increases. When the maximum frequency is reached, C_1 shunts out R_5 and L_1 and opens up R (because of the high reactance of L_1). Thus, the pad loss is theoretically zero.

With a single equalizer of this configuration, 20 dB of equalization is the maximum we should attempt. If a greater amount of equalization is required, two or more equalizers may be connected in tandem. The total equalization will be the algebraic sum of the two equalizers.

The phase shift of a bridged-T equalizer is about 40°. The amount of equalization at the lower frequencies is limited by the reactive elements, particularly the inductance. Only coils of the highest Q should be employed in conjunction with high-grade or mica capacitors. The coils

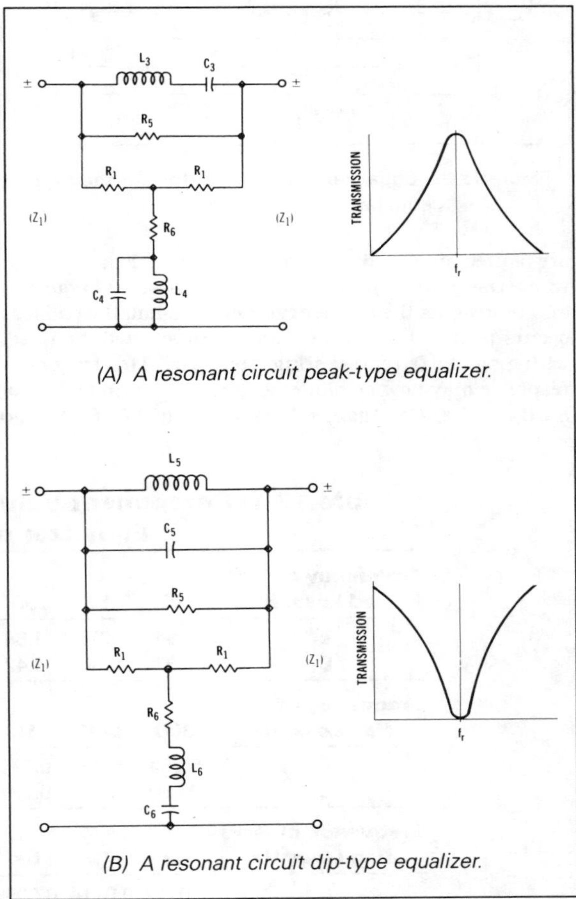

(A) A resonant circuit peak-type equalizer.

(B) A resonant circuit dip-type equalizer.

Figure 17-37 Resonant circuit equalizers.

should have their maximum Q (at least 25) at the resonant frequency.

Charts are available to simplify the mathematics to design a bridged-T pad.

17.2.7.1 Shelving Equalizers[3]

For designing the shelving equalizer shown in Figs. 17-36 and 17-38, transmission curves are used. The curves

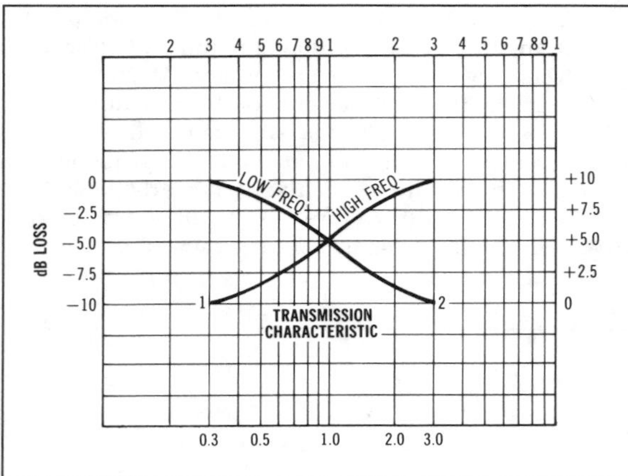

Figure 17-38 Equalizer design chart for the shelf-type equalizers given in Fig. 17-36.

are plotted for a 10-dB loss pad. The figure 1.0, at a point where the curves cross, is termed the *crossover frequency* and represents the frequency where one-half the pad loss occurs (−3 dB). For an example, curve 1 will be used, with point 1.0 representing 1500 Hz. The frequency response may now be plotted by first indicating a loss of 5 dB at 1500 Hz. Again referring to Fig. 17-38 at 3000 Hz (2.0), the loss is 1.25 dB; at 4,500 Hz (3.0), the loss is negligible; at 750 Hz (0.5), the loss is 8.75 dB; and at 500 Hz (0.3), it is 10 dB.

To make the curve fit a particular requirement, the frequency at the crossover point (1.0) is shifted up or down on the curve, as required.

After the frequency response has been plotted, the values of C_1 and L_1 are selected from Table 17-1. Under the 1.5-kHz column, L_1 equals 0.053 H, and C_1 is 0.147 μF. After having determined the circuit element values and the frequency characteristics, the configuration may be converted to an impedance other than 600 Ω by multiplying C_3, C_5, L_1, L_2, L_4, and L_6 by K and dividing C_1, C_2, C_4, C_6, L_3, and L_5 by K, where $K = Z_{new}/600$ and for a pad loss greater than 10 dB by the use of the simple conversion factors in Table 17-2.

Table 17-2. K Factors for Pad Losses Other than 10 dB

dB_{loss}	K	dB_{loss}	K
3	0.30	11	1.12
4	0.38	12	1.25
5	0.48	13	1.38
6	0.57	14	1.50
7	0.67	15	1.62
8	0.78	16	1.75
9	0.89	17	1.87
10	1.0	18	2.00
		19	2.12
		20	2.25

A low-frequency shelving equalizer uses curve 2 of Fig. 17-38 and Table 17-3 for component values. Impedance and attenuation values are changed as for the high-frequency shelving.

Table 17-1. Component Values for 600-Ω, Shelf-Suppressor Equalizer of Fig. 17-37A

Frequency of 3-dB Pad Loss, Hz	30	40	50	60	80	100	120	150	200
L_1	2.64	1.98	1.58	1.32	0.990	0.792	0.658	0.531	0.396
C_1	7.33	5.50	4.42	3.66	2.750	2.210	1.84	1.470	1.100
Frequency of 3-dB Pad Loss, Hz	**300**	**500**	**1k**	**1.5k**	**2k**	**2.5k**	**3k**	**4k**	**5k**
L_1	0.264	0.158	0.079	0.053	0.039	0.0316	0.0264	0.0198	0.0158
C_1	0.650	0.441	0.221	0.147	0.110	0.0884	0.0733	0.0550	0.0441
Frequency of 3-dB Pad Loss, Hz	**6k**	**7k**	**8k**	**9k**	**10k**	**12k**	**15k**	**20k**	
L_n	0.0132	0.0114	0.0098	0.0086	0.0079	0.0066	0.0052	0.0039	
C_1	0.0366	0.0316	0.0275	0.0242	0.0221	0.0183	0.0147	0.0110	

Table 17-3. Component Values for 600-Ω, Shelf-Type Suppressor Equalizer in Fig. 17-37B

Frequency of 3-dB Pad Loss, Hz	30	40	50	60	80	100	120	150	200
L_2	3.84	2.88	2.30	1.92	1.44	1.15	0.96	0.767	0.576
C_2	10.07	8.00	6.40	5.34	4.00	3.20	2.67	2.130	1.610
Frequency of 3-dB Pad Loss, Hz	**300**	**500**	**1k**	**1.5k**	**2k**	**2.5k**	**3k**	**4k**	**5k**
L_2	0.384	0.231	0.115	0.0768	0.0576	0.0455	0.0384	0.0288	0.0231
C_2	1.065	0.640	0.320	0.2130	0.1610	0.1260	0.1060	0.0800	0.0640
Frequency of 3-dB Pad Loss, Hz	**6k**	**7k**	**8k**	**9k**	**10k**	**12k**	**15k**	**20k**	
L_2	0.0192	0.0168	0.0144	0.0132	0.0115	0.0096	0.0077	0.0058	
C_2	0.0530	0.0460	0.0400	0.0367	0.0320	0.0267	0.0213	0.0161	

17.2.7.2 Resonant Peak-Type Equalizers[3]

A *resonant peak-type equalizer*, as shown in Fig. 17-37A, is designed by using the charts in Fig. 17-39, and the component values are given in Table 17-4. Impedance and attenuation is varied as the high-frequency shelving equalizer.

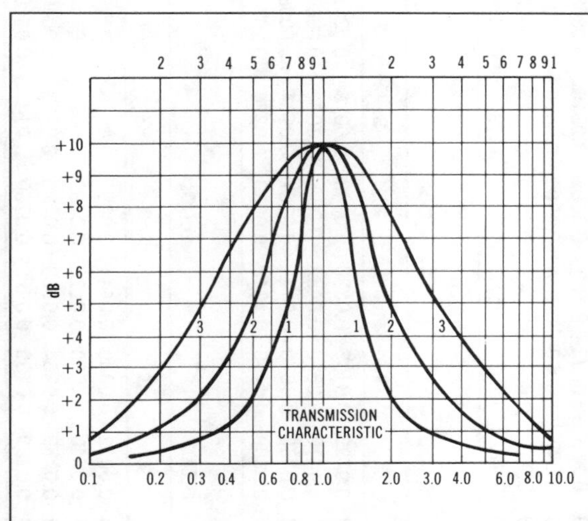

Figure 17-39 Equalizer design chart for equalizer shown in Fig. 17-37A.

17.2.7.3 Resonant Dip-Type Equalizers[3]

A *resonant dip equalizer*, as shown in Fig. 17-37B, is designed with the graph in Fig. 17-40, and the components are determined from Table 17-5. Changes in impedance or attenuation are done the same way as for the high-frequency shelving equalizer.

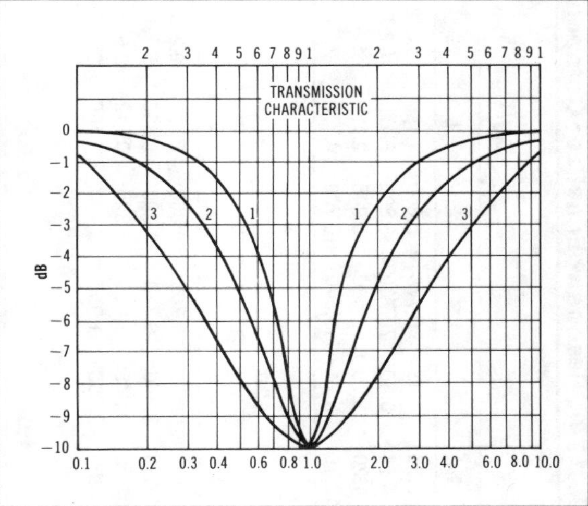

Figure 17-40 Equalizer design chart for equalizer shown in Fig. 17-37B.

17.2.8 Impedance Conversion

Whenever a filter of known impedance is being converted to another impedance the following equations are used:

$$L_x = (Z_1/Z_O)L \quad (17\text{-}43)$$

$$C_x = C(Z_1/Z_O) = (Z_O/Z_1)C \quad (17\text{-}44)$$

where,

L_x is the new value of inductance,

L is the original value of inductance,

Table 17-4. Resonant Equalizer Component Values

Resonant Frequency	30			40			50			60			80		
Response	1	2	3	1	2	3	1	2	3	1	2	3	1	2	3
L_3	4.42	1.99	1.05	3.30	1.48	0.778	2.660	1.190	0.632	2.210	1.01	0.537	1.650	0.715	0.398
C_3	6.38	14.10	26.80	4.84	10.80	20.700	3.800	8.470	16.10	3.200	7.00	13.400	2.420	5.540	10.000
L_4	1.60	3.53	6.70	1.20	2.78	5.080	0.948	2.120	4.00	.800	1.75	3.350	0.604	1.390	2.540
C_4	17.60	8.00	4.21	13.16	5.74	3.140	10.700	4.770	2.53	8.800	4.04	2.100	6.580	2.870	1.570

Resonant Frequency	100			120			150			200			300		
Response	1	2	3	1	2	3	1	2	3	1	2	3	1	2	3
L_3	1.290	0.592	0.316	1.100	0.505	0.265	0.868	0.396	0.210	0.666	0.296	0.158	0.442	0.199	0.105
C_3	1.970	4.300	8.050	1.610	3.540	6.720	1.290	2.850	5.390	0.965	2.140	4.030	0.638	1.410	2.680
L_4	0.487	1.070	2.010	0.398	0.875	1.680	0.325	0.712	1.350	0.246	0.533	1.010	0.160	0.353	0.670
C_4	5.220	2.370	1.300	4.400	2.000	1.050	3.480	1.590	0.835	2.620	1.180	0.630	1.760	0.800	0.421

Resonant Frequency	500			1,000			1,500			2,000			2,500		
Response	1	2	3	1	2	3	1	2	3	1	2	3	1	2	3
L_3	0.2660	0.119	0.0632	0.129	0.0592	0.0316	0.0868	0.0396	0.0210	0.0666	0.0296	0.0158	0.0532	0.0236	0.0127
C_3	0.3800	0.847	1.6000	0.197	0.4300	0.8050	0.1290	0.2850	0.5390	0.0965	0.2140	0.4030	0.0757	0.1690	0.3200
L_4	0.0948	0.212	0.4000	0.049	0.1070	0.2010	0.0325	0.0712	0.1350	0.0246	0.0533	0.1010	0.0190	0.0424	0.0807
C_4	1.0700	0.477	0.2530	0.522	0.2370	0.1300	0.3480	0.1590	0.0840	0.2620	0.1180	0.0630	0.2140	0.0960	0.0506

Resonant Frequency	3,000			4,000			5,000			6,000			7,000		
Response	1	2	3	1	2	3	1	2	3	1	2	3	1	2	3
L_3	0.0442	0.0199	0.0105	0.0330	0.0148	0.0078	0.0266	0.0118	0.0063	0.0221	0.0101	0.0053	0.0188	0.0085	0.0044
C_3	0.0644	0.1410	0.2680	0.0482	0.080	0.2020	0.0380	0.0850	0.1600	0.0322	0.0700	0.1340	0.0275	0.0610	0.1180
L_4	0.0160	0.0350	0.0670	0.0121	0.0267	0.0504	0.0095	0.0212	0.0400	0.0080	0.0175	0.0335	0.0069	0.0152	0.0296
C_4	0.1760	0.0800	0.0420	0.1310	0.0590	0.0320	0.1070	0.0480	0.0253	0.0880	0.0400	0.0210	0.0750	0.0340	0.0180

Resonant Frequency	8,000			9,000			10,000			12,000			15,000		
Response	1	2	3	1	2	3	1	2	3	1	2	3	1	2	3
L_3	0.0165	0.0072	0.0040	0.0141	0.0065	0.0035	0.0129	0.0059	0.0032	0.0110	0.0050	0.0027	0.0087	0.00396	0.0021
C_3	0.0242	0.0540	1.1000	0.0223	0.0480	0.0093	0.0197	0.0430	0.0805	0.0161	0.0350	0.0670	0.0130	0.02860	0.0540
L_4	0.0060	0.0139	0.0254	0.0053	0.0120	0.0223	0.0049	0.0107	0.0201	0.0040	0.0087	0.0170	0.0033	0.00712	0.0135
C_4	0.0660	0.0290	0.0160	0.0590	0.0260	0.0140	0.0520	0.0240	0.0130	0.0440	0.0200	0.0110	0.0348	0.01590	0.0085

All Values of Inductance in Henrys All Values of Capacitance in Microfarads

Table 17-5. Component Values for a 500-Ω Resonant Equalizer

Resonant Frequency	30			40			50			60			80		
Response	1	2	3	1	2	3	1	2	3	1	2	3	1	2	3
L_5	2.30	5.08	9.680	1.74	4.000	7.300	1.40	3.100	5.75	1.15	2.520	4.840	.870	2.000	3.650
C_5	12.20	5.55	2.900	9.14	4.100	2.280	7.40	3.280	1.70	6.15	2.800	1.500	4.570	1.990	1.110
L_6	3.07	1.39	0.730	2.28	0.100	0.550	1.85	0.828	0.438	1.53	0.700	0.370	1.140	0.497	0.273
C_6	9.20	20.30	38.600	6.96	16.400	29.200	5.60	12.200	23.00	4.60	10.100	19.340	3.480	8.000	14.600
Resonant Frequency	**100**			**120**			**150**			**200**			**300**		
Response	**1**	**2**	**3**	**1**	**2**	**3**	**1**	**2**	**3**	**1**	**2**	**3**	**1**	**2**	**3**
L_5	0.702	1.550	2.890	0.573	1.270	2.420	0.460	1.030	1.940	0.354	0.767	1.450	0.230	0.508	0.965
C_5	3.620	1.640	0.878	3.070	1.380	0.750	2.420	1.100	0.582	1.800	0.829	0.439	1.220	0.556	0.290
L_6	0.900	0.410	0.219	0.767	0.343	0.182	0.603	0.276	0.146	0.448	0.208	0.110	0.307	0.139	0.073
C_6	2.810	6.200	11.600	2.290	5.100	9.670	1.870	4.100	7.750	1.420	3.060	5.800	0.920	2.030	3.860
Resonant Frequency	**500**			**1,000**			**1,500**			**2,000**			**2,500**		
Response	**1**	**2**	**3**	**1**	**2**	**3**	**1**	**2**	**3**	**1**	**2**	**3**	**1**	**2**	**3**
L_5	0.137	0.3050	0.575	0.0702	0.155	0.2890	0.0468	0.1030	0.1940	0.0354	0.0767	0.145	0.0273	0.0617	0.1160
C_5	0.738	0.3320	0.176	0.3620	0.164	0.0880	0.2420	0.1100	0.0580	0.1800	0.0830	0.044	0.1490	0.0660	0.0350
L_6	0.185	0.0828	0.044	0.0903	0.041	0.0219	0.0603	0.0276	0.0146	0.0448	0.0208	0.011	0.0374	0.0165	0.0088
C_6	0.548	1.2200	2.300	0.2810	0.620	1.1600	0.1870	0.4100	0.7750	0.1420	0.3060	0.580	0.1100	0.2470	0.4640
Resonant Frequency	**3,000**			**4,000**			**5,000**			**6,000**			**7,000**		
Response	**1**	**2**	**3**	**1**	**2**	**3**	**1**	**2**	**3**	**1**	**2**	**3**	**1**	**2**	**3**
L_5	0.0230	0.0508	0.0965	0.0174	0.0385	0.0725	0.0137	0.0305	0.0575	0.0115	0.0252	0.0483	0.0099	0.0219	0.0426
C_5	0.1220	0.0560	0.0300	0.0910	0.0410	0.0220	0.0740	0.0330	0.0180	0.0620	0.0280	0.0150	0.0520	0.0240	0.0120
L_6	0.0307	0.0140	0.0073	0.0227	0.0103	0.0055	0.0185	0.0083	0.0044	0.0153	0.0070	0.0037	0.0130	0.0059	0.0030
C_6	0.0920	0.2030	0.3860	0.0700	0.1540	0.2900	0.0550	0.1220	0.2300	0.0460	0.1000	0.1930	0.0400	0.0880	0.1710
Resonant Frequency	**8,000**			**9,000**			**10,000**			**12,000**			**15,000**		
Response	**1**	**2**	**3**	**1**	**2**	**3**	**1**	**2**	**3**	**1**	**2**	**3**	**1**	**2**	**3**
L_5	0.0087	0.0200	0.0363	0.0070	0.0173	0.0322	0.0072	0.0155	0.0289	0.0058	0.0126	0.0250	0.0047	0.0103	0.0194
C_5	0.0460	0.0200	0.0110	0.0410	0.0180	0.0100	0.0360	0.0160	0.0090	0.0310	0.0140	0.0075	0.0242	0.0110	0.0058
L_6	0.0114	0.0050	0.0027	0.0103	0.0045	0.0024	0.0090	0.0041	0.0022	0.0077	0.0035	0.0018	0.0060	0.0028	0.0015
C_6	0.0350	0.0800	0.1460	0.0310	0.0690	0.1290	0.0280	0.0620	0.1160	0.0230	0.0500	0.0970	0.0187	0.0410	0.0775

All Values of Inductance in Henrys All Values of Capacitance in Microfarads

Z_O is the characteristic impedance,
Z_1 is the new impedance,
C_x is the new value of capacitance,
C is the original value of capacitance.

17.2.9 Frequency Conversion

If a filter is being changed to another frequency the following equations are used:

$$C_x = C(f_O/f_1) \tag{17-45}$$

$$L_x = L(f_O/f_1) \tag{17-46}$$

where,
C_x is the new value of capacitance,
C is the original value of capacitance,
L_x is the new value of inductance,
L is the original value of inductance,
f_O is the original frequency,
f_1 is the new frequency.

17.2.10 Combination Series and Parallel Circuits

Filters to be operated in either series or parallel require special treatment, because the impedances are joined to a common source impedance. Since filter impedances vary with frequency in the stopband, both the parallel impedance and the insertion loss are affected. The loudspeaker crossover networks of Fig. 17-41 are typical examples of parallel and series filter combinations.

For parallel operation, the low- and high-pass sections must employ T-type intermediate sections with an L-type input half-section, designed for m equal to 0.6. With equal load impedances at the output terminals of each filter, a normal impedance match is achieved by omitting the shunt impedance (Z_1 and Z_2) at the input of each filter section. For series operation, the filter sections are designed using pi intermediate sections, with pi input half-sections. Using a value of m equals 0.6 and equal termination impedances at the output, a normal impedance match is obtained by omitting the series impedance at the input of each filter section.

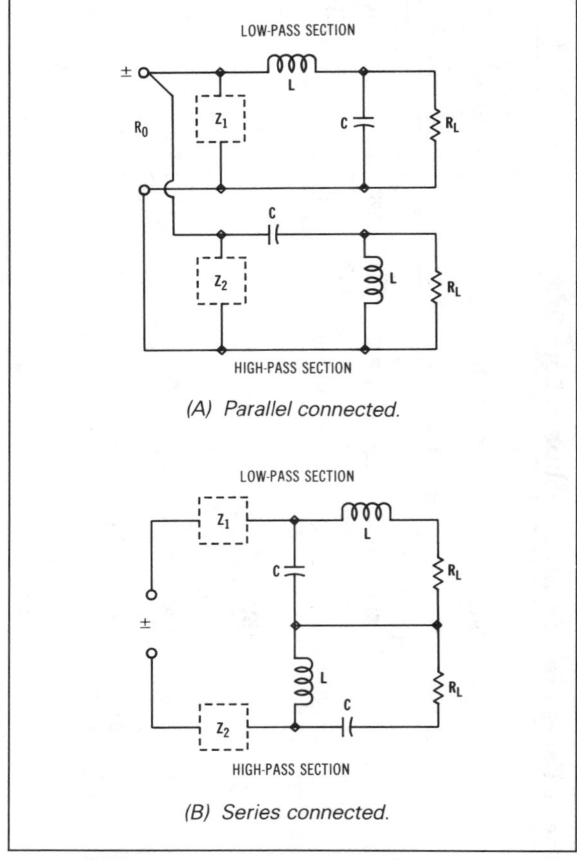

Figure 17-41 Filters connected in parallel and series.

17.3 ACTIVE FILTERS[2]

Active filters can produce the same or better results than passive filters with lower cost and smaller, lighter components. Active filters eliminate the need for large, heavy inductors. They can also be made as low pass, bandpass, high pass, or any combination without affecting the others.

Active filters can be easily cascaded to sharpen cutoff. They usually have high-input and low-output impedance, which produces good isolation; they are easily tuned; and they can produce gain. Because of the absence of chokes or coils, shielding can be kept at a minimum.

Active filters do have disadvantages, however. They require a power supply and are usually less reliable than passive filters (coils and capacitors have an extremely low mortality rate). They also have smaller dynamic range, the lower limit is controlled by circuit noise, and the upper limit is controlled by clipping.

The most popular active filters are Sallen Key; equal-component Sallen Key; unity gain, state variable; and variable-gain-state variable filters.

A filter design is normalized to resistors of 1 Ω, capacitors of 1 F, and a frequency of 1 rad/s. Active filter design is made simple by normalizing a filter design to 10 kΩ and 1 kHz. To normalize to 10 kΩ and 1 kHz, all resistors are multiplied by 10 kΩ, and all capacitors are divided by 6.28×10^7 (Fig. 17-42A and B). The same circuit, with a cutoff frequency normalized to 588 Hz, is shown in Fig. 17-42C.

The damping of the filter is changed by changing the

value of d in the equation. The value of d can vary from zero to two. If d is zero, the circuit will change into an oscillator, and while at two, the damping will be equivalent to two isolated resistance-capacitance filters. A *d* of 1.414 is considered critical damping and gives maximum flatness without overshoot. A *d* of 1.73 gives maximally flat signal delay while a *d* of 1.059 produces a 1-dB peak and a *d* of 0.766 produces a 3-dB peak.

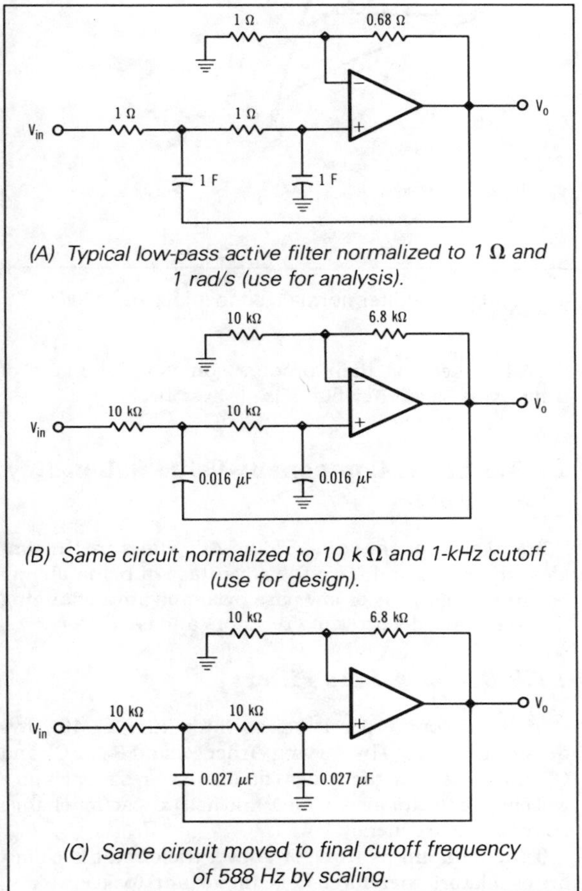

(A) *Typical low-pass active filter normalized to 1 Ω and 1 rad/s (use for analysis).*

(B) *Same circuit normalized to 10 k Ω and 1-kHz cutoff (use for design).*

(C) *Same circuit moved to final cutoff frequency of 588 Hz by scaling.*

Figure 17-42 Normalization and scaling techniques to simplify active-filter design.

The filter design determines the shape of the filter response and the filter delay.

A Bessel filter has the best signal delay and minimum overshoot; however, it also has a droopy passband and a broad knee.

A Butterworth filter has the flattest passband with a good knee and reasonable overshoot.

The Chebychev filters have a ripple in the passband that can be designed to be from 0.3 to 3 dB in concert with increasingly sharp knee and overshoot.

17.3.1 Simple Low-Pass Active Filters

The simple 12-dB/octave low-pass active filter in Fig. 17-43 is actually two resistance-capacitance filters followed by an emitter follower. The response is the same as the response from a resistance-capacitance filter with a high-Z load. The input impedance is high, and the output impedance is low. The gain is always less than one.

This filter simply uses an emitter follower for impedance matching and isolation.

17.3.2 Unity-Gain Sallen-Key Filters

17.3.2.1 Low-Pass Filters

The *unity-gain Sallen-Key filters* are very simple to design and make. A disadvantage is that the frequency and damping cannot be adjusted independently. Fig. 17-44 is a simple 12-dB/octave active low-pass filter using positive capacitive feedback to produce the effect of an inductor in a passive circuit. At low frequencies, C_1 has too high a reactance to feed back the signal, and at high frequencies the signal is too low to affect the circuit. In

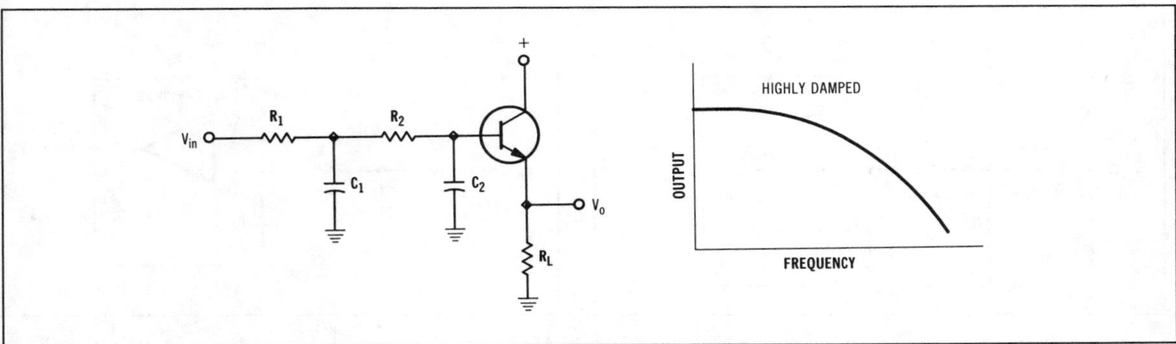

Figure 17-43 Simple 12-dB/octave low-pass filter.

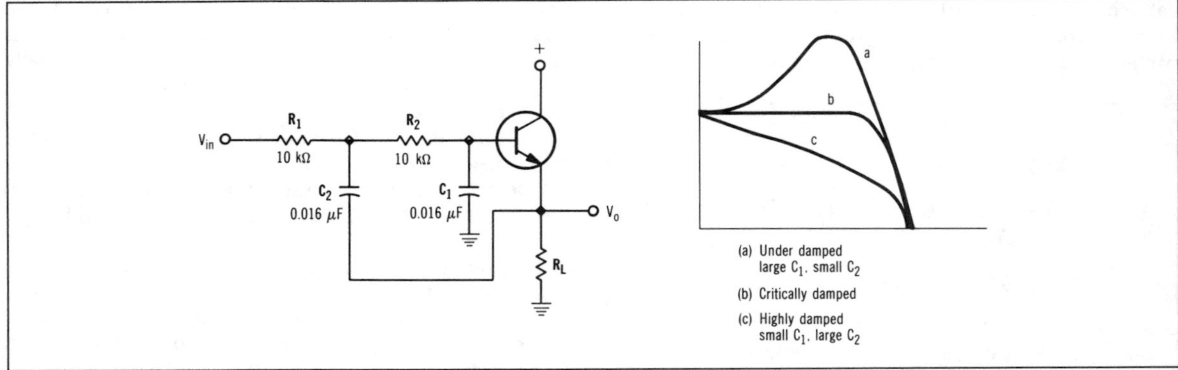

Figure 17-44 Simple 12-dB/octave active low-pass unity-gain Sallen-Key filter normalized to 1 kHz and 10 kΩ.

the vicinity of critical frequency, the capacitor feedback loop C_2 feeds back excessive energy, therefore, increasing the output. By changing the ratio of the two capacitors, the damping can be changed. The cutoff frequency is controlled by the values of C_1, C_2, R_1, and R_2.

The cutoff frequency can be changed by varying R_1 and R_2 keeping both values identical or by varying C_1 and C_2. A 10:1 variation in R provides a 1:10 frequency change, and a 2:1 change in capacitance changes the frequency 1:2. The value of C_2 should always be $(4/d^2)C_1$.

Damping is changed by changing the ratio of C_1 to C_2, giving $Q = \sqrt{C_2/C_1}$. The product of C_1 and C_2 must always remain the same.

17.3.2.2 High-Pass Filters

A high-pass second-order filter is shown in Fig. 17-45. The cutoff frequency can be adjusted by changing C_1 and C_2, by keeping their values identical, or by varying R_1 and R_2, by keeping $R_1 = (4/d^2)R_2$. A 10:1 change in C produces a 1:10 frequency change. A 2:1 change in R produces a 1:2 frequency change.

Damping is changed by changing the ratio of R_1 and R_2, while keeping their product constant. The gain of unity-gain Sallen-Key filters is always one.

17.3.3 Equal Component-Value Sallen-Key Filters

Equal component-value Sallen-Key filters are the simplest to design and have the advantage of being able to be either high pass or low pass by simply interchanging the frequency-determining resistors and capacitors.

17.3.3.1 Low-Pass Filters

In the second-order low-pass filter (Fig. 17-46), frequency is changed by varying either R_1 and R_2 or C_1 and C_2, always keeping the values equal. A 10:1 resistor change will change the frequency 1:10, and a 2:1 capacitor change changes the frequency 1:2.

If the damping is three or above, the circuit becomes an oscillator; therefore, it is important to keep $R_4 = (2 - d)R_3$. To keep the offset at a minimum, it is best to have $R_3 = R_{in} + R_1 + R_2$.

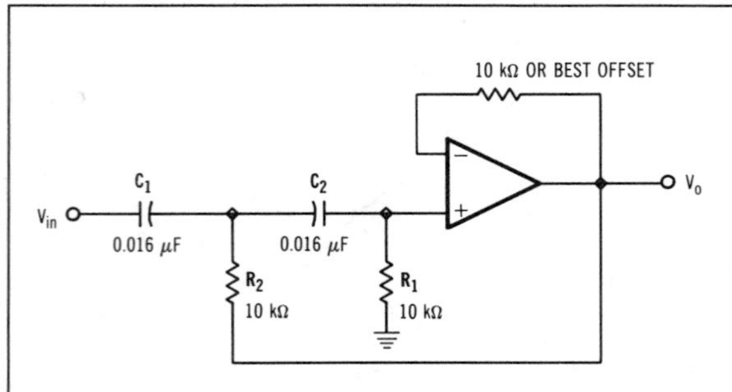

Figure 17-45 Unity-gain Sallen-Key high-pass filter normalized to 1 kHz and 10 kΩ.

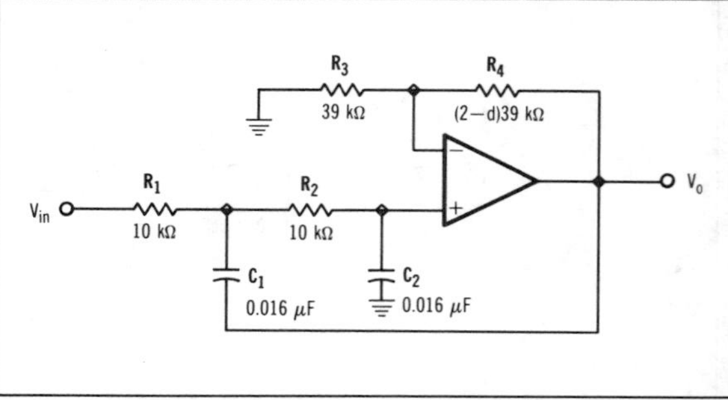

Figure 17-46 Equal-component-value Sallen-Key 12-dB/octave low-pass filter normalized to 1 kHz and 10 kΩ.

The gain of the circuit is fixed at (3 − d) or about +6 dB.

17.3.3.2 High-Pass Filters

A second-order high-pass filter is shown in Fig. 17-47. The frequency is changed by varying either C_1 and C_2 or R_1 and R_2, keeping the values equal. A 2:1 capacitor change will change the frequency 1:2, and a 10:1 resistor change changes the frequency 10:1.

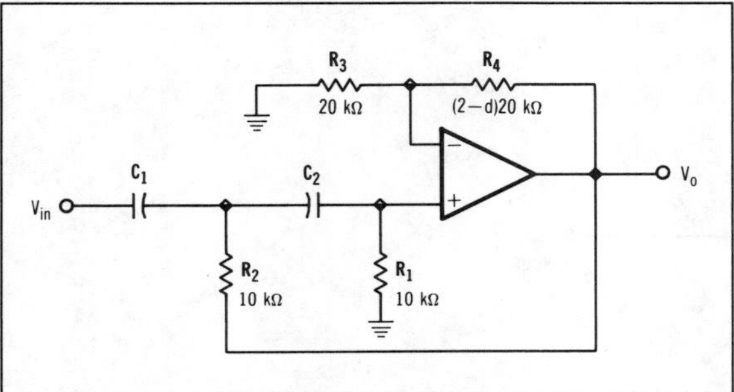

Figure 17-47 Equal-component-value Sallen-Key 12-dB/octave high-pass filter normalized to 1 kHz and 10 kΩ.

The damping is adjusted by varying the ratio of R_3 and R_4. Be sure $R_4 = (2 - d)R_3$.

The gain of the circuit is fixed at about +6 dB.

17.3.4 Unity-Gain-State Variable Filters

The frequency of the circuit in Fig. 17-48 can be changed as in the preceding circuits by varying R_1 and R_2 or C_1 and C_2, keeping the values identical. A 10:1 resistor change produces a 1:10 frequency change, and a 2:1 capacitor change produces a 1:2 frequency change.

The damping is varied by changing the ratio of R_3 and R_4 by making $R_4 = [(3 - d)/d]\ R_3$. For stability, R_3 and R_4 should be adjusted to produce a bandpass gain of 1.

R_5, R_6, and R_7 must have a ratio of 1:1:1, and R_8 and R_9 can be any value including a short. Ideally the values of R_8, R_9, and R_3 should be picked to keep the offset voltage of the ICs at a minimum.

17.3.5 Variable-Gain-State Variable Filters

The variable-gain-state variable filter shown in Fig. 17-49 is the same as the unity-gain-state variable filter except the damping feedback is inverted and summed with the input and feedback on the inverted input, which makes gain and damping completely independent.

The frequency is adjusted the same as in a unity-gain-state variable filter. The damping is changed by varying the ratio of R_3 and R_4 by making $R_4 = (d)R_3$. This filter gain can be adjusted by adjusting R_{12}. If R_1, R_2, and R_{12} are equal, the gain is one. R_{12} is determined by dividing it by G, the desired gain.

The values of $R_8 - R_{11}$ are not critical and should be picked for minimum offset.

17.4 GRAPHIC EQUALIZERS

A graphic equalizer is most often used to shape the signal during recording. It is called "graphic" because the output frequency response follows the shape of the adjustable slides. Graphic equalizers are normally two-thirds or full-octave devices.

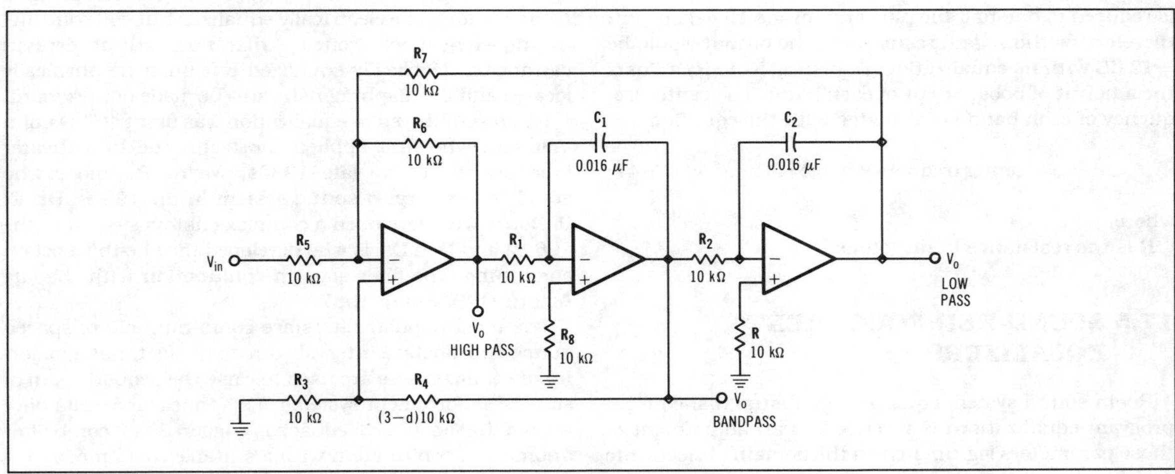

Figure 17-48 Unity-gain, state-variable second-order low-pass, high-pass, bandpass filter normalized to 1 kHz and 10 kΩ.

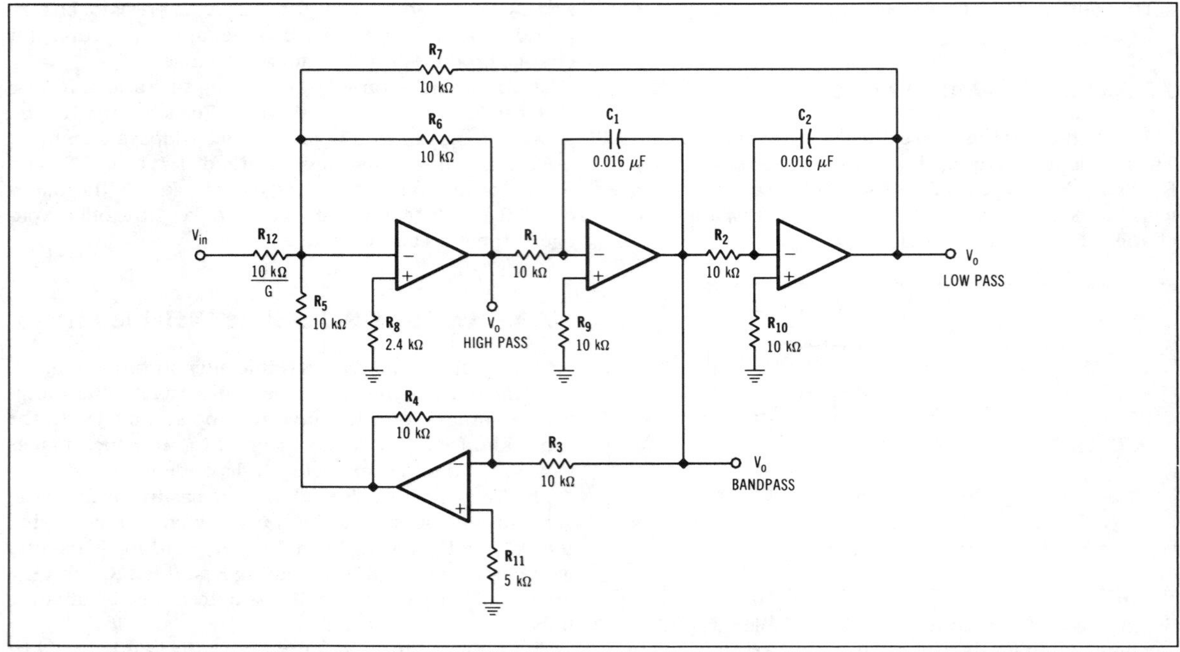

Figure 17-49 Variable-gain, state-variable second-order low-pass, high-pass, and bandpass filter normalized to 1 kHz and 10 kΩ.

Graphic equalizers may be passive or active. A simple equalizer is shown in Fig. 17-50[4]. This is called a *subtractive equalizer* and only uses the integrated circuits to isolate and sum. IC_1 isolates the preceding circuit and its impedance from the equalizer, and IC_2 sums all the Wein-bridge tonearms and isolates the effects of the next circuit on the equalizer.

The wideband signal enters the equalizer tonearm and is reduced to one-half the plus and minus 12-dB output; therefore, without gain restoration, the output would be −12 dB with no equalization. Adjusting R_1 to R_7 adjusts the amount of boost or cut of each band. The center frequency of each band is calculated with the equation

$$\text{center frequency} = 1/2\pi CR \qquad (17\text{-}47)$$

where,

R is the resistance in megohms.

17.5 SOUND-REINFORCEMENT EQUALIZERS

Room sound system equalization, distinguished from program equalization, is intended as an adjustment of those parameters legitimately in the domain of electronic equalization that optimizes the acoustic response of the loudspeaker in its interaction with the acoustic environment.

Three main domains predominate in room equalization:

1. The acoustic environment's domain.
2. The electrical or electronic domain.
3. The transducer's domain.

For example, an undamped resonant "bump" in a transducer can be electrically equalized but will continue to ring when shock excited. A diaphragmatic absorption cannot be electrically equalized but must be physically located and the diaphragmatic area be made nonresonant.

Room sound system equalization was first tried by John Volkman who first applied the technique to a theater loudspeaker in the late 1930s; Wayne Rudmose who equalized an airport sound system in the 1950s; Dr. C. P. Boner who developed a complex custom system in the 1960s; and Don Davis who developed the one-third-octave combining-type filter sets (in conjunction with the late Arthur C. Davis) in 1967.

The most popular filters are combining filters spaced at one-third-octave intervals due to the fact that a majority of equalizer sets are used to raise the acoustic gain of sound-reinforcement systems. TEF™ measurements have shown that acoustic feedback is triggered by a comb filter anomaly in conjunction with a suitable room mode.

What has been called a room ring mode is actually a transducer ring mode—that is, an undamped resonance in a microphone or loudspeaker that finds an acoustic

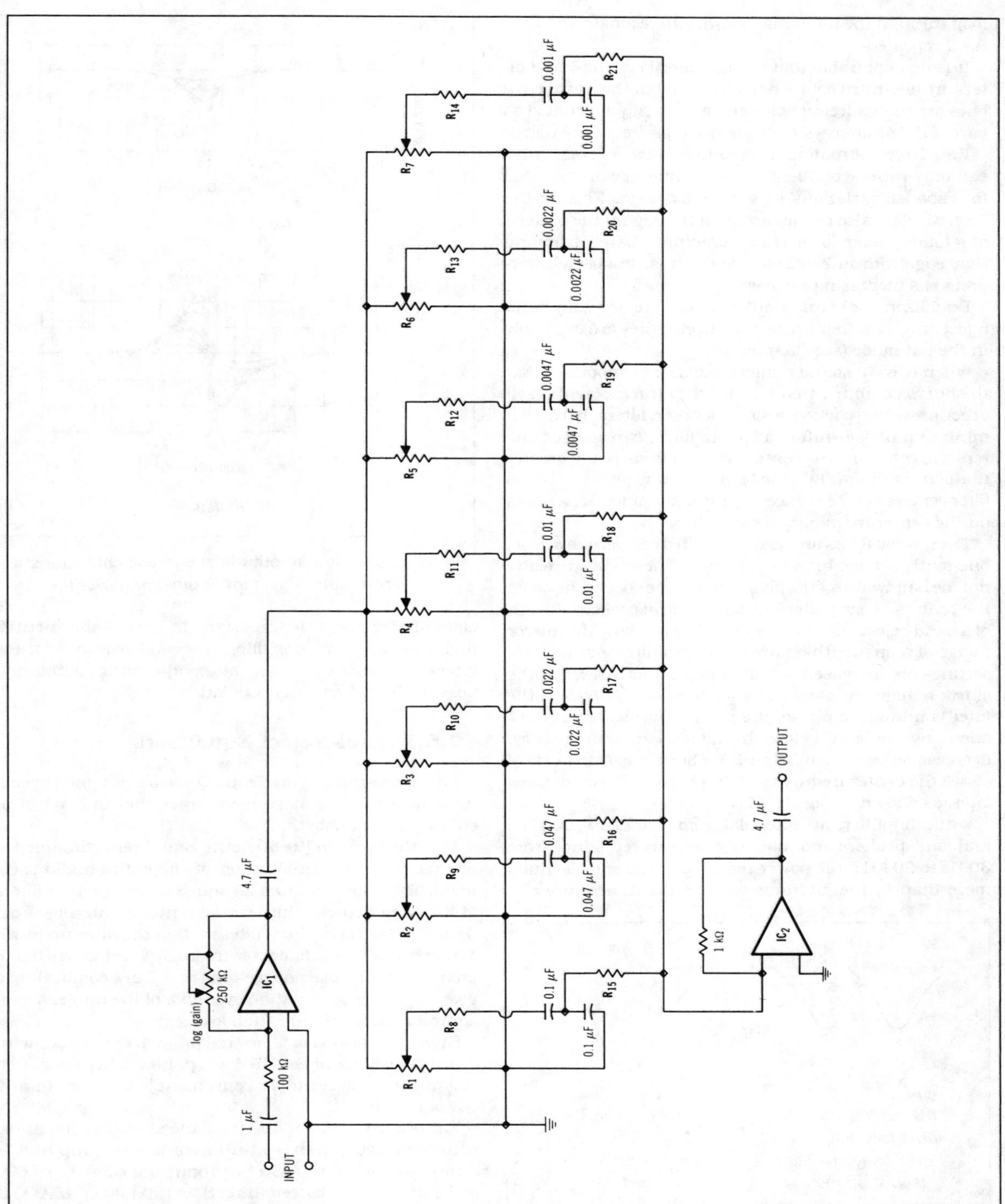

Figure 17-50 A subtractive equalizer.

loop through the room that allows it to resonate and hear itself repeatedly.

It is demonstrable that a vast majority of the comb filters are one-third octave or wider and that the few narrow ones are higher frequencies and are usually alternated as part of the desired system response high-frequency rolloff.

Equalizers cannot improve loudspeaker coverage; they can only raise acoustic gain and remove coloration due to response variations in the loudspeaker. Raising the acoustic gain also causes areas on the edge of the pattern of a loudspeaker to increase sometimes barely bringing that edge into intelligibility and, thus, is falsely interpreted as increasing the coverage.

Equalizers for sound reinforcement are normally band reject only, or if they are boost and cut, they are used only in the cut mode (see Chapter 26).

When used in sound reinforcement, it is important that the filters combine, that is, that they interact with each other providing a smooth slope between filters. In a good, minimum phase-shift combining filter, two adjacent filters will combine, the center between them being greater than either filter (Fig. 17-51). In this way peaks between filter centers can be reduced by the same amount as peaks on the center frequency of each filter.

The normal filters are called one-third octave, one octave, one-tenth octave, broad or narrow. These are in reality not the bandwidth of the filters but are the spacing between the centers of each adjacent filter. The actual bandwidth of a band-reject one-third-octave filter is nearly the mirror image of a one-tenth-octave bandpass filter. As the filter settings are increased, the filter depth increases, but the skirts remain the same, as shown in Fig. 17-52A. If the filter is minimum phase, the phase angle will start at 0° about two octaves below the filter's center frequency, decrease to a minus 40° to 50° about one-third octave above the center frequency, going back to 0° two octaves later, as shown in Fig. 17-52B.

While amplifiers are often flat from near dc to 100 kHz, and loudspeakers and microphones can reproduce from 30 Hz to 20 kHz, the power required at the ends is much more than in the midranges where the devices are efficient. Therefore, it is important to have a sharp cutoff high-pass and low-pass filter. A second reason for these filters is to reduce floor and air-conditioning rumble and possible high-frequency oscillation.

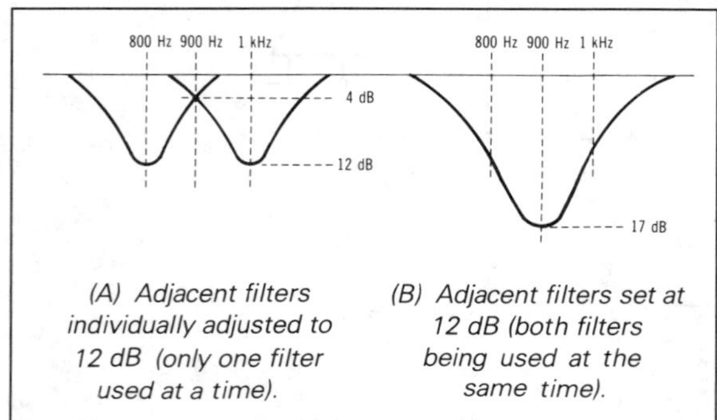

(A) Adjacent filters individually adjusted to 12 dB (only one filter used at a time).

(B) Adjacent filters set at 12 dB (both filters being used at the same time).

Figure 17-51 Combining filter characteristics.

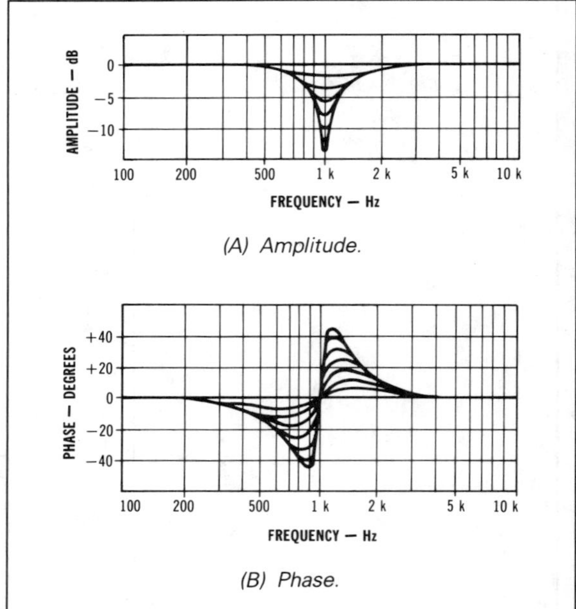

(A) Amplitude.

(B) Phase.

Figure 17-52 Filter amplitude and phase characteristics. *From Sound System Engineering (REFI)*

17.5.1 Band-Reject Equalizers

These one-third-octave equalizers are designed specifically for sound reinforcement since they only reject or cut and do not boost.

The Altec Lansing 1650 Active Equalizer is designed to provide accurate equalization of the entire audio spectrum. The 1650 contains 28 active band-rejection filters at ISO-preferred one-third-octave center frequencies from 31.5 to 16,000 Hz. Each filter section provides up to 15-dB attenuation at its center frequency and is skirted to crossover with adjacent sections at −7 dB, combining to give ripple-free summation over 85% of the range. A gain control restores equalization losses.

High- and low-pass filters roll off at 18 dB/octave with continuously variable 3-dB down points. A bypass switch allows the filter set to be conveniently switched in and out of the circuit.

The output is 150 or 600 Ω balanced and is compatible with high-level (up to +21-dBm) or low-level (up to +1-dBm) systems. The 1650 has input impedances of 600 or 15,000 Ω unbalanced (direct) or 150,600 or 15,000 Ω balanced (with accessory transformers). Filter characteristics are shown in Fig. 17-53.

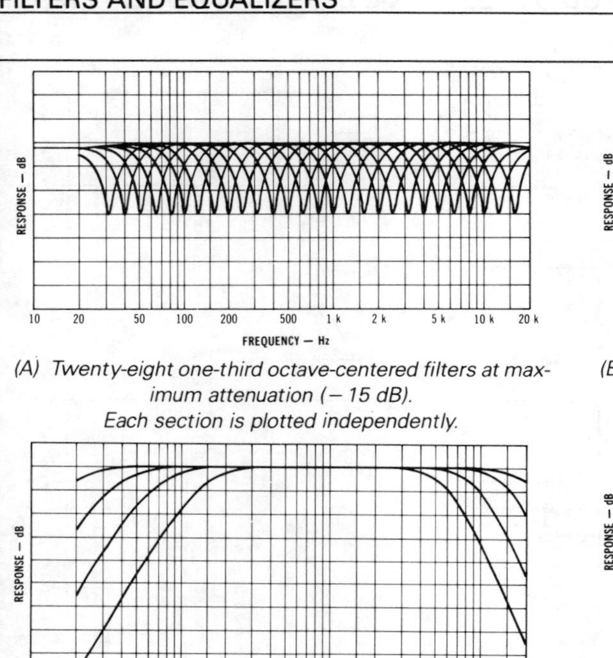

(A) Twenty-eight one-third octave-centered filters at maximum attenuation (– 15 dB). Each section is plotted independently.

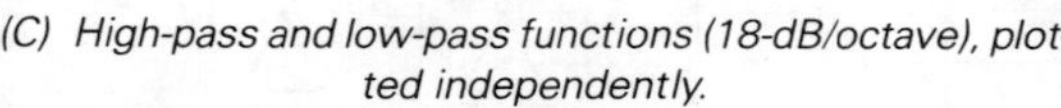

(C) High-pass and low-pass functions (18-dB/octave), plotted independently.

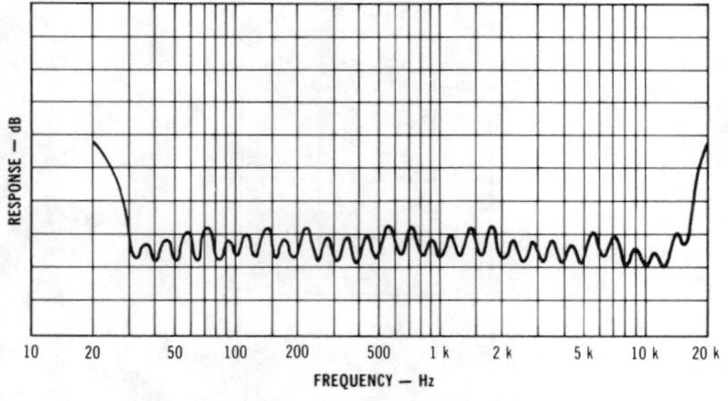

(E) All filter sections set for full attenuation.

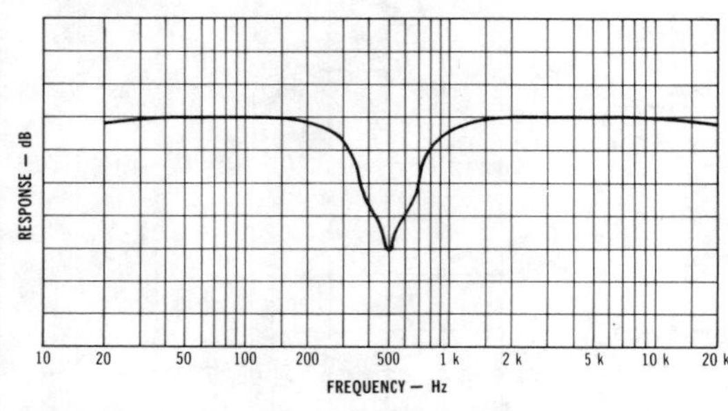

(G) 500-Hz filter set at – 15 dB, 400-Hz and 630-Hz filters set at – 8 dB.

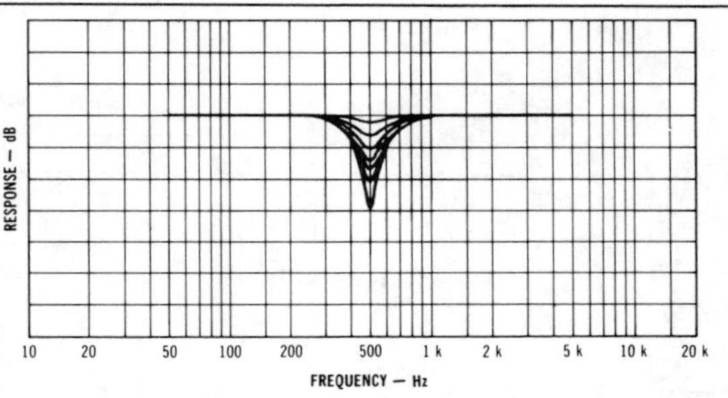

(B) Single filter, 500 Hz, shown in each detented position of attenuation.

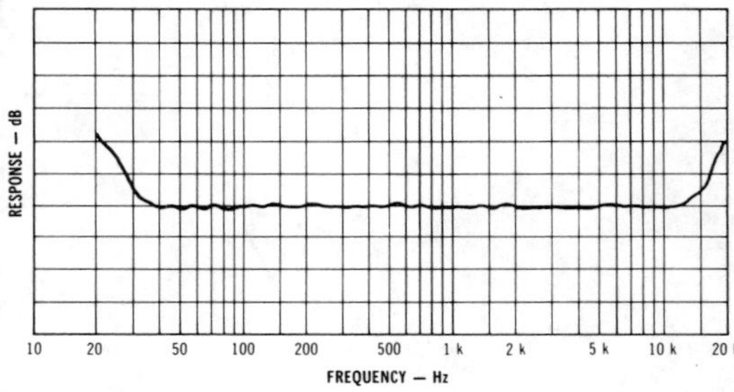

(D) All filter sections set at – 7-dB attenuation illustrating a slight degree of ripple (± ½ dB), characteristic of proper interaction between sections.

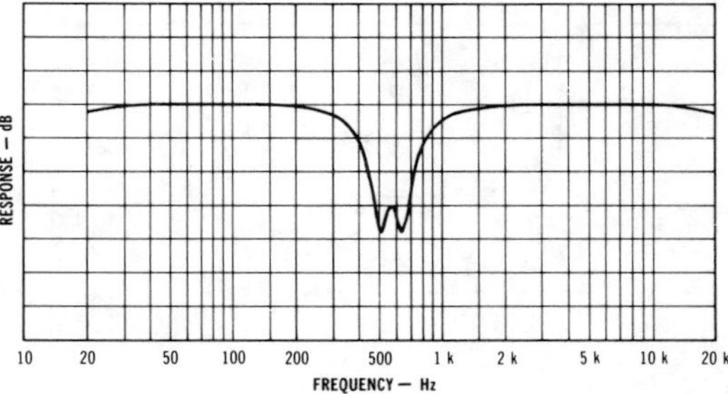

(F) Two adjacent filters, 500 Hz and 630 Hz, set for full attenuation.

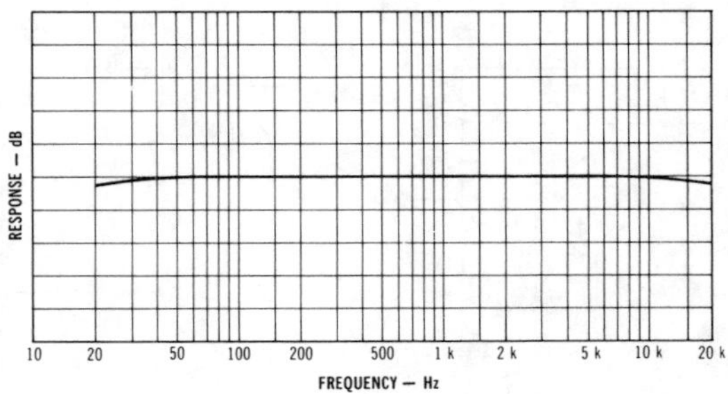

(H) All filters at 0 dB, high-pass and low-pass at off.

Figure 17-53 Filter characteristics *(From Sound System Engineering, Reference 1.)*

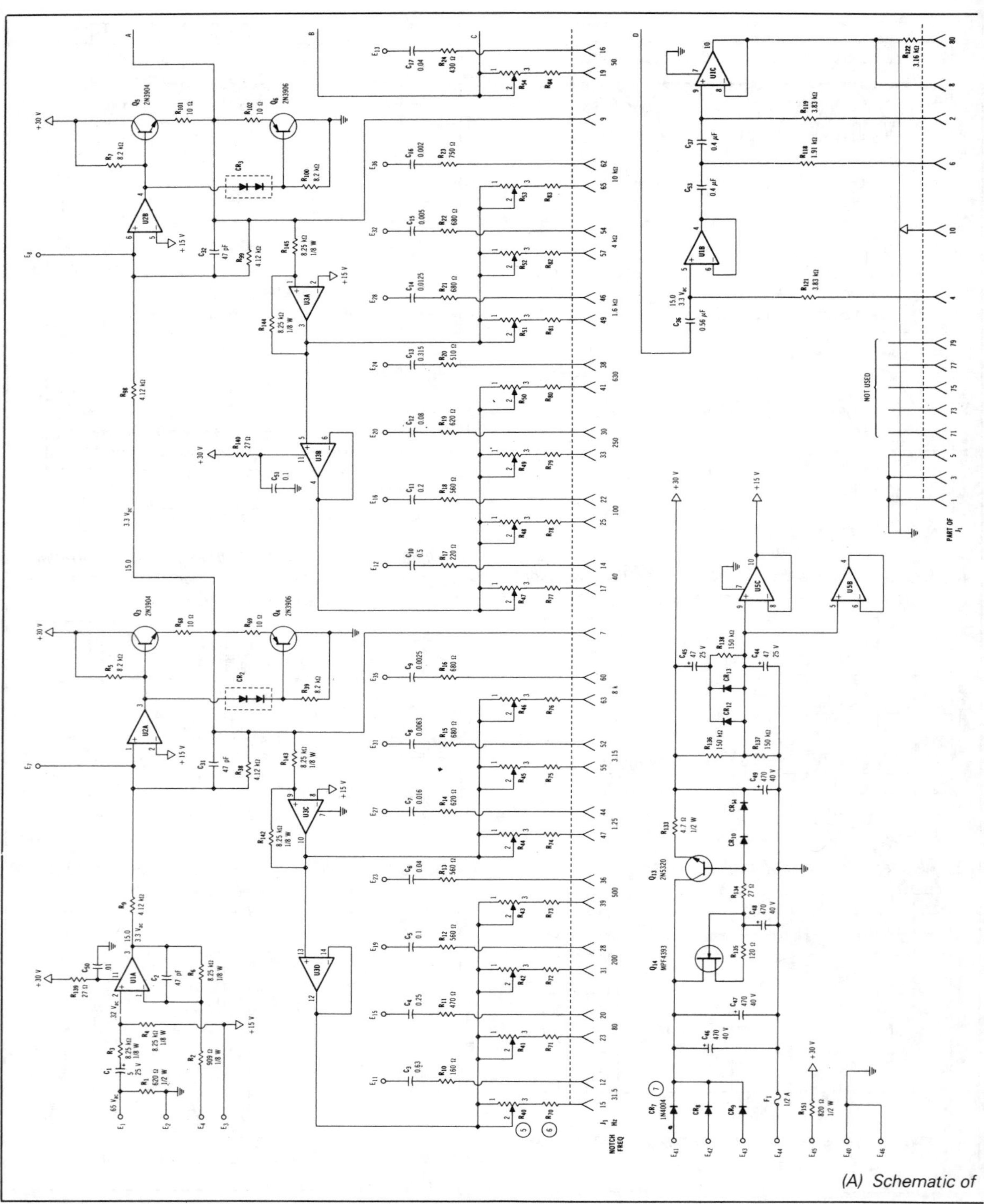

(A) Schematic of

Figure 17-54 Schematics for the Altec

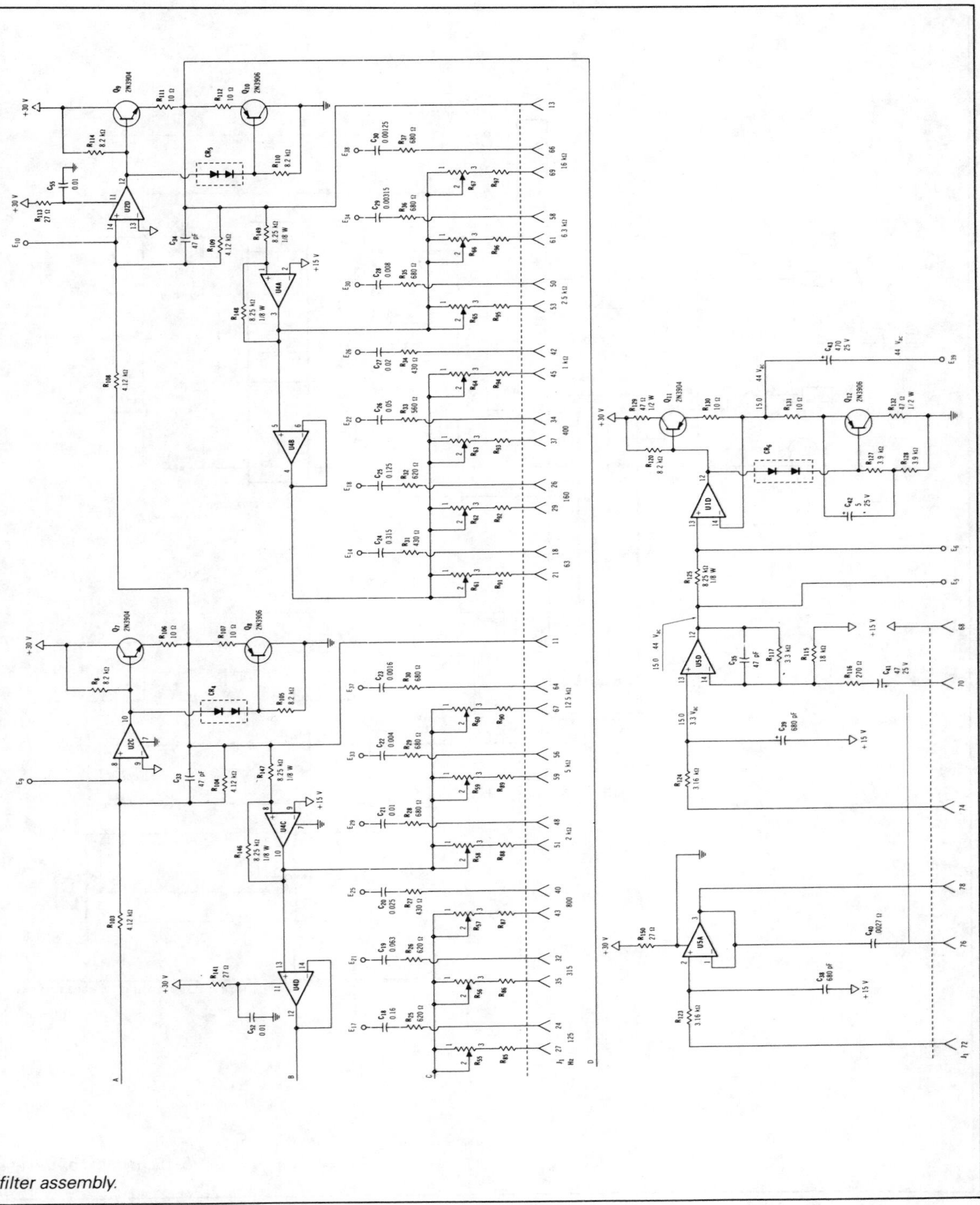

filter assembly.

1653A. *(Courtesy Altec Lansing Corp.)*

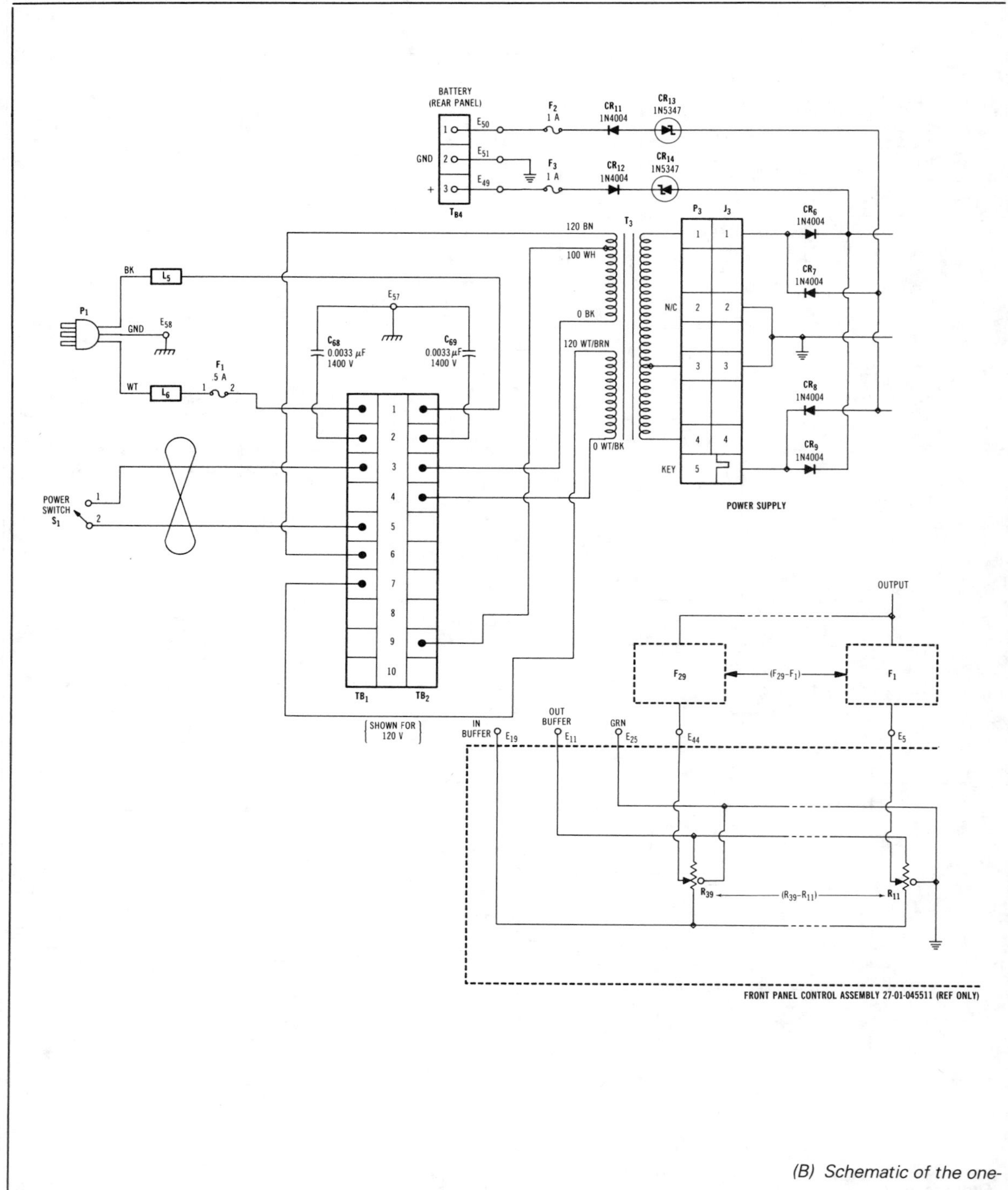

(B) Schematic of the one-

Figure 17-54—cont. Schematics for the

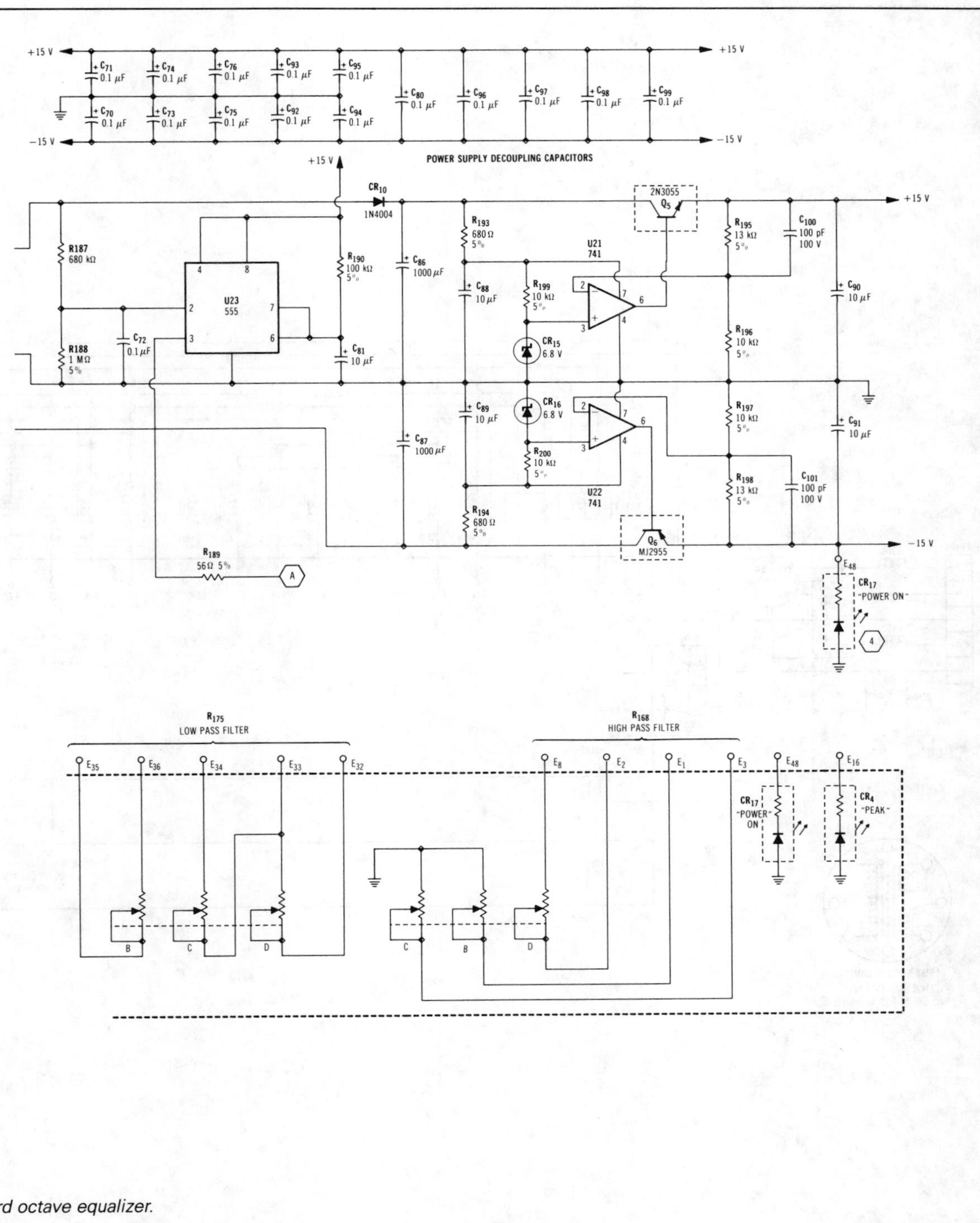

third octave equalizer.

Altec 1653A. *(Courtesy Altec Lansing Corp.)*

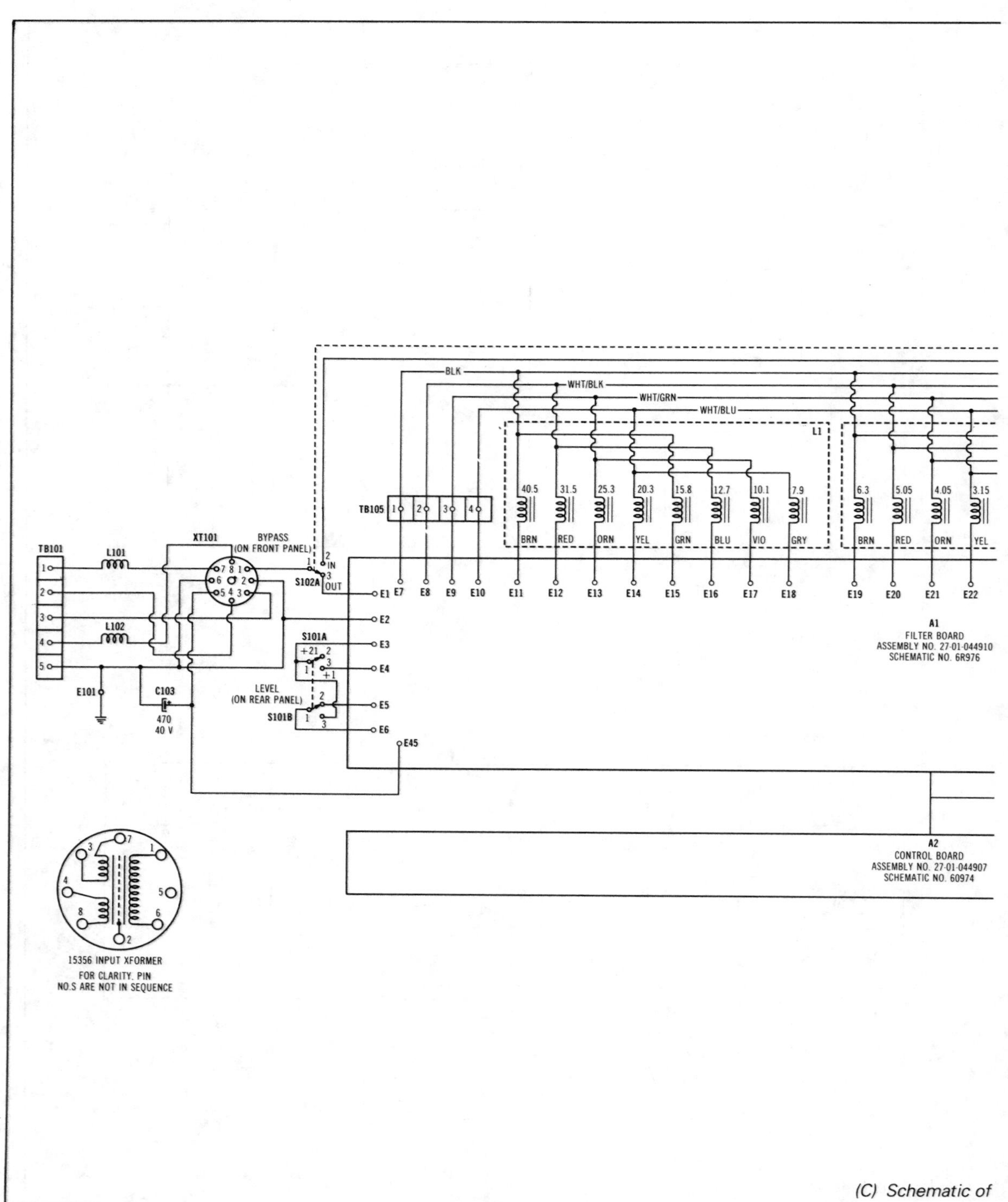

(C) Schematic of

Figure 17-54—cont. Schematics for the

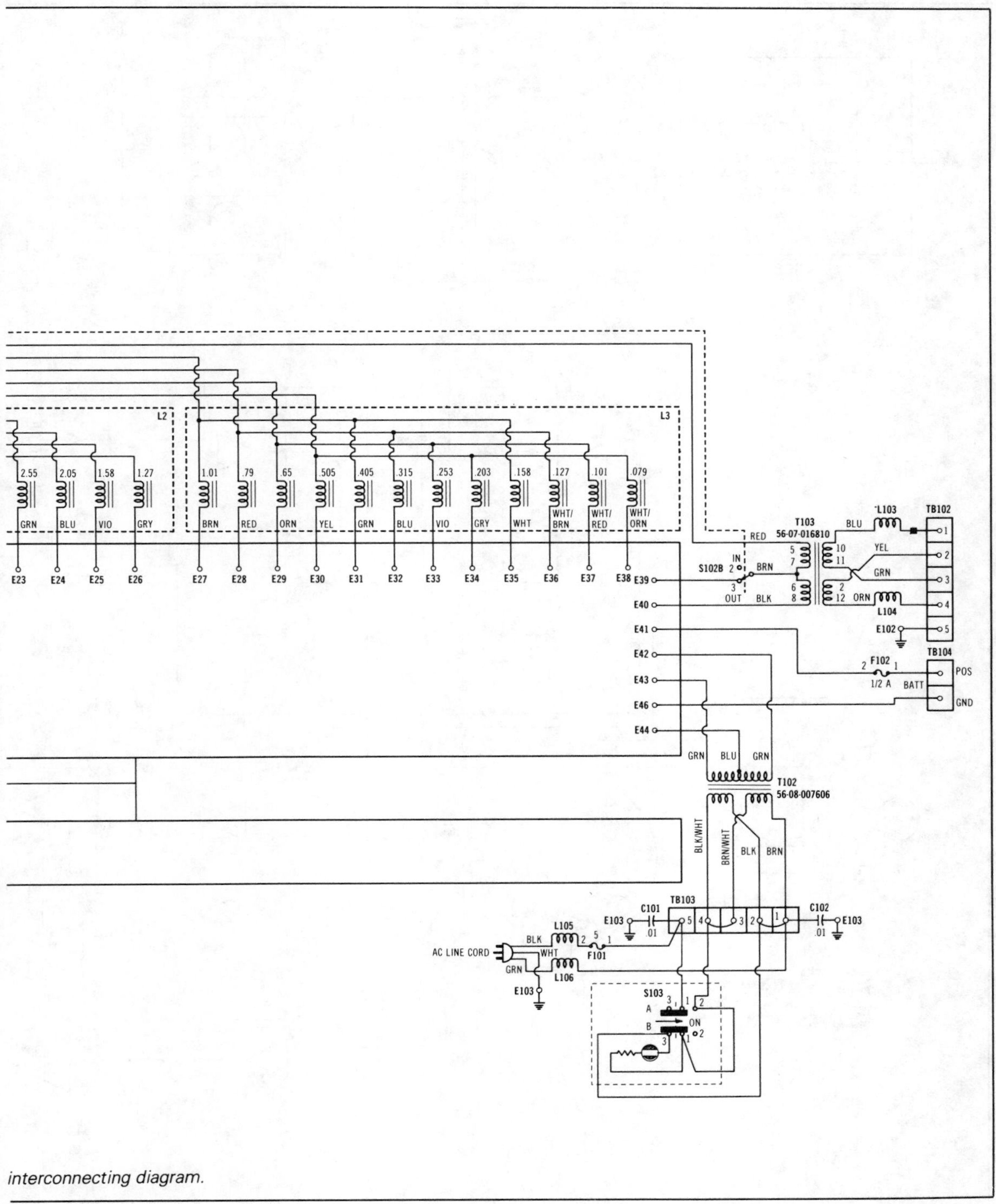

interconnecting diagram.

Altec 1653A. *(Courtesy Altec Lansing Corp.)*

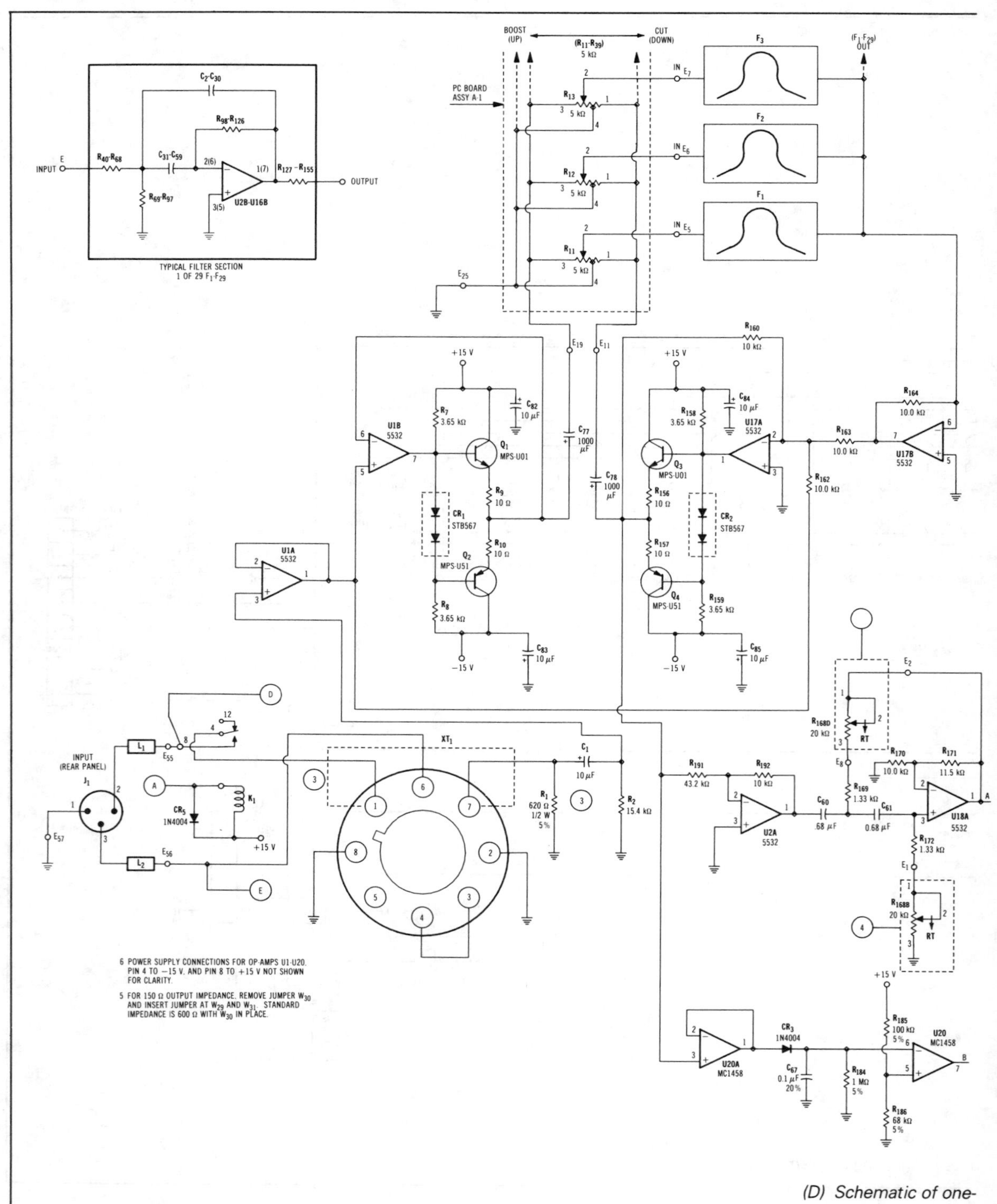

(D) Schematic of one-

Figure 17-54—cont. Schematics for the

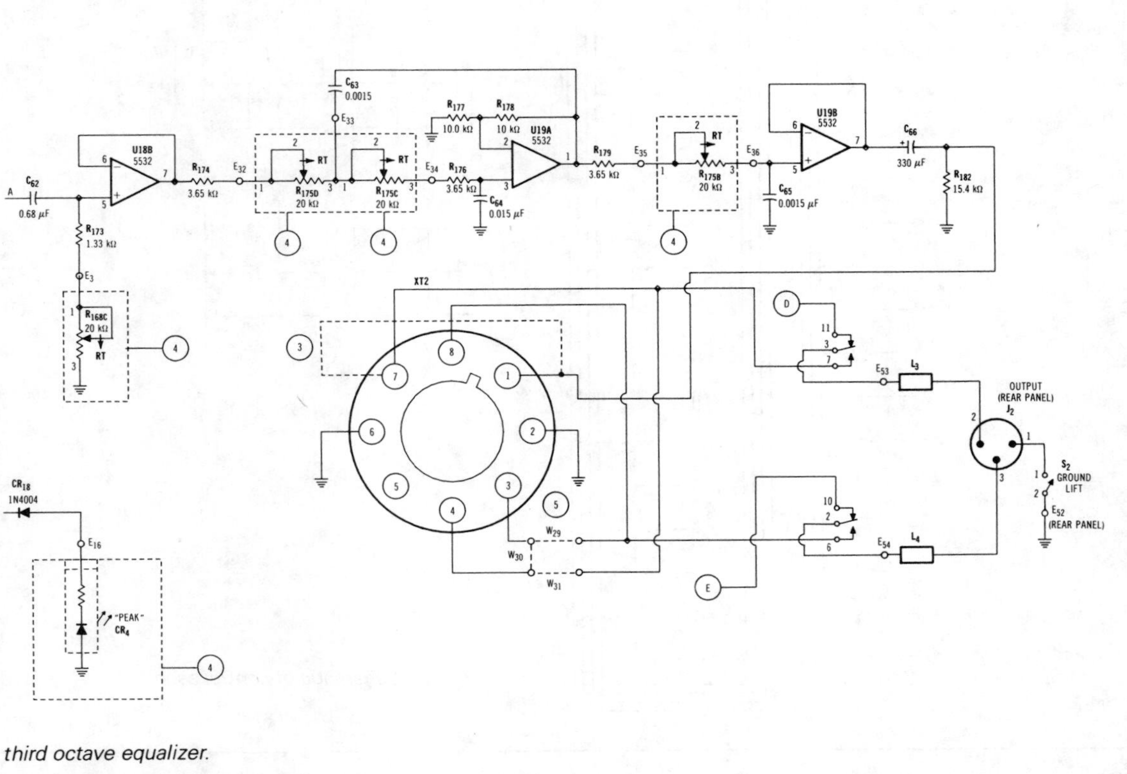

third octave equalizer.

Altec 1653A. *(Courtesy Altec Lansing Corp.)*

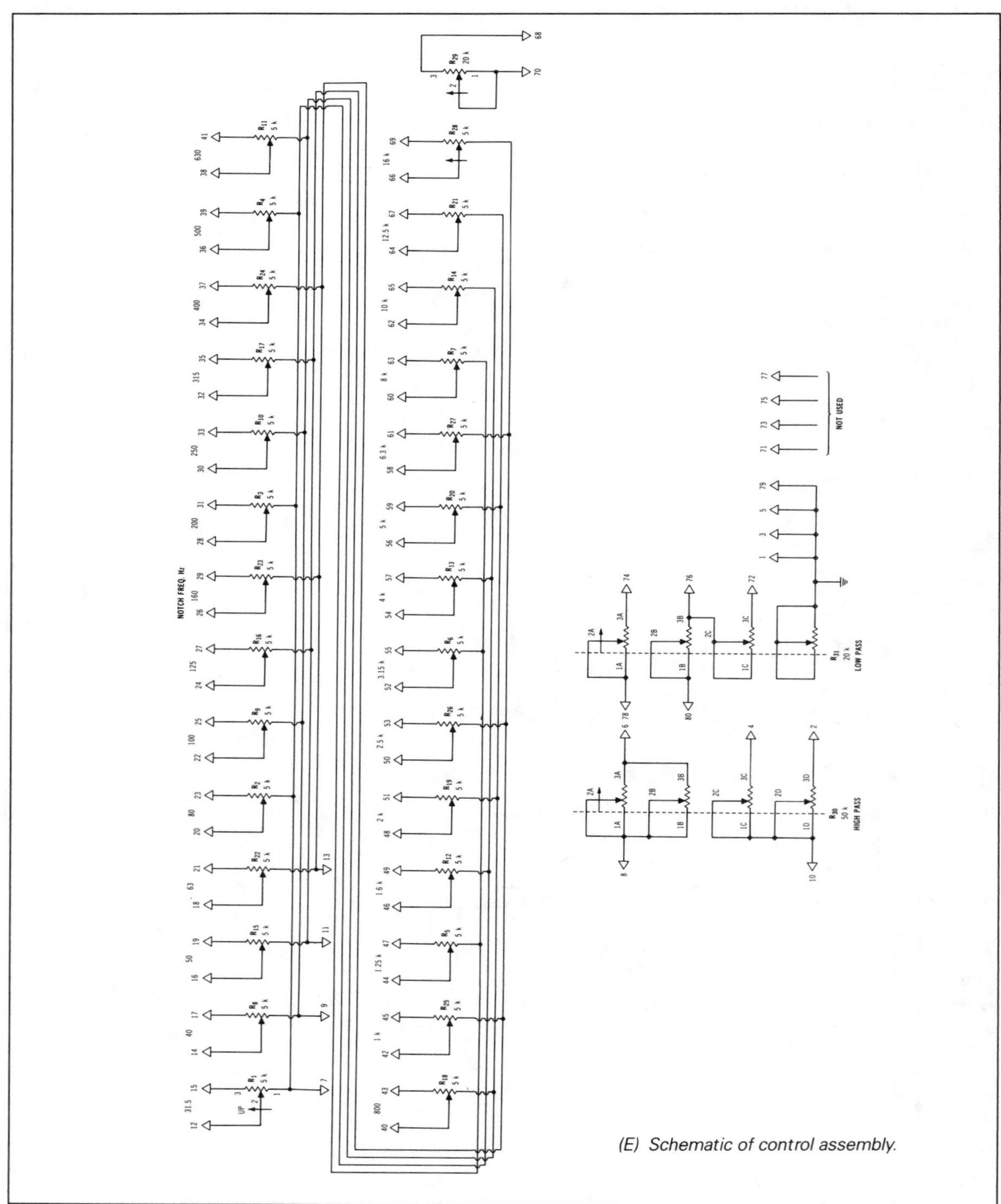

(E) Schematic of control assembly.

Figure 17-54—cont. Schematics for the Altec 1653A. *(Courtesy Altec Lansing Corp.)*

17.5.2 Cut-and-Boost Equalizers

A one-third-octave active equalizer, Altec Lansing model 1653A, is shown in Fig. 17-54. The unit consists of 29 one-third-octave minimum-phase-shift active filter sections from 25 Hz to 16 kHz. Each section provides 12 dB of boost and cut. An 18-dB/octave high-pass and low-pass filter is also included.

XT1 and XT2 are sockets for installing isolation transformers as equalizers may be mounted a considerable distance from the console or power amplifiers. With the power off, the equalizer is bypassed by relay K_1, therefore, making it "fail safe." Because active circuits can be overloaded easily, a peak indicating light is provided.

As in the graphic equalizer the input and output are isolated from the external circuits with op amps.

17.5.3 Synergistic Equalizers

Another equalizer is the Crown International EQ-2. The EQ-2 is basically two systems in one package. It consists of a very powerful hinge point (shelving) tone control system in conjunction with a one-half-octave equalizer that has adjustable frequency center points. The two systems coupled together make a strong equalizer system, hence the term *synergistic equalizer.*

The EQ-2 operates in the following manner. By using the balanced input, the user can select either unity gain or +10-dB gain. When the unbalanced input is selected, the unit operates only at unity gain. From the input, the signal is switch selected through the tone control system.

The tone control system allows the user to make drastic changes in the audio spectrum, such as raise the entire

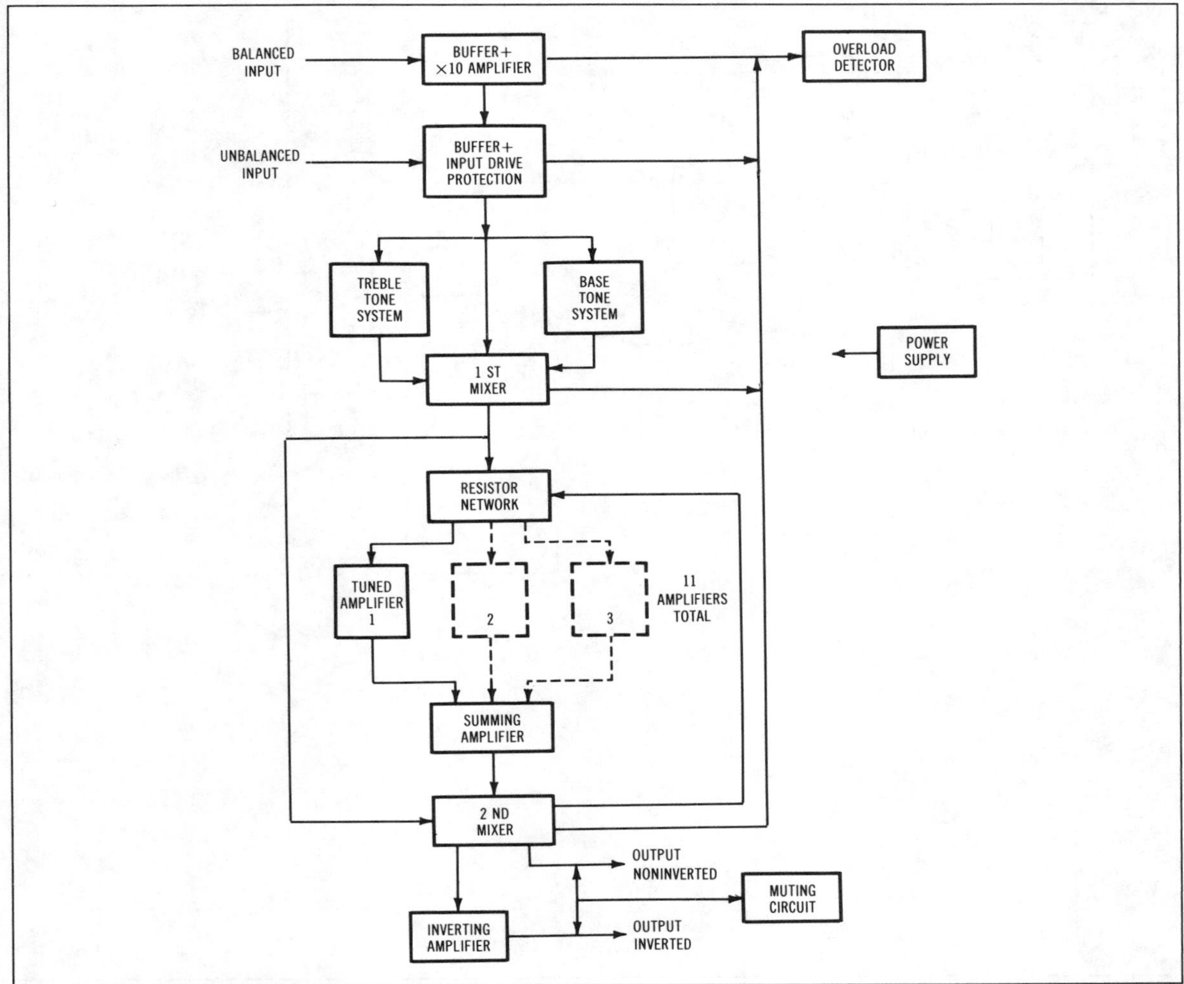

Figure 17-55 Block diagram Crown EQ-2 equalizer. *(Courtesy Crown International, Inc.)*

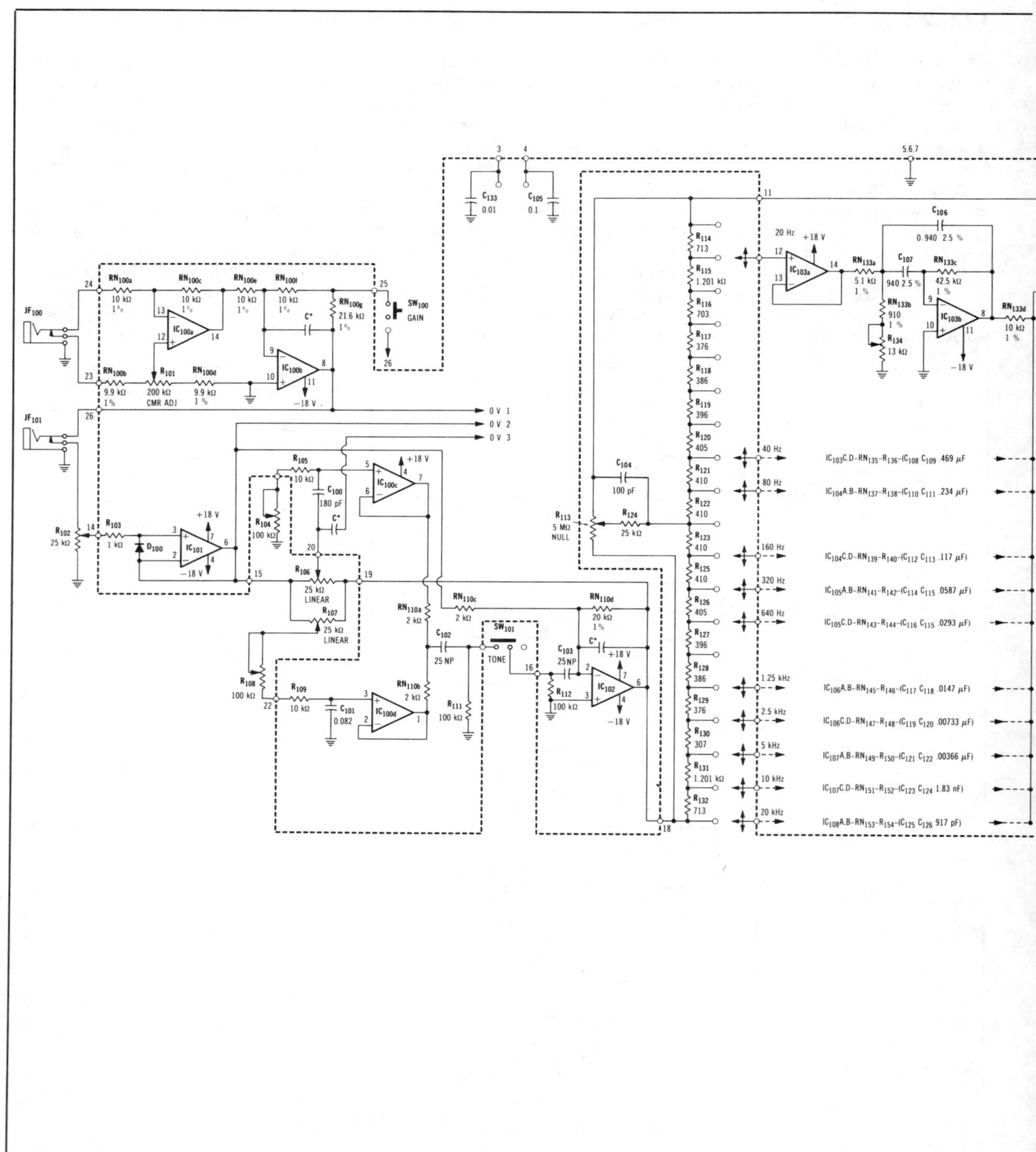

Figure 17-56 Schematic of the Crown EQ-2

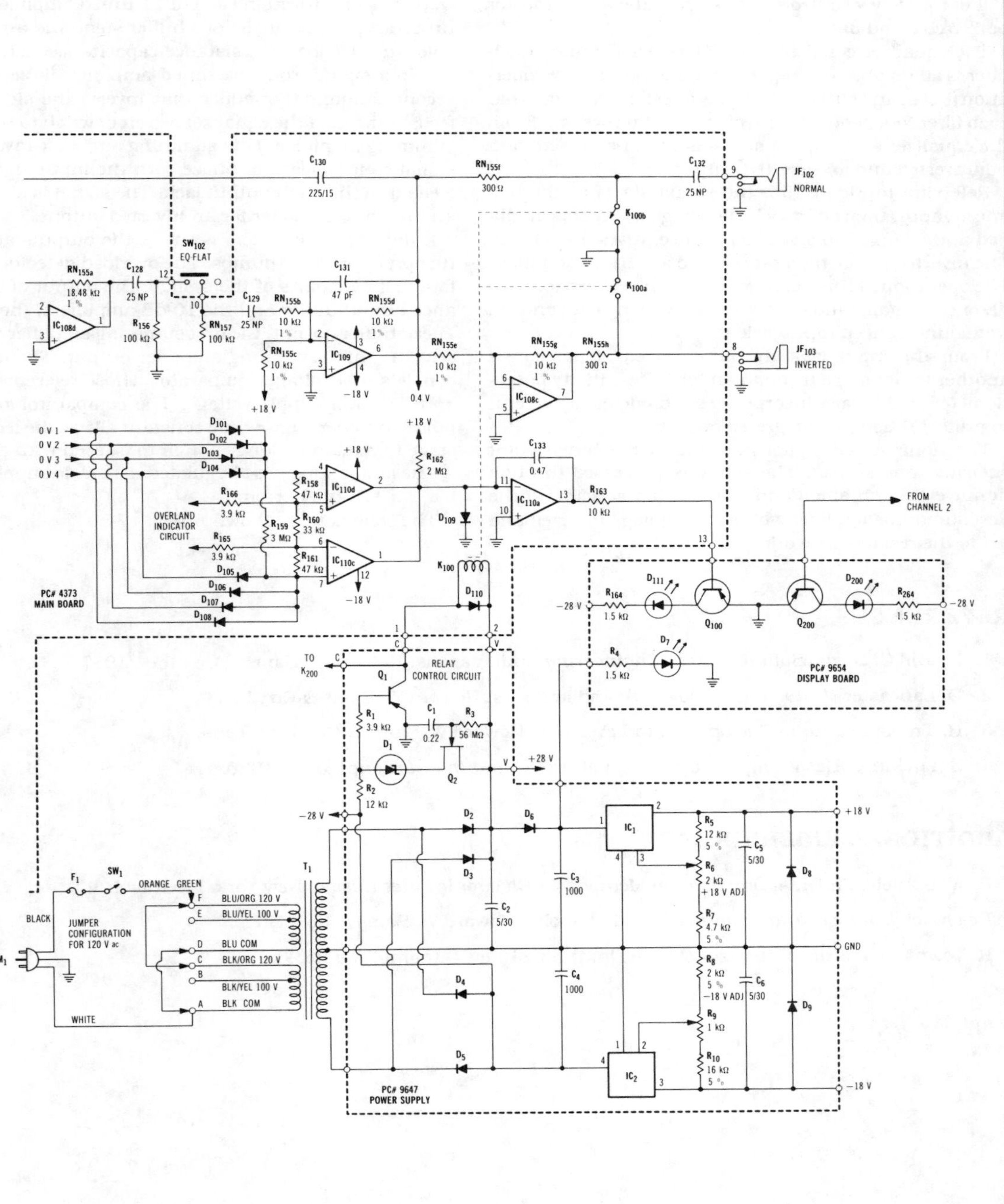

equalizer. *(Courtesy Crown International, Inc.)*

high-end frequencies or lower them. These controls consist of frequency controls and boost-and-cut controls for both treble and bass.

The equalizer consists of 11 filters per channel. Each filter is adjustable to a frequency center point. Filter operation (boost and cut) is selected by a resistor network that each filter independently selects from a bus system. From the equalizer section, the signal is then processed for a noninverted and an inverted output.

Referring to Fig. 17-55, the signal starts at the balanced input, then enters a buffer stage where it is amplified and changed to a low-impedance, high-level signal. The inverted signal then proceeds to a +10-dB amplifier. The operation of this amplifier is switch selected for +10 dB or unity gain, and the signal is inverted again and fed to the unbalanced input jack.

From the input jack the noninverted signal enters another buffer stage through an input sensitivity potentiometer. This stage incorporates a diode clamp circuit to protect the input integrated circuits.

The noninverted signal now enters the hinge point shelving tone system. The signal is processed through noninverting op amps and then switch selected to the first summing amplifier where the signal is inverted and fed to the resistor network.

Next, the signal is processed through the resistor network bus and through each of 11 tuned amplifiers. The tuned amplifiers consist of a buffer stage and an adjustable full feedback resistance-capacitance filter. The inverted signal from the tuned amplifiers is fed to the second summing amplifier that inverts the signal and feeds it through the equalizer selector switch to the third summing amplifier. This summing amplifier inverts the signal so it is again in phase with the input signal and feeds it to the main output jack. The signal is also fed to an inverting amplifier for an inverted output.

A muting relay system grounds the outputs at initial turnon to prevent thumps. The overload detector senses four critical points of the system: the output of the balanced input buffer and the 10-dB amplifiers, the unbalanced buffer output, the first summing amplifier output, and the third summing amplifier output. The detector consists of a voltage comparator whose reference is the ±18-V power-supply voltage. The comparator drives a pulse stretcher whose time constant allows the led driver stage to remain on long enough to be seen with the eye.

The power supply is a regulated ±18-V dc supply capable of a 175-mA current.

The schematic is shown in Fig. 17-56.

REFERENCES

1. D. and C. Davis, *Sound System Engineering*, Indianapolis: Howard W. Sams & Co., Inc., 1987.
2. D. Lancaster, *Active-Filter Cookbook*, Indianapolis: Howard W. Sams & Co., Inc.
3. H. Tremaine, *Audio Cyclopedia*, Indianapolis: Howard W. Sams & Co., Inc., 1969.
4. S. Lucking, "Designing a Graphic Equalizer," *Sound International*, June 1980.

ADDITIONAL BIBLIOGRAPHY

R. W. Daniels, Ph.D., *Approximation Methods for Electronic Filter Design*, New York: McGraw-Hill.

Reference Data for Radio Engineers, Indianapolis: Howard W. Sams & Co., 1975.

R. Townsley, *Passive Equalizer Design Data*, Blue Ridge Summit: Tab Books.

CHAPTER **18**

Delay

by Mahlon Burkhard

Delay is the amount of time by which an event or a signal is retarded. Its application to sound system design and installation began with the invention of vacuum-tube amplifiers although designers of concert halls and theaters used reflection of sound from walls and ceilings for delay long before. Electronically produced delay has become a practical tool in sound systems and for electronic enhancement of the sound in auditoriums with the availability of large-sized semiconductor memories at reasonable prices. This chapter will give a historical review of the delay mechanisms, go into the characteristics of delay systems in use today, and then review some of the psychoacoustic factors that form the basis for its use in sound systems. A brief overview of special-effects applications is included.

An event can be delayed and a signal can be delayed. The measure of the delay is a unit of time. Thus, a signal or an event can be delayed by a number of seconds, milliseconds, microseconds, and so on. Time is not delayed, contrary to common usage.

18.1 DELAY DEVICES

Although many delay devices have probably been replaced in recent years with digital delays, many sound systems were successfully installed with various magnetic tape and acoustic tube delays. A brief description of these and other older types will help to emphasize the impact of solid-state digital delay on sound systems.

18.1.1 Lumped-Element Transmission Lines

At one time the most reliable method of producing audio frequency delay was through a periodic-wave filter network. A low-pass inductor-capacitor section that is terminated in its matching or characteristic impedance can produce a smooth frequency response for frequencies below a cutoff frequency and a small amount of delay. The delays of sections in series are additive so that useful but bulky (and expensive) delay systems are possible. Somewhat more compact analog delays can be obtained with all-pass amplifier chains, but they are not competitive with digital methods when delays longer than a few milliseconds are required. An all-pass amplifier section that produces phase shift proportional to frequency and hence delay is shown in Fig. 18-1.

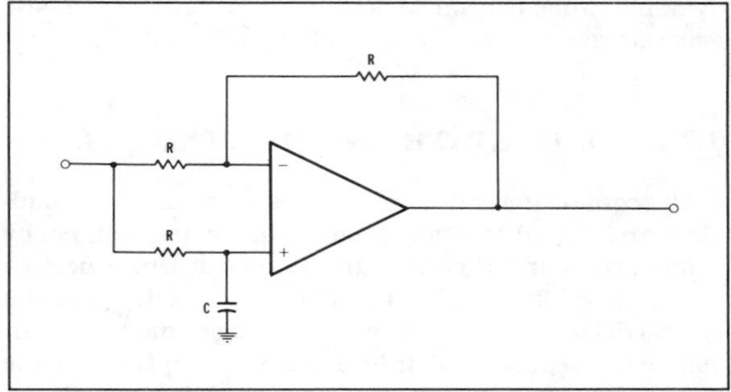

Figure 18-1 An all-pass amplifier having phase shift proportional to frequency and exhibiting a small amount of delay.

18.1.2 Magnetic Tape Delays

A patent filed by Bascom in 1917 and issued in 1920 described a device for "providing some means to delay the electrically transmitted waves by an amount sufficient to bring them into phase at the receiving point with the waves transmitted through the air" in auditoriums. The delay was composed of a long loop of magnetizable wire passing a "recording magnet" and "several reproducing magnets."[1] We now know that "exact phase" is not necessary.

Magnetic tape recorders constructed according to this basic concept were used until the early 1970s. To obtain a wide bandwidth, the tape on one version ran at 30 in./s. This higher speed also permitted smaller delay increments to be set with the relatively large pickup heads. The loop was 70 cm long and passed in succession over an erase head, a record head, and up to 13 pickup heads arranged in a circle. Other versions used more typical 7.5 or 15 in./s speeds and obtained appreciably longer tape life, but with longer delay-setting intervals. The delay t is easily calculated by dividing the distance d from the record head to the playback head by the tape speed s:

$$t = d/s \tag{18-1}$$

A tape speed of 30 in./s and a head spacing of 1 in. produces a delay of 33.3 ms.

Maintenance is required on a regular basis. The tape must be replaced frequently to maintain good signal-to-noise ratios and low distortion. Heads must also be cleaned and normal mechanical maintenance schedules followed. Signal quality comparable to a tape recorder may be expected. Very long delays can be obtained relatively inexpensively with several heads on a reel-to-reel system.

18.1.3 Acoustic Delay Tube

A tube or pipe fitted with a sound source at one end and one or more microphones positioned along its length has been used for delay. The other end of the tube is closed and has a sound absorber to prevent reflections and thus eliminate standing waves. Attenuation of sound in such a tube depends on frequency and increases in proportion to the length of the tube so that large amounts of equalization and microphone signal amplification are necessary. Practical delays using tubes are limited by dynamic range to around 50 ms. Vibration and acoustic isolation are an essential part of any installation.

18.2 SOLID-STATE AND DIGITAL DELAYS

All acoustic delay devices and systems based on solid-state and digital technology store the electrical signal by some means and then feed the signal to output devices at a specified later time. Fig. 18-2 is a block diagram of a typical delay path. The incoming analog audio frequency signal is preprocessed into a form appropriate to the memory or delay medium, fed to the delay medium, extracted from the delay medium, and then postprocessed prior to output. With solid-state delays, the signal is sampled, the samples are stored for the desired time, and then the signal is reconstructed from the samples for further amplification, application to loudspeakers and so on. Various processing steps used in these types of delay include companding, antialias filtering, and sample and hold. A distinction needs to be made between analog types, which use bucket brigade or certain types of charge-coupled-device (CCD) memory elements, for example, and true, digital-memory-based systems. For convenience, the former will be discussed as analog shift-register-based memory. The discussion in the following two sections applies equally to analog and digital delay systems. The extension to coding of amplitudes for digital delay will be considered in section 18.3 after the discussion of analog shift-register type delays.

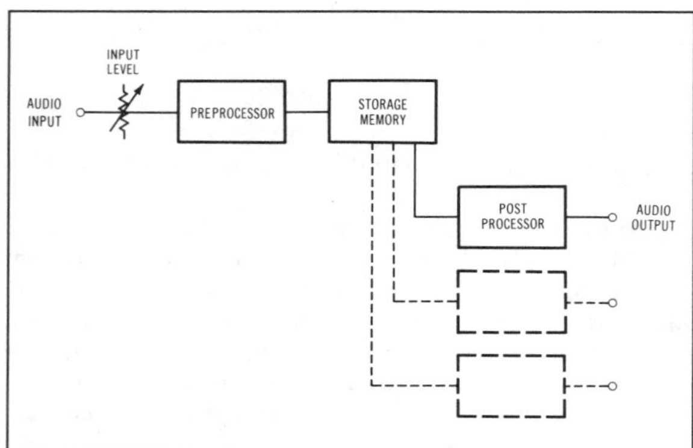

Figure 18-2 Block diagram of a delay.

18.2.1 Sampling Theory I

A signal is sampled by looking at its amplitude at regular intervals and disregarding its amplitude at other times. The procedure is illustrated in Fig. 18-3. A sequence of sampling pulses acts like a switch that turns on the signal for a brief instant and then disconnects for the remainder of the sampling interval. The result is a sequence of pulses having amplitudes corresponding to the signals (i.e., an amplitude-modulated pulse train). According to the *sampling theorem*, a continuous-bandwidth limited-signal waveform that contains no frequency components higher than frequency f_c can be recreated if it is sampled at a rate greater than $2f_c$ samples per second. Since the real world never completely satisfies the theoretical conditions, sampling frequencies are usually $3f_c$ or higher. Thus, 15-kHz bandwidth delays will be found with clock frequencies of 50 kHz or more. There are several reasons for this larger than theoretical sampling frequency. (Other considerations apply to delta modulation, which is discussed later.)

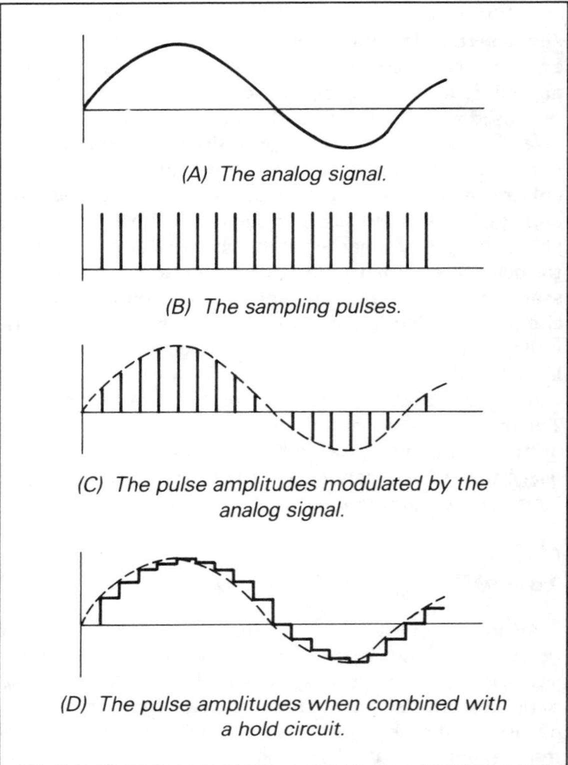

(A) The analog signal.

(B) The sampling pulses.

(C) The pulse amplitudes modulated by the analog signal.

(D) The pulse amplitudes when combined with a hold circuit.

Figure 18-3 The process of signal sampling.

A small, but significant, amount of time is required to establish that the signal sample is of a particular amplitude for both analog shift register and digital types of delay. The time is usually longer for digital delay to allow for the additional time required for the analog-to-digital conversion process.

18.2.2 Antialias Filters

As stated previously, sampling of the audio signal is a form of modulation. Modulation of a band-limited signal with upper frequency, f_c, by the sampling frequency f_s, shifts the original spectrum out to f_s, $2f_s$, $3f_s$, and so on

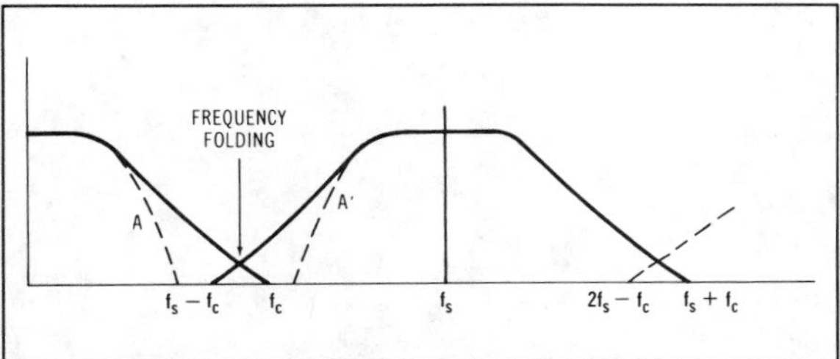

Figure 18-4 Frequency spectrum envelope showing the effect of the sampling theorem.

in addition to the one at the origin. If the sampling frequency is not high enough or the band is not adequately limited, part of the spectrum centered on f_s will fold over into the original signal spectrum. See Fig. 18-4. The fold-over components become a part of the signal in the recovery process. They produce distortion components that cannot be filtered out. In practice there is always some frequency folding because of imperfect band limiting, noise, and some high-frequency energy that may be present.

An antialias filter is a sharp cutoff low-pass filter that limits the bandwidth of the signal, such as A in Fig. 18-4. It is typically sixth order or higher. One is required on the input, before the sampling takes place, and one, at the output as part of the reconstruction circuit. Aliasing and fold-over must be eliminated or reduced by selection of a high sampling frequency and an adequately sharp filter.

The economics of delay design dictate a relatively low sampling frequency because less memory is required. Memory required is proportional to the sampling frequency. The required rate of cutoff of the antialias filter and its cost is inversely proportional to the separation between the upper frequency (f_c) and the sampling frequency (f_s). As the rate of cutoff is increased, antialias filters tend to be less stable.

18.2.3 Analog Shift Register Delays

Analog shift registers have appeared in two forms, the bucket brigade and the analog charge-coupled device (CCD). They are shift registers because they move a sample in the form of an electrical charge from one stage or register to the next in response to timing signals. The delay of a shift register is proportional to the number of registers (N) and inversely proportional to the frequency (f) of the timing signals.

$$T = N/f \tag{18-2}$$

The f here would most likely equal the sampling frequency f_s, discussed previously.

The term *charge transfer device (CTD)* has been applied generically to bucket brigade and CCD-based structures and will be used here for convenience. The idea of a CTD is that it stores a sample of analog information, such as might result from the sampling process, as a packet of charge on a capacitor and, under the control of a timing signal or clock, transfers it to the next storage site. One performance parameter for a CTD is its *transfer inefficiency* ϵ. Charge transfer inefficiency is the fraction of charge left behind in each transfer. A second parameter of performance is the leakage of charge from a cell between transfers. A third parameter is the leakage of charge into an empty cell due to thermal agitation of the semiconductor. Taken together these effects degrade the signal-to-noise ratio of the signal as it passes through the CTD. CTDs, therefore, have been used in applications requiring less than 50 to 100 ms or where the signal-to-noise ratio is not so critical. They have appeal because the expense of analog-to-digital (a/d) conversion and digital-to-analog (d/a) conversion is avoided. All the requirements of the sampling theorem and audio frequency band limiting should be met, however.

18.3 DIGITAL DELAYS

Digital delay operating principles have undergone a number of important changes since they were first used in sound systems. Probably the most significant change is in the type of storage or memory. Shift registers were almost universally used in the first commercially produced units. Digital shift registers are conceptually similar to analog shift registers, with the important advantage that only the presence or absence of a charge carries the significant signal information. Now, random-access memory (RAM) provides flexibility and economic trade-offs for design. As the cost of memory decreases, more sound systems can be designed to include delay. Until recently, the cost of the memory dominated delay design considerations. Currently analog-to-digital (a/d) and digital-to-analog (d/a) costs are equally important design and cost considerations.

The digital delay device shown in Fig. 18-5 is typical of a basic unit that is used in sound systems. The memory is RAM (random-access memory). Delay is set by a combination of coarse, 24-ms, and fine, 3-ms, step controls for a total of up to 192 ms. One, two, three, or four independently settable output taps may be specified. As noted in section 18.6.1, sound arrival time differences of 50 ms or more are unacceptable so that the combination of total available delay and number of delay taps satisfies the requirements of a large number of sound system installations.

18.3.1 Analog-to-Digital Conversion

Details of the large number of methods of analog-to-digital conversion and digital-to-analog conversion are outside the scope of this discussion. However, the efficiency with which it is accomplished is so important to

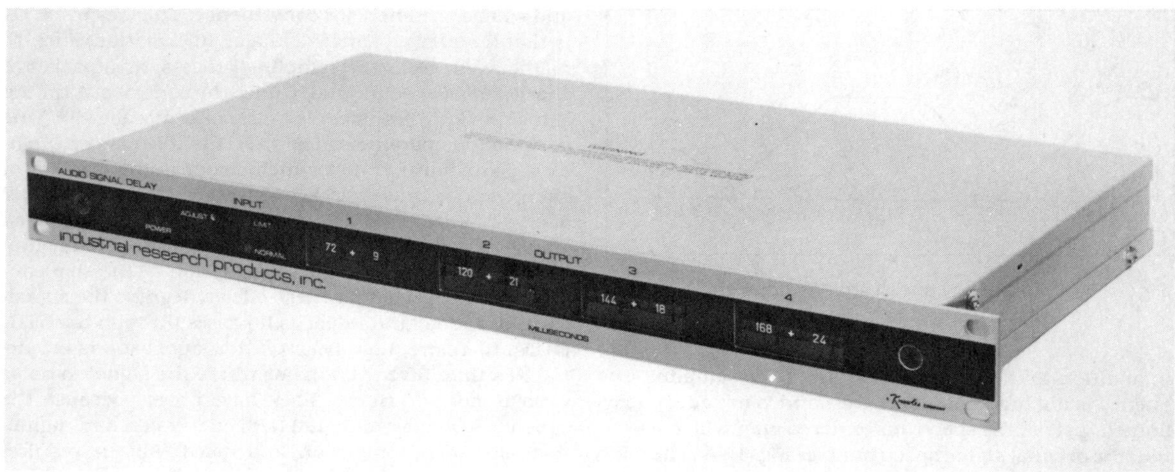

Figure 18-5 A popular digital delay, used in sound systems and other applications *(Courtesy Industrial Research Products Subsidiary of Knowles Electronics, Inc.)*

the success and acceptability of the particular delay that an overview of the common conversion principles is useful. We will first discuss *PCM* or *pulse-code modulation*. Delta modulation is the second commonly encountered method of digital coding for audio frequency signal delays in sound systems.

18.3.2 Pulse-Code Modulation

The PCM method of analog-to-digital conversion is essentially a two-step process: *quantizing*, followed by *coding*. Quantizing is the process of converting the continuously varying analog signal into a set of discrete states. Coding is the process of assigning a digital code word to each of the states. The code word consists of a defined series of pulses. Digital-to-analog conversion is the reverse process by which the series of pulses or codes is converted into quantized levels that yield the analog signal after smoothing or filtering.

The sampling process discussed previously in connection with analog shift register delay is essentially a quantizing process with a nearly infinite number of levels possible since the actual voltage of the sample is permitted.

18.3.3 Coding

When using a digital word to define the analog voltage, it is not always possible to code the signal voltage exactly. This is illustrated in Fig. 18-6 with a three-bit a/d converter. The analog range of the converter is 0 to 10 V. A total of eight output states is possible. Only eight voltages over the 10-V range can be outputted with no error. The resolution of the quantizer is defined as the number of output states expressed in bits. The number of possible states for a quantizer is 2^n, which is 2^3 or eight in this example.

Fig. 18-6 also illustrates that, unless the analog voltage exactly matches a decision point or value, there is an error range of ± ½ of the voltage between successive decision points. This quantizing error results because there is a range of voltages that will yield the same output code

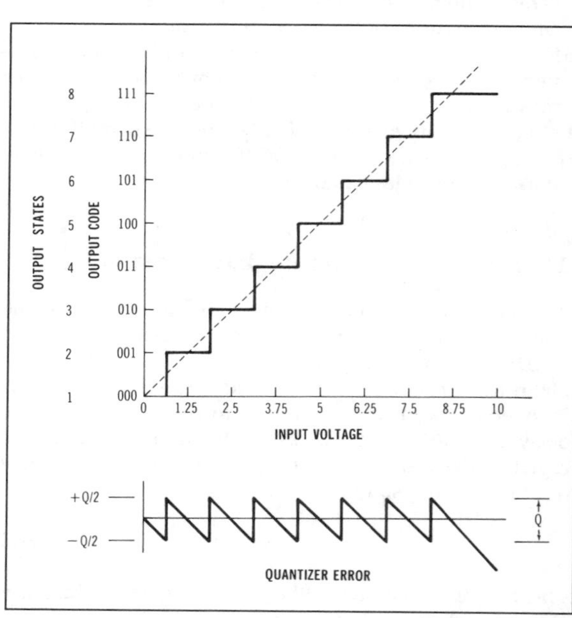

Figure 18-6 Conversion or transfer function of a three-bit quantizer.

word. It is frequently called the *quantization noise* or the *quantization uncertainty*. Quantization error is given by

$$Q = FS/2^n \qquad (18\text{-}3)$$

where,

Q is the smallest analog difference that can be resolved by the converter,
FS is the full scale,
n is the number of bits.

For a full scale of 10 V and a 12-bit quantizer, Q = 2.44 mV.

There are many digital codes that might be used to convert the sample. *Natural binary* or *straight binary* is popular and may be used in its fractional form to represent a number (N) as follows:

$$N = a_1 2^{-1} + a_2 2^{-2} + a_3 2^{-3} + \cdots + a_n 2^{-n} \qquad (18\text{-}4)$$

Each coefficient (a) assumes a value of zero or one. The number N has a value between zero and one. As an example, a binary fraction might normally be written as 0.11010110, but the decimal is omitted and the code word represents a fraction of full scale. This particular 8-bit code word represents the decimal fraction (1 × 0.5) + (1 × 0.25) + (0 × 0.125) + (1 × 0.0625) + (0 × 0.03125) + (1 × 0.015625) + (1 × 0.0078125) + (0 × 0.00390625) = 0.8359375 or 83.6% of full scale. It would represent 8.359375 V if the full scale were 10 V. The first bit in the sequence has the most weight and is called the *most significant bit (msb)*; the last, the *least significant bit (lsb)*. The least significant bit has the same significance and analog equivalent value as Q discussed previously, namely,

$$\text{lsb (analog value)} = FS/2^n \qquad (18\text{-}5)$$

Table 18-1 gives a useful set of relationships among the parameters of a/d conversion.

The *dynamic range (DR)* of a PCM converter in decibels is calculated with the following equation:

$$\begin{aligned} DR &= 20 \log 2^n \\ &= 20(n)\log 2 \\ &= 20n(0.30103) \\ &= 6.0206n \end{aligned} \qquad (18\text{-}6)$$

Note that a code word with all ones does not add up to one, but lacks one least significant bit. In other words, the maximum value that can be converted is FS $(1 - 2^{-n})$; it never quite reaches the value defined as analog full scale.

Offset binary, two's complement, and *binary-coded decimal (BCD)* are other examples of binary coding. Each method of coding has an advantage for particular applications. *Offset binary* is a common coding for analog audio signals because the signals have both positive and negative values. This is also referred to as bipolar operation of the converter. The analog range is offset by one-half of the full scale or the MSB value. Thus, the most significant bit becomes a sign or polarity indicator. This is illustrated in Fig. 18-7, for a three-bit a/d converter. The code 000 indicates −5.00, 100 indicates 0, and 111 indicates +3.75. By reserving the most significant bit for

Table 18-1. A Set of Relationships Among the Parameters of A/D Conversion

Resolution Bits n	Number of States 2^n	LSB Weight 2^{-n}	Dynamic Range dB
0	1	1.0	0
1	2	0.5	6
2	4	0.25	12
3	8	0.125	18.1
4	16	0.0625	24.1
5	32	0.03125	30.1
6	64	0.015625	36.1
7	128	0.0078125	42.1
8	256	0.00390625	48.2
9	512	0.001953125	54.2
10	1024	0.0009765625	60.2
11	2048	0.00048828125	66.2
12	4096	0.000244140625	72.2
13	8192	0.0001220703125	78.3
14	16384	0.00006103515625	84.3
15	32768	0.000030517578125	90.3
16	65536	0.0000152587890625	96.3

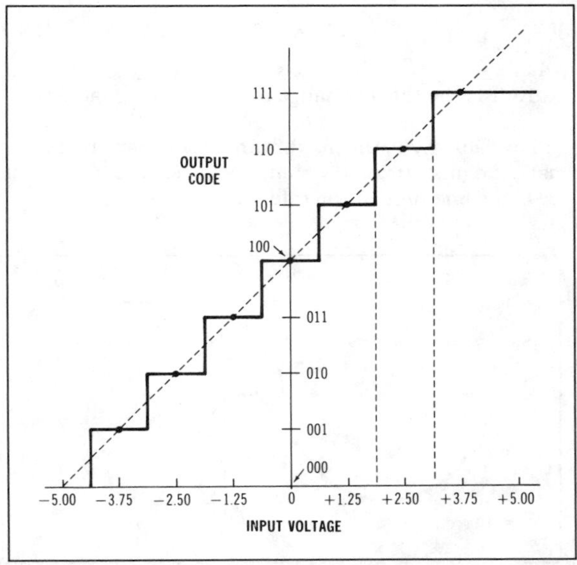

Figure 18-7 Conversion or transfer function of a bipolar three-bit quantizer.

polarity indication, the peak value that can be coded or decoded is half the peak-to-peak range, so a 12-bit code has an 11-bit or 66-dB dynamic range in terms of peak value. FS in the a/d or d/a sense refers to the 0 to 10 range of a dc level and a 0 to 5 range in the sinusoidal case.

It may be noted that the quantizer output is essentially the analog input with the quantization noise added to it. The noise has a peak-to-peak value of Q, an average value of zero (as with other types of noise), and an rms value of $Q/2\sqrt{3}$ because of its triangular waveshape. This noise also has a wide bandwidth although being audible as a "noise behind the signal" contributes to the distortion in a total harmonic distortion (THD) measurement.

The dynamic range and signal-to-noise ratio of a digita delay are set almost entirely by the properties of the a/d and d/a processors and to a small extent by the integrity of the memory.

18.3.4 Sampling Theory II

The new sample of a signal cannot be taken before the present sample has been converted to a digital word. The time required depends on the resolution, the conversion technique, and the speed of the components used in the converter. Conversion time, frequently called *aperture time*, describes the time window required to do the conversion and leads to an amplitude uncertainty or error if the signal is changing during this process.

The resulting error may be considered a timing error or an amplitude error, as illustrated in Fig. 18-8. The signal changes by an amount ΔV during the aperture time t_a required for the a/d conversion. They are related as follows:

$$\Delta V = t_a(dv/dt) \tag{18-7}$$

where,

dv/dt is the rate of change of the input signal, v(t).

The value ΔV is the maximum error caused by the signal changing during the sampling interval and it should be 0 at some time in the interval.

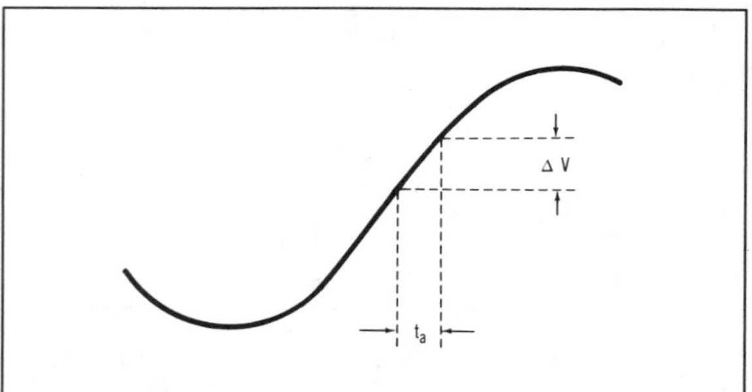

Figure 18-8 Relationship between aperture time and signal amplitude, showing the amplitude uncertainty.

For sinusoidal signals, the maximum error is at zero crossing when the slope or rate of change is largest,

$$\begin{aligned} \Delta V &= t_a(d/dt)(A \sin \omega t)(t = 0) \\ &= t_a(A)\omega \end{aligned} \tag{18-8}$$

In terms of the full scale peak-to-peak value of the signal, the resultant error (e) is

$$\begin{aligned} e &= \Delta V/2A \\ &= \pi f t_a \end{aligned} \tag{18-9}$$

As an example, the aperture time required for a 12-bit a/d system, having a 72-dB range or a resolution of one part in 4000 to convert a 10-kHz signal, is

$$\begin{aligned} t_a &= e/\pi f \\ &= 8 \times 10^{-9} \text{s} \end{aligned} \tag{18-10}$$

The aperture time is only 8 ns.

An a/d converter this fast is difficult to find at any price, but since the sampling need only be done at three to four times the highest audio frequency, a sample and hold is a convenient and cost-effective way of extending the effective aperture time to the period of the sampling frequency, which is within the speed range of a number of converters.

18.3.5 Sample and Hold

A hold circuit forces the amplitude of the sample to have constant value throughout a sample period. In Fig. 18-3, for example, the sample amplitude is set at the beginning of the sample period. It may also be at the end of the sample period shown in Fig. 18-3D. A basic sample-and-hold circuit is shown in Fig. 18-9. The signal amplitude is "frozen" for a brief time in the form of a charge on a capacitor until the next sample period is initiated, at which time the new sample amplitude is transferred to the capacitor. The switch S is momentarily closed, synchronously with the sampling pulse, and then it is disconnected. The voltage or charge on the capacitor establishes a steady value to be used by another part of the circuit. The amplifier A_1 must be able to charge the capacitor rapidly. Low-leakage capacitors, high-impedance amplifiers with very low bias current, and fast switches with very low off-state leakage are used. A sample and hold is basically an accurate energy storage circuit. In reality, a sample and hold takes a very fast sample of the analog signal and then changes into a hold mode.

18.4 DELTA MODULATION

A quite different method of digital coding is based on whether the newest sample in a sequence of samples is larger or smaller than the preceding one. It is called *delta modulation*. In contrast to the PCM encoder that generates multibit binary words representing the amplitude of samples at regular intervals, a delta modulator produces single-bit words representing the quantized error between a tracking signal and the actual input signal. The delta modulation digital coding method is used in several delay products. Basically, a delta modulator is a closed-loop sampled data system. It includes a sampled data element that transmits binary output pulses whose polarity depends on the instantaneous amplitude difference between the input signal being sampled and a quantized approximation of the preceding signal sample. As illustrated in Fig. 18-10, a simple delta modulation encoder can be made with a comparator, a type D flip-flop, and a low-pass or integrating feedback composed of resistance and capacitance. The output of the comparator is high or low depending on whether the feedback or tracking

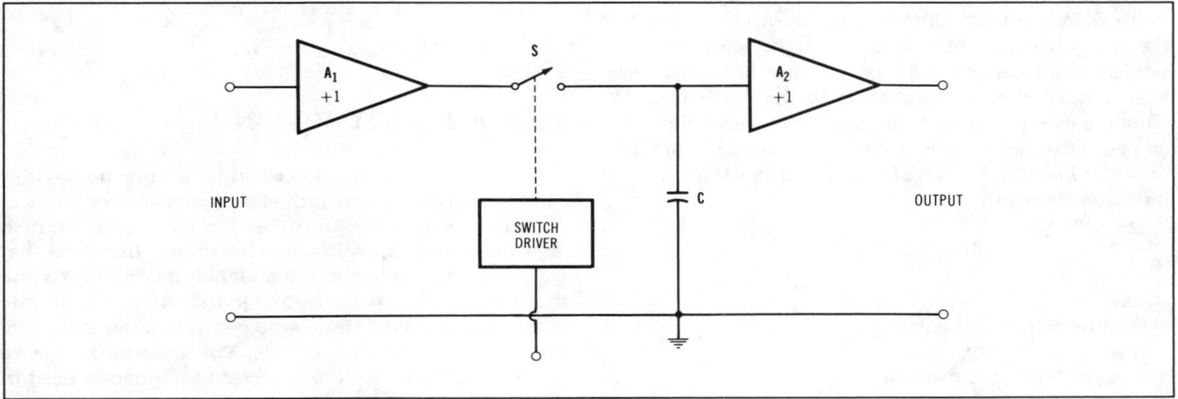

Figure 18-9 A commonly used sample-and-hold circuit.

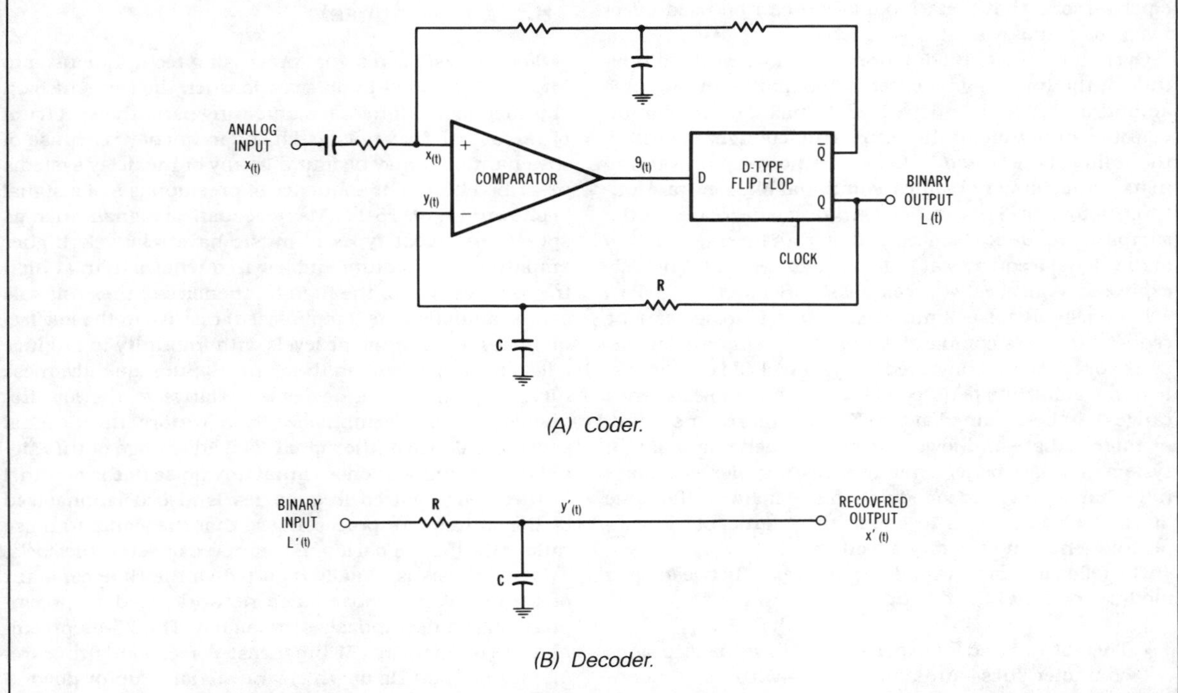

(A) Coder.

(B) Decoder.

Figure 18-10 A delta-modulator system.

signal y(t) is smaller or larger than the input x(t). The output of the comparator is sampled in the flip-flop at a rate set by the clock and produces the binary output L(t). Since the signal y(t) is an approximation of the input signal, the decoded output x′(t) will also be the same approximation of the input signal if the binary L′(t) from the memory is decoded in the same way that L(t) was decoded to produce y(t) in the encoding process. The simplicity of the coding and decoding schemes has resulted in the use of delta modulation in delays and communication as well as motor control. The simplest integrating network for a delta modulator consists of a capacitor, but the quantization noise is quite high. More practical implementations and the basis of successful delay systems employ double integration in the feedback path, which is closely related to what is sometimes referred to as predictive delta modulation. For these delta modulators, the maximum ratio of signal-to-quantization noise for a sine wave is

$$S/N = 0.026\, f_s^{5/2}/f_a f_o^{3/2} \tag{18-11}$$

where,
f_s is the sampling frequency,
f_a is the audio frequency,
f_o is the audio bandwidth.

The signal-to-noise ratio is a strong function of the sampling frequency and, to a lesser extent, the audio bandwidth. These important dependencies are the principal reasons that delta modulation can be used effectively for audio delay.

Overload in delta modulation occurs when the amplitude of the input signal exceeds the maximum possible amplitude of the reconstructed signal. The maximum possible amplitude of the reconstructed signal is set by the ability of the system to follow the more rapidly varying instantaneous signal values, somewhat like slew rate limiting distortion. This overload limitation decreases as the sampling frequency is increased. It is an inverse function of the signal frequency at high frequencies and is usually expressed as an effective preemphasis. (See section 18.5.1.)

A no-signal noise limit, called *idling noise*, can be reduced to levels comparable to good-quality analog circuits so that when compared with many PCM coding systems on a total bits-per-second basis, comparable dynamic ranges can be obtained at 500 Kbits or more per second. At intermediate and lower bit rates, a delta modulation system may have better dynamic range and signal-to-noise ratio than a pulse-code modulation system (with the same bit rate, where the bit rate equals the product of the sample frequency and the digital code bits).

The following important differences exist between delta modulation and PCM coding:

- There is no need for expensive filters with steep slope characteristics—antialias filters—with delta modulation.
- There is great simplicity in delta modulation coding and decoding, an important consideration when a number of outputs on a single delay line are called for.
- There is no sharp limiting of the upper voice spectrum in delta modulation.
- Delta modulation is less sensitive to errors in storage and recovery of the digital signal.
- Delta modulation is less suitable for arithmetic manipulation in the digital form.

18.5 NOISE REDUCTION

All the delay systems described here with the possible exception of the passive inductance-capacitance lumped-element transmission line in section 18.1.1, have limited signal-handling capability. It is important, therefore, that signal processing to maximize signal-to-noise ratios and dynamic range be used. Although increasing the bit rate is feasible in digital delay systems, it is often more economical to use other methods. Preemphasis and companding are two types of processing frequently used in delay system design and supplement the signal processing described previously.

18.5.1 Preemphasis

Preemphasis is a signal-processing technique used to improve the signal-to-noise ratio when the transmission channel has a limited dynamic range and the spectrum of the signal does not match the frequency response of the channel. It may be found in any of the delay systems described here. The sequence of preemphasis of a signal is shown in Fig. 18-11. Many acoustical signals such as speech and most types of music have relatively higher amplitudes at medium and low frequencies than at high frequencies. Thus, the high frequencies of these signals can be amplified (i.e. emphasized) relative to the low frequencies up to the same levels with impunity to produce a flat signal spectrum in the channel. Subsequently, these high frequencies are decreased relative to the low frequencies (i.e., deemphasized) to restore the original spectral balance of the signal. The advantage of this signal-processing sequence is that any noise in the channel at these emphasized frequencies is also deemphasized by the subsequent processing so that the signal-to-noise ratio of the final signal may be improved by several decibels.

Preemphasis is usually reported as the time constant of the resistance-capacitance network used to preemphasize and deemphasize the signal. The 75-μs preemphasis common in FM broadcast corresponds to a frequency of 2000 Hz at which the signal is up or down 3 dB. By contrast, a 35-μs preemphasis corresponds to 4000

Hz. Because the cost of a digital delay increases rapidly with the increase of coding word size, preemphasis has been a cost-effective way to get acceptable signal-to-noise ratios and dynamic ranges by permitting smaller memories and smaller binary coding words in PCM systems. Preemphasis is inherent in some forms of delta modulation and, therefore, need not be added as separate signal-processing steps.

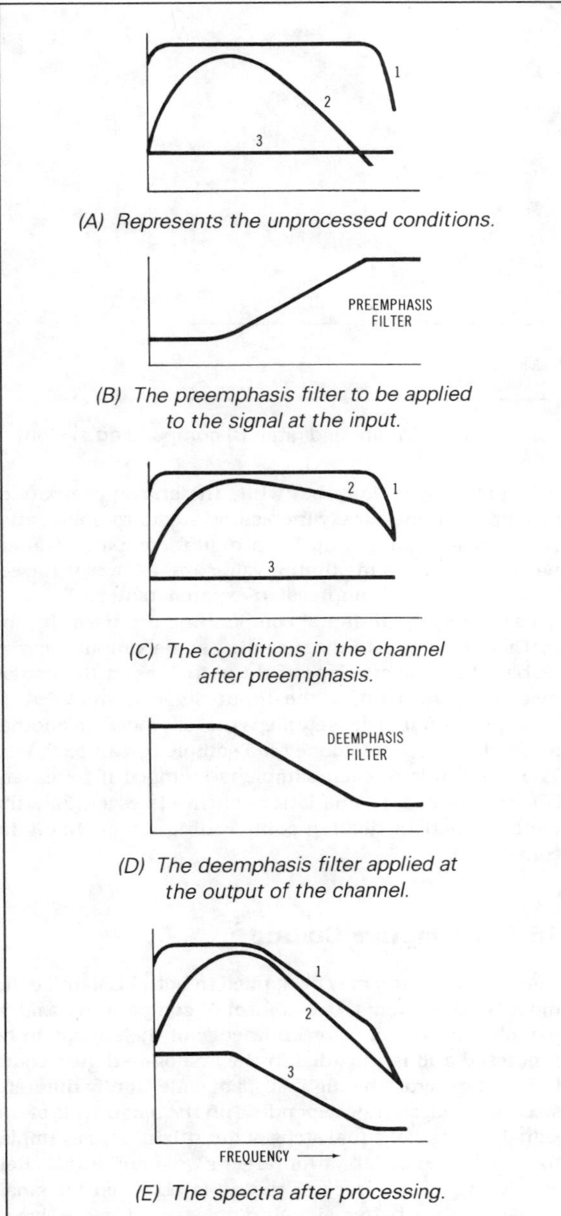

1
2
3
(A) Represents the unprocessed conditions.
PREEMPHASIS
FILTER
(B) The preemphasis filter to be applied
to the signal at the input.
2
1
3
(C) The conditions in the channel
after preemphasis.
DEEMPHASIS
FILTER
(D) The deemphasis filter applied at
the output of the channel.
1
2
3
FREQUENCY
(E) The spectra after processing.

Figure 18-11 The preemphasis processing of a signal. Curve 1 is the maximum signal permitted. Curve 2 is the signal spectrum. Curve 3 is the noise spectrum.

Preemphasis enforces some signal-handling limitations in the form of reduced headroom at high frequencies because the effective maximum signal-handling capability decreases with frequency in the preemphasis region. However, as stated previously, the distribution of signal energy across the audio frequency spectrum does not cause a problem for most signals, especially when the channel signal-to-noise ratio is high enough that a 35-μs preemphasis can be used.

18.5.2 Companding

Companding (i.e., compression followed by expansion) is used in digital delays to improve dynamic range, since the cost of digital conversion and memory increases significantly with dynamic range. As with preemphasis, it may be used in any of the delay systems described here. Both analog and digital signal-processing methods of compression are used. Regardless of the method of companding, the dynamic range and signal-to-noise ratio of the signal storage channel should be in excess of 66 dB, or the "noise-behind-the-signal" breathing of the compander will probably be audible. Compression of at least 24 dB is thus required to reach the accepted performance of a 90-dB dynamic range with a signal-to-noise ratio of 66 dB.

18.5.3 Analog Companding

Analog compression is applied to the analog signal prior to conversion to digital form; *expansion* is done after conversion from digital back to analog form. Simple and elaborate methods of analog compression and expansion of signals have been devised as evidenced by the standalone noise-reduction equipment available. Typically, a compressor consists of a voltage-controlled amplifier with its control voltage being the envelope of the amplifier output signal. Thus, control is a form of negative feedback that strives to reduce the ratio of output-to-input signal level as the output level increases. Expansion reverses the process by detecting the envelope of the converted analog output signal and applying it to a voltage-controlled amplifier in a feed-forward mode that strives to increase the gain of the output amplifier in proportion to the signal envelope amplitude. The detector in the expander is sufficiently like the detector in the compressor so that good tracking occurs. It is at this point in the processing that the noise behind the signal becomes audible if the channel does not have adequately low noise.

The relation between signal-to-noise ratio and input level for a typical delay with analog companding is shown by curve A in Fig. 18-12. This type of companding senses

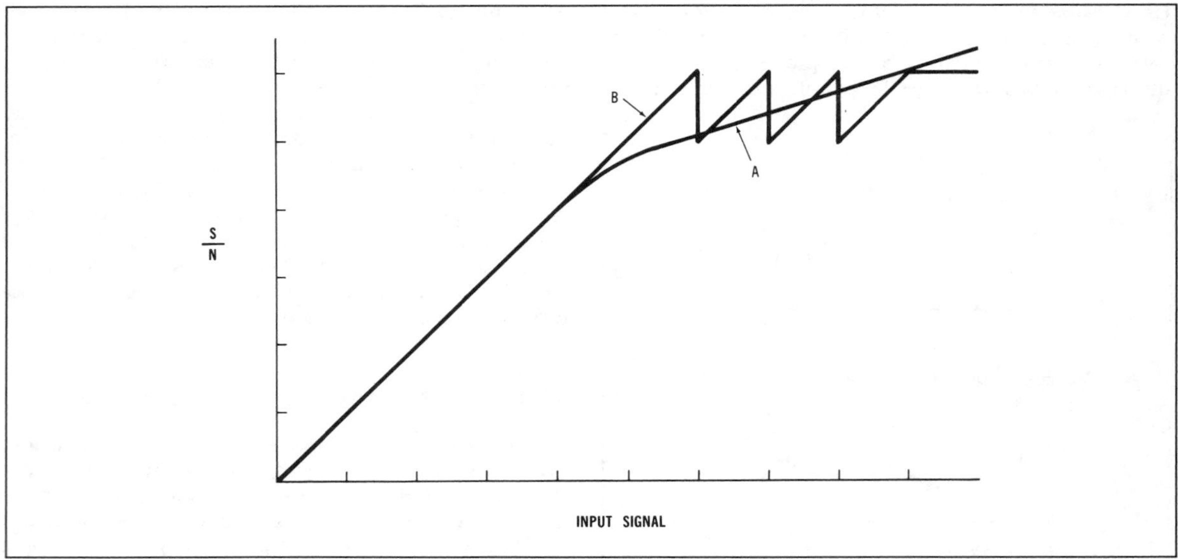

Figure 18-12 Signal-to-noise ratio versus input signal level for an analog (A) and a digital (B) companding system.

the signal magnitude before acting on the signal in a proportional control manner.

18.5.4 Digital Companding

Just as in analog companding, the level of the input signal is adjusted to be most favorable for the delay channel in digital companding. In this case, the gain-setting parameters are captured as explicit signal parameters or codes and transmitted along with the signal codes to the output. The gain-setting parameters are then used at the output to restore the original signal level relationships. A digital word carries the gain information. It is desirable that the digital word have as few bits as possible. Consider a rather typical delay with a 10-bit PCM and 60-dB dynamic range such that 2 more bits of code can be added. What is the best way to use the added bits? If the PCM code is increased to 12, the dynamic range and signal-to-noise ratio will increase 12 to 72 dB. On the other hand, if the input stage gain is changed in 10-dB steps, the 2 bits of code may indicate 0, 10, 20, or 30 dB of attenuation at the input and corresponding gains at the output. Now, a 12-bit code provides a 90-dB dynamic range, an increase of 30 dB, but the signal-to-noise ratio remains at 60 dB. This is a method of digital companding. Depending somewhat on the application, once the signal-to-noise ratio of the channel is in the vicinity of 66 dB, added bits should probably be used for increased dynamic range via companding in a delay.

The signal-to-noise ratio versus input level for a typical delay with digitally coded companding is shown by curve B in Fig. 18-12. Note that while the analog compander produces monotonically increasing signal-to-noise ratio, the signal-to-noise ratio for a digital compander alternates between its maximum value and a lower value set by the size of the compression-expansion steps.

Two methods of digital companding are used. In one method, detection of the incoming signal amplitude may be based on the envelope of the signal, as in the analog methods. The gain of the input stage is modified as appropriate, but in discrete steps that are coded. In another method, detection is done on a sample-by-sample basis. The amplitude of each sample is changed if necessary before it is coded. The latter scheme is essentially the method used in floating-point coding analog-to-digital conversion.

18.5.5 Adaptive Coding

Adaptive coding may be applied in both PCM and delta modulation systems. It is a form of companding that is usually based on a prior knowledge of the signals to be processed and is included in the analog-to-digital coder itself. In general, the digital bits of code signify different sizes of signal change depending on the magnitude of the signal. Instead of equal steps of quantizing, for example, the steps become larger for larger signal amplitude. Relatively higher accuracy of coding is obtained for small signals with a better signal-to-noise ratio, while lower accuracy of coding results for large signals where signal masking can compensate to some extent for coding inaccuracy. Coding inaccuracy is audible as noise behind the signal and distortion.

18.6 HOW DELAY IS USED

18.6.1 Criteria

People with normal hearing in both ears fuse complex acoustic signals from two sources into one if their spectra and time histories are alike, their levels are within 10 dB of each other, and the delay of one relative to the other is less than 35 ms. Fig. 18-13 shows the relationship between delay and relative levels of sounds from two different sources. A sound will appear to originate at the location from which the signal first arrives even though the second arriving sound has a 10 dB higher level. The delay between speech signals arriving by different paths to the ears of a listener at similar levels should be limited to a maximum of 40 to 50 ms. To preserve directional realism or apparent source location for these two (or more) signals, more stringent conditions must be satisfied. (1) The signal from the desired direction must arrive first (ideally 5 to 15 ms sooner, although a range of 2 to 35 ms may be satisfactory). (2) The level of the signal from the desired direction must not be 10 dB less than that of the other(s) if the spectrum is the same and the delay is optimum, or several decibels higher if the spectrum is not the same or the delay is not ideal. In other words, directional realism is lost in the sound system if the sound from the loudspeaker is heard before the sound from the original source, or if the sound from the loudspeaker is much louder than the original sound at the listener's location. Listeners will hear a confused sound when it does not arrive at their ears from the various reflecting surfaces or the reinforcing speaker within this quite well-defined time interval and limited range of levels. Judicious use of delay in a sound system can achieve both better intelligibility and directional realism.

It is important to note, though, that fusion of the sounds takes place in the processes of the human brain and results in a subjective impression of increased loudness or level. Exact phase or time alignment is not necessary for this effect and, in fact, is virtually impossible to achieve except under controlled conditions.

18.6.2 Application to Sound Systems

Sound travels through the air at 344 m/s or 1129 ft/s. Thus, there will be delay of 2.9 ms for each meter, 0.88 ms for each foot, the sound travels. At 60 ft this delay amounts to 53 ms. A sound picked up by a microphone, amplified, and emitted by a loudspeaker at the 60-ft distant location suffers essentially no delay so that a person next to the loudspeaker would hear it 53 ms before the airborne naturally arriving sound. A 53-ms delay is long enough for most persons to perceive the combination as having an echo that would be annoying and tend to be fatiguing, and have degraded intelligibility and sound quality unless one of the signals is more than 10 dB larger. Stated another way, a delay of the electrical signal between the microphone and the loudspeaker equal to the transit time of the sound through the air will cause the two sounds to be coincident and much more acceptable.

A general and much simplified approach to establishing the optimum delay and levels of amplified sound is to first overlay a plan view of the listening area with a series of concentric circles with origins at the principal natural sound source location. Space the circles 33¾ ft (to scale)

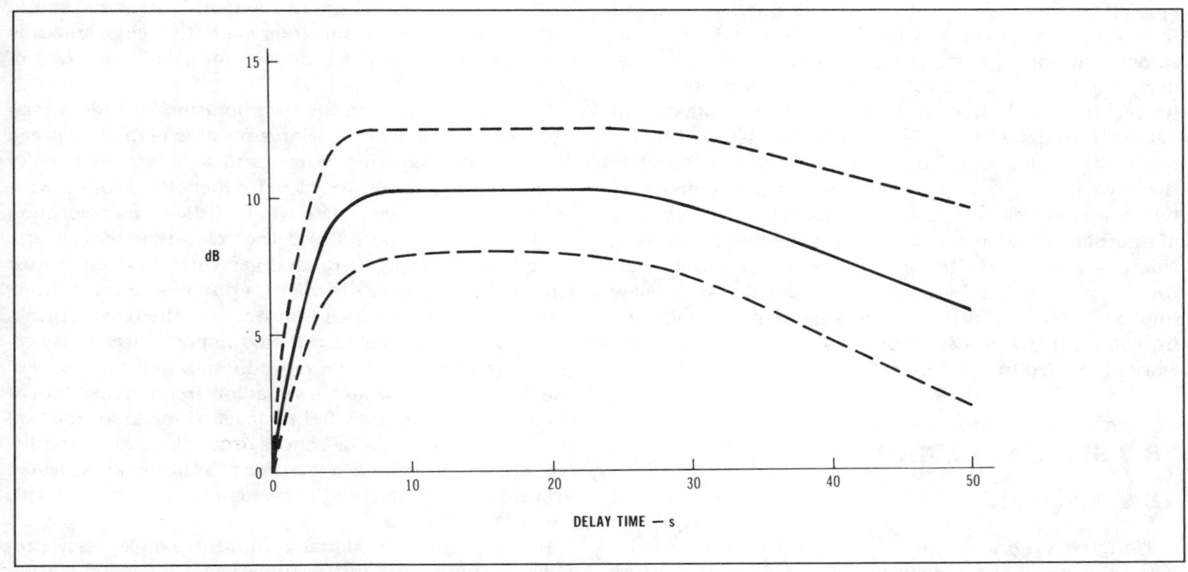

Figure 18-13 Relationship between relative arrival time, or delay, of two signals and their levels for a typical listener.

apart, corresponding to about 30 ms of delay from one to the next. Label the circles according to the delay: 30 ms, 60 ms, and so on. Next, do the same for the loudspeaker(s) in the sound system with centers on the respective locations. The delay to be added to the loudspeaker signal channel is the time in milliseconds for the natural source-centered circle minus the time for the loudspeaker centered circle plus a small amount, usually 5 or 10 ms. Next, analyze the sound levels at various distances from the loudspeakers, using the −6 dB per doubling of distance rule, and set the levels so that they are in the ranges suggested by Fig. 18-13 over their respective coverage areas. Actual installation requirements very quickly get much more complicated than this simple example, and we can expect to repeat the analysis by altering delay and level several times before a reasonable design is achieved. Some trimming of the delay to different zones in a sound system is the rule rather than the exception.

18.6.3 Time Align®

If the virtual or effective sources for the elements of a loudspeaker cluster are not in the same location, a different effect, interference in the form of additions and cancellations of the sound waves from the individual elements, occurs. This is a phase incoherence problem that may be audible as a change in signal quality, usually most pronounced within the critical distance for the loudspeaker system. It occurs where the respective signals overlap in space and/or frequency. *Time Align®* is the term that identifies the small amount of delay that might be applied to the electrical signal for an element of a cluster to bring the virtual source locations into coincidence. Delay applied in this way may improve the quality of sound from some clusters or may improve the sound quality at some locations in front of the cluster. In other words, delay applied to portions of a cluster will frequently alter its resulting radiation or coverage pattern. Maximum delays of 10 ms with 0.05- or 0.1-ms adjustment increments seem adequate. Time alignment can be used effectively when construction and architectural considerations cause one element of an array to restrict the coverage of another; all elements of the array may be placed in a common plane and their effective source locations can then be brought into the same effective position with delay. Implementation of a good time alignment should take into account the delay and phase shift in crossover networks included in the system.

18.7 SPECIAL EFFECTS

18.7.1 Flanging

Flanging originated with reel-to-reel tape recorders, when the speed of a tape was modulated by application of drag to the flange of one of the reels. The digital equivalent of the effect is produced with digital delay by controlled variation of the clock frequency of the delay. The frequency and phase modulation of the signals has been used effectively by performers and recording engineers.

18.7.2 Frequency Shifting

For a variety of reasons, it may be necessary or desirable to change the frequency of a signal, to produce special effects, to improve the intelligibility of "helium speech" of divers, or to compensate for the frequency decrease or increase associated with tape playback at a speed different from the record speed. Delay forms the basis of one method of frequency shift. Samples of the signal to be processed are fed into the memory of a delay at one rate and extracted from the memory at a different rate. The signal frequency increase or decrease is the difference between the two rates (i.e., the difference between the frequency at which the signal samples are entered into the memory and the frequency at which the signal samples are withdrawn from the memory). Signal samples, when joined together, have waveform discontinuities at the junctions and several signal-processing techniques have successfully reduced their audibility.

18.7.3 Synthetic Reverberation

Delay is often the basis of reverberation synthesis because it provides a convenient method for storing the signal and releasing it at a later time. To appreciate the requirements for good reverberation synthesis, it should be recalled that the sound decay in a room has many modes of decay that result in a smooth, uncolored sound throughout the decay time interval. Rather large amounts of delay or memory are needed for good synthesis of reverberation.

Some of the criteria for reverberation include a relatively smooth decay rate, a large number of modes spread out over the frequency range, and an adequate density of modes even at relatively low frequencies. From the listener's point of view, there will be little or no coloration of the decaying sound, and the coloration that is produced has the spectrum changes with time associated with familiar rooms, theaters, churches, auditoriums, and so on. This requires that not only the reverberation or delay time is created but also important early reflections are provided in the reproduction and the decay of the signal is somewhat slower at low frequencies than at intermediate and high frequencies. *Directional realism* (i.e., the impression of echoes from all around the listener) usually requires a number of loudspeakers located around the perimeter of the room or space being fed with the delayed signals.

Recirculating the signal through a single delay provides a simple but rather unsatisfactory reverberation synthesizer. The output of the delay is reduced in amplitude a small amount and added to the input signal. In addition to creating a decaying sound, modes with period equal to the amount of the delay and quality of a comb-filtered sound are produced. If each mode so produced is equivalent to one mode of the decaying sound in a real room, the equivalent of a large number of such recirculating delay modes, randomly spaced, have to be created for good synthesis of room sound decay. Computational methods using microprocessors may be used with delays to create a variety of sound decay patterns.

18.8 DIGITAL FILTERS

This is a good place to mention digital filters because they depend in large part on adaptation of digital delay technology. At this time they are not a big factor in sound system and studio equipment, except indirectly for special effects like the reverberation synthesis. As used in electrical engineering, a filter transforms an electrical signal from one form to another and, in particular, is used to eliminate or filter out various frequencies in a signal. Similar transformation of signals can be performed either in the familiar continuous variable-analog domain or by processing in the sampled and quantized signal domain. An in-between type of filter is possible in the sampled data domain, such as is found in analog shift register systems mentioned previously. It is recommended that treatises on the subject be consulted for more detail by interested readers.

There are two basic types of digital filter: (1) *nonrecursive,* which may also be known as a finite impulse response (FIR) filter, a transversal filter, a tapped delay line filter, or a moving average filter; and (2) *recursive,* which may

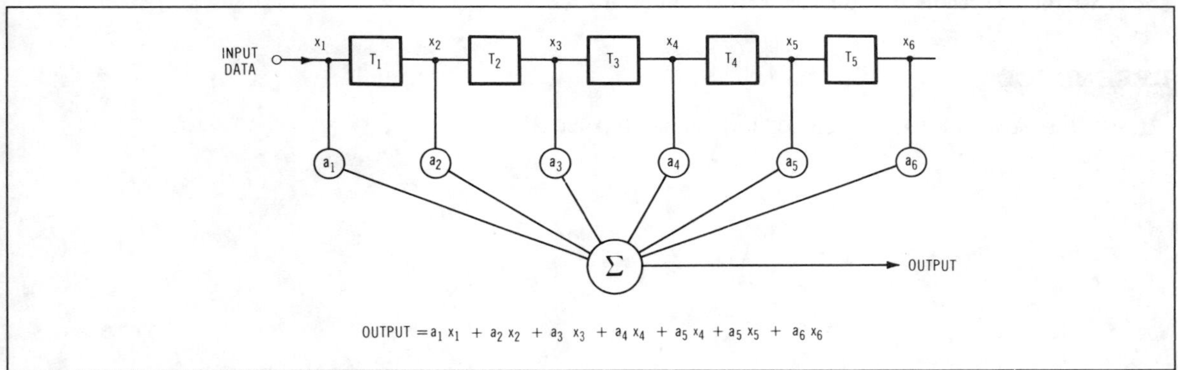

Figure 18-14 Nonrecursive transversal or finite impulse response filter block diagram.

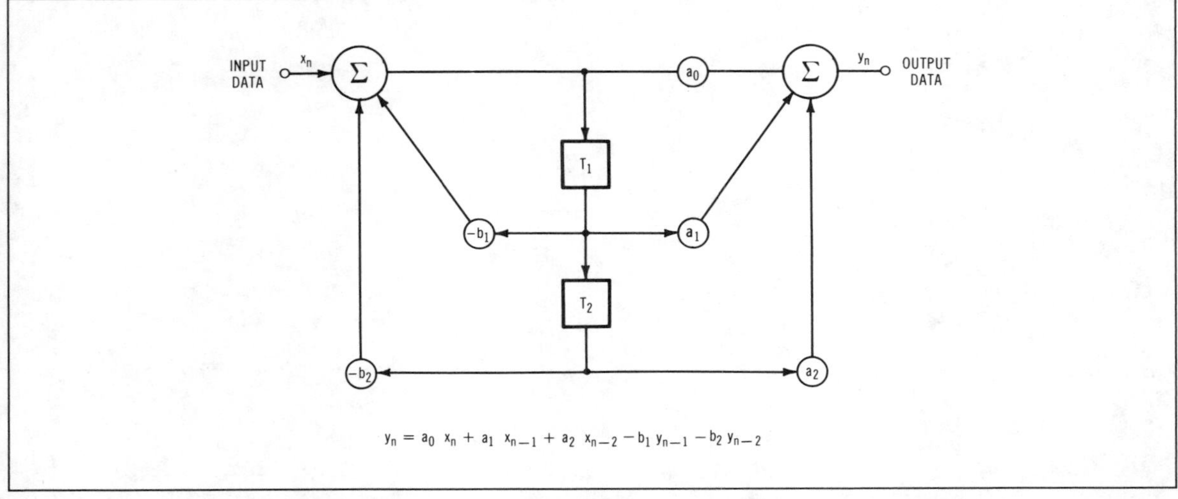

Figure 18-15 Recursive or infinite impulse response filter block diagram.

also be known as infinite impulse response (IIR), filter ladder filter, lattice filter, or wave digital filter. In addition, combinations may be found that give a wide variety of properties.

A block diagram in Fig. 18-14 shows an example of the basic elements of a nonrecursive-type digital filter. The analog-to-digital and digital-to-analog portions are omitted; the tapped delay line property is apparent. Taps spaced at equal intervals along the line provide signals that are summed to produce the filtered signal output. Imagine the digital data samples being stepped sequentially through the delay line. At every step a new combination of signals is summed. There will be a new waveform created by the linear summing at the output of the filter. The particular filter characteristic is determined by the relative amplitudes or weights and phases of the summed signals, the length of the delay line and the spacing or the time interval between the taps. In a true quantized and coded digital system, the sums are carried out prior to digital-to-analog conversion. It should be noted that a signal sample contributes to the output only while it is in the delay memory; it contributes for a finite time.

A simple form of a recursive-type digital filter is shown in Fig. 18-15, again omitting the a/d and d/a details. The recursive filter inserts delayed signals back into its input at various levels and phases to be added to the input so that its output is also the sum of a number of signal samples. In this case once the signal enters the system, it continues to circulate within the system almost indefinitely, hence the name of infinite impulse response (IIR). Since recursive filters depend on recirculation or feedback, care must be taken to ensure stability. Recursive filter elements are the basis of many reverberation synthesizing schemes. It is evident that the recursive filter remembers all the past data. These digital filter techniques enable the substantial improvements in the signal-to-noise ratio obtained in some rereleased recordings.

REFERENCE

1. H. M. Bascom, US Patent 1,358,053, November 9, 1920.

CHAPTER 19

Power Supplies

by Glen Ballou

19.1 POWER-SUPPLY TERMINOLOGY[1]

A *power supply* is a unit that supplies electrical power to another unit. Power supplies usually obtain their prime power from the ac power line. A power supply is normally thought of as a device used to produce the necessary dc power for various electronic circuits; however, it can also be a device that supplies special power to the lines, such as motor generators, inverters, and converters. This chapter will discuss dc and ac power supplies.

19.1.1 Rectifiers

A *rectifier* is a device that passes current in only one direction. The rectifier consists of an *anode* and a *cathode*, the anode being positive and the cathode being negative. When a positive voltage is applied to the anode of the rectifier, the voltage minus the voltage across the rectifier will appear on the cathode and current will flow.

When a negative voltage is applied to the anode with respect to the cathode, the rectifier is turned off and only the rectifier leakage current will flow.

There are various types of rectifiers; however, silicon rectifiers are almost universal today.

19.1.2 Forward Resistance

The *forward resistance* of a rectifier is the resistance of an individual cell measured at a specified forward voltage drop or current.

19.1.3 Forward Voltage Drop

The *forward voltage drop* is the internal voltage drop of a rectifier resulting from the current flow through the cell in the forward direction.

19.1.4 Reverse Resistance

The *reverse resistance* is the resistance of the rectifier measured at a specified reverse voltage or current.

19.1.5 Reverse Current

The *reverse current* is the current flow in the reverse direction. Reverse current is usually a very small value (microamps).

19.1.6 Maximum Peak Current

The *maximum peak current* is the highest instantaneous anode current a rectifier can safely carry recurrently in the direction of the normal current flow.

The value of the peak current is largely determined by the constants of the filter sections. With the large choke at the filter input, the peak current is not greater than the load current. However, if a large capacitor is used at the input of the filter section, the peak current may be many times the load current. The current is measured with a peak-indicating meter or oscilloscope.

19.1.7 Peak Inverse Voltage

The maximum *peak inverse voltage* is the highest instantaneous voltage that the rectifier can withstand recurrently in the direction opposite to which it is designed to pass current. Referring to Fig. 19-1, when anode A of a full-wave rectifier is positive, current flows from A to C, but not from B to C because B is negative. At the instant anode A is positive, cathodes A and B are positive with respect to anode B. The voltage between the positive cathode and the negative anode B is inversely related to the voltage causing the current flow. The peak value of this voltage is limited by the resistance and nature of the path between the anode B and the cathode. The maximum value of voltage between these points, at which there is no danger of breakdown, is termed maximum peak inverse voltage.

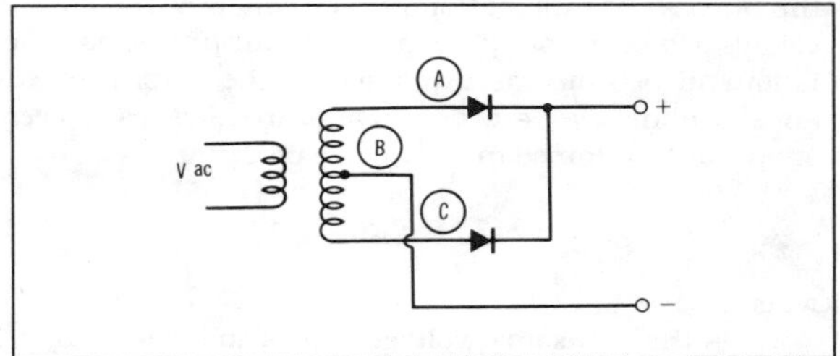

Figure 19-1 Peak inverse voltage analysis.

The relationship between peak inverse voltage, rms value of ac input voltage; and dc output voltage depends largely on the individual characteristics of the rectifier circuit. Line surges, or any other transient or waveform distortion, may raise the actual peak voltage to a value higher than that calculated for a sine-wave voltage. Therefore, the actual inverse voltage (and not the calculated value) should be such as not to exceed the rated maximum peak inverse voltage for a given rectifier. A peak-reading meter or oscilloscope is useful in determining the actual peak inverse voltage.

For single-phase, full-wave circuits with a sine-wave input and no capacitance at the input of the filter section, the peak inverse voltage is approximately 1.4 times the rms value of the anode voltage. For a single half-wave circuit, with a capacitor input to the filter section, the peak inverse voltage may reach 2.8 times the rms value of the anode voltage.

19.1.8 Ripple Voltage/Factor

Ripple voltage is the alternating component (ac) riding on the dc output voltage of a rectifier-type power supply. The frequency of the ripple voltage will depend on the line frequency and the configuration of the rectifier. The effectiveness of the filter system is a function of the load current and the values of the filter components.

The ripple factor is the measure of quality of a power supply. Ripple factor is the ratio of the rms value of the ac component of the output voltage to the dc component of the voltage:

$$\text{ripple factor} = V_{rms}/V_{dc} \qquad (19\text{-}1)$$

19.1.9 Internal Impedance

The *internal output impedance* of a power supply is the impedance presented to the equipment receiving the power supply voltage. In the operation of many devices, it is necessary that the internal power supply impedance be as near to zero as possible. Since most load devices consist of both passive and active elements, the current drawn from the supply consists of an ac component superimposed on the dc output of the supply. This ac component is generally of a nonsinusoidal nature. For the purpose of explanation of how constant the output voltage of a power supply can remain in spite of load variations, it becomes useful to specify the output impedance in ohms over a wide range of frequencies. Power-supply output impedance (Z_o) may be defined

$$Z_o = E_{ac}/I_{ac} \qquad (19\text{-}2)$$

where,

E_{ac} is the sinusoidal voltage across the power supply terminals,

I_{ac} is the sinusoidal current flowing through a series loop consisting of the power supply and load equipment.

To measure the output impedance of a power supply at any frequency, it is necessary to draw a sinusoidal current from the power supply and measure the ac component of the voltage that results across the output terminals. Dividing this ac voltage by the ac component the load current yields the output impedance at a frequency of the sine-wave load. A circuit for the measurement of the ac output impedance is given in Fig. 19-2. A signal current I_{ac} is caused to flow through the output terminals of the power supply and a series current-monitoring resistor R_1. The output impedance (Z_o) is then

$$Z_o = R_1 E_o/E_R \qquad (19\text{-}3)$$

where,

R_1 is the series resistor,

E_o is the superimposed sinusoidal voltage,

E_R is the voltage across the series resistor.

19.1.10 Static Line Regulation

Static line regulation is the output voltage variation as the line voltage is varied slowly from rated minimum to rated maximum with the load current held at the nominal value.

19.1.11 Dynamic Load Regulation

When the load change is sudden, the power supply may be unable to respond instantaneously, and an additional momentary excursion in the output voltage may result, subsiding afterwards to the static load regulation level.

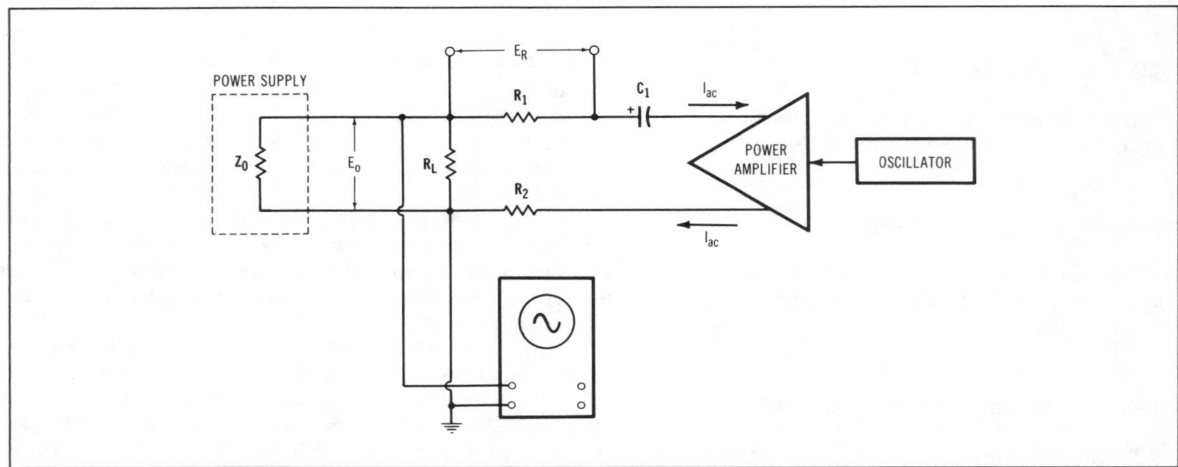

Figure 19-2 Circuit used for measuring the internal ac output impedance of a dc power supply.

The positive and negative excursion limits are superimposed on the static line and load regulation region. The positive and negative components are not necessarily equal or symmetrical. The most stringent rating is for a change from no load to full load or from full load to no load.

19.1.12 Dynamic Line Regulation

As in the case of the dynamic load regulation, the supply may not respond instantly to a step change in line voltage, and a momentary additional excursion of output voltage can result.

19.1.13 Thermal Regulation

Ambient temperature variations can influence conductivity of the power supply components and alter the output voltage level over the rated operating temperature range. This is also known as thermal drift.

19.2 POWER SUPPLIES

19.2.1 Simple DC Power Supplies

The simplest type of dc power supply is a rectifier in series with the load. As more rectifiers are installed into the circuit, along with filters, the power supply becomes more sophisticated. However, this type of supply will always remain simple and have poor regulation and transient response. Table 19-1 shows various power supplies and their characteristics.

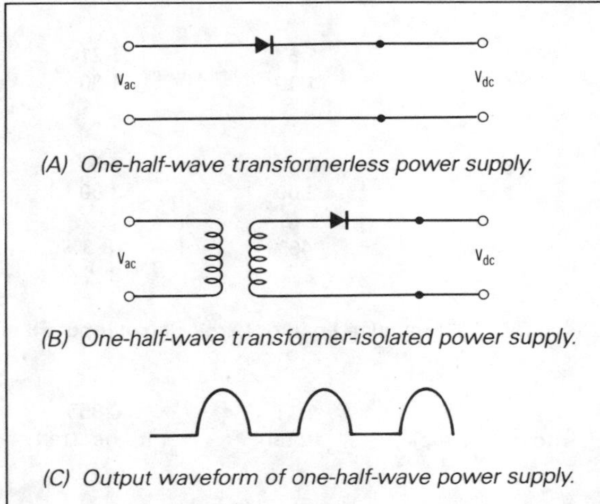

V_{ac}
V_{dc}
(A) One-half-wave transformerless power supply.
V_{ac}
V_{dc}
(B) One-half-wave transformer-isolated power supply.
(C) Output waveform of one-half-wave power supply.

Figure 19-3 Two one-half wave power supplies.

19.2.2 One-Half Wave Supplies

The simplest power supply is a one-half wave unit. This supply can be connected directly off the ac mains (Fig. 19-3A), or off the mains through a transformer (Fig. 19-3B). Since a rectifier only passes a current when the anode is more positive than the cathode, the output wave-form will be one half of a sine wave (Fig. 19-3C). The dc voltage output will be 0.45 of the ac voltage input, and the rectifier current will be the full dc current; the peak inverse voltage (piv) rectifier will be 1.414 ac, and the ripple will be 121%. In the transformerless power supply, the 115-V ac power line is connected directly to the rectifier system. This type of power supply is dangerous to both operating personnel and to grounded equipment. Also, power supplies of this type will cause hum problems that can only be solved by the use of an isolating transformer between the line and power supply.

19.2.3 Full-Wave Supplies

The full-wave supply is normally used in electronic circuits because it is simple, yet has a good ripple factor and voltage output. A full-wave supply is always used with a transformer. Full-wave supplies may be either of a single-phase center tap design or as a full-wave bridge. In either case, both the positive and negative cycles are rectified and mixed to produce the dc output.

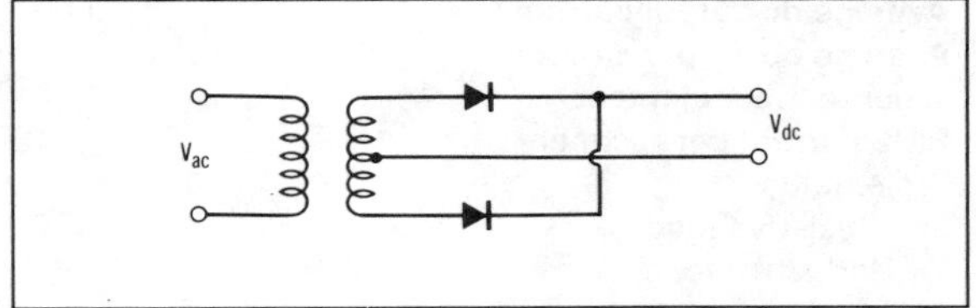

Figure 19-4 Full-wave center-tapped power supply.

The center tap configuration (Fig. 19-4) uses two rectifiers and a center tap transformer. The V_{dc} is approximately V_{ac} where V_{ac} is from one side of the transformer to the center tap. Because the output is from each half wave, ripple is only 48% of the output voltage and at twice the input frequency. Each rectifier carries one-half of the load current. The piv/rectifier is 2.828 V_{ac}.

The chief advantage of the full-wave bridge rectifier is its ability to supply full-wave rectification without a center tap on the transformer. However, the bridge rectifier is not a true single-ended circuit, since it has no terminal common to both the input and output circuits.

A full-wave bridge rectifier consists of four rectifier elements, as shown in Fig. 19-5. This circuit is the most familiar and is the one most commonly employed in the electronics industry. The circuit functions in the following manner:

When the ac input terminal 1 is positive, current flows

Table 19-1. Rectifier Circuit Chart. The Data Assume Zero Forward Drop and Zero

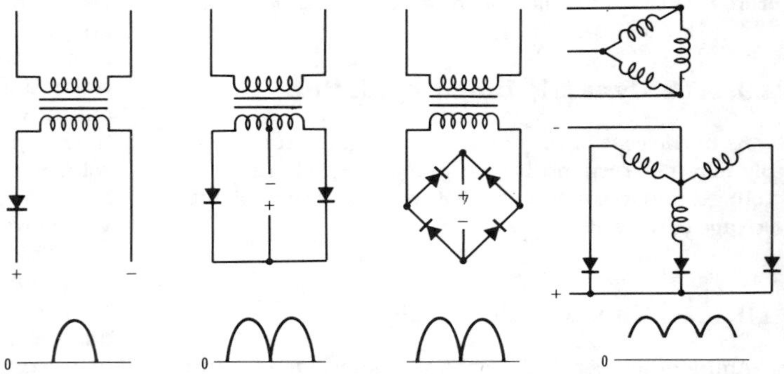

Type of Circuit→		**Single-Phase Half Wave**	**Single-Phase Center Tap**	**Single-Phase Bridge**	**Three-Phase Star (Wye)**
Primary→					
Secondary→					
One Cycle Wave of Rectifier Output Voltage (No Overlap)					
Number of rectifier elements	=	1.	2	4	3
RMS dc volts output	=	1.57	1.11	1.11	1.02
Peak dc volts output	=	3.14	1.57	1.57	1.21
Peak reverse volts per rectifier element	=	3.14	3.14	1.57	2.09
	=	1.41	2.82	1.41	2.45
	=	1.41	1.41	1.41	1.41
Average dc output current	=	1.00	1.00	1.00	1.00
Average dc output current per rectifier element	=	1.00	0.500	0.500	0.333
RMS current per rectifier element:					
Resistive load	=	1.57	0.785	0.785	0.587
Inductive load	=	—	0.707	0.707	0.578
Peak current per rectifier element:					
Resistive load	=	3.14	1.57	1.57	1.21
Inductive load	=	—	1.00	1.00	1.00
Ratio of peak to average current per element:					
Resistive load	=	3.14	3.14	3.14	3.63
Inductive load	=	—	2.00	2.00	3.00
% ripple (rms of ripple/ average output voltage)	=	121%	48%	48%	18.3%
Ripple frequency	=	1	2	2	3
		Resistive Load	Inductive Load or Large Choke Input Filter		
Transformer secondary rms volts per leg	=	2.22	1.11 (to center-tap)	1.11 (total)	0.855 (to neutral)
Transformer secondary rms volts line-to-line	=	2.22	2.22	1.11	1.48

Table 19-1—cont.

Type of Circuit→		Single-Phase Half Wave	Single-Phase Center Tap	Single-Phase Bridge	Three-Phase Star (Wye)
Secondary line current	=	1.57	0.707	1.00	0.578
Transformer secondary volt-amperes	=	3.49	1.57	1.11	1.48
Transformer primary rms amperes per leg	=	1.57	1.00	1.00	0.471
Transformer primary volt-amperes	=	3.49	1.11	1.11	1.21
Average of primary and secondary volt-amperes	=	3.49	1.34	1.11	1.35
Primary line current	=	1.57	1.00	1.00	0.817
Line power factor	=	—	0.900	0.900	0.826

(From *Reference Data for Radio Engineers,* Indianapolis: Howard W. Sams & Co., Inc., 1975.)

Reverse Current in Rectifiers and No Line or Source Reactance

Three-Phase Bridge	Six-Phase Star (Three-Phase Diametric)	Three-Phase Double Wye With Interphase Transformer	Note: Assumes perfect rectifiers and zero reactance of ac line and source To Determine Actual Value of Parameter in Any Column, Multiply Factor Shown by Value of
6	6	6	
1.00	1.00	1.00	× Average dc voltage output
1.05	1.05	1.05	× Average dc voltage output
1.05	2.09	2.42	× Average dc voltage output
2.45	2.83	2.83	× Rms secondary volts per transformer leg

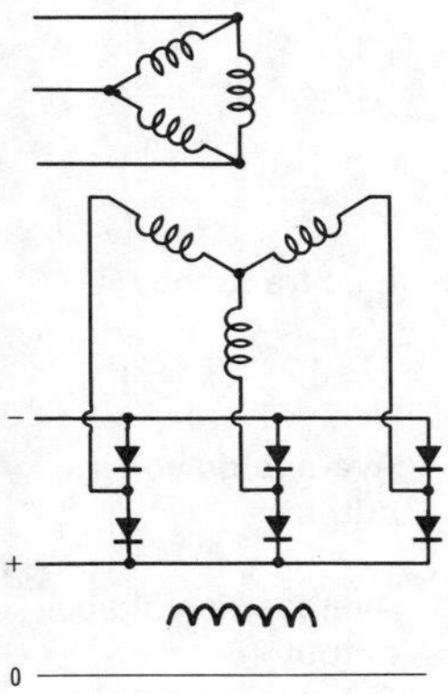

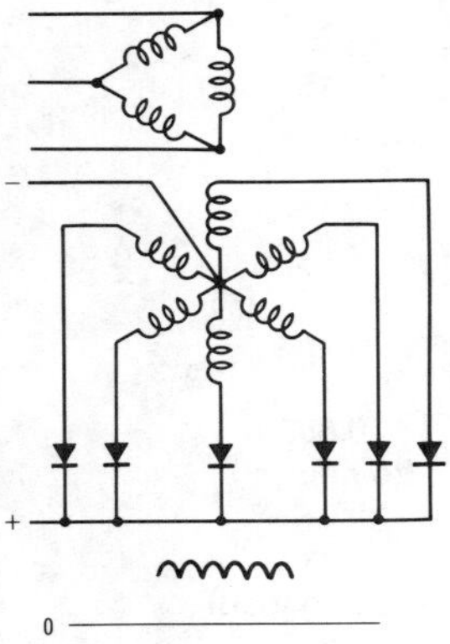

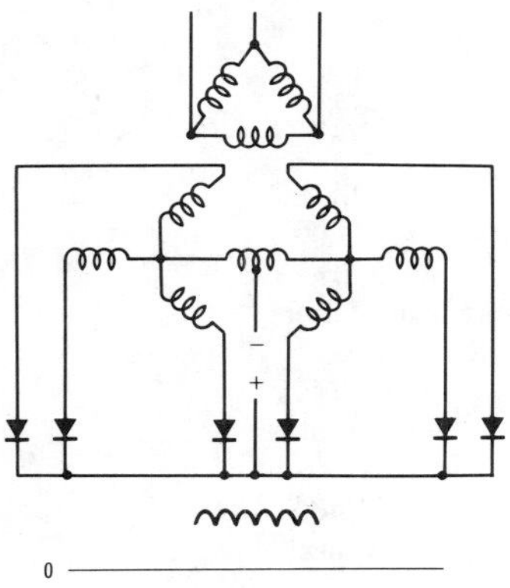

cont. on next page

Table 19-1.—cont.

Type of Circuit→		**Single-Phase Half Wave**	**Single-Phase Center Tap**	**Single-Phase Bridge**	**Three-Phase Star (Wye)**
1.41	1.41		1.41 (diametric)	×	Rms secondary volts line-to-line
1.00	1.00		1.00	×	Average dc output current
0.333	0.167		0.167	×	Average dc output current
0.579	0.409		0.293	×	Average dc output current
0.578	0.408		0.289	×	Average dc output current
1.05	1.05		0.525	×	Average dc output current
1.00	1.00		0.500	×	Average dc output current
3.15	6.30		3.15		
3.00	6.00		3.00		
4.2%	4.2%		4.2%		
6	6		6	×	Line frequency *f*
Inductive Load or Large Choke Input Filter					
0.428 (to neutral)	0.740 (to neutral)		0.855 (to neutral)	×	Average dc voltage output
0.740	1.48 (max)		1.71 (max-no load)	×	Average dc voltage output
0.816	0.408		0.289	×	Average dc output current
1.05	1.81		1.48	×	Dc watts output
0.816	0.577		0.408	×	Average dc output current
1.05	1.28		1.05	×	Dc watts output
1.05	1.55		1.26	×	Dc watts output
1.41	0.817		0.707	×	(Avg. load current × leg voltage)/primary line voltage
0.955	0.955		0.955		

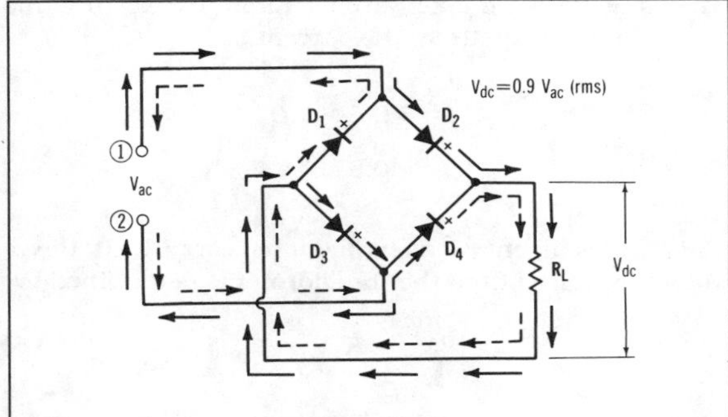

Figure 19-5 Full-wave bridge rectifier power supply.

in the direction of the solid arrows from terminal 1, through the low forward resistance of rectifier D_2, through the load resistance R_L, rectifier D_3, and, finally, to terminal 2, which is negative at this instant. Conduction through D_1 and D_4 is negligible because these rectifiers present their high back resistance when terminal 1 is positive and terminal 2 is negative.

On the next half-cycle, when terminal 2 swings positive, current flows in the direction of the dotted arrows from terminal 2, through the low forward resistance of rectifier D_4, through the load resistance R_L, rectifier D_1, and, finally, to terminal 1, which is negative at this instant. Conduction through rectifiers D_2 and D_3 is negligible because these rectifiers present their high back resistance when terminal 2 is positive and terminal 1 is negative. Note that the rectified current indicated by the solid arrows for one half cycle and the dotted arrows for the other half cycle always pass through the load resistance R_L in the same direction. The top of R_L is always positive, and the bottom is negative. Thus, full-wave rectification is obtained.

With the full-wave bridge circuit, the dc output voltage is equal to 0.9 of the rms value of the ac input voltage.

Bridge rectifier circuits may be grounded by four methods shown in Fig. 19-6. Either the input (ac source) or output (dc load) may be grounded, but not both simultaneously. However, if an isolation transformer is used between the ac source and the input to the rectifier, as shown in Fig. 19-6C, both ac and dc sides may be grounded permanently. An alternate method of grounding is shown in Fig. 19-7 where the center tap of an isolation transformer is grounded.

An advantage of the bridge rectifier is its ability to utilize the full winding and total voltage of a conventional center-tapped transformer, providing full-wave rectification, while the conventional full-wave, center-tapped circuit utilizes only one-half the total voltage. The power capabilities of the transformer remain the same.

Although twice the dc output voltage is available with the bridge rectifier under these circumstances, the permissible power drain will be only one-half that allowed with full-wave, center-tapped operation.

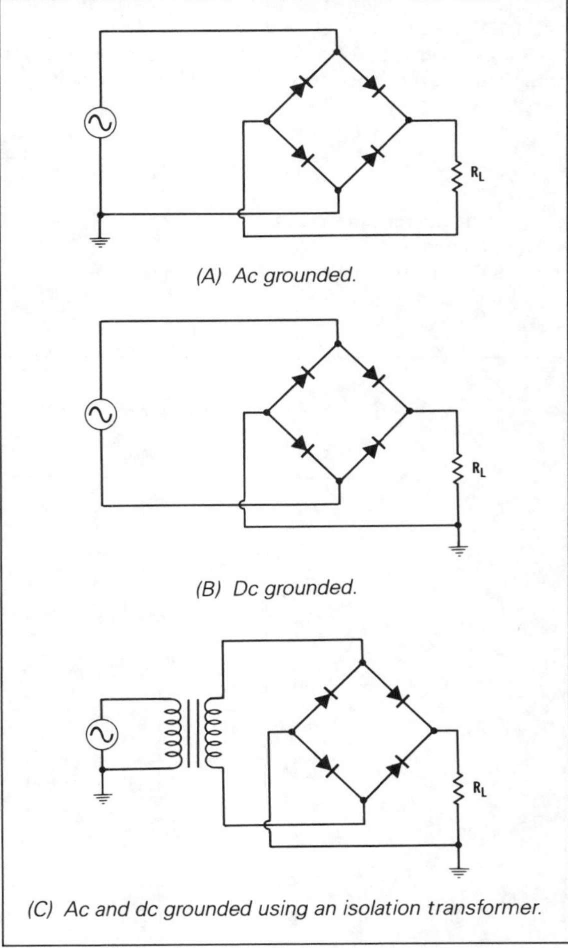

Figure 19-6 Methods of grounding a bridge rectifier power supply.

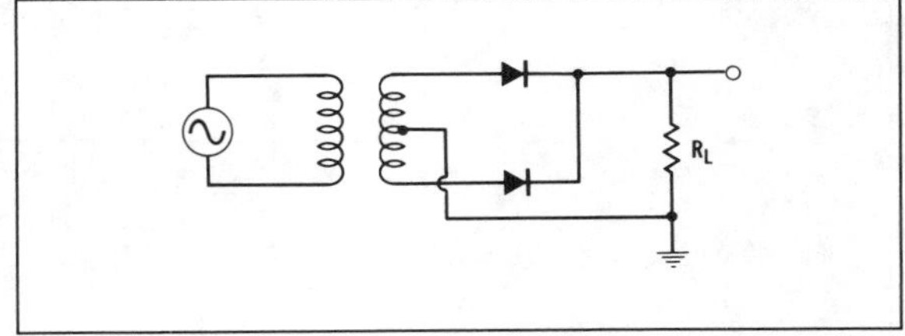

Figure 19-7 Full-wave center-tapped power supply with load.

When designing rectifier circuits, several factors must be taken into consideration. They are dc load current, dc load voltage, peak inverse voltage, maximum ambient temperature, cooling requirements, and overload current. Assume that a full-wave rectifier using silicon rectifiers is to be designed as in Fig. 19-7 and the dc load voltage V_{dc} under load is 25 V at 1 A.

Using the chart of Fig. 19-8, the first step is to determine the current (per rectifier) in terms of a half-wave rectifier using

$$I_{eq} = K_2 I_{dc} \quad (19\text{-}4)$$

where,

I_{eq} is the current per rectifier,
K_2 is a constant,
I_{dc} is the rectified ac current or dc current.

The value for K_2 is taken from column 5. Inserting this factor into the equation, the current is

$$I_{eq} = 0.5 \times 1.0$$
$$= 0.5\,A$$

This is the current each rectifier must carry. Next, the ac voltage required from the transformer is determined by

$$V_{ac} = K_1 V_{dc} \quad (19\text{-}5)$$

1	2	3	4	5	6
NAME	DIAGRAM	OUTPUT WAVEFORM	K_1 V_{ac}	K_2 CURRENT RECTIFICATION	K_3 PIV RECTIFICATION
1-PHASE HALFWAVE	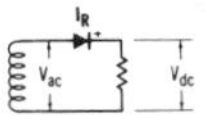	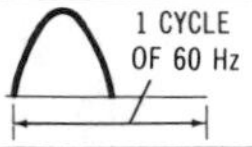 1 CYCLE OF 60 Hz	2.22	1.0	1.414
1-PHASE CENTER-TAP	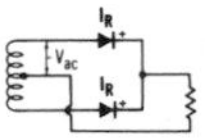	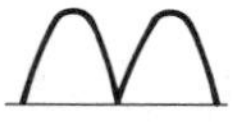	1.11	0.5	2.828
1-PHASE BRIDGE	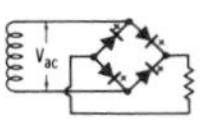		1.11	0.5	1.414
3-PHASE HALFWAVE	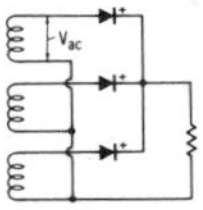	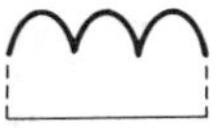	0.86	0.374	2.45
3-PHASE CENTER TAP	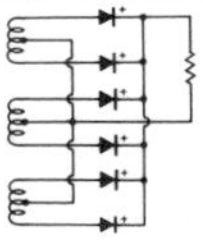		0.74	0.261	2.828
3-PHASE DOUBLE-WYE	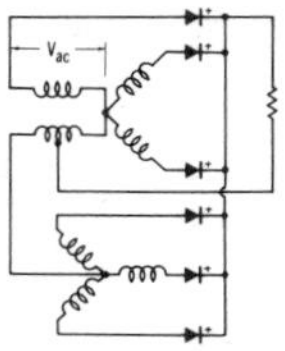	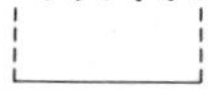	0.86	0.187	2.45
3-PHASE BRIDGE (Δ SEC.)	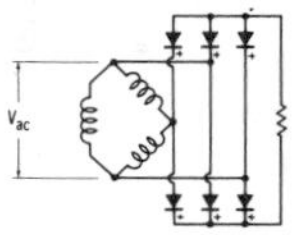	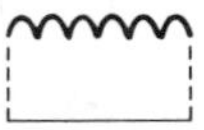	0.74	0.369	1.414
3-PHASE BRIDGE (Y SEC.)	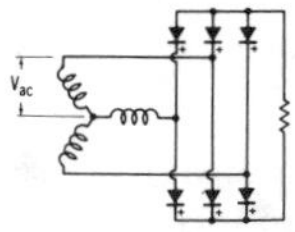	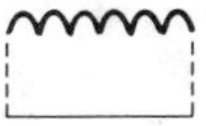	0.43	0.369	2.45

Figure 19-8 Basic rectifier circuits using a resistive load, and K values used for design.

where,
V_{ac} is the transformer voltage,
K_1 is a constant from column 4.

$$V_{ac} = 1.11 \times 25$$
$$= 27.75\,\text{V rms}$$

This is the voltage as measured from each side of the transformer center tap; the total voltage across the secondary is 55.50 V rms.

The peak inverse voltage is

$$\text{piv} = K_3 V_{ac} \quad (19\text{-}6)$$

The value for K_3 is taken from column 6 and equals 2.828; therefore,

$$\text{piv} = 2.828 \times 27.75$$
$$= 78.4\,\text{V rms}$$

A manufacturer's catalog can be consulted to find a rectifier with a piv rating of 78 V or greater, at a current of 1 A. A good selection would be a rectifier with a piv rating of 100 V and a capability of carrying 1000 mA or more. If the rectifier is to carry several amperes, it must be mounted on a heat sink; otherwise, it will be severely damaged within the first few seconds of operation. If a rectifier with the required piv rating is not available, two or more may be connected in series to obtain the desired piv rating. An example would be two units each having a piv rating of 50 V at 1 A connected in series. Unequal values of piv ratings may be used, provided the lowest rating is greater than half of the total piv rating needed.

Parallel operation of rectifiers is also possible to obtain higher current ratings. However, because of a possible unbalance between the units due to the forward voltage drop and effective series resistance, one unit may carry more current than the other and could conceivably fail. To prevent this, small resistances are connected in series with each individual rectifier to balance the load currents, as shown in Fig. 19-9.

Combination power supplies use a single power transformer serving as a voltage source for more than one rectifier section.

A single power supply serving two full-wave, high-voltage sections is shown in Fig. 19-10. In Fig. 19-11, a single power transformer serves a full-wave and a half-wave rectifier. This is a very common type of rectifier circuit and is used mainly in oscilloscopes. Note the high-voltage output is negative with respect to ground.

A dual power supply employing a full-wave rectifier circuit using two rectifiers is shown in Fig. 19-12. Two completely separate filter sections, consisting of an inductance-capacitance network and a resistance-capacitance network, are connected at the output of rectifiers D_1 and D_2. Filter capacitors C_1 through C_5 are all returned to a common ground.

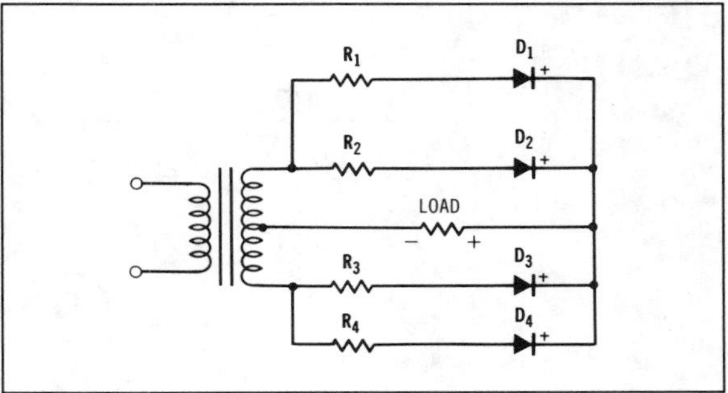

Figure 19-9 Parallel operation of rectifiers, small resistors are connected in series with each rectifier to balance the current through each unit.

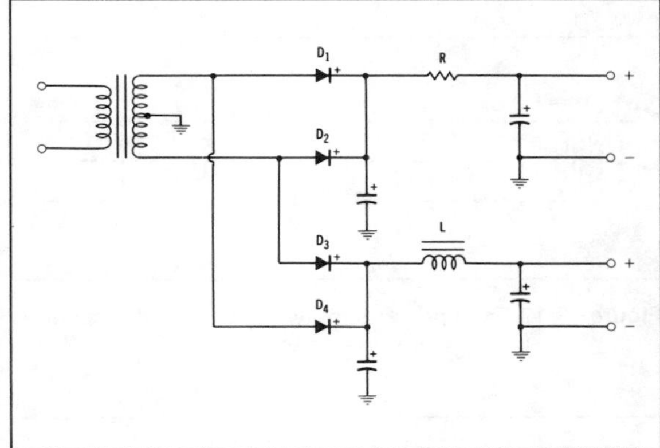

Figure 19-10 Combination power supply using a common power transformer two full-wave rectifier sections.

19.2.4 Voltage Doublers

A *voltage-doubler* circuit (Fig. 19-13) has the rectifiers connected in series, resulting in twice the voltage output as for a single rectifier.

Referring to Fig. 19-13, on the positive peak of the input voltage V_{ac}, capacitor C_1 is charged through rectifier D_2 to the peak voltage of V_{ac}. The negative half of the cycle charges capacitor C_2 through rectifier D_1. The polarities are such that the voltages are additive. Voltage V_{dc} at the output is approximately double the peak voltage of V_{ac}.

Voltage doublers may be used directly from the line or from a power transformer. The circuit shown is a half-wave doubler and delivers 2.82 times the rms value of the secondary voltage. Voltage doublers may also be designed for a symmetrical configuration (Fig. 19-14). The advantages of this circuit are that it is a full-wave circuit, with lower ripple content, better voltage regulation, and a ripple voltage frequency double that of the half-wave config-

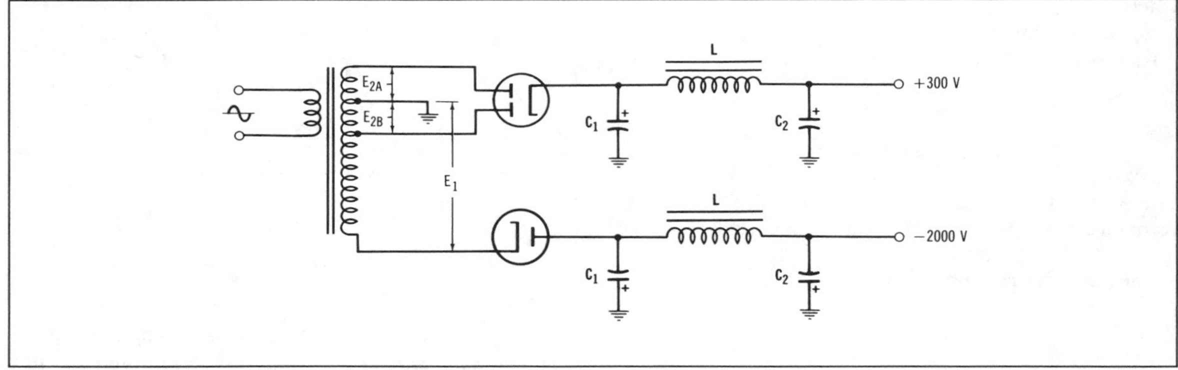

Figure 19-11 Combination power supply as generally found in an oscilloscope. A single transformer supplies both a full-wave and half-wave rectifier tube.

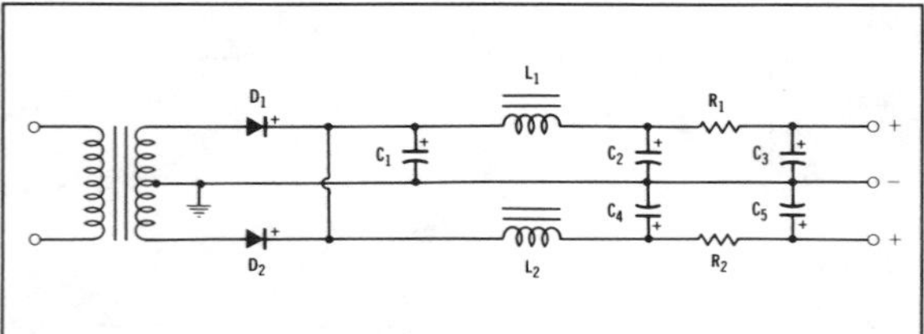

Figure 19-12 Dual power supply using two filter sections from one dc source.

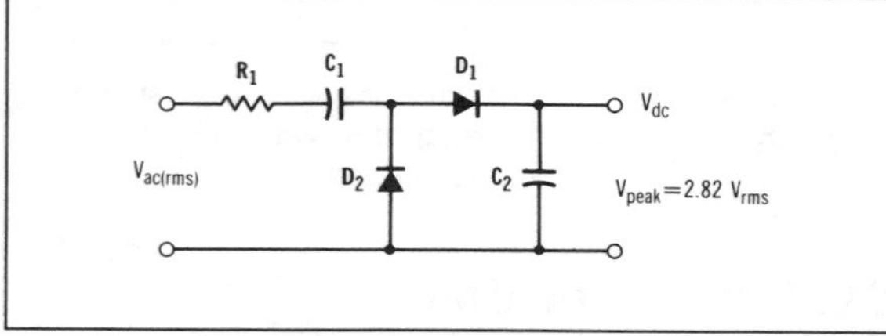

Figure 19-13 Voltage-doubler circuit.

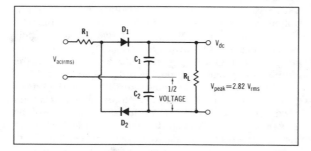

Figure 19-14 Full-wave symmetrical voltage-doubler circuit.

uration. It is quite important that the capacitors in the doubler circuit (also for triplers and quadruplers) be close to the same capacitance value, to keep the load evenly divided between the two rectifiers. A half-voltage point is also available by tapping off at the junction of the two capacitors.

Resistor R_1 in the solid-state doubler is a current-limiting resistor used to reduce the in-rush current until the load current becomes normal. If a transformer is used, resistor R_1 can usually be omitted, since the dc resistance of the transformer acts as a current-limiting resistor.

19.2.5 Voltage Triplers

A *voltage tripler* triples the ac voltage. Referring to Fig. 19-15, during the first half cycle of the source voltage V_{ac} charges C_1 through rectifier D_1 to the peak voltage value of V_{ac}. During the other half cycle, the voltage across C_1 and V_{ac} are in series-aiding and charge C_2 to the same voltage through rectifier D_2. The voltage across C_3 is now the voltage across C_1, plus the peak voltage of V_{ac}.

The voltage across C_3 is now brought to the same value as C_2 through rectifier D_3. The output voltage V_{dc} is approximately three times the peak voltage V_{ac}.

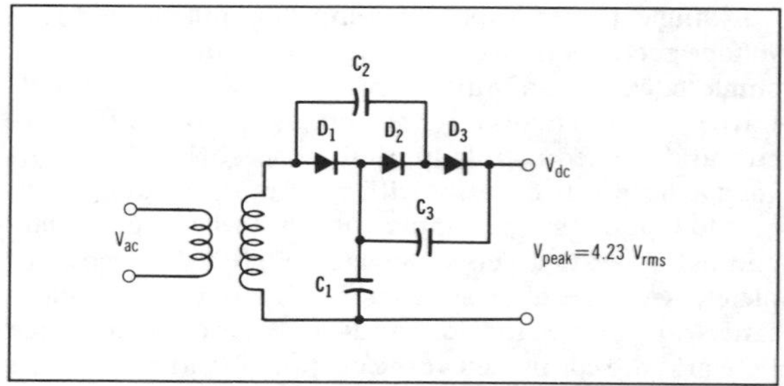

Figure 19-15 Voltage-tripler series multiplier circuit.

Theoretically, it is possible by adding successive stages of rectification and capacitor combinations to raise the voltage indefinitely; however, from a practical standpoint, this becomes economically unsound.

19.2.6 Three-Phase Power Supplies

Three-phase power supplies are common in industry; however, they are seldom used in audio. To see the characteristics of three-phase supplies, see Table 19-1.

Three-phase half-wave V_{dc} is 1.16 V_{ac} per phase, the current/rectifier is 0.374 I_{dc}, and the ripple is 18.3%.

A three-phase, full-wave center-tapped supply has V_{dc} equal to 135% of V_{ac}, each rectifier carries 0.26 I_{dc}, and the ripple is 4.2%.

19.3 FILTERS

A *power-supply filter* is a series of resistors, capacitors, and/or inductors connected either passively or actively to reduce the ac or ripple component of the dc power supply.

19.3.1 Capacitor Filters

A *capacitor filter* employs a capacitor at its input, as shown in Fig. 19.16. Capacitor filter power supplies have a higher output voltage than one without a capacitor because the peak value of the rectifier output voltage appears across the input filter. As the rectified ac pulses from the rectifier are applied across capacitor C_1, the voltage across the capacitor rises nearly as fast as the pulse. As the rectifier output drops, the voltage across the capacitor does not fall to zero but gradually diminishes until another pulse from the rectifier is applied to it. It again charges to the peak voltage. The capacitor may be considered a storage tank, storing up energy to the load between pulses. In a half-wave rectifier, this action occurs 60 times per second, and for a full-wave rectifier, it occurs 120 times per second.

For a single-phase circuit with a sine-wave input and no capacitor across the output, the peak inverse voltage at the rectifier is 1.414 times the rms value of the voltage applied to the rectifier. With a capacitor input to the filter, the peak inverse voltage may reach 2.8 times the rms value of the applied voltage. This data may be obtained by referring to Tables 19-1 and 19-2.

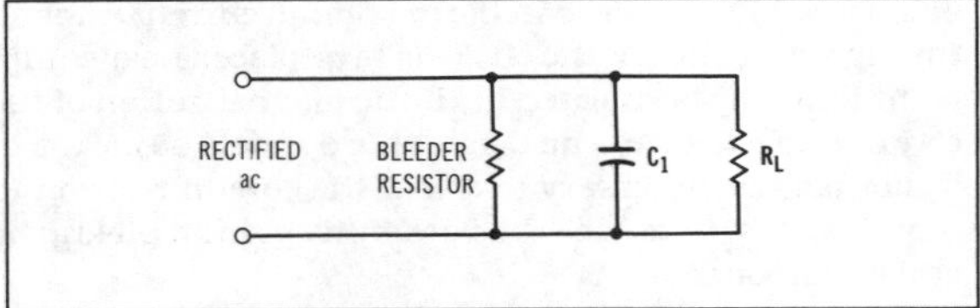

Figure 19-16 Capacitor filter.

As a rule, the value of the input capacitor is in the order of 20 to 40 μF for high-voltage, low-current supplies and 1000 to 20,000 μF for low-voltage, high-current supplies.

Using a low value for the input capacitance will permit the output voltage to be adjusted to a given value. However, this type of design affects the regulation and is not recommended unless the load demands are small and constant. A capacitor-input filter section does not have as good a regulation as the choke input, but it does have the advantage of a higher voltage output.

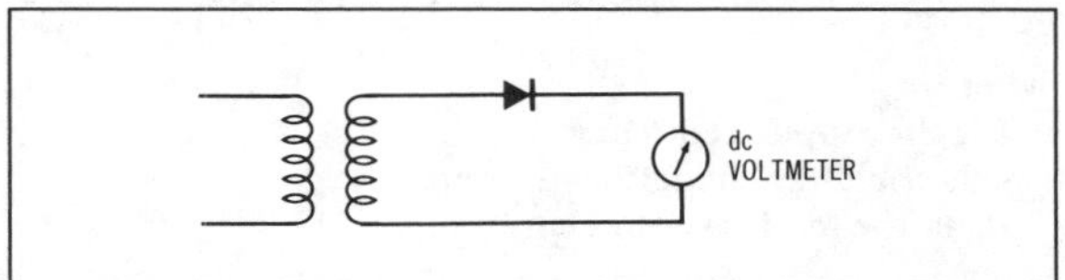

Figure 19-17 Measurement of average rms voltage across the output of a half-wave rectifier. Waveform shows half-wave pulses of current.

When a conventional dc voltmeter is connected across the unfiltered output of a rectifier, the voltage read will be the average voltage. As an example, assume a dc voltmeter is connected across the output of a half-wave rectifier, as shown in Fig. 19-17. Because of the inertia of the meter pointer movement, the meter does not respond to the rapidly changing pulses of the half-wave rectified current but acts as a mechanical integrator. The pointer will be displaced an amount proportional to the time average of the applied voltage waveform. If the secondary voltage of the transformer is, say, 25 V rms, the peak voltage V_p will be

$$\begin{aligned} V_p &= 1.414\,V_{rms} \\ &= 1.414(25) \\ &= 35.35\,\text{V} \end{aligned} \tag{19-7}$$

The average voltage (V_{av}), as read by the dc voltmeter, will be

$$\begin{aligned} V_{av} &= V_p/\pi \\ &= 35.35/3.14 \\ &= 11.25\,\text{V} \end{aligned} \tag{19-8}$$

For a full-wave rectifier circuit, the average voltage at the output of the rectifier will be double that of the half-wave rectifier (assuming each half of the transformer is equal to the voltage of the half-wave transformer secondary) because there are two pulses of rectified current per cycle instead of one. This is approximately 90% of the rms voltage. Therefore, if the voltage rating of the capacitor is based on a measurement made by a dc voltage, it will be in error. The voltage rating must be calculated and determined by mathematically calculating the peak value of the voltage applied to the rectifier. The voltage rating of the capacitor must be greater than the peak voltage at the output of the rectifier.

If the voltage at the output of the rectifier is too high for the conventional electrolytic capacitor, two capacitors may be connected in series. To balance the capacitors, they should be the same value, and each, bypassed with a high-value resistor.

The ripple factor from equation 19-1 would be

$$\gamma = I_{dc}/4\pi\sqrt{3}\,fCV_{dc} = 1/4\pi\sqrt{3}\,fCR_L \qquad (19\text{-}9)$$

where,
f is the ripple frequency,
C is the filter capacitor in farads,
R_L is the load resistance in ohms.

Capacitor filters operate best with large filter capacitors and high-resistance loads. As the load resistance is lowered, ripple increases and regulation decreases.

A *bleeder resistor* is often connected across the dc output of a power supply, as shown in Fig. 19-16. The bleeder functions to protect the filter capacitors when the load is removed and also to drain off the charge from the filter capacitors when the power supply is shut off. If the bleeder resistor is of the correct value, it will tend to improve the voltage regulation.

The current taken by a bleeder resistor is generally in the order of 10% of the total load current. Bleeder resistors are only used with unregulated power supplies.

Lowering the value of the bleeder resistance will improve the regulation at the expense of consuming more current.

Filtering efficiency is reduced, and the internal leakage is increased when the power factor increases. Electrolytic capacitors should be removed when their power factor reaches an excessive value. In an ideal capacitor, the current would lead the voltage by 90°. However, capacitors are never ideal, as a small amount of leakage current always exists around the dielectric. Also, a certain amount of power is dissipated by the dielectric, the leads, and their connections. All this adds up to power loss. This power loss is termed phase difference and is expressed in terms of power factor (pf). The smaller the power factor value, the more effective the capacitor. Since most service capacitor analyzers indicate these losses directly in terms of power factor, capacitors with large power factors may be readily identified. Generally speaking, when an electrolytic capacitor reaches a power factor of 15%, it should be replaced. However, the data sheet of the manufacturer should be consulted before replacing certain types of electrolytic capacitors, because they may be designed to operate with a relatively high power factor. Filtering efficiency for different values of power factor can be read directly from the following table:

% Power Factor	Filtering Efficiency
5	0.999
10	0.995
15	0.989
20	0.980
25	0.968
30	0.955
35	0.935
40	0.915
45	0.895
50	0.857
60	0.800
70	0.715
80	0.600
90	0.436
100	0.000

19.3.2 Inductive Filters

An *inductive filter* employs a choke rather than a capacitor at the input of the filter, as shown in Fig. 19-18. Although the output voltage from this type filter is lower, the voltage regulation is better.

A choke filter operates best with maximum current flow. It has no effect on a circuit when no current is flowing. The critical inductance is the inductance required to assure that current flows to the load at all times. An inductor filter depends on the property of an inductor to oppose any change of current.

To assure that current flows continuously, the peak current ($\sqrt{2}\,I_{rms}$) of the ac component of the current must not exceed the direct current $I_{dc} = (V_{dc}/R_L)$. Therefore,

$$X_L \geqslant \sqrt{2}/3\,R_L$$

and

$$L_C = R_L/3(2)\pi f \qquad (19\text{-}10)$$

where,
L_C is the critical inductance,
R_L is the load resistance.

Filter chokes should be selected for the lowest possible dc resistance commensurate with the value of inductance.

To prevent saturating the core, the current rating should be at least 25% higher than the maximum current demand through the choke. If the choke is to be placed near equipment that may be affected by the dc magnetization of the core or ripple voltage, a moderate shield should be included. It may also be necessary to orient the core in relation to other devices, to reduce the possibility of hum pickup by other components.

When the direct-current rating of a filter choke is

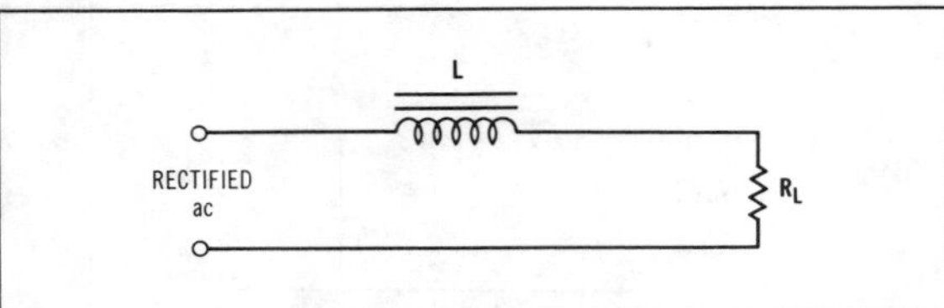

Figure 19-18 Choke input filter.

exceeded, the core becomes saturated, which reduces the inductance and, in turn, reduces the filtering action of the choke. Under these conditions, the ripple voltage will rise to a value that may render the supply useless.

19.3.2.1 Swinging Chokes

A *swinging choke* is used in the first filter section of a power supply having a wide range of load current. The choke is designed so that its inductance varies inversely with the load current. The core has little or no air gap, which permits it to saturate at high current, thus decreasing its inductance. The important points of its construction are the inductance, the core gap, and the dc resistance. Because the inductance of the choke varies with the load currents flowing through it, the inductance falls very sharply when the current becomes high enough to saturate the core. Therefore, a point of critical inductance is reached for each change of load current.

To determine the critical inductance, the load resistance must be calculated. Assume that a power supply is to deliver 400 V of 100 mA and the dc resistance of the swinging choke is 200 Ω. The load resistance will be

$$400\ \text{V}/0.100\ \text{A} + 200\ \Omega = 4200\ \Omega$$

Assuming that the load current falls to 40 mA, the load resistance then becomes

$$400\ \text{V}/0.040\ \text{A} + 200 = 10{,}200\ \Omega$$

The critical inductance (in henrys) then becomes approximately:

$$L_C = \text{load resistance}/1000\ @\ 60\ \text{Hz}$$

For the previous example, the critical inductance at full-load current is 4 H, and 10 H at minimum-load current. The optimum inductance is twice the value of the critical inductance. Using the previous information, a swinging choke of 8 to 20 H at 100 mA is required.

19.3.2.2 Ripple Factors

The *ripple factor* (γ) for an inductive filter is

$$\gamma = (R_L + R_C)/[3\sqrt{2}\,(2\pi f)] \qquad (19\text{-}11)$$

where,
R_L is the load resistance in ohms,
R_C is the choke resistance in ohms,
f is the ripple frequency.

19.3.3 Combination Filters

Combination filters use a combination of resistors, capacitors, and inductors to improve the filtering, the simplest being a resistor-capacitor filter and the more complicated being a series of inductance-capacitor (LC) circuits.

19.3.4 Inductance-Capacitance (LC) Filters

Inductance-capacitance (LC) filters, sometimes called *L filters,* use an inductor as an input filter and a capacitor as the second stage of the filter (Fig. 19-19). LC filters operate well under varying load conditions.

In an LC-type filter section, the inductive reactance of the choke tends to oppose any change in the current flowing through the winding; therefore, it has a smoothing action on the pulsating current of the rectifier. The capacitor at the output of the choke stores and releases electrical energy, thus it also smoothes out the ripple voltage. The result is a fairly smooth output current. Adding a second filter section results in a steady direct current. The choke-type filter has another advantage in that its low dc resistance induces only a small voltage drop across its winding, which becomes quite important at heavy load currents. The ripple factor for an LC filter is

$$\begin{aligned}\gamma &= \sqrt{2}X_C/3X_L \\ &= \sqrt{2}/(3)(2\pi fC)(2\pi fL) \qquad (19\text{-}12) \\ &= 0.01/f^2CL\end{aligned}$$

where,
X_C is the capacitance reactance in ohms,
X_L is the inductive reactance in ohms,
f is the frequence of ripple,
C is the capacitance in farads,
L is the inductance in henrys.

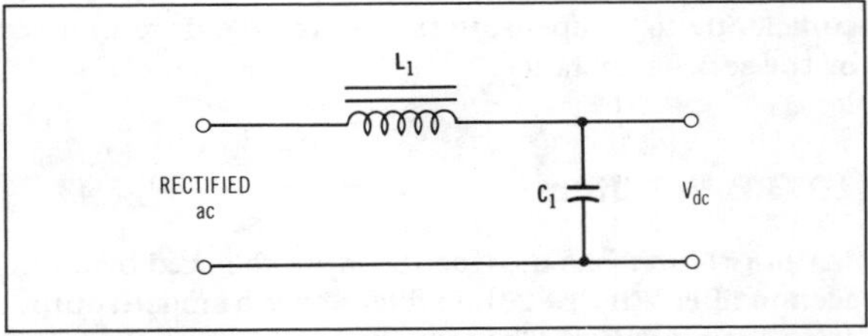

Figure 19-19 Inductance-capacitance or L filter.

When multiple LC filters are connected together, the ripple factor is

$$\gamma = (\sqrt{2}/3)/(16\pi^2 f^2 LC)^n$$
$$= 0.47/(157.9f^2 LC)^n$$

where,
L is the inductance in henrys,
f is the ripple frequence,
C is the capacitance in farads,
n is the number of sections.

19.3.5 Resistance-Capacitance Filters

A *resistance-capacitance (RC) filter* employs a resistor and capacitor rather than an inductor and capacitor, Fig. 19-20. The advantage of such a filter is its low cost, weight, and reduction of magnetic fields. The disadvantage of such a filter is that the series resistance induces a voltage drop that could be detrimental to the circuit operation. An RC filter system is generally used only where the current demands are low. RC filters are not as efficient as the LC type, and they may require two or more sections to provide sufficient filtering.

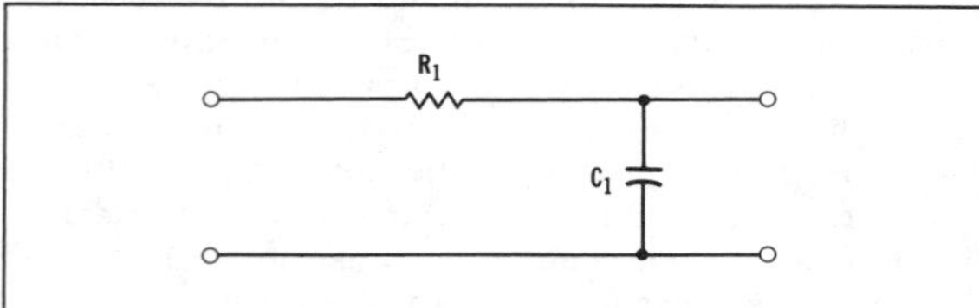

Figure 19-20 Resistance-capacitance filter.

A rule-of-thumb design for RC filters is to first determine the value of the series resistance, based on the load current through the resistor. Capacitors are then selected that offer a low impedance at the power-supply ripple frequency. Thus, a small power supply may use a 250- to 1000-Ω series resistor, and a capacitor of from 40 to 100 μF. For a low-voltage power supply of 30 V, two filter sections using 1500-μF capacitors could be used. The important point to remember in the use of RC filter sections is that the voltage at the rectifier must be increased sufficiently to compensate for the voltage drop induced by the series resistance.

19.3.6 Pi Filters

A *pi (π) filter* has a capacitor input followed by an LC section filter (Fig. 19-21). Pi filters have a smooth output and poor regulation. They are often used where the transformer voltage is not high enough and low ripple is

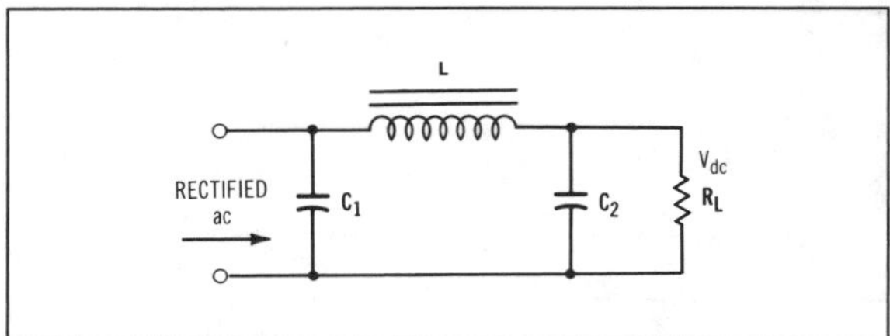

Figure 19-21 Pi (π) filter.

required. By using the input capacitor, the dc voltage is boosted to the peak voltage.

The ripple factor for a pi filter is

$$\gamma = \sqrt{2}\,(X_{C1}X_{C2}/R_L X_{L1}) \quad (19\text{-}14)$$

where,
X_{C1} is the capacitive reactance of the first capacitor,
X_{C2} is the capacitive reactance of the second capacitor,
R_L is the load resistance,
X_{L1} is the inductive reactance of the choke.

When the choke is replaced with a resistor, the ripple factor becomes

$$\gamma = \sqrt{2}\,(X_{C1}X_{C2}/R_L R) \quad (19\text{-}15)$$

19.3.7 Tuned Filters

A *tuned filter* has the LC network tuned to the ripple frequency to reduce ripple, as shown in Fig. 19-22. The capacitor C_1 and the choke L_1 form a resonant circuit that is tuned to the second harmonic frequency of the rectifier circuit. For a 60-Hz full-wave rectifier, the resonant frequency is 120 Hz. To eliminate the higher harmonics, a second section should be used as shown.

A second tuned filter is shown in Fig. 19-23 and consists of a series-resonant circuit L_1 and C_2, with a par-

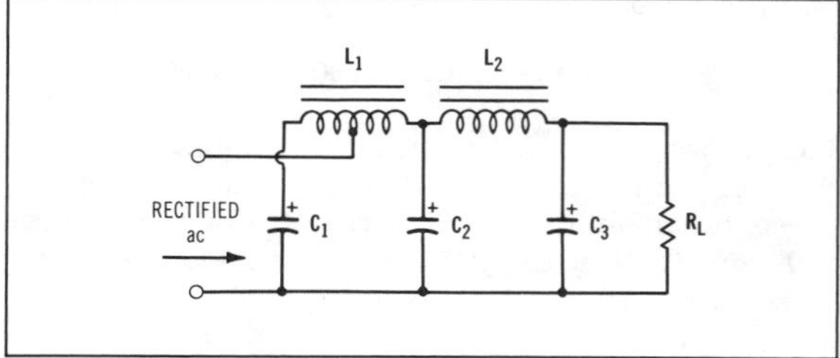

Figure 19-22 Tuned or hum-bucking filter L_1 followed by a single-section filter L_2. For a 60-Hz line supply voltage and a full-wave rectifier, L_1 and C_1 are resonated to 120 Hz.

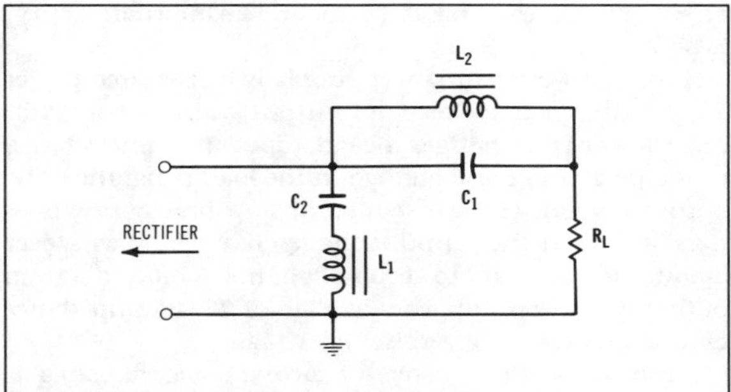

Figure 19-23 Tuned filter section using both series- and parallel-tuned circuits.

allel-tuned circuit L_2 and C_1 in series with the high potential. The filter sections for a half-wave rectifier are tuned to a frequency of 60 Hz; for a full-wave rectifier they are tuned to 120 Hz.

19.4 RESISTANCE VOLTAGE DIVIDERS

A *resistance voltage divider* is shown in Fig. 19-24.

In this system of voltage division, the resistors are connected in series with the particular load they feed. The resistors are calculated by means of the simple Ohm's law ($R = V/I$). The wattage is computed by $P = V^2/R$ or I^2R.

Generally, when a series-resistance voltage divider is used, a separate bleeder resistor is also used to secure better regulation.

Each section should have a separate bypass capacitor of 10 μF or more to ground. The bypass capacitors stabilize and improve the filtering. This is particularly true for the series-type voltage divider.

There are two common types of voltage dividers, the *shunt* and the *series* types. The shunt type shown in Fig. 19-24 is designed to supply three different voltages to external devices. The upper circuit supplies 75 mA at 40 V, the second circuit supplies 30 mA at 25 V, and the third circuit supplies 15 mA at 15 V. All circuits are common to ground.

The total current required is the total current of the three external circuits, or 120 mA, plus an additional current called the bleeder current. This bleeder current flows only through the resistors and not through the external circuits. It is generally 10% of the total current. For this illustration, the bleeder current is 12 mA, making a grand total of 132 mA.

Resistor R_3 is calculated first. Because only bleeder current flows through this resistor, it may be calculated using

$$R_3 = V/I$$
$$= 15/0.012$$
$$= 1250\,\Omega$$

where,

V is the voltage across R_3,
I is the bleeder current.

The voltage at the top of R_2 is 25 V to ground. Subtracting the voltage drop across R_3 results in a voltage across R_2 of 10 V. The current through R_2 is the current of load 3 plus the bleeder current, or a total of 27 mA. Therefore,

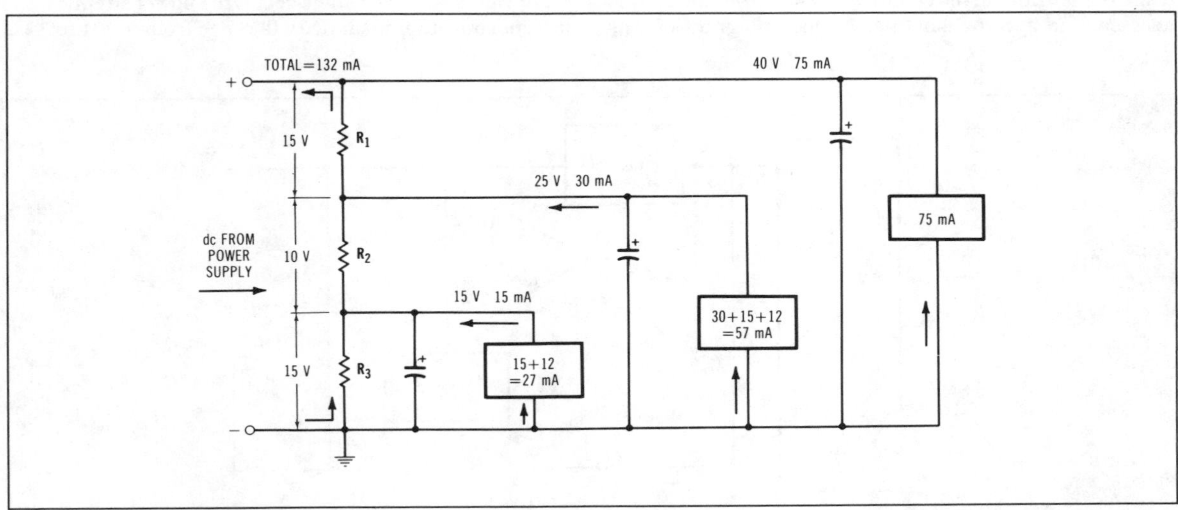

Figure 19-24 Shunt-type voltage-divider system showing the current flow in the various branches.

$$R_2 = V/I$$
$$= 10/0.027$$
$$= 370\ \Omega$$

Resistor R_1 has the current of loads 2 and 3 plus the bleeder current flowing through it, making a total current of 57 mA. Therefore,

$$R_1 = V/I$$
$$= 15/0.057$$
$$= 263\ \Omega$$

The current of load 1 does not flow through any part of the voltage-divider system; therefore, it requires no further considerations.

19.5 REGULATED POWER SUPPLIES

A *regulated power supply* holds the output constant with variations in load, current, or input voltage.

Regulated supplies may be simple shunt or series regulators with 1 to 3% regulation, to high gain supplies with 0.01% regulation and 0.01% ripple.

A regulated power supply can hold either the voltage or current constant, and it is called a *voltage-regulated* or *current-regulated supply*.

A constant-voltage power supply is a regulated power supply designed to keep its output voltage constant, regardless of the changes in load current, line voltage, or temperature. For a change in the load resistance, the output voltage remains constant to a first approximation, while the output current changes by whatever amount is necessary to accomplish this. A block diagram of this type supply appears in Fig. 19-25, and its impedance curve is shown in Fig. 19-26.

A constant-current power supply is a regulated power supply designed to keep its output current constant, regardless of the changes in load impedance, line voltage, or temperature. For a change in the load resistance, the output current remains constant to a first approximation, although the output voltage changes by whatever amount is necessary to accomplish this. A block diagram of this type supply appears in Fig. 19-27. Its impedance characteristics are given in Fig. 19-28.

A *constant-voltage, constant-current power supply* acts as a constant-voltage source for comparatively large values of load resistance and as a constant-current source for comparatively small values of load resistance. An automatic crossover (or transition) between these two modes of operation occurs at a critical or crossover value of load resistance (R_c) where

$$R_c = V_s/I_s \qquad (19\text{-}16)$$

where,

V_s is the voltage-control setting,

I_s is the current-control setting.

A block diagram of this type supply appears in Fig. 19-29.

An ideal constant-voltage power supply would have zero impedance. A constant-current supply would have infinite impedance at all frequencies. However, these ideals are not achieved; therefore, a practical power supply has a very low impedance at the lower frequencies, and the impedance rises with frequency. The constant-current supply has a rather high impedance at the lower frequencies and decreases at the higher frequencies.

For well-designed voltage-regulated power supplies, the internal output impedance will range from 0.001 to 32 Ω

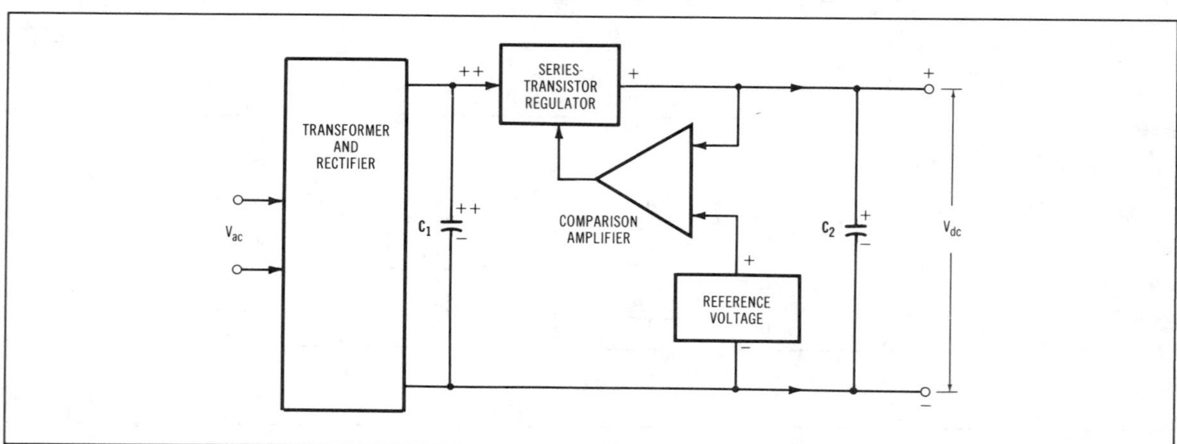

Figure 19-25 Block diagram for a constant voltage-regulated power supply.

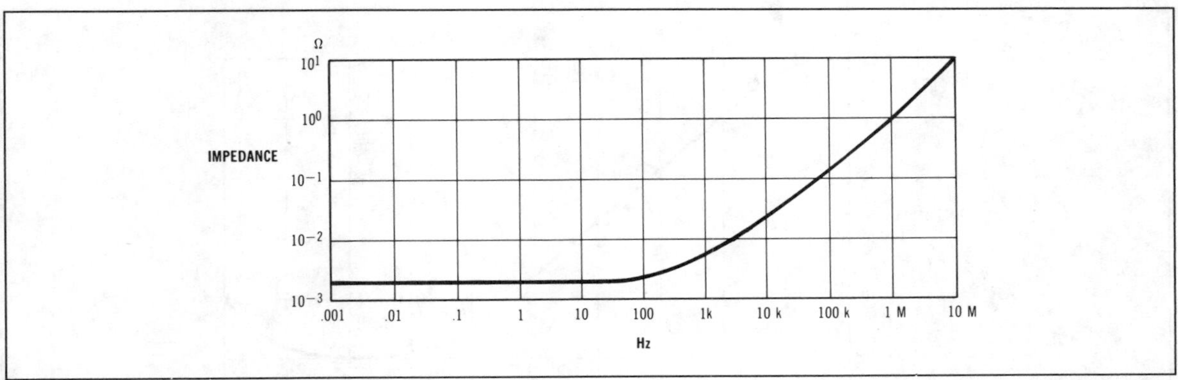

Figure 19-26 Typical internal impedance characteristics for a constant-voltage power supply.

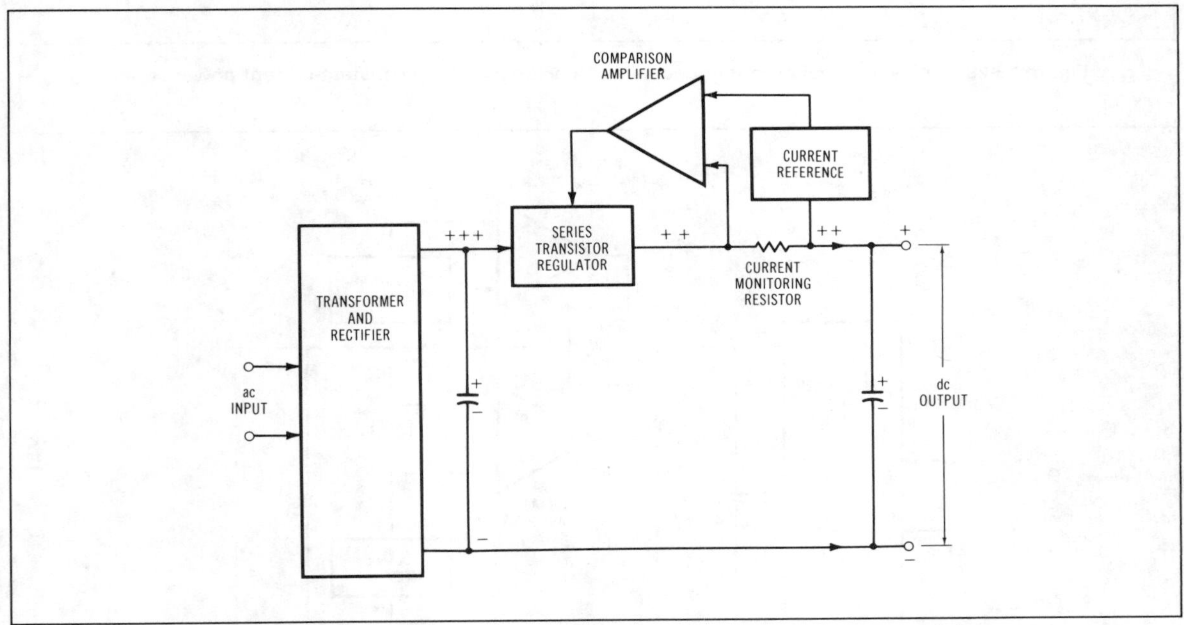

Figure 19-27 Block diagram for a constant-current regulated power supply.

for frequencies of dc to 1 MHz. The actual impedance is a function of the load and the type equipment being fed by the supply. However, the impedance of most high-quality supplies ranges from 0.001 to 3 Ω.

Power supplies may be connected in parallel, but the supplies must all have the same maximum compliance voltage ratings. If they do not and if the load circuit is opened, the terminal voltage will rise to the maximum voltage of the highest rated supply. If this voltage is greater than the rating of the other supplies, damage may result. To prevent this possibility, diodes are connected in the positive lead of each power supply, as shown in Fig. 19-30. When the diode is in its normal conducting mode, it must be capable of withstanding the short-circuit current of its regulator. The piv rating of the diode must be equal to or greater than the maximum open-circuit potential of the highest-rated power supply.

Regulated power supplies can also be connected in series if certain precautions are observed. The isolation voltage rating of the individual power supplies must not be exceeded, and the power supplies must be protected against reverse potential. Diodes are connected in the nonconducting direction across the output of each supply unit (Fig. 19-31). These diodes will start to conduct the instant a reverse potential appears, providing a path for short-circuit current. If possible, the regulating cir-

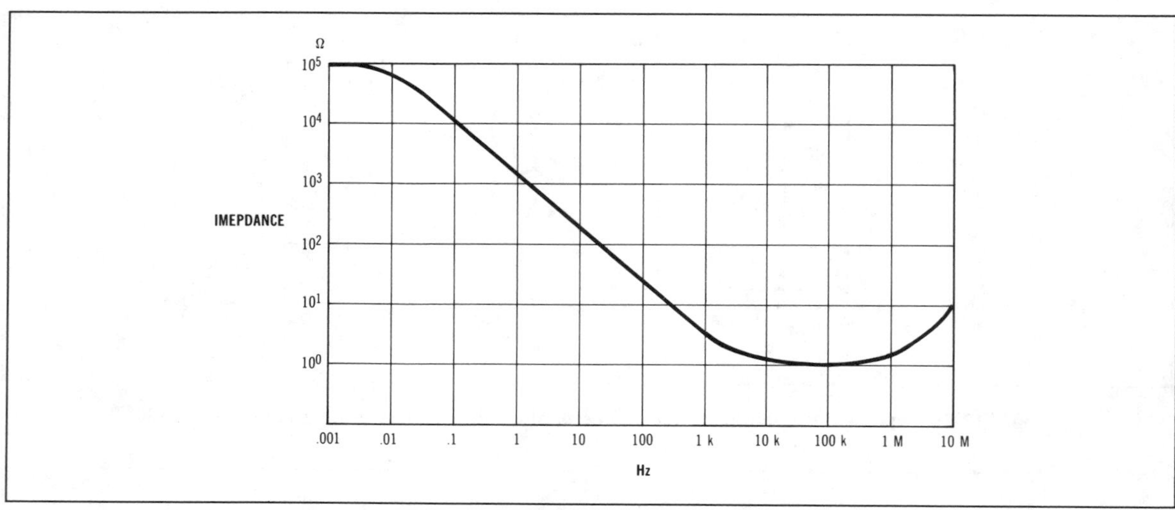

Figure 19-28 Typical internal output impedance characteristics for a constant-current power supply.

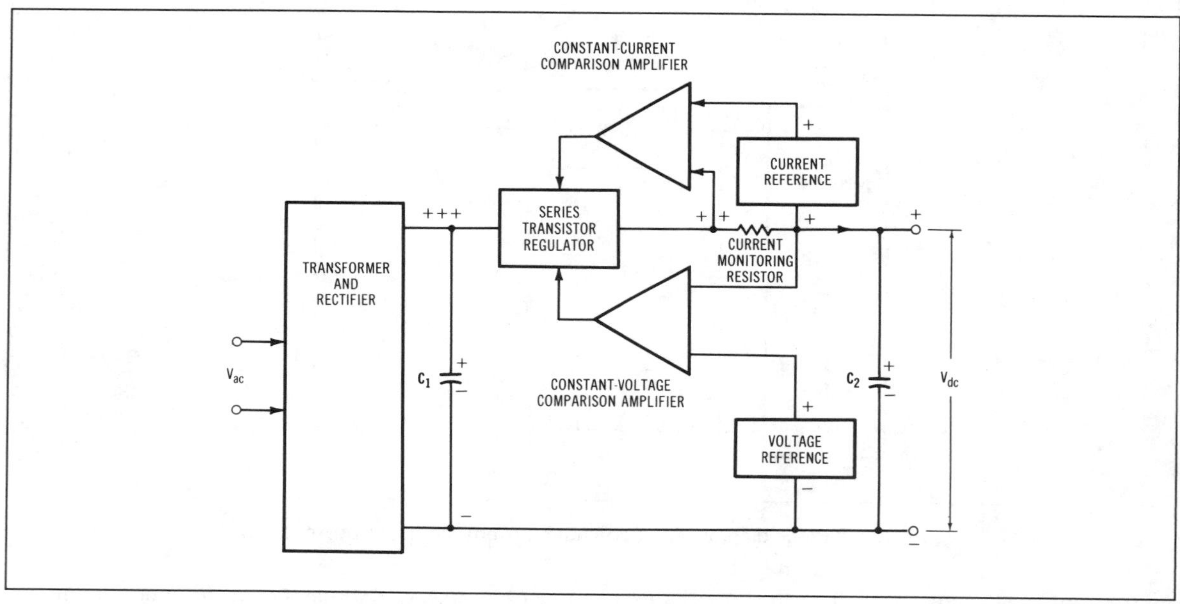

Figure 19-29 Block diagram for a constant-voltage constant-current power supply with automatic crossover.

cuit for one supply should be connected as a master and the other as slaves. The voltages of the supplies do not have to be the same.

All regulated supplies have a reference element and a control element. The amount of electronics between the two elements determines the quality and regulation of the supply.

The reference element is the unit that forms the foundation of all voltage regulators. The output of the regulated power supply is equal to or a multiple of the reference. Any variation in the reference voltage will cause the output voltage to vary; therefore, the reference voltage must be maintained as stable as possible (Fig. 19-25).

The control element is that unit that maintains the output voltage constant. The regulator type is named after the control element, namely, series, shunt, or switching (Fig. 19-25). The control element is an electronic variable resistor that drops voltage either in series with the load or across the load. Control element configurations are shown in Fig. 19-32.

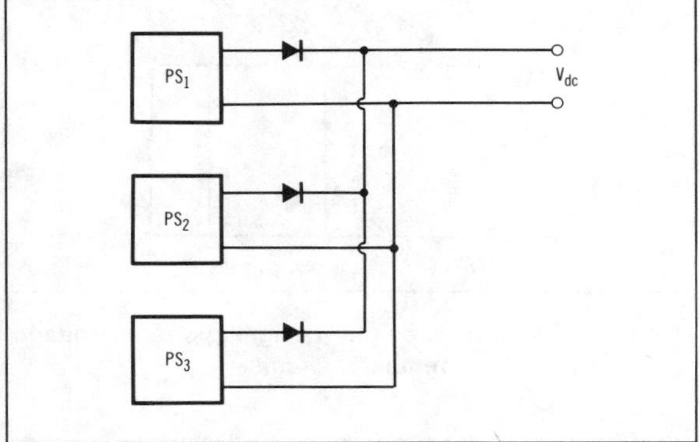

Figure 19-30 Three regulated power supplies connected in parallel, with diodes connected in series with a plus side to prevent damage from a voltage reversal.

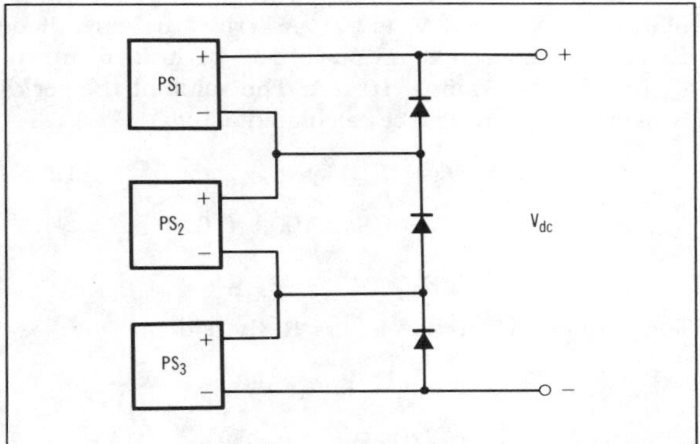

Figure 19-31 Three regulated power supplies connected in series with diodes connected across each supply to prevent damage because of voltage reversal.

All regulated supplies draw standby current which is the current drawn by the power supply with no output load.

The input voltage to regulated supplies is filtered dc. The smoother the input voltage is, the smoother the output will be. The capacitor C_1 shown in Fig. 19-25 is used to smooth the output (reduce ripple).

Because the comparison amplifier is constantly monitoring the output, it also reduces ripple because the reference voltage is smooth dc and the output attempts to have ripple. The output ripple voltage appears to the comparator like a varying load; therefore, the regulator or pass transistor attempts to follow it, reducing ripple.

19.6 SIMPLE REGULATED SUPPLIES

A simple supply consists of only the control element and the reference element.

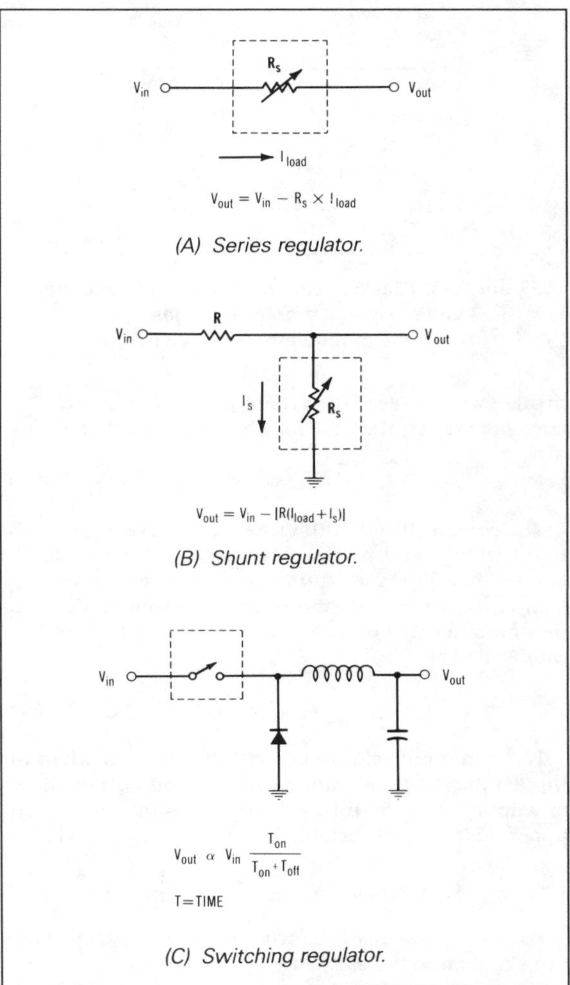

Figure 19-32 Example of various control elements.

19.6.1 Gaseous Voltage Regulators

The *gaseous voltage regulator (VRT) tube* was the standard reference element for many years (see electronic components). These tubes were normally used to regulate high voltage (over 90 V).

The basic circuit for a VRT is shown in Fig. 19-33. The input voltage to the regulator tube is designated V_1; the nominal or regulated output voltage, V_2. Variable quantities are the tube current (I_1), the load current (I_2), and the load R_L. There are several variables to be considered in the design, so several separate calculations are required. These calculations are based on the following conditions: the current through the tube must fall within the minimum and maximum current limits, and the supply voltage must be equal to or be greater than the maximum

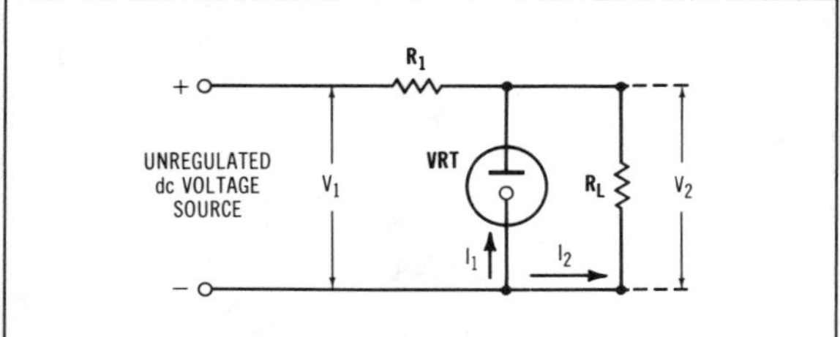

Figure 19-33 Basic circuit for designing a regulated-voltage circuit employing a gaseous voltage-regulator tube (VRT).

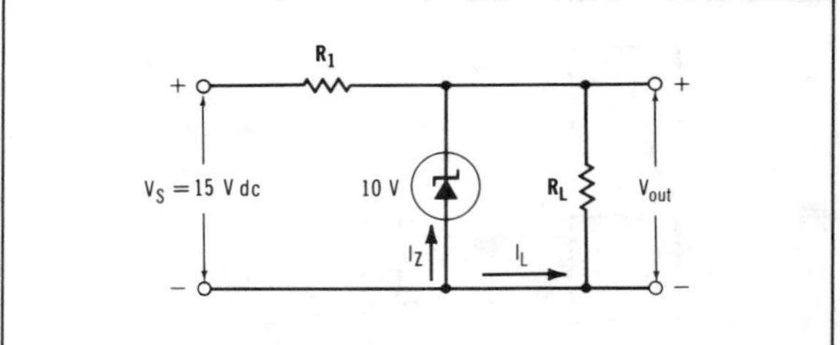

Figure 19-34 Basic circuit for designing a zener voltage regulator circuit.

breakdown voltage of the VRT plus the IR drop of R_1. The current through the tube may be expressed using

$$I_1 = [(V_1 - V_2)/R_1] - I_2 \qquad (19\text{-}17)$$

The current through the tube varies directly with the input voltage and inversely with the load current. The current I_1 will be maximum when V_1 is maximum, the load current I_2 is minimum, and the voltage V_2 is the minimum for this current. Thus, the lower limit of R_1 is established as

$$R_1 = (V_{1\,max} - V_{2\,max})/(I_{1\,max} + I_{2\,max}) \qquad (19\text{-}18)$$

The minimum value of current (I) will occur when the input voltage (V_1) is minimum, the load current (I_2) is maximum, and the tube voltage (V_2) is maximum. The upper limit for R_1 is established as

$$R_1 = (V_{1\,min} - V_{2\,max})/(I_{1\,min} + I_{2\,max}) \qquad (19\text{-}19)$$

To assure that the tube will fire, the following conditions must also be satisfied:

$$(V_{1min} \times R_L)/(R_L + R_1) > V_{breakdown}$$

VRTs can be connected in series. Each tube can be a different voltage rating, and voltage taps can be taken at each tube. This connection is satisfactory only if each tube meets the minimum and maximum current ratings. The starting voltage applied to each tube in the string will be determined by the individual leakage resistances. If a resistor of 200,000 Ω to 1 MΩ is connected across one of the tubes, the remaining tubes will fire first, thus assuring the instant firing of all tubes when the voltage is applied. A slight reduction in the regulation effectiveness may be noted for the shunted tube.

19.6.2 Zener Diode Voltage Regulators

The *solid-state zener diode* has replaced the gaseous tube reference element because it is smaller and has better regulation, wide voltage range, and wide power range. Referring to the basic design in Fig. 19-34, the zener diode is connected in series with the limiting resistor R_1 and in parallel with the source of voltage to be regulated. Assume that a 10-V regulated dc voltage V_{out} is desired at a maximum load current of 100 mA, and the unregulated voltage source V_S is 15 V. As a rule, the zener diode current I_z is chosen for a value of 10% of the load current I_L, or for this example 10 mA. The value of the series resistance R_1 can now be calculated using

$$R_1 = (V_S - V_{out})/I_L + I_Z) \qquad (19\text{-}20)$$

$$= (15 - 10)/(0.100 + 0.010)$$

$$= 45.5\,\Omega$$

The power dissipated in R_1 is I^2R; therefore,

$$P = (I_L + I_Z)^2 \times 45.5$$

$$= 0.55\,W$$

For practical purposes, a 47-Ω, 5%, 1-W resistor is used. The power dissipated by the diode is equal to

$$V_{out} \times I_Z = 10 \times 0.01$$

$$= 0.10\,W$$

The dissipation is only for a condition where the load current remains constant at 100 mA. If the load current is completely removed, the current through the diode increases to 100 mA, and the zener wattage dissipation rises to 1.10 W. In this instance, a diode capable of dissipating 2 W is required.

Several voltage-regulating circuits are shown in Fig. 19-35. Zener diodes can be connected in series across the output of a dc supply, provided the power-handling capabilities and the current-operating ranges are similar.

A cascade shunt regulator is given in Fig. 19-36. The zener diode controls the base potential of transistor Q_1, which functions as an emitter follower and circuit amplifier. The voltage V_{CB} of Q_1 determines the bias of Q_2, the shunt regulator. This circuit is used where large current variations are encountered. Transistor Q_2 may consist of several parallel-connected transistors. Q_2 current is max-

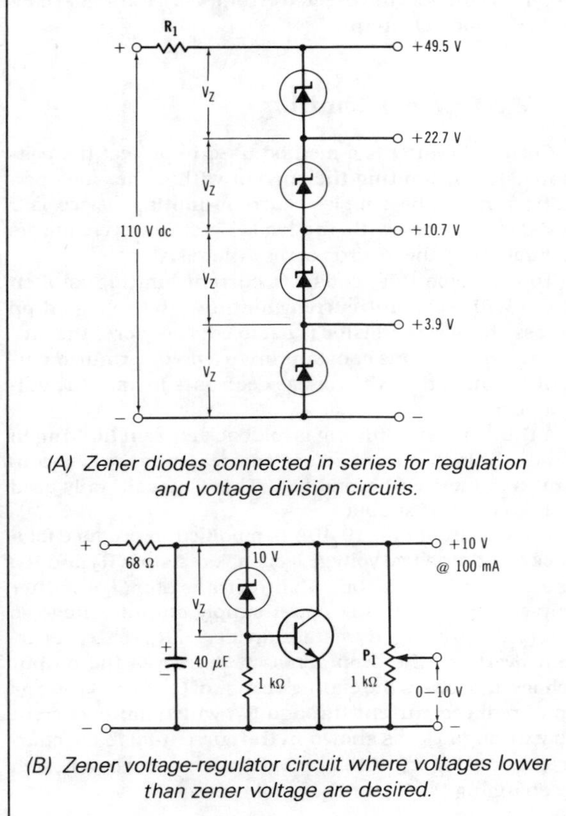

(A) *Zener diodes connected in series for regulation and voltage division circuits.*

(B) *Zener voltage-regulator circuit where voltages lower than zener voltage are desired.*

Figure 19-35 Various regulator circuits.

imum when the load resistance is minimum and is most useful when the load currents remain high.

If only a small voltage drop is required, say, 5 or 6 V, the configuration in Fig. 19-37 might be employed. In this instance, the entire load current plus the current through R_1 must flow through the diode, and it could be easily damaged.

A current-regulator circuit is shown in Fig. 19-38. Basically, the circuit consists of a grounded-base transistor and a variable resistor R_2. By changing the value of R_2, the emitter current flowing through R_3 is changed. Resistor R_3 serves as a keep-alive current for the zener diode. With the load R_L, the transistor supplies a small portion of the current drawn by R_3; therefore, less current will flow through the reference diode. Resistor R_3, however, must draw enough current through the reference diode so the voltage drop across the diode remains at 8 V as the current regulator is loaded. The load current remains essentially constant until R_L increases to where the average voltage drop across R_L is as large as the voltage drop across R_3. The transistor must be mounted on a heat sink of approximately 165 in^2.

Zener diodes, ranging from 2 to around 200 V and covering a large range of current operation, can be obtained

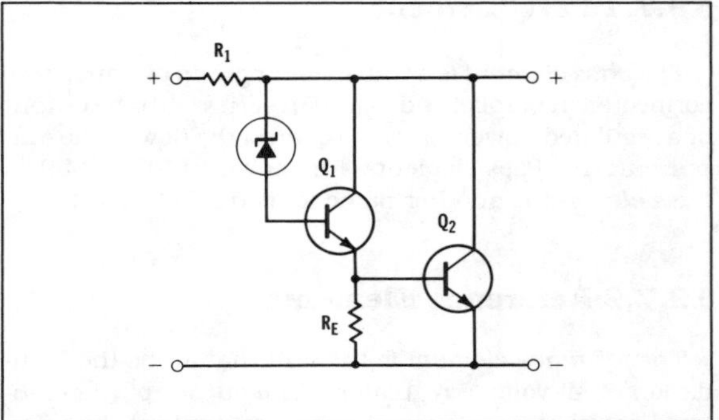

Figure 19-36 Cascade-shunt zener-diode voltage-regulator circuit. Transistor Q_2 may consist of several units in parallel for higher current ratings.

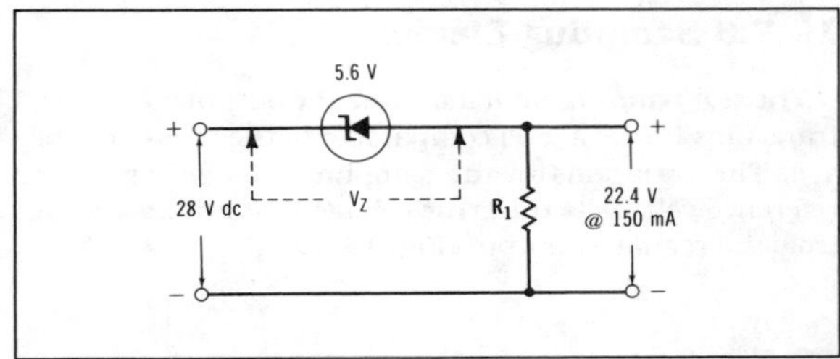

Figure 19-37 Series connection for a zener diode when only a small voltage drop is required.

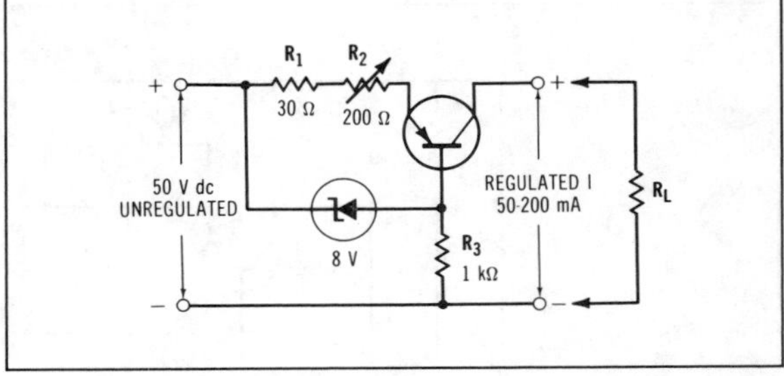

Figure 19-38 Current-regulator circuit using a transistor and zener diode.

for voltage regulation and reference use. In using higher-current types, the power dissipated by the diode must be given consideration. This latter information is found from the data sheet of the manufacturer.

19.7 COMPLEX SUPPLIES

Complex supplies include a pass element, a sampling element, and a comparator element, and they may include current limiting, undervoltage and overvoltage protection, and remote sensing.

19.7.1 Pass Elements

The *pass element* is a transistor or group of transistors connected in parallel and placed in series with the output of a regulated power supply to control the flow of the output current. Pass elements are shown in Fig. 19-39. A *pass element* is another name for control element.

19.7.2 Reference Elements

The *reference element* is the unit that forms the foundation of all voltage regulators. The output of the regulated power supply is equal to or a multiple of the reference. Any variation in the reference voltage will cause the output voltage to vary; therefore, the reference voltage must be maintained as stable as possible (Fig. 19-25).

19.7.3 Sampling Elements

The *sampling element* monitors the output voltage and translates it into a level comparable to the reference voltage. The variations in the sampling voltage versus the reference voltage is the error voltage that ultimately controls the regulator output (Fig. 19-39).

19.7.4 Comparator Elements

The *comparator element* compares the feedback voltage from the sampling element with the reference and provides gain for the detected error level. This signal controls the control circuit.

19.7.5 Current Limiting

Current limiting is a method used to protect the pass transistor by limiting the current within the safe operating range. The simplest current-limiting device is a resistor in series with the load. This, however, affects regulation by the IR drop across the resistor.

To overcome this, constant current limiting is often used. With constant current limiting, the voltage drop across the series resistor is sampled; therefore, the output voltage remains constant up to a predetermined current at which time the voltage decreases to limit the output current.

A third current limiting is foldback current limiting in which the load current actually decreases as the load continues to increase beyond I_{max}. This is usually only used in high current supplies.

The circuit of Fig. 19-40A is modified to produce foldback by adding two voltage feedback resistors R_3 and R_4, as shown in Fig. 19-40B.[2] Control transistor Q_1's emitter voltage depends on the power-supply output voltage as sampled by the R_3, R_4 voltage divider. If R_1 senses a current overload, the drop across it decreases the output voltage and lowers the emitter voltage of Q_1. Then Q_1 turns on at reduced current through R_1, which limits current flow through Q_2, as shown in the current-foldback characteristic of Fig. 19-40B. The foldback ratio can be adjusted by changing R_3, R_4, or R_1, or all three.

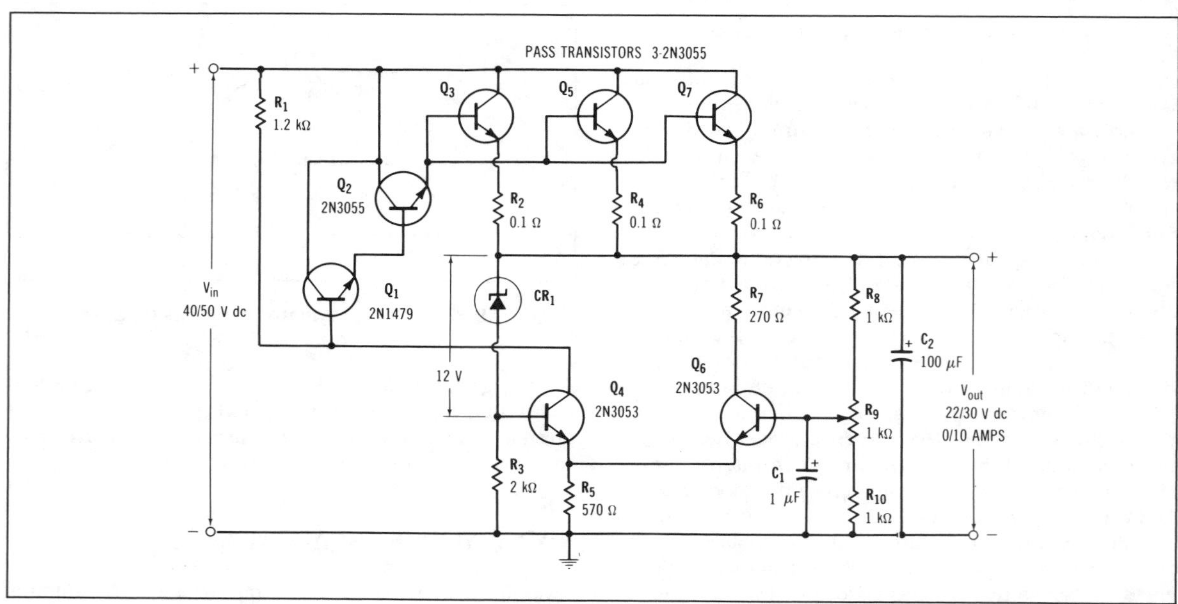

Figure 19-39 Series-type transistor voltage regulator. Load regulation 0.5%, input 1%. The output voltage is adjustable within 22 to 30 V. *(Courtesy Radio Corporation of America)*

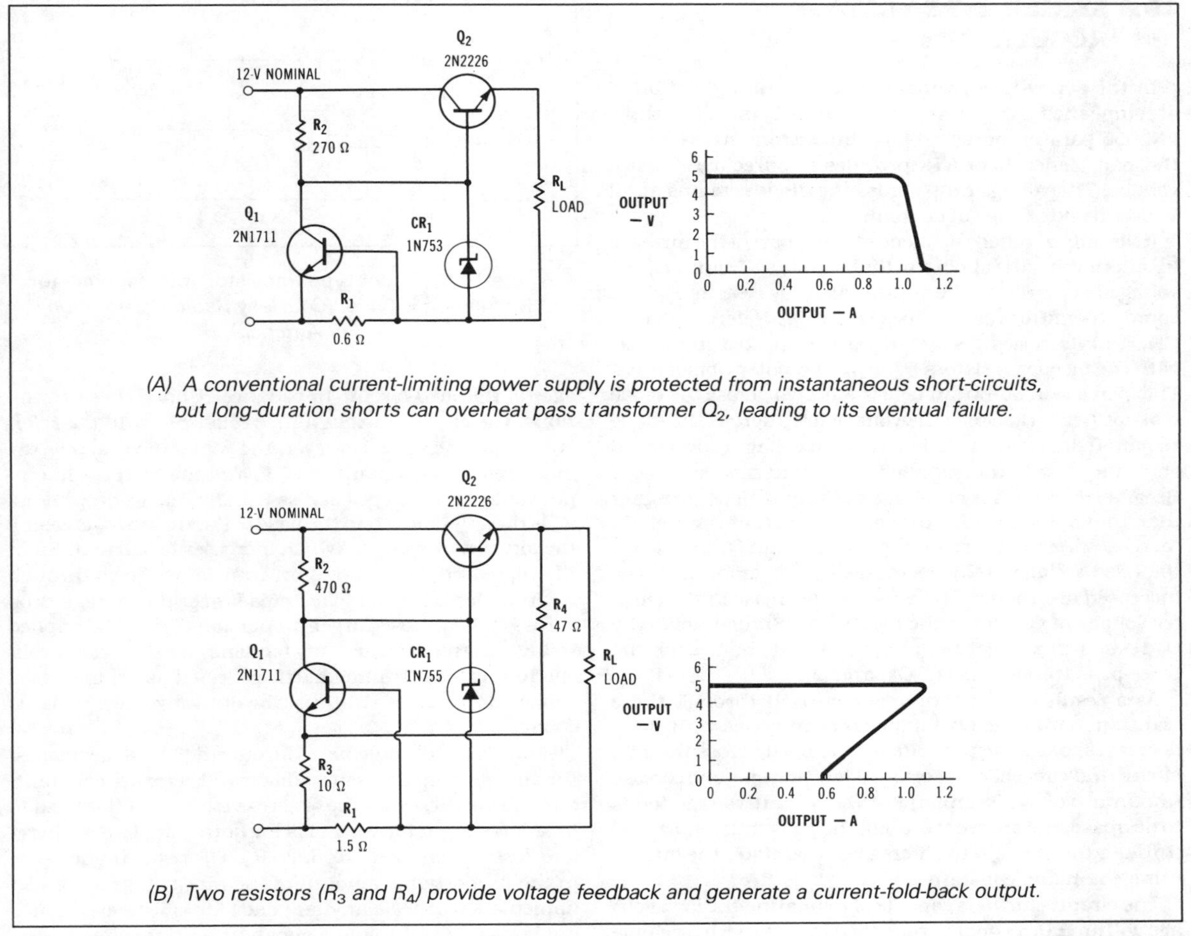

(A) A conventional current-limiting power supply is protected from instantaneous short-circuits, but long-duration shorts can overheat pass transformer Q_2, leading to its eventual failure.

(B) Two resistors (R_3 and R_4) provide voltage feedback and generate a current-fold-back output.

Figure 19-40 Current limiting circuits.

19.7.6 Overvoltage Protection

Overvoltage protection protects the load from overvoltage. This may be accomplished internally or as an add-on to the power supply. A crowbar circuit is a typical overvoltage protector.

The circuit monitors the output voltage of a power supply and instantaneously throws a short circuit across the output terminals when a preset voltage is reached. This is generally accomplished by the use of a silicon controlled rectifier (SCR) connected across the output terminals of the supply unit.

19.7.7 Remote Sensing

By means of two extra wires between the supply and the load, the *remote sensing* circuit permits the supply to achieve its optimum regulation at the load terminals, rather than at the power supply output terminals. In this manner, the circuit compensates for the IR drop in the line from the power supply to the equipment receiving its voltage. The current through the sensing lines is quite small; therefore, the voltage drop is negligible.

When remote sensing accuracy is not required, the remote sensing terminals can be connected directly to the output terminals. In this manner, the output is regulated at the output of the supply rather than the input to the load.

The wire size and voltage drop for regulated power supplies can be determined by Ohm's law. However, with the use of the nomograph in Fig. 12-8, the problems are simplified. Since regulated power supplies are designed to control the output at the power supply output terminals, the conductors used for the supply line must be considered as a part of the power supply load.

19.8 SERIES-TYPE VOLTAGE REGULATORS

In the series-type regulator (Fig. 19-39) regulation is accomplished by varying the current through three 2N3055 parallel-connected pass transistors in series with the load. Zener diode CR_1 provides a source of reference voltage. The voltage drop across the diode remains at 12 V, over a wide range of current.

If the output voltage V_{out} tends to rise, part of the increase in output voltage is applied to the base of Q_6. This increased voltage is coupled to the emitter of Q_4 by resistor R_5, the common-emitter resistor for Q_4 and Q_6. Reference diode CR_1 and its series resistor R_3 are connected in parallel with the bleeder resistors R_8, R_{10}, and potentiometer R_9. The increase in output voltage is reflected across the diode resistor network. Since the voltage drop across the diode remains constant, the full increase in voltage is developed across R_2 and is thus applied directly to the base of Q_4. Because the increase of voltage at the base of Q_4 is higher than that of the emitter, the collector current through Q_4 increases. As the collector current through Q_4 increases, the base voltage of Q_1 decreases by the amount of the increased drop across R_1, causing a decrease in the emitter voltage of Q_1 and in the base of Q_2. Similar action by Q_2 results in a negative-going voltage at the base of the three pass transistors Q_3, Q_5, and Q_7.

As a result of this action, the current through these transistors and the load impedance in series with them decreases, reducing the voltage developed across the load circuit and canceling the original tendency for an increase in output voltage. Similarly, if the output voltage tends to decrease, the current through the pass transistors and through the load circuit increases; therefore, the output voltage remains constant.

The circuit shown is capable of regulating the load voltage within ±0.5% for currents of 0 to 10 A, with a voltage output of 22 to 30 V.

19.9 SHUNT-TYPE VOLTAGE REGULATORS

A *shunt-type voltage-regulator circuit* is not as efficient as the series regulator. However, it does have advantages because of its simplicity. In the shunt regulator (Fig. 19-41) the current through the shunt element transistors Q_1 and Q_2 varies with the load current of the input voltage. The current variations are reflected across resistor R_1 in series with the load so that output voltage V_{out} is maintained nearly constant. This regulator circuit can provide a regulated output voltage within ±0.5% of 28 V dc, with a current capability of 500 mA, for inputs of 45 to 55 V dc. The zener diode is rated at 27 V.

With a 28-V output, the reference diode CR_1 voltage drop remains constant (27 V) over a wide range of currents through the diode. The output voltage will tend to rise with an increase in either the unregulated input voltage or the load-circuit impedance. Under these conditions, the current through the resistor R_2 and the reference diode increase. However, the voltage drop across the diode remains constant at 27 V, and the increase in output voltage is developed across R_2. The voltage drop across R_2 is directly coupled to the base of Q_2, thereby increasing the forward bias on Q_1, which increases its current. Since the increased current of both transistors flows through R_1 in series with the load impedance, the voltage drop across R_1 becomes a larger proportion of the total applied voltage. In this manner, any tendency for the output voltage to increase is immediately reflected as an increased voltage drop across R_1; thus, the output voltage remains constant.

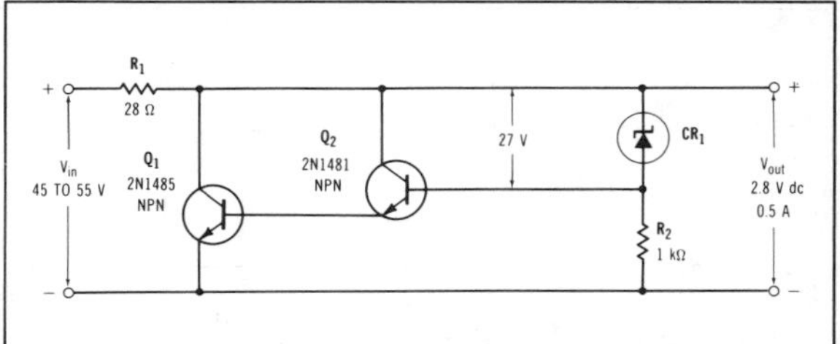

Figure 19-41 Shunt-type transistor voltage regulator. Regulation is 0.5%. *(Courtesy Radio Corporation of America)*

Under a condition where the output voltage decreases, the voltage drop across the diode still remains constant, and the full decrease occurs across R_2. This action results in a decrease in forward bias for both transistors; therefore, less current flows through R_1. The resultant decrease in the proportional amount of the input stage across R_1 immediately cancels any tendency for a decrease in output voltage, resulting in a constant output voltage.

Shunt regulators should only be used when the load current is fairly constant and is seldom removed. When the load is removed, the shunt transistor absorbs all the current of the load plus the normal regulation current, causing heat in the transistor.

19.10 MONOLITHIC VOLTAGE REGULATORS

Monolithic voltage regulators are grown on a single chip by etching, scribing, diffusing, and so on. The result is a chip that includes all the transistors, diodes, capacitors, resistors, and interwiring. A monolithic voltage regulator includes all the components required for voltage regulation, thermal overload, current limiting, and short-circuit protection. See Fig. 19-42. In this Lambda 1.5-A regulator, dc is applied between pin 1 and the case, and the regulated output is between pin 2 and the case. This regulator has a 0.69% load regulation and a 58-dB ripple attenuation.

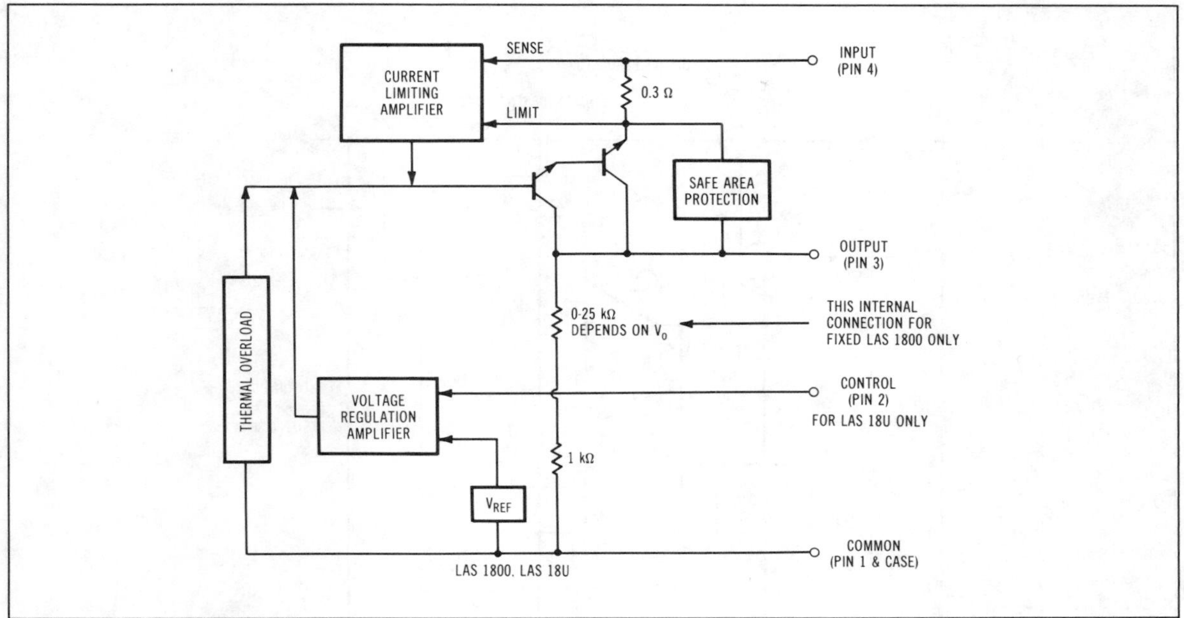

Figure 19-42 Lambda monolithic regulator *(Courtesy Lambda, Subsidiary of Veeco Instruments Inc.)*

19.11 HYBRID VOLTAGE REGULATORS

A *hybrid voltage regulator* incorporates transistor chips and integrated circuit chips in a single enclosure. These regulators are used where higher current than that obtainable from a monolithic regulator is required. In Fig. 19-43, the series regulator transistor is capable of 15 A and is a separate chip from the low-current devices. This unit has a 0.01% line, a 0.2% load regulation, and a 0.007%/°C temperature coefficient. The regulator has remote sensing capabilities and individual supplies for the V_{in} for the load and the V_{in} for the control amplifier to improve regulation.

19.12 SWITCHING REGULATORS

In a *switching regulator* the pass transistor operates in an on-off mode, increasing efficiency and reducing heat. The simple switching regulator shown in Fig. 19-44, incorporates a pulse generator circuit that pulses on the pass transistor as the output voltage decreases. As the output voltage increases, the comparator circuit reduces the pulse generator, reducing the on time of the pass transistor and, therefore, reducing the average output voltage. Since the output voltage is a series of pulses, a filter is required to smooth the dc output. An inductance-capacitance filter is commonly used.

Switching regulators normally operate at 20 kHz or higher, which has three main advantages:

1. Filter components and transformers can be smaller.
2. The frequency is above audibility.
3. To eliminate weight, no 60-Hz transformer is used, rather the ac line is rectified, filtered, and then switched at a 20-kHz rate, as shown in Fig. 19-44.

The 20-kHz switching creates an alternating current that can be transformed to a low-voltage, high-current supply at low weight. The transformer output is then rectified and filtered to produce dc output. The output is regulated through an error amplifier/comparator. The pulse-width modulator and driver must have a fast rise time and must completely saturate and turn off the pass transistor to ensure high efficiency.

19.12.1 Switching Advantages[3]

Because switching regulators are basically on-off devices, they avoid the higher power dissipation associated with the rheostatlike action of a series regulator. The switching transistors dissipate very little power when either saturated (on) or nonconducting (off); most of the power losses occur elsewhere in the supply. Efficiencies ranging from 65 to 85% are typical for switching supplies, as com-

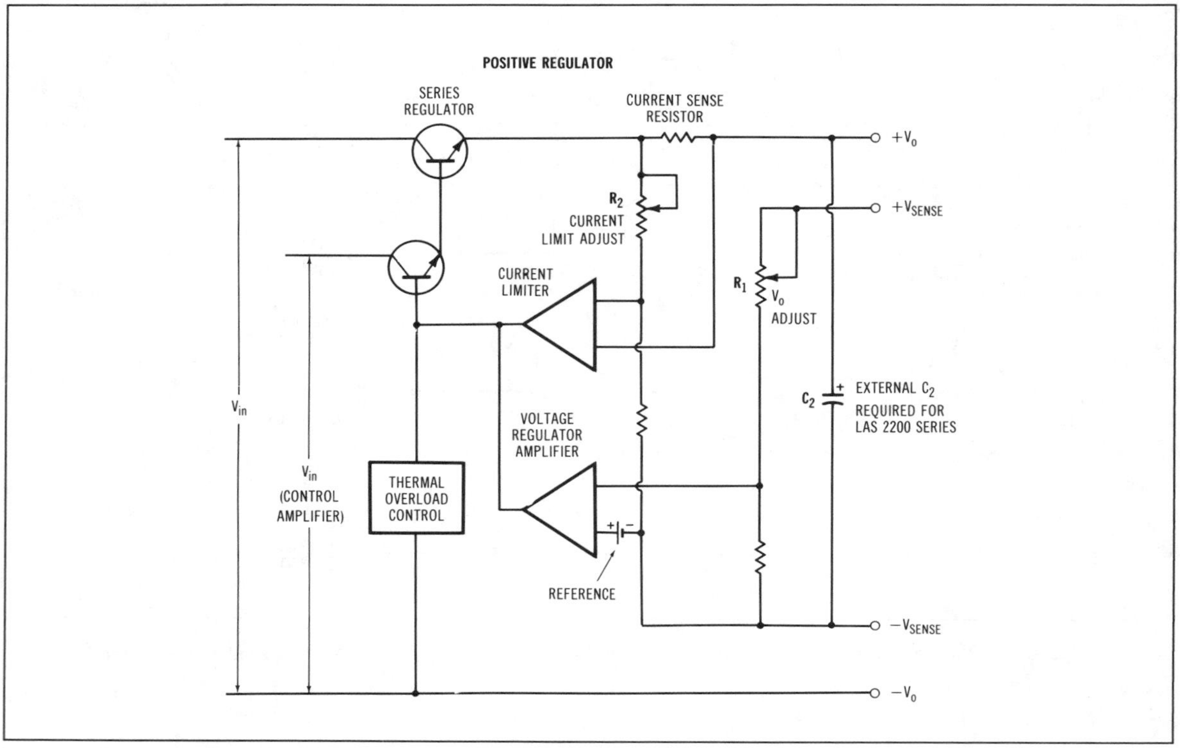

Figure 19-43 Lambda hybrid regulator. *(Courtesy Lambda, Subsidiary of Veeco Instruments Inc.)*

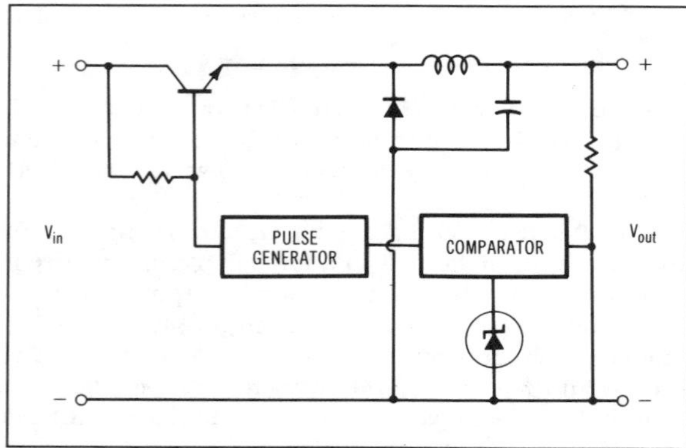

Figure 19-44 Basic switching regulator.

pared to 30 to 45% efficiencies for linear types. With less wasted power, switching supplies run at cooler temperatures, cost less to operate, and have smaller regulator heat sinks.

The size and weight reductions for switching supplies are achieved because of their high switching rate. Typically, a switching supply is less than one third the size and weight of a comparable series-regulated supply.

Another aspect of performance is the switcher's ability to operate under low ac input voltage (brownout) conditions and sustain a relatively long carryover (or holdup) of its output if input power is lost momentarily. The switching supply is superior to the linear supply in this regard because more energy is stored in its input filter capacitance. In a switching supply, the input ac is rectified directly, and the filter capacitor charges to the voltage peaks on the ac line, as opposed to the ac input of the linear supplies being stepped down through a power transformer, then rectified, which results in a lower voltage across its filter capacitor.

Since the energy stored in a capacitor is proportional to CV^2 and V is higher in switching supplies, their storage capability (and thus their holdup time) is better.

19.12.2 Switching Disadvantages[3]

A switching supply has some inherent operating characteristics that could limit its effectiveness in certain applications. One is that its transient recovery time (dynamic load regulation) is slower than that of a series-regulated supply. In a linear supply, recovery time is limited only by the speeds of the semiconductors used in the series regulator and control circuitry. While in a switching supply, recovery is limited mainly by the inductance in the output filter.

Electromagnetic interference (emi) is a natural by-product of the on-off switching. This interference can be conducted to the load (resulting in higher output ripple and noise), it can be conducted back into the ac line, and it can be radiated into the surrounding atmosphere.

19.12.3 High-Power Regulation[3]

A *high-power switching regulator* by Hewlett Packard Co. is shown in Fig. 19-45. Regulation is accomplished by a pair of push-pull switching transistors operating under control of a feedback network consisting of a pulse-width modulator and a voltage comparison amplifier. The feedback elements control the on periods of the switching transistors to adjust the duty cycle of the bipolar waveform (E) delivered to the output rectifier-filter. Here the waveform is rectified and averaged to provide a dc output level that is proportional to the duty cycle of the waveform. Hence, increasing the on times of the switches increases the output voltage and vice versa.

The waveforms of Fig. 19-45 provide a more detailed picture of circuit operation. The voltage comparison amplifier continuously compares a fraction of the output voltage with a stable reference (V_{REF}) to produce the $V_{CONTROL}$ level for the turn-on comparator. This device compares the $V_{CONTROL}$ input with a triangular ramp waveform A, occurring at a fixed 40-kHz rate. When the ramp voltage is more positive than the control level, a turn-on signal (B) is generated. Notice that an increase or decrease in the $V_{CONTROL}$ voltage varies the width of the output pulses at B and thus the on time of the switches.

Steering logic within the modulator chip causes switching transistors Q_1 and Q_2 to turn on alternately so

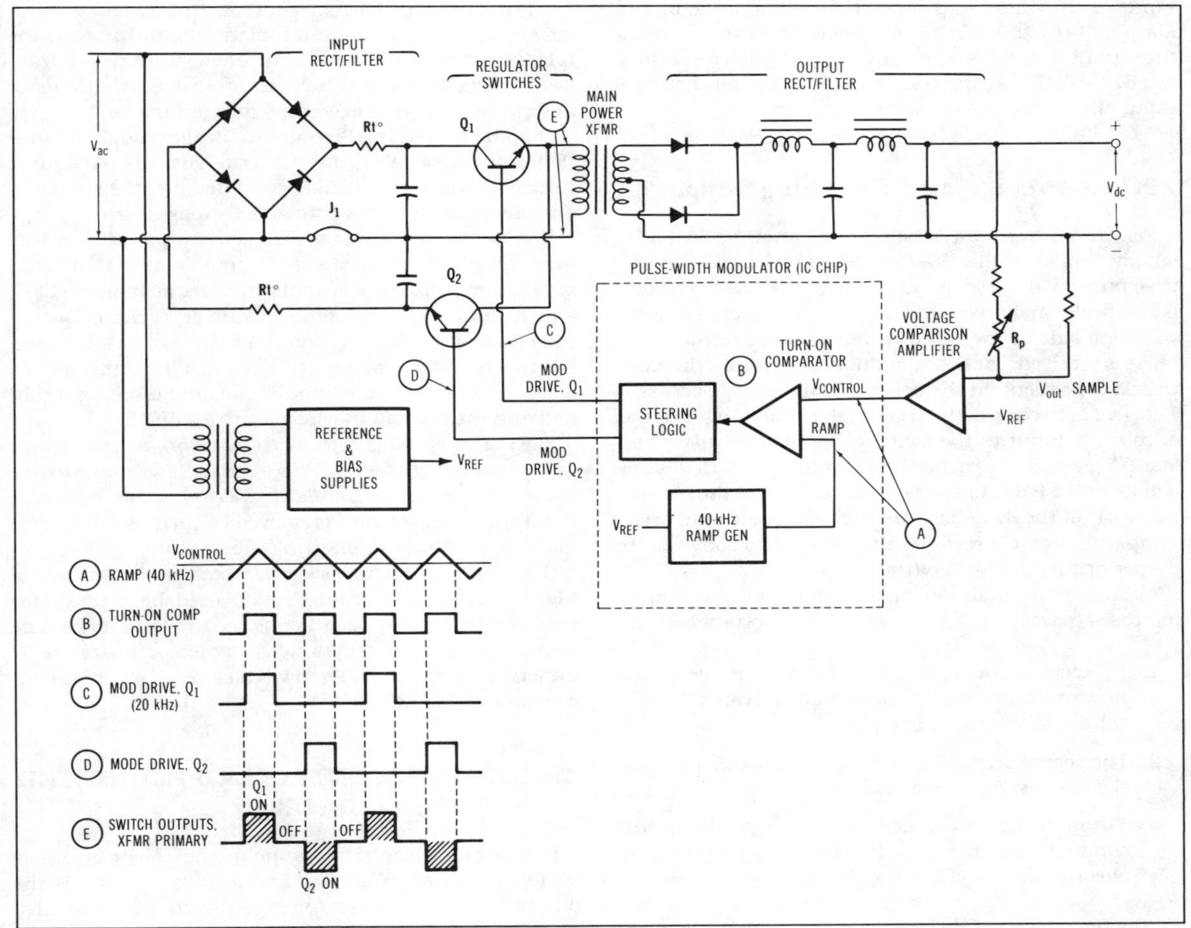

Figure 19-45 Switching supply with push-pull transistors and feedback for regulation. *(Courtesy Hewlett-Packard Co.)*

that each switch operates at one-half the ramp frequency or 20 kHz.

Included, but not shown, in the modulator chip are additional circuits that establish a minimum dead-time (off-time) for the switching transistors. This ensures that both switching transistors cannot conduct simultaneously during maximum duty-cycle conditions.

Because the input filter capacitors are connected directly across the rectified line, some form of surge protection must be provided to limit line surge currents at turnon. If not controlled, large surges could trip circuit breakers, weld switch contacts, or affect the operation of other equipment connected to the same ac line. Protection is provided by a pair of thermistors (Rt°) in the input rectifier circuit. With their high negative temperature coefficient of resistance, the thermistors present a relatively high resistance when cold (during the turnon period) and a very low resistance after they heat up.

A shorting strap (J_1) permits the configuration of the input rectifier-filter to be altered for different ac inputs. For a 174- to 250-V ac input, the strap is removed and the circuit functions as a conventional full-wave bridge. For 87- to 127-V ac inputs, the strap is installed and the input circuit becomes a voltage doubler.

19.12.4 Preregulated Switching Supply[3]

Fig. 19-46 shows a schematic of another switching supply similar to Fig. 19-45 except for the addition of a triac preregulator and associated control circuit. The triac is a bidirectional device and is usually connected in series with one side of the input primary. Whenever a gating pulse is received, the triac conducts current in a direction that is dependent on the polarity of the voltage across it. The goal is to control the triac so that the bridge rectifier output (dc input to the switches) is held relatively constant. This is accomplished by a control circuit that issues a phase-adjusted firing pulse to the triac once during each half cycle of the input ac. The control circuit compares a ramp function to a rectified ac sine wave to compute the proper firing time for the triac.

Although the addition of the preregulator circuitry increases complexity, it provides three important benefits:

1. By keeping the dc input to the switches constant, it permits the use of more readily available lower voltage switching transistors.
2. The coarse preregulation it provides allows the main regulator to achieve a finer regulation.
3. Through the use of slow-start circuits, the initial conduction of the triac is controlled, providing an effective means of limiting input surge current.

Note that the preregulator triac is essentially a switching device and, like the main regulator switches, does not absorb a large amount of power. Hence, the addition of the preregulator does not significantly reduce the overall efficiency of this supply.

19.12.5 Protection Circuits[3]

Fig. 19-47 shows typical protection circuits that are used in Hewlett Packard Co. (HP) switching regulated power supplies. The following is a brief description of those protection circuits shown.

A is the emi filter, which helps prevent high-frequency spikes (RFI) from being conducted to the load or back into the ac line. HP switching supplies also contain built-in shields for additional control of conducted and radiated interference.

B is the thermistor. It limits ac input surge current by its negative temperature coefficient of resistance. It has a high resistance when cold (during turnon) and low resistance after it heats up.

C is the regulator overcurrent limit. This circuit is much faster than the current limit comparator and protects the regulator switches from overcurrent conditions of a transient nature. It monitors current flow through the switches and prevents it from exceeding a harmful level.

D is the output rectifier diodes. Besides final rectification, these diodes also protect internal components against reverse currents that could be injected into the supply by an active load or series-connected supply.

E is the ac undervoltage. This circuit performs a dual function. It protects the supply from damage that could result from a prolonged condition of low ac input voltage, and it limits output overshoot during turnon. During undervoltage or turnon conditions, the low ac input level reduces the V_{BIAS} voltage and activates the undervoltage detector. When activated, the modulator pulses are inhibited and the regulator switches turned off.

F is the overvoltage detector. It monitors output voltage and turns off regulator switches if output attempts to rise above a preset value. Similar to a crowbar circuit except that the output voltage is removed by turning off the regulator rather than by shorting the output.

G is the temperature switch, which opens in case of high ambient temperature that could be caused, for example, by a misapplication or cooling fan failure. The switch opens and removes V_{BIAS}, which activates the ac undervoltage detector. The switch closes again after temperature cools to a safe level.

19.13 PHASE-CONTROLLED REGULATED POWER SUPPLIES

In the *phase-controlled supply*, the pass element is switched on and off at line frequency and controls the output voltage by a varying pulse width. This is most often accomplished by using an SCR as the pass element. By delaying the firing point of the SCR in each cycle, the output voltage can be varied. In Fig. 19-48, the SCR is

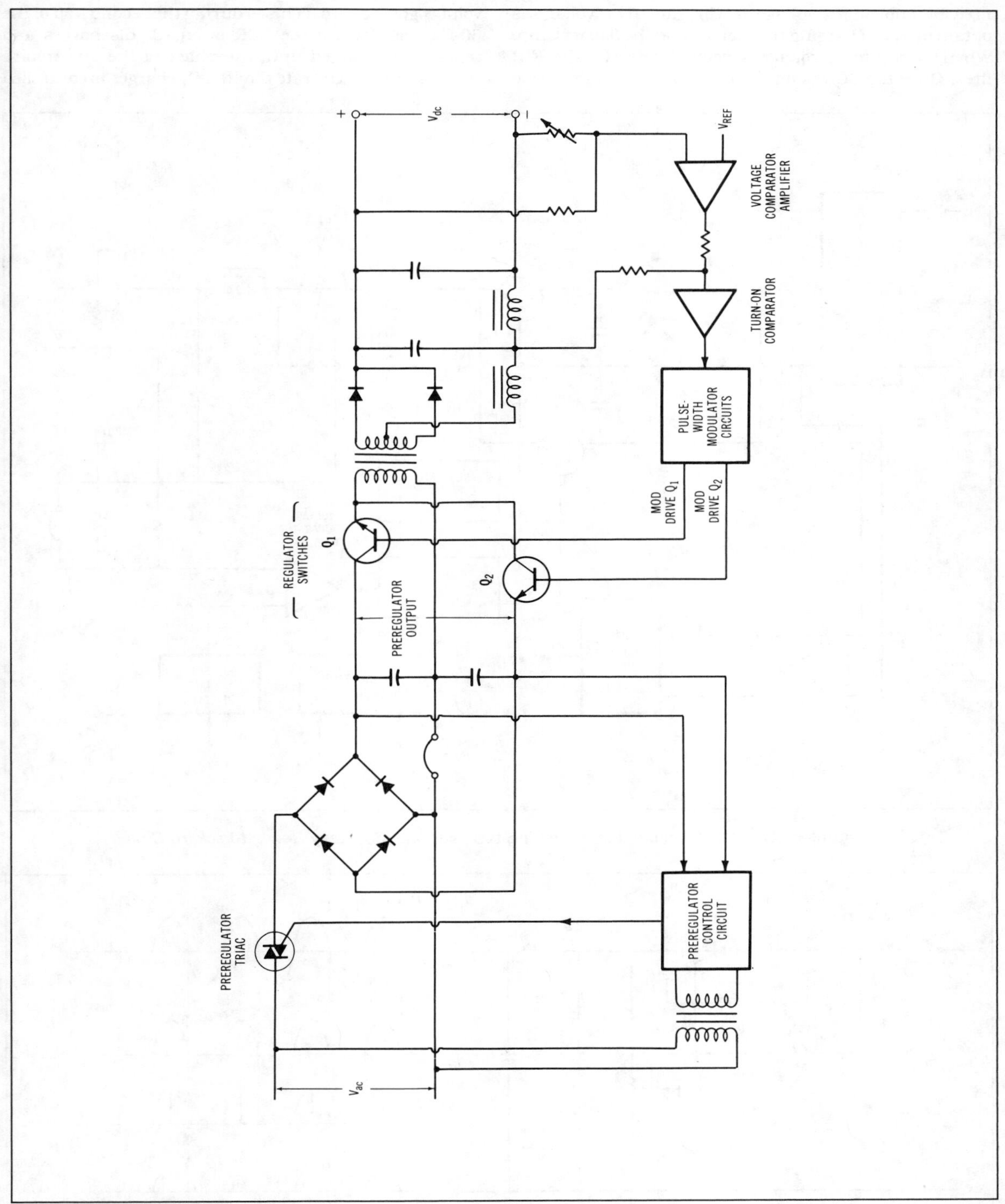

Figure 19-46 Push-pull switching supply with triac preregulator. *(Courtesy Hewlett-Packard Co.)*

fired by applying a voltage to the gate. The voltage is obtained by C_1 charging through R_2 and the ballast lamp. When the gate firing voltage is reached across C_1, the SCR fires. Once the SCR is on, it remains on until its anode voltage goes to zero. (This is during the second half of the 60-Hz cycle.) Once the SCR is on, C_1 discharges and remains discharged until the phase of the line voltage returns to zero. The rate that the C_1 charges is controlled

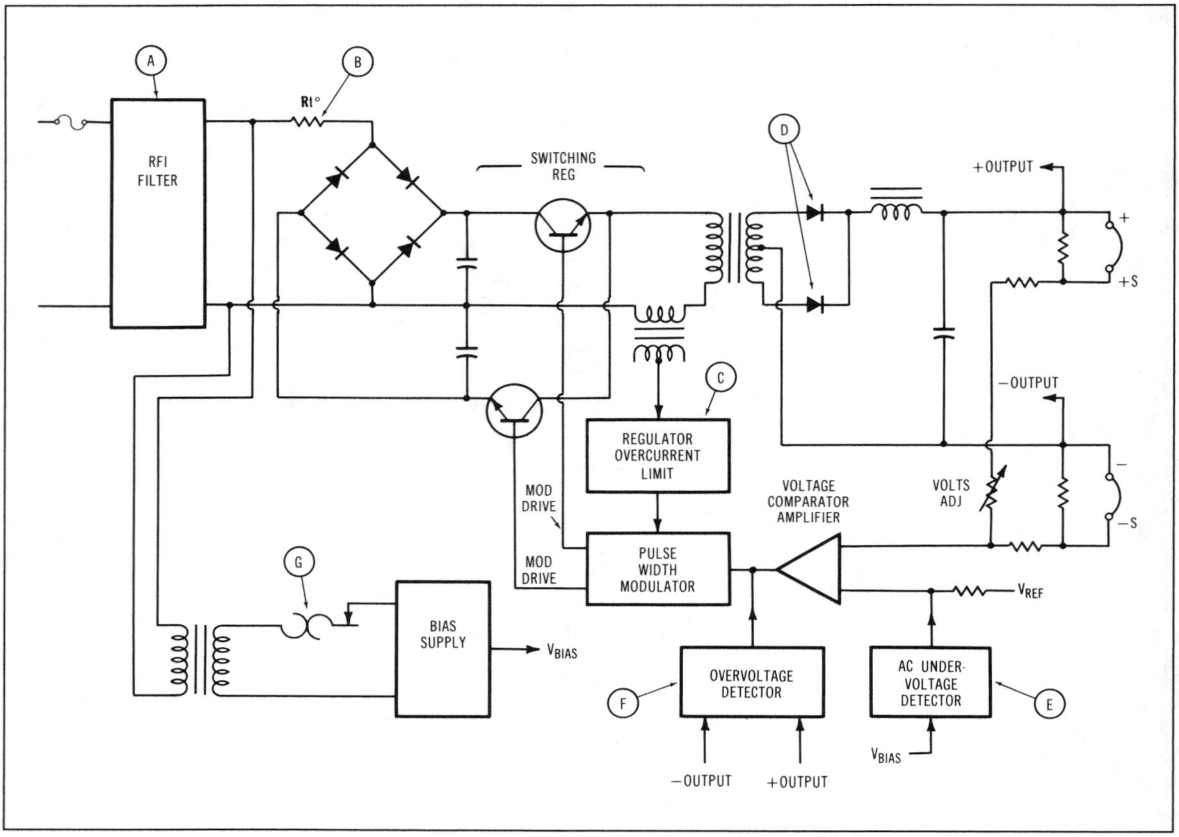

Figure 19-47 Protection circuits, switching-type supply. *(Courtesy Hewlett-Packard Co.)*

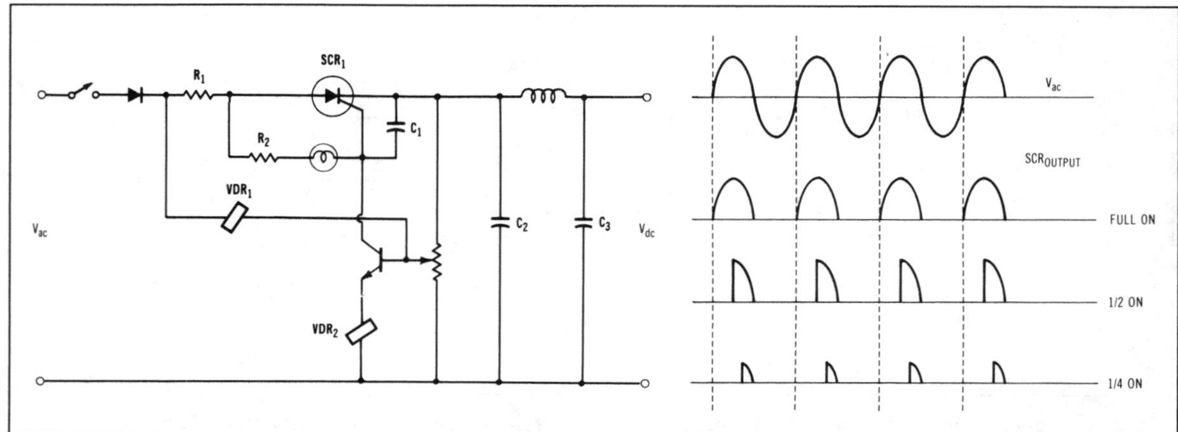

Figure 19-48 Phase-controlled regulated supply and waveforms.

by T_1. When T_1 is turned on, much of the C_1 charging current is shunted around C_1, requiring a longer time to charge C_1, thus delaying the firing of the SCR. As the line voltage increases, the resistance of VDR_1 and VDR_2 decreases, turning T_1 on more and thus slowing the charging rate of C_1. Since the output is a series of pulses with a high rise time of the leading edge, a filter is required on the output to smooth the dc.

19.14 RIPPLE FILTERS

Power supply ripple voltage can also be reduced by electronic means. A *ripple filter* is used to supplement conventional filter systems to achieve exceptionally low values of ripple voltage.

Fig. 19-49 is the basic circuit, and the circuit in Fig. 19-50 is a practical circuit. In designing such a circuit, pass transistor Q_3 should be biased so that the collector-to-emitter voltage V_{ce} is equal to or greater than the input peak-to-peak ripple

$$V_{ce} \geqslant (\text{input p-p ripple}/2) + 1.5\,\text{V dc} \qquad (19\text{-}21)$$

This design is used to prevent the pass transistor from going into saturation. With the transistor at saturation, ripple reduction is greatly reduced because a small change in V_{be} no longer has any control of the collector current.

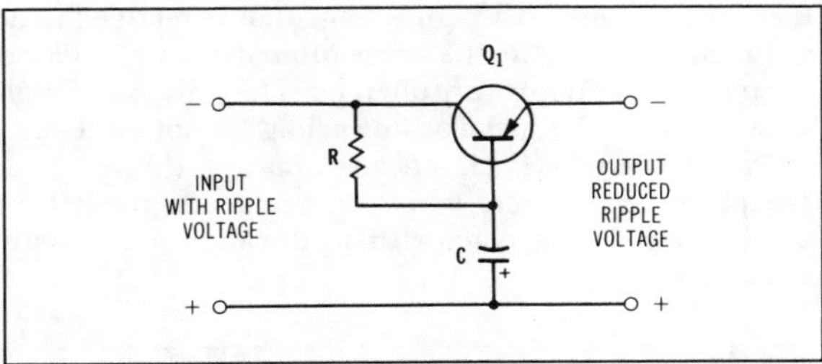

Figure 19-49 Basic circuit for electronic filter.

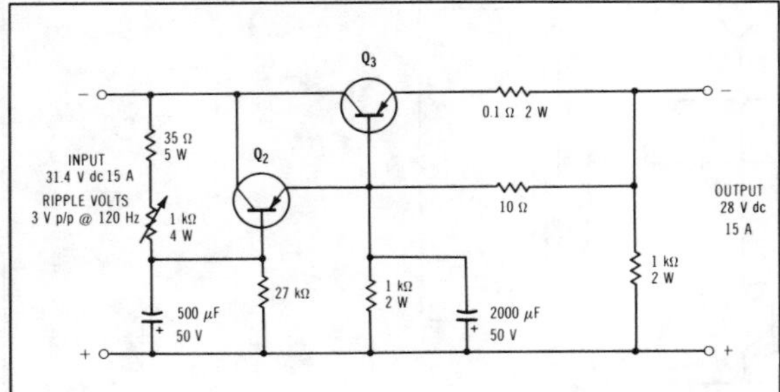

Figure 19-50 Electronic ripple filter. Ripple reduction ratio 250:1. *(Courtesy AC-Delco, Division of General Motors Corp.)*

Excess V_{ce} will increase the transistor dissipation, which means additional transistors must be used in the pass section of the circuit. The transistor V_{CEO} rating should be equal to about 1.4 times the supply voltage. This is necessary in order to allow the peak supply voltage to initially appear across the transistors while the filter capacitors charge through the series resistor.

19.15 BATTERY CHARGERS

Batteries can be charged by constant current or constant voltage.

When charged by the constant-current method, care must be taken to eliminate the possibility of overcharging; therefore, the condition of the battery should be known before charging so that the charger can be removed when the ampere-hour rate of the battery is met.

Charging with the constant voltage method reduces the possibility of overcharging. With the constant voltage method, charge current is high initially and tapers off to a trickle charge when the battery is fully charged. Two requirements must be met when using the constant-voltage method:

1. The charging voltage must be stable and set to 2.4 V per cell for a lead-acid battery and 2.30 V per cell for a Gel cell[1] battery. Gel cell open-circuit voltage is 2.12 V per cell.

2. A current-limiting circuit must be employed to limit charge current when the battery is fully discharged.

It is often desirable to have the charging circuit automatically disconnect from the battery when the battery is fully charged and reconnect to the battery when the battery is discharged.

The circuit in Fig. 19-51 is a hybrid charger that could be considered a current-limited, constant-voltage circuit with automatic cutoff. The circuit is only constant voltage at cutoff as controlled by the battery voltage and the 8.2-V zener diode. When the battery voltage is below the value set by R_5 (14.4 V), the SCR is turned on, and the battery charges through the SCR. Current is limited by the internal resistance of the transformer. When the battery voltage reaches 14.4 V, SCR_2 energizes and turns off SCR_1, disconnecting the battery from the charge circuit. The battery voltage will begin to drop to its normal open-circuit voltage, which will turn SCR_2 off and SCR_1 on, recharging the battery. This charger will charge heavily on the dead battery and very slowly on a charged battery.

19.16 INVERTERS

An *inverter* converts direct current to alternating current. Inverters are used in applications where the primary source of power is direct current. Because direct current cannot be transformed, it is convenient to con-

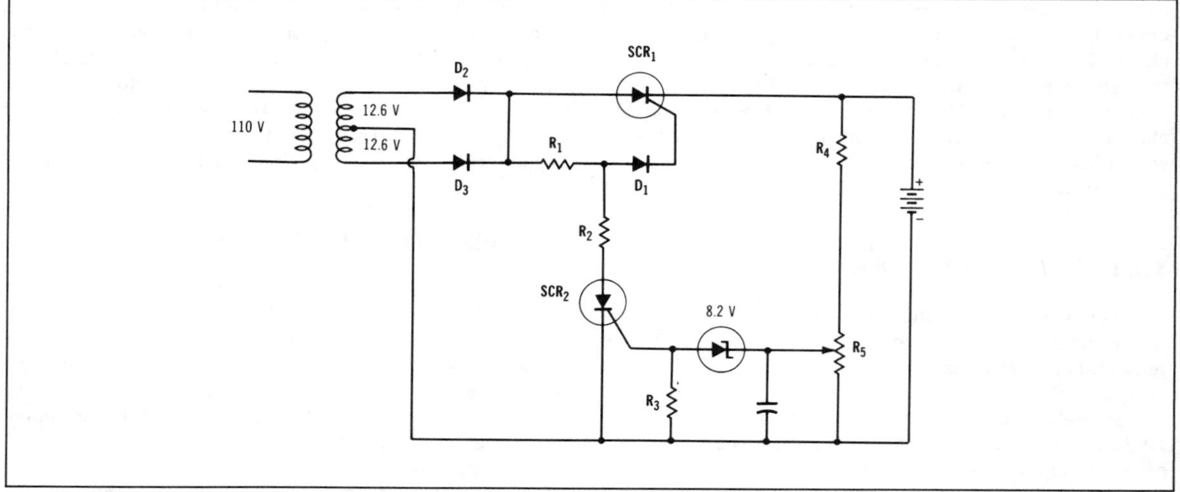

Figure 19-51 Battery charger with automatic cutoff.

vert direct current to alternating current so that alternating current output from the inverter may be applied to a transformer to supply the desired voltage.

An inverter operates much like the switching circuit and transformer section of a converter. In Fig. 19-52, R_1 and R_2 assure that the oscillator (switch) will start. T_1 is a saturable base-drive transformer that determines the drive current to turn on Q_1 or Q_2. T_2 is a nonsaturable transformer; therefore, collector current through Q_1 and Q_2 is dependent upon load. Base resistors R_b are current-limiting resistors, and capacitors C can be used to decrease the transistor storage time and assure rapid turn-off of the switching transistors. By adding a rectifier and filter section, this inverter can be changed to a converter.

19.17 CONVERTERS

A *converter* changes low-voltage dc to high-voltage dc. Basically, a dc-to-dc converter consists of a dc source of potential (generally a battery) applied to a pair of switching transistors. The transistors convert the applied dc voltage to a high-frequency ac voltage. The ac voltage is then transformed to a high voltage that is rectified to dc again and filtered in the conventional manner. Power supplies of this nature are often used for a source of high voltage, where the usual ac line voltage is not available.

The circuitry for such a device appears in Fig. 19-53. The power transformer is rather special and consists of a Deltamax toroidal core, with a saturation flux density of 14,000 G.

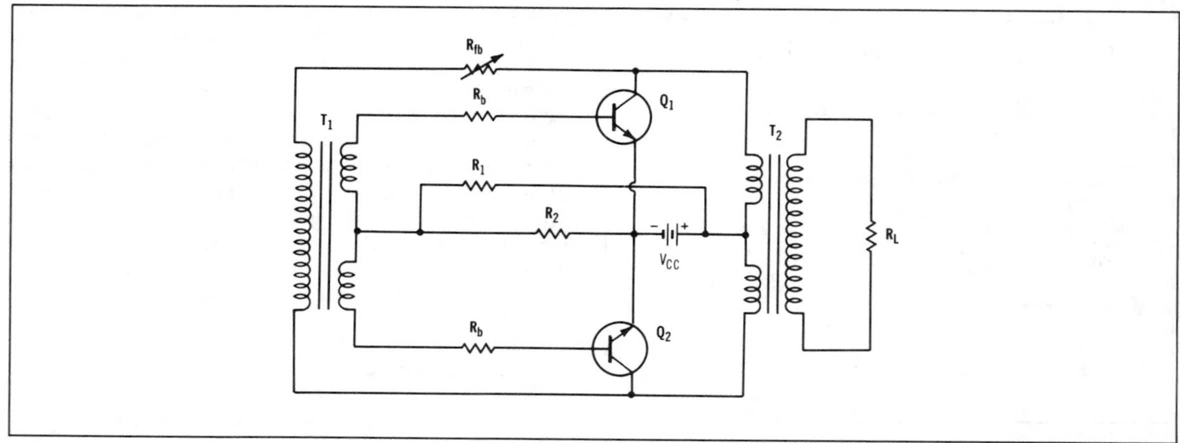

Figure 19-52 Two-transistor, two-transformer, push-pull inverter that uses a resistive voltage-divider network to provide starting bias.

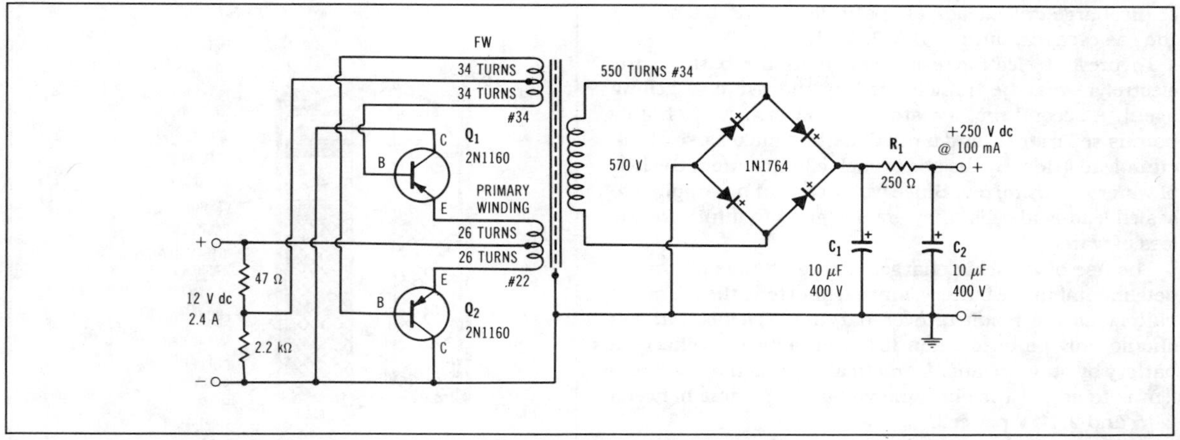

Figure 19-53 A dc-to-dc converter using switching transistors at a switching frequency of approximately 1600 Hz.

The primary and feedback windings are bifilar wound to obtain a tight coupling between the two halves of the winding on each side of the center tap. The switching frequency is generally on the order of 1000 to 2000 Hz to reduce the size and weight of the transformer and filter chokes (if used).

Applying a voltage from the positive input terminal of the battery causes a current to flow to the emitter of Q_1 and induces a voltage in the *feedback winding* (*FW*) in such a manner that the base of Q_2 is made positive with respect to the base of Q_1. These polarities at the bases of Q_1 and Q_2 cause an increase in the current through Q_1. At the same time, they cause the current through Q_2 to decrease, which amounts to positive feedback. Therefore, transistor Q_1 is turned on and Q_2 is turned off.

The current continues to increase from the input terminal until the core becomes saturated. The induced voltage in the feedback winding then drops to zero, turning off transistor Q_1. The collapsing field of the core induces a voltage of opposite polarity in the feedback winding, which further turns off Q_1 and turns on Q_2. Current then flows from the plus voltage to the emitter of Q_2 through the feedback winding. Saturation again takes place—this time in the negative direction. This action provides suitable conditions for oscillation repeated at a frequency dependent on the circuit constants.

The voltage at the secondary is of a square-wave nature and is rectified by a full-wave bridge-rectifier-circuit and filtered in the usual manner. The frequency of the described circuit is about 1600 Hz and is capable of supplying 250 V dc at a current of 100 mA.

19.18 BATTERIES

Batteries offer a means of producing a smooth, ripple-free, hum-free, portable power supply.

All batteries have internal resistance that causes the battery voltage to fluctuate with the load. To calculate the internal resistance of a single cell or battery, the open-circuit voltage is measured using a meter with an internal resistance of 1000 Ω/V. Suppose this voltage (V_1) is 10 V. The battery or cell is then loaded with a 50-Ω resistance R_1, and the voltage across the resistor is measured. Assume this voltage V_2 to be 9 V. The current through the resistor R_1 is

$$V_2/R_1 = 9/50$$
$$= 0.180\,\text{A}$$

The internal resistance (R_i) of the battery may now be calculated using

$$R_i = (V_1/I) - R_1 \tag{19-21}$$
$$= 9/0.180 - 50$$
$$= 55.5 - 50\,\Omega$$

The internal resistance equals 5.5 Ω.

19.18.1 Sealed Lead-Acid Batteries

The lead-acid storage battery was invented by Gaston Planté in 1860 and is one of the most widely used forms of battery power. The principal drawback to this type of battery has been the liquid electrolyte and the fumes given off when charging and discharging. However, due to new developments in sealing and venting, the sealed lead-acid battery may now take its place with other rechargeable batteries such as the nickel-cadmium battery. Lead-acid batteries are now available with voltages ranging from 2 to 8 V and in 1- to 8-A capacities. Since small amounts of gas may be generated in any battery during the charge or discharge cycle, lead-acid batteries are vented so that the gas escapes, but not the electrolyte.

To prevent electrolyte movement in the battery, the electrolyte may be immobilized by the use of a gelling agent. A second method stores the electrolyte in highly porous separators, and a third method makes use of calcium-lead grids. By the use of such construction, the loss of water is minimized. Since water cannot be supplied to sealed lead-acid cells, they are designed to minimize the loss of water.

The use of a trickle charger with a storage battery is detrimental to the battery, since it shortens the life of the battery as the result of overcharging. Trickle chargers should only be used when it is impractical to charge a battery by other means. A practical approach to the problem is to adjust the charging voltage to a value between 2.15 and 2.17 V per cell.

A better, but more elaborate, method is to check the specific gravity of the cells over a period of several months and to adjust the charging voltage to a value where the specific gravity is maintained at 1.250. Compensation must be made for temperature changes when reading the specific gravity. Four gravity points are added to the reading for every 10° the electrolyte is above a temperature of 80°F.

The freezing point of a battery electrolyte depends on the specific gravity of the electrolyte as shown:

Specific Gravity	Freezing Point
1.275	−85°F
1.250	−62°F
1.225	−35°F
1.200	−16°F
1.175	+ 4°F
1.150	+ 5°F
1.125	+13°F
1.100	+19°F

The specific gravity readings of a storage battery are interpreted as follows:

1.275 to 1.300	A high state of charge.
1.250	A medium state of charge.
1.200	A low state of charge.

If a storage battery is left in a discharged condition for any length of time, the plates may be damaged due to sulfation.

19.18.2 LeClanche (Zinc-Carbon) Batteries

A cross-sectional view of a typical zinc-carbon (LeClanche) cell is given in Fig. 19-54 with its principal components called out. Basically, the cell consists of a zinc anode, manganese-dioxide cathode, and electrolyte solution of ammonium chloride, zinc chloride, and mercury chloride in water. The nominal voltage is 1.5 V. This type of cell is quite inefficient at heavy loads, and its capacity depends considerably on the duty cycle. Less power is available when it is used without a rest period. Maximum power is produced when it is given frequent rest periods, since the voltage drops continuously under load. Shelf life is limited by the drying out of the electrolyte. A typical discharge curve is given in Fig. 19-55.

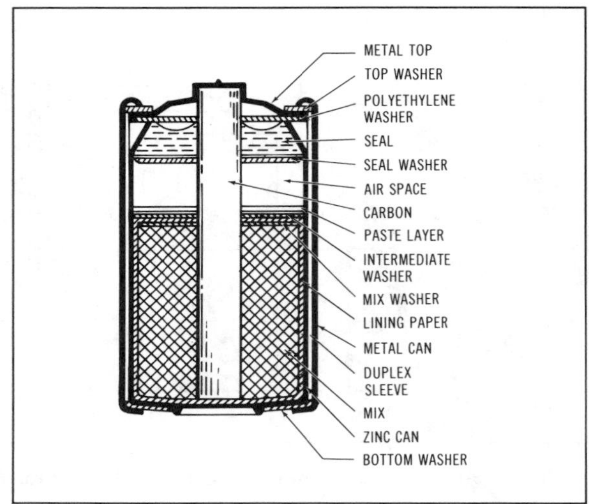

Figure 19-54 Interior construction of a zinc-carbon (LeClanche) cell.

Zinc-carbon cells may be recharged for a limited number of cycles. The following information is extracted from the National Bureau of Standards Circular 965:

> The cell voltage for recharge must not be less than 1 V and should be recharged within a short time after removing from service. The ampere-hours of charge should be within 120 to 180% of the discharge rate. The charging rate is to be low enough to distribute the recharge over 12 to 16 hr. Cells must be put into service soon after recharging as the shelf life is poor.

19.18.3 Nickel-Cadmium Batteries

Nickel-cadmium batteries are used in portable electronic and portable recording equipment. A cell consists of sintered positive and negative plates, separators, safety vent cap, electrolyte, and plastic container.

The plates are made by firing a microfine nickel powder at high temperature until the particles weld or sinter together to form a porous structure. The porous structure is sintered on a fine-mesh nickel screen. These plates are put through electrochemical processes designed to deposit active nickel and cadmium oxides in the fine pores of the plate. The cells are assembled, connected to the terminals, and mounted in a polystyrene or nylon case.

The selected construction eliminates the need to add

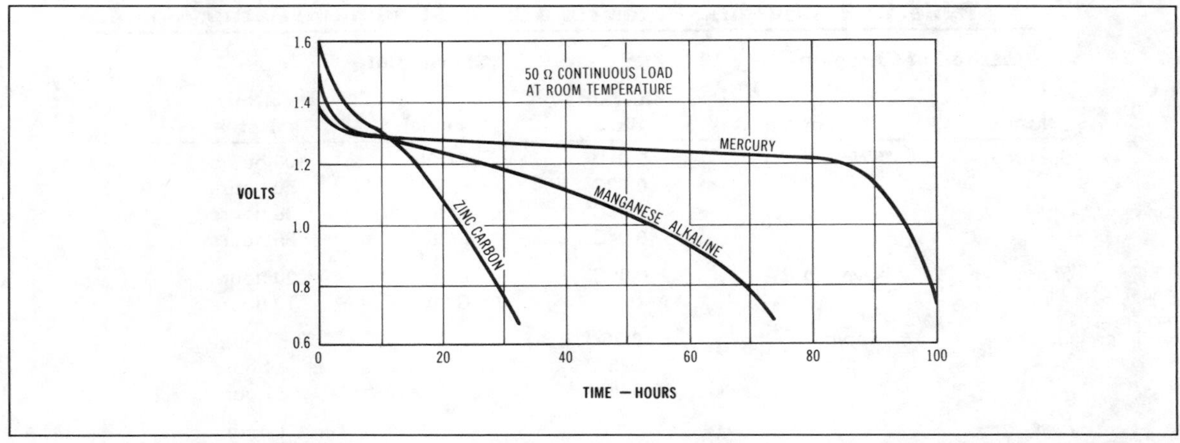

Figure 19-55 Typical discharge curves for three different type penlight cells discharged continuously into a 50-Ω load.

water or electrolyte, and, under certain conditions, the cell will operate on overcharge for an indefinite period. A typical discharge curve for a cell, rated at 25 Ah and weighing approximately 2 lb, is given in Fig. 19-56.

The charge retention varies from 75% for one month to 50% for five months. Storage at high temperatures will reduce high retention. Cells should be charged prior to use to restore full capacity. Nickel cadmium eventually fails due to permanent or reversible cell failure. A reversible failure is usually due to shallow charge and discharge cycles and the battery appears to have lost capacity. This is often called the "memory effect." This problem can be removed by deep discharge and a full recharge. A loss of capacity can also come from extended overcharging. If this should occur, full capacity can be restored by a discharge followed by a full recharge.

Permanent failures are normally related to time, temperature, rate and depth of discharge, and general application of the cell or battery. The failure is usually caused by an internal short within the cell or by an open circuit within the cell. Internal shorts can be either high resistance or low resistance and prevent the cell from accepting a full charge or delivering capacity after charging. This normally comes from deterioration from the separator material in the cell. Open circuits come from premature dryouts of the cell and loss of electrolytes. This loss is caused by high temperatures, high drain rates, and high charge rates, all of which produce venting of the cell.

When three or more cells are series connected for higher voltages, the possibility exists that one of the cells, which may be slightly lower in capacity than the others, will be driven to a zero potential and then into reverse during discharge. At *discharge rates* (C) in the vicinity of C/10, cells can be driven into reverse without permanently damaging the cell. Prolonged, frequent, or deep reversals should be avoided since they shorten cell life or cause it to vent. Cell voltage should never be allowed to go below −0.2 V.

Nickel-cadmium batteries may be charged using either

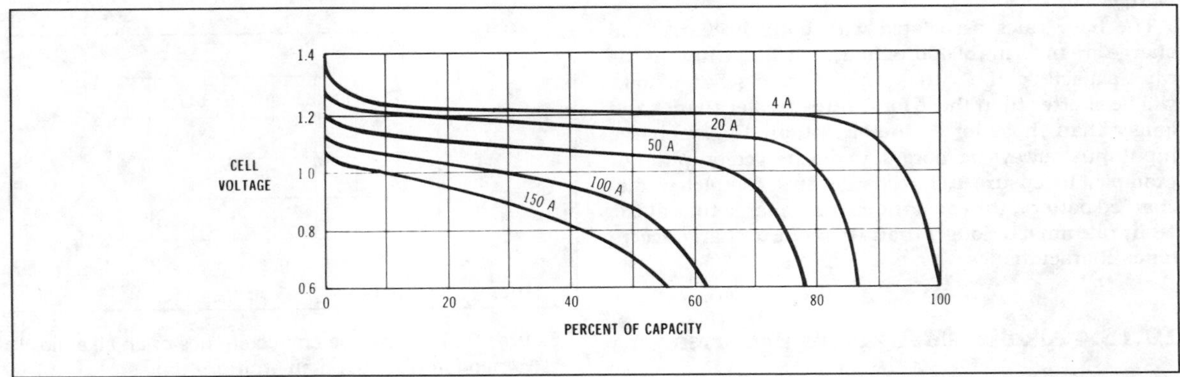

Figure 19-56 Discharge characteristic for Sonotone type 20L420 nickel-cadmium battery, rated 25 Ah.

Table 19-2. Charging Rates for a Nickel-Cadmium Battery

Method of Charging		Charge Rate		
Name	**Nickname**	**Current Rate**	**Fraction**	**Hour Rates**
Standby	*"Trickle"*	0.01C	C/100	100 hours
		0.02C	C/50	50 hours
		0.03C	C/30	30 hours
		0.04C	C/25	25 hours
Slow	*"Overnight"*	0.05C	C/20	20 hours
		0.1C	C/10	10 hours
Quick	*"Rapid"*	0.2C	C/5	5 hours
		0.25C	C/4	4 hours
		0.3C	C/3	3 hours
Fast		C	C	1 hour
		2C	2C	30 minutes
		3C	3C	20 minutes
		4C	4C	15 minutes
		10C	10C	6 minutes

a constant-current or constant-voltage charger. There are four major factors that determine the charge rates, which can be used on nickel-cadmium batteries. They are charge acceptance, voltage, cell pressure, and cell temperature.

No charge control is required for *charge rates* up to C/3. This allows the use of the least expensive charger design.

When charging rates equal or exceed 1.0 C, the charging current must be regulated to prevent overcharge. At this extremely high rate of charge, as much or more current is being put back into the battery as the rated ampere-hour capacity. Unless charging is terminated, pressure and heat will build up to undesirably high levels in the cells.

In Table 19-2, the notation that includes the letter C is used to describe current rates in terms of a fraction of the capacity rating of the battery. A comparison of cells from different manufacturers requires rationalization to a common standard for capacity rating at the same discharge rate.

The hour rates associated with both discharge and charge are in terms of approximate discharge time at the rated capacity of the battery. In general, discharge times will be shorter than those for C rates greater than 1 and longer than those for C rates less than 1. The charge input must always be more than discharged output. For example, to ensure full recharge of a completely discharged battery, the constant-current charge time at the 10-hr rate must be longer than 10 hr due to charge acceptance characteristics.

19.18.4 Alkaline-Manganese Batteries

The *alkaline-manganese battery* is gaining considerable importance in the electronic field since it is a primary battery and is rechargeable. This cell uses a cylindrical depolarizer in contact with a cell container of nickel-plated steel. Because of the passivity of steel in alkaline electrolytes, there is no chemical reaction between the depolarizer and the steel, thus permitting the latter to be both a current collector and container. The depolarizer surrounds a cylindrical, granular, zinc anode, with the two electrochemical components being separated by porous material.

The polarity of this cell is reversed from the conventional zinc-carbon cell, in which the can is negative. However, because of packaging, the outward appearance is similar to the zinc-carbon cell, with the same terminal arrangement. Although this cell has an open-circuit voltage of approximately 1.5 V, it discharges at a lower voltage than the zinc-carbon cell. Also, the discharge voltage decreases steadily but more slowly. Alkaline-manganese batteries have 50 to 100% more capacity than their zinc counterparts. Zinc-carbon cells yield most of their energy

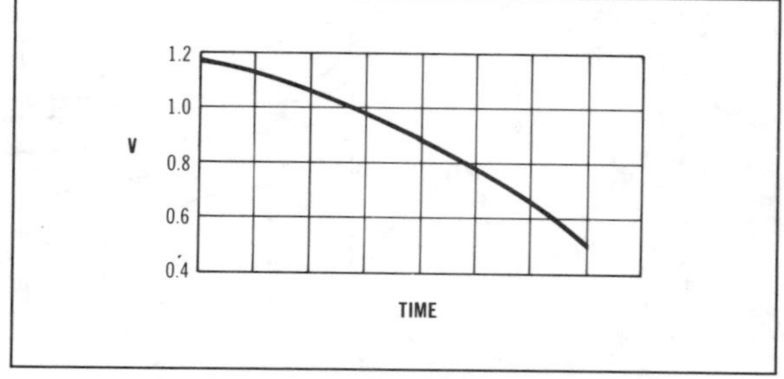

Figure 19-57 Discharge characteristics of an alkaline-manganese cell, on an arbitrary time scale. The cell discharges at lower voltages as compared to a zinc-carbon cell.

above 1.25 V and are virtually exhausted at 1 V, while the alkaline cell yields most of its energy below 1.25 V with a considerable portion released at less than 1 V.

If the discharge rate is limited to 40% of the nominal capacity of the cell and recharge is carried out over a period of 10 to 20 hr, alkaline-manganese cells can be cycled 50 to 150 times. A typical discharge curve is shown in Fig. 19-57.

19.18.5 Mercury Dry Cells

The *mercury dry cell* using a zinc-mercury oxide alkaline system was invented by Samuel Ruben during World War II. There are two kinds of mercury cells: one with a voltage of 1.35 V and one with 1.4 V. Both have pure zinc anodes amalgamated with mercury and an electrolyte of potassium hydroxide solution with some zinc oxide. The difference between the two cells lies in the cathode material.

The 1.35-V cell has a pure mercuric-oxide cathode. On discharge its voltage drops only slightly until close to the end of the cell life when it then drops rapidly. The 1.4-V cell has a cathode of mercuric oxide and manganese dioxide. On discharge, its voltage is not quite as well regulated as the 1.35-V cell, but it is considerably better than the manganese-alkaline or zinc-carbon cell.

Mercury cells have excellent storage stability. A typical cell will indicate a voltage of 1.3569 V, with a cell-to-cell variation of only 150 μV. Temperature variation is 42 μV/°F ranging from −70 to +70°F, with a slight increase of voltage with temperature. The internal resistance is approximately 0.75 Ω. Voltage loss during storage is about 360 μV per month; therefore, a single cell can be used as a reference voltage of 1.3544 V, ±0.17%. The voltage is defined under a load condition of 5% of the maximum current capacity of the cell. Normal shelf life is on the order of three years.

Recharging of mercury cells is not recommended because of the danger of explosion. A typical discharge curve for mercury cells appears in Fig. 19-55, and the stability characteristics for a single cell over a period of 36 months are shown in Fig. 19-58. The drop in voltage over this period is 13 mV.

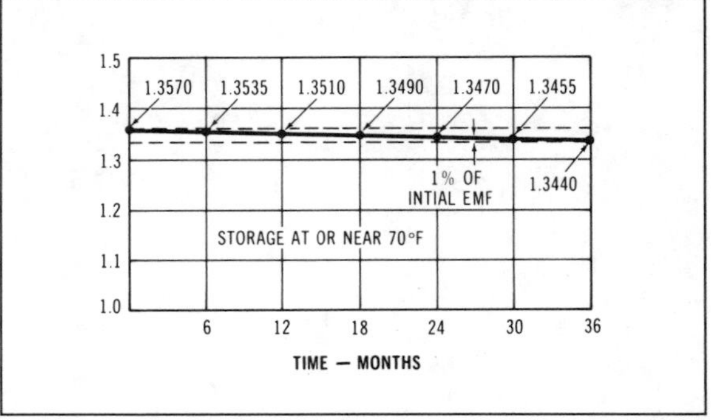

Figure 19-58 Stability curve for a single-cell mercury battery. The drop over a period of three years is 13 mV.

19.18.6 Lead-Dioxide Batteries

A *lead-dioxide battery* is a gelled electrolyte, maintenance-free type that exhibits high capacity and long life when properly applied and charged. The Gel/Cell, as produced by Globe Battery Division of Johnson Controls, incorporates lead dioxide (PbO_2) positive plates, a gelled dilute acid (H_2O and H_2SO_4) electrolyte, and sponge lead (Pb) negative plates. The terminal voltage of each cell is approximately 2.12 V. The cell voltage is higher for a battery that has just been taken off charge, but in all instances it should adjust to about 2.12 V after a period of time.

As the battery is discharged, the terminal voltage will slowly decrease. For instance, when the rated capacity of the battery is removed over a 20-hr period, the terminal voltage would decrease to 1.75 V per cell. These batteries are rated at a 20-hr current rate and room temperature. This means a 2.6 Ah battery would put out 0.13 A for 20 hr. This does not mean, however, that it will put out 2.6 A for one hour. The battery would put out about 1.7 A for one hour.

Lead-dioxide batteries can be charged by the constant-current or constant-voltage method. The constant-current method is used when charger cost is the primary consideration, such as in some equipment modification programs or trickle charge for emergency power source. This is a constant-current charging technique, which in its simplest form is like force-feeding. The battery is forced to receive a constant amount of current regardless of its needs. Although charger component economy is achieved, it is sometimes done at the expense of recharge time or service life if the current is not properly set.

When charging with the constant-voltage method, a voltage of 2.25 to 2.30 V per cell should be used. To maintain the battery of 100°F, a voltage of 2.2 V per cell is required, while at 30°F, 2.4 V per cell is required.

REFERENCES

1. H. M. Tremaine, *Audio Cyclopedia,* Indianapolis: Howard W. Sams & Co., Inc., 1969.
2. F. S. Griffin, Vice-President, Ordnance Research Inc., "Add Foldback Protection to Your Supply and Stop Pass Transistor Failures," *Electronic Design* 3, February 1, 1978.
3. R. Tomasetti, "Switching Power Supplies," *Bench Briefs,* Hewlett Packard Co., November 1978, April 1979 (parts copied with permission).

CHAPTER **20**

Constant- and Variable-Speed Devices

by Glen Ballou

The search for obtaining a constant linear speed is one that has been going on for years. The paper by Dr. E. W. Kellogg, "A Review of the Quest for Constant Speed," *Journal of the SMPTE*, April 1937, is a classic on this subject. For the recording and reproduction of sound, many drive systems have been developed, and ingenious new devices are still appearing. This section discusses the fundamental principles of constant- and variable-speed driving systems, single- and three-phase, power-factor correction, motors, and inverters. This same information and design can be used to produce power of a frequency different from the input power. For instance, using a 50-Hz motor and a 60-Hz generator can give a 60-Hz output in countries operating on 50 Hz. The output frequency of the 60 Hz will be dependent on the stability of the input motor. The voltage regulation, however, will be dependent on the output generator.

Constant speed means a device that moves in a given direction without a change in velocity. The term *constant speed* is used in the recording industry to indicate devices used for driving recording and reproducing equipment.

If the speed of a recording device is increased above normal during recording, when the recorder material is played back at the correct speed, the pitch will be lowered, and the playing time, increased. The reverse is true if the recording speed is below normal.

Motors used for driving studio recording and reproducing equipment are dc synchronous, multiduty (dual-purpose), and selsyn interlock motors. The ac motors may be used with either single- or three-phase power. The selsyn interlock motors are driven from a selsyn generator. Motors are rated in horsepower and torque.

20.1 HORSEPOWER

Horsepower is a unit of power that, in the foot-pound-second (fps) system is equal to 33,000 ft.lb/min. For instance, a machine would be considered capable of delivering 1 hp if it could lift a weight of 33,000 lb a height of 1 ft in a period of 1 min.

Horsepower can be calculated in watts as 1 hp equals 746 W in the fps system and 735.5 W in the SI system.

The relationship of electrical horsepower to watts may be defined as follows:

SI system: 1 hp = the work done by 75 kg of force moving a particle a distance of 1 m in 1 s. Also, 1 hp is equal to 735.5 J/s = 735.5W.

fps system: 1 hp = the work done by 550 lb of force moving a particle a distance of 1 ft in 1 s. Also, 1 hp is equal to 746 W.

20.2 TORQUE

Torque is a force that produces or tends to produce rotation. A force of 1 N applied to the handle of a crank, the center of which is displaced 1 m from the center of the shaft produces a torque of 1 N·m on the shaft. In the fps system, torque is usually measured in pound-feet or ounce-inches. For example the term *ounce-inches* is the weight in ounces that a motor will lift at a distance in inches from the centerline of the motor shaft. An example would be a motor with a 6-in radius pulley lifting a 10-oz weight would produce a torque of 60 oz-in.

Torque can be converted to watts with the equation:

$$\begin{aligned}\text{watts} &= (5.325 \times 10^{-7})(\text{kg}\cdot\text{m})(\text{rpm}) \\ &= (7.4 \times 10^{-4})(\text{oz}\cdot\text{in})(\text{rpm})\end{aligned} \quad (20\text{-}1)$$

and to horsepower by the equation:

$$\begin{aligned}\text{horsepower} &= (7.24 \times 10^{-10})(\text{kg}\cdot\text{m})(\text{rpm}) \\ &= (9.92 \times 10^{-7})(\text{oz}\cdot\text{in})(\text{rpm})\end{aligned} \quad (20\text{-}2)$$

where,
watts is the power consumed by the motor,
rpm is the motor shaft speed,
kg·m and oz·in are torque.

20.3 SPEED REDUCTION AND CONTROL[1]

Several methods used to obtain speed reduction in recording and reproducing equipment are shown in Fig. 20-1. Among these various systems will be found gear reducers, intermediate idler rollers, and belt drives. Fig. 20-1A shows three types of puck or idler drive systems. Fig. 20-1B illustrates two types of gear reducers; Fig. 20-1C shows two types of belt-speed reducers, and Fig. 20-1D shows a Gilmer Timing Belt drive system. For the sake of clarity in the drawings, *decoupling devices* (compliance) generally connected between the motor and the driven member have been left out.

Decoupling devices are generally of a loose coupling design; that is, the motor shaft is connected to the driven member through a piece of rubber, felt, leather, or adhesive tape to reduce the transmission of vibration from the motor to the speed-reduction system. In some systems, a second decoupler is used to isolate the gearbox vibration from the driven system. Pucks, idlers, and belts serve as their own decoupling devices.

Intermediate rubber-covered idler roller drives are used in magnetic recorders and other types of recording equipment because of their low cost and smoothness of operation. Also, they serve as decoupling devices and prevent hunting in the drive system. The principal objection to their use is slippage due to the deformation of the rubber at the point of surface contact. This slippage may be reduced to a minimum by the use of multiple pucks with narrow faces. Wide faces are not always the best because the wide contact surface does not bear uniformly over the entire surface.

Rim drive or drives on the outer surface of a flywheel damp out the action the flywheel is intended to impart to

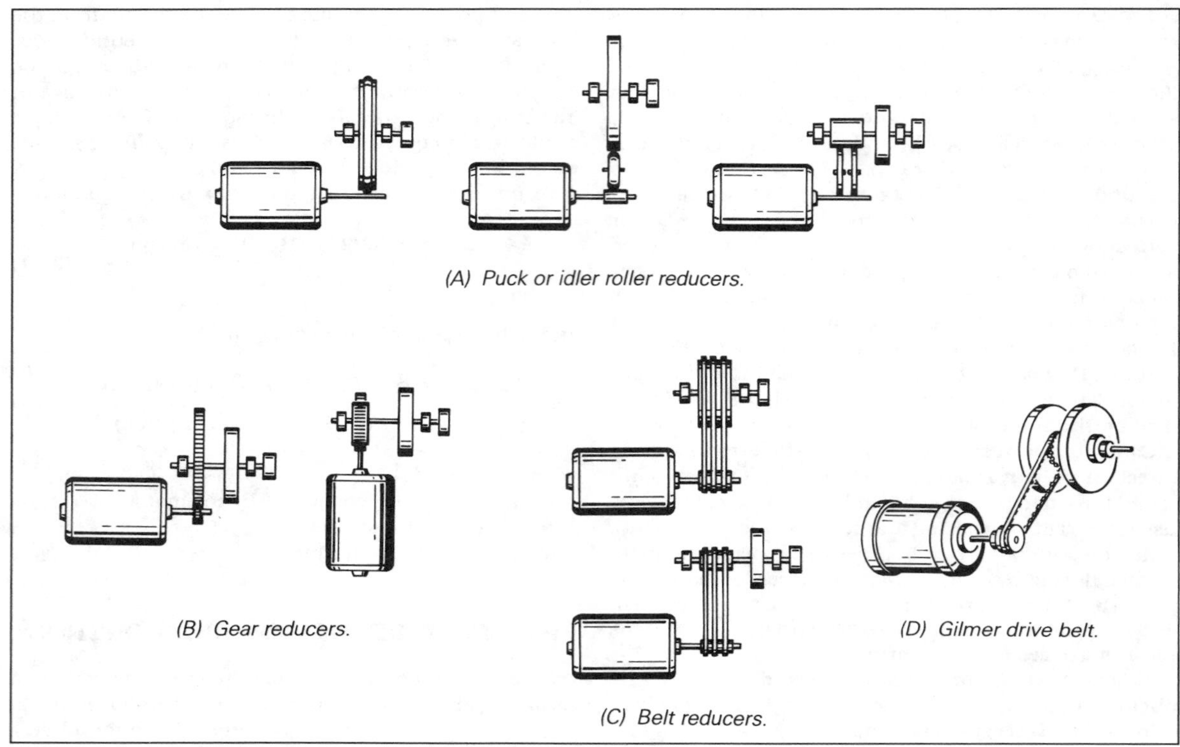

Figure 20-1 Drive systems used to reduce speed through pucks, gearing, and belts.

the drive system, which is the smoothing out of the rotational irregularities and surface imperfections of the idler or puck surfaces.

Frequency meters on camera supply units are generally calibrated to read in both frames per second and hertz. This enables the recordist to increase or decrease the speed of the camera motor for special effects. If the camera is run overspeed, when the picture is projected later, the action will be slowed down. If the camera is run underspeed, the action will be sped up. In these instances, the camera is run wild, without sound. The relationship of frequency to frames per second is

40 Hz, 16 frames/s

45 Hz, 18 frames/s

50 Hz, 20 frames/s

55 Hz, 22 frames/s

60 Hz, 24 frames/s

65 Hz, 26 frames/s

When a change of frames per second is required and a calibrated scale is not readily available, the corresponding frequency may be determined by multiplying the desired frames per second by a factor of 2.5, which is derived by

$$60/24 = 2.5$$

where,

24 is the frames per second for a standard frequency of 60 Hz.

A mechanical method of controlling the speed of a motor is with a *centrifugal governor.* Centrifugal governors are used with both series and shunt ac or dc motors and generators. The governor consists of an insulated plate, mounted on one end of the armature shaft, with two stationary and two movable weighted contacts. As the speed increases beyond its rated speed, centrifugal force moves the weighted contacts outward, opening the contacts and reducing motor input voltage, and hence speed.

20.4 POWER FACTOR

The *power factor* (pf) of an alternating-current circuit or motor is the ratio of active power to apparent power. When an alternating current circuit contains inductance, the current will lag behind the voltage. When the circuit contains capacitance, the current will lead the voltage. In each instance, the current and the voltage reach their maximum values at different instants, and the product of the voltage and the current at any given time is less than it would be if the two were in phase. If the voltage and current are measured separately, the voltmeter and the ammeter will indicate the mean effective values. If the power in the circuit is measured using a wattmeter, the meter indicates the combined efforts of the voltage and current synchronously, not the product of their effective values, which occur at different instants. Consequently, a wattmeter indication will be less than the product of separate voltmeter and ammeter readings.

The ratio of the power read by the wattmeter and the power read by the voltmeter and ammeter is the power factor (pf) of the circuit.

$$\text{single-phase pf} = \text{watts}/[\text{V(A)}] \qquad (20\text{-}3)$$

and for a three-phase circuit:

$$\text{three-phase pf} = \text{watts}/\sqrt{3}\,(\text{line-to-line V})\,(\text{line A}) \qquad (20\text{-}4)$$

where,

watts are read on a wattmeter,

volts and amperes per phase are read on individual meters.

A single-phase motor drawing 5 A at 220 V, as shown by the voltmeter and ammeter, and 880 W as shown on the wattmeter has a pf $= 880/[5(220)] = 0.8$.

When electric motors are connected to a power source, the power factor lags due to motor inductance. To correct this condition, capacitors, which have a leading power factor, are connected across the load to bring the power factor back toward unity. If the power factor cannot be measured, it can be estimated.

20.5 WIRE INSULATION

Motor design, manufacturing techniques, and newly developed insulating materials have advanced to where a given size motor of a few years ago is now considerably smaller and more efficient. The minimum physical size of a motor and its life expectancy are limited and determined by the destructive effects of internal operating temperature and winding insulation. The materials for a motor winding are divided into groups and standardized by the Institute of Electrical and Electronic Engineers (IEEE).

Class	Maximum Spot Temperature
0	90°C
A	105°C
B	130°C
H	180°C
C	No limit set

The electrical and mechanical properties of the insulated windings must not be impaired by the application of a permissible temperature for a given classification. Cotton, silk, paper, and similar materials may be used as a Class-0 insulation; however, if these materials are to be used as Class A, it is necessary that they be impregnated or immersed in a liquid dielectric to afford greater insulation. Other Class-A insulations are molded and laminated materials with cellulose filler, phenolic and other similar resins, also films and sheets of cellulose acetate or other cellulose derivatives. Conductors are varnished. Class B and Class H make use of materials such as mica, asbestos, fiberglass, and so on, with suitable binding substances. Where the temperature may be higher in Class-C, materials such as mica, porcelain, quartz, and glass may be required.

20.6 THREE-PHASE POWER

Three-phase power can be connected in either a delta or wye (star) connection. Each phase is separated by 120 electrical degrees from the other windings.

The delta connection is wired in the form of the Greek letter delta, as shown in Fig. 20-2. Delta connections are never grounded; therefore, all three legs are floating. When a delta-connected motor is connected across the main power, each leg has full voltage across it.

The wye or star connection has the windings connected in the form of the letter gamma (γ) as shown in Fig. 20-3. The voltage from the mainlines is across two wind-

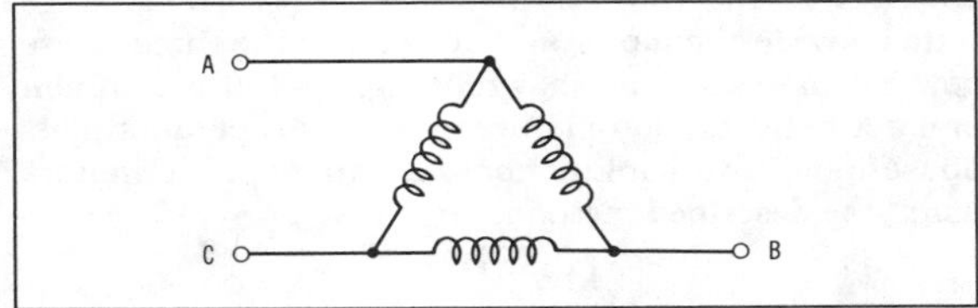

Figure 20-2 Delta connection for motors, generators, and transfomers.

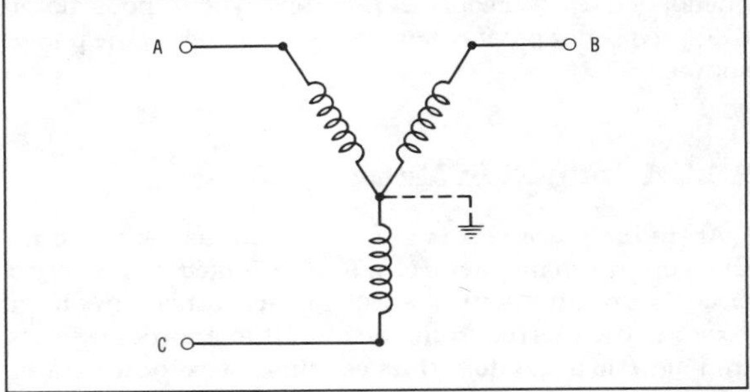

Figure 20-3 Wye or star connection for motors, generators, and transformers.

ings so each winding only has ($V_{line\ to\ line}/\sqrt{3}$) the mains voltage on each leg. A wye connection can be grounded at the center of the wye as shown by the dotted lines in Fig. 20-3. A grounded wye connection circuit is also called a four-wire system. A four-wire, three-phase wye connection power supply is often 208 V across each phase, which gives 120 V between each phase and common:

$$\text{voltage}_{\text{line to common}} = \text{voltage}_{\text{line to line}}/\sqrt{3} \quad (20\text{-}5)$$

The current per phase of an electrical system can be calculated by the following equations:

For a single-phase system,

$$I = W/V(pf) \quad (20\text{-}6)$$

For a two-phase system,

$$I = W/2V(pf) \quad (20\text{-}7)$$

For a three-phase system,

$$I = W/\sqrt{3}V(pf) \quad (20\text{-}8)$$

where,
I is the line current,
W is the power delivered in watts,
V is the potential existing between the main lines,
pf is the power factor.

Single-phase motors can be operated on three-phase power. By connecting a transformer of the correct voltage ratio between the motor and one pair of the three-phase power source leads, as shown in Fig. 20-4. It is common practice in the motion-picture industry to operate single-phase motors in conjunction with three-phase motors using the described method.

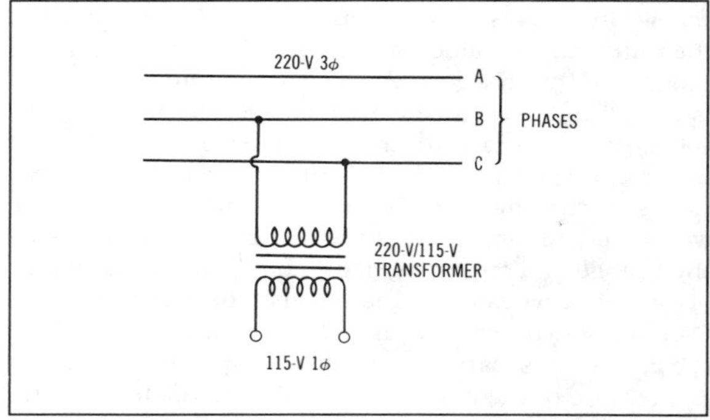

Figure 20-4 Transformer connections for single-phase operation from a three-phase source.

20.7 TYPES OF MOTORS[2]

Ac motors are either *synchronous* or *asynchronous*. In a synchronous motor the speed is proportional to the frequency of the power source, and in an asynchronous motor the speed is not proportional to the frequency of the power source.

20.7.1 Induction Motors

An *induction motor* is an asynchronous, ac machine that contains a magnetic circuit interlinked with electric circuits, rotating with respect to each other, in which power is transferred from one circuit to another by electromagnetic induction, thus causing the rotor to rotate.

Induction motors are of two types: *wound rotor* and *squirrel-cage rotor*. The wound rotor motor is an induction motor in which the secondary circuit, the rotor, consists of a polyphase winding or coils whose terminals are closed through a suitable external circuit. This circuit, which could be a dc supply, allows the speed to be adjusted ±8% and the torque to be controlled.

The squirrel-cage rotor has the winding permanently short circuited, usually uninsulated, having its conductors uniformly distributed around the periphery of the machine and joined by continuous end rings, as shown in Fig. 20-5. Thus, circulating currents will be induced in them by the field (stator) windings. The synchronous speed of an induction-motor rotating field is calculated by

$$N = 120f/p \quad (20\text{-}9)$$

where,
N is the speed in revolutions per minute (rpm),
f is the frequency in hertz,
p is the number of poles/number of phases of the power source.

The speed of an induction motor is affected by the fre-

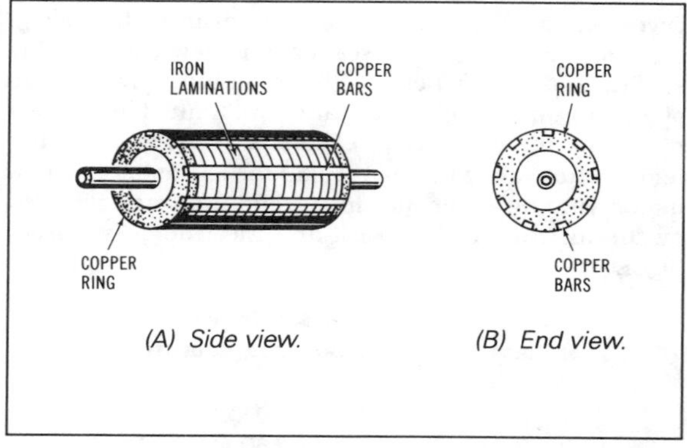

Figure 20-5 Rotor for a squirrel-cage motor.

quency of the source and the load. Induction motors are not absolute constant-speed devices and should not be used when a constant speed is essential.

The *slip speed* is the difference in revolutions per minute between the synchronous speed and the actual speed.

Exciting the field windings sets up a rotating electric field that rotates around the motor and is called the *synchronous speed*. The actual rotor speed is somewhat less than this because a difference between rotor speed and synchronous speed is required to make the motor rotate.

Slip can be given in the difference of revolutions between synchronous and rotor speed or as percent slip

$$\%\ \text{slip} = [(\text{rpm}_{sync} - \text{rpm}_{rotor})/\text{rpm}_{sync}] \times 100 \qquad (20\text{-}10)$$

Motor horsepower rating is proportional to the product of line voltage (V_R), full-load current in amperes (I_M), full-load efficiency (Eff), and full-load power factor (pf), where efficiency and power factor are expressed in per-unit values (e.g., 0.95 equals 95% efficiency). For any three-phase motor, full-load horsepower may be defined as

$$\text{rated horsepower} = 1.732 V_R I_M (\text{Eff}) \text{pf}/746 \qquad (20\text{-}11)$$

The relationships between power factor, efficiency, and current at various partial loads are shown in Fig. 20-6.

The percent of full-load slip-speed curve in Fig. 20-6 is a straight line between a 10% and a 110% load, indicating that slip speed is directly proportional to the horsepower load in this range. This relationship provides an accurate means of estimating loads carried by squirrel-cage induction motors in integral-horsepower sizes.

A squirrel-cage induction-motor no-load speed is slightly less than synchronous speed. In the example in Fig. 20-6, the no-load slip is approximately 1 rpm, which is equivalent to 1,799 rpm no-load speed. This no-load slip causes a no-load current to flow, thus supplying the motor losses. The no-load current also includes the current necessary to produce the rotating magnetic field; this is called magnetizing current and is approximately constant for all loads, with the constant voltage applied.

The direction of the rotation of a three-phase motor is reversed by reversing any two power-source wires.

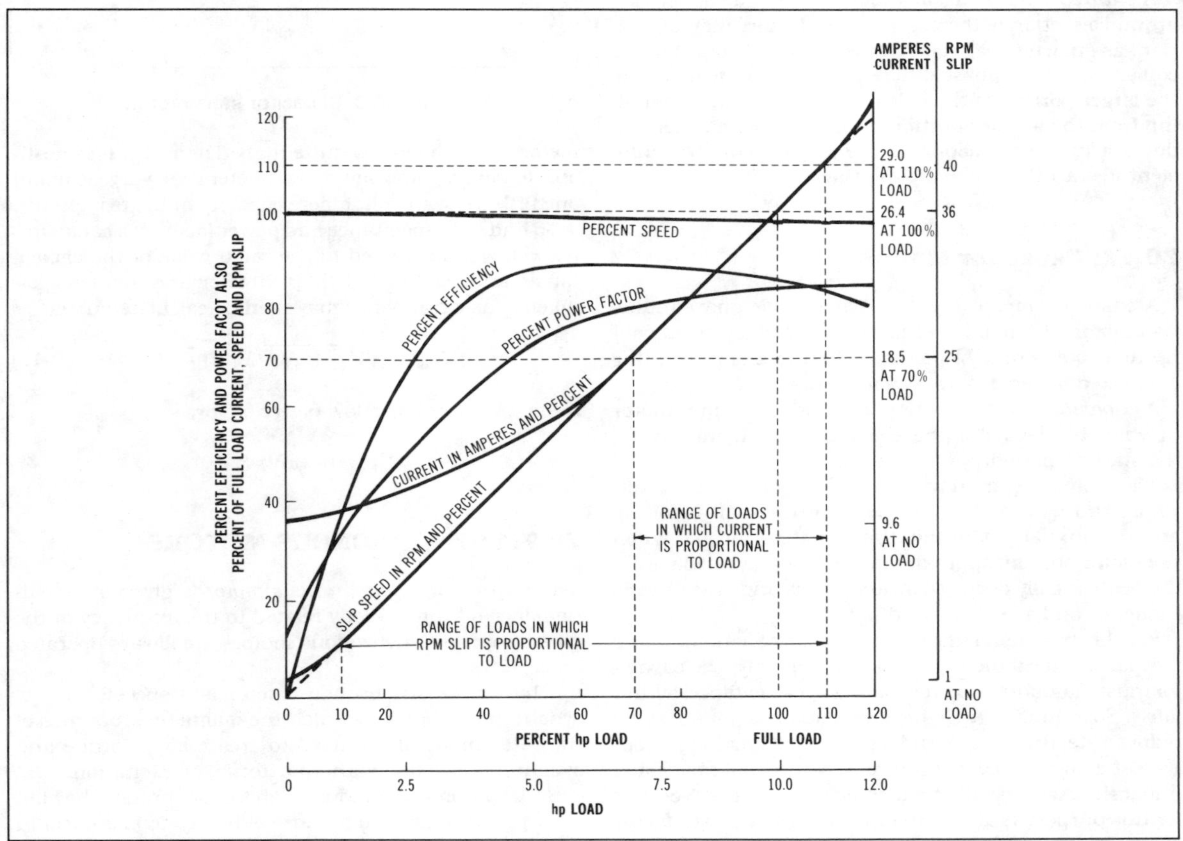

Figure 20-6 Performance curves of a typical 10-hp 1800-rpm squirrel-cage induction motor at rated voltage and frequency.

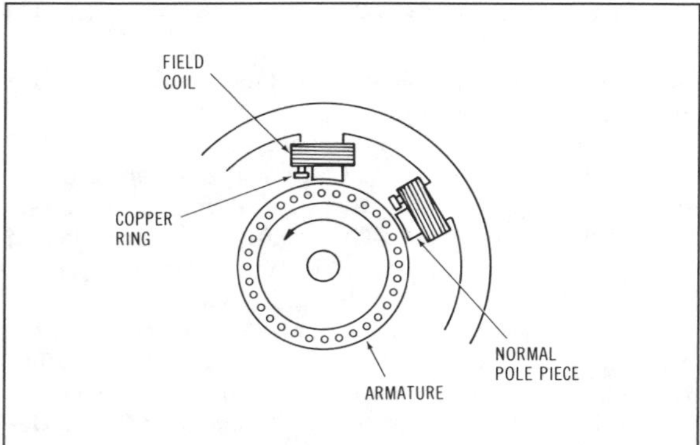

Figure 20-7 Shaded-pole motor with a single-turn copper coil on a pole piece.

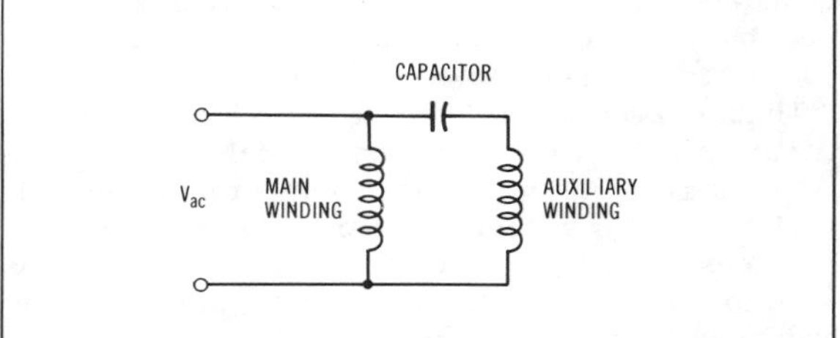

Figure 20-8 Capacitor single-phase induction motor.

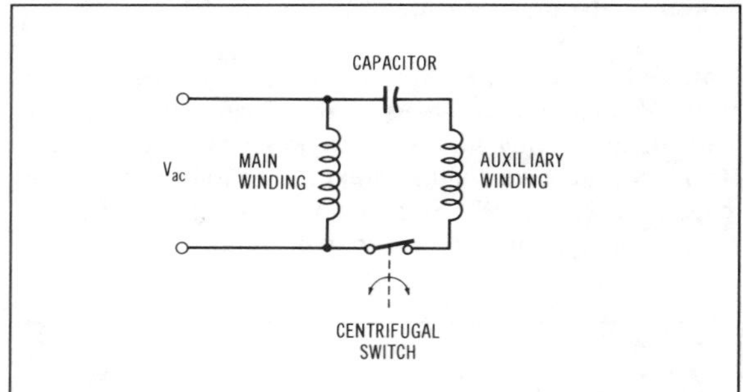

Figure 20-9 Capacitor-start motor.

20.7.2 Shaded-Pole Motors

A *shaded-pole motor* is a motor having a copper ring around a section of the pole piece in the direction of rotation, as shown in Fig. 20-7. This coil is called a shading coil and causes a phase difference between the flux from the larger portion of the pole piece and the flux emanating from the smaller portion of the pole piece. This produces a two-phase action in the armature and is sufficient to start the armature rotating.

20.7.3 Capacitor Motors

A *capacitor motor* (Fig. 20-8) is a single-phase induction motor with a main winding arranged for direct connection to a source of power and an auxiliary winding connected in series with a capacitor.

A *capacitor start motor* (Fig. 20-9) is a capacitor motor in which the capacitor phase is in the circuit only during the starting period.

The motor is started with the capacitor in the circuit, which causes a phase shift between the main winding and the auxiliary winding, thus creating torque. When the motor obtains approximately 80% of its rated speed, the centrifugally operated switch opens and cuts out the capacitor and auxiliary winding.

For the proper starting and operation of a motor using a capacitor permanently or for starting only, the capacitor must maintain its power factor and capacitance, within fairly close limits. A high power factor is manifest by reduced starting torque and a prolonged starting period. To test a starting capacitor properly, it should be tested under the exact conditions in which it operates. A circuit for this purpose is shown in Fig. 20-10. The power-factor wattmeter must be capable of reading quite low values, since the losses of a good capacitor are quite low, although the product of current and voltage as read on the voltmeter and ammeter is quite high. Therefore, it is desirable to have a power-factor wattmeter that will read about one fifth the watt voltampere capacity of the test circuit.

To find the capacitance and power factor of a capacitor, the voltage is adjusted to the rated value of the capacitance, and readings of the voltmeter and ammeter are taken. The capacitance may then be calculated using

$$C_{\mu F} = [\sqrt{I^2 - (P/V)^2}/2\pi fV] \times 10^6 \qquad (20\text{-}12)$$

If the capacitor has a low power factor,

$$C_{\mu F} = (I/2\pi fV) \times 10^6$$

20.7.4 SYNCHRONOUS MOTORS

The speed of a *synchronous motor* is given in revolutions per minute directly related to the frequency of the power source. Synchronous motors are always operated on ac.

A hysteresis synchronous motor is a special form of synchronous motor in which the magnetic properties of the rotor material are used to create large torque and synchronous action without external dc excitation.

Hysteresis motors produce high torque through the high rotor power consumed because of the hysteresis effect in the rotor. The speed of a synchronous motor is determined by equation 20-9.

The synchronous motor employed for driving recording

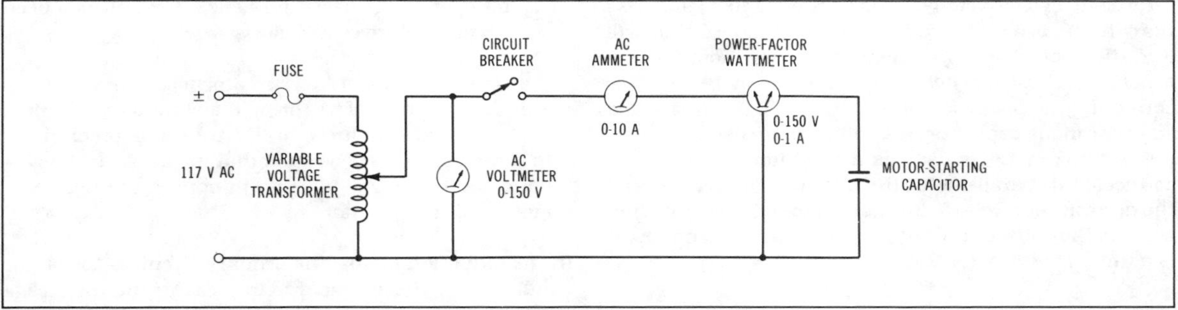

Figure 20-10 Circuit for testing motor starting capacitors.

and projection equipment is not the conventional synchronous motor generally found in an industrial plant. Motors for sound work are of special design and are of the variable reluctance type, using squirrel-cage construction for the armature, with salient poles milled in the armature laminations. Such armatures are constructed by using heavy copper bars running lengthwise of the armature and shorted at each end by a heavy copper ring. Salient poles are milled the length of the armature laminations, at an angle of 7° to 10°, using the armature shaft as a reference, as shown in Fig. 20-11.

If the bars of the squirrel-cage rotor are of a sufficiently low resistance to bring the rotor to synchronous speed, the salient poles will pull the armature into step with the points of greatest flux density of the rotating field. Since there are no windings, the armature requires no maintenance.

Synchronous motors may be designed to operate over a limited speed range by changing the frequency of the driving-power source. This design usually requires a change in the supply voltage to maintain a satisfactory power input. Synchronous motors may also be provided with stator windings to produce a number of different pole combinations, and, by using a suitable rotor, the motor may be made to operate at a number of different speeds.

Because of the quick-starting characteristics of squirrel-cage motors due to the copper bars, shorting rings, and salient poles, they have a high starting torque and are brought into synchronism very quickly. Since this is somewhat of a disadvantage, particularly for the cameras and projection machines, some steps must be taken to provide a soft start, such as putting resistors in the power source and cutting them out of the circuit as the motor comes up to speed.

Fractional horsepower synchronous motors of the previously described type are characterized by their high starting torque, rapid acceleration, low power factor (because the exciting current is taken from the line through the stator winding), and efficiency. The power rating is low, generally on the order of ⅙ to ⅓ hp.

A special type of hysteresis motor is the *inside-out* motor, called so because the stator revolves rather than the

Figure 20-11 Squirrel-cage motor armature showing the copper rods, rings, and salient poles. *(Courtesy Bodine Electric Co.)*

armature. This type of motor is used extensively for the driving of ¼-in. magnetic tape recorders, at speeds of 1⅞ to 30 in/s. Such motors are available in dual- and triple-speed designs. Common speeds for the dual type are 300/600, 360/720, 450/900, and 600/1200 rpm; and 300/600/900 for the triple speeds. A nonmagnetic puck or capstan is pressed on the motor spindle to obtain the desired linear speed for magnetic tape. Hysteresis synchronous motors provide the exact constant-speed required for magnetic recorders, with high torque and constant angular velocity. The rotor (stator) is a dynamically balanced flywheel that assures a constant speed under changing load conditions. A Mumetal shield is placed over the stator winding and rotor to eliminate the high flux-torque from the region of the motor shaft. Impellers on the rotor circulate air to provide forced ventilation for the motor and associated equipment.

The average power consumed by this type motor is approximately 30 to 40 W, at 117 V, with a rotor torque of 7 to 10 oz. The bearings may be ball bearing or oil-less sleeve type. The motor has a single hold mounting and uses a capacitor ranging from 1.5 to 3.0 μF.

A special job for synchronous motors is to correct the power factor of a line. If the synchronous motor is driven from an external source of power and variable dc voltage is applied to the rotor windings and set to a value that will be called for the sake of illustration 100%, no current will flow from the stator windings to the rotor windings. Under these conditions the voltage generated in the stator windings (counter electromagnetic force) exactly balances the voltage applied to the stator from the external voltage source.

If the dc exciter voltage is now reduced to a value less than 100%, a reactive component is produced that will lead the applied voltage. The machine will now act as a capacitor. Thus, a synchronous motor may be used for correcting the power factor and, when so used, is called a synchronous capacitor or a rotary condenser.

When the motor is used as a capacitor, the motor is connected in parallel with the line to be corrected, and the dc excitation voltage is adjusted to produce a leading current that offsets the lagging line current. The result is a unity power factor.

20.7.5 Braking of AC Motors[3]

In many applications where induction motors are used, it is desirable to provide a retarding force to slow or stop the motor by a means other than a mechanical brake or to supplement a mechanical brake.

There are several methods of electrically braking induction motors. These include dc braking, plugging, regenerative braking, and capacitor braking. Some of the characteristics of each of these methods are noted in the following:

1. With *plugging* the power is applied (usually through suitable resistors) in reverse phase rotation, causing a reversed torque. However, to prevent actual rotating reversal, a zero speed switch is necessary to remove power as the speed approaches zero. Here, if this switch fails or is maladjusted, reversed rotation may actually occur, and in many applications this is not permissible. Also, motor losses during plugging are about 300% of starting losses and, in addition to possible motor overheating, may cause severe line disturbances if a large motor is involved.
2. *Dynamic braking* occurs when, after voltage is removed, a resistive load is shunted across the motor terminals. With this method, however, the braking torque decreases as the motor slows and becomes zero at zero speed, thus limiting its usefulness to motor loads that also have appreciable frictional-retarding forces.
3. *Capacitor braking* is obtained when capacitors are connected across two or three phases of the induction motor. (Resistors may also be connected in parallel with the capacitors during the braking period.) Very little braking torque is obtained below about 30% of synchronous speed; therefore, like dynamic braking, this method also is limited to motor-load systems having considerable frictional retarding forces.
4. *Regenerative braking* is provided by applying a dc voltage to one phase of a polyphase induction motor, usually from a transformer-rectifier power supply. (This method is also applicable to single-phase induction motors.) The principle by which dc braking operates is based on Lenz's law and has been stated by Maxwell as follows:

> If a constant current flows in a primary circuit "A," and if, by motion of "A" or by the secondary circuit "B," a current is induced in "B," the direction of this induced current will be such that, by its electromagnetic action on "A," it tends to oppose the relative motion of the circuits.

In the induction motor, the primary circuit is the stator winding, and the secondary circuit is in the rotor cage (or winding if a wound rotor motor is used). The braking force results from the opposition to relative motion between these two circuits while the dc current is flowing. This braking method exhibits many of the advantages of the other methods, with very few of the disadvantages. These attributes may be explained as follows:

1. It is effective on single-phase and polyphase squirrel-cage and wound rotor induction motors.
2. The amount of braking torque and the rate of braking are easily adjustable over a wide range, and the braking rate, when once correctly adjusted, will maintain and duplicate the retarding cycle accurately each time the cycle is initiated.
3. A smooth, rolling stop is obtained by this method; however, like the other methods, there is no holding power at the end of the braking cycle. On loads that must be firmly held, an auxiliary mechanical brake is required.
4. For rapid braking, dc currents in excess of rated motor, full-load currents are required. Therefore, similar to plugging, overheating of the motor can occur if the power is applied for extended periods. Accordingly, a timer is usually used to remove the dc power after the motor has stopped, however, for an equal braking effort, the dc braking losses are less than those of plugging.

The basic circuit, Fig. 20-12, shows a three-phase transformer and rectifier feeding the motor terminal through the *braking contacts* of a reversing contactor. When the motor contactor (C) is de-energized, the braking contactor (C_b) is energized and applied dc power until the timer contact (C_t) disconnects the circuit.

For small motors, the braking power may often be supplied by a charged capacitor in a manner similar to Fig. 20-13.

In the case of capacitor-stored energy braking (Fig. 2-13) the circuit constants may be designed by knowing the number of seconds allowed to brake the motor and the dc voltage and the current calculated as noted previously. From these, calculate the necessary watt-seconds of energy using

$$V_{dc}I_{dc} \text{ seconds}$$

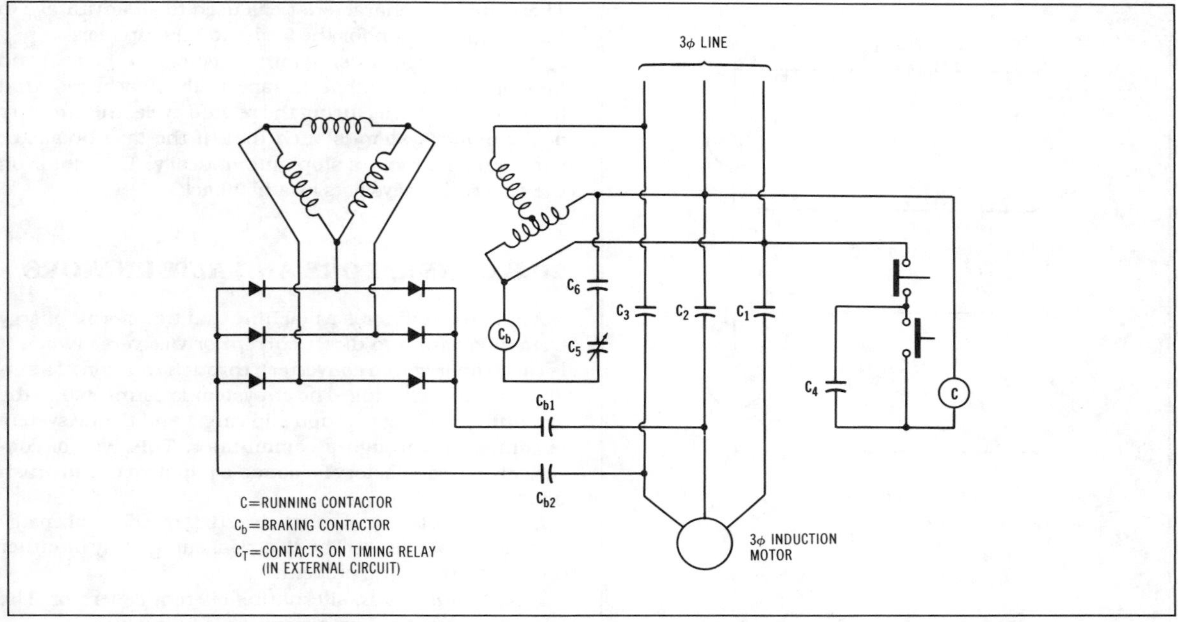

Figure 20-12 Basic circuit for "braking" an ac motor.

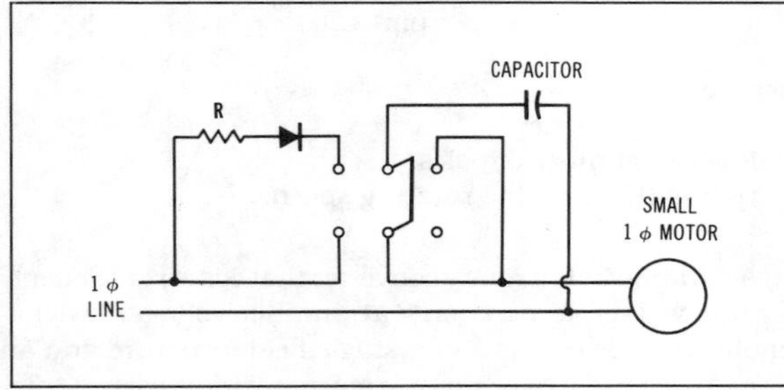

Figure 20-13 Capacitor braking for small motors.

Then from the stored energy equation,

$$\text{watt-seconds} = CV_{dc}^2/2 \qquad (20\text{-}13)$$

where,

C is the capacitance in farads,

V is the dc voltage to which the capacitor is charged.

The size of the capacitor and the voltage to which the capacitor must be charged may be calculated and components selected by usual design methods.

20.7.6 DC Motors

A dc motor operates on direct current. Dc motors can be series connected, shunt connected, or compound connected.

Series-connected motors (Fig. 20-14A) have high starting torque and poor speed control and run away under no-load conditions.

Shunt-connected motors (Fig. 20-14B) have fair starting torque and good speed control, and they are self-regulating.

Compound-connected motors (Fig. 20-14C) have both the features of shunt and series motors.

A dc motor is reversed by reversing the polarity. The dc motor speed is varied by varying the input voltage, the load, or the field or armature voltage.

The dc motor speed is held constant by using a feedback system that monitors the motor's revolutions per minute and varies the voltages inversely to the speed.

This is often accomplished with a servoamplifier (Fig. 20-15). This differential amplifier monitors a feedback generator physically connected to the motor shaft. When the generator voltage is different from the reference voltage, the motor source voltage is either increased or decreased to regulate the speed and make the generator voltage the same as the reference voltage.

20.7.7 Torque Motors

Manufacturers of professional (and some nonprofessional) magnetic recording and reproducing equipment make use of torque motors mounted on the spindles for the feed and take-up reels to provide a constant tension on the film or tape, regardless of the diameter of the recording media on either reel. The motors may be of the

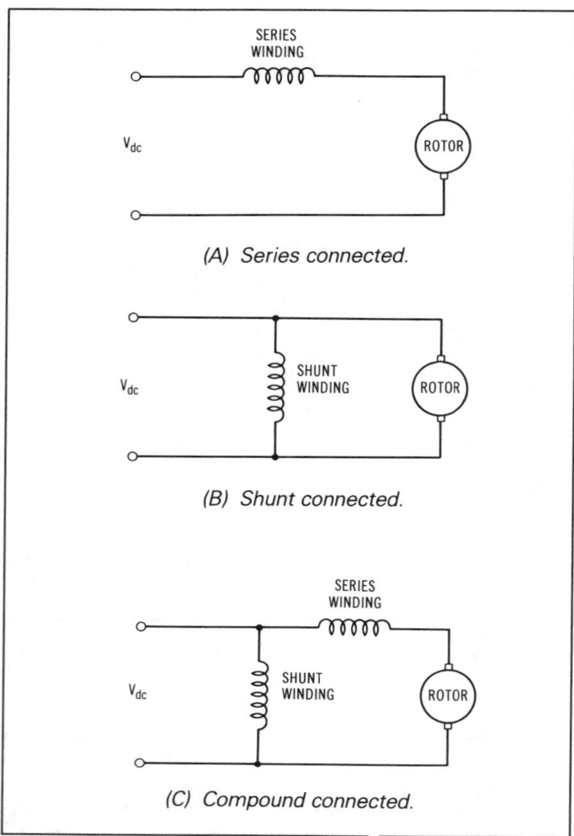

Figure 20-14 Dc motor configuration.

induction type or of the single-phase shaded-pole design. Resistors connected in the ac supply line are used to control the speed and to provide an adjustment for the desired tension. The power drops off proportionally to the increase in speed and develops maximum power at stall speeds. Therefore, this characteristic is used to an advantage to control the tension for the feed and take-up reels.

One advantage of using torque motors in the feed and take-up positions is that the tape or film may be rewound in either direction. During the rewind cycle, the circuitry of the motor system is such that, if the tape breaks or runs out, the motors stop automatically. The motor on the feed reel always acts as a holdback.

20.8 GENERATORS AND ALTERNATORS

A *rotary converter* is a machine that transforms energy from alternating to direct current or vice versa (when it is called an inverted converter), through rotation of a single armature winding. The ac system is connected to the armature winding through slip rings, and the dc system is connected through a commutator. This type of converter is not satisfactory for sound equipment due to brush noise.

A *generator* is a device for converting mechanical energy into electrical energy. The electrical energy may be either direct or alternating current.

An *alternator* is an alternating-current generator. The output frequency of an alternator is found by

$$f = (P/2)(rpm/60s) \quad (20\text{-}14)$$
$$= P(rpm)/120$$

where,

f is the frequency,
P is the number of poles,
rpm is the machine rotating speed.

A *dynamotor* is a rotary converter that converts dc energy at one voltage to dc energy at another voltage. A dynamotor usually consists of a single field structure and an armature with two or more armature windings and commutators. One armature winding is the motor or input winding and the other windings are the dynamo or generator (output) winding.

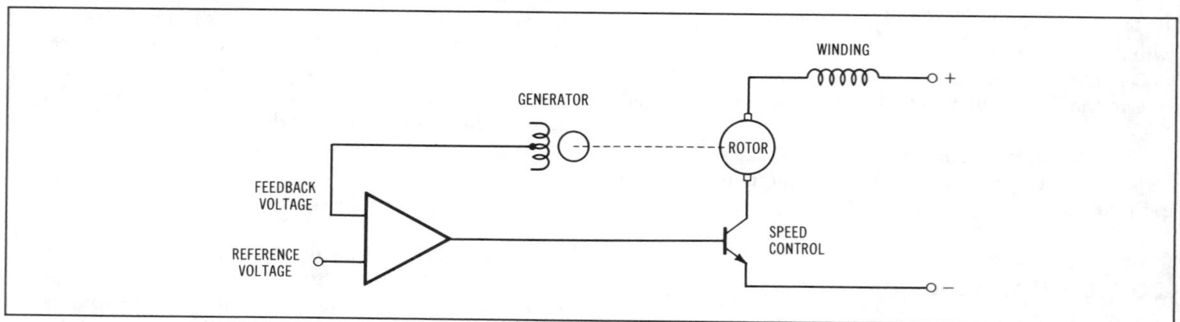

Figure 20-15 Servo-controlled dc motor.

20.9 SELSYN INTERLOCK SYSTEMS

The sole purpose of an interlock system for rerecording and other purposes is that all the machines in the system, including the projection machine (which is the heaviest to start), must be brought up to speed in synchronism, from a standing start, in about 6 s. This gain in speed must be accomplished in a smooth manner to avoid breaking film and sound track.

Selsyn distributors are sometimes referred to as rotary transformers, because of the 1:1 ratio of the two windings. As a rule, the internal windings of the distributor unit are star connected. The rotor windings of the distributor unit and the remote meters are connected in parallel. The stator windings of the distributor and remote motors being driven are also connected in parallel and to the three-phase power. Phasing of each unit is accomplished by connecting similar numbers of the windings together and to the same place.

Because the distributor unit is always the largest unit in the system, it becomes the master, and all other units become the slaves. When properly phased, absolute synchronism is maintained.

Under these conditions the system may be termed as a constant-speed device.

The diagram for such a device appears in Fig. 20-16. Starting at the left is a control box consisting of a group of relays, resistors, and three solenoids, one connected in each phase of the incoming power source. Solenoids normally have low impedances; however, at the instant current flows through the coil, a soft iron plunger is pulled upward into the coil, increasing its impedance. As the driving motor starts to rotate, the initial current drops, and as it does, the plunger falls out of the coil, lowering its impedance to the original value. The pulling up of the plungers into the starting coils prevents the system from making a sudden start that might break the film or damage the equipment. When adjusted properly, a slow, smooth start is obtained, even with 10 to 20 machines being driven simultaneously. The driving motor is a three-phase, 220-V, synchronous type turning 1200 rpm and is mechanically coupled to the selsyn distributor unit. A

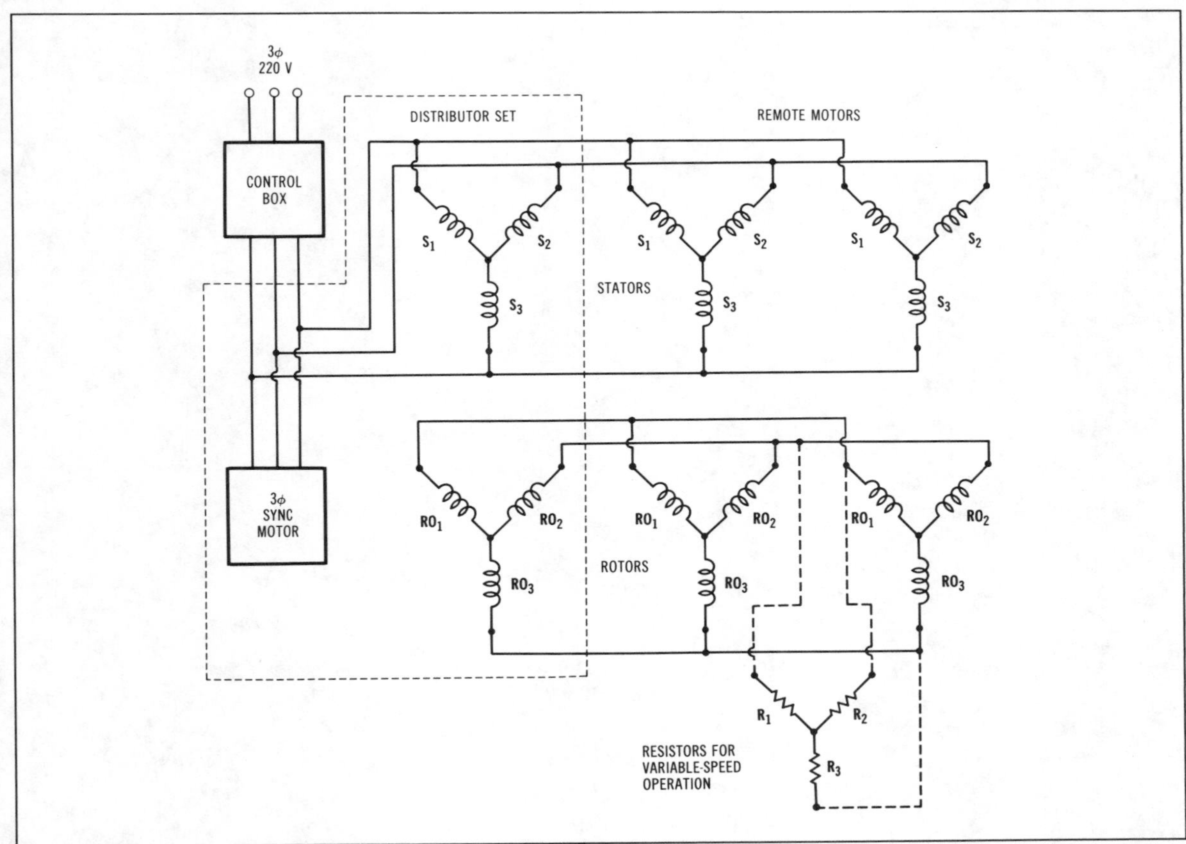

Figure 20-16 Three-phase selsyn-interlock distributor system.

heavy flywheel is mounted on the shaft to provide a large amount of inertia for a soft start and gradual slowdown. When running, it also helps to iron out small irregularities in the speed. An electrically controlled brake may be applied to the outer rim of the flywheel to bring the system to a gentle stop when the circuit to the drive motor is opened. When the circuit for running is closed, the brake is lifted automatically.

At times during the rerecording of a motion picture, a variable-speed distributor system is required to obtain a particular sound effect. If a separate distributor system is available, it may be made to run at variable speeds by connecting three variable resistors (R_1, R_2, and R_3) across the rotor windings, as shown in Fig. 20-16. If the values of the three resistors are varied the same amount simultaneously, the speed of the system may be controlled. If the three resistors are shorted, the machine will run at 1800 rpm.

REFERENCES

1. H. M. Tremaine, *Audio Cyclopedia*, Indianapolis: Howard W. Sams & Co., Inc., 1969.
2. C. C. Libby, *Motor Selection and Application*, New York: McGraw Hill.
3. F. W. Parrish, *Direct Current Braking for AC Induction Motors*, International Rectifier Corporation.

CHAPTER **21**

VU and Volume Indicator Meters and Devices

by Glen Ballou

To operate a sound-recording or -reproducing system properly, some method for determining the signal levels in different parts of the system to avoid overloading, noise, and distortion is required. This is the purpose of the volume unit (VU) or volume indicator (VI) meter.

21.1 DEFINITIONS

21.1.1 Volume Indicator Meters

A *volume indicator (VI) meter* is a meter used to measure power levels of audio-frequency signals. The term volume indicator is generally associated with meters calibrated in decibels.

21.1.2 VU Meters

A *volume unit (VU) meter* is a special form of VI meter used for monitoring broadcast and recording circuits. Such meters employ special ballistics that average out complex waveforms to properly indicate program material that varies simultaneously in both amplitude and frequency. Complex waveform changes can only be measured in volume units. For complex waveforms, such as speech, a VU meter reads between the average and the peak values of a complex wave. No simple relationship exists between volume measured in VU and the power of a complex waveform. The indicated reading will depend on the particular waveshape at the moment. For sine-wave measurements, a change of one VU is numerically equal to a change of 1 dB.

VU meters are designed to have a dynamic characteristic that approximates the response of the human ear. When a speech waveform is applied to a VU meter, the movement will indicate peaks and valleys in the signal. The average of the three highest peaks in 10 s (disregarding occasional extremes), is taken to be the indication of the meter movement.

Many meters marked as VU meters are not actually such meters, since they have normal movements without the special characteristics of the standard VU meter.

21.1.3 Power-Level Meters

A *power-level meter* is a VI meter calibrated in decibels. As a rule, this type meter is confined to test equipment for steady-state measurements and is not used for monitoring program material.

21.1.4 Power-Output Meters

A *power-output meter* is used for measuring the power output of audio amplifiers and other devices. It may also be used to determine the characteristic and internal output impedance, the effect of load-impedance variation, and other applications involving the measurement of output power and impedance with respect to frequency.

21.2 VU METERS

The *volume-unit meter* is a device whose standard has remained the same since 1961.

The meter consists of a 200-mA dc D'Arsonval movement fed from a full-wave, copper-oxide rectifier unit mounted within the meter case. VU meters are calibrated in reference to 1 mW of power into a 600-Ω load. A typical VU meter is shown in Fig. 21-1.

Because of the inaccuracies inherent in the early copper-oxide rectifier power-level meter and because it was not satisfactory for program monitoring, the development of an entirely new meter was jointly undertaken by the Bell Telephone Laboratories, Columbia Broadcasting System (CBS), and National Broadcasting Company (NBC). The results of this research were not only the development of a new type volume indicator meter but also the standardization of a new reference level of 1 mW, a unit that was adopted by the electronics industry in May 1939.

Figure 21-1 Typical VU meter.

The current standard is United States of America Standards Institute (USASI), formerly the Acoustical Society of America (ASA) C16.5-1961.

The characteristics of this meter are as follows:

General—The meter consists of a dc meter movement with a noncorrosive, full-wave, copper-oxide rectifier unit (mounted in the instrument case) and responds approximately to the root-mean-square (rms) value of the impressed voltage. This value will vary somewhat depending on the waveforms and the percentage of harmonics present in the signal.

Instrument scale—The face of the instrument may have either of the two *scale cards* shown in Fig. 21-2. Each card has two scales: a VU scale ranging from −20 to +3 VU and a percent-modulation scale ranging from 0 to 100%, with 100% coinciding with the 0 point on the VU scale. The normal point for reading volume levels is at 0 VU or 100%, which are located to the right of the center at about 71% of the full scale arc.

Dynamic characteristics—With the instrument connected across a 600-Ω external resistance, the sudden application of a sine-wave voltage, sufficient to give a steady-state deflection at the 0 VU or 100 scale point, shall cause the pointer to overshoot not less than 1% nor more than 1.5% (0.15 dB). The pointer shall reach 99 on the percent scale in 0.3 s.

Response versus frequency—The instrument sensitivity shall not depart from that at 1000 Hz by more than 0.2 dB, between 35 and 10,000 Hz, nor more than 0.5 dB, between 25 and 16,000 Hz.

Impedance—For bridging across a line, the volume indicator, including the instrument and proper series resistor (3600 Ω), shall have an impedance of 7500 Ω when measured with a sinusoidal voltage sufficient to deflect the meter to 0 VU or the 100% scale point.

Sensitivity—The application of a sinusoidal potential of 1.228 V (4 dB above 1 mW in a 600-Ω line) to the instrument in series with the proper resistance (3600 Ω) will cause a deflection to the 0 VU or 100% point.

Harmonic distortion—The *harmonic distortion* introduced in a 600-Ω circuit, caused by bridging the volume indicator across it, is less than 0.3%, under the worst possible condition (no loss in the variable attenuator).

Overload—The instrument must be capable of withstanding, without injury or effect on the calibration, overload peaks of ten times the voltage equivalent to a reading of 0 VU or 100% for 0.50 s and a continuous overload of five times that voltage.

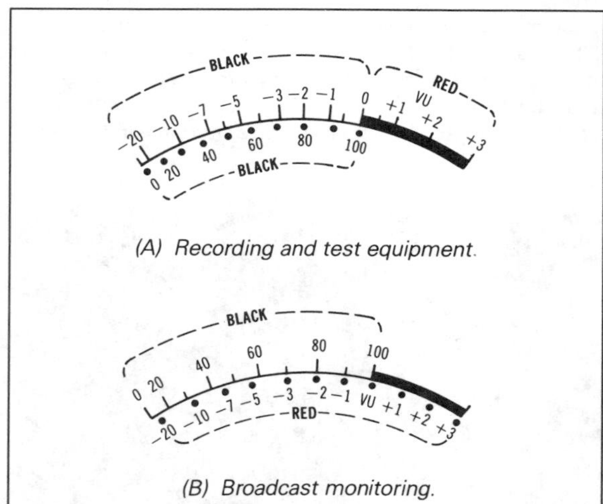

(A) Recording and test equipment.

(B) Broadcast monitoring.

Figure 21-2 VU meter scales.

21.2.1 Meter Ballistics

Meter ballistics are the mechanical and electrical characteristics built into the meter movement. A given characteristic may be obtained by shaping the pole pieces and counterweighting the pointer mechanism. Shunts are sometimes used across the meter terminals, but this use will reduce the sensitivity of the movement.

The ballistics characteristics of a typical old-style VI meter or voltmeter and a standard VU meter, when a 1000-Hz signal is applied for a period of 1 s, are shown in Fig. 21-3. Note the VU meter comes to a steady state at the end of 0.30 s, while the VI meter continues to oscillate showing peaks and valleys over a period of 1 s. This clearly indicates why the ballistics of the VU meter are desirable for monitoring program material containing complex waveforms.

A VU meter reads the rms value of the waveform. On a sine wave, the rms VU indicator of the peak is only 3 dB above the reading; however, on voice or music, the peak may be 10 to 12 dB above the VU reading. This difference is called the *crest factor* and is illustrated in Fig. 21-4.

Because of the meter ballistics, a VU meter indicates somewhere between the average and the peak values. Program material is of a complex and transient nature; therefore, the VU meter indicates considerably under the instantaneous peak program level. This means that 8- to 14-dB peaks present in the program material are not indicated by the meter because the meter movement cannot follow small instantaneous peaks. Even if they could be seen, it would be too late to reduce the level. Therefore, the meter must either be set or caused to indicate in a manner that will not overload the system in which it is operating.

Since VU meters do not include the true peak values of program material (complex waveforms), it is quite easy to overload a recording system. To protect against these unseen peaks, a lead or margin of safety is inserted in the VU meter circuit.

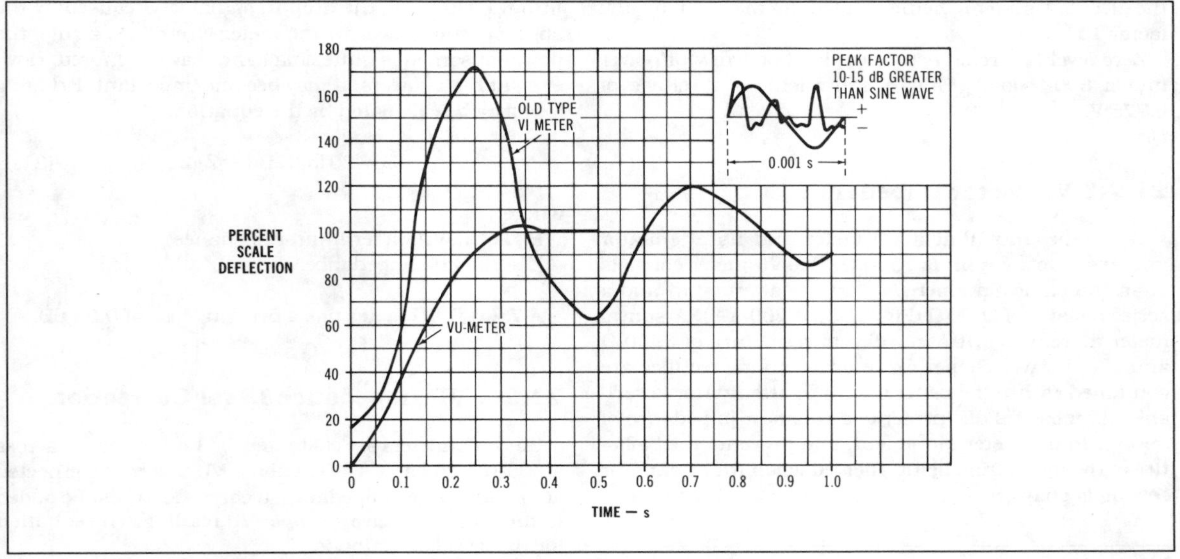

Figure 21-3 Comparison of the original VI meter and the present VU meter ballistics when a 1000-Hz signal is applied for 1 s.

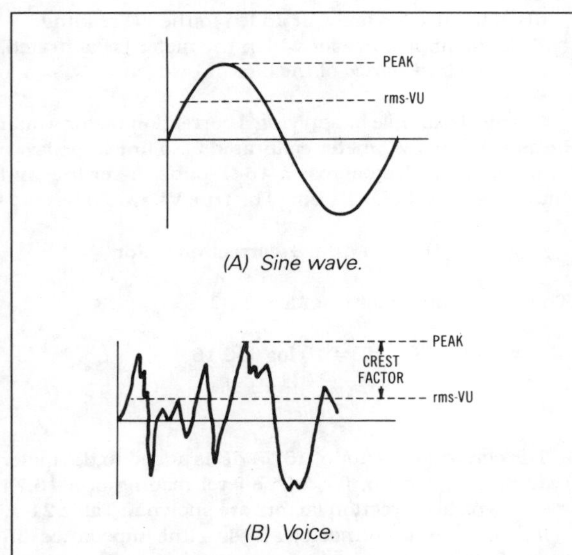

Figure 21-4 Crest factor caused by the peak of music or voice being greater than $\sqrt{3}$ rms.

To insert a lead into a VU meter circuit, the VU meter is connected across a bridging bus with a sine-wave level of +14 dBm. A 400- or 1000-Hz signal is sent into the input of the recording console. The mixer control is set to its normal operating range, and the signal level is adjusted to bring the bus level to +14 dBm (the VU meter reads 100% or 0 dBm).

Remove the input signal and return the VU meter attenuator to its +6-dBm position. This inserts an 8-dB lead or margin of safety in the VU meter by making it 8 dB more sensitive, thus protecting the system against unseen peaks up to 8 dB. The program material is now mixed in the usual manner. Some recording activities, because of the heavy peaks and overloads encountered in some types of music, use a 10- to 12-dB lead in the VU meter.

Radio transmitters are adjusted in a similar manner: only in this instance the percentage modulation indicated by the VU meter indicates the percent modulation of the radio transmitter.

21.2.2 Reference Levels

In the early days of broadcasting and recording, both 10 and 12.5 mW into a 500-Ω line were used as a reference level. However, later this was changed to 6 mW. In May 1939 the present standard of 1 mW into a 600-Ω line was adopted.

This reference level was selected as a level that would conform to the telephone company's standards of limiting the signal level on a transmission line to a value that would produce a minimum of crosstalk and still provide a satisfactory signal-to-noise ratio. The 1-mW reference level is a unit quantity and is readily applicable to the decimal system, being related to the watt by the factor 10^{-3}.

Zero level is a reference power level of 1 mW of power into a 600-Ω load. This is equivalent to a voltage of 0.775 V.

21.2.3 VU Meter Impedance

The impedance that a VU meter and its attenuator impress onto a circuit is 7500 Ω. The VU meter consists of an indicator movement, a variable attenuator, and a series resistor of 3600 Ω (Fig. 21-5). A 200-μA D'Arsonval meter movement with an internal resistance of 3900 Ω and a full-wave, copper-oxide or selenium rectifier are contained within the meter case. The attentuator is variable in steps of 2 dB, presents a constant impedance of 3900 Ω to the meter movement, and prevents the ballistics of the meter from being affected when the attenuator setting is changed.

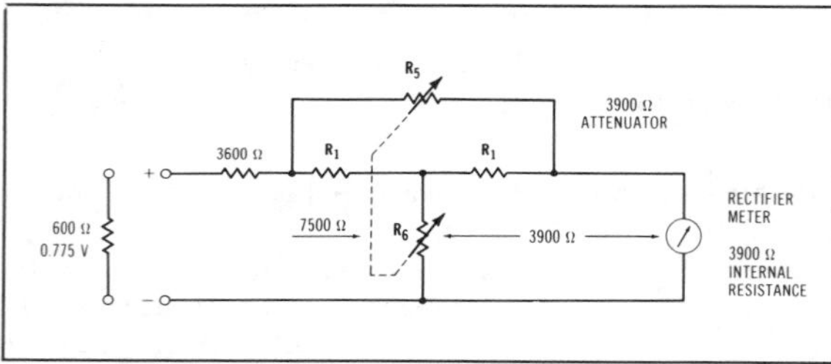

Figure 21-5 Schematic diagram for a 7500-Ω VU meter, calibrated for 1-mW reference level or 0.775 V across 600 Ω.

Standard VU meters are designed to read 0 VU, or 100%, with 1.228 V (+4 dBm) applied to the instrument. If the meter is used with the attenuator but without the 3600-Ω series resistor and is connected across a 600-Ω load in which 1 mW of power is flowing, the movement will be deflected to the 100% calibration point.

This method is not recommended since the impedance looking back into the meter is only 3900 Ω and loads the 600-Ω circuit. It is the usual practice to keep the impedance of bridging devices at a ratio of 10:1 or greater.

Increasing the input impedance of the VU meter from 3900 to 7500 Ω creates a 4-dB loss across the 3600-Ω resistor. If a signal of 1 mW (0.775 V) is impressed across the input terminals of the circuit in Fig. 21-5, it will not deflect the meter to the 0 VU calibration but only to the −4 VU (or decibel) mark, or approximately 65%. This means that if the meter is to be deflected to the 100% point, the input signal must be increased to a +4 dBm. This is the reason why 1 mW of power will be indicated at the −4 calibration mark.

Attenuators used with VU meters start at a +4 dBm. The bridging loss caused by the VU meter being inserted into the circuit is the drop in signal level caused by the absorption of power by the meter circuit. As a rule, the power absorbed is quite small and may be ignored. However, at high powers, it may become important. Bridging loss may be calculated by the equation

$$dB = 20 \log [2B_R + Z)/2B_R] \qquad (21\text{-}1)$$

where,

B_R is the VU meter input impedance,
Z is the line impedance.

A 7500-Ω VU meter has a bridging loss of 0.34 dB.

21.2.4 VU Impedance Level Correction

Since VU meters are calibrated for 1 mW of power across a 600-Ω load as − 4 VU, when a VU meter is connected across any other impedance, a correction must be added to the reading to give a proper VU reading. The equation for the level correction is

$$dB = 10 \log (Z_2/Z_1) \qquad (21\text{-}2)$$

where,

dB is the decibel amount added to the VU reading,
Z_2 is the impedance for which the meter is calibrated,
Z_1 is the impedance of the circuit bridged.

A typical example of applying a correction factor would be as follows: a VU meter calibrated for a line impedance of 600 Ω is bridged across a 16-Ω loudspeaker line and indicates a level of +1 dBm. The true VU would be

$$VU = +1\,dBm + \text{correction factor}$$

The correction factor from Eq. 21-2 is

$$\begin{aligned} dB &= 10 \log 600/16 \\ &= 10(1.574) \\ &= 15.74 \end{aligned}$$

The correction factor of 15.74 dB is added to the meter reading of +1 dBm, for a true level reading of +16.74 dBm. Typical correction factors are shown in Table 21-1.

If a VU meter is connected across a line impedance different from that for which it was originally calibrated, the voltage supplied to the meter will either be lower or higher than the original calibration; therefore, the meter would indicate incorrectly. Two circuits are shown in Fig. 21-6, one a 600-Ω circuit and the other a 16-Ω circuit. Both are dissipating the same amount of power; yet the voltage for the 600-Ω circuit is 0.775 V, and for the 16-Ω circuit it is 0.127 V. As can be seen, if a VU meter is connected across the 16-Ω circuit, it will not deflect the same amount as for the 600-Ω circuit, although the same amount of power is flowing in each circuit. To arrive at the correct

Table 21-1. Correction Factors To Be Applied To a dBm (VU) Meter When Connected Across an Impedance Other Than 600 Ω

Line Impedance, Ω	Meter Cal 600 Ω, dB
10,000	−12.22
5,000	− 9.21
2,500	− 6.20
1,000	− 2.22
600	0.000
500	+ 0.791
250	+ 3.800
200	+ 4.770
150	+ 6.020
125	+ 6.810
100	+ 7.780
50	+10.790
30	+13.010
16	+15.740
15	+16.020
8	+18.750
4	+21.760

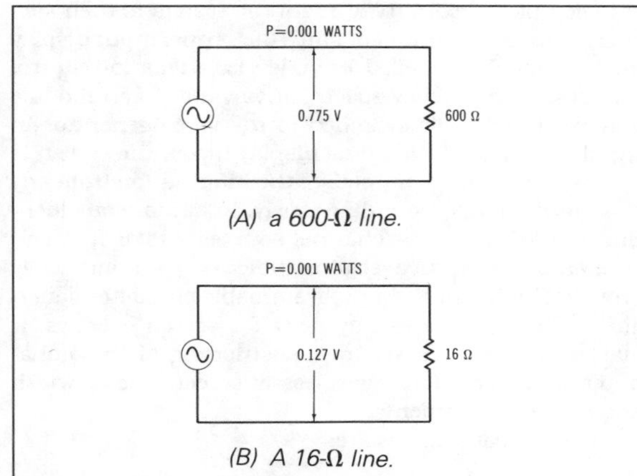

Figure 21-6 Voltage across lines of different impedance but with the same power in milliwatts.

power level in the 16-Ω circuit, a correction factor must be applied to the meter indication.

21.2.5 Voltages at Various Impedances

If the line voltage for a given level at 600 Ω is known, voltages for other line impedances may be calculated using

$$V_x = V\sqrt{Z/600} \qquad (21\text{-}3)$$

where,

V_x is the unknown voltage,
V is the voltage for 600 Ω,
Z is the new impedance.

As an example, assume voltage V_x is required for a line impedance of 150 Ω at a level of +4 dBm. Referring to Fig. 21-7, the voltage for a level of +4 dBm at 600 Ω is 1.23 V. The new voltage may now be calculated using

$$V_x = 1.23\sqrt{150/600} = 0.615\,V$$

Voltages for a line impedance of 600 Ω for levels between 0 and + 50 dBm may be taken from Fig. 21-7. Volts across 600 Ω can be calculated from dBm with the following equation:

$$V = (0.6)\,10^{dBm/10} \qquad (21\text{-}4)$$

21.3 WIDE-RANGE VU METERS

Standard VU meters measure only the upper 23 dB of the signal level. From the practical standpoint, this limits the display to about 20 dB below the reference level of the 0 indication.

This short range of operation limits its usefulness, particularly when it is connected across a bridging bus for monitoring program information. A wide-range program-monitor meter displays the program information over a 60-dB meter scale, spread from −57 to +3 dB. The large spread of program material permits the very low-level signals to be observed as well as the noise between program pauses.

The instrument was not designed to replace the conventional VU meter; however, its characteristics are compatible with the VU meter. In addition, a dc output is provided for connection of a linear tape recorder for logging program levels over a range of 60 dB. The 0-dB indication may be set to represent a reference level from −22 to + 18 dBm.

Referring to the block diagram in Fig. 21-8, the basic component is a logarithmic amplifier, with a nonlinear feedback circuit, a preamplifier, a 15,000-Ω bridging input transformer, a reference-level selector switch, and a sensitive indicating meter movement. The total range of measurement is a −79 to +21 dB, with a frequency response of ±1 dB from 50 to 15,000 Hz.

21.4 LIGHT-EMITTING DIODE VU METERS

A light-emitting diode (LED) VU meter uses LEDs for the display. Fig. 21-9 shows the four-channel VU meter panel on the Altec Lansing 1690 console with nine LEDs

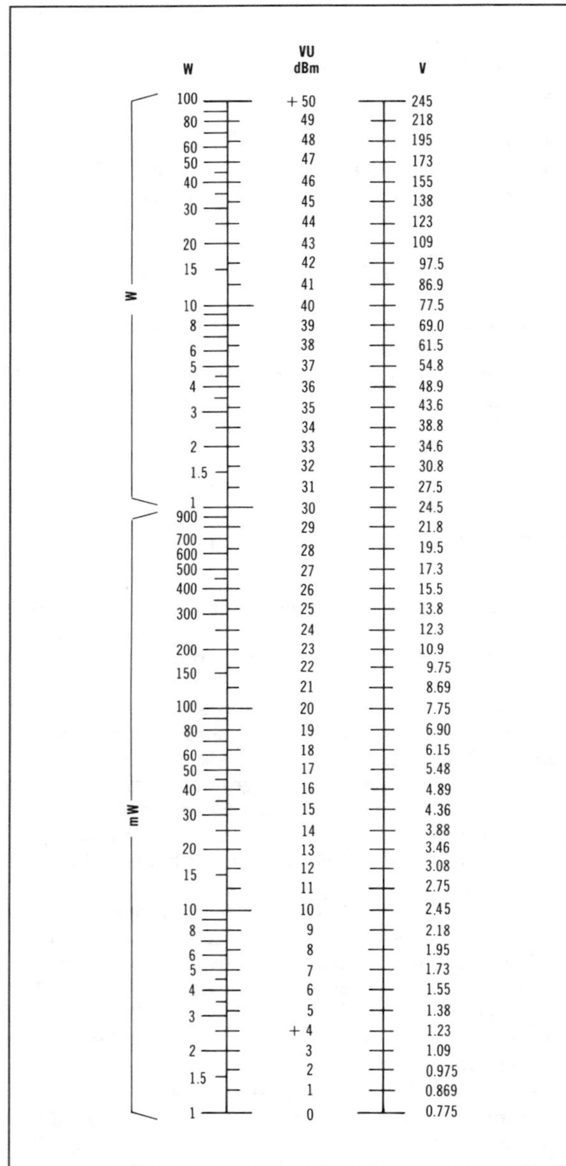

Figure 21-7 Relationship of VU and dBm to power in watts and voltage in a 600-Ω line.

arranged vertically, displaying a dynamic range of 40 dB from −20 to +20 VU. Segments are calibrated at −20, −10, −6, −3, and 0 VU (all green indicators); +3, +6, and +10 VU (yellow indicators); +20 VU (red indicator). The average responding (33-ms time constant) is −20 to +10 VU, and the +20 VU is peak responding with a 50-ms sample-and-hold enhancement. A 0 VU corresponds to a + 4 dBm or 1.23 V across 600 Ω.

21.5 PEAK-READING VU METERS

A peak-reading meter reads the peak level of the applied signal. Because audio signals are not made up of sine waves, standard meters read a value between average and peak. Many instruments have a crest factor of 12 dB or more. To assure the signal is not clipped, a peak reading meter is used. Peak meters respond to the peak value of the signal and are clamped at their maximum level for a period long enough to be read on a meter or a screen.

21.6 BAR GRAPH VU AND SPECTRUM ANALYZERS

The United Recording Electronics Industries (UREI) Model 970 Vidigraf is a bar graph display generator that operates any National Television System Committee (NTSC) standard video monitor or (with an inexpensive accessory) black-and-white television receiver. The system provides both a VU level display and the frequency-spectrum-level information. It is designed primarily for multitrack recording studio applications. However, its dc to 20-kHz input capability suggests its use for a wide range of dc or ac analog voltage measurements.

The 970 Vidigraf's modular construction provides users with complete flexibility to adapt the system to their specific needs. A maximum of four 16-channel input display modules may be installed for VU level, automation control voltages, or frequency-spectrum viewing. Each module may be individually switched to the video generator in the single mode. In the dual display mode, the screen is split vertically to accommodate the information from any two input modules simultaneously. Instantaneous identification of the input channel sources and/or frequencies, as well as vertical scaling indices are automatically provided by the built-in programmable character generators. This eliminates any need for screen overlays or masks and ensures accurate positioning of the alphanumeric information regardless of screen size or width and height adjustments.

Some typical displays are:

16 or 32 simultaneous VU channels.

16 or 2 × 16 bands of frequency spectrum (1 or 2 channels).

16 VU channels, plus channels of automation control voltages.

16 VU channels, plus 15 bands of frequency spectrum and 1 composite level.

A single *VU module* provides 16 bar graphs with standard VU ballistics over a display range of 30 dB. Each bar has two shades of gray, with the lighter shade above 0-dB reference. When a signal is applied to any of the 16 inputs, a bright bar moves up and down with the signal

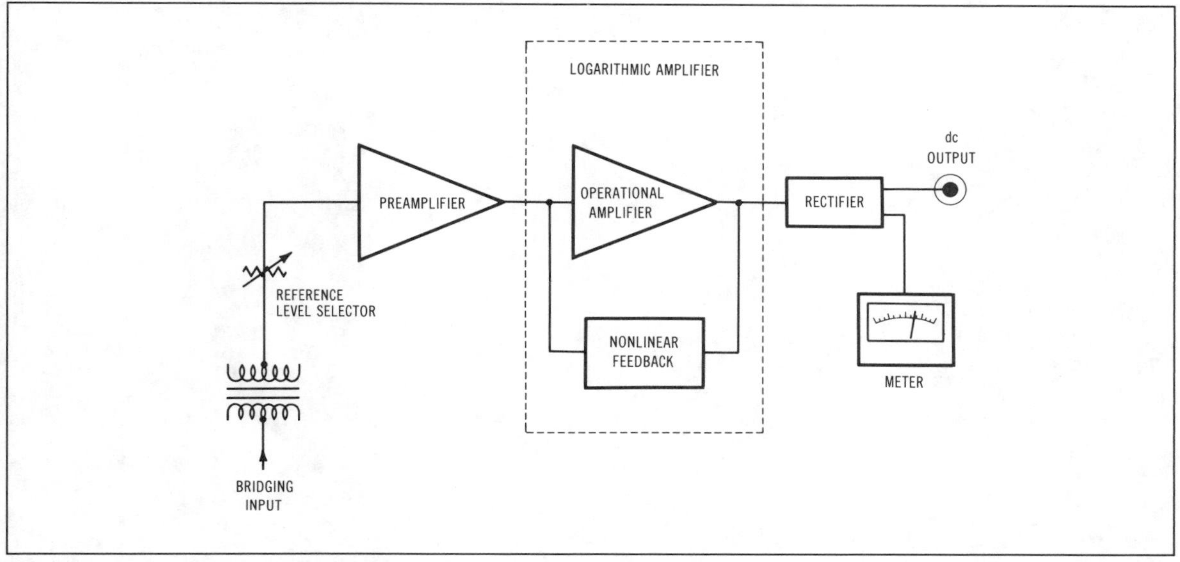

Figure 21-8 Block diagram of a wide-range program—monitor VU meter.

Figure 21-9 Altec Lansing 1690 mixer console with light-emitting diode VU meters in upper right corner. *(Courtesy Altec Lansing Corp.)*

level, clearly visible against the background. The 0-dB reference point is continuously adjustable to any standard from 0 to +8 dB. The signal inputs accept 16 balanced or unbalanced sources, through the module's edge connector. The VU module is user programmable to display a logarithmic scale from −20 to +3 dB when measuring audio signals or to read linearly from 0 to 10 for display of ac or automation dc control voltages. Also user programmable is the nomenclature to be displayed beneath the bars, either 1 through 16 or 17 through 32.

The *spectrum* module provides visual real-time display of VU level versus frequency of an audio signal, as an aid to setting equalization and adjusting frequency balance. This module provides 16 bar graphs with visual characteristics similar to those of the VU module. One bar is assigned to the full spectrum of the audio signal, and the other 15 channels display increments of the frequency spectrum, centered on standard ISO two-thirds-octave filter frequencies. Nomenclature and scales are user programmable. Additionally the display may be visually identified as channel A or channel B. Two independent controls adjust the level of the full spectrum bar relative to the spectrum analysis bars.

A *remote control center* is available as an accessory. It duplicates all front panel operating controls of the Vidigraf for convenient operation at a recording console for other remote locations.

BIBLIOGRAPHY

H. M. Tremaine, *Audio Cyclopedia*, Indianapolis: Howard W. Sams & Co., Inc., 1969.

CHAPTER **22**

Consoles and Systems

by Steve Dove

The establishment of consoles was a slow and gradual process. Similarly, *systems*—or pre-organized arrangements of devices—evolved slowly, too. In most audio work the two are now considered as almost synonymous; the greatest departure from this is the inclusion of a console as part of a system. But even then, there is no doubting that the console is the heart of the system.

The history of consoles reaches back to the time when the recording process was purely mechanical (Fig. 22-1) and then to its electrical analog (Fig. 22-2) which includes a source transducer (in this instance a microphone), a means of gain (an amplifier), and an output transducer (a disk-cutting head). It doesn't take a staggering amount of imagination to extend this system to embrace other applications: public address; acoustic enhancement of natural sound by electronic means (Fig. 22-3); disk replay (Fig. 22-4); and broadcasting by replacement of a simple electromechanical transducer by a radio transmitter (Fig. 22-5). So it goes on. The objective of the system is to facilitate the transfer of a signal from one source—be it a simple transducer or another system—to another.

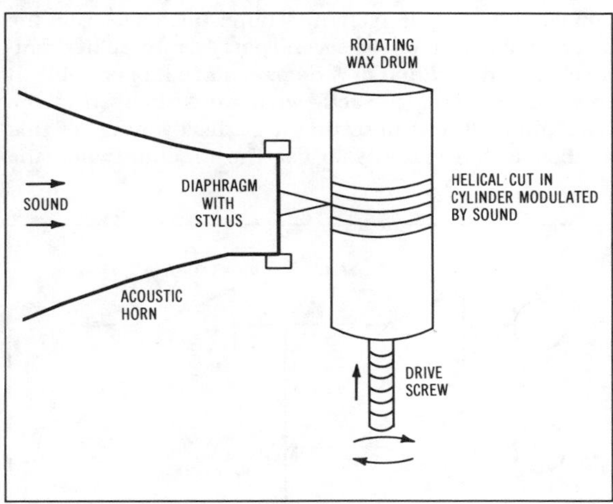

Figure 22-1 Mechanical recording or early drum recording.

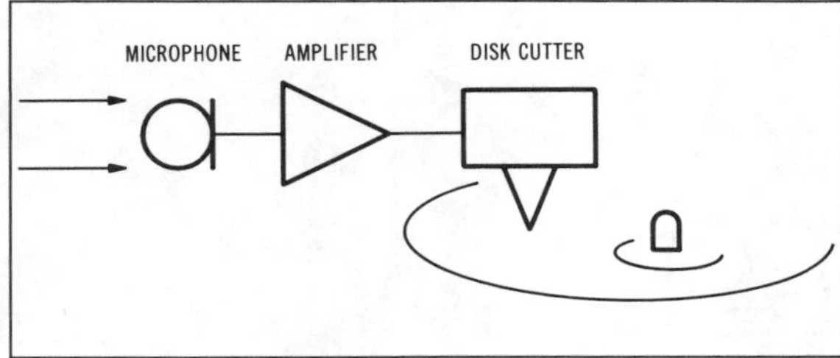

Figure 22-2 Electrical recording (disk cutter driven by electricity).

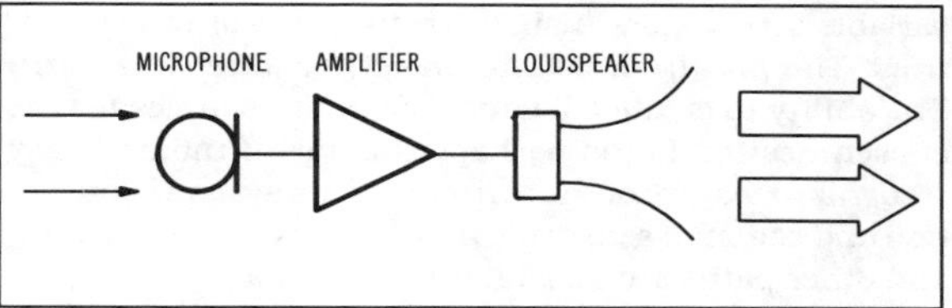

Figure 22-3 Public address system.

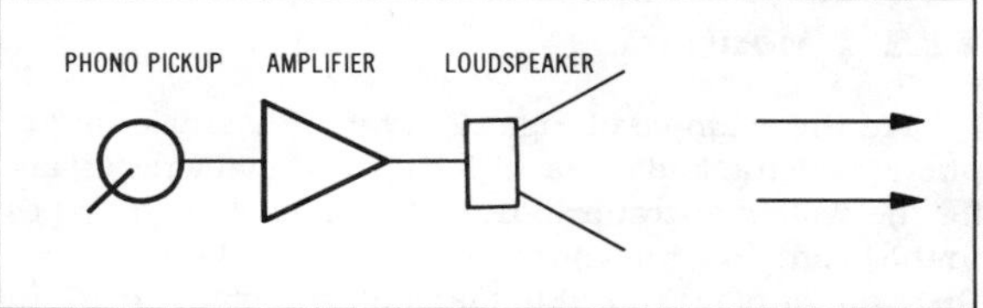

Figure 22-4 Disk replay.

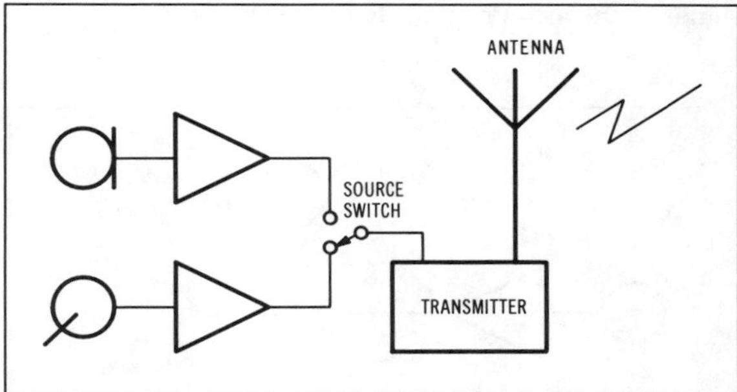

Figure 22-5 Simplified broadcast system.

Of course things get a bit more complex than that, and to demonstrate this complexity, the evolution of what is probably the most important subsystem to our industry—*tape recording*—will be used to explain how it, almost single-handedly, made everything as wretchedly complex as it is now. Disks were a bit permanent. You got it right or you didn't. Tape at least gave the chance of "one more take."

Mixing in the early days of system development was surprisingly easily achieved—just cobbling together the outputs of the various source input amplifiers did it perfectly adequately. It's important to understand that the technology of the day facilitated this simplicity far more, paradoxically, than today's gear. Tube amplifiers, such as were then used, needed to be terminated at their outputs by a specific impedance for proper operation, which for reasons discussed later was universally 600-Ω floating balanced. By simply connecting amplifier outputs together, a mix of sources was achieved, provided each of the source amplifiers saw 600 Ω. It was only a very minor step for interspersed networks to become constant-impedance variable attenuators, usually in the form of rotary controls. The *pot* (from potentiometer) or *fader* was born. The ability to create a balance of sundry sources for the chosen destination is perhaps the most fundamentally recognized feature of the console and its system. Convention and common sense rule this as the *main signal path*, and other paths are subsidiary or auxiliary to it.

22.1 AUXILIARY PATHS

21.1.1 Monitoring

Take the example of Fig. 22-6, where a single microphone is being laid on tape. It's operationally necessary for the system operator to hear the signal going to tapes in the headphones or control-room monitor loudspeaker; therefore, a parallel feed is taken off the machine input to the operator's monitoring. *Monitoring* is perhaps the most important of the auxiliary signal paths, for upon it are based the qualitative decisions of the nature of the signal in the *main path*. It is the reference.

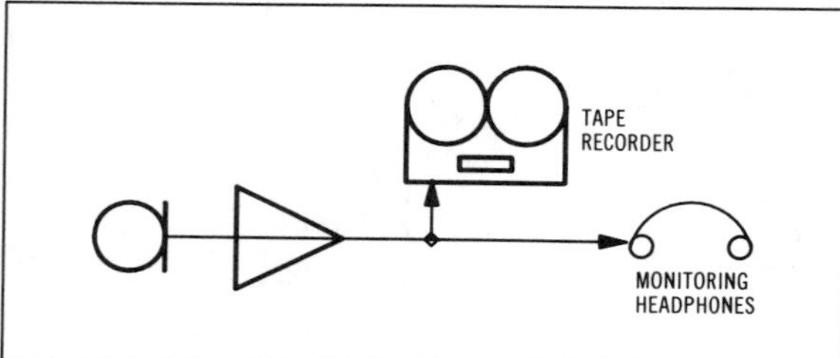

Figure 22-6 Simple microphone-to-tape monitoring (source only).

Fig. 22-7 applies a small extension to the basic monitoring path in the form of a *source/replay switch*, enabling operators to hear the aftermath of their efforts! If the recorder has separate record and play heads and electronics, they can even toggle between them while actually recording for immediate quality assessment. The *monitoring section* is born.

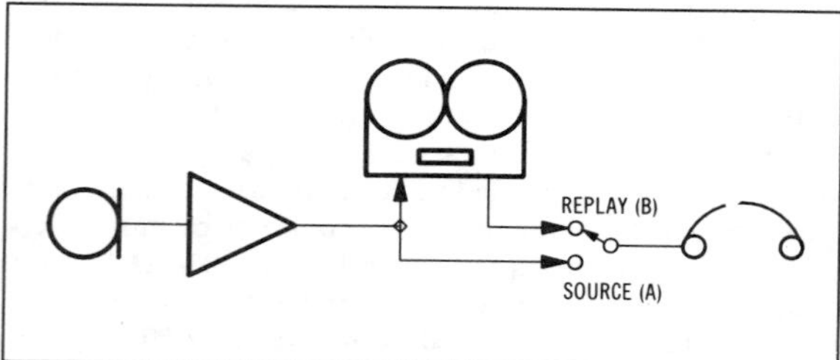

Figure 22-7 Tape monitoring (source and tape)

22.1.2 Prefade Listen and Audition

When a multiple-source system is established (similar to Fig. 22-8), another monitoring requirement, prefade listen (PFL) and audition, soon rear their heads. Imagine the case of a radio broadcaster, where the sources consist of disk replay units and microphones; it's an obvious necessity to be able to listen to a source prior to its being put on air to check that (1) the microphone is set at the correct position, level, or even working! Or (2) that the required section of a disk or tape is cued-up or ready to play. There are two basic methods of arranging this prehear function, as shown in Fig. 22-9. They owe their existence primarily to slightly different operating practices on opposite sides of the Atlantic. The first (Fig. 22-9A) involves switching the signal immediately prior to the fader on the selected source path into the monitoring chain. This is called *prefade listen (PFL)*. A useful but not immediately obvious virtue of this arrangement is that it is possible to listen to a channel's contribution to a mix of which it is part without disturbing that mix. It is, therefore, a *nondestructive monitoring function*. The alternative method shown in Fig. 22-9B consists of removing the required channel (after the fader) from the mix and placing it onto a second parallel mix facility commonly called *audition* or *rehearse*, since it is possible in this mix to emulate exactly what would happen in the "real" mix without upsetting it. A disadvantage of this method is the inability to use the function when the

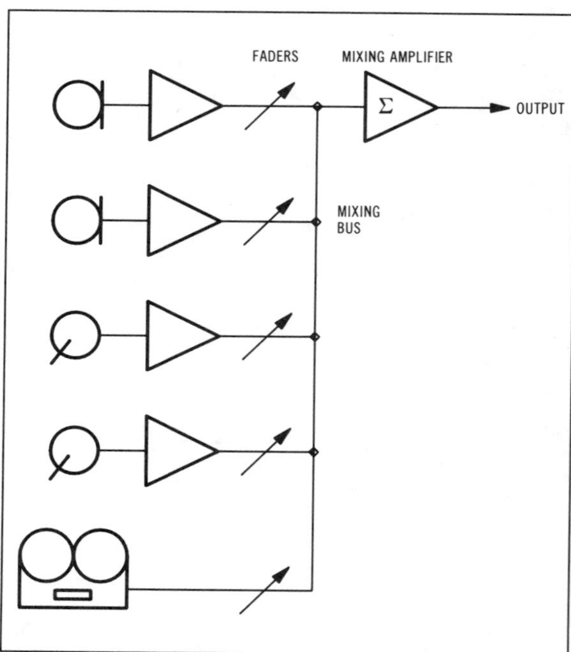

Figure 22-8 Multisource mixer.

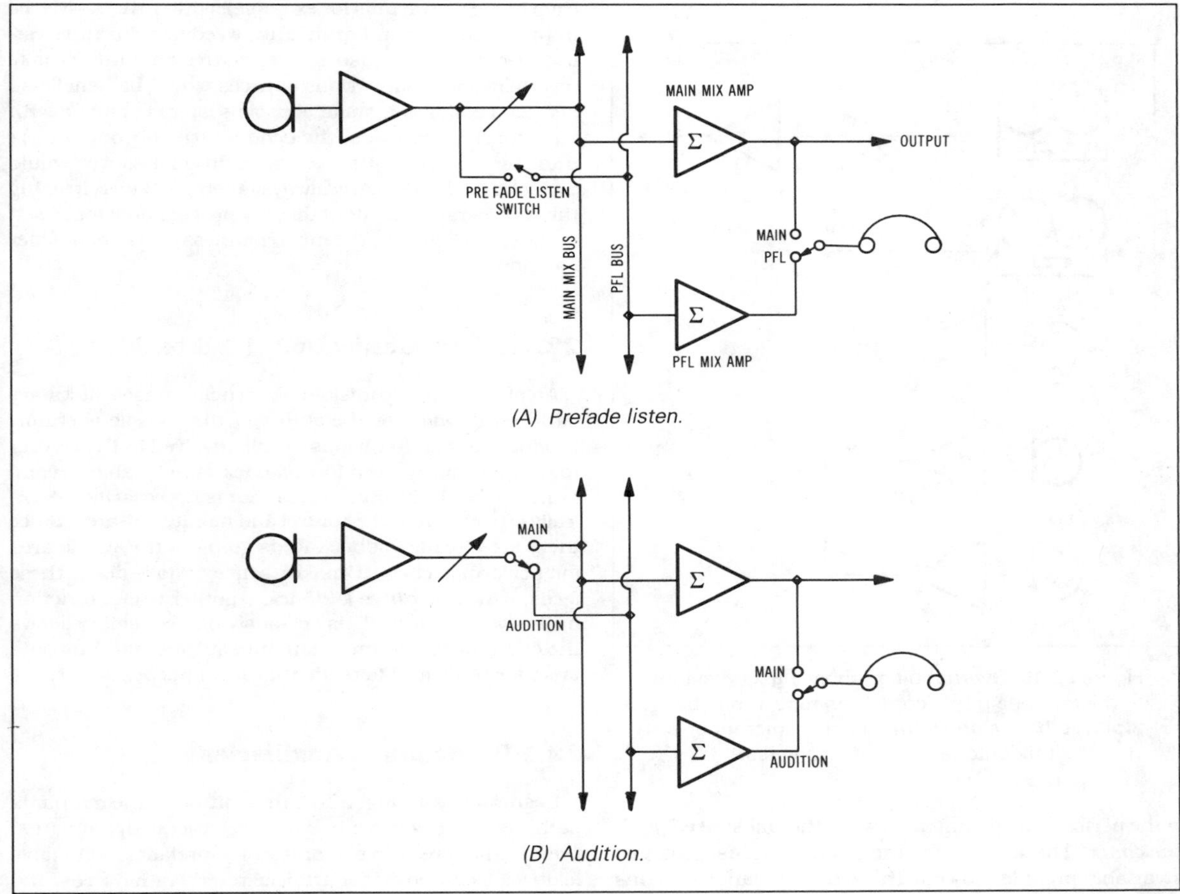

Figure 22-9 Prefade listen (PFL) and audition.

channel is live since it would disrupt that source going to the mix. It is a *destructive* monitoring technique. Each method has its virtues, though, and most modern consoles use both techniques to an extent.

22.1.3 Overdubbing and Foldback

While broadcasting lends itself to explaining the need for individual channel monitoring, original material generation onto tape serves best to explain another crucial auxiliary signal path.

It didn't take long before studios were using more than one tape machine in a technique known as *overdubbing*. Briefly, this involved recording a *backing track* (say a rhythm section) on one machine, then playing that back while vocalists or soloists sang or played along with it; the whole was mixed together and recorded on a second machine, Fig. 22-10. This could be carried on ad nauseam or until the subsequent machine-to-machine generation losses became too objectionable (although that never seemed to bother many early producers!). Naturally, it was essential that the musicians in the studio were able to hear via loudspeakers or headphones that to which they were supposedly playing along; this is where *foldback* comes in. In its simplest form, it could be a straight derivative of the main mix output, since this output has basically everything necessary in it. This system, however, has a few shortcomings due primarily to conflicts between what the final mix is intended to be and what the artist(s) needs to hear to perform satisfactorily. A prime example of this dilemma is in the recording of backing vocalists' sections; usually they take a fairly minor part in a mix, being balanced well down. Contrary to this is the need of the vocalists to not only hear the track played back to them but to hear themselves sufficiently well—usually enhanced—to pitch and phrase themselves effectively. These conditions are next to impossible at the final mix. A solution lies in Fig. 22-11 where a separate balance of the relevant sources is taken and fed separately

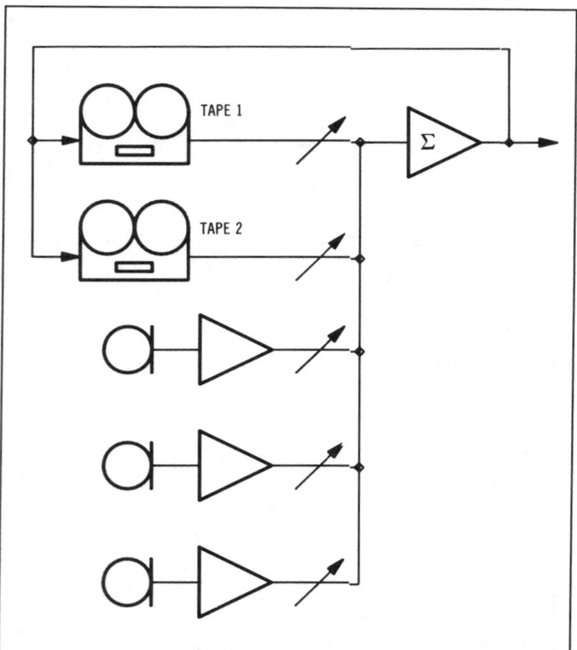

Figure 22-10 Overdubbing/'bouncing', a previous microphone mix recorded on tape 1 may be played back along with a further microphone mix onto tape 2 and vice versa.

to the performers, giving them what they most need, *foldback mix*. The take-off for the foldback feeds is almost invariably prefader so that the artist's balance remains unaffected regardless of what machinations may be necessary for the main mix.

22.1.4 Echo and Effects Send

The move (regrettable as it may seem) from natural performing acoustic environments to the more cultured, drier, closer mic'ed techniques brought with it a hoard of problems attendant to the advantages. How do you make a sound seem as though it were recorded in Albert Hall if it was done in a broom closet? Reverberant chambers were an initial answer, being relatively small rooms acoustically treated (or neglected!) to have an extended reverberation time (bathroom effect). Driven obliquely at one end or corner by a loudspeaker and sensed by a microphone at the other end, which is amplified and balanced into to the main mix, a fairly convincing large room reverberant effect can be achieved. Simplistically, all that's needed to feed the loudspeaker in this room is a derivation of the main mix, but similar to the problems with foldback mixes, artistic judgments dictate something more complex. Some instruments and sounds benefit greatly from being dry (drums for example), while others—vocals in particular—sound quite arid, weedy, and uninteresting. A means of adjusting the relative amounts of fake reverberation from various sources would be beneficial. Fig. 22-12 shows a small console system complete with an *echo send* mix bus; the *echo return* is brought back into the main mix just as any additional source would be. Echo feeds are nearly always taken postfader, keeping the reverberation content directly proportional (once set) to the clean signal in the mix regardless of the main fader position.

22.1.5 Communications (Talkback)

An often mentally mislaid but crucial console auxiliary path is *talkback*, or the ability of the console operator/producer to talk to various people involved in the recording. The primary need for talkback is to be able to communicate with the studio area that is necessarily acoustically separate from the control and monitoring area. Since there are already foldback feeds going to the studio area for performer cues, it makes sense to talk down these feeds, which is *talk to foldback*. Another useful function in this vein is *slate*. This curiously named facility allows the operator to talk into main mix output and thus onto tape, for track and take identification purposes.

22.1.6 Combined Auxiliaries

In summary, in Fig. 22-12 in addition to the main mix path, a usable console has to have several signal paths: overall and presource monitoring, prefader adjustable foldback feeds, postfader artificial reverberation feeds, and communication (talkback) feeds.

22.2 STEREO CONSOLES

Stereo predated multitrack recording, but technically the required console techniques were not very far removed from those just described. Assuming the same bouncing (machine-to-machine overlay and transfer system described earlier in the section on overdubbing), stereo just means two of everything in the main signal path.

22.2.1 Panning

Panning is the technique of positioning a single (monophonic) source within a stereophonic image. It isn't true stereo, which can only be achieved from coincidentally aligned microphones, but panned mono. Simply, the ear is deceived by pure level differences between the left and right paths of a stereo pair into perceiving differing image position; fortunately for the entire industry, this is a trick

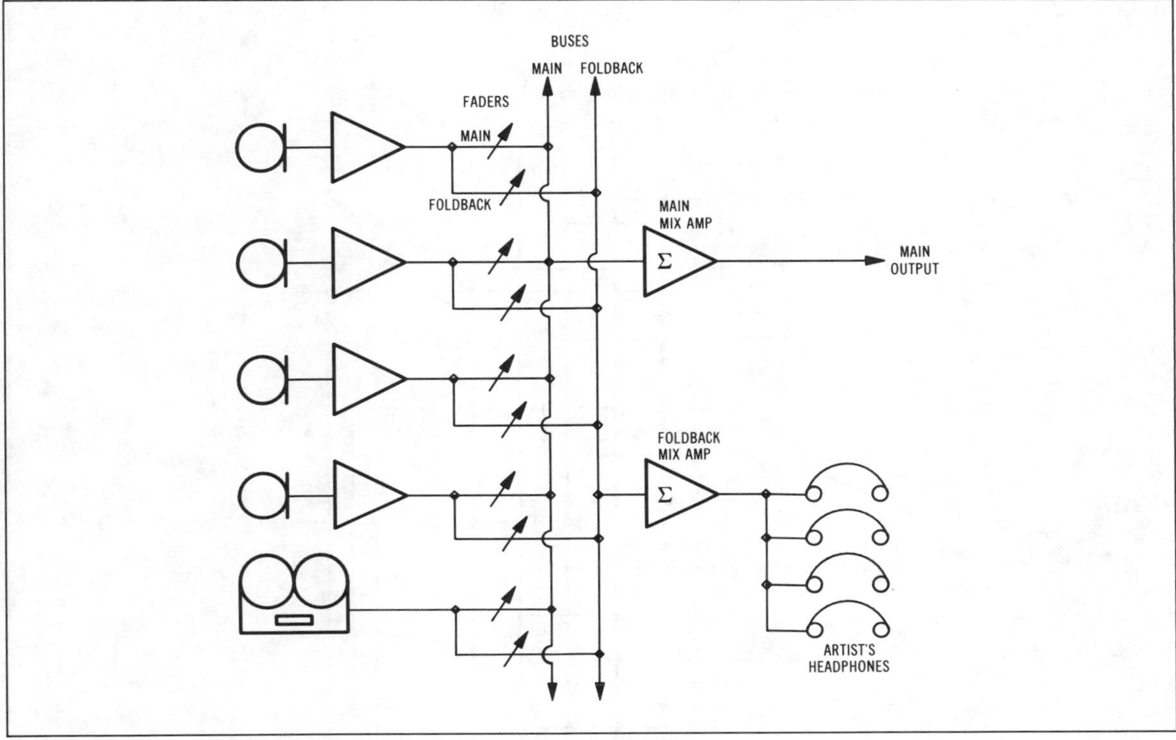

Figure 22-11 Foldback mix.

quite simply realized. Complementary attenuators (one increasing attenuation, one reducing with rotation) feeding the L and R mix paths from a mono source is the most common method, as Fig. 22-13A elucidates. The *panpot* is generally inserted after the source fader. An alternative arrangement shown in Fig. 22-13B with the panpot prior to the fader demands a ganged matched fader. This arrangement can be useful, however, when stereo PFL is required, although there are other ways of achieving stereo in-place monitoring for sources, as will be shown later.

22.2.2 Auxiliaries for Stereo

Auxiliary paths remain largely untouched by the upgrade to stereo of the main mix path; the monitoring section stays just the same in systemic function (but obviously with two paths instead of one to cope with stereo feeds. Both the prefader foldback and PFL take-offs are still in mono. The postfader *echo-send feed* is usually taken out before the main path panpot, so they remain mono, but the returns pass through their own panpots such that the reverberant image may also be spatially determined in the mix. It's become quite normal practice to make echo-send feeds stereo in their own right, (Fig. 22-14) via their own panpots' mixing to two outputs. Many reverberation rooms and reverberation plates are capable of supporting a diffuse stereo field. The purpose of this is to excite the reverberant chamber (or plate or springs or little black box) spatially, conjuring a more solid and credible reverberative effect in the main mix. If a panned echo-send output isn't available, it's common to use a pair of separate postfader feeds and juggle the levels between them.

22.2.3 Multiple-Effect Feeds

In the present day there is a whole gamut of electronic "toys" applied to mixdown to achieve specific sounds: harmonizers®, delays, flangers, phasers, automatic panners, artificial reverberators of various sorts, and so on. These all need to be fed from their own effects mix paths. Similarly, studio foldback mixes have grown more profuse with changing music, increasing musician sophistication and awareness of studio techiniques; consequently, the number of auxiliary mixes within modern consoles has risen quickly. A rationalization of this is to make those auxiliary mixes multipurpose, usually by allowing them to be switchable between prefader and postfader feed on their appropriate sources.

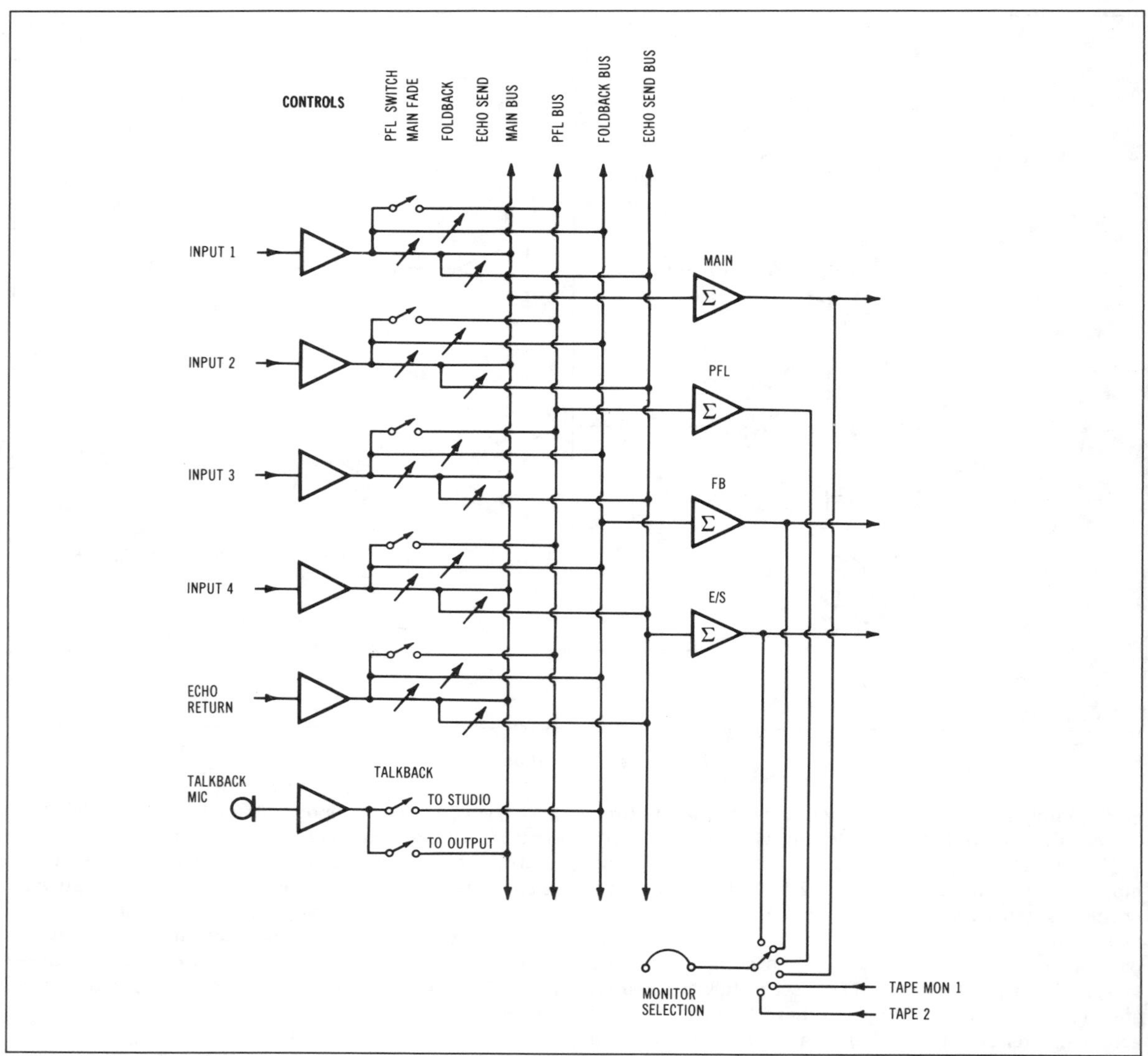

Figure 22-12 Small mixer system showing auxiliary functions.

22.3 DAWNING OF MULTITRACK

Multitrack operation is when a number of separate parts of the recording are laid onto separate tracks on a tape machine, and subsequently remixed down onto another machine (be it mono or stereo) or even interim onto spare tracks on the same machine.

Stereo recording using two-track tape technology seemed to many to be the zenith of professional audio. Many will argue the point even today. There is inescapable evidence of that opinion's validity in that some of the finest stereo recordings, especially of classical works, were done using fundamental microphone techniques straight onto two track. Even in the field of pop records from a technical standpoint, the final master represents the first generation of the last overlay. (In retrospect that is an advantage over contemporary multitracking where the master is at best the second generation of everything.)

Multitrack soon reared its head(s?) in the early 1960s initially as three track and four track across 1 in. tape; there are those who regard *that* as the zenith. Although their argument relies on a slightly stretched point (many

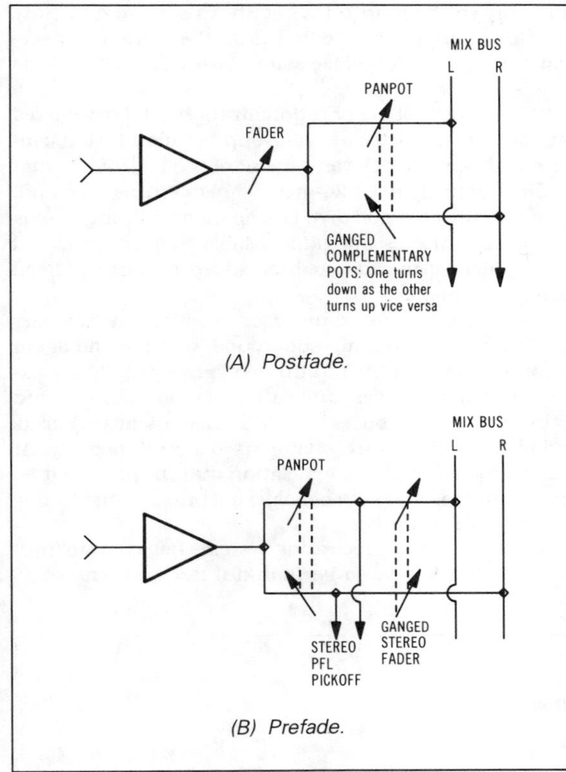

Figure 22-13 Panpots.

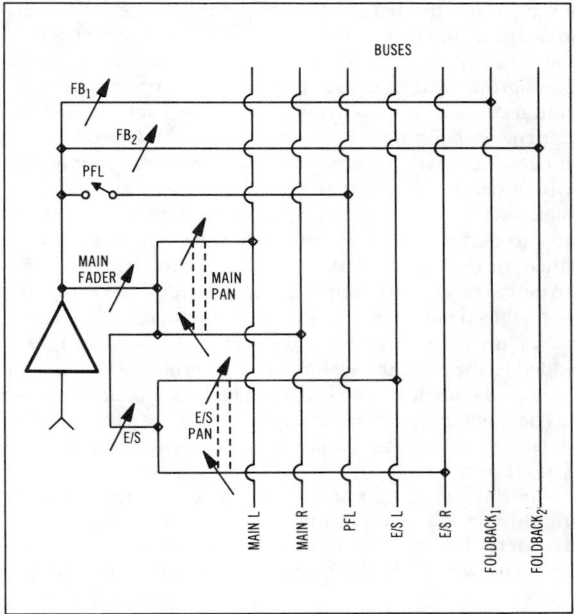

Figure 22-14 Channel feeds showing foldback and stereo echo-send feeds.

parts were done on a pair of loosely synced four-track Studer J-37s), comparing a quick 1967 burst of "A Day in the Life" with most of today's "Meisterwerks" does rather put things in perspective. How much more technology is needed for what?

Three track afforded a great advantage over two track for modern music producers at the time. Two-track recordings were always hampered by the need to make sure that all the earlier things done in a bouncing sequence were right to begin with; there was no chance of subsequently altering them. Three-track recordings, typically in a "Track/Vocals/The Rest" format, took a little of that pressure away. Already producers and performers were taking advantage of the multilayered production approach to take the heat out of recording; it was no longer necessary for everyone from lead vocalist to third trianglist to be present all at once for a momentous occasion. Bits could be done one at a time. The extension to this given by multitrack is simple to see: the more tracks, the smaller those bits need be and the fewer things needed to be incontrovertibly mixed. Putting off the day of reckoning—the final mixdown—is one of the strongest appeals of multitrack.

22.4 GROUPING AND THE MONITORING SECTION

Each signal source in the console needs some *routing* to determine the machine track on which it is going to end up. It's a situation that hardly existed previously, since it was pretty sure that the mono or stereo output of the console was going to go straight to the respective mono/stereo inputs on the tape machine(s). There were on a stereo console just two *groups* where all the sources were summed together; for multitrack as many groups as there are tape tracks are switch selectable from the sources—any source to any machine track. The alternative hard way, patching everything across on a jackfield, was and is exceedingly tedious, messy, and expensive.

Four track set the mold for console design for many years. The *monitoring section* evolved. Fig. 22-15 can be compared to the simpler back-end of a stereo mixer in Fig. 22-12. The main difference can be seen as the addition of an entirely separate mixer within the console just to handle the multitrack monitoring. Fortunately, it's a fairly bare-bones mixer; it's all at high signal levels, and little, if any, gain is required except as makeup gain in the monitor mix bus.

While all these tracks are being laid, it's necessary to hear what has been done previously in the control room and studio. In the same way that source/return listen of stereo machines was needed, so each individual track of a multitrack needed similar treatment. It grew, though. Initially, as the number of tracks per machine increased, the number of mixer groups increased correspondingly. Each group had its own A/B switch relating to that individual console track output and the associated machine return, with its own level and pan controls feeding an altogether separate stereo monitor mix. This new *monitor mix* appeared as another source on the main monitor selector. This, alas, was insufficient. Foldback prefade mix feeds no longer became a luxury but a necessity, since the desk stereo output or a derivation thereof could no longer be relied upon to be even roughly what the artist needed to hear. There *was* no proper console stereo output at any time other than mixdown. Foldback feeds were added to the monitor system on each group. Effect sends were also added, just to let the monitoring sound pretty.

The monster has split itself amoebalike into two entirely separate signal-processing systems: the main mixer and a monitor mixer.

A curious situation occurs: the mix used for monitoring during the original multitrack recording had to be transferred over to the main system entirely at some time for mixdown. Ordinarily, tape-machine returns are not only brought back into the monitoring section but are also tied to high-level line inputs on the main mixer section. The remix takes place using those channels into the main stereo mix bus.

Perhaps the first major rationalization (which occurred long after many X-input, 24-group, 24-monitoring consoles had been made) was a result of the realization that we don't actually need 24-group faders sitting there full up, collecting dust and dirt. Losing them instantly avoids a normally unnecessary gain-variable stage in the signal path, which, if maladjusted, could upset noise or head room performance.

Individual channel outputs together with a much smaller number of stereo mixing subgroups, which could again be routed to any of the multitracks, proves easily as flexible. But still there was duplication of monitor buses and main stereo mixing buses both with their attendant effects and foldback feeds rarely being used simultaneously. At least the dawning of the realization that the pair, that is, the monitoring and stereo mastering buses, could be one and the same thing.

In-line monitoring recording systems had come to fitful fruition. We all have to be thankful for the cranks and

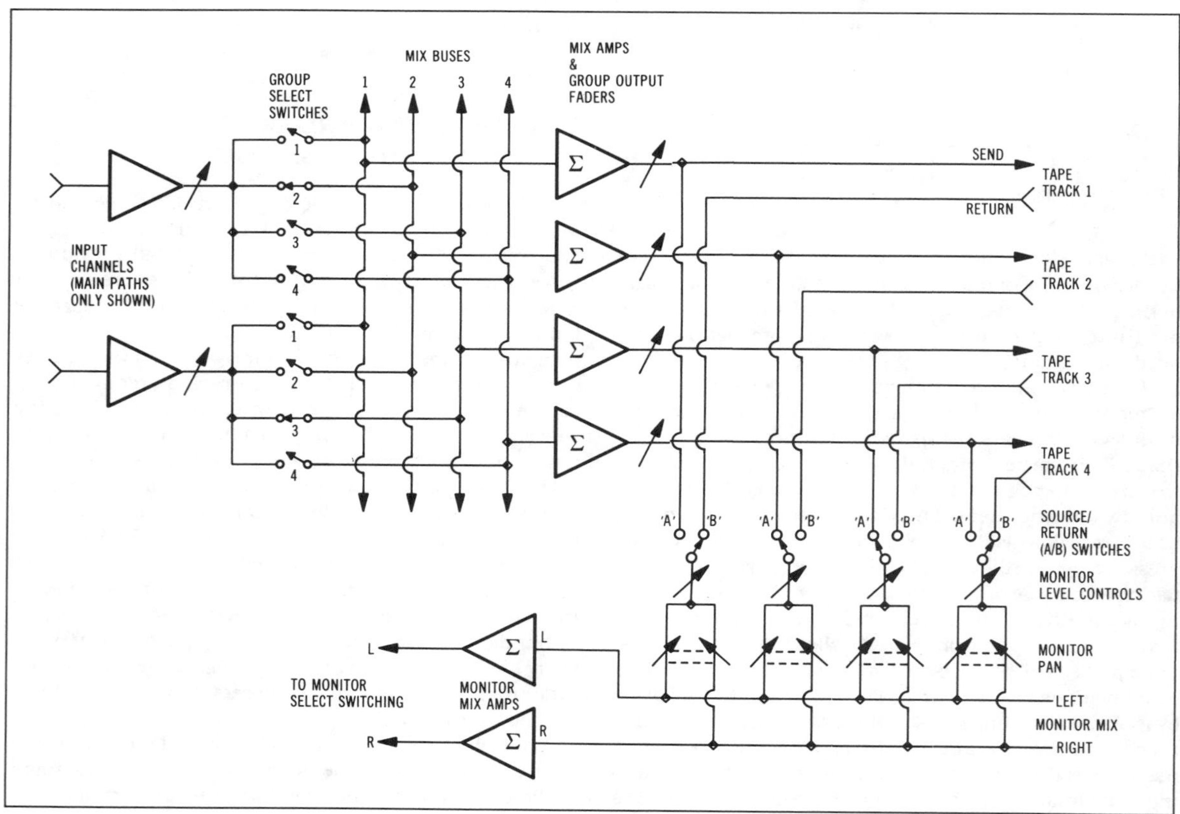

Figure 22-15 Four-track monitoring.

visionaries along the way (often the same) who have manipulated or shocked the industry into grudgingly lurching back into step with technology's capability. These milestones represent significant plateaus of thinking that point the way to today's console concepts.

22.5 CONSOLE DESIGN DEVELOPMENTS

Two distinct considerations interplay in determining the ability of a console to fulfill a given appplication. These two, the system and the electronics, have entirely differing parameters that need to be defined but are, nevertheless, completely indivisible.

The electronics, as much as being designed to perform required functions, have been very carefully designed not to be a major influence on the sound of the console. Most causes of sonic disturbance can be attributed or predicted, and still dubious circuit configurations can be avoided altogether. To the shock of some purists, commonly available integrated circuit operational amplifiers are used throughout. The reasons why (other than the obvious convenience) together with the reasons why they acquired a bad reputation are treated in depth in section 22.6.

Operational amplifiers, known as *op-amps*, have in recent years revolutionized the concepts and systems capability of full-performance audio consoles. Allowing system elements to be thought of, designed, and implemented as building blocks simplifies matters considerably, but it also entertains the valid criticism that console design can be relegated to a "do-it-by-numbers" status. Fortunately, device idiosyncrasies, subleties, and the entirely separate science of getting heaps of individual system elements to behave successfully as a total console prevent this.

Fortunately for the console industry, the large proportion of the current console manufacturers started off in life as small groups of studio engineers furtively constructing mixers for their own ends, resulting in grassroots system design owing everything to immediate operational needs. Continuing in this vein in production, the manufacturers are listening to and, most importantly, relating to customer needs because they've played this game for themselves.

Once upon a not so distant time, systems and mixers as such didn't exist. All the bits of electronics used in the control room sat there with all their inputs and outputs accessible by way of a jackfield for the prosperous or by small screwdriver and sore knees for those who weren't.

Mixing sources was accomplished by directly paralleling amplifier outputs (possible because all the old tubed gear has a finite and predictable output impedance usually arranged to be a conventional balanced 600 Ω) and either hoping or arranging that the destination had enough gain in hand to make up the accrued loss. Crude as that may seem today from an engineering viewpoint, it has a sheen of pure elegance. An amplifier was just that, a box that had a balanced 600-Ω source and termination impedances. It might also have an alternative bridging (> 10 kΩ) input terminal and a selectable amount of gain and universal application from microphone amplifiers through mixing amplifiers to headphone amplifiers. To do more things, more boxes were added. Equalizers and limiters, a treasured few if there were any, were similarly universally applicable. Variable-level control was again attained by true balanced 600-Ω source, and termination, via studded rotary attenuators. The utter beauty of the systemless studio was that anything could go to anywhere via anything else and be mixed or distributed at any point on the way.

Soon enough amplifiers were hardwired to attenuators and designated specifically a *microphone amplifier* or whatever, and a system had been created. Some of these together with a mixing gain makeup amplifier were thrown in a box. The mixer was born.

It has been downhill all the way since, with ever-increasing numbers of system elements being tied together in increasingly knotted manners in order to maintain some kind of flexibility. In other words, a system can be defined as a means of reducing the ultimate versatility of its constituent parts.

Once a *mixer* was accepted as a system element itself, the problem set in further. There was no need to provide for convenient connection of its internal interconnections to the outside world, so the balancing transformers disappeared, and more economic alternatives to the stud attenuators operating at more convenient internal impedances evolved. By a more positive token, the electronics were gradually becoming optimized for specific functions to which they were designated, such as the microphone amplifier and the mixing amplifier. (The question nags us whether a universal amplifier, by now all but obsolete, could be optimized for all the varying requirements.) Still, at least all the inputs and outputs of the mixer were conventional. This held true until the slow demise of tubes in professional audio.

22.5.1 Transistors

Transistors were justifiably unpopular for a long time because of the numerous limitations they placed upon design: headroom was severely limited because of the low supply voltages that could be applied to the early devices. They were noisy, the lower operating impedances and differing modes to tubes took some getting used to, and when they clipped, they actually clipped rather than gracefully bending (characteristic of tubes that people had known, loved, and frequently taken advantage of). To realize a reasonably low stage distortion, many transistors in compound configurations using heavy amounts of negative feedback were used—a far cry from a single tube stage operating virtually wide open with little feedback. This gave rise to a peculiar phenomenon that sounded as if it hailed from science fiction—*zero impedance*.

The heavy negative voltage feedback employed around transistor circuits could be made to render the output of an amplifier insensitive to varying load impedances; they would deliver the same output voltage level almost regardless of their termination impedance. This eliminated the termination problems with the attendant worry of compensating in level for differing load hookups. With the exception of long-line feeds, 600-Ω terminations were dead. High-level balanced inputs were now almost exclusively bridging; they had a sufficiently high impedance (usually > 10 kΩ) not to disturb the level of the source to which they were tacked on. For better or worse, it has become the conventional studio interconnection technology. It has taken until fairly recently for a distinction and separate level specification for the two technologies to be accepted.

22.5.2 Level Specifications

The original *transmission line level specification* referred to a power level of 1 mW at whatever the impedance was. It was a universal specification applicable to any signal of any frequency being transmitted along any bit of wire for any purpose at any rated impedance, and it is used extensively in radio-frequency work and other things entirely unrelated to audio. The dBm definition is sacred and can't be changed. Zero dBm in a 600-Ω load works out to 0.775 V rms; this was adopted de facto as the reference for use in general audio work. With zero impedance technology, although the working voltage is specified, the impedance isn't. It can be anything, as long as the power varies; 0.775 V rms across say a 100-Ω load works out at +7.78 dBm while across 10 kΩ it would be −12.22 dBm.

The reference level for zero impedance thinking is a voltage, and the one chosen is the familiar 0.775 V rms with which everyone was used to dealing. That voltage is distinguished as 0 dBu. Some have tried to impose the universal reference based around a voltage level of 1 V called the dBV for audio, which made some sums nice and easy, looked neat, and proved confusing to anyone brought up on the dBm.

22.6 OPERATIONAL AMPLIFIERS IN CONSOLES

Consoles utilizing integrated circuit operational amplifiers (IC op-amps) have suffered from a curious syndrome, collecting in the early days a (sometimes deserved) dreadful reputation, which has stuck.

This section is an attempt to explain the history, shortcomings, and attributes of IC op-amps from conception to present day; to point out how some shortcomings are overcome; and to provide reassurance that there is nothing really evil about those square black spiders after all. It is also an example to those prone to ill-informed wistful opining that this, along with most other technology, is well understood and quantified, the concepts if not the details having been defined many years ago.

Many years ago, I remember deeply coveting then eventually giving in and forking out nearly five late-1960s Pounds Sterling for a tiny transistor-sized eight-legged queer-thing. At long last I actually held between quivering fingers a real, live Fairchild μA709!

This breakthrough opened up whole new avenues of creative ways to generate spurious oscillations. Many happy (and otherwise) hours were spent trying to get the wretched thing to do anything other than squeal, hiss, and squeg. Never the most stable of creatures, the 709, once tamed, provided a faltering education in the idiosyncrasies of op-amp circuit design. My first 709 expired as I attempted to drive +15 dBu into a screwdriver. Output stage protection was not one of its notable strong points.

At this stage in the game, discrete transistor circuitry still ruled supreme in audio. The new-fangled ICs were eventually compensated sufficiently to remain operationally stable, but little high-frequency loop gain remained to guarantee enough feedback for adequately low high-frequency distortion. Also, they were very noisy. Although their parameters could be set up to be acceptable for any set application and gain setting, the very nature of control in consoles is variable, so the devices would almost inevitably end up operating away from their optimum.

Hot on the heels of the 709 came the now much-loved-and-despised, but always revered, 741. Best known in its plastic encapsulated eight-pin dual in-line incarnation, it still took our industry many years to catch on to the fact that here existed a seemingly almost vice-free op-amp. Well, at least, it was free of some of the 709s vices. It was heavily internally compensated so it was stable, but the penalty for this was rapidly disappearing open-loop gain with increasing frequency. There was just enough gain left to get away with 20 dB of broadband gain safely over a 20-kHz bandwidth.

Some IC manufacturers came up with pleasant 741s, which were usably quiet and did not have output offset voltage problems on the scale of earlier devices. The 741 was also output-protected to the extent of being short-circuit proof, much to the relief of all.

Subsequent generations of op-amps to the 709 included the 748 (the uncompensated sister to the 741) and the 301, again, some versions of which were excellent for the class of device. The 748 and 301 being user compensated did allow for more optimal parameter setting and in most circuits only required one capacitor to achieve this (as opposed to the necessary two-resistor/capacitor networks for the 709).

This, although on the surface appearing to be of great convenience to the user, disguised the fact that far superior bandwidth and phase-margin performance could be obtained by carefully considering the nature of the com-

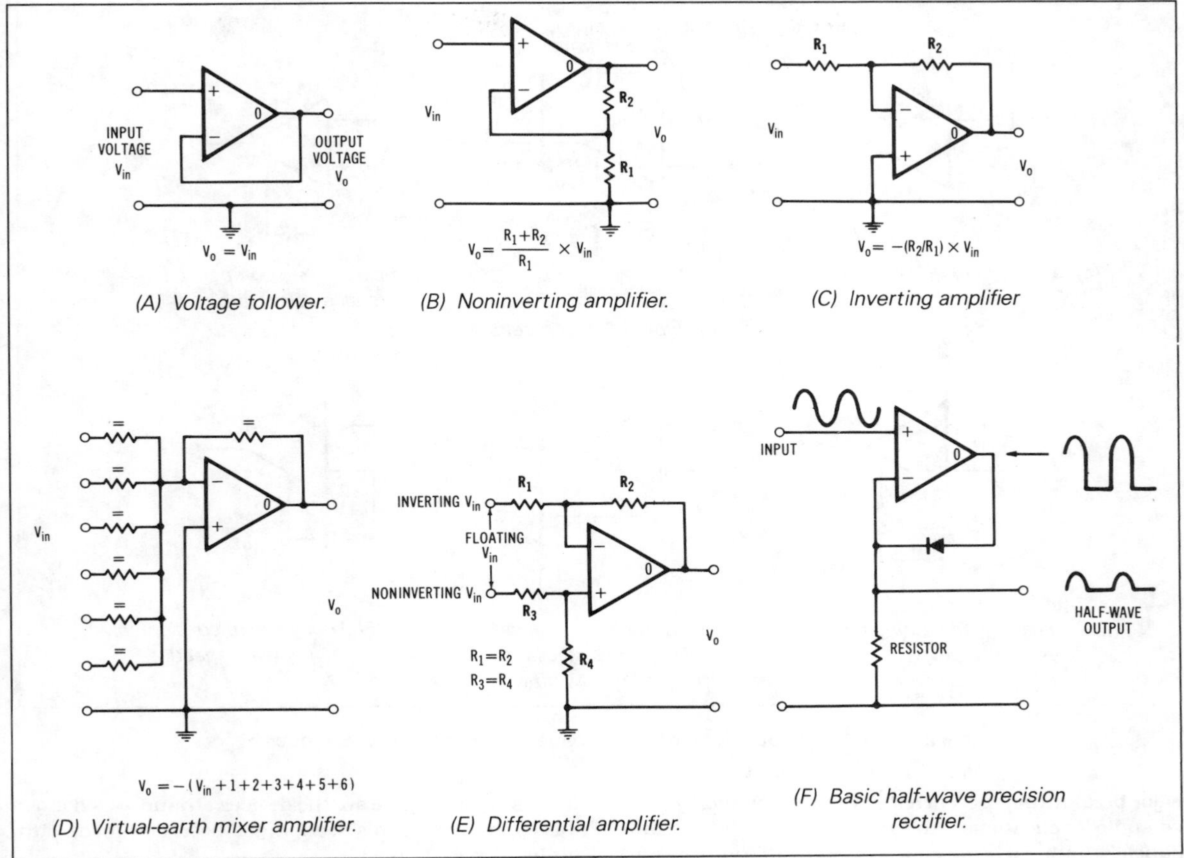

Figure 22-16 Basic operational-amplifier configurations.

pensation network. Rather than just a simple capacitor of sufficient value to hold the amplifier stable (which also turned the internal compensated transistor into a Miller integrator doing absolutely nothing for the speed of the device), a more complex network such as a two-pole resistance-capacitance network (Fig. 22-16) improved matters greatly.

External feed forward, while in use as an inverting or virtual-earth mixing stage, also enabled a dramatic increase in bandwidth and speed over the more conventional compensation arrangements, as shown in Fig. 22.17.

22.6.1 Slew-Rate Limitations

All these early devices had one great failing, one that has quite recently been leaped upon vigorously by the hi-fi fraternity and audio engineers alike. *Slew rate* is the speed (measured usually in volts per microsecond, V/μs) at which an amplifier output shifts when a step source of extremely high speed is applied to the input. All the early-generation op-amps had slew rates in the order of 0.5 V/μs, but no one really understood it then, and it was not the issue it is now.

The speed limitation was nearly always in the differential and dc level-shifting stages of the devices. It is quite difficult to fabricate on the IC wafer ideal classes of transistors in configurations necessary to improve matters without compromising other device characteristics (such as input bias current, which affects both input impedance and offset performance).

Feed forward, in which a proportion of the unslewed input signal is fed around the relatively slow-responding lateral pnp stages improving slew-rate and bandwidth appreciably, is used to great effect in the LM318. This device still has a notable number of devotees, and a slew rate of some 70 V/μs is achievable by this technique. It was in this area of slew rate, combined with a significantly improved noise performance (again another parameter suffering from difficulty in fabricating appropriate devices in a relatively dirty wafer), that the next

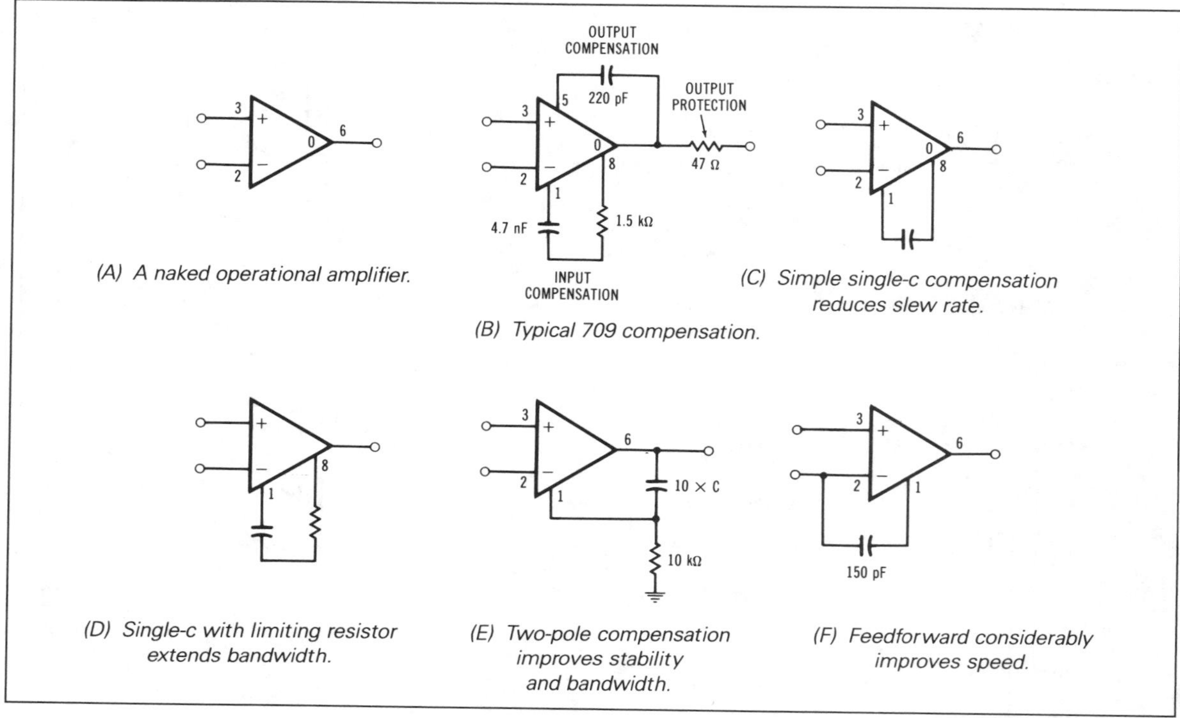

(A) A naked operational amplifier.

(B) Typical 709 compensation.

(C) Simple single-c compensation reduces slew rate.

(D) Single-c with limiting resistor extends bandwidth.

(E) Two-pole compensation improves stability and bandwidth.

(F) Feedforward considerably improves speed.

Figure 22-17 Various operational amplifier compensation techniques.

major breakthrough occurred in devices commonly used for audio applications—the Harris 911. Although dramatically improved, the slew rate was still not fast and was also asymmetrical (+5 and −2 V/μs).

22.6.2 Bipolar Field-Effect Transistors (BiFETs)

In recent years a breed of op-amps called *biFETs* or bipolar field-effect transistors has emerged. These devices have a closely matched and trimmed field-effect transistor input differential pair (hence, the typically unimaginably high 10-MΩ input impedance) and a reasonably fast 13-V/μs structure throughout. These devices are typified by the TLO series from Texas Instruments, Inc. and devices such as the LF356 from National Semiconductor Corp. Selected versions can, when source impedance is optimized, give noise figures bettering 4 dB at audio, which is thoroughly remarkable for units costing very little more than a 741.

The speed of the devices has been achieved by the replacement of the conventional bipolar transistor differential input and level-shifting circuitry with FET configurations. Incidentally, the intrinsic noise characteristic of these FET front ends is significantly different from that of bipolars and seems perceptually less objectionable. Needless to say, these are the devices around which most of the circuitry in this section has been designed, with minimal exceptions.

There is one IC device that was designed specifically and optimized totally for inclusion in high-quality audio equipment. With a quoted noise figure of better than 1 dB at audio, a slew rate of 13 V/μs, and the ability to drive a 600-Ω termination at up to +20 dBm, the Signetics Corp.'s NE5534 (or TDA1034) is truly a quality chip among chips. It is, despite an initial rapid plummeting of price, still significantly more expensive than the humble biFET types. The price is a perfectly valid reason for not using them everywhere; but more to the point, how many actual circuitry circumstances demand each and all of these characteristics? There are not many; although a fairly detailed reasoning of design criteria is given in each of the circuit descriptions, a brief explanation that would put to rest the minds of the "purists" who would otherwise demand using 5534s throughout is in order here.

Noise in any competently designed and operated console can be attributed mostly to two sources: (1) mixing amplifiers with an appreciable number of sources and, hence, a lot of makeup gain, but predominantly (2) the input stage, especially a microphone amplifier with a fair amount of gain in it. Once a background noise level is established from the front-end stage (at a level obviously dependent on the amount of gain employed there), the difference in noise contribution between an amplifier with a typical unity gain noise of − 120 dBu and one of − 115 dBu is for the vast majority of considerations totally insignificant.

The output driving capability of the 5534 is not really worth putting to the test since conventional line-amp designs are usually cheaper to construct. The performance and ease of using the 5534 as a microphone amplifier far outweigh the hassle of a similarly performing discrete transistor design, which in this specific area is still its main close rival.

22.6.3 Discrete Operational Amplifiers

In the realm of altogether more esoteric devices fall the purpose-designed encapsulated discrete amplifier modules such as the JE990, designed by Deane Jensen of Jensen Transformers and manufactured by Hardy Co. of Evanston, Illinois. Many fascinating solutions to op-amp internal design problems (some of which even IC designers evidently haven't realized existed) are implemented in this design whose features demand a total reappraisal of contemporary audio circuit design and philosophy. Optimum input source impedance (normally about 10 kΩ with most IC and discrete amplifiers) is reduced to about 1 kΩ by the use of an IC multiparallel input transistor differential pair. Small inductors in the emitters provide isolation from potential high-frequency instability due to the gain/bandwidth characteristic of the first differential stage shifting with varying source impedances. Unity-gain noise is a quoted staggeringly low − 133.7 dBu, while the output is capable of delivering full voltage swing into a 75-Ω load. This permits the use of exterior circuit elements of far lower impedance, reducing thermal noise generation due to them.

This elegant device inevitably carries an elegant price tag. Its many attributes point to the direction for design. It is well ahead of any devices available in IC form and also, to the author's knowledge, of any universal discrete circuitry elements used to date in console manufacture. This device begs the question of the wisdom of the complex multiamplifier, multistage mixer configurations versus true minimum-path circuit philosophy.

22.6.4 Instability

An unexpected thrill facing designers as they upgraded to newer, much faster devices was the tendency for all their previously designed circuits to erupt in masses of low-level instabilities even in what had been perfectly tame boards.

Layout anomalies, such as track proximity, were a major contributor toward the stability problems, so new layouts had to be generated with a whole new set of conditions added to the already hazardous game of analog card design. However, the real roots to this problem are with the devices themselves and a lack of appreciation of the relationship between their internal configurations and the outside world. Everyone who had been brought up designing around 741s had become too used to treating them in a somewhat cavalier fashion and for good reason. There was precious little you could not do with them without their even showing a hint of oscillation. People got used to treating ICs as plug-in blocks of gain with little consideration for the fact that inside was a real, live collection of electronic bits that still had all the problems real electronics always had. The reason the 741 was relatively impervious to user-inflicted problems is analogous to the fact that it's quite difficult to get anything that is bound and gagged to not behave itself.

Mistake number one with the new devices was believing that they were unity-gain stable because the data sheets said so. What that really means is "does not burst into oscillation at unity gain," which is not the same thing at all.

22.6.5 Phase Margin

It is important to maintain as large a margin as possible between the internally structured gain-bandwidth rolloff set for open loop and the rolloff around the external circuitry determining the closed-loop gain. This is to preserve sufficient phase margin at all frequencies for which the circuit has gain. Failure to do this can result in the feedback being shifted in phase sufficiently to become reverse phase to that intended (positive feedback) with oscillation resulting. Even if the phase isn't shifted quite that far, the feedback tends toward positive and damped ringing when transients hit the circuit. Also, these resonance effects are extremely high in frequency, typically many megahertz, so any radio signal that gets as far as the circuitry will absolutely adore an amplifier that is critically resonant at its frequency! A reasonable phase margin to aim for at all gain frequencies is better than 45°. In practice a compromise between desired circuit bandwidth traded off against the need to tighten that bandwidth for the sake of phase margins can be fairly easily reached with the newer devices, provided the need to do so is recognized!

The normal, easiest, and most flexible way to determine the closed-loop rolloff of a circuit is by means of a feedback phase-leading capacitor across the main output-to-inverting-input feedback resistor. A typical arrangement is shown in Fig. 22-18. Generally, the need to properly define the bandwidth of a gain block by just such a means automatically takes care of the matter, although it's dangerous design practice to assume that the two requirements—phase-margin determination and bandwidth limitation—are always mutually satisfiable.

A fairly common eroder of phase margin and progenitor of instability is stray capacitance from the inverting input of the amplifier to ground. This capacitance, a combination of internal device, pinout, and printed-circuit lay-

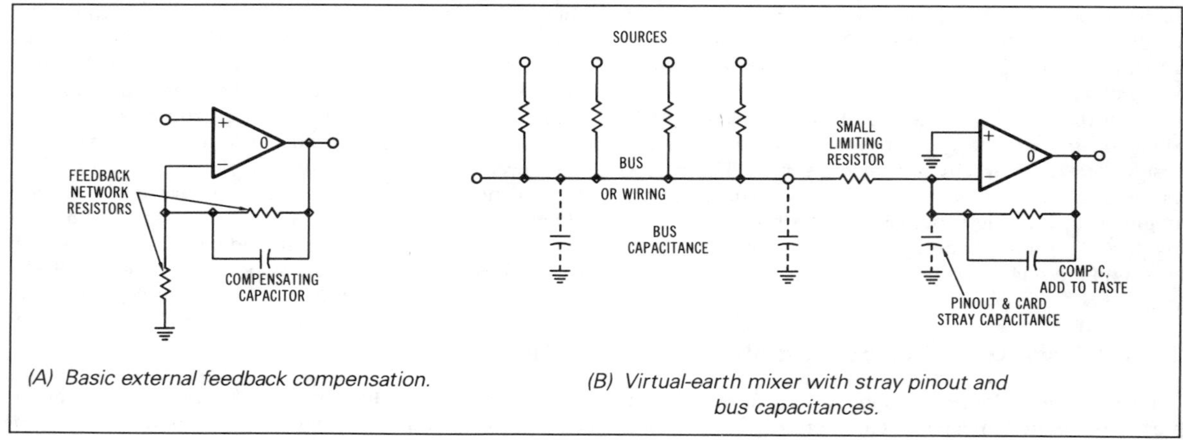

(A) Basic external feedback compensation.

(B) Virtual-earth mixer with stray pinout and bus capacitances.

Figure 22-18 Feedback phase-leading stability compensation.

out proximity capacitances, reacts against the feedback impedance to increase the closed-loop gain at high frequencies. In normal circuits, even the typical 5 pF or so is enough to tilt up the closed-loop gain parameters, threatening stability. Far worse is the situation where the inverting input is extended quite some distance along wiring, and a bus—as in a virtual-earth mixing amplifier—containing hundreds of picofarads may be present there. It can arise that despite a sizable time constant being present in the feedback leg, none of the expected high-frequency rolloff occurs since it is merely compensating for the gain hike created by the bus capacitance. Ensuring required response and phase characteristics using any virtual-earth mixer can only be done properly with at least two orders of compensation around the mix-amp and with the finished system up and running completely, since any additional sources modify the impedance presented by the bus.

To define just how much this unwanted gain can rise, a small limiting resistor may be added as close to the amplifier inverting input terminal as possible; this is at the expense of the virtual-earth point now having a minimum impedance based on the value of that resistor. The resistor, incidentally, is also a measure of protection against any radio-frequency signals on the bus being rectified by the input stage's junctions.

22.6.6 Time-Domain Effects

There is invariably a finite time taken for a signal presented at the input of any amplifier to show an effect at the output of the amplifier—the so-called *transit time.* Every tiniest capacitance and consequent time constant in the internal circuitry of the amplifier makes this inevitable; electronics takes time to do things. This transit time becomes an appreciably greater proportion of the wavelength of the wanted signal as the frequency increases, and as such it has to be taken into account. Fig. 22-19 shows how the fixed transit time becomes more relevant to increasing signal frequency. Ultimately, of course, the transit time will become half the time necessary for a wavelength of the signal frequency. At that stage what emerges from the amplifier will be a half-wavelength (i.e., 180°) out-of-phase. Before this point, its detraction from phase margin with increasing frequency can start to cause serious problems; at this ultimate state, though, the negative feedback on which the amplifier depends for predictable performance is now completely upside down and becomes positive feedback and oscillation.

22.6.7 Transient Intermodulation Distortion (TID)

The TID effect is due almost totally to amplifier transit times and not surprisingly, since it is nearly always the case with fad problems (as was TID during the 1970s). TID has been known and appreciated for as long as there have been negative feedback amplifier circuits—some 65 years. It is and always has been totally predictable.

TID is a direct result of the servo nature of an amplifier with a large amount of negative feedback. The feedback is intended to provide a correction signal derived as a difference between the amplifier output and the applied input signal. It is a simple concept: any difference between what goes in and what comes out is error in the amplifier. All we need do is subtract the error. There is, however, a problem. Since there exists a time delay in the amplifier, the circuit has to wait for that amount of time before its correction signal arrives. The output during this time is uncontrolled and just flies off wildly in the general direction the input tells it to. Once the correction arrives, the amplifier has to wait *again* to find out how accurate that correction was and so forth, see-sawing on and on until the amplifier output settles. Fortunately, this all takes

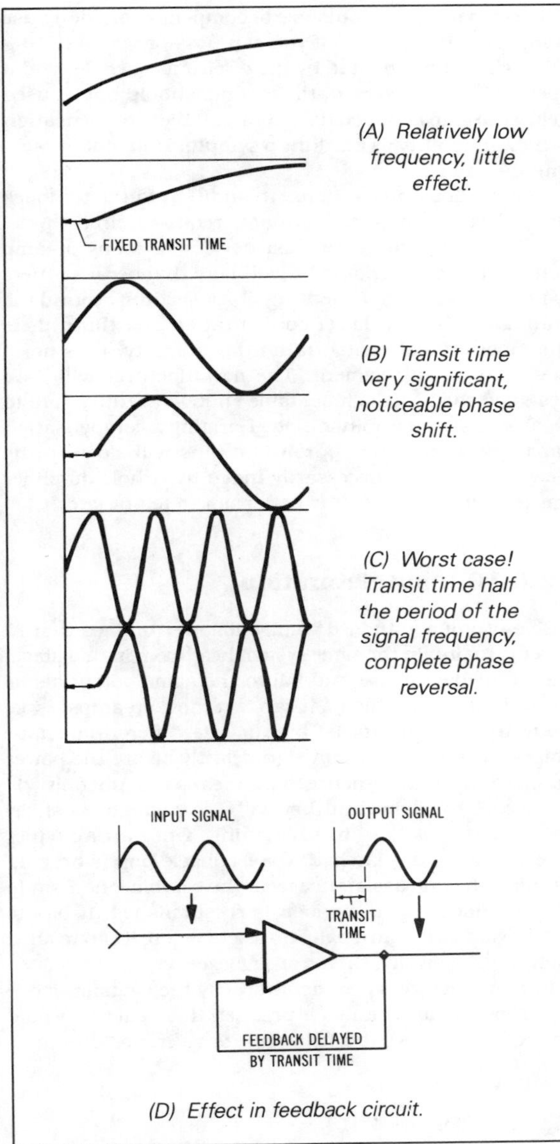

Figure 22-19 Transit-time effects with increasing signal frequency.

place rapidly (dependent on the amplifier external circuitry), but it *still* represents a discrepancy between input and output. It is an effect peculiar to amplifiers with large amounts of negative feedback (typical of most contemporary circuitry), frequently displaying itself quite audibly—especially in power amplifiers where transit time is quite long with the usual huge, slow output devices.

Amplifiers that rely on their own basic linearity (such as tube amplifiers), rather than on a servo-type nonlinearity correction system, are often held to be subjectively smoother. A whole sub-industry thriving on the virtues of feedbackless circuitry has evolved. Nowadays though, with device speeds improved as they are, settling times are becoming insignificant in relation to the signal transients they are expected to cope with.

22.6.8 Output Impedance

Most newer devices, particularly the TLO series of biFETs have a quite significant open-loop output impedance. This is because the IC designer obviously thought that instead of an active output current-limiting circuit (standard on most op-amps up until then), a simple resistor would do instead. Although this built-in output impedance—by virtue of the enormous amount of negative feedback used—is normally reduced to virtual zero at the output terminal, it is still present and included as part of the feedback path (Fig. 22-20). Any reactive load at the output is going to materially affect the feedback phase and phase margin.

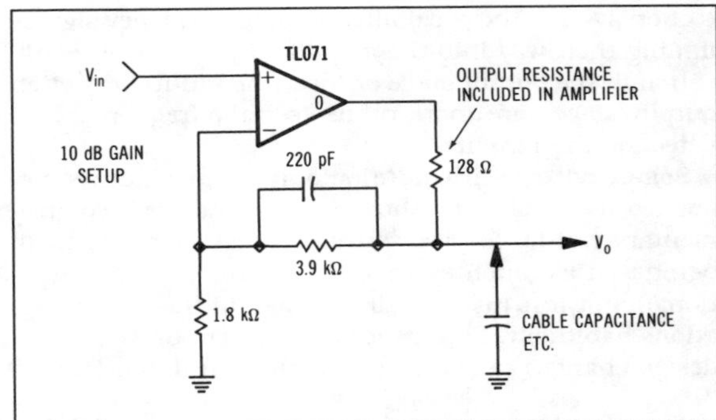

Figure 22-20 Output impedance as part of the feedback loop.

Any capacitance from the output to ground will form a feedback phase-lagging network. This shifts the phase inexorably toward the point where the total amplifier and network phase shift reaches 180° at the inverting input (therefore, a full 360° total), and the circuit oscillates. The frequency at which it oscillates is inversely relative to the capacitance value. It isn't unusual, with small values, to find oscillations right at the edge of the high-frequency sensitivity of an oscilloscope. Hanging a long bit of wire on the amplifier output (especially shielded cable with its high shield to inner capacitance) is a surefire guarantee of instability for this very reason. It has the added complication that there is a measure of inductance there, too. It is conceivable that a long cable might start to look like a mismatched tuned stub at a frequency where the amplifier still has some gain, creating a good, stable radio-frequency generator.

What this extra resistance-capacitance output circuit is in effect doing is to add dramatically to the transit time of the amplifier where actually the termination problem is creating far more delay than could possibly exist within the device itself. That the cures for the two are similar shouldn't be a surprise. Fortunately, a simple cure for this instability is to buffer away the load from the output-feedback termination with a small resistor of typically 33 to 150 Ω. This usually does it, but at the expense of headroom loss due to the attenuation from the buffer resistor against the load termination. Provided the load is greater than about 2 kΩ, which it would really have to be in order to prevent getting close to current drive saturation in the IC output stage, this headroom loss should not exceed 0.6 dB. An altogether more elegant way is to buffer off with a small inductance, giving increasing isolation with frequency; a phase-shifting characteristic opposite to that of the (normally) capacitative load provides a total termination that is phase constant at the higher frequencies. At the lower audio frequencies, of course, the inductive reactance is very low, and the load sees the very low dynamic output impedance of the amplifier. The buffering inductance becomes virtually transparent.

Both of these techniques also provide a measure of protection against the possibility of radio-frequency signals finding their way into the amplifier by means of rectification in the output stage or inverting input. Very often output stages are more prone to radio-frequency field detection than inputs.

Some devices with a quite low output impedance before applied feedback (say, those with unbuffered, complementary emitter-follower output stages) are not likely to be phased as much by these effects (pun totally intentional), but it is just as well to design in these considerations habitually. Emergency replacement or IC internal design changes can evoke this problem unintentionally.

22.6.9 Compensating Operational Amplifiers

Op-amps generally have a couple of pins dedicated for *compensation*, which is the way manufacturers say that their product isn't stable under certain conditions of usage—usually at low closed-loop gain where the bandwidth is at its most extreme. The classic solution is to shrink the bandwidth of the amplifier by slowing the amplifier down. This wrecks the slew rate that's been paid for.

The most ordinary means of slowing down the devices is to slug an internal gain stage, leaving the other stages intact. On the bright side, if it is this internal gain stage around which the external compensation capacitor is hung that is tending toward instability, the capacitor should cure it. Nevertheless, it rarely is that stage. If a previous stage, say, the input differential amplifier, is unstable, all the capacitor will do is slow up the amplifier and reduce the slew rate to the extent that the oscillation is no longer visible at the output. It does not cure the instability. It's still in there, hiding.

There is a moral to this tale of compensation: don't use compensating op-amps if you can possibly avoid it. Stability should be ensured by the circuit as a whole, and if speed is to be preserved, the op-amp should not be used below the gain at which it's happily stable. Compensation achieves stability by masking a symptom and not by tackling the cause.

The previous precautions, in addition to the feedback phase-leading capacitor, are now required circuit practice for using the newer, fast devices in many op-amp configurations. It should be said here that because there is no facility for implementing phase-leading around the standard voltage-follower configuration and that this is the most critical configuration for stability, it is not a preferred circuit element. The manufacturer will have designed the IC to be just stable enough at unity gain to be able to say so unblushingly. Hanging a compensation capacitor across the appropriate pins will slow up the slew rate and not necessarily make the whole amplifier any less unstable, yet it is better not to tempt fate.

22.6.10 Input Saturation

The use of a standard voltage-follower implies that in order to maintain the same system headroom in that stage, the input has to rise and fall to the same potentials as the output is expected to. It can't. In most op-amps, especially those with bipolar inputs, the differential input stages saturate or bottom significantly before the power supply outputs are reached. This means that not only will they cease to follow, but they will also spend a considerable amount of time in unlatching. Once an amplifier internal stage has latched, the feedback loop is broken; the stage has no assistance from the servomechanism to unstick itself. Once the loop is reestablished, it has to settle again as if from a hefty transient before it can resume following. Basically, this is an ugly scene.

IC manufacturers commonly specify the common-mode input voltage range, and it is precisely this limit that would be exceeded in use as a follower. For reference they are:

± 13 V for the 5534,

± 11.5 V for an LM318,

$+15$ V to -12 V for a typical biFET.

All fall far short of the power supply maxima. Provided enough gain is built around the amplifier to prevent these common-mode limits from being reached, there should be no latching hang-ups; the feedback network also provides some substance to hang closed-loop compensation around in addition to enabling the full output voltage swing of the amplifier to be utilized.

Similar settling-time problems occur any time any stage is driven into clipping, but given the high power-supply voltages, hence, large headroom common today, clipping should be rare.

22.6.11 Front-End Instability

Altogether the most obscure potential instability-causing effect relates directly to the behavior of the input stage in bipolar front-end op-amps. The gain-bandwidth characteristic of the input differential stage is greatly dependent upon the impedance presented to the input, the gain-bandwidth increasing with reducing source impedance. There is the possibility that given an already critical circumstance, the erosion in phase margin due to this effect can cause instability. This instability can be mitigated by limiting the gain-bandwidth excursion by means of a resistor, typically 1 kΩ, in series with the input. Ordinarily, this would have little effect on circuit performance but may, especially in microphone amplifiers, detract from noise performance. Noise performance is largely dependent on the amplifier being fed from a specific source impedance, and 1 kΩ would be a sizable proportion. However, it's usually fairly easy to arrange in the design stage so the IC doesn't have a zero impedance at either of its inputs.

Fortunately, because of the far greater isolation between the FET gates and their channels, this is a problem that FET-input op-amps do not have. A similar approach to that proposed for output isolation (i.e., an inductor rather than a resistor) in series with the affected input seems, on the surface, an equally good idea. The impedance of the inductors would be low at audio (so not affecting noise criteria significantly) and high at radio frequencies where the low source impedance phenomenon does its work. Unless the value is critically defined, an inductor of sufficient value to provide a usefully high reactance at radio frequencies is also likely to be self-resonant with circuit stray and its own winding capacitances at a frequency probably still within the gain-bandwidth capability of the amplifier.

Those who have experienced design with discrete circuitry will not be surprised that this source impedance instability effect is also the reason emitter-followers are the most instability-prone of the three basic transistor amplifier configurations. The cure is the same. Not only does the series resistor limit the source impedance before zero, it also acts together with any pinout and base-emitter capacitance as a low-pass filter helping to negate further external phase shift that may detract from stability. This base source-impedance instability is quite insidious in that it can either contribute to instability of the amplifier loop if it is already critical or it can be a totally independent instability local to the affected devices with nothing whatsoever to do with the characteristics of the external loop.

22.6.12 Band Limiting

One of the first great superficially appealing results of using the enormous feedback inherent from using op-amps at the relatively low gain requirements of the audio world was a close approach to dc-to-light frequency response. The author remembers well the hysterical peals of laughter as the response of a new mixer was measured as still ±0 dB right to the end of the testing ranges of the oscillator and the badly disguised puzzled looks and worried glances when we listened to it.

Most audio signals, especially live ones from microphones and tape-machine returns with a high-bias content, have a fair amount of ultrasonics present.

We see here the old story: the wider the window, the more muck flies in. It would be perfectly all right if the circuitry were capable of dealing with signals much higher than the audio band; sadly at the time (and even now) that is not so. The root of the difficulty is the worsening open-loop gain of the individual op-amps. As it drops off at 6-dB/octave with increasing frequency, it can be seen that less closed-loop feedback is available to maintain the op-amp's linearity.

Fig. 22-21 is representative of the open-loop input-output transfer characteristic of an op-amp. (Incidentally, most big power amps have similar unseductive curves.) The good in-band linearity and low distortion of op-amps comes from the application of monstrous amounts of feedback; take the case of a noninverting 741-type amp with 40 dB of gain around it (Fig. 22-22). At

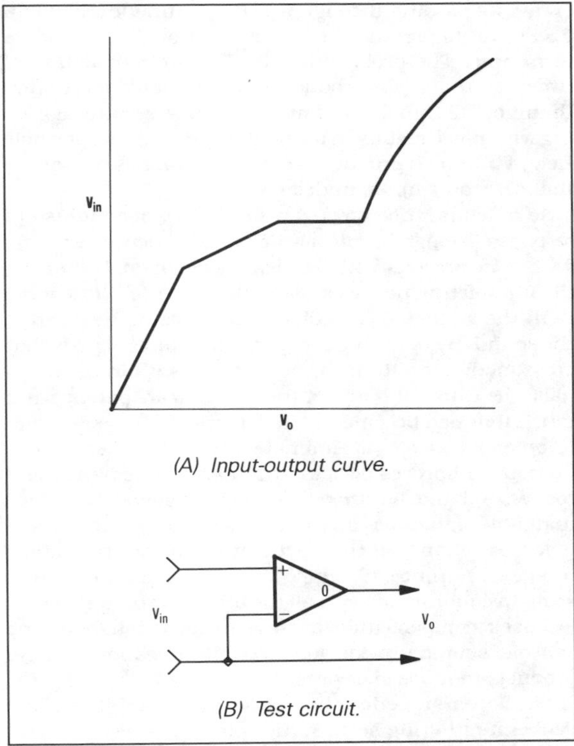

Figure 22-21 Operational amplifier open-loop gain curve typical of a bipolar device.

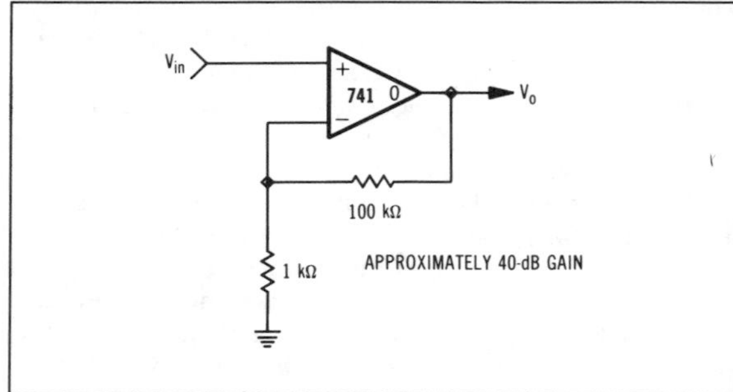

Figure 22-22 A 741 with 40-dB gain.

100 Hz there can be 60 dB of feedback, which is great! However, the open-loop gain plummets above this frequency, leaving a still respectable 40 dB of feedback at 1 kHz. (This figure of 40 dB is widely regarded as the lowest amount of feedback for good performance from an op-amp.) At 10 kHz it's down to 20 dB; it is 14 dB at 20 kHz; and at an ultrasonic 40 kHz, there is a bare 8 dB! There is still gain, though, and the amplifier is quite capable of supporting the signal up at those frequencies; it's just not very good at it.

Harmonic distortion of ultrasonics that would be generated by passing through a transfer function like Fig. 22-21 is unimportant; the frequencies would be even more ultrasonic. The problem lies in the intermodulation of two or more signals, products of which would more often than not fall into the audible band; even reciprocal mixing with noise results in in-band noise products. A whole slew of intermod products were produced; it is no wonder that early op-amps sounded bad.

So much for the expected result of *improved transient response* through having a wide-open frequency response. As is now obvious with hindsight, deliberately limiting the input frequency response of the mixer to a little more than the audio band results in an amazing clean up of the sound. By removing a lot of the inaudible signals that cross modulate within themselves and with in-band signals, the cause of much of the lack of transparency and mush that had become the trademark of first-generation IC op-amp consoles is eliminated.

Despite improved devices, this approach remains valid today. By band limiting the program signal to reduce inaudible signals as early in the chain as possible, there is far less chance of their generating unwanted audible products. A front-end, single-order, low-pass filter, operating in conjunction with all the other low-pass effects of feedback compensation arrangements throughout the console, should provide adequate minimization of these products in modern devices.

"Purist" arguments about the undesirability of any deliberate filtering seem rather futile in a world of real devices and final signal destinations such as tape (with its generally anything other than linear phase and frequency characteristics and bias frequencies), disk, radio (rapid filtering above 15 kHz), or digital processing/recording (very, very rapid low-pass filtering to avoid frequency folding or aliasing).

22.6.13 Slew-Rate Effects

Slew-rate limiting occurs when the fastest signal rise time the amplifier is expected to pass exceeds the speed of the fastest stage in the amplifier, giving rise to intermodulation effects that are dependent upon both frequency and signal level. A common subjective result of this limiting is for the high end of a drum-kit to change in character of sound with differing levels of the lower-frequency instruments on which it is riding. Another favorite is the "disappearing snare drum" in which, again, the sound radically alters with changing level.

22.6.14 Device Idiosyncrasies and the Future

Many of the circuits described rely a little on the extremely high input impedances of the biFET devices and, hence, the very low bias currents required. Gaily stuffing in bipolars may result in generated output offset voltages that could manifest themselves in extreme instances as switch clunks and scrappy pots. Also, the feedback phase-leading compensation may or may not be adequate for devices other than the biFETs, especially some bipolars with less than ideal internal poles. If we're tempted to use more conventional bipolar devices, particularly in quad packages, it is also worthwhile examining their characteristics when inputs or outputs are taken above or below the power supply potentials. If the device structure under such circumstances is unprotected and turns into a silicon controlled rectifier that deftly shorts the power supply, you are better off without it.

The proliferate use of amplifier elements in modern console design has mushroomed in recent years with the availability of compact and extremely low-cost IC op-amps. Increasingly complex functional blocks are becoming increasingly commonplace. If, in order to improve their electrical and sonic characteristics, it would mean an increase in size and cost of well over an order of magnitude, would they still be quite as popular? In the "good old days" of tubes, it was not through any lack of expertise that equalizers even of today's complexity did not exist; it was just the size and cost of the concept that would have made even the reckless shudder. Also, it is to be noted, they were not really thought necessary.

Could it be that the next level of enlightenment in consoles is going to demand more simple and concise systems traded for a far higher and thorough level of elemental electronic design?

22.7 GROUNDING

A human working visualization of anything electronic soon becomes impossible without a mental image of the solid, infinite, immovable, dependable *ground*. It has many other names too: *earth*, *0 V*, *reference*, *chassis*, *frame*, *deck*, and so on, each of differing interpretation but all, ultimately, alluding to the great immovable reference.

Electrons could not care less about all this. They just go charging about as potentials dictate; any circuit will work perfectly well referred to nothing but itself. (Satellites, cars, and flashlights work, don't they?) Ground in these instances is but an intellectual convenience.

Interconnection of a number of circuit elements to form a system necessarily means a reference to be used between them. To a large degree, it's possible to obviate a reference even then by the use of differential or balanced interfacing, unless, of course, power supplies are shared.

So, having proved that ground is seemingly only a mental crutch, why is it the most crucial aspect of system design and implementation?

22.7.1 Wire

Fig. 22-23A shows a typical, ordinary, long, thin bit of metal known more commonly as wire and occasionally as printed-circuit track. However short it is, it will have resistance, which means that a voltage will develop across it as soon as any current goes along it. Similarly, it has inductance and a magnetic field will develop around it. If it is in proximity to anything, it will also have capacitance.

So, Fig. 22-23A actually looks more like Fig. 22-23B with resistive and distributed reactive components. Admittedly, these values are small and seem of little significance at audio frequencies, but clues have already been laid (particularly in section 22.6 on op-amps) that believing the world ends at 20 kHz is not so much myopic as naive.

A radio engineer looking at Fig. 22-23B would mumble things like "tuned line," "resonance," or "bandpass filter," maybe even "antenna." Radio-frequency technology and thinking may seem abstruse and irrelevant to console design until it is considered that devices commonly used nowadays have bandwidths often dozens, sometimes hundreds, of megahertz wide. An even more frightening realization is the enormous quantity of RF energy present in the air as a consequence of our technological being.

A more obscure collection of equivalents is shown in Fig. 22-24. Fig. 22-24A represents a wire into a bipolar transistor input; Fig. 22-24B shows a wire from a conventional complementary output stage; and, for reference sake, Fig. 22-24C shows a basic crystal-set radio receiver. It may be quaint, now, but for the presence of considerably more volts per meter radio-frequency field energy compared to the heyday of wireless it's the same. In all the three circumstances, radio frequencies collected and delivered by the antenna tuned line are rectified (hence, demodulated) by a diode (the base-emitter junctions in Figs. 22-24A and B). As contrary as it may seem for demodulation to occur at an amplifier output, it is perhaps the most common detection mechanism with the demodulated product finding its way back to the amplifier input by means of the conveniently provided bypassed negative feedback leg.

Making our bit of wire fatter and thicker has the effect of lowering the resistance and inductance while increasing capacitance (greater surface area exposed to things nearby). So, although the resonant frequency of the wire stays about the same, the dynamic impedance (hence, Q) reduces. Although in general this is deemed a good thing, in some instances it can merely serve to improve the matching and coupling of the radio-frequency source to the resonance.

Carried to an extreme, even the console frame constitutes a big fat resonant tank at a surprisingly low (mid-vhf) frequency, and frame resistance, however heavily constructed, cannot be disregarded and treated as a universal ground path.

For the purposes of practical design, these considerations perhaps become a little better defined. The reactive elements of capacitance and inductance with the atten-

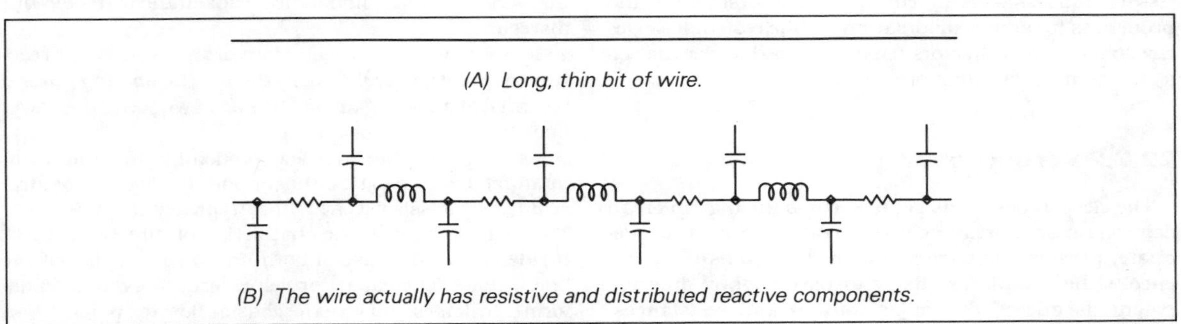

(A) Long, thin bit of wire.

(B) The wire actually has resistive and distributed reactive components.

Figure 22-23 What is a bit of wire?

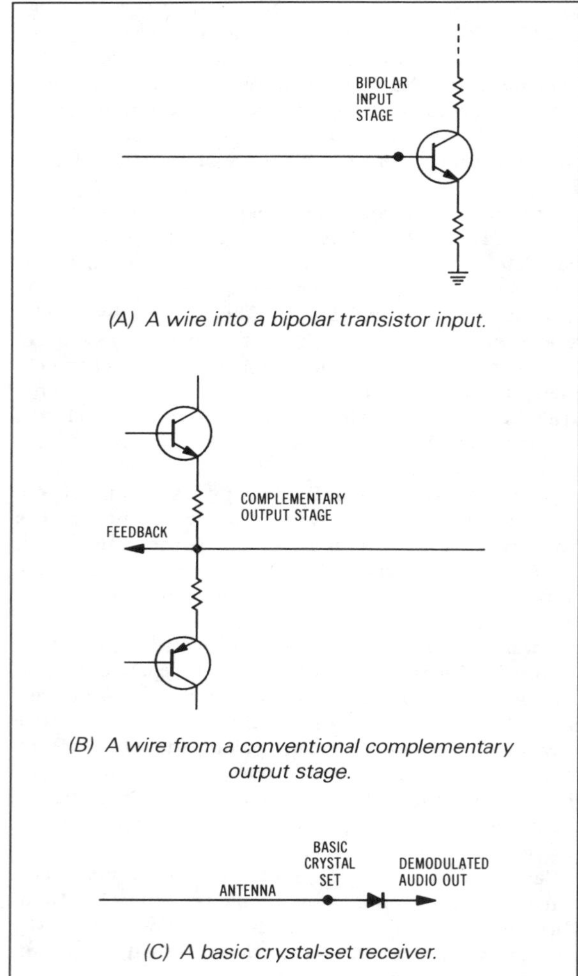

Figure 22-24 A collection of equivalents.

dant effects of resonance and filtering are concerned with less obvious aspects (such as electronic stability and proneness to radio demodulation), while resistance gives rise to most of the horrors usually lumped under the collective term "grounding problems".

22.7.2 Earth Ground

The closest most of us get to earth is the big pin on an ac power plug. Fortunately for most purposes, it is adequate, provided just the one point is used as the reference. Other points are likely to have slightly differing potentials due to dissimilar routing and resistances. Compared to a technical earth ground (e.g., a water pipe, if we make sure the plumbing isn't plastic, or alternatively a fortune in copper pipe hammered into the earth), conventional earth grounds can have a surprisingly high potential, a volt or two, considering it is principally a safety facility not ordinarily carrying current. Any potential implies resistance in the earth path, which is bad news about something intended as a reference while also detracting from the safety aspect. Practically, though, it does not matter too much if everything is waving up and down a bit provided everything, including even unrelated things in proximity, are waving up and down in the same manner. The potential is usually small, meaning that the ground impedance is reasonably low to the extent it may be considered zero.

22.7.3 Why Ground Anything to Earth?

With all our component system parts tied together by a reference ground and everything working as expected, the question arises as to why it is necessary to refer our ground to earth. If the internal grounding is completely correct, our system will operate perfectly, quietly, and tamely regardless of what potential (with respect to earth) it is tied to. If not tied, it will derive its own potential by virtue of resistive leakages, inductive coupling, and capacitance to things in its environment. For an independently powered system (for example, batteries), these leakages and couplings will be of very high impedance and, hence, easily swamped by human body impedance to earth.

If, as is most often the case, most of the system is powered off the ac lines, this floating ground potential becomes of far lower impedance and consequently is much more capable of dragging current through the human load. (It's the current that kills, not the voltage.) A telltale sign is a burring, tingling feeling as you drag a finger across exposed metalwork on something that is deriving its own ground potential.

The mechanism for this lower impedance is fairly straightforward. Power transformers are wound with the optimum transfer of energy at 50 to 60 Hz and very high flashover voltages (2 or 3 kV), while the finer points of transformers such as leakage inductance, interwinding, and winding imbalance capacitance are all but disregarded.

Being far greater in scale than ordinary ambient reactive couplings, they primarily dictate the floating ground potential at anything up to 240 V ac or whatever the power lines happen to be locally.

A strange practice by a few, predominantly American, manufacturers is to tie either or both the live and neutral ac lines to chassis via capacitors (typically of 1 to 100 nF). The result is that, if the chassis is not directly earthed, it rides at (in the case of both lines being tied) half the line voltage. The capacitor values grossly swamp transformer leakages and give the chassis floating potential an uncomfortably (literally) low impedance. The chassis tingle changes from "Mmm—interesting" to vile oaths with attendant flailing limbs.

A system composed of many separately powered units will almost certainly hum, buzz, and sound generally uneasy, which is seemingly in direct contradiction to the earlier statement that ". . . the system will operate perfectly . . . regardless of what potential it is tied to. . . ." Being tied to a lot of different potentials at a lot of different points along a ground path is definitely not proper.

Each different power transformer will have different amounts and permutations of leakage and, hence, propagate different potentials and degrees of power-line-borne noise into our otherwise perfect grounding path. Assorted ground potentials mean assorted ground currents, meaning assorted noises.

Tying the entire grounding path to earth is the ultimate "swampout" of leakage impedances. A connection to a (nearly) zero impedance makes a nonsense of most other potential-creating paths, most of which have reactances exceeding 1 kΩ.

Ordinarily in such a multisupply circumstance, regardless of earth termination, significant currents exist along the ground reference lines. The resultant interelement noise and hum voltages (developed across the inevitable line resistances) quickly become intolerable in unbalanced systems. Any wobbling of the ground reference becomes directly imposed upon the required signal.

Balanced, or pure differential, transmission helps obviate these perturbances by rendering them common mode in a system that is (theoretically) only sensitive to differential information. In reality, practical transformers can afford a good 70- to 80-dB common-mode isolation at low audio frequencies. They deteriorate in this respect at 6 dB/octave with increasing frequency around the winding resonance frequencies unless considerable effort is made to fake a more accurate balance externally. Although transformer balancing does effect a dramatic improvement in noise levels, it is far greater for fundamental hum (50 to 60 Hz) than it is for other power-line-borne noise. This explains why in tricky systems, lighting dimmer buzz, motor spike noise, or any source with a high-frequency energy or transient content is so persistent.

The golden rule is to treat the grounding of any balanced system as if it were unbalanced. This minimizes the inevitable reference ground currents.

There is one good reason not yet mentioned for grounding to earth. The consequences of a piece of chassis from a gear becoming inadvertently at the power-line potential are obvious. We would much rather see death to a fuse or breaker than one of us.

22.7.4 Console Internal Grounding

Let us assume that the grounding for the studio control room is all sensible and that our console has a solid earth termination. What about the intraconsole grounding paths? This is perhaps the ultimate unbalanced signal path.

Most conventional amplifier stages rely on a voltage difference between their input and reference in order to produce a corresponding output voltage (referred, naturally, to the reference of the input). If the input is held steady while the reference is wobbled, a corresponding (amplified) inverted wobble will appear at the output.

It is plain, then, that any signal the reference sees that is not also common to the input (e.g., ground noise) will get amplified and summed into the output just as effectively as if it were applied to the proper input. The obvious (and startlingly often overlooked) regimen to render extraneous noise unimportant is to ensure that the point at which an amplifier source is referred to is tied directly to the reference, while that amplifier output is only taken in conjunction with the reference. Successive stages daisy chain similarly—source reference to destination reference, and so on.

This thinking is called ground follows signal.

22.7.4.1 Ground Follows Signal

Ground follows signal is a classic maxim and one that has dictated the system design of nearly every console built. It was particularly true in the era of discrete semiconductor design, where ground was not only audio ground but also the 0-V power-supply return. As an added complication, the power-supply positive lines, being heavily regulated and coupled to ground, were an equal nightmare as they too became part of the grounding path. This could be fairly simply avoided by spacing each circuit element away from the supply line by an impedance considerably greater than that offered by the proper ground path—achieved by either separately regulating or simply decoupling by a series resistor, parallel capacitor network, as shown in Fig. 22-25.

Accelerating technology has for once, actually made life a bit simpler—specifically, the trend toward IC op-amps with their required differential ($+V_e$ and $-V_e$) power supply. This, thankfully, removes electronic operating current from the audio system ground, while individual stage supply decoupling is rendered unnecessary (in most instances) by the excellent power supply noise rejection ratio of most popular op-amps. Nevertheless, correct grounding paths still apply; the removal of supply current just exposes and highlights audio ground subtleties.

Unfortunately, although op-amps have simplified matters in one respect, their ease of use and versatility have been largely responsible for the creation of enormous systems with so many stages, break points, mix buses, and distribution networks that the simple daisy chaining of ground follows signal becomes unwieldy, if not unworkable. Alternate grounding schemes, such as star grounding where every ground path and reference is taken to a central ground or earth, tend to play an increasingly important role.

In practice, a necessary compromise between these two prime systems occurs in most console thinking. Daisy chain applies mostly to on card electronics (e.g., in the

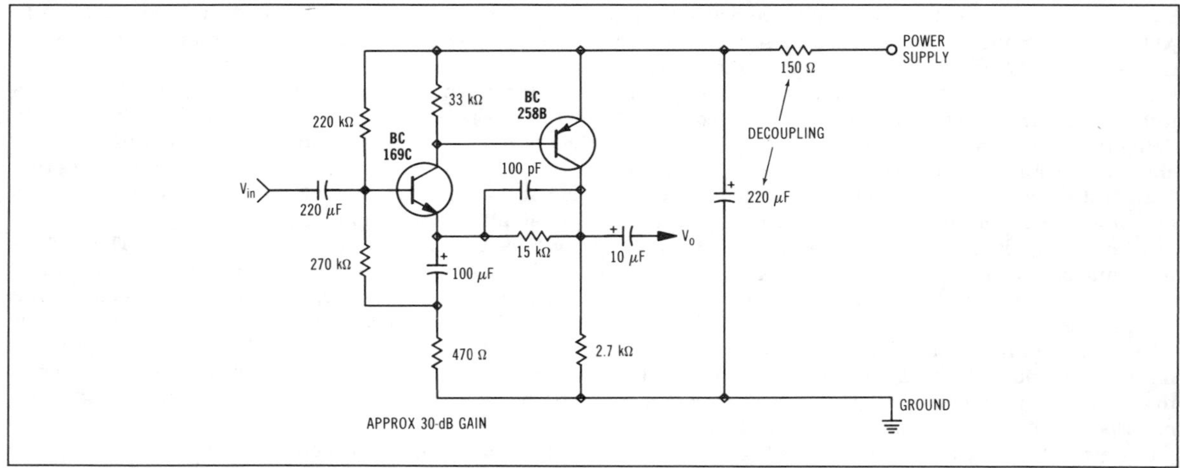

Figure 22-25 Power-supply decoupling: A typical discrete amplifier with the power supply isolated.

microphone amplifier sections), while systems switching and routing rely on star connections.

22.7.4.2 Ground Current Summing

A principal grounding-related manifestation is crosstalk, or the appearance in a signal path of things that belong elsewhere. Other than airborne proximity-related reactive crosstalk, the most unwanted visitations are by the resistive ground path mechanism. In Fig. 22-26A, R_1 represents the load of an amplifier output (what it is in actuality, for example, the 10 kΩ of a fader or a 600-Ω line termination, is immaterial for the present). The resistor R_G represents a small amount of ground path wiring, loss resistance, and so on. It is quite apparent that the bottom end of the termination is spaced a little way from true ground by the wiring resistance, and the combination forms a classic potentiometer network. The fake ground has a signal voltage present of the amplifier output voltage attenuated by R_1 into R_G.

In a practical circumstance with a 600-Ω termination (R_1) and a ground loss (R_G) of 0.6 Ω, the fake ground will have a signal voltage about 60 dB down. The use of the fake ground as a reference for any other circuitry is a surefire guarantee of injecting −60-dB worth of crosstalk.

Two identical terminations sharing the same fake ground (Fig. 22-26B), happily inject a small proportion into each other by generating a common potential across the ground loss R_G.

Should the second termination be far higher in impedance (the 10 kΩ of a fader), its contribution to the common fake ground potential will be far less (−86 dB) since the ground impedance is much smaller in relation to the source. Correspondingly, though, this higher impedance termination is more prone to be crosstalked into from the lower impedance contributors to the common ground.

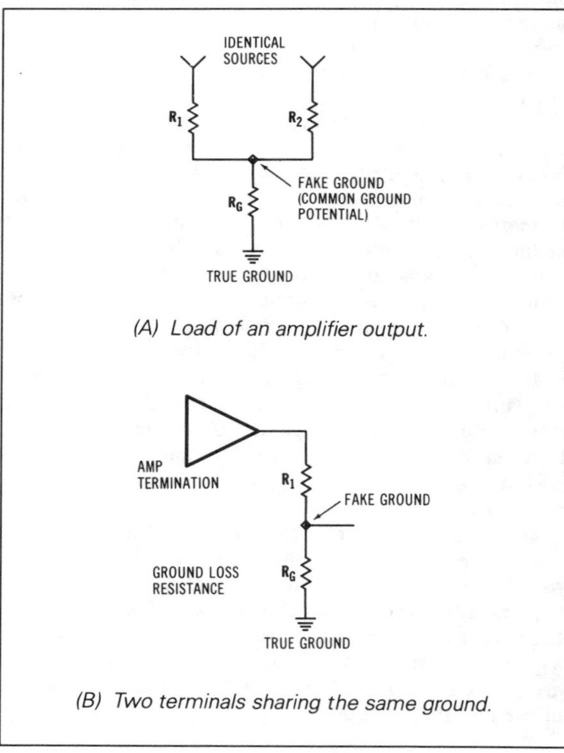

(A) Load of an amplifier output.

(B) Two terminals sharing the same ground.

Figure 22-26 Ground current summing.

22.7.4.3 Typical Grounding Problems

Let us take a fairly unusual (but definitely not unknown) grounding anomaly caused as a result of inattention to

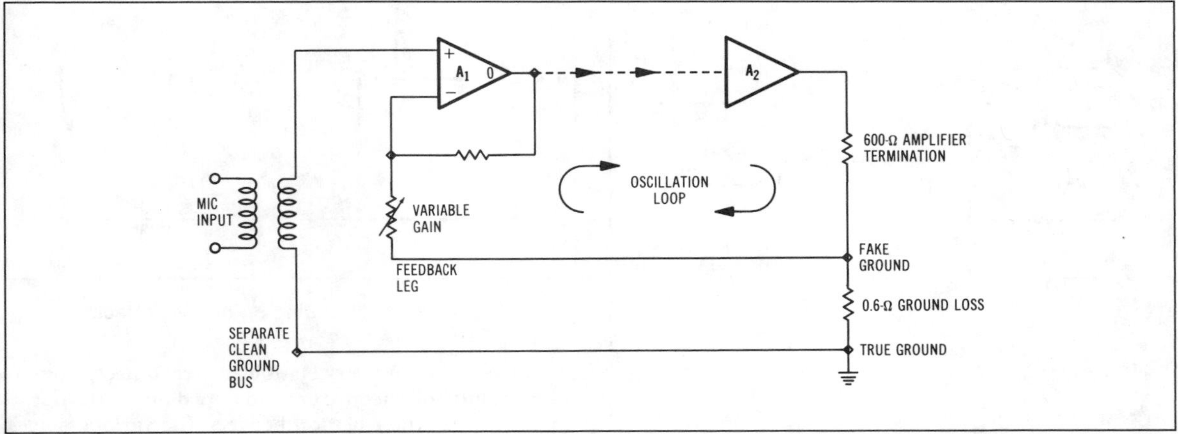

Figure 22-27 Feedback and oscillation via poor grounding.

the grounding paths. In Fig. 22-27 A_2 is a line amp feeding a termination of 600 Ω into a lossy ground of 0.6 Ω resulting in a fake ground potential 60 dB below the output of the amp. An earlier stage in the chain A_1 (in this example a microphone amplifier, with a considerable amount of gain) has its feedback leg (amplifier reference) tied to the same fake ground. Its input ground reference (here lies the problem) is taken from a separate bus supposedly to provide a nice, clean ground. This, of course, it does admirably, the bus being tied straight to true ground and having no sources of great substance going to it.

Any signal present on the fake ground is duly amplified by the microphone amplifier (in its inverting mode) and is attenuated at the line amplifier output back into the fake ground. Then, as soon as the microphone amplifier gain exceeds the output attenuation, the entire chain bursts into glorious oscillation.

A very similar mechanism was responsible for an owner's criticism of his well-known console that whenever he attempted to use the track routing on any channel modules, the sound of that channel discernibly altered. It was found that ordinarily nothing in the channel drew much current; all ground impedance requirements were quite light. That is, they were light until the track routing line amp was accessed with its load of routing resistors and the terminated output transformer demanded a relatively large ground current. This output stage current shared the only ground access point of the module (two paralleled connector pins) with all the rest of the module electronics, with the notable exception of the mic and line input transformer ground returns. The resultant feedback, although nowhere near enough to promote oscillation, did by virtue of the phase shifting of the output transformer at both high and low frequencies result in distinct coloration.

A purist answer to these fake and loop problems is to choose one grounding point for the entire console and to take every reference and ground return directly to it through separate ground wires.

A few minor problems would ensue. The enormous number of ground lines would soon outstrip the capacity of the module connectors, and the mass of wiring would cause apoplexy if not dark mutters of evildoing from the wiremen. Fortunately, a working compromise suggests itself based upon separating the different classes of ground requirements by impedance.

Bucket grounding refers to tying fairly high impedance sources to a common ground point, bus, or line (since the ratio of their impedances is so great that resultant fake ground potentials will be normally low enough to ignore). Anything that is likely to draw current (any kind of output or line amplifier stage) should go directly to ground, will not pass through any bus, and will not collect shared ground paths on the way to the bucket.

Any ground bus will have a measure of resistance and must, therefore, be fake to a certain degree. If we do our sums right, ground bus signal levels can be kept acceptably low, say below −100 dBu.

Smugly, we can expect to ignore figures like that until we (almost inevitably) amplify them up. If you're wondering what crazy circuit arrangement unavoidably amplifies up ground noise, it's called the *virtual-earth mix-amp*.

22.7.4.4 Ground Noise in Virtual Earth Mixers

Fig. 22-28A tells the story. For instance, a multitrack mix-amp can typically have 32 sources applied to it; the through gain from any source is unity (assuming the source resistors equal the feedback resistor), but the real electronic gain of the circuit is 33 or about 30 dB. Redrawing the circuit slightly in Fig. 22-28B shows exactly what this 30 dB is amplifying. Consider as a clue that which is directly applied to the noninverting input of the

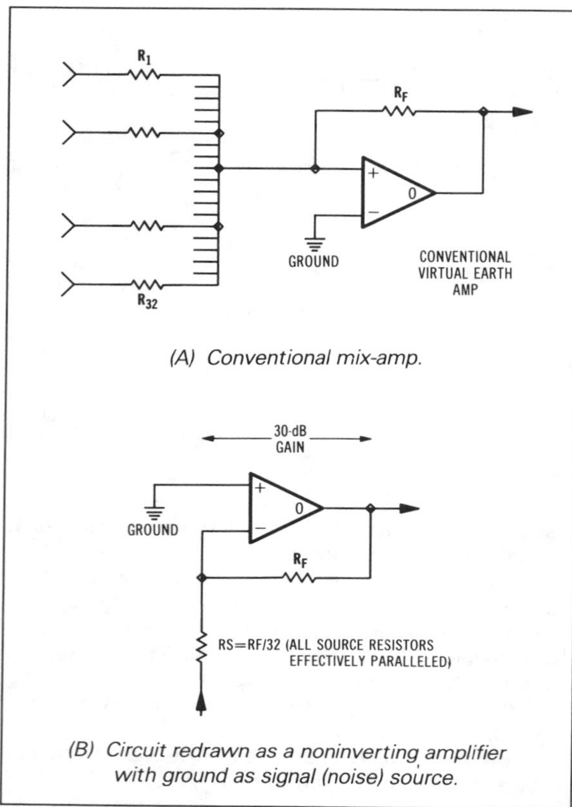

(A) Conventional mix-amp.

(B) Circuit redrawn as a noninverting amplifier with ground as signal (noise) source.

Figure 22-28 Virtual-earth mix amplifier as amplifier of ground-borne noise.

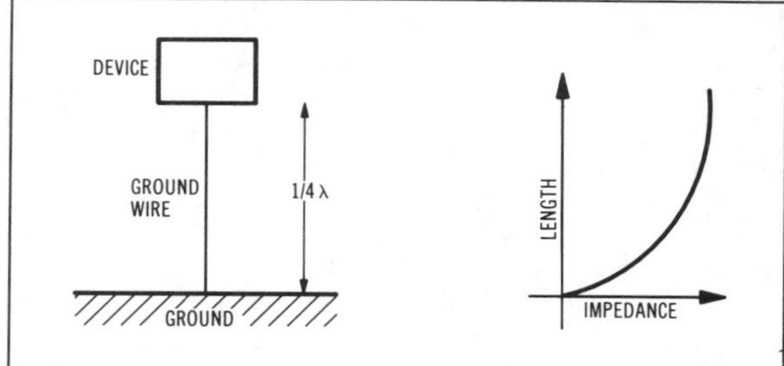

Figure 22-29 "Standing on one leg effect."

op-amp—the ground! True, it is also merrily amplifying the noise due to the resistors and the internal noise mechanisms of the device, but for our argument here, it is amplifying ground.

In any reasonably sized console, providing no sources are grossly out of proportion to the majority, ground noise is pretty random and noisy in character. The result is that, on being amplified up, it serves to make the mix-amp apparently noisier than would be expected from calculation. In suspect systems it has been found to be the predominant noise source. It is truly astonishing what loving care and attention to virtual-earth mixer grounding can have on bus noise figures.

For mix-amps, practical noise performance has little to do with the device employed and nearly everything to do with grounding.

22.7.4.5 Reactive Ground Effects

Noise generation due to grounds is not limited to the resistance predominant in the ground wiring at audio frequencies. At radio frequencies well within the bandwidths of modern op-amps, even fairly short ground wires and buses can have very significant reactances dramatically raising the effective ground impedance. This not so much reduces the isolation between the various stages as directly couples them together. All the inherent radio-frequency noise instabilities of the stages become intermodulated (by the nonlinearity of the device at those frequencies) to make their presence felt as yet more audible and measurable noise.

A good "shock horror" example, which although described in simplistic theoretical terms, manifests itself sometimes dramatically in practice and can be called the "standing on one leg effect."

The box in Fig. 22-29 represents a device that relies on the wire to be connected to the ground mass. It looks all right, and it is, apart from the fact that at certain radio frequencies the wire is electrically 0.25 wavelength or an odd multiple of 0.25 wavelength. Our innocuous bit of wire turns into a tuned line transforming the zero impedance of the ground to an infinite impedance at the other end. The result is that the device is totally decoupled from ground at those frequencies. Practical consequences of this, of course, vary, from instability at very high frequencies on cards with long supply and ground leads to my most memorable encounter where an otherwise incurable case of television signal demodulation in an electronic keyboard was fixed just by snipping a foot off the power-line lead.

22.8 SIGNAL SWITCHING AND ROUTING

Signal routing within the channel and other areas of the system is a touchy problem that has always been an area of much discontent for console designers, especially since the advent of in-line consoles and projected remotable and assignable systems. There are the old, standard relays, but these have lost, justifiably, a lot of appeal in the light of current technological advances.

22.8.1 Relays

Unless they are of the expensive miniature IC package variety, relays tend to be big, heavy, eventually unreliable, mechanically noisy, and a nuisance to implement electronically. They also demand support circuitry such as back-emf protection diodes and drive transistors for a realistically operable system. The coils, being inductive in nature, draw a surprisingly large instantaneous on current and release an equally surprisingly large amount of back-emf energy when deactivated. Both of these—through mutual-inductance coupling, dubious common ground paths (even as far back as the master ground termination in separated supply systems), twitchy power supplies, and even mechanical microphonic effects—tend to impinge themselves on audio signal paths as clicks, splats, and other assorted bumps. Of course, it's possible to have silent relay switching. However, after designing in separate ground unrelated power supplies of considerable heft, spatially separating the relays from the audio (preferably on another card), working out the drive interfaces, and liberally sprinkling the whole issue with diodes, resistors, and capacitors to tame the spiky transients, you'll wish you'd taken up making telephone exchanges instead.

Certain routing applications do implicitly require relays and their lack of concern about the amount of dc and either common-mode or differential signals of absurd quantities that may accompany the audio in balanced networks. Such circumstances are to be found anywhere a telephone line is used.

Primarily, then, this is almost specifically a broadcaster's problem, where many external high-quality sources appear down phone lines and need to be routed before hitting either the internal distribution amplifier system of the station or even a desk line input directly. *Outside source selection*, as it's called, does not, fortunately, have the same splat-elimination constraints as intraconsole switching, since the signal is nearly always of high level, balanced, and riding with at least a little dc (which will unavoidably click upon switching), but most importantly the selector is very unlikely to be switched while actually on air.

22.8.2 Electronic Switching

The basic outline characteristics for an audio switch are simply that it:

1. has an infinite off impedance,
2. a zero on impedance,
3. a control signal that is isolated from and does not impinge upon the through signal path.

In the real world, of course, some leeway has to be given, but, fortunately, more must be given in subtleties than in these basics.

Transistors are out right away despite their splendidly high on-off impedance ratios, because they are essentially unidirectional in current flow, and the control port (the base) is actually half of the signal path as well.

Field-effect transistors have been and still are used extensively for switching. They again have a high on-off ratio, and the control port (the gate) is of extremely high impedance and well isolated from the signal path, but the gate on-off voltage levels are a bit awkward for interfacing with logic control signals. They also define signal head room through the switch. It is bidirectional, its channel path being essentially just a voltage-controlled resistor, but the on resistance tends to vary with the varying audio voltage across it (auto modulation); hence, distortion in the more basic FET switching configurations can be a problem.

22.8.3 MOSFETS and CMOS

Closely related to FETs are *metal-oxide-semiconductor field-effect transistors (MOSFETs)*. They have a different chemical structure and physical construction but have essentially similar characteristics with the pleasant exceptions that the gate is of even higher impedance and is better isolated, and the control voltage swing required is easier to deal with. *Complementary MOSFET (CMOS) elements*, connected back to back to form virtually ideal bidirectional analog transmission gates, are nowadays manufactured in all manner of variations and packages by IC manufacturers. Early versions of CMOS transmission gates had some rather untoward vices. They were raw CMOS elements, and one of their main attributes, the extremely high impedances in their off states and of their control ports, made them liable to destruction by fairly everyday amounts of static electricity. Also, they tended to latch up easily should any of the MOS junctions inadvertently get reverse biased into conduction; this happened easily if the signal voltage passing through a gate even momentarily exceeded the supply voltage. Most current devices are now gate protected to prevent static blatting, and the worst that happens with the audio signal exceeding the switch supply voltage by a small amount is that the switch breaks over, not resulting in the fatal consequences it once did.

Perhaps the best-known and most-used switch of this kind is the 4016 (and its younger brother the 4066, which is essentially identical but for a lower on resistance). It is a 14-pin dual package containing four independently controllable CMOS transmission gates. Each gate can pass up to the ICs supply voltage (typically 18 V) into a load exceeding 10 kΩ with a distortion of about 0.4% in the most basic of switching formats. Obviously, both the distortion figure and the headroom availability of 18 dB above 0.775 V (for an 18-V supply) are both woefully inadequate by today's expected console standards. Another less obvious pitfall is the decreasing switch isolation at high frequencies due to leakage capacitance across the gate.

Fig. 22-30A gives a typical representation of the variation of the on resistance of a CMOS transmission gate

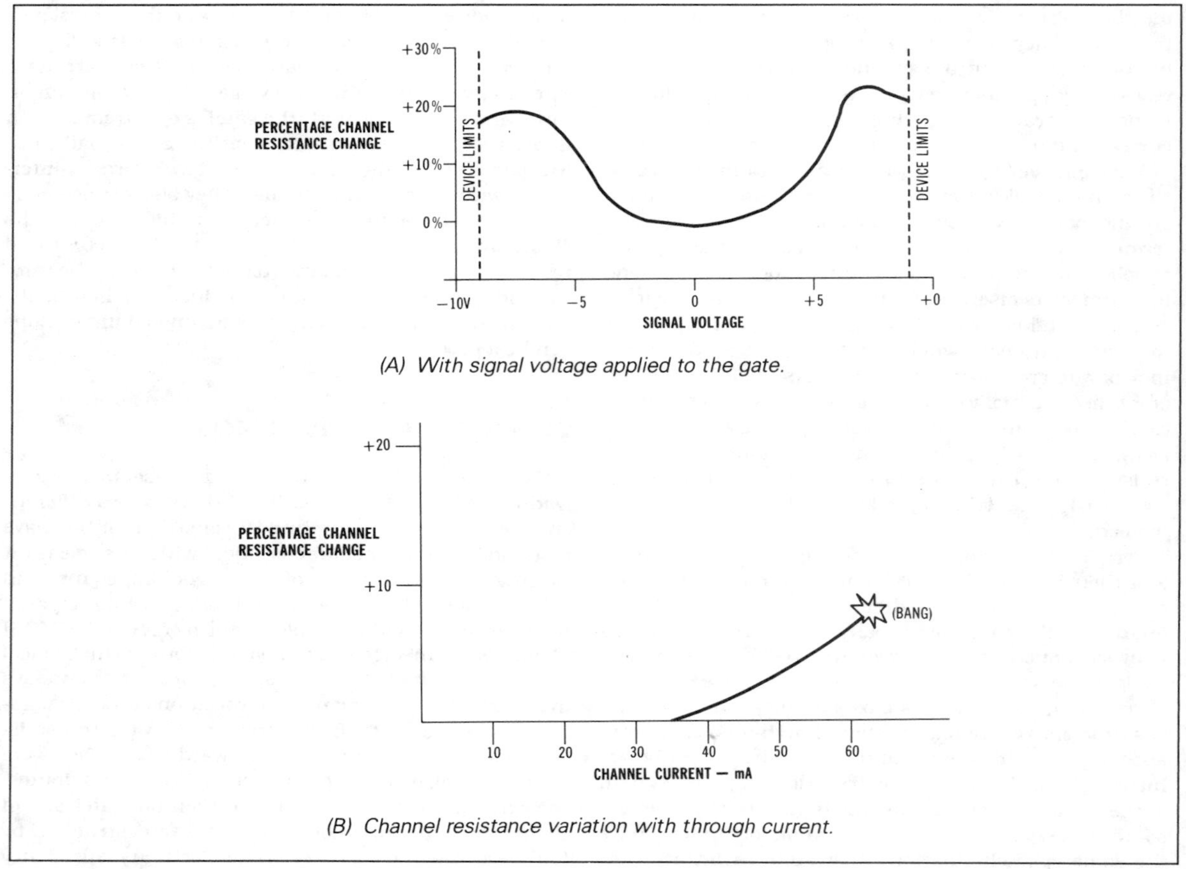

(A) With signal voltage applied to the gate.

(B) Channel resistance variation with through current.

Figure 22-30 Typical CMOS transmission gate linearity.

with signal voltage applied to the gate. This variation in resistance is, of course, the source of the distortion. If we could restrict the signal voltage to within that (linear) bit in the middle, or better still virtually eliminate the signal voltage altogether, our problem would be solved.

Placing the switching element right up against a virtual-earth ground point, as in Fig. 22-31A, achieves this signal voltage elimination; the switch now behaves as a two-state resistor. When closed, the on resistance variation, which will be small anyway because of the very low voltage swing across it, will be effectively swamped by the (relatively) much larger series resistance. When open, the off resistance extends the total series resistance to a value approaching infinity. In practice, the on-off ratio is not really adequate. Capacitance across printed-circuit tracks and in the device encapsulation itself, combined with common-ground current and other essentially flat-response crosstalk mechanisms, results in a cross-switch leakage characteristic ultimately rising 6 dB/octave against frequency. Also, despite the fact that the distortion problem is now largely resolved, there still remains a head room problem when the switch is open. If the source voltage presented to the series resistor exceeds that of the power supply of the CMOS gates, the gate will break over, turning on for that excessive portion of the input waveform.

Attenuating the source signal by the needed amount before it hits the gate skirts this hang-up, unfortunately, by worsening the noise gain of the virtual-ground amplifier by the amount of that attenuation. In Fig. 22-31B dropping to ground an equal-value resistor to the series resistor from its junction with the gate is a working approach. The maximum signal that can be present across the gate when off is now half that previously, which is usually more than enough attenuation to prevent breakover. This 6-dB loss is magically made up for in the on mode because the source resistance of the signal into the amplifier is now halved (series resistance effectively in parallel with the dropped resistor). Incidentally, the crosstalk improves as a consequence by almost 6 dB—less signal voltage actually within the chip. For many practical purposes, this switching configuration, with its

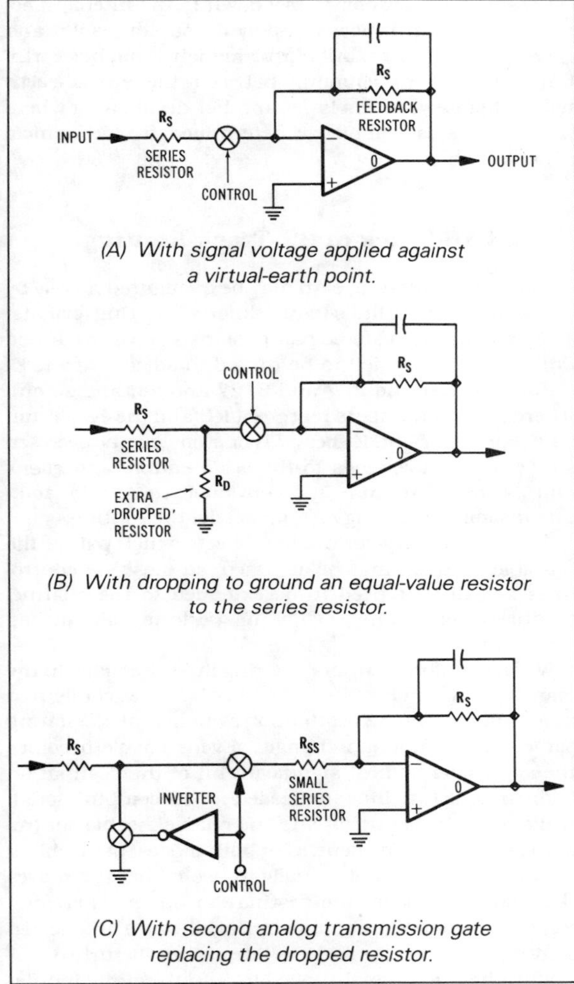

(A) With signal voltage applied against a virtual-earth point.

(B) With dropping to ground an equal-value resistor to the series resistor.

(C) With second analog transmission gate replacing the dropped resistor.

Figure 22-31 Switching arrangements using CMOS transmission gates.

performance limitations as defined, is quite adequate. For instance, the noise and crosstalk characteristics are a good order of magnitude superior to any analog multitrack recorder, so this element can be a good choice for a track assignment routing matrix.

22.8.4 Potentiometric Switching

A refinement of this element—in fact, really an extension of the same principle—is shown in Fig. 22-31C. Here, a second analog transmission gate replaces the dropped resistor and is driven through an inverter from the control line for the original gate, arranging for it to be on when the other is off and vice versa. When the original gate is on, there is very little potential across either of the gates (they're both at virtual ground from the op-amp). Similarly, there is little potential across either of the gates when the second gate is on, since it is tying the series resistor to ground and the open gate is between ground and virtual ground. Crosstalk is dramatically improved when the element is off because any signal present at the series resistor faces the double attenuation of the series resistor tied to ground by the on second gate followed by the off original gate into the virtual-earth input of the op-amp. In the on mode of the element, there is no input attenuation, hence, no gain and no extra noise contribution from the amplifier. The only limitation now to the cross-switch leakage characteristic of this switching element is printed-circuit card layout and grounding arrangements. Given a good home, this element is virtually unmeasurable.

It does, however, have one quirk that may preclude its use in some places. Unless a great deal of care is used to arrange complementary on-off switching timing for the two gates, they are both momentarily partially on together during a switching transition. This, for an instant, ties the virtual-earth amp input to ground via the quite low half-on impedances of the two series gates, creating an instantaneous burst of extremely high gain from the amp; this shows as a transient of noise or worse still as a splat if any dc offset is present at the virtual-earth point. It can be minimized, or at least the extent of the transient defined, by a small value resistor in series with the input (Fig. 22-31C). This will, of course, increase the signal voltage across the gates and increase the distortion, so a compromise has to be struck to suit the given application. However, excessive distortion owing to this has never shown itself to be a problem.

22.8.5 Minimizing Noise

To reduce the thermal noise contribution to the circuit noise performance, the resistances involved in switching should be as low as practically possible, consistent with device limitations and the ground current arrangements. The feedback resistor around the virtual-earth stage is limited by the output drive capability of the op-amp, bearing in mind it has to drive its load, too. Fig. 22-30B demonstrates a typical channel resistance variation of a CMOS switching element with through current. It behaves linearly until about 40 mA, which actually compares more than favorably with the output drive current capability of an op-amp. (FETs are excellent constant-current sources, self-limiting in nature.) As a rule of thumb then, the resistors used around analog gate switching circuits can be as low as 2.2 kΩ without exceeding device limitations; the high-output current capability of the 5534 can be used in effect here if the drive for the diamond of lowest possible thermal noise is that important. Generally, ground-borne noise kindly provides a noise floor well before this theoretical limit is attained; the whole lowest-impedance question becomes self-defeating eventually. The more current we have, the worse the ground noise is going to become.

22.8.6 Practical Matrix

The 4000 series of CMOS devices, which are very commonly used, have one important feature at odds with general mixer technology—their maximum supply voltages. The earlier 4000 A series were limited to a 15-V total (as compared to the 30- or 36-V total commonly used in console design), while the more recent buffered B series can stand 18 V. Although power supply limitations are fairly immaterial (given the virtual-earth switching technique), it is a pain having to provide for and derive a differential ±5-V supply either centrally or on each card in addition to the main differential 18-V supply. Many IC manufacturers, however, notably Siliconix and Harris, produce analog switching packages not only capable of running directly off the full console supply voltages, but also capable of switching configurations that can be directly and usefully applied to our purposes (despite the fact that they were designed for something else completely). Fig. 22-32 shows one mixer channel's worth of a digitally assigned 32-track routing matrix, designed around a pair of Harris HI506A 16-way multiplexers.

The 506A contains 16 analog transmission gates tied to one common output (which we will cross out and pencil in input instead). Each of the free ends of the gates ties directly to a mix bus. They all share a common series source resistor via the input port. Since only one of these gates can be open at a time (the one corresponding to the binary four-bit address code on the address inputs), there is no possibility of two or more buses being inadvertently shorted together. The device manufacturers proudly point out the break-before-make delay in switching, meaning that a newly selected gate waits until the previous one has delatched, so there is no momentary switching short.

22.8.7 Matrix Crosstalk

Crosstalk with this configuration, which you will notice is a variation between Figs. 22-31A and C, is extremely good. Again, there is the double attenuation of the series resistor via an on-gate to a virtual-earth bus (some 20-dB isolation to start with), followed by the internal isolation between buses owing to the off-gate impedances into all the other virtually zero impedance mixing buses (some additional 70 to 80 dB). A slightly more critical crosstalk situation could exist when all the gates are turned off (by tying the 506 enable low [pin 18]) since the first set of attenuation no longer exists; the switches common point would no longer be tied to a virtual earth by any of the elements. This is why external switching elements (IC_{3a} and IC_{3b}) are arranged to tie the end junction of the series resistor and the 506 input common point to ground whenever the enable lines are low.

Crosstalk is now completely down to the interconnections to this card, power supply decoupling, solid and correct ground paths, but mostly inductive and bus/earth/bus eddy-current coupling between the virtual-earth buses themselves; this is yet another design area where performance is completely determined by mechanical considerations.

22.8.8 16-Track or 32-Track Routing

The same switching card may be configured merely by changing two wire links in two different routing formats. The first enables a stereo pair of signals (say the panned outputs of a channel) to be routed to adjacent pairs of outputs (i.e., 1 and 2, 7 and 8, 27 and 28, and so on), where the odd numbers represent left and the even numbers represent right. Either odds or evens may be accessed singly by suitable feeds to the *odds enable* and *evens enable* control inputs. Quite obviously these also facilitate disabling (turning off completely) the routing.

A four-bit binary control bus selects which pair of the possible 16 pairs may be accessed, so these six control lines are all that need to be extended to the channel module where simple switching performs all routing requirements.

When the aforementioned wiring links are made in the fashion shown in Fig 22-32, the card becomes configured as a 1-source-into-32 destination switcher, necessitating some control function changes. Evens enable becomes the additional highest significant bit of the destination address code (five bits are needed for 32 combinations), while odds enable turns into the enable/disable control of the switcher. (The benefit, in both modes, of disabling the switcher when not actually in use is that it removes the feed totally from the destination buses. Therefore, their performance is not impaired at all, and a preselected routing set up on the address lines is not disturbed.)

With the same signal applied to both the audio inputs, it is now possible to access any one of the 32 buses.

22.8.9 Processor Control

The seemingly great mass of logic circuitry enclosed in the dotted lines allows the card to be controlled by a computer or central processing unit (CPU). It's really just six flip-flops acting as memory elements (so that the card can remember what the CPU has told it to do) and six tristate buffers that, on request, tell the CPU what the card is actually doing. These little chunks of memory both save the CPU from having to store the matrix routing information somewhere else and also act as a very useful diagnostic aid to help find out what isn't doing what, where, and why.

For ordinary direct operation, this logic can be left off the card completely and linked across (between the x's on the diagram). The NAND gates in the top left-hand corner merely organizes the CPU bus information to fire the appropriate clock, enables, and resets to the memory elements.

CMOS 4000 series logic operating at 5 V is not the fastest logic family in existence and is too slow for most microprocessor CPUs to drive directly. The circuitry shown here will operate successfully from a microprocessor running at a 500-kHz clock rate, which is woefully slow in this world of 16-MHz microclocks and buses. This slowness is not a problem in reality, since the practical way of dealing with this is to hang the entire switching matrix logic system off a bunch of the CPU input/output ports, masquerading as a local address/data/control bus system at a fairly leisurely software-controlled rate.

A convenient 16 input-output (i/o) line is required (two lots of eight, handy for micros). A single 8255 or 6850 Peripheral Interface Adapter (PIA) would handle this matrix. A suggested format is in Table 22-1. Being software controlled, the i/o lines may be timed a little more gently than the hardware-determined processor buses.

A separate address decoder card takes however many of the card address bits that are required (5 for 32, 6 for 64, 7 for 128) and generates the decoded feeds for the card enable (CE) on each matrix card. This is very simply accomplished with a daisy chain of 4028 binary-to-decimal decoders (Fig. 22-33).

22.8.10 Audio Path

In the bottom left-hand corner of Fig. 22-32 hides a good old-fashioned analog mix-amp and line amp, which are the group output stages for the channel to which the particular matrix card is relevant. Where else to put them except on the matrix card where they cannot get any closer to the buses?

The mix-bus input is tied on the back of the edge-connector to the bus it is responsible for sensing. This ensures card replaceability and redundancy; individually doctored cards are the kiss of death from a maintenance standpoint since there is no means of getting a given path going again (in the event of a failure) without actually fixing the fault. The old standby of swapping cards wouldn't work; it is best to keep individualisms off the cards.

Note that no values are attributed to the feedback capacitor around the mix-amp, since this not only has to compensate for the amplifier's own tendency to instability but for the added irritation to this of the bus impedance—an unknown until actual construction. Similarly, astute circuitophiles will note a capacitor across part of the switcher input series resistance. This provides a variable high-frequency kick, which can be of assistance in sorting out frequency and phase response quirks in particularly horrid bus systems. This is, fortunately, very rarely needed and is provided just in case.

Fig. 22-34 shows the audio path through the switcher, devoid of frills. The mystery 1-kΩ resistor R_S, which does not appear on Fig. 22-32, is internal to the HI506A, appearing on each of the switch inputs. Although a minor nuisance in this application, which means the CMOS switches are not actually switching a zero impedance, they are part of the device's internal protection against, principally, static electricity damage—a worthwhile sacrifice. Harris does make an unprotected version, the HI506, with all the switching elements exposed, which would mean that the on-impedance of the device would be down to the 300 Ω of the element as opposed to the 1.3 kΩ of the HI506A, but the use of an expensive unprotected IC on a plug-in card such as this has a very high cringe factor.

The total source impedance before the bus is around

Table 22-1. Processor I/O Lines Dedication

	Line	Function	Description
CPU I/O	1	CARD ADDRESS	—least significant bit (LSB)
	2	CARD ADDRESS	
	3	CARD ADDRESS	(Seven binary bits allow up to 128 matrix routing cards to be separately addressed)
	4	CARD ADDRESS	
	5	CARD ADDRESS	
	6	CARD ADDRESS	
	7	CARD ADDRESS	—most significant bit (MSB)
	8	$\overline{\text{R}}$ $\overline{\text{RESET}}$ or $\overline{\text{CLEAR}}$	(When this bit is *down*, all memory is cleared)
	9	$\overline{\text{W}}$ $\overline{\text{WRITE}}$	(This bit down allows data on lines 11–16 to be stuffed into memory)
	10	ϕ2 MID–PHASE CLOCK	(Clock pulse delayed slightly to allow data and address to settle before enabling the memory)
CPU I/O	11	DATA	Matrix card, output or memory
	12	DATA	—least significant bit (LSB)
	13	DATA	Matrix card, output or selection
	14	DATA	—most significant bit (MSB)
	15	DATA	—even enable (or MSB is one-of-32 mode)
	16	DATA	—odds enable (or on/off)

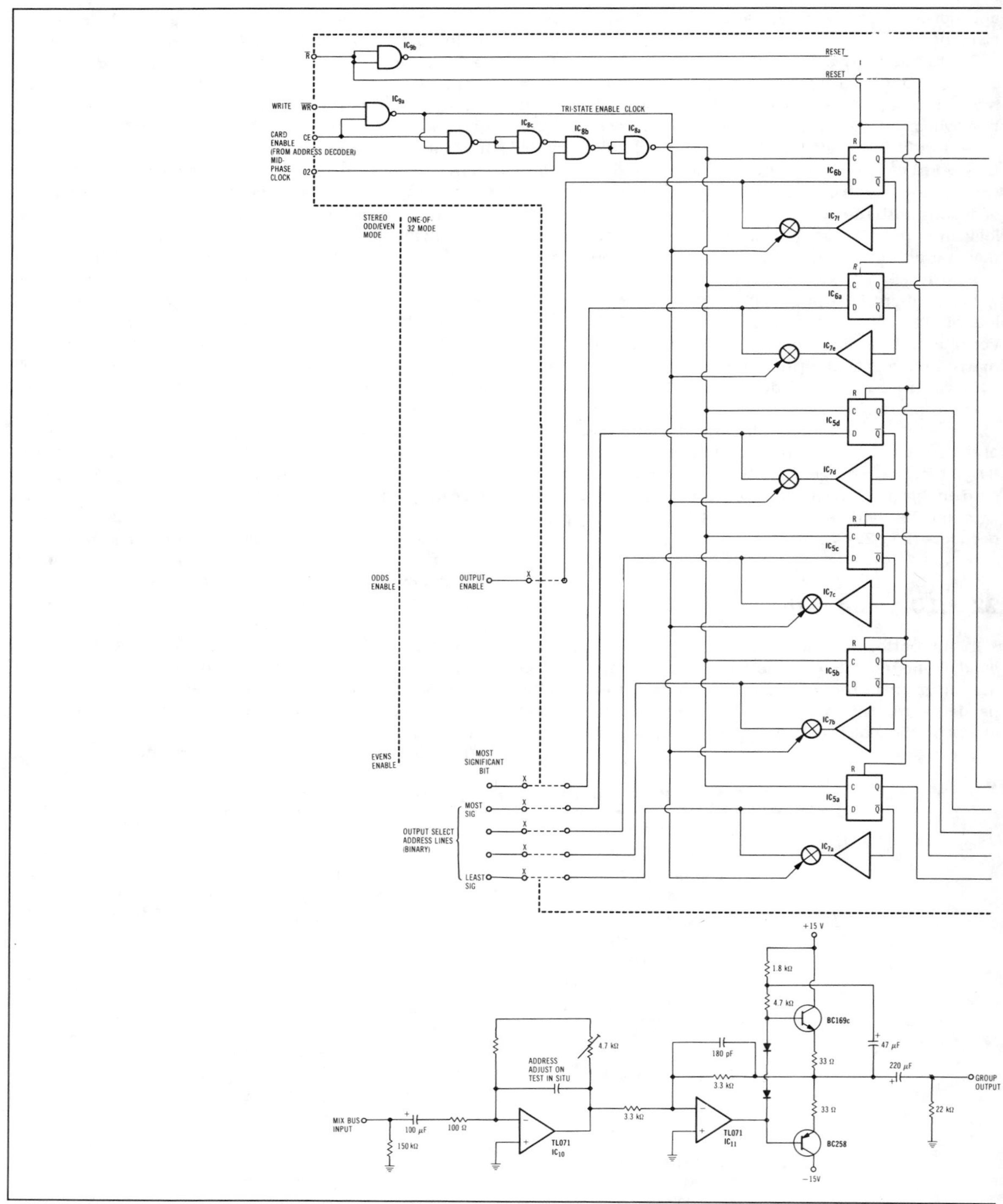

Figure 22-32 Processor-controllable

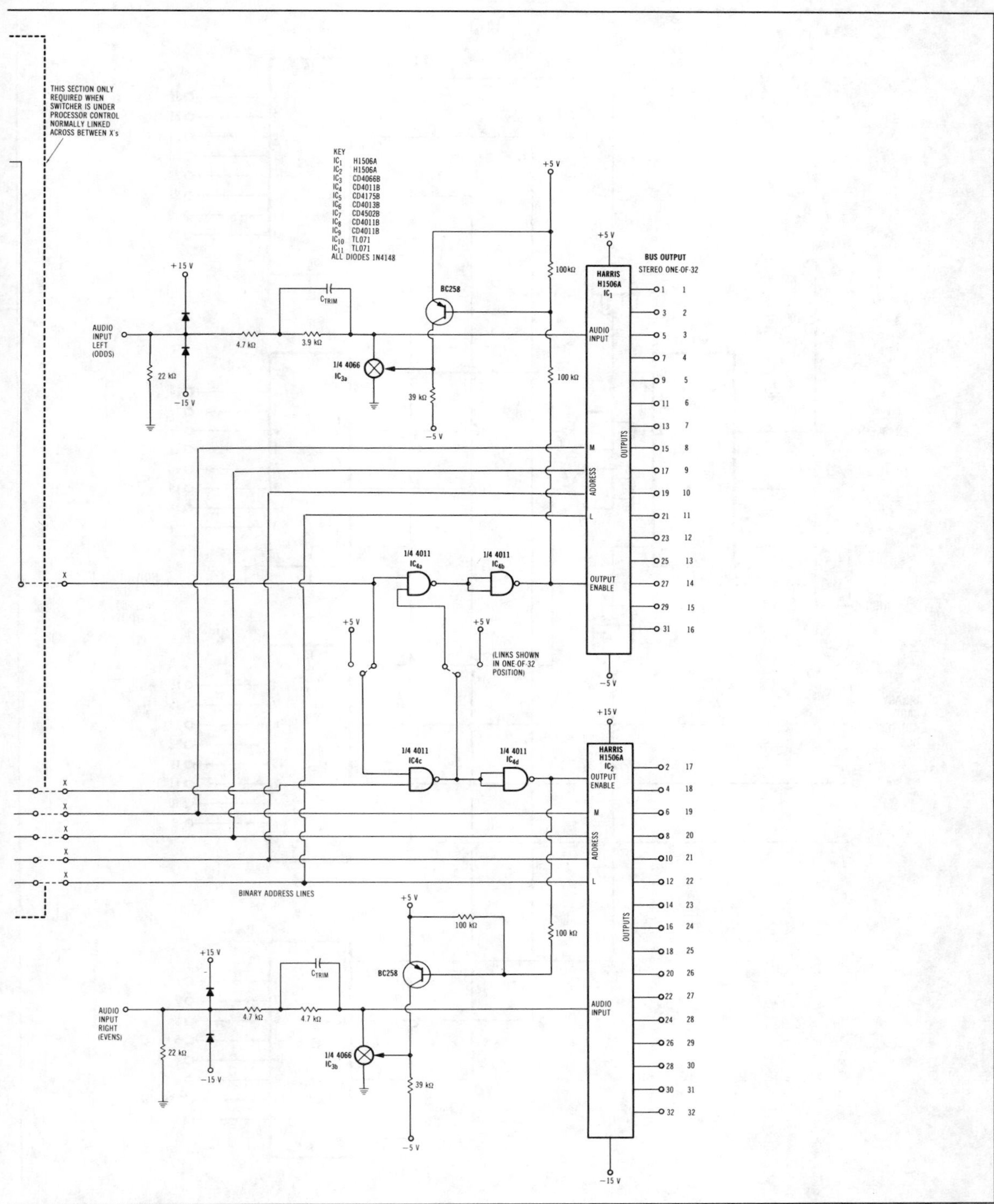

matrix routing circuit.

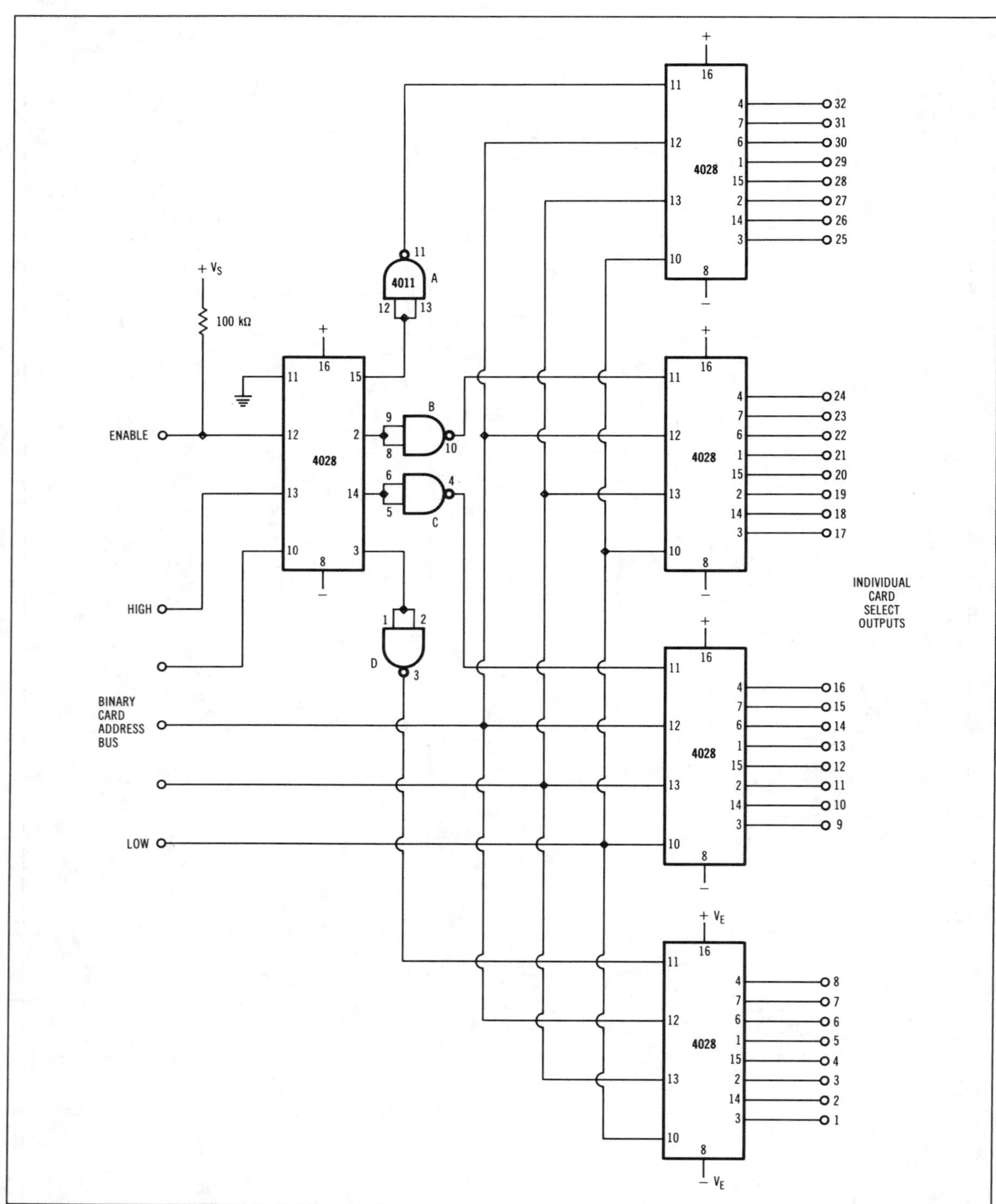

Figure 22-33 Matrix channel-decoding logic.

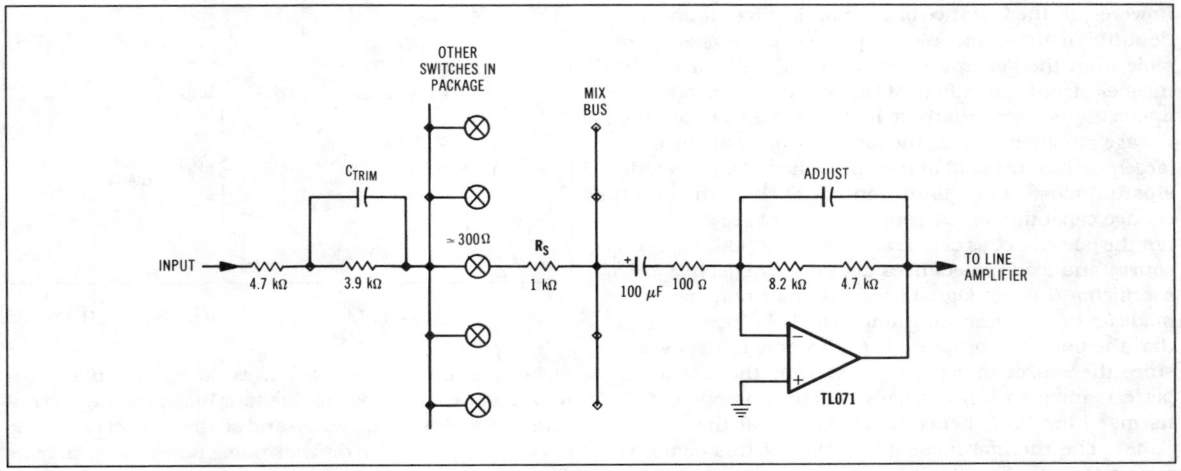

Figure 22-34 Switcher audio path.

9.9 kΩ, which with the addition of the 100-Ω buffering resistor becomes 10 kΩ before the virtual-earth input of the mix-amp. A 4.7 kΩ gain trim preset in series with 8.2 kΩ gives a gain determining feedback resistor swing of approximately 8.2 to 12.9 kΩ, which corresponds to a swing of −1.7 to 2.2 dB.

The line amp is quite unremarkable. It is a simple beefed-up inverting amplifier necessary to maintain the absolute input-output phase relationship.

22.9 INPUT AMPLIFIER DESIGN

A console is expected to accept any signal in the way of input level and impedance while producing a uniformly consistent output capable of being deposited in the tightly defined container that is a tape track.

Fortunately, industry standards provide at least some clues as to what mixers are likely to have stuffed in them. Nevertheless, these standards can obviously do nothing to alter the physics of the operation of the assorted transducers and sources used and the disparity in the treatment required for a dynamic microphone, and a tape machine output totally precludes a universal input stage.

Mixer front-end design tends to be a little like working on a grown-up jigsaw puzzle where all the important pieces perversely refuse to fit. It's really delightful to find or develop some that fit beautifully—as in line-level input stages. This euphoria is ground away by the problems inherent in other areas, notably microphone input stages.

Optimizing input noise performance in a dynamic microphone preamp is a performance, juggling a seemingly endless number of variables. A dynamic microphone may be represented (a little simplistically) as a voltage source in series with a fairly lossy inductance representing a midband impedance typically of between

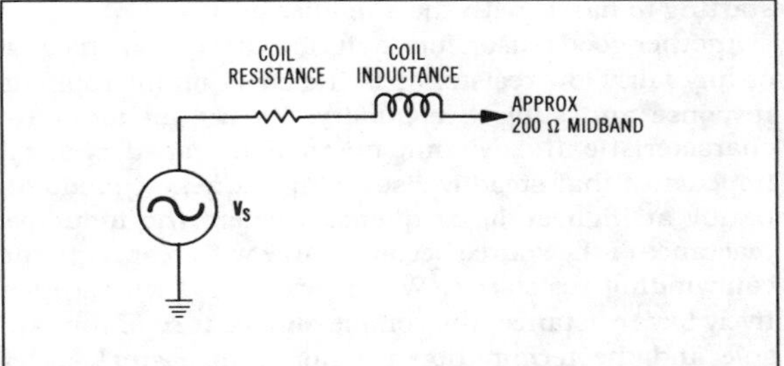

Figure 22-35 Simplistic dynamic microphone model.

150 and 300 Ω (Fig. 22-35). Being a transducer and, of necessity, mechanical in nature, many complex varying motional impedance effects contribute to the overall scene, but for most design purposes, the specified electrical analog can suffice. The low impedance commonly and conventionally used is primarily to mitigate high-frequency attenuation effects due to the inevitable cable capacitance, which in practical circumstances mounts up to horrifying values of capacitance that the transducer must drive along with its load. Unfortunately, the impedance is not low enough that it may be treated as a pure voltage source; there exists a tiny signal at a finite impedance that must be daintily ferreted out for optimum performance.

22.9.1 Power Transfer and Termination Impedance

Textbooks on electrical theory quite correctly state that to extract maximum power from a given source the optimum load is equal in value to the source impedance. This, however, in the instance of a dynamic microphone, is of doubtful (if any) value. We've squeezed all the energy possible from the generator, but to what end? Given that most electronic amplifiers of the type useful in low-noise applications are of relatively high input impedance (i.e., voltage amplifiers), then the terminating resistance that largely defines the load of the microphone is, in fact, dissipating most of our hard-won power. It is the output voltage capability of the source that is of greatest value, not the power. So, as can be seen in Fig. 22-36, matching source and load impedances does a very effective job of sacrificing 6 dB of signal level that naturally has to be made up in the succeeding amplifier. This does not imply that the noise performance is 6 dB worse than possible, since the source impedance as seen by the (assumedly perfect) amplifier is now a parallel of the microphone and its matching load; hence, it is about half the value of either. The thermal noise generation of this combined source is consequently 3 dB less; hence, the noise performance is only degraded 3 dB by such a termination. Still, who wants to throw away a good 3 dB before even starting to hassle with the amplifier itself.

Another good reason for not terminating with an equal or any fairly low resistance is the effect on microphone response and subjective quality. Having an inductive characteristic, the dynamic microphone capsule has an impedance that steadily rises with frequency, predominantly at high audio frequencies where the inductive reactance of the source becomes large with respect to the coil-winding resistance. When terminated with a relatively low resistance, the complex impedance of the capsule and the termination resistor form a single-order 6-dB/octave low-pass filter, gracefully rolling off the top.

With a fairly hefty cable capacitance, the system is no longer graceful, since the complete network now looks like a rather poor second-order filter. Still, regardless of termination method, we are stuck with cable capacitance. It is always a consideration unless the preamp is remoted to or close to the microphone itself.

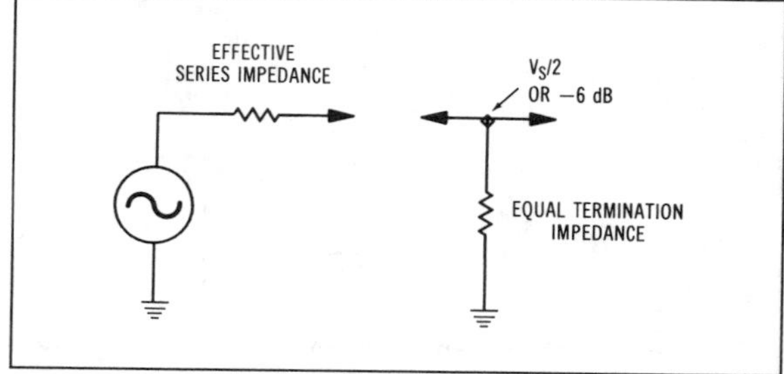

Figure 22-36 Matching—how to lose 6 dB.

22.9.2 Optimizing Noise Performance

Amplifiers are not perfect. For noise criteria, the first device that the signal hits in the amp is the key one, since the noise it generates usually masks, by a large margin, noise due to all succeeding stages.

All practical amplifying devices are subject to a variety of internal noise-generating mechanisms, including thermal noise generation. When measured, these give rise to some important values, namely, input noise voltage and input noise current.

For the most part, ordinary bipolar transistors are used as front-end devices both in discrete designs and op-amp IC packages so much of the following is specific to them.

These noise voltages and currents alter in both individual magnitude and ratio to each other with differing electrical parameters, especially collector current. Predictably, as this current decreases, so does the noise current (most of the noise is due to minor random discontinuities in device currents), and so the ratio between the noise voltage and current, or noise impedance, may be altered.

Thermal noise generation is common to all resistive elements, its amount being related to both temperature and the bandwidth across which it is measured; an increase in either will increase proportionally the noise power generated. Under identical circumstances, the noise power that is generated by any values of resistance is the same. Differing resistor values merely serve to create differing ratios of noise voltage and noise current, the product of the two always equaling the same noise power. This particular noise phenomenon is totally unavoidable, since the nature of atomic structure is that, when things get hot, they grind and shuffle about randomly, creating electrical disturbances white in spectra (i.e., equal energy per bandwidth).

Even the real (resistive) part of the complex impedance of a dynamic microphone generates thermal noise, and this ensures that there is a rigidly defined noise value that cannot in any way be bettered.

22.9.3 Noise Figure

The difference between the noise floor defined by thermal noise and the measured noise value of a practical system is known as the *noise figure (NF)* and is measured in decibels (Noise figure = System noise − Theoretical noise). The noise output from a resistor is predictable. Therefore, a direct comparison of the noise voltage measured at the output of an amplifier from a resistor applied to the amplifier input and the noise voltage expected of the resistor on its own is possible just by simply subtracting the measured gain of the amplifier. This is a measure of NF.

An interesting effect occurs when, with any given set of electrical parameters set up for the amplifier front-end device, the source resistance is steadily changed in value. A distinct dip in the NF occurs (Fig. 22.37), and the value of the resistor at which this dip occurs changes as the device parameters are changed (collector current primar-

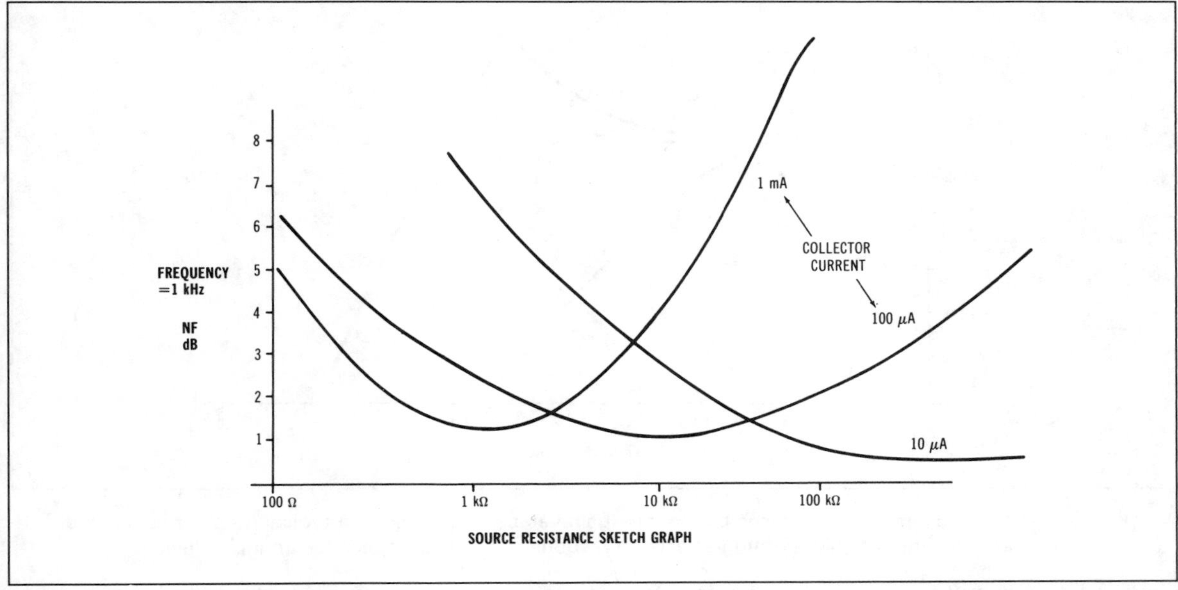

Figure 22-37 Bipolar noise curves (noise figure curves for a good pnp front-end transistor for collector current versus source resistance).

ily). For the usually predominant noise mechanism (thermal noise), a minimum NF occurs with a tiny amount of collector current (5 to 50 μA) and a high source resistance (50 kΩ up). Without diving into the mathematics, the nulling is a balancing of interaction between the external noise source and the internal voltage and current noise generators.

22.9.4 Inverse-Frequency Noise

There is another major noise mechanism inherent to semiconductors. It is the low frequency (inverse level with respect to frequency) noise—a burbly, bumping type noise caused by the semiconductor surface generating and recombining sporadic currents—most prevalent in dirty devices but present to a degree in all. It is subjectively apparent and has to be considered. Measured alone, low-frequency noise has its own set of collector current and source resistance nulls, usually far higher in current and lower in resistance than for thermal noise.

22.9.5 Optimum Source Impedance (OSI)

A compromise has to be struck. To make a generalization, a 100-μA collector current and a 10-kΩ source impedance for a typical low-noise pnp transistor seem about right. (Pnp transistors are commonly used in this area due to marginally better low-frequency performance figures over npn types.) The source resistance value is that at which the device is optimally quiet for audio purposes and is known as the *optimum source impedance (OSI)*. Incidentally, this impedance has absolutely nothing to do with the kind of circuit configuration that the device may be in. Whether it be in a common-base amplifier with an input impedance of 50 Ω or in a totem-pole front end with bootstrapping and a consequential input impedance of over 10 MΩ, it doesn't matter. The source impedance for optimum noise performance stays at 10 kΩ, or whatever, provided that the collector current is the same in all cases. Optimum source impedance has nothing to do with input impedance.

This optimum impedance varies dependent on the type of input device used. For a field-effect transistor, the noise figure typically obtainable drops to an amazingly low value but, unfortunately, at an impedance of several dozen megohms. Even supposing it were practical to provide a source impedance of that magnitude, the whole arrangement would be so sensitive to any electromagnetic fields (such as RF) that even tiny amounts present would obliterate the noise advantage. The design and construction of capacitor microphones using FET front-ends highlight the hazards; the end results more often than not show such capacitor microphones to be several dB noisier than a well-designed dynamic microphone/front-end combination.

Good bipolar transistors have OSIs in the region of 5 to 15 kΩ, whether discrete or as part of an IC amplifier package. By happy accident, these values closely coincide with the source resistance value that provides for optimum flatness of device transfer characteristics. This helps

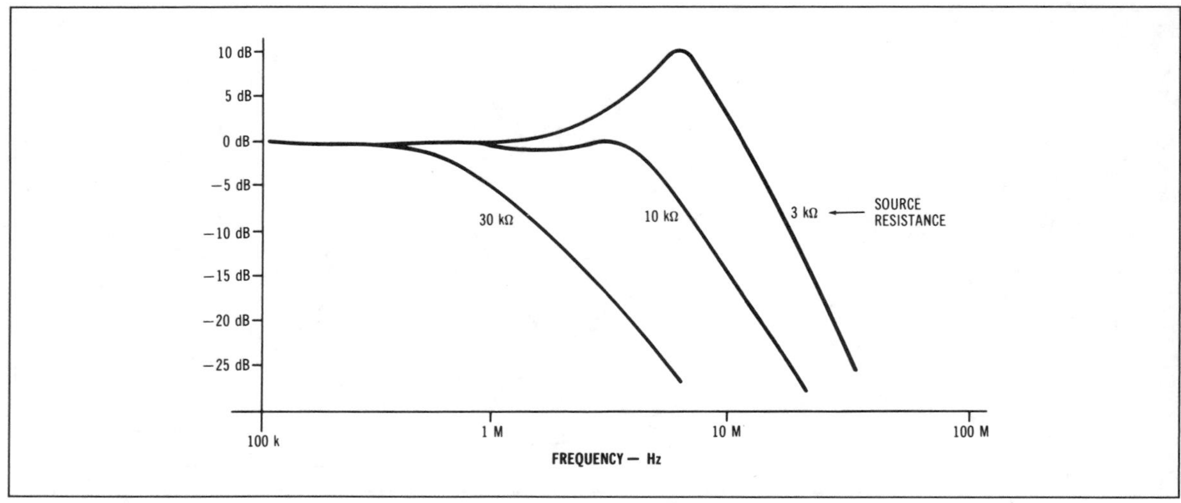

Figure 22-38 Source impedance versus bandwidth (gain versus frequency for a typical follower-connected operational amplifier highlighting effects on response of source impedance on input device.

a long way toward best frequency, phase linearity, and hence, stability in a typical high negative-feedback amp configuration.

Fig. 22-38 shows the effect of altering the source impedance into such an amplifier (using a conventional bipolar transistor input device) on output frequency response. The droop is due to the excessively high source impedance reacting against the device base-emitter, board, and wiring capacitances to form a low-pass filter. The *high-frequency kink* is a practical effect of the curious mechanism; when a bipolar transistor is fed from an impedance approaching zero, its high-frequency gain-bandwidth characteristic extends dramatically, radically altering the phase margin and, consequently, the stability of an amp designed and compensated for more ordinary operating circumstances. The *kink* is a resonance within the amplifier loop caused by erosion of phase margin resulting from this mechanism. It is only an uncomfortably short step from oscillation.

As can be seen from the graph, the response is maximally flat at a source resistance of around 10 kΩ, about the same value as the OSI for optimum noise performance for the same configuration.

A problem to reconcile is that our practical source impedance is nominally 200 Ω for a dynamic microphone, whereas the OSI for the best conventional input devices is around 10 kΩ. How do we make the two fit?

22.9.6 Microphone Transformers

You've undoubtedly heard some horrible stories about how nasty transformers are. However, properly designed and used they do offer a good solution to impedance matching and sundry other problems.

Simplistically, a *transformer* is a magnetically soft core around which are two windings, the voltage ratio between the two being equal to the ratio of the number of turns on each. The impedance ratio is the turns ratio squared (e.g., a 10:1 turns ratio corresponds to a 100:1 impedance ratio) because power output cannot exceed power input. If the *voltage* is stepped up ten times, the output *current* must be stepped down ten times. Impedance, which is the ratio of voltage to current, is, consequently, the square of the transformed voltage or current ratio.

Given this, it is a simple matter to calculate the ratio necessary to match the microphone impedance to the OSI that is actually achievable. Since few people are intense enough about the whole affair to bother measuring microphones, the convention that 200 Ω is a good midpoint for source impedance serves well. The assumption that most bipolar input amplifiers have an OSI of between 5 and 15 kΩ indicates that the transformer ratio should lie somewhere between 1:5 and 1:8.7.

Many consoles use higher ratios (typically 1:10), probably in the belief that the noise advantage of a step-up input transformer stems from the free gain it affords. Although on a basic level it would seem to make sense that the less electronic gain we need to use, the quieter the system must be, this fallacy is completely belied by the truth that the transformer merely allows you to *choose* and *alter* the impedance at which your amplifier is optimally quiet. Increasing the turns ratio beyond this easily defined optimum can and will actually make the amplifier noisier.

In practice the free gain can be more of a nuisance than a benefit. It is not unusual for microphone inputs to receive transients exceeding +10 dBu and mean levels of −10 dBu, especially in a rock-and-roll environment. Even dynamic capsules can deliver frightening levels, and this can pose headroom problems in the mixer front end. A typical 1:5 transformer has a voltage gain of 14 dB (at 1:10, 20 dB), which would mean that even with no electronic gain after the transformer, normal mixer operating levels are being approached and possibly exceeded. These circumstances make worrying about a dB or two of noise performance total nonsense to be sure; it just serves to point out that our microphone front end has to be capable, if not perfectly optimized, for elephant herds as well as butterflies.

22.9.6.1 Transformer Characteristics

Transformers have numerous limitations, inadequacies, and problems resulting from their physical construction that make their actual performance differ (in some respects radically) from that expected of the theoretical model.

The heart of the transformer is the magnetically pliable material into and out of which the energy is induced. Virtually any material: nickel, steel, iron, ferrous derivatives, and substitutes have the same basic limitations: saturation at a magnetic level beyond which they are incapable of supporting further excursion, and hysteresis–a crossoverlike nonlinearity at low levels responsible for a significantly higher distortion at low levels than anything else likely to be found within a signal path.

These two effects at opposite ends of the dynamic spectrum mean that all transformers have a well-defined range within which they must be operated and which is less than the range of levels they are expected to pass in mic-amps. This is especially true at low frequencies where the core is prone to saturation far earlier. Optimization begins here. Is it to be designed for minimum hysteresis (butterflies) or with plenty of material to be tolerant of monstrous (elephantine) signal levels?

Windings are made of wire, which has resistance. Resistance means loss and lack of efficiency and noise performance. By the time there are enough turns on each of the windings to ensure the inductive reactances are high enough not to affect in-band use, the winding resistances can no longer be ignored.

Capacitance exists between things in close proximity and that includes transformer windings—between each other, between adjacent turns and piles in the same winding, and from the windings to ground. In this given instance it is nothing but bad news. Capacitance between windings means unwanted leakage and imperfect isolation, while winding self-capacitance reacts with the winding inductances to form resonances. Resonances, even if way out of the audio band, invite response trouble, and disturb in-band phase linearity. Combinations of these capacitances greatly affect one of the most touted advantages of transformers, *common-mode rejection (CMR)*.

22.9.6.2 Common-Mode Rejection

Common-mode rejection is the ability of the transformer to ignore signals present in identical amplitude and phase on the two input legs and not transfer them across the secondary as differential information.

Principally, it is imbalanced distribution of capacitance along the length of the two windings, both with respect to each other and to ground that makes CMR less than perfect. Co-winding capacitance has the effect of directly coupling the two wiring masses together permitting common-to-differential signal passage, which worsens with increasing frequency at 6 dB/octave. Electrostatic shielding (a Faraday shield) between the windings helps alleviate, but certainly does not eradicate, co-winding capacitance coupling.

Further CMR worsening can be expected even if the two windings are perfectly balanced with respect to each other, if the primary winding is not end-to-end capacitatively matched with respect to ground. Any common-mode signal from a finite impedance source (almost always the case) when confronted with such a capacitatively unbalanced winding sees it as being just that —unbalanced (becoming more so with increasing frequency)—again, transferring input common-mode signals across to become output differential information indistinguished from the wanted input differential source.

Broadcasters particularly are concerned with winding balance, not only on microphone transformers but also on line-output transformers, reasoning that common-differential transference is as likely to occur at a source as at an input.

22.9.6.3 Microphone Transformer Model

Fig. 22-39 gives a better idea of what our microphone's small signal has to suffer. The winding capacitances (C_P and C_S) form lovely resonances with the inductances, while the transformed up primary winding resistance (R_P) added to the resistance of the secondary winding (R_S) merely serves to increase the effective source impedance of the microphone and, hence, produce inefficiency.

The frequency response of the transformer fed from a 200-Ω source and measured at high impedance across the secondary looks something like Fig. 22-40, where the low-frequency droop is attributable to one or both of the winding inductive reactances becoming relevant to signal impedances, while the high-frequency peak is the aforementioned secondary winding self-resonance. Usually the primary self-resonance is fairly well damped by the source impedance, but occasionally added cable capacitance can play cruel tricks here, too.

The mic-amp itself, as discussed, has a high input impedance (megohms and up) while its optimum source impedance is defined at around 5 to 15 kΩ.

It's good engineering practice to consider how the cir-

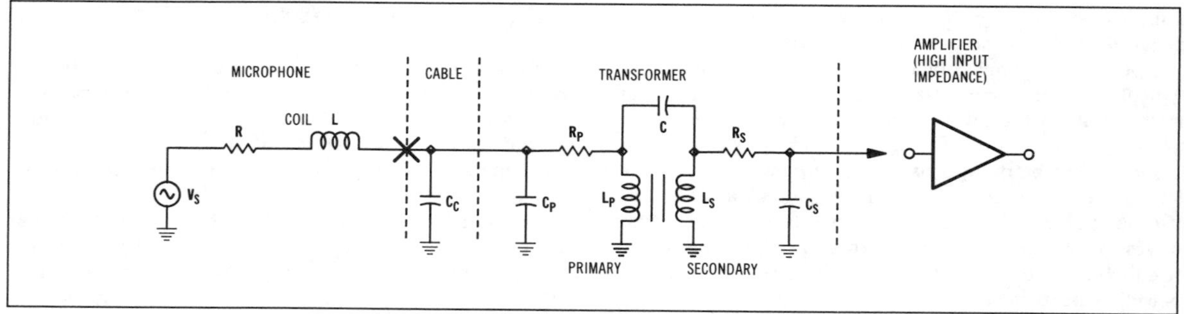

Figure 22-39 Transformer coupling model showing major elements.

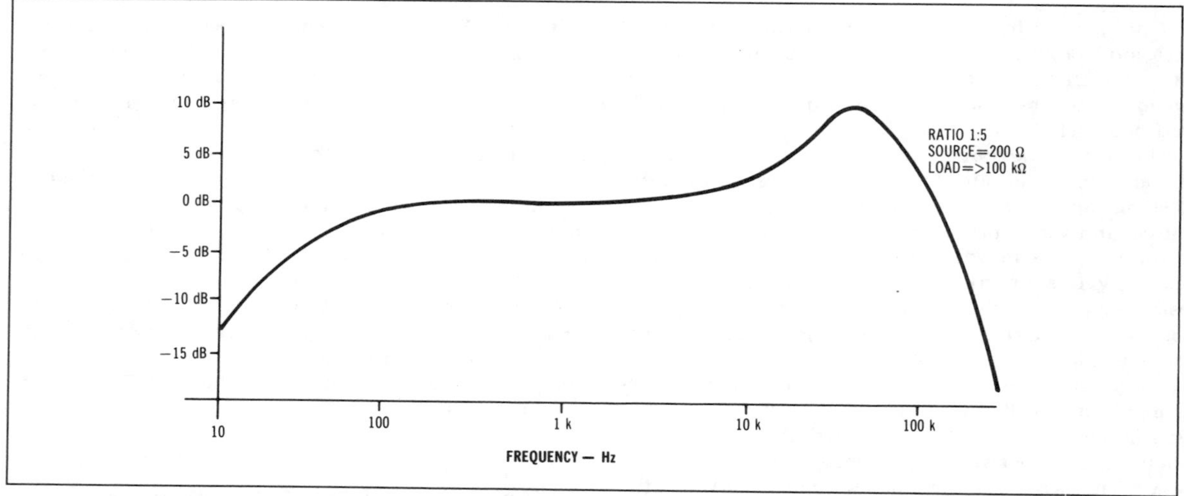

Figure 22-40 Typical transformer transmission response.

cuit behaves when the operating impedances are no longer defined by the microphone (i.e., when it is unplugged). Ordinarily, the circuit of Fig. 22-39, with the microphone disconnected, would probably scream merrily away in oscillation, as would any circuit with a high-gain, high-input-impedance amp terminated only by the collection of vile resonances and phase-shifting elements that are an open-circuit transformer. An open-circuit impedance-defining resistor (R_O in Fig. 22-41) with a value 10 or 20 times that of the amp OSI, helps tame this. It also marginally tames the secondary resonance.

There are a variety of techniques for dealing with this resonance. They vary from pretending it doesn't exist to actually using it as part of a front-end, low-pass filter. The usual way is to try to eliminate it as much as possible passively prior to the amp; the taming network in Fig. 22-41 represents a typical approach. Here, a series resistor-capacitor combination in conjunction with the open-circuit, impedance-defining resistor is used. The values are calculated to produce a step type response (Fig. 22-42) which when combined with the hump at the high-frequency end of the transformer response produces a more acceptable rolloff characteristic. Naturally, the interreaction between this network and the complex impedance of the transformer is not quite that simple. The network capacitance reacts heavily with the transformer inductance, shifting the resonance frequency in the process. It is this fact that has led to the misconception that the capacitance somehow magically tunes out the resonance.

Open-circuit stability is dramatically improved (Fig. 22-42). The network takes an even larger slice out of the overall high-frequency response, keeping impedances at the top end comfortably low.

22.9.6.4 Bandwidth

Providing the compensating high-frequency rolloff around a subsequent amplifier in the form of exaggerated feedback phase-leading, even around the mic-amp itself

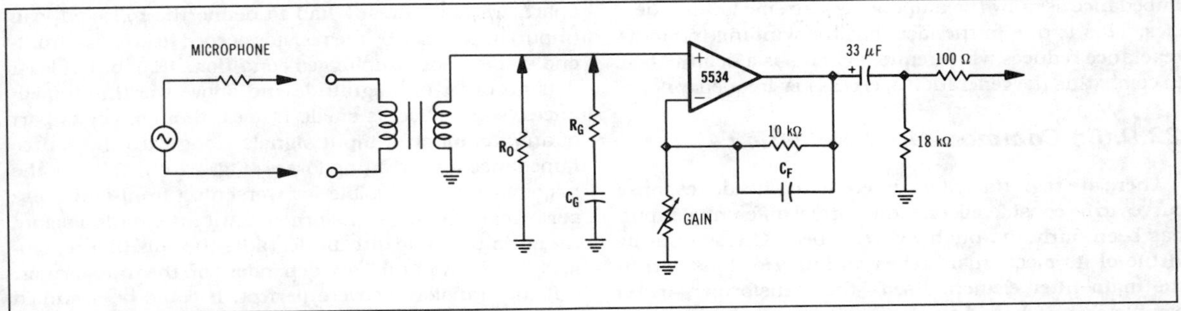

Figure 22-41 Basic microphone preamplifier showing compensation components.

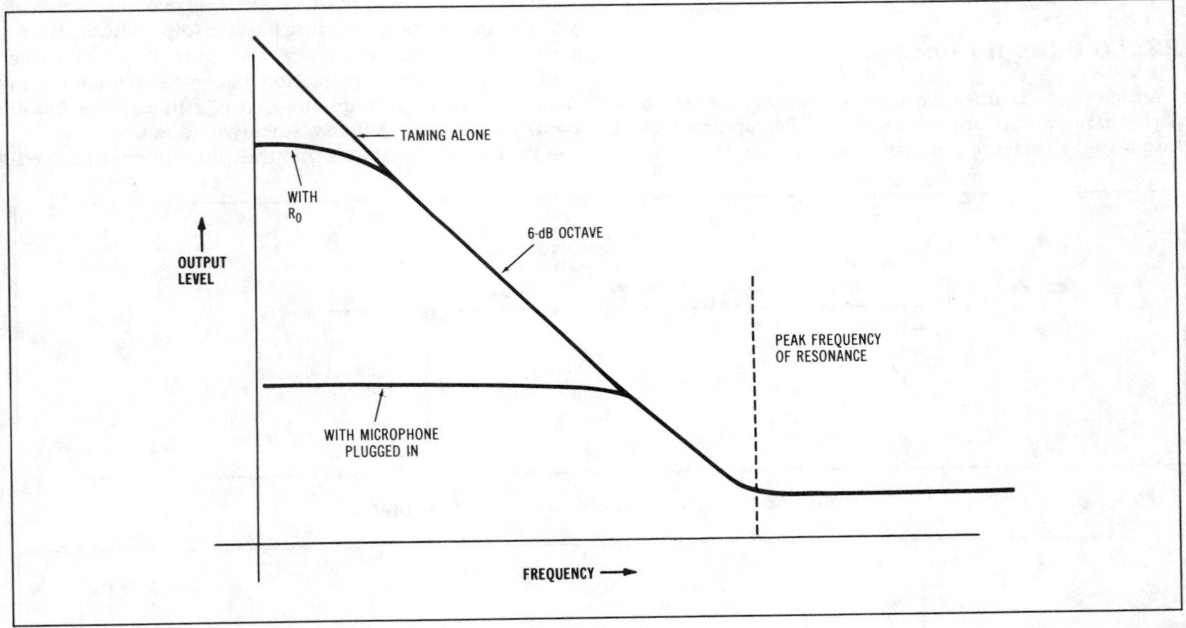

Figure 22-42 Frequency response of taming network.

(C_F), has the advantage in that the noise performance of the combination at the higher frequencies remains unimpaired by an impedance mismatch resulting from a passive network.

Problems result in several areas. Compensation around the mic-amp becomes limited when the electronic gain approaches unity, while compensation around a late fixed-gain stage means that all stages prior to it, including the mic-amp, have head room stolen at the frequency of the resonance and to a degree of the magnitude of the resonance. This may or may not be a problem dependent on how far the lower side of the resonant curve invades the audio band.

The passive method reduces the magnitude of the resonance. The ultimate low-pass, rolloff slope is that of the high-frequency side of the resonance, which more accurately is a lightly damped inductance-capacitance, low-pass 12 dB/octave filter. The active method uses an additional 6-dB/octave curve in the compensation making a total 18 dB/octave, but it relies on the resonance being of a manageable quantity to begin with. Consequently, a measure of both techniques is usually required; their balance and relationship is an experimental process to optimize for each different type of transformer.

This enforced filtering is of considerable advantage, helping to keep all sorts of unwanted ultrasonic noise from finding its way into the mixer. It also represents a major advantage of transformer inputs over solid-state varieties.

A further advantageous filtering is the falling source

impedance seen by the amplifier at extreme low frequencies. This is due to the fact that the winding inductive reactance reduces with frequency. This is a definite help in combating the generation of excess low-frequency noise.

22.9.6.5 Common-Mode Rejection

There are regrettably two different amplitude response curves to be considered: one, the normal differential input, has been fairly thoroughly determined. The second, by virtue of its mechanism relies on imperfections within the main filter element itself—the transformer—rides completely roughshod over and oblivious to our carefully calculated filter responses. Common-mode unrejected signals still appear at the amplifier input as if nothing had happened.

22.9.6.6 Input Impedance

As determined earlier, we would end up with better noise performance and cleaner sounds if the microphone looked into a high, preferably infinite, impedance. Preferences apart, we have already had to define the reflected load (input) impedance by the resistor needed to keep the front-end stable under unplugged conditions (R_0), but at least it is an order of magnitude and above working impedances, so its effect is small. It does, though, act as part of an attenuator of input signals along with the source impedance and winding losses (Fig. 22-43). This is the major factor responsible for worsening front-end noise performance using transformers. Any attenuation before the optimized amp directly degrades the noise figure, typically between 1 and 6 dB, dependent on the transformer.

If the transformer were perfect, it could be assumed that the reflected impedance, as seen by the microphone, would be constant over the audio band. At the low-frequency end (Fig. 22-44), the diminishing inductive reactance (it tends to zero with frequency) becomes a term of greater importance, affecting parallel impedances, attenuation, and, hence, efficiency. Winding self-capacitances and the passive compensation networks are largely to blame for the high-frequency droop, although the list of contributing mechanisms is nearly endless.

A good rule of thumb is that the midband input imped-

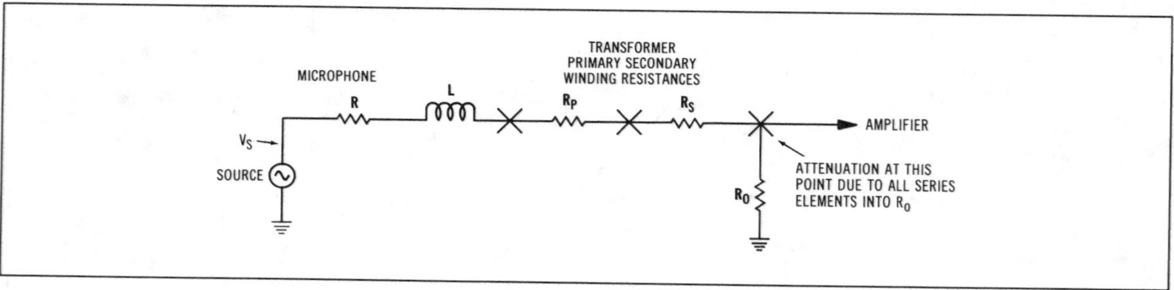

Figure 22-43 Input losses—worsening noise figure.

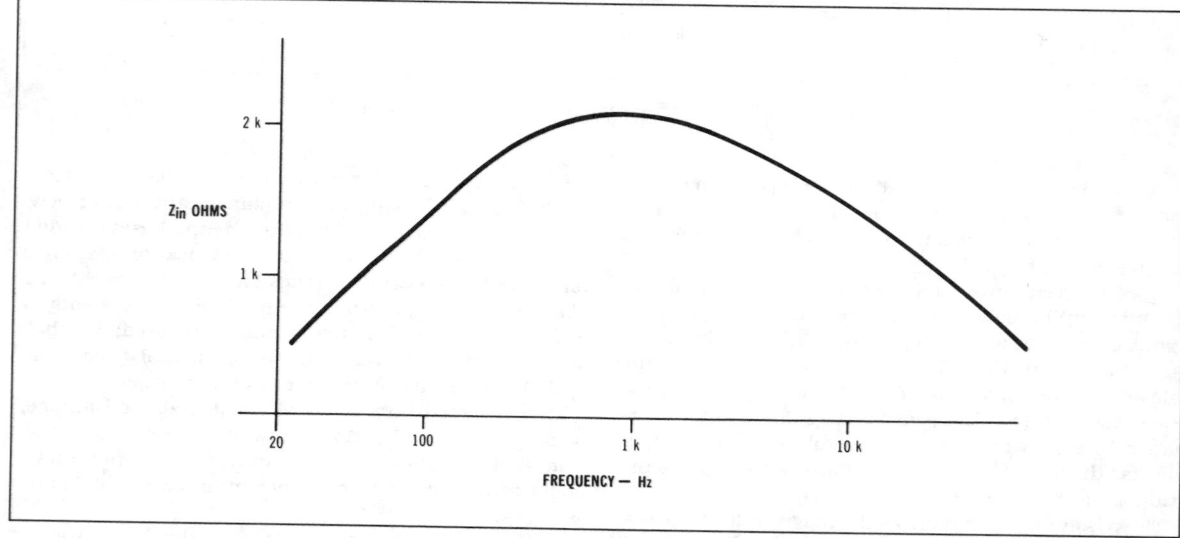

Figure 22-44 Typical input impedance curve.

ance should exceed ten times the source impedance, or about 2 kΩ. Any wild variation in this impedance is obviously going to result in frequency and phase response aberrations, which are probably the greatest single drawback to transformer front ends.

22.9.6.7 Attenuator Pads

Attenuator pads, regrettably necessary in many instances to preserve headroom and prevent core saturation with elephant sources, should maintain expected operating impedances when introduced. The transformer primary should still be terminated with a nominal 200 Ω, while the microphone should still look at 2 kΩ or above. Departure from these will cause the microphone/amplifier combination to sound quite different when the pad is thrown in and out, as would be expected from altering source and load impedances in and around complex filter characteristics.

22.9.6.8 Transformerless Front Ends

Bringing the amplifier optimum source impedance down to that of conventional dynamic microphones is possible by means other than transformers. Reducing the ratio of amplifier-inherent voltage and current noises has this effect, being managed by somewhat of a fiddle—namely paralleling up lots of identical input devices—maintaining about the same noise voltage but proportionally increasing noise current and, therefore, reducing the ratio between them (i.e., noise impedance).

The usual technique is to place two of these multidevice input front-end amps ahead of an electronic differential amplifier, as shown in Fig 22-45. All the amplifier gain is made within the first pair of stages, differentially cross-coupled. This gain arrangement, rather than referring to ground, greatly assists the ignoring of common-mode signals. Differential input signals are amplified since the reference for each of the two amplifiers is the other amplifier, tied to an identical signal of opposite polarity.

If the input signals to the two amps are identical in phase and amplitude (common), the references for each of the amplifiers are waving up and down identically to the signal. There is no voltage difference for the individual amplifier to amplify; consequently, there is no gain. For ordinary differential input signals, the amplifiers operate conventionally, their ground reference being a zero voltage point half-way along the gain-determining variable resistor. This point is a cancellation null between the opposite sense polarity swings of the two amplifiers.

These amplifiers feed a conventional electronic differential amplifier running usually at unity gain, and in order to maintain stage noise as low as possible, the resistors are made as low in value as the devices can sensibly stand. Optimization of impedances is not necessary since the outputs of the front-end pair can be assumed to be feedback-derived zero impedance. This arrangement is unmistakably a bastardized instrumentation amplifier that is a well-documented circuit configuration; the only thing of remark is the low-impedance, optimized, front-end stages.

Although potentially offering far higher and flatter input impedances than transformer inputs, there are, as always, snags. Common-mode signals directly gobble up headroom in the first pair of stages even if those are operating as followers and are subsequently cancelled in the differential amplifier. There is also the great danger that common-mode signals (in addition to normal differential signals) can exceed the input swing capability of the input devices.

Radio frequencies adore base-emitter junctions, and this configuration gives them a lot to play with. Filtering microphone inputs sufficiently without sacrificing noise performance or input device high-frequency gain (hence, high-frequency distortion and so on) is not a simple task.

22.9.6.9 Line Level Inputs

High-level balanced interconnections and systems (regrettably) have been largely relegated these days to the outside world or intersystem interfacing; internal interconnects are usually left unbalanced. The wisdom was that balancing implied transformers and performance limitations.

The search was on for electronic equivalents to transformers for both input and output applications, a moderate degree of success being achieved early on for input stages with classic circuits such as Figs. 22-46 and 22-47. These are simple differential input amplifier and instrument amplifier configurations with op-amps.

Line inputs are commonly simple differential amplifiers, rather than unity-gain transformers, similar to the one used in the transformerless mic-amp, but with the resistor values elevated to bring the differential input impedance up to over the 10 kΩ required of a bridging termination (Fig. 22-46). The noise of these stages is directly attributable to these resistor values, so the lower resistor values are better. An instrumentation amplifier configuration would seem to offer possibly better performance for noise (the differential amplifier resistor values may be small) but entails the use of undesirable voltage followers (see section 22.6) with potential stability problems, input voltage swing limitations, and unprotected (for RF) input stages. At least with a simple differential amplifier, the impedances are comfortably low and the inputs buffered by resistors from the outside world.

The dc blocking series capacitors have, unfortunately, to be large in value to maintain an even input impedance at the lowest used frequencies and, being necessarily unpolarized, physically large and expensive. This is a small price to pay, though, for such a simple but important circuit element.

The circuit in Fig. 22-46A suffers from a slight problem. As common and popular as it is, it only works properly under ideal circumstances, offering still some but not total isolation from ground under usual use. This is because the input impedance on the noninverting leg is permanently defined by the resistor values while that on

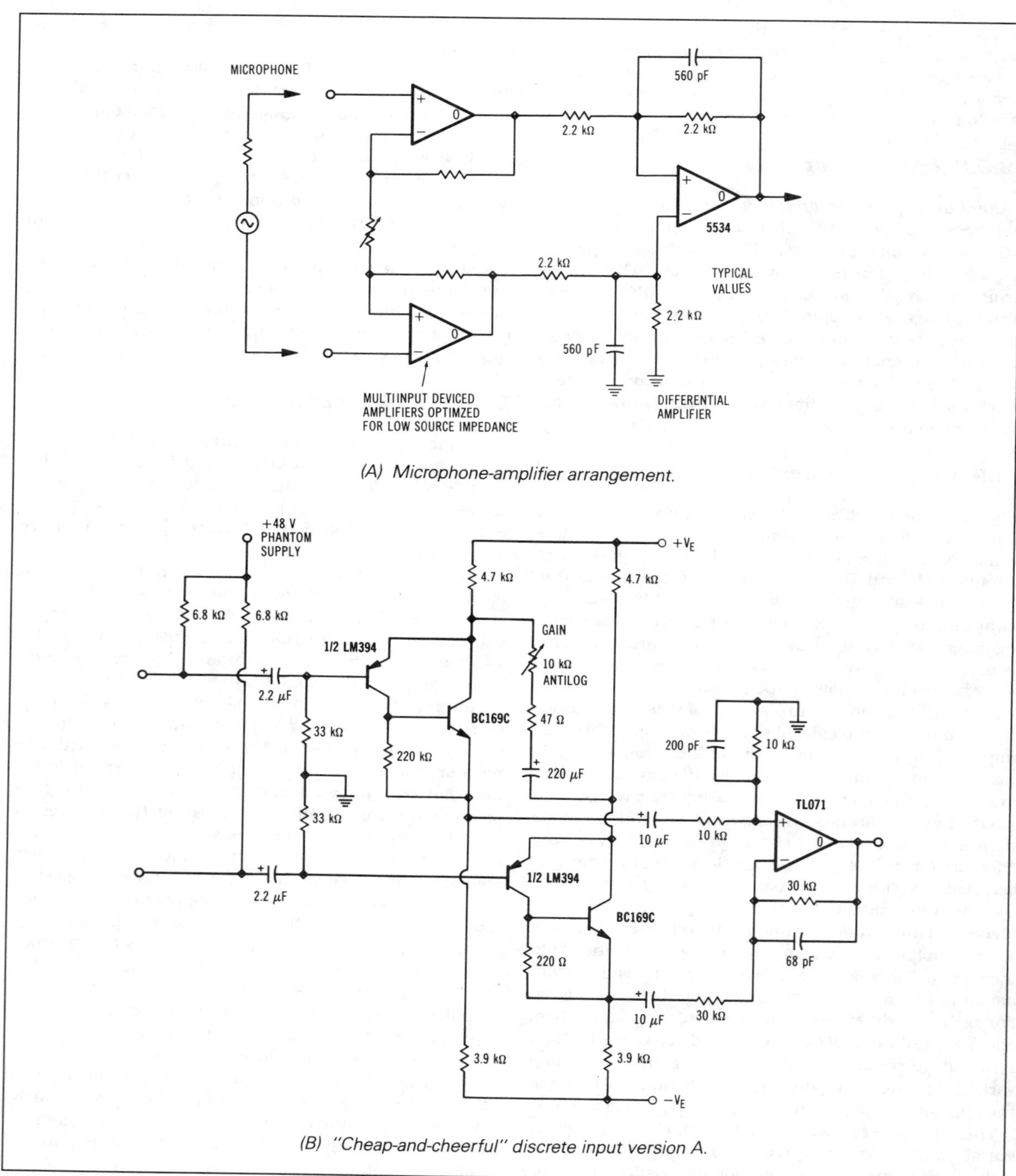

(A) *Microphone-amplifier arrangement.*

(B) *"Cheap-and-cheerful" discrete input version A.*

Figure 22-45 Basic transformerless microphone-amplifier arrangement.

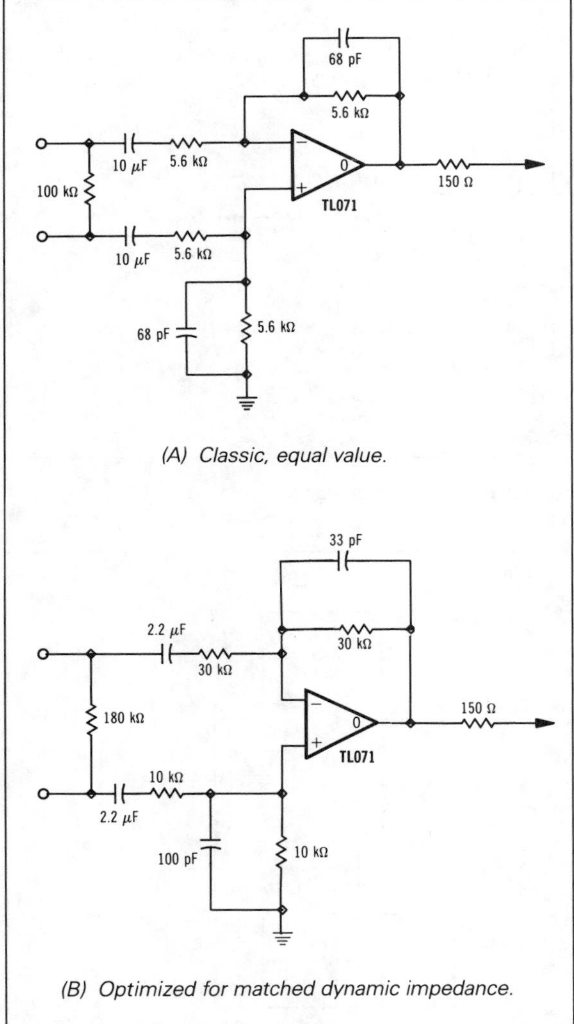

(A) Classic, equal value.

(B) Optimized for matched dynamic impedance.

Figure 22-46 Electronic differential input amplifier.

the inverting input leg is dynamic. If the noninverting leg is stationary, the inverting leg will see the value of the input resistor, and the circuit behaves as a straight ground-referred inverting amplifier. If the noninverting input is moving, however, the reference point for the inverting leg is changing, and the impedance it's seeing is changing, too. The negative input leg impedance is continually being variably bootstrapped by common-mode voltages and nondifferential sources.

It's possible to match the two input impedances of the input legs for differential signals. It's also possible to match them for common-mode signals by altering the resistor values in one or the other leg—but not for both at the same time. The values shown in Fig. 22-46B are suitable for the latter case, the ones in Fig. 22-46A are suitable for the former. Both cases fall apart if the signal source has a significant impedance. The instrumentation amplifier presents a very high, nonground-referred differential termination and has the great advantage that gain may be easily invoked between the two input amps at no cost to the excellent common-mode rejection (Fig. 22-47).

A pair of inverting amplifiers, as shown in Fig. 22-48, provides a simple, hardy, easily defined differential (not true floating balanced) input stage. A really fascinating and distinctly immoral-looking circuit known as the superbal input is depicted in Fig. 22-49; this is a balanced differential virtual-earth amplifier, referred to ground solely by one op-amp input and capable of quite astonishing common-mode rejection. Accepting any lopsided input signal, it delivers a differential output perfectly symmetrical to ground, making it a splendid input conditioning amplifier.

The capacity of both these circuits to be differential virtual-earth points makes them ideal for use in balanced mixing bus systems.

22.9.6.10 Electronic Balanced Outputs

The simplest balanced outputs configuration is given in Fig. 22-50. This is a pure, no-nonsense, inverter-derived differential feed. For many internal interconnections and especially in differential balanced mixing systems it works well. But, as regards the outside world, forget it.

Ideally, there must be no discernible difference in characteristics between the output circuit and a transformer (hopefully without the core-saturation and reactive problems of the latter!). Regardless of the common-mode potential, the differential output potential must not change. Also the output should be insensitive to any imbalance in termination, even to the extent of shorting one leg or the other to ground. This is the floating test. For example, the simple inverter circuit of Fig. 22-50 fails the floating test since, if one leg is shorted to common, the overall output has to drop by one-half (6 dB). (The question of what happens to ground noise with a shorted amplifier bucketing current into it will be sidestepped here.) Two basic circuits have emerged as being close approximations to a transformer. Not only are they fairly closely related, but most balanced output topologies are also derived from them. They both depend on cross-coupled positive feedback between the two legs to compensate for termination imbalance.

In Fig. 22-51 a unity-gain inverting stage provides out-of-phase drive for the two legs, each output leg of which is a −6-dB gain inverting amplifier with error sensing applied to its reference (positive) inputs. Under normal operation, there is no error-sensing voltage; the two inverse outputs cancel at the midpoint of the equal sense resistors. The two amps invert merrily away, a differential voltage equal to the unbalanced input voltage appearing between their outputs. (Two −6-dB quantities make a

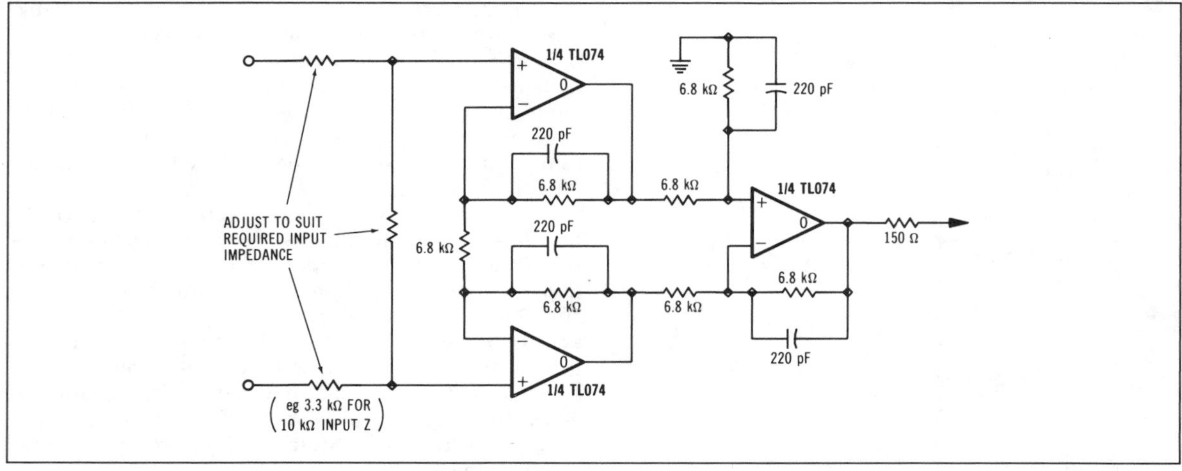

Figure 22-47 Instrumentation amplifier-type line-input stage.

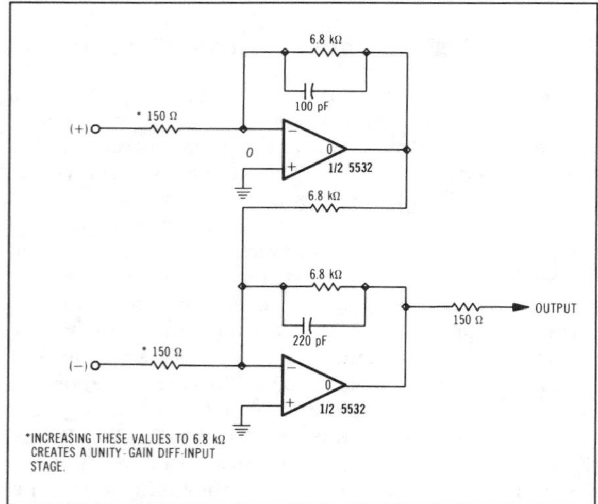

Figure 22-48 Differential mix/input amplifier.

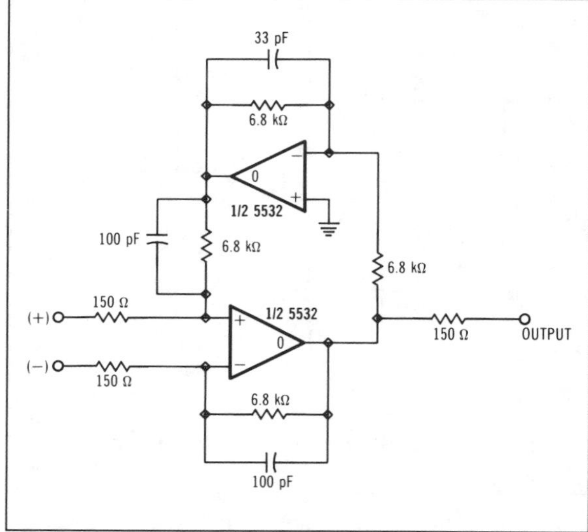

Figure 22-49 "Superbal" differential mix/input amplifier.

zero gain.) Take the case of one output—say, the upper one—being shorted to ground. An error potential is derived of such a phase and level on the error-sense line that positive feedback increases the gain of the unshorted amp by 6 dB, while matching on the positive input of the shorted one the signal on the negative input, cancelling its amplification. Closing the shorted amp down prevents ground-current problems; therefore, any measure of output termination imbalance is reasonably dealt with by this arrangement.

A major problem with any circuit depending upon high levels of positive feedback, such as these, is their instability. Both these are right on the edge of instability; a measure of margin has to be given for peace of mind and component tolerances. This backing-off compromise affects primarily common-mode rejection and output level against lopsided terminations. A loss of about 0.5 dB in differential output level can be expected when one side is shorted to ground.

Curiously, instability tends to show itself as common mode. This fault manifested itself for the first time early one morning when a peak programme meter (PPM) across such an output read nothing. On listening to it there was a little bit of hum, but from either leg to ground were 10-V peak-to-peak square waves, driving the tape-machine to which the output was connected into shock!

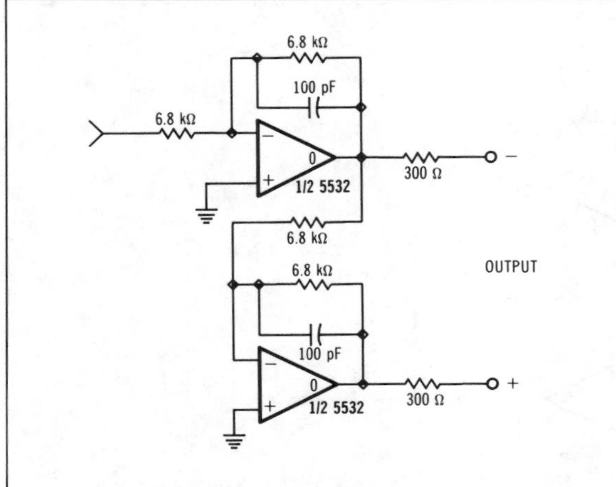

Figure 22-50 Inverter-type differential output.

22.9.7 A Practical Microphone-Amplifier Design

Optimizing front-end sound is nothing more than shrewd judgment in juggling the nearly endless electronic operating conditions so that adequate performance is obtained over the wide range of expected and common input signals. Any wrinkles should be arranged to exert influence only under quite extraordinary operational conditions.

The microphone amplifier described here is a somewhat developed version of a basic front-end design (Fig. 22-52), which is in grave danger of becoming an industry standard. The precise origins of this rather clever two op-amp arrangement are obscure, but it's been around a few years now.

Initially most striking is the manner in which a single-track potentiometer is used to vary simultaneously the gains of two amplifying elements—the front-end (noninverting) stage and the succeeding inverting amplifier. Since the first stage is (as far as its inputs are concerned) a conventional noninverting amplifier, transformer input coupling is not any more problematic than with simpler microphone amplifiers (e.g., Fig. 22-41, a standard generic microphone amplifier).

With maximum gain distributed between two stages, large gain is possible without any danger of running out of adequate steam at high frequencies for feedback purposes in either of the two amplifiers. This, incidentally, also makes for reasonably simple stabilization of the amplifiers, something not easily accomplished with more simple single-amplifier circuits achieving the same gain swing. Other than the obvious neatness of one-pot gain control, two nice features are inherent in the design that are delightful from the points of view of system level architecture and of operation, respectively.

22.9.7.1 Level Architecture

System level architecture is largely concerned with operating all the elements of a system at the optimum levels and/or gain for noise and headroom (i.e., at a comfortable place somewhere between the noise floor and clipping ceiling). Where gain is involved, it's important that the resultant noise be due primarily to the gain stage that has been optimized for noise (or rather lack of it) such that it can then mask all the other, hopefully, minor contributions. At no point in the gain swing—particularly at minimum gain—should it be necessary to attenuate unwanted residual gain. This amount of attenuation gets directly subtracted from overall system headroom. What good is 24 dB of headroom everywhere else, if you've only 16 dB in the front end?

In this respect circuits similar to Fig. 22-52 score well, and the graphs of Fig. 22-53 show why. Fig. 22-53A represents the gain in dB of a simple noninverting amp varying with the percentage rotation of an appropriately valued linear pot in its feedback leg. This is like the gain/rotation characteristic of the first amp of Fig. 22-52. Similarly, Fig. 22-53B is the gain/rotation plot for a linear pot as the series element in an inverting amp, such as the second gain stage of Fig. 22-52. For the first half of the rotation, the first stage provides all the gain swing and most of the gain, only about 6 dB being attributable to the inverting stage at midpoint. Toward the end of the rotation, this position reverses with the front end remaining comparatively static in gain, the extra swing and gain coming from the inverting stage. Noise criteria are met, since the first (optimized) stage always has more than enough gain to allow its noise to swamp the second stage, with the exception of minimum gain setting. There it hardly matters anyway because the front-end noise contribution is going to be at a similar level to the overall system noise floor (i.e., really quiet!). The impedances around the second stage largely determine the noise performance of the amplifier, and this is such that it need not be considered in relation to input noise at any sensible gain setting. Headroom is satisfactory as no attenuation after the first gain stage is needed for any gain setting.

An operational advantage can be gleaned from Fig. 22-53C. This is the combined gain/rotation curve for the total two op-amp circuit. Note that for a very large percentage of rotation around the middle (where it's most often used) the dB gain change per rotation is as good as linear. It gets a bit cramped at the top and bottom, but you can't win them all. For reference a little later on, it may be noted that there are two available resistors (R_2 and R_3) that may be used to modify the gain structure independently of the potentiometer.

22.9.7.2 Input Coupling

As a microphone amplifier, the fairly high optimum source impedance of the op-amp used (a Signetics NE5534)

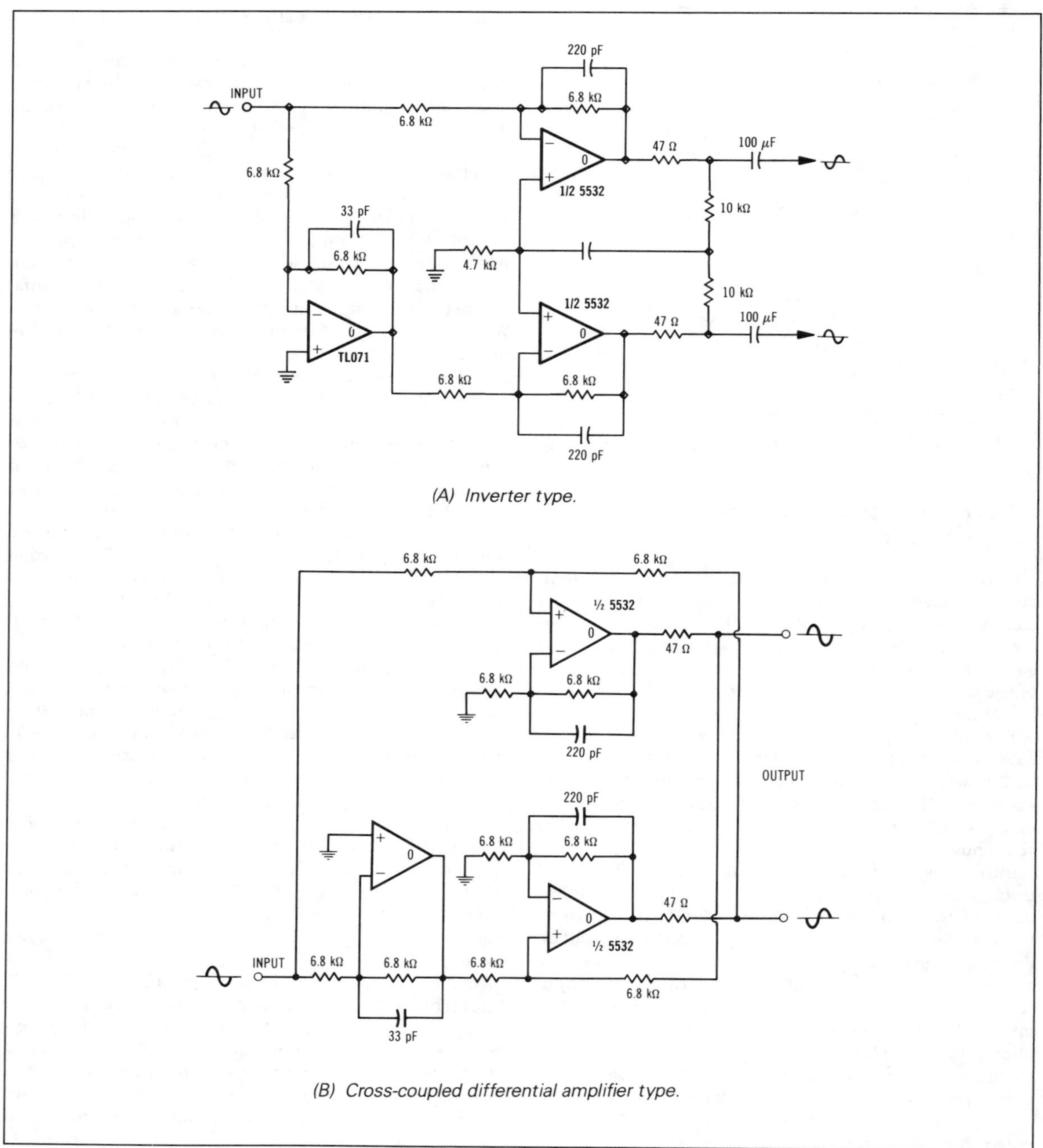

(A) Inverter type.

(B) Cross-coupled differential amplifier type.

Figure 22-51 Electronic floating differential output stages.

needs to be matched to the likely real source impedance of some 150 to 200 Ω. No apologies are offered for the use of transformer input coupling, as grossly unfashionable as this may presently seem.

A Sowter type 3195 (1:7 ratio) transformer is used here. Many circuit values (marked with an asterisk in Fig. 22-54, with some in quite unexpected places) are dependent on the specific transformer type in use. Other excellent

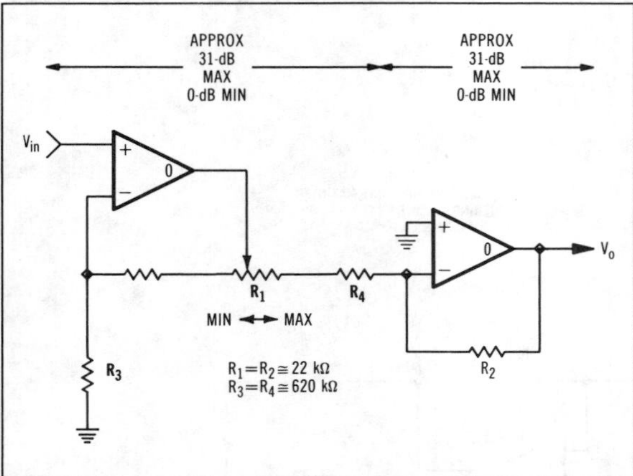

Figure 22-52 Shared-gain two operational-amplifier input stage.

transformers, notably those from Colne (Reading, Berks, England) and the Jensen JE-115-K, can be very successfully used provided the differing ratios are taken into account in level calculations. Phase and response trimming values will vary significantly. With Deane Jensen's JE-115-K, it is simpler than with Dr. Sowter's. Despite the apparent simplicity of the circuit, a lot of effort has gone into defining the front-end bandwidth and straightening out the phase response at audible extremities. Taming the high-frequency transformer resonance for example is quite tiresome.

On the front of the transformer hang the usual components to make the microphone amplifier useful in this world of capacitor microphones: a 20-dB input attenuator and 48-V phantom power via 6.8-kΩ resistors per leg carried common-mode along the microphone line.

22.9.7.3 Line Level Input Facility

A line-in option is brought in via the transformer also. It features far stiffer input attenuation (about 36 dB) while simultaneously disabling much of the gain swing of the first amp. The resultant gain swing of 35 dB (between −25- and 10-dBu input level) with a bridging-type input impedance of some 13 kΩ should accommodate most things that the microphone input or machine-return input differential amp can't or won't. A small equalization network is used in the attenuator to bolster the extreme low-frequency phase response.

22.9.7.4 Common-Mode Rejection Ratio

Common-mode rejection ratio (CMRR) in the transformer is dependent mostly on the physical construction of its windings. The Sowter, in common with most other transformers, may be in need of compensation by deliberately reactively unbalancing the primary winding to

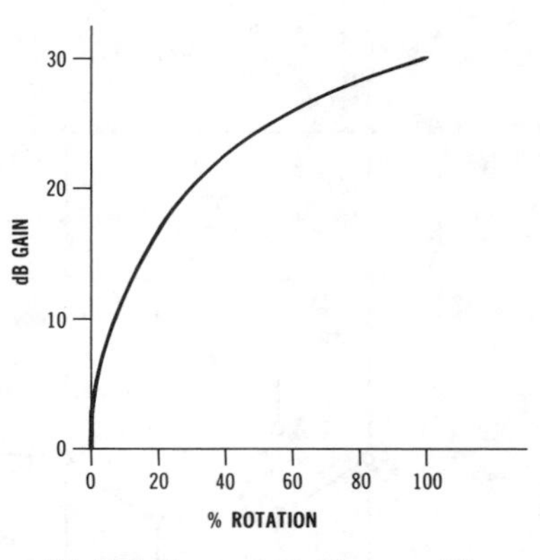

(A) Gain for noninverting amplifier.

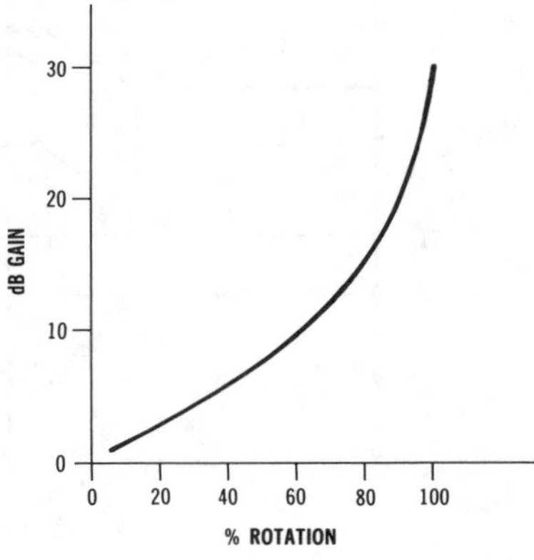

(B) Inverting amplifier.

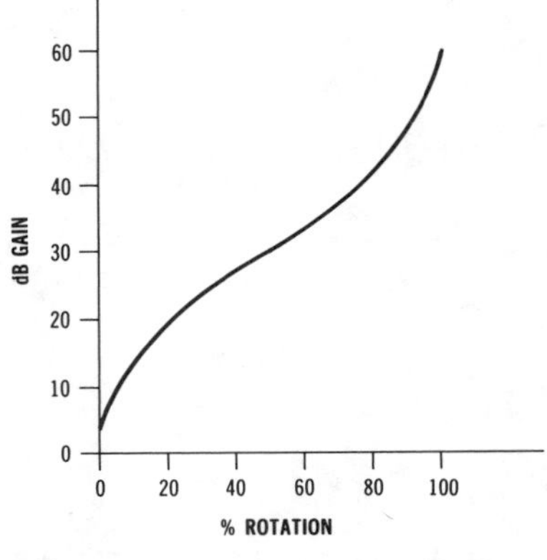

(C) Combined noninverting and inverting gains as in CCT of Fig. 22-52.

Figure 22-53 Gain versus pot rotation for two-operational-amplifier input stage.

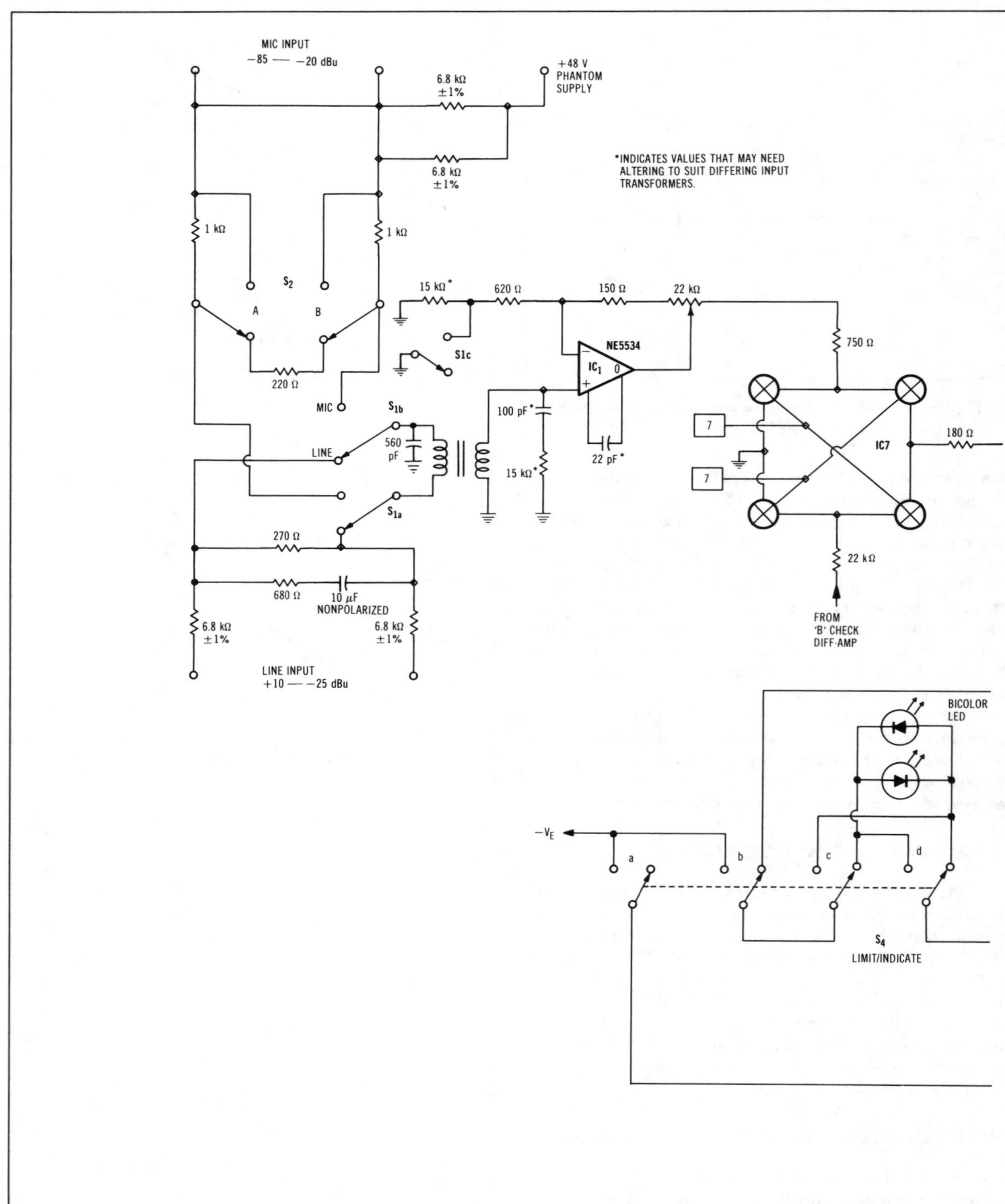

Figure 22-54 Channel input

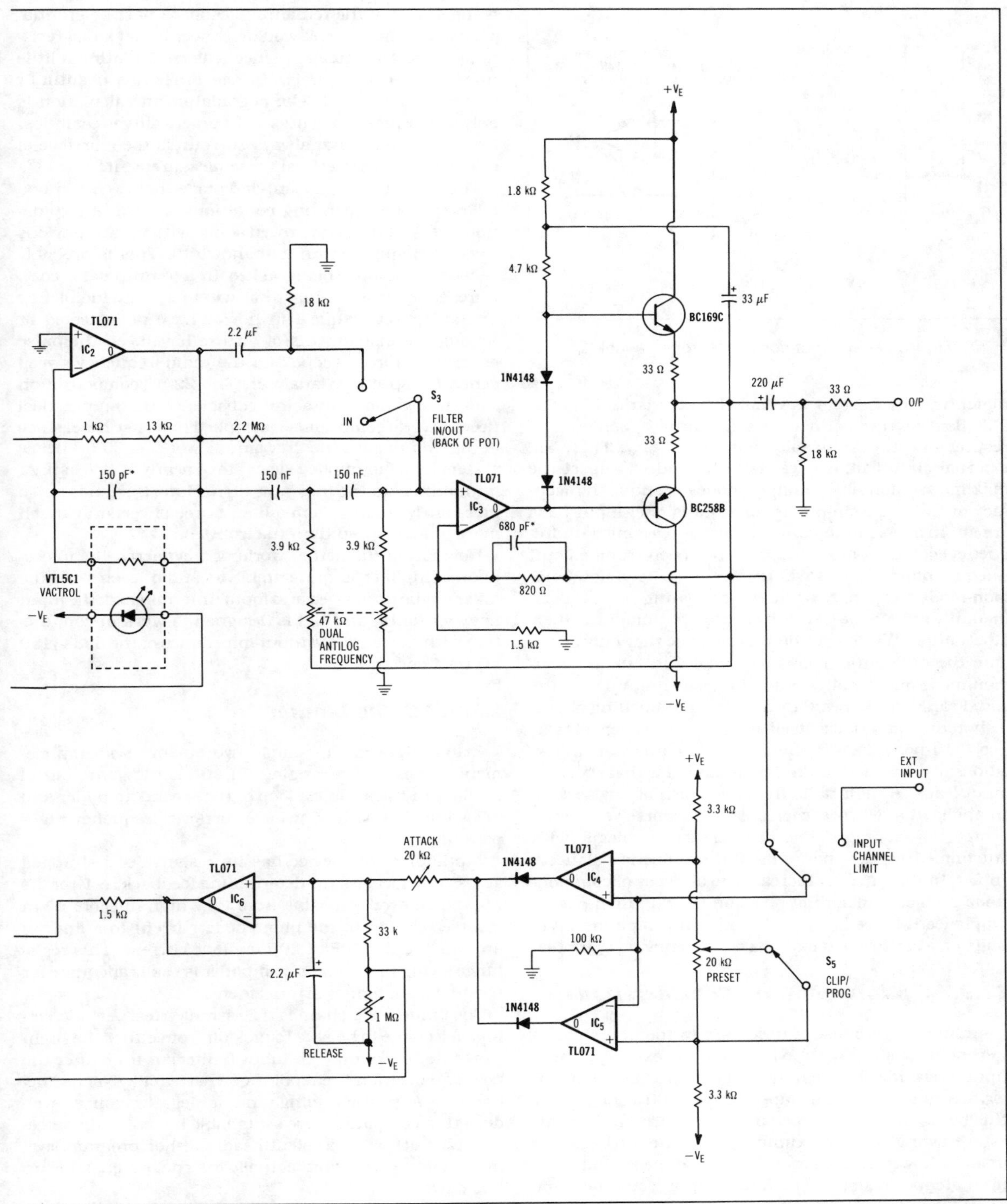

amplifier, high-pass filter and limiter.

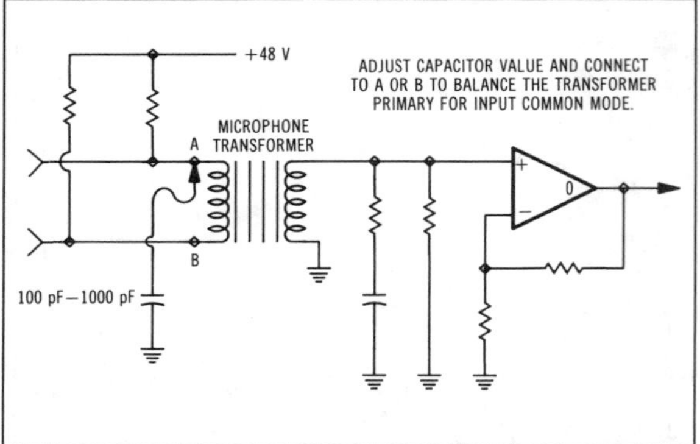

Figure 22-55 Input common-mode "tweak."

match the inadvertent internal characteristics (Fig. 22-55). Jensen transformers are uncannily good in this respect—no tweaks usually being necessary. There are external circuit influences that can and will upset the maximum obtainable common-mode rejection. The accuracy of the phantom-power resistors is one; input pads are another. Assuming any reactive (i.e., rising with frequency) common-mode response has been trimmed out, unequal phantom-legs will enforce a lopsided flat, common-mode response while true floating input pads instantly reduce the CMRR by nearly the amount of their attenuation. Why? They do this because they only attenuate the differential (wanted) signal and not the common-mode one. A half-way solution is to ground refer the pad. Frankly if there's *that* much signal hurtling about, it shouldn't materialize itself as a problem. Given all that, less than perfect CMR shouldn't cause any ill manifestations in a typical recording environment with fairly short input leads. A high radio-frequency field of any sort, or an application with very long leads (or worse yet, a multicore), is far more likely to create problems with untrimmed inputs than with those properly balanced. Vulnerability is greatly increased to all types of common-mode problems including noise on the phantom power-supply feed. Indeed, this is a common compounding of faults on a console that exhibits consistently noisy inputs.

22.9.7.5 Minimum-Gain Considerations

A minor compromise is necessary in the first stage to prevent it gasping with exhaustion on extremely high input levels. Ideally, the output of the operational amplifier has to look into an impedance of 600 Ω or greater (this being the lowest impedance it can drive full output voltage swing into). Maximum gain state isn't really a problem, however, if it's overdriving into the second-stage input stopper resistor. The filter output would be some 30 dB into clipping, and someone might notice.

The problem would be at minimum gain where the first stage is operating almost as a follower, its output load being 770 Ω of the remaining feedback path to ground. That's safe; however, it would be nicer if that small resistance were a lot smaller, since it is contributing a little unwanted thermal noise to the otherwise beautifully optimized front end. The degradation in calculation is only minor points of a dB and in practicality is easily lost in the gray mist that always surrounds the marriage of calculation with practical noise measurement.

The idea of using a front-end stage that turned into a follower under operating conditions did cause trepidation at first, but it has proved stable without any obvious trace of ringing within its bandwidth. This is probably because it is only being asked to look into safe, cozy, unreactive loads. Things that will make any incipiently unstable circuit squeal in horror have not affected it. Among the instruments of torture have been the pulse generator/storage scope and the radio-frequency sweep generator/spectrum analyzer. The 22-pF compensation capacitor is more an act of conscience than a practical necessity. No compromise is implied in its use here, since at maximum gain the first amp is working 30 dB below system level (an implied slew rate of nearly 200 V/μs!). At minimum gain the incoming signal level is such that it's most likely coming from a line source of certainly much more limited speed than the front end.

Down from the nether world of megahertz, the microphone amplifier is quite stable at audio, even with the microphone unplugged and input unterminated; the input network (of R_G and C_G) is designed to work in conjunction with the fairly low input impedance of the 5534 (150 kΩ the book says).

22.9.7.6 The Limiter

Elaboration on the simple two op-amp mic-amp element consists of arranging an automatic gain control element in the feedback loop of the second amplifier and following that with a variable turnover frequency high-pass filter.

A photoresistor device has its resistive end strapped across the normal gain-determining feedback resistor. Its resistance drops in value from very high (megohms) in inverse relation to the photodiode current to a limit of around 300 Ω at about 20-mA diode current. This resistance swing in the second amplifier is easily adequate for use in a peak limiter arrangement.

The limiter side-chain is true symmetrical peak-detecting, selectable to be able to pick off from either the high-pass filter output (as an input limiter) or from after the post equalization breakpoint downstream (as a channel limiter). A positive-going and a negative-going level-detecting comparator are switchable between clip detection (2/3 dB before system headroom) or program level (nominally) +8 dBu but actually internally adjustable up and down.

A bicolor LED blinks red to indicate limiting in action, and it blinks green when the limiter is disabled to signify that the selected level (clip or program) is being reached or exceeded. In this "indicate" mode, the limiter integration time constant is deliberately shortened to make the green flashing similar in character to the red flashing in limit.

The difference is due to the nature of servo loops, of which a feedback limiter such as this is an example. In limit, the loop is self-regulating, the gain-control element holding back the audio level so that it's just tickling and topping up the side chain. In indicate, the loop is broken, and there is no such regulation. The green light stays on whenever the threshold is exceeded and tends to hang on for a bit while the time-constant capacitor discharges. With even a minor overload, this hangover could extend for quite a few seconds; hence, the shortened time constant.

As an experimental aid, both the attack and release time constants for the side chain are on presets, although it's suggested that once settings are found, fixed-value resistors of the measured value should be substituted for them. There are two reasons: good presets are unbelievably costly these days, and trying to get a number of channels exactly the same by ear is a mission for fools.

This limiter is not subtle. The comparators deliver a full-sized, power-supply wallop to the integrator upon threshold, softened a bit by the attack preset in conjunction with the output impedance of the comparators. This rather unusual approach is to help wake up the photoresistor that has a relatively leisurely response time. The combination can be adjusted to be slow enough such that it doesn't clip yet fast enough to prevent an audible snap. Overshoot is generally well within 1 dB on a normal program, given a release time long enough to prevent pumping.

As a rough guide, if it's intended to use the limiter for sporadic transient protection, it's best to aim for short attack and release times, bearing in mind that such settings will behave more as a clipper to the lower frequencies. For continual effect use, longer time constants will be less gritting and more buoyant. This side-chain arrangement certainly behaves differently from more conventional field-effect transistor or voltage-controlled amplifier (VCA) linear proportional systems and needs a slightly different approach in setting up.

From a design viewpoint, there is an awful lot of spikey current hammering about into the integrator and through the LEDs of the indicator and photoresistor. This current is kept well away from ground, because flowing through the low-level microphone amplifier ground path makes it sound reminiscent of—only slightly louder than—a machine gun. It is best to keep it all in the power supply where it belongs.

22.9.7.7 High-Pass Filters

Constructed around the line output amplifier of the front end is a second-order, high-pass filter. It is a completely ordinary Sallen-Key type filter, arranged to use a dual-gang equal value potentiometer to sweep the 3-dB-down turnover frequency from between 20 and 250 Hz. A click-stop switch at the low-frequency end (counterclockwise) negates the filter, replacing it with a very large time-constant, single-order, dc decoupler. These are both tied to reference in order to minimize clicks. Fortunately, the TL071 in the filter barely uses any input bias current, so there is little developed offset voltage from that source to worry about. Being an equal-value filter, the Q or turnover would be very lazy indeed if the feedback were not elevated in level to compensate for the upset resistor ratio. Here a compromise is struck. A low Q gives a very gentle rolloff (which is sonically good), and high Q results in a much more rapid attenuation beyond the cutoff frequency at the expense of a more disturbed in-band frequency response—pronounced bumps—and frantic temporal and phase responses exhibited as ringing and smeared transients. Luckily, the majority of control-room monitors exhibit far worse characteristics at the low-frequency end! A maximally flat response midway between the two extremes is chosen by an appropriate amount of elevated feedback (around 4 dB in this case). This gain is taken across the filter as a whole, with the second stage of the microphone amplifier arranged to sustain a 4-dB loss to compensate. It all works out in the end, with no compromise of headroom. With minimum gain set, there is still unity electronic gain front to back. An added convenience of gain is that it provides a better chance of shoring up feedback phase margin, which is quite important in a line-amp that may have to drive a lot of heavily capacitative cable. Also, it provides yet another single-order, low-pass pole to help iron out the high-frequency resonance of the microphone transformer.

22.10 EQUALIZERS AND EQUALIZATION

The term *equalization* is strictly a misnomer. It was originally utilized to describe flattening and generally putting to rights the response of systems in which by a matter of course or by design it has got a bit bent out of shape (e.g., telephone lines and tape machines). (In the latter case, equalization refers to the adjustment tweaks to the preemphasis and de-emphasis curves—not necessarily the curves themselves.)

In search of a name for the deliberate modification of amplitude and phase versus frequency responses for taste and the occasional genuine creative effect, the contraction *EQ* is well understood as both a noun and verb.

This sonic mutilation uses response curves, shapes, and limits that have grown through an uneasy mixture of operator needs and technical expedience/feasibility. One of today's multiparametric console channel EQs would have needed a rack full of tubes 25 years ago.

The delight (and maybe curse) of IC op-amp design is that active filter (hence, EQ) implementation and techniques have blown wide open, limited only by the largeness of the printed-circuit board and the smallness of the user's fingers.

EQ curves can be roughly lumped into three user categories:

garbage disposal,

trend,

area.

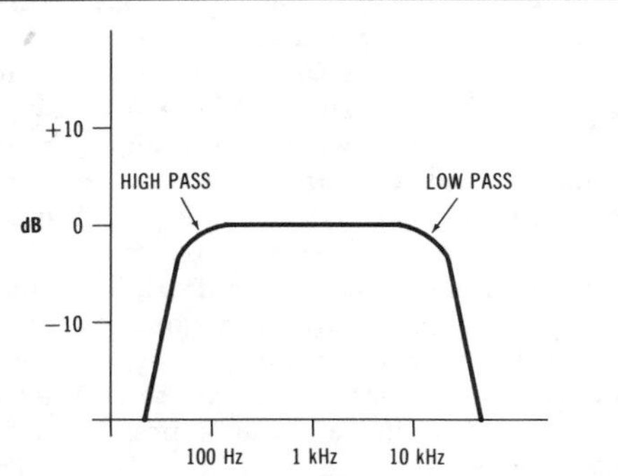

(A) High-pass and low-pass typical responses.

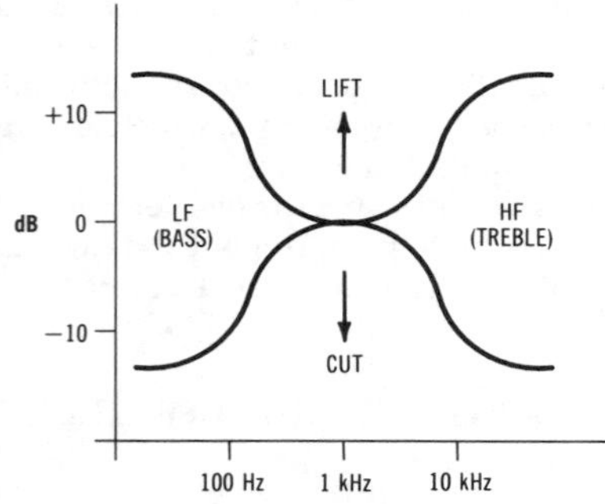

(B) Treble and bass shelving responses.

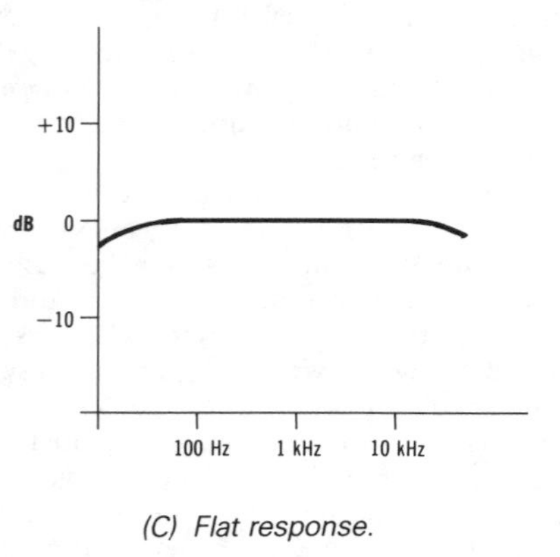

(C) Flat response.

Figure 22-56 EQ responses.

High-pass and low-pass filters that eliminate air-conditioning, mic-stand rumble or breathing, and excessive noise are obviously enough in the business of garbage disposal. Fig. 22-56A shows the sort of responses to be expected from these. Gentle hi-fi type, treble and bass slopes, and shelving establish response trends shown in Fig. 22-56B, while resonancelike, bell-shaped, lift-and-cut filters manipulate given areas of the overall spectral response. These are used to depress unwanted or irritating aspects of a sound or, alternatively, to enhance something at or around a given frequency that would otherwise be lacking. As the curves differ, so do the design techniques required.

22.10.1 Single-Order Networks

You can't build a house until you have the bricks, so they say. Fig. 22-57 has those bricks, in the form of combinations of basic passive components with a rough guide to their input-output voltage transfer functions (essentially the frequency responses). Assumptions are that the V_{in} source impedance is zero and the V_o termination is infinite impedance.

Capacitative reactance decreases with increasing frequency, working against the resistance to increasingly short the output to ground with increasing frequency in Fig. 22-57A, while in Fig. 22-57B the capacitance steadily isolates the output from the input with reducing frequency (rising reactance).

Inductors have entirely the opposite reactive characteristics. Inductive reactance is directionally proportional to frequency, so the curves in Figs. 22-57C and D will be of no surprise at all, being complementary to those involving capacitance.

22.10.2 Single-Order Active Filters

More useful curves are derived when the passive R, C, and L elements are wrapped around an op-amp in the classic inverting and noninverting amplifier modes, as shown in Figs. 22.57E to L. All the curves in Fig. 22-57 are normalized to unity gain and the same center frequency at which the curve departs significantly from flat.

Standard arithmetic formulas normally consider or obtain a frequency at which the curve has departed 3 dB from flat, the 3-dB down point, and it is usually also where the phase has been shifted 45°. This is only partially useful in the design of filters for use in practical eqs; *departure point* is generally more relevant.

22.10.3 Changing Filter Frequency

With any of these filters, moving the frequency at which the filter "bites" can be achieved by altering any of the R,

L, or C values. Making any value smaller moves the frequency higher, while making the value larger moves the frequency lower.

There are an infinite number of combinations of element values to create the same curve at the same frequency. In Fig. 22-57A, if the value of the capacitor were reduced (increased in reactance), the filter curve would shift up in frequency. A corresponding proportional increase in the series resistor value would result in the original turnover frequency being restored; therefore, we have an identical filter with a different resistor/reactor combination. What does remain the same is the ratio or relationship between the two elements. It is only the filter impedance (the combination of resistance and reactance) that varies.

With the exception of a devious and evil few, the operation of any active filter can eventually be guessed referring to these basic, single-order filter characteristics in Fig. 22-57.

There is one particular combination of two reactive elements (capacitance and inductance) that is of prime relevance to the construction of eqs. This is shown in Fig. 22-58 and is called a series-tuned circuit.

22.10.4 Reactance and Phase Shifts

In, for example, the context of a simple resistor/reactor filter (Fig. 22-57A), the reactance not only causes an amplitude shift with frequency but also a related phase shift. A fundamental difference between the two types of reactance (C and L) is the direction of the output voltage (V_o) phase shift with respect to the source (V_{in}). More specifically, the capacitor in Fig. 22-57A causes the output voltage phase to lag further behind the input as the rolloff progressively bites to a limit of −90° at the dregs of the curve, while the inductor of Fig. 22-57C imposes an increasing voltage phase-lead as the low frequency rolloff descends with a limit of +90° at maximum attenuation.

The two reactances, in their pure unadulterated forms, effect phase shifts of +90° to −90° to an ultimate extent of 180° opposed; they are in exact opposition and *out-of-phase* with each other.

Referring again to Fig. 22-58, a slightly different light shines. The two reactances are working in direct opposition to each other with the inductive reactance trying to cancel the capacitative reactance and vice versa. Arithmetically, it is surprisingly simple when two opposing reactance values are directly subtracted from each other; the whole network behaves as a single reactance of the same reactive character as the one predominant in the network.

For example, if for a given frequency, the inductive reactance is a (+) 1.2 kΩ (the + indicating the phase shift character of inductance) and the capacitive reactance is (−) 1.5 kΩ, then the effective reactance of the entire network is that of a capacitor of (−) 300-Ω reactance. Because there are *two* reactive effects operating simultaneously in this network, it is said to have *second-order characteristics.*

22.10.5 Resonance

Resonance is the strange state where the reactances of both the L and C are equal. For any inductor-capacitor pair at resonance, the two reactances will still be equal. If you subtract two equal numbers, the answer is zero. So, for the series tuned-circuit arrangement of Fig. 22-58 at resonance, there is no impedance. The two reactances have cancelled themselves out. It is a short circuit at that one frequency of resonance, disallowing component losses and is, in effect, a frequency-selective short circuit. Either side of that frequency, of course, one or the other of the reactances become predominant again.

22.10.6 Resonant Q

Like the single-order networks, there is an infinite number of combinations of C and L at any given frequency that will achieve resonance (i.e., the two reactances are equal). Similarly, it is the scale of impedance that alters with such value changes; the magnitude and rate of change of reactance on either side of resonance (off tune) hinges on the chosen combination.

At resonance, although the two reactances negate each other, they both still individually have their original values. Off resonance, their actual reactances matter. If each of the reactances is 400 Ω at resonance, then 10% off tune either way they are going to become 440 and 360 Ω, respectively. A 10% change in this instance equates to about a 40-Ω change either way, up or down. Now imagine that a smaller capacitor and a larger inductor were used to obtain the same resonant frequency. Their reactances will be correspondingly larger. If they're five times larger with reactances of 2 kΩ each, then at 10% off tune their reactances will become 2.2 and 1.8 kΩ or 200 Ω change each. The higher the network impedance, the more dramatic the reactance shift off tune.

On its own, the series-tuned circuit with whatever impedances are involved doesn't amount to much; however, in relation to the outside world, it becomes interesting. In Fig. 22-58C the series-tuned circuit is fed via a series resistor the output being sensed across the tuned circuit. Fig. 22-58D shows input-output curves for three different tuned-circuit impedances based on low, medium, and high reactances with the series resistor kept the same in all cases. The detune slopes are steeper with higher reactance networks than with lower ones. In other words, higher reactance networks have a sharper notch filter effect, less bandwidth, and a higher Q than lower reactance networks.

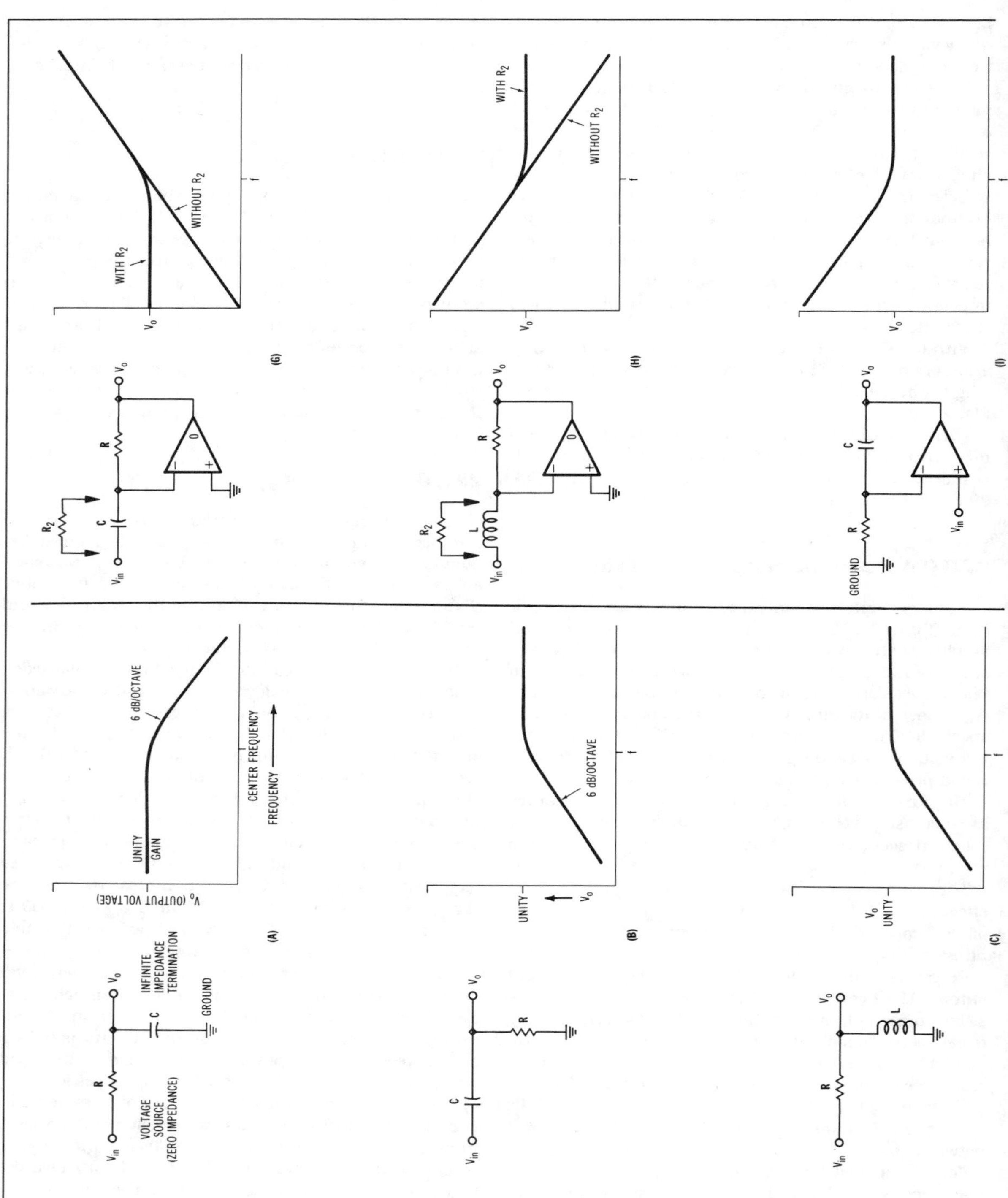

V_{in}
VOLTAGE SOURCE (ZERO IMPEDANCE)
R
C
V_o
INFINITE IMPEDANCE TERMINATION
GROUND
(A)
V_o (OUTPUT VOLTAGE)
UNITY GAIN
6 dB/OCTAVE
CENTER FREQUENCY
FREQUENCY
(B)
UNITY
6 dB/OCTAVE
f
(C)
L
(G)
R_2
WITH R_2
WITHOUT R_2
(H)
(I)

Figure 22-57

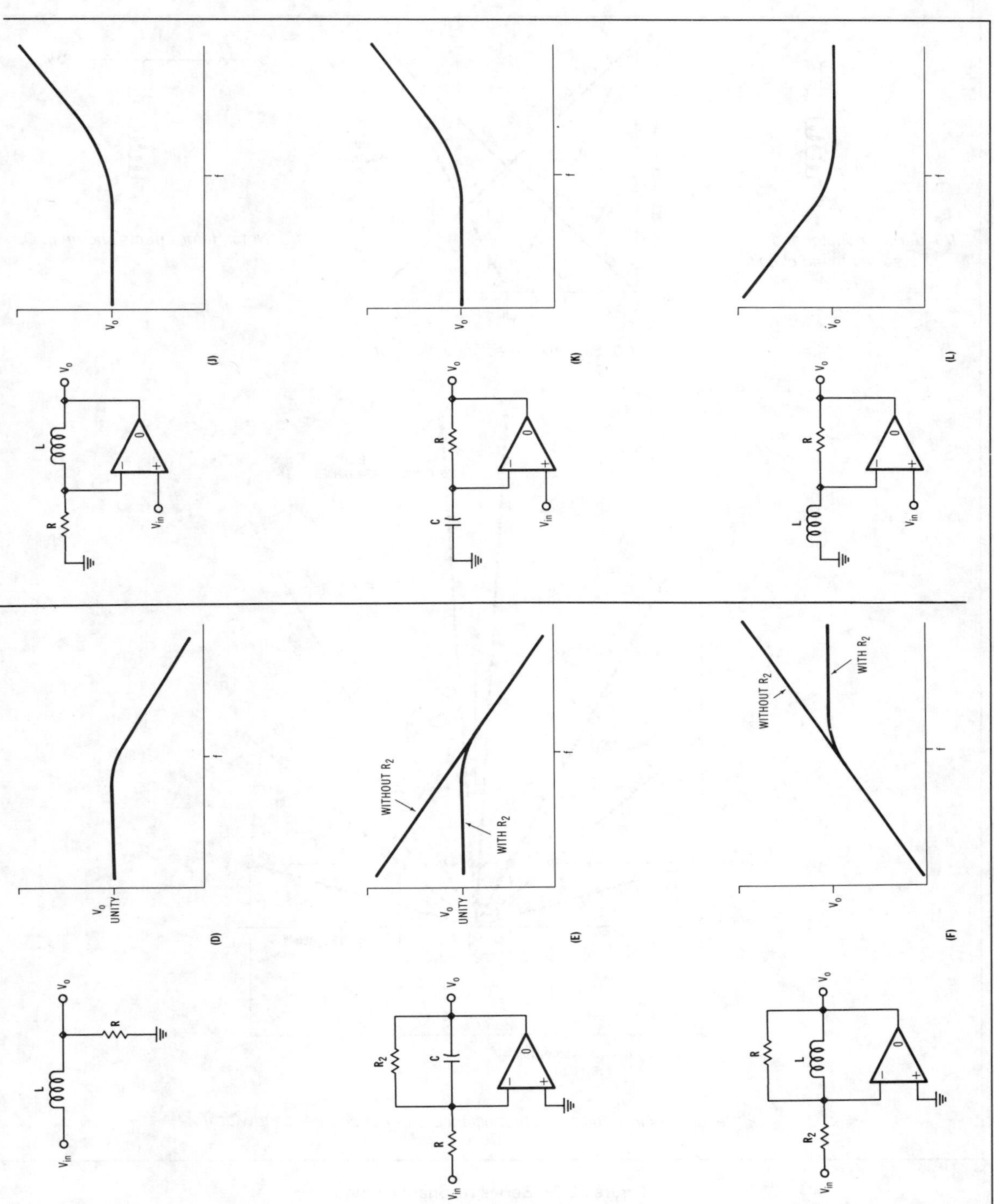

Single-order filters.

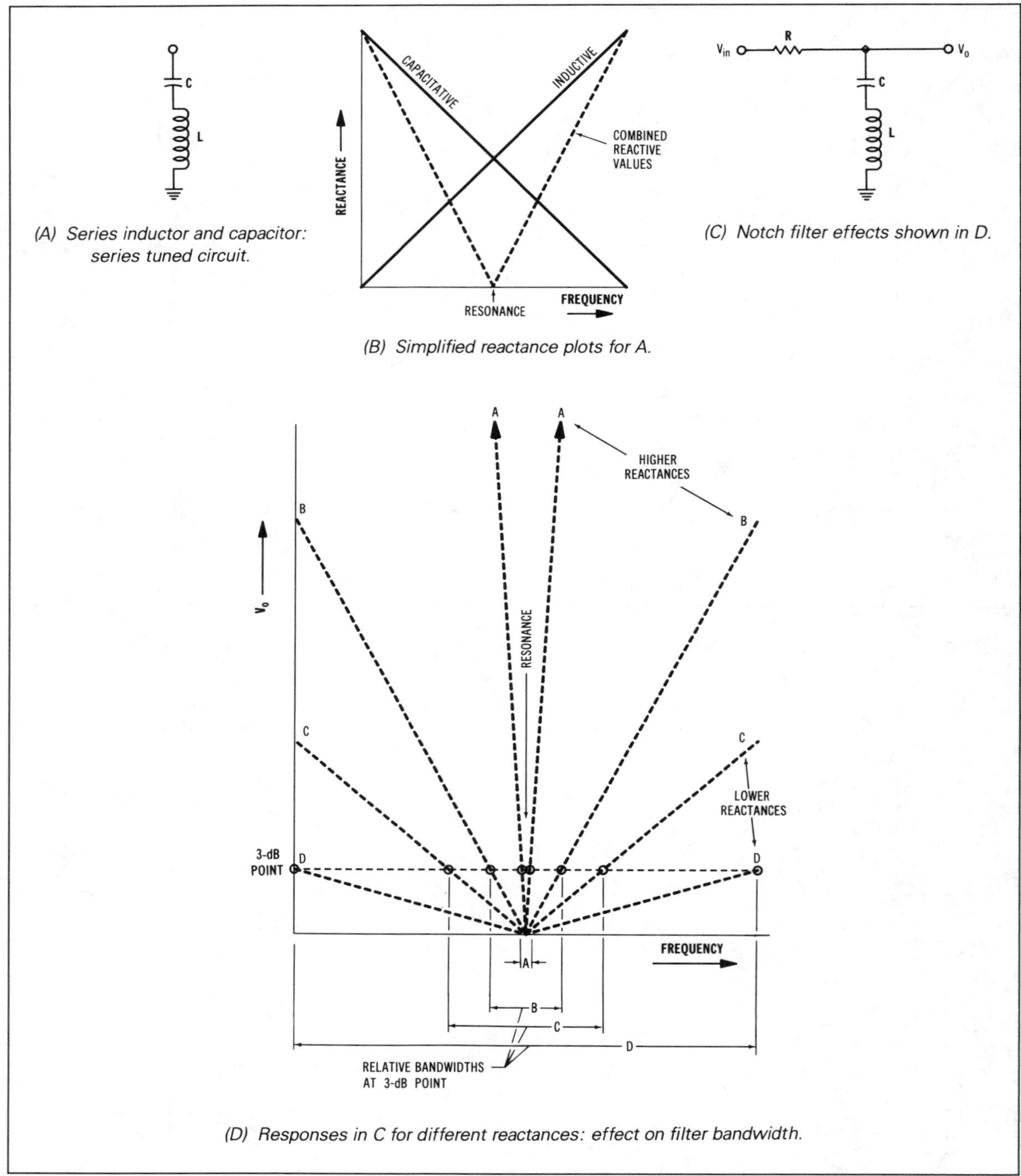

(A) Series inductor and capacitor: series tuned circuit.

(B) Simplified reactance plots for A.

(C) Notch filter effects shown in D.

(D) Responses in C for different reactances: effect on filter bandwidth.

Figure 22-58 Series resonant circuits.

22.10.7 Bandwidth and Q

There are direct relationships between the network reactances, the series resistance, the bandwidth, and the Q. Q is numerically equal to the ratio of elemental reactance to series resistance in a series-tuned circuit (Q = X/R); on a more practical level, the Q can also be determined as the ratio of filter center frequency to bandwidth (Q = f/BW). Bandwidth is measured between the 3-dB-down points on either side of resonance where the phase has been shifted ± 45°. If a tuned circuit has a center frequency of 1 kHz and 3-dB-down points at 900 Hz and 1.1 kHz, the bandwidth is 200 Hz and the network Q is 5 (frequency/bandwidth). The greater the Q, the smaller the bandwidth.

The filter resonant frequency may be altered by changing either the inductance or capacitance. Q is subject to variation of the resistor or simultaneously juggling the reactances in the inductance-capacitance network, while maintaining the same center frequency.

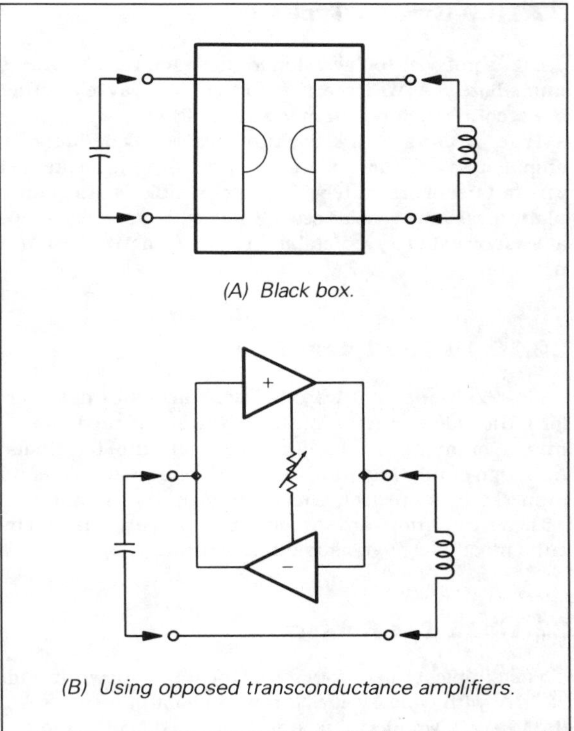

(A) Black box.

(B) Using opposed transconductance amplifiers.

Figure 22-59 Gyrators.

22.10.8 Creating Inductance

It is most efficient (electrically and financially) in the majority of console-type circuitry for inductance to be simulated or generated artificially by circuits that are the practical implementation of a mathematical conjuring trick known generically as *gyrators*.

A true gyrator is a four-terminal device that transmutes any reactance or impedance presented to one port into a mirror image form at the other port (Fig. 22-59A).

A capacitor on the input (with its falling reactance versus frequency) creates inductance at the output port. The scale of inductive reactance generated may be easily and continuously varied by altering the internal gain-balance structure of the gyrator in Fig. 22-59B by changing the transconductance of the back-to-back amplifiers, creating a continuously variable inductor.

Real inductors have a justifiably bad name for audio design. They are big and heavy, and they saturate easily. Their core hysteresis causes distortion, and they are subject to pickup of nearby electromagnetic fields (principally power line ac hum and RF unless well screened, which makes them even bigger and heavier). The windings and terminations are prone to break, and they are *expensive.*

It is quite easy to see why it is popular to avoid using real inductors. Naturally, the simulated inductive reactance is only as good as the quality of the capacitative reactance it is modeled upon and the loading effect of the gyrator circuit itself, the major limitation. Degradation of the inductance takes the general form of effective series lossy resistance, the Q of the inductors suffering (Q = X/R). Leakage resistance across or through the image capacitor is partially to blame here. Fortunately, for the purposes of normal equalizers, very large Qs are not necessary, so selecting capacitor types to this particular end is hardly necessary.

An obvious extension of the continuously variable inductor is the continuously variable bandpass filter formed by adding a capacitor either in series or parallel with the gyrated inductor, forming series- and parallel-tuned circuits to make notch and peak filters, respectively. Although ideal for fixed-frequency filters with the Q of the network or sharpness defined by a resistor in series with the gyrator resonator, the idea falls down when the resonance frequency is moved.

If the frequency is moved higher by altering either the L or C, the reactances of the element at resonance become lower; consequently, the ratio of the reactances to the fixed-series resistor (this is the ratio that determines the Q) becomes smaller, and the Q of the filter becomes broader in response. In order to maintain the same Q over the projected frequency variation, the series resistor has to be ganged with the frequency control, which is not easy. Should it be necessary to make the Q a variable parameter also, as in a parametric-type eq section, it would mean devising quite a complex set of interactive variable controls. For this reason parametric-type equalizer sections are ordinarily constructed around second-order, active-filter networks, not individual tuned circuits whether real or gyrated.

22.10.9 Gyrator Types

Let us not write off gyration for function variable filters immediately. As we'll see, they form in one way or another the second reactance in many active filters.

True gyrators of the back-to-back transconductance amplifier variety are an unmitigated drag to make, set up, and use. Fortunately, there are simpler ways of simulating variable reactances—if not with pure reactance at least by using a predictable effect of a reactive, resistive network.

22.10.10 The Totem Pole

Fig. 22-60 may not ward off evil spirits but does perform the magic transformation of the single capacitor C_1 into a simulated inductance between the terminals. Although emulating quite a pure inductance when set up properly, it is precisely that setting up that is not altogether straightforward. In fact, it is high on a list of circuits most likely to do something curious.

22.10.11 The Bootstrap

The simplest fake inductor of the lot is shown in Fig. 22-61A, with typical values thrown in for argument's sake. It relies on a wonderful technotrick called *bootstrapping*. The fundamental principles are shown in Fig. 22-62. A 1-kΩ resistor with 1 V across it will pass 1 mA. Without changing the source potential of 1 V, the bottom end of the resistor is tied to 0.8 V. There is 0.2 V across the resistor, and so a current of 0.2 mA flows through the resistor. The source (still at 1 V) sees 0.2 mA flowing away from it, the amount of current it would expect to see going to a 5-kΩ resistor value (1 V/0.2 mA = 5 kΩ). It thinks it's looking at a 5-kΩ resistor! Continuing this, stuffing a potential of 1 V (not the same source) at the bottom end of the resistor means there is no voltage across the resistor, so there is no current flow. Our original source thinks it's seeing an open circuit (infinite resistance) despite the fact that there is still a definite 1-kΩ resistor hanging on it.

This phenomenon holds true with any source voltage, ac or dc, provided the instantaneous bootstrap voltage is the same as the source. Any phase difference creates an instantaneous potential difference across the resistor; therefore, current flows, and so on.

This fake inductor works on frequency-dependent bootstrapping, the terminal being almost totally bootstrapped to high impedance via the 150-Ω resistor at high frequencies and the bootstrap voltage reducing (together with its phase being shifted) with falling frequency. At very low frequencies the capacitor behaves as a virtual open circuit. No bootstrap exists, so the terminal is tied to ground via the 150-Ω resistor and the effectively zero output impedance of the voltage follower. The circuit emulates an inductor reasonably well; it has a very low impedance value at low frequencies, increasing with frequency to a relatively high impedance.

The problem with this simple circuit is that at high frequencies a parallel impedance (consisting of the variable resistor and capacitor chain) hangs directly from the terminal to ground. Buffering the chain from the terminal by a follower eliminates this (Fig. 22-61C).

Fig. 22-61A creates an analog of an inductor with the losses shown in Fig. 22-61B. The series resistor is the 150-Ω bootstrap resistor; after all, a proper inductive reactance tends to zero at low frequencies, not 150 Ω. Therefore, the resistor is effectively in series. The R/C network across the lot represents, again, the high-pass filter impedance, which upon the addition of the follower, disappears to be replaced in Fig. 22-61D by the much greater input impedance of the follower, which is enough to be ignored.

As a short footnote to this gyrator epic, consider what happens to either Fig. 22-61C or F if the high-pass resistance-capacitance filter is replaced by a low-pass filter by swapping R with C. It may seem a bit strange to use circuitry to imitate a capacitor, but imitating a continuously variable capacitor does not make sense. Real variable capacitors of the large values needed in eqs and easily created by gyrators simply don't exist otherwise.

22.10.12 Constant-Amplitude Phase-Shift Network

A constant-amplitude phase-shift (CAPS) circuit of previously little real worth smiles at us in Fig. 22-61E. Bearing more than a little resemblance to a differential amplifier, this circuit can rotate the output phase through 180° with respect to the input, at around the frequency primarily determined by the high-pass RC filter. In addition, the input and output amplitude relationship remains constant throughout.

How? This is dealt with in Fig. 22-61G and H where the simplistic assumptions that a capacitor is open circuit at low frequencies and a short at high frequencies show that at low frequencies the circuit operates as a straightforward unity-gain inverting amplifier (−180° phase shift), while at high frequencies it operates as a unity-gain noninverting amplifier (0° shift). The mechanism for the latter mode is interesting. The op-amp is actually operating at gain-of-two noninverting; this is compensated for by the input leg *also* passing through the still operating unity inverting path, which naturally subtracts to leave unity gain, noninverting.

22.10.13 Simulated Resonance

We now possess all the variables we need to create single- and second-order filters. Higher-order networks can be made with combinations of the two. Tracking variable

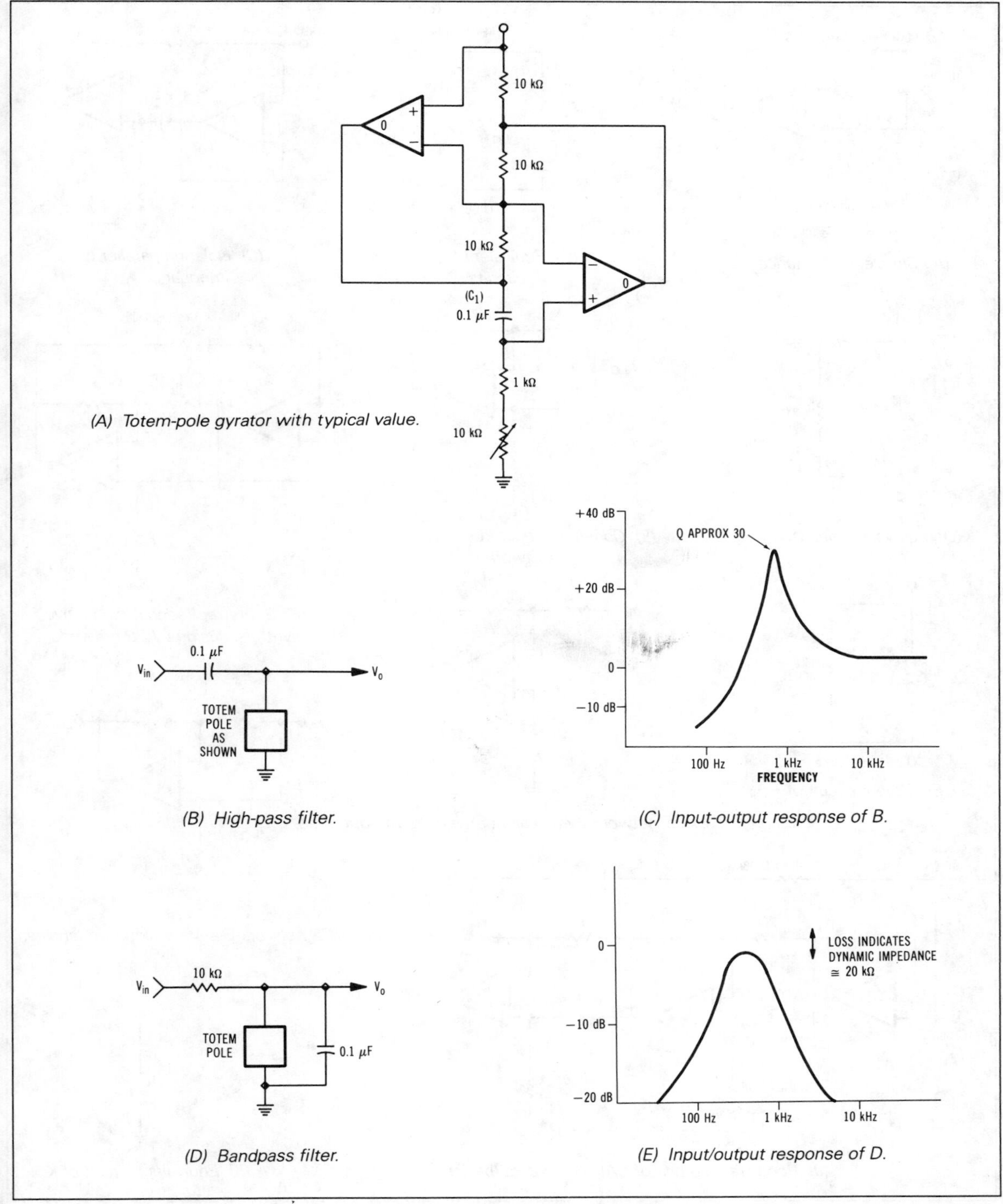

(A) Totem-pole gyrator with typical value.

(B) High-pass filter.

(C) Input-output response of B.

(D) Bandpass filter.

(E) Input/output response of D.

Figure 22-60 Totem-pole gyrators.

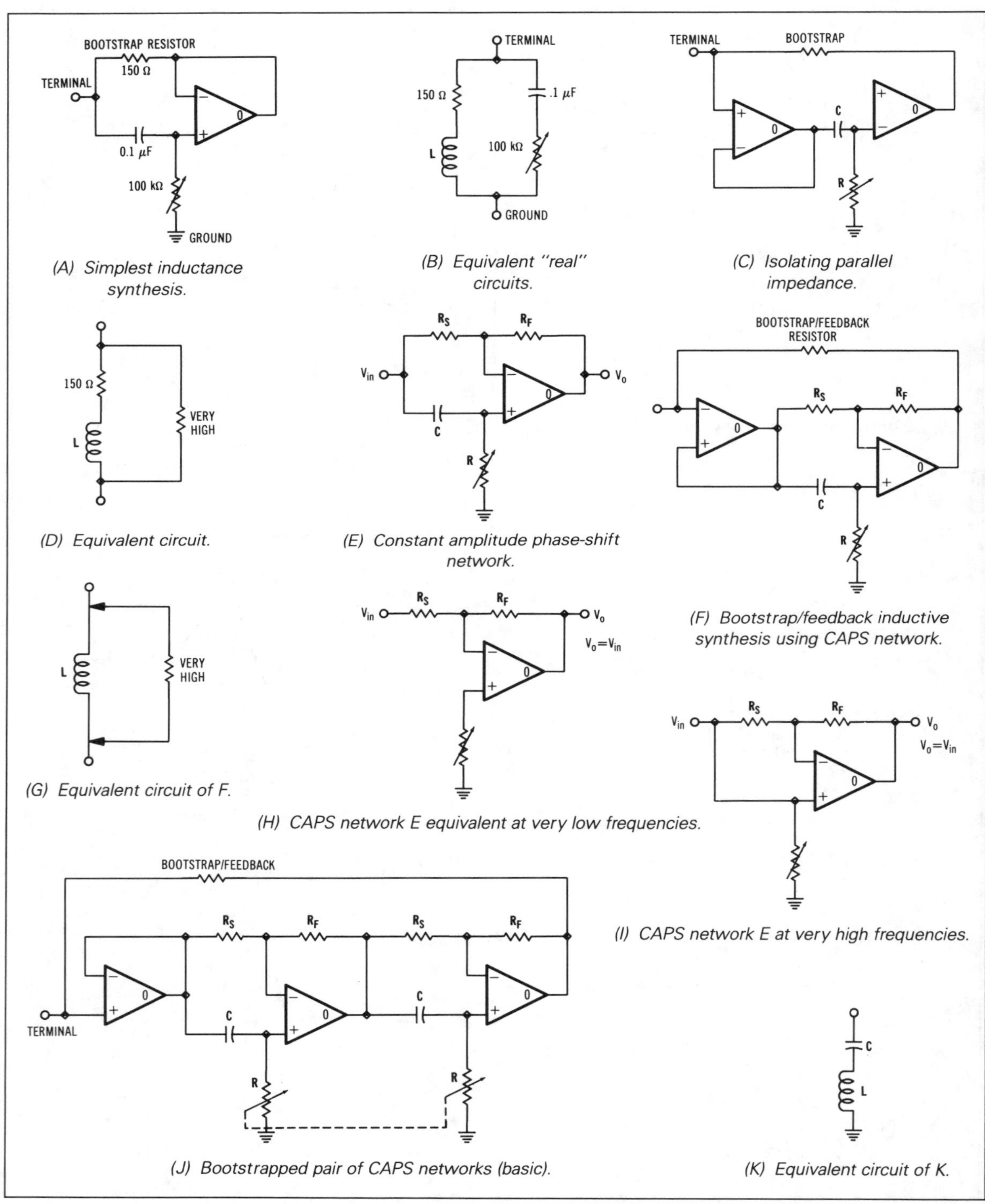

Figure 22-61 Inductive reactance synthesis.

capacitors and inductors allows us to manufacture constant Q bandpass filters irrespective of frequency. This realization itself brings a dawning of understanding in how the much-touted integrator-loop filters such as the *state variable* actually operate. The clue lies with the 180° phase-shift circuit of Fig. 22-61E. Connecting two such filters (with the variable resistor elements ganged) in series produces a remarkably performing circuit. At any frequency within the design swing, it is possible for the circuit output voltage to be exactly out-of-phase (−180° phase shift). By summing input and output, direct cancellation at that frequency and at no other is achieved. In short a variable-frequency notch filter with a consistent resonant characteristic is produced. Alternatively, bootstrapping the input from the output actually changes that input port into something that behaves exactly like a series-tuned circuit to ground (Fig. 22-61J). The circuit is continuously variable in frequency with a constant Q by virtue of the simultaneously tracking simulated inductor and capacitor maintaining exactly the same elemental reactances at whatever the selected operating resonant frequency. This creates the same source resistance, same reactance, same Q.

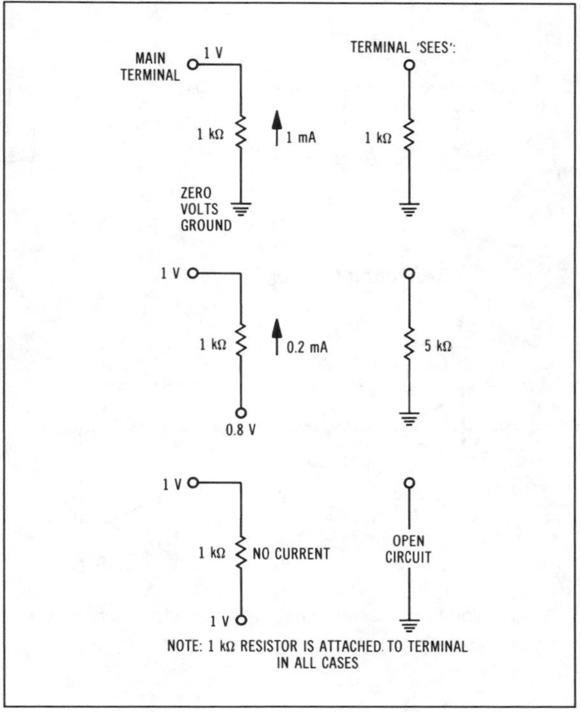

Figure 22-62 Bootstrapping analysis.

22.10.14 Constant Q and Constant Bandwidth

The same Q definitely does not imply the same bandwidth. As the resonant frequency changes, the bandwidth changes proportionally. Bandwidth is, after all, the ratio of frequency to Q. Some active filters, such as the multifeedback variety, exhibit a constant bandwidth when the resonant frequency is changed: a 10:1 variation of center frequency, a 10:1 variation of Q. This, of course, is rarely useful for real eq; however, it is very interesting in that the change in Q with frequency happens in the opposite sense to that expected from a normal-tuned circuit. The Q sharpens with increasing frequency. It is a perfect example of a constant-bandwidth filter.

22.10.15 Q, EQ, and Music

The almost insistence on resonant-type filters being constant in Q when varied in frequency is not through an industry-wide collective lack of imagination or desire to keep things tidy. It stems from psychoacoustics, from the way humans react to audible stimuli, and also from the way nature deals with things acoustic.

If something is acoustically resonant, it will need a similar electrical resonance response shape to compensate for, extract, or imitate it in the console. Acoustics are defined by exact analogs of the first- and second-order filters and the time-domain effects that we've been delving into here in eq; nature is nothing if not consistent.

22.10.16 Bandpass Filter Development

Methods of filtering come thick and fast once the basics are established. The development of a popular bandpass filter arrangement is shown in Fig. 22-63. It starts as two variable passive single-order filters of a common crossover frequency point, ganged so that they track. Reconfigured slightly (Fig. 22-63B) to minimize interaction, they are shown with their drive and sense amplifiers. Wrapping the two networks around an inverting amp isolates them completely from each other, improving the filter shape. The bandpass Q is rather low, well under one, leaving it rather limited in scope for practical applications. A discretionary degree of positive feedback from the amplifier output back to the noninverting input sharpens the Q, if a little unpredictably and certainly more than critically of component tolerances.

Yes, it does look rather like a Wein Bridge oscillator, doesn't it? Attempting to get the Q too high proves the point unquestionably!

22.10.17 Listening to Q

This raises the problems of excessive Qs. Fortunately, extremely high Qs (greater than ten) are unnecessary or

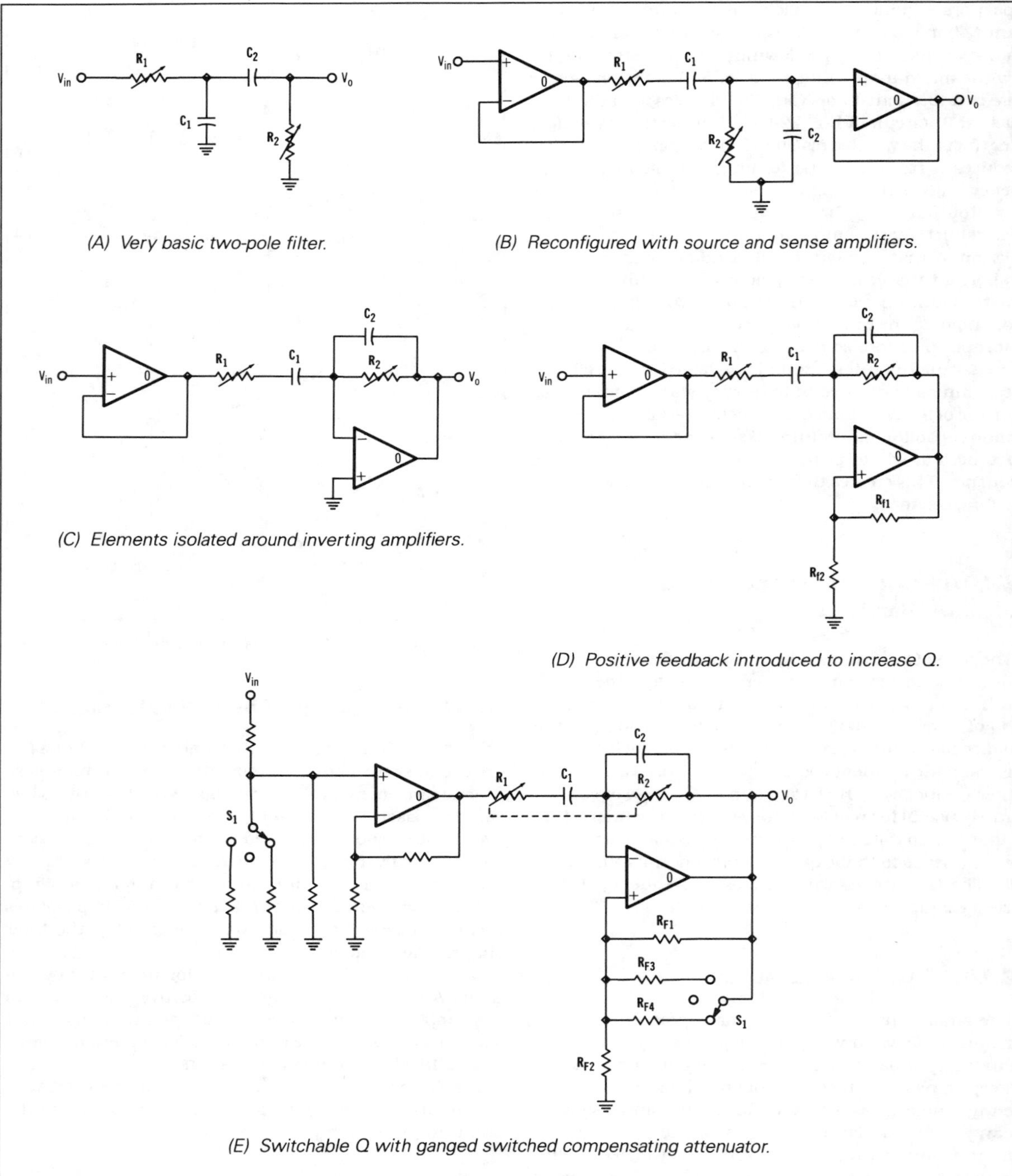

(A) *Very basic two-pole filter.*

(B) *Reconfigured with source and sense amplifiers.*

(C) *Elements isolated around inverting amplifiers.*

(D) *Positive feedback introduced to increase Q.*

(E) *Switchable Q with ganged switched compensating attenuator.*

Figure 22-63 A bandpass filter development.

unusable for eq purposes. The higher the Q becomes, the less actual spectral content of the signal it modifies, so despite the fact that its peak gain or attenuation is the same as a lower Q filter, it seems to do subjectively less. Judicious care is required in setting up the filter to enhance or trim exactly what is required. Accidental overkill is easy.

There comes a breakpoint with increasing Q where you are not so much listening to the effect of the filter as to the filter itself. Resonant-tuned circuits are to a degree electrical storage media, where energy inside the circuit shuffles backward and forward between the two reactive elements until the circuit losses waste it away. The greater the Q (and by definition the lower the included losses), the more pronounced the signal storage is.

Despite being good for a laugh, hearing frequencies triggered by notes trailing off into the sunset and extremely high Qs are of no value at all in practical EQ. A transient hitting such a filter fires off a virtually idential series of decaying sine waves at the frequency of the filter.

Square waves sent through audio paths are good for kicking resonant ringing off at almost any frequency. It's a convenient means of unearthing inadvertent response bumps, phase problems, and lurking instabilities. The breakpoint, where we start to hear ringing as much as signal, is quite low, a Q of between five and ten depending on the nature of the program material.

22.10.18 Squegg or Slug?

It is not too difficult now to appreciate that resonant circuits and oscillators are very close cousins—often indistinguishable, except for maybe an odd component value here and there. There are two fundamental approaches to achieving a resonant bandpass characteristic using active-filter techniques.

The first is to start off with a tame, poorly performing, passive network and then introduce positive feedback to make it predictably (we hope) unstable. The feedback exaggerates the filter character and increases the Q to the desired extent. A perfect example of this is the Wein Bridge development of Fig. 22-63. The major disadvantage of such methods is that the Q is disproportionately critical with respect to the feedback adjustments.

The second approach is to start off with an oscillator, then slug it until it's tame enough. This is the basis of the state variable, the biquad, and similar related integrator-loop-type active filters.

22.10.19 The Two-Integrator Loop

Three inverting amplifiers connected together in a loop, as shown in Fig. 22-64, seem a perfectly worthless circuit and, as such, it is. It's there to demonstrate (assuming perfect op-amps) that it is a perfectly stable arrangement. Each stage inverts (180° phase shift), so the first amplifier section receives a perfectly out-of-phase (invert, revert, invert) feedback, cancelling any tendency within the loop to drift or wobble. Removing 180° of phase shift would result in perfect in-phase positive feedback; the result is an oscillator.

Arranging for the 180° to be lost only at one specific frequency results in the circuit being rendered unstable at just that one frequency. In other words, it oscillates controllably. Creating the 180° phase loss is left to two of the inverting amps being made into integrators (Fig. 22-64B), so called because they behave as an electrical analog of the mathematical function integration.

The integrator you may recognize from a single-order filter variation in Fig. 22-58. It's not so much the amplitude response that's useful here as the phase response, which at a given frequency (dictated by the R and C values) reaches −90° with respect to the input. Two successive ganged-value integrators create a 180° shift.

Slugging the loop to stop it from oscillating can be achieved in a variety of ways:

1. Trimming the gain of the remaining inverter. This is unduly critical like the Wein Bridge for Q determination.
2. Doping one of the integrator capacitors with a resistor (Fig. 22-64C). This in essence is the biquad. The Q is largely dependent on the ratio of the capacitive reactance to the parallel resistance; consequently, it varies proportionally with frequency. For fixed-frequency applications the biquad is easy, docile, and predictable.
3. Phased negative feedback. This is not true negative feedback but taken from the output of the first integrator (90° shift). It provides an easily managed Q variation, is constant, and is independent of filter frequency (Fig. 22-64C). Forming the basis of the state-variable filter, this has turned out to be "The active filter most likely to succeed," if the majority of current commercial console designs are to be believed.

Loop filters, such as described in Fig. 22-64, have a number of inherent problems that are usually glossed over for the sake of the operational simplicity and elegance of the design.

22.10.20 Stability and Noise Characteristics

Each amplifier within the loop has a finite time delay, which together add up to significant phase shifts within the open-loop bandwidths of the amplifiers. Some simply add to the delay imparted by the integrators, but the total time discontinuity around the summing amp can pro-

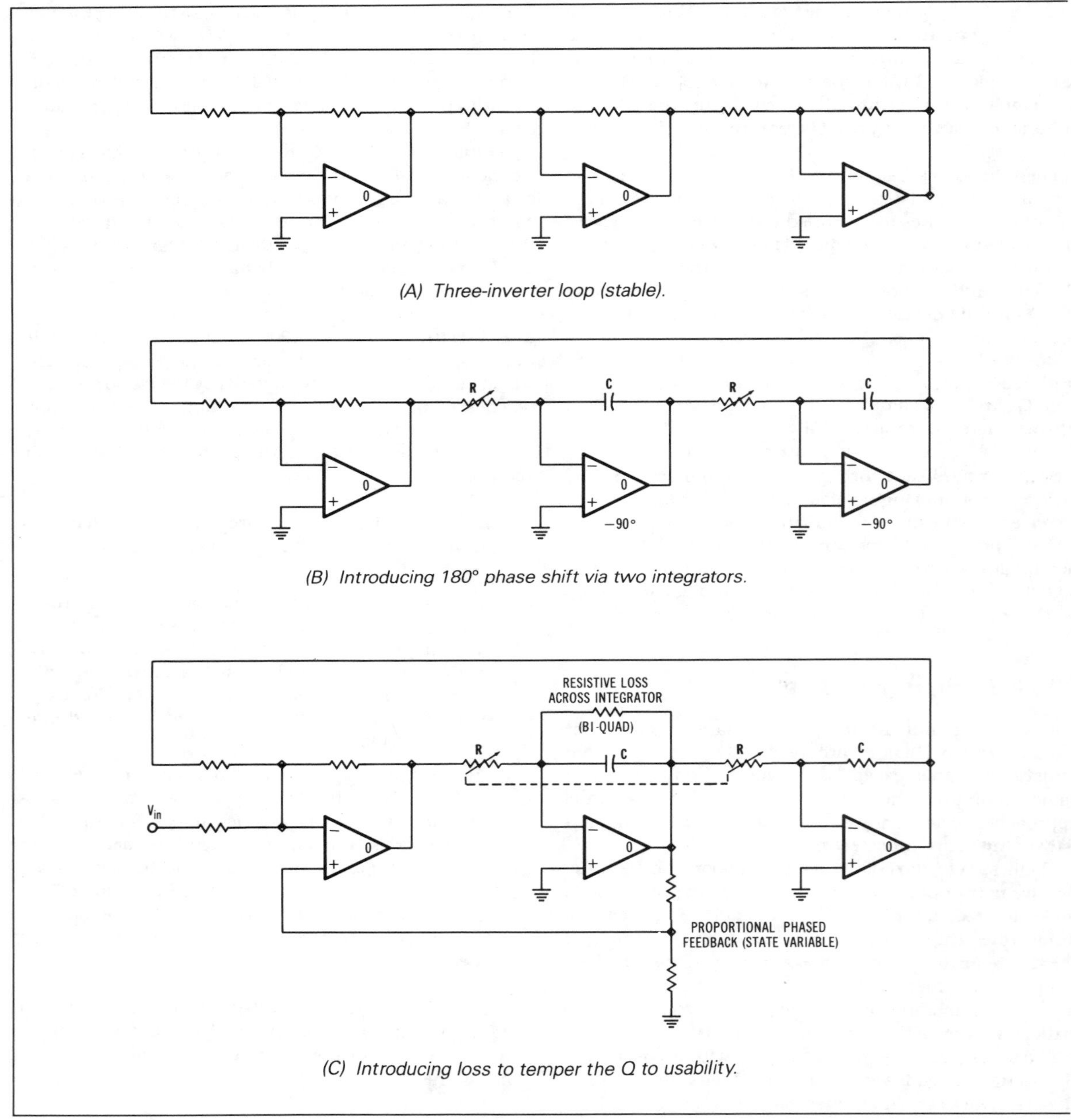

(A) Three-inverter loop (stable).

(B) Introducing 180° phase shift via two integrators.

(C) Introducing loss to temper the Q to usability.

Figure 22-64

mote instability in the multimegahertz region. Compensation for this around the summing amplifier can introduce further phase shifts, upsetting the filter performance at high frequencies.

Two major problems are due to the nature of the integrator arrangement itself. They come to light at the extremes of the feedback capacitive reactance (i.e., at very low and very high frequencies where, respectively, the reactances are virtually open circuit and short circuit).

Open circuit at low frequencies means the op-amp is infinitely amplifying external resistor noise and internally generated thermal and (mostly) low-frequency noise,

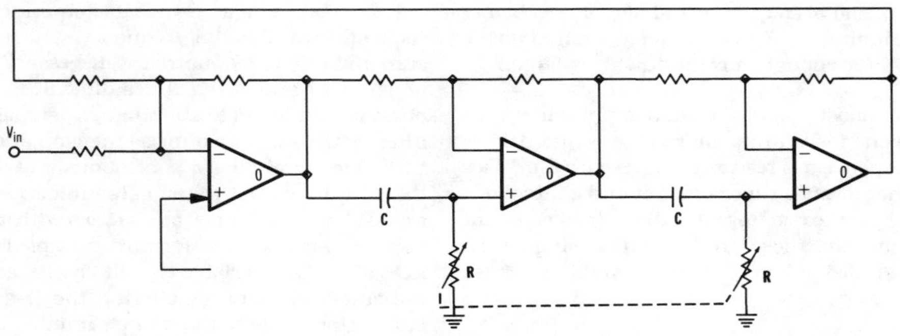

(D) CAPS—variable filter, Q determined as for state variable.

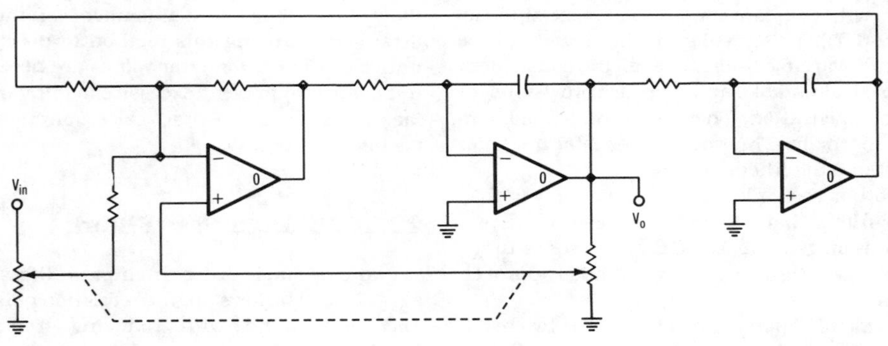

(E) Ganged potentiometer simultaneously altering Q and input attenuator.

Loop filters.

plus any low-frequency noise presented to the input along with the signal. There is *a lot* of generated and circulating low-frequency noise.

At high frequencies, the reactance approaches a short circuit, connecting the output back around to the inverting input. This arrangement, zero closed-loop gain, is about as critical in terms of device instability as we can get. It is analogous to a grounded-input follower (see section 22.6), since there is no possible way of further externally defining the closed-loop characteristics beyond that of the integrating capacitor itself, which may or may not be adequate. For audio frequencies, the integration capacitor value can be quite sizable, up to 1µF. Two problems appear:

1. An immediate problem of the current output capacity of the op-amp being incapable of charging such a capacitor instantaneously; this will result in a low maxima of signal frequency and signal level before slew-rate limitation. The amplifier just might not be able to deliver enough current quickly enough.

2. There will almost certainly be another problem related to the open-loop output impedance of the device; this corresponds to a resistor in series with the device output that forms a time constant and a filter with the integrator capacitor. Another time constant means more time delay in the loop causing a seriously degraded (already critical) stability phase margin.

As tame as it may superficially seem, the state variable is not an unconditionally or reliably stable arrangement, with out-of-band dynamic problems potentially degrading its sonic performance.

With the exception of inevitable loop effects (usually time related), most of the undesirable things about the state variable can be eliminated or mitigated by replacing the integrators with constant-amplitude, phase-shift elements (Fig. 22-64D). This results in what could best be known as a CAPS-variable filter. Here, all the constituent elements are basically stable, and there are provisions for independent compensation. There is no undefined gain for any of the spectrum. This seems to be a far healthier format to start making filters around.

There is another way of looking at the state variable/ CAPS-variable filters that will suddenly resolve the previous discussions on gyrators, L and C filters, series-tuned circuits, and so on with the seemingly at-odds approach of active filters.

Resonance depends upon the reaction of the two reactances of opposite sense, 180° apart in phase effect. Rather than achieve this in a differential manner, one element +90° with the other −90° at a given frequency, active filters achieve the total difference by summing same-sense phase differences (−90°) + (−90°) (i.e., still 180°). Two reactive networks are still involved; hence, it is still a second-order effect. At the end of the day, the principal difference is that such loop-type active filters have their median resonance phase displaced by 90° from their input as a result of both reactances going the same way, as opposed to the nil phase shift at resonance of a real LC network.

22.10.21 Q and Filter Gain

Pretty much every resonant-type active filter has the unfortunate characteristic of its gain at resonance being at least related and often directly proportional numerically to the Q of the filter. This means a filter with a Q of ten usually has a voltage gain of 10 (or 20 dB) at resonance. Naturally, this is not on. Even specifying a maximum Q of five only helps by losing 6 dB of boost with respect to a Q of ten.

That represents a very sizable chunk of system headroom stolen at the filter frequency, which also makes the sum-and-difference matrixing necessary to provide the usual boost-and-cut facilities difficult to configure. The obvious solution is to attenuate the signal going into the filter by the same amount as the gain and Q expected of the filter. Arranging a continuously variable Q control that also attenuates the signal source appropriately is not a conspicuously simple task, at least with most filters. Perhaps the most straightforward example is shown in Fig. 22-64C, a state-variable type filter with an attenuator in the slug-back network altering the Q ganged with an attenuator ahead of the input/summing amplifier.

Within a couple of decibels, this holds the resonant peak output constant over a considerably useful Q range.

Most other filters are not so obliging in terms of continuously variable Q. Switching between a few values of Q while substituting appropriate input attenuation is quite often a practical and operationally acceptable solution, applicable to nearly any filtering approach. Fig. 22-63E illustrates a further development of the Wein Bridge arrangement using this method to provide three alternative Qs. The attenuator values are necessarily high in impedance to prevent excessive loading of the source, a factor that in some practical eq circumstances is important.

22.10.22 High-Pass Filters

Two old, single-order, high-pass filters are shown in Fig. 22-65. The keys are the reduction of inductive reactance to ground with reducing frequency in Fig. 22-65F and the increasing of capacitative reactance with reducing frequency in Fig. 22-65G.

How about combining the two and omitting the resistors as in Fig. 22-65A? As expected, the combining of the two opposing reactances causes an ultimate rolloff twice as fast as for the single orders; however, they have also resulted in a resonance peak at the point of equal reactance. Resonance Q is the ratio of elemental reactance to resistance; so deliberately introducing loss in the circuit in the form of a termination resistor tames the resonance to leave a nice, flat, in-band response (Fig. 22-65B).

Substituting a basic gyrator or simulated inductance for the real one (Fig. 22-65C) naturally works just as well and even better than expected. The filter output can be taken straight from the gyrator amplifier output, eliminating the need to use another amplifier as an output buffer.

Second, we can automatically introduce the required

amount of loss into the inductor by increasing the value of the bootstrap resistor and get the resonance damping right. (Refer to the discussion of gyrators in section 22.10.9.)

Third, we can easily change the turnover frequency of the filter by varying what was the tuning resistor. In doing this, of course, the elemental reactance-to-loss ratio will change, causing the Q (hence, damping factor) to change with it. The frequency change and required damping change are directly related and may be simultaneously altered with a ganged control—even if we do our sums right, with the two ganged tracks having the same value!

A slight redraw of Fig. 22-65C gives Fig. 22-65D, a more conventional portrayal of the classic Sallen-Key high-pass filter arrangement.

As the Sallen-Key filter evolves, it is seen that an *equal value filter* (where the two capacitors are equal and the two resistors are equal) results in a less than adequate response shape. An expedient method of tailoring and smartening up response (working on the assumption that a few more resistors are cheaper than a special two-value ganged potentiometer) is to alter the damping by introducing gain into the gyrator buffer amplifier (also providing a means of stability and compensating it correctly). See Fig. 22-65E. A side effect of this technique of damping adjustment (which, incidentally, is independent of filter frequency) is that an input-output in-band gain is introduced. This may or may not be problematic. The 4-dB gain introduced necessary to render the filter frequency response maximally flat could be included in

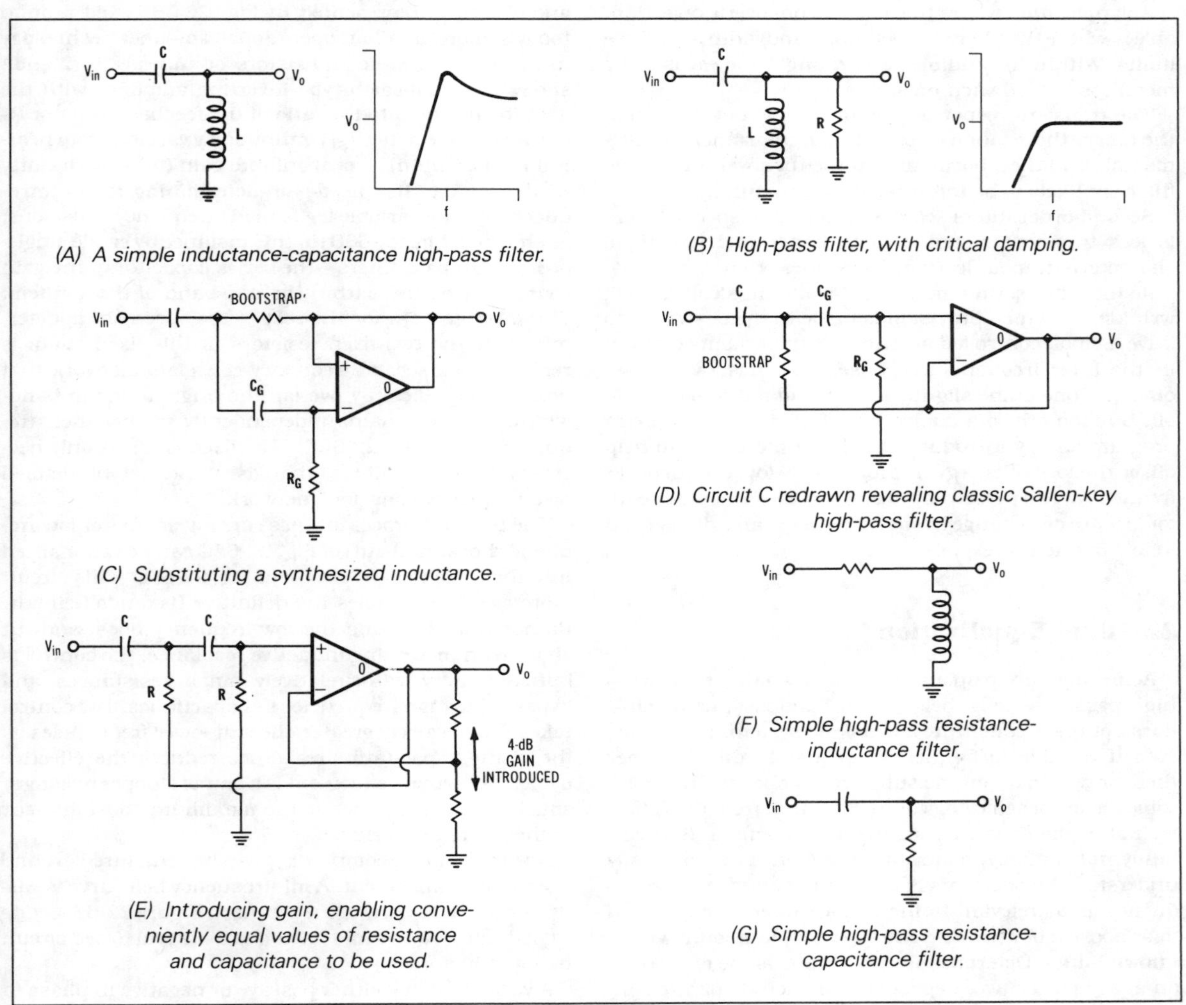

Figure 22-65 High-pass filter development.

overall system gain, or alternatively a compensating attenuator could be instituted ahead of it. This could as well be arranged to be a fixed-frequency, band-end, single-order, high-pass filter to accelerate the rolloff slope out of band.

22.10.23 Second or Third or More Order?

Without delving too deeply into psychoacoustics, the ear notices easily a third or more order filter being introduced for much the same reasons as a high-Q bandpass filter is obvious. There are severe modifications to the transient response of the signal path and ringing-type time-related components are introduced into the signal spectrum.

An application where this effect is not overly objectionable is where the filters are defining bandwidth at audible limits. Within the audible band though, the ear is quite merciless toward such noises.

The transient response modification is not the end of the story; the relationships between instrument fundamentals and their harmonics in the turnover area of the filter are likely to be interpreted as unnatural.

Second-order filters score well in both respects. There is less transient response disturbance and less tonal characteristic modification. There are few who would dispute that they sound more natural and musical. A small wrinkle, for which provision is made in the design, is to leave a small controlled amount of under-damped bump in the filter frequency response. This has two consequences: one is the slightly more rapid out-of-band rolloff, but the other, a subjective effect, is that the extra program energy introduced by the hump serves to help offset the loss of energy in programs below the turnover frequency. The perceived effect upon introducing the filter is more of a change in sound rather than a direct drop in low-frequency response.

22.10.24 Equalization Control

Achieving bare response shapes of whatever nature—high pass, low pass, bell-shaped bandpass, or notch—does not really constitute a usable eq system. The shape, even if variable in frequency and bandwidth, is either there or not, in or out, no subtleties or shades; therefore, some means of achieving control over the strength of effect is vital to the cause. By far the most common (but certainly not the only) control requirement and one easily understood by operators is boost and cut, where the frequency areas relevant to the various filters are required to be boosted or attenuated by any variable amount within known limits. Determining these limits alone is good for an argument or two, dependent on such disparate considerations as system headroom, operator maturity, and, obviously, application. An EQ created specifically for horrific effects is not a subtle beast. An adjustment of 20 dB is not unknown (and not, unfortunately, unheard); a 6-dB adjustment, though, is often far more than enough particularly in self-operated, on-air control suites. A general median accepted by most manufacturers is to provide between ± 12- and ± 15-dB level adjustment on channel-type EQs.

22.10.25 The Baxandall

Hi-fi-type tone controls needed similar basic operational high-frequency and low-frequency boost-and-cut facilities, and a design for this dating from the 1950s by Peter Baxandall has since been an industry standard in assorted and updated forms. A development of the Baxandall idea is represented in Fig. 22-66 based around today's more familiar operational amplifier technology rather than discrete transistors or tubes. Fig. 22-66A shows a virtual-earth-type inverting amplifier with the gain (being equal to the ratio of the feedback resistor R_F to the series resistor R_S) continuously variable from near-infinite loss (min) to near-infinite gain (max) with unity in the middle. If a fixed-gain-determining leg is introduced and the variable leg is made frequency conscious, as shown in Fig. 22-66B (in this instance by crude single-order, high-pass filters—the series capacitors), the gain swing only occurs within the passband of those filters. The through gain for the rest of the spectrum is determined by the two fixed resistors. If this fixed chain is replaced by a second frequency-conscious network that does not significantly overlap the original one in bandwidth, the two chains independently modify their frequency areas (Fig. 22-66C). The fixed chain is only necessary where the gain is otherwise unpredictably defined by a frequency-conscious network.

The belt-and-braces low-pass arrangement (for low-frequency boost-and-cut) of Fig. 22-66C can be rationalized into the more elegant circuit of Fig. 22-66D. This circuit more closely resembles the definitive Baxandall circuit. Rather than isolating the low-frequency boost-and-cut chain with increasing inductive reactance, the control is buffered away with relatively small resistances and bypassed to high frequencies by capacitance. The control takes progressively greater effect at lower frequencies as the rising capacitative reactance reduces the effective bypass. A further refinement is a pair of stopper resistors, small in value, that define the maximum boost-and-cut of the entire network.

Naturally, more complex EQ can be configured around the same arrangement. A midfrequency bell curve is easily introduced by any of the means in Figure 22-67, giving a good clue how to avoid having to use a real tuned circuit using inductors.

A variable signal either positive or negative in phase to the source V_{in} can be picked off from a pot straight across the existing high-frequency and low-frequency chains, taken to an active-filter arrangement to derive the needed amplitude response shape, then returned into the loop at either the virtual-earth point (to which the high-frequency and low-frequency chains are tied) or to the non-inverting reference input (Fig. 22-67D) dependent on whether the absolute phase of the filter is positive or negative, respectively. Industry favorites seem to be this approach using either a Wein Bridge bandpass (Fig. 22-63E was evolved specifically to such an end) or a state-variable integrator-loop type, as shown in Fig. 22-64E.

cranked for maximum, will not give the expected additional 15-dB gain. The overall loop is already operating close to the maximum gain defined by the stopper resistors. A notable measured result is for the maximum boost-and-cut capability of a sweep midbell curve to be restricted at the extents of its range where it overlaps into the shelving high-frequency and low-frequency curves.

A rough rule born from hard experience of squeezing the most eq from the least electronics is to not allow overlap incursion beyond the point where either curve has

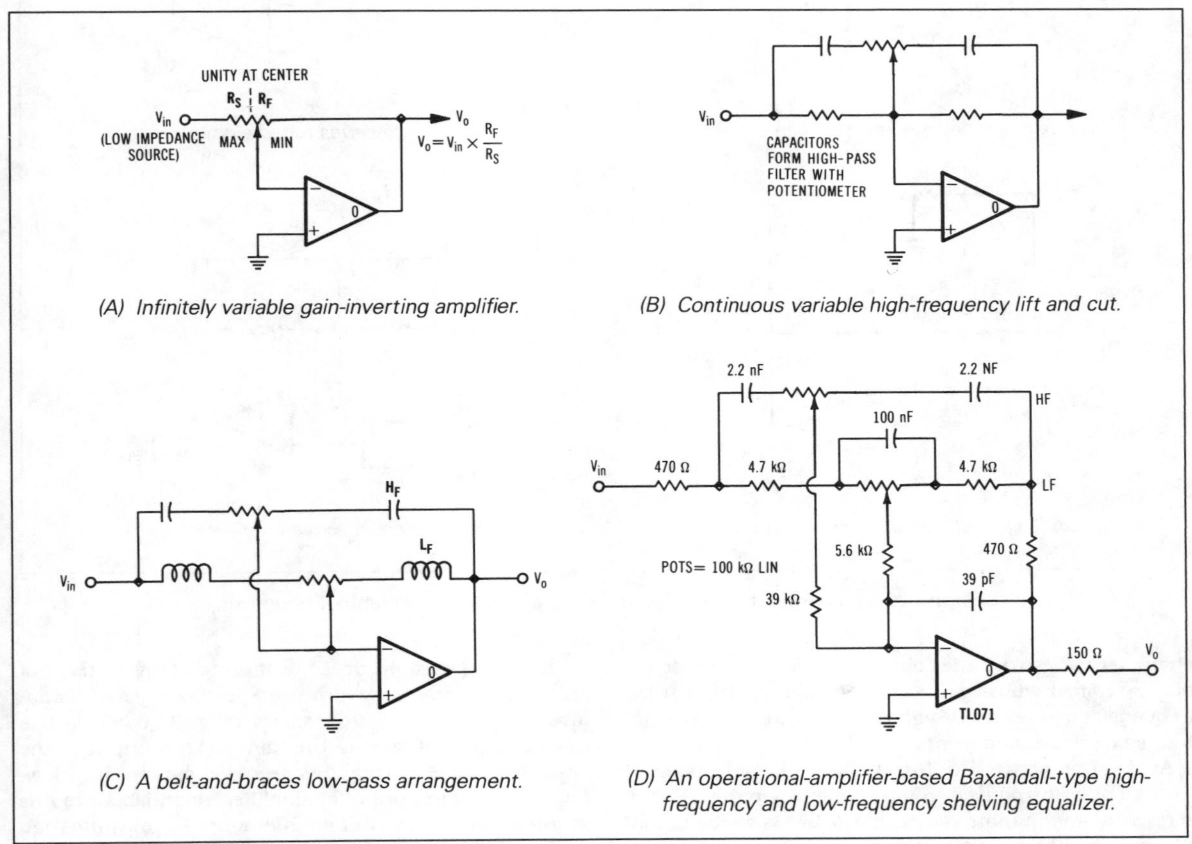

(A) Infinitely variable gain-inverting amplifier.

(B) Continuous variable high-frequency lift and cut.

(C) A belt-and-braces low-pass arrangement.

(D) An operational-amplifier-based Baxandall-type high-frequency and low-frequency shelving equalizer.

Figure 22-66 Development of Baxandall-style equalizer.

Any number of such active chains may be introduced, provided two great hangups don't intrude excessively.

Hangup 1 is the interaction between frequency groups. Hanging on two control chains that operate at the same frequency either adjustably or through overlap can at best be deceiving or at worst self-defeating. In the Baxandall (as with most other arrangements, as we shall see), if maximum gain (say 15 dB) is attained at a given frequency by one control, a second similarly tuned chain,

±6-dB eq effect individually. Overlapping is best achieved from the comfort of another EQ stage, although that too invokes other compromises.

Hangup 2 is noise. The basic Baxandall, using purely passive frequency-determining components, is a fairly quiet arrangement. With controls at flat, it is theoretically only 6 dB noisier than the unity-gain noise of the amplifier plus additional thermal noise due to network resistances—probably in the −100-dBu region. The noise

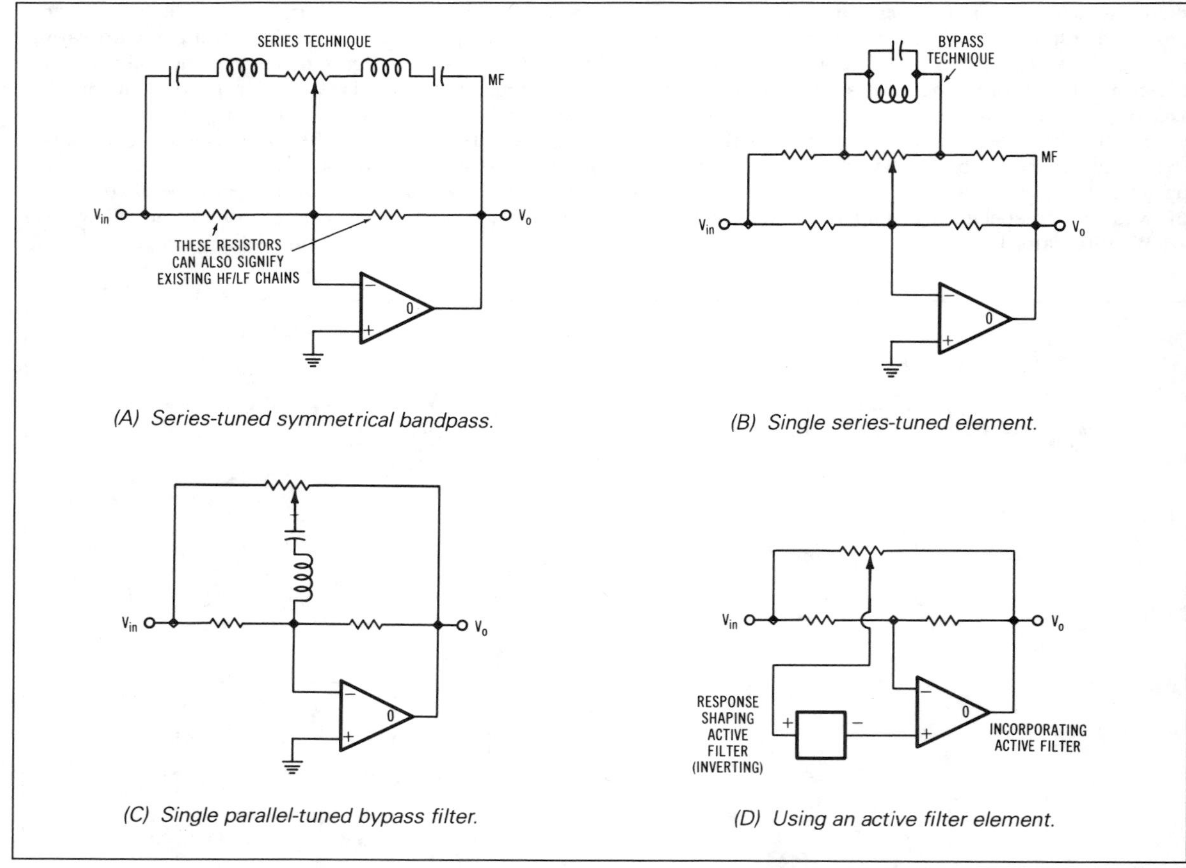

(A) Series-tuned symmetrical bandpass.

(B) Single series-tuned element.

(C) Single parallel-tuned bypass filter.

(D) Using an active filter element.

Figure 22-67 Resonant frequency selective elements in Baxandall Equalizer.

character varies with the controls, as would be expected, of an amplifier whose gain is directly manipulated at the frequencies in question—high-frequency boost, more high-frequency noise, and so on.

As soon as active filtering is involved, more noise is unavoidably introduced, often highly colored and, consequently, much more noticeable. What is worse is that it's present all the time irrespective of control positions. Even with its appropriate control at neutral center, it is quite usual to hear a mid-sweep "swoosh" in the noise changing with filter frequency. This is, along with the strange spectral character of the noise emergent from some filters, notably the integrator-loop variety, a result of unoptimized impedances and dubious stability almost inherent to the design.

22.10.26 Swinging Output Control

The source impedance versus feedback impedance ratiometric approach of the Baxandall is not the only way of achieving symmetrical boost-and-cut. A method of enclosing the controls within the feedback leg of a noninverting amplifier is developed in Fig. 22-68. This has the advantage of leaving the noninverting input of the op-amp free, obviating the need for a preceding low-impedance source or buffer amplifier. Roundabout to this swing is the necessity of a buffer amplifier or quite high destination load impedance since the output is variable in impedance and included within the feedback loop of the op-amp. Heavy control modification, potential phase margin erosion with consequent instability, and certain headroom loss are among the penalties for careless termination.

Unity gain in Fig. 22-68A is achieved when the attenuation in the feedback chain equals the output attenuation; the feedback attenuator causes the op-amp to have as much voltage gain as the output attenuator losses. Replacing the two bottom legs of the attenuators with a swinging potentiometer (Fig. 22-68B) provides a boost-and-cut facility; when the pot is swung toward min, the feedback leg is effectively lengthened to ground, and the

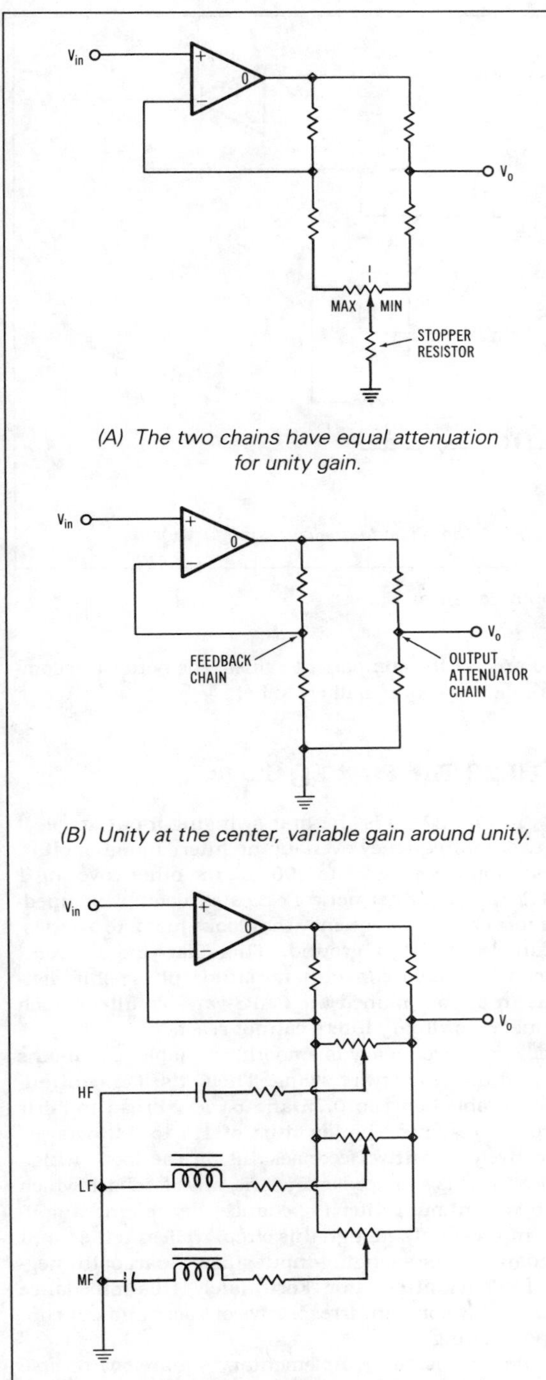

(A) The two chains have equal attenuation for unity gain.

(B) Unity at the center, variable gain around unity.

(C) Multiband equalizer system approach.

Figure 22-68 Swinging output equalizer.

amplifier gain is reduced somewhat. Meanwhile, the output attenuator is shortened considerably, reducing the output accordingly. At max the reverse occurs. The feedback leg is shortened, increasing the loop gain of the op-amp while the output attenuator is lengthened, losing less of the available output. A small stopper resistor defines the overall gain swing about unity, which would otherwise range from zero to earsplitting, respectively.

Introducing reactances and complex impedances into the potentiometer ground leg (or legs as in Fig. 22-68C) results again in boost-and-cut control over the frequency bands in which the reactances are lowest (i.e., high frequency for capacitors, low frequency for inductors [real or fake] and so on). This arrangement, which has been spotted in a few odd places professionally and in some Japanese hi-fi, has only one major drawback other than the previously mentioned output-loading considerations. In order to achieve reasonable control dB-per-rotation linearity, the two attenuators (feedback and output) need to be of about 3-dB loss each with the control at center. This implies that the obtainable output voltage is 3 dB below the output swing capability of the op-amp, meaning a headroom deficit of that amount in the equalizer stage—probably where it is most needed.

22.10.27 Swinging Input Control

Avoiding the headroom headache but utilizing a rather similar technique, the swinging-inputs gain block of Fig. 22-69 is very promising. Here, the feedback attenuator remains unchanged, but the output attenuator is shifted around to the noninverting input of the op-amp. At minimum, the input attenuation is quite vicious while the feedback leg is long, making the op-amp deliver only a small amount of gain. When the attenuation characteristics are reversed for maximum, the op-amp works at a high loop gain, while the input is only slightly attenuated. Unity is achieved at control center where the input attenuation equals the make-up gain of the amplifier.

There is a fascinating trade-off between noise mechanisms in this circuit arrangement. Assuming a maximum of three controls (for fairly standard high-frequency, low-frequency, and mid-sweep curves) before interaction becomes a major hassle, the amplifier can have between 10 and 20 dB of fairly frequency-conscious background gain (i.e., with all controls flat) rendering it at first sight significantly noisier than a Baxandall. However, the impedances around the amplifier are around a decade lower. This considerably reduces thermal noise generation due to resistive elements and op-amp internal mechanisms.

In addition, the noise generated by the active frequency-determining filters is, with the controls neutral, injected equally into the inverting and noninverting inputs of the op-amp. Differential amplifiers being what they are, common-mode signals (such as this equally injected filter noise) get cancelled out and do not appear at the output.

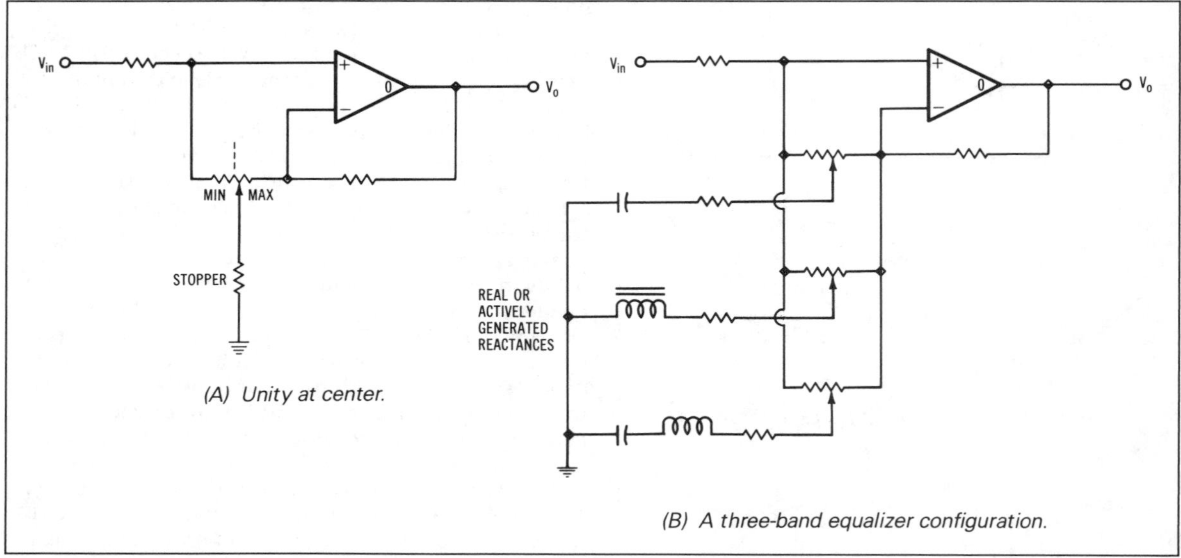

Figure 22-69 Swinging input equalizer.

Interaction can still intrude, and care is required to prevent excessive frequency band overlap. Center-tapped pots (the tap grounded) eliminate many interactive effects but at the cost of increased invariable background gain (noise) and peculiar, almost intractable, boost-and-cut gain variation linearity versus control rotation.

22.10.28 A Practical EQ

A three-section parametric eq with additional versatile shelving-type high- and low-frequency controls is detailed in Fig. 22-70. It is designed to be easily shortened to high-frequency, low-frequency, plus a single midband parametric section, for applications that don't demand the full complement of facilities. Each individual selection is switchable in or out to allow preset controls, and simple in-and-out comparisons with tie-down resistors maintain the dc conditions of the unused filters to minimize switch clicks. Even a brief look at the circuit reveals a major benefit. The signal path through the EQ is merely via three op-amps, IC_2 is an input differential amplifier, and IC_3 does duty as the output line-amp. In the shortened version this path is reduced to only two op-amps, IC_1 and IC_3, which serve also as a swinging-input EQ gain block. IC_2 and its associated circuitry are unused in this simplified version.

Perplexed by the strange-looking values around the differential input stage? Without lurching into tedious sums, those values provide unity differential in unbalanced out levels while providing an identical impedance (with respect to ground) on each of the two input legs. Naturally, the more precise the component values, the better the common-mode rejection is likely to be.

22.10.29 The First EQ Stage

IC_2 in Fig. 22-70 is the first swinging-input stage. It has two nonfrequency overlapping filters hanging off it, one section covering 25 to 500 Hz, the other covering 1 to 20 kHz. Each filter network creates a complex impedance form against frequency that looks just like a series-LC-tuned circuit to ground. This fake-tuned circuit (formed from two constant-amplitude phase-shift networks in a loop, named the CAPS-variable filter) reach parameters ordinary filters cannot reach.

The center frequency is smoothly variable; Q remains constant over the entire swing. The Q itself is continuously variable between 0.75 and 5 (very broad to fairly sharp, representing bandwidths of 1.5 to 0.2 octaves, respectively). Positive feedback inside the loop, which defines the Q is balanced against negative feedback which controls minimum filter impedance, hence, and amplitude. Interestingly enough this circuit relies on the input impedance of the swinging-input stage as part of the negative feedback attenuator. Fortunately, this impedance is reasonably constant irrespective of boost-and-cut control positioning.

In the absence of complementary square-law/reverse square-law dual-gang potentiometers ideally required for the purpose, readily available log/antilog dual-gang pots, slugged a bit to a reasonable approximation, control the positive/negative feedback balance. As a result of this compromise, the filter crest amplitude (maximum effect) varies within ±1 dB as the Q control is swept; however, in comparison to the dramatic sonic difference from such a Q variation, this tends to insignificance. The result of all this, at the output of IC_2, is a pair of resonant-type curves of continuously variable place, height, depth, and width.

22.10.30 Second EQ/Line Amp

A reasonably hefty pair of transistors is hung on the end of IC_3 to provide a respectable line-drive capability, in addition to the use of the amplifier as a swinging-input EQ section. There is enough open-loop gain in the combination of the op-amp and transistors (over a much greater bandwidth than mere audio) to cope with 15 dB of EQ boost and output stage nonlinearities.

Differing from the last EQ stage, this one only has a single midfrequency bell-curve creator, operating over a range of 300 Hz to 3 kHz, together with deceptively simple looking but fascinating high- and low-frequency impedance generators.

22.10.31 Low-Frequency Control

Gyrating inductance to create a conventional low-frequency shelving response (variable in turnover frequency by a 220 kΩ antilog pot) is achieved around IC_{11}. A fairly large (2.2 μF) series capacitor forming a resonance is switchable in and out. The value of the capacitor is carefully calculated to work with the circuit impedances to provide an extreme low-frequency response that falls back to unity gain below the resultant resonant frequency. The Q of this arrangement reduces proportionally to increasing frequency. Typical resultant response curves (Fig. 22-71) show just what all this means, demonstrating an extraordinarily useful bottom-end control.

22.10.32 High-Frequency Control

Unusual is one way to describe the high-frequency impedance generator and its EQ effect. It is essentially a super capacitor, or capacitative capacitor. If both of those are meaningless, it's a circuit that, when in conjunction with a resistor, causes a second-order response as would normally be expected of an inductor and capacitor combination—a slope of 12 dB/octave as opposed to a single-order effect of 6 dB/octave. Fig. 22-72 shows what it does as an EQ element.

The response is hinged about 1 kHz. The control varies the frequency (between 5 and 20 kHz) at which the gain reaches maximum (or minimum if the boost-and-cut control is cut). The slope between 1 kHz and the chosen maximum frequency is virtually a straight line representing a nearly constant dB-per-octave characteristic, with a nearly flat-top shelving characteristic.

In electronic terms, this is achieved by progressively degenerating the super capacitor until it gives in, that is, until it eventually ends up looking like a simple, single capacitor.

22.11 MIXING

22.11.1 Virtual-Earth Mixers

The circuit diagram of Fig. 22-73 in its simplicity belies the hidden design that is in the relationship of the circuitry to its mechanical and electrical environment.

This is where the care and feeding of op amps (section 22.6) and grounding paths (section 22.7) really pay dividends. Mix-amp stages, with large numbers of permanently assigned sources such as in the main mix buses, are as crucial to the overall well being of a console as any front-end stage could be. In a typical situation, as a unity-gain virtual-earth mixing stage with 33 sources (channels plus access), the amplifier is being asked for about 30 dB of broad band gain, as much as any other stage in the chain including both the microphone preamp and/or secondary input stage.

22.11.2 Noise Sources

That this mix-amp gain is sometimes referred to as *noise gain* is not accidental. Unless care is taken to balance fader-back channel noise contributions against this self-generated mix-amp noise, the latter could well predominate and arbitrarily determine the noise floor for the entire console. Similarly, channel noise contribution due to gainy buffer amplifiers should equal or outstrip mix-amp noise. Self-noise generation in the mix-amp is predominantly the amplified thermal noise of the source and feedback resistances, device input current noise, and surface generation and recombination noise. The last two can be minimized by device choice. Thermal noise is physics and is here to stay. Common sense on first glance says to make the mix resistors as low in value as possible. Too low a value would cause quite large signal (hence, ground) currents to be thundering about. On a less technical level, it would necessitate yet another tier of buffer amplifiers to feed the buses after the pan controls. The bus feed resistors are also deliberately used to modify the law of the log/reverse-log pots used for the panning. While not materially affecting the center-pan attenuation, this trick can help the subjective linearity of an image sweep across stereo versus control rotation, which could otherwise be a little too concentrated at the ends of the control range.

Ordinarily though, the mix resistors are of such a value that, in the context of a complete mixer, the combined

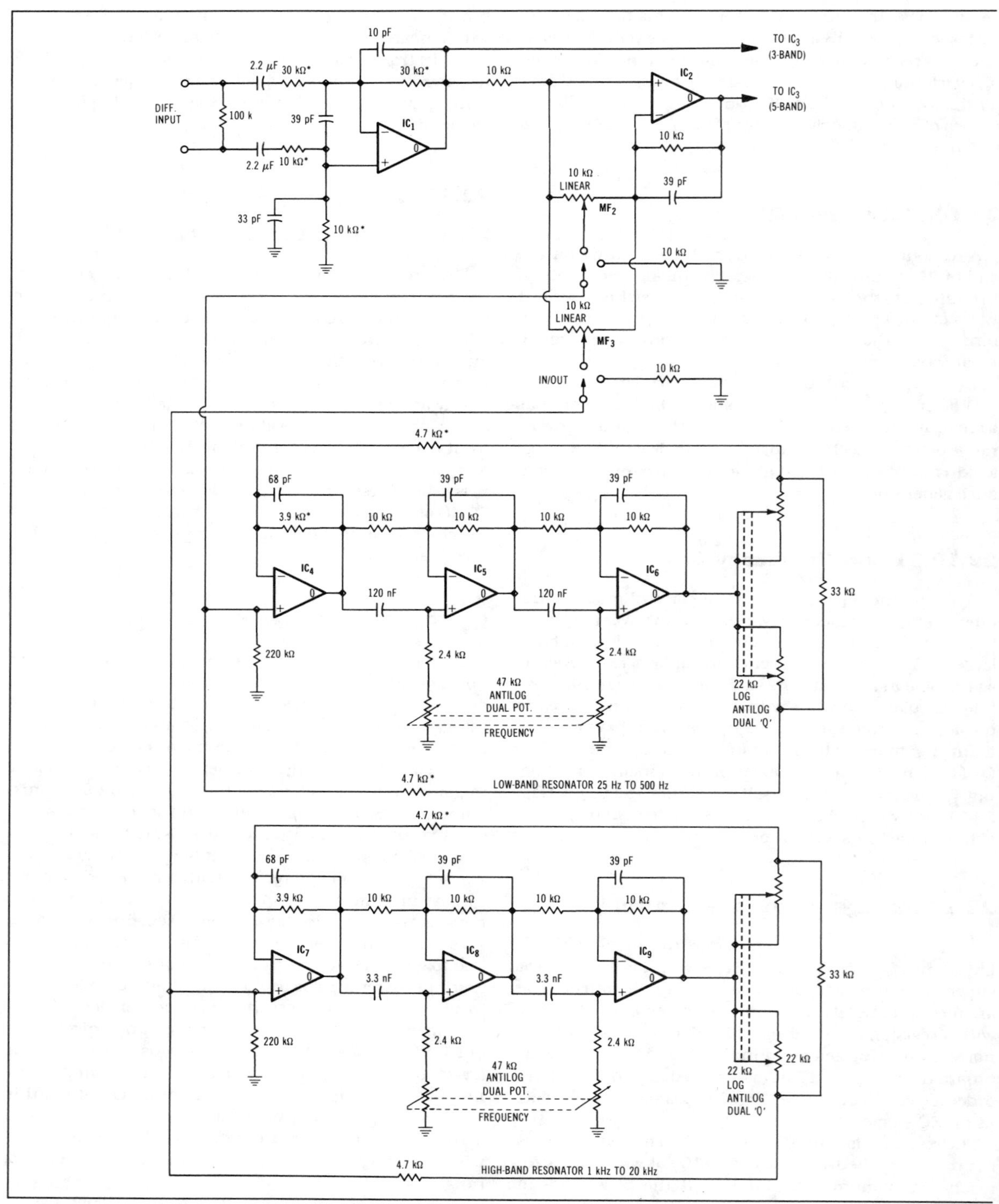

Figure 22-70 Five-band

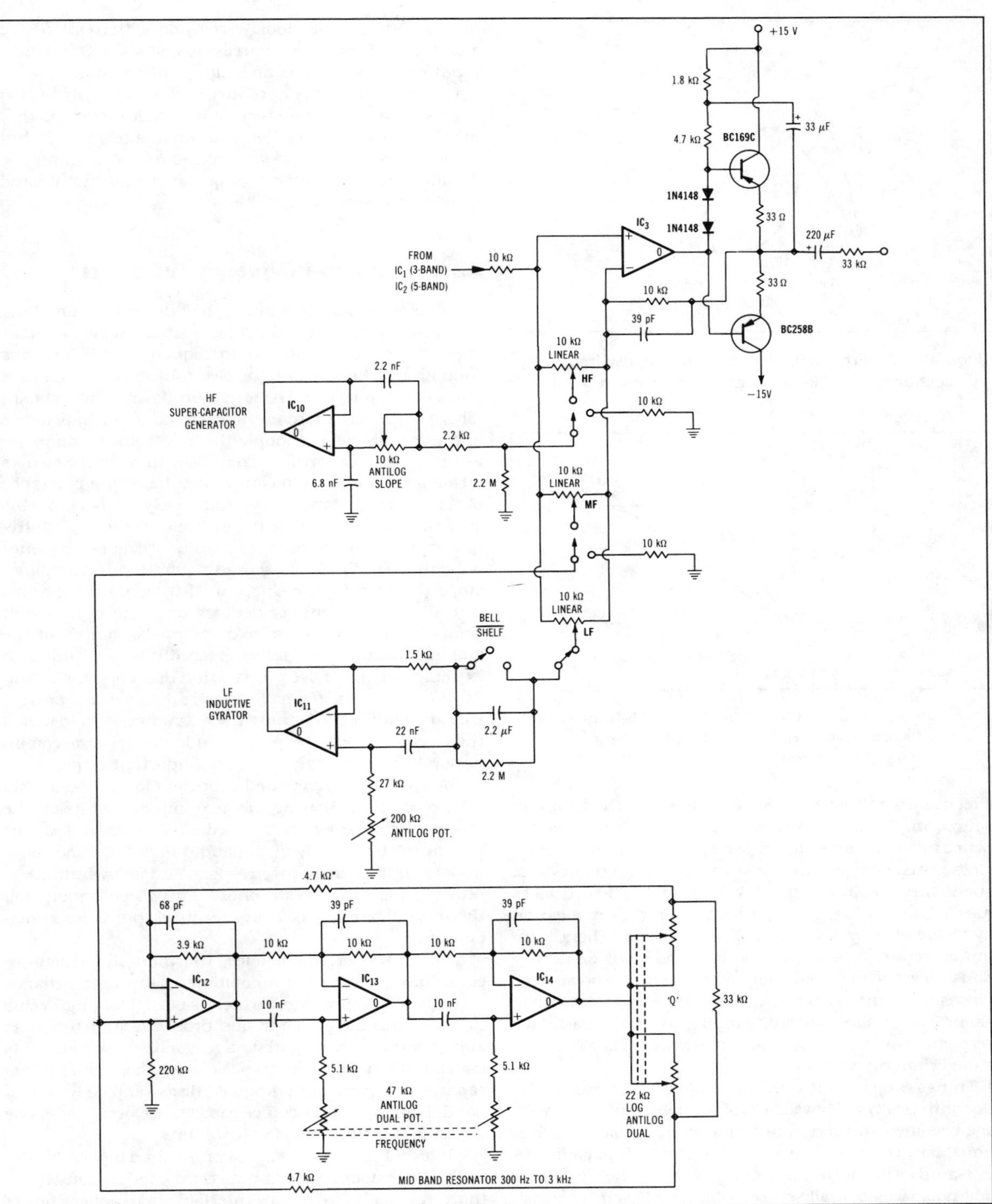

equalizer circuit diagram.

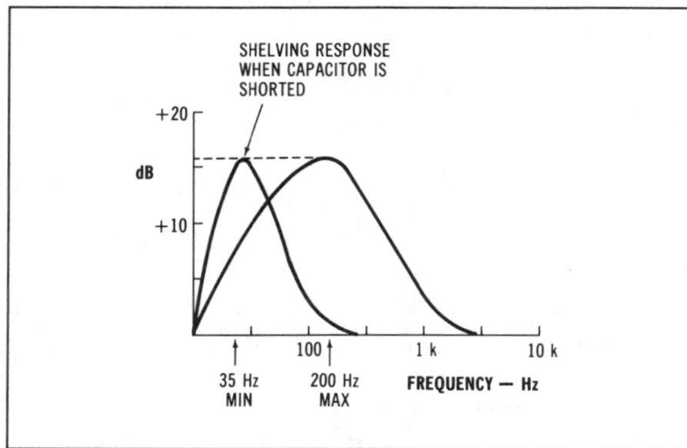

Figure 22-71 Frequency response of the low-frequency section of Fig. 22-70 (control at maximum gain).

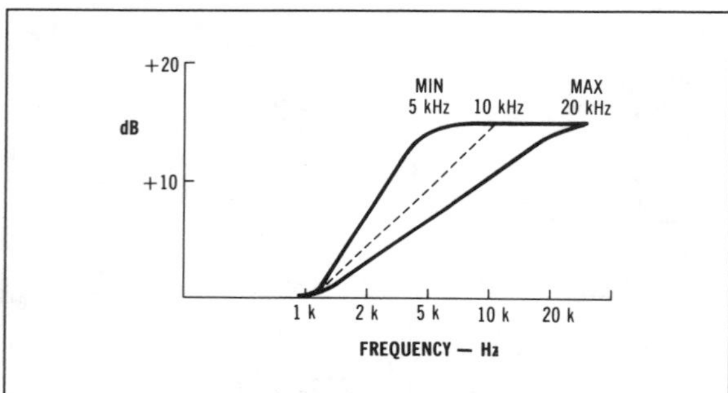

Figure 22-72 Characteristics of the high-frequency section of Fig. 22-70 (lift/cut control at maximum lift).

effectively paralleled resistance is well below the optimum source impedance of the mix-amp device used, so the primary noise modes are those above-mentioned device vices. This isn't too difficult with FET front-end devices, such as the TL071 with their high OSI. These devices have a couple of other major benefits in this application by virtue of their FET inputs. Input current (hence, input current noise) is extremely low, and being FETs they don't have the many low-frequency junction and surface noises inherent to bipolar devices. It seems a paradoxic absurdity to use an ultrahigh input impedance device for zero impedance mixing, but in many ways they're better suited than bipolars.

Things can get a bit startling if the resistance/OSI relationship is awry. Above the OSI, device input noise voltage becomes an increasingly important noise contribution. Many years ago in a mixer design with bipolar device mix-amps and quite high mix resistors, the measured bus noise was actually more quiet on a 20-channel version than on the 10-channel original. It wasn't until much later that what was actually happening finally dawned. Increasing the number of source resistors reduced the bus impedance, previously well above the OSI of the amplifier with only ten sources, to below the OSI, where input noise voltage was no longer contributing.

Theoretical source impedance and device contribution tell less than half the story in a practical design; they may be quantifiable in the isolation of a test bench, but thrown into a system, they can all seem a bit meaningless. It's all largely a matter of grounding and out-of-band considerations.

22.11.3 Radio-Frequency Inductors

Inductors are used between the bus and the amplifier input in Figs. 22-73 and 22-74. A simplistic view is that they are there to stop any radio frequency on the mix-bus from finding its way into the electronics, but this is only part of their purpose. The ferrite beads and small chokes (about 5 μH) are there to increase the input impedance and hopefully help decouple the bus from the amplifier at very high frequencies. The larger inductance creates a rising reactance in to counteract the falling reactance of the bus capacitance. If left completely unchecked, this capacitance would cause the mix-amp extreme high-frequency loop gain to turn it into a lovely radio-frequency oscillator. Feedback phase leading around the amplifier stops the gain from rising, but if it were not for some series loss (accidental or deliberate) in the input leg, it would be insufficient to hold the phase margin of the amplifiers within the limits of stability of the bandwidth extremes where device propagation delay become significant in the loop. A small series resistance can provide this loss while also defining the maximum gain to which the circuit can rise. A parallel inductor/resistor combination improves on this in a few important respects.

The inductor is calculated to present low in-band (<20 kHz) reactance, allowing the mix-amp to operate on the bus in a virtual-earth (zero-impedance) configuration. The reactance rises gently at the audio high-frequency end, imparting little frequency response anomaly but a definitely beneficial partial phase straightening against the inevitable effect of heavy feedback phase-lead compensation.

At even higher frequencies, the inductive reactance continues to rise until the combined network impedance is limited by the resistor, which is of high enough value to afford sizable choke-to-bus problems and to define amplifier out-of-band gain to a reasonably low value. It is low enough, however, to stop the inevitable inductor/bus capacitance resonance from getting completely out of hand. Making an inductance-capacitance oscillator is one way of preventing spurious instability.

While FET inputs are far less prone than bipolar inputs to the intermodulation and direct demodulation effects that cause radio-frequency interference to appear out of nowhere, this fairly healthy brace of filtering may be helpful to those living near a source of high-powered very high frequencies, such as a group of television transmitters.

22.11.4 Virtues of Grounding

Grounding paths for virtual-earth mixing, especially in long mixers, are always the final arbiter on how far down the system noise floor will go and how susceptible the mix stage is to extraneous fields and earth currents. In this age of digits, ground paths are especially crucial. Remember from Fig. 22-64 how the ground on the non-inverting input of an op-amp mix-stage gets amplified up by the *noise gain* of the stage? This implies that a ground noise of −100 dBu will end up at about −70 dBu for a 32-source mixer, which is barely adequate. A simple, but so often ignored, rule with virtual-earth stages is to make sure that the ground reference has got the same "dirt" on it as the signal and vice versa. Yes, ground follows signal. If both ground and signal have the same noise in the same phase, there is a chance that the noise will get ignored as common mode and not amplified in the mix-amp. Thus, for each mix bus, there is a parallel ground bus being fed by the last relevant ground reference from each channel. Avoiding a major bus length ground loop (otherwise known as a single-turn transformer!) means that all the heavyweight signal current in the fader/mute/mode switchery has a direct wire to central ground while the mix-amp has a respectable output referenced ground to work against, clean of channel signal currents but representative of the reference of the buffer amplifier in the case of the stereo mix-bus. The mixer amplifier does not take a direct system central ground of its own.

22.11.5 Passive Mixing

There are, of course, alternatives to single-bus virtual-earth mixing. Passive resistor mixing (Fig. 22-75) is quite viable for fixed-assignation systems that are not going to be chopped, changed, or switched in and out. A major advantage is that bus capacitance is merely something to be taken into account in terms of frequency response and phase, rather than directly imperiling the stability of the mixer amplifier. For passive mixing, the mixer amplifier is just a buffer amplifier to make up the loss in the resistor tree; RF filtering becomes simple with known filter source and load impedances together with the ability to refer against ground. The primary hangup is that the bus is unbalanced and has an impedance at audio (albeit fairly low due to paralleled sources). Hence, it lays itself wide open to induced noise and capacitatively coupled crosstalk. Despite this, it is a method used with considerable success for many years in quite a few production mixers.

22.11.6 Devolved Mixing

Distributed or devolved mixing (Fig. 22-76) uses local mix-amps to sum blocks of channels; the outputs of these local amplifiers is then taken to a common summing point. This quite neatly obviates having to deal with a long bus but does create a practical problem of locating the distributed summers.

Both passive and devolved systems have the advantage that large amounts of the bus can be run in shielded single cable. The extra capacitance here does not have the awful consequences it does with virtual-earth summing amplifiers.

For consistency all buses would be run devolved. This means the sub-mix facilities for the PFL buses, the four effect sends, the four foldbacks, the main stereo/monitor mixer; and the eight subgroups (if used). Also, provisions must be made to arrange the master mixer for each of those at the grouping end.

22.11.7 Balanced Mixing

The earliest form of signal mixing consisted of directly paralleling the sources, which were generally medium-impedance (nominal 600 Ω) and balanced. This form of passive balanced mixing persisted until semiconductor electronics and the easily achieved zero impedance transpired. The balancing was done entirely by transformers; again, things that have fallen at least partially by the wayside.

As a technique it was simple (for the technology at the time) and had all the advantages the balanced systems have in general—principally an astonishing robustness with respect to interferences, induced noise, or crosstalk. Recently, balanced or differential mixing has become practical again with the development of simple electronic differential and floating balanced input and output circuits (see sections 22.9.6.1 to 22.9.6.4). Fig. 22-77 shows how differential sources of the trivial kind (straight and inverted) can be mixed onto a balanced virtual-earth mixing bus, created and sensed by a superbal input stage.

Although requiring a fairly large number of bits, the performance of such an arrangement in the context of a large multitrack console is truly staggering, especially noise, headroom, radio-frequency rejection, and crosstalk. The noise improves in two respects:

1. No longer is the mix-amp amplifying up the noise on its reference ground. It is referenced to itself, effectively.

2. Square-law noise summation—twice the signal (coherent) means 6-dB gain, two lots of incoherent noise 3-dB gain, and, therefore, 3-dB noise advantage.

Headroom, by virtue of two signal paths carrying the same information differentially, is 6 dB higher. (Naturally the noise and headroom are interrelated; whichever is more pressing in a given circumstance necessarily takes precedence.) The radio-frequency field and crosstalk rejection improvements are dramatic, but they really ought

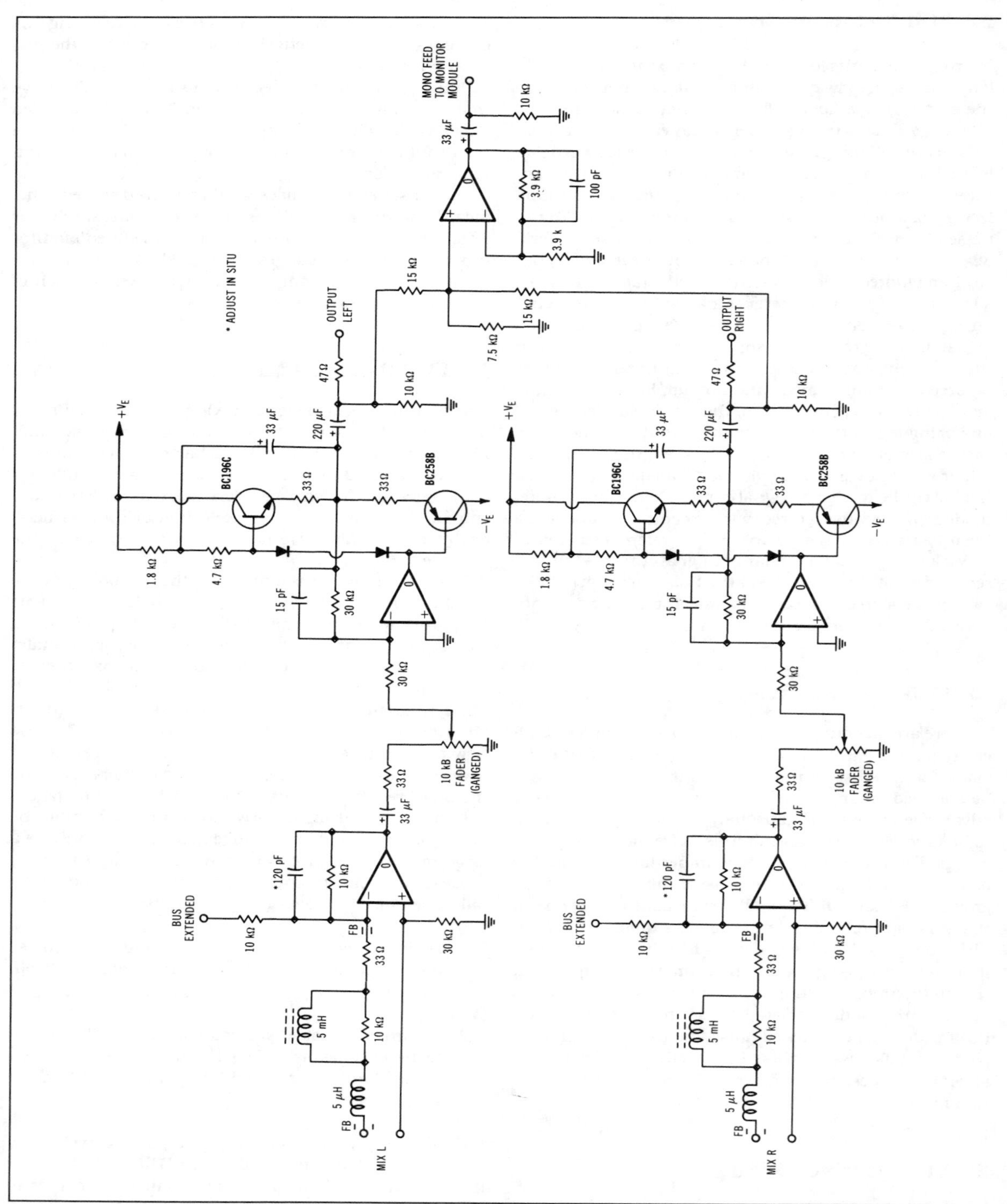

Figure 22-73

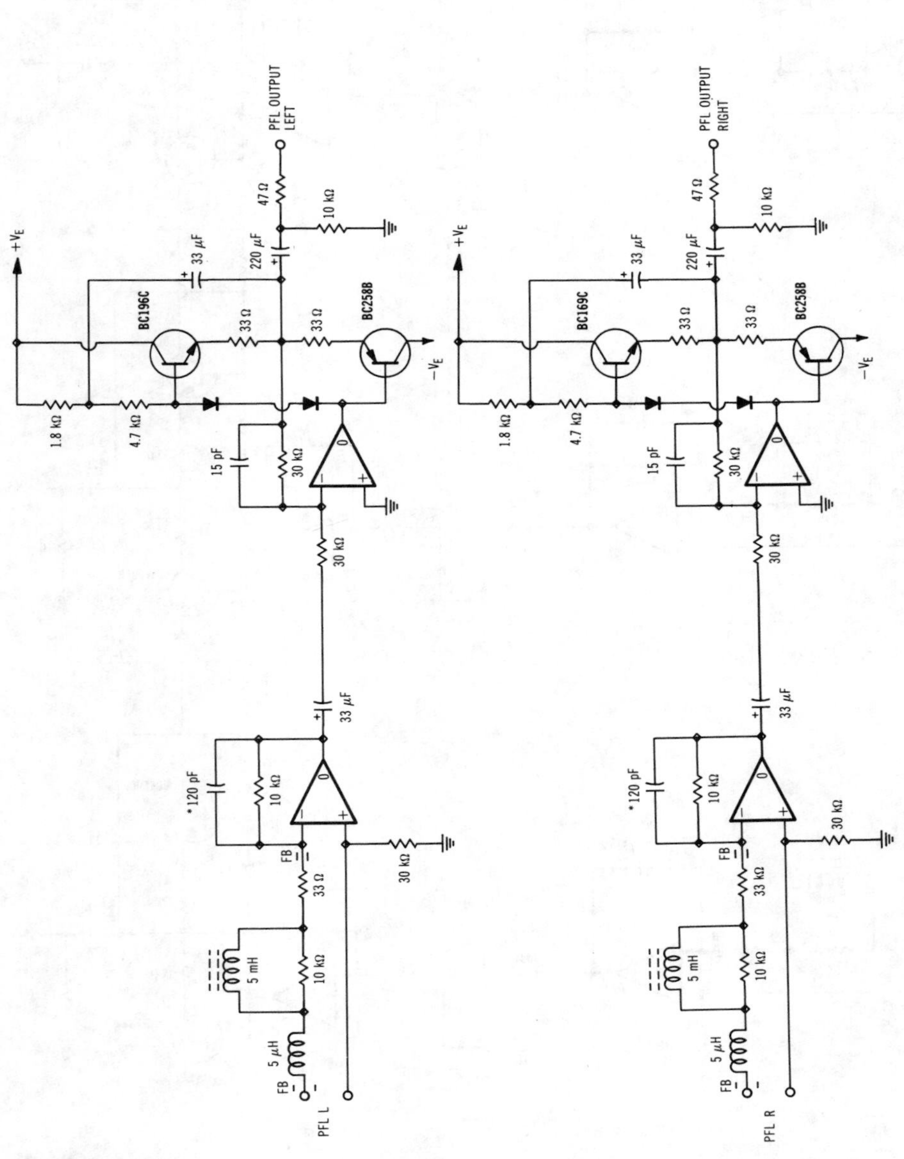

Master group electronics.

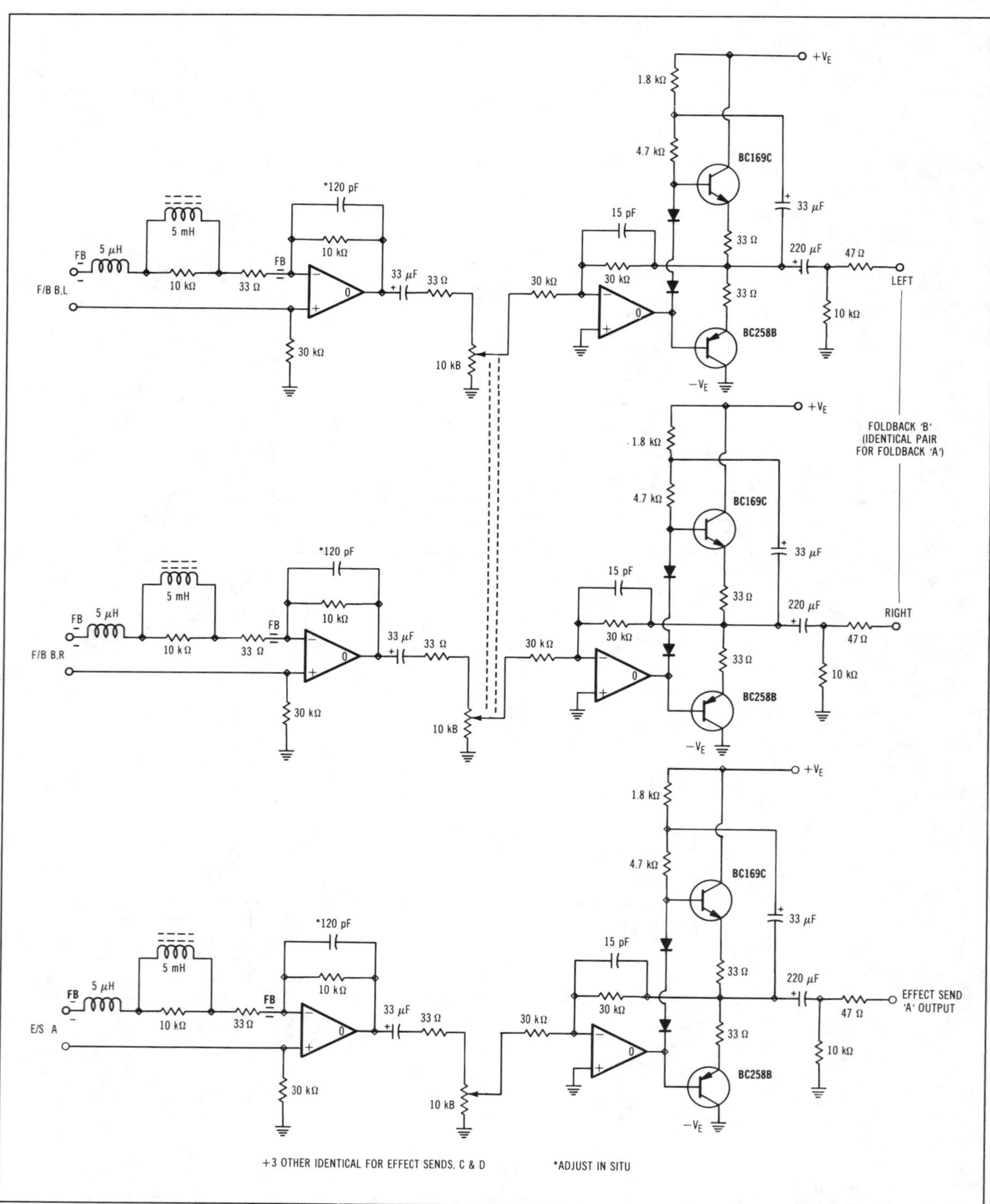

Figure 22-74 Auxiliary group electronics.

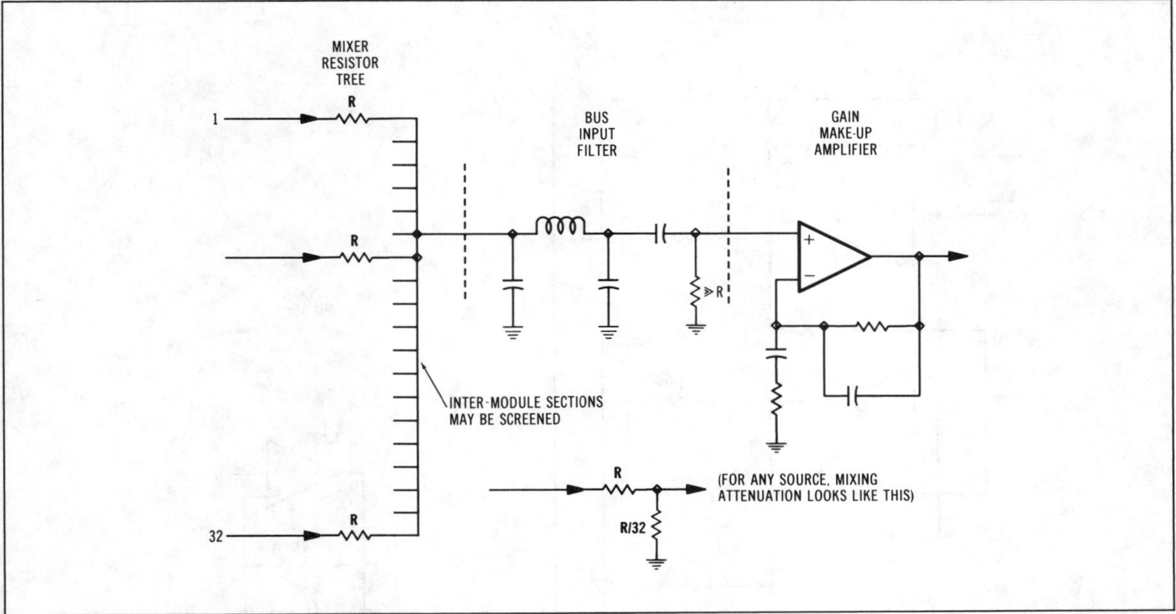

Figure 22-75 Passive mixing arrangement.

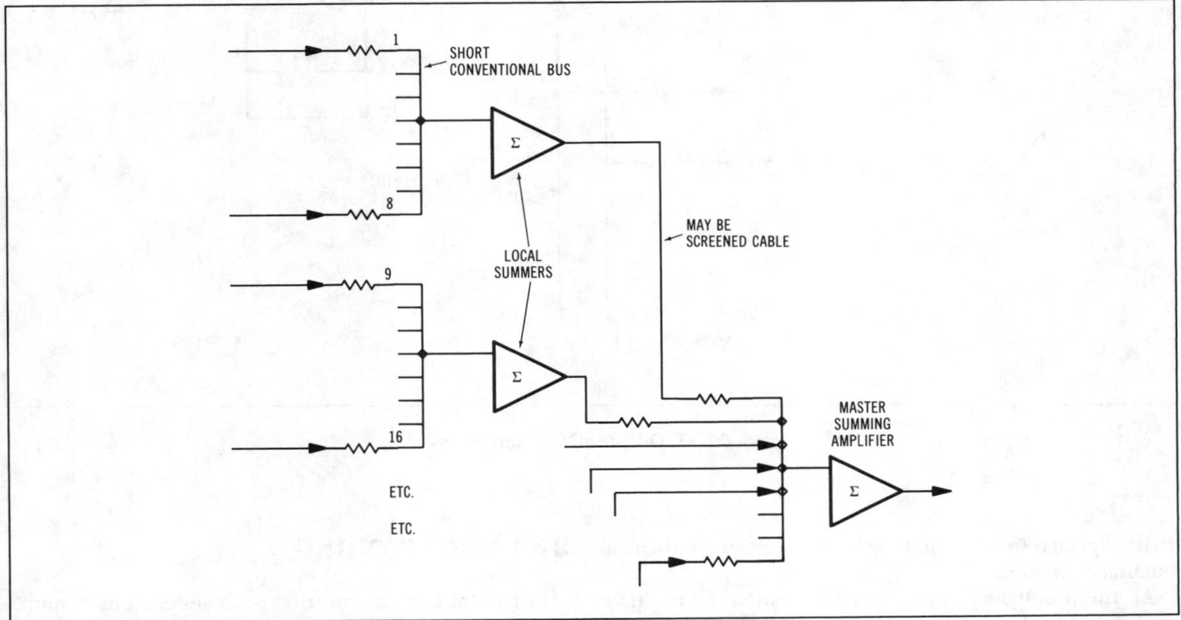

Figure 22-76 Distributed or devolved mixing.

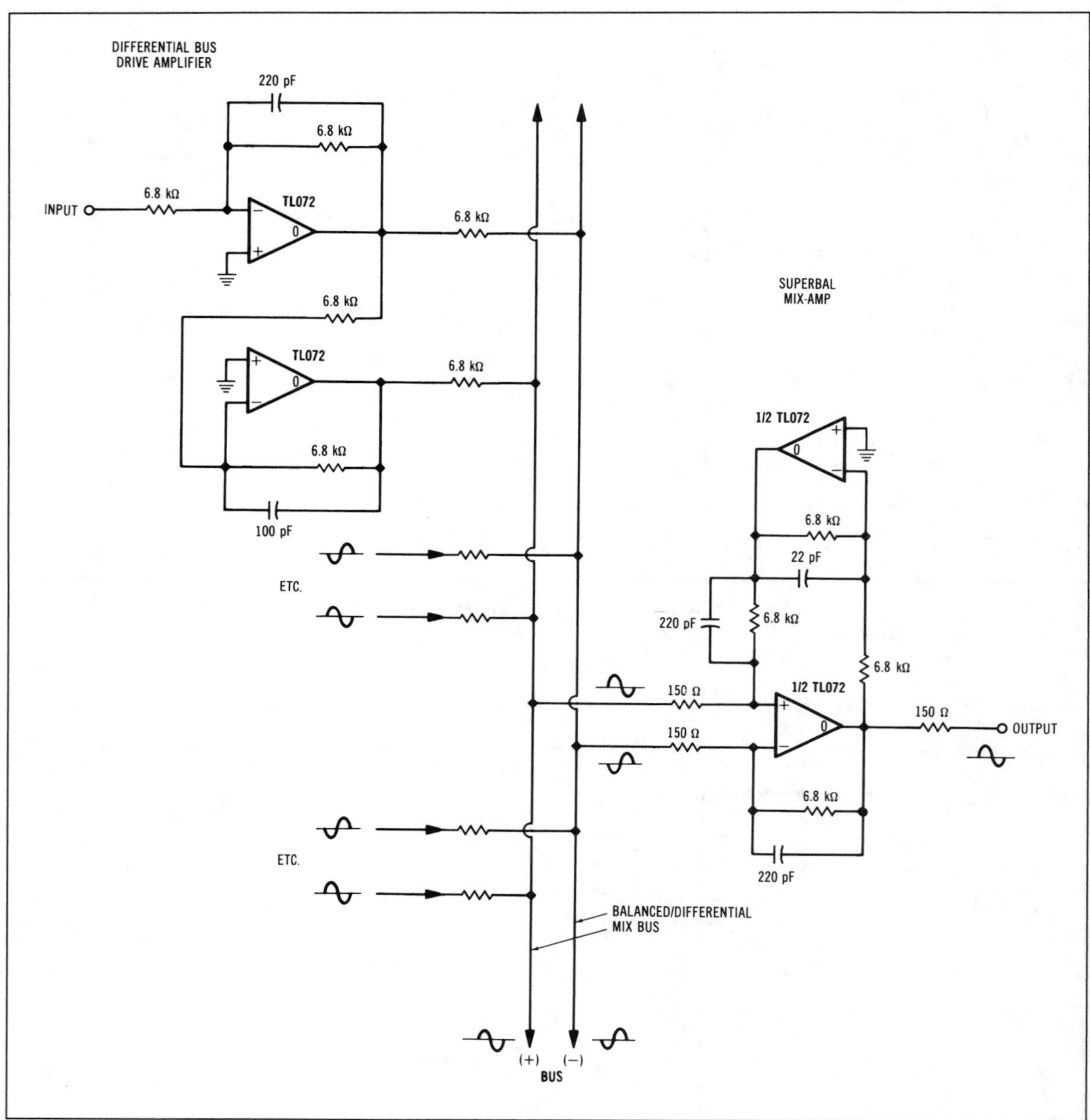

Figure 22-77 Differential balanced mixing.

to be expected from the naturally self-canceling nature of balanced systems.

All the problems of keeping virtual-earth mixers tidy and stable apply twofold here; of course, bus buffering is strongly recommended, mostly to allow the bandwidth-defining poles around the superbal to be effective.

22.12 MONITORING

At its simplest, monitoring consists of a power amplifier and loudspeakers hung across the main output(s) of the console, with the auxiliary functions either unused or preset. In public address (pa) work the pa actually is the monitoring; the only other function necessary is prefade listen (PFL) and then only during panic mode. Alternatively the monitoring demands for multitrack recording extend to an entire secondary sub-mixer replete with panning and pre/post foldback effect feeds, stand-alone soloing together with listen access to all console send and return ports. The in-line console principle makes efficient use of electronics to combine often coincident signal and monitoring path requirements for the multitrack machinery to the extent that it is operationally rare to need to listen to anything other than the main stereo bus output; this output serves as both the multitrack monitoring bus and the stereo mixdown bus.

Three distinct types of monitoring activity evolve in multitrack work:

1. Mainline—The stereo bus encompasses the multitrack machine sources/returns and stereo mixdown.
2. Transient—This allows short-term check listening of individual channels for reassurance or adjustment, using PFL or solo functions.
3. Auxiliary—This provides access to the assorted foldback/effect feeds, effect returns, mastering machine, and subsidiary two-track and cassette machine returns.

From an operating point of view, the foregoing activities seem to be the division. From a technical stance, it's a different matter entirely. The solo function is very closely related to the stereo bus. In fact, it uses exactly the same signal path throughout—and can be seen simply as a modification of it. PFL though, despite a similar operation (only prefade as opposed to post-pan listening) actually requires an entirely separate bus and mixing system. Its output is switched to override the main path into the monitors. (It may seem a bit strange to go through all this for a spot-check function that tells less than the stereo in-place solo, until we remember that a solo disrupts the mix while a PFL is nondestructive.) Conversely, an operator usually has a psychological hook about the main stereo bus monitoring being the umblemished signal path and that all the auxiliary functions are somehow tarnished and unclean.

In reality, the monitoring chain selects directly between all its sources, merely treating the stereo mix as one of the many. No special treatment is desired or given.

22.12.1 Solo, Solo-Free, and Prefade Listen

An assumption is made that the *solo* function is such that if a console channel is *soloed*, all other sources contributing to the main stereo bus are muted, leaving the desired channel in isolation at its set level and panned position. An exception and extension to this is for other channels (principally those returning effects to which our soloed channel may be contributing) to remain unmuted in the stereo mix during solo operation; this is done by using the *solo-free* button on those channels still needed. Solo-free detaches the channel from the solo activation logic.

The upshot of this is that solo monitoring is inherent to the stereo mix path. If that path isn't selected for monitoring, then neither is the solo. So, although a solo overrides the main stereo mix (unless disabled altogether by the master function, *solo safe*), it cannot override anything else, unlike the prefade listen.

Although PFL could just be brought up as another monitored source, it is made to emulate solo in single-button touch operation, with the added advantageous capability of overriding everything—whatever is selected to monitoring.

This gives a logical priority on which to base the monitoring routing system.

22.12.2 Monitoring Controls

Now we've worked out how to get what signal and at what priority into the monitoring chain. What other torture do we put it through?

- Level control: used to adjust the volume.
- Mute: used to turn the row off occasionally.
- Dim: used so that you can hear what people say.
- Mono: still used in radio.
- Phase reverse: used to make sure you haven't already done it inadvertently. (This function with the mono makes for one of the quickest ways in history of lining up machine azimuth.)
- Split: unashamedly borrowed from broadcast monitoring technology. This routes a mono sum of the main stereo mix bus continually to the left side of the monitor chain and a mono sum of whatever source is selected (including PFL override) to the right side, providing simultaneous monitoring of two different sources—one of which would almost certainly be console output anyway.

  (Split's origins lie in network radio, where announcers on the air have to talk up to program junctions and smoothly hand over to another studio or network feed, news, or whatever at a cue. In order to do this, they have to be able to hear both themselves and the network they are opting into to hear the lead-up and handover cue.)

  Other than its primary design use, the *split function* is used considerably under other normal programming, affording random source monitoring without losing track of what the main console output is doing. It's also used extensively in program prerecording and production enabling, with practice, real-time multisource edits without recourse to razor blades and tape.

Split will eventually find a niche in multitrack recording techniques; if nothing else, it can fulfill the requirement for single-loudspeaker mono monitoring, by simply selecting the right side to a dead source.

- Desk-top loudspeakers: used to do transistor-radio and cheap hi-fi impersonations, also affording a respite of sorts from the deafness-inducing normal monitor loudspeakers.

22.12.3 Related Crosstalk

In a program sense, two forms of crosstalk are relevant. The first—related crosstalk—is a signal bleeding over into another signal path that is carrying a musically and temporally related signal (e.g., between the left and right of a stereo pair or between adjacent tracks of a multitrack recorder). It happens (a lot) and is fortunately not often subjectively obvious or embarrassing; usually they're playing the same song!

Crosstalk within multitrack recording systems is usually little short of horrifying. As a result of the large physical size of the console, ground paths are unavoidably long, and ground currents generate (and cross-inject into other paths) crosstalk voltages across the resultant ground impedances. Capacitance between interconnecting cabling, looms, modules, buses, indeed everything results in a reasonably suspect overall crosstalk performance electrically. Naturally, the better the design and construction (and the more intimidating the cost), the better a console tends to be in this respect.

This is overshadowed and mitigated by multitrack machine crosstalk between tracks—a safe order of magnitude worse than even a horrid console ever could be. Machines not only have the same electrical problems as consoles but also have many magnetic heads all in very close proximity, all dealing with a tape medium not notable for magnetic isolation anyway. It is all tolerable and usable simply because all the crosstalk is related and blends in unnoticeably.

22.12.4 Unrelated Crosstalk

The only area where unrelated crosstalk is not necessarily that is in monitoring, where a hostile signal (say a delayed replay B check of a master) can be screaming about in uncomfortable proximity to the main stereo mix paths. Broadcasters face this problem all the time. All their sources are hostile unless brought up on air.

This is unrelated crosstalk where the bleeding signal is totally dissimilar and irrelevant to the interfered signal. Basically, if any unrelated crosstalk is audible above system background noise, *it will be noticed.*

A fairly recent and insidious sort of unrelated crosstalk comes in the forms of assorted chirps, buzzes, and sizzles stemming from the relentless march of digits into console design and operations. The Society of Motion Picture and Television Engineers (SMPTE) time codes and automation codes were bad enough, but trying to get a computer clock droning out of the mixing buses and audio paths is not one of life's most enjoyable tasks.

22.12.5 Quantifying Crosstalk

A very reasonable quantitative measurement technique of all such effects is specified in the British Independent Broadcasting Authority (IBA) Independant Local Radio Code of Practice. This is a technical standard that effectively says, "If you can hear it or measure it, it's failed. . . ." Originally the test for interchannel crosstalk (i.e., between any channels in a console), it's also used for any dissimilar path crosstalk measurements. In short, it asks for better than 60 dB of isolation of 6 kHz between the paths, measured with a standard peak programme meter (PPM) with a CCIR 468 weighting filter in line. Since this CCIR curve has 12 dB of gain at its crest (at 6 kHz), the specification is actually calling for better than 72 dB of isolation at 6 kHz, which is neither easy nor very realistic. Such a figure is not far above system noise floors, generally. Remember, it's a peak measurement; an rms measurement would be 7 to 10 dB lower.

This discussion about crosstalk is not without a point, since it is actually concerned with the physical construction of the monitoring switches.

22.12.6 The Switcher

The selecting switcher (based on electronics for outside source selection matrices) is contained in a remote rack mounting box; the routing is controlled by digital logic lines from the console. In this way only a single pair of hostile signals is returned into the console, far easier to engineer away from things that may be unduly influenced by them. All the required sources, including PFL, main stereo output, auxiliaries, and two-track machine returns, are accessible from the console as a matter of course. Jumping links to the terminations on the switcher replace all the messy hassle of getting dozens of bits of signal via motherboard or hardwired connectors into the back of a conventional monitoring module within the console. The monitor control electronics (mono, split, volume, and so on) are conventionally located at hand on the console itself.

22.12.7 The Control Link

Communications between the console controls and the switcher rack is via a six-line data bus. Four lines form a 1-of-16 binary code to select the source; the other two are control bits (Fig. 22-78). The write command line goes high immediately when a different routing is elected, enabling the 4175 (IC_5) at the rack end in Fig. 22-79 to

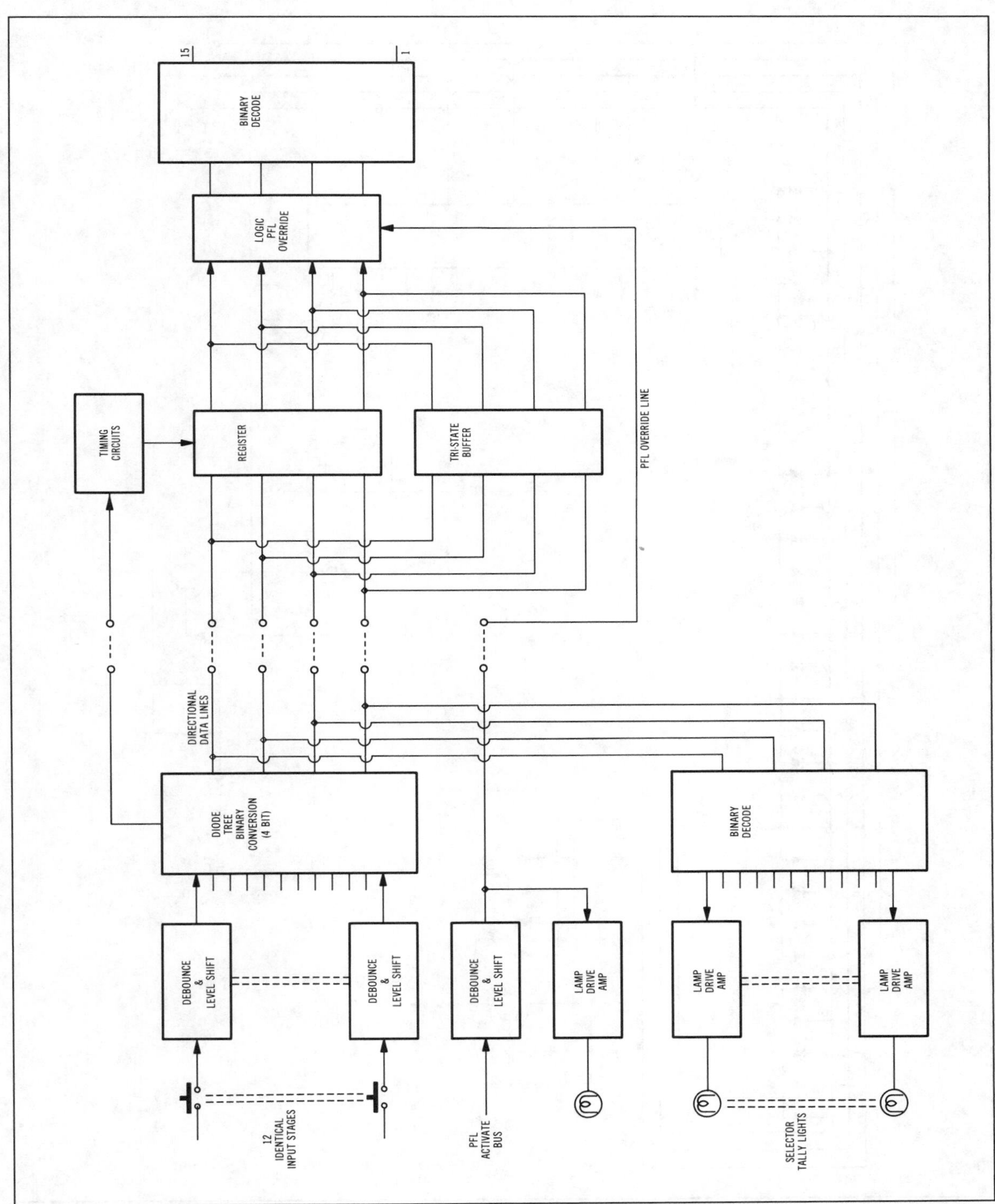

Figure 22-78 Block diagram of monitor select control logic.

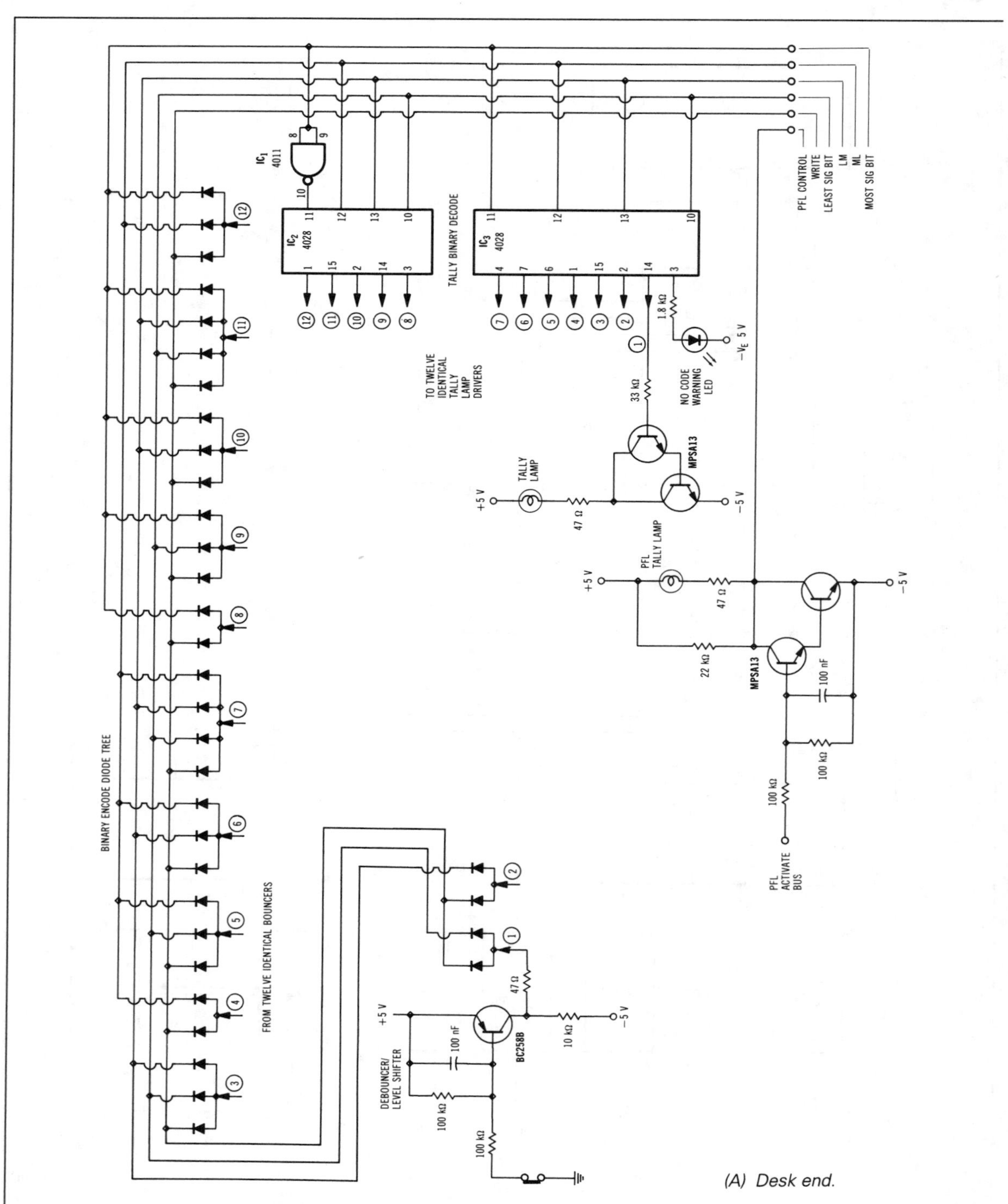

(A) Desk end.

Figure 22-79 Monitor

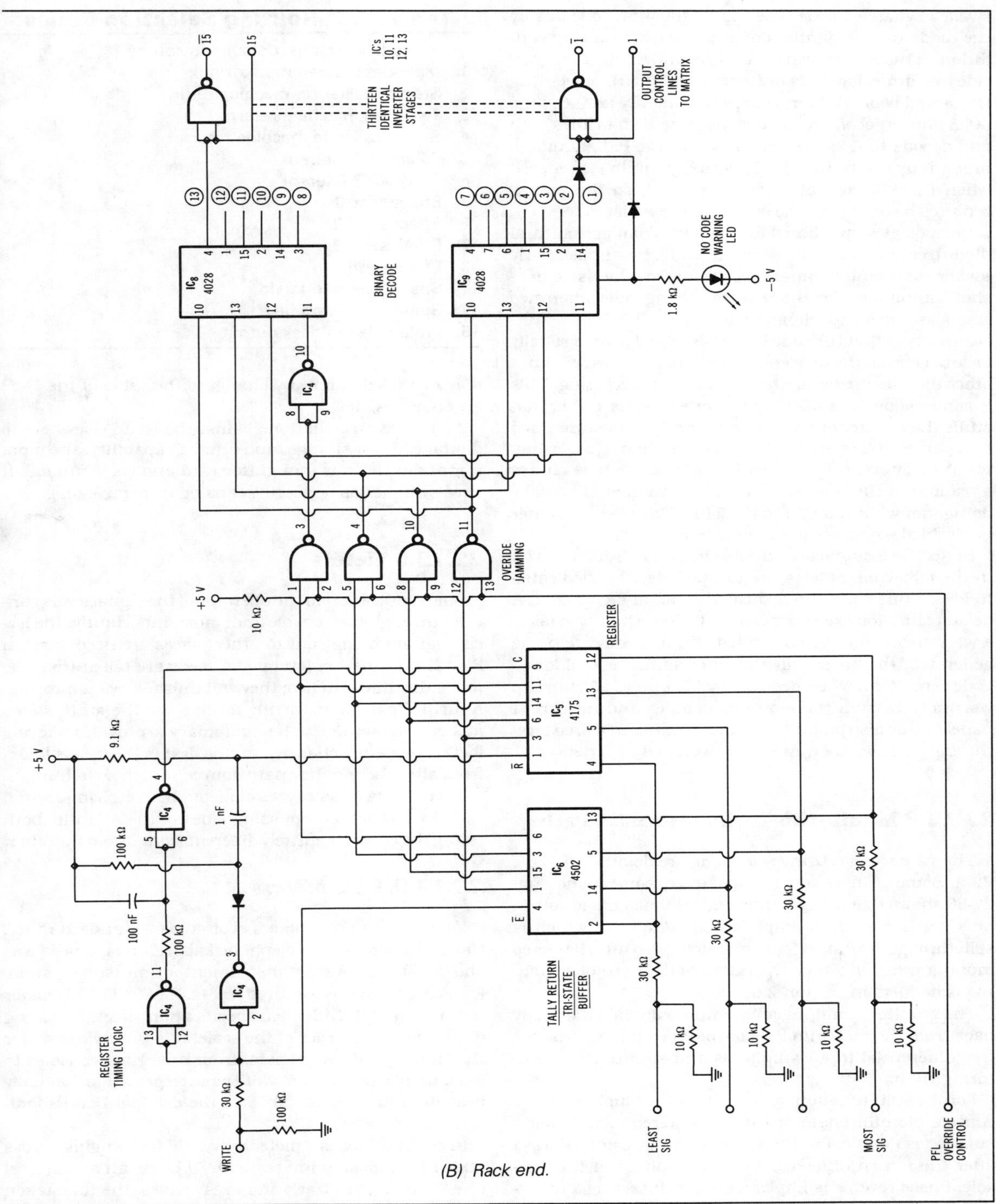

(B) Rack end.

select control logic.

swallow whatever code is set up on the 4-bit code bus by the diode tree. Regardless of any other monitoring condition, if the PFL activate bus is grounded, the PFL override line drops low (it is ordinarily tied high), preventing the stored code in the register reaching IC_8 and IC_9, the 4028 binary decoders. Instead, they see all data lines high and decode that as source 15, where the PFL (audio) is brought up on the matrix. This code jamming is relieved when the PFL activate line is released, so the matrix reroutes back to the code stored in the register.

No apologies are offered for the somewhat agricultural diode tree approach to binary encoding. It's simple, fairly inexpensive, and bomb-proof. Similarly, why use a one-shot timing chip for the register timing logic when two resistors and a capacitor will do?

A nicety is that the code bus is also used to bring a tally code back from the rack end to the console end at all times other than the instants when rerouting is occurring. This is achieved by the 4502 (IC_6) tri-state inverter/buffer that stuffs the register output back up the lines to be decoded by a pair of 4028s (IC_2 and IC_3), which then, via Darlington transistors, drive indicating lamps. There is always a readout at the console of what the switcher is actually doing, not what it ought to be doing. The tri-state buffer is disabled whenever the write line goes high.

Sixteen selections are possible (0 to 15), but as shown in the following, only 14 are used. Code 15 is dedicated to PFL, while code 1 is dedicated to main stereo mix. A default situation exists, whereby if the code bus logic takes a walk or becomes disconnected and no codes are being generated, the buses will almost certainly rest all low—code zero. Zero, when decoded by IC_8 and IC_9, brings up warning LEDs on the monitor modules and rack front panels while also pulling on source one (main stereo mix) through the switcher. At least it won't all go quiet.

22.12.8 Monitoring Switcher Audio Path

The 12 normal routing selections are detailed in Table 22-2. Some of these sources are stereo, some mono. Fig. 22-80 shows that the only difference is that a mono source only needs one input amplifier, the output of which is split through two analog transmission gates into the stereo monitor select mix bus. Operation of this type of switching is detailed in section 22.8.

The monitor summing amp outputs are taken directly back from the rack into the console via a pair of ground-free differential input amplifiers and so into the monitoring chain.

For the split function, a mono sum is brought into the console monitor chain of the main stereo mix. A mono sum is also derived of the switcher output immediately after the return differential input amplifier in the console. Phase reverse is implemented by inserting a unity-gain inverter into the right path. The rest of the monitor chain is self-explanatory (Fig. 22-81). Dim attenuation

Table 22-2. Routing Selection Codes

0	No code warnings, defaults to source 1
1	Main desk stereo monitor/mix
2	Stereo mastering machine return
3	Two-track machine return
4	Stereo cassette machine return
5	Foldback 1 (stereo)
6	Foldback 2 (stereo)
7	Effect send 1
8	Effect send 2
9	Effect send 3
10	Effect send 4
11	Spare, access on field
12	Spare, access on field
15	Prefade listen desk output

may be varied simply by changing the value of the 1-kΩ lower-leg resister.

Almost as a retaliation against the trend elsewhere to digital control, storage, and remote capability, the monitor audio chain is straightforward and conventional. It uses switches as opposed to analog transmission gates.

22.12.9 Meters

Some indication to the operator of the signal levels running through the console and, most importantly, the levels that are being sent to other places are necessary. In Fig. 22-81 a pair of level meter feeds are taken from the top of the dim switches; they will thus follow monitoring. A further pair permanently hung cross the *main stereo mix output* is optional. It's customary to provide metering facilities on each channel; in this design the feed is taken from after the monitor path source/return switching.

There are two basic types of meter, both evolving around the same period on opposing sides of the Atlantic, both telling the observer entirely different things from the other.

22.12.9.1 VU Meters

Volume unit (VU) meters evolved as a standard in the United States by Bell Telephone Laboratories. A need was shown for a consistent instrument for measuring audio levels on lines; it is pictured in Fig. 22-82. The VU meter has a quite tightly defined specification sheet, including down to the buff color of the scale! It is the style of meter that finds itself everywhere, from broadcast consoles to cassette players, very few of the interpretations actually bearing much resemblance to the original Bell Laboratories' intentions.

In essence, it was a meter only valid for hanging across 600-Ω tranmission lines, the 0 VU being an actual level of +4 dBm. The attack and decay times (the time taken for the meter to indicate a steady input signal of 0 VU accurately and the time taken for the needle to fall back

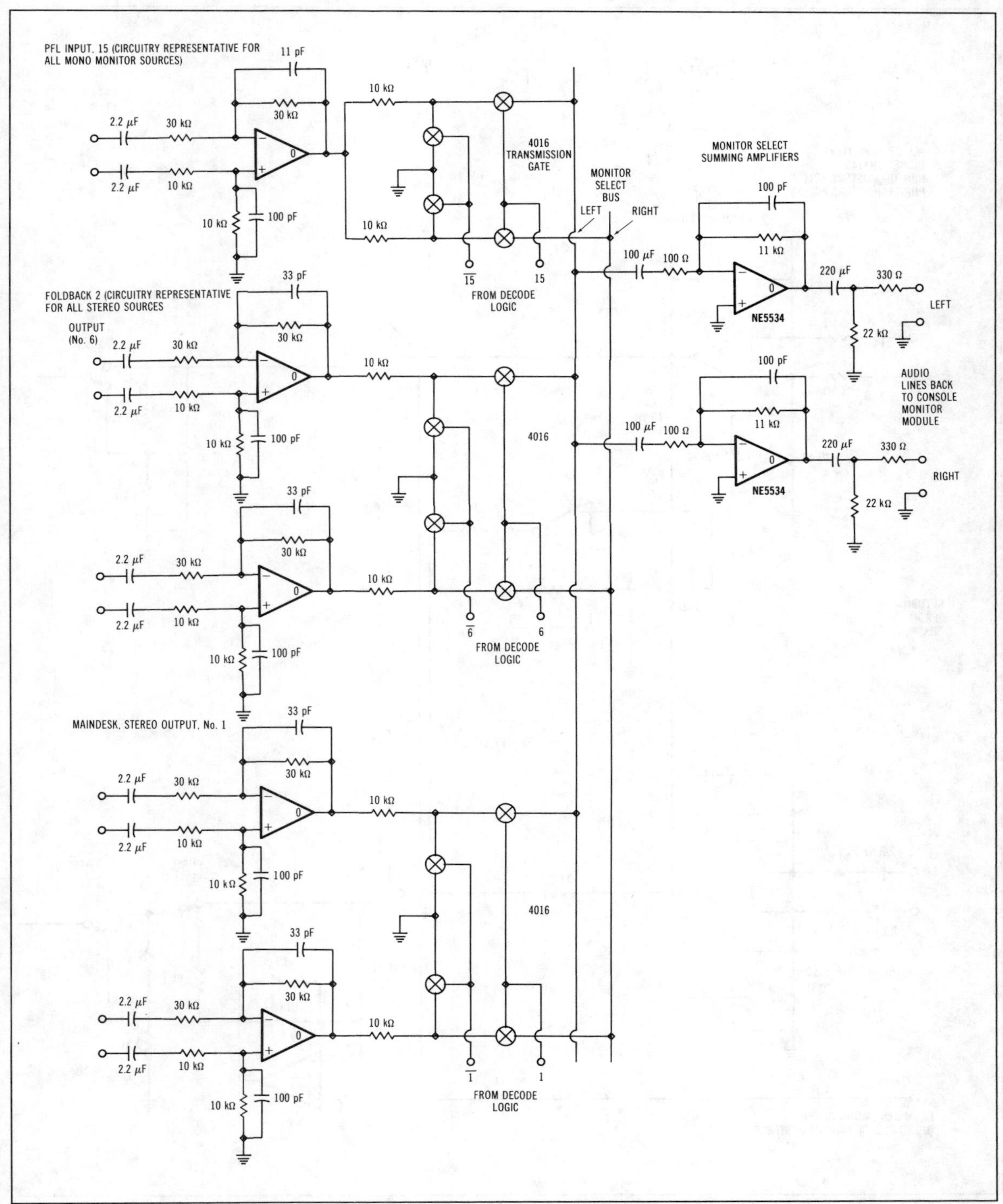

Figure 22-80 Monitor select switcher.

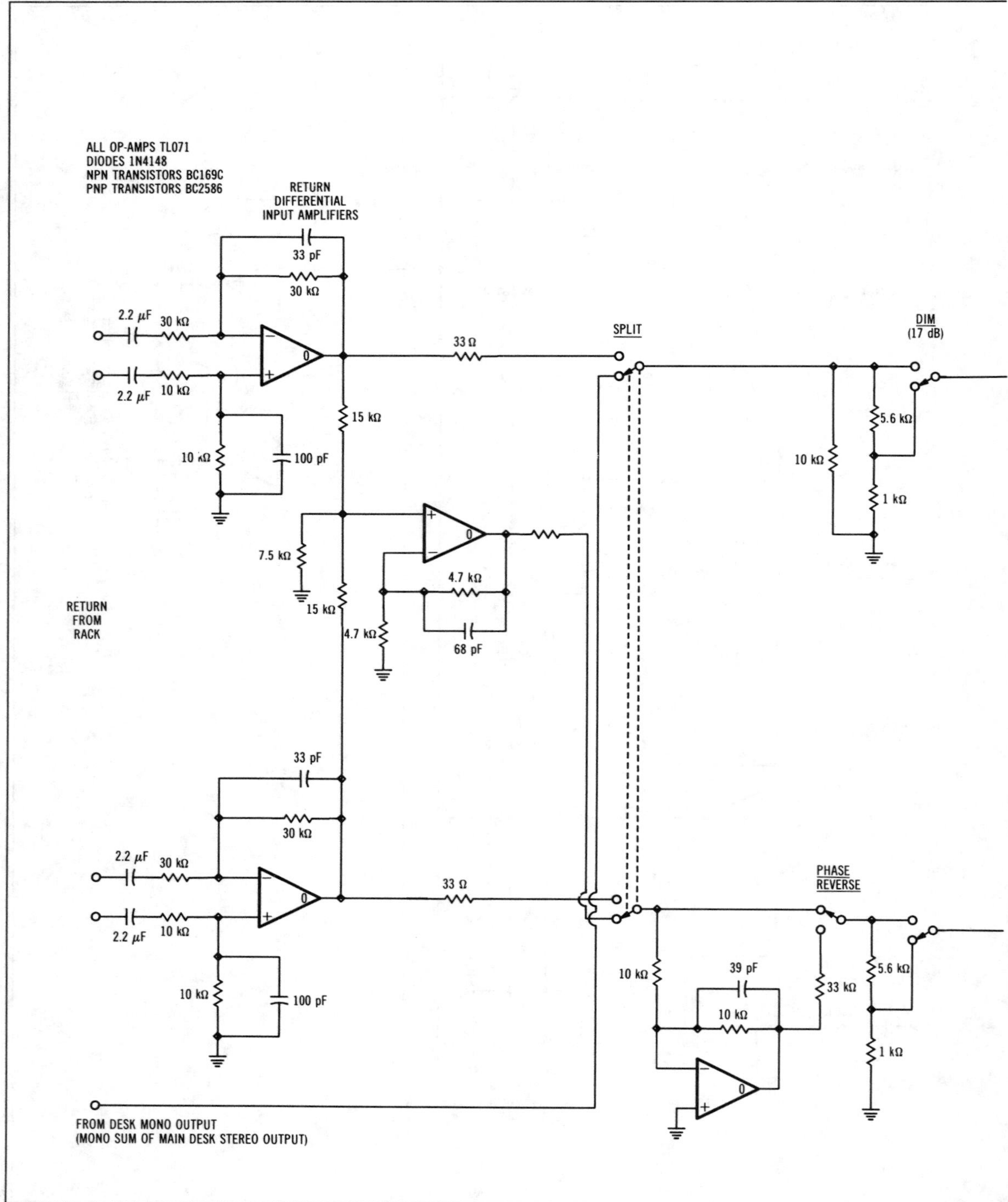

Figure 22-81 Monitor

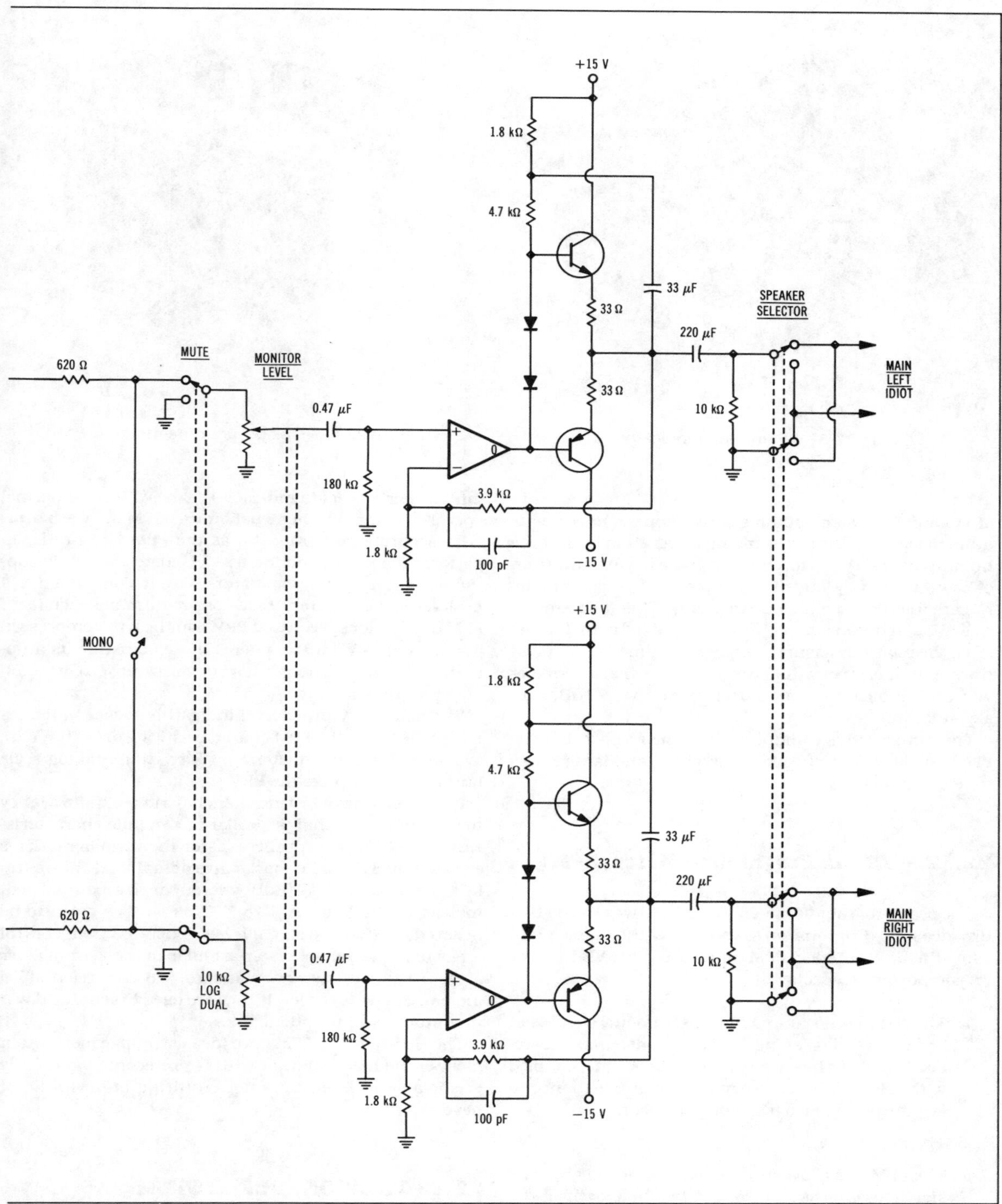

audio path (desk end).

Figure 22-82 Volume-unit indicator. (VU)

Figure 22-83 Peak programme meter. (PPM)

afterwards) are some 300 ms; this happens to correlate quite nicely with the level-sensing integration time of the human ear. The VU is intended to give a useful indication of how subjectively loud different pieces of program material are in order to match them evenly. This it does quite well. What it doesn't do is give any idea of the actual signal level; the relatively leisurely integration time misses most transients altogether with the consequence that a VU meter will underindicate actual signal level by up to 20 dB, usually at least 8 to 10 dB.

The underread is unimportant in the respect that the VU does allow subjective level matching and is very easy to read and use.

22.12.9.2 Peak Programme Meter (PPM)

The peak programme meter (Fig. 22-83) was the British Broadcasting Corporation's answer to the same problem—the BS4297 spec. PPM differs from the VU in three very important respects:

1. The PPM is a peak-reading instrument, capable of accurately displaying signal transients. Correspondingly, it has a very short attack time, coupled with a long fallback decay time to give a chance to see the peaks once it's captured them.
2. The PPM is black.
3. The PPM has a logarithmic scale, allowing accurate signal-level measurements to be made over all the scale range.

The scale consists of seven marks, numbered 1 to 7, each division representing 4-dB level change. PPM 4, the middle mark, is set to indicate 0 dBm/0 dBu. The normal operational maximum signal limit is PPM 6, or +8 dBu.

As accurate and as useful as the PPM is, in order to perform the same function as a VU meter, which is subjective level matching, operators have to consult a list of peak levels for different types of program material (e.g., PPM 5 to 5½ for speech and PPM 4 for heavily compressed pop music). A VU meter makes these adjustments automatically since, although it's worthless for peaks, it follows program density.

Virtually every other level-indicating device emulates either the VU or the PPM characteristics—or both. There are other European meters; peak reading and log scale but otherwise unlike the PPM.

Proper American broadcasters have taken quite a fancy to a mutant PPM that is similar in dynamic characteristics to BS4297, except the level for the various marks is elevated by 8 dB. The marks give actual level values (up to a maximum of +16 dB whereupon it's painted red) instead of the familiar 1 to 7. This is, it is given to be believed, so that the signal levels generated from control areas using these meters are similar to those from older areas using (curiously nonstandard) +8 dBm-referred VU meters. Such are the levels they are used to sending down interstudio and telephone lines.

The elevated-level PPM is an idea with some merit when most of the material dealt with is prerecorded and fairly predictable in level, thus not requiring an awful lot of headroom.

22.13 THE CONSOLE SYSTEM

A system is a means of reducing the versatility of its component parts. Ideally, there should be no system, but practicality dictates that there must be one. The thought is mortifying: hundreds of elements, the microphone amplifiers, differential input amplifiers, line amplifiers, equalizers, filters, and routing matrices roaming loose and needing to be coupled together for each individual operational requirement.

We need a saving grace, and fortunately there is one. Engineering and balancing habits are pretty well entrenched giving rise to a few well-defined, commonly used elemental combinations. Rationalizing these combinations and arranging easy selection of them as necessary is a good compromise. We've not so much lost versatility as gained a family of operating modes.

22.13.1 Channel System

The entire channel subsystem relies on the electronic switching elements used being entirely transparent, noiseless, distortionless, clickless, and other impossibilities. Noise due to the potentiometric CMOS switching employed here is very largely due to the individual summing amplifiers, scaled by the gain asked of them.

Noise resultant from them is defined to low (− 100 dBu or better) floor levels—fairly meaningless under the stampede of typical front-end or machine noise.

Distortion is primarily due to the automodulation of the CMOS transmission gates; that is, the path resistance varies with the instantaneous signal voltage. This, at zero level, is typically a nonsensical value. Both the harmonic and intermodulation products are almost unmeasurably low principally because of the near virtual-ground operation of the active CMOS elements. There is no voltage swing, no automodulation.

22.13.2 Function Modes

Reference should be made to Figs. 22-84 through 22-87 during this discussion of the channel system. These illustrations show the overall channel in block diagram form and the various ways the circuit blocks are configured for the different functions expected of the channel in use. Fig. 22-84 has all the reconfiguration represented by diagrammatically accurate but forbiddingly incomprehensible mechanical switching. Figs. 22-85 and 22-86 replace those in the main signal paths with electronic switching elements, which may seem more or less of a jungle, dependent on whether you were brought up on hard-gold contacts or silicon.

Certainly there are fewer electronic switchpoints than there were mechanical. This rationalization is primarily due to yet another incursion of esoteric (for audio) digital things.

A simplified representation of the four basic channel operating modes is given in Fig. 22-87A for recording, Fig. 22-87B for mixdown/direct to stereo, and Fig. 22-87C for overdubbing. The Xs show the switching points. Briefly, main multitrack operating modes and their implementation in this system are outlined here.

22.13.3 Recording Mode

In the recording mode, the object is to get a live source (e.g., microphone) through the signal modification chain (i.e., limiting, equalization) and on to a track or tracks of the multitrack machine. Level control on this path is by the main fader (or VCA fader if automation is applicable). Before and after monitoring of the tape track dedicated to the channel is routed on to the main stereo monitoring/mix-bus via the secondary level control.

22.13.4 Mixdown Mode

The machine return is brought through the modification chain and mixed onto the main stereo monitoring/mix-bus via the main/VCA fader. The machine monitoring chain is disabled.

Since a major justification for keeping the multitrack routing open during mixdown is to provide additional effects feeds, this is best served if the secondary level control is fed post main fader and post mute/solo switching. To enable this, a crossfeed electronic routing is included Fig. 22-87B. However, independent control is restored when required if a fader reverse is called.

Another mode, *direct to stereo*, is a derivative of *mixdown*. It enables live sources to be mixed straight on to the main stereo bus obviating the need to use multitrack routing.

22.13.5 Overdub Mode

A halfway house between *record* and *mixdown*, overdub mode is intended for use when most of the console is in mixdown but individual channels are being laid or touched up. Signal flow is as record, only with the main/VCA and secondary level controls interchanged. The main/VCA fader in this mode, therefore, controls the monitor feed into the main stereo mix-bus, which ties in with the operation of this fader on all the other channels that are in mixdown.

A handy interlock exists in this mode to facilitate single button drop-in. When the channel system function is selected to overdub and the monitoring path is set to A check (machine input), a relay closing pair is made that may be plumbed into the remote control access of the machine. Provided the track is armed ready to record, hitting A check automatically drops the machine in simultaneously.

22.13.6 Logic Control

A distinction is made in Figs. 22-85 and 22-86 between the analog signal switches and their digital control electronics not purely because of the differing disciplines but for clarity's sake—that is, to avoid too many lines running all over the place.

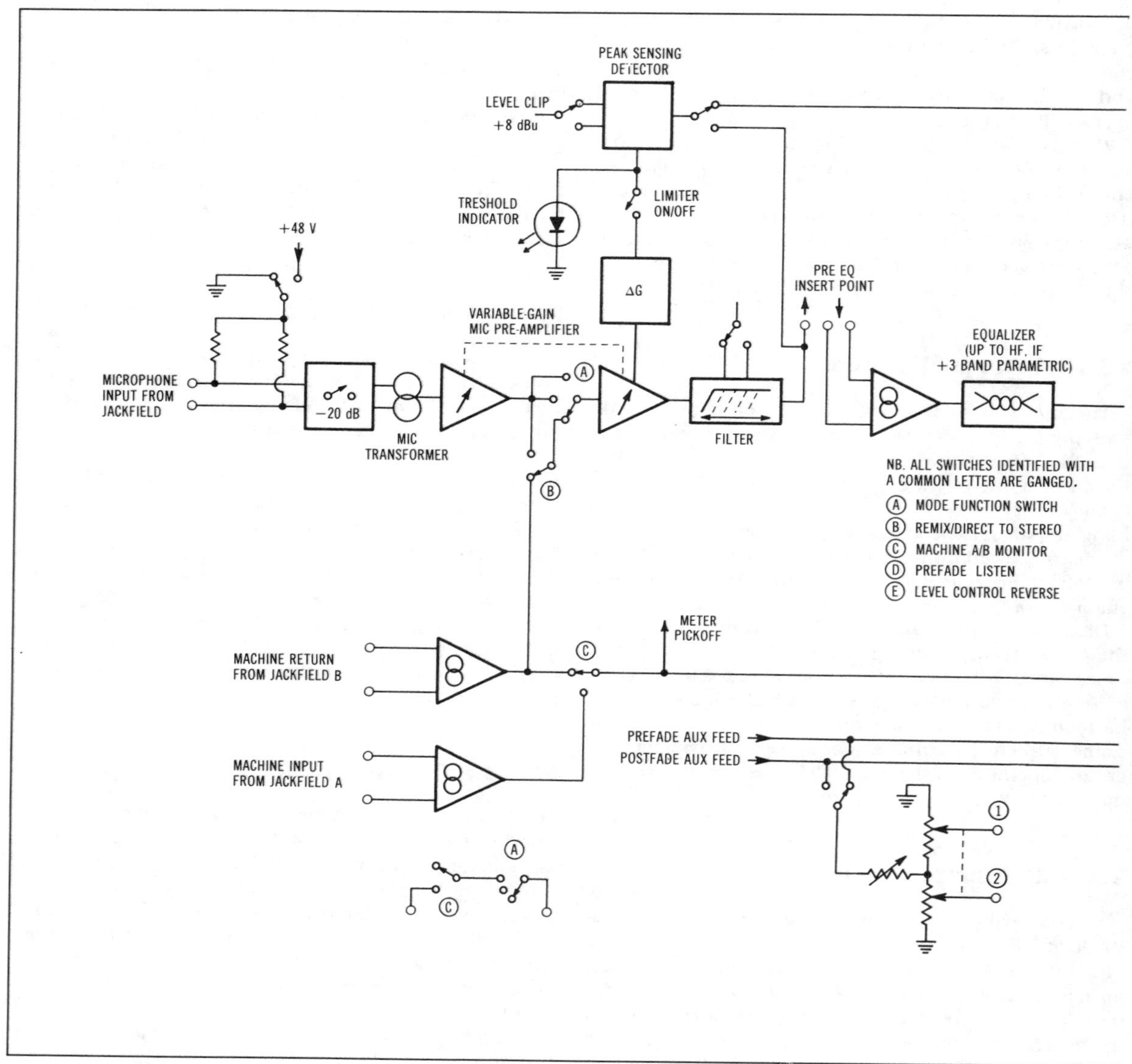

Figure 22-84 In-line multitrack

Each top-panel switch is a momentary-action touch switch with an associated LED indicator (with the exception of the function mode switch). The toggle push-on and push-off characteristic is provided by the basic debouncer/flip-flop circuit, as shown in Fig. 22-88. This action is not only fun, play-worthy, and therefore, fashionable, it scores in a couple of other important respects:

- Cost—The combination of a small, mechanically simple, nonlatching, push-to-make switch and a fairly small amount of silicon bits is much less expensive than latching pushbutton switches.
- Versatility—Using electronic latching rather than mechanical catches makes remote/automatic function presetting and triggering comparatively simple.

22.13.7 Switch Debouncing

Debouncing is removing the ragged edges from a switching signal. Switch contacts do not simply make contact when pressed and break contact on release. The two bits of metal grind against each other or bounce a

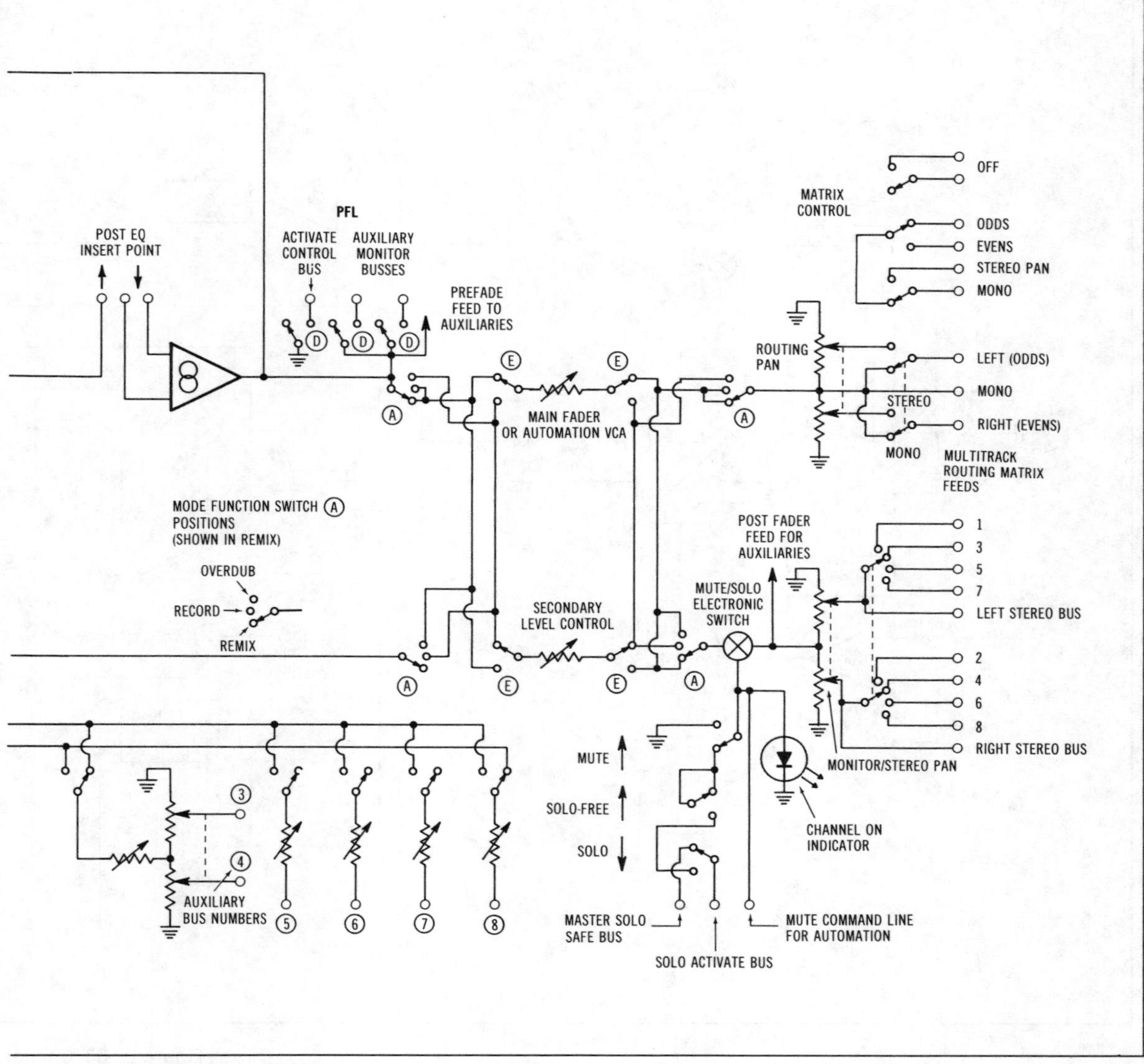

recording and monitoring channel.

few times while moving together or apart, resulting in a series of ragged, spiky "almost contacts" rather than simply touch or not touch.

Ordinarily, this doesn't matter too much, but, if the switch is feeding a bistable flip-flop (as here), the fun begins. Flip-flops are usually edge triggers; on a positive-going transition, another pulse flops it back and so on. A string of rapid, unpredicatable pulses, as provided by nearly any mechanical switch, sends flip-flops frantic.

Slugging the switch with time constants is nearly foolproof, but the arrangement in Fig. 22-88 is practically faultless.

The 4098 contains two monostables, which are handy since the 4013 contains two flip-flops. It can sense either positive or negative transitions, positive in this application, catch the very first input transition, and stuff out a uniform, clean, predictable clock pulse for the flip-flop. Subsequent bounces and scrunches merely extend the output pulse slightly but don't generate any spurious output transitions.

Flip-flops can have their outputs jammed by stuffing the required state up set (making the Q output go positive) or reset (negative)—an invitation for remote processor control.

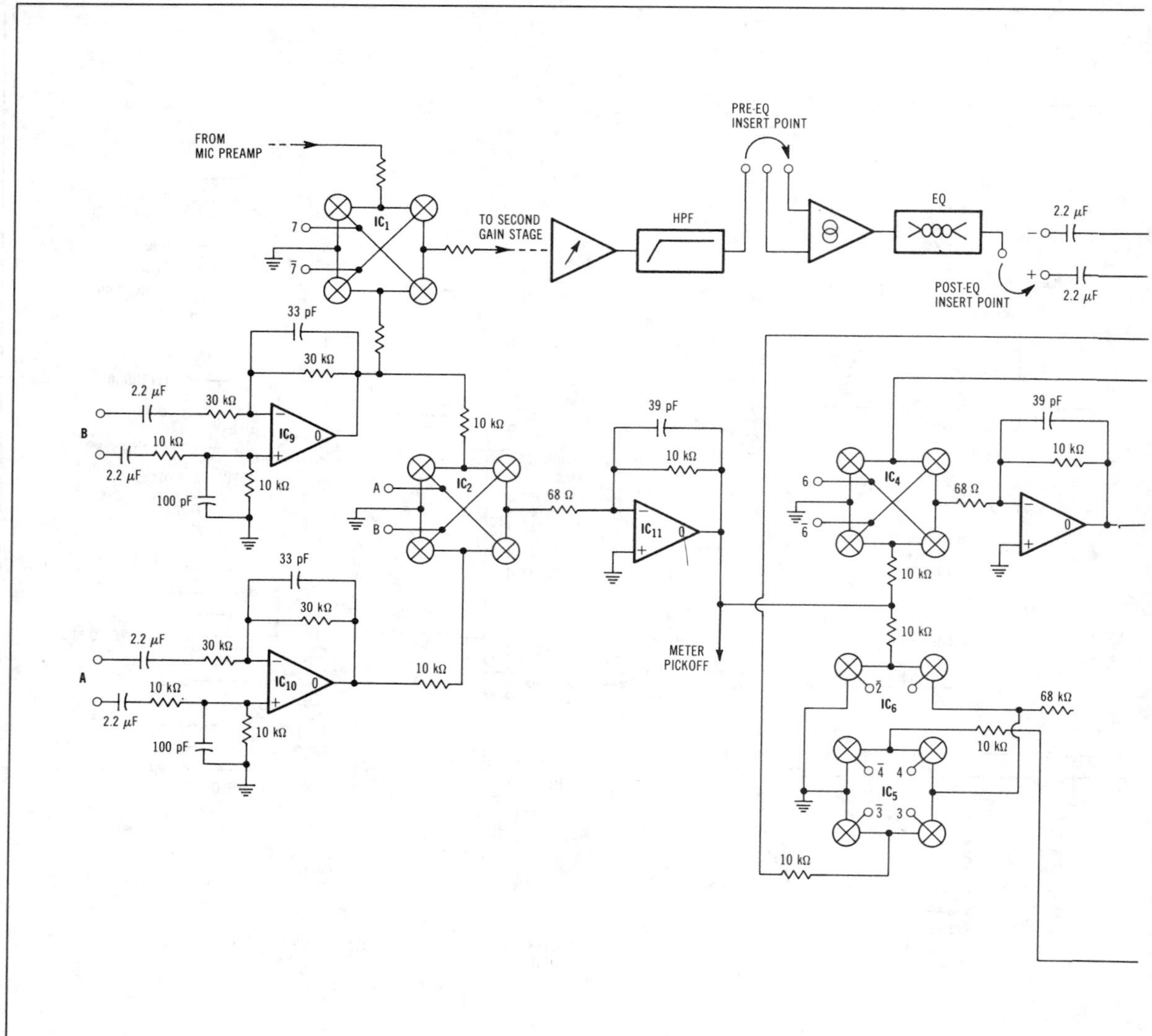

Figure 22-85 Channel

22.13.8 Logic Sense

Some of the logic design is unconventional, all done in the name of reducing component count, largely obviating level-shifting transistors while maintaining the inviolable ground-for-active law of control interfacing. This is a common-sense rule that simply means that any accessible control line should just need to be taken to some reasonable ground in order to activate whatever it's supposed to, not a specific voltage above or below ground. This helps avoid the "should this go to +5 or −24 V" routine, while greatly simplifying system design—grounds are omnipresent.

The main reason for the unusual logic powering (Fig. 22-86) stems from the use of a bipolar PROM in the assignment logic. This needs a tightly controlled 5-V supply unlike the CMOS ICs, which will run off nearly anything with "volts" on it.

22.13.9 What Is a PROM?

PROMs (or progammable read-only memories) are digital devices used extensively in computer technology for storing individual items of information or sequences of information that are regularly referred to.

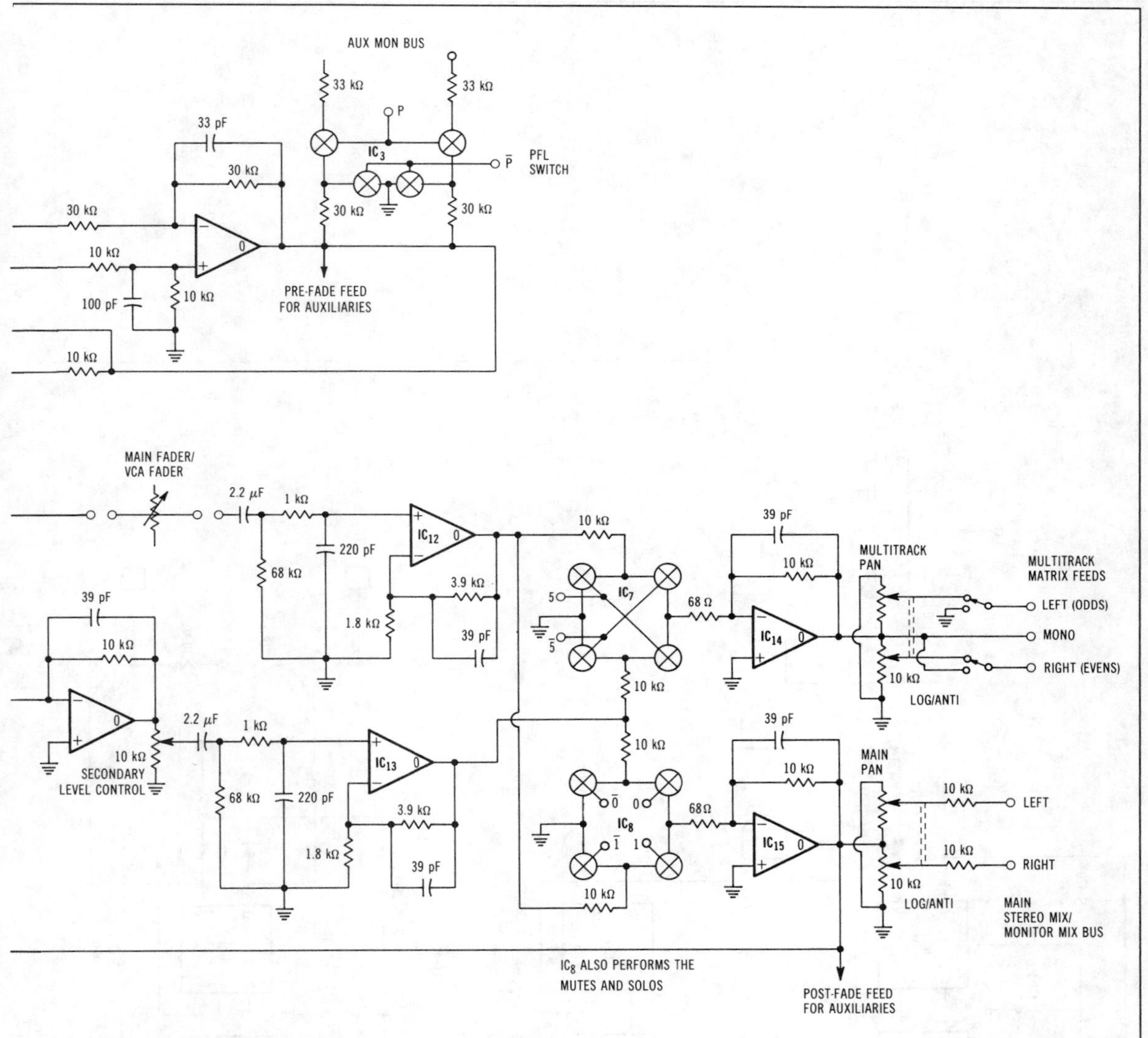

system—audio paths.

Memory is self explanatory.

Read-only means that in normal operation it's only possible to retrieve the information that's stored. New information cannot be put in or the contents modified.

Programmable means, given the right gear and software, prepared information can be written into the PROM. The type used in this design can't be restuffed though, since the programming is achieved by literally blowing tiny internal fuses in the "shape" of the data. This seeming inversatility is reasonable with such devices where the device cost is cheap compared with programming costs (human time).

The information stored is, of course, binary in nature—a 0 or a 1, up or down, there or not, and so on. The number of these binary bits contained in each PROM can be up to 65,000, 8192 and 16,384 being very common. For this channel system control, the PROM used stores 256 bits, which, in fact, is still a wee bit overkill, but they don't really come much smaller.

This baby PROM, a Harris 7602, is much like most adult PROMs in that the bits are organized internally in chunks eight wide, as in a digital word (byte). Eight happens to be the byte width of most popular microprocessors. In the baby PROM there are 32 such bytes of stored data (32 × 8 = 256), each being accessible with a specific 5-bit wide address code (given by the binary numbers

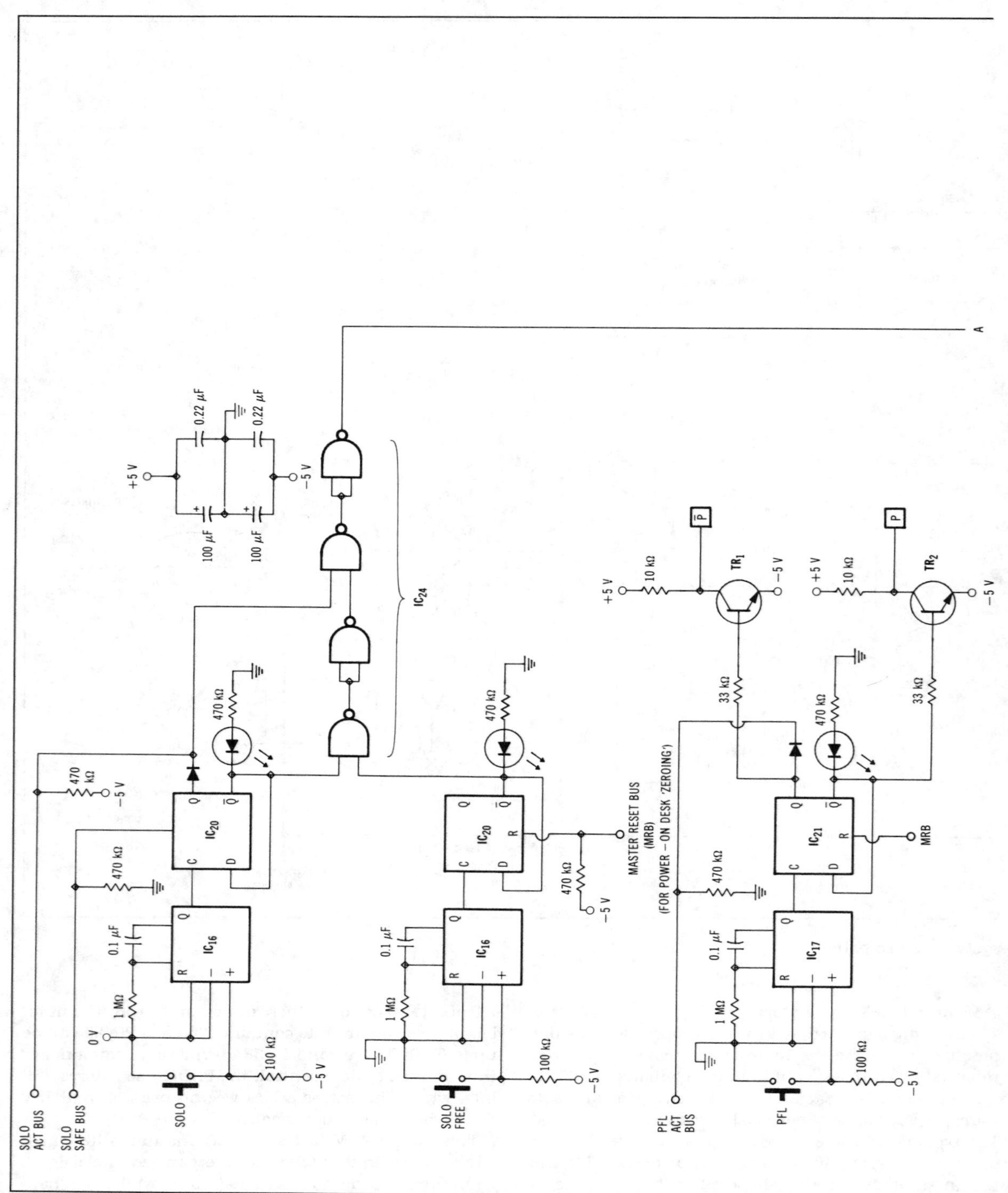

Figure 22-86 Channel

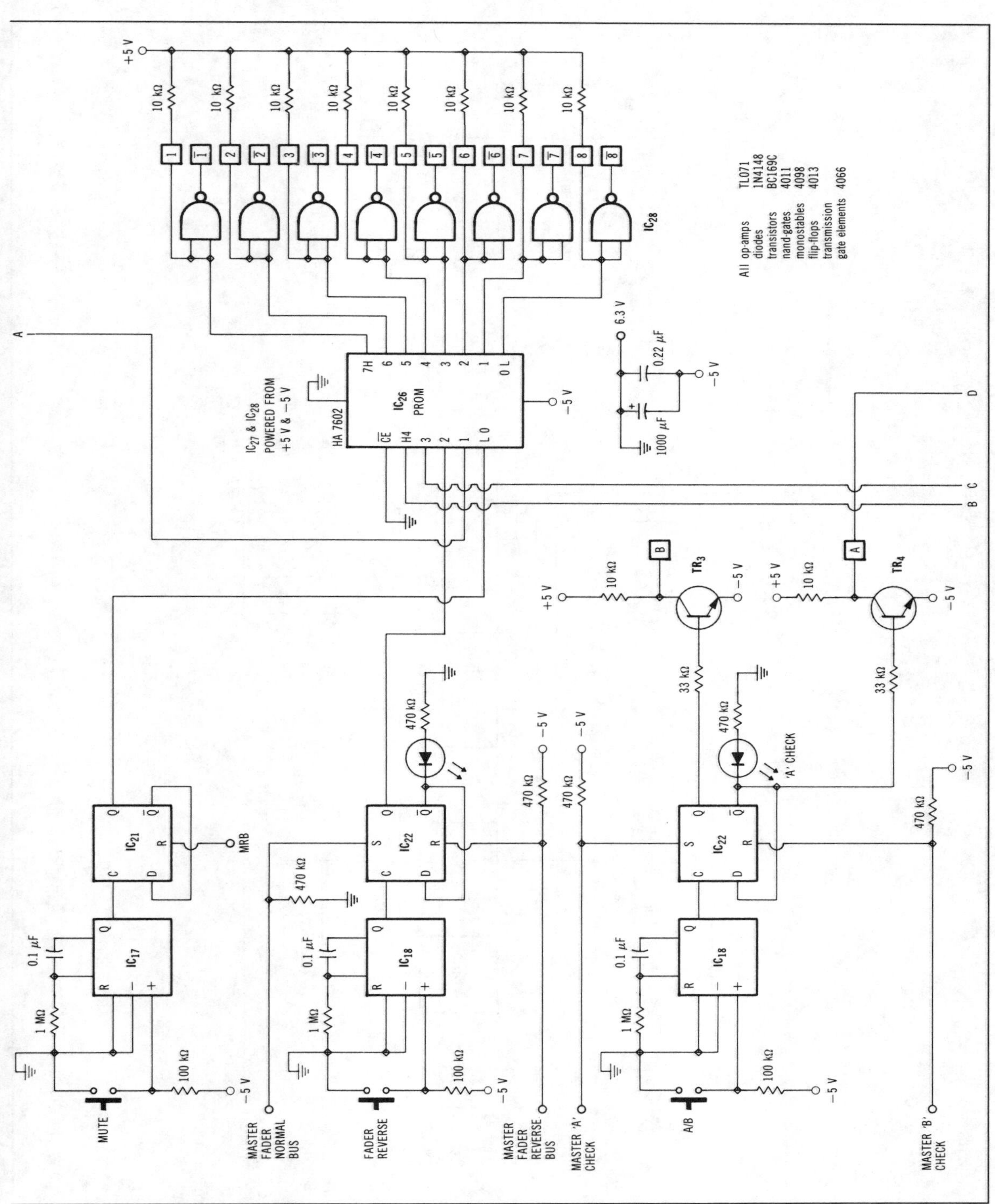

system—control logic.

cont. on next page

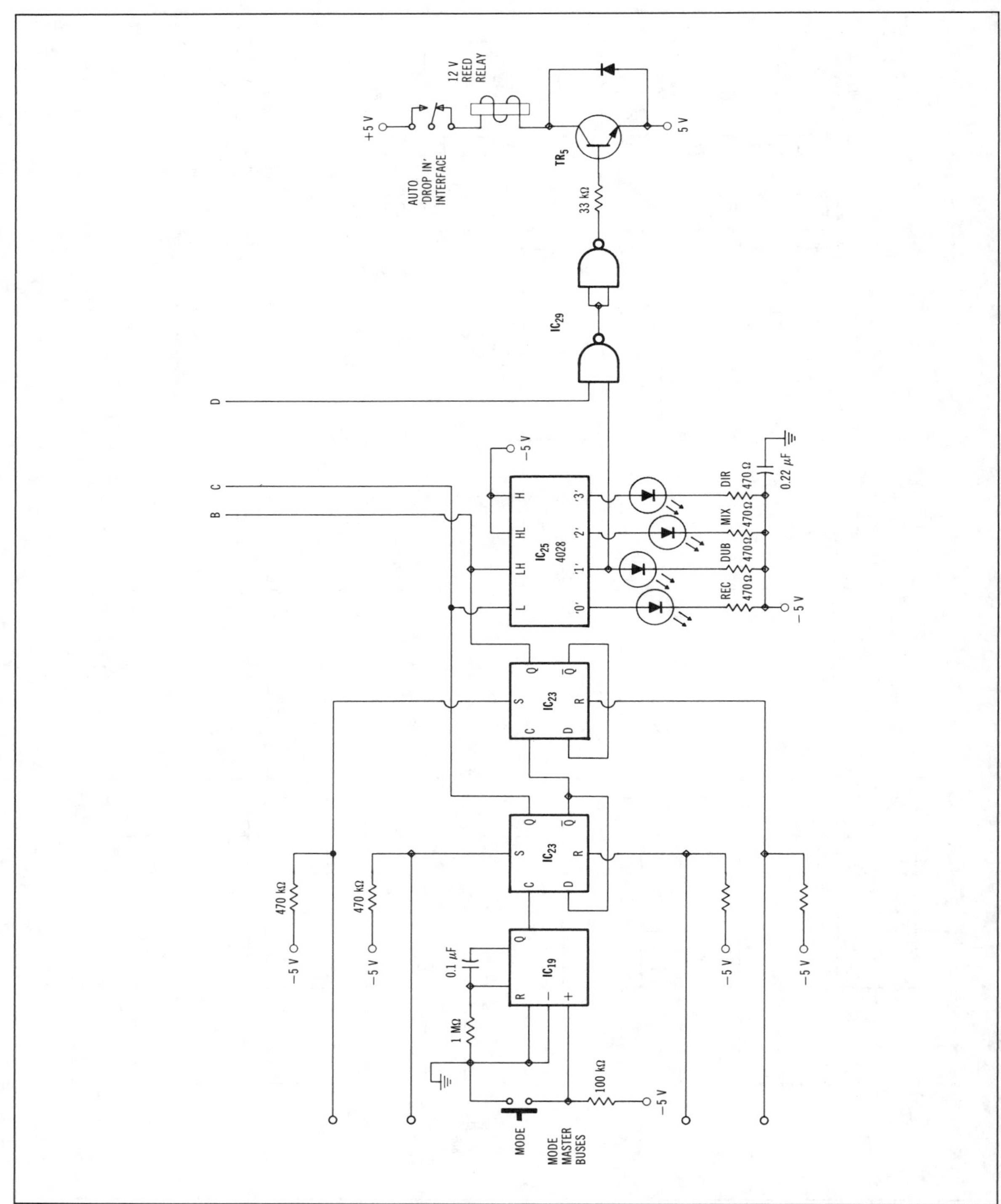

Figure 22-86-cont. Channel system—control logic.

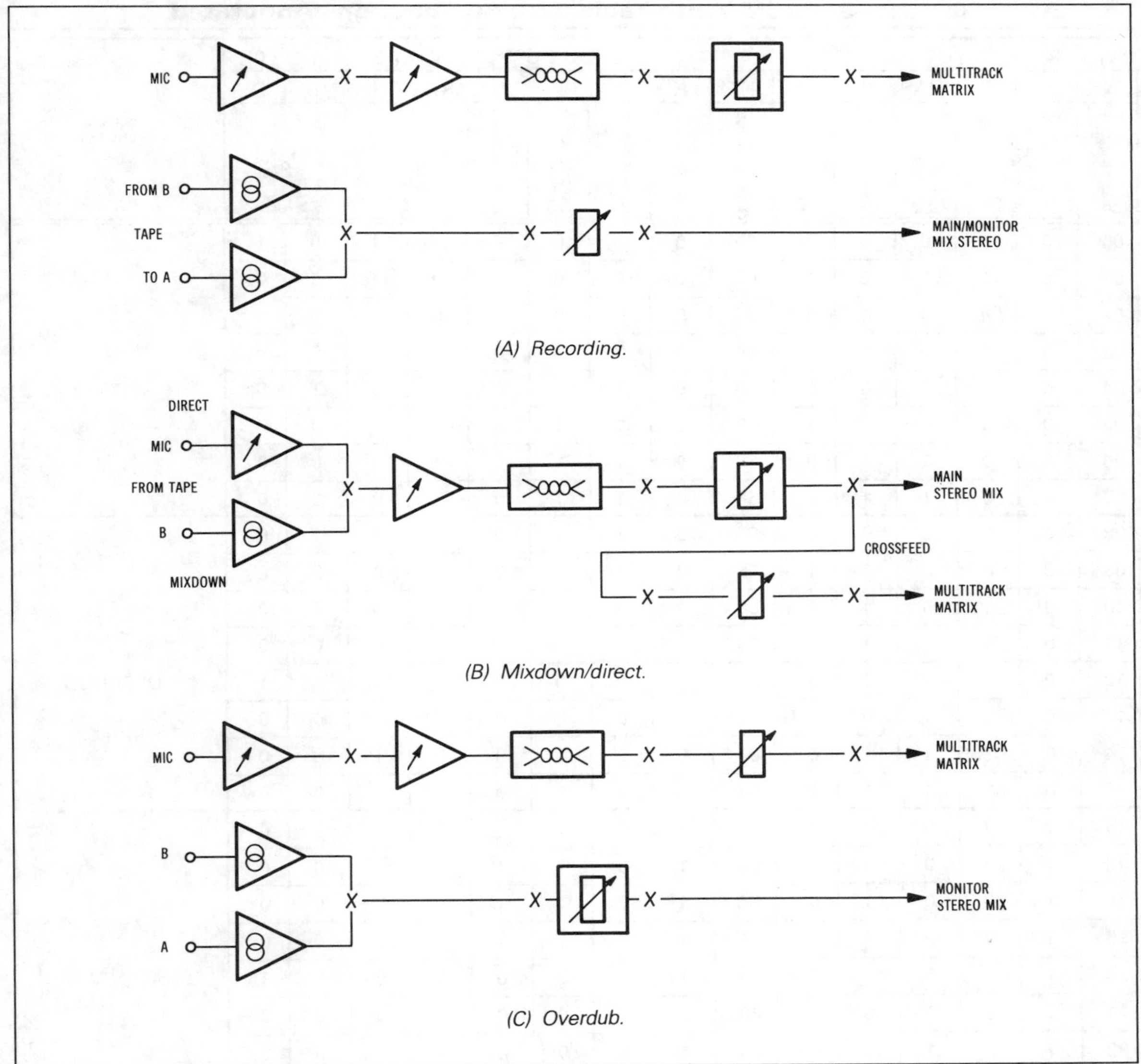

Figure 22-87 Channel function modes.

from 0 to 31). This format is diagrammatically represented in Fig. 22-89. For any of up to 32 command states, preprogrammed responses for eight output lines are immediately accessible.

(This particular type of baby PROM is usually used at the top-end of microprocessor memory maps where a *page* (256 bytes) is given over to the function of the processor *vectors*, such as interrupts. As an example, if the processor receives a *nonmaskable interrupt (NMI)*, it usually means "Panic! The power is collapsing!" or some other similar situation. NMI makes the processor look at a certain address in the page of the baby PROM, which tells it where to find in memory a program to "save the environment" (i.e., hide safely all the crucial operating data, quickly).

In the context of our channel system, the PROM outputs drive the analog switches (organized per Fig. 22-85) to route and control the channel and monitor signal paths through the system elements. This occurs in accordance with and under the command of the PROM address inputs, which are indicators of selected channel function (Record/Mixdown/Overdub), local or remote fader reverse commands, and, importantly, mute and solo status.

Table 22-3 is the input-output truth table for the pro-

Table 22-3. PROM Truth-Table with Bit Functions Annotated

	4	INPUT			1		7	6	OUTPUT		3	2	1	0	
No.	H	BINARY			L	HEX	H	BINARY						L	
DECIMAL	CHANNEL FUNCTION MODE		FADER REVERSE	SOLO	MUTE	HEXADECIMAL	MIC/LINE	MAINFADER INPUT	MULTITRACK OUTPUT	CROSSFEED	SECONDARY FADER INPUT		MAIN STEREO OUTPUT		CHANNEL FUNCTION
00	0	0	0	0	0	05	0	0	0	0	0	1	0	1	
01	0	0	0	0	1	04	0	0	0	0	0	1	0	0	
02	0	0	0	1	0	04	0	0	0	0	0	1	0	0	
03	0	0	0	1	1	04	0	0	0	0	0	1	0	0	
04	0	0	1	0	0	6A	0	1	1	0	1	0	1	0	RECORD
05	0	0	1	0	1	68	0	1	1	0	1	0	0	0	
06	0	0	1	1	0	68	0	1	1	0	1	0	0	0	
07	0	0	1	1	1	68	0	1	1	0	1	0	0	0	
08	0	1	0	0	0	6A	0	1	1	0	1	0	1	0	
09	0	1	0	0	1	68	0	1	1	0	1	0	0	0	
10	0	1	0	1	0	68	0	1	1	0	1	0	0	0	
11	0	1	0	1	1	68	0	1	1	0	1	0	0	0	
12	0	1	1	0	0	05	0	0	0	0	0	1	0	1	OVERDUB
13	0	1	1	0	1	04	0	0	0	0	0	1	0	0	
14	0	1	1	1	0	04	0	0	0	0	0	1	0	0	
15	0	1	1	1	1	04	0	0	0	0	0	1	0	0	
16	1	0	0	0	0	B2	1	0	1	1	0	0	1	0	
17	1	0	0	0	1	B0	1	0	1	1	0	0	0	0	
18	1	0	0	1	0	B0	1	0	1	1	0	0	0	0	
19	1	0	0	1	1	B0	1	0	1	1	0	0	0	0	
20	1	0	1	0	0	89	1	0	0	0	1	0	0	1	MIXDOWN
21	1	0	1	0	1	88	1	0	0	0	1	0	0	0	
22	1	0	1	1	0	88	1	0	0	0	1	0	0	0	
23	1	0	1	1	1	88	1	0	0	0	1	0	0	0	
24	1	1	0	0	0	32	0	0	1	1	0	0	1	0	
25	1	1	0	0	1	30	0	0	1	1	0	0	0	0	
26	1	1	0	1	0	30	0	0	1	1	0	0	0	0	
27	1	1	0	1	1	30	0	0	1	1	0	0	0	0	
28	1	1	1	0	0	09	0	0	0	0	1	0	0	1	DIRECT
29	1	1	1	0	1	08	0	0	0	0	1	0	0	0	
30	1	1	1	1	0	08	0	0	0	0	1	0	0	0	
31	1	1	1	1	1	88	0	0	0	0	1	0	0	0	

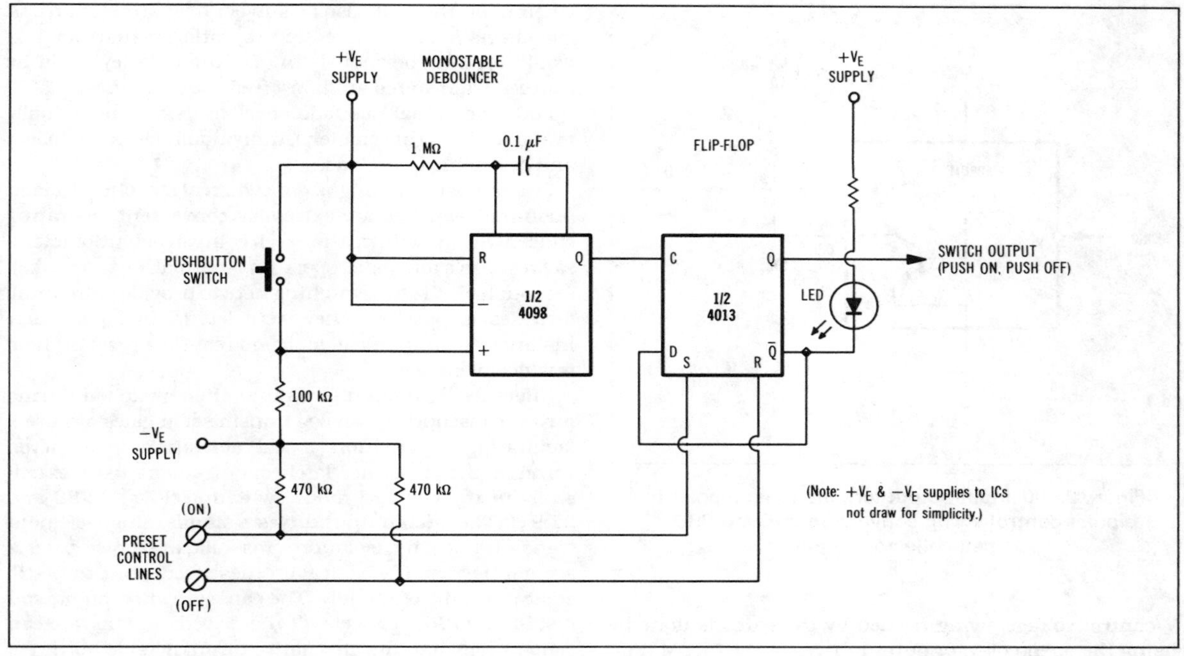

Figure 22-88 Pushbutton interface circuit.

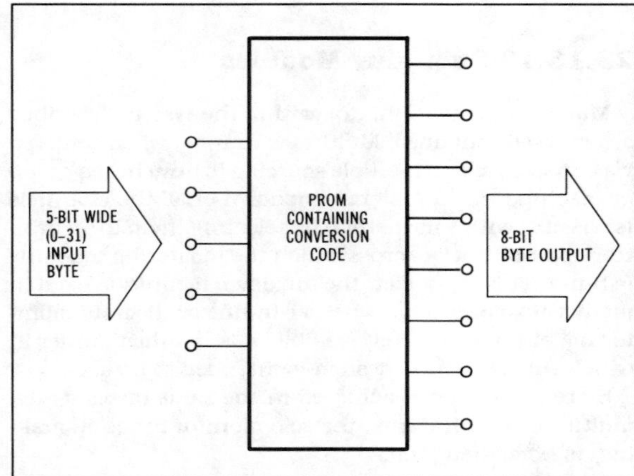

Figure 22-89 PROM input/output format.

gram burnt into the baby PROM. The input and output binary lines are tagged as a guide to their function in the real world of the channel system. The O/P HEX column is the numerical value in hexadecimal notation for programming.

Insomniacs will be able to pass much time referring the truth table to the channel circuits working out exactly what happens to the channel under all control conditions.

Most of the control logic is still done in hardware, largely consisting of jammable debouncer/flip-flops. For the channel function control, a single pushbutton that steps through the four functions is realized by a simple 2-bit counter (IC_{23} in Fig. 22-86). This generates a 2-bit code that feeds both the PROM control inputs and a 4028 binary to decimal decoder IC_{25}, which drives the relative status indicating front-panel LEDs.

Solo, solo free, and solo safe are dealt with in IC_{16}, IC_{20}, and IC_{24}, but the relevant action on the analog circuitry is still executed via the PROM. It can be deduced that the solo command and mute of the PROM do just the same thing, resulting in a fair number of duplicated and redundant program codes within the PROM. At least this gives room for expansion or function modification (if and when required) by simple card link changes and a differently programmed PROM.

22.13.10 Logic Meets Analog

The 7602 PROM hangs between logic ground and −5 V (of the split ±5-V logic supply) thus necessitating all input feeds to be similar in swing—0 to −5 V. All the drive logic flip-flops, debouncer, and master bus logic are similarly powered.

Analog transmission gates, such as the design of Fig. 22-85, are required to pass (and stop) analog signals referred to ground and, therefore, of both polarities, so the gates have to be fed from a split supply (in this instance the ±5 V logic supply).

Converting between the 0 and −5-V logic and the ±5-

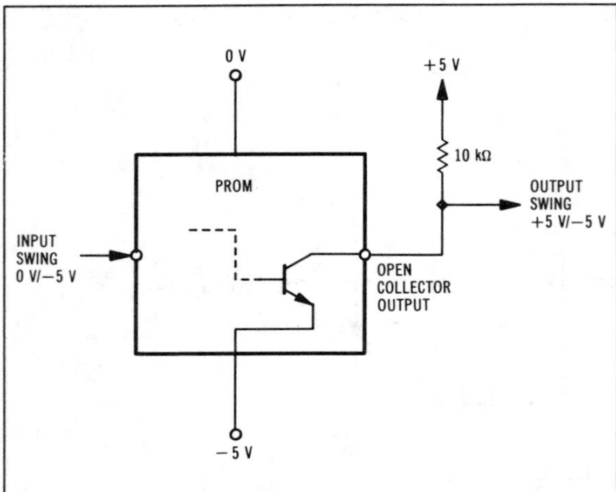

Figure 22-90 Input/output termination (unipolar to bipolar control swing conversion utilizing PROM open-collector output).

V control voltage swing needed by the gates is done by using the open-collector output drives of the PROM (Fig. 22-90). Open-collector is exactly that—there is no positive output pull-up internal to this PROM. The idea is that it may be paralleled with other open-collector devices in a wired-OR bus configuration. When the output transistor is turned off, the collector is at a high impedance state. The collector is pulled up an extra 5 V above the internal supply of the PROM. When the transistor turns on, the collector dutifully zaps down to the −5-V supply. It doesn't care what is at the other end of the load pulling resistor provided it isn't of excessive potential (12 V is safe; the output ports are, in fact, the programming path with these devices and much above that may induce some involuntary reprogramming).

Some of the analog switches are driven directly off the PROM outputs, while others have the necessary inverse-switching feed provided by a conventional inverter.

As a note to the unwary, bipolar memories such as the 7602 use a lot of power when being switched. This explains the large amount of decoupling festooned around it and the logic supply generally. Needless to say, the analog transmission gates are referred to audio ground, not the click-infested logic ground, despite the fact that they are powered off the logic supply.

22.13.11 Auxiliary Channel Feeds

Two prefade (and so premute) feeds are provided on each channel, each with a level control and pannable across a stereo pair of mix-buses. This provides a versatile facility enabling separate stereo foldbacks or four separate feeds. Each of the pairs is selectable to postfade should extra effect feeds be needed during a heavy mixdown, whereupon they will also be subject to channel mutes. A few effects such as stereo reverberation plate/black box would benefit enormously in operation if they could be sourced from stereo auxiliary feeds such as these.

Four individual postfade effect feeds are individually mutable (locally or remotely), individually level controlled, and selectable to prefade.

Pre- or postswitching is done via real switches. In fact, push-pull switches are extremely convenient, operating concentrically within the level control potentiometers, saving hassle and panel space (in—normal, out—reverse). Although electronic switching here to provide store/recall facilities is possible, they were left in this particular instance as mechanical, since no real-time reset of them was deemed likely.

Effect feeds, though, are quite often switched during mixes; consequently, analog transmission gates are used, facilitating automation. Local activation is achieved through the debounce/latch arrangement used extensively in the channel mode switching (Figs. 22-88 and 22-91). The latch output drives a simple, single-element transmission gate. Isolation, crosstalk, and noise criteria are not particularly critical on these feeds, but they still come out quite creditably. The console switch-on *master reset bus (MRB)* cancels all these feeds leaving a clean slate rather than the alternative unpredictable hordes of ons, offs, and maybes in the event of a power interruption or control zeroing.

22.13.12 Summing Modules

Much of the actual mixing within the system described so far is self-contained. Multitrack routing, when achieved via a matrix, allows multiple sourcing to any chosen group or machine track. A stereo mixdown of all the channels is possible with this method by selecting them to an arbitrary pair of tracks across which the mastering machine is hung. This is, in fact, the mixdown technique used in many console systems whether in-line or discrete monitoring; although entirely feasible, it is not the manner in which this particular system is intended to be used.

Stereo mixdown is achieved in the same buses as the multitrack monitor mix, the solo monitor function making its home here, too.

A master group module contains the mix-amps, fader, and line amps pertaining to the stereo bus together with sundry other related things, like mono summing (required for a monitor feed) and clean auxiliary bus access for extending the monitor mix (for effect returns or temporary extra channels).

22.13.13 Mixes to Outputs

The virtual-earth mixing buses of the console all end up in identical mix-amp, attenuator, line amp configurations. Exceptions are the mono sources (effect sends)

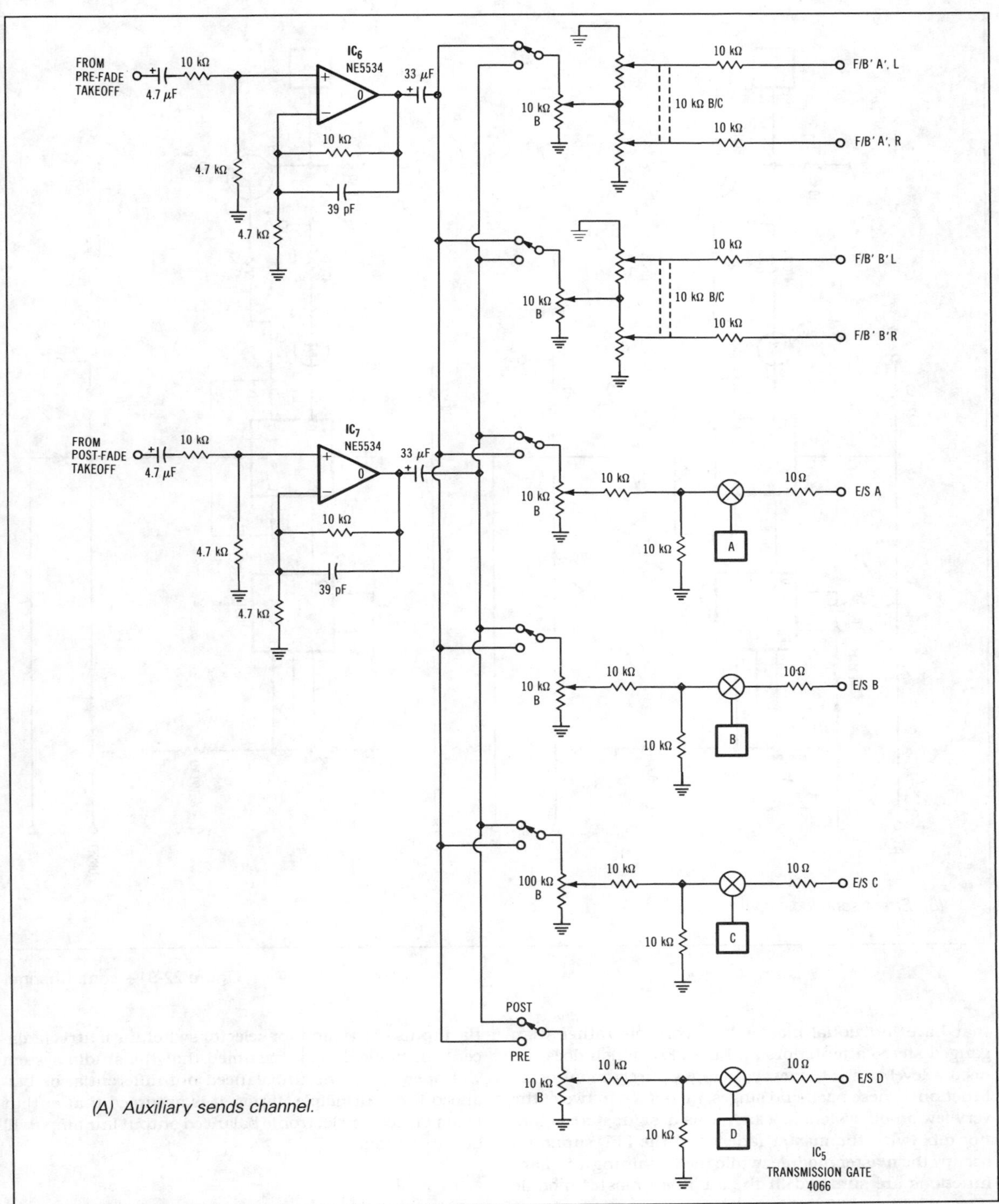

Figure 22-91 Channel auxiliary sends and logic control.

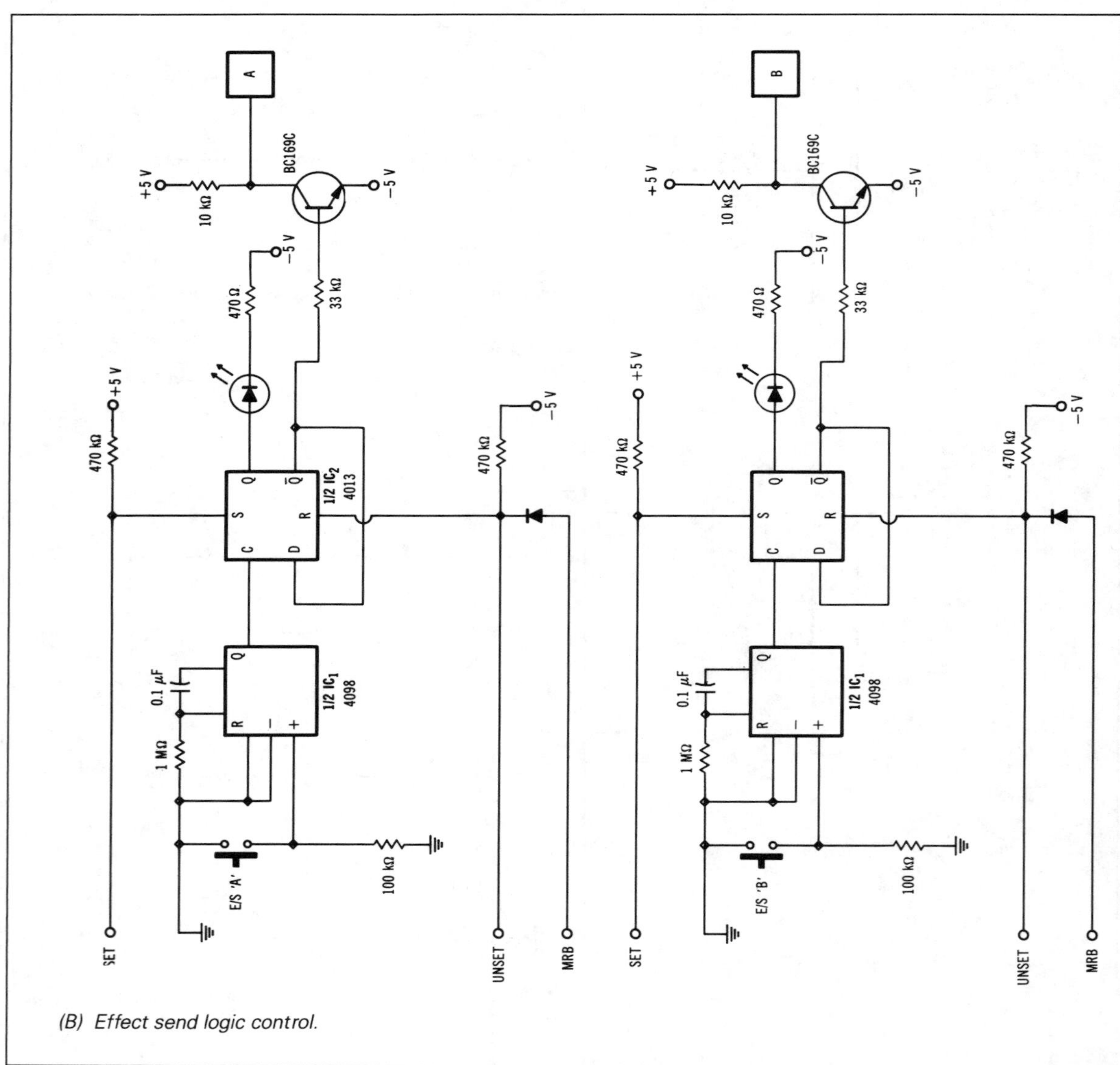

(B) Effect send logic control.

Figure 22-91—cont. Channel

that have individual master level controls rather than ganged stereo attenuators and the PFL (which does not need a level control anyway, being a purely monitoring function). These back-end stages are homed in two of the very few on-off system blocks in this design: stereo monitor/mix (with the master fader) and the PFL summing occupy the master module, while the remaining auxiliary functions are summed in the auxiliary master module (Figs. 22-73 and 22-74).

The outputs, each low impedance unbalanced, are taken to the jackfield, where they are normalized to their appropriate destinations and directly bridged by the differential inputs of the monitor selector switching matrix (adjacent to the field). It is assumed that the studio system will operate on the unbalanced out/differential or balanced input principle. If not, it is assumed that output transformers or electronic balanced output line amps will be substituted.

22.13.14 Master Functions

Fig. 22-92 shows the devastatingly simple console master function circuitry. All the clever switching is done in

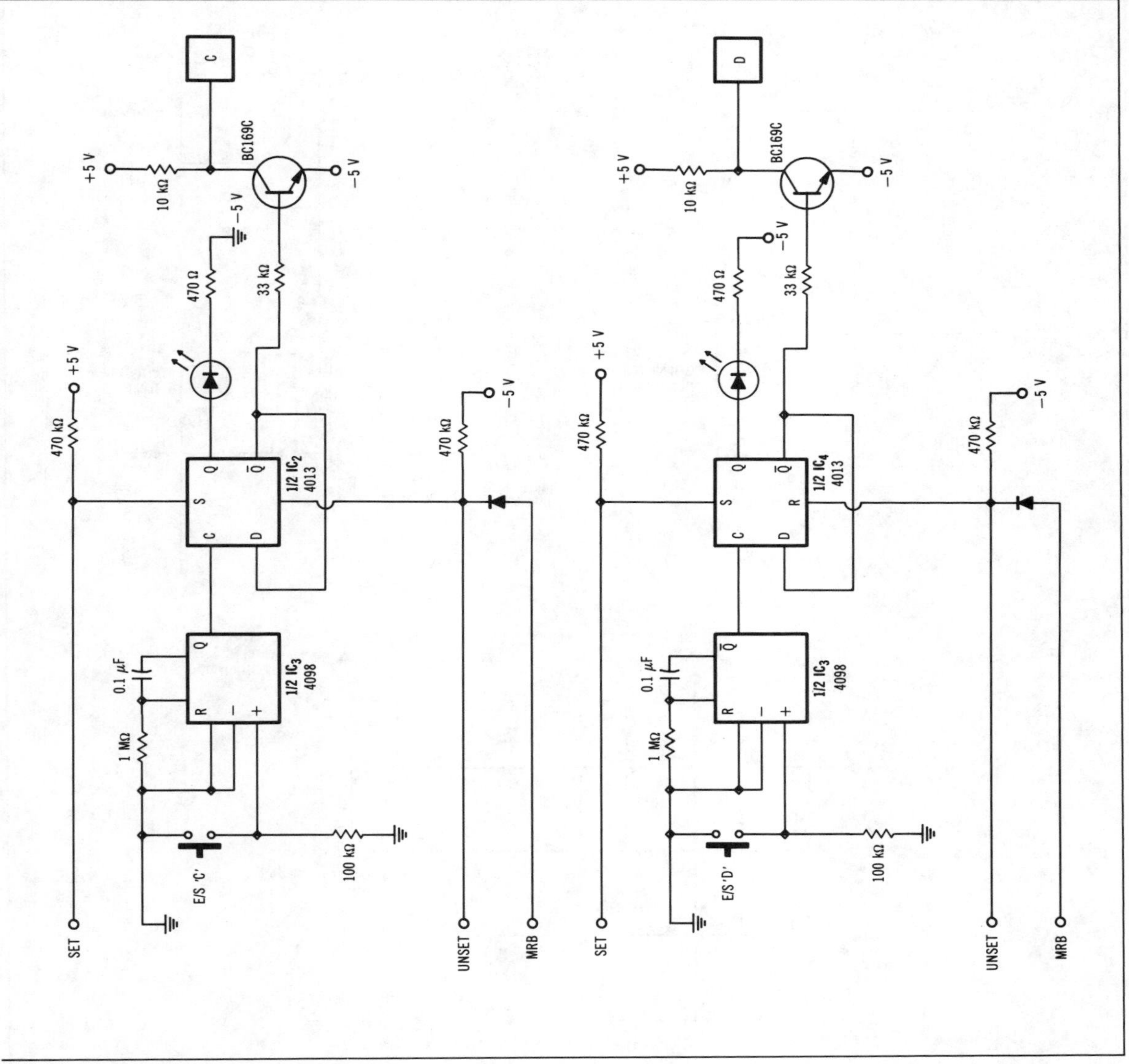

auxiliary sends and logic control.

the channels, allowing this unit to be little more than switch contacts. No debouncing is necessary since the master buses directly actuate the set and reset latch functions of the channel function registers.

Lockouts are arranged on the fader main/reverse selection and master monitor A and B switching to prevent both of the relevant control buses from being switched at the same time: this could otherwise lead to some very odd things happening inside the channel signal routing. Similarly, a ground follow-through lockout arrangement is used on the master function mode selection. Otherwise, the consequences of more than one button being pushed simultaneously would be to select a virtually random mode.

Note that all the switching is to ground from the logic −5-V supply. This interfaces with the majority of the channel logic as described. An important feature is the master reset bus and its control. Ordinarily, an array of random logic circuitry dependent on flip-flops and latches (of which this design is an example) would, on power up, tend to settle into whatever state these registers felt like at the time. The result would depend on device symmetry, temperature, and humidity, but worse still, the results not usually repeatable. An intriguing exception to this is

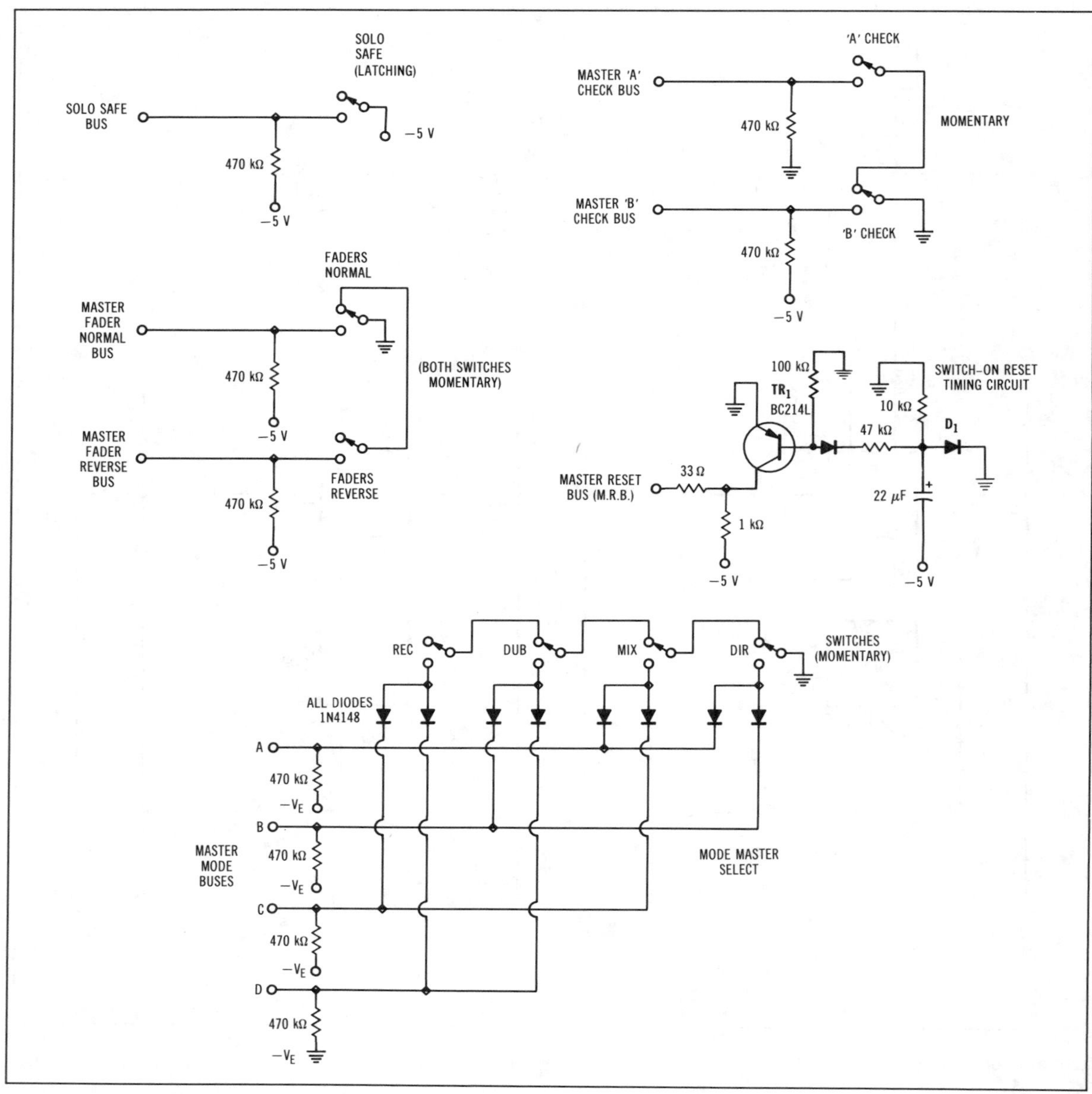

Figure 22-92 Desk master function control circuitry.

the knack of CMOS flip-flops to come back up in their previous state after a short power disablement, probably a function of small charge storage.

22.13.15 Power on Reset

Wisdom and common sense dictate that on power-up the console should come on neutral, with all channels muted and with monitoring functions such as PFL and solo disabled. As well as providing a frame of reference from which to start reusing the console, it saves all the aggravation of finding the one function that's killing the montoring. Console mode and basic monitoring conditions can be set up just by pushing the relevant master controls.

TR_1 grounds the master reset bus (MRB) for as long as the 22-μF capacitor takes to charge up—around a quarter of a second. This charging takes place when the −5-V logic supply appears. Should the supply collapse, the capacitor is rapidly discharged via D_1 ready to reinitialize the MRB signal as soon as power is reestablished.

Although it would be extremely simple to do, no top-panel master reset control is made available because sooner or later someone would hit that button at exactly the wrong moment.

22.13.16 Meters and Headroom

There are plenty of proprietary meters of the popular standards and types, plus quite a few strange ones, too. It's all a matter of personal preference and the information we hope to glean from the assorted needles, lights, and cathode rays dancing before our eyes.

Without jumping into the argument of average versus peak-reading instruments, it is relevant to state that the choice will directly affect the operational levels, the level architecture, the machine line-ups, and the various tweaks, notably the input stage limiter threshold. Out of habit, this console was designed with standard PPMs in mind, where the peak operational level throughout the system is expected to be PPM 6, or +8 dBu. Line-up level (i.e., the system and output level for which the front-end gain stage is calibrated), is 0 dBu, PPM 4. This will suit any current or expected PPMs.

Users of PPMs and VUs tend to fall into the respective category types of "We'll only peak up to the 3% tape distortion point" and "Let's wind it up until just before it comes back sounding bent." VUs are very good for giving an idea of subjective loudness and not worrying you about transients that can often be anything up to 20 dB above the indicated value.

22.13.17 System Level Architecture

Given standard +4 dBm referred vu meters, under normal operational circumstances, headroom in any console is perilously skinny. Various ways of dealing with potentially inadequate headroom are in use (Fig. 22-93). A favorite is to run the entire console system at a depressed level, usually −4 dB, the necessary 4-dB make-up at the end being done passively by an output transformer ratio step up. This is a poor choice for two reasons. The transformer step-up arrangement is overly critical to termination impedance, and the frequency response could suffer with a heavily reactive load such as a long line.

Headroom is mostly a problem in input channels, before the channel gain-controlling element, the fader. Both ragged unpredictable input sources and equalizer gain gobble up the nonmargin. Hopefully, beyond that point the levels and, hence, the mix are easily and well regulated by the faders. Dropping the channel operating level by 6 or 10 dB helps matters tremendously, and the gain is made up either in the mix-amps or the postfader buffer amps (the latter being normal). This does compromise bus noise (quiescent console output noise), but since the main justification for doing it is the high level of signals present, its pulses outweigh its problems. This depressed channel system is worthwhile in any circumstance, regardless of metering type, where there is likely to be a great unknown lurking on the end of an input line.

Some of the disadvantages are that all the channel insert points operate at the depressed (10 dBu) level, which may or may not give problems in some less than versatile outboard devices. The more immediate concern is that other internal channel circuits will need adjusting.

Machine line-in feeds from the A′ and B′ input differential amplifiers will need to be dropped by 10 dB. This drop is easily accomplished by altering the values of the resistors around electronic switches to scale down a factor of 3.16 (10 dB), as shown by Fig. 22-94A. The PFL bus mix-amp gains are required to increase 10 dB (the extra bus noise here is no great crime), and an extra 10 dB of gain is put into the prefader auxiliary feed buffer amplifiers. Reestablishing main path gain to unity is simply achieved by upping the gain of the post fader buffer amplifier in Fig. 22-94B and by changing the feedback bottom leg resistors in Fig. 22-85 from 1.8 kΩ to 430 Ω. This provides for 10 dB of fader back off and the necessary 10 dB reinstatement.

If all that sounds complicated, just bear in mind that it's all achieved with resistor changes.

It doeesn't matter that the machine monitor differential input amplifiers are still operating at a normal undepressed level. The A′ check is directly monitoring a console output, which is at normal level anyway, so there is no headroom problem. As for the B′ check, if we have more level coming back from the machine than we're putting in (A′ check), then it's time for realignment.

It is entirely possible to recalculate the values around the differential amplifier to drop 10 dB and still maintain input balance, but that would greatly increase the number of component changes necessary to alter channel system level. This is no mean consideration should you choose to do so on a console full of 32 or 48 channels.

22.14 CONSOLES AND COMPUTERS

Recording consoles especially and broadcasting consoles to a less marked extent have been growing in size and complexity far faster than human ability to operate them. People usually have two arms, ten fingers, and two eyes with a concentrated 10° viewing angle and an overall nervous reaction time of 0.1 second. Expecting this humble piece of bioengineering to deal effectively with over 2000 controls, indicators, meters and switches, often spread over an area 6 × 3 ft is downright cruel. Add to this the constraints of operating in tight coordination of musical time keeping and cues, and the problems for the human multiply.

A recording console features many identical discrete audio channels—both physically and technically—usually around 30 and often up to 60. Each displays dozens of controls. Many of these controls are strictly local in

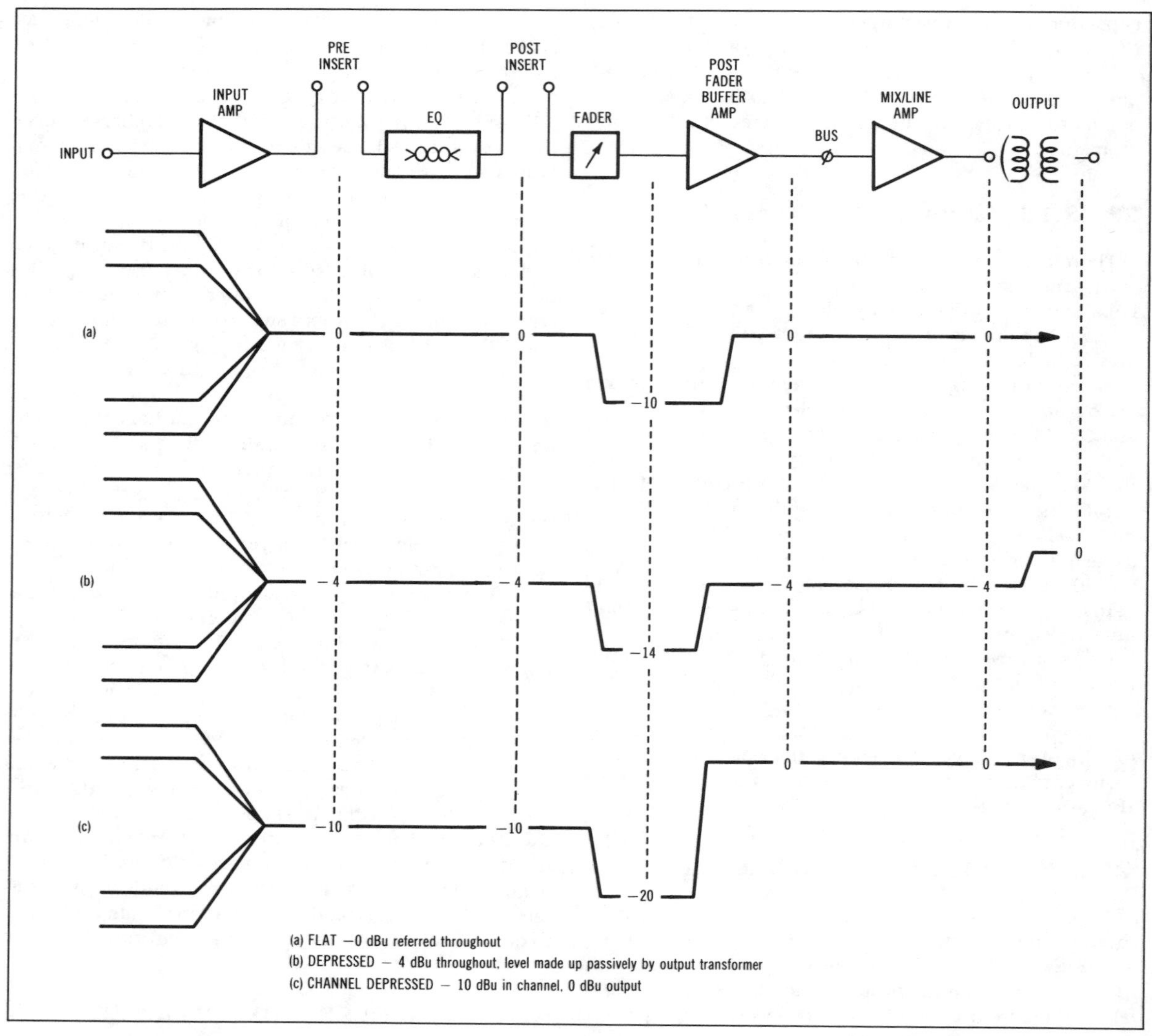

Figure 22-93 System level architectures.

nature, and little mileage would be made from remoting or storing their operation. This is not true of some of the more commonly used controls where allowing a machine to take over the more humdrum mechanistic routines can free the creative human to lend energy more usefully to a mix. Much effort is made during the early stages of a mixdown to sort out the odds and ends that got away during the initial recording process. This is quite a tedious process necessitating lots of irritating tweaks and even total removal—muting—of things that would rather not be heard at all!

With 24, or quite often 46, recording tape tracks, it is necessary to mute out those tracks not immediately contributing musically, simply because the additive quiescent background noise from them can get simply horrible. All these tidying-up routines, which do not really fall into the category of artistic, are ideal applications for computerized help.

In practice, it's quite difficult to know where to draw the line for computerized intervention in consoles. Some operations scream for it, while others would gain nothing operationally. Present thinking is toward not drawing one at all.

It's not entirely obvious which came first in the application of digital storage techniques to analog audio consoles: the need to provide the storage or the technology capable of doing it! Whichever, it now seems (from a possibly jaundiced viewpoint) that things are happening to consoles simply because it is now not just technically feasible but increasingly simple.

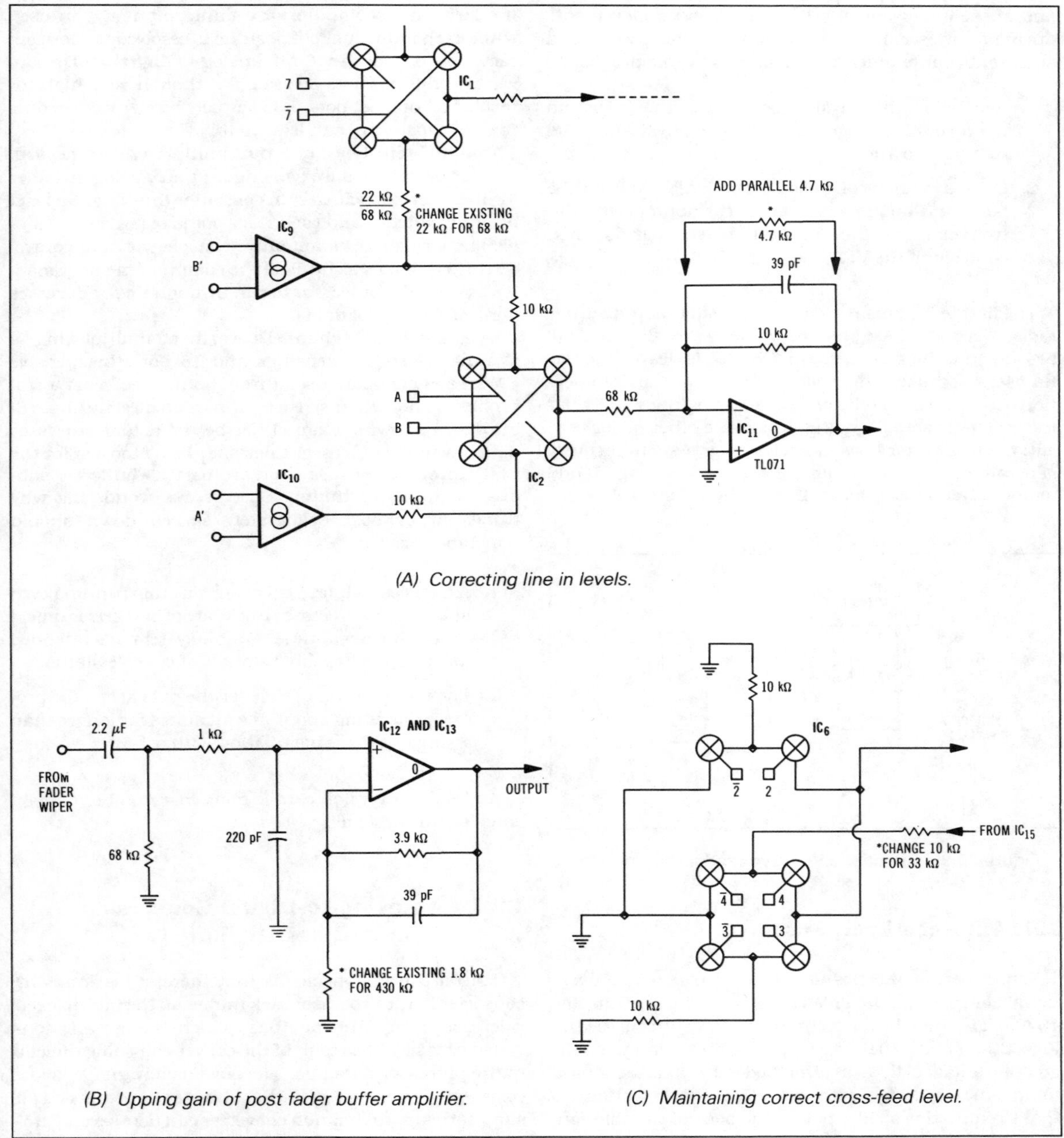

(A) Correcting line in levels.

(B) Upping gain of post fader buffer amplifier.

(C) Maintaining correct cross-feed level.

Figure 22-94 Component changes to operate channel at a depressed (−10 dBu) level. (Refer to Fig. 22-85.)

22.14.1 Fader Automation

The first victims of automation were the faders: once heavy multitrack (16/24 track) had become common, a severely limiting factor of human physiology—only ten fingers—proved something of an obstacle in a mixdown situation demanding considerably in excess of that number. The hitherto classic solution—reduction mixes of subgroups of tracks to a more manageable quantity—forced another tape generation. To be able to remember, and subsequently modify if need be, fader movements during a mix seemed like a good idea. There were, and still are, two fundamental approaches to this problem:

1. Remember the physical position of the fader and upon recall arrange for it to move physically to its required position.
2. Drive a voltage-controlled amplifier (VCA) from the fader and upon recall reapply the appropriate control voltage to the VCA—the fader itself not then controlling the VCA. (see Fig. 22-95.)

The first technique is used by one major manufacturer today (Neve's NECAM system), while nearly all others fall broadly into the second camp. NECAM is dearly loved by its users because it does give an unequivocable indication at all times—by the actual fader positions—of what the system is actually doing. It has one other major benefit: the involuntary hysterical laughter it spontaneously generates from anyone for the first time seeing 30-odd motor-driven faders dancing about on their own.

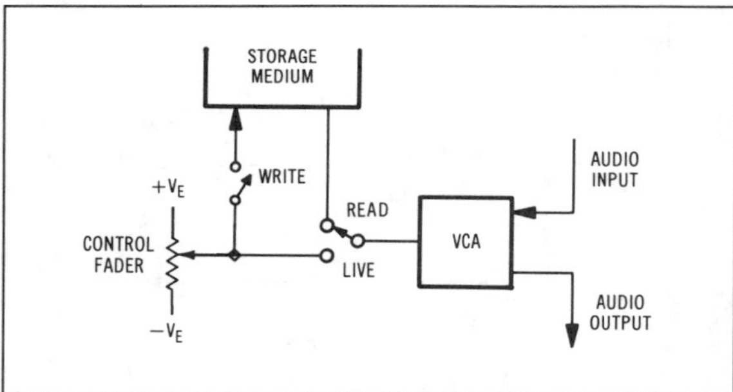

Figure 22-95 Simplistic VCA-type fader automation.

22.14.2 Recall and Reset

Remembering the position of controls in a conventional console was the great innovative burst of the late 1970s. The niceties of techniques vary, of course, but Figs. 22-96 to 22-101 are reasonably representative. The great advantage of this sort of method is that it can be applied to an existing design with virtually no modification; all that's required is a rider pot on the back of variable controls (although this can be a bit difficult with dual-concentric pots) and an extra pair of contacts on switches.

22.14.3 Data Acquisition

The digital data-capture system is fairly straightforward. Switch closures are sensed in batches of 8 (or 16 if a large microcomputer or a minicomputer is in use), while each individual pot position is resolved to the accuracy afforded by an 8-bit analog-to-digital (A/D) converter—256 possible positions. Although very high for resolution of most pots, it is actually harder work reducing the capability than leaving it be!

Two different types of input multiplexers are needed, one for switch closure sensing and an analog switcher for the rider-pot voltages. In computer thinking, each set of eight switches and each rider-pot is regarded as a single memory address; an entire console worth of control settings occupies a chunk of the computer memory map. It's easy for the processor to run through these addresses and collect a set of data.

In Fig. 22-96 a channel's worth of multiplexing is shown—32 switch sensings and 16 pots. Inexpensive CMOS switchers are used throughout; speed isn't a real problem. The switch-sense multiplexers directly hit an 8-bit data bus, which can either be the actual processor data bus (if the processor clock speed isn't too fast for the CMOS propagation delays) or, ordinarily, a buffered "sub-bus" with slower timing. Speedfreaks wondering why things are almost deliberately slowed down should remember two things:

1. A data acquisition system such as this running even at a leisurely processor clock rate of 500 kHz is quick! This is *not* a real-time variable system, it's intended mostly for "snapshot" storage of console status.
2. The A/D conversion time for the pots keeps the processor hanging about in wait states far longer than a single address acquisition with a 1-MHz clock.

And A/D conversion can be done in a number of fashions for this system.

22.14.4 Analog-to-Digital Conversion: Central or Distributed?

Central conversion means that there is just one A/D converter in the processor rack frame. All the multiplexed rider-pot voltages hit one bus, which is then A/D converted centrally, the result of the conversion going directly to the processor data bus. The obvious advantage is low cost—only one converter. Disadvantages are speed (a successive-approximation converter can take several processor clock cycles to perform a conversion; this can be gotten around by using a very high-speed comparator-type flash converter) and bus slewing (caused by bus capacitance, mostly). Since each rider-pot source is not zero impedance unless it's at one end of its track or the other and CMOS analog transmission gates have a finite on impedance, there is a definite time constant involved with the bus capacitance needing a certain amount of time to charge to the correct potential (as determined by the rider pot). The previous bus potential can, of course, be anywhere dependent on the previously selected position of the pot. Even if this time-constant can be made short with respect to an acquisition cycle, it even then really does make a nonsense of 256-level, 8-bit resolution!

Buffering each rider pot to present a known zero impedance to the multiplexer is a partial solution; buffering the multiplexer output—a seemingly obvious solution—creates more problems. First, the buffer output needs to be gated away from the bus for the times it's not addressed, so there is a transmission gate impedance there regardless. Second, it has to be a very fast follower if it isn't to create worse slewing than the bus! Remember that the multiplexers are switching at processor or subbus speed. Suitable amplifiers tend to be as expensive as they are fast.

Distributed A/D essentially means having a converter on each sub-assembly (channel). The main idea is that it allows the processor to work unhampered by conversion-related hangups while also keeping all system interconnections digital. Similarly, this system avoids gross bus-slewing (there would no longer be an analog bus). This, however, creates problems:

1. Although 8-bit successive approximation A/D chips are now cheap, the number has grown.
2. There are more bits on the channel subassembly.
3. The multiplexers feeding the on-board converter are still switching at processor-defined speed—slewing inaccuracies are still possible. Clever priming algorithms can increase conversion accuracies while maintaining a high overall acquisition rate, almost as high as for switch-closure bytes. These set in motion a conversion on one channel allowing plenty of time for switcher settling and so on before the result is looked for on the bus. During the idle period the computer is dealing with other setups and results from other channels.

Both central and distributed systems are successfully used in circumstances where the ultimate speed isn't that important. Accurate enough resolution is reasonably easily achieved.

22.14.5 Display

Figs. 22-98 to 22-100 describe how all the relevant console control positions can be digitized into processor-manageable form. Storage on a mass medium such as floppy or hard disk is a fairly simple computer file-management exercise, as is recalling it. What to do with the recalled information is now the question.

It is assumed that this particular requirement is informational recall only, not hardware reset (i.e., setting up the parameters of the channel to their stored values). Eyeball comparison and human tweaking is the resetting mechanism employed. The comparison is between a recalled value displayed on a meter, LED column, bar display, null indicator, or video display unit (VDU) and the immediate real value read from the control in question and displayed on an adjacent like display. As the relevant control is tweaked, its indicated value will be higher or lower than the stored value; when the two are matched, then the control position is the same as it was when the snapshot was taken. Fig. 22-99 shows in simplistic form the basis of the matching process, while Fig. 22-100 is a photograph of a VDU matching display for a set of channel controls on the Solid-State Logic, Total Recall system. VDUs are presently the easiest way of performing this matching—so much information is visible at once, which is a blessing in this circumstance.

22.14.6 Nulling

Null indicators are particularly easy to use. They usually take the form of a pair of LEDs adjacent to the relevant control. If the real value is higher than the recalled value, the upper LED lights; if it is less, the lower one lights. If they both come on, the two values are matched. Even simpler nulling indicators take the form of a single LED that only comes on (or alternatively goes out) when the two values match. A nicer arrangement is a single-cell green/red LED giving an unequivocable "go" or "no go" indication. This device makes it particularly easy to spot anything out of order on a channel.

A fairly elaborate demultiplexing system has to be plumbed onto the channel board, however, to deliver the software-derived nulling indications to the front-panel LEDs; Fig. 22-101 is representative. A further amount of processor memory area needs to be dedicated for this output facility in addition to that already spoken for by the input multiplexing.

Another software consideration when using null indicators is that the chance of actually finding the 1-in-256 position that is correct is pretty slim. Reducing the effective resolutional accuracy to 5 bits (32 levels) makes the operation a lot simpler. Even 6 bits gets a bit touchy.

As laborious as these facilities may operationally be, a complete reset of console parameters can be achieved. It is considerably less laborious and inaccurate than writing everything down, though.

Interestingly enough, any bus-slew inaccuracies engendered on storage tend to be canceled during recall. When all the controls on a channel are reset at or close to their original settings, all the bus errors will be very similar to those present when stored.

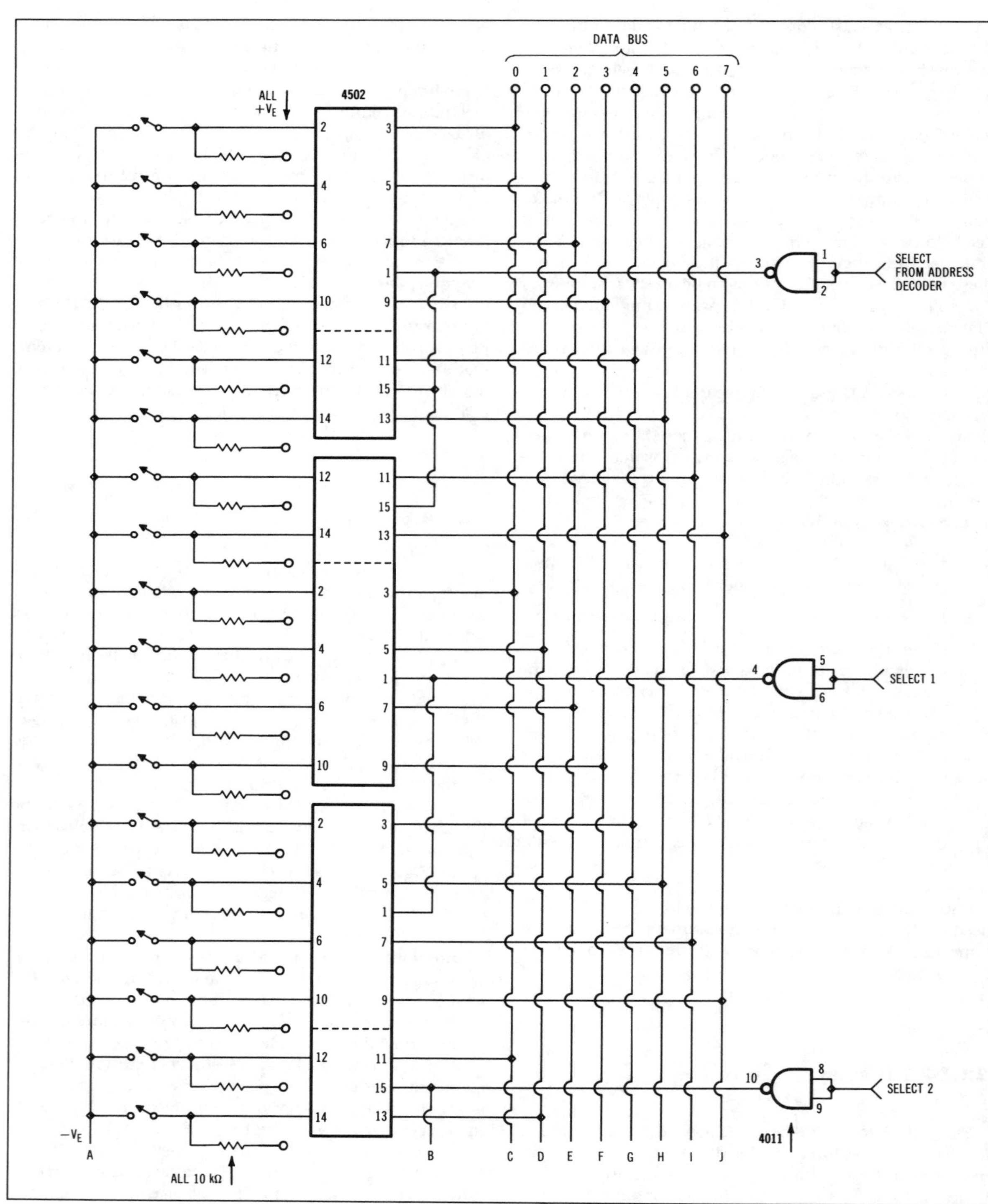

Figure 22-96 Rider

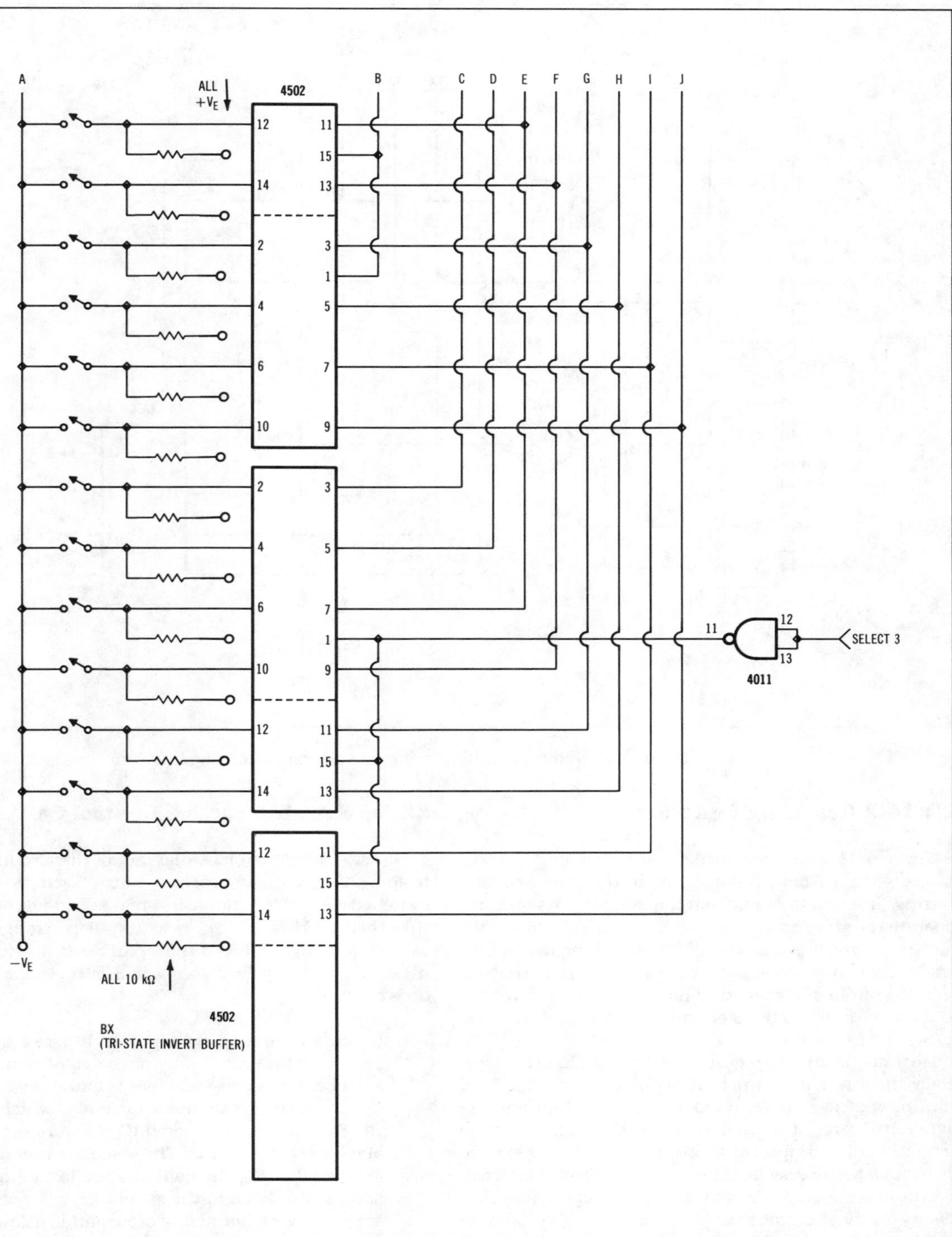

switch multiplexing.

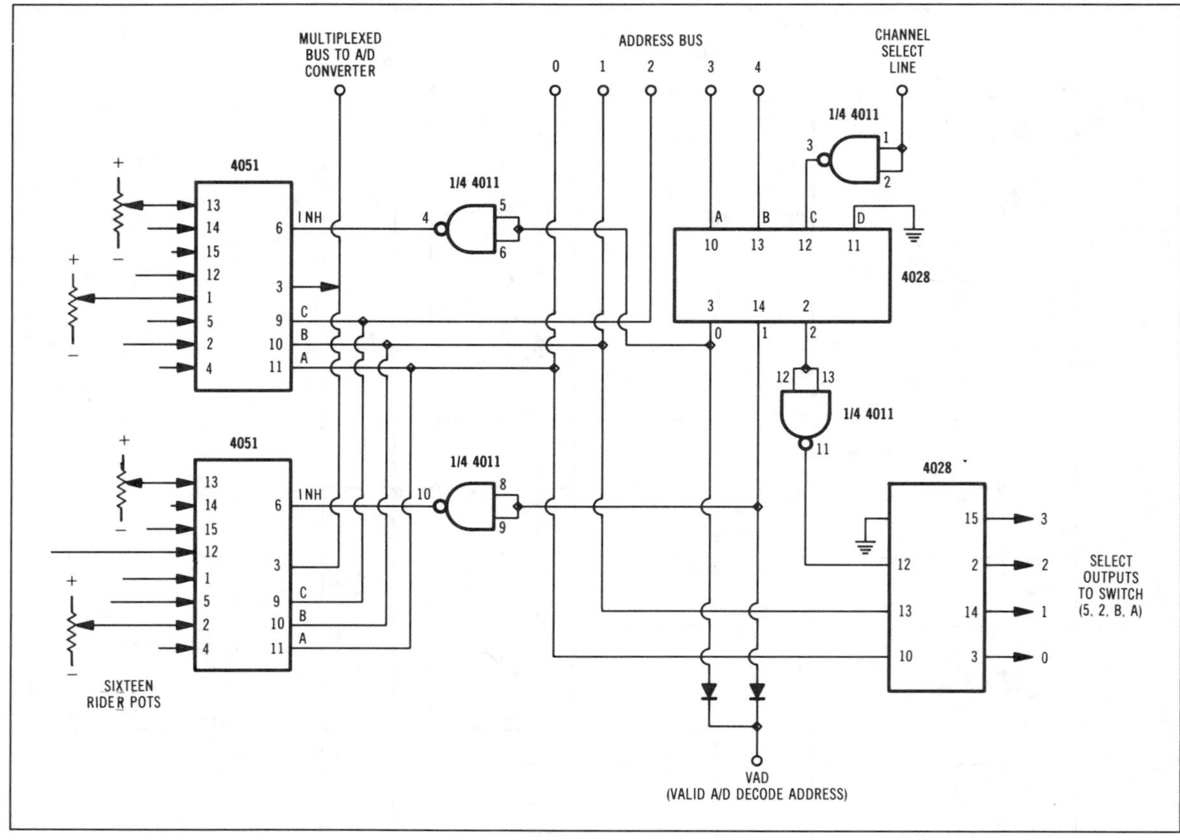

Figure 22-97 Rider pot mulitplexing and address decoding.

22.14.7 Resetting Functions

The next logical step in developing computer assistance is for the machine not only to remember console settings but also to reestablish the console to its previous operational state upon command. This means that if the multitrack routing on channel 27 were going to machine track 15 when the console status was stored, then regardless of what has happened or how the routing may have altered or configurations changed, upon recall channel 27 will go to track 15.

Most of the circuitry described in this chapter, especially the internal channel routing system, muting, and routing matrices, is from a generation of design where active resetting of all major switched functions was a requirement. Variable controls were not even considered as candidates for resettability since it demanded too great a shift in technology. As we will see, the techniques necessary for that become instrumental in a deeper, broader change of console design, structure, operation, and philosophy.

22.14.8 An Interactive Control Cell

Fig. 22-102 is the block diagram of the circuit shown in Fig. 22-103, an interactive control section for eight switched control functions. Its great advantage over multiple "belt and braces," set/reset, flip-flop arrangements, as shown in Fig. 22-88, is the significantly less pc board it takes up. It is quite a complex circuit element, but it does a lot too:

1. IC_1 is a commutating input multiplexer that senses, one at a time, if any of the eight nonlatching switches are depressed. If one is found, a write pulse is generated by the monostable IC_2, which causes the 8-bit addressable latch IC_3 to store the inverse of its present contents. The inversion is done by the D-type latch IC_4. Its contents are loaded from the addressable latch at the same time as a switch closure is sensed; because of propagation delays, it has time to settle before the write pulse arrives. Anyway, in effect the circuit is eight self-debounced flip-flops.

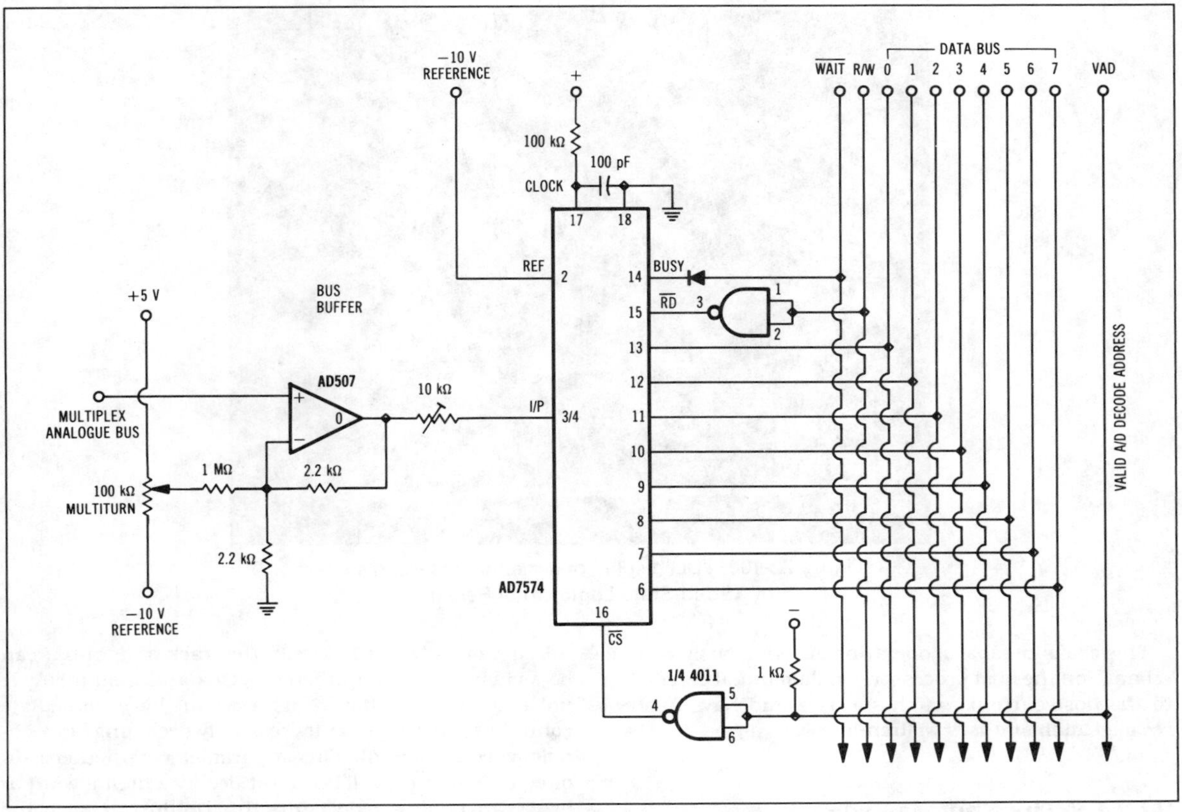

Figure 22-98 An analog-to-digital converter (as part of the system in Fig. 22-97).

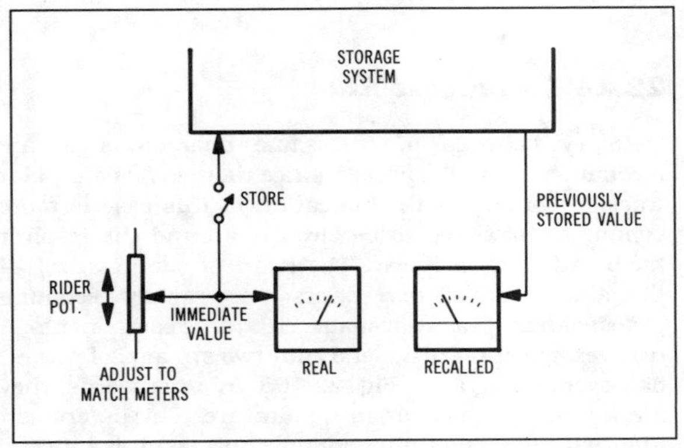

Figure 22-99 Simplistic manual reset system.

2. LEDs adjacent to (or inside) the switches indicate the status of each latch. (Incidentally, the commutation of the multiplexer and addressable latch is done by a 3-bit address line common to both, clocking from 0 to 7 [000 to 111] continuously at up to 1 MHz.) From these indicator points are also taken the control feeds to whatever the switches are controlling. Handily enough, these can be of either sense (up for active or low for active) simply by arranging the LED to be current sourced or sunk (i.e., tied to + or 0-V supply) from the latch output.

3. Data may be extracted by an external machine by its pulling down the read line; this causes the addressable latch active at that instant to have its output routed via the buffer and internal routing switcher IC_5 onto an external data bus. (If the host computer is an 8-bit machine, then eight of these switching cells may occupy the width of a byte and would require eight contiguous memory locations to store all the commutated switches; the bottom three address lines of the processor are arranged to drive the three-cell address lines while it is accessing.)

4. If the host processor pulls down the write line, then the data present on the external data bus gets transferred through into the active addressable latch; an internal write pulse is generated to facilitate this.

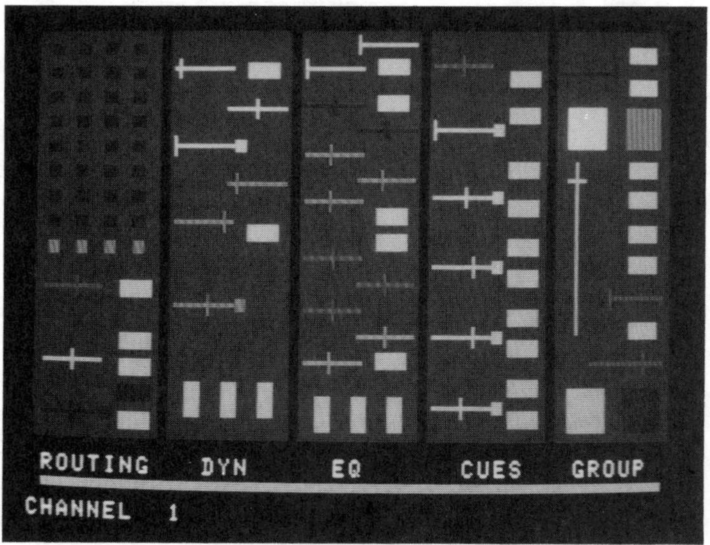

Figure 22-100 VDU display of a manual resetting system (Solid-State Logic; Total Recall).

This cell is capable of operating autonomously with no reliance on the host processor. On demand, it can deliver to the host current switch statuses and have fresh or recalled latch statuses written into it.

22.14.9 The Endless Fader

This virtually unheard of device (which is just crying for a more elegant name!) is crucial to the continuing development of audio consoles. With a conventional fader, the knob serves as both the manipulating control and indicator; an endless fader separates these two functions. Indication takes the form of a bar-graph-type display of a row of LEDs, LCD column, fluorescent bar, or other similar linear indicator about the same length of a present fader. The control of the up and down motion of this light-bar, which directly relates to the gain of a VCA, is achieved not by a knob but by a caterpillarlike track running parallel to it. Fig. 22-104 gives the general idea—an *endless* or *knobless* fader.

The divorce of control and indication is the key to new system philosophy and development.

Agility is what *endless faders* are about. In a simple automated fader setup, the VCA level can be seen directly all the time. Normally the indicated level will follow the track up and down. In replay the light-bar can move freely while any movement of the track performs any manual up-or-down tweaks necessary. The important thing is that the track doesn't have to be zeroed or made to match the VCA level before it can take effect; it always can take effect, since it has no physical reference, unlike the knob of an ordinary fader.

In a more advanced system, the track or light-bar can be switched between different VCAs and instantly give not only an indication of its level but have immediate control over it. VCAs are increasingly becoming old technology; soon all audio circuit parameters, whether gain or eq or whatever, will be quantified by a digital word or byte. Our endless fader suits this bill just as well; the light-bar can just as easily indicate a byte's value while the track can (more easily in fact) be arranged to increment or decrement that byte's value.

22.14.10 Endless Knobs

Rotary controls of the same characteristics are mechanically much simpler, since there is no caterpillar track to contend with. Indication in this case is more commonly arranged to be circular around the resolver knob rather than linear. The heart of such controls—digital shaft encoders/resolvers— are rapidly becoming pedestrian and easily available electronic components. A resolver, when rotated, sends out two streams of pulses, half overlapping as in Fig. 22-105; in other words, they are 90° out-of-phase or in quadrature. This is enough information to determine not only how fast it is rotating (by counting the number of pulses from one of the trains) but also in which direction. These two, rate and direction sense, are enough for a controlling processor to analyze and appropriately perform control.

The simple circuit of Fig. 22-106 sorts it out; it's a 4013 D-type latch. The data port is fed by one train, while the edge-triggered clock input is fed by the other. If the clock is triggered by the rising edge of the A train and the B

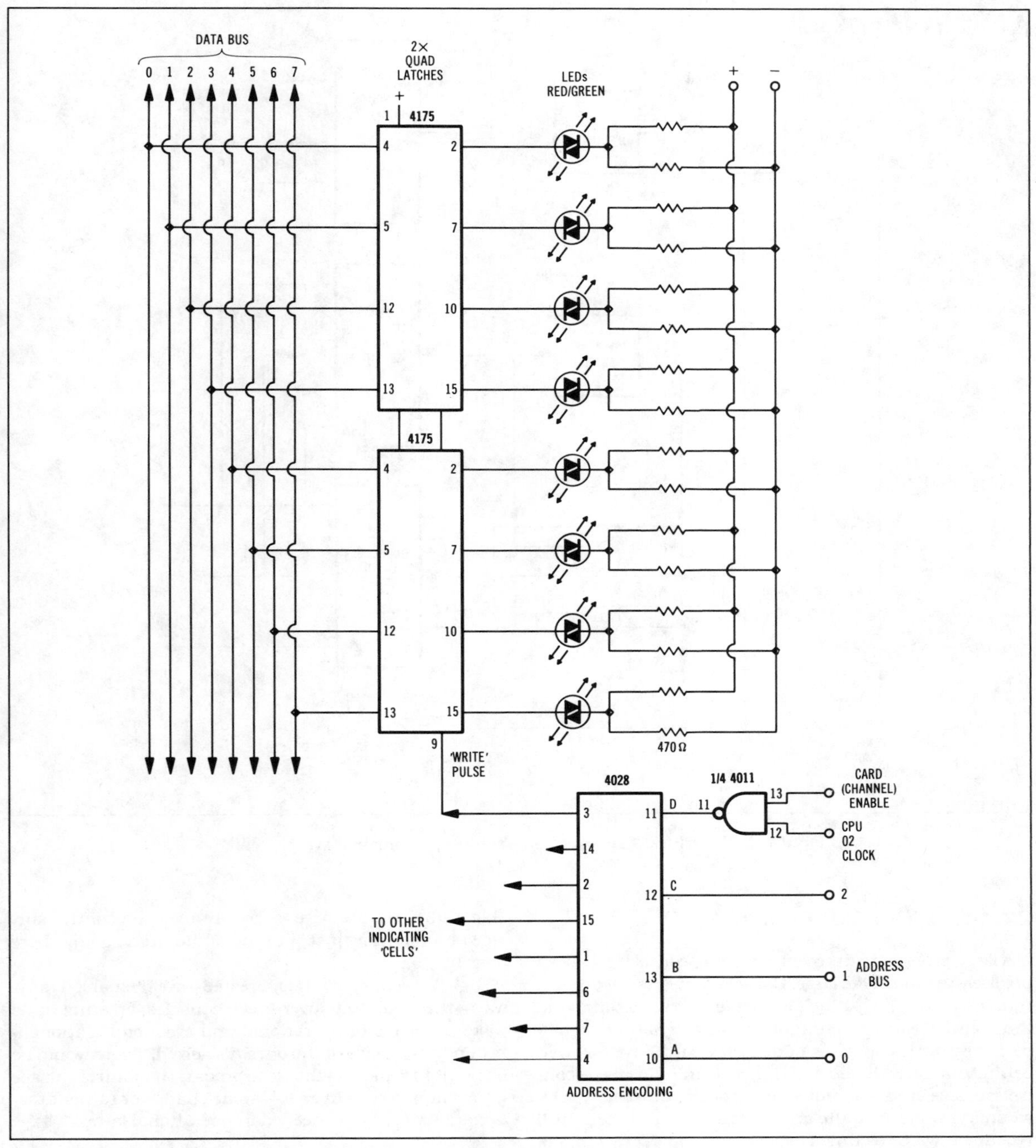

Figure 22-101 Nulling indicator decoding.

train is active, then the latch output goes high, indicating one direction of rotation (left to right in Fig. 22-105). In the other direction, the rising clock edge from A corresponds to B being inactive, so the latch output goes low.

It is rather a simplistic circuit that assumes that the making contacts of the resolver are perfect and no false triggering will occur. With more swanky optical resolvers this may be true, but with mechanical ones a little clean ing up prior to the D-latch gates may be advisable.

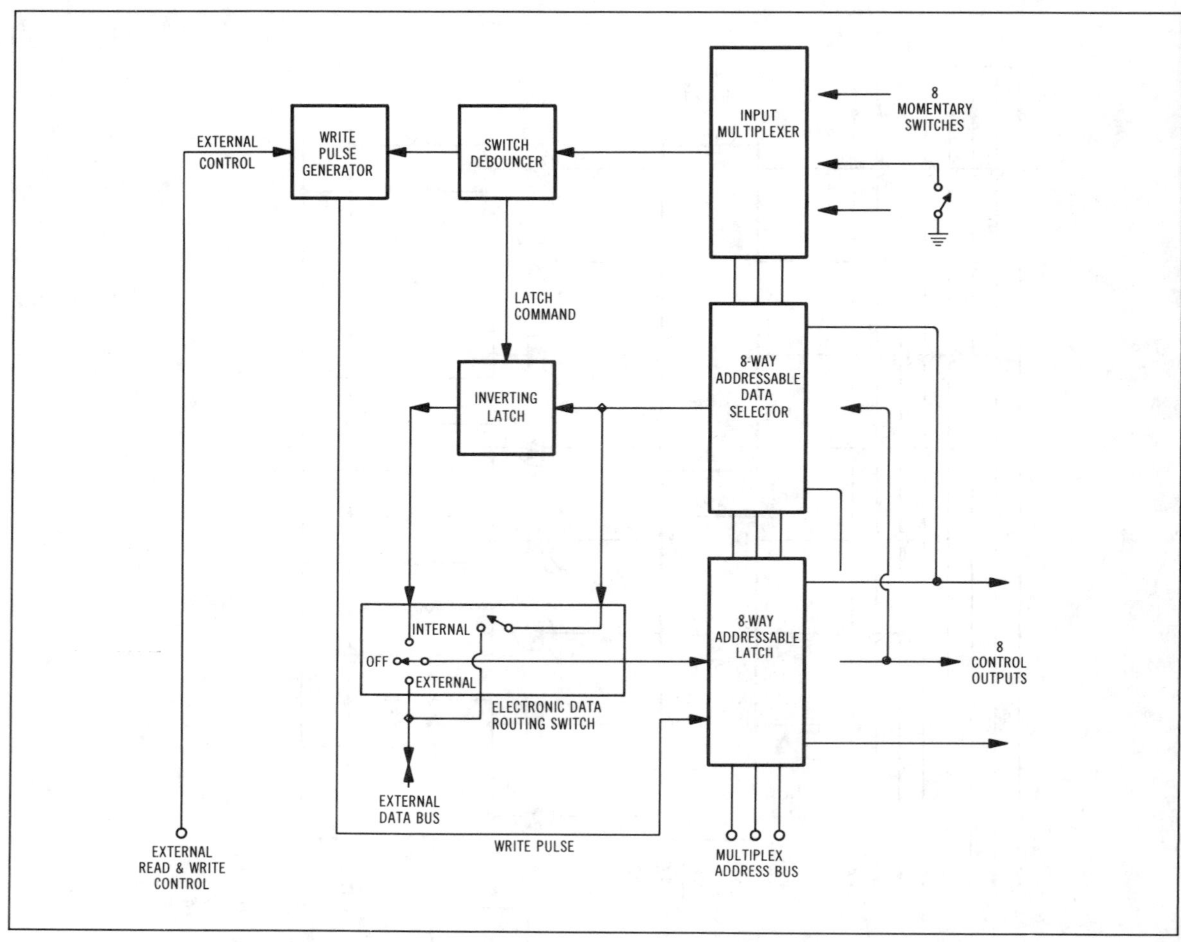

Figure 22-102 Block diagram of an eight-way interactive switch "cell."

22.14.11 The Soft Console

A large problem with recent recording consoles has been precisely that—they're large. Console channels have grown into long, thin strips for purely historical reasons, and the manufacturing technique of hanging all the signal-path electronics on acres of dense pc card have followed behind similarly. Removing the electronics from the control surface into a remotely controlled equipment rack where it belongs is quite an obvious step, although until recently it was a technically unwieldy one. Many types of electronic circuits lend themselves to direct remoting. For example, VCAs for level control need, in essence, a single dc control line. Others, such as equalizers and microphone preamplifiers don't. Noise and difficulties in extending nonzero-impedance configurations are both significant problems. As with everything else, these areas of difficulty look quite different given a dose of digits. With only minor compromises, digitally controlled remotable audio circuits of all sorts are real: the control surface becomes now just that, no audio need go anywhere near it.

Digital technology has created—well, enabled anyway—the solution to overgrown consoles, creating in its wake problems of operational and ergonomic rationalization in the place of the ones it's solved. There would be no point in remoting the electronics if the control surface were going to remain as is—some change or rather drastic rationalization is needed in operational layout.

22.14.12 Operational Redundancy

There is an immediately apparent redundancy with large consoles—rows and rows of identical channel modules. The first intuitive step would be to reduce all those to just one set of channel controls that is selectable or assignable to any channel that needs tweaking. The first modifica-

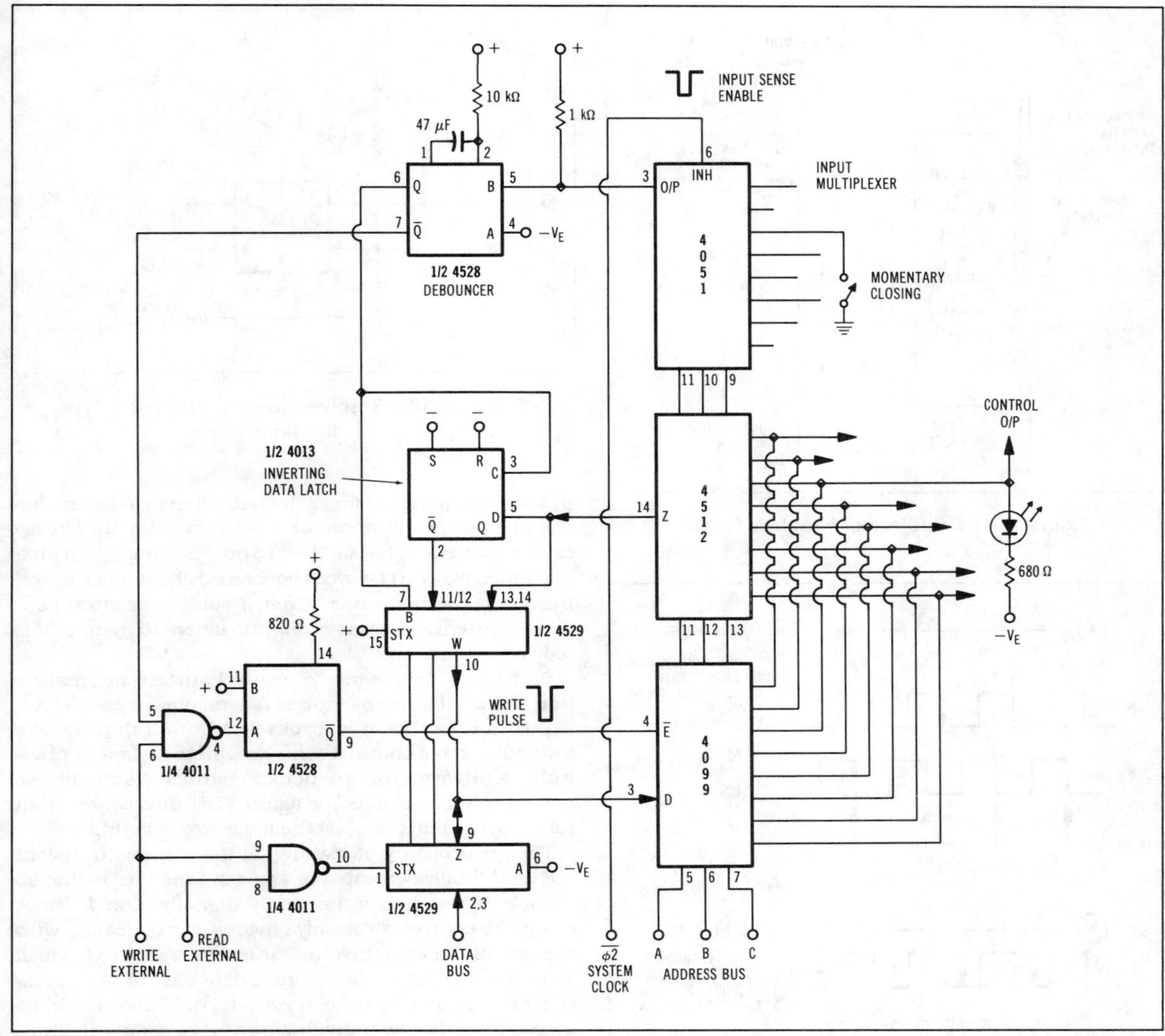

Figure 22-103 Circuit diagram of an eight-way interactive switch "cell."

tion to this rather simplistic rationalization is that the main level faders need to be kept continuously available in front of the operator; a button adjacent to each of the individual faders calls the set of assignable channel controls to the channel to which that fader is related.

The second modification concerns the assigned controls. Like the knobless fader, they have to be separately acting for indicating. Upon being called, the indicating part of the control adopts the settings pertinent to that channel; the control whether it be knob style or switch style can then act on the selected channel with the indicators folowing their action on the remote circuitry. A ready alternative to knobs, switches, and indication is an interactive VDU screen. This indeed is the route to control presently most favored, whether the control manipulation is by joystick, trackball, mouse, touch-sensitive screen, or digitizing tablet (again, the favorite).

A third modification to the initial rationalization concerns the many auxiliary mixes found in a console, whether they be for effect feeds, foldback, or, perhaps most importantly, multitrack monitoring. Although the controls for these are traditionally regarded as channel controls, intuitively they are thought of and operated on horizontally across the console; if someone's setting up a foldback mix they'd most likely be working along the row of controls for that mix bus (to which they'd also almost certainly be listening via monitoring) and have very little interest in any other channel controls at all. Making the

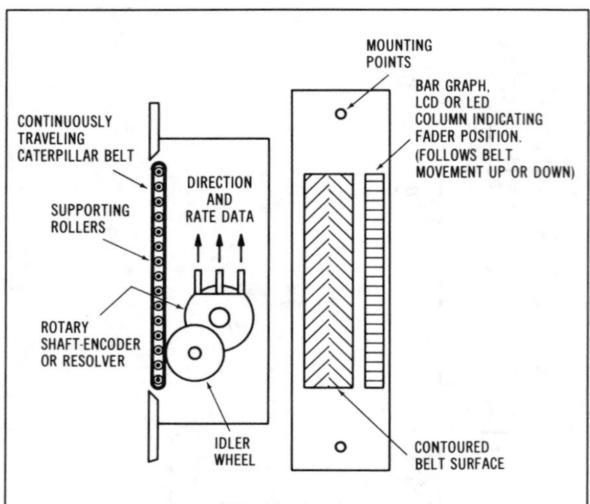

Figure 22-104 Endless or knobless fader.

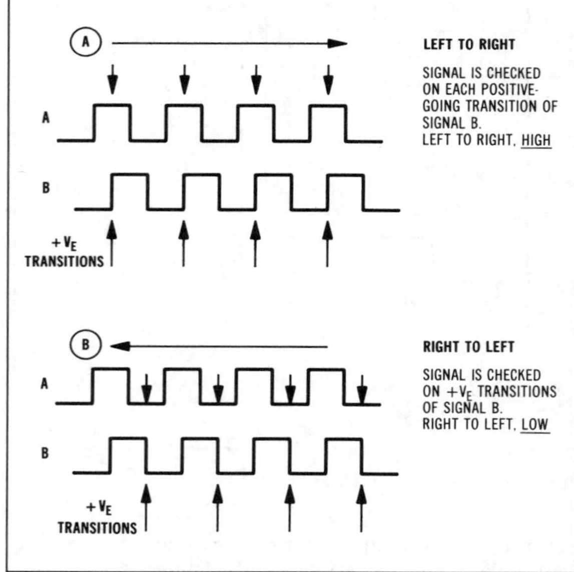

Figure 22-105 Quadrature streams from resolver indicating how speed and directions are sensed.

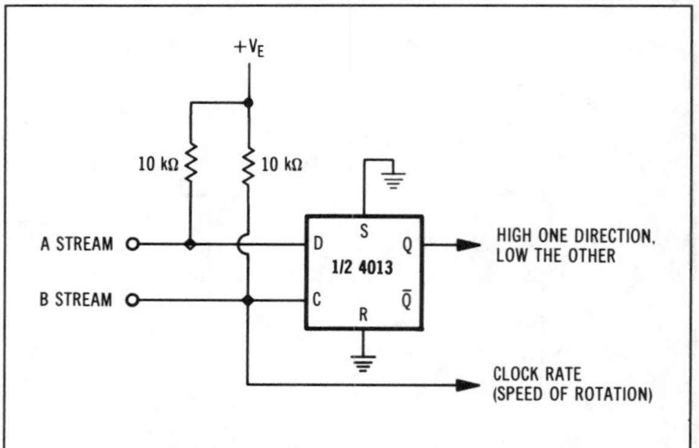

Figure 22-106 Resolver decoder (using a D-type flip-flop).

operator have to select each channel at a time to do such a routine mix setup would be a very retrograde move. Quite sensibly then, any same-function bus-orientated controls become accessible together. This is precisely the rationale behind the channel faders all being accessible simultaneously. A neat bit of further rationalization comes into play here: the console-wide set of controls implied in having parallel access to auxiliary buses (meaning that in addition to a fader for each channel there'd be an auxiliary bus control also) can be avoided by using the already existent faders. After all, if we're busy setting up an auxiliary mix, we won't be overly concerned about other mixes, including the main one. Even if something does need instant attention, reassigning the faders to main mix is only a button away.

So here is the essence of control surface rationalization. We want a row of endless faders, one for each channel, with an adjacent control select button that renders a singular set of channel controls (whether glass or physical) operative on that particular channel. We would also have a row of buttons (or again VDU interaction) that selects which mix-bus(es) the fader row is acting.

The great beauty of making all the controls transient (i.e., not totally dedicated to any one function) is that all console functions are implicitly digitally stored. Since computer control is the only obvious way of dealing with the amount of logic involved, it is only a relatively small step to construct a mass-storage data base of past, present, and future console control setups. These should be accessible either as individual setups or sequentially, at virtually any sequence rate and predictably locked against a time-code-type reference.

22.14.13 Goodbye Jackfields

Considering that one of the easiest audio subsystems to organize using computer technology is switching, it's astonishing jackfields still exist.

Analog switching matrices are now at such a level of development that they can be considered transparent to the system. They in no way, even when many are cascaded, create limiting parameters. They are dense (over a thousand crosspoints will fit in the same rack space as 144 jack holes) and decreasingly expensive, much less expensive per crosspoint than a comparable jack circuit.

Control is soft (i.e., computer driven) and the operation

can thus be anything from a humble computer terminal to hardware switching from a console. Of course, within assignable systems, the matrix is controlled by the VDU interactive control surface of the operator, all routings and parameters being storable, recallable, and resettable as are the rest of the parameters of the console. This can be accomplished in real time if desired. Try that with 50 patch cords!

Inputs and outputs of everything internal to the console (equalizers, dynamics sections, front-end amplifiers, line-output amplifiers, and so on) and everything external to the console (effects, machine input and outputs, and so on) all appear as sources or destinations on the matrix. The concept of insert point has disappeared; anything can go in anywhere. After decades of things getting more complex suddenly things have become simple again—there is no system, no prewired interconnections. A system to fit a given circumstance is built up from scratch using all the circuitry building blocks interconnected as required via the matrix. A repertoire of usual starting points—preassembled patches—is stored and recalled as needed.

22.14.14 Integrated Control of Outboard Gear

A great many bits and pieces of *outboard signal-processing gear* (known vernacularly as "toys") are involved in the successful production of present-day program material. Already the term *outboard* is flimsy since via the system matrix, their signal paths are already firmly internalized. The hitherto missing link—control of outboards—has found itself. Most serious rack-gear manufacturers now fit the remote-control interfaces of either IEEE 488 or RS232c persuasion. The centralized control point for these is the interactive main control surface for the operator.

At last the impossible console, completely automated and resettable in real time in conjunction with other systems such as video, has arrived.

22.14.15 Multiuser, Multifunction

"Multiuser" and "multifunction" are familiar terms in the computer world and only entering the confines of the audio industry as a counter to one of the more intelligent user objections to the above rationalized control surface concept. The argument runs something like, "But we might want to change several things at once, and Fred the producer likes to look after the monitor mix while I do the rest."

The control software would naturally allow simultaneous control actions on a pair or across a group of channels to be ganged, which is fairly trivial and not the point being addressed. The main engineer console can be regarded and would be regarded by the computer in the rack, as simply a terminal, albeit the main one. There is nothing to stop other terminals of greater but probably lesser or deliberately limited facilities having access to the main body of electronics. In practice they would have access to and be able to manipulate a preprogrammed subset of the total capability (e.g., our producer friend's monitor mix) concurrent to the main terminal or control surface. Another obvious secondary terminal would be a second or even third set of assignable channel controls for multi-op situations, although we can't help wondering how often they would be redundant. As a capability it would go a long way to soothing the frustration of engineers new to the concept who are wary of losing so many controls at once! Simultaneous access to the same set of information is what the term *multiusers* is all about.

In computer terms the system described bears more than a passing resemblance to a hardware-related database. Again, in computer terms, it's a pretty small one, too. As a practical side-step development in consoles, it has three great things going for it:

1. At last console size becomes manageable again; it is no longer necessary to knock down walls or saw mixers in half to get them in the room or up the elevator! Room design becomes more sensible, acoustic considerations are lessened, and there are no more worries about cloning engineers with 6-ft long arms.

2. The similarity of the digital control to presently well-established computer data-handling techniques makes the realization far less frightening than it could be. Original software techniques are required for the manipulation of the specialized hardware involved, but this is softened if the hardware is designed to fit easily into the grand software scheme of things; nothing exists in a technological vacuum. Interactive VDU control and graphics again are something that mainstream computer technology is well on top of and developing fast.

3. The signal-processing hardware can live in a rack where it belongs; the cards can be laid out most efficiently, not to suit vagaries of top-panel control layouts. Racks are designed for maximum density of electronics and ease of interconnection. If only the same could be said for traditional console frames! Pure hardware costs, despite the additional electronics for digital manipulation, could actually work out to be less expensive. Esthetic considerations only apply now to a much-shrunk control surface rather than a whole huge piece of furniture. The number of expensive and difficult to source controls, knob pots, and switches is also drastically reduced.

PART 5

Recording and Playback

CHAPTER **23**

Disk Recording and Playback

by George Alexandrovich

23.1 HISTORY OF SOUND RECORDING

In 1877 Thomas A. Edison invented a cylindrical phonograph that was capable of recording sounds by means of converting vibrations of air into an engraved groove in the aluminum foil that covered a rotating cylinder, Fig. 23-1. Although this device demonstrated the feasibility of recording and reproducing sound, it proved to be impractical for large-scale production and use. Future models of the phonograph used special wax as a recording surface and many cylinders can be found even today in private and government archives preserving historical recordings.

Figure 23-1 Thomas A. Edison with his original tinfoil phonograph, taken in Washington, DC, April 18, 1887, where he demonstrated the machine before the National Academy of Science. *(Courtesy Smithsonian Institution)*

The first talking motion pictures used film synchronized to wax cylinders. The cylinders, however, were difficult to duplicate and to store. Soon afterwards Emil Berliner, in 1887, invented "flat disk recording" working on the principle in use today. Although flat disk records could be easily mass produced, they were noisy, the sound was distorted and the frequency response was poor.

Until 1925 all recordings were made acoustically and were reproduced by mechanical pickups through the acoustical horns. The invention of the vacuum tube made it possible to convert sound into electrical impulses using a carbon microphone, which was invented by Berliner. Electrical signals, after being amplified, were fed into the cutterhead which was cutting the groove. Since that time the endless research began to improve recording materials, cutterheads, turntables, pickups and recording techniques.

The important milestones in the history of sound recording were the invention of the electrical pickup by Western Electric in 1918, the invention of the Rochelle crystal pickup in 1931 by Sawyer, the invention of multichannel modulation by Arthur Keller of Bell Labs in 1929 and later formulated by Blumlein in 1931. Then, the method of cutting stereo records was not taken seriously, and this last method was abandoned shortly after being invented. This method used a 45°/45° modulation of the record groove to record stereo programs with two independent channels and, though abandoned earlier, is still being used successfully today.

In 1921, Edison used a dc motor to drive his phonograph. In 1938, the rim-drive idler system was developed, and in 1948 the first long-playing record was introduced. The era of high fidelity began. Commercially available stereo records made their debut in 1957, and in 1960 FM stereo broadcasts started. In the 1970s, CD-4 discrete four-channel stereo and four-channel matrix technologies were made possible through the use of new transducer developments and improvements in recording techniques. However, they never became a marketing success.

The technology of sound recording using disk records made remarkable strides, advancing from shellac pressings to vinyl, from course-pitch mechnical modulation to microgroove stereophonic recordings with a dynamic range close to 80 dB and a frequency range from subsonic to supersonic frequencies. Today we are witnessing technological breakthroughs in using pulse-code modulation for storing audio and video information in digital form on disks and for producing superior recordings, impervious to wear and quality degradation due to a nondestructive method of playing back the information using a laser beam.

23.2 DISK-CUTTING HEADS AND RECORDING LATHES

This section discusses both monophonic- and stereophonic-type recording heads and their associated equipment and cutting techniques. Various types of cutting heads are discussed, as well as their calibration. Hot- and cold-stylus recording techniques are also discussed.

A cutting head is an electromechanical transducer that translates electrical waveforms into mechanical vibrations. These vibrations are applied to the cutting stylus, which in turn cuts and modulates a record groove on the surface of the nitrocellulose disk. Cutting heads may be designed to vibrate the stylus in a lateral or vertical direction or a combination of both for stereophonic recording.

The original method of recording sound was using sound waves to actuate a diaphragm to which a stylus was attached. The stylus pressing on the recording medium mechanically engraved a sound track, which corresponded to the impressed sound waves. This method was used before the advent of electrical recording. Acoustic recording is also called mechanical recording.

Figure 23-2 A recording session in the early twenties at the RCA Victor plant in Camden, NJ. *(Courtesy Radio Corporation of America)*

Because the acoustical output of most of the instruments used for recording was low, and a considerable amount of energy was required to obtain a satisfactory level on the record, horns were attached to the string instruments to reinforce their acoustic output. A typical recording session in the early 1920s is pictured in Fig. 23-2.

The sound-level control consisted of a ball of yarn in a tube attached to the large horn at the left. The position of the ball of yarn in the tube was varied to regulate the volume of sound fed to the recording diaphragm and stylus.

Naturally, all acoustical recordings were monophonic, and the motion of the vibrating diaphragm produced hill-and-dale cuts or vertical modulation.

With the invention of electrical recording, lateral modulation became easy and soon replaced vertical modulation. The first cutting heads were monophonic and operated using electromagnetic and piezoelectric principles.

23.2.1 Piezoelectric Cutting Heads

A typical crystal (or piezoelectric) monophonic cutting head is shown in Fig. 23-3.

A crystal cutting head employs a piezoelectric crystal for the stylus-actuating mechanism. The crystal is similar (except heavier) to that used in a crystal pickup.

The audio signals cause the crystal to twist in a lateral direction. A recording stylus mounted in a chuck is attached to the crystal slabs for the purpose of engraving the sound track on the recording disk.

Ceramic crystals have, to some extent, replaced the Rochelle salt crystal; however, because of the greater sensitivity, Rochelle salt crystals find their greatest usage in pickups, microphones, and headphones. Generally, ceramic crystals are treated both electrically and mechanically in much the same manner as Rochelle crystals. The impedance of an average crystal cutting head at 1000 Hz is approximately 22,000 Ω (Fig. 23-4).

Crystal cutting heads may be coupled to an amplifier output stage in a number of ways. The output stage may be single or double ended (Fig. 23-5).

If a constant voltage is applied to the crystal slabs, the amplitude motion of the recording stylus will be constant, regardless of the applied frequencies. Recordings made with a crystal cutting head require no equalization in either the recording or reproduction circuits if played back with a crystal pickup (Fig. 23-6).

The primary function of a cutting head is to engrave on the disk a faithful reproduction of the applied electrical waveforms.

The cutting head converts electrical energy into mechanical energy; therefore, it is similar to an electric motor or a loudspeaker. For present-day requirements, a cutting head must be capable of recording with uniform characteristics up to at least 10 kHz, and preferably up to 20 kHz or higher.

Because angles, mechanical mounting and alignment, and amplifiers are critical, an understanding of physics, mechanics, and electronics is useful in the understanding of disk-cutting heads (recording heads) and their behavior.

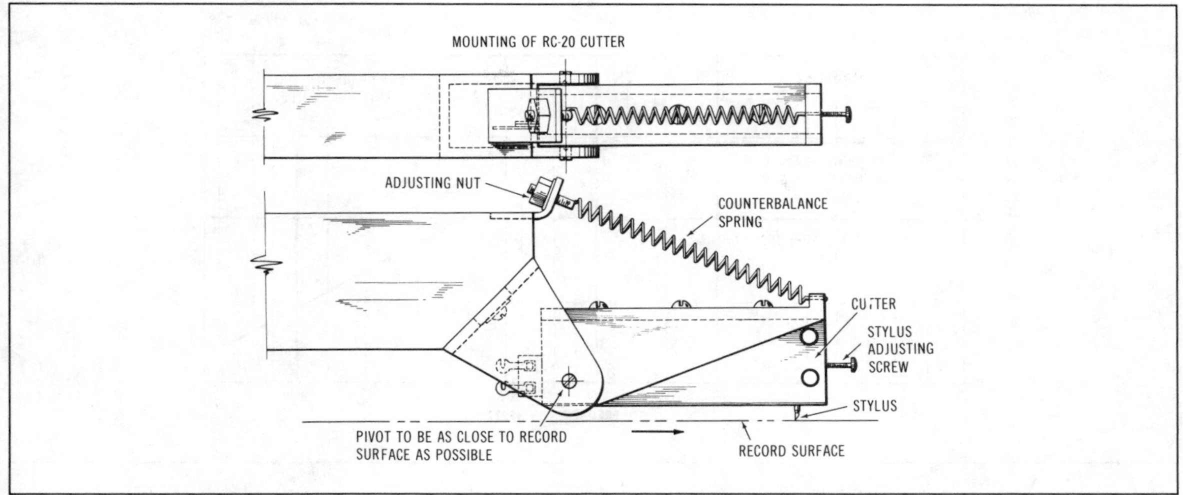

Figure 23-3 Crystal cutting head and recorder mount. *(Courtesy Clevite Corp., Piezoelectric Div.)*

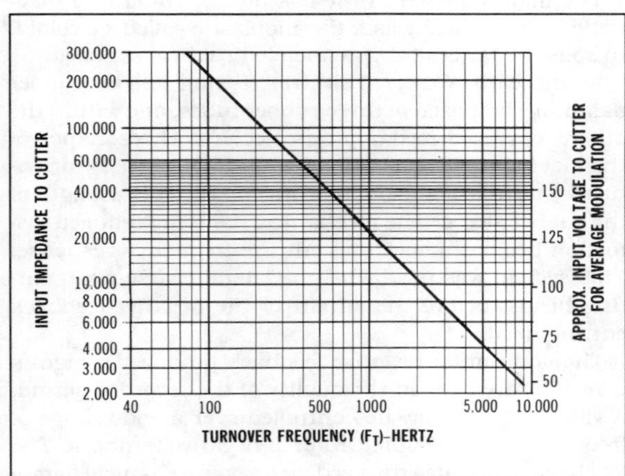

Figure 23-4 Electrical impedance of a piezoelectric cutting head as a function of frequency.

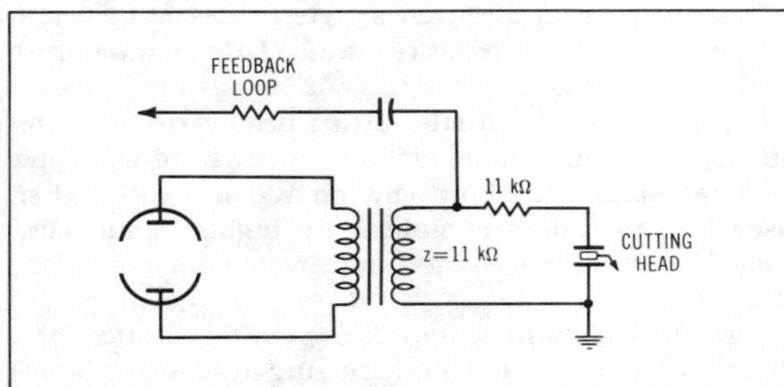

Figure 23-5 Coupling circuit for driving a crystal cutting head, constant amplitude, constant velocity with a turnover frequency of 1000 Hz.

23.2.2 Balanced-Armature Cutting Heads

The interior construction for a typical monophonic balanced-armature cutting head is shown in Fig. 23-7. In Fig. 23-7A, a balanced armature A is placed in a permanent magnetic field supplied by a permanent magnet B. Actuating coils C, connected in series, are placed at the upper and lower ends of the armature. The use of two coils in series cancels the even harmonics and reduces the distortion. The armature A is constructed of laminated steel with a V-shaped saddle D at the center. The saddle rests on a ground knife-edged support E. Steel rod F balances the armature in the exact center of the gap between the pole pieces. Two steel rods G with offset loops are used to supply pressure to the outer ends of the saddle mount D, to balance the armature in the center of the magnetic structure.

The rear end of the armature is connected to a thermoplastic damper H, which removes resonant peaks and helps to smooth out the frequency response. A metal washer I secures the damping member to the armature. A side view showing how the damping material is secured to the magnetic structure appears in Fig. 23-7B. The cutting head just discussed is of the nonnegative feedback type.

The essential parts for a lateral-type head designed by Miller are shown in Fig. 23-8. A permanent magnetic field is supplied by a magnet, indicated by north and south poles, N and S. A soft-iron armature A is supported and centered in the magnetic field on a bearing B. Coil C surrounds the end of the armature and carries the audio-frequency currents, which induce a magnetic field in the armature that is continuously changing polarity, causing the armature to be attracted or repelled by the permanent magnet in accordance with the strength of the induced audio current. Thus, the stylus D mounted in

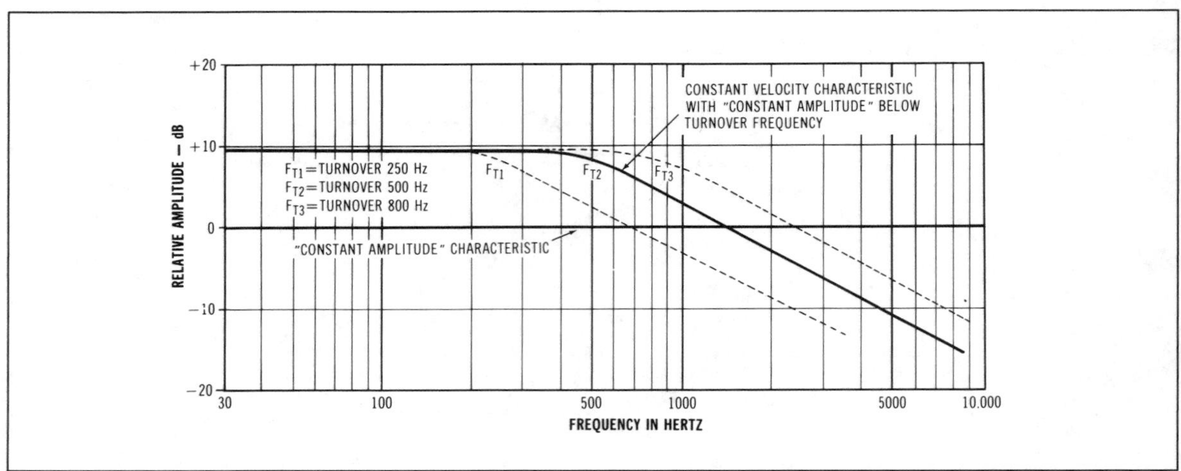

Figure 23-6 Frequency characteristics of a crystal cutting head operating constant amplitude and constant velocity. *(Courtesy Clevite Corp., Piezoelectric Div.)*

chuck E inscribes the electrical waveform applied to the coils C in a disk record. In the back of armature A is a vibrating reed R with damping blocks V, supported by foam blocks F_1 and F_2. This reed is resonated to counteract the main mechanical resonance peak of the cutter, which is around 1 kHz. Although some cutting heads still being used are similar to the basic construction previously discussed, better commercial recording heads generally make use of negative-feedback coils within the heads, since such a design reduces distortion and improves frequency response, such as the Grampian cutting head shown in Fig. 23-9.

The adjustment of a cutting head without feedback to secure a desired recording characteristic is both tedious and difficult and is somewhat of a cut-and-try job.

The calibration should be carried out at normal room temperature, since temperature has a pronounced effect on the final response. The calibration is made by recording light patterns (see section on test records and calibration) and measuring the response visually or by playing back and measuring the output on an ac voltmeter. A typical frequency response plotted from a light pattern is shown in Fig. 23-10. If the cutting head is calibrated at normal room temperature and then operated at a low room temperature, the frequency characteristic may change.

When calibrating a cutting head, single frequencies should not be applied to the head for extended periods of time as the damping material becomes overheated and softens, permitting the calibration to change. If the head has been subjected to overheating, it should be permitted to cool slowly and then should be rechecked for calibration. Unlike recording sustained tones during normal recording of music, only bursts of audio power are sent into the cutting head, and there is very little heat being generated because the average power dissipated is low.

The material used in the past for damping in a magnetic cutting head was a thermoplastic called Viscoloid. In some instances tungsten-loaded rubber was used.

In the early Western Electric cutting heads, rubber damping composed of three rubber tubes, one within the other, was used to damp out mechanical resonance of the moving parts. The rubber was attached to the armature by means of a metal fin running the entire length of the rubber sleeve. The mechanical damping reduced distortion besides smoothing out the frequency response. This system was used with the lateral coarse-pitch cutting heads, before the advent of the negative-feedback cutting heads.

The addition of negative feedback produced a significant improvement in the quality of the recorded sound. A vibrating coil may be controlled over a wide range of frequencies by the application of negative feedback. The feedback eliminates the need for heavy mechanical damping materials and reduces the effects of the disk material on the tip of the recording stylus. Negative feedback governs the power rather than absorbing it in the control process. Furthermore, the use of viscous damping offers difficulties since its effectiveness deteriorates over a period of time and its characteristics are affected by temperature changes resulting from the use of a hot stylus.

Impedance of a magnetic cutting head varies with frequency. As a rule, the magnetic cutting head will show its stated impedance only between 400 and 1 kHz, then rise to several thousand ohms at the higher frequencies. Below 1 kHz the impedance may drop to one-tenth that at 1 kHz.

Fig. 23-11 shows the impedance characteristics for a typical nonfeedback magnetic cutting head, rated 500 Ω at 1 kHz. As may be seen, this head has an impedance of 90 Ω at 40 Hz, 500 Ω at 1700 Hz, and then rises to over 3000 Ω at 10 kHz.

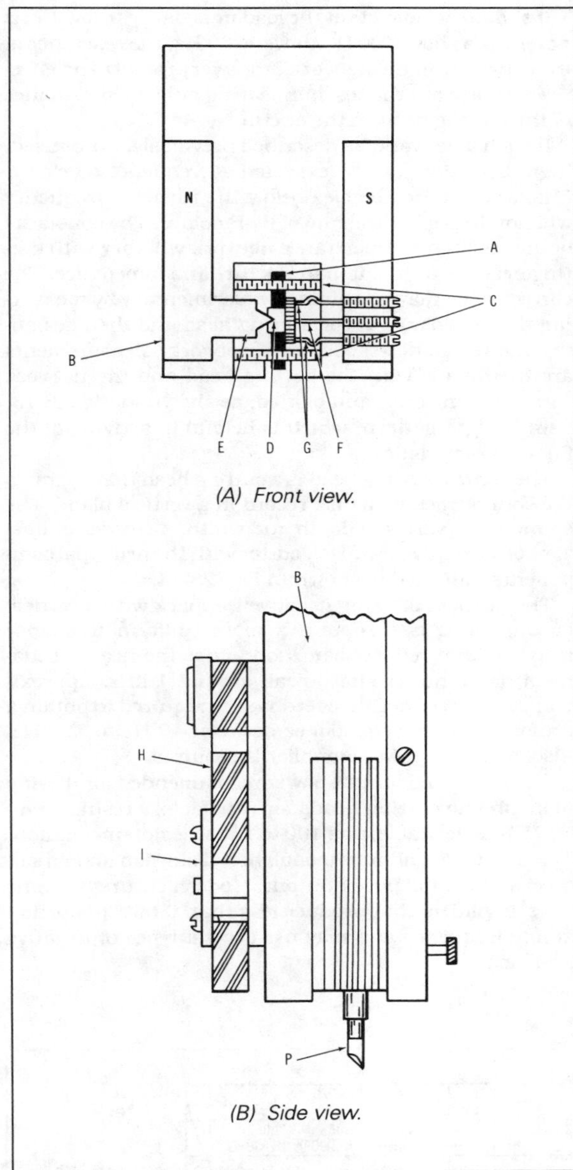

(A) Front view.

(B) Side view.

Figure 23-7 Interior view of typical monophonic balanced-armature cutting head.

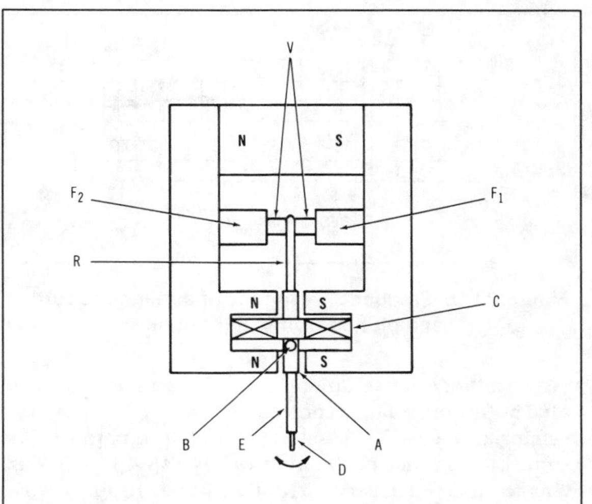

Figure 23-8 Miller cutting head.

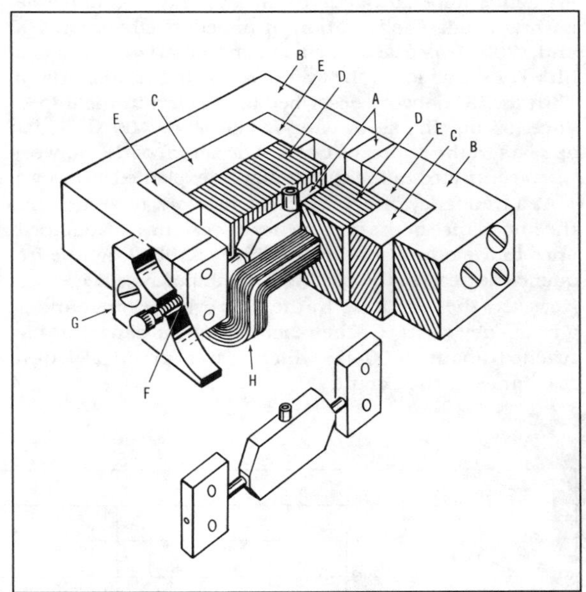

Figure 23-9 Grampian cutting head—inverted interior view of balanced-armature, moving-vane magnetic cutting head, using negative feedback, for monophonic recording.

With the cutting head described previously connected across the output of a driving amplifier, the amplifier output sees 500 Ω at only one frequency (1700 Hz). This means the amplifier will be overloaded at the lower frequencies because of the lowered impedance of the cutting head decreasing the power output and increasing the harmonic distortion. The impedance rise above 1700 Hz will have little effect on the amplifier as it acts as a bridging load across the output. To prevent the low impedance of the cutting head from disturbing the output stage of the driving amplifier (to maintain a constant amplitude and a constant velocity frequency characteristic), a resistance-capacitance network is connected in series with the output circuit, as shown in Fig. 23-12.

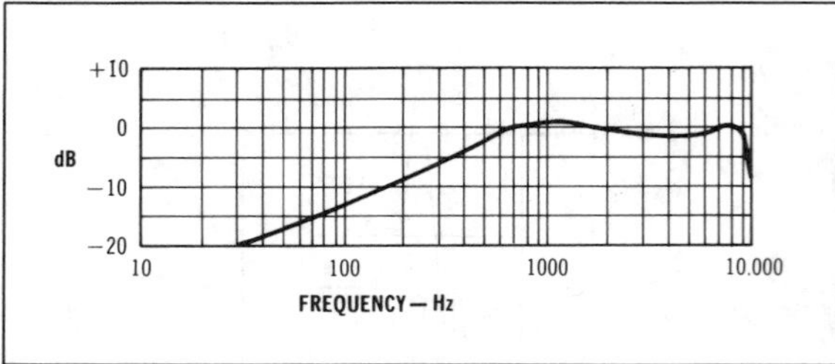

Figure 23-10 Frequency response of a magnetic cutting head plotted from a light pattern.

A resistance-capacitance network for a cutting head rated 500-Ω impedance consists of a 400-Ω noninductive resistor and a 1-μF capacitor connected in parallel. The parallel impedance of this network is 148.4 Ω at 1 kHz. When connected in series with the cutting head, the load impedance seen by the amplifier output is the network impedance plus the impedance of the cutting head, as shown by the dotted line in Fig. 23-11. The curves shown are actual impedance curves measured on a commercial cutting head. The variation in impedance between 100 and 1700 Hz is due to the head characteristics and is of little consequence to the overall recording characteristic. With the RC network described in the circuit, the impedance, as may be seen, cannot fall below 400 Ω, which appears in the region of 1 kHz. The action of the network when connected in the circuit may be explained as follows.

At a frequency of 1700 Hz, the network in series with the impedance of the cutting head presents a load impedance to the output of the amplifier of 500 Ω. As the frequency decreases, the cutting-head impedance decreases. However, the reactance in the network is rising, and at a frequency of 40 Hz, the reactance of the capacitor has reached about 4000 Ω, which leaves practically pure resistance in the circuit.

It should be noted that the load impedance below 1 kHz never rises above 400 Ω. Above 1700 Hz, the reactance of the capacitor in the network drops very rapidly and effectively shorts out the resistor, leaving only the impedance of the cutting head in the circuit.

If such a network, as described previously, is not used, high distortion may be expected at frequencies below 1 kHz, and the frequencies below the turnover frequency will not drop off at the rate of 6 dB/octave. The constants of the resistance-capacitance network will vary with cutting heads of different manufacture and impedance. The correct value may be obtained experimentally by measuring the impedance of the cutting head and then designing the resistance-capacitance network. Measurements are then made with the cutting head and the network connected in series and plotted, as shown in Fig. 23-13, using a light pattern, which is helpful in arriving at the final characteristic.

The vertical cutting head is a cutting head that engraves the sound track on a disk record in a vertical plane. The sound track varies in depth and width. A cross-sectional view of a negative-feedback cutter with the principal components indicated is shown in Fig. 23-14.

The purpose of using negative feedback with a vertical cutting head is to obtain a more uniform frequency response and reduce distortion, since the head mechanism has a rather sharp peak around 1 kHz. Approximately 43 dB of negative feedback is required to obtain a uniform frequency response between 40 Hz to 12 kHz. Also, a special power amplifier is required.

The minimum output power recommended for driving monophonic cutting heads for satisfactory results is 40 W; 75 W is desirable, and 100 to 150 W is not uncommon. The harmonic and intermodulation distortion should not exceed 1% at full power output. Modern cutting systems have amplifiers that produce less than 0.05% distortion at any frequency and may use several types of negative feedback.

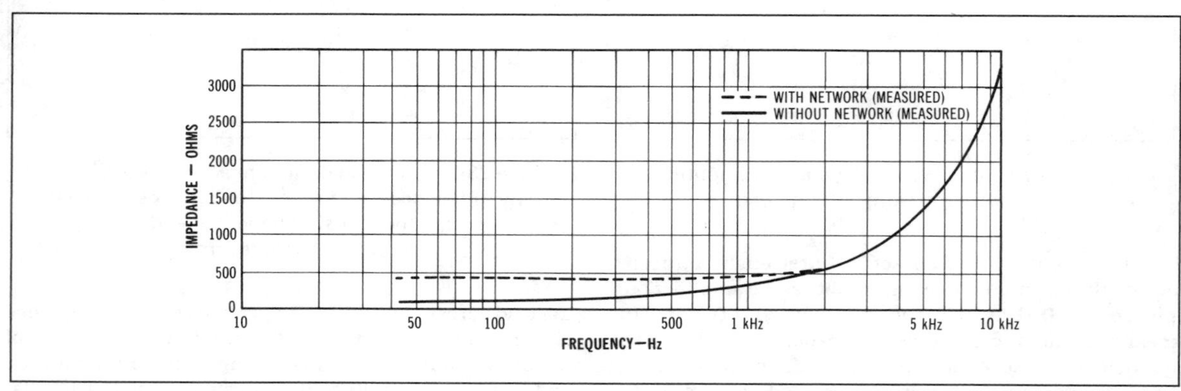

Figure 23-11 Impedance characteristic of a typical nonfeedback cutting head, with and without resistance-capacitance network.

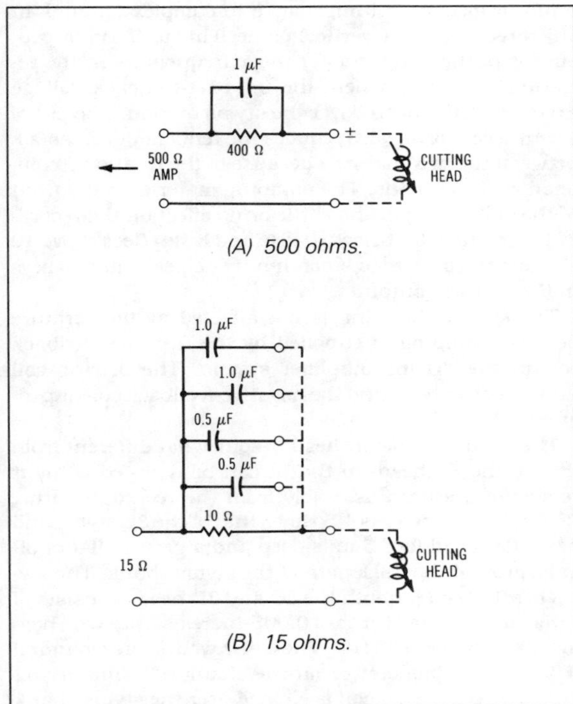

Figure 23-12 Resistance-capacitance networks used with nonfeedback cutting heads to maintain a constant-amplitude, constant-velocity frequency characteristic.

23.2.3 Stereo Cutting Heads

Stereo cutting heads differ from monophonic cutters because they provide a means of moving perpendicular to the surface of the record and to the direction of the groove.

Because of this, the groove can be modulated in lateral and vertical directions as well as in any other direction, depending on the phase relationship between the two signals driving the cutting heads.

23.2.3.1 Westrex Cutting Heads

A simplified constructional diagram of the Westrex Corp. Model 3C and 3D StereoDisc recording heads (Westrex refers to cutting heads as recording heads) is given in Fig. 23-15. The following discussion holds true, generally, for both the 3C and 3D heads, except for certain modifications mentioned in the discussion.

The cutting-head assembly contains two magnesium coil form assemblies, each associated with a given recording channel. Each coil assembly contains a driving coil and a negative-feedback coil located in separate pole pieces with annular gaps. The pole pieces are attached to a single Alnico V permanent magnet. The magnetic gaps of the driving and feedback coils are arranged in a series-parallel fashion to ensure equal flux densities in the corresponding gaps.

Copper slugs or shields are used to reduce crosstalk between the driving and negative-feedback coils. These shields or slugs can be seen in the shaded areas near the coils. The springs supporting the coils are made out of beryllium copper and are V-shaped to maintain the alignment of the coils.

The coil assemblies are attached to the stylus holder through links that are stiff longitudinally, but flexible laterally. These links are braced in the center to prevent excessive lateral compliance. This structure results in a stiff forward driving system with a high compliance in the lateral direction.

The supporting member for the model 3C stylus consists of a tubular cantilever spring (Fig. 23-16) with the support used in the model 3D shown in Fig. 23-15. This type of support was selected because the compliance of a cantilever spring will be the same for all directions of motion. This compliance permits the stylus to present a

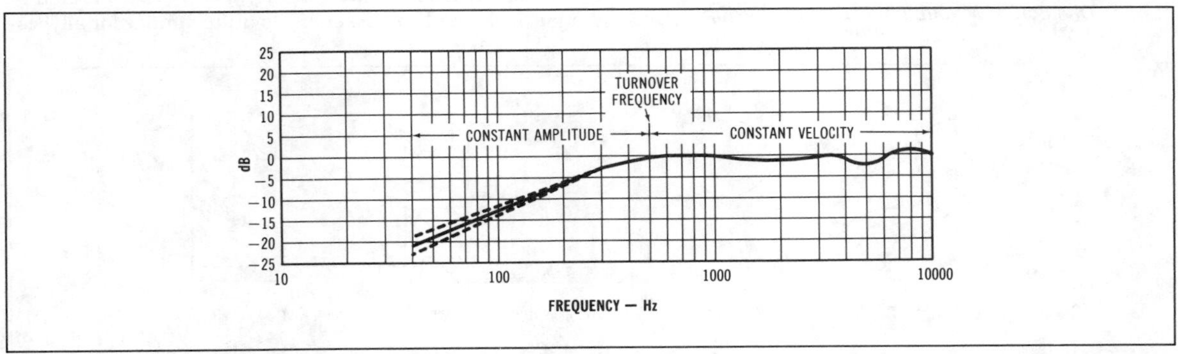

Figure 23-13 A typical response for a nonfeedback monophonic cutting head plotted from a light-pattern measurement.

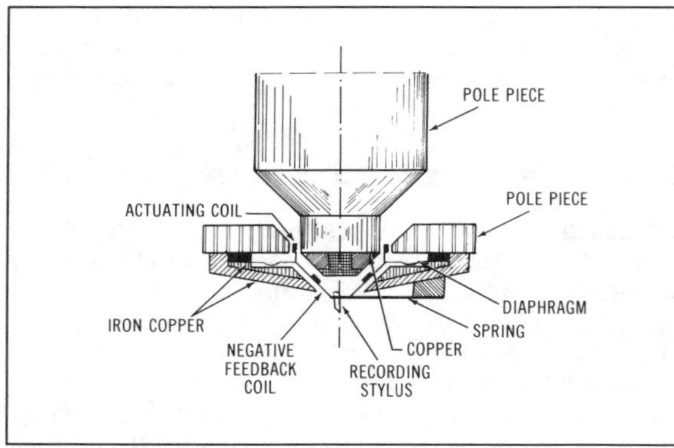

Figure 23-14 Cross-sectional view of a vertical, negative-feedback cutting head. *(Courtesy AT&T Bell Laboratories)*

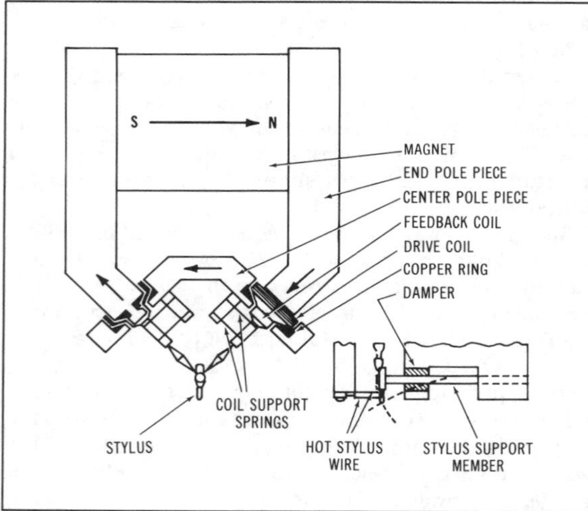

Figure 23-15 Simplified cross-sectional view of Westrex stereophonic cutting head. *(Courtesy Westrex Corp., Division of Mitsubishi Pro Audio Group)*

uniform mechanical impedance to complex motions in any direction in the vertical plane. This uniform impedance is particularly true for those frequencies in the recording spectrum where the negative-feedback voltage exercises little control over the stylus motion. The use of a cantilever spring also reduces the tendency of crosstalk between the two channels because of the rotational compliance of the stylus. The damping material at the front of the stylus support has little or no effect on the recording at frequencies below 10 kHz and little effect above 10 kHz. Its purpose is to smooth out the peaks and valleys in the monitor output.

The system damping is not affected by temperature because damping is supplied by the negative-feedback coil in the driving amplifier system. The driving coil impedance is 10 Ω, and the negative-feedback coil impedance is 11 Ω.

The stylus for the 3D head is somewhat different from that of the 3C head, in that it can be replaced without removing the head assembly from the recording lathe. The stylus diameter is 1.5 times that of the 3C stylus and has a flattened face 5 mils deep and a ground flat of 39 mils, ground the full length of the stylus shank. The stylus heating coil for both the 3C and 3D heads consists of seven and one-half turns of 0.005-in. resistance wire having a resistance of 32 Ω/ft. The coil is wound on a mandrel 0.038 in. in diameter or on the shank of a number 62 drill. The completed coil is slipped over the stylus shank and held in place either by the natural spring tension of the wire or special epoxy. The heating current for the coil can be taken from a 6.3-V transformer with a resistance in series with the coil or from a Variac® in the primary winding.

Fig. 23-17 is an underside view of the 3B head, with its principal components called out. They are (A) advance ball, (B) advance ball lateral adjustment, (C) stylus tip, (D) heater coil, (E) chip suction pipe, (F) stylus linkage, (G) coil assembly, (H) groove depth, (I) stylus support, (J) damping member, and (K) driving and negative-feedback coil leads.

A Westrex Model 3A recording head mounted on a recording lathe is pictured in Fig. 23-18. This method of mounting the head assembly is quite similar for all Wes-

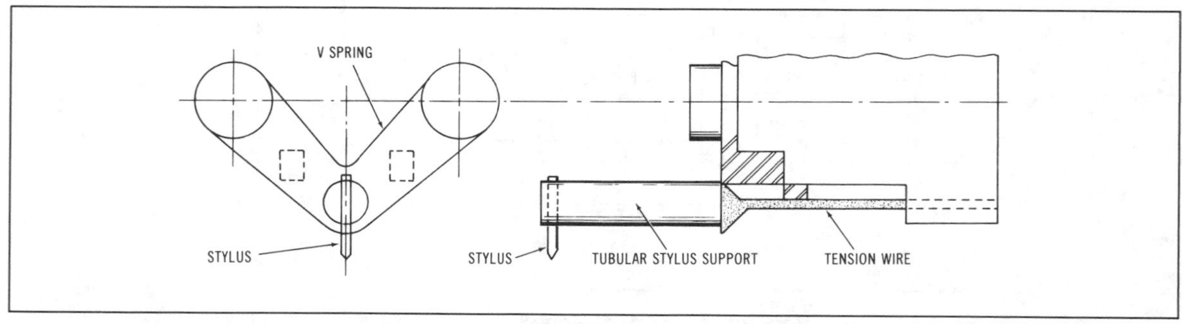

Figure 23-16 Stylus support member of Westrex model 3D stereophonic recording head. *(Courtesy Westrex Corp., Division of Mitsubishi Pro Audio Group)*

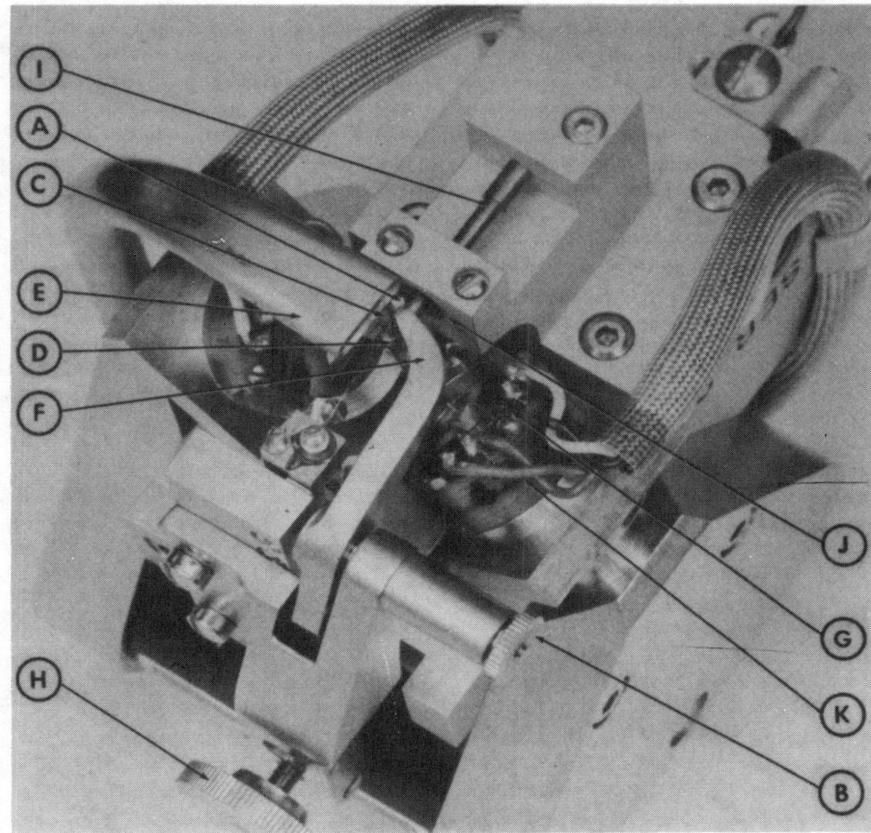

Figure 23-17 Underside view of Westrex StereoDisc recording head.
(Courtesy Westrex Corp., Division of Mitsubishi Pro Audio Group)

trex heads. Vertical adjustment screw A and lateral screw B are for adjusting the angle of the recording stylus. Westrex recommends a cutting angle of 23°, established with the Model 3C recording head. Distortion versus the effective vertical-cutting angle is a complex problem involving many factors, and it will be discussed separately.

The negative-feedback circuit in both the 3C and 3D heads displays a resonant peak around 1300 Hz (Fig. 23-19). Applying a 27-dB negative feedback to the 3C head or 28 dB to the 3D head, the frequency response appears as given in Fig. 23-20. After connecting the head to a special amplifier (RA-1574D) with its equalizers, the frequency response at both the low and high ends is flattened out to within ±1 dB, 50 Hz to 12 kHz, and ±2 dB, 12 kHz to 15 kHz. Recording Industry Association of America (RIAA) equalization is provided from 30 Hz to 1 kHz. The 3D head has an overall increase in sensitivity of about 25%, as compared to that of model 3C.

23.2.3.2 Neumann Disk-Cutting Heads

The Neumann SX74 stereo cutting head works on the same principle as a Westrex cutting head. As can be seen from Fig. 23-21, the SX74 has separate magnets for each channel, and the cutter is smaller than 3C or 3D cutters. The clear tube attached to the front supplies the cutting head with inert gas to cool the coils, which often dissipate hundreds of watts of audio power.

The SX74 cutter is shown mounted on a Neumann cutting lathe. The round cylindrical device just above the cutting head is a dashpot-oil-filled cup. The dashpot's piston is attached to the vertical mounting plate holding the cutting head. The dashpot helps the cutting head follow the surface of the record without bouncing or vibrating.

23.2.4 Disk Recording Lathes

A disk recording lathe, basically, is a special precision turntable that is designed to rotate a disk to be cut at the precise speed and, at the same time, support and move the cutting head over the surface of the record radially, to cut a continually spiraling groove. Modern cutting lathes are very sophisticated, almost totally automatic machines, capable of cutting modern records of exceptional quality,

Figure 23-18 Westrex StereoDisk cutting head mounted on a recording lathe. *(Courtesy Westrex Corp., Division of Mitsubishi Pro Audio Group)*

to the highest technological standards. Since there are only a couple of manufacturers of these machines left, we shall start with a description of a disk-cutting lathe, available from Neumann.

23.2.4.1 Neumann Disk-Cutting Lathe

A commercial recording lathe, manufactured by Neumann of West Germany, is pictured in Fig. 23-22, with its principal components indicated. Basically, the recorder consists of a heavy steel base, mounted on shock mounts supported by a steel cabinet A. The turntable B weighs 65 lb, with three stroboscopic rings on its outer rim for three speeds that are illuminated by a neon light. The turntable is isolated from the drive system below by means of an oil-filled coupling, thus preventing rumble and flutter from being transmitted from the drive to the turntable. The turntable is driven by a film of oil between two concentric cylinders at C. The lathe bed D is of the slide type, with two ball bearings riding on top of the bed to relieve strain placed on the sled E by the weight of the cutter suspension and cutting head F.

Directly below the lathe bed is a calibrated scale on which are mounted the starting cams and end-groove stop.

Three cams for 7-, 10-, and 12-in. disks are provided. An adjustable end-groove stop for the three standard RIAA groove diameters causes the cutting head to lift with an adjustable delay, to provide for a locked groove. A lead screw engaging lever G is interlocked in such a way that the cutter will lift at any time it is not being driven by the lead screw, with a braking assembly to prevent the lead screw from coasting when the end is reached. A vacuum system provides a means of holding down blank disks from 10 to 17¼ in. in diameter on the turntable, with a disabling valve to shut off the vacuum holes when they are not in use.

As shown in Fig. 23-22, cutting-head connections are brought to the rectangular box on the transport sled by means of a plug to permit the exchange of cutting heads without disturbing the alignment. The connector plugs (for stereo) consist of six pins that carry the audio signal, feedback loop, and dc for the stylus heating coil. A release solenoid lifts the cutting head whenever the stop button

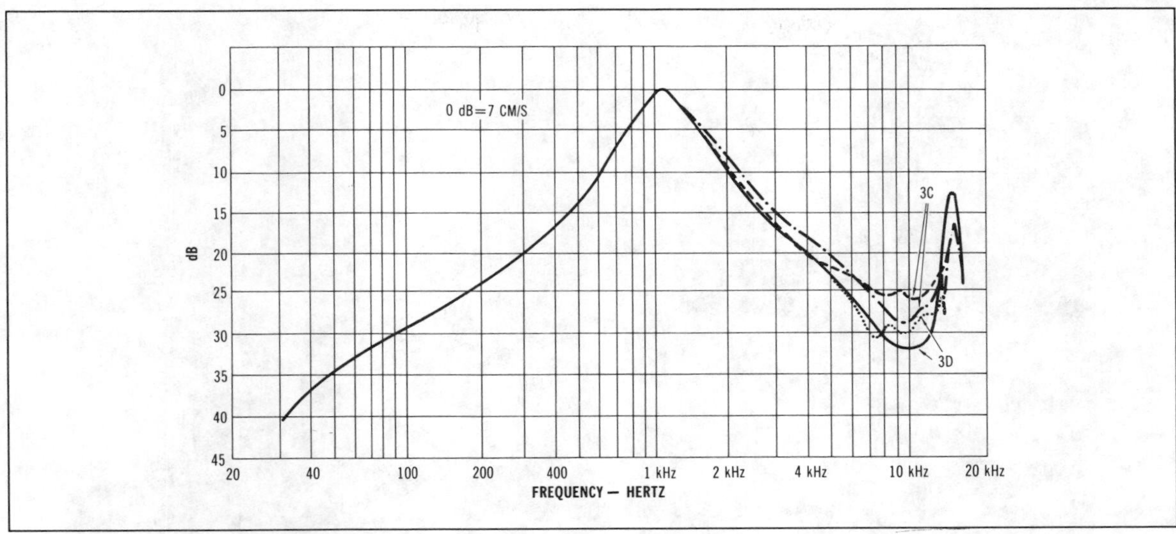

Figure 23-19 Resonant-frequency characteristic, without feedback, of Westrex model 3C and 3D negative-feedback recording heads. *(Courtesy Westrex Corp., Division of Mitsubishi Pro Audio Group)*

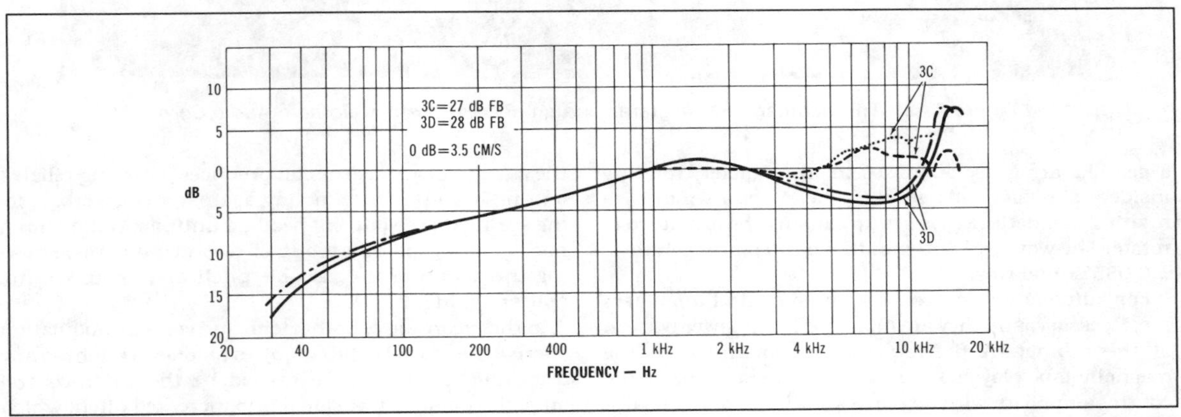

Figure 23-20 Frequency characteristics, with feedback, of Westrex model 3C and 3D negative-feedback recording heads. *(Courtesy Westrex Corp., Division of Mitsubishi Pro Audio Group)*

is depressed, when the sled hits the end groove stop, or when the lead screw is disengaged. A dashpot on the front of the cutting-head suspension mechanism is equipped with a perforated piston, with an adjustable shield over the perforations, to allow a wide latitude of adjustment. A tilting mechanism is connected to a moving-coil system, which, together with the depth-of-cut control, provides electronic-depth variation, thus eliminating the advance ball generally used.

The depth-of-cut control supplies direct current to a moving-coil system in the cutting-head suspension mechanism, thus relieving the cutting-head pressure on the disk. This operation is controlled by a potentiometer, which is adjusted while observing the cut through a microscope J. A second control presets the increased depth used with the lead-in, lead-out, and spiraling grooves. The variable-pitch control K is a separate piece of equipment situated at the left end of the lathe. The pitch-control mechanism is self-driven and coupled to the lead screw by a four-way, shock-isolated coupling. The variable-pitch motor is connected by means of a belt, and through an oil-filled flexible coupling to the lead screw. A generator coupled to the shaft acts as a feedback generator to maintain rigid speed control. A second motor, identical to the belt-connected motor, connected to an overdrive in the gear train, serves for the speed up of pitch for lead-in and lead-out spiraling.

The turntable motor is of the synchronous type. It has

Figure 23-21 The Neumann SX-74 stereo cutting head. *(Courtesy Gotham Audio Corp.)*

a gearlike armature about 10 in in diameter, rotating inside a similar inside gear. By means of a winding, a rotating magnetic field is set up causing the armature to rotate. The wow and flutter of this particular machine is ±0.035% total rms.

For automatic pitch control, three control amplifiers are necessary, and they are mounted in the lower portion of the cabinet. A preview head is mounted on the magnetic-tape playback transfer machine to provide the control amplifiers with advance knowledge of the modulation to be fed to the cutting head (see Fig. 23-23). (Note the long delay path between the program and preview heads.) The output of the control amplifiers associated with the preview head is fed to the control amplifiers. For monophonic recording, the depth of cut is held constant, and the pitch is varied as a function of the preview information. In stereophonic recording, the pitch control is actuated by the sum of the left and right channel signal, although the depth of cut is varied according to the difference signal obtained from a stereophonic preview head. It is the function of the pitch-control amplifier to translate the preview signal through an equalizer into variations of braking current, which in turn are applied to the pitch-control motor to vary its speed and, with it, the lines per inch of recording.

The depth-control amplifier is identical to the pitch-control amplifier; however, its output to the solenoid in the cutting-head suspension produces a varying relief of cutting-head pressure, acting against a counterbalancing spring on the cutting-head mounting mechanism. A microphotograph of a group of recorded grooves, showing the action of the variable pitch and depth control appears in Fig. 23-24.

In the recording of both lateral and vertical modulation (stereo), increased depth requires increased pitch, so any deepening of the groove caused by the depth-control amplifier must be translated into increased pitch, which is accomplished by an integrating amplifier. This amplifier adds to the pitch-control current whenever increased depth is required. It is claimed that such a system, when properly adjusted, can add up to 6 min of recording time on a 12-in. record.

The microscope is 156 power with concentric illumination, brightly lighting the groove and leaving the land between the grooves dark, and is moved across the turntable by means of a rack-and-pinion gear. The microscope support arm also acts as the vacuum conductor for the vacuum-chuck turntable. The microscope graticule is calibrated to read in 0.001-in. graduations. The chip collector is contained in the lower portion of the cabinet. A pickup arm is generally mounted at the left for playback purposes, and it may be used for simultaneous monitoring of the playback signal, while also monitoring the signal from the negative-feedback loop to the cutting head.

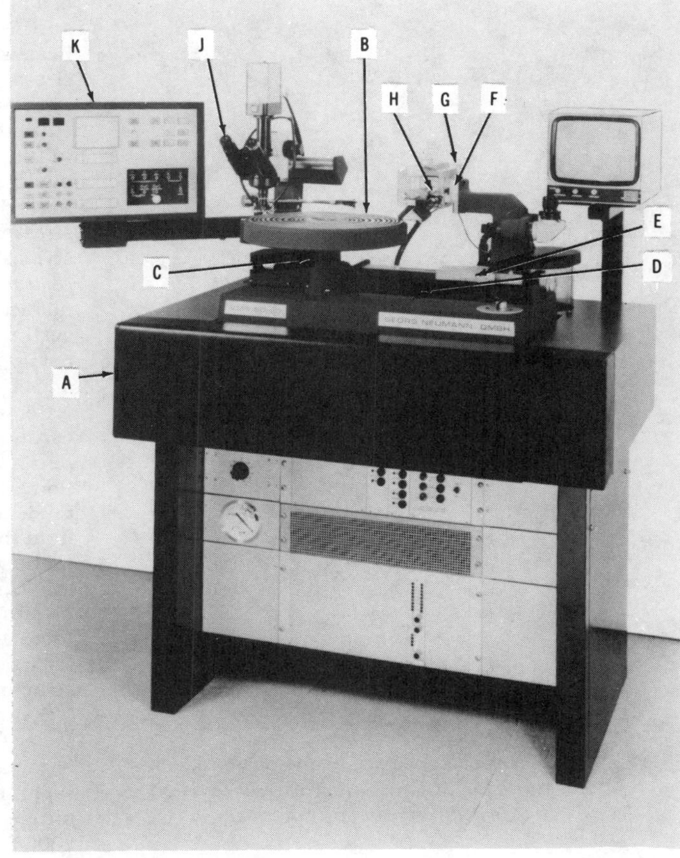

Figure 23-22 Neumann master disk recording lathe model AM-32b with automatic pitch and depth control. *(Courtesy Gotham Audio Corp.)*

A half-speed converter permits the turntable to be rotated at 16⅔ rpm, and half-speed for 45 or 78 rpm for experimental work or for cutting frequency disks.

23.2.4.2 Scully Mastering Lathe

A second recording lathe, manufactured by the Scully Recording Instrument Corp., appears in Fig. 23-25. Like the Neumann lathe, it also has variable pitch and depth control and many of the features previously described. At A and B is the microscope and its light; C, the turntable; D, a vacuum-suction pipe for removing the chip from the disk; E, the cutting head; F, depth-control adjustment; H, cutting-head dashpot; I, plug connection for the cutting head; K, sled; L, leveling screws; M, push-button control panel; O, carriage hand knob; P, recorder base; O, feed-nut adjustment; R, carriage-limit stop; and S, line-per-in. indicator scale. The motor with its gear box and mechanical filter is mounted below the table.

The lines per inch may be varied over a range from 70 to 400 lines/in. Automatic control of pitch and depth are accomplished in a manner somewhat similar to the Neumann lathe. A more recent Scully machine is shown in Fig. 23-26.

23.2.5 Cutting Styli

A recording stylus is a sharp-pointed, gouge-shaped instrument for engraving a sound track on a cylindrical or disk record. The tip may be a precious or semiprecious stone or metal. Commercial recording styli use sapphire tips. (See Fig. 23-27.)

The recording stylus is one, if not the most important, component in a recording system and, as far as is known, was first used by Edison in 1877. With the advent of present-day high-quality sound, wide frequency range, low distortion, increased signal-to-noise ratio, long-playing and stereophonic recordings, and improved recording media, a great responsibility is placed on both the recording and reproducing styli. Since its first use, many different materials have been used for their manufacture—steel alloys, sapphires, and diamonds. However, over the years it has been found that *corundum* is the

Figure 23-23 A disk mastering tape playback unit manufactured by MCI. *(Courtesy MCI, A Division of Sony Corporation of America)*

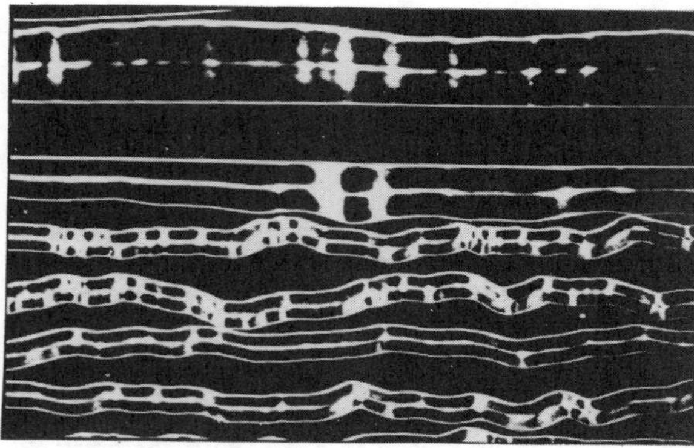

Figure 23-24 Variable depth at work deepening the groove as needed.

most practical of all materials for recording styli. Corundum can be obtained in several different colors, such as red, blue, green, violet, yellow, and colorless, which are often used for identification. Both the natural and synthetic sapphire (blue, ruby red, etc.) are corundum (Al_2O_2) of a hexagonal crystalline structure with a hardness of 9 on the Moh scale and 1525 to 2000 on a Knoop scale. Because of its lack of grain, crystalline structure, and cleavage, sapphire may be ground to very accurate dimensions and angles, while still retaining a very fine cutting edge. This latter property is of prime importance in the manufacture of recording styli. Although the diamond is much harder than corundum for use in recording styli, it is impractical because of its grain and internal stresses, as well as its cost. However, as a reproducing stylus, it is ideal because of its long life and ruggedness. As a recording stylus, the sapphire is much more economical than a diamond, but it has to be replaced after cutting 15 to 18 long-playing sides. Diamond styli are being used with modern techniques of cutting in metal and in preparation of some digital video and audio records.

Commercial sapphire is manufactured from synthetic corundum. For all practical purposes, synthetic sapphires are identical in physical and chemical composition to the natural mineral. The name sapphire is used to identify clear synthetic corundum and differentiate it from the more familiar blue variety of this mineral. Synthetic white sapphire is a single, homogeneous crystal that can be given an exceptionally smooth surface polish by either flame or mechanical processes. There are no interruptions on their mirrorlike surfaces and no potential weak spots such as might develop in multicrystalline structures and offer locations for wear.

Synthetic corundum has a hardness rating on Moh's scale of 9 as compared to 10 for diamond and 5.5 to 7 for hardened steel. Laboratory tests show synthetic white sapphire has a tensile strength of the same order of magnitude as steel. When heat treated between 1700 and 2000°C (3090 and 3632°F), this material exhibits a plasticity that will permit it to be worked by flame-forming techniques.

Although some work has been done with making styli out of diamond, synthetic ruby and sapphire remain the jewels of choice, due to their ease in forming and absolute control of the grain. The latter is most vital in assuring good chip removal.

Several views of a recording stylus are shown in Fig. 23-28. The stylus consists of a sapphire held in a dural shank (Fig. 23-28B). The sapphire tip has a flat face ground on one side. The end of the sapphire is ground to a point with a rounded tip. Extending from the tip upward and along its edges are burnishing facets, the most difficult and exacting part of the stylus grinding, as the dimensions are only a few ten-thousandths of an inch. The *burnishing facets* polish the groove as it is cut. The length of the burnishing facet not only affects the signal-to-noise ratio, but also the frequency response. A cold-stylus coarse-pitch recording with a burnishing facet of 0.4 to 0.6 mil will effect a loss at 10 kHz, compared to 1 kHz of 3 to 6 dB. Only a very small portion of the stylus tip is used to engrave the sound track on the record (Fig. 23-28C). An enlarged view of the burnishing facet is shown in Fig. 23-28D.

For high-quality recording of any type, the noise level

Figure 23-25 Scully Recording Co. mastering disk recording lathe with automatic pitch and depth control. *(Courtesy L. J. Scully Manufacturing Corp.)*

produced by the stylus itself must be at least 55 dB, and as a rule, if not abused, will run 57 to 60 dB below the reference level of 7 cm at a frequency of 1 kHz. The noise level is measured while playing back an unmodulated groove. It is important that the unmodulated groove used for measurement is normal in every respect, that the chip has cleared the groove properly, that the stylus heat current is optimum, and that the disk is of good quality.

For stereophonic recordings, both the shape and length of the shank (Fig. 23-29) have considerable effect, as shown in the plots in Fig. 23-30. The frequency response of each recording stylus should be measured before using and graded. An ANM recording stylus is a special *antinoise modulation stylus* developed by Capps and Co. to reduce modulation noise while recording. The stylus is ground with two or more burnishing facets compared to the single facet of the conventional recording stylus. A cross-sectional view of a conventional recording stylus with a single burnishing facet in an unmodulated groove is shown in Fig. 23-31A.

In Fig. 23-31B, the stylus is shown in a groove with a 20° slope, and in Fig. 23-31C it is shown with a 30° slope. Note the burnishing angle made by the facet is increased depending on the stylus motion. When the modulation is high, the burnishing facets cannot function properly and leave rough places in the groove, as shown in Fig. 23-31D, resulting in increased noise. This type noise is particularly noticeable because the rough spots are on the side of the groove that has the greatest effect on the stylus.

An ANM stylus has three burnishing facets on each side of the tip, as shown in Fig. 23-31E. In Fig. 23-31F, the additional facets permit the groove to be polished even at high percentages of modulation. The angles of the facets are leading facet 60°, center facet 25°, and last facet 10°. ANM styli are used for both standard and microgroove recording.

The life of a recording sapphire stylus, if treated with care, is about six to eight hours. The tip of the stylus should be wiped off with lacquer solvent after each use to prevent small microscopic particles from sticking to the tip and fouling the groove while recording.

Mounting styli in a stereophonic recording head is shown in Fig. 23-32 and used in both the Westrex 3C and 3D cutting head. In the 3D head, the design of the stylus and the torque tube are such that the cutting head does not have to be removed from the recording lathe to replace the stylus. The stylus is 1.5 times the diameter of the one used in the 3C head and has a flattened face 6 mils deep and 39 mils wide, ground the full length of the sapphire. The ground surface serves as the stylus cutting face and as a flat for mating to the precision mount, designed to result in a precision alignment of the burnishing facets and cutting face.

Figure 23-26 "The Lathe"—current model of L. J. Scully Recording Instruments Corp. A Westrex cutterhead is mounted in the carriage assembly. Variable pitch computer by Capps shown in front. *(Courtesy L. J. Scully Manufacturing Corp.)*

A recording stylus can be aligned vertically by observing the reflection of the recording stylus on the surface of the recording blank, as shown in Fig. 23-33. When the reflected image is in perfect alignment with the actual stylus shank, the alignment is correct.

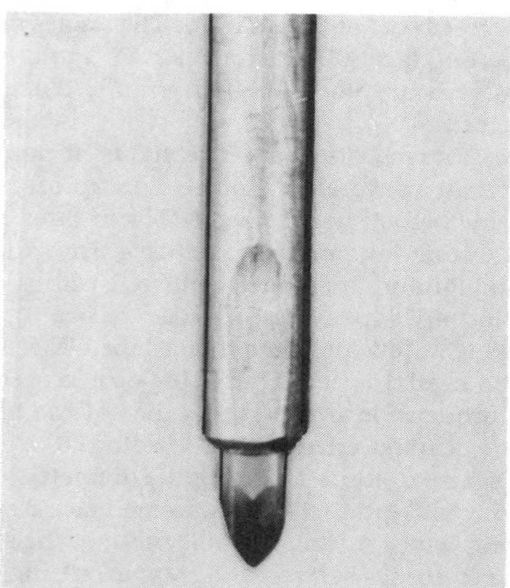

Figure 23-27 A coarse-pitched recording stylus with 87° included angle, 1.5-mil tip radius.

Because of the nature of the stylus suspension in a stereophonic cutting head, the stylus describes an arc in the vertical mode, and because of this motion, the cutting face is tilted back from the vertical (Fig. 23-34). This results in an increase of the included angle of the groove (Fig. 23-35). In view of this fact and that the reproducing stylus rides on the wall of the groove and not the bottom, the waveform is distorted and increases with an increase in the recorded level. For the Westrex stereo system, the recording angle is specified to be 23°; however, studies show that the angle of the recording stylus can change. It is hard to predict the final angle, since factors other than stylus angle inject themselves into the study. Among these factors are fitting of the recording stylus in the recording head, stylus shank material, and bonding of the jewel in the stylus shank. Any shifting of the jewel tip because of the bonding will cause resonance and also affect the vertical angle. The jewel and stylus shank must act as an integral part.

When reproducing a record cut at a 23° angle (or greater), the reproducer stylus angle is set to an angle of 20° to reduce the distortion caused by the difference in the angle of the recorded groove. It has been agreed by the manufacturers of sound-reproducing equipment that the angle for the reproducing stylus is to be 20°. At the present time, this leaves the record manufacturer with the problem of establishing the correct angle for the recording stylus to produce a 20° groove in the finished product. Unfortunately, many recording companies still cut records with a vertical angle less than 20°, sometimes closer to 10° or even less.

The scoop-shaped stylus is used to reduce the error of the vertical groove motion, as discussed in the last paragraph. The scooped stylus is manufactured by Capps & Co., Inc. Its construction is shown in Fig. 23-36.

By making the cutting face of the stylus a circular arc, it is possible to reduce considerably the deviation of the cutting head face from the perpendicular to the record surface. In addition, the curved surface of the stylus facilitates the removal of the chip, while improving the signal-to-noise ratio for an average of 3 dB compared to the conventional flat-faced stylus. Based on considerable research and study, the conclusions reached were that groove walls recorded using a flat-faced stylus are not actually straight, but are concave, due to the nature of the lacquer disk and the motion of the stylus. This may be verified by a study of the chip, which is not a true triangle.

The *hot-stylus recording* is a technique using a stylus that is heated to a rather high temperature by a small heating coil wound around the recording stylus tip. When a hot stylus is used, the horns caused by cold flow at the upper edges of the record groove are made smaller, permitting a higher level to be recorded. A lower noise level results when cutting with heated stylus and the signal-to-noise ratio is improved by as much as 18 dB. With hot-stylus techniques, diameter equalization is not required because of the improved high-frequency response.

Operating temperatures of the cutting stylus vary from 350°F upward. In a series of tests conducted by Jackson, under controlled conditions, it was learned that the particular coil in use produced the highest output level at a current of 500 mA. Current used to heat a stylus can be either alternating or direct current.

The average coil consists of about 7.5 turns of nichrome wire, 0.005 in. in diameter, having a resistance of 32 Ω/ft. The coil is closely wound over the stylus and held in place by the special high-temperature epoxy. As the current through the coil is increased, the signal-to-noise ratio will be increased, up to a certain point. Beyond this point, the chip may be caused to burn and adhere to the stylus so that its removal will damage the tip. Under no circumstances should the recording be made without the suction pump being on.

There are several types of vacuum systems in use today. One of the oldest and quietest pumps used was the Van-Eps bellows pump for church organs. Vacuum cleaners with Variacs® had been used as have other types of vane pumps. But they all had a jar with water to collect the highly flammable chip, as shown in Fig. 23-37. With the new technique of cutting directly in metal (Fig. 23-38), the chip is metallic, and there is no fire danger. It is of interest that the use of a hot stylus was experimented with in 1891 using a flame.

23.3 DISK CUTTING AND RECORD MANUFACTURING

Many years ago when there were no tape recorders or electron tubes, the only kind of recording that existed was acoustical. It meant that for the sound to be recorded it had to be collected by huge horns and directed toward the membrane of the cutting head, which vibrated the cutting stylus attached to it. This stylus, as it was cutting the groove either in the surface of the rotating cylinder or the disk, was modulating it in accordance with the sound waves that were being received. This primitive type of direct-to-disk recording, in the beginning, produced very dramatic results. Playback of such a recording was also mechanical. The needle or the stylus, in following the excursions or modulation of the groove, vibrated the membrane, which acted as a loudspeaker, in turn vibrating the air and producing sound.

With the invention of the electron tube, the new world opened up for the art of sound recording. The newly invented carbon microphone was converting the sound waves into electrical signals, which in turn were amplified electronically and used to drive the electrical cutters. The whole idea of the disk record was to make it possible to mass produce the recordings easily and inexpensively. In order to achieve this, several compromises were allowed over the cylindrical recordings. The most significant one was the varying groove velocity as seen by the playback stylus. The groove velocity varied as the speed of the turntable remained constant. This affects the quality of the sound being reproduced from the inner grooves because the modulation is condensed and the playback stylus cannot follow excursions with the same accuracy. In earlier days of disk recording, this phenomenon was quite severe because of inadequate playback equipment, so to rectify it, the so-called diameter equalization was used during the recording. It consisted of amplifying more high frequencies as the cutting head was approaching the center of the disk record.

Today, the technology of disk cutting has been perfected to the point where, under certain playback conditions, it is hard to distinguish the live sound from the sound electronically reproduced. It is truly amazing that after all the transformations of signal and manufacturing processes involved in manufacturing records, the sound we hear as an end product is so crisp and clean.

The first step in producing the disk record is to cut the *master*. This process is called *mastering of the record*. The mastering process involves cutting the modulated groove in the lacquer according to developed standards dealing with dimensions of the record and the processing of the signals being recorded.

The construction of the lacquer disk for cutting appears simple; however, it consists of a precision aluminum blank disk coated with an extremely uniform layer of nitrocellulose lacquer on both sides. The surface of the disk has a mirrorlike surface finish with maximum roughness not exceeding 2 μin. or 500 Å. The recording blanks are usually classified by their surface roughness and selected either for demo or trial cutting (lower grade) or for a mastering (high-precision cutting surface). The lacquer disks are produced in different sizes normally larger than the record being cut. For instance, to cut a master for a 12-in. long-playing disk, a 14-in. blank is used. This extra area gives enough time to properly adjust the cutter, the stylus heat, and the groove depth.

23.3.1 Record Dimensions

Excerpts from the EIA standard for producing analog disk records follow.

The diameter of records shall be as follows (Figs. 23-39 and 23-40).

23.3.1.1 Diameter of Record

11.875 ± 0.031 in. (301.6 ± 0.8 mm) (12-in. lp disk)
9.875 ± 0.031 in. (250.8 ± 0.8 mm) (10-in. disk)
6.875 ± 0.031 in. (174.6 ± 0.8 mm) (7-in., 45-rpm disk)

The recorded surface shall start with at least one turn of unmodulated groove.

23.3.1.2 Maximum Outer Diameter

The maximum outer diameter of a recorded surface shall be as follows:

11.500 in. (292.1 mm)
9.500 in. (241.3 mm)
6.625 in. (168.3 mm)

23.3.1.3 Groove Dimensions

The groove dimensions shall be as follows:

Minimum top width (monophonic only)—0.0022 in. (0.56 mm)
Maximum bottom radius—0.00025 in. (0.006 mm)
Included angle—90° ± 5°

On stereophonic records, the instantaneous groove width should be not less than 0.001 in. (0.025 mm). The average groove width should preferably be not less than 0.0014 in. (0.035 mm).

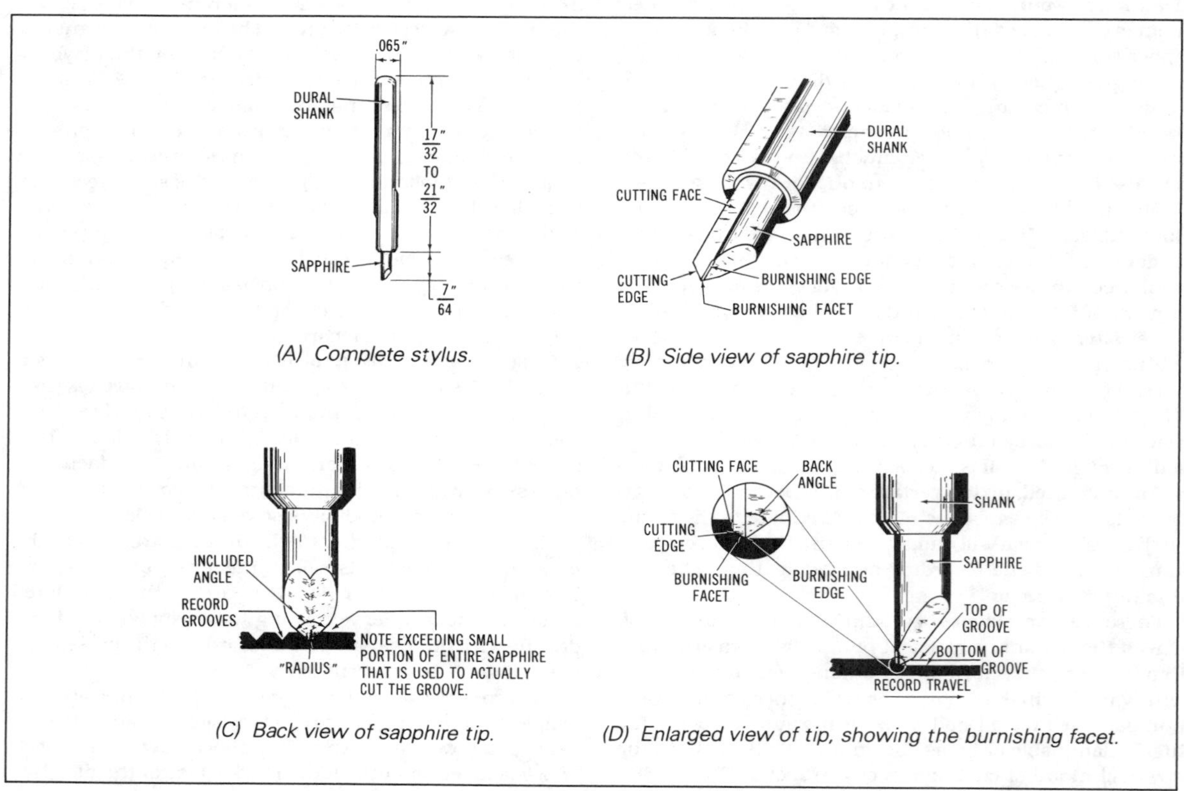

(A) Complete stylus.

(B) Side view of sapphire tip.

(C) Back view of sapphire tip.

(D) Enlarged view of tip, showing the burnishing facet.

Figure 23-28 Essential

23.3.1.4 Stereophonic Groove

The *stereophonic groove* shall carry two channels of information. The two channels shall be recorded in such a manner that they can be reproduced by movement of a reproducing stylus tip in two directions at 90° to each other and at 45° to a radial line through the stylus tip and the center of the record. The reproducing stylus tip motion shall be tangential to, or lie in a plane through, the stylus tip and the record center, preferably inclined at an angle of 20 ± 5° clockwise to the normal to the record surface through the stylus tip, as viewed from the record center. In practice, angles of between 0 and 25° may be encountered.

23.3.1.5 Channel Orientation

The groove shall be recorded for reproduction with the right-hand loudspeaker(s), as viewed from the audience, actuated by movement of the groove wall, which is further away from the center of the record.

23.3.1.6 Channel Phasing

The phasing of the two recorded signals shall be suitable for reproduction on equipment so connected that movement of the reproducing stylus tip parallel to the record surface (as with a monophonic record) produces

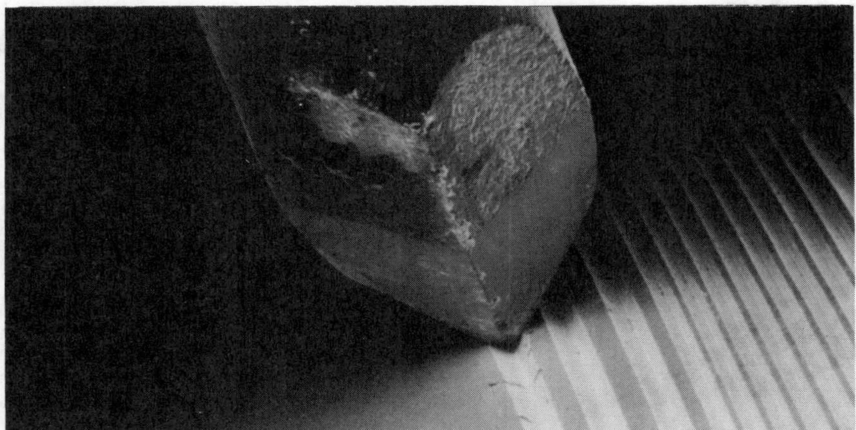

(E) Back view of disk cutting, magnification 50 times. (Courtesy Stanton Magnetics, Inc.)

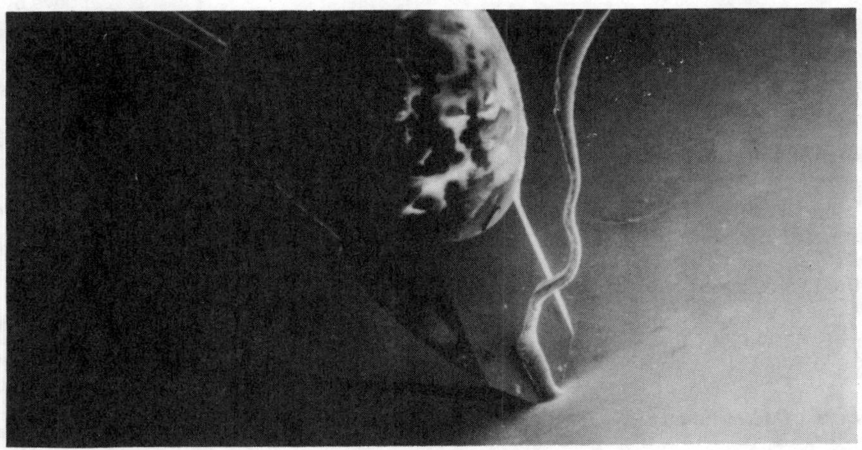

(F) Actual cutting groove and formation of chip, magnification 50 times. (Courtesy Stanton Magnetics, Inc.)

parts of recording stylus.

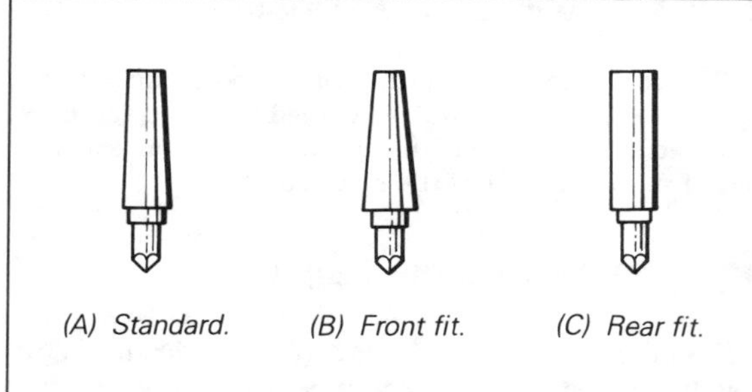

Figure 23-29 Stylus shanks.

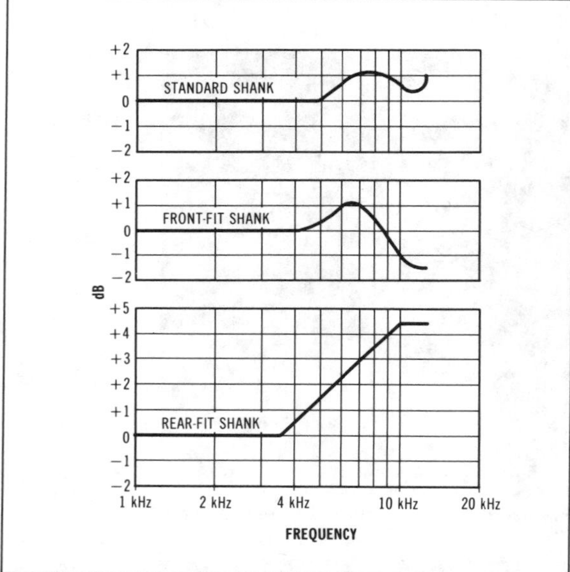

Figure 23-30 Frequency response of recording styli using different shank tapers.

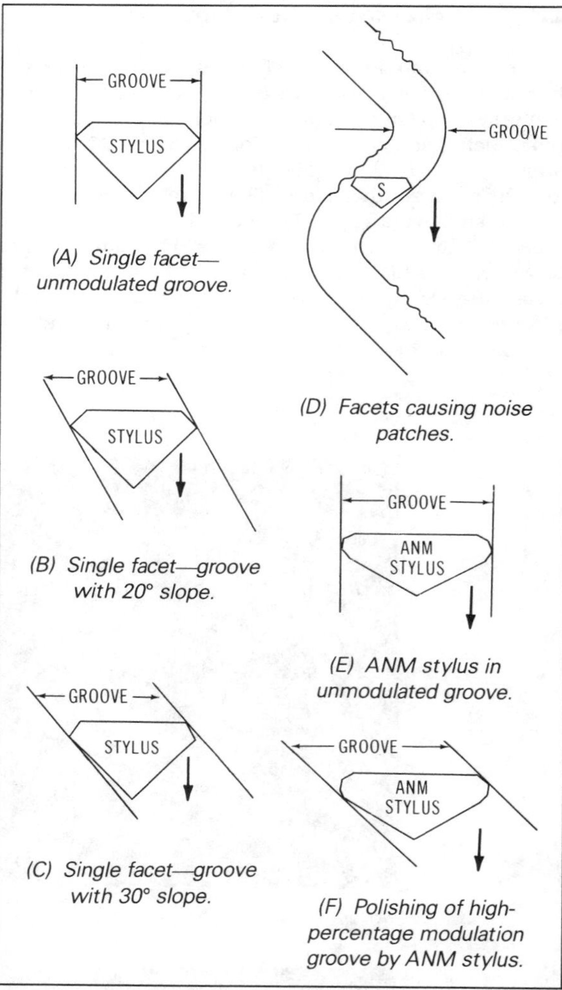

Figure 23-31 Single and multiburnishing facet recording styli. *(Courtesy Audio Devices Inc.)*

in-phase signals across the output terminals of the phono cartridge.

23.3.1.7 Channel Levels

The levels of the two recorded signals should be such that peak excursions of the groove should not exceed 100 μm or 0.004 in. in lateral plane and 50 μm or 0.002 in. in vertical plane.

23.3.1.8 Speed of Rotation

Records shall be recorded for reproduction at one of the following speeds:

50-Hz electric supplies	60-Hz electric supplies
45.11 rpm ± 0.5%	45.00 rpm ± 0.5%
33⅓ rpm ± 0.5%	33⅓ rpm ± 0.5%

23.3.1.9 Lead-In Groove Pitch

The pitch of the lead-in groove shall be 16 ± 2 lines/in.

23.3.1.10 Lead-Out Groove Pitch

The pitch of the lead-out groove shall be 2 to 6 lines/in.

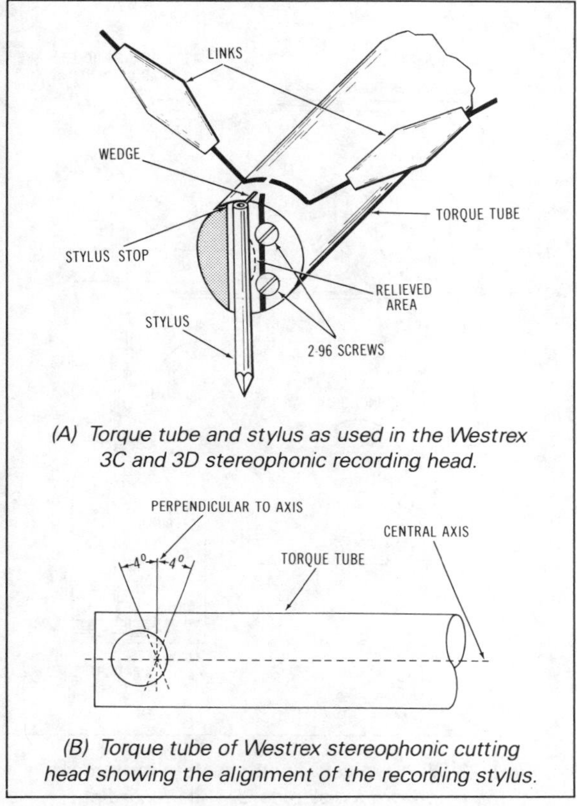

(A) Torque tube and stylus as used in the Westrex 3C and 3D stereophonic recording head.

(B) Torque tube of Westrex stereophonic cutting head showing the alignment of the recording stylus.

Figure 23-32 Torque tube and stylus. *(Courtesy Westrex Corp., Division of Mitsubishi Pro Audio Group)*

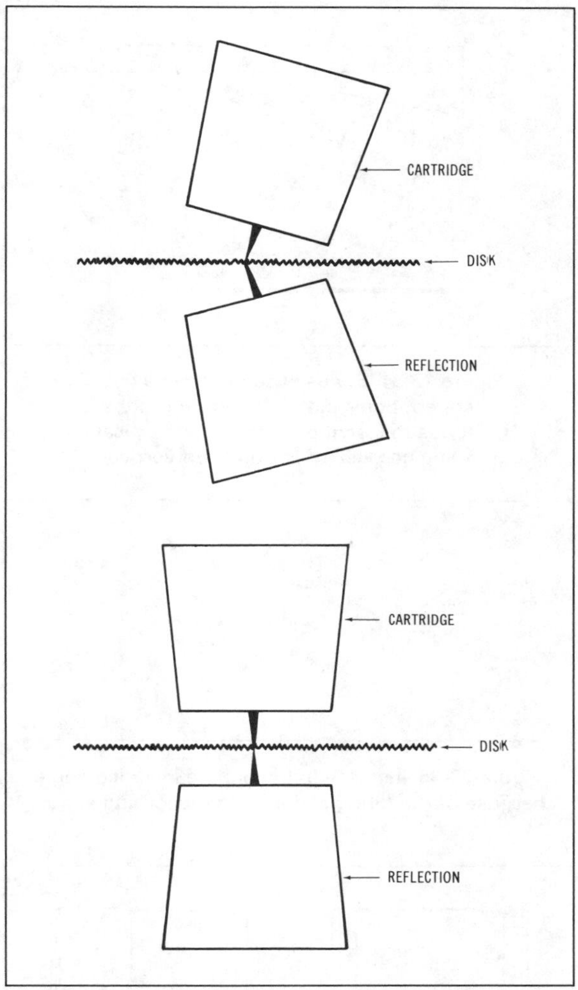

Figure 23-33 Vertical alignment of stylus by observing its reflection on the surface of the disk.

23.3.1.11 Lead-Out Groove Width

The top width of the lead-out groove shall increase to a minimum of 0.003 in. (0.076 mm) when the pitch exceeds ¼ in. (6.4 mm).

23.3.1.12 Finishing Groove

The diameter of the finishing groove shall be as follows:

4.187 ± 0.31 in. (106.4 ± 0.8 mm)	12- and 10-in. disks
3.875 ± 0.078 in. (98.4 ± 2 mm)	7-in. disks

23.3.2 Disk Cutting

The procedure of cutting the disk record starts with placing the blank lacquer disk on the cutting lathe platter and activating the suction hold-down system, which holds the recording blank flat against the surface of the turntable and prevents it from slipping after the cutting starts.

Start the turntable spinning at the desired cutting speed. The standard speeds are 33⅓ rpm and 45 rpm. However, in some instances when it is desirable to extend the upper portion of the frequency range, half-speed mastering is practiced. This procedure is not as straightforward as it seems at first, since it involves adjusting equalization of the tape machine and disk-cutting amplifier in order to end up with a flat frequency response in the finished product. Not all disk-cutting lathes are designed to run half speed.

Once the recording blank is rotating, position the cutting head carriage so that the cutting head is just above the outer portion of the disk lacquer. Before lowering the cutter onto the surface of the disk, turn on the suction

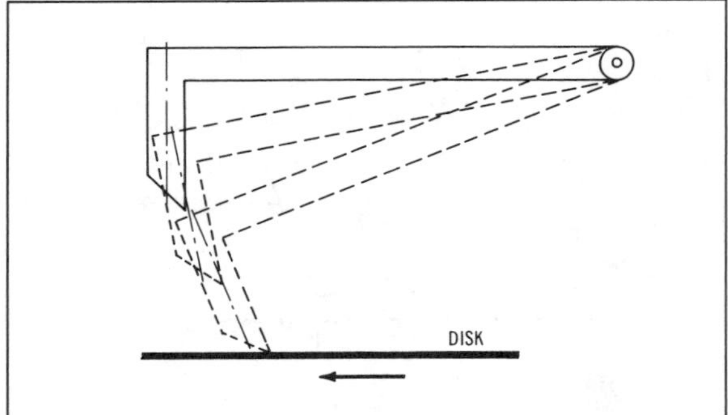

Figure 23-34 Stylus suspension in a 45°/45° stereophonic cutting head causes the stylus to inscribe an arc in the vertical mode because of the tilt from vertical.

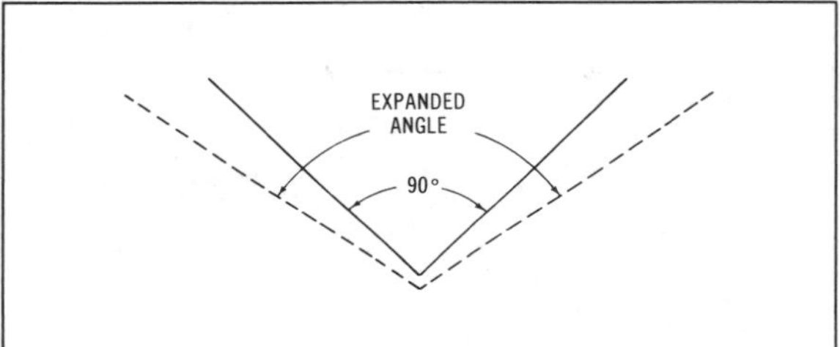

Figure 23-35 Increase in the groove included angle because of the tilting action of the recording stylus.

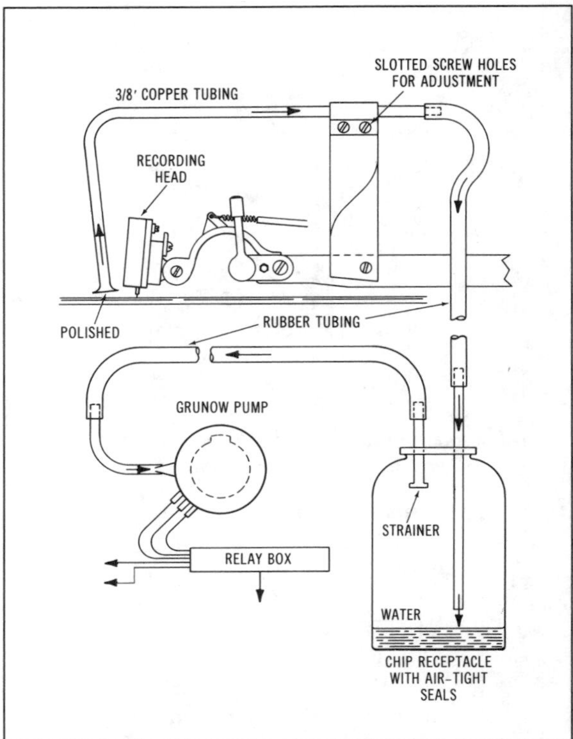

Figure 23-37 A typical vacuum system for removing the chip from a disk record while recording. *(Courtesy Audio Devices Inc.)*

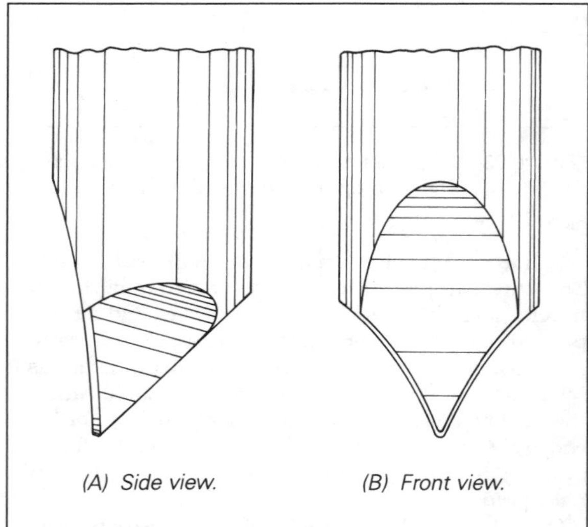

Figure 23-36 Cappscoop recording stylus for stereophonic microgroove recording.

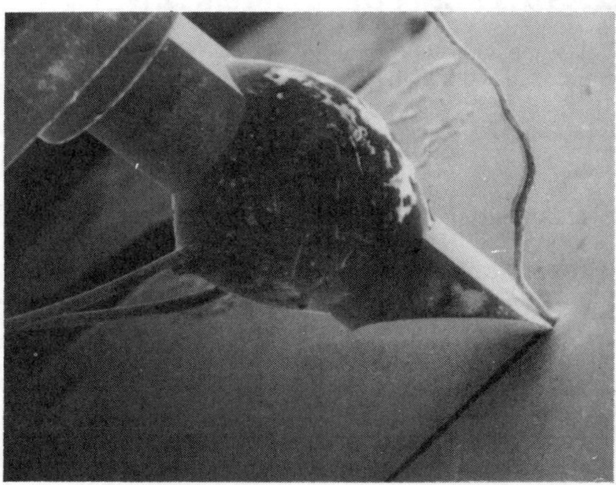

Figure 23-38 Cutting stylus with heater coil. *(Courtesy Stanton Magnetics, Inc.)*

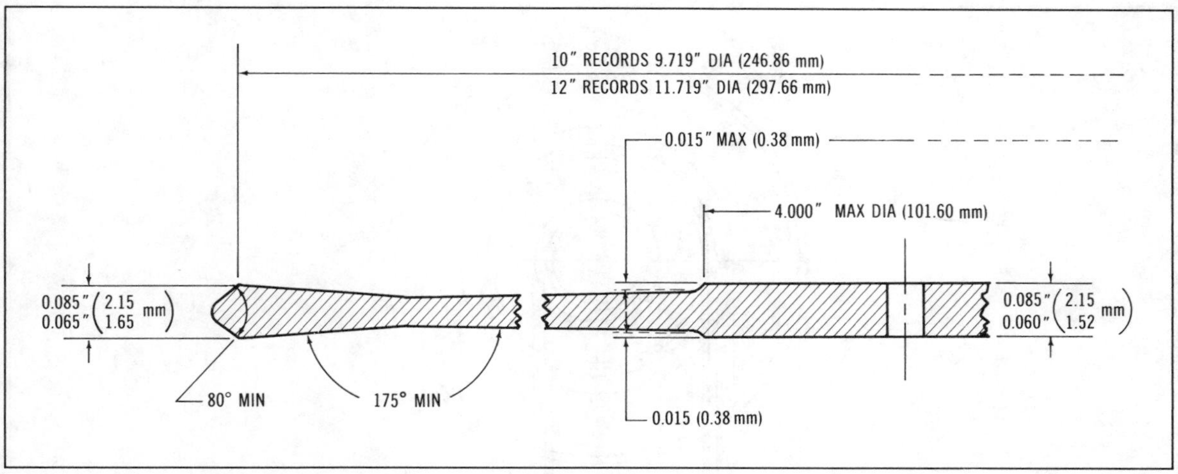

Figure 23-39 Profile and dimension of a 12-in. long-playing record.

for chip removal, and turn on the stylus heat (if it is not automatic). Finally, slowly lower the cutter to start cutting the groove.

At this time you should have your tape machine ready to play the master tape, your cutting amplifier turned on, your cutting pitch adjusted, your recording level set, and your monitor system ready to be turned up.

As the cutter is lowered and the groove is being cut, check and adjust the groove width using the microscope. Check the amount of heat by either checking the current through the heater wire or by placing the auxiliary tonearm into the test groove being cut and turning up the monitor speaker and listening to the surface noise of the cut. By varying the amount of heat, you can minimize the surface noise as you listen to it.

Lift the tonearm and don't use it any further to play the musical portion of the recording unless you are making a test and do not intend to use the disk as a master. Now you are set to cut the lead-in groove. Press the spiral button on the control panel of the cutting lathe until the pointer of the carriage reaches the proper diameter to start the modulated groove. Most modern machines have automatic start circuits for the tape recorders so that no time is wasted in starting the program. Momentarily press the button for spiraling between the individual selections to separate individual songs or parts of the program.

As the cutting takes place, variable-pitch and depth-control systems will adjust the spacing between the adjacent grooves in order to conserve the recording space and to prevent overcutting during the loud passages, which have strong low-frequency signals. As the last selection approaches the end, be ready to press the spiral button to produce lead-out, and locking groove. If the cutting was successful and there are no mistakes or flaws that would cause later mistracking or skipping the groove, remove the master disk from the lathe and store it in a dust-free container or a box designed to transport the lacquers. To produce the complete two-sided record, you should cut two separate lacquer master disks, rather than one, recorded on both sides.

As the last music groove has been cut and the spiraling mechanism moves the cutter to produce the locking groove, be ready to lift the cutter up from the lacquer as soon as the locking groove is completed and do not allow the cutter to cut the same groove twice. As the cutter is lifted, shut off the heater current first (unless it is done automatically), turn the turntable drive off, and stop the suction.

23.3.3 Lacquer Processing

Finished lacquers are marked (scribed) with the disk number and side designation and then placed in a special shipping box and sent to the plating plant for further processing.

This described procedure does not mention many of the preparatory steps necessary for successful mastering. Since this is not the manual for mastering engineers, we will restrict ourselves to mentioning rather than listing all of the necessary adjustments. It is appropriate to mention that the previous procedure considers the use of prerecorded programming, which was carefully edited, remixed, and prepared for disk cutting, including separating the individual selections with leader (nonmagnetic) tape to keep the noise down. Also, it is assumed that the cutting system has been calibrated and adjusted for the proper preemphasis curve, levels have been set so that no overcutting will take place, and the cutting stylus was checked for wear and alignment. And these tests are only a small part of what one has to think of before any

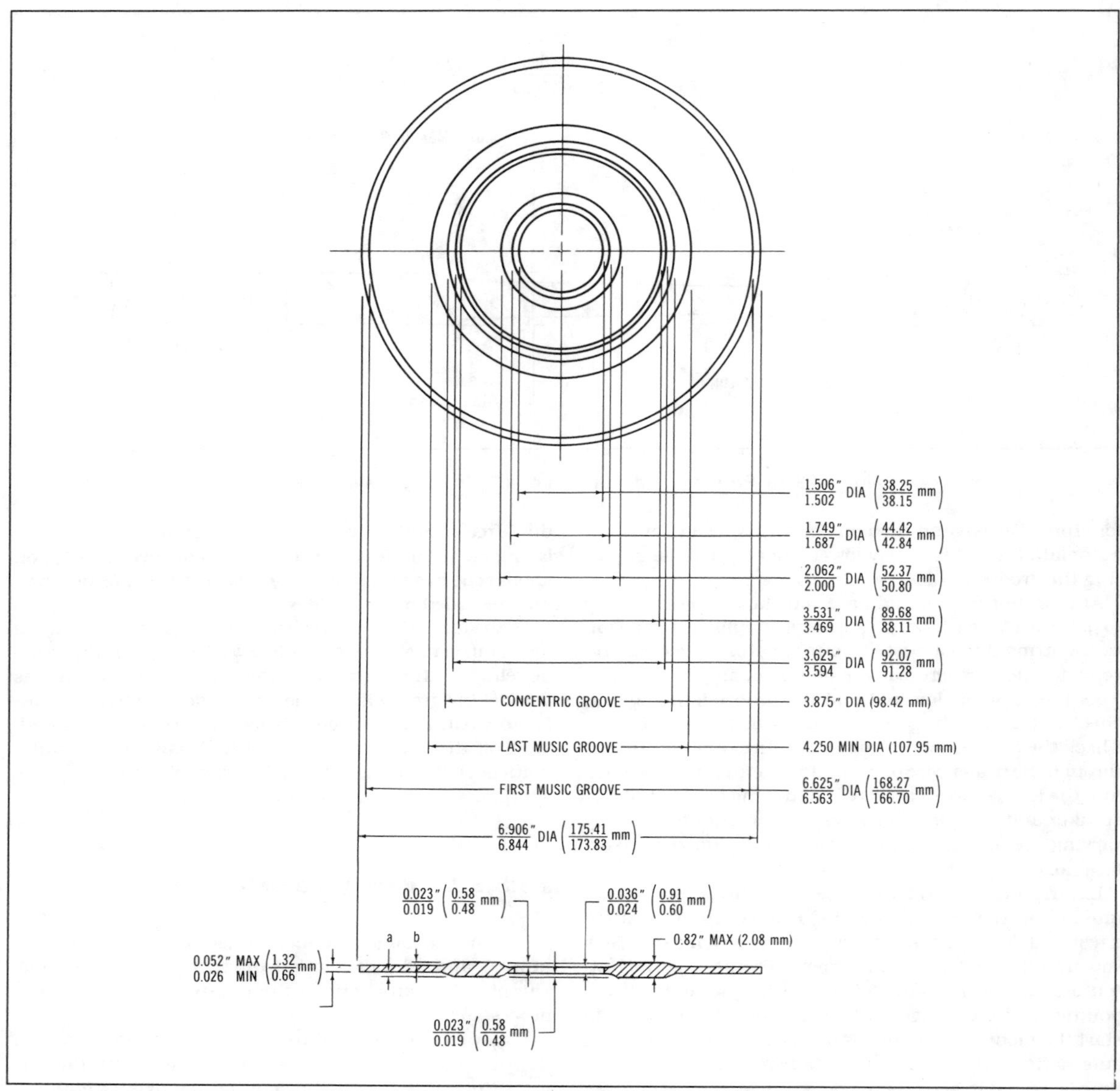

Figure 23-40 45-rpm 7-in. record dimensions.

master disks are cut because mistakes made in system alignment ruin many recordings.

One lacquer master disk can produce thousands of first grade records, and the quality of each pressing depends on the quality of the original master. Therefore, the extra care in the process of turning the cut lacquer into vinyl records is so important and requires thorough knowledge of all processes involved.

As seen in Fig. 23-41, a cut lacquer master is plated, and a metal master is formed from it. From the metal master or father, a metal mother is derived by a second plating. The mother is the second step in the process and produces the first positive metal duplicate of the original cut. It is possible to produce or pull several mothers from a single metal master, depending on many factors starting with careful plating, cutting, and separating of the plated parts. The metal mother is usually made much thicker and stronger so that in the next step of plating,

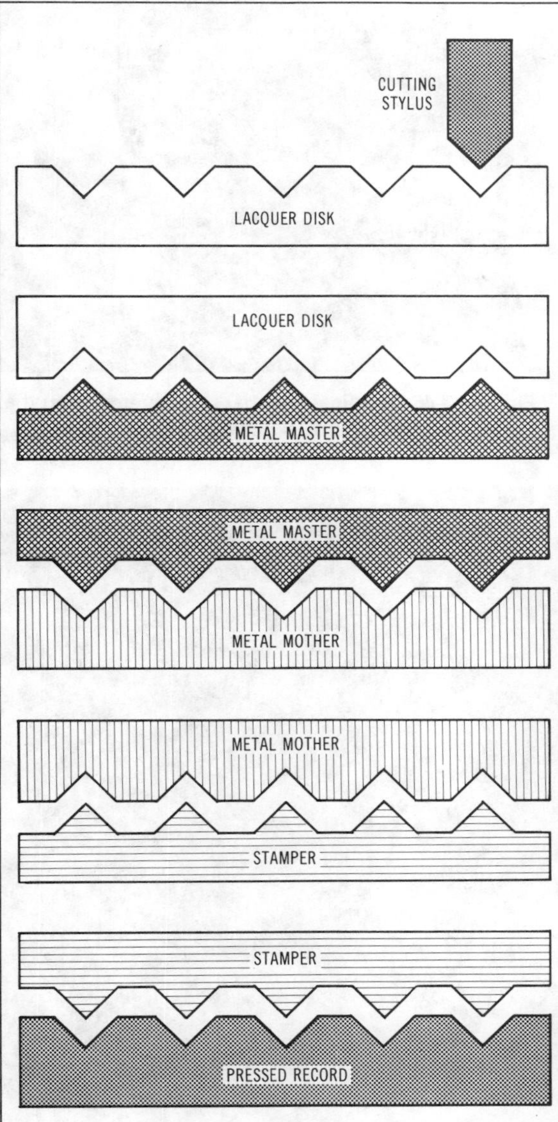

Figure 23-41 The various stages in the pressing process. Noise and other flaws can be introduced at any stage. *(From* Basic Disc Mastering, *Courtesy Larry Boden)*

many metal stampers can be generated, each capable of pressing tens of thousands of records. In order to manufacture one double-sided long-playing record, it is necessary to cut two lacquer masters, have two metal masters, at least one metal mother per side, and many metal stampers per each side.

23.3.4 Plating of Master, Mother, and Stamper

The process of plating the lacquer disks starts with washing the surface of the lacquer with mild detergent and distilled water to remove dust or dirt. After that, the master is immersed into a solution of stannous chloride.

Next, the disk is rotated and sprayed at the same time with a silvering solution (silver nitrate) to make the surface electrically conductive (Fig. 23-42). Once the surface of the lacquer disk is coated with silver, it is immersed into the nickel sulfamate solution to be nickel plated. After enough nickel has been deposited on the surface, the deposited layer of nickel is carefully peeled off, and this negative impression is called the metal master (Fig. 23-43). This metal master is then chemically treated to produce the second metal impression from it and form the so-called mother. Nickel is plated onto the metal master and when a sufficiently thick coating is formed, it is separated from the master, as shown in Fig. 23-44.

Figure 23-42 Silvering the master lacquer. *(Courtesy Stanton Magnetics, Inc.)*

Figure 23-43 Once coated with nickel at the proper thickness, the acetate is removed from solution. *(Courtesy Stanton Magnetics, Inc.)*

Figure 23-44 Separating the acetate and the metal master. *(Courtesy Stanton Magnetics, Inc.)*

Figure 23-45 The final stamper is separated from the metal mother. *(Courtesy Stanton Magnetics, Inc.)*

The metal mother is the first positive impression of the record, and it can be played the same way conventional records are reproduced. At this time if there are any pops and clicks heard during the playing of the metal groove, a special heavy tracking playback stylus is used to burnish the groove walls, thereby, removing annoying pops and clicks.

In the last several years it became popular to polish the surface of the metal mother in order to remove the horns of the groove. The horns are curled up edges of the groove produced by the stylus in the process of cutting. The size and shape of the horns depend on the amount of heat used, the sharpness of the stylus, and the lacquer itself. It is desirable to remove horns because in the process of plating, the horns turn into one continuous curl, which interlocks with the material being plated on. Also, in the negative or stamper, the next step after the mother, horns become a tiny groove on both sides of the ridge and in the procees of pressing the vinyl record interfere with easy separation of the stamper and finished record.

After the removal of the horns, or after dehorning, the metal mother is plated again, and this time the second record negative, the so-called stamper, emerges (Fig. 23-45). The mother can be plated many times and produce many stampers. The quality of plating can be checked using a Stanton Bi-pointed stylus, which plays negatives (Fig. 23-46). However, frequent handling and bending of the mother slowly damages the metal surface and makes the part useless.

Each stamper, before it can be used for pressing the records, has to be properly trimmed and shaped in order to fit the record-pressing machine. One of the most important things being done to a stamper is finding the true center of the recording and punching the center hole. Unless the stamper is perfectly centered, there will be bad eccentricity of the recorded groove that will result in a bad once-around wow. The back of the stamper is cleaned and made smooth in order to keep the record surface flat.

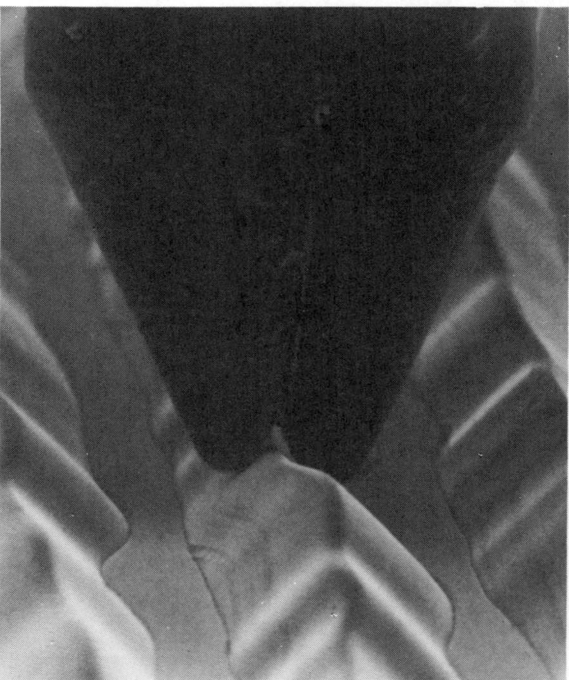

Figure 23-46 Bi-pointed stylus used to test stampers. *(Courtesy Stanton Magnetics, Inc.)*

Once the stampers are mounted into the press, we are ready to press the records. By the way, two stampers are required to press one double-sided disk.

The pressing of the record consists of placing the preheated, premeasured doughnut of vinyl between the two stampers and then applying the pressure until the two stampers are within the thickness of the record being

Figure 23-47 The warm vinyl biscuit placed in the center of the stamper. *(Courtesy Stanton Magnetics, Inc.)*

produced to each other (Fig. 23-47). Once the material cools and solidifies, the two stampers are pulled apart, and the newly pressed record emerges. The small excess of vinyl material is immediately trimmed from the record, which is placed between the two rotating metal disks the size of the record, exposing only the excess material. After the trimming, the record is inserted into the sleeve, and it is ready for sale and to be played.

It is not possible to mention all the details of record pressing, but just to name a few. The vinyl biscuit is preheated to the temperature of 300°F and is extruded from vinyl granules, which are usually stored outside the pressing plant in large holding silos and then pumped automatically to the presses through the system of pipes. This system is used to prevent the exposure of the compound to the moisture and contaminants in the air. In the early days pressings were made using slate powder and shellac as a binding agent, which is why they were called shellac records. The idea then was to have the record surface abrasive to keep the steel stylus worn down to the shape of the groove. These records are obsolete today. Today for reasons of economy, many record-pressing plants have been using polystyrene, not vinyl, to produce 45-rpm disks. Unfortunately, the properties of this material are such that after several playings of the groove, the outer layer of the material peels off exposing course and granule inner layers of the record. Broadcasters who rely heavily on playing popular disk records live on the air usually backcue the records. In other words, with the stylus placed in the groove they rotate the turntable backward until the desired part of the groove is reached and then, when ready, spin the record in order to start the song or musical selection without losing precious time. In the process of backcueing, the record groove takes the beating, and the polystyrene records exhibit so called *cueburn*, the worn spot, just before the start of a musical selection, which has high surface noise, usually over 10 dB above the quiet portion of the groove. It is hoped that new pressing materials could be found to replace inferior polystyrene for this application.

In the process of extruding the vinyl on the stampers in automatic machines, two labels are placed over the center pin on both sides of the biscuit prior to closing the press, so that when the record emerges from the press it already has both labels. However, the process may vary depending on construction and vintage of the machines.

In the record-pressing machine both stampers are attached to two heavy metal plates that have water passages. They are attached to the superheated steam and cold water piping. As the mold is in the process of closing, the hot steam is fed into the passages to help heat the stampers and allow easy flow of the vinyl. Once the mold closes, the cold water is circulated, cooling the vinyl.

Because of a certain amount of abrasiveness of the vinyl, both stampers wear and, after several thousand copies, have to be replaced.

23.3.5 Direct Metal Mastering (DMM)

The process of making records has undergone many changes since the day it was invented and until its present form. And yet many new improvements are being added. For one, the cutting of the original is being done directly into the copper by a select group of recording and cutting companies.

This method promises simplification of the entire manufacturing process and considerable improvement in the quality of reproduced signal. It consists of electroplating pure copper onto the optically flat metal disk (Fig. 23-48). Once the sufficient amount of copper has been deposited, it is separated from the metal disk and used instead of lacquer (Fig. 23-49). To cut into the copper, a special cutting stylus has to be used with the modified cutting head (Fig. 23-50). This cutter makes the cutting stylus vibrate at a very high supersonic frequency, thereby easing the chip-removal process. The advantage of this method is that during cutting, no heat is required and no horns are formed on the sides of the groove. Also, there is no electrostatic charge to attract dust to the surface of the disk, and there is no groove deformation or cold-flow after the cutting is finished. There is no need to silver the finished master because the surface is already conductive, and the original automatically becomes the metal mother from which stampers are made. If the old procedure called for three-step plating processes, this one is a one-step process, just as if the lacquer master was plated and the metal negative was used to press the record (the old, one-step process produced so-called strikeoffs when a very small quantity of records were to be produced, a few hundred at the most). But because this technology requires the use of a few proprietory techniques and is subject for licensing agreements, it may not become as widespread as we might wish it would, at least not at the present time.

Figure 23-48 Europafilm (plating system for the creation of the DMM) copper blank. *(Courtesy Teldec/Baerthel)*

23.3.6 Direct-to-Disk Mastering and PCM Technology

Another old method of producing records was revived recently, the so-called direct-to-disk recording, which consisted of bypassing the tape recorder altogether and setting up the cutting machines and feeding them directly from specially beefed-up consoles. This cuts onto the disk signals with the least amount of degradation, the largest dynamic range, and the lowest noise because tape has inherently higher noise than a disk, and signal degradation during the remixing and editing procedures used in conjunction with multitrack tape machines reduces the quality of recorded music.

But the economic considerations and practical inconveniences of this method have all but forced the curtailment of production of records using this approach. Instead, the new technology, based on conversion of signals into the digital *PCM (pulse-code modulation)* format has emerged. One of the biggest advantages of the digital format, is that it allows preservation of the original signal in almost perfect form, from the moment the signal comes from the recording console, and is converted into digital form until it is reconverted back into an analog signal just before the cutting of the master disk. The PCM format has its own weak points and disadvantages, for instance, the cost of the equipment and the cost to operate it. The analog signal is chopped into very short pulses, and each pulse is converted into a set of numbers. In order to make such chopping of the signal appear smooth and continuous, very high sampling rates have to be used with each sample byte, requiring large numbers of bits of information. This requires the use of a tape recorder system capable of recording very high frequencies like video signals. This digital technology creates new demands for rerecording equipment, such as equalizers, echo and reverberation devices, or so-called signal-sweetening equipment, since all have to process numbers rather than

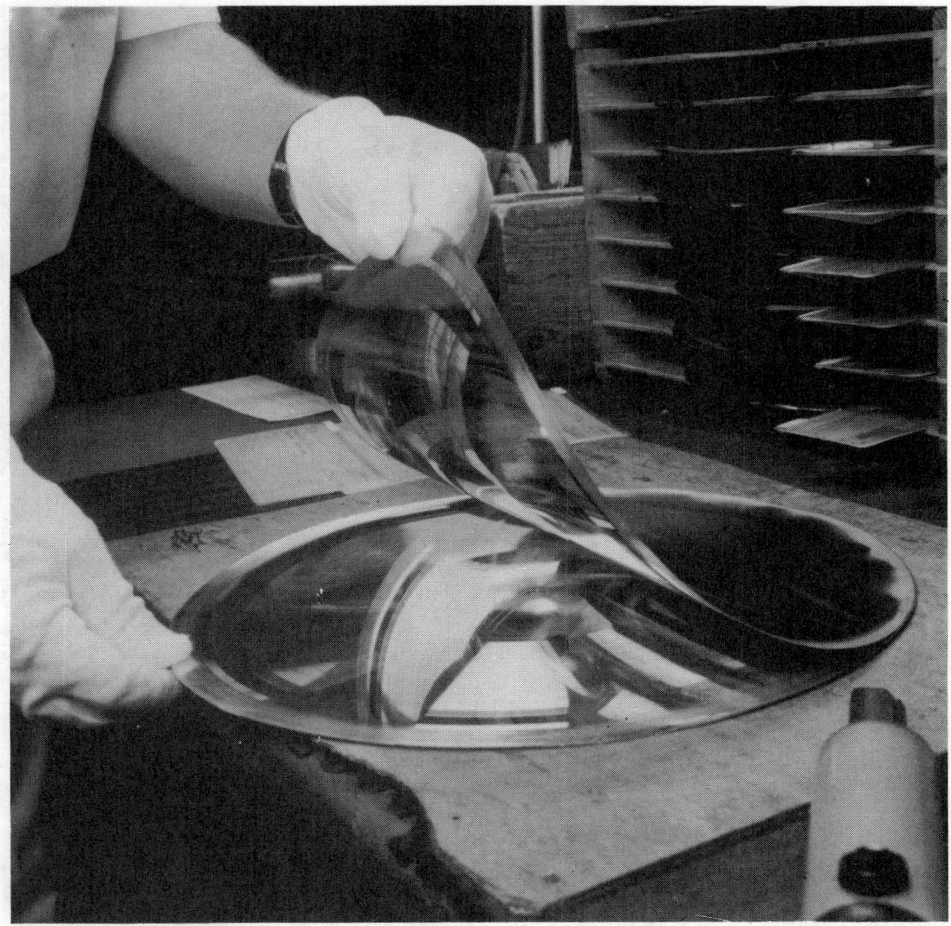

Figure 23-49 DMM (direct stamper production) separation of the stamper from the copper master. *(Courtesy Teldec/Baerthel)*

sine waves and analog signals. The weakest point of digital is in dealing with the highest frequencies of recorded spectrum.

PCM in its present form goes only up to 20 kHz and there it stops. Normally, this bandwidth would be sufficient, but there are only four bits per sine-wave cycle available to describe the signal, which may be considered a deviation from the road to perfection by restricting the bandwidth and losing the infinite resolution found in analog processes.

Another drawback of the system at present is the lack of standardization. There are too many formats and incompatible machines being used to reach the practicality of analog technology where any studio in the world can play tapes made elsewhere. The digital technology in its present form bears little compatibility with previous technologies. Besides, there are strong indications that this may not be the final format the digital world can offer us.

There are very stringent requirements for mechanical parts used in the equipment, especially in the latest *digital compact disk (CD)* development. A digital audio disk has only two things in common with the present analog audio record. First, it is also a disk, and second the end product is sound. Here the resemblance ends. The CD is only about 5 in. in diameter and has to rotate with a varying speed of 500 to 200 revolutions/min. It uses a laser beam to read the modulation encoded on the tracks (there are no grooves), which are only 1.6 μm wide representing approximately 15875 lines per inch. Present long-playing records have only 150 to 200 lines or grooves per inch (except when variable pitch is used where it can reach close to 1000, which is not very practical). The CD record stores up to 60 minutes of programming with a

Figure 23-50 Neumann cutting lathe with direct metal mastering (DMM) cutterhead. *(Courtesy Teldec/Baerthel)*

dynamic range of close to 90 dB and a signal-to-noise ratio of 90 dB, and it does it without variable pitch.

It also maintains perfect speed because the turntable speed is controlled by the encoded information within the signal itself. There is no wow and flutter for the same reason, and there is no stylus wear because there is no stylus and no physical contact with the record. The record cannot be scratched easily or made noisy as in an analog disk. Also, it cannot be cut or pressed in a conventional way, and that limits its acceptance to few of today's record-manufacturing companies who are capable of processing this high-technology product. Only time will tell if this record format will be accepted and survive in its present form. See section 23.12 for more on PCM digital recording.

23.4 TURNTABLES AND TONEARMS

To play a record, the turntable or device to rotate the disk at the required speed is needed. This is the basic requirement for all turntables. However, the construction and execution of the requirement may differ greatly between the models and the designs of different manufacturers. The history of evolution of the record drive mechanisms takes us from the days of hand-cranked cylinder machines, through the age of spring-wound phonographs with mechanical governors for speed control, and into the age of electrically driven machines having the sophistication of modern computers. But even in this day and age when the accuracy of turntable speed is measured in small fractions of 1% in deviation from the desired speed, there is enough mystery and lack of understanding without the question, "What makes the turntable sound good?"

23.4.1 Drive Systems

At first we shall examine the types of drives that exist and underline the advantages and weak points of each type.

The turntables that are found today are all driven by electric motors. The method by which the power from the motor is transferred to the turntable platter classifies the drive mechanism.

The turntable platters can be belt driven, puck or idler driven, and driven direct. The first category, the *belt-driven type*, encompasses all models that have motors mounted to the side of the platter with the belt stretched over the motor pulley and outer rim of the platter (Fig. 23-51). Some platter designs have an additional internal rim to hide and to protect the belt.

Many turntables have synchronous motors or motors with some type of speed control mechanism, such as a centrifugal switch that disconnects the power to the motor when the speed exceeds the preset value. The later type motors are usually low-voltage, battery-driven motors used in portable equipment. Also, in portable turntables we find an application of an electrical feedback to control the speed of the low-voltage motor with a potentiometer. Many of the newest types of consumer turntables operate using these types of drives.

Another version of the same idea uses a low-voltage ac motor driven by a self-contained, crystal-controlled oscillator allowing variation of the speed of the platter and achievement of the great speed precision. The only source of speed variation can come from the belt slippage or defective belt. Belt-driven turntables have been known to be the quietest turntables of them all. The speed selection of the belt-driven turntable can be accomplished either by changing the speed of the motor or by having the stepped pulley on the motor and by shifting the belt from one pulley onto another.

The second type of turntable is a *puck-driven type* (Fig. 23-52). The coupling between the platter and the motor shaft is achieved through the intermediate idler wheel or puck, which has the outer edge covered with neoprene rubber or polyurethane for positive drive and isolation of the motor vibration from the platter. This idler wheel rotates on the shaft that is attached to a sliding bracket when the contact between the inner side of the rim of the platter and the idler pulley (or puck) on one side and the motor shaft on the other, is established, the idler wheel will transmit the motor rotation to the turntable platter. This mechanism is designed so when the motor is turned off the idler wheel is retracted away from the motor shaft to protect the rubber ridge from forming a flat spot.

The advantage of the rim drive is that it provides positive torque to the platter, and if the motor is strong enough, it can bring the turntable to the desired speed

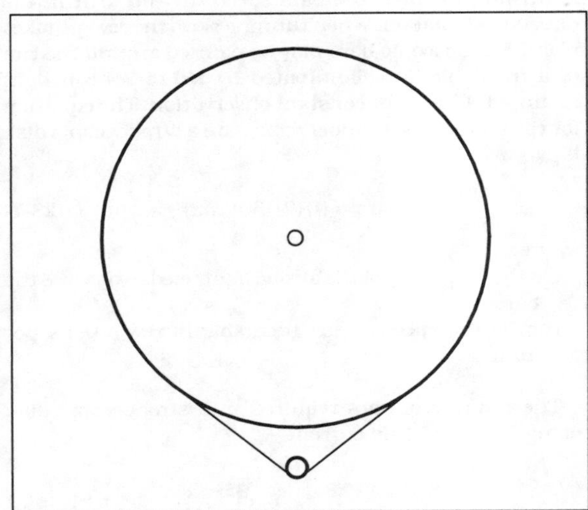

Figure 23-51 Diagram of a single-motor belt-drive system.

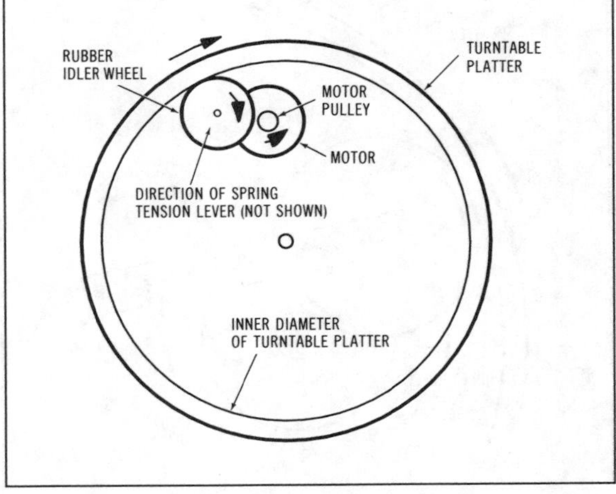

Figure 23-52 Diagram of a puck- or idler-driven turntable.

almost instantly. The mechanism is simple, and it is the most reliable type of drive, but it is also the noisiest. Because of the positive coupling between the motor and the platter idler or puck, it transmits a certain amount of the motor vibrations to the platter and consequently to the record, as shown in Fig. 23-53.

The third kind of turntable drive is the *direct type*. What this means is that the motor is driving the shaft of the platter directly. There are also variations of the design. Some turntable designs are very sophisticated, using the platter itself as a rotor of the motor and drive is provided by the self-contained, quartz-controlled oscillator. The motion is extremely accurate and the speed of rotation may be displayed on the digital display, which is part of the control panel. There is also a weak point in this seemingly perfect drive. Because of the slow speed at which the turntable rotates, and because the motor has a finite number of poles, there is a slight cogging action in the platter motion, which may manifest itself with increased loads. However, this handicap is only related to turntable platters with fairly small mass and small moments of inertia. If the platter is heavy, it will overcome this problem. The best example of this is the drive system in the Neumann disk-cutting lathe. Aside from the platter being extremely heavy, it is also decoupled from the motor by the soft coupling, which isolates all vibrations of the motor. The Neumann recording lathe cannot start by itself but has to be spun manually close to the synchronous speed until the motor takes over and falls into synchronism.

The performance of the turntable depends very little on the type of drive used but rather on the correct execution

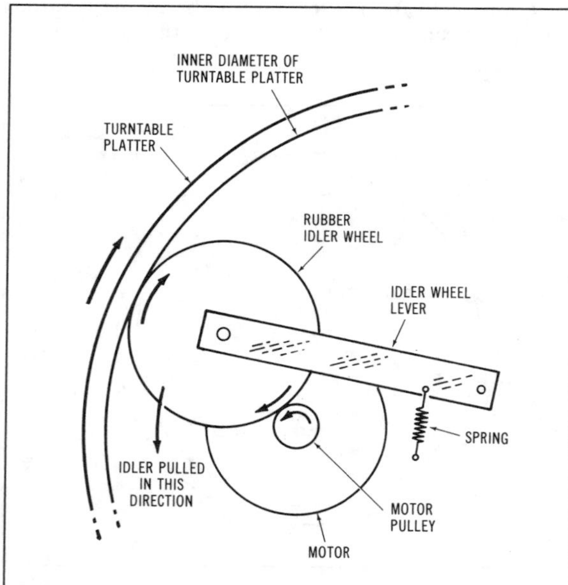

Figure 23-53 This lever system jams the idler wheel between the motor pulley and the platter rim.

of the design by understanding of problems involved. The ideal turntable should have the following properties:

1. It will start fast without hesitation.
2. It will rotate with exact speed without variations.
3. There will be no motor noises or vibrations heard while the system is in operation, nor will they be transmitted to the platter.
4. The turntable should be adequately shock mounted and isolated from the surface on which it stands to prevent building rumble and vibrations of the furniture produced by the loud sounds to shake the platter and the tonearm.
5. The platter should be treated against ringing either by using a turntable mat with damping properties or by undercoating the platter.
6. The turntable shall be easy to maintain and to repair.

Not many turntables meet all these criteria; therefore, in order to know how to evaluate the unit, we should know how it works.

But before we get into evaluation of the entire system, there are tests that can be performed on the turntable alone. The first one is speed of rotation. There are many ways of checking the speed of rotation, but the simplest one is by using the stroboscopic disk.

A *stroboscopic disk* is a circular disk containing a number of black-and-white bars, which are used for checking the speed of turntables and other rotating machines (Fig. 23-54). The disk is placed on the turntable, and the bars are observed under a light source fed from the normal ac lighting circuits. When the speed of the turntable is correct, the black bars will appear to stand still. If the table is turning too fast, the bars speed up and drift in the direction of rotation. When running slow, the reverse takes place. Stroboscopic bars may be painted around the rim of a turntable and illuminated by a 115-V neon light mounted close by for constant observation. The equation for calculating the number of bars on a stroboscopic disk is

$$\text{bars} = (f)(2)(60)/\text{rpm} \qquad (23\text{-}1)$$

where,

f is the frequency of the strobe light used to observe the bars,

rpm is the speed of the turntable in revolutions per minute.

The number of bars required in a stroboscopic disk using 60-Hz lighting current is

RPM	Bars
16	450
33.3	216
45	159
78.26	92

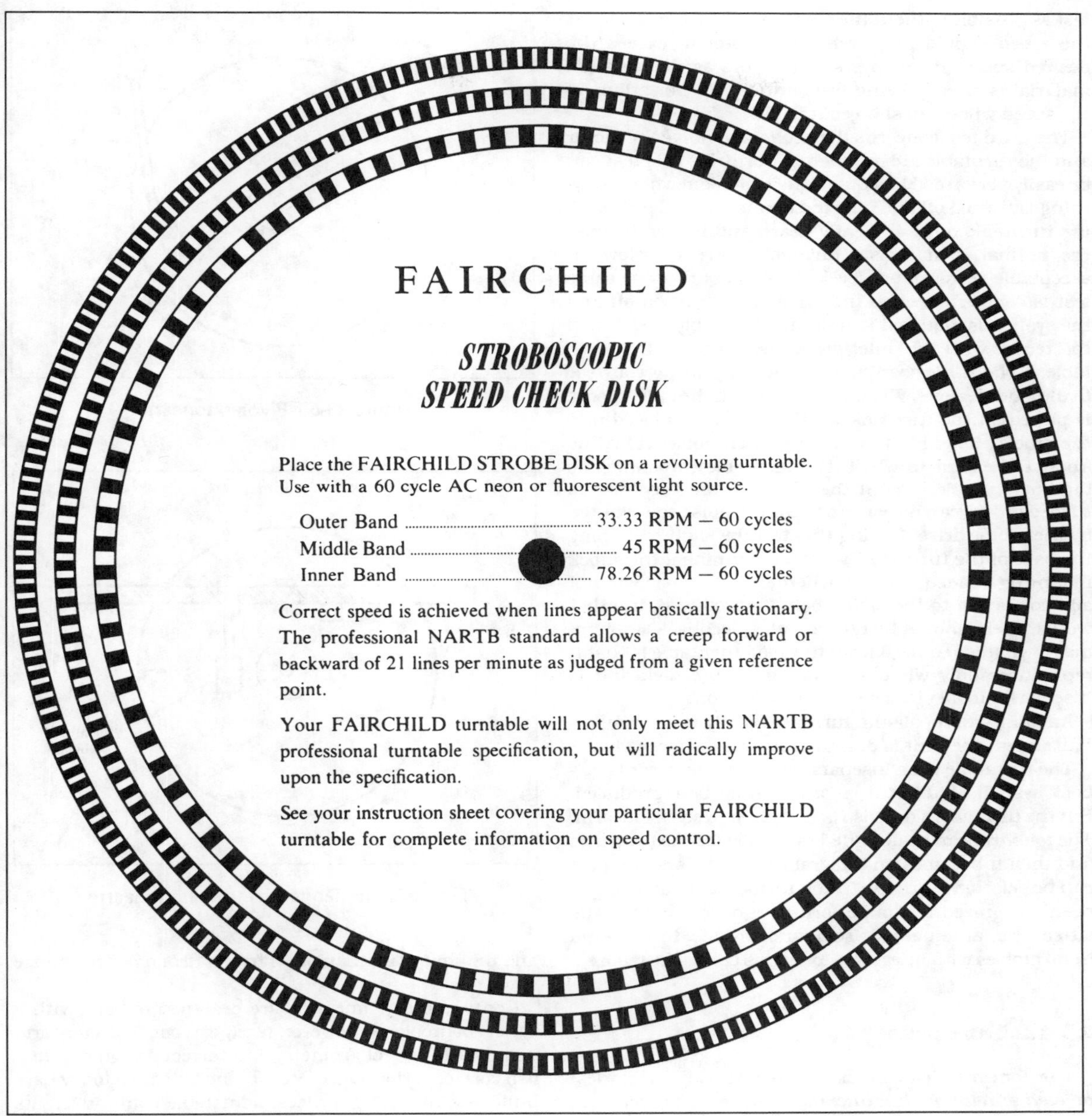

Figure 23-54 A stroboscopic disk used for checking the rotational speed of a turntable. *(Courtesy Fairchild Recording Equipment Corp.)*

The next test we can perform is starting time, or the time it takes for the platter to reach its operating speed from a complete stop. This time period is important to know for professionals who have to begin playing the song or selection at the exact moment. To check the starting time requires either a stop watch or timing device. This test requires the use of a strobe disk or the test record. As soon as the lines on the strobe disk appear stationary, the turntable has reached its operating speed. In playing the test tone on the record, we can listen to the pitch change as the correct speed is attained. Starting time may vary anywhere from a fraction of a second to two or more seconds, depending on the construction of a turntable. Turntables used by disk jockeys have to start as fast as possible without the overshoot, which means that the speed should not, even for a moment, exceed the desired speed. If this overshoot occurs as the program material is already being transmitted, the variations of the speed will be most objectionable.

The third test concerns the *acoustical noise* the motor and the turntable are producing. Normally, this test can be easily performed in a quiet listening room when everything is turned off and only the turntable is energized. If the turntable noise is clearly heard and it overshadows the normal room noise, turntable drive is below an acceptable performance level. A second part of the same test is conducted when the turntable is turned off and the system is adjusted to a normal listening level. When the record with the quiet groove is placed on the turntable, a slight hiss can be heard when putting your ear to the loudspeakers. When the record with the quiet groove is placed on the turntable and the stylus is placed into the groove, listening to the increase in noise will let us know the extent to which the turntable transmits the building rumble. Now if the power to the turntable is turned on, we can measure or hear the noise contributed by the motor drive. During this test, by slightly tapping the base of the turntable, we can determine if the shock mounting is adequate and whether loud music will not add coloration to the signal being reproduced, in other words, there should be no acoustical feedback. In summary, what is required from the good turntable is that it reproduces only what is recorded on the disk and is insensitive to all other sources of vibration.

An ability to repair the turntable easily is very important unless the unit is designed as a throw-away.

The turntable is an inseparable part of the record playback system. Without it records cannot be reproduced. But the turntable alone also is useless; it needs a tonearm. The *tonearm* can be designed especially for the turntable and then it becomes an integral part of the system, or it can be selected for use with the turntable because it has been recognized for its performance or features. In the latter case, automatic or semiautomatic features found in turntables with integrated tonearms cannot be realized.

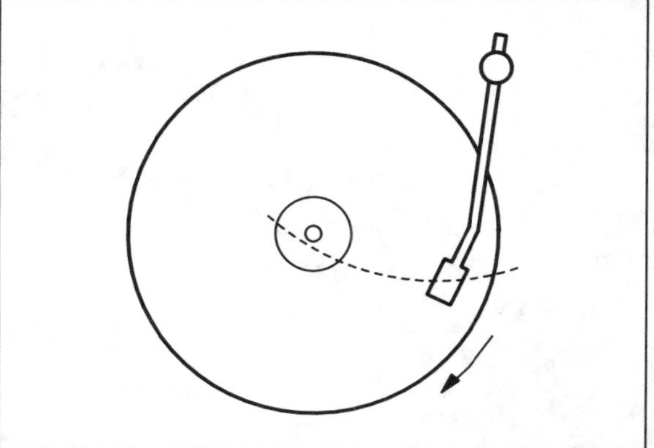

Figure 23-55 Pivoted tonearm.

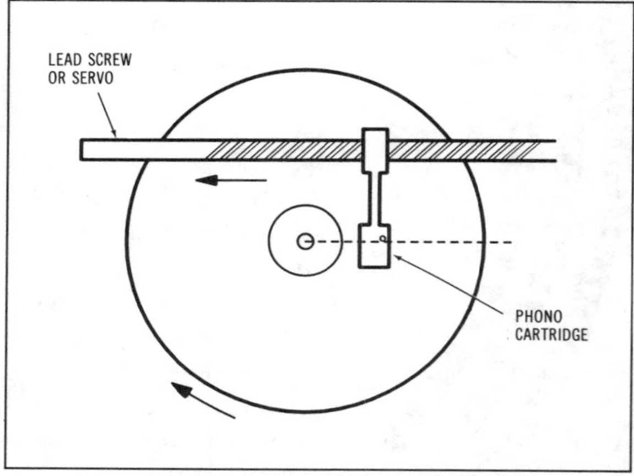

Figure 23-56 Tangential tracking tonearm.

23.4.2 Tonearms

The tonearms can be classified into two categories: *pivoted* and *tangential tracking*. The first type, *pivoted*, is shown in Fig. 23-55. It originated at the time of invention of the disk record. The *tangential* tracking, as shown in Fig. 23-56, was actually the first one ever used by Edison, who played the embossed foil on the cylinder by moving the horn-type pickup using the feed screw. Today's designs are an improvement of these old units. Contemporary pivoted tonearms are designed to ease the work the cartridge stylus has to perform, which includes tracking the groove, supporting the tonearm at an appropriate height above the surface of the disk, and moving it across the record until the end of the groove is reached and the shutoff mechanism is triggered or a record change takes place.

Contemporary tonearms are designed to cope with a variety of problems, however, rarely can one find a tonearm with nearly perfect geometry and correct design to establish correct performance. Most of the tonearms today have built in antiskating devices, adjustable counterweights to accommodate a variety of cartridge weights and tracking forces, vertical height adjustment to set the tonearm parallel to the record, and a variety of features to facilitate installation and operation of the device. But as far as the ideal tonearm is concerned, all tonearms are at best all but a compromise. Very few tonearms are dynamically balanced, and most of them rely on dynamic unbalance to produce vertical tracking force. The dynamically balanced tonearm is the tonearm that is capable of playing a record with the turntable tipped at almost any angle without changing the tracking force and tracking ability.

23.4.2.1 Tonearm Geometry

Today's tonearms are designed to retrace the modulation of the groove in the same way as it was recorded. Design of the tonearm takes into consideration the diameter of the records or the turntable, and the distance between the center of the platter and the pivot of the tonearm. The older tonearms have suffered from a tangent error when the cartridge was aligned properly only at one point on the record. Today's pivoted tonearms have a built-in so-called offset angle at which the cartridge is positioned so it is always perpendicular to the radius of the disk within a couple of degrees reducing the distortion in the lateral plane and improving tracking. There are many protractors available today using different approaches to help position the cartridge as accurately as possible in the tonearm to minimize tracking error.

When a disk record is being cut, the cutting head is carried across the face of the recording disk following the radius. However, when in playback, the pickup is at the right angle to the radius of the disk only, at two points, because the pickup arm is pivoted in such a manner that it swings across the face of the disk in an arc, as shown in Fig. 23-57.

Generally, the manufacturer of the arm supplies a template and mounting instructions for a particular arm. However, in the absence of such information, the pickup arm is mounted in such a manner that the tangent error is at a minimum. One method of mounting the arm is shown in Fig. 23-58. A template is plotted (Fig. 23-59), to indicate the inner and outer areas of modulation, and

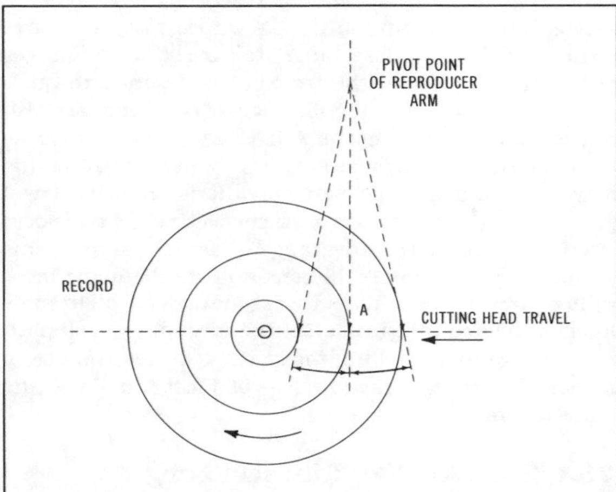

Figure 23-57 Tangent error in a reproducing arm. The error is zero at point A only.

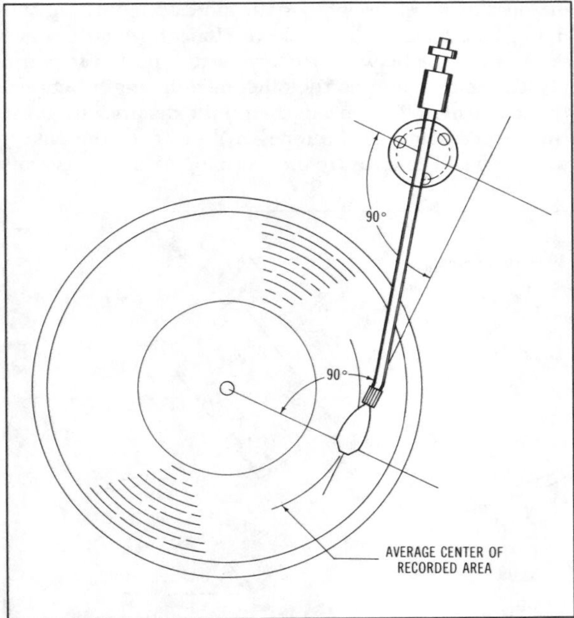

Figure 23-58 Typical mounting for an offset pickup arm.

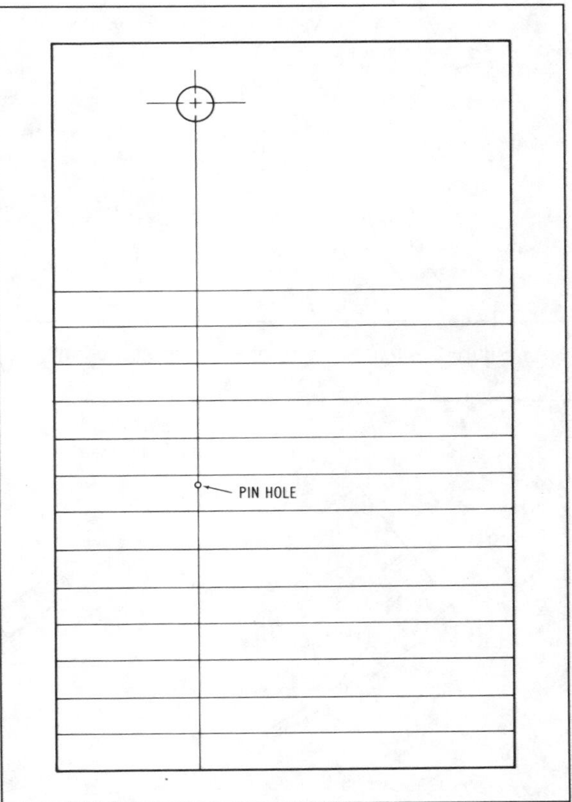

Figure 23-59 Tonearm alignment protractor.

the arm is so placed for a minimum tangent error. The procedure is the same for any length arm and diameter platen. It can be shown, regardless of where the pivoted arm is placed, that a tangent error cannot be eliminated entirely.

However, the error can be made so small that, for all practical purposes, it can be neglected. In offsetting the tonearm by bending it into an S or J shape (Fig. 23-60), it is possible to achieve positioning of the cartridge so that at two points on the record the error shall be zero. The deviation from this ideal groove-cartridge interface will be only 2° to 3° in the horizontal plane (Fig. 23-61). By offsetting the tonearm, we are introducing the new force that pulls the tonearm toward the center of the record, which we call skating force. In tonearms without the offset angle the skating force is zero at one point and increases as the tonearm moves away from this position. The zero tangent error point in this tonearm coincides with the zero skating force position, and it is point A in Fig. 23-57.

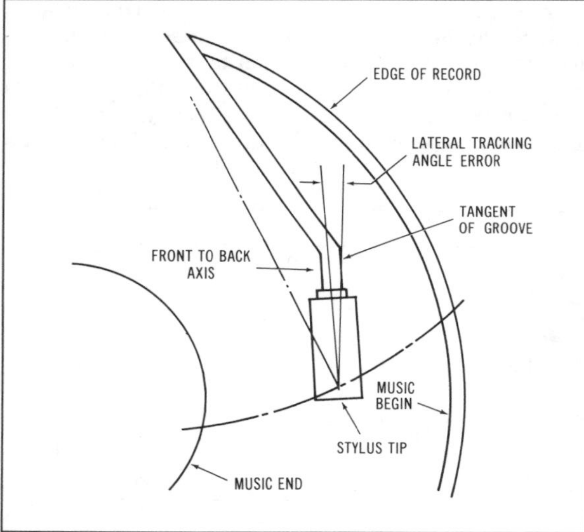

Figure 23-60 Geometry of a modern tonearm.

Theoretically, the pivoted tonearm without the offset angle and without any tangent error has to be infinitely long. However, the tonearm designed by the Rabinoff brothers revived the principle of tangential tracking used by Edison and found application in many turntable systems. There the tonearm motion has been achieved using servomechanisms and utilizing various types of arm position sensors. These tangential tracking turntables practically eliminated the tracking error and are quite popular with many hi-fi enthusiasts. But there are also drawbacks to this design as well. Usually, such tonearms cannot be moved as fast as pivoted counterparts, and this may become a handicap in operations when speed of positioning the tonearm is of essence. Consider disk jockeys, for instance. The advantage of tangential tonearms is that they are shorter, lighter, and can be made more rigid to prevent many tonearm resonances found in some inferior pivoted tonearms. But the mechanical complexity of tangential tracking tonearms requires the use of modern technology including special integrated circuits and sensors.

23.4.2.2 Effective Tonearm Length

The table for mounting the tonearm correctly is shown in Table 23-1. The values have been calculated for tonearms of different lengths and with different offset angles. The accompanying drawing of the turntable platter and spindle location in relationship to the tonearm mounting hole in Fig. 23-62 identifies the effective tonearm length, which is the distance between the stylus tip and the tonearm pivot. The overhang is the difference in length between the tonearm's effective length and the distance from the turntable spindle to the tonearm's pivot. In the past it was fairly easy to measure the overhang because tonearms

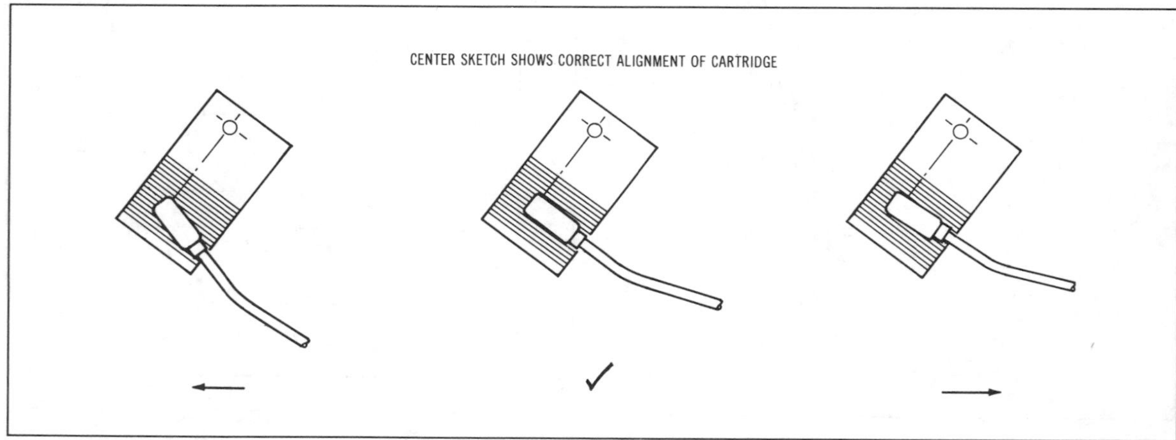

Figure 23-61 The proper use of a protractor.

Table 23-1. Measurements for Correctly Mounting Tonearms

Effective Length, Inches	Pivot-to-Spindle Distance, Inches	Offset Angle, Degrees
7.87	7.04	27.85
7.91	7.08	27.70
7.95	7.13	27.55
7.99	7.18	27.40
8.03	7.22	27.26
8.07	7.26	27.12
8.11	7.30	26.97
8.15	7.35	26.83
8.19	7.39	26.70
8.23	7.44	26.56
8.27	7.48	26.42
8.30	7.52	26.29
8.35	7.56	26.15
8.38	7.61	26.02
8.42	7.65	25.90
8.46	7.69	25.76
8.50	7.74	25.63
8.54	7.78	25.50
8.58	7.82	25.38
8.62	7.87	25.26
8.66	7.91	25.13
8.70	7.95	25.01
8.74	8.00	24.89
8.78	8.04	24.77
8.82	8.08	24.65
8.86	8.13	24.54
8.90	8.17	24.42
8.94	8.21	24.31
8.98	8.26	24.19
9.02	8.27	24.06
9.05	8.34	23.97
9.09	8.39	23.86
9.13	8.42	23.75
9.17	8.47	23.64
9.21	8.51	23.53
9.25	8.56	23.43
9.29	8.60	23.32
9.33	8.64	23.21
9.37	8.68	23.12
9.41	8.73	23.01
9.45	8.77	22.91
9.49	8.81	22.81
9.53	8.85	22.71
9.57	8.89	22.61
9.60	8.93	22.52
9.65	8.98	22.42
9.68	9.02	22.32
9.72	9.06	22.23
9.76	9.11	22.13
9.80	9.15	22.04
9.84	9.19	21.95

were constructed so that they could swing over the turntable spindle.

Modern tonearms have a built-in stop preventing them from moving further than the locking groove. Therefore, the term *overhang* is no longer a meaningful measured magnitude. Only three dimensions are of importance: effective tonearm length, tonearm pivot-to-spindle distance, and the offset angle.

Table 23-1 was developed to be used with the protractor shown in Fig. 23-59. The accuracy of the cartridge tracking and mounting depends on the effective length of the tonearm. If the effective length of the tonearm (distance between the stylus tip to tonearm vertical pivot) is 7.87 in., and it is properly mounted (7.04 in. away from the turntable spindle), the cartridge will track to within +2¼° and −1½°, providing the cartridge is mounted at an offset angle of 27.8°, which can be verified with the protractor in Fig. 23-59. By observing the dimensions given in the table and using the protractor, almost perfect alignment of the cartridge can be achieved. If the tonearm is longer, the lateral tracking error gets smaller so that the tonearm with the effective length of 10 in. will have a maximum tracking error of less than 1° at the smaller disk radii and a 1.7° error at the maximum radius.

23.4.2.3 Skating Force

In an effort to achieve nearly perfect lateral tracking of pivoted tonearms, we should not forget that there is a force that can all but upset the best aligned tonearm and cause considerable tracking error. The force in question is a *skating force*. The skating force is the result of tonearm geometry and the friction between the stylus and the record groove. Because of the offset angle and the overhang, this force is acting upon the stylus, pulling it in the direction away from the pivot point of the tonearm with one of the vectors of this force pulling the tonearm toward the center of the turntable (Fig. 23-63). If this skating force is not compensated for during the playing of the record, then the stylus will be deflected toward the outside of the disk at the angle much greater than the error angle encountered in tracking the groove at different radii (Fig. 23-64). The skating force compensation consists of applying a force to the tonearm that is equal to but opposite in direction to the skating force (Fig. 23-65). For all practical purposes, the skating force is constant for all radii of the music groove, if the tracking error is small and the tonearm alignment is correct (Fig. 23-66). There are slight variations of the skating force due to heavy modulation and groove wall plastic deformation caused by the sharpness of the new stylus, but the largest deviation in skating force is due to the variations in record material. From the study of various materials, it was established that the softest materials produce more friction and larger skating force. Lacquer masters produce up to 25% more friction (i.e., skating force) than vinyl records. Consequently, metal stampers and shellac records (mostly made out of slate powder) exhibit three times less skating force than vinyl records. Styrene records,

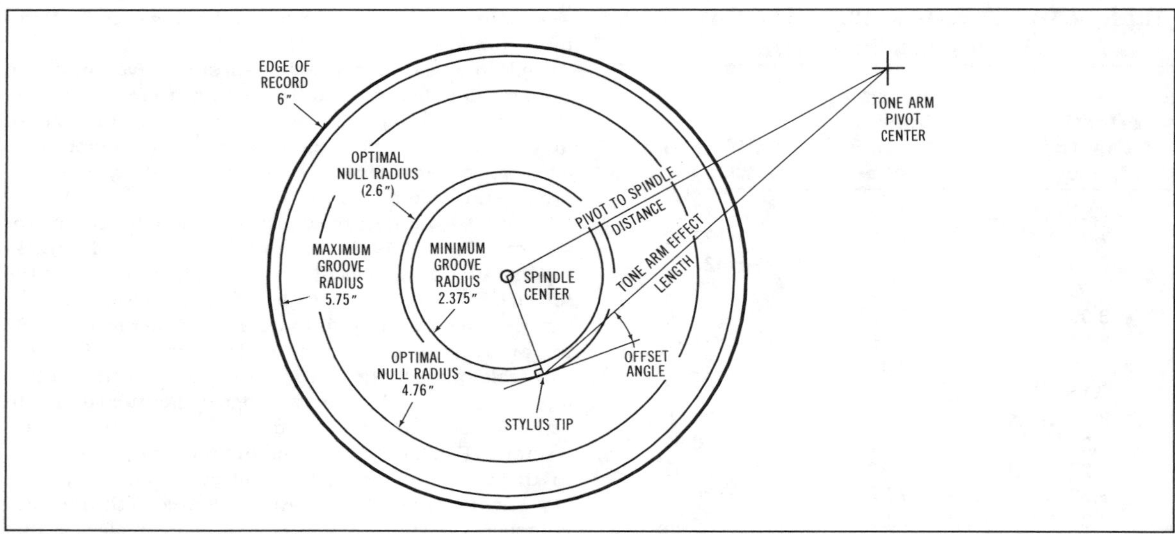

Figure 23-62 Relationship of the lateral components of a tonearm.

today's 45-rpm disks, have approximately 30% less friction than vinyl, requiring less antiskating compensation than vinyl lp's (Fig. 23-67).

There are many different ways to generate the antiskating force. It is incorrect to assume that increasing the drag on the horizontal motion of the tonearm will compensate for skating. Skating force is independent of groove spiraling speed; drag is not. Also, because of the variable pitch common to all present-day recordings, the speed with which the tonearm moves across the record varies and at times may even be zero. Because of this variation, the mechanism that generates the antiskating force should be able to generate a uniform force at all times, regardless of the motion of the tonearm. Antiskating force can be generated by using springs, magnets, weights with pulleys, electrical devices, and mechanical linkages and weights (Fig. 23-68). Any method to apply the clockwise bias in a horizontal plane to the tonearm to counteract the skating force produces positive results; however, compensation may not be accurate for all types of systems.

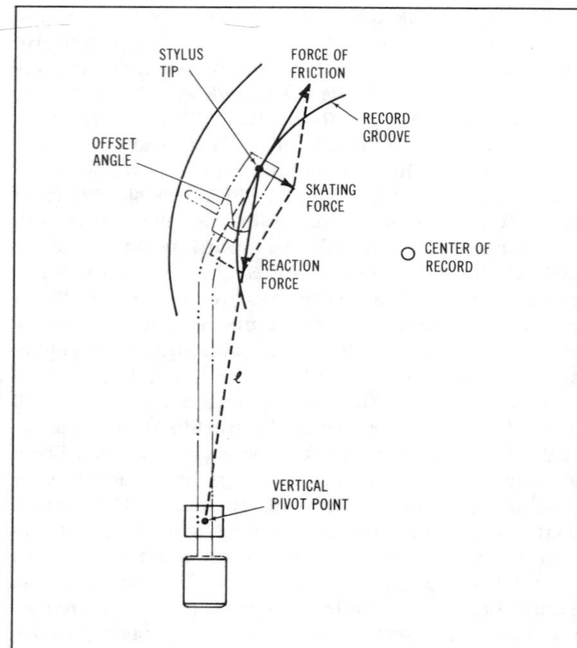

Figure 23-63 Position of the arm on the record and the forces acting on it. *(Courtesy G. Alexandrovich)*

It was discovered that most of the tonearms have the calibration of their antiskating force dials done incorrectly, placing more emphasis on the shape of the stylus than on the type of record material. The device used to detect the amount of skating force that exists as the tonearm plays the record is a dynamic bias balance gauge, consisting of a headshell that pivots on a precision bearing in the lateral plane with respect to the tonearm (Fig. 23-69). The cartridge mounted in it contacts the groove in a conventional way with the exception that any imbalance of pressures exerted by the two groove walls on the stylus results in swaying of the entire cartridge and headshell. The only time when the headshell with the cartridge aligns with the zero mark is when the skating force is accurately compensated for. To check the calibration of the tonearm, it is necessary to use a record with a quiet unmodulated groove and to set the tonearm antiskating

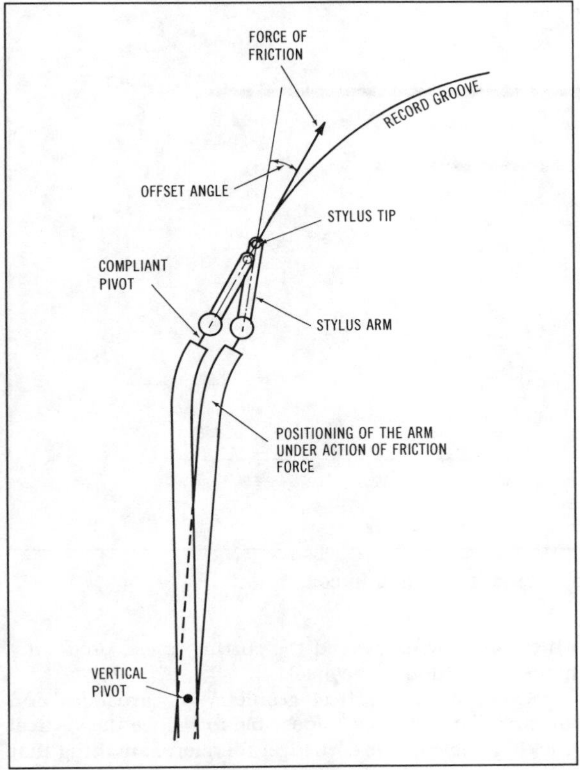

Figure 23-64 Effect of friction on tracking error. *(Courtesy G. Alexandrovich)*

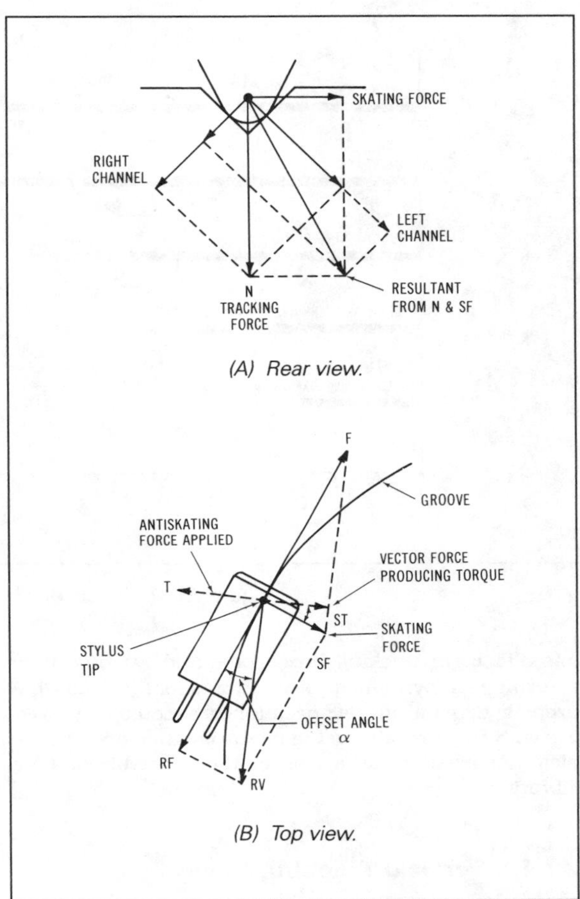

Figure 23-65 Skating and antiforces in a record groove. *(Courtesy G. Alexandrovich)*

at different diameters with the bias balance gauge. If the compensation is correct, the gauge will show zero deviation at any radius.

If it is desired to see how modulation affects the skating force (or force of friction), then all one has to do is to play a record that has quiet and loud passages and to observe the behavior of the gauge. The same way, one can measure the relative coefficient of friction of different record materials as well as effects of different stylus shapes. The simplicity of the gauge and the accuracy it possesses makes this tool indispensable for precision alignment and adjustment of the antiskating force and the design of the mechanism itself. The effectiveness of the antiskating force mechanism depends to a high degree on the dynamic behavior of the tonearm. If the tonearm is not dynamically balanced (and most of them are not), then any tilt of the turntable may result in a change of skating force, endangering the tracking ability of the pickup. As was mentioned before, the dynamic balancing of the tonearm implies that the pivot point of the tonearm is also the center of mass. In most modern tonearms this center of weight is shifted toward the cartridge end in order to produce tracking force (Fig. 23-70). In a dynamically bal-

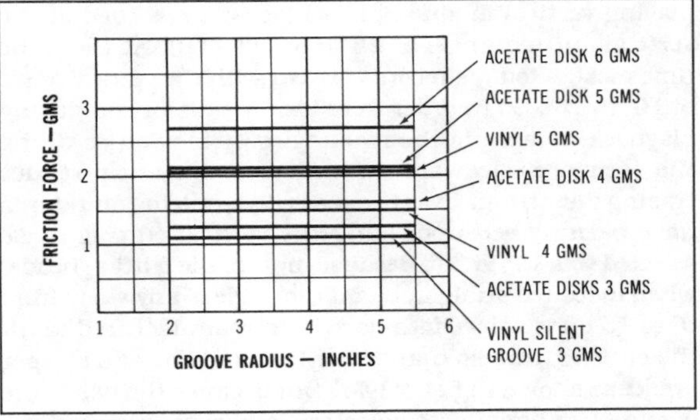

Figure 23-66 Effect of record materials and record radii on the skating force. *(Courtesy G. Alexandrovich)*

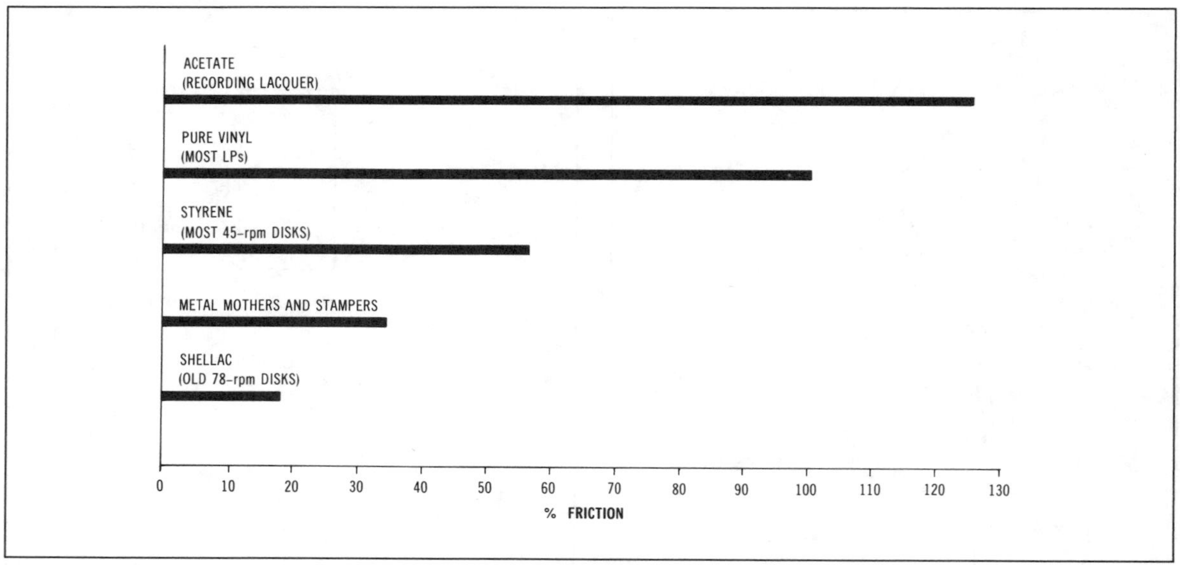

Figure 23-67 Effects of record material on skating force.

anced tonearm, tracking force is produced by using either a spring or a permanent or electromagnet (solenoid). A properly dynamically balanced tonearm could play a record with the turntable being in any position and is completely insensitive to jarring of the turntable or floor vibrations.

23.4.3 Vertical Tracking Angle

An important adjustment of the tonearm is in positioning the cartridge over the surface of the disk. Cartridges are mounted in tonearms so that the mounting surface of the cartridge is parallel to the record surface, as shown in Fig. 23-71A. Sometimes tilting the cartridge fore or aft results in lower tracking distortion. Some cartridges are designed to produce lowest distortion when playing vertical modulation, which was recorded at the vertical cutting angle of 25° (Fig. 23-71B). At the same time most of today's records are cut with the vertical angle of 10° to 15°. So in order to reduce the distortion during playback, matching the two angles by moving or tilting the cartridge backward a few degrees may help reduce tracing distortion. Over the years disk-cutting standards have been agreed upon, and the vertical cutting angle selected was 15° to 20°. Because most of the cutting heads, when mounted straight, cut at the angle of anywhere from 0° to 15°, special wedges have been manufactured to tilt the cutting head so that the stylus would be at a steeper angle, as shown in Fig. 23-72. But because the use of the cutting head at such a steep angle involved the use of a special cutting styli, wedges slowly disappeared and cutting heads returned to their original vertical position, which, of course, lowered the cutting angle, producing higher distortion in playback.

Because of the vertical geometry of cartridges and tonearms, it is almost impossible to reduce the vertical tracking angle in the cartridge; therefore, anything that will reduce this angle (like tipping the cartridge backward) will reduce the distortion in playback. This problem of vertical cutting angle and distortion was attended to by RCA in the late 1960s when Dynagroove records were cut with the signal predistorted to compensate for the difference in the recording and playback angles. But because of the lack of standardization, the idea was not applicable for all types of cartridges. Instead of reducing distortion, in some cases the distortion was higher. The idea had bearing on work done by Dr. Woodward at RCA. The problem of the vertical angle becomes more acute as the tonearm is called to play warped records. As the cartridge moves up and down, the cartridge stylus, in following the contour of the record warp, changes its position with respect to the record and the cartridge body itself (Fig. 23-73). The heavier the tonearm and the more compliant the stylus, the larger the change will be in vertical tracking angle due to the warp.

23.4.4 Tonearm Resonance Damping

Studies of tonearms were conducted by many research laboratories and individuals, but the most acclaimed is the work by the Shure Brothers, Inc., staff. They have experimented with many warped records and have compiled enough data to draw conclusions and to pave the way for a better understanding of the behavior and con-

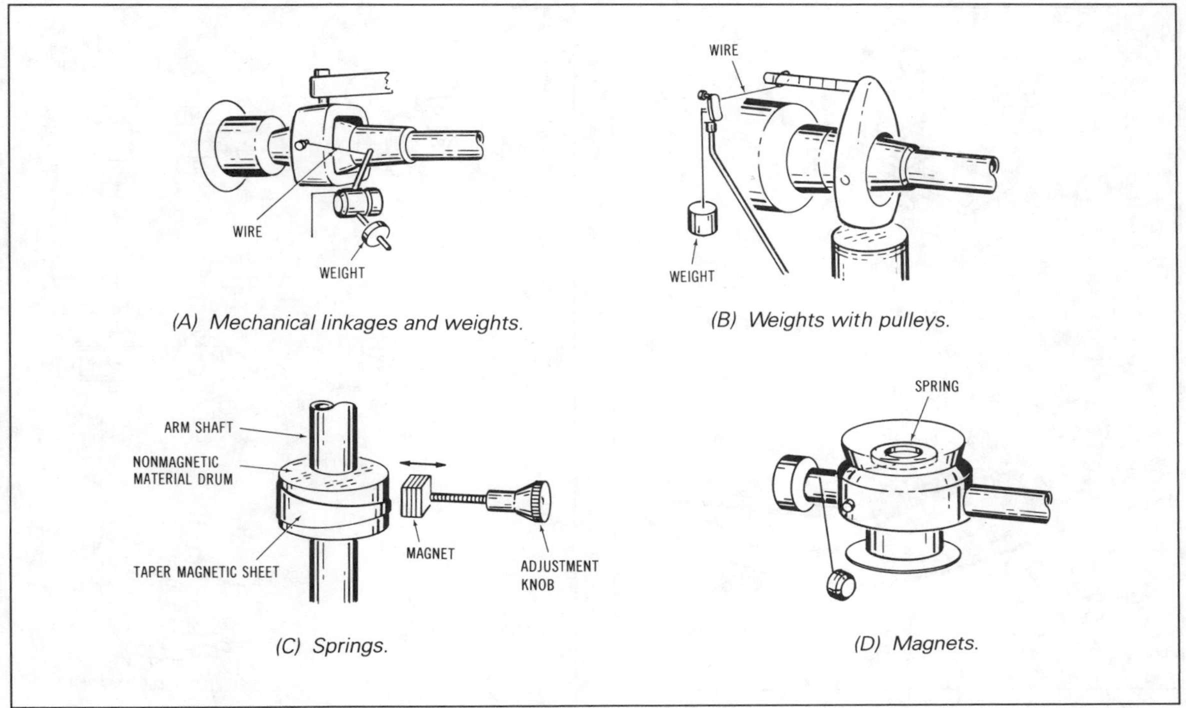

Figure 23-68 Different methods of generating antiskating force.

sequently have produced better sound from records. The Shure study revealed that the warp frequencies of lp records lie in the region from once around (0.5 Hz) peaking at 3 Hz and tapering down to 7 and 8 Hz. Because the audible range of frequencies starts at around 20 Hz, tonearm resonance placed between the warp frequency region and the audible region will allow minimum distortion of the signal due to tonearm bounce. (See Fig. 23-74.) As a result of this research, improvements were made in the tonearms starting with applying vertical damping to the tonearm. The vertical tonearm motion control was attacked by the Discwasher, Inc., by designing a special damping mechanism named Disctracker, which attached to the cartridge and acted pretty much as the advance ball in disk cutting, as shown in Fig. 23-75. Next, Shure Brothers introduced their stabilizer brush as shown in Fig. 23-76, which attached to the cartridge similar to the brushes invented and used by Pickering and Stanton since 1971, as shown in Fig. 23-77, except that the Shure stabilizer brush had its pivots filled with damping fluid. These devices helped to various degrees to stabilize the tonearm as the brush cleaned the record groove.

The other approach was to adjust the effective mass of the tonearm by pivoting only the front part of the tonearm and selecting a cartridge with compliance that would match the mass of this portion of the arm (Fig. 23-78). Dynavector tonearm is an example of such design. One of the latest variations of the same attempt is the design by Sony that employs electronic control of the tonearm motion. Instead of relying on weights, springs, or magnets, the Sony tonearm uses linear dc electromotors driven, operated, and controlled by electrical signals. Unfortunately, not all functions of the tonearm are controlled automatically and are subject to misadjustment.

23.5 PHONOGRAPH PICKUPS

In order to reproduce signals recorded on the phonograph record, a *transducer*, a device that converts the groove modulation into the electrical signals, has to be used. Such a transducer presently is referred to as a phonograph pickup, phono cartridge, or just needle. Unlike microphones, loudspeakers, and other types of devices or transducers that convert one form of energy into another, the phonograph pickup is the most difficult one to design and construct because it has to perform more than one function. The phonograph pickup or cartridge, called so since the invention of the removable stylus or needle assembly, has to convert modulation of the record groove into the electrical signals, and at the same time support the tonearm at the proper height above the record surface, all while moving the tonearm across the surface of the record. In the beginning of the sound-record-

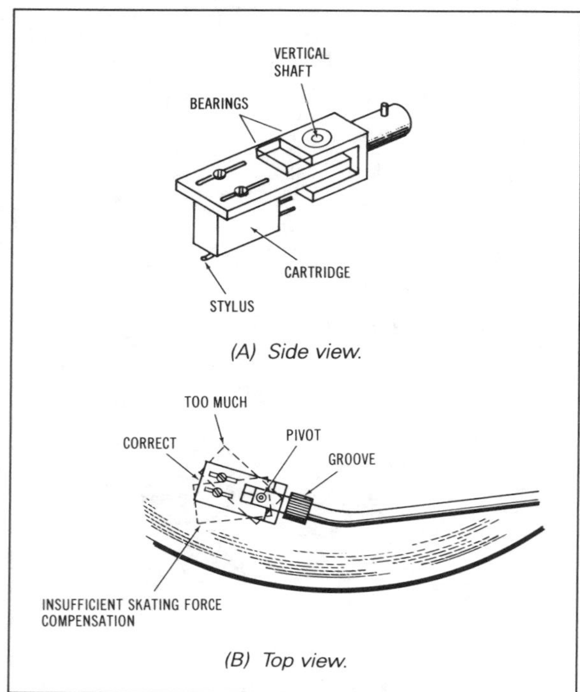

Figure 23-69 Bias balance gauge to detect and measure balance between skating and antiskating forces. *(Courtesy Dynamic Sound Devices)*

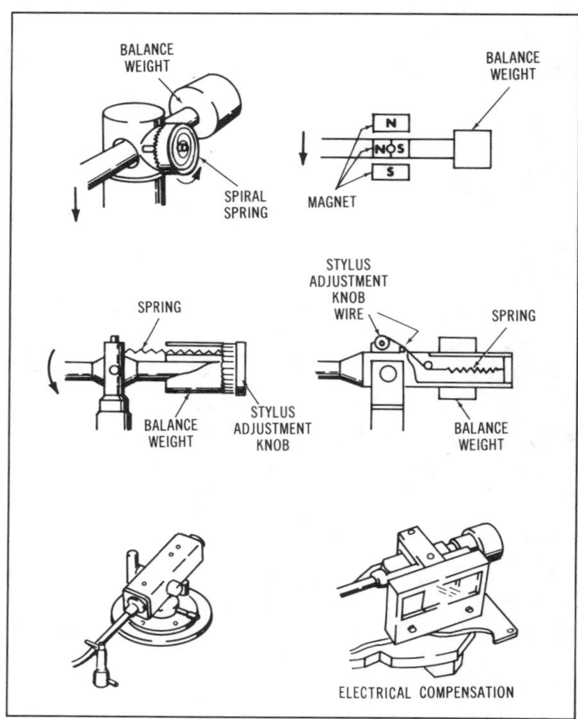

Figure 23-70 Examples of how dynamic balance of the tonearm can be achieved.

ing era, cartridges were heavy, crude, and noncompliant. Tracking forces used were measured in tens of ounces and tonearms weighed pounds. But the need and the desire to improve the quality of the reproduced sound forced the manufacturers and designers of sound equipment to improve the sensitivity of pickups, improve their frequency response, and reduce the distortion they produced. The long and difficult road from early, simple devices to the present-day refined technology was paved by the many talented and dedicated engineers and scientists whose names are associated with companies like Pickering, Shure Brothers, GE, Fairchild, Stanton, RCA, Ortofon, Neumann, Elač, Westrex, and many others. People like Dr. Hunt, Dr. Olson, Messrs. Pickering, the Shure Brothers, Bauer, Stanton, Badmaieff, and Fairchild have inspired the progress that led to the realization of the concept of high fidelity.

This section deals with the phonograph cartridge itself, with its mechanical and electrical properties and construction. Since the cartridge is the most delicate and critical link in the chain of equipment used in sound reproduction, its effect on the quality of the sound as an end product will be evaluated.

The phonograph cartridge is an electromechanical device designed to track or follow the excursions of the record groove and convert this motion with the help of a tracking mechanism-stylus assembly into electrical signals.

Cartridges usually are classified by the principle by which they convert mechanical motion into the electric current or signal. The main two principles used in generating electrical energy are *electrodynamic* and *piezoelectric*. There are also pickups designed to operate using strain gauges, variable capacity, and light as sensors. The last type is presently being perfected for use with digitally recorded disks that are reproduced by reflecting a laser beam off the surface of the record. The detailed description of this method can be found in section 23.12 on digital recording. The largest number of cartridges produced are of the piezoelectric type because the crystal element is the least expensive to produce and the voltage produced from this type of cartridge is the highest. The quality of sound derived from this type of cartridge restricts its use to inexpensive stereo equipment.

The electrodynamic type cartridges are subdivided into three categories: *moving magnet, moving coil,* and *induced magnet* or *moving-iron type*. The electrodynamic principle consists of using a magnetic field that, when it intersects the coil windings, generates electric current. The construction of the cartridge classifies the type. If the magnet is attached to the stylus tube or cantilever and the coils are stationary, it is called a *moving-magnet cartridge*. If the magnet is made stationary and

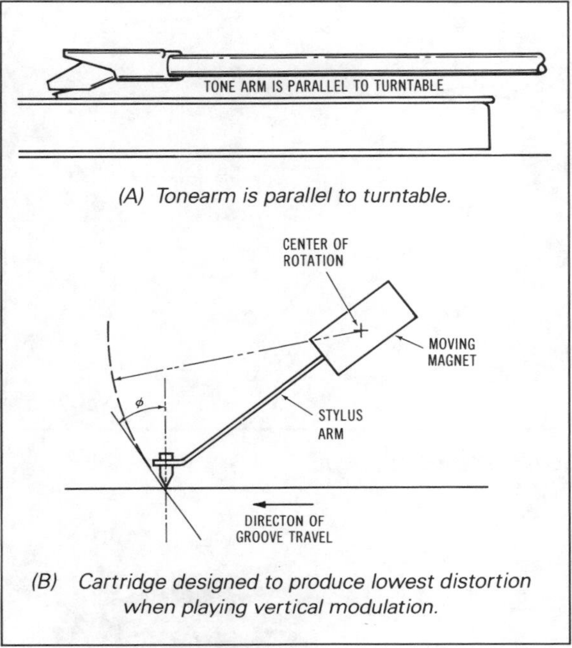

(A) Tonearm is parallel to turntable.

(B) Cartridge designed to produce lowest distortion when playing vertical modulation.

Figure 23-71 Schematic representation of the moving system of a pickup, illustrating the vertical tracking angle.

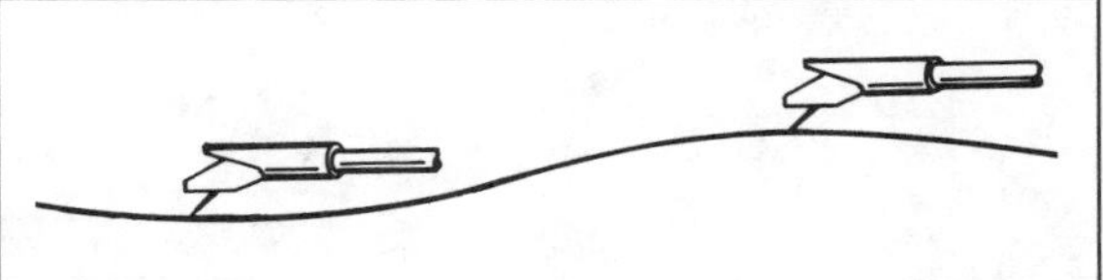

Figure 23-73 Change in vertical tracking angle due to warped records.

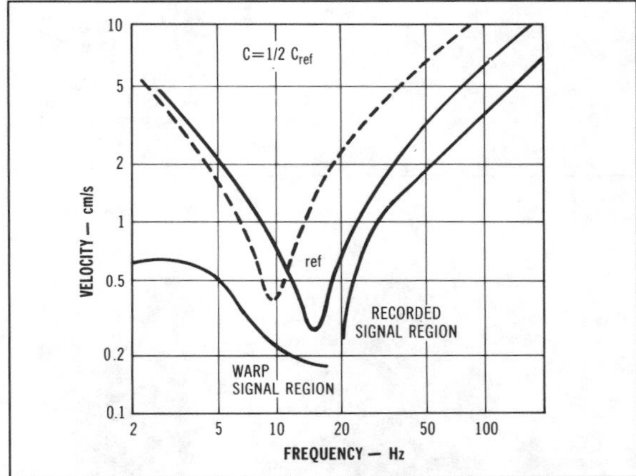

Figure 23-74 Warp frequency range as researched by Happ and Karlof.

Figure 23-72 Cutter mounted with the wedge to cut a 15° to 20° vertical angle. *(Courtesy Ortofon Inc.)*

the coils move in the magnetic field, it is a *moving-coil cartridge*; and if the magnet and the coils are made stationary and there is a slug of soft magnetic iron moving in place of a magnet while being magnetized by the stationary magnet, it is called a *moving-iron* or *induced-magnet cartridge*.

23.5.1 Balanced-Armature Pickups

One of the earliest types of pickups designed was the balanced armature, which can be classified as a moving-iron type. The basic principle of this early magnetic pickup, used for record reproduction, is shown in Fig. 23-79. Although present-day designs are quite different, the same principles of operation still apply. The essential parts were a permanent magnet A, with its pole pieces B, and a soft-iron armature C, pivoted at D and mounted between the pole pieces of the magnet in rubber bearings E. Movement of the armature by the stylus H disturbs the magnetic lines of force (shown by the dotted lines) causing a voltage to be generated in coil F. Two tungsten-loaded rubber damping blocks G were used to center the armature in the center of the magnetic field.

In these early model pickups, the stylus pressure was several ounces (at least 3 to 4 oz [or 85 to 113 g]), while the modern pickup uses 1 to 2 g. The stylus was generally a steel needle. The greatest drawback to this design was the frequent replacement of rubber bearings E and damping blocks G and the centering of the armature C in the magnetic field. The output voltage was proportional to the stylus velocity, and since there were no standards for recording and reproduction, little or no equal-

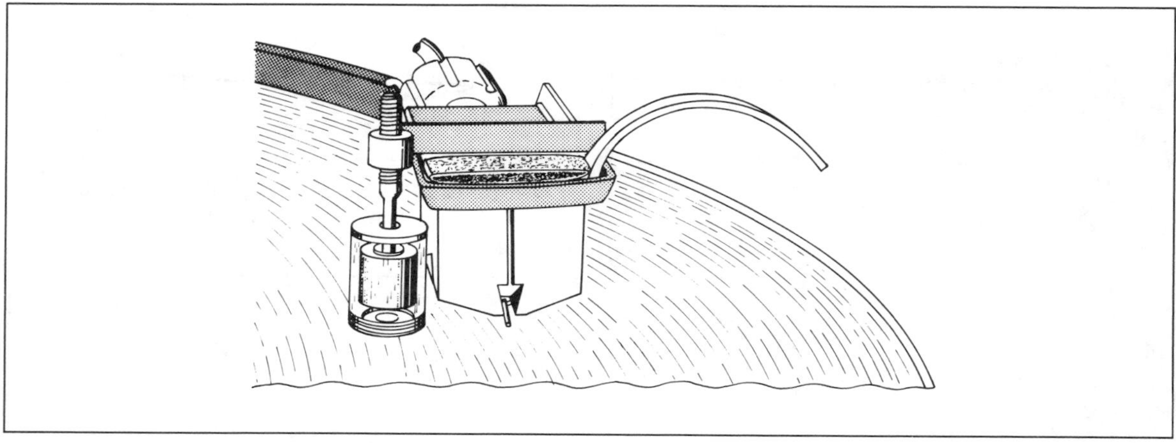

Figure 23-75 Disctracker. *(Courtesy Discwasher, Inc.)*

Figure 23-76 Shure dynamic stabilizer. *(Courtesy Shure Brothers, Inc.)*

Figure 23-77 Pickering dustamatic brush. *(Courtesy Pickering and Co., Inc.)*

ization was used. If the armature was not accurately centered in the magnetic field, the distortion was quite high and was compensated for by attenuating the high frequencies with a fuzz filter (a simple low-pass filter), consisting of a coil and capacitor. This filter also helped in reducing the surface noise of the shellac pressings used at the time.

23.5.2 Variable-Reluctance Pickups

Since the introduction of the original variable-reluctance pickup, many different versions of its design have appeared. One of the earliest was that by Clark in 1947 and is given in Fig. 23-80. In principle, it is still used for both monophonic and stereophonic design. The magnetic structure consisted of two pole pieces A, with a small permanent magnet B between them. At one end, coil C is mounted with a soft rubber insert D.

The stylus E, which is also the armature, is held in the exact center of the magnetic structure by the rubber insert. When the stylus is actuated, its movement causes a voltage to be generated in the coil. Because of its construction, the frequency response extended beyond the normal audio-frequency band. Output voltage was on the order of 100 mV at 1 kHz, with an output impedance of 500 Ω. The recommended stylus pressure was 15 to 20 g. The stylus weighed 31 mg and was removable. Although the recommended pressure was 15 to 20 g, the pressure could

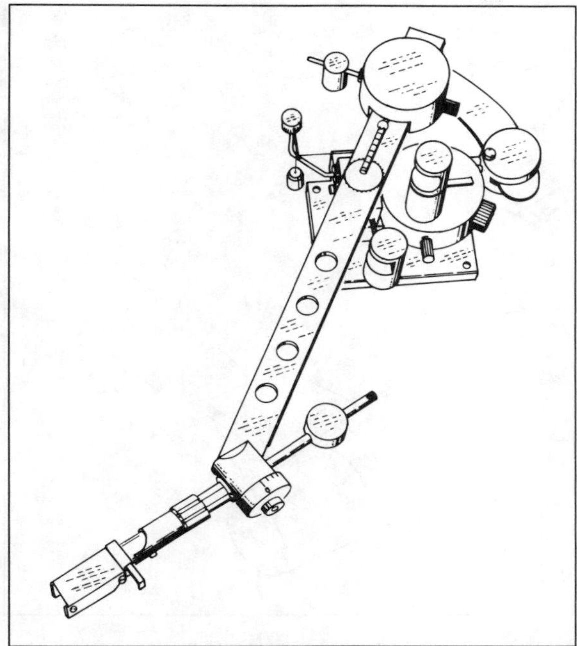

Figure 23-78 Dynavector tonearm with pivoted front portion for lower dynamic tonearm mass. *(Courtesy Onlife Research, Inc.)*

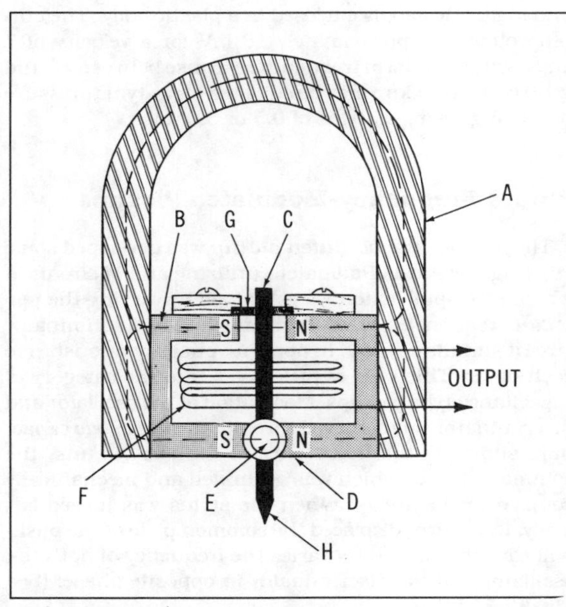

Figure 23-79 Construction of a balanced-armature type pickup, showing the magnetic lines of force.

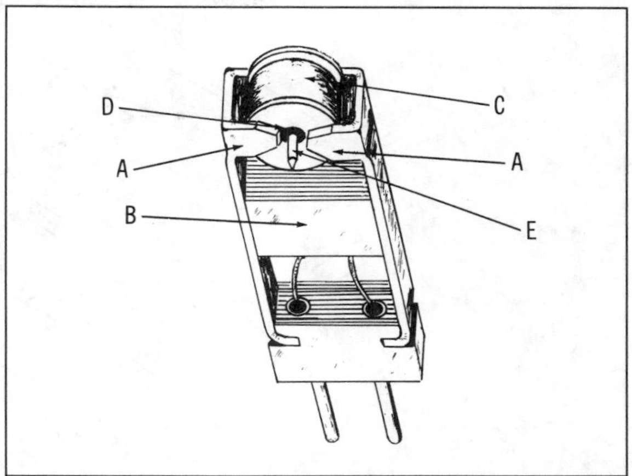

Figure 23-80 Variable-reluctance magnetic pickup. *(After Clark.)*

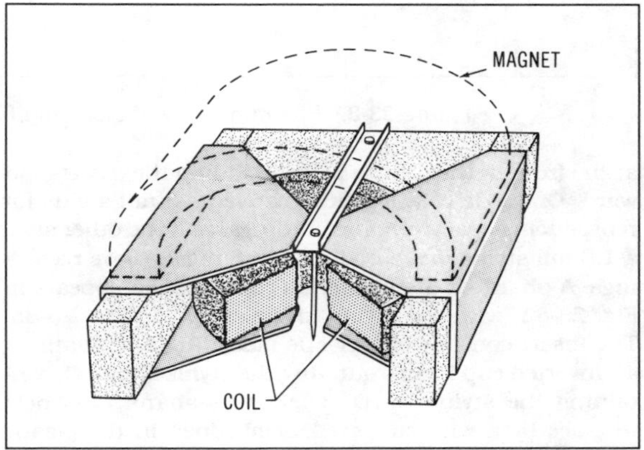

Figure 23-81 Internal construction of early model Pickering variable-reluctance pickup.

be as low as 7 g. The frequency response was ±2 dB, 20 Hz to 20 kHz.

A second variable-reluctance pickup to make its appearance was that by Pickering (Fig. 23-81). It was of similar construction and design. This early model used a stylus pressure of 15 g and developed an output voltage of 17 mV for an impedance of 500 Ω. The magnet was placed as shown by the dotted lines. The frequency range was about the same as for the first structure by Clark. The compliance was 1×10^{-6} cm/dyn. The stylus was not replaceable.

In about 1956, a decided improvement was made in the design of the variable-reluctance pickups, with the appearance of the Pickering Fluxvalve, designed by Stanton. The pickup was manufactured in two models: a single pickup mechanism and a dual type in which two replaceable styli inserts were used and could be removed

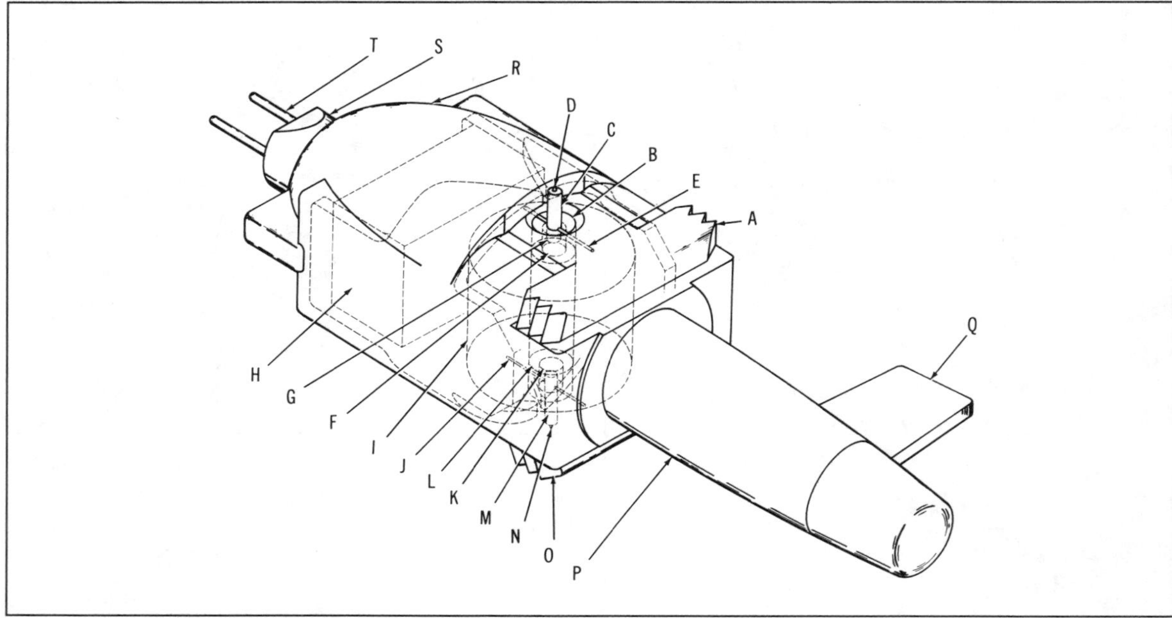

Figure 23-82 Phantom view of Pickering Fluxvalve variable-reluctance magnetic pickup.

at the front of the pickup body by sliding the inserts forward. One side of the pickup carried a 3-mil stylus for reproducing coarse-pitch recordings, and the other side, a 1.0-mil stylus for reproduction of microgroove recordings. A phantom drawing of its construction appears in Fig. 23-82, with the stylus insert shown in Fig. 23-83. The insert consists of a plastic mounting A, containing an inverted cup B, surrounding the stylus shank C, containing the stylus tip D. The stylus shank C is held in place by a wire support E, embedded in the plastic insert A.

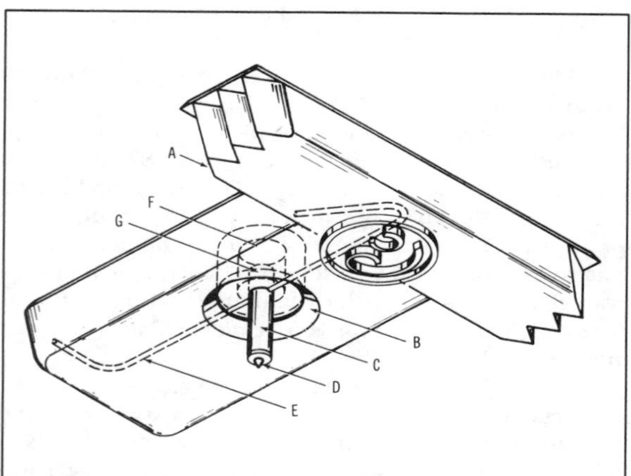

Figure 23-83 Removable stylus mounting used in the turnover pickup of Fig. 23-82.

The vibratory mass of the Pickering Fluxvalve is comprised of only the stylus shank and tip; thus, the mass is kept to a very low value. Armature resonance occurs above 30 kHz, which removes any peaks in the audible range. The entire mechanism, including the magnet, coil, and magnetic gap, is enclosed in a plastic body. The output voltage is approximately 18 mV for a velocity of 7 cm/s, with a uniform frequency response between 10 and 20 kHz. This pickup may be adjusted for a stylus pressure of 2 to 6 g, using a stylus of 0.5 or 3.0 mil.

23.5.3 Frequency-Modulated Pickups

The *frequency-modulated pickup* was developed some years ago by Alexis Badmaieff, utilizing an FM circuit in which push-pull action was obtained by varying the resonant frequencies of an oscillator and a discriminator circuit simultaneously, in opposite phase relationship to each other. This type of pickup fell into the category of capacitance-type pickups. Modulation of the oscillator and discriminator was achieved through the use of two capacitors shunting the inductance of the two circuits, the common plate of which was grounded and mechanically coupled to the stylus. When the stylus was moved laterally, it, in turn, displaced the common plate of the push-pull capacitor and thus varies the frequency of both the oscillator and the discriminator in opposite phase. (See Fig. 23-84.)

The output signal was audio frequency in character, with an output level of minus 45 dBm, after passing through the output filter. The arm resonance was low

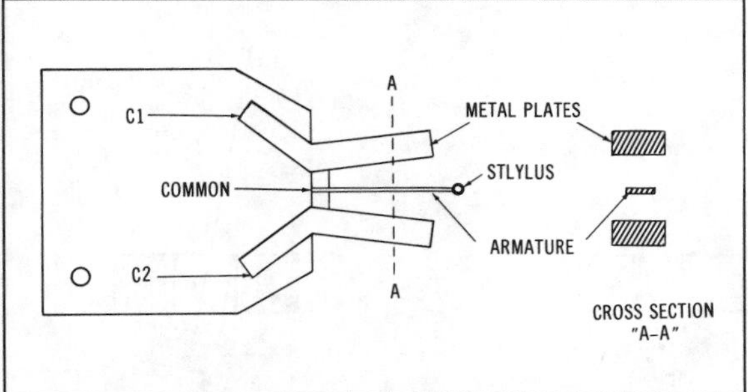

Figure 23-84 Simplified form of an fm pickup head consisting of a push-pull capacitor with grounded center plate.

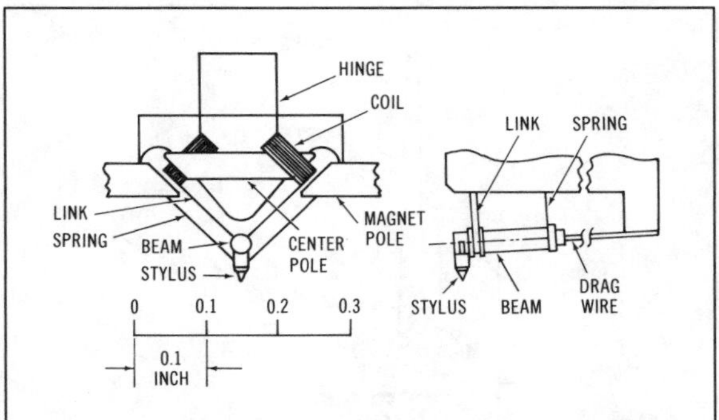

Figure 23-85 Simplified cross-sectional drawing showing the interior construction of a moving-coil stereophonic pickup.

(about 12 Hz) and was damped mechanically by means of a high-viscosity oil in a special ball-bearing pivot. The vertical motion of the arm was damped to prevent the head from bouncing. A variable filter or equalizer supplied the desired reproducing characteristic. The mechanical resonance of the armature and stylus was above 15 kHz, thus enabling the pickup to reproduce frequencies within the audio spectrum without appreciable peaks or dips, over a range of 20 Hz to 15 kHz.

The distortion was on the order of 0.5% below 5 kHz, and above this frequency, 1.5%. The oscillator frequency was approximately 40 MHz and was adjusted for a maximum output by playing a record with a 1-kHz signal. The output impedance was 250 Ω and could be used with any normal low-impedance input circuit.

23.5.4 Moving-Coil Stereophonic Pickups

One of the first moving-coil stereo pickups was the Western Electric 9A, which reproduced both lateral and vertical coarse-pitch records, using a single stylus. Several different types of moving-coil pickups have been developed for both stereophonic and monophonic reproduction. Among the first for stereo was the Westrex Model 10A, now obsolete but shown in Fig. 23-85. The two self-supporting voltage-generating coils were mounted on Mylar™ hinges with the axes of the coils at right angles to each other and mounted 45° to the horizontal. The lower edge of each coil was connected mechanically through a wire to a beam that supported the stylus. This beam consisted of a small metal tube with an outside diameter of 0.031 in. and an approximate length of 0.15 in. The stylus beam or tube was not subjected to twisting or bending. A drag-wire consisting of a flat spring was connected to the rear of the stylus beam and then to the reproducer housing to prevent the beam from rotating. Thus, an equal compliance was obtained at the stylus for any vertical direction. The drag-wire also prevented any longitudinal motion of the stylus.

A semisolid damping material between each link and the reproducer housing (near the coils) provided mechanical damping to the system to remove high-frequency peaks and also helped to reduce crosstalk between the two channels.

The vertical angle of the stylus was set to 15°; however, in early pickups of all manufacturers the stylus angle was what the individual manufacturer thought best. The magnetic path of the pickup structure consisted of two pole pieces, a center pole, and a permanent magnet. One edge of each voltage-generating coil was placed over the end of the center pole piece, in the gap formed by the center and outer pole pieces.

The coils were phased to produce in-phase output voltages when the stylus was actuated by a laterally recorded groove.

The compliance of the Westrex stereo pickup was about 2.5×10^{-6} cm/dyn. The stylus included angle was 40° to 55°, with a tip radius of 0.5 or 0.7 mil. The output voltage averaged about 2 mV per coil for a peak velocity of 10 cm/s. Separation was in the order of 25 to 30 dB at 1000 Hz.

23.5.5 Moving-Coil Cartridges

Modern moving-coil cartridges are represented by a variety of designs. All of them have coils that move, but not all of them are entitled to be called moving-coil type. Designs that depend for their functioning on the motion of the soft iron core rather than on the motion of the coil itself should not be classified as a pure moving-coil device. There the motion of the coil is coincidental. To this class belong a great many models of moving-coil pickups manufactured all over the world. Fig. 23-86 shows the cross sections of such moving-coil stylus assemblies as they move during the playing of the record. From these drawings it can clearly be seen how magnetic flux is directed by the iron core or armature of the coil. If the coil is made stationary and the core is vibrated, the signal will be generated anyway. This fact prevents it from being classified as a pure moving-coil device.

To this class belongs the MC-20 cartridge produced by

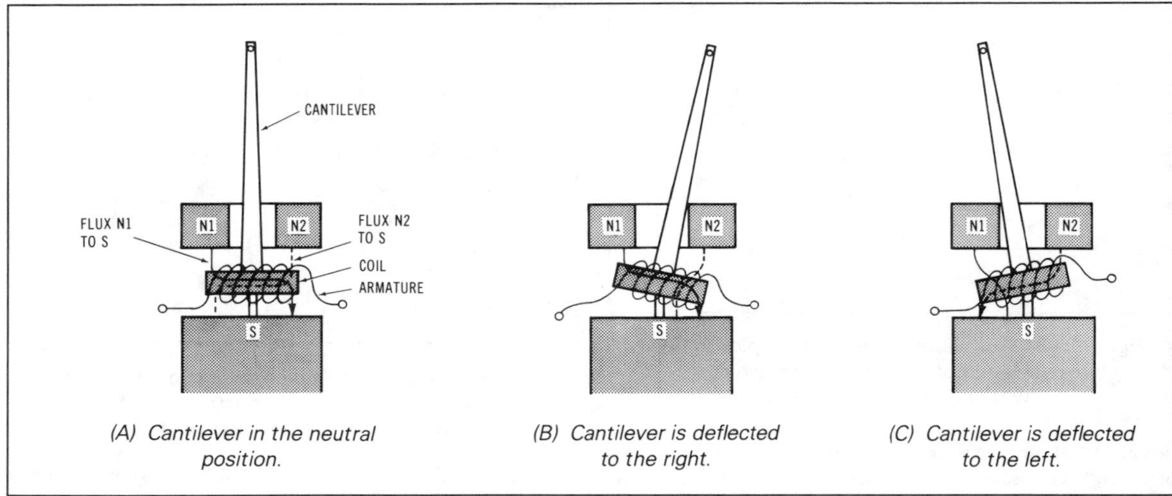

(A) Cantilever in the neutral position.

(B) Cantilever is deflected to the right.

(C) Cantilever is deflected to the left.

Figure 23-86 Bottom view of the moving-coil cartridge generator assembly.

Ortofon Manufacturing. Fig. 23-87A shows the layout of all major parts of the assembly. The design uses one heavy magnet and the cantilever assembly, which is not user replaceable. The advantage of this design is that it features extremely low impedance, and the cartridge is insensitive to capacitive loading, allowing the use of very long cables without the fear of altering the frequency response of the device. On the negative side, the output of the cartridge is very low, measuring in the tenths of a millivolt and, therefore, requiring extra amplification to bring the electrical signal to the required level. A step-up transformer or an extra stage of amplification, which may be added to the system, usually introduces additional noise and possibly the sensitivity to capacitive loading, as in the case of the transformer. Other drawbacks of such design are the weight of the cartridge and the need to use a heavier tracking force.

One of the debatable points about MC cartridges is the sound they produce. Because of very low inductance and the impedance of the coils, there is a very fast response to the transients aided by the very rigid cantilever, which has to be strong in order to move a relatively heavy coil assembly. Another factor in this type of design is the construction of the coil assembly, which may have a number of turns in the coil unsupported and free to vibrate, producing random signals at higher frequencies. Also lead-in and lead-out wires may not be secured properly and can vibrate in the magnetic field producing random coloration of the signal. Lead dressing, coil impregnation, and gluing techniques control the purity of the sound produced by this design.

Enormous strides have been made to preserve the purity of the MC principle and to raise the output voltage. The Yamaha International Corp. Model MC-1X/1S (Fig. 23-88) is a perfect example of such an effort. A cutaway view of this cartridge shows two magnetic gaps each of which have two magnets directing flux in two directions. Fig. 23-89 shows that the entire coil that moves inside the field will generate the electric current, which is contrary to many other MC pickups that utilize only one-half of each coil while the other half is only contributing to the overall mass of the stylus assembly. Yamaha's cartridge is designed with two printed-circuit microminiature flat coils (Fig. 23-89). In spite of all attempts to increase the output voltage, the signal voltage produced by playing the reference level of 5 cm/s at 1 kHz is only 0.2 mV. Because of the different way these coils are made, this design does not suffer from the spurious resonances due to loose wires found in other cartridges.

Moving-coil cartridges existed since the days of the invention of electronic playback and amplification. The amount of additional amplification needed usually varies from 20 to 30 dB, as referenced to an established sensitivity of 1 mV of output for 1 cm/s of recorded velocity.

Step-up transformers have to have winding ratios of 1:10 or more. The transformer's high-impedance secondary winding is reflected back into the primary, and any loading of the secondary in excess of the specified value affects the signal output level and electrical damping of the coils. Theoretically, shorted coils produce maximum damping, while an unterminated winding of the transformer's secondary will emphasize electrical resonances and unchecked mechanical motion. It is important to locate the step-up transformer near the preamplifier input to minimize the capacitive load of the shielded wires between the transformer and the input stage of the amplifier. Because the levels handled by this input transformer are extremely low, good transformer shielding is necessary.

In lieu of the step-up transformer, a pre-preamplifier may be used. Additional preamplification, obtained from active gain circuits, requires super low-noise transistors

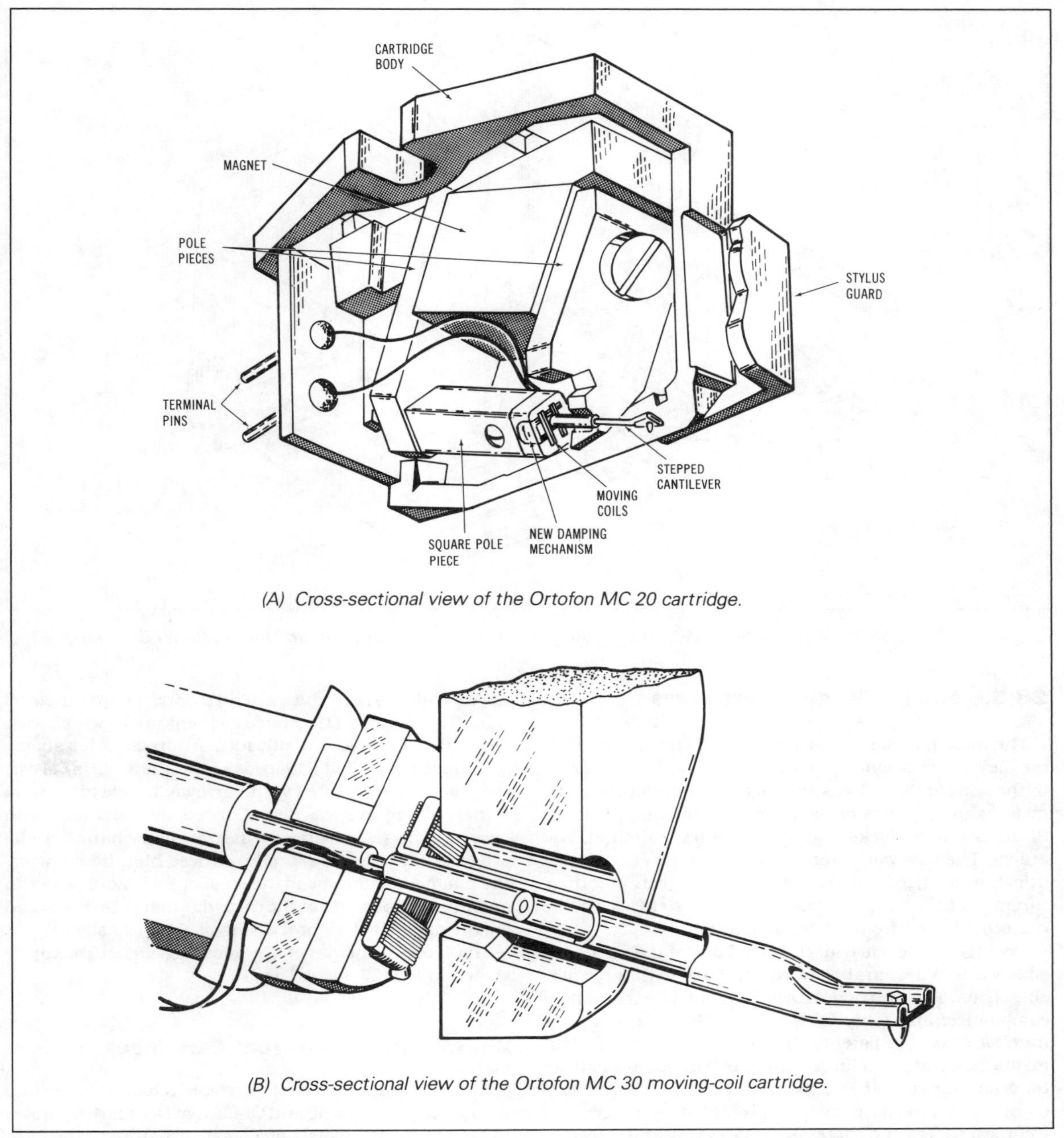

(A) Cross-sectional view of the Ortofon MC 20 cartridge.

(B) Cross-sectional view of the Ortofon MC 30 moving-coil cartridge.

Figure 23-87 Cross-sectional views of the Ortofon MC 20 and MC 30. *(Courtesy Ortofon Inc.)*

and special circuits in order to preserve an acceptable signal-to-noise ratio. There have been many such pre-preamplifiers designed using the most exotic devices and circuits, operating with batteries or special ac power supplies with maximum filtering and voltage regulation, and using magnetic shielding.

A typical pre-preamplifier circuit designed by Marshall Leach for battery operation is shown in Fig. 23-90. It features a floating power supply with two grounded base pnp and npn transistors. Since most of the MC cartridges operate well into a 100-Ω load, this preamplifier can be used with most of the cartridges, it is not sensitive to the magnetic fields, and it features very low noise and very small power consumption.

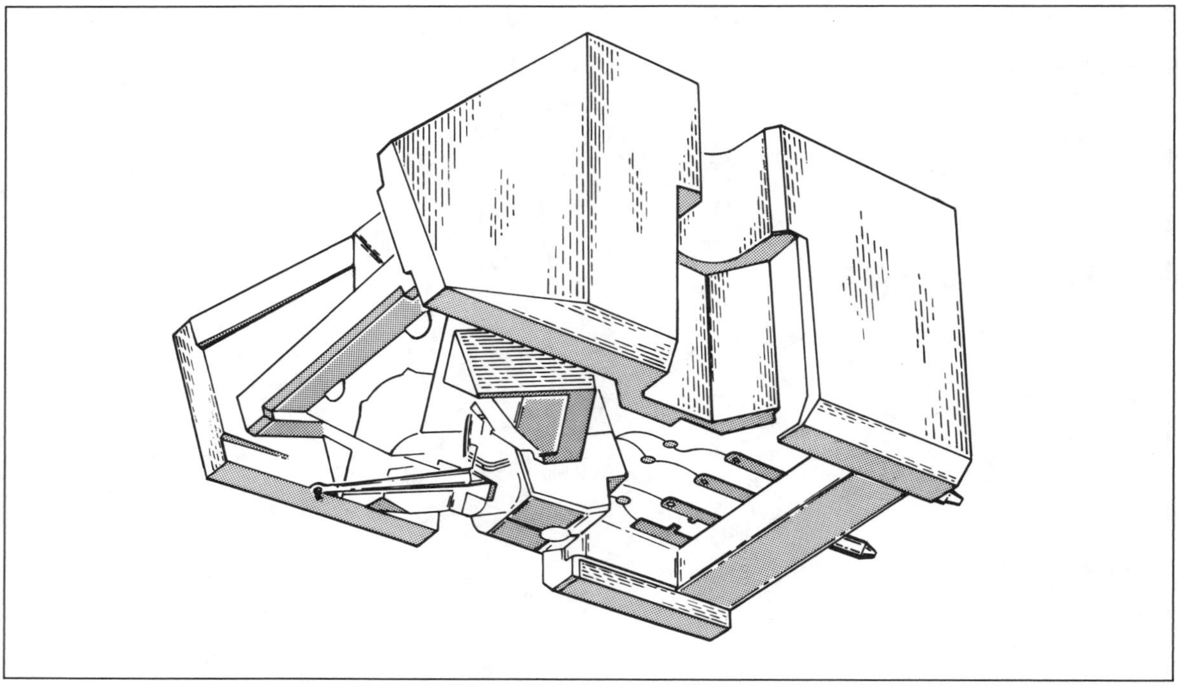

Figure 23-88 Yamaha MC 1X1.5 true moving-coil pickup. *(Courtesy Yamaha International Corp.)*

23.5.6 Moving-Magnet Cartridges

The most popular high-performance stereo cartridges are the moving-magnet type. The idea originated in Europe in the late 1950s and was adopted almost immediately by major manufacturers of transducers in the United States: Shure Brothers, Pickering, ADC, Empire, Fairchild, and others. The idea was patented, and it took a great deal of litigation and cross-licensing until American manufacturers could produce moving-magnet cartridges and be protected by law from other competitors.

Moving-magnet cartridges offered one of the most sensible ways to design the stereo cartridge with a replaceable stylus. This cartridge has low dynamic tip mass, high compliance, and fairly high output. Because of a large number of design patents that were issued for moving-magnet cartridges, a large variety of cartridge constructions sprang up in the period from 1960 to 1980. Refinements of the basic principle, prompted by a series of technical papers and aggressive engineering and research, produced cartridges that outperformed any other type of transducer. By using the most powerful rare earth magnets and using the most modern manufacturing methods, the frequency response was extended from almost direct current to well past the threshold of hearing, up to 50 kHz, which happened when the idea of discrete four-channel recording and reproduction of sound was in its full bloom in the late 1970s. The idea of CD-4 called for the cartridge to reproduce a 30-kHz carrier superimposed on both channels of the stereo base channels, which were restricted to a 20-kHz bandwidth. A special stylus shape, introduced by Shibata, helped recover the 30-kHz FM carrier that was modulated with narrower bandwidth audio signals. When this was demodulated and combined with base channels, it produced a discrete four-channel audio program. In order to reproduce these high frequencies, the magnets had to be made smaller and more powerful and the moving parts of the cartridge had to be optimized for the most efficient processing of electrical signals.

The basic principle of the moving-magnet pickup is shown in Fig. 23-91.

23.5.7 Induced-Magnet Cartridges

An induced-magnet or variable-reluctance pickup manufactured by Bang and Olufsen of Denmark is shown in Fig. 23-92. It consists of a small armature in the form of a cross, made of Mumetal, which swings between four pole pins, as shown in Fig. 23-93. A stylus bar constructed of aluminum tubing 0.002-in. thick is attached to the Mumetal armature cross at one end. The stylus is secured to the other end of the tube. Four pole pins with four coils are placed at each end of the cross. With a 45° motion to the right, a reverse voltage induction takes place. Such action permits the coils to be connected push-pull,

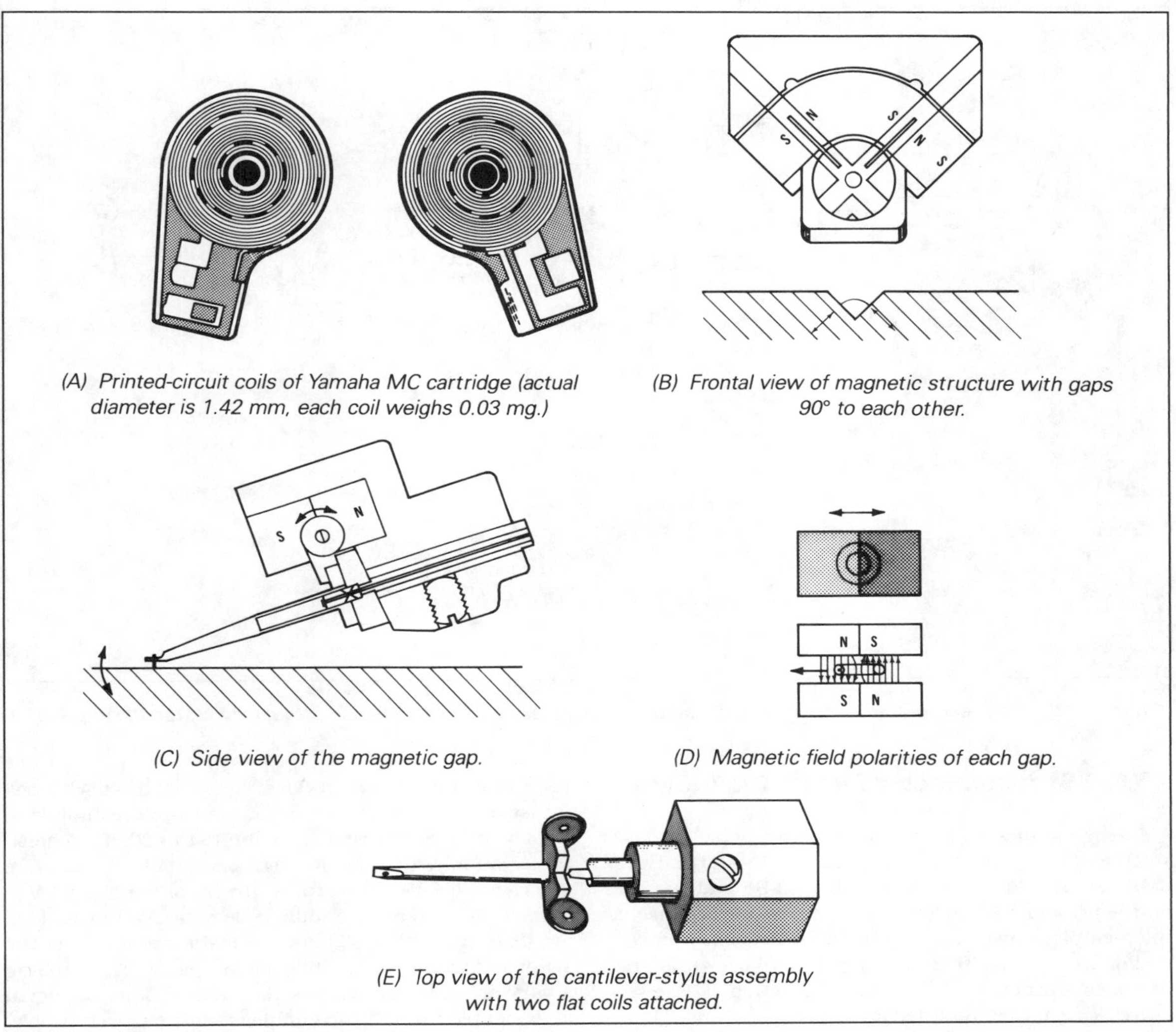

(A) Printed-circuit coils of Yamaha MC cartridge (actual diameter is 1.42 mm, each coil weighs 0.03 mg.)

(B) Frontal view of magnetic structure with gaps 90° to each other.

(C) Side view of the magnetic gap.

(D) Magnetic field polarities of each gap.

(E) Top view of the cantilever-stylus assembly with two flat coils attached.

Figure 23-89 Parts of the Yamaha 1X1.5 moving-coil pickup. ***(Courtesy Yamaha International Corp.)***

thus reducing harmonic distortion induced by the nonlinearity of the magnetic field. In addition, the coils provide an effective hum-bucking circuit.

Crosstalk between the left and right channels is minimized, since such components are bucked out. The overall crosstalk level is quite low for any frequency, since the voltage induction comes only from changing the spacing of the armature cross arms and the pole pieces. Modulating one channel 45°, the cross arms on the orthogonal channel rotate without changing the spacing; therefore, there is no induced voltage in this channel, assuming the positioning of unit, with respect to the groove, is correct.

A cross-sectional view of the magnetic circuit is shown in Fig. 23-94 and is similar to the magnetic structure of a loudspeaker employing a center magnet. Thus, a closed magnetic circuit, which prevents leakage of the magnetic field, is provided and being nonmagnetic, it cannot be attracted to the steel turntable plate. It also provides an effective shield for the coils. The stylus bar pivots on a nylon thread, bonded to a plastic support. The armature cross bears on a resilient disk (Fig. 23-95), which controls compliance and supplies damping for the moving system. The rotational point of the system is at the junction of the armature cross and the nylon thread support. The output voltage is 7 mV for each channel for a 5-cm/s cut. The stylus has an angle of 15° (at 2 g of tracking force) and may be operated at a pressure of 1 to 3 g. Compliance is 15×10^{-6} cm/dyn for both directions of motion. Frequency response is ±2.5 dB, 20 Hz to 20 kHz.

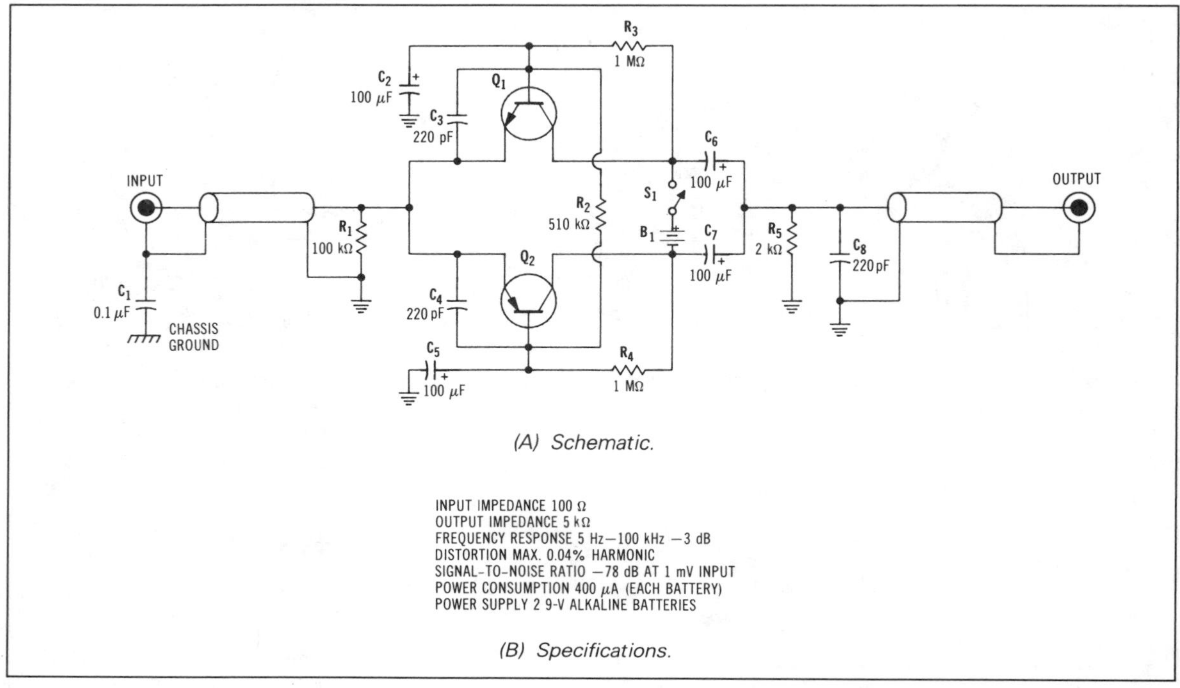

Figure 23-90 Pre-preamplifier for moving-coil cartridge designed by Marshall Leach. *(Courtesy Marshall Amplifiers)*

23.5.8 Semiconductor Pickup Cartridges

A semiconductor pickup cartridge developed by J. F. Wood and George Grover of the Euphonics Corp., Guaynabo, Puerto Rico, is shown in Fig. 23-96 and operates on the principle of the strain gauge. The pickup mechanism employs two small, highly doped silicon semiconductor elements (0.008 × 0.005 in.) whose resistance varies as a function of the stylus deflection. These sensitive elements are mounted on laminated beams of lightweight epoxy with gold-plated surfaces, as shown in Fig. 23-97. A notch in the beam under the assembly acts as a hinge for stress concentration. Referring to Fig. 23-98, the construction for a stereophonic cartridge is shown. In this structure two beams are used, each driven by an elastic yoke, coupled to the stylus. Aside from the compliance of the yoke and mounting pads, a mechanical advantage of over 40:1 can be attained in the beam and stylus lever. This mechanical transformer provides high compliance and reduces the mass of the elements reflected to the stylus. This stylus, elliptical in shape, is set at an angle of 15°.

Since the semiconductor elements are sensitive modulating devices and not generators as in the conventional pickup, very little energy is required for their operation. The compliance at 1 kHz is approximately 25 × 10^{-6} cm/dyn. Because of the low mass of the semiconductor elements and driving mechanism, the frequency response is carried out beyond 50 kHz. Actually, the device will measure down to dc, but because of the preamplifiers, the low-frequency response is limited to 20 Hz. A small power supply, two single-stage preamplifiers, and one inverter stage are required. A current of 6 mA at 14 V is supplied to each semiconductor element. As the elements are deflected by the stylus action, the resistance of the semiconductors (about 800 Ω) changes slightly, causing a varying dc voltage across the output. This dc signal is ac coupled to the preamplifiers in the power supply, providing an output voltage of 0.4 V for each side. The cartridge employs mechanical equalization which, in combination with the RC equalizer at the output of each preamplifier, results in an RIAA reproducing characteristic.

Because of the importance of maintaining symmetry in a stereo cartridge, the beams are oriented with the silicon elements upward in each channel. Such an arrangement gives out-of-phase signals for lateral motion of the stylus. Since the elements have no inherent polarity, reversing the terminals does not change the phase. To phase the output signals properly, the left side is passed through a phase inverter.

Using a standard test record with 400 Hz and 4 kHz, the intermodulation distortion for a stylus pressure of 2 g at a velocity of 13 cm/s is 2%; for a velocity of 15 cm/s and a stylus pressure of 1 g, the distortion rises to about 10%. Separation is 25 dB up to 11 kHz and better than

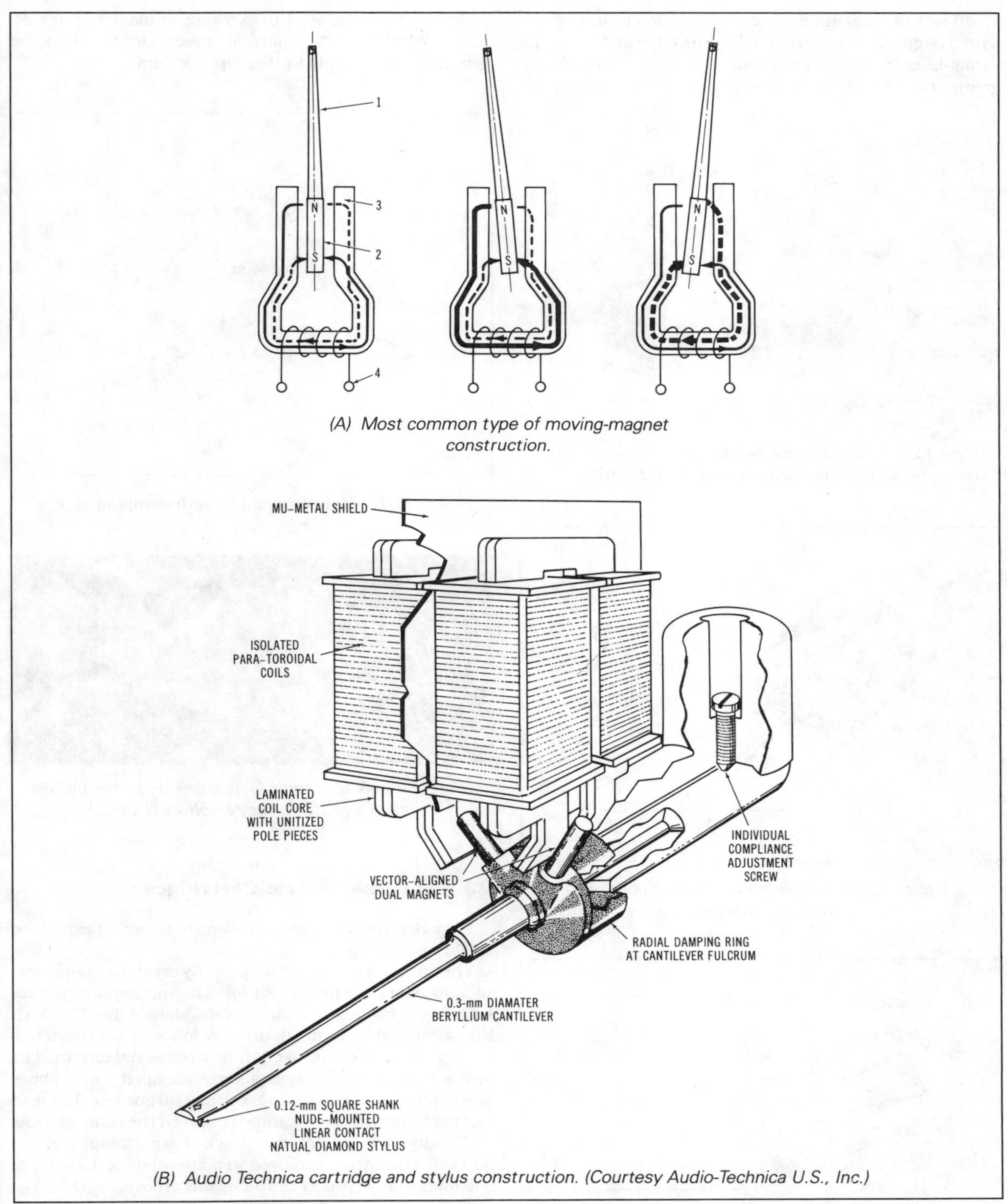

(A) Most common type of moving-magnet construction.

(B) Audio Technica cartridge and stylus construction. (Courtesy Audio-Technica U.S., Inc.)

Figure 23-91 Basic principle of the moving-magnet pickup.

15 dB to 20 kHz. Square-wave reproduction is quite good, with a slight overshoot on the leading edge at 1 kHz. The signal-to-noise ratio at the output of the preamplifier is greater than 80 dB below a reference level of 1 mW. Such pickups are not subject to extraneous magnetic or electrostatic fields. The normal precautions taken for grounding also apply to this type pickup.

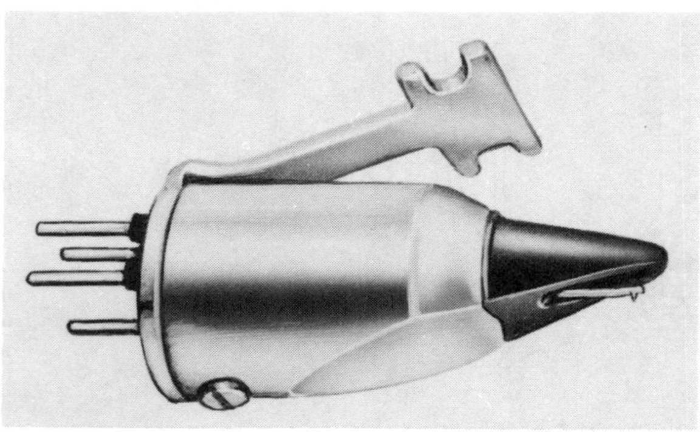

Figure 23-92 Stereodyne Model SP-6, 15°, push-pull stereophonic pickup. *(Courtesy Bang and Olufsen Co.)*

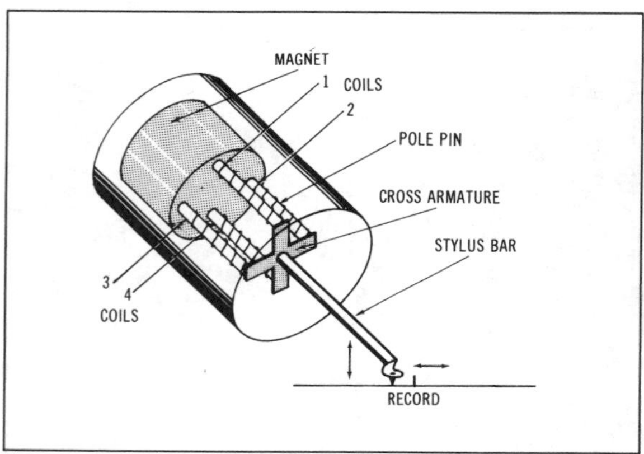

Figure 23-93 Simplified drawing of coils and cross armature.

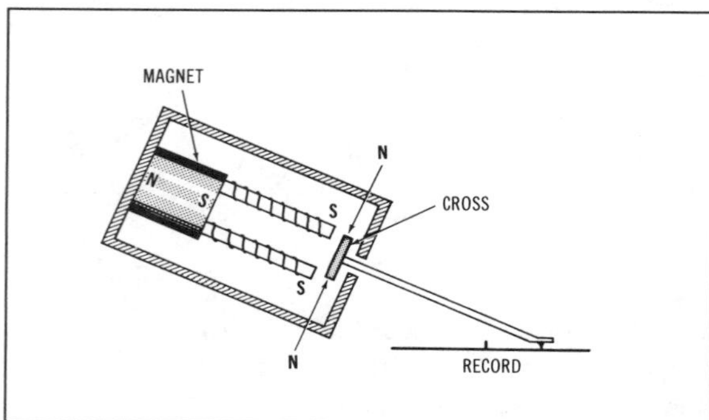

Figure 23-94 Magnetic circuit.

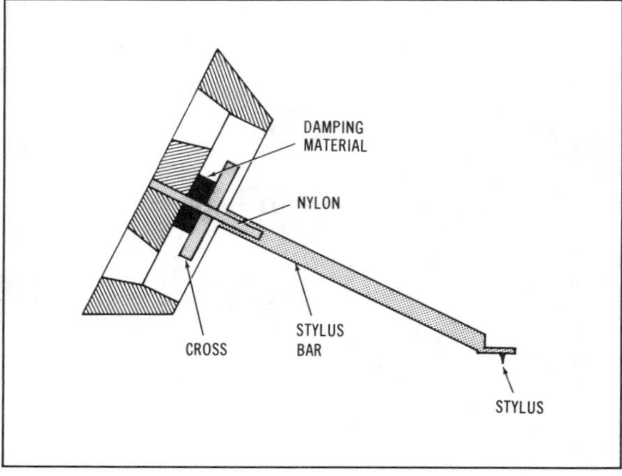

Figure 23-95 Stylus mounting with damping control.

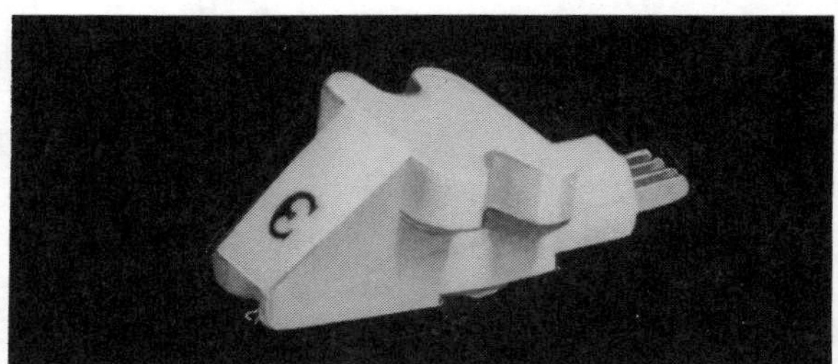

Figure 23-96 Miniconic U-15 semiconductor pickup cartridge. *(Courtesy Euphonics Corp.)*

23.5.9 Piezoelectric Cartridges

Piezoelectricity is pressure electricity and is explained in Chapter 13.

The basic construction for an early crystal monophonic pickup is shown in Fig. 23-99. The motional structure consists of two Rochelle salt crystal slabs A and B, which are separated by a metal foil C. A foil lead D is attached to each crystal for connection to an external circuit. The opposite ends of the crystals are clamped in a rubber sleeve mounted in a clamp E called a torque jaw. The lead ends of the crystals are clamped between the rubber blocks F. The stylus G is held in a chuck H and clamped by the screw I. The chuck is moved in a lateral direction due to the motion of stylus G in the record groove.

The twisting motion of the torque jaw causes the crystal slabs to generate a voltage due to the piezoelectric characteristics of the crystals. The voltage generated by the crystals is proportional to the amplitude of the stylus

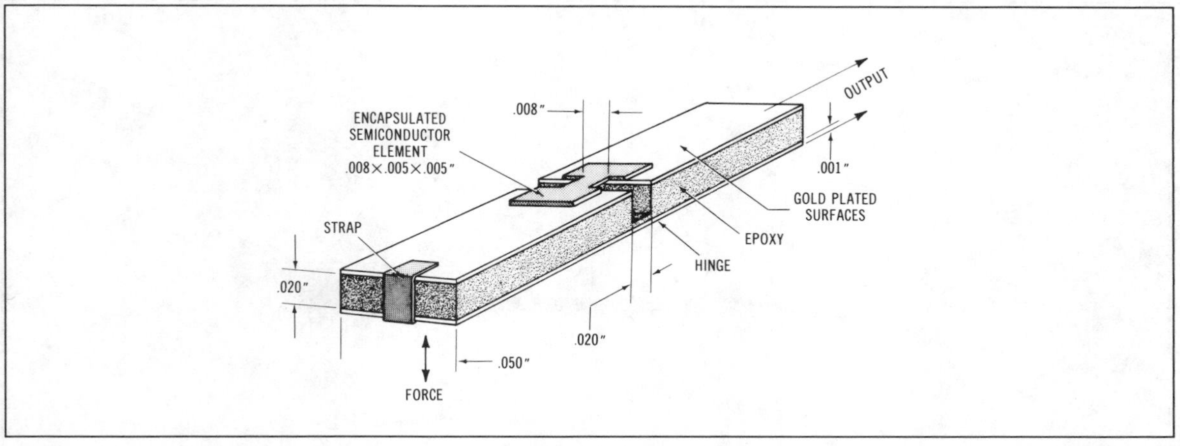

Figure 23-97 Beam construction of Euphonics semiconductor stereophonic pickup. *(Courtesy Euphonics Corp.)*

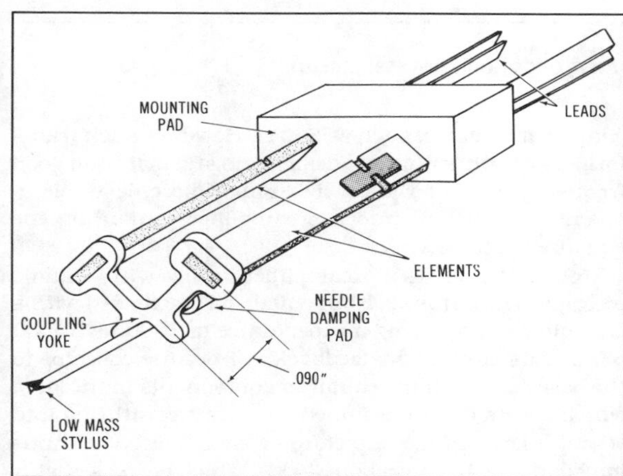

Figure 23-98 Cartridge construction of Euophonics semiconductor stereophonic pickup. *(Courtesy Euphonics Corp.)*

displacement. The rubber sleeves J, K, and L are used to hold the crystal assembly in its case, as shown in Fig. 23-99.

The output voltage of the average piezoelectric pickup is considerably higher than for other type pickups. Piezoelectric pickups are treated electrically as a capacitive-reactance device since the impedance rises with a decrease of frequency, and vice versa. Simple RC networks are used with this type pickup to obtain a frequency response corresponding to the standard RIAA reproducing characteristic. Records recorded using a constant-amplitude characteristic may be reproduced without equalization.

A simplified diagram for a ceramic stereophonic pickup unit is shown in Fig. 23-100. The moving system consists of two piezoelectric crystal slabs of lead-zirconium titanate, or similar material. This particular material offers good mechanical and electrical properties, with high sensitivity and high capacitance. The ends of the slabs are mounted rigidly in a mounting block, and the front end is connected by a yoke made of injected molded plastic. This coupling is most critical because upon it depends the electrical performance and the mechanical impedance seen at the stylus point by the record groove. The coupling system is defined as that portion of the mechanism that lies between the stylus tip and the ceramic slabs.

The stylus bar is made from heat-treated, thin-walled aluminum alloy tubing, with one end flattened to hold the stylus at the desired angle. The other end of the stylus bar is held in place by the stylus mounting block. The coupling yoke is connected at a point about midway on the stylus bar. This point is chosen because it affords the most desirable electrical performance and substantially reduces the mechanical impedance of the yoke and ceramic elements as seen by the stylus tip.

Better designs have four output terminals, two for each channel, to ensure the complete isolation of one side from the other. Damping in the form of a viscous material is used to control the frequency characteristics. These pickups are of the constant-amplitude type; therefore, an RC network is required to reproduce the RIAA curve. The output voltage for such a device is approximately 10 mV for a peak velocity of 5 cm/s. Ceramic pickups are not affected by magnetic or electrostatic fields.

RC equalizer networks for both crystal and ceramic pickups are shown in Fig. 23-101. The networks are connected between the output of the piezoelectric pickup and the input of the preamplifier. The characteristics of these networks are such that they correspond to the standard RIAA reproducing curve.

The internal impedance of the average crystal pickup is approximately 100 kΩ, with a capacitance of 0.001 to 0.0015 μF. Special impedance-matching transformers are available for matching the ceramic and crystal pickup to

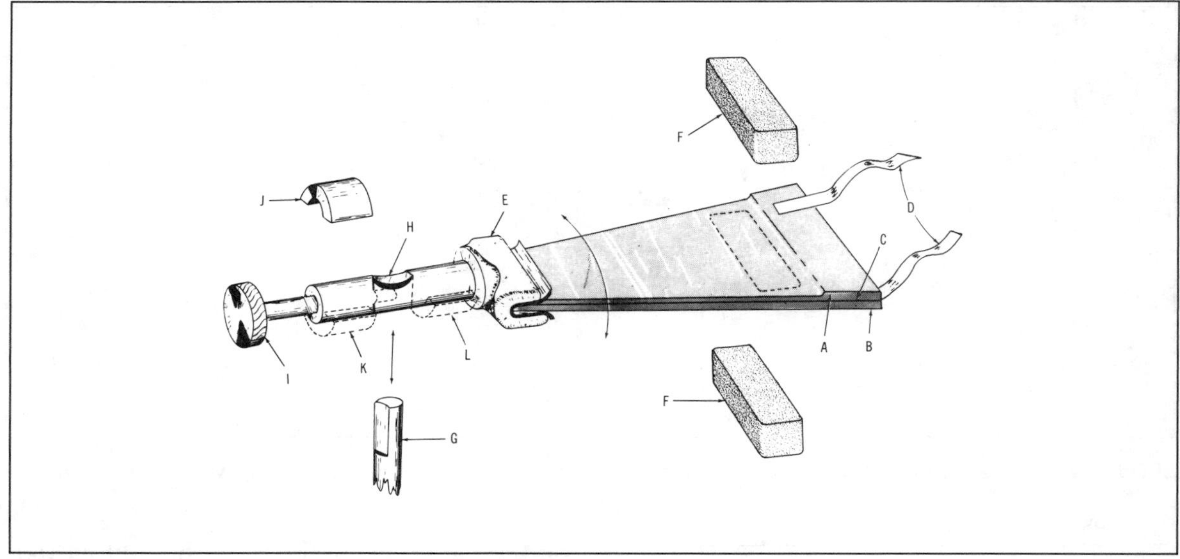

Figure 23-99 Interior mechanism of a monophonic crystal pickup.

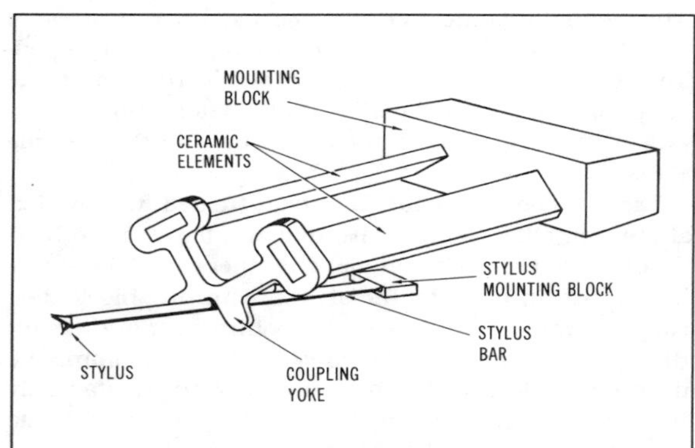

Figure 23-100 Simplified drawing showing the construction of a ceramic stereophonic pickup.

a lower impedance, such as 600 Ω. However, such transformers are rather hard to design and still maintain good frequency characteristics. It is much more desirable to operate the pickup into a preamplifier containing the equalizer networks.

Fig. 23-102 shows a preamplifier for use with ceramic pickups. The output is RIAA equalized when used with a ceramic pickup having a capacitance of 1000 to 10,000 pF. In this circuit, the feedback is from the collector to the base of T_1 with the equalizer components in the loop, which lowers the input impedance, thus permitting it to accept a large range of pickup capacitances. The input impedance at 40 Hz is about 30 kΩ, which decreases with an increasing frequency causing a velocity response from the cartridge. The frequency response is within ± 1.5 dB from 40 Hz to 12 kHz, with a signal-to-noise ratio of 70 dB. Harmonic distortion is less than 0.1% at 1.25 V output.

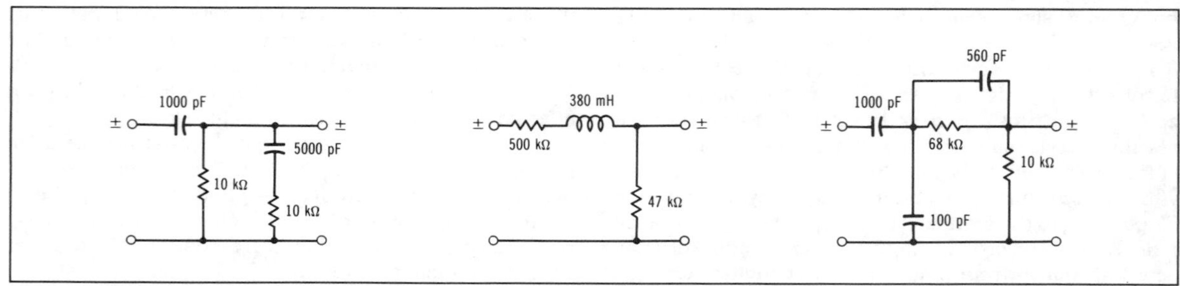

Figure 23-101 Resistance-capacitance frequency-correction networks for ceramic pickups to reproduce the RIAA characteristic, using a pickup with a compliance of 15×10^{-6}cm/dyn or greater. Response can be within ±2 dB.

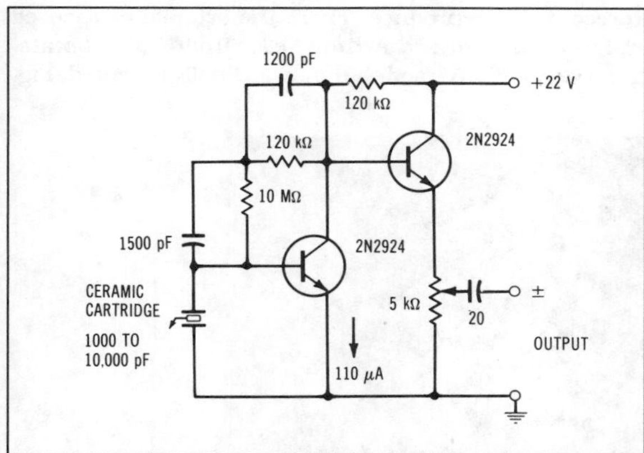

Figure 23-102 Transistor preamplifier designed for use with ceramic pickups of a 1000- to 10,000-pF capacitance.

Exceptionally good results may be obtained by using field-effect transistors in pickup preamplifiers, since a greater signal-to-noise ratio can be obtained by their use. The circuit shown in Fig. 23-103 has a signal-to-noise ratio 7 dB lower than the best vacuum-tube amplifier of similar design, with a 5 dB higher overload factor.

23.5.10 Phonograph Cartridge Styli

23.5.10.1 Stereo Disk Groove

The playback stylus (Fig. 23-104) is the first link between the information stored in the record groove and the playback system. The quality of the reproduced sound is influenced by the precision with which the stylus follows the record modulation. In order to understand what is required from the stylus and what it takes to reproduce the modulation with the least amount of distortion, let us analyze the groove and see how it is modulated.

The record groove is cut so that two walls of the V groove are at a 45° angle to the surface of the record and 90° to each other.

The stereo groove can carry several types of modulation, as shown in Fig. 23-105. The first type of modulation ever used was vertical modulation. If the groove was observed from above, its width changes symmetrically. With the advent of disk records, lateral modulation became popular. The laterally modulated groove has a constant depth, and the modulation deflects the groove sideways.

In the stereophonic recordings, the two channels are isolated from each other because modulation of each channel is at 90° to the other. In the first attempts to store stereo information in a single groove to be reproduced with the single stylus, one channel was modulated

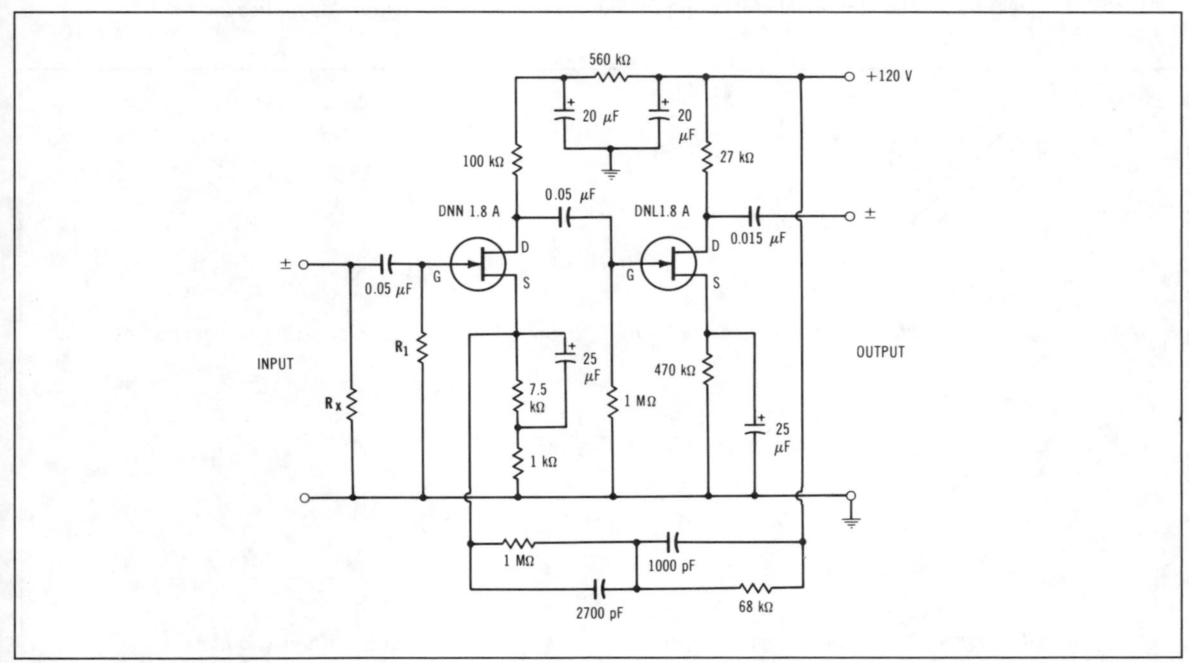

Figure 23-103 Pickup preamplifier using field-effect transistors. Resistor R_x and R_l are to be of a value specified by the pickup manufacturer. *(After Rheinfelder.)*

in a lateral plane while the second channel was modulated in a vertical plane. But very soon it was realized that the vertical channel had more distortion and was harder to record and reproduce. Then, the originally proposed and developed idea by Arthur Keller from Bell Laboratories, using 45°/45° modulation, was finally accepted (Fig.

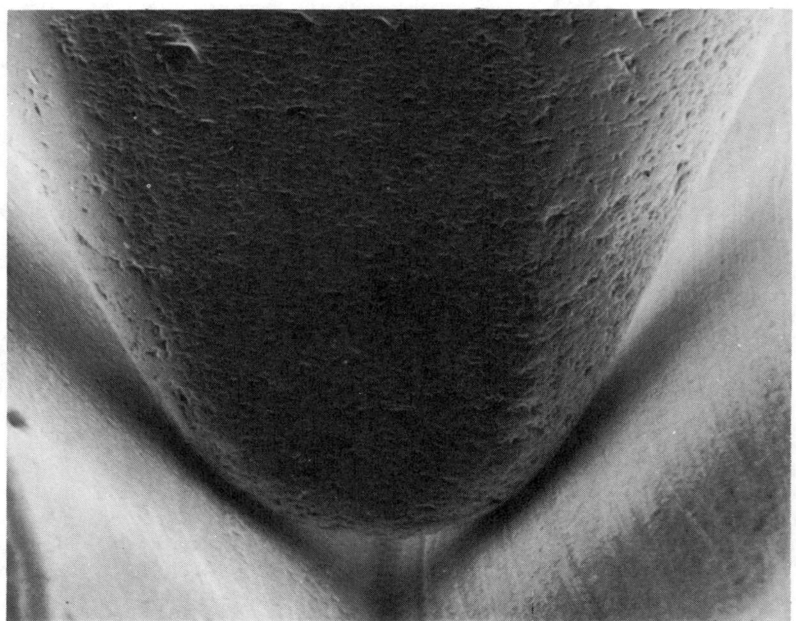

Figure 23-104 Spherical stylus tip in the groove. *(Courtesy Stanton Magnetics Inc.)*

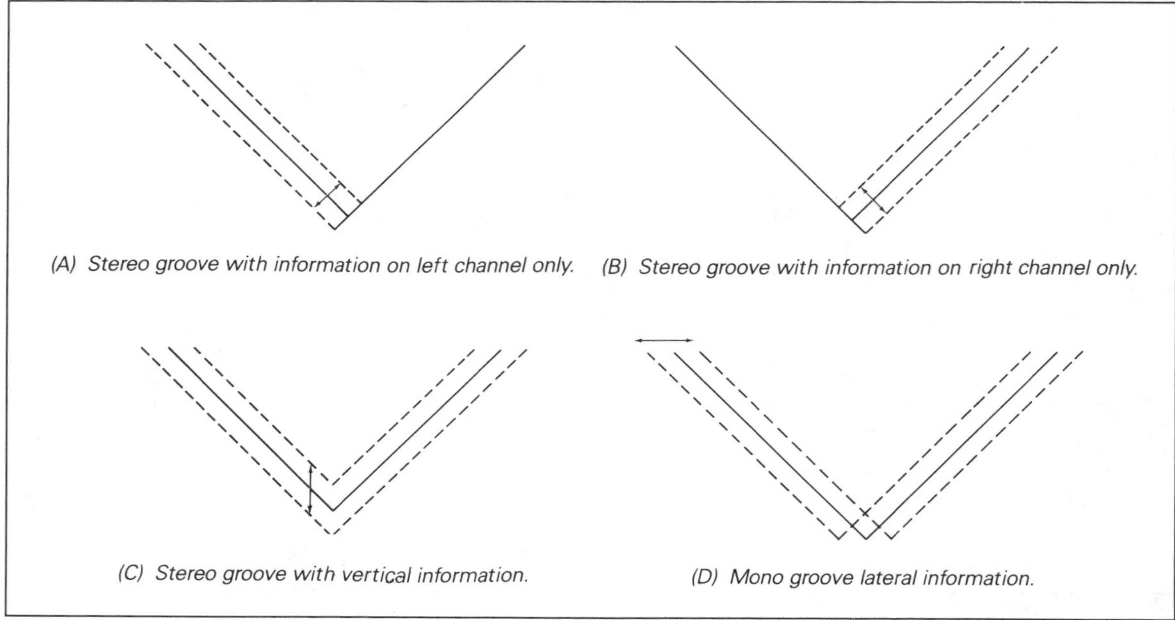

(A) Stereo groove with information on left channel only.
(B) Stereo groove with information on right channel only.
(C) Stereo groove with vertical information.
(D) Mono groove lateral information.

Figure 23-105 Types of groove modulation. *(From* Basic Disc Mastering, *Courtesy Larry Boden)*

23-106). Faults of vertical recording were divided between the two symmetrical channels, and new ways were found to minimize them without affecting the frequency response or the separation between channels (Fig. 23-107). In order to further minimize the effects of vertical excursions at low frequencies, the phase of both channels was adjusted in such a way that low-frequency signals be in phase in order to produce lateral modulation. Even special equipment was designed to cancel or suppress out-of-phase low-frequency, large-amplitude signals (Fig. 23-108). The phase relationship of the two channels determines the location of the signal between the two loudspeakers, and in some cases the phase is a deciding factor as to whether there is going to be a signal reproduced at all.

23.5.10.2 Stylus Tip

The function of the playback stylus of the cartridge is to follow all deflections of the groove. Since the stylus is attached to the end of the cantilever, any motion of the stylus tip is transmitted to the other end of the tube or shank, where the electrical signals are generated by a moving magnet, a moving coil, or a crystal. The shape of the playback stylus differs from the shape of the cutting stylus. The playback stylus, although it has to duplicate motion of the cutting stylus, should not destroy or alter the existing groove. Therefore, it has rounded off edges that are polished for smooth tracking, as shown in Fig. 23-104. Ideally, the playback stylus should be centered

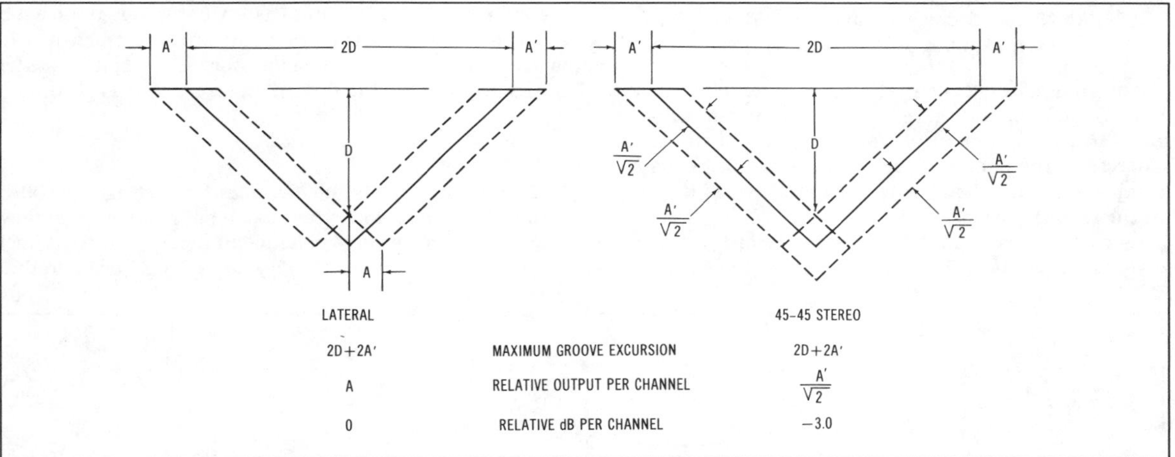

Figure 23-106 Comparison of 45°/45° stereophonic groove with standard lateral groove.

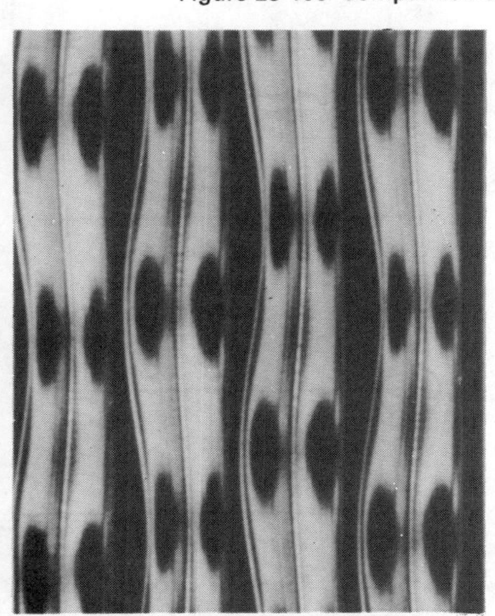

(A) Left channel modulation.

(B) Right channel modulation.

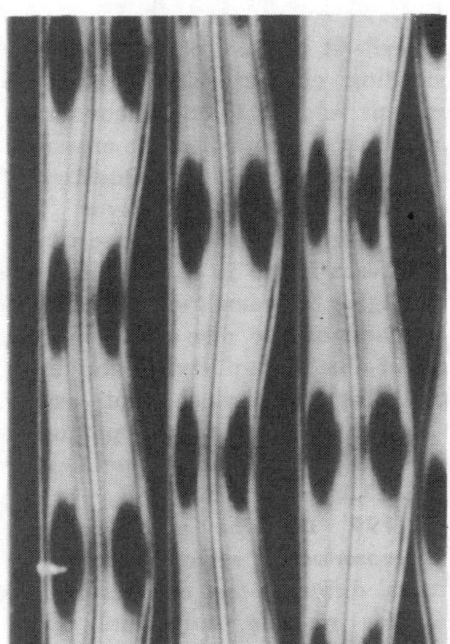

Figure 23-107 Left and right channel modulation.

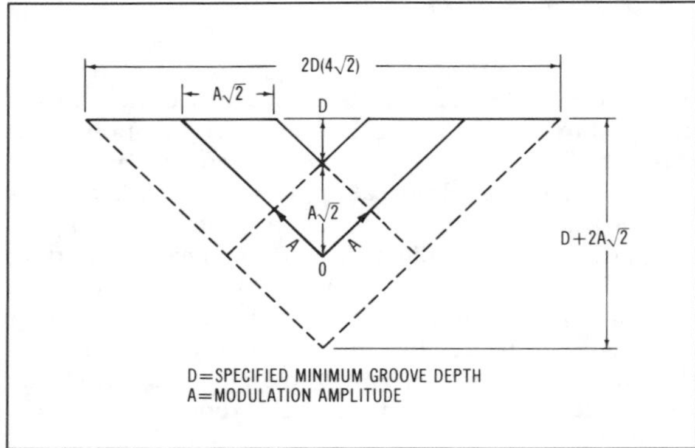

Figure 23-108 Cross section of 45°/45° groove for maximum groove excursion.

in the groove, and its centerline should match that of the cutting stylus. But there are always minute imperfections in the alignment of the stylus and of the groove. Therefore, the shape of the playback stylus is made to compensate and allow some misalignment of the stylus in the record groove.

As can be seen from the frontal view of the spherical stylus (Fig. 23-104), the stylus touches the groove walls at two points. The contact area is curved and is a part of the tip radius so that if the stylus is slightly tilted due to misalignment of the cartridge or the tonearm, tracking will not be affected.

Spherical Stylus

There are several types of styli today. The simplest and the oldest one is the *spherical tip*. The spherical stylus is a tiny diamond or sapphire cylinder with one end ground to a cone shape with its tip polished to an accurate sphere. The included angle of the cone is about 55°, and the tip radius is about 0.0007 in. or 0.7 mil. Older styli had much larger tip radii, which were determined by the depth and the size of the groove. Because modern grooves can be as narrow as 0.001 in., the stylus tip has to be equal to or smaller than the groove in order to track it. The standard tip radius dimensions for today's spherical styli range from 0.0005 to 0.0007 in. or 12.7 to 17.7 μm.

Elliptical Stylus

The second type is the *elliptical stylus* (Fig. 23-109A). From the front it looks just like a spherical stylus; however, there are two flats polished in the front and the back of the stylus, as shown in Fig. 23-109B. The side radius

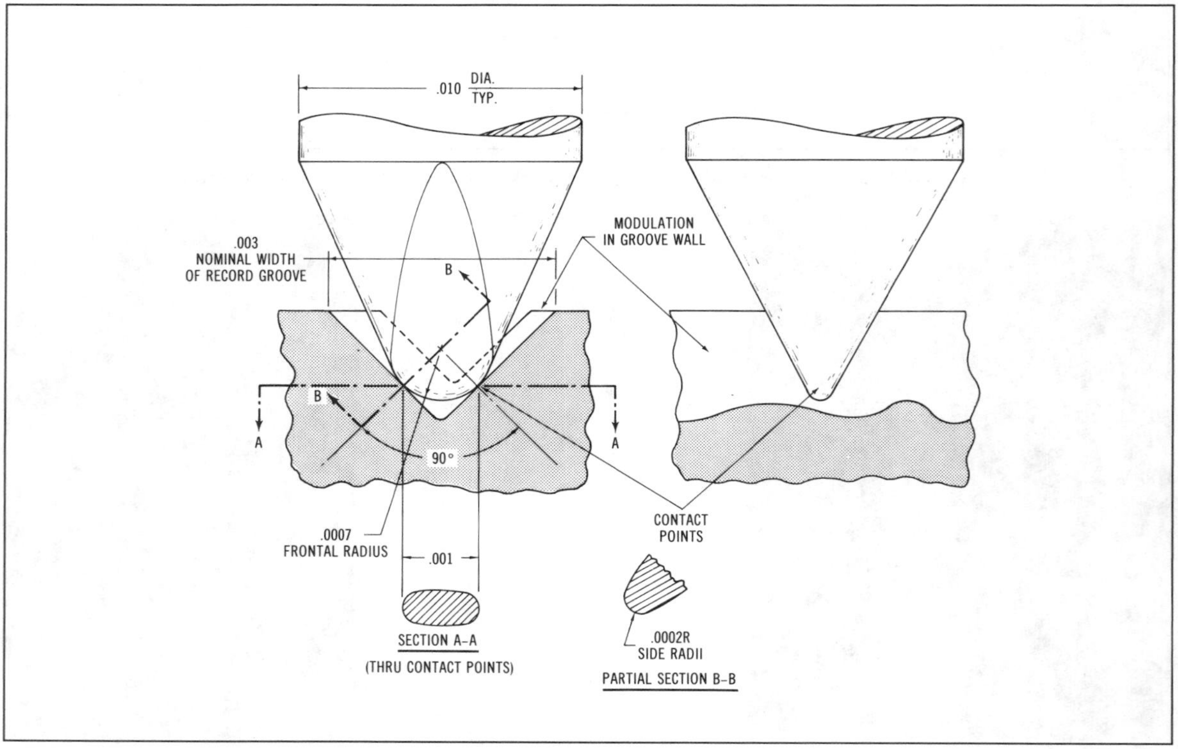

Figure 23-109 Bilateral-elliptical pickup stylus dimensions and radii. *(Courtesy Shure Brothers, Inc.)*

of the elliptical tip is much slimmer than that of the spherical stylus. The intersections of the two flats are polished to form small radii called the "tracing radii," which measure about 0.0002 in. These small side radii are actually in contact with the modulation of the groove and, because they are small, they follow the high-frequency excursions of the groove easier.

Figure 23-110 Quadrahedral stylus tip with a playing groove with a 30-kHz carrier (CD-A record). *(Courtesy Stanton Magnetics, Inc.)*

Figure 23-111 Stereohedron stylus tip in the stereo groove.

Fine-Line Stylus

The third type of stylus shape is represented by several designs of tip configurations that have much longer contact area than the elliptical stylus but with the same scanning or tracking radius. Sometimes this type is known as a *fine-line stylus, Shibata, biradial,* or *CD-4 type*. This type was developed in the days of CD-4 (four-channel discrete stereo) or quadraphonic research, when extremely high-frequency modulation had to be reproduced without destroying it. The first line stylus that was designed was called Shibata, followed by quadrahedral (Figs. 23-110 and 23-111), stereohedral, hyperelliptical, premanic, fine-line, and others.

Stylus Characteristics

Modern records contain signals with large amplitudes and hard-to-track modulation. The cutting stylus cuts a narrower groove when the stylus moves sideways, as shown in Fig. 23-112. This narrowing of the groove produces the *pinch effect*, which is responsible for lifting the playback stylus out of the groove and producing second harmonic distortion in the vertical direction. The pinch effect is much more noticeable with spherical styli and is less troublesome with fine-line shapes because the fine-line playback stylus is slimmer and fits into the curvature of the groove better.

All playback styli are designed to contact only the walls of the groove; therefore, the stylus tip has to ride without touching the bottom of the groove (Fig. 23-113). Since the diamond gets slimmer as it wears down, the tip gets closer and closer to the bottom of the groove (Fig. 23-114). When it starts touching it, noise increases because debris has accumulated on the bottom of the groove and is scooped up by the stylus. This is a clue to change the stylus in order to reduce the noise and to preserve the record from being destroyed by the sharp edges of the worn diamond (Fig. 23-115).

Presently, almost all styli manufactured are made out of diamond. The quality and the price of the stylus depends on whether it is made out of a solid piece of diamond or a small chip bonded onto another material that acts as an extension or pedestal for the diamond tip. The technology of manufacturing diamonds has advanced significantly so that chip bonding and encasing can be favorably compared to solid or nude diamond tips. In view of the fact that the area of contact is only 0.2 millionths of a square inch and as long as this area is made out of a diamond, the overall performance of the stylus will not be affected. All this is true providing, naturally, that the mass of the bonded stylus assembly is not higher than that of a conventional diamond and not larger than the nude stone (Fig. 23-116).

Playback stylus orientation has to match very closely the orientation of the cutting stylus to achieve maximum channel separation at middle and high frequencies. The phase relationship between the channels may also be

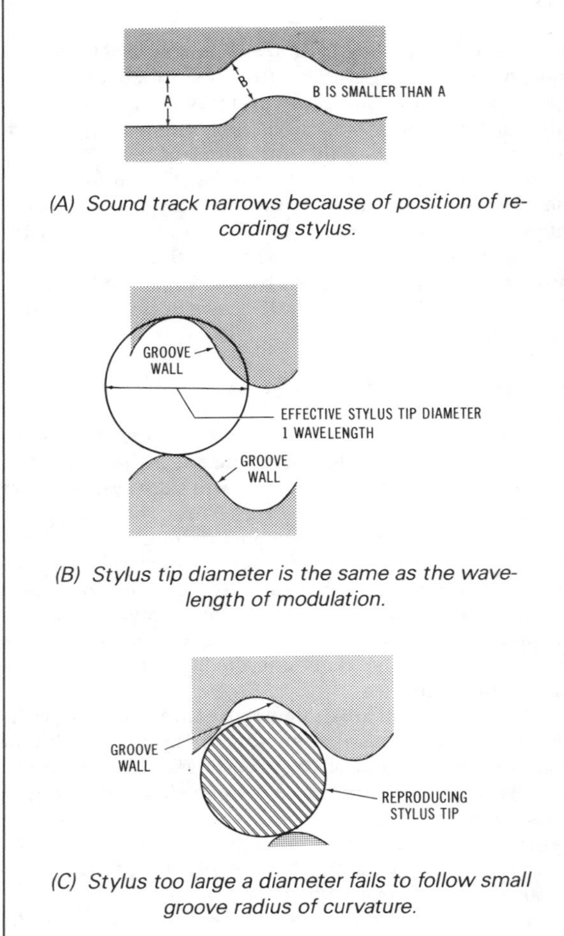
B IS SMALLER THAN A
A
B
(A) Sound track narrows because of position of recording stylus.
GROOVE WALL
EFFECTIVE STYLUS TIP DIAMETER
1 WAVELENGTH
GROOVE WALL
(B) Stylus tip diameter is the same as the wavelength of modulation.
GROOVE WALL
REPRODUCING STYLUS TIP
(C) Stylus too large a diameter fails to follow small groove radius of curvature.

Figure 23-112 Causes of tracking problems.

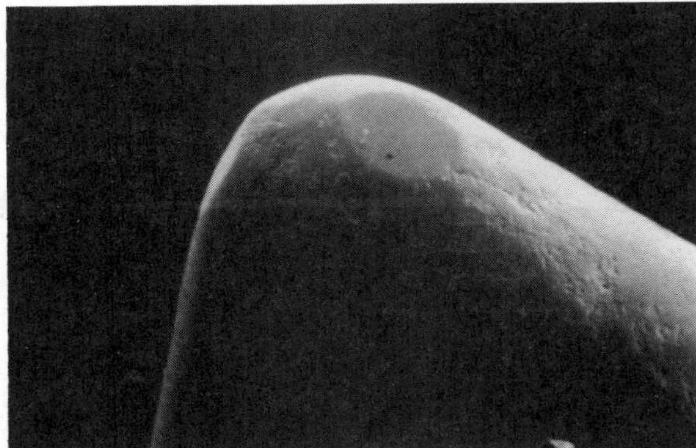

Figure 23-113 Slightly worn spherical tip. Note contact areas and worn tip from landing on flat portion of the record before sliding into the groove. *(Courtesy Stanton Magnetics, Inc.)*

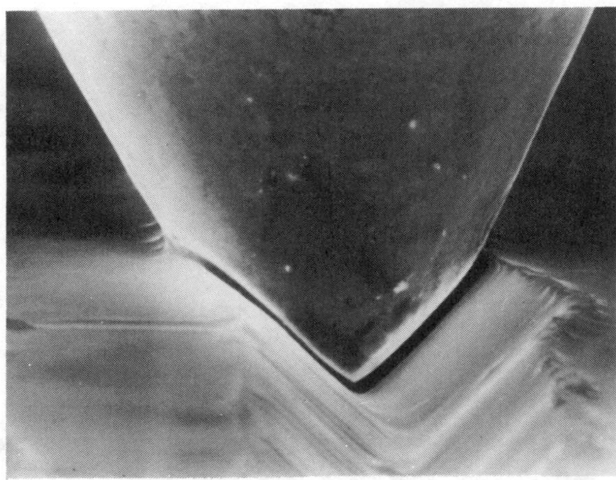

Figure 23-114 Excessively worn stylus in the groove, shaving all modulation. *(Courtesy Stanton Magnetics, Inc.)*

affected. Contrary to the fears of many about the accuracy of the diamond orientation, the phase between the high-frequency signals varies so much due to other reasons caused by the short wavelengths that it becomes less critical. If the speed of sound is 1200 ft/s in round numbers, then the wavelength of the 12-kHz signal is one-tenth of the foot. Since the wavelength represents 360° of phase rotation, the signal image shifts every 180° or every one-twentieth of a foot or 5/8 in. Therefore, if you are listening to the same 12-kHz signal coming from two loudspeakers and you move your head a little more than a ½ in., you will hear wandering of the signal source due to phase reversal. However, for proper seating of the stylus of the complex shape in the groove, correct orientation is a must.

The vertical tracking force applied to the stylus is divided between the two walls. Each wall is experiencing force that is equal to the total vertical force times the cosine of 45° or 0.707 (Fig. 23-117). For instance if the vertical tracking force (VTF) is 1 g, then each groove wall will experience a force of 0.7 g. This wedge effect plays an important role in understanding the dynamic behavior of the stylus in a compliant groove and its effect on electrical separation between the channels.

Because of the small area of contact that exists between the stylus tip and the groove, the pressure against the groove wall can rise up to many thousands of pounds per square inch. For instance, if each wall receives 0.7 g of force applied through the contact area equal to 2/10 millionths of an inch (0.2×10^{-6}), the pressure is 7726

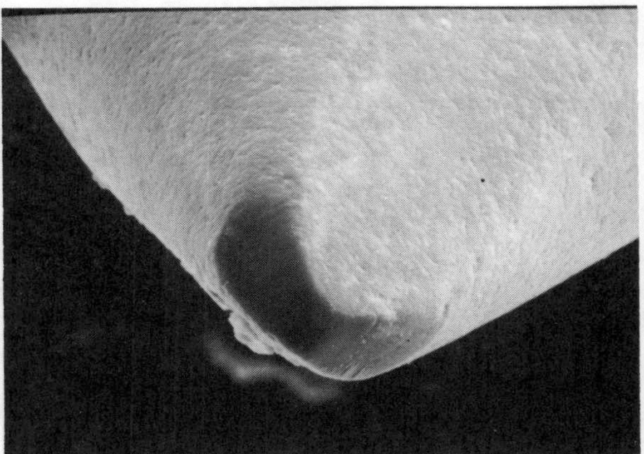
Figure 23-115 Badly worn elliptical stylus tip magnified 1000 times. *(Courtesy Stanton Magnetics, Inc.)*

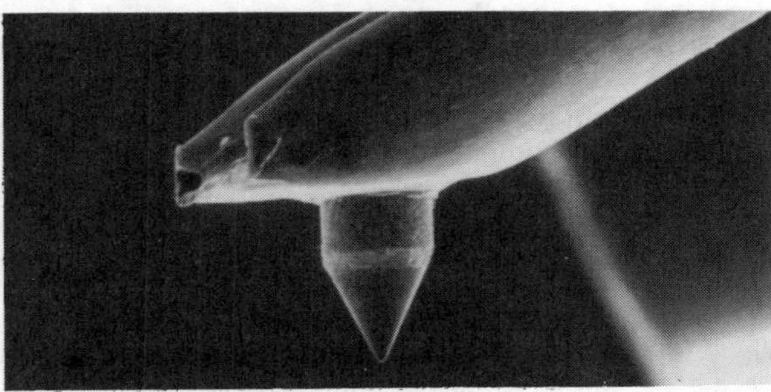
Figure 23-116 Bonded spherical tip in final assembly. *(Courtesy Stanton Magnetics, Inc.)*

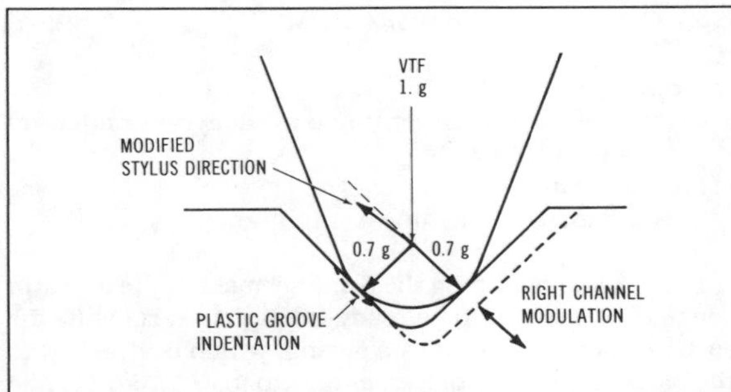

Figure 23-117 Stylus motion and forces acting upon it in a stereo groove.

lb/in.^{2} It has been experimentally shown that with such high pressures and force of friction between the stylus and the vinyl, that the outer skin layer of the record material melts as the tip slides over the plastic and then refreezes almost as fast as it melted. It has been suggested that since the melting temperature of the vinyl is about 480°F

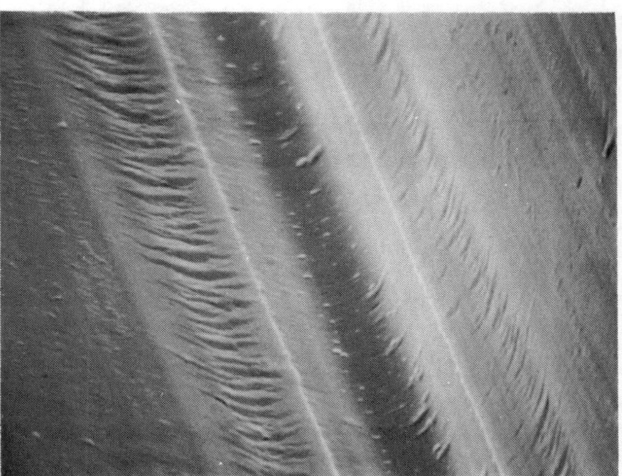
Figure 23-118 Tracks left by the stylus after 100 plays. *(Courtesy Stanton Magnetics, Inc.)*

that the same temperature exists in the contact area. If the record material is metal, which happens when metal mothers are played, then the pressure increases to 20,000 to 30,000 lb/in.^{2}, and the temperature can reach 2000°F because there is no plastic deformation of the groove wall. This explains why styli made out of diamond, which is nothing more than carbon, literally burn up or wear out in a couple of hours when they are used to play metal mothers. If liquids are used to cool the contact area, then the diamond wear diminishes drastically, but the metal surface of the record is burnished. If the liquid is applied to the vinyl surface, then the temperature of the plastic surface cannot increase and melt; therefore, the scouring of the groove wall can be observed, as shown in Fig. 23-118.

23.5.10.3 Stylus Cantilever

The stylus is attached to some type of coupler or cantilever that connects it to the generating element of the cartridge, which could be a magnet, a piece of iron, a coil, or a ceramic element. Because of a very wide range of frequencies this stylus assembly has to transmit, the construction material and shape of the cantilever is very important. Theoretically, it has to be very light and rigid. Over the century of existence of mechanical sound recording, styli were made out of cactus needles, whale bones, and all kinds of metal, gems and stones, plastic, and wood. The final choice seems to be centered around an aluminum alloy thin-wall tube. It is fairly strong, light, noncorrosive, nonmagnetic, electrically conductive, and easy to manufacture, as shown in Fig. 23-119.

The average diameter of the aluminum cantilever tube is around 0.03 in., and the length may vary from ¼ to ½ in. A few exotic cartridges have cantilevers made out of solid ruby or even diamond, and some from boron or beryllium copper alloy. Although ruby and diamond are extremely rigid materials, because of manufacturing dif-

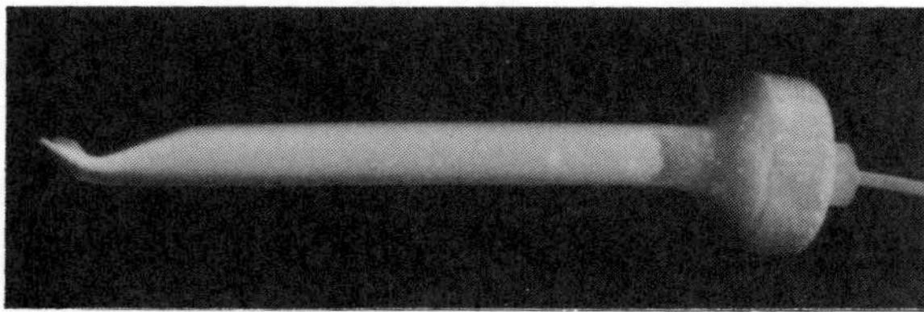

Figure 23-119 Cantilever tube assembly connecting stylus (left) and ring magnet (right). *(Courtesy Stanton Magnetics, Inc.)*

ficulties and high weight/length ratio, they are made very short. This, in turn brings the pivot point much closer to the stylus tip that moves in a much smaller arc when reproducing groove modulation. Since the grooves are modulated by the cutting stylus that has its pivot quite a distance away and is moving in an arc of much larger radius, the larger the difference between the motions of the cutting and of the playback styli, the larger the distortion, as shown in Fig. 23-120.

On the other hand very long playback cantilevers are unable to produce sufficient motion of the generating element that results in a very low electrical output.

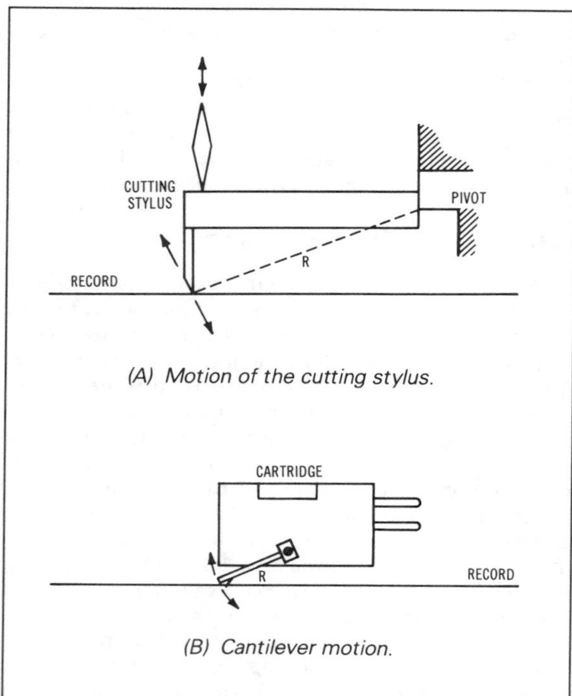

Figure 23-120 Vertical motion of cutting and playback styli.

Compliance

The amount of force required to move the playback stylus depends on several factors; the first is the *compliance* of the stylus, and the second is *mass*.

Compliance of the cantilever or the stylus is the ability of the stylus assembly to react to the groove modulation. It is measured in cm/dyn or μm/mN (metric) and gives the amount of stylus tip deflection for the given force. Compliance is measured *statically* and *dynamically*.

Static compliance is the amount of deflection of the cantilever when a constant force is applied to the stylus tip. The *dynamic compliance* is a measure of tip deflection as it is reproducing the frequency of known amplitude at which the measurement is being made.

The static compliance of the cantilever can be measured simply by observing the amount of stylus deflection as the known amount of force is applied to the stylus tip. The static compliance is only an indicator of the sensitivity to the vertical tracking force rather than the tracking ability. Because the stylus damping, which is one of the forces affecting the stylus suspension system, has no affect on the static compliance, static compliance is usually larger than the dynamic compliance.

The dynamic compliance is useful to know because it is not only the measure of tracking ability at low frequencies, but it also allows us to calculate the resonant frequency of the tonearm/cartridge combination and to measure the effective mass of the tonearm.

The method developed to find precisely the dynamic compliance of the stylus begins with the measurement of the dynamic mass of the tonearm and the resonance of the tonearm/cartridge combination. Because there are three variables, we have to know two of them to find the compliance. The equation for the compliance is

$$c = 1/(4\pi^2 f^2 M) \qquad (23\text{-}2)$$

where,

c is the compliance in centimeters per dyne (or micrometers per millinewton),

f is the frequency in hertz,

M is the mass of the tonearm in grams.

The method of finding the dynamic mass of the tonearm consists of suspending a ready-to-play tonearm with the cartridge mounted in it by a spring, which is attached to the loudspeaker type driver, as shown in Fig. 23-121. The spring is attached just above the stylus pivot. By exciting the spring vertically at various frequencies, the resonance of the tonearm is found and the frequency is noted. Next, the tonearm is disconnected from the spring, and known weights are attached to the end of the spring until the resonance at the same frequency is found. The sum of all the attached weights equals the dynamic mass of the tonearm.

The reason the tonearm has to be adjusted to play the records is because that is the condition that really exists

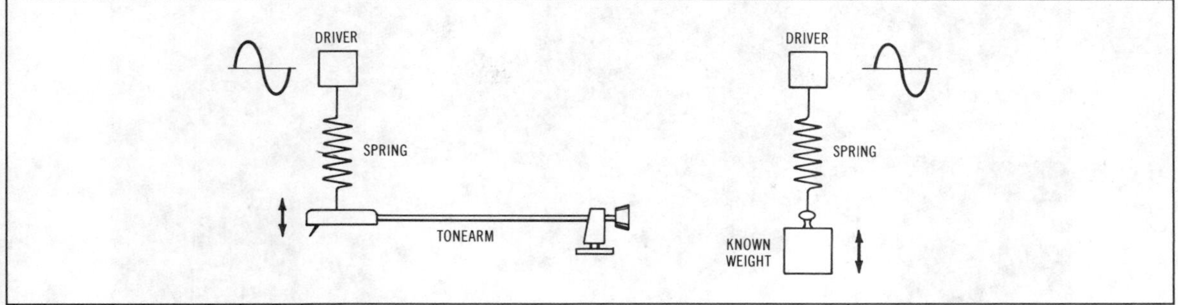

Figure 23-121 Method of measuring dynamic mass of a tonearm.

and for which the formula is valid. If the tonearm is balanced without adding the tracking force, the position of the counterweight will be different, and the dynamic mass of the tonearm will be different.

Vertical Resonance

The second variable in the equation is the *tonearm/cartridge vertical resonance*. It can be found by playing the special test record with a range of vertical signals at known frequencies. The frequencies at which the cartridge output is the highest is the frequency of the resonance. The tonearm can be placed on the platform driven in the vertical plane by the oscillator and the output of the cartridge monitored by an ac voltmeter or scope. The frequency is varied until the peak in the response is found. Modern tonearms and cartridges resonate anywhere from 5 to 15 Hz, but the most desirable range is between 8 to 12 Hz. Resonance below 8 Hz will produce instability of the tonearm and will result in poor tracking of moderately warped records. If the tonearm resonance happens to be a multiple of or at the resonant frequency of the turntable suspension, even a slight shift between the two frequencies may result in trouble-free tracking or tonearm instability with possible loss of a groove contact.

When both variables are known, the values can be substituted into an equation, and the compliance calculated. The value of the dynamic compliance calculated is at the tonearm resonance frequency. The compliance can be measured in the lateral and in the vertical plane, but only the vertical compliance is important to match the tonearm to the cartridge. Most of today's stereo cartridges have fairly uniform compliance in all planes of stylus motion. It should be pointed out that cartridges with higher compliance work best with light tonearms, and heavy tonearms should be set up with cartridges having low compliance. Many cartridge manufacturers offer a wide selection of cartridges with different compliances. Also, replacement styli having different compliances are available for the same cartridge. It should be remembered that if the stylus compliance is low, the tracking force applied to the stylus should be higher than for a high-compliance stylus, and that it has to be increased until satisfactory performance is achieved. Generally, the tracking force is recommended by the manufacturer, but in some cases there are records that were cut with exceedingly high levels of modulation so that some experimentation with tracking force is required (Fig. 23-122).

23.5.11 Cartridge Voltage Output

The electrical output of the cartridge depends on its design and the type of generator system used. Ceramic or crystal cartridges produce the highest voltage. Next are the moving-magnet cartridges and then the induced-magnet pickups; the last group is the moving-coil cartridges. If we measure the amount of power each cartridge produces, we will see that the moving coil produces higher power output than other types; therefore, moving-coil cartridges can work with step-up transformers to increase the output voltage. There is generally enough magnetizing current for the transformer laminations to do a good job of increasing the voltage 10 to 20 times or 20 to 26 dB, bringing the output voltage in line with the voltage produced by the moving-magnet cartridges. On the other hand, some high output voltage ceramic cartridges are connected to the loss pads and response-shaping networks to reduce the voltage down to the average output level of the moving-magnet cartridges. Since most of the preamplifiers are designed for moving-magnet cartridges, it is only natural that the industry should standardize around the moving-magnet principle and performance.

23.5.12 Electrical Loading

With various output levels and different source impedances, cartridges respond differently to electrical loads. For instance, crystal or ceramic cartridges are the most susceptible to capacitive loading. The entire frequency response is dependent on the loading of the cartridge. In the moving-magnet cartridge, only the highest portion of the frequency range is affected by the capacitive loading, and the moving-coil cartridges are almost completely

Figure 23-122 Stereo groove with high level of modulation. *(Courtesy Stanton Magnetics, Inc.)*

immune to the loading effects. However, once they are connected to the step-up transformers, the secondary of the transformer becomes very sensitive to loading, and excess capacity can play havoc with transformer resonance and the impedance of the secondary transformer winding. Therefore, cartridge manufacturers specify the recommended resistive and capacitive loads.

For the moving-magnet cartridges, the most common resistive load is 47 kΩ (50 kΩ for Europe), paralleled by 200 to 400 pF of capacitance, depending on the manufacturer and on the cartridge model. For a long time, it was not emphasized enough that the capacitive loading for the cartridge included capacitance of all interconnecting cables and tonearm wiring to ground (or between the conductors); capacity added by the connectors, switches, internal wiring of the preamplifier circuit; and most of all preamplifier input circuit capacitance, which varies widely depending on the circuit design (Fig. 23-123). In many cases the total capacitance that appeared as a capacitive load for the cartridge exceeded 1000 pF, which resulted in an electrical resonance peak around 7 to 8 kHz followed by premature response rolloff at frequencies above this point (Fig. 23-124).

In the specifications for the moving-coil cartridges, we often see a specified low-value load impedance, which doesn't mean that the cartridge will not work well into any other input impedance but simply that this is the optimum design impedance, so if a step-up transformer is used, the secondary voltage will be within the range accepted by the preamplifier input. Unfortunately, the recommended load impedance, as shown on the chassis of the preamplifier next to the input connector, does not necessarily reflect the actual input impedance of the preamplifier input. After a detailed testing of a majority of the preamplifiers having moving-coil inputs, it was established that a vast majority of the preamplifiers had an input impedance of 100 Ω or higher across the entire audio band.

Some ceramic cartridges, as mentioned earlier, have been operated through pads and networks to make them look electrically like the moving-magnet cartridge. By doing so the dependency on capacitive loading is minimized and the source impedance of the cartridge looks constant, which is an advantage when the preamplifier input circuit is sensitive to the variations of the source impedance (Fig. 23-125).

The cartridge design in question is by Microacoustics. The two thick-film circuits inside the unit are built on small ceramic substrate that has thick-film resistive and capacitive components for conversion of the voltage from the bimorph element, which is a constant amplitude device, to the constant velocity characteristic, typical to the moving-magnet cartridges. This cartridge, because of this network, is classified with the rest of the dynamic cartridges but is referred to by the manufacturer as an electret device. Aside from the immunity to magnetic fields and capacitive loading (within certain limits), this cartridge is similar in its characteristics to other dynamic cartridges.

High-frequency cartridge performance, aside from being influenced by the electrical loading, is also dependent on the effective mass of the cantilever assembly. Especially important is the effective mass of the tip, because the reliability of the coupling between the stylus tip and the groove walls depends on it. The record material is relatively soft and compliant, and in order to move larger mass, greater groove deformation takes place. This phenomenon causes the delay in accelerating the stylus tip and consequently in reproducing sound recorded in the groove. The square-wave test used in evaluating transient response of cartridges is designed to detect this delay in response of the stylus tip to changes in direction of the groove (Fig. 23-126). Although this test is used very widely to evaluate cartridges, it is also subject to questionable results. The correct interpretation of the results depends on knowing exactly the limitations of the cutting equipment as well as the formulation of the record material, the temperature at the time of the test, and the calibration of the monitoring equipment oscilloscope. It was determined through the photographic studies with the scanning electron-beam microscope that the rise time or reaction time of the cutters used in cutting the test records was inadequate and that the parasitic vibrations of the cutting stylus were superimposed on the test signal. As a result, many good cartridges tested with this record responded to all the flaws encountered in the recording and were unjustly labeled as underdamped and producing so-called overshoot and ringing. The cartridges that were insensitive to vibrations that modulated the square-wave signal were judged as well damped. Specifically, the overshoot and the dip that follows were attributed to the cartridge behavior rather than the cutting head characteristic. The method and interpretation of results are based on the ideal conditions that exist when the square-wave signal is fed into the amplifier and the output of the amplifier is observed on the scope. There, we can monitor the shape of the waveform as it enters the amplifier. In the disk playback, this is impossible, and the only means of analyzing the quality of the recorded signal is through microscope photography.

23.6 CUTTING AMPLIFIERS

Amplifiers used to cut records are designed to deliver large amounts of audio power to a small impedance load. Because today's records are cut using RIAA or NAB preemphasis equalization, the amount of power demanded by the cutting head at high frequencies is very large. Some cutting systems have amplifiers capable of delivering peak power of up to 1000 W. Consider the fact that the armature of the stereo cutting head has a mass usually of several grams that has to be accelerated to a velocity of up to hundreds of centimeters per second in a fraction of a millisecond and that this process may be repeated up to several thousand times a second. Although most cutting heads require very little power in the region of the system's primary resonance (about 1 kHz), the amount of power required at 10 kHz rises by at least 13.7 dB and by 19.6 dB at 20 kHz because of the preemphasis curve. Because of cutter sensitivity at 10 kHz, the cutter may require up to 30 times more power than at 1 kHz.

The demand for power at the low frequencies is low because the preemphasis curve calls for −19.3-dB signal attenuation at 20 Hz referenced to 1 kHz.

Today's stereo cutting head amplifiers have very effective motional negative feedback, which tends to correct most nonlinearities in frequency response produced by the mechanical transducer, in this case the cutting head armature. Since no feedback system is perfect, additional equalization is usually needed to achieve the desired frequency response. See section 23.2 for schematics of equalization circuits.

In this era of fast technological advances, it is impossible to stay current with all new variations in power amplifier design. However, each system has to be analyzed and judged on its own merits. In a disk-cutting system's amplifier, requirements are more stringent than for those used in conventional applications in typical sound reinforcement or playback-monitoring setups.

Designers of power amplifiers for disk-cutting systems go to great length in eliminating all obvious sources of distortion and noise. The amplifiers are transformerless, have low-noise preamplifier stages, and use premium components for ultimate reliability and circuit performance. Most solid-state power amplifiers have their power stages operate in class AB, which means that at low power levels the amplifiers behave like a class A amplifier producing low distortion, and when called for to deliver large amounts of power they operate as a class B amplifier, drawing the current from the power supply only as required.

There is a constant discussion going on regarding the question, "What makes the amplifier good or not so good?" We can summarize from all research efforts conducted with power amplifier circuits; the quality of the signal from the power amplifier depends greatly on the basic design of the circuit and proper use of components.

What makes amplifiers perform and sound differently is *distortion*. There are different types of distortion, and there are various causes of it. One of the most neglected causes of distortion revealed recently is improper use of polarized electrolytic capacitors. Although dc biasing of the electrolytic capacitors may be correct, ac signals may reverse bias the capacitor and produce distortion. When electrolytic capacitors are reverse biased, there is a *diode effect* that degrades the signal. These electrolytic capacitors are used in complementary symmetry circuits for an isolation bypass and filter capacitors used in power supply circuits and decoupling networks. Electrolytic capacitors are also known to have internal inductance that becomes important in low-impedance transistor circuits. Since tube circuits are of higher impedance, these shortcomings of electrolytics were not detrimental to the operation of the tube amplifiers. Consequently, the sound of tube amplifiers was considered to be superior to that of transistor circuits. With special care in designing transistorized power amplifiers, using up-to-date technology VFETs and premium grade electrolytics, circuits can be built to be superior to anything else in existence.

23.7 DISK MASTERING

The procedure for cutting records was covered in general terms in section 23.3. This section will cover more

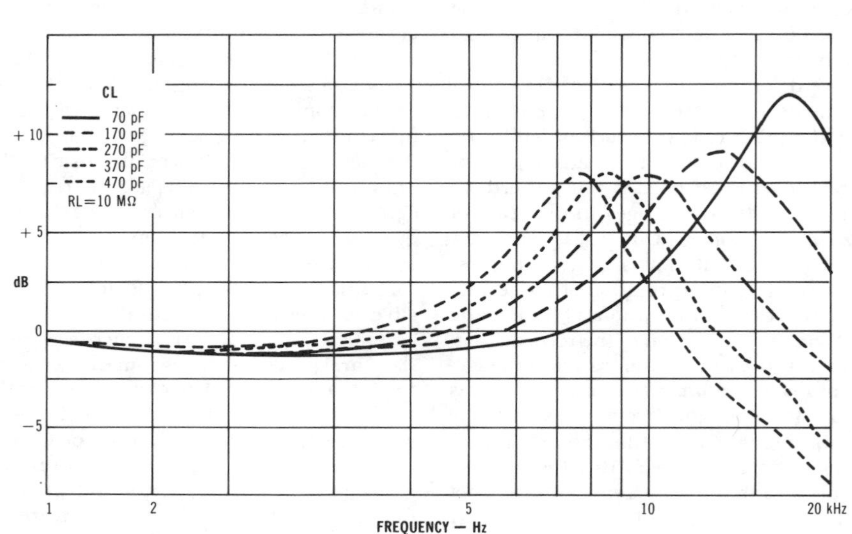

(A) Effect of varying capacitive load on resistively unterminated cartridge.

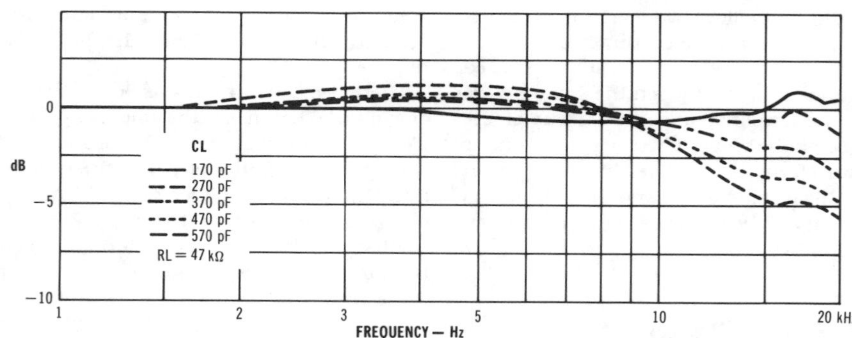

(C) Effect of varying capacitive load on cartridge terminated with 47 kΩ.

Figure 23-123 Effect of cartridge loading on frequency

detailed requirements imposed today on recording engineers and their cutting equipment.

It is generally agreed that having the best equipment available does not necessarily produce an adequate quality product. On the other hand, even with relatively primitive equipment, it is possible to achieve excellent results if one knows the limitations of the equipment and how to overcome them. In this section different methods of mastering will be mentioned that were tried and used by many outstanding engineers in the disk-cutting field.

23.7.1 Setting Up for Disk Cutting

One of the most critical phases in mastering is a preparatory phase. It involves selection of lacquers, adjustment

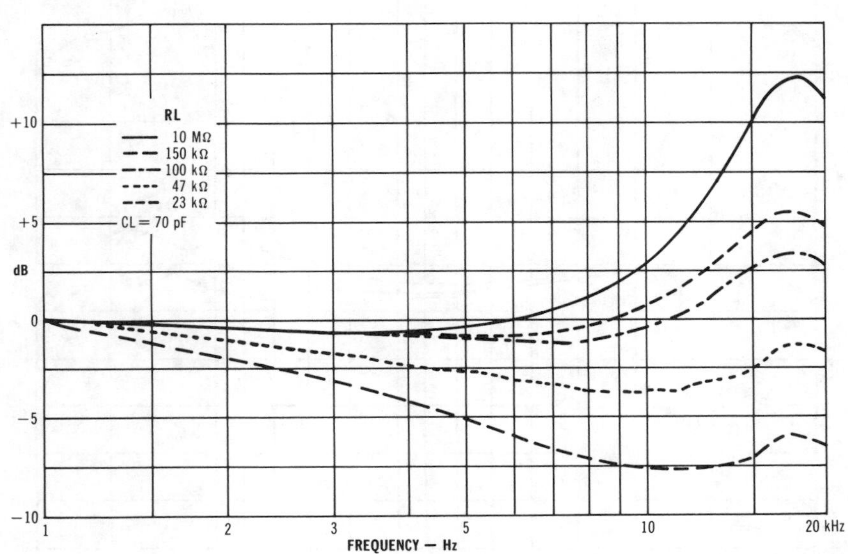

(B) Effect of varying resistive load on capacitively unterminated cartridge.

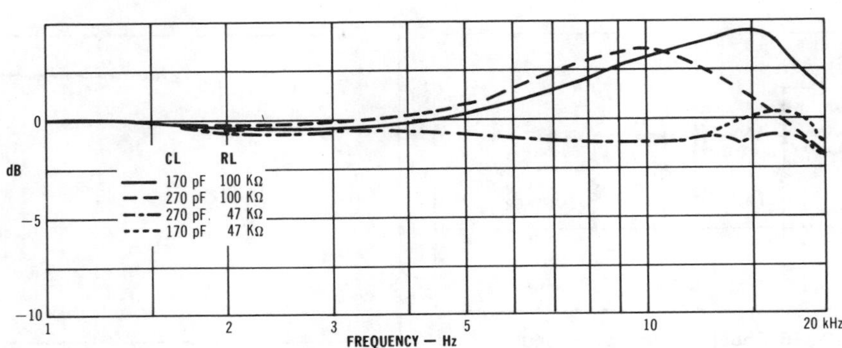

(D) Various load combinations.

response. *(Courtesy Stanton Magnetics, Inc.)*

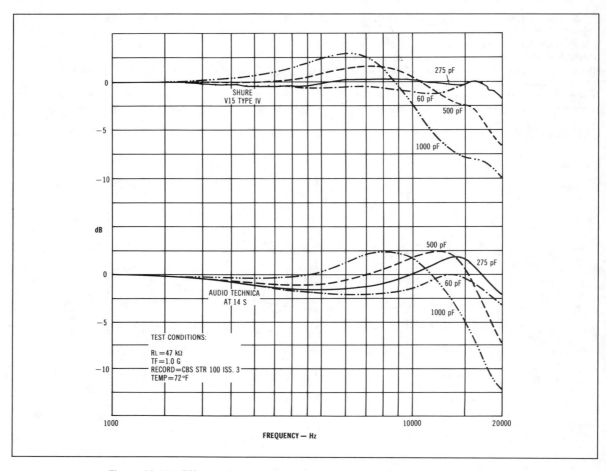

Figure 23-124 Effects of capacitive loading. *(Courtesy Stanton Magnetics, Inc.)*

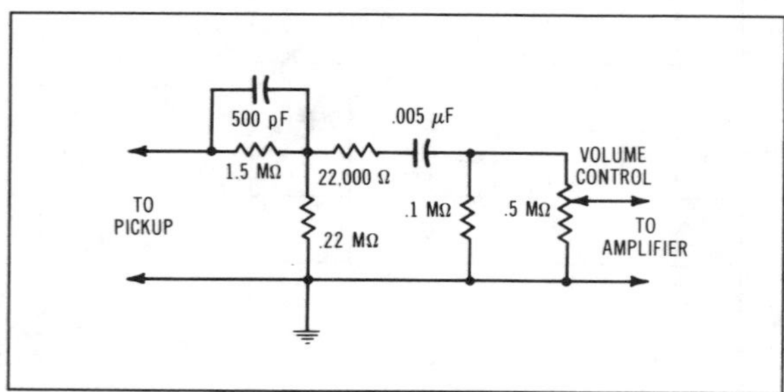

Figure 23-125 Equalizer circuit and pad for ceramic pickup.

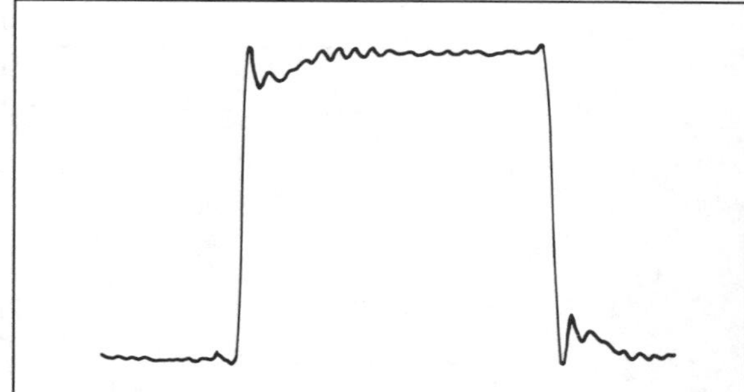

Figure 23-126 Square wave produced by the phonograph pickup.

of the cutting system, setting up of levels, and adjustment of variable-pitch and variable-depth systems. The most common problems observed in finished records indicate that the most basic preparatory steps have been overlooked or forgotten. Sometimes these problems can be attributed to the lack of understanding of the requirements.

23.7.2 Stylus Orientation

Quite often, the cutting stylus is inserted into the cutting head and aligned "by eye." The error can easily exceed 5° in misalignment. The use of jigs and fixtures supplied by the cutter manufacturer is strongly recommended. A small pocket flashlight or microscope lamp can be used to bounce the beam off the front face of the sapphire cutting stylus and to observe its reflection. This method may not work with diamond cutting styli, which are very small and covered with metal in the front preventing reflection of light. This method was used years ago with great success. In the early days of stereo, when separation was marginal and systems lacked the sophistication of today's models, every decibel of separation was precious, and a great deal of attention was paid to small details. Today, we can easily cut a record with 35 to 40 dB of separation between channels if the necessary precautions are taken.

23.7.3 Lead-In Groove

Another problem that is not being readily recognized is the depth of the lead-in groove. The profile of finished records is such that the outer edge has a *groove guard*, or thick section designed to protect the grooves during the stacking of records. The lead-in groove spirals over the inclined area between the outer rim of the record and the modulated portion of the disk's surface. Because this area is inclined, the stylus of a phonograph cartridge sometimes skids over the inclined portion and on to the modulated grooves, not necessarily into the first one. The problem is that quite often the lead-in groove is not cut deep enough. The maximum prescribed depth is 0.005 mil, which gives a width of 0.010 mil. The IEC standard calls for lead-in pitch of 1.0 ± 0.2 mm and minimum groove width of 0.050 mm, which is far from being adequate (0.002 in.). Even the lead-out groove is specified to be 0.07 mm wide (minimum) or 0.0027 in.

23.7.4 Pitch

It has also been established that the pitch of many recordings is not adjusted properly. The much talked about groove echo, the cause of improper pitch control, can be minimized if spacing between the modulated grooves is closely observed. The desire to cut 40-min sides on a long-playing size lacquer will result in groove echo, especially if the levels are not kept within safe limits. The exception to this condition is if mastering is done in copper using the Teldec DMM method.

When the program material contains a lot of low-frequency information, we should not expect to achieve a loud record with 30-min playing time. A fairly accurate set of rules applies to selecting levels and timing in order to maintain sound quality. The running time for the program equals the product of the radial length of modulation and lines per inch divided by the speed of the records.

$$T = (R_{max} - R_{min})\ LPI/rpm \qquad (23\text{-}3)$$

where,
R_{max} is the maximum radial length,
R_{min} is the minimum radial length,
LPI is the lines per inch,
rpm is the revolutions per minute.

For example, if we use 300 lines per inch at 33⅓ rpm we can cut a 30-minute record. If we calculate the amplitude of a 1-kHz signal at the level of 7 cm, we will find that the peak-to-peak displacement is 0.88 mil. To calculate the peak-to-peak displacement of the groove at other frequencies so that variable pitch can be set and monitored accurately, we use the equation:

$$A = V_{peak}/(2\pi f) \qquad (23\text{-}4)$$

where,
A is the amplitude of displacement,
V_{peak} is peak recorded velocity in centimeters,
f is the frequency in hertz.

To find the peak-to-peak value, the result has to be doubled.

23.7.5 Equalization and Phasing

Another object of concern is *equalization*. It is a fact that cutting heads are designed to record music and not the sustained tones. If a signal generator is fed into the input of the cutting amplifier to record the RIAA curve in short bands at normal recording levels, the cutting head fuses will blow, or the cutter will burn out. To record a steady signal, the overall gain of the system should be lowered by about 10 dB. How will we know that the cutter will behave the same way at the increased levels? (See section 23.11.) To keep modern cutters cutting at the required program levels, inert gas such as helium, argone, or nitrogen is pumped into the coil assembly of the cutting head to conduct the heat away from the coils that dissipate enormous amounts of power (Fig. 23-21).

Theoretically, there is no limit to the levels that can be cut on the record. The limitation comes from the thickness of the lacquer coating (there was no such limitation in cutting wax) and the ability of the phonograph cartridge to track the modulation. Generally speaking, excursion of 100 μm or 4 mils at 300 Hz is the maximum better cartridges can track. High-frequency playback is controlled by the effective mass of the stylus tip and the tracing radius of the stylus. The maximum excursion that would be tracked without skipping can be calculated easily from the stylus dimensions, frequency, and groove speed. If the tracking radius of the stylus is 0.0003 in. then half the wavelength will be 0.0004 mil.

Recording 10 kHz on the innermost radius of the disk (2.2 in.) at 33.3 rpm requires a linear groove speed of 7.84 in./s. The wavelength of a 10-kHz signal is 0.00078 in. or a half cycle is 0.00039 in., meaning that the stylus will just about fit the curvature of the modulation. For higher frequencies at the inner diameter, either the linear speed has to be higher (not practical), or the level of the signal should be lowered. Boosting the high-frequency level at that point is almost pointless; therefore, the diametric equalization has been abandoned.

The question of phasing is important because it will determine whether low-frequency signals will end up as a lateral signal (as they should) or will become vertical excursions, impossible to track and record. It is a goal of recording engineers to produce tapes where two stereo channels would be in phase, especially at low frequencies. Signal phasing at high frequencies is hard to control on tape; however, the proper orientation of the cutting stylus controls this in cutting similar to azimuth alignment of the multitrack tape recorder head.

23.7.6 Stylus Heat Adjustment

The *stylus heat adjustment* that was covered in section 23.3, "Disk Cutting and Record Manufacturing" is also important. Every new lot of lacquers must be tested for quality and for the amount of heat needed for the quietest groove. It goes without saying, heat is not required in cutting copper (DMM system). (The same is also true for cutting in wax.)

23.7.7 Half-Speed Mastering

In an attempt to overcome some of the limitations of the cutting head, *half-speed mastering* is being practiced on a limited scale. The drawbacks of this method are too serious for half-speed mastering to become universally accepted. Not only is the mastering time twice the normal time, but the equalization of the system also has to be changed. Also older systems that used transformers could not keep up with the low-frequency requirements. A 20-Hz signal has to be recorded as a 10-Hz signal. The high frequencies sound better at the expense of required additional mastering time and signal quality at the low end. In a cassette field we find the trend in just the opposite direction. Rerecording takes place at many times the original speed with quite favorable results.

23.7.8 Direct to Disk

Another attempt to overcome some of the distortions produced by the tape recorders is direct-to-disk recording. Although the disks produced using this method are extremely good, the method is expensive and hard to execute because it requires a full complement of performers performing in real time without mistakes for 25 to 30 minutes. This method also requires more than one disk-cutting machine for safety reasons and produces a limited number of copies because only two masters at best can be cut from two machines during the 30-minute session. However, this method produces the most natural sounding disks. When done with great care, it offers the widest frequency range any medium can ever hope for. The disadvantage of the direct-to-disk method is that there is no way to use variable pitch or depth controls, unless adjustments are made manually by following the musical score.

23.7.9 Digital PCM Recording

In competition with direct to disk is the newly developed digital pulse-code modulation (PCM) technology. As can be seen in section 23.12, digitally encoded audio signals only approximate the waveshapes of higher-order harmonics; however, they produce midrange frequencies with astonishing exactness. They lend themselves to be stored in digital form and retrieved at any time without degradation. The recording industry has been using digital equipment extensively since 1980 for disk mastering, and it seems that the 16-bit systems with 48-kHz sampling rate will become the standard for professional recording.

23.8 SIGNAL EQUALIZATION IN DISK RECORDING

To overcome the limitations found in the basic disk-cutting and reproducing process, special equalization of the signals before and after the recording was developed. When all signals that appear in the program bus are analyzed, we can see that the amplitude is the highest at low frequencies and the lowest at high frequencies. The relationship between the frequency of the signal and its amplitude where amplitude is inversely proportional to frequency is called a *constant velocity characteristic* (Fig. 23-127).

If we try to record the signals without equalization, we would run out of space on the disk because low-frequency excursions would take all the space. The high frequencies would be of such a low amplitude that during the playback, high-frequency signals could be very close to the noise level of the system. The signal-to-noise ratio then would be extremely small; in other words, recording would be very noisy. This problem was recognized in the early days of disk recording, but the remedy used was only partial. At first only the low end of the audio spectrum was equalized. The cutting head sensitivity was decreased at low frequencies so that the amplitudes in midrange and at high frequencies could be recorded at higher levels (Fig. 23-128). Then, the playback amplifiers were adjusted to boost the low frequencies to compensate for the losses

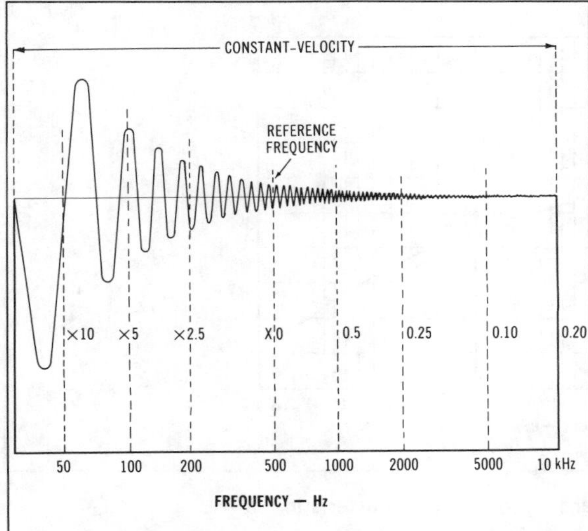

Figure 23-127 Constant velocity characteristics.

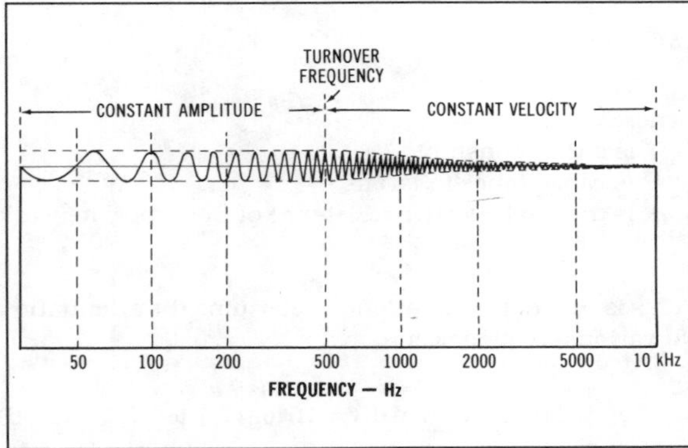

Figure 23-128 Frequency characteristic of a magnetic cutting head adjusted for a constant-amplitude, constant-velocity recording characteristic.

introduced in recording. From this point on, the equalization used for cutting was called preemphasis, and equalization used in playback equipment, postemphasis (Fig. 23-129).

The 1-kHz signal was chosen as the reference point because it was a convenient half-way point between the low and high frequencies. As the time went by and further improvements were made, the equalization was extended to the higher frequencies as well. What emerged from the long and at times controversial subject of equalization are the RIAA and NAB equalization curves. The first curve was used by the Record Industry Association of America (RIAA) and the second, which is almost iden-

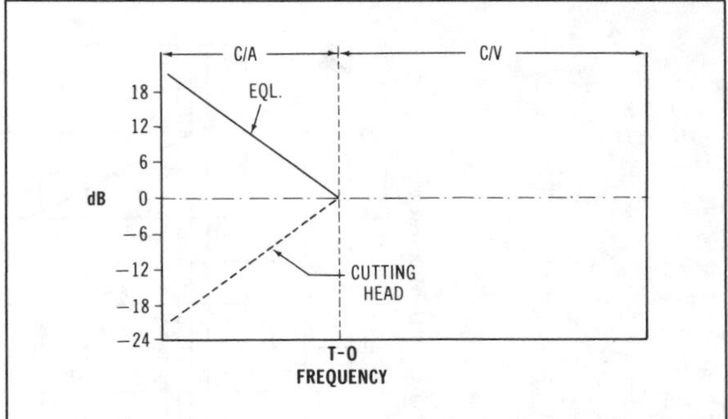

Figure 23-129 Equalizer frequency characteristics required to compensate for the constant-amplitude characteristics of the cutting head when reproducing.

tical to the first curve, by the National Association of Broadcasters (NAB).

Even today, so many years after the standardization, we debate about two versions of the recording equalization. The DIN standard used in European countries calls for additional equalization at the extreme low end during playback to improve the signal-to-noise ratio and stability of the system due to mechanical disturbances (turntable rumble for instance), which can affect the overall performance of the system.

The NAB (RIAA) curve used presently in the playback equipment is shown in Fig. 23-130. The numerical values for the characteristic are shown in Table 23-2. For recording, the inverse curve is used. It means that if the playback signal is boosted 19.3 dB, the same signal should be recorded at the level of − 19.3 dB so that the overall result will be 0-dB deviation from the ideal flat response curve.

The whole idea of equalization is to be able to record the sound at the most advantageous levels for the best results as far as distortion and noise are concerned and to reproduce it so that the original balance between the frequencies can be restored. The NAB or RIAA curves we are discussing are used for phonograph disks. Tape recorders record signals on tape, and tape recording has limitations that differ from the limitations found in mechanical recording and, therefore, require different preemphasis and postemphasis for best results.

The difference between the NAB and RIAA curves is in the NAB curve that is used by broadcasters who have limited bandwidth in their transmitting equipment; therefore, the curve is limited to the range of 30 Hz to 15 kHz. The RIAA curve on the other hand covers the range from 20 Hz to 20 kHz. With the advent of FM broadcasting, the RIAA curve is used more often for high-quality radio sound. The DIN curve (Deutsche Industrie Norm), as shown in Fig. 23-131, extends the control over playback down to 2 Hz where the equalization returns back to 0 dB. As can be seen from the graphs, the curves have

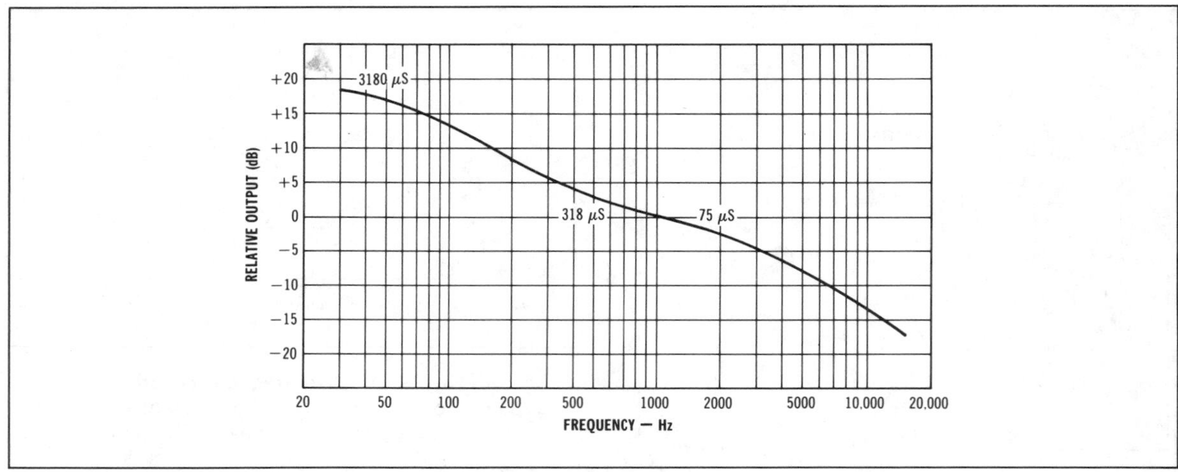

Figure 23-130 NAB (RIAA) standard reproducing characteristic.

Table 23-2. Preferred Frequencies and Newly Calculated Recording Characteristics

Frequency, Hertz	Recording Characteristic, Decibels
20.0	−19.3
25.0	−19.0
31.5	−18.5
40.0	−17.8
50.0	−16.9
63.0	−15.8
80.0	−14.5
100.0	−13.1
125.0	−11.6
160.0	−9.8
200.0	−8.2
250.0	−6.7
315.0	−5.2
400.0	−3.8
500.0	−2.6
630.0	−1.6
800.0	−0.8
1,000.0	0.0
1,250.0	0.7
1,600.0	1.6
2,000.0	2.6
2,500.0	3.7
3,150.0	5.0
4,000.0	6.6
5,000.0	8.2
6,300.0	10.0
8,000.0	11.9
10,000.0	13.7
12,500.0	15.6
16,000.0	17.7
20,000.0	19.6

complex shapes; equalizer circuits use capacitors and resistors, and their values determine the amount of signal equalization that can be expressed as a function of a time constant in microseconds as derived from the formula

$$T = CR \tag{23-5}$$

where,
T is a time constant,
C is capacitance in farads,
R is the total effective resistance of the supply network in ohms.

This is part of the equation to determine the attenuation at various frequencies:

$$\text{attenuation in dB} = 10\log(1 + \omega^2T^2) \tag{23-6}$$

where,
ω is $2\pi f$,
T is CR.

To achieve the desired shape of the NAB curve, the combination of several time constants has to be used. The transition point from one slope to another is called a knee, and a −3-dB point on the curve is the center of the knee and the reference point for the transition frequency.

The RIAA curve consists of three time constants; 75 μsec to roll off the high frequencies, 318 μs to produce the slope below 1 kHz with a knee at 500 Hz, and a 3180-μs time constant to flatten the low end of the curve. In today's modern amplifiers, the equalization is accomplished by placing the network with proper time constants into the negative feedback loop of the amplifier, thereby achieving lower distortion, better signal-to-noise ratio, and improved, signal-level-handling capability of the circuit.

Since there are many records cut with older type recording characteristics, it is appropriate to mention and show the curves so that appropriate playback equalization could be applied when playing these recordings, as shown in Figs. 23-132, 23-133, and 23-134. Because the recording space on the record disk is limited, records are cut with constant amplitude characteristics of the signals in the upper half of the frequency range (Fig. 23-135). When reproduced by the pickup, these signals are equalized to a constant velocity characteristic. In playing back these preemphasized disk recordings, different equalization has to be used for different types of cartridges. For instance, dynamic cartridges, which include moving-magnet, moving-iron, moving-coil, and variable-reluc-

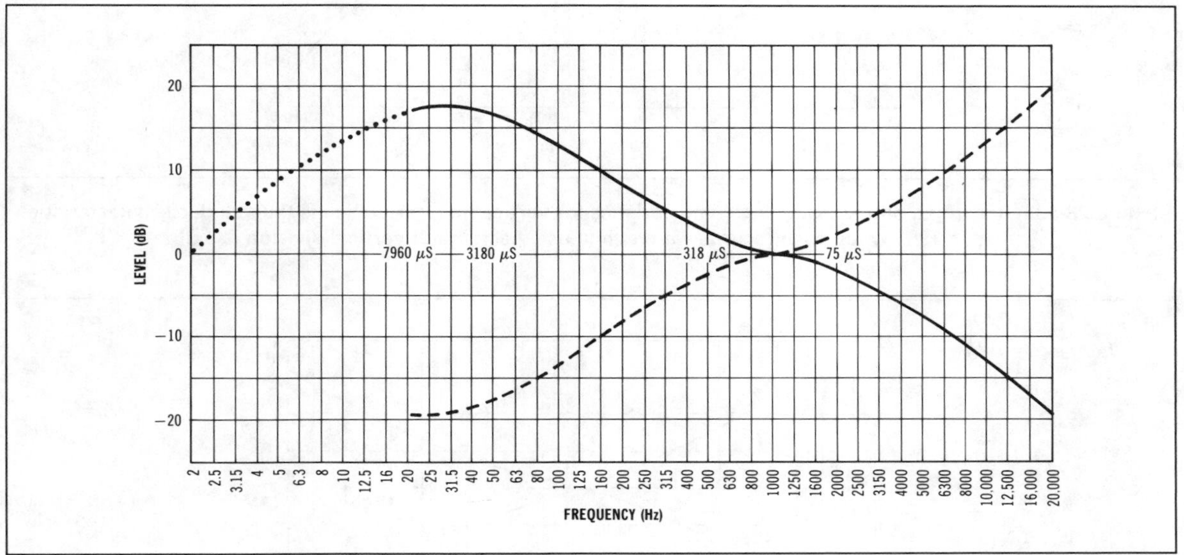

Figure 23-131 DIN recording and playback characteristics.

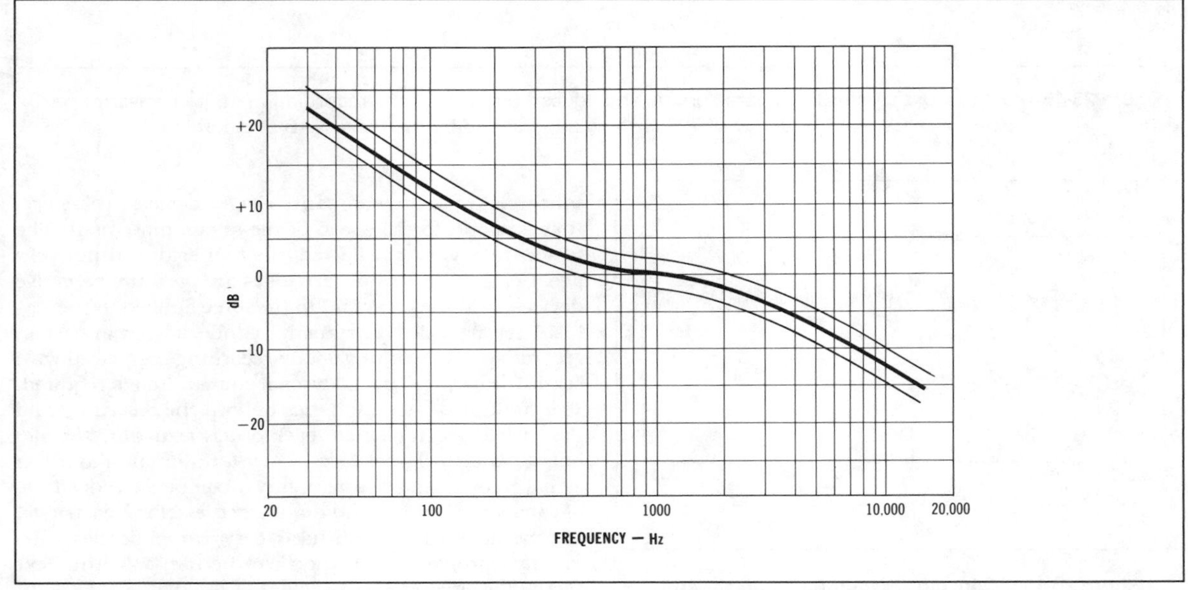

Figure 23-132 The original AES reproducing characteristics (now superseded by the RIAA characteristics).

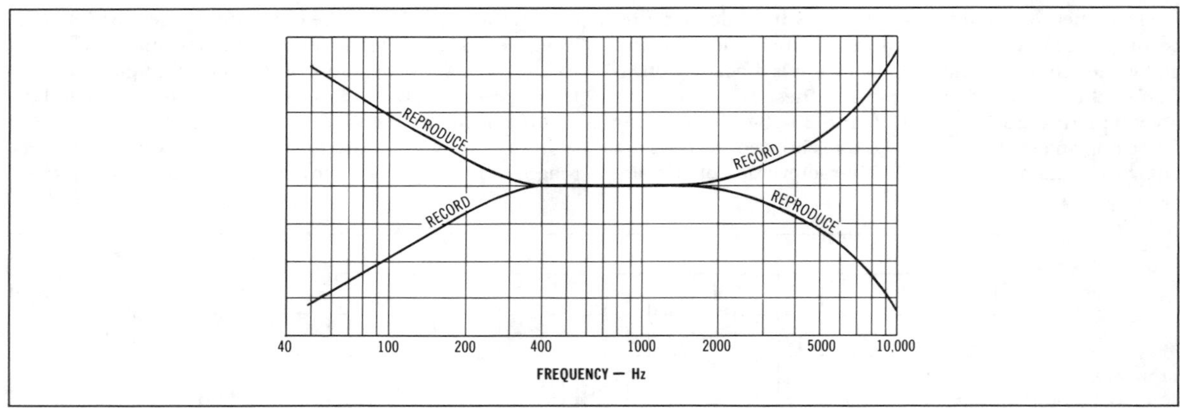

Figure 23-133 Recording and reproducing characteristics for vertical records, which is the standard characteristic used in 1953 when such records were still in use. Each major vertical division is 5 dB.

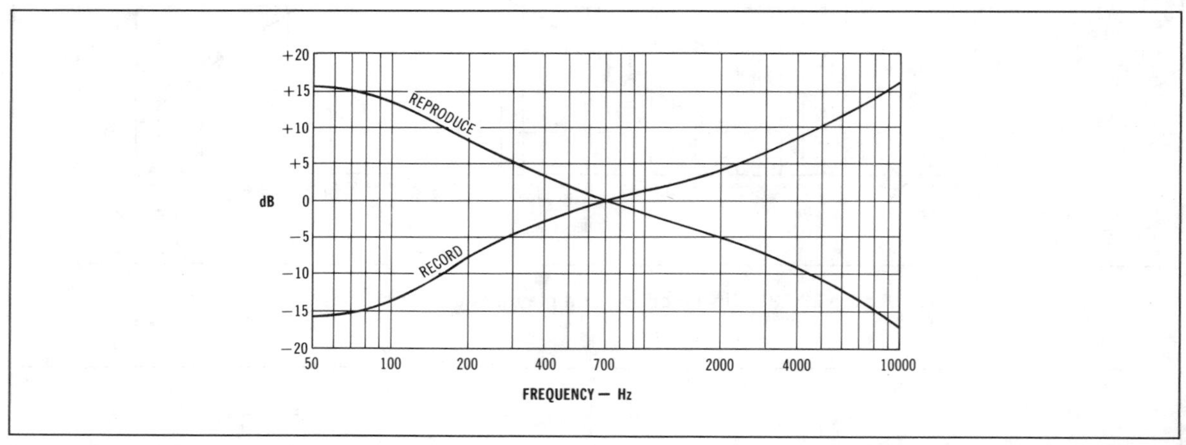

Figure 23-134 Orthocoustic recording characteristic, introduced by RCA for the recording of 16-in. transcriptions, using a crossover frequency of 700 Hz now superseded by the RIAA-NAB standard.

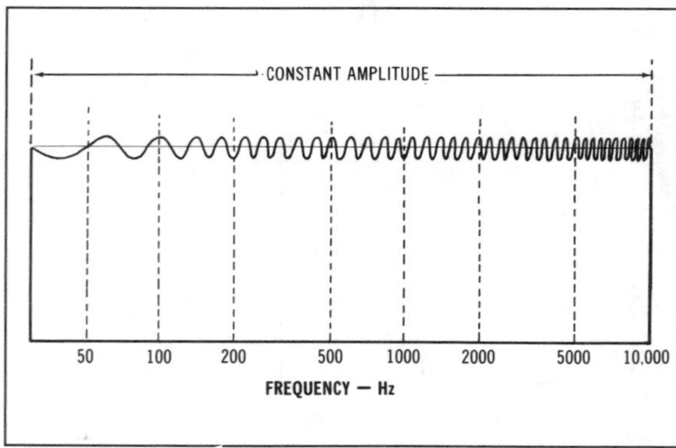

Figure 23-135 Constant-amplitude characteristic.

tance pickups, are constant velocity devices; therefore, they respond to the speed of the stylus movement. The faster the stylus is deflected, the higher the output voltage. Ceramic or crystal cartridges are pressure-sensitive devices, and they respond to the force applied to the stylus. They are called constant amplitude devices, and when records with constant velocity recording are played with ceramic cartridges, no additional equalization is required. The combined characteristics of both the recording and the cartridge complement each other, returning the signals to their original form. Only a minimal amount of signal grooming may be necessary to compensate for effects of capacitive loading and nonlinearities of the cartridge. The methods and circuits used in a preamplifier designed to enact proper equalization can be found in the next section on preamplifiers.

23.9 PHONO PREAMPLIFIERS

23.9.1 Design Requirements

Phonograph cartridges require a special type of amplification to reproduce the recorded sound the way it existed during the recording session. The tiny electrical signals from the cartridge, measuring only a few millivolts rms have to be amplified into signals of many volts, capable of driving an array of loudspeakers and producing sound pressure levels sometimes close to the threshold of pain. And, this has to be accomplished with a minimum distortion and flat frequency and an excellent signal-to-noise ratio. The role of the preamplifier is a most difficult one. The phono preamplifier has to amplify a cartridge signal without changing its phase, without adding more than a small percentage of harmonic and intermodulation distortion, and without adding to the noise content of the original signal from the cartridge. In addition, it must have enough reserve power to handle any unusually high transient signals. In terms of electrical performance, the requirements for the average preamplifier can be summed up in the following data.

23.9.2 Voltage Amplification

The average required voltage amplification, depending on the output of the cartridge, is 40 to 50 dB. The dynamic cartridge of today produces approximately 4 to 5 mV of output for the average recording signal. A preamplifier gain of 45 dB will boost the signal output to nearly 1 V, the level required to drive most power amplifiers to full output. The noise contribution of the cartridge and of the recording medium requires that the preamplifier should have its noise level at least 70 dB below the average input signal of 10 mV.

23.9.3 Frequency Response

The frequency response of the circuit should follow the RIAA characteristics. In other words, low frequencies should be boosted by about 20 dB, and the high frequencies should be attenuated by the same amount, with respect to 1 kHz, which implies that the preamplifier with 40 dB of gain at 1 kHz will have as much as 60 dB of gain at 20 Hz and only 20 dB of gain at 20 kHz; see section 23.8.

23.9.4 Power-Handling Capability

The power-handling capability of the preamplifier is of great importance to the professional users of the equipment. The preamplifiers in most of the radio stations are connected to circuits that operate with nominal levels of 0 dBm or 1 mW; therefore, the output circuit should produce 0.707 V across a 600-Ω load. However, to process all peaks and transient information, an additional output is required, which may be an additional 10, 14, 18, 24, or even 30 dBm, which is 1 W of power or 1000 times the power at reference nominal level. If the preamplifier output is limited to +10 dBm, then there is a chance that some signal peaks may exceed the output capability of the output circuit and be clipped. Not only may the output circuit be the limiting factor, the input stage is also subject to overload if the cartridge output is too high and spikes exceed the overload point of the input stage. It is not unusual for a cartridge producing an output of several millivolts for the average modulation found on the records today to produce voltage peaks that are over 100 mV of peak amplitude. Most of the preamplifiers are capable of handling signals from 80 to 120 mV at the input before overload occurs. This is one of the reasons that cartridges are designed to produce an output voltage of around 1 mV for each centimeter per second of recorded velocity. This way for the average recorded level of 5 cm/s, the cartridge output is 5 mV. It has been confirmed that we may anticipate on some disks recorded velocities as high as 100 cm/s, which translates into 100 mV of peak voltage. Some preamplifier circuits when overloaded by fast spikes can recover in a matter of microseconds and resume their normal operation. There are some other preamplifiers that are incapable of recovering fast and once overloaded stay in this unbalanced state long enough to produce audible distortion of lower-level signals that follow. This primarily happens because large electrolytic capacitors, used for coupling the stages and decoupling the ac and dc circuits, are easily charged by current drivers and take a long time to discharge. Directly coupled stages, which don't employ large capacitors and inductors, have much higher slew rates and consequently react much faster and with less distortion to audio signals. One of the reasons that transistor circuits are so sensitive to overloads and clipping is because of the inherent characteristics of the transistors when operated with large amounts of negative feedback. Transistors go from a low distortion region into full clipping suddenly, unlike tubes that go into saturation gradually as the operating signals increase. The design of the preamplifier is a compromise between the power-handling capability of the circuit, low-noise performance, overload characteristics of the input stages, and limitation of the semiconductor devices.

23.9.5 Distortion

Distortion characteristics of the preamplifiers depend greatly on the amounts of negative feedback present in the design. Modern circuits contribute to the signal distortion to such a small degree that it may be measured in hundredths of 1%. Often the preamplifier has less distortion than the test equipment or the oscillator that is used in testing. Almost all preamplifiers today use integrated circuits that utilize temperature-compensated operational amplifiers with differential inputs, which results in superb performance of most preamplifier circuits. The difference between models is usually in peripheral features that enhance the cartridge-preamplifier interface and control the circuit parameters to suit the operating conditions. These include adjustable gain and variable-frequency response (referred to in consumer units as tone controls), a switchable rumble filter circuit, selectable input loads, a choice of RIAA, NAB, or FLAT response characteristics, and special inputs and controls to handle either lower or higher levels other than the accepted standards. Since the revival of moving-coil cartridges, many preamplifiers are designed with special inputs with a step-up transformer or low-noise pre-preamplifier stage to boost low-voltage signals from the moving-coil pickup.

The average MC cartridge produces from 0.1- to 0.6-mV output with the source impedance of the cartridge being around a few ohms and an inductance of a few millihenries at most, meaning that 20 to 30 dB of additional voltage gain is required from the pre-preamplifier. Because the output level of the cartridge is so low, an extra demand for low-noise performance is placed on the circuit. To maintain the same signal-to-noise ratio as in high-output moving-magnet cartridges, the pre-preamplifier (or head-amplifier) circuit should have 20 dB lower noise than the preamplifier for the moving-magnet cartridges. The only way to achieve this lower noise is by using a step-up transformer. But transformers have their own shortcomings. Head-amplifier circuits utilize exotic circuits and components in order to lower the noise of the input stage. The power supply for the low-level amplifiers has to be special. It requires excellent regulation and extremely low ripple voltage, which with today's voltage-regulator ICs is not hard to achieve.

23.9.6 Input Matching and Termination

The preamplifier input for the moving-magnet cartridges has to have a 47-kΩ input resistance and a low, preferably adjustable, capacitive load. The proper termi-

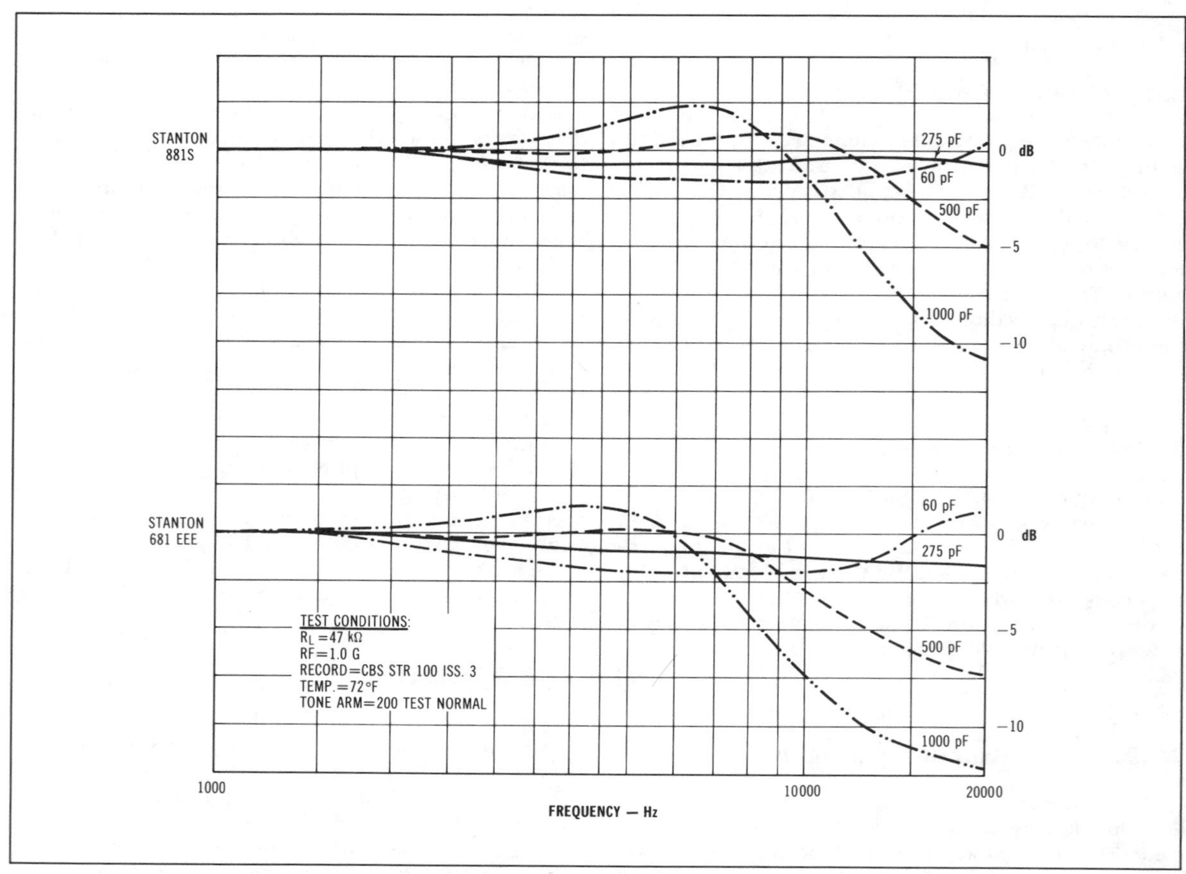

Figure 23-136 Effects of capacitive loading on the frequency response of a cartridge.

nation of the moving-magnet cartridge is of most importance for the correct performance of the transducer. Because of the resistive and inductive nature of the moving-magnet cartridges, designers today are specifying the capacitive load. Fig. 23-136 shows the frequency response of the cartridge loaded with different capacitive loads. It should be noted that the capacitive load consists of the sum of all the capacitances appearing across the terminals of the cartridge, including the interconnecting cables, connectors, and, most of all, the input capacity of the preamplifier circuit. Therefore, if the specified capacitive load is higher than the total capacity of the circuit, the preamplifier should have a provision to add capacitance to the cartridge termination as required. If the total capacitance is larger than needed, cables can be made shorter or replaced with ones having lower capacitance.

23.9.7 Typical Preamplifier Circuit

The phono preamplifier schematic in Fig. 23-137 meets almost all of the requirements mentioned previously. This preamplifier has continually adjustable gain from 30 to 60 dB, power-handling capability of 20 dBm, switchable input capacity from 15 to 350 pF in 50-pF steps, selection of flat response or NAB equalization, and high-frequency trim, as well as a switchable rumble filter and an active filter in the power supply with an LED indicator to monitor dc current flow and presence of an ac signal. As the current demand increases in the class AB output stages, the light-emitting diode glows brighter.

The noise of the circuit depends on the integrated circuit used. In this case it is the industry-acclaimed NE5533. The measured noise at the output is below the −70-dB level with an input level of 10 mV, at 1 kHz with NAB equalization.

23.10 NOISE-REDUCTION TECHNIQUES

Every recording medium adds noise to the audio signal. In tape recorders there is a tape noise; in disk recording there is a surface noise, noise of the preamplifiers and noise of the tape recorders used to store the audio signals before records are cut. Since the recording of sound has reached the levels of high-technological excellence, the only way to improve the playback further is to resort to electronic means of separating useful information from noise.

23.10.1 Compression

The electronics and recording engineers first method of noise reduction was *simple compression* and *limiting*. Compression of the audio signal consists of automatically reducing the gain of the amplifier as the input signal increases beyond a preset threshold. The resultant input-output curve shown in Fig. 23-138 represents a typical compression curve with a 2:1 compression ratio. A 2:1 ratio means that for every 2 dB of input-level increase above the threshold, there is 1-dB increase in the output level. Compressing the signal as it is being recorded produces a louder recording with less noise because the low-level information is recorded at a higher level. The only drawback of using compression is a smaller dynamic range, meaning that the level difference between the quietest and the loudest signals is smaller.

23.10.2 Limiting

Another type of level control technique is *limiting*. Limiting means there is a preset level or threshold above which an increase in the input level results in practically no increase in the output level. Limiting ratios can be 10:1, 20:1, or even higher (Fig. 23-139). Limiting allows a much greater increase of input signal and a much higher signal-to-noise ratio. But the penalty for such a dramatic increase in signal level often results in a very unpleasant pumping effect, along with a dramatic decrease of dynamic range. Also, as the signal fades after heavy compression or limiting takes place, there is an increase in amplifier gain and, consequently, noise level.

The use of limiting action with discretion may be beneficial in protecting against clipping and overloading of the amplifier chain or recording medium. Compression and limiting were used extensively for many years with different degrees of success. It soon became obvious that indiscriminate compression of the entire audio range is not necessary, and if selective compression of different parts of the audio spectrum is used, better results may be obtained without affecting noise.

23.10.3 Expansion

Along with the selective limiting and compression, expansion, the inverse of compression, was applied to the reproduced sound. If the signals were compressed by the ratio of 2:1 in recording and if a 1:2 expansion ratio was applied in playback, the signals would be restored to the original dynamic levels shown in Fig. 23-140, which also shows the expander curve.

23.10.4 Loudness Contours

The combination of the compression and expansion was tried in many different ways resulting in a variety of useful effects. One of the applications was an automatic loudness control circuit. Based on the sensitivity curves of the human ear as researched by Fletcher and Munson, the circuit was designed to automatically boost (expand) the frequencies the human ear was not sensitive to at the lower levels (i.e., the low and the high end of the audio

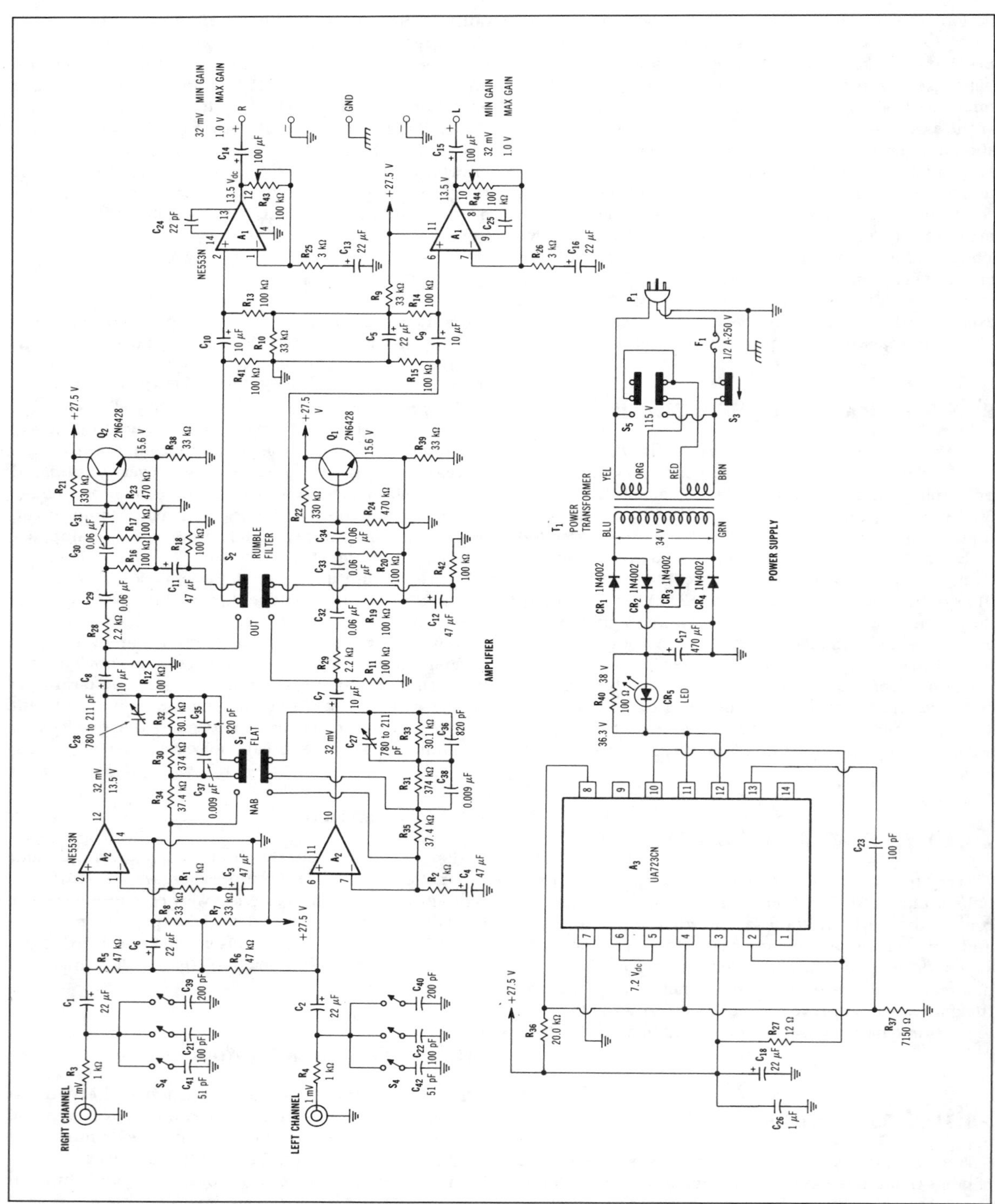

Figure 23-137 Professional phono preamplifier. *(Courtesy Stanton Magnetics, Inc.)*

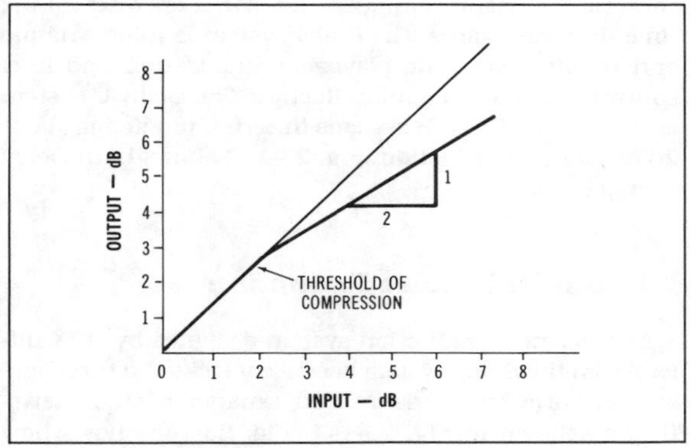

Figure 23-138 Compression curve with 2:1 ratio.

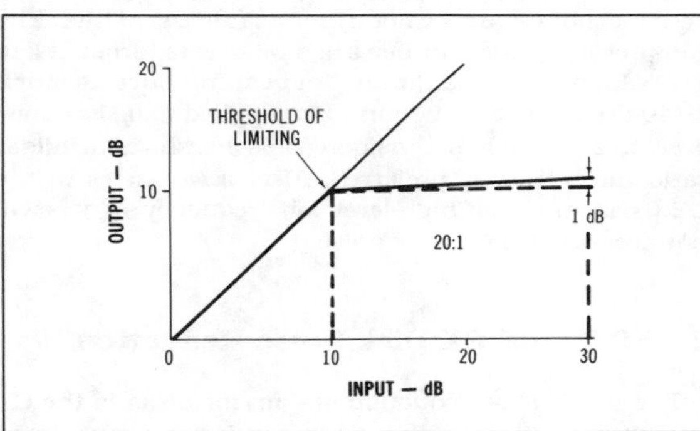

Figure 23-139 Limiter curve with 20:1 ratio.

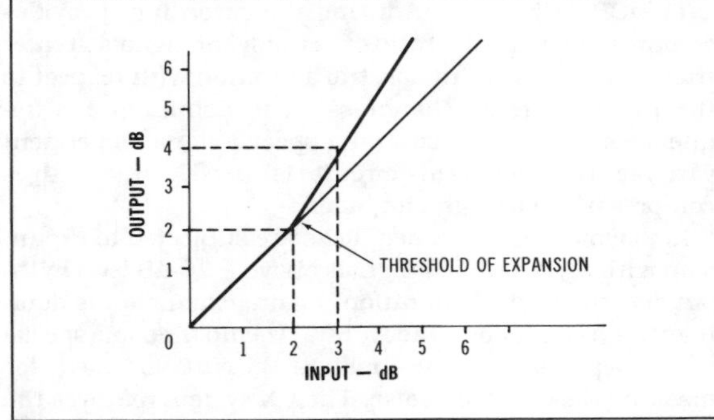

Figure 23-140 Expander curve having 1:2 ratio.

spectrum). The human ear is most sensitive to the frequencies in the middle of the audio spectrum, as shown in the Fletcher-Munson curve shown in Chapter 2. The circuit is used as an automatic loudness control in some high-fidelity amplifiers and tuners. One of the major radio and TV networks in the early 1960s designed a special expander-compressor to be used for broadcasting radio

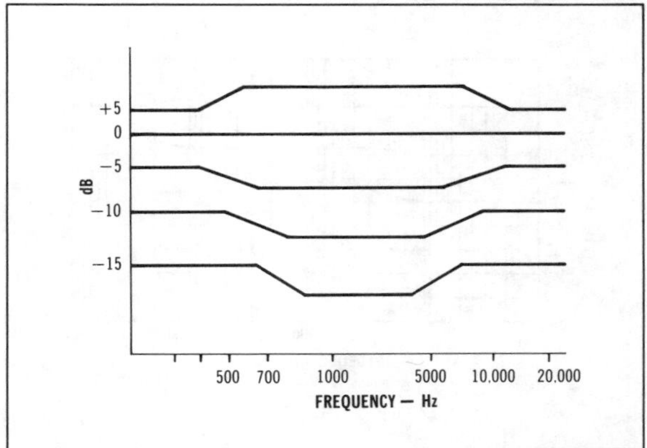

Figure 23-141 Automatic loudness contours.

programs and to achieve a louder signal without overmodulating the transmitter. At the high levels, low and high frequencies were compressed; at normal output levels, the response was flat; and at the low levels, both ends of the spectrum were boosted, as shown in Fig. 23-141.

A similar approach was tried with disk records, but the noise spectrum of the disk medium and recording characteristics made the method less effective.

23.10.5 Dolby Noise Reduction

The first effective noise reduction was developed by Ray Dolby. The *Dolby system* was designed primarily for tape recording. It requires that the tape carries a reference tone for adjusting the threshold of the circuit, and in playback this test tone is used to set the playback level.

The Dolby system scans the audio program and increases the volume of the passages and sounds that are closest to the noise-producing frequencies and are lowest in level during the recording. In Dolby-encoded recordings, parts of the music that were expanded stand out clearly from the noise, which makes the recording sound loud if the program is not properly decoded. During the decoding, loud passages are brought back to their original levels, which reduces the noise. Dolby divided the spectrum into four bands. Figs. 23-142A and B show Dolby input and output curves.

Dolby presently has several types of record/reproduce curves each tailored for a specific application. The original Dolby A system was designed for professional use, and then came type B (Fig. 23-142C), which was later modified with HX circuits to raise the headroom. Recently the type C was introduced to increase the effect of noise reduction.

Although the Dolby system leaves the high levels almost untouched during the recording, high frequencies are boosted 10 dB at levels below −40 dB. The process depends not just on level changes but also on an electronically

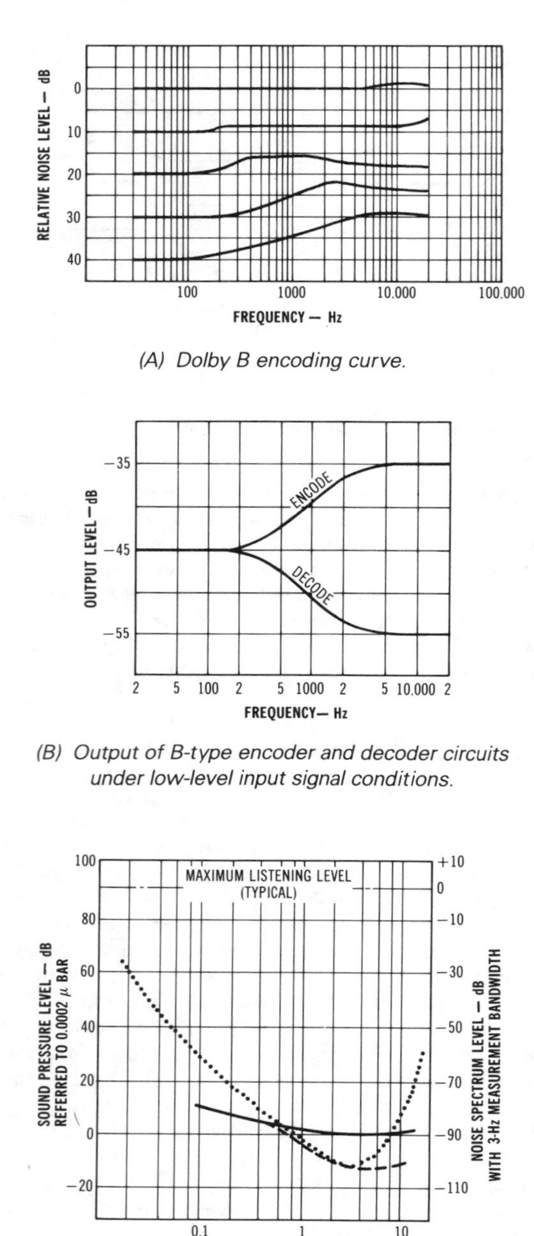

(A) Dolby B encoding curve.

(B) Output of B-type encoder and decoder circuits under low-level input signal conditions.

(C) Effectiveness of Dolby B system.

Figure 23-142 Dolby input and output curves.

controlled, variable, bandpass filter that operates all the time. In other words, the Dolby system is fully dynamic and requires accurate playback equalization and level control in order to be fully effective. The Dolby C system is actually two Dolby B systems in series, producing about 20 dB of noise reduction. Fig. 23-143 shows both Dolby curves B and C.

23.10.6 DBX Noise Reduction

Another noise reduction system designed by DBX differs from the Dolby system because it lacks of a threshold and uniform compression and expansion characteristics, as shown in Fig. 23-144. Fig. 23-145 shows how *DBX noise-reduction characteristics* differ from the Dolby system. The DBX system is a basic *compander system*, compressor for recording and expander for playback. The action is not frequency nor dynamic range sensitive. The compression ratio can be varied or selected from 1:1 to 2:1, which is the maximum, and can produce as much as 40 dB of noise reduction when applied to disks. However, a 2:1 factor is considered too harsh, and milder ratios are generally preferred. Also, a weakness in the DBX system is that high-level, low-frequency signals will not necessarily mask the noise.

23.10.7 CBS CX Disk Noise Reduction

The third noise reduction system for disks is the CX system by CBS. It is also a compander-type system, in some ways resembling the DBX system, but it doesn't function over the entire audio range, making its presence and action more discrete and less objectionable.

The CBS CX system, during the recording, provides compression with the ratio of 2:1 only for signals greater than −40 dB, without spectral alteration with respect to the reference level. Compression is dominant for frequencies above 500 Hz, and a special signal-dependent variable time-constant circuit is used, which gives compression a benign character.

In playback, CX-encoded disks are subjected to expansion with a 1:2 ratio for signals above −20-dB level without signal, spectral alteration. Again, expansion is dominant for all frequencies above 500 Hz, and the same special signal-dependent, time-constant circuit is used for masking disk surface noise. The CX system requires the playback threshold to be adjusted for each cartridge only once during the installation of the cartridge.

The time-constant network provides a variable attack and decay time as well as high ripple rejection. The basic attack time constant is 1 ms for *fast, large* increases in signal amplitude. For slow, large increases the attack time constant is 30 ms. For *small* changes in signal amplitude the time constant is 2 s. The release time constant varies from 200 ms for *large* signal decreases to 2 s for *small* decreases. Because the time-constant circuit responds

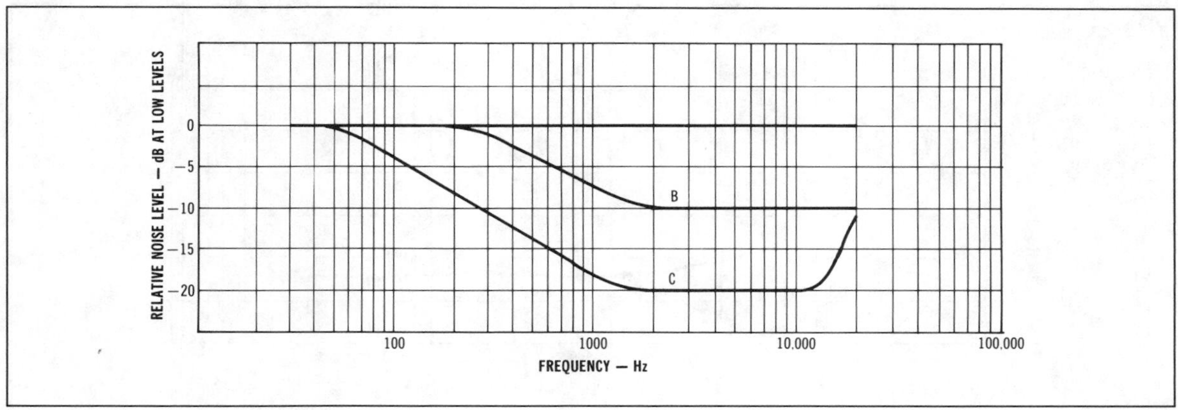

Figure 23-143 Dolby B and C curves compared (low-level signals).

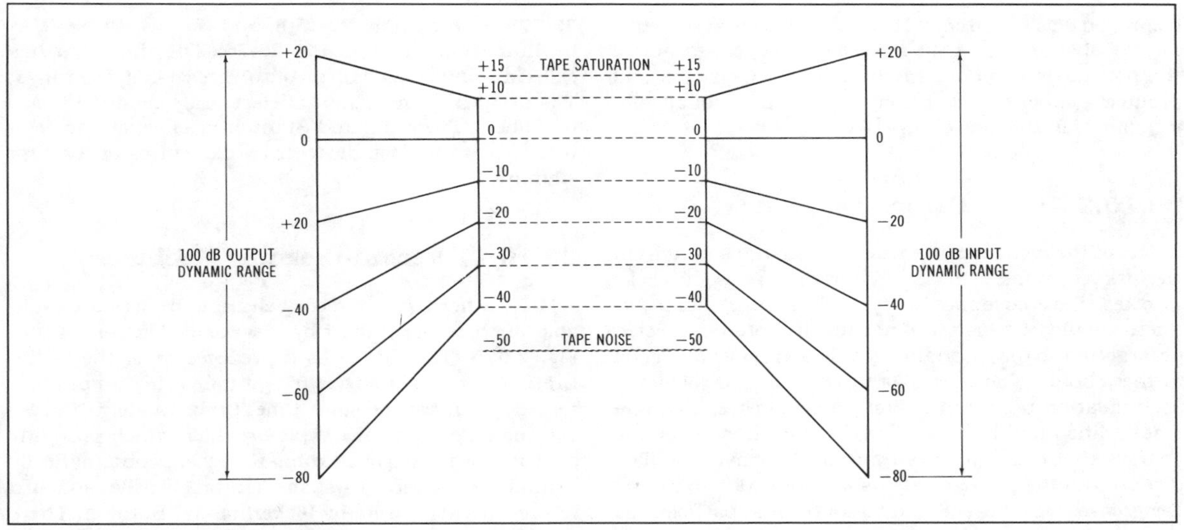

Figure 23-144 A compression and expansion level diagram in a DBX system.

fast only to large changes in envelope, there is no ripple or steady-state tones, thereby preventing distortion due to self-modulation. The curves for the CX noise-reduction system are found in Fig. 23-146.

23.10.8 Dynamic Noise Reduction

Another unique noise-reduction system that is used only in playback has been labeled *DNR*, which stands for *Dynamic Noise Reduction*. DNR was designd by Burwen from KLH and later packaged by National Semiconductor Corp. into a two-channel integrated circuit. The DNR circuit consists of a variable low-pass filter that is controlled by the presence of high-frequency signals. When there are strong high-frequency signals present, there is no filter action, and the noise-masking effect is at its maximum. But as soon as the signal amplitude falls, the bandwidth is instantly reduced, cutting down the background noise (Fig. 23-147). The filters have to be fast enough to open up to avoid transient clipping. Typical attack time is 1 ms with release time of 20 ms, long enough to retain the musical ambience. The DNR circuit can be used with almost any program source and presently is being actively utilized in car radios and tuners.

All noise-reduction techniques mentioned previously are presently being used. The advances in large-scale integration have permitted very complex functions to be

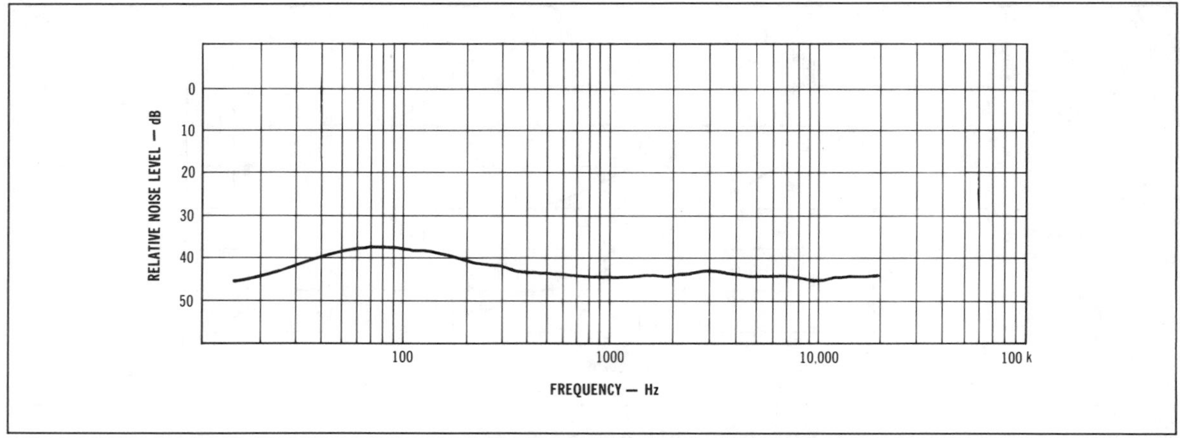

Figure 23-145 Potential noise reduction with DBX.

combined on a single chip. It is conceivable that someone may be able to extract the most desirable features of all the previously mentioned noise-reduction systems and produce a superior circuit that could be used for all analog signals in the quest for perfection.

23.10.9 Record Care Suggestions

One of the most effective ways to keep the sound from the disk record free of noise and unwanted pops and clicks is to keep the groove and the stylus clean. Although cleanliness should be a matter of routine, it is often neglected or forgotten so that soon the records don't sound as good as they should. The causes for dirty records are obvious; accumulation of airborne dust, finger grease, cigarette smoke, and anything that can be attracted by the static charges that exist on the surface of the vinyl disk. The dirt around the playback stylus is mainly due to raking the groove (Figs. 23-148 and 23-149). Dust particles, as they settle down on the record surface, are attracted by the stylus, especially if it has a static charge on it. Better cartridges have their styli electrically grounded to bleed any static potential from the cantilever assembly to ground.

23.10.10 Brushes

Another way to keep room dust out of the record groove is to have the cartridge work with the dust-collecting brush shown in Fig. 23-150. The principle of brush operation is simple. In sliding over the surface of the vinyl record, the electrically insulated brush produces a static charge of its own that attracts and holds the dust particles from the surrounding area. The stylus cantilever that is metallic and electrically neutral because of grounding, stays clean and free to vibrate and track the modulation of the groove. Such cartridges are produced by Pickering (Fig. 23-77); Stanton (Fig. 23-150); and the newest model is by Shure Brothers, Inc. (Fig. 23-76). The Shure brush is called a stabilizer, which pivots on grease-filled bearings. The bristles are made out of electrically conductive carbon fibers. Pickering and Stanton brushes are made of nylon fibers and clean the record while controlling tonearm stability.

23.10.11 Record-Cleaning Machines

Many other types of record-cleaning devices are available, such as Disctracker by Discwasher, Inc., shown in Fig. 23-75. This device is a predecessor of the Shure Brothers, Inc., stabilizer. It is a tone-arm damper and record cleaner at the same time. Unfortunately, it never became as popular as simple brushes, which presently are the only means of cleaning the records automatically in multiple-play record systems. The first brushes attached to the cartridges were by Pickering and Stanton. There were many imitations of the same idea, and some brushes were made to attach to the side of the tonearm.

The ultimate methods of cleaning records were developed recently by the Keith Monks (Audio) Ltd. in England (Fig. 23-151). The record is placed on the turntable, and a special brush with a liquid dispenser (Fig. 23-152), is used to apply a mixture of alcohol and distilled water to the record surface to loosen up the debris. As soon as the surface is brushed, a special tubular tonearm with the vacuum cleaner nozzle is moved over the surface of the rotating disk sucking up the liquid along with the suspended dirt and dust (Fig. 23-153). It is considered that this machine is one of the most efficient devices to restore the disk to as close as possible to its original cleanliness. But even the Keith Monk machine cannot remove some record preservatives that have a fluorocarbon base and that once clung to the surface of the vinyl; they cannot be washed away, only scraped off. Today, there are literally hundreds of different record-cleaning liquids, sprays, brushes, cloths, pads, and devices being offered. Efficiency of these devices varies with the methods of application and use and with the material that the record is made of. It is strongly advised that before using any cleaning device that the instructions be followed precisely and some experimentation be done on a few records before the entire library is cleaned or covered with a preservative coating (Fig. 23-154). A word of caution, if too much record preservative is used, it will do more harm than good (Fig. 23-155). Not only does excess of material not lower the surface noise, but it contaminates the stylus tip to the extent that it is no longer able to stay in the groove. Accumulation of the cleaning or antistatic substance on the stylus tip also increases its dynamic tip mass, interfering with tracking of high-frequency modulation. Consequently, cleaning the cartridge stylus becomes as important if not more important than cleaning records (Figs. 23-156 and 23-157).

Methods of playing records wet have been developed, which benefited the quality of sound while playing but caused problems later when the wet surface of the record is left to dry as it accumulates airborne dust and debris. (See Fig. 23-158.) Records that are played wet should be thoroughly cleaned before using again.

23.10.12 Damaged Grooves

Worn styli can easily damage the record groove in very few playings. Therefore, it is advisable to change the styli regularly, depending on the amount of tracking force used and the type of stylus. Diamond styli can last as long as 1000 hours when operated at a tracking force of 1 g or less. However, if the tracking force is increased to 2 or 3 g, the tip can become worn in less than 300 hours. The end of the stylus life is when the diamond tip starts touching the bottom of the groove, increasing noise and accelerating groove damage. The stylus wear is fastest in the beginning when the tracing radii are round and the pressure per unit area is very large. As the stylus wears, this area increases, and the record wear is slowed down. The fastest stylus wear occurs when playing metal parts (mother) because there is no deformation of the record surface. In addition, the pressures are so great that the heat generated because of friction literally burns the diamond away. (Diamond after all is compressed carbon.) It has been established that serious stylus wear in playing a metal mother can occur in only 8 to 10 hours of playing time. If a cooling liquid is applied to the surface of the disk, the life of the stylus is prolonged. But the presence of any liquid has its own drawbacks, such as contamination of the stylus tip and of the cantilever. Photographs of worn styli made with an electron beam microscope clearly show sharp edges surrounding the areas of contact, which act as a cutting tool for modulated portions of the groove (Fig. 23-114).

23.11 TEST RECORDS

The test record provides a rapid, accurate, and inexpensive way to make measurements and accurately adjust and check a recording or playback system. Recording engineers can make a routine frequency response check of their entire system—from tape to disk—in minutes by using a test record as the basis for their calibration.

Test records serve many purposes and are used by recording studio engineers, broadcast engineers, pickup manufacturers, research-oriented professionals, and home high-fidelity enthusiasts, which explains the wide variety of test records and the variations in technical specifications describing them.

23.11.1 Modulation Direction

In stereophonic recording we can have left-channel, right-channel, lateral, or vertical modulation. In monophonic recording, only lateral modulation is present. In either left- or right-channel modulation, the direction of the groove bottom is 45° to the surface of the record. When both channels are equal in amplitude and recorded in phase, the resultant direction is lateral (monophonic), and the motion of the groove bottom is parallel to the record surface. When both channels are recorded out of phase, we have vertical modulation, and the direction of the groove bottom is perpendicular to the surface of the record.

Amplitude is the displacement of the groove bottom in the modulation direction. *Peak amplitude* (usually called amplitude) is the maximum displacement from its mean position. *Wavelength* is the linear distance covered by one complete cycle of the wave.

23.11.2 Linear Velocity

The *linear velocity* of the record groove at the point of contact with the recording or playback stylus is in a direction perpendicular to the record radius drawn to that point of contact. The linear groove velocity depends upon the rotational speed and the record diameter.

When the groove is moving at a given linear velocity, the recorded wavelength will determine the number of cycles of modulation that the pickup will scan each second, which is the *playback frequency*.

23.11.3 Modulation Velocity

From a playback viewpoint the modulation velocity—or simply velocity—refers to the velocity of the groove bottom away from and toward the position of the groove centerline if no modulation were present. Referring to Fig. 23-159 the groove bottom of a laterally modulated groove is shown, although a single channel or vertically

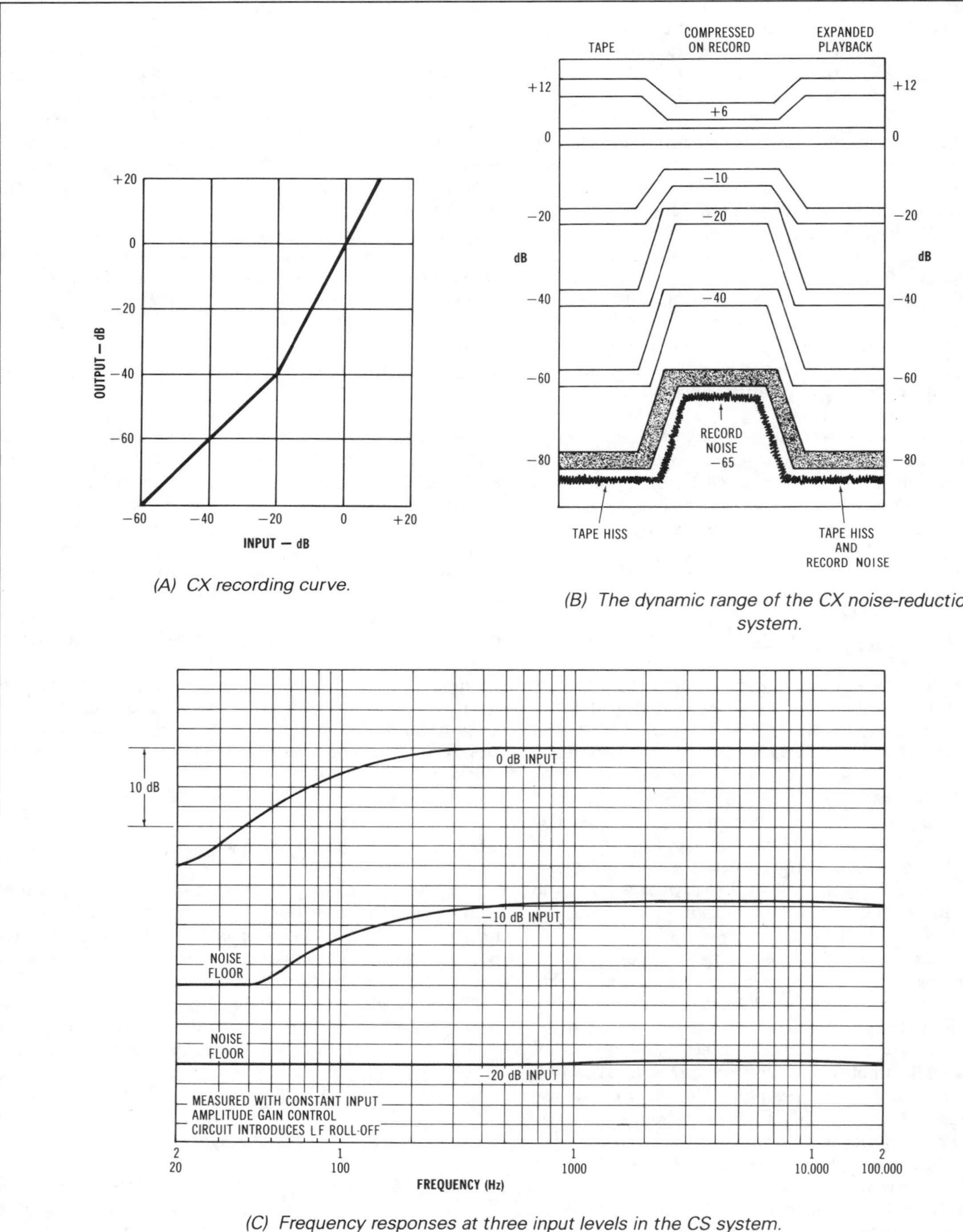

(A) CX recording curve.

(B) The dynamic range of the CX noise-reduction system.

(C) Frequency responses at three input levels in the CS system.

Figure 23-146 Curves of the CX

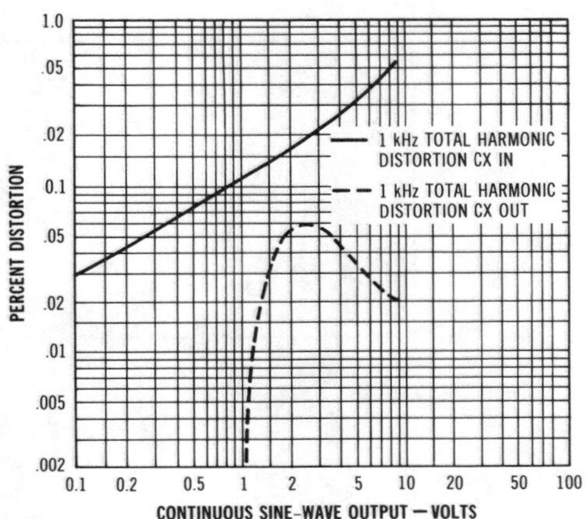

(D) Distortion with decoder in and out of system.

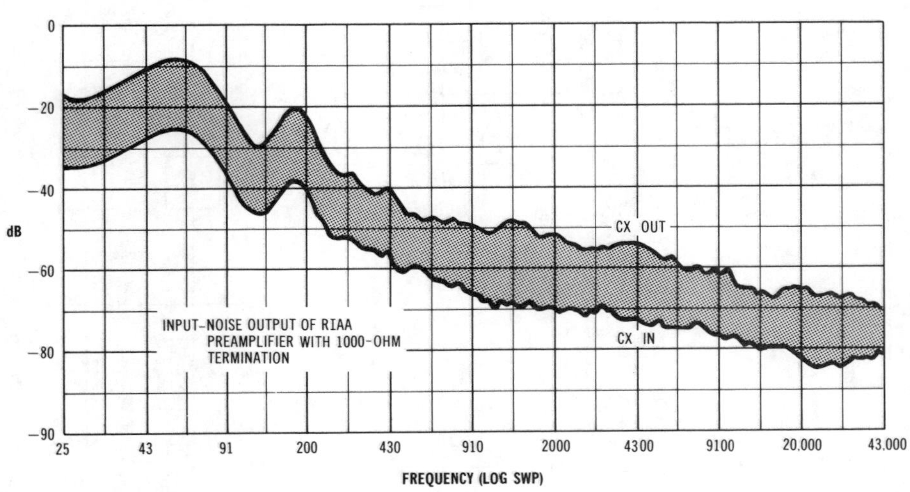

(E) Noise reduction using a CBS CX noise reduction system.

noise-reduction system.

cont. on next page

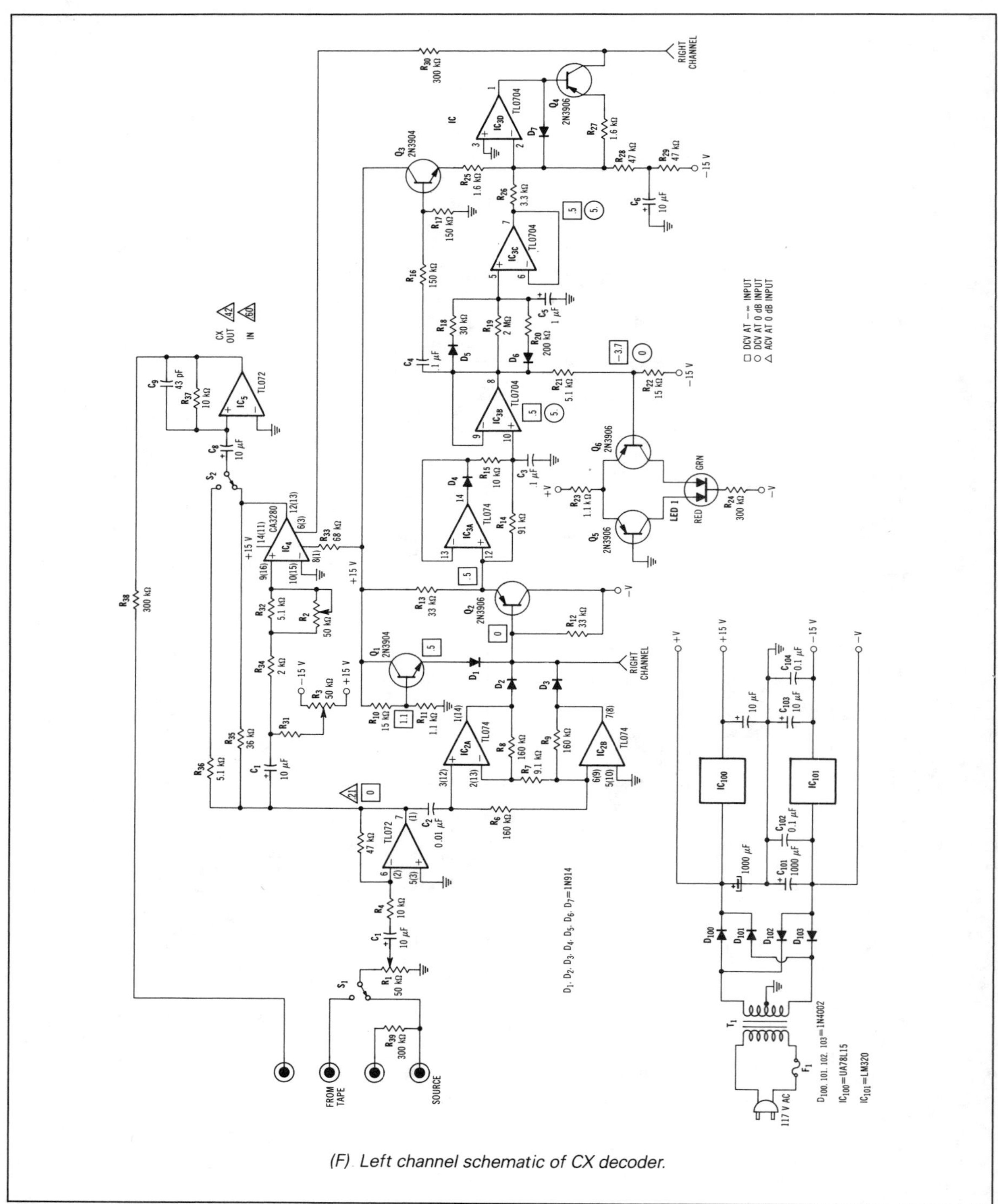

(F) Left channel schematic of CX decoder.

Figure 23-146-cont. Curves of the CX noise-reduction system.

modulated groove would serve equally well as an example. If we imagine the groove moving in the direction of the arrow due to linear groove velocity, an observer looking down at the centerline of the moving groove would see that centerline move right and left alternately. As point A passes the observer the velocity of the groove bottom is maximum to the right. As point B passes the observer the velocity of the groove bottom in the modulation direction is zero for an instant, and the motion of the groove is actually parallel to the linear groove velocity. As point C passes the observer, the velocity is again maximum but in opposite direction from point A. The maximum instantaneous velocity, as represented at points A and B, is called the *peak velocity*. The rms velocity is 0.707 of the peak velocity and is analogous to the relationship of rms voltage to peak voltage.

Velocity and amplitude are related by the equation

$$V_p = 2\pi f a_p \qquad (23\text{-}7)$$

where,
V_p is the peak velocity,
f is the frequency,
a_p is the peak amplitude.

Another way of expressing the peak velocity is in terms of the wavelength λ, and the linear groove velocity V_g:

$$V_p = 2\pi V_g a_p/\lambda \qquad (23\text{-}8)$$

23.11.4 Standard Reference Level

A recorded single-channel peak velocity of 5.0 cm/s at 1000 Hz is the standard reference level. (At this velocity and frequency the peak single-channel amplitude is 0.8 $\times 10^{-3}$ cm.) When both channels are modulated in phase (lateral) or out-of-phase (vertical), the resultant peak velocity is 3 dB greater or 7.0 cm/s. Standard reference-level test bands can be left channel, right channel, lateral, or vertical.

The standard reference level band is used for absolute calibration of the playback and record systems. With the pickup on the appropriate standard reference level band, the playback gain of each channel is adjusted. The output signal level is set at 0 VU re 1 V, or 0 dBm—whichever level is the conventional standard signal or power reference used in your system.

A lateral reference level band can be used to calibrate a stereophonic playback system. The lateral modulation is then considered as left- and right-channel modulations being present simultaneously. All levels will be referred to in decibels relative to the standard reference level.

23.11.5 Frequency Response

The recorded velocity or amplitude of a frequency response test band is related to the frequency by the recording characteristic. In a constant-velocity characteristic, the recorded velocity is constant at all frequencies. Similarly, a constant-amplitude characteristic has constant recorded amplitude at all frequencies. A combination of constant-velocity, constant-amplitude characteristic is frequently used; the RIAA or NAB curve is this type.

Frequency response tests can be spot frequencies, or a sweep or glide tone. Spot frequency recordings have a series of frequencies bands that are spaced at uniform intervals. The sweep-frequency band employs a continuously varying tone that covers the entire frequency range. Sweep-frequency bands require a specialized recording apparatus to be fully utilized. For the recording studio and broadcaster, the frequency-response test using the RIAA (NAB) recording characteristic is most useful since the standard playback electronics have the RIAA playback characteristic. The output of an ideal playback system (pickup and associated electronics) with RIAA playback characteristic will be flat when playing a frequency response test band with the RIAA recording characteristic.

23.11.6 Crosstalk

Stereo standard reference level and stereo frequency response test bands provide a means for measuring pickup *crosstalk*. Crosstalk is a measure of the loss of stereophony. When the left channel only is modulated, the right-channel crosstalk signal is measured in decibels below the left-channel output. The reverse procedure is used to measure the left-channel crosstalk.

23.11.7 Pickup Tracking

Tracking refers to the ability of the playback stylus to maintain continuous contact with the groove walls in the presence of modulation. When, due to high modulation levels, the playback stylus is only intermittently in contact with the groove walls, audible distortion will occur. On rare occasions the pickup can be thrown completely out of the groove, although this is not likely in modern pickups. Harmonic and intermodulation measurements can be used to determine the distortion caused by mistracking.

The test record provides, with either single-tone or two-tone recordings, successively higher levels of modulation. The pickup output will sound normal or undistorted at low modulation levels. When the critical modulation level is exceeded, beyond which the pickup cannot track, the output becomes noticeably distorted, which then is the maximum undistorted level that can be played back by the pickup.

23.11.8 Turntable Performance

Turntable rumble can be measured by playing the pickup on a quiet groove and measuring the pickup output rel-

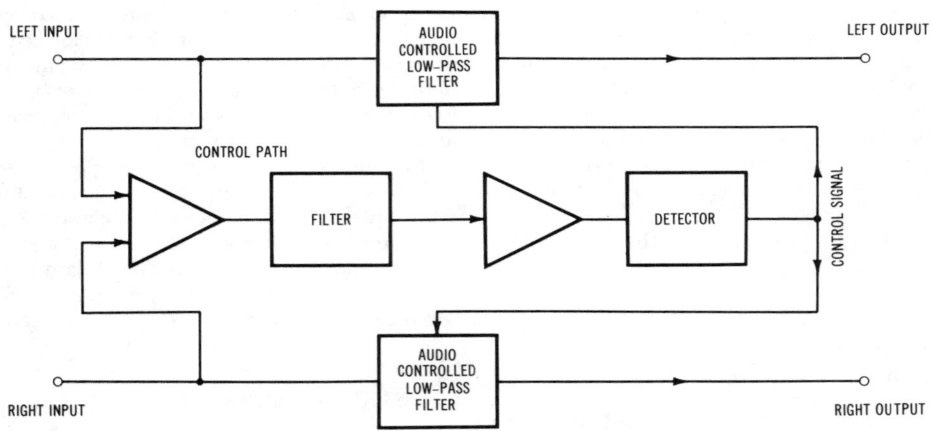

(A) DNR system block diagram.

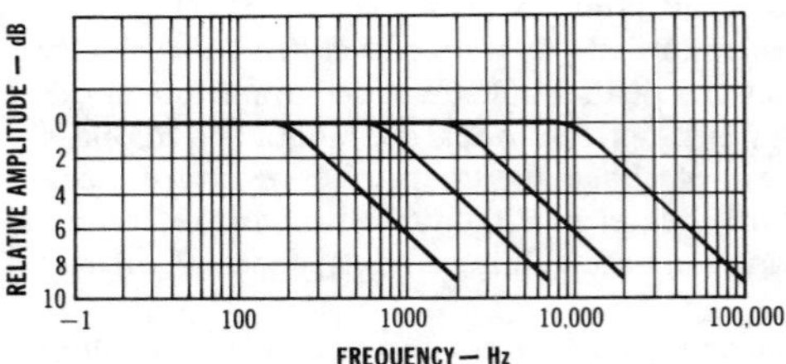

(B) DNR noise reduction of four different levels.

Figure 23-147 DNR system diagram, noise

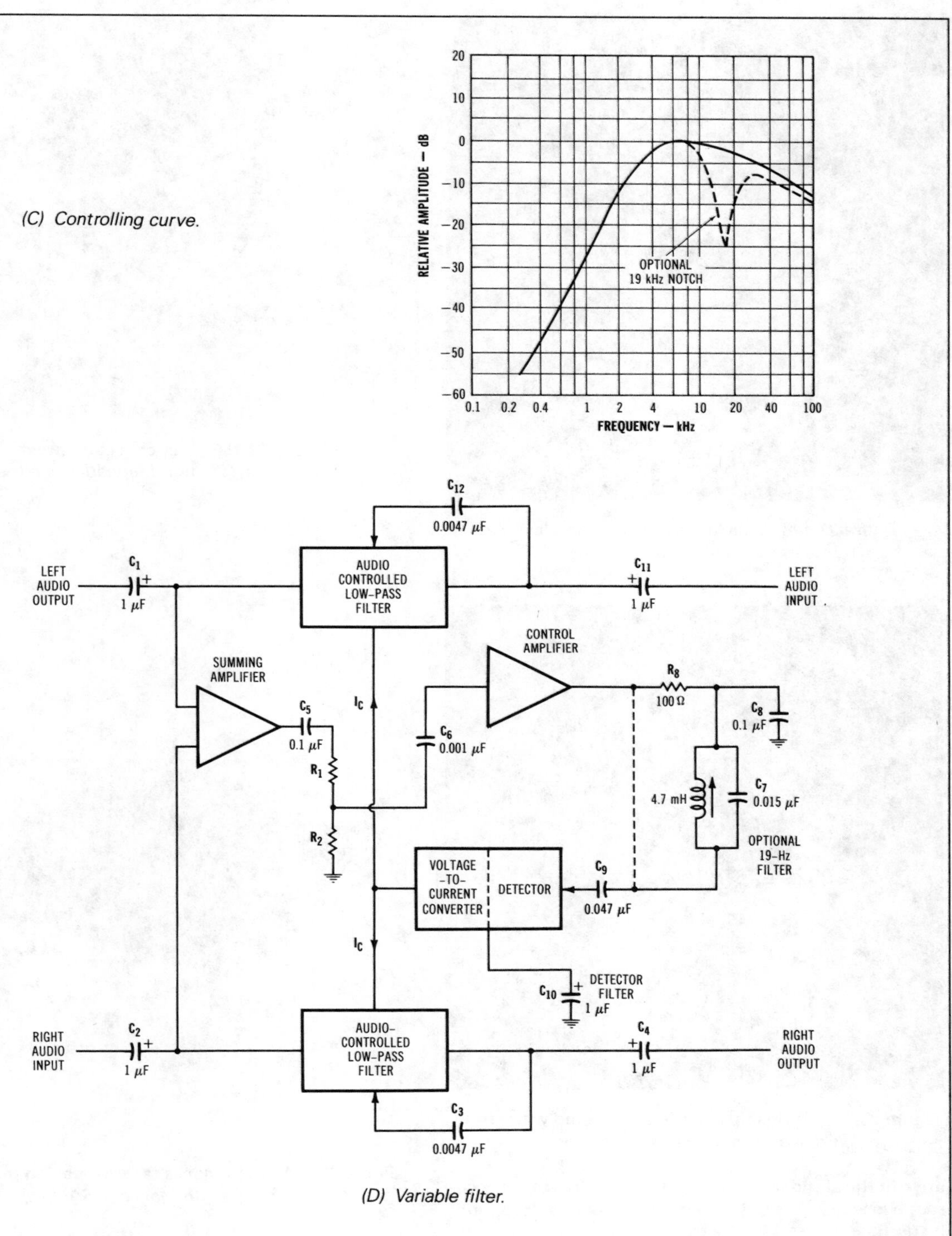

(C) Controlling curve.

(D) Variable filter.

reduction, controlling curve, and variable filter.

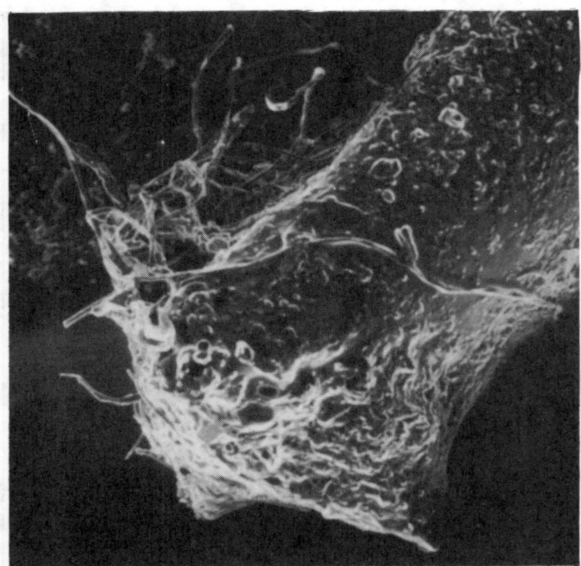

Figure 23-148 Badly contaminated but playable stylus tip.

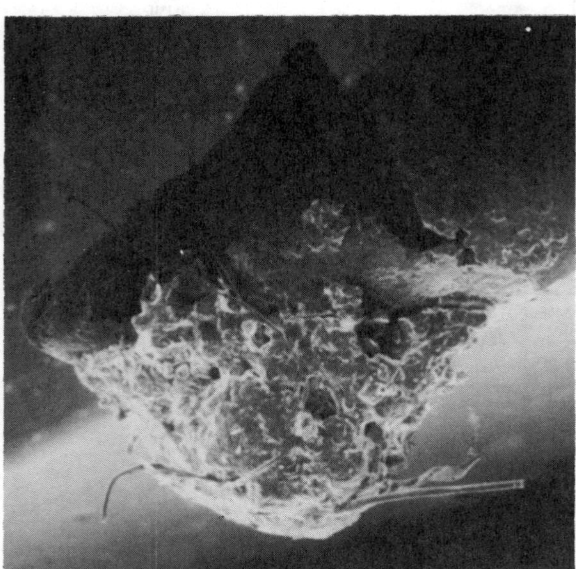

Figure 23-149 Stylus tip completely covered with grime. *(Courtesy Stanton Magnetics, Inc.)*

ative to the standard reference level. For increased accuracy a low-pass filter with a cutoff around 300 Hz should be used.

Wow and flutter can be measured with a *wow and flutter meter*. A 3000-Hz tone is provided on the CBS STR 150, the NAB Test Record, and the RCA 12-5-65 for this purpose.

Figure 23-150 Dust-collecting brush. *(Courtesy Stanton Magnetics, Inc.)*

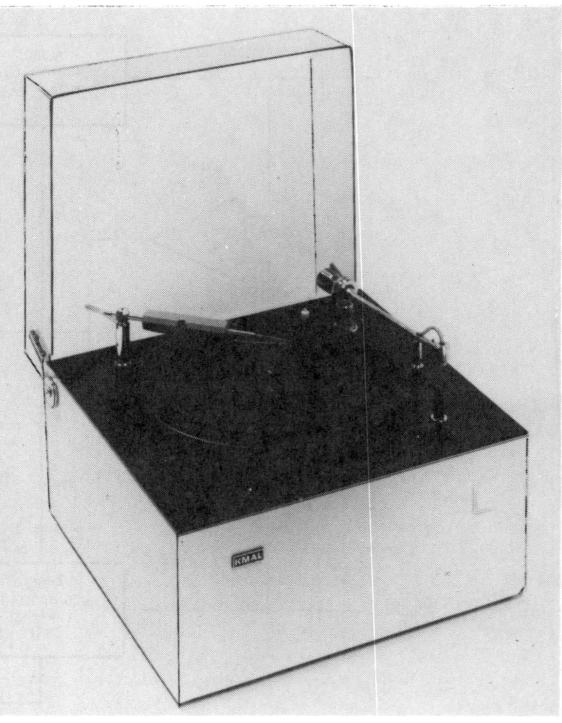

Figure 23-151 Keith Monks record-cleaning machine. *(Courtesy Keith Monks [USA] Inc.)*

23.11.9 System Phase and Balance

A system phase and balance check is used to verify the following: channel balance, the fact that in-phase signals

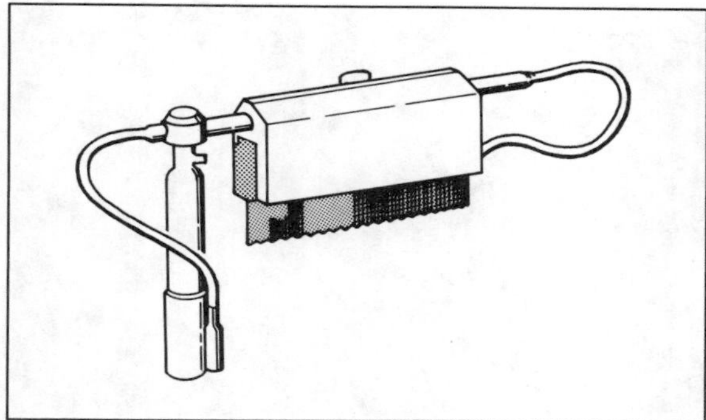

Figure 23-152 Liquid dispenser and groove cleaning brush. *(Courtesy of Keith Monks [USA] Inc.)*

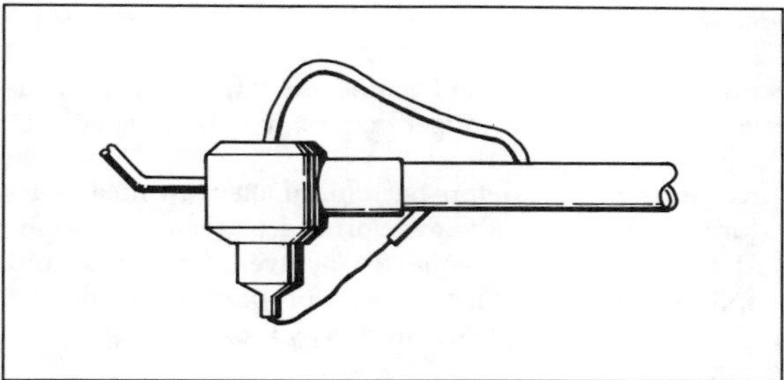

Figure 23-153 Suction arm. *(Courtesy Keith Monks, [USA] Inc.)*

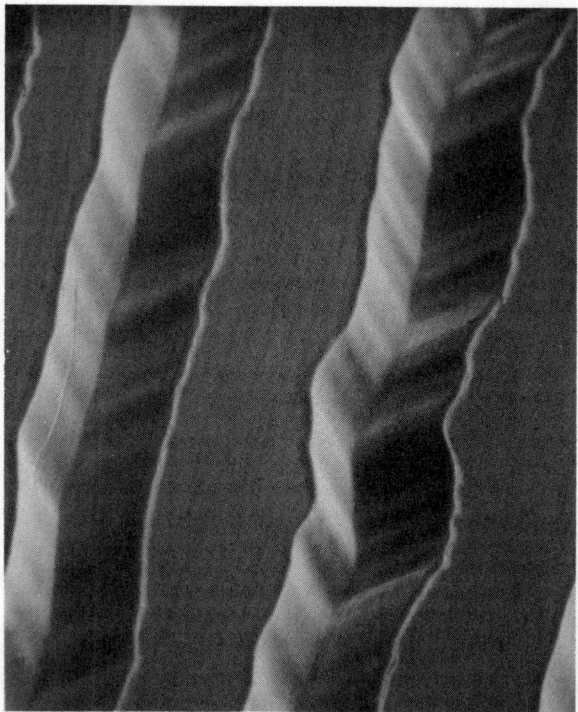

Figure 23-154 Clean record grooves. *(Courtesy Stanton Magnetics, Inc.)*

are present at the playback system output for lateral recordings, and the fact that out-of-phase signals are present at the playback system output for vertical recordings.

In order to design and cut test records, it is important to know how to verify the levels, frequencies, phase, and distortion levels of modulation.

As the disk-recording technology advanced, so did the art of making test records. But even today, when the disk recording technology can be considered being at a very advanced stage, test records from several major record manufacturers played back on the same system vary greatly from record to record (Fig. 23-160). This is because they are cut with different cutters and standards for records are incomplete and at times vague. Also, most of the time the results of a cutting are checked using cartridge playback. Since cartridges introduce additional error, the overall result is inaccurate.

An old method of checking the accuracy of levels being recorded is the *light method*. The making of light patterns for plotting the frequency characteristics of cutting heads and disk-recording channels was first devised by Buchman and Meyer. Light patterns are recorded by applying frequencies of constant amplitude to the recording channel and then recording them on a disk record. Each frequency is recorded for approximately 10 s with an unmodulated groove of 5 s. The recording is started with the highest frequency on the outside of the record to reduce the effect of lower groove velocities at the smaller diameters. A typical light pattern made with a magnetic cutting head using a modified constant-amplitude, constant-velocity recording characteristic is shown in Fig. 23-161.

The usual manner of reading a light pattern is to view it in sunlight or by means of a small light located some distance away from the disk so that the light rays strike the disk nearly parallel to its surface. The pattern is then observed from a distance of about 4 ft, using one eye, or it may be photographed and read (Fig. 23-162). Light patterns are a simple and effective means of making an overall calibration of a recording channel or checking the frequency characteristics of a cutting head.

The theory of the light pattern is as follows. At the center of the pattern, an unmodulated groove makes an angle of 90° with the incident ray and reflects a beam of light to the eye (Fig. 23-163). Other parts of the groove appear dark. When the groove is modulated, reflections are visible despite the departure of the groove axis from the 90° direction. A point will exist on each waveform where the angle due to the modulation cancels the 90° angle because of the change in mean direction.

Again, for a short distance within each waveform, the groove is at the 90° position or parallel to the tangent at the center of the pattern. At a given distance from the

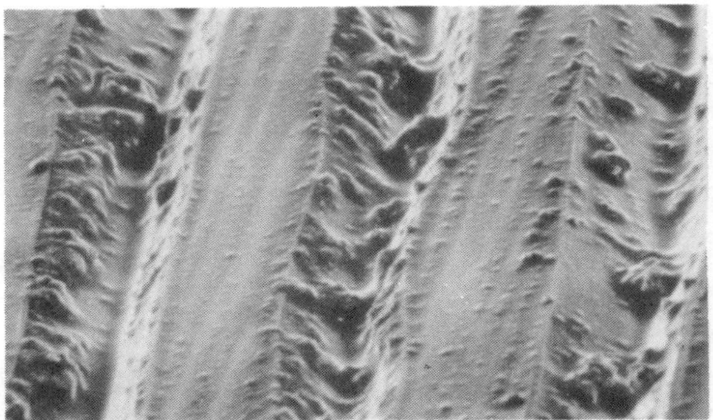

(A) Overapplied record preservative.

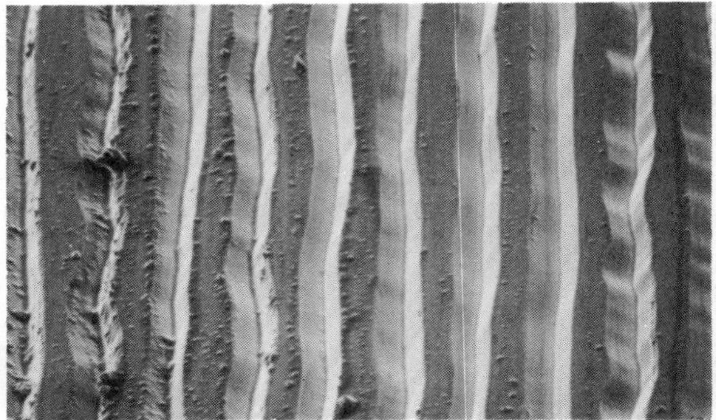

(B) Gradual cleaning of the record groove with a brush attached to the cartridge.

Figure 23-155 Cleaning of record grooves. *(Courtesy Stanton Magnetics, Inc.)*

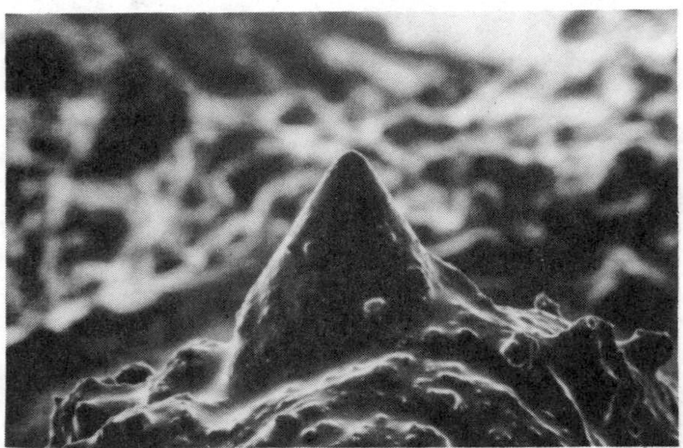

Figure 23-156 Stylus tip surrounded by excess record preservative. *(Courtesy Stanton Magnetics, Inc.)*

Figure 23-157 Stylus tip of Fig. 23-156 after cleaning. *(Courtesy Stanton Magnetics, Inc.)*

center, the groove angle becomes so large that the cancellation of angles no longer occurs, which is the edge of the pattern.

As the groove diameters become smaller, the mean curvature increases, but the waveforms are becoming shorter and the modulation slope for a given frequency and amplitude increases in the same proportion. Thus, the width of the pattern is not affected by the changing groove diameter.

Figure 23-158 Globules of dust after playing a record wet then allowing it to dry. *(Courtesy Stanton Magnetics, Inc.)*

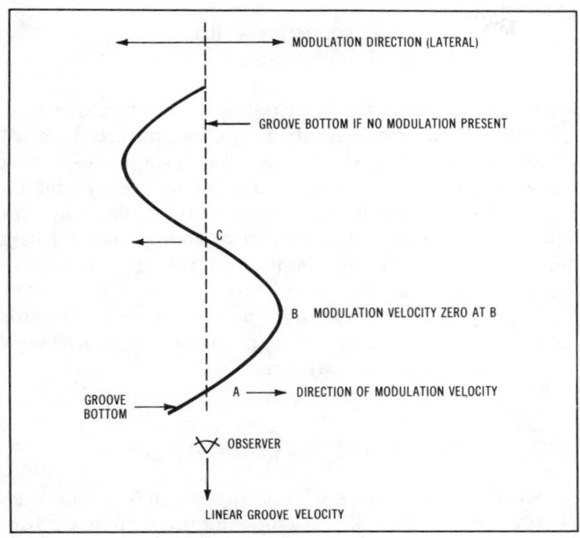

Figure 23-159 A diagram of the modulation velocity of a disk.

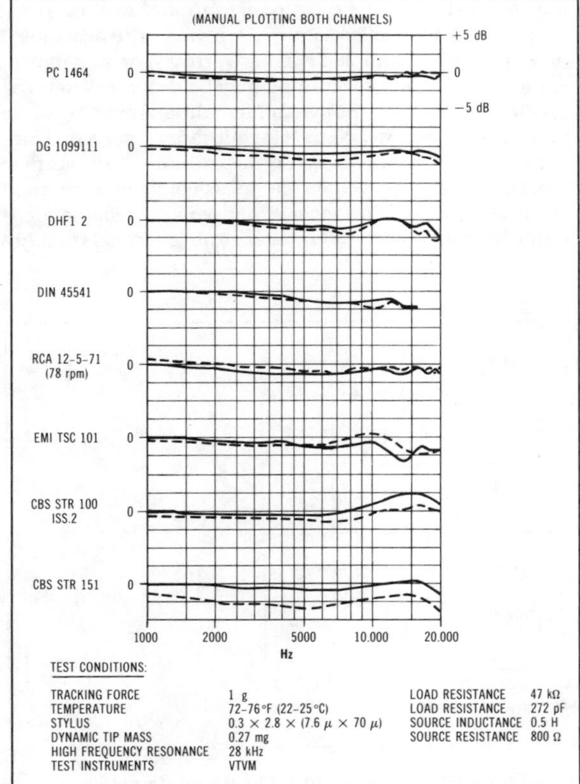

Figure 23-160 Frequency response study of test records taken with the same cartridge.

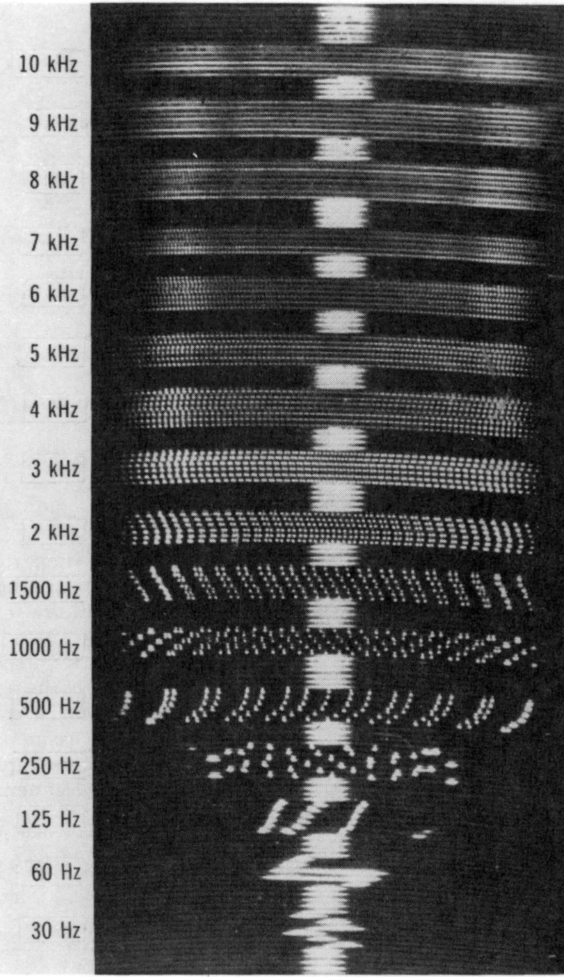

Figure 23-161 Typical monophonic light pattern made with a magnetic cutting head using a modified constant-amplitude, constant-velocity recording characteristic (RIAA), speed 33 1/3 rpm.

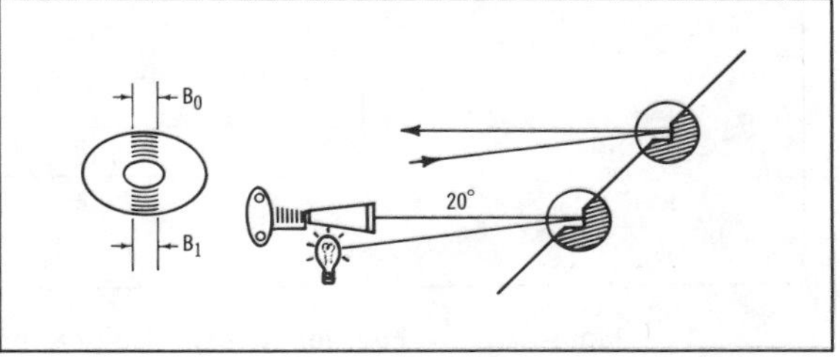

Figure 23-162 Arrangement of apparatus to obtain equal pattern width.

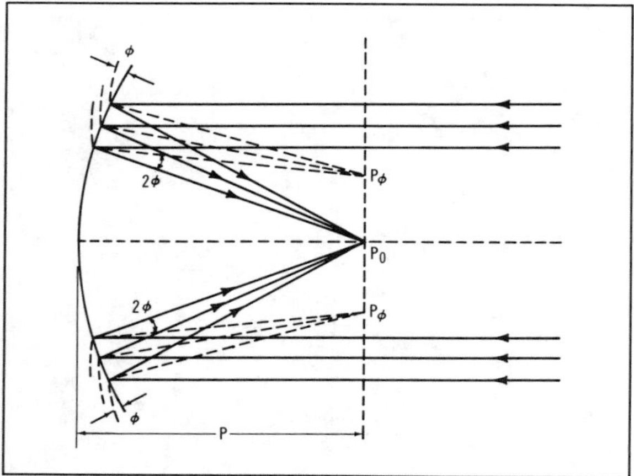

Figure 23-163 Formation of pattern by one circular groove.

A light pattern is principally a method of comparing the width of various frequency bands with each other, one band being a reference frequency. Light patterns may also be measured by playing back the pattern using a magnetic pickup. The results are plotted as the frequency versus the output level in decibels. The width of the pattern is proportional to the voltage output from a constant-velocity pickup. If the amplitude of the frequency bands is measured mechanically, either by photographing or by viewing, variations from the reference frequency may be plotted in decibels:

$$dB = 20 \log (f_1/f_2) \qquad (23\text{-}9)$$

where,

f_1 is the reference frequency width,

f_2 is any frequency of interest.

A light pattern recorded using a modified constant-amplitude, constant-velocity recording characteristic will show whether the velocity is constant, by its having straight sides between the turnover frequency and the highest frequency at the outside of the disk. Below the turnover frequency, the frequency characteristic slopes off at a rate of 6-dB/octave if amplitude is constant, as shown in Fig. 23-164.

Although the described light patterns were made using a monophonic cutting head, the procedure is the same for stereophonic light patterns.

23.11.10 Vertical Tracking Angle

Most manufacturers of high-quality pickups for stereophonic phonographs attempt to design their pickups to conform to a standard 15° vertical tracking angle. Various techniques are employed for ascertaining the angles of such pickups. Ordinarily, static methods of measuring the angle, either from the mechanical dimensions of the moving system of the pickup or from measured vertical and longitudinal deflections of the stylus in an assembled pickup, are not completely trustworthy. The angle measured under static conditions may be different from the effective angle under the dynamic conditions existing while playing a record. An accurately calibrated test record provides the most meaningful measurement of vertical tracking angles as well as the most convenient method of measurement. The most sensitive and reliable technique known at present for determining vertical tracking

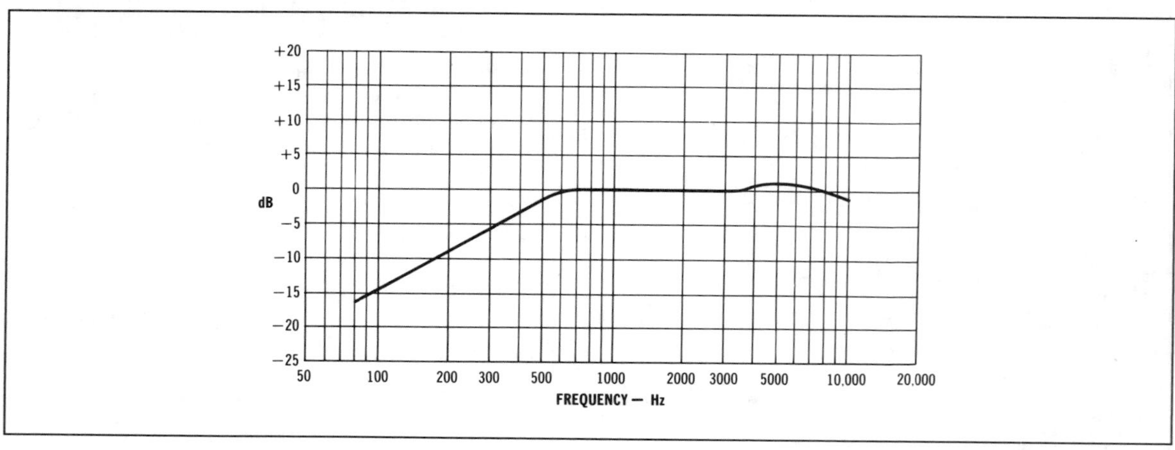

Figure 23-164 Frequency response of a magnetic cutting head plotted from measurements of frequency-band amplitude.

angles by playback of a test record is based on measurements of the phase modulation occurring with a 400 + 4000-Hz recorded signal. The frequency modulation of the 4000-Hz component at the 400-Hz rate is measured with instrumentation consisting of limiters, filters, and a discriminator. A test record containing this two-component signal has a series of bands in which the vertical recorded angle is varied from −12° to +44°. By means of this test record, the vertical tracking angle of a pickup under actual playback conditions can be found within ±0.5°, the calibration accuracy of the record, as shown in Fig. 23-165. Since the production of such a record was not feasible prior to the development of the electronic delay modulator, this test record represents the first application of a new recording technique that permits control of the vertical angle during the recording of stereo disks.

Although a number of test records are available that permit measurement of frequency response and playback losses at all frequencies of interest for phonograph systems, the pickup tracking and tracing problem at high frequencies is virtually unexplored territory.

There exists a notable lack of instrumentation and techniques for measuring the total performance of stereophonic phonograph pickups in the frequency range from approximately 7.5 to 20 kHz. The only test that shows promise of yielding significant results at high frequencies is the CCIF intermodulation test in which two closely spaced tones of equal magnitude are recorded. A number of such tests have been made using a test record on which the primary CCIF tones were 400 Hz apart and glided from a center frequency of 2 to 20 kHz in synchronism with a chart recorder that plotted the magnitude of the difference tone as a function of frequency. The results show the usefulness of this type of test in studying such factors as side thrust, pickup mechanical impedance, stylus-tip size, groove-wall deformation, and vertical tracking angle, all at high frequencies.

Observations of the frequency response and/or the reproduced waveform allow us to make certain inferences regarding the mechanical impedance and the tracing and tracking capability of a pickup. However, the interpretation of such inferences is subject to considerable uncertainty. Indeed, even the meaning of tracing and tracking becomes a bit fuzzy for short-wavelength recorded modulation. In principle it is possible to design electromechanical devices to drive a pickup stylus and make a direct measurement of the driving-point mechanical impedance of a pickup as a function of frequency. Unfortunately, the practical design problems involved are severe, and such devices have found only limited use with modern pickups in the high-frequency region.

23.11.11 Available Test Records

Table 23-3 is a list of some available test records for determining characteristics and quality of cartridges.

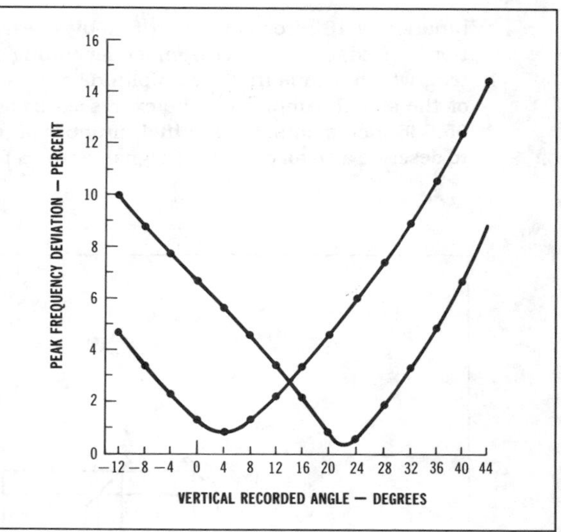

Figure 23-165 Plot of results of playback of the first group of bands of test records 12-5-78 for two pickup angles.

These test records are designed to be used by broadcasters, recording studio engineers, audio equipment designers, engineers, retailers, and users.

23.12 DIGITAL RECORDING AND PLAYBACK

For the past several years in the laboratories of major manufacturers of video and audio equipment, research has been conducted to develop and perfect new ways to record, store, and reproduce video and audio signals. The desire to find a perfect storage medium for video programs led to the experimentation with existing methods of recording, but instead of recording signals in analog form, conversion to digital format was used. The a/d (analog-to-digital) conversion of the signal was achieved by chopping up the signal into small intervals at the rate at least twice the highest frequency desired to reproduce. Then, each part or pulse sampled was coded using the binary numbering system and recorded as pulses. The original experiments were conducted using tape as a storage medium, but later flat disks like ones used for lp records were used because of much higher storage density. This world of zeros and ones used in digital recording is the language similar to the one used in computers, as shown in Table 23-4.

In chopping up the signal at the rate of 44.1 kHz (sampling frequency used in today's digital disks), the amplitude of each part of the waveform sampled is expressed as a binary number containing the equivalent of a combination of 16 zeros and ones (if 16-bit linear quantization is used) or any lower number depending on the system, which means that the amplitude of this small part of the signal sampled can be expressed in as many as 65,536 increments. Such a high number of increments to describe a small part of the signal requires fast recording speeds. Therefore, video tape recorders are us[e] record digitally processed signals. Disks carrying v[ideo] frequencies are made to rotate up to 1800 rpm and bet[ween] 150 and 400 rpm for audio programs.

The first video disks by Teldec used a mechanical [con]tact between the surface of the disk and the play[back]

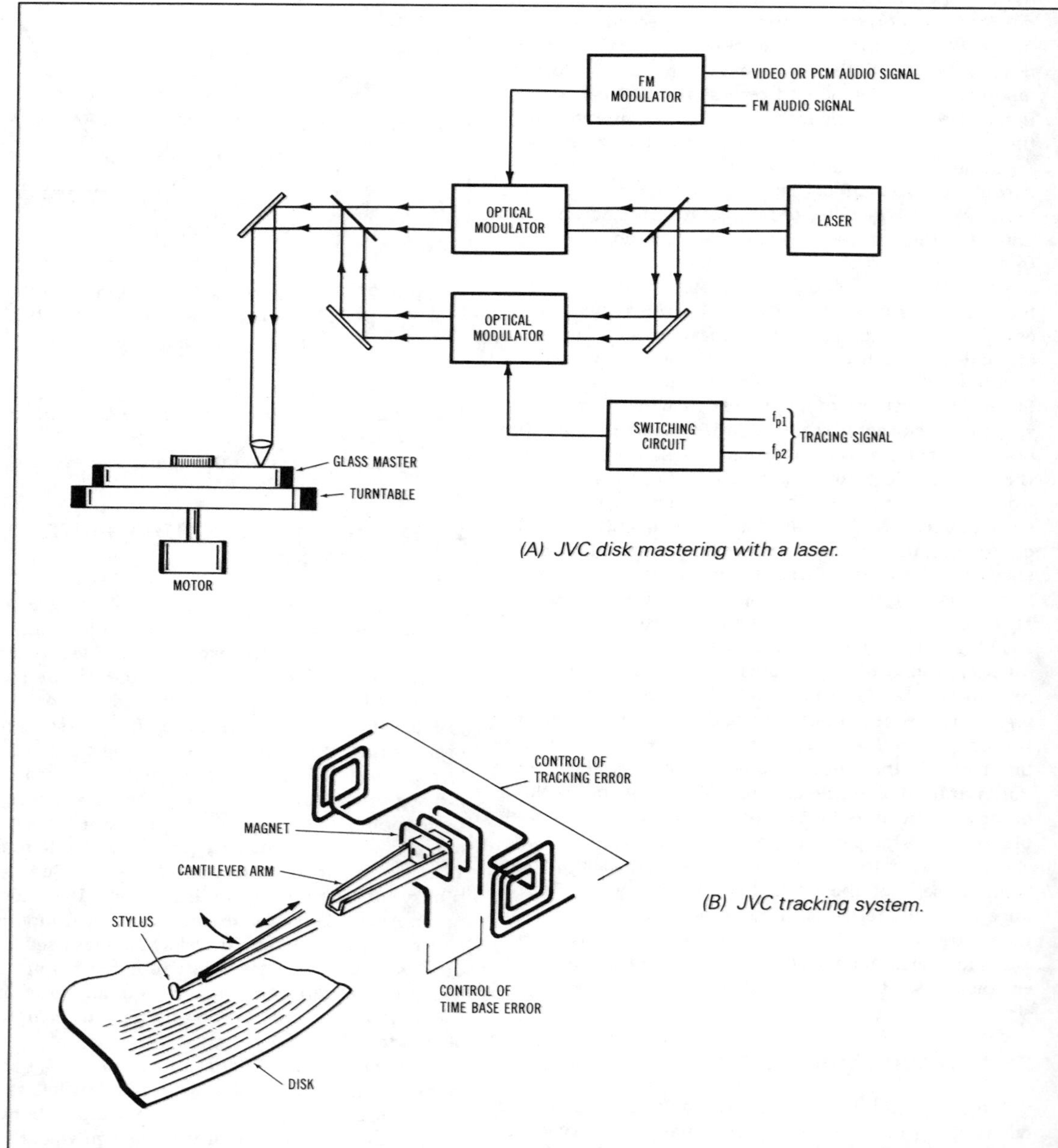

(A) JVC disk mastering with a laser.

(B) JVC tracking system.

Figure 23-166 JVC capacitance-type dig[ital]

stylus. The stylus was made of ceramic and responded to television frequencies. Because the groove had to be wide and the speed of rotation fast, the disk contained only a few minutes of television program. RCA then developed a capacitance-sensing system. The grooves resembled ocean waves, and the stylus had an electrode that scanned the surface of the record, which contained modulation in the form of pits. JVC improved the RCA system by eliminating the grooves and using a flat disk, as shown in Fig. 23-166. The record material and the underlying surface is conductive and grounded so that the stylus senses variations of capacitance to ground. These variations in

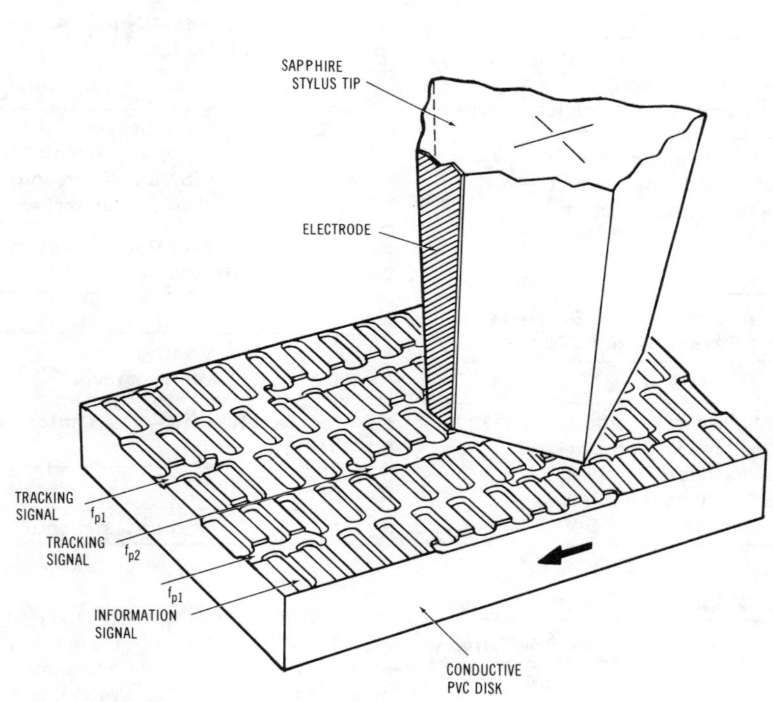

(C) JVC disk surface with stylus. The longitudinal tracking signal is now left and right of the information track.

pickup. *(Courtesy JVC Co. of America)*

Table 23-3. Test Records Available From Various Manufacturers

DIN Test Records—Gotham Audio Corp., 1790 Broadway, New York, NY 10019-1412

Number	Title
DIN 45 541	Stereo frequency and crosstalk test record
DIN 45 542	Vertical tracking angle (FIM) test record
DIN 45 543	Crosstalk test record
DIN 45 544	Rumble test record
DIN 45 545	Flutter test record—3150 Hz

CBS Test Records—CBS Technology Center, 227 High Ridge Rd., Stamford, CT 06905

Number	Title
CTC-300	Phonograph cartridge test record
CTC-310	Distortion test record
CTC-320	High-frequency response test record
CTC-330	Studio test record
CTC-340	Acoustical test record
CTC-350	Turntable and tonearm test record
SQT-1100	Quadraphonic test record
STR-101	Seven steps to better listening

Shure Brothers Test Records—Shure Brothers, Inc., 222 Hartrey Ave., Evanston, IL 60204

Number	Title
TTR 103	Trackability test record
TTR 109	Level and crosstalk test record
TTR 110	Obstacle course for V15-III
TTR 115	Obstacle course for V15-IV
TTR 117	Obstacle course for V15-V

JVC Test Records—JVC Cutting Center, 6363 Sunset Blvd., Hollywood, CA 90028

Number	Title
TRS-1001	Mono-frequency response TR
TRS-1002	Stereo-frequency response TR
TRS-1003	High-frequency response sweep spot TR
TRS-1004	Quick check for pickups
TRS-1005	High-frequency response (sweep) TR
TRS-1006	CD-4 adjustment
TRS-1007	Stereo sweep frequency
TRS-2001	Quick-frequency response check for players

Denon Test Records—Denon America Inc., 27 Law Drive, Fairfield, NJ 07006

Number	Title
XZ 7002	Pickup test record 1
XZ 7003	Pickup test record 2
XZ 7004	Turntable test record
XZ 7005	RIAA system test record

Audio Technica Test Record—1221 Commerce Drive, Stow, OH 44114

Number	Title
AT 6606	Multitest record
AT 6607	Multitest record

Ortofon Test Record—122 Dupont St., Plainview, NY 11803

Number	Title
2	Ortofon test record

Table 23-4. Binary Code

Decimal	Binary	Decimal	Binary
0	0	9	1001
1	1	10	1010
2	10	11	1011
3	11	12	1100
4	100	13	1101
5	101	14	1110
6	110	15	1111
7	111	16	10000
8	1000		

capacitance affect the resonant frequency of the tank circuit, which includes the stylus. Because the pitch of the spiraling groove is constant, the stylus can be driven by the tangentially driven tonearm mechanism in synchronism with the groove motion. This system was chosen by RCA and JVC because of ease of manufacturing, relative simplicity of the playback system, and, consequently, cost considerations. The RCA system, operating at 400 rpm,

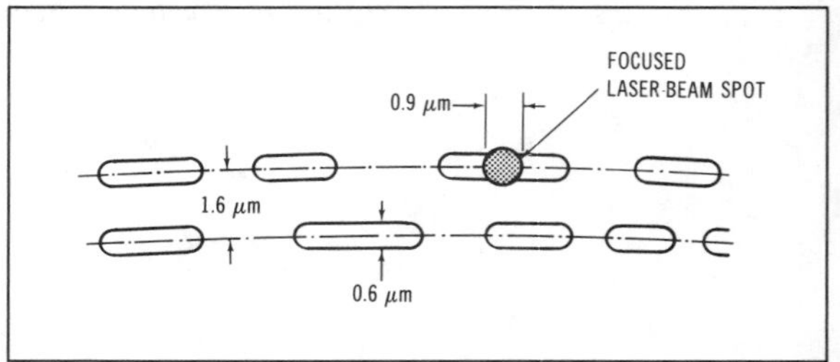

Figure 23-167 Two PCM tracks of Philips/Sony audio disks. *(Courtesy Philips Industries)*

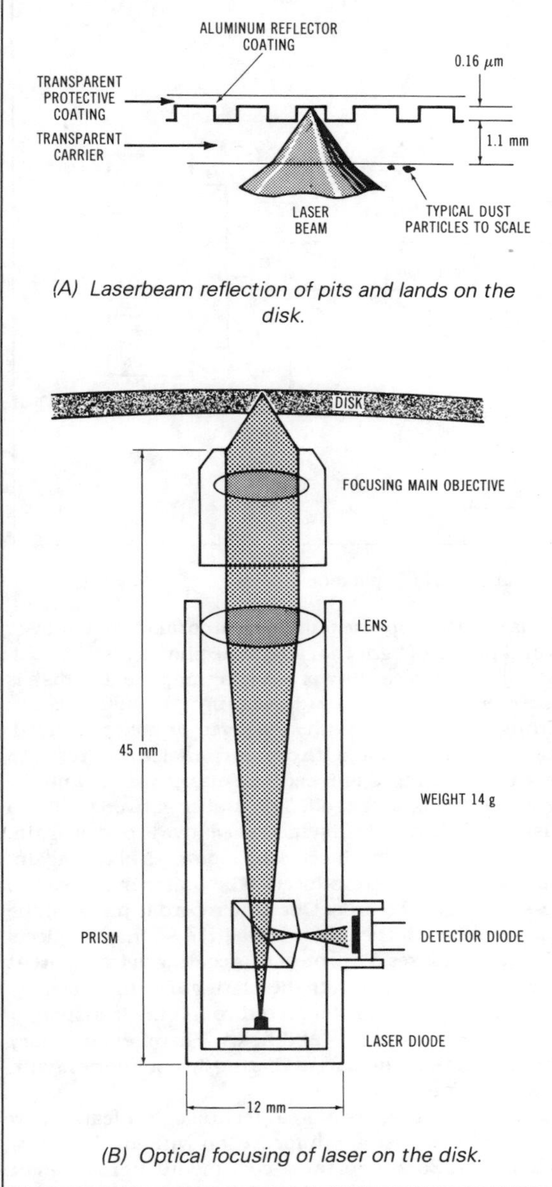

(A) Laserbeam reflection of pits and lands on the disk.

(B) Optical focusing of laser on the disk.

Figure 23-168 Laserbeam reflection and optical focusing.

can also offer two high-quality audio channels along with a high-quality television signal.

Parallel to the RCA efforts, a number of Japanese companies and Philips (Netherlands) have developed records that use a laser beam for cutting and playing back digitally encoded signals. The advantage of this method is nondestructive reproduction of the groove modulation. The laser-beam recording is produced on an optically flat glass surface covered with a vapor-deposited metal by burning the "pits" using a highly focused laser beam. The track is less than 1.6 μm wide, or about 60 such tracks would fit into the single long-playing groove (Fig. 23-167). These pits are later placed on the surface below a 1.2 mm thick protective clear plastic layer that prevents damage to the modulated surface of the disk. A disk can hold up to one hour of stereo sound. The laser output is fed through a complicated optical system that focuses the beam on the area beneath the protective clear plastic layer so that dust or scratches cannot interfere with the signal reproduction. The reflection of the laser beam is diverted by the half mirror to the photo diode, which differentiates between the light reflected from the pit or the land between the pits (Fig. 23-168).

The Philips audio disk, which was fashioned after the video counterpart, uses the same technology and methods except that it is 4½ in. in diameter and carries 60 minutes of stereo sound information per side (Fig. 23-169). The mechanism that rotates the CD (compact disk)

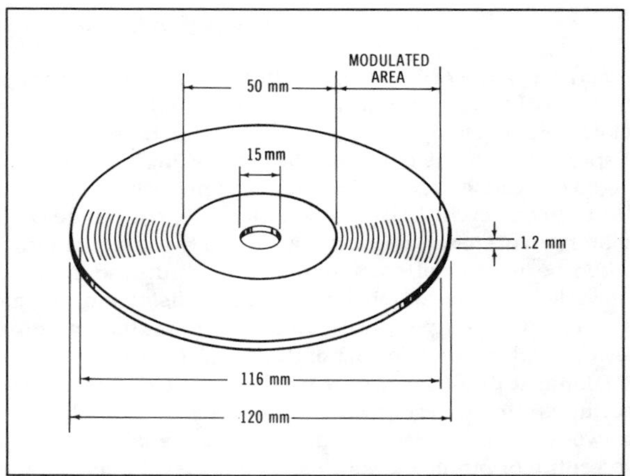

Figure 23-169 CD dimensions.

is servo-controlled so that the linear speed of the groove is constant. The disk rotates at 500 rpm when the laser-beam assembly is at the inside; as it moves toward the outside of the disk, the rotational speed reduces to 215 rpm (Fig. 23-170).

To better understand the coding process, Fig. 23-171 shows how an ordinary sine wave is converted into the pulse code and reconverted back to analog, which is the process that takes place in manufacturing and playing of digital records. The signal is first chopped up into short intervals according to the sampling frequency, which is 44.1 kHz. Then, the amplitude of each part is measured, and the measurement is expressed in binary code (Table 23-4).

Using the code shown in Fig. 23-171, we construct a 16-bit word. In playback this information is used to

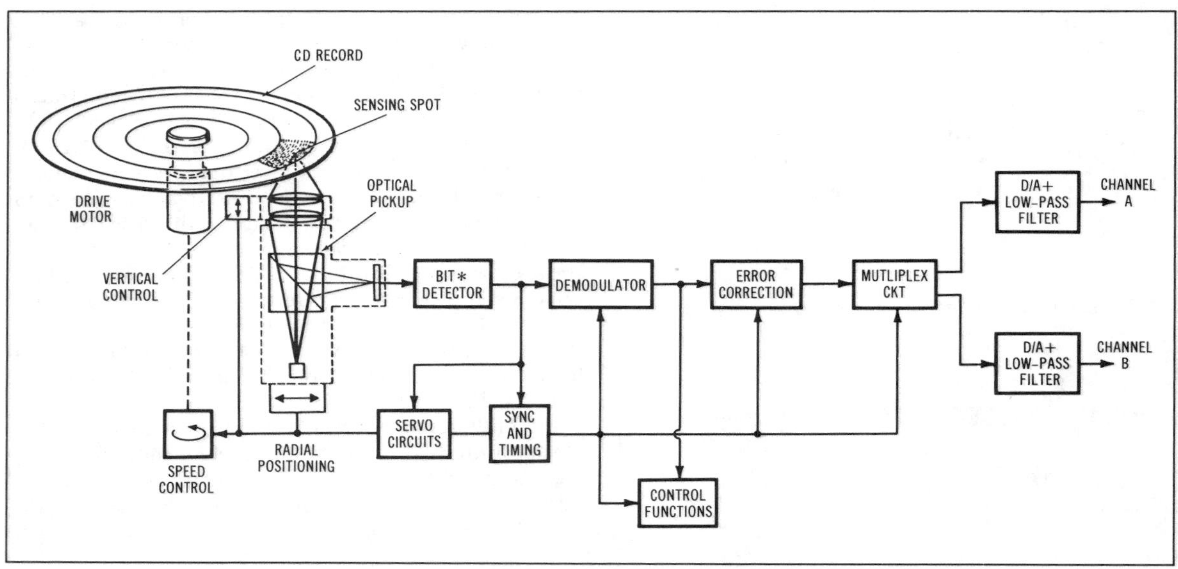

Figure 23-170 Functional block diagram of CD player.

reconstruct the original signal, but it is only an approximation of the original. It takes special circuits and special filters to restore the signal with reasonable precision. Especially difficult is restoration of the high-frequency signals because the signal is sampled only as little as four times in one cycle. Luckily, the human ear cannot detect distortion of signals of short duration at high frequencies when harmonics of such signals are at supersonic frequencies. In order to ensure that such distortion never appears at the output of the digital player, a sharp cutoff low-pass filter is made part of the circuitry.

Digital technology is so attractive because digital recordings offer no record wear, complete absence of flutter or wow, no print through, no signal degradation in rerecording or storage, and no scrape flutter. In addition, they offer a signal-to-noise ratio of 90 dB, and harmonic and intermodulation distortion of less than 0.03%. Crosstalk is less than 90 dB, and the bandwidth is from 20 Hz to 20 kHz to within a fraction of 1 dB. Noise is astonishingly low at −90 dB. However, scratches on the transparent side of the disk that follow the path of the track can cause mistracking and skipping.

The most critical part of the system is the laser-beam tracking mechanism and the error-correction system. Several digital systems on the market differ primarily by their error-correction method.

The laser assembly is a complicated system composed of several lenses, a half mirror and a prism, a motor, and the semiconductor laser with life expectancy of better than several thousand hours (Fig. 23-172). Recording and processing of the digital record is shown in Fig. 23-173. The process starts with fabrication of a polished glass disk. This disk is next coated with a photosensitive film that is used to store the pulse-code information. The laser flashes pulses of light that affect the photosensitive coating. When the recording process is complete, the disk is processed like a film by developing its photosensitive coating. The coating is then silvered or gold sputtered, much the same way as with ordinary analog disk records. Once the silvering is finished, the disk is plated, and the metal coating is peeled off. The first negative is called a master or *father*. This first metal negative is plated again, and the *mother* is produced. The *mother* is plated again, and the stamper is produced. The stamper is used to press the digital records. Once the record is pressed, the side covered with the pits is metallized so that it reflects light from the laser. To protect this coating, a transparent layer of plastic is put over the plating. During the playback, the laser beam is focused through the transparent layer to the track of pits and holes. Therefore, ordinary scratches in the transparent coating do not interfere with the sensing process.

Digital technology is a great technological feat, a new way to store almost any information without deterioration, forever. Because of pulse-code modulation, it can be recorded and stored as pits on digital disks, it can be written down as numbers, or it can be recorded on tape or stored on photographic film. In analyzing some of the possibilities using digital technology, we can see that the present way of storing this information in a form of a fast-rotating disk may only be a stepping stone to a more advanced and perhaps simpler method of recording, such as using a stationary card and an electronic beam scan of the face of the card resembling the bar-code reading technique.

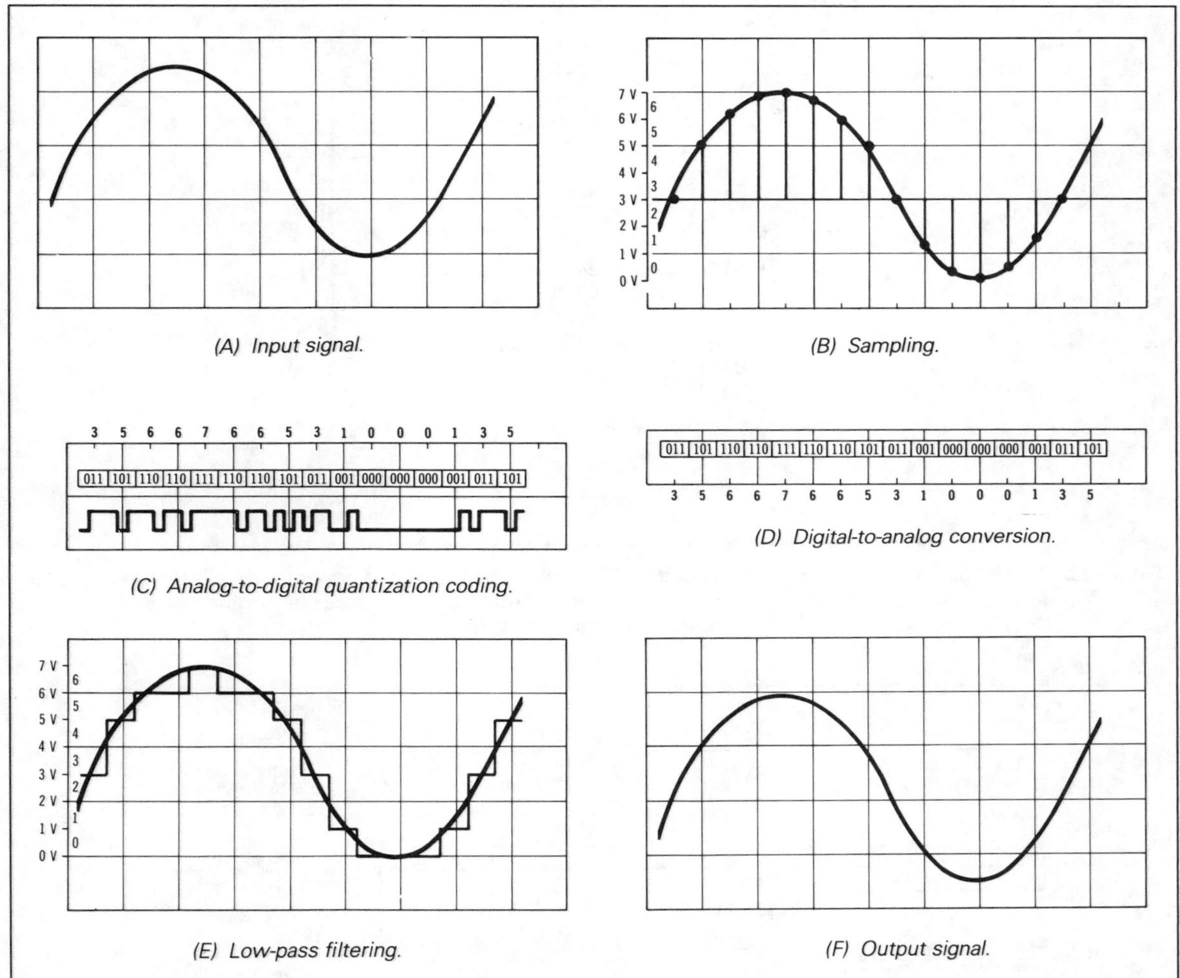

(A) Input signal.

(B) Sampling.

(C) Analog-to-digital quantization coding.

(D) Digital-to-analog conversion.

(E) Low-pass filtering.

(F) Output signal.

Figure 23-171 Digital encoding and recording of audio signal.

BIBLIOGRAPHY

G. Alexandrovich "New Approach to Tone Arm Design," AES Preprint 149, Oct. 1960.

G. Alexandrovich, "Phono Cartridges and Communications," *Broadcast Engineering*, 1982.

R. Berkovitz and K. Gundry, "Dolby B-Tight Noise Reduction System," *Audio*, September and October 1973.

L. Blakely, dbx Inc., "Using Noise Reduction to Reduce Disc Surface Noise," *Recording Engineer/Producer*, vol. 4, no. 6, December 1973.

L. Boden, *Basic Disc Mastering*, 1980.

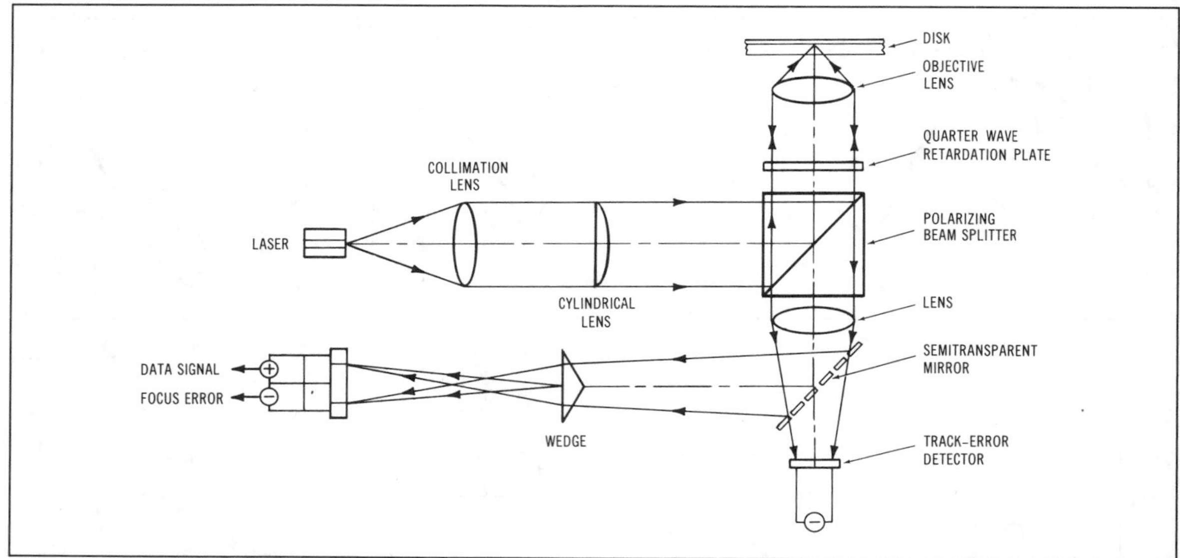

Figure 23-172 The optical-disk recorder developed by Philips Research Laboratories employs a laser-diode source and sophisticated lens systems to read recorded information and to focus its writing beam. *(Courtesy Philips Industries)*

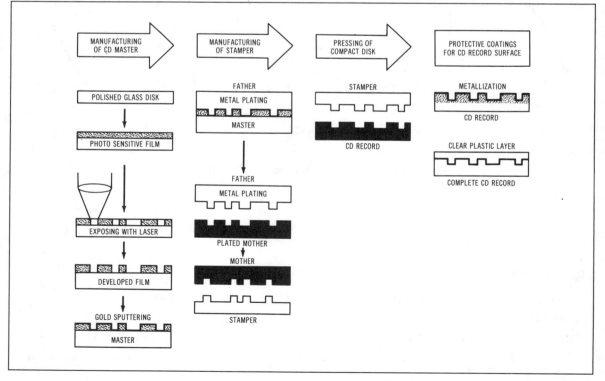

Figure 23-173 Sequence of manufacturing of the CD.

"Digital Audio Discs," *Studio Sound*, July 1979.

W. M. Leach, "Building a Pre-Preamp," *Audio*, February 1978.

J. Roberts, "$70 Decoder for New CX Records," *Popular Electronics*, January 1982.

"Studio Audio Discs," *Studio Sound*, July 1979.

G. W. Tillett, "A Look at Noise-Reduction Systems," *Stereo Guide*, Winter 1982.

H. M. Tremaine, *Audio Cyclopedia*, Indianapolis: Howard W. Sams & Co., Inc., 1969.

CHAPTER **24**

Magnetic Recording and Playback

by Dale Manquen

24.1 INTRODUCTION

The ability to store and recreate audio events has led to fundamental changes in our society. In less than 40 years, magnetic tape recording has risen to a dominant position in the audio industry due to its versatility and ease of use. The quick acceptance of tape as a primary recording medium for radio and music was due to several factors, including improved sound quality, longer playing times, and, perhaps most importantly, the ability to edit by physically cutting and rearranging the original recording without degradation. The continued success of tapes in new applications can be attributed to not only the steady improvements in recording technology, but also the recording format flexibility that permits the optimization of specialized recorders and tapes for specific applications such as critical professional studio applications or economical dictation storage.

All magnetic tape recorders are members of the family of storage devices that utilize moving storage media. (Other members of this family include phonograph disk recorders, motion picture cameras and projectors, optical laser disks for video and audio, and magnetic disk devices for computer data storage.) These storage devices share one very important characteristic—they all are complex electromechanical devices. In addition to electronic circuits that amplify, process, and control the basic signal that is to be recorded, each device also contains numerous mechanical devices ranging from drive motors for turntables and tape drive capstans to focusing actuators for optical lenses. These devices not only move the media past the recording and reproducing transducers but also position the transducers for optimum performance.

Each combination of media and transducers presents a unique set of capabilities and requirements. For example, the cutting head, lacquer master, electroplating, and disk-pressing characteristics of a phonograph record are a set of interrelated phenomena that differ greatly from the recording and playback processes and magnetic characteristics of a tape recorder. Each type of recording device must be optimized to achieve maximum performance within the limitations and features of its own media and of the intended application.

For magnetic tape recording, the dominant features are

- The recording process is instantaneous, requiring no processing.
- The tape can be easily erased and rerecorded.
- The magnetic recording process exhibits Reciprocity, permitting one transducer head to be used for data recording and reproducing.
- The filamentary nature of the tape permits editing by cut-and-splice techniques.

These features are exploited by a recording system consisting of precision mechanical devices to move the tape, sophisticated magnetic heads and tape to record and reproduce the magnetic audio signal, distortion-free audio electronics for recording and reproduction, and intricate logic circuits to provide ease of operation. Since these functions have been implemented in many different ways by various manufacturers, it is not surprising that all tape recorders are not created equal.

The audio engineer must choose an optimum tape recorder and tape that best suits the application. The freedom of choice, however, requires adequate knowledge to weigh the alternatives and properly select the appropriate device. The following discussion is intended to provide the engineer with adequate familiarity to select and use a recorder properly.

Understanding why a recorder *doesn't* work is often more important than understanding proper operation. To assist in these times of panic, the maintenance procedures included herein are general in nature, but they are still very thorough. These sections warrant repeated careful study by anyone who must operate or maintain recording equipment so that problems can be recognized before they develop into critical failures.

24.1.1 Tape Recorder as a Transformer

A magnetic tape recorder can be visualized as a specialized form of audio transformer. In a conventional audio transformer, an electrical signal on the input or primary winding is converted to a magnetic energy in the magnetic core of the transformer. This magnetic energy is immediately reconverted to an electrical signal in the output or secondary winding.

For a tape recorder, the input and output windings consist of the record head and reproduce head. The magnetic core, which couples the windings, is a conveyor belt in the form of the magnetic tape. Unlike the transformer core, which is very loss-free in coupling flux from winding to winding, the recording tape is fraught with numerous losses and imperfections that require correction or minimization.

The following discussion of these shortcomings begins with the problems associated with moving the tape conveyor at constant speed with the tape transport. Next, the effects of the record and reproduce heads will be introduced to bridge the gap between time and distance relationships. Then the conveyor belt of magnetic tape will be examined in detail. Finally the electronic circuits required to move the tape and to record and reproduce the magnetic signals correctly on the tape with a minimum of loss and distortion will be described.

24.1.2 Changes with Time and Space

The performance of a magnetic tape recorder is determined by two types of frequencies. Cyclic variations with respect to time in the input and output electrical signals are examples of "temporal" frequencies measured in hertz or cycles per second. An equivalent set of spatial frequencies in cycles per inch or wavelengths in inches per cycle can also be calculated for a moving piece of recording tape. If the tape is moving at a fixed speed of V inches per second, the cyclic variations that repeat every L inches of length are related to the time frequency f by

$$V = L(f) = \text{frequency}_{\text{temporal}}/\text{frequency}_{\text{spatial}} \qquad (24\text{-}1)$$

(This expression is also used in acoustics to relate frequencies and wavelengths of sound waves.)

The first step toward understanding tape recorders is recognizing the transitions from temporal to spatial and from spatial to temporal frequencies, which occur in the recording and playback processes. The performance of the tape transport and tape are almost exclusively spatial; the magnetic heads are roughly 75% spatial and only 25% temporal. The audio electronics are strictly temporal.

The dominance of spatial characteristics illustrates the importance of maintaining precise control of the tape speed. Since the electrical-to-magnetic-to-electrical transformations that occur during a record/reproduce cycle are controlled by the tape speed, any speed variations will distort the audio signal much as an imperfect mirror creates a distorted image. Perfect speed control, on the other hand, produces a perfect image with no time distortions.

Deliberate speed changes are sometimes introduced for special applications, such as to permit the duplication of tapes at high speed. Commercial tape duplicators operate at from 32 to 100 times normal speed, permitting both sides of a 30-min cassette to be copied less than 10 seconds. Other applications of speed change include rapid dumps of spacecraft data and the stretching of the time scale of a rapid event to permit detailed analysis. (Slow motion video is *not* an example since the speed of the video head across the tape remains constant.)

24.1.3 Analog Versus Digital

Contrary to popular opinion within the audio industry, the technology that is utilized to store audio information in digital form is not new and revolutionary. The recording of digital data that represents an analog audio signal is merely an extreme case of trading increased bandwidth for reduced signal-to-noise ratio. These tradeoffs will be covered as part of the general discussions of performance parameters. The new developments in error detection and correction of this digital data are described in the section 24.3.7.2. (For details of the methods used to convert the incoming analog signal to digital values prior to recording and to restore the analog signal on playback, consult Chapter 25.)

24.2 TAPE TRANSPORTS

The beginnings of modern-day tape transports can be traced to Vlademar Poulsen, the inventor of the magnetic wire recorder. Poulsen's experiments in 1898 consisted of moving an electromagnet along a piece of steel wire to record and reproduce sound. He soon learned, just as every tape recorder operator today learns, that the relative motion between the transducer (the electromagnet) and the storage medium (the wire) must be uniform and repeatable. The world's best tape, electronics, and record/reproduce heads are useless if the recording tape does not move!

Many of Poulson's solutions to this problem, such as sliding the electromagnet down a long, sloping wire attached to the ceiling of his lab, would be quite intolerable in a modern 24-track recording studio. (Imagine ceilings 300 ft high to accommodate a 3-min song or trying to cut and edit 24 wires!) The functions of his transport device, however, were the same as our modern tape recorders, specifically:

1. To drive the tape at a repeatable—and preferably constant—speed over the surface of the transducer heads.
2. To maintain a fixed mechanical alignment of the tape as it crosses the heads.
3. To provide contact pressure between the tape and head by either tensioning the tape or pushing the tape against the head.
4. To provide the necessary auxiliary motions of the tape required for rewind, search, editing, and so on.

The typical degree of precision that is available today in a professional recorder includes a tape speed variation of a few hundredths of a percent, mechanical alignments of less than one-thousandth of an inch and three-thousandths of a degree, and tension variations of a few percent. Even these seemingly small variations create readily observable errors in recordings, leaving opportunity for future improvements.

24.2.1 Tape Metering

Although the basic speed requirement for a tape recorder is repeatability of speed—which would permit fluctuations if these fluctuations were always repeated exactly—the need for interchangeability of tapes between machines and the need to splice random segments of a program together without pitch changes require that all tape machines run at the same speed.

One way to achieve this objective would be to record a speed reference track on the tape. This reference could then be used as a speed control for all subsequent work. Unfortunately, this leads to the paradox, "What controls the tape speed while the reference track is being recorded?" Editing of segments at different speeds would also produce a momentary pitch error since the transport would require a finite amount of time to complete the jump in speed that is required at each splice.

A second and more universal approach is to equip each recorder with a measuring or metering device that will provide absolute speed accuracy. Most designs therefore include a rotating capstan that is driven at constant rotational speed by a motor. The surface of this capstan drives the tape at a constant linear velocity.

The drive system for the capstan can be either an implied (open-loop) or measured (closed-loop) system. Older recorders using the implied technique assume that the drive motor and coupling components such as belts and pulleys are ideal. A constant drive voltage or frequency to the motor should therefore produce a constant tape speed. Unfortunately, mechanical irregularities and motor torque variations introduce errors at the capstan, which are not detected and corrected by this system.

Newer recorders overcome this problem by including a measuring device on the capstan in the form of a high-resolution optical or magnetic tachometer. By comparing the speed sensed by the tachometer to a high-accuracy reference, any variations or errors in speed are immediately detected. The control circuits sense this error and generate corrections in the signal driving the motor to cancel the error. The accuracy of the system is primarily dependent upon the accuracy of the tachometer and the amount of error signal that can be generated by the control circuit.

The block diagram of a typical capstan speed control is shown in Fig. 24-1. Commonly referred to as a phaselock servo, the system is, in essence, a clocked position detector.

The reference voltage generates a nominal command that would drive the motor at the desired speed if no errors or disturbances were present. Under normal conditions, however, an error correction command is subtracted from this nominal value to correct for variations in the external loading due to the tape and in the internal friction and torque of the motor.

The crystal oscillator/counter provides a highly accurate clock reference by dividing the frequency of the crystal oscillator down to a convenient lower frequency. The switching transition of the clock serves as a strobe to sample the position of the tachometer. If the motor is running exactly at the desired speed, each tachometer transition will coincide exactly with a clock transition. The phase comparator compares the tachometer and clock signals to determine which signal arrives first and the amount of timing error between the sources. This error signal is amplified and filtered and then subtracted from the nominal drive voltage to correct the motor speed error.

If the tachometer is accurately mounted, if the tachometer samples occur frequently enough to provide precise sensing, if the control circuit sends the correction signal to the motor quickly so that errors are sensed as they start, and if the motor can respond swiftly to corrections in its control voltage, then the motor will turn at a constant speed. The string of "if's" in the previous sentence is a clue to the complexity of this servo design. The results, however, of a good design are very impressive, with professional recorders being able to maintain mechanically induced speed variations to below 0.05% rms at 15 in./s on a routine basis.

The speed-sensing device need not be attached to the driving capstan for phaselock operation. The tachometer can be mounted on a free-running idler that is driven by the tape, but the extra time delay introduced into the error signal renders the system more difficult to control. This delay usually requires a reduction in the "stiffness" and bandwidth of the servo loop, requiring either an improvement in the inherent errors that are to be corrected by the servo or a decrease in the expected level of performance.

The phaselock servo permits convenient speed control for multiple tape speeds by changing the frequency divider ratio.

A *variable-speed oscillator (VSO)* can also be substituted for the fixed reference to provide infinitely variable speeds. Professional machines typically accept an external frequency of 9600 Hz from accessories for nominal speed. The ease with which external accessories such as film resolvers, television synchronizers, and multiple-machine controllers can be interfaced through the servo variable-speed connector has greatly expanded the use of tape recorders in film and video production and post production.

To achieve constant tape velocity, the tape must maintain intimate contact with the rotating metering capstan. A driven capstan must have enough traction on the tape due to friction to exert a driving force on the tape that is at least equal to the difference in the tape tensions on the

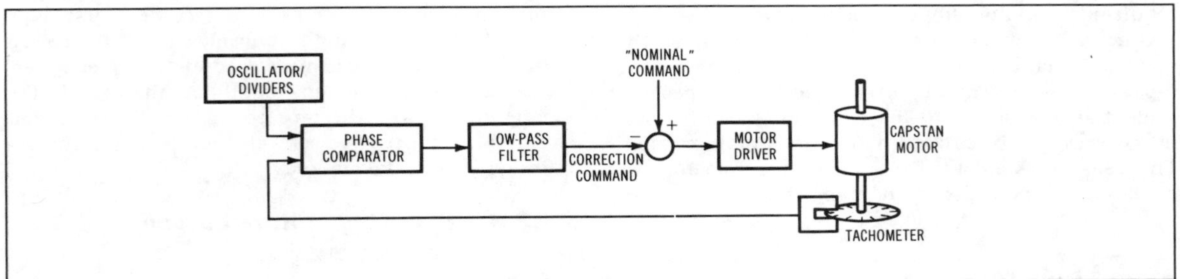

Figure 24-1 Capstan speed control block diagram.

ingoing and outgoing side of the capstan. The conflicting objectives of low tape tension and firm capstan contact usually require various active and passive contact enhancement techniques to achieve adequate drive force.

Active contact devices such as rubber pinch rollers push the tape against the capstan surface to maintain firm contact. Unfortunately, numerous undesirable side effects are also produced, including:

1. Heavy side loads on the capstan that produce bearing wear and can even cause small-diameter capstans to bend or tilt.
2. Speed errors due to the elastic deformation of the rubber roller at the point of contact.
3. Increased variations in speed created by inhomogeneities of the rubber, eccentricities of the roller, and bearing rattle.

In spite of the abundance of pinch-roller-equipped tape transports, the interaction of the driven capstan, tape, and rubber roller is not well understood. Conflict abounds, with some designers advocating pinch rollers that are narrower than the tape and others advocating wide pinch rollers that overhang the tape at the edges to achieve additional contact with the capstan. Indeed, three product development teams at a leading manufacturer once were simultaneously developing similar products with narrow rollers, overhanging rollers, and no pinch rollers. The heated debates between groups added new meaning to the term "bigotry." (All three machines were produced and sold!)

The clamping force of a pinch roller can also be produced by pulling the tape against the capstan with a vacuum. Although computer tape drives frequently use hollow vacuum capstans for this purpose to achieve rapid tape shuttling, the noise and complexity of such systems have stifled their use in recording studios.

Passive contact enhancement methods concentrate on maximizing the traction between the tape and capstan surface. Roughening of the capstan surface by sandblasting or coating the surface with urethane rubber or diamond-impregnated grit yields an improvement in the coefficient of friction. After heavy usage, however, the roughening will be polished away by the abrasive surface of the tape, or the urethane surface will glaze and harden, requiring reconditioning to avoid slippage.

Other passive techniques concentrate on eliminating any loss of contact due to air being trapped between the tape and capstan. This air bearing effect, which becomes evident at tape speeds as low as 30 in./s, can be minimized by cutting bleed slots in the surface of the capstan. These slots are similar to the tread on an automobile tire, providing escape paths for the trapped air.

24.2.2 Flutter

Regardless of the passive and/or active contact enhancements, servo design, and workmanship standards employed in a given transport, some residual amount of tape speed variation will still be present. The long-term or fixed component of this speed error is denoted as speed accuracy, timing accuracy, or drift. The small, rapid changes in instantaneous speed are referred to as flutter.

Flutter is further broken down into three frequency bands, based upon the perception of a human listener. Speed variations at rates up to a few cycles per second are termed *wow*, with the listener perceiving a cyclic pitch variation in music. The most common source of wow is eccentric rotating parts. Faster flutter rates due to motor torque pulsations and rattling bearings add a fluttering sound to the music. As the flutter rate increases beyond a few hundred hertz, the listener no longer distinguishes the flutter components from the music. Instead, the listener notices a loss of crispness and clarity, with high frequencies created by percussion, strings, and brass sounding dull or mushy. These high-frequency, scrape flutter components are generated as the surface of the tape scrapes over stationary elements such as fixed guides and heads, creating vibrations in the tape similar to the plucking of a stringed instrument.

Historically, wow and mechanical flutter have received much more attention than scrape flutter. In fact, tape recorders were used for music recording for nearly 20 years before the first transport with low scrape flutter content was introduced. Even today designers of both transports and tapes treat scrape flutter more as an afterthought than as a primary problem, failing to quote any specifications for scrape flutter performance. Unfortunately for the user, the subjective evaluation of the clarity of a recording is very dependent upon the content in all three flutter bands.

24.2.3 Tape Tensioning

Magnetic recording tape, like all elastic media, must be stretched slightly to produce tension within the tape. For normal recording applications, the tape is stretched approximately 0.1% to achieve a typical tension of 4 oz per ¼ in. of tape width. To create permanent deformation or stretching of the tape, the yield stress point, which is 10 to 30 times greater than this running tension, must be reached.

Three separate and often conflicting functions are performed by tape tension on a tape recorder. First, tape tension holds the moving tape firmly against the record and playback heads to achieve good high-frequency performance. Second, the tension stiffens the tape on the tape guides so that the tape position will remain constant. Third, the tension controls the stacking of the layers of tape on the takeup reel.

24.2.3.1 Spooling Motor-Derived Tensioning

The present-day, top-of-the-line professional recorders with tension servos on the spooling motors use only one tension, which is constant throughout the tape path.

Although this technique avoids speed variations since the tape drive and metering devices see no tension differentials, the guides, heads, and spooling devices are all forced to operate at the same tension. Depending upon the tradeoffs chosen in a given design, this may lead to either nonoptimal winding tension or poor tape-to-head contact.

The tape tension is altered to some degree by every component that comes into contact with the tape. One type of these tension modifiers that is usually more parasitic than deliberate in nature is the tension generated by friction as the tape slides over any stationary guide or head surface. (The bearing friction and viscous drag of rotating guides is usually negligible.) The relative contribution of friction tension to the total tape tension ranges from a low of 5% for transports with only rotating guides to over 50% for transports with numerous fixed guides and/or large tape deflection angles around fixed guides.

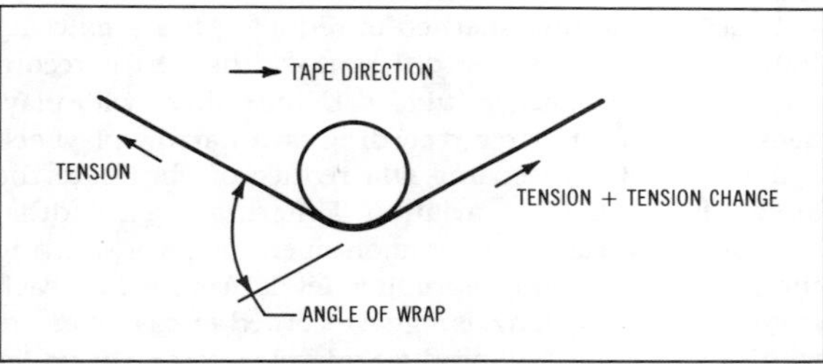

Figure 24-2 Tension increase due to guide friction.

The amount of drag tension generated by a cylindrical post is shown in Fig. 24-2 and given by the expression:

$$\text{tension change} = \text{tape tension (angle of wrap)} \times (\text{coefficient of friction}) \quad (24\text{-}2)$$

Note that although the diameter of the guide does not appear in the tension expression, the pressure exerted by the guide against the tape surface increases as the diameter increases. This increased pressure makes small guides wear faster and accumulate dirt more quickly. Since a speck of dirt trapped on the surface of a small guide would also be more prone to scratch the tape surface, small-radius fixed guides must be kept very clean. (My experience indicates that any stationary guides less than ½ in. in diameter require frequent cleaning.)

The coefficient of friction for different tape types varies greatly. On transports with either high amounts of drag tension or very little capstan contact enhancement, a change of tape type may necessitate a readjustment of the tape tension (Fig. 24-2), to achieve optimum performance and avoid tape slippage.

24.2.3.2 Capstan-Derived Tensioning

To achieve more flexibility, the tape path can be broken into segments of differing tape tensions. One common approach is to use a driven capstan and pinch roller as an isolation device, with the capstan motor supplying the power needed to overcome the tension differential across the capstan. This isolation can then be used, for example, to achieve low head tension and high spooling tension.

Rather than rely upon the spooling or drag tensions to control tape tension at the head, two driven capstans can be used to isolate both the incoming and outgoing tape paths from the heads. The tension in the tape at the heads can be produced by a controlled stretching of the elastic tape between the two capstans by using a slightly faster surface velocity on the outgoing capstan than on the incoming capstan. If the capstans are free of flutter, this tight- or closed-loop design will yield low mechanical flutter and wow since the heads are isolated from spooling disturbances and low-scrape flutter because only a short span of tape is free to vibrate at the heads.

The added complexity of two capstan and pinch roller assemblies makes the isolated loop more expensive to manufacture, but several clever designs have been developed to minimize the cost differential. One design uses a single motor to drive two identical capstans with a single rubber belt. Stretching the drive belt causes the capstans to turn at slightly different speeds. A similar design using a stiff plastic belt and slightly different capstan or drive pulley diameters also achieves the required speed differential.

Yet another design achieves the effect of two capstan diameters by using a single capstan with multiple alternating rings of large and small diameters. The step between rings is so small, on the order of 0.1%, that specially contoured pinch rollers can press the tape against the smaller-diameter rings on the incoming side and against the larger-diameter rings on the outgoing side of the capstan.

Unlike recorders that derive tape tension by controlling torque on the spooling motors, the tension of the closed-loop drives varies slightly with tape thickness. Since the *change* in tape length is always constant, lower tensions are generated in thin tapes that stretch more easily. This decrease in tension is generally unnoticed since the thinner tape conforms more readily to the face of the heads, offsetting any pressure reduction.

The advent of economical integrated circuits has led to a shift in emphasis from the mechanically complex tight-loop drives toward active tension servo controls in which the tape tension is directly sensed by a spring-loaded surface in contact with the tape. A position sensor, which senses the tension-induced displacement of the sensing surface, provides an electrical signal proportional to tension that can be used to control the spooling motor drive voltage.

An alternative to tension *sensing* is to determine actively the diameter of the tape pack on each reel and then set the motor voltage to the value that was known beforehand to give the desired tension for that diameter. By sensing the rotational velocities of the spooling motors with tachometers attached to the spooling motors shafts and comparing these values with a signal from the capstan servo, which is proportional to tape velocity, the diameter of the tape packs on the reels can be calculated.

The desired motor voltage is determined by

$$\text{motor voltage} = \text{tension adjustment factor} \times (\text{tape speed/rotational rate}) \quad (24\text{-}3)$$

The multiplication is easily implemented by a potentiometer; the division requires an analog multiplier/divider integrated circuit.

Although the calculated method cannot detect tension abnormalities due to bent reels, motor problems, or changes in friction; during normal operation, tension is held very constant over a wide range of tape speeds and pack diameters.

Regardless of the method employed to achieve constant tension, the results are always worthwhile. For nearly 25 years the recording industry was forced to struggle with recorders that had a doubling of tape tension from beginning to end of reel, with attendant speed variations, splicing problems, and tape guiding variations. Today these problems need no longer be endured.

24.2.4 Tape Guiding

For proper recording and playback of a magnetic recording to occur, the tape must move over the heads in a very precise path. This tape path should be the natural path that the tape would follow without any external vertical constraints. The purpose of the guiding system is only to protect the tape and to overcome the slight reel-to-reel variations in tape such as twists and bends due to tape-manufacturing tolerances, but not to force the tape to perform any unnatural acts. Any such use of brute force will lead to tape damage, excessive guide wear, and/or instabilities and jumping of the tape.

The tape guiding system deals with three aspects of the tape motion—height, azimuth, and zenith, with primary concern for the motion of the tape at the heads. Each aspect is in turn composed of two components—fixed errors due to misadjustment and dynamic errors due to tolerances and tape variations.

24.2.4.1 Tape Height

Height must be controlled so that the recorded tracks on the tape will pass directly over the pickup areas of the head. The required degree of height accuracy increases as the tracks become narrower. Table 24-1 shows signal loss due to height errors for several popular tape formats.

For a tape guide to position the tape accurately, the tape must fit snugly into the guide, but not squeeze the tape edges. The typical manufacturing tolerances of 2 to 4 mils on tape width and 1 to 3 mils on tape guide width result in a loose fit for many rolls of tape.

Sources of height error also include fixed errors in head and guide height and core placement tolerances within the heads. A good alignment should contain no more than 1 mil combined error for the head and guides, but this degree of accuracy requires the use of optical measurement devices that are not commonly available in a recording studio. Typical maintenance shop practices will yield typical errors in the range of 2 to 3 mils. When this alignment error is added to a typical core placement error of 1 mil and a tape guide clearance error of 2 mils, the signal loss or variation can easily exceed 1 dB on a 24-track recorder.

A relatively simple method of reducing the sensitivity to height errors is to use different widths for the record and reproduce head core widths. Using either a wide playback head on a narrow recording or a narrow playback head on a wide recording will reduce or eliminate the losses due to height variation. Differing track widths, however, give rise to a common operator error. Setting the normal and sync reproduce levels from a full-track alignment tape, which has signal recorded across the entire width of the tape, will produce a level error on the wider of the two heads. The amount of error, which depends upon the ratio of the core widths of the two heads, must be subtracted from the actual meter reading of the wider core to determine the true flux level. For example, a recorder with 37-mil record cores and 43-mil reproduce cores would be set to read 0 vu in sync playback and + 1.3 vu in normal playback from a full-track alignment tape.

24.2.4.2 Head Azimuth

Not only must the tape pass across the head be at the correct height, but the recorded signal on the tape must be parallel to the pickup gap in the reproduce head. Any angular error is referred to as azimuth error. Table 24-2 gives the amount of signal loss due to azimuth error for a 15-kHz signal at 15 in./s (a l-mil wavelength).

Table 24-1. Loss Due to Height Error

Loss		Height Errors for Various Trackwidths			
dB Loss	**%**	**70 mil**	**43 mil**	**37 mil**	**21 mil**
0.1	1.16	0.81	0.50	0.43	0.24
0.3	3.51	2.46	1.51	1.30	0.74
0.5	5.93	4.15	2.55	2.19	1.25
1.0	12.20	8.54	5.25	4.51	2.56

70 mil—4 track 1/2 in., 8 track 1 in., 16 track 2 in.
43 mil—24 track 2 in. (on some systems)
37 mil—4 track 1/4 in., 24 track 2 in.
21 mil—stereo cassette, 8 track 1/4 in.

Table 24-2 Azimuth Loss at 15 kHz, 15 in/s (1-mil wavelength)

	Azimuth Error (minutes)			
dB Loss	250 mil	70 mil	37 mil	21 mil
0.5	2.55	9.1	17.3	30.4
1.0	3.6	12.9	24.3	42.8
3.0	(6.1)	21.7	41.1	72.4
6.0	8.3	27.3	56.0	98.6

Loss = 20 log {sin [($\pi\omega \times \tan\alpha$) / λ]}/[($\pi\omega \times \tan\alpha$) / λ]

For a typical professional recorder with guides spaced 6 in. apart, the worst case combination of guide and tape sizes could produce a maximum dynamic guiding error of ±5 mils at each guide, yielding an azimuth error of ±0.1° or ±6 min. This error would generate a signal fluctuation of 3 dB for a 250-mil track width as indicated by the circled entry in Table 24-2. Overlapping heads or tracks offer no azimuth loss improvement.

For multitrack recorders, the time and phase relationship between audio channels that are recorded on separate tracks may be more critical than the level of short-wavelength signals. Azimuth errors contribute to differential timing errors between tracks, since the azimuth tilting causes one track to be reproduced slightly later than the other. As the distance between tracks becomes large, such as for 1- and 2-in. formats, the timing error becomes critical. A typical method to measure this timing error is to record the same high-frequency signal on two tracks, and then measure the phase difference between tracks. Table 24-3 shows the amount of worst-case phase difference and timing difference at a 1-mil wavelength introduced by a 0.5-dB head azimuth error for the outer pair of tracks.

Table 24-3. Errors Due to 0.5-dB Azimuth Error (1-mil wavelength)

Format	Phase Error	Timing Error
1/4-in. stereo	151°	0.28 ms
1-in. 8 track	867° (2.4 rotations)	0.16 ms
2-in. 24 track	3500° (9.7 rotations)	0.65 ms

The magnitude of both the height loss and the azimuth loss could be greatly reduced if the widths of the tape guides and tape matched perfectly. One method to achieve this objective is to use adapting guides with spring-loaded movable flanges so that the guide adjusts itself to the tape width.

A similar effect can be achieved with fixed-flange guides if a curvature is deliberately introduced into the tape path. Fig. 24-3 illustrates two possible methods to achieve this curvature. Typically, an offset of less than 5 mils is adequate to overcome the worst-case combination of clearance between the tape and guides and the maximum amount of natural bowing in the tape due to slitting and subsequent handling distortions.

Although the dynamic guiding variations are greatly reduced by forcing the tape to maintain a distorted tape path, the increased force applied to the edges of the tape produces new problems. Not only do both the guides and the edges of the tape experience higher wear rates, but scrape flutter is also increased dramatically. The edges of a tape are very rough due to the shearing action used in the tape-slitting process. When these rough edges slide firmly against the distorting guide flange, tape vibrations are excited, producing scrape flutter. The author has noted increases in scrape flutter of over 50% on one transport design as the center guide was brought into contact with the edge of the tape to produce curvature.

24.2.4.3 Tape Guides

Tape guides come in many shapes, sizes, and basic types, as shown in Fig. 24-4. Each guide contains flanges that press against the edges of the tape to steer it. In all cases except the edge-only guide, the tape wraps around the guide to generate stiffness so that the steering force exerted by the flange can move the entire width of the tape and not just buckle the edge. Typically, at least 10° of wrap is required for adequate stiffness.

Rotating guides are generally less effective than stationary guides. Since the tape is in firm contact with the spinning surface of a rotating guide, rather than in sliding contact as with the stationary guide, the force required to slide the tape up or down is determined by the tape tension and the coefficient of *static friction*. The tension component is identical for the stationary guide, but in this case the coefficient of *sliding friction*, which is typically half the static value, is used.

Although both stationary and rotating guides are commonly used in tape transports, rotating guides are slightly more prone to damage the edge of the tape. Guides with large rotating flanges can produce ruffles on the edge of the tape if the tape edge contacts the outer radius of the moving flange. Most guide designs taper the flange to minimize this hazard, but a small flat area at the bottom

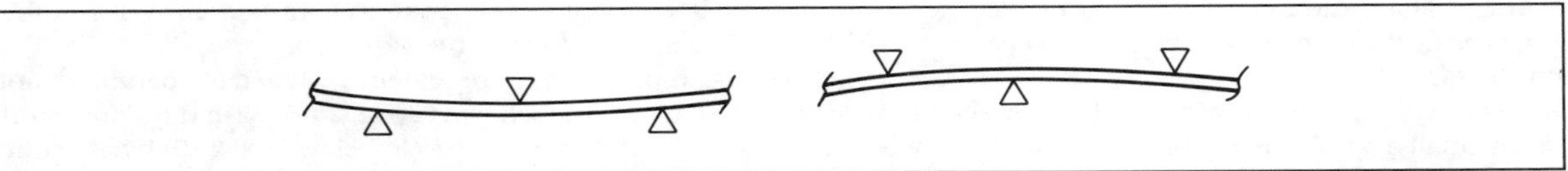

Figure 24-3 Deliberate tape curvature to reduce guiding errors.

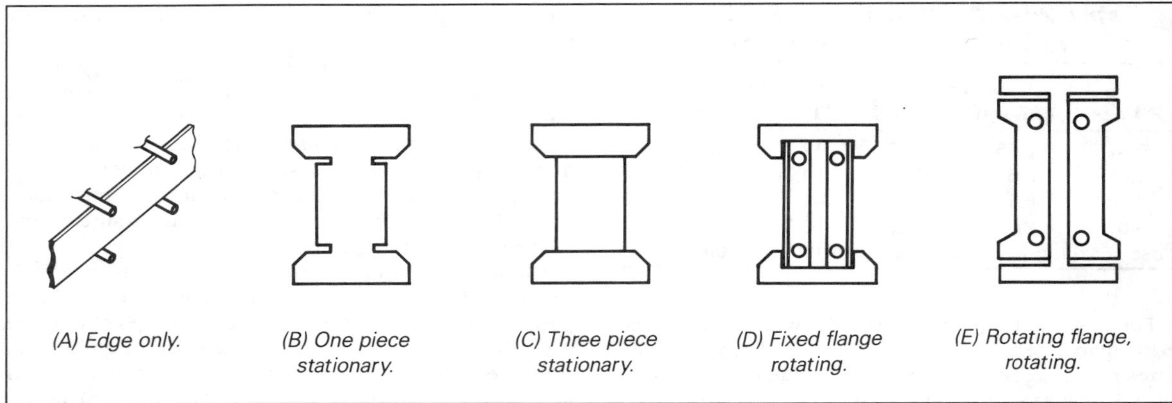

Figure 24-4 Five styles of tape guides.

of the taper is still required if the guide is used for precise tape positioning.

The edge-only guide is very limited in effectiveness since any appreciable force on the edge of the tape may cause the tape to twist rather than move up or down.

24.3 MAGNETIC HEADS

Although magnetic tape is covered in detail in a later section, the following discussion of magnetic heads requires a few very simple assumptions regarding the composition and dimensions of the magnetic tape. First, assume that the magnetic coating consists of microscopic particles of magnetic materials that have been bonded to one surface of a thin plastic backing or substrate. Second, each magnetic particle is assumed to function as a small independent magnet, allowing patterns of varying magnetic polarity and intensity to be stored along the tape. Last, the thickness of the magnetic coating will be assumed to be 0.6 mil.

24.3.1 Spatial Characteristics

24.3.1.1 Gap Length Loss

Each of the tiny magnetic particles on the surface of the tape produces a magnetic force or flux in the space surrounding the particle. This invisible magnetic effect, called a *magnetic field*, will interact with other nearby magnetic particles. To measure the strength of this field, a flux concentrator in the form of a reproduce head is scanned along the tape. The resulting electrical output from the head is dependent upon the flux pattern recorded on the tape.

To read changes accurately in flux patterns that may be as small as 100 millionths of an inch in wavelength, the reproduce head must be able to collect flux selectively from a very small span of tape. To achieve this fine resolution, a small gap can be created in a ring of magnetic material, as shown in Fig. 24-5A.

The length of the gap, denoted as L in the figure, ranges from two ten-thousandths of an inch (2×10^{-4} in.) for studio mastering recorders down to less than 50-millionths of an inch (5×10^{-6} in.)—the wavelength of red light—for cassette and high-density digital recorders. Since no slicing technique is available to cut accurate gaps that narrow, the core is usually fabricated as two pieces that are fastened together with a shim spacer of the desired dimension inserted in the gap. Fig. 24-5B shows a typical studio head drawn full size, with the critical gap area and adjacent tape magnified in Fig. 24-5C.

The operation of the gap, which serves as a sensing aperture, can be analyzed in terms of a flux pickup focused at the surface of the tape. The amount of flux picked up by the core, and thus made available to generate an output voltage in the winding, is determined by the *net* magnetic flux at the gap area. If the tape segment at the gap consists of a strong magnetization of only one polarity, the flux in the core will be maximized. If, on the other hand, the segment contains two strong portions of opposite polarity that cancel each other, the net flux in the core will be zero.

The efficiency of the gap due to this averaging effect is illustrated in Fig. 24-6. The output of the head declines—slowly at first, and then quite rapidly—to zero as the wavelength decreases to the length of the gap. When the gap length is longer than the wavelength, an output of opposite polarity will appear. When the wavelength drops to half the gap length, another null will occur. This pattern is repeated over and over, with nulls occurring at each wavelength that produces an odd or even number of complete cycles in the gap.

Audio recorders are seldom designed to operate beyond the dashed lines shown in Fig. 24-6. With this constraint, gap length loss can be held below 1 or 2 dB by choosing an appropriate gap length for a given application and

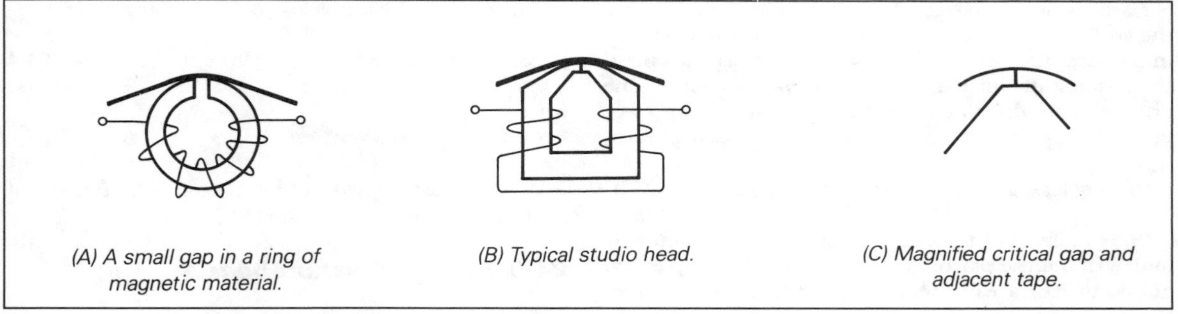
(A) A small gap in a ring of magnetic material.
(B) Typical studio head.
(C) Magnified critical gap and adjacent tape.

Figure 24-5 Three types of magnetic heads.

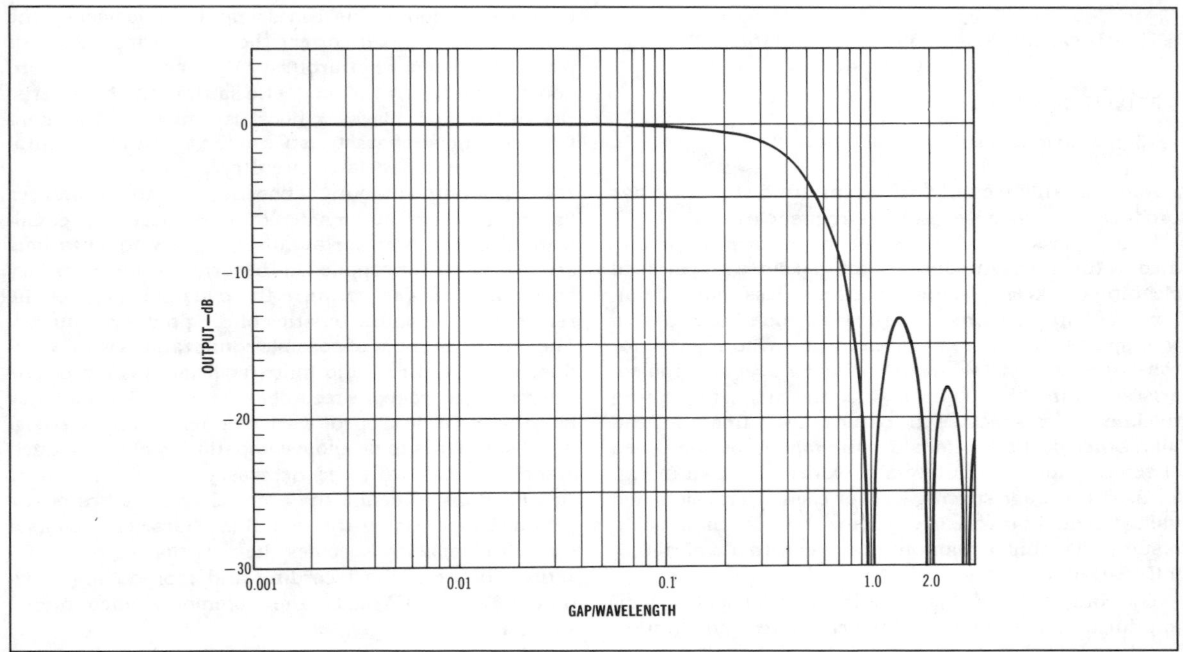

Figure 24-6 Loss due to ratio ot gap length to wavelength.

minimum wavelength. Use of an excessively narrow gap will cause an additional loss in overall head sensitivity due to shunted flux that jumps the gap rather than traveling through the core, as shown in Fig. 24-7.

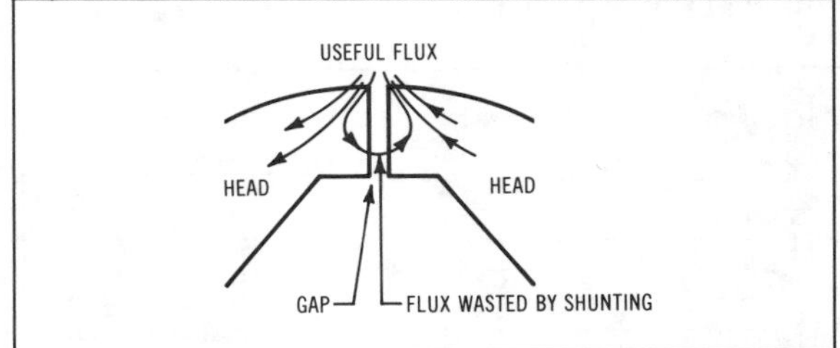

Figure 24-7 Gap shunting loss.

24.3.1.2 Spacing Loss

Gap length loss and shunting loss are not the major determiners of the performance of an audio recorder. The most critical parameter is the relative thickness of the magnetic coating on the tape. The ratio of tape thickness to the shortest wavelength to be recorded has a profound effect upon the frequency response, maximum output, noise, and signal-level fluctuations. The cause is quite simple—the reproduce gap is *nearsighted*! The magnetic particles at the surface of the tape are very tightly coupled to the core of the head, producing a maximum amount of playback flux in the core. Particles that are buried below the surface of the tape, however, produce a weaker flux in the core. The amount of flux that is lost depends upon the spacing distance and the wavelength—just as fine print is more difficult to read at a distance than large print. An approximate expression for this spacing loss is

$$\text{spacing loss}_{dB} = 55\ (\text{distance/wavelength}) \qquad (24\text{-}4)$$

One example of the use of this spacing loss formula is to determine the playback signal loss due to a piece of dirt on the surface of a reproduce head. Assuming a typical recording studio tape speed of 15 in./s, a dirt speck only one ten-thousandth of an inch high will produce losses at the following frequencies of

$$\text{150-Hz spacing loss} = 55 \times [0.0001/(15/150)] = 0.055\ \text{dB}$$

$$\text{1500-Hz spacing loss} = 0.55\ \text{dB}$$

$$\text{15-kHz spacing loss} = 5.5\ \text{dB}$$

Note that this seemingly insignificant dirt particle has produced a serious loss in high frequencies.

Spacing loss due to dirt is not the major problem created by the nearsightedness of the gap since proper head cleaning will keep spacing distances to less than 10-millionths of an inch, producing virtually no error at studio tape speeds. (The problem is eight times more severe for cassette speeds of 1⅞ in./s.) The major spacing problem arises within the tape itself since the magnetic coating thickness spaces most of the particles away from the head *with other particles*. Consider the tape to be composed of several independent layers of oxide, as shown in Fig. 24-8. The average spacing loss for each layer, calculated using the midpoint of each layer to determine the spacing distance, is tabulated for our example with a typical 0.6-mil coating thickness.

The contributions of layers 2 through 6 fall off so rapidly due to spacing loss that their *combined* contribution is only equal to layer 1 by itself at this wavelength. Indeed, shaving off layer 6, which constitutes 17% of the coating thickness, would produce a loss of only 2% or 0.18 dB is output at this wavelength.

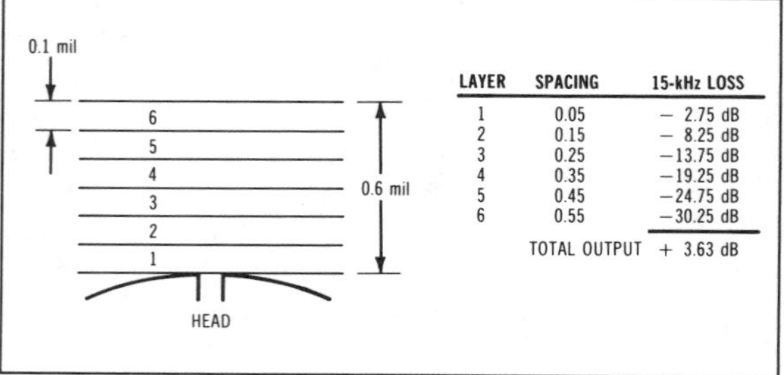

Figure 24-8 Tape thickness loss.

This coating thickness loss can be expressed as

$$\text{coating thickness loss (dB)} = 20 \log[x/1 - \epsilon^{-x}] \qquad (24\text{-}4)$$

where,
x is 2π thickness/wavelength

This expression yields a typical drop of 6 dB/octave of *spatial frequency*, as shown is Fig. 24-9.

24.3.1.3 Equalization Boosts

This thickness loss of Fig. 24-9, which is the dominant loss of a tape recorder, must be corrected by applying compensating boosts in either the record or reproduce circuitry. Although this loss is a playback deficiency, the choice of whether to correct the loss during record or playback is somewhat arbitrary. The amount of record boost is limited by the magnetic saturation characteristics of the tape; playback boost is limited by the high-frequency noise characteristics of the tape and the reproduce head and associated circuitry.

The minimum amount of boosting required to achieve flat response can be considered to be a necessary equalization. In addition, certain discretionary equalizations are also sometimes applied in the form of complementary boosts and cuts to optimize the dynamic range of the recorder to the characteristics of the program material. The infinite number of possible equalizations would produce chaos in the audio industry if tapes could not be interchanged from one recorder to another. The industry has therefore developed a set of internationally recognized standards to promote compatibility of tapes. Each standard deals with the necessary and discretionary equalizations to define the exact characteristics of the recorded tape. Using the tape flux characteristics as a standard implicitly specifies the partitioning of equalizations between the recording and reproducing functions. Table 24-4 lists the commonly encountered standards.

Unlike the absolute nature of the reproduce characteristics, the record characteristics of the recorder must have enough flexibility to accommodate a number of different tape sensitivities and frequency characteristics. Once the reproduce section has been calibrated to the standard with a standard alignment tape, all further adjustments are to produce a recorded tape on the machine that accurately matches the standard tape.

The amount of thickness loss can always be reduced by utilizing thinner coatings, but any decrease in thickness also causes an equal drop in low- and mid-frequency output and signal-to-noise ratio. To preserve the existing standards, the tendency has been to adjust the coating thickness of new tapes to emulate the high-frequency losses of the older tape types while trying to achieve maximum low-frequency output. This somewhat self-defeating strategy has been overcome in recent thin-coat high-energy tapes that retain the low-frequency output

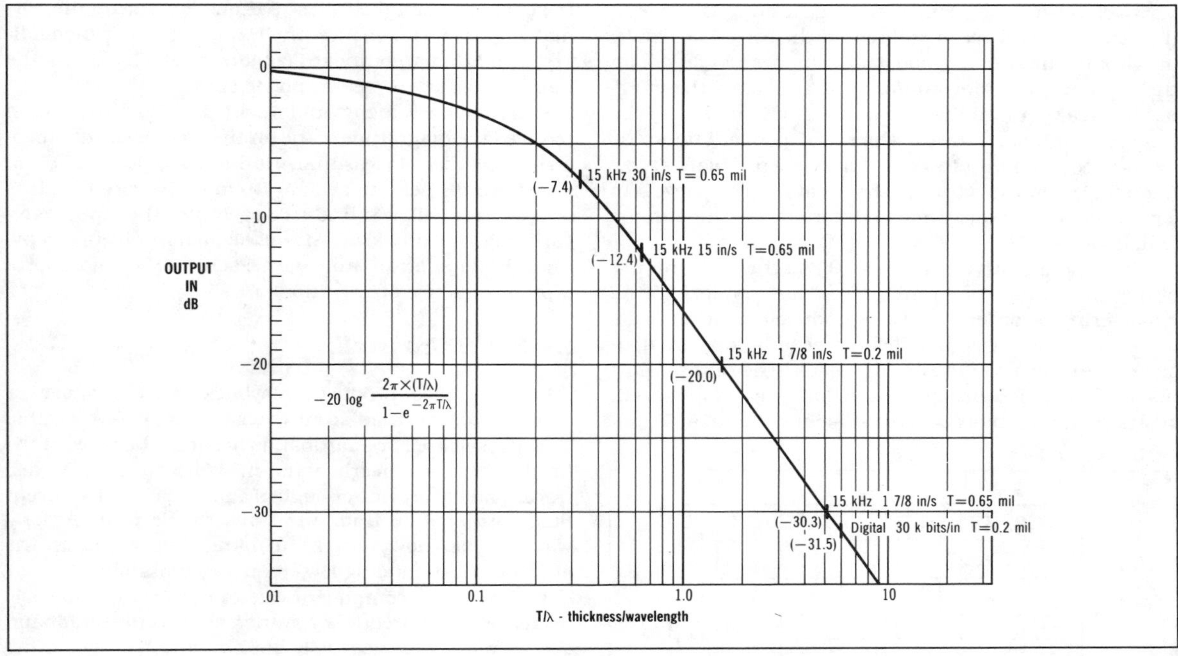

Figure 24-9 Loss due to ratio of coating thickness to wavelength.

Table 24-4. Common Tape Record-Playback Equalization Standards

Standard	Tape	Rollover Frequencies at Various Speeds, in./s 1 7/8	3 3/4	7 1/2	15	30
IEC	Fe_2O_3	100/1326	50/1768	0/2274	0/4547	0/9095
	Metal	100/2274				
NAB		50/1768	50/1768	50/3180	50/3180	0/9095

capability of older tapes, but utilize new equalization curves optimized for the new tape thickness.

24.3.1.4 Fringing

Spacing loss is evident not only at high frequencies, but it also shows up at very long wavelengths. For the long wavelength cases, however, the spacing is sideways rather than vertical. Flux that is recorded off to the sides or fringes of the area normally scanned by the reproduce head core will begin to be sensed if the wavelength becomes longer than the separation distance. At studio operating speeds of 15 and 30 in./s, for which low-frequency wavelengths reach 1/2 and 1 in., this fringing leakage becomes very evident. For example, for the case of an oversized record track mentioned in 24.2.4 section, the signal level may rise by the ratio of the track width to the core width. A typical 24-track format on 2-in. tape would encounter a 1.3-dB rise at frequencies below 500 Hz for record and reproduce cores of 43 and 37 mils.

A similar case arises when alignment tapes made with a single full-width record head are utilized for level and response checks. The sideways fringing will produce significant level and response errors. The actual amounts of error depend upon both the track format and the playback head design. Some alignment tape manufacturers roll off the low frequencies in an attempt to offset the rise in a nominal head, but the amount of this fringing compensation is not absolutely correct for all head designs.

One additional pitfall to be avoided is the fringing differences between center tracks and edge tracks. Since the edge cores run very near the physical edge of the tape, these cores sense only one-half the amount of fringing flux sensed by the inner cores. During a frequency check from a full-width alignment tape, the two edge tracks should therefore be slightly lower in output at the low frequencies than the remainder of the tracks.

24.3.1.5 Contour Effect

At very low frequencies, the wavelength of the recorded signal may become as long as the magnetic core of the playback head. These long wavelengths enter the core at the gap and at the sides and rear of the core. The resulting flux in the core will consist of the desired flux from the gap plus additions and/or subtractions of the fringing flux leaking into the core at the sides and back. The voltage output of the head, which is dependent upon the net flux coupled into the windings, will undulate at low frequencies as the wavelengths create varying levels of constructive and destructive interference due to the fringing flux.

The response curve in Fig. 24-10 illustrates the nature of the undulations or "head bumps" for a typical 15-in./s mastering recorder using a reproduce head that has a 0.5-in. core face. Two well-defined head bumps are usually evident for such mastering heads. The bumps shift up an octave in frequency for each doubling of tape speed, creating an even more severe problem at 30 in./s.

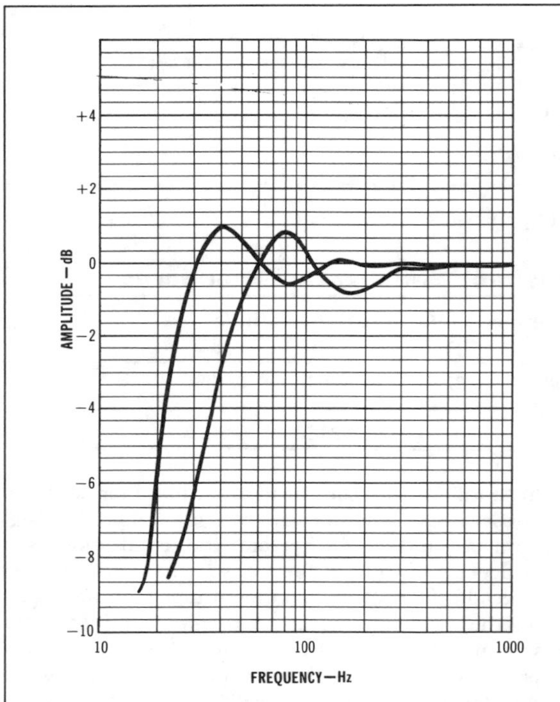

Figure 24-10 Contour effect.
(Courtesy of Sony Corporation of America)

Heads with either very small cores or only a small window in the head shielding at the gap area can produce numerous ripples in the low-frequency response. Such heads should be avoided unless the tape speed is slow enough to avoid serious problems within the normal band of audio frequencies.

The exact shape of the head bumps is determined by the size and shape of the reproduce core, surrounding shielding material, and angle of wrap of the tape. Since the user cannot adjust these parameters during the normal alignment procedure, the bumps can only be modified by adding an outboard equalizer, which cancels the bumps with an inverse response curve.

Recent improvements in the control of head bumps has reduced the magnitude of the bumps in present-day mastering recorders to less than 1 dB peak-to-peak at 15 in./s and 1.5 dB peak-to-peak at 30 in./s. Beware that this level of error will be introduced each time the tape is rerecorded during mixdown and subsequent protection copying. The total error can easily reach 5 dB or more for a typical sequence of operations.

24.3.1.6 Crosstalk

Fringing also produces playback signal leakage or crosstalk between adjacent tracks at long wavelengths. The unused area or guardbands between the cores of the head, which are nearly equal in width to the recorded track, usually provide enough of a physical gap to prevent flux from spilling from one track to the next. At long wavelengths, however, the fringing flux will jump the guardband, producing low-frequency crosstalk.

The crosstalk component due to fringing will initially decrease as the frequency is increased, but at midband the decrease will eventually bottom out. The remaining residual level of crosstalk is not due to fringing, but rather it is a direct transformerlike coupling of leakage flux between the adjacent cores in either the record or reproduce head. A layer of magnetic shielding material is typically placed between the cores of the head as a crosstalk shield to reduce this flux leakage.

The presence of transformer crosstalk is normally only a minor concern in a reproduce head. However, if adjacent cores are simultaneously being used to record and reproduce signals, as when a core of the record head is used to reproduce previously recorded material to feed studio headphones for overdubbing, the crosstalk may rise to intolerable levels. Although the *ratio* of flux leakage remains constant, the greatly increased flux *level* in the recording core that is required to align the tape particles during recording produces a higher crosstalk output level. A recorder with a crosstalk ratio of −50 dB in playback may give a crosstalk of only −20 dB or worse during overdubbing.

This problem is further increased by the lack of any wavelength-related losses in the transformer crosstalk phenomenon. Thus, all the high-frequency boosts in playback sensitivity for wavelength compensation due to thickness and gap length loss are added to the basic signal to produce a crosstalk signal at high frequencies that may actually exceed the signal level being recorded. This uncontrollable signal, which is being fed to the recording musicians via headphones, may confuse the artists and degrade their performance.

Another situation in which excessive crosstalk during overdubbing is detrimental is during an attempt to rerecord one or several tracks onto an unused track to make space for new overdubs. In this case, excessive crosstalk can produce feedback oscillations that make copying difficult or impossible.

The amount of overdub crosstalk is primarily a function of the tape speed and head design. Unfortunately, the design constraints are sometimes conflicting. For example, some of the newer multiple-winding recording heads (see section 24.3.2), which are intended to individually optimize the record and overdub functions, can suffer from increased crosstalk. As with all aspects of the recorder, the design engineer must choose a set of compromises that fit a particular intended application.

24.3.2 Temporal Characteristics

24.3.2.1 Inductive Rise

Up to this point, most of the losses and response anomalies have been governed by the wavelength performance of the interface between the tape and the head. An additional set of temporal characteristics due to the internal frequency-dependent operation of the head must also be considered.

The most striking characteristic in the frequency response of a conventional coil-and-core playback head is a continuous 6-dB/octave rise in output voltage with rising frequency. The core and winding of the head form an inductor in which the ouput voltage is proportional to the rate of change of the flux in the core. In terms of the core flux and number of turns in the winding N, this voltage is expressed as

$$\text{head output voltage} = \text{number of turns (change in flux/time interval)} = N(\Delta\phi/\Delta t) \qquad (24\text{-}5)$$

The symbol for Greek delta Δ is used to represent a small change in a quantity. For example, a leak in a water tank can be represented as

$$\begin{aligned}\text{leakage rate} &= (\Delta\text{water}/\Delta\text{time})\\ &= (10\ \text{gal}/5\ \text{min})\\ &= 2\ \text{gal/min}\end{aligned}$$

Any ratio of the form $\Delta x/\Delta t$ is called a differential with respect to time, and the device creating this rate of change is called a *differentiator.*

If a sine-wave signal is used for testing the output voltage of a head, the voltage expression can be further simplified to

$$\text{head output voltage}_{max} = 2N\pi\ \text{frequency}\ (\text{flux}_{max}) \qquad (24\text{-}6)$$

This output voltage can be increased by adding more turns to the coil, increasing the frequency, or using a stronger input flux. In the case of the reproduce head, the number of turns is fixed when the head is constructed. The maximum flux is determined by the composition of the tape and the wavelength performance of the head.

24.3.2.2 Hysteresis Loss

The constantly changing magnetic flux in the core of the reproduce head gives rise to losses within the core of the head. One source of these losses is the amount of energy that is required to change the magnetization state of the core material. Every time the flux in the core reverses polarity, a small amount of energy is lost in overcoming the magnetic memory or hysteresis of the core material. The hysteresis power loss increases with both increasing flux magnitude and frequency.

24.3.2.3 Eddy Current Loss

The changing core flux generates a voltage not only in the winding of the head, but also within the core itself. If the core is metallic, this voltage will cause a current to flow within the core, as shown in Fig. 24-11. The core currents, referred to as "eddy currents" because of their similarity to swirling eddies in a stream of water, dissipate energy that should be going to the reproduce signal.

The amount of power (P) dissipated in the eddy currents is given by the general power formula of

$$\begin{aligned}P &= V^2/R\\ &= I^2R\end{aligned} \qquad (24\text{-}7)$$

The previous discussion on the inductive rise of voltage with increasing frequency in the reproduce head also applies to these eddy components, producing a rapid rise in eddy current power loss.

The eddy currents of the solid core of Fig. 24-11A rise to an unacceptable level even before the upper limits of the audio band are reached. Fortunately, this drastic loss can be decreased by dividing the core into many thin insulated layers or laminations, as shown in Fig. 24-11B. For M laminations, each lamination would generate only $1/M$ of the core voltage and $1/M^2$ of the loss power produced by a solid core. The core resistance for each lamination drops only slightly since the width of the lamination remains unchanged. The net improvement for M laminations of $M\text{-}1/M^2$ yields a $1/M$ reduction in the eddy current power loss. (Professional audio heads, which are typically constructed with laminations 2 mils thick, will contain 20 to 120 laminations per track, depending upon the track width.) Further improvements can be achieved by reducing the core size and using high-resistivity core materials such as ferrites.

24.3.3 Combined Characteristics

Fig. 24-12 illustrates some of the individual and composite effects of the foregoing reproduce head character-

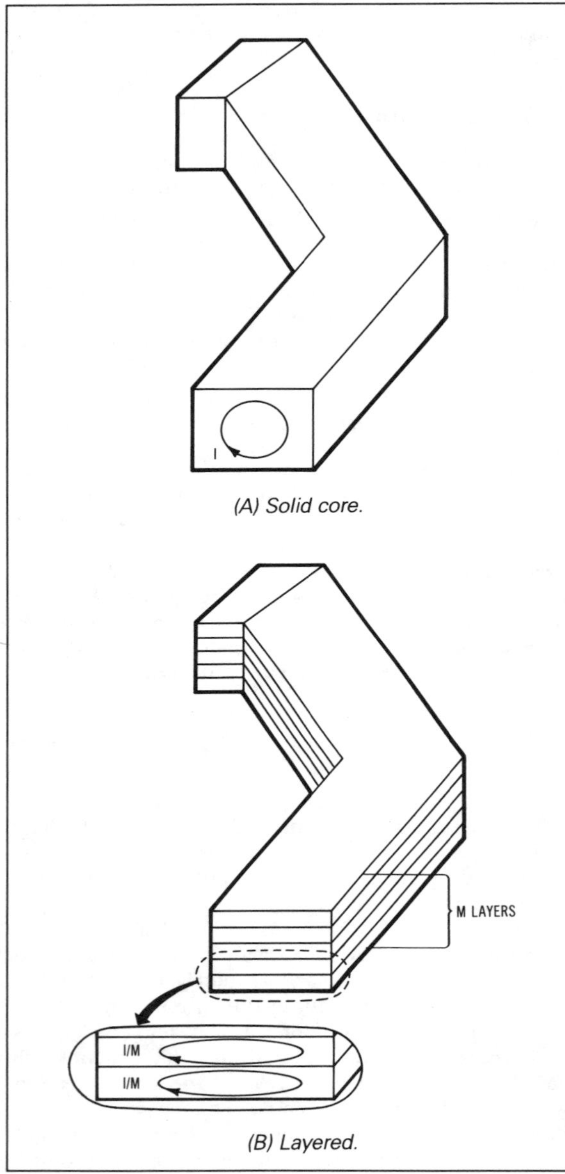

(A) Solid core.

(B) Layered.

Figure 24-11 Eddy current.

istics. The constant 6-dB/octave inductive rise of the head has been omitted in the figure to accentuate the undesired departures from flat response.

Curves A, B, and C illustrate the gap length, tape thickness, and spacing losses, respectively.

Curve D represents a typical resonant rise due to head inductance and the capacitance of the head cable and head winding. The playback amplifier high-frequency response boost dictated by the National Association of Broadcasters (NAB) equalization standard for 15 in./s is represented by curve E. The combination of all of these effects in curve F yields a response that is flat within ± 1 dB. This simplified model does not include relatively minor contributions at mastering speeds due to eddy currents and hysteresis, self-demagnetization effects, recording equalization, and the effects of nonuniform distribution of recorded flux due to coating thickness. In spite of these omissions, the dominant nature of the coating thickness loss is readily apparent. The equalization standards have been chosen primarily to offset this thickness loss.

The composite curve F represents the overall playback performance from an ideal tape of finite thickness. All the indicated response anomalies within the audio band must be either corrected or tolerated. In some cases, one effect can be used to offset others, such as shaping the resonance curve to correct for the gap length loss. (Unlike the resonance, the gap length loss increases with decreasing tape speed, upsetting the correction at lower tape speeds.)

24.3.4 Noise

The useful range of signal levels that pass through the tape recorder is limited at the top by the maximum signal at which all the magnetic tape particles become completely magnetized or saturated, and on the bottom by the amount of noise that remains when the input signal is removed. The residual noise is contributed by a number of sources distributed throughout the record/reproduce process. Discussion of the tape- and electronics-related noises will be deferred to later sections; only head-induced noise will be covered here.

The distortion content of the signal from a tape recorder rises so dramatically near tape saturation that the normal operating range must be limited to less-than-maximum levels. For the purpose of specifying and comparing tape recorders, the distortion-free maximum operating level is typically considered to be the output signal level at which the *total harmonic distortion (THD)*, which is dominated by third harmonic and other odd components, reaches 3%. The ratio of the level for 3% THD at medium wavelength to the residual noise is defined as the *signal-to-noise ratio* or *(SNR)* of the recorder. (Note that the 3% THD point in a magnetic recording corresponds to a compression of 0.8 dB from an ideal linear transfer characteristic.) The magnetic tape should determine both the maximum operating level and the residual noise of the system. For this to be true, the noise and distortion contributed by the heads and electronic circuitry must typically be 10 dB better than the tape-related components. This margin is usually attained for professional recorders using relatively wide tracks and 15 or 30 in./s tape speeds, but consumer-oriented machines may fall short of this goal.

Two factors compromise the performance of the consumer products. First, the use of slower tape speeds

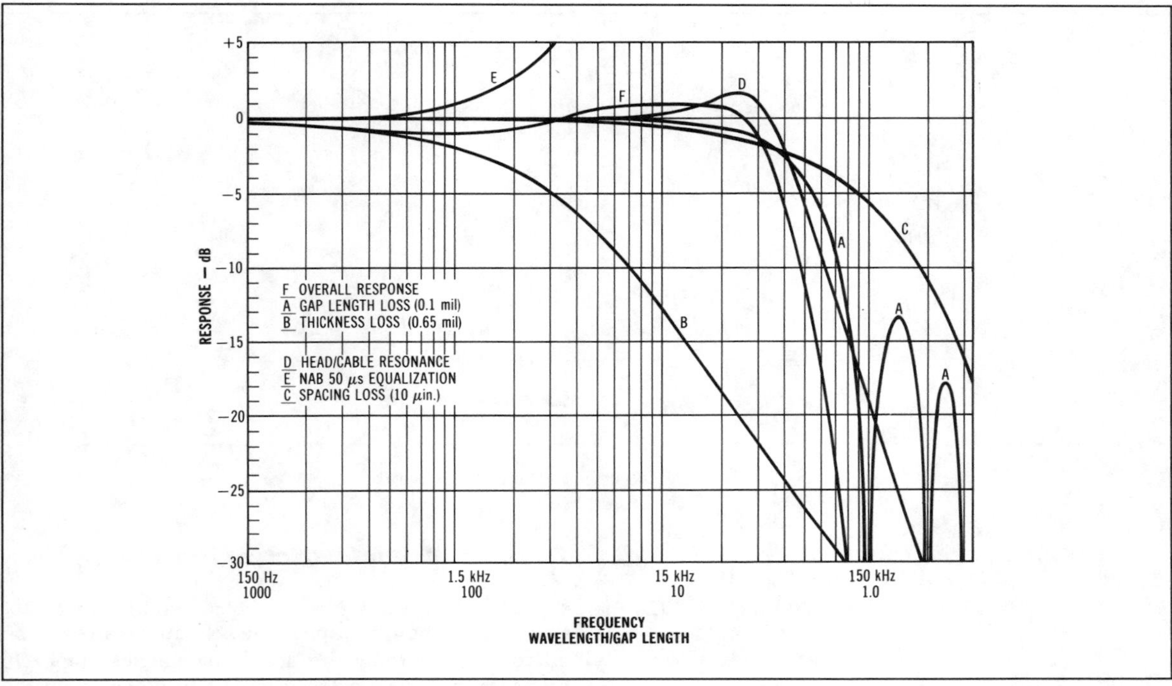

Figure 24-12 Playback loss components at 15 in./s for 0.65-mil coating thickness.

requires shorter wavelengths, which result in increased tape thickness loss. When the high-frequency gain of the reproduce amplifier is increased to compensate for this loss, the residual high-frequency noise of the head and electronic circuitry is also increased.

24.3.4.1 Track Width

The second factor relates to the difference between the ways that random noise sources and coherent signals increase. The noise due to the tape, heads, and electronics is a random combination of many small independent noise bursts. If two equal and independent random noise sources of this type are added together, the noise *power* is doubled, producing an increase of 3 dB on a voltmeter.

Coherent sources, on the other hand, are merely duplicates of the same waveform. If two identical sources are added together, the value at each point on the output waveform is exactly twice the value of either of the input waveforms. In this case the output *voltage* is doubled, producing a 6-dB increase on a voltmeter.

Consider the case of two tracks of a tape recorder that have recorded the same signal. If the output signals of the two tracks are added, the noise will add randomly and the signals will add coherently. The overall signal-to-noise ratio of the combined tracks has 6 dB more signal and 3 dB more noise, yielding a net improvement of 3 dB. Using a single track of double the original track width would produce the same result *if the noise sources were statistically independent in nature.*

The tape noise will follow the 3 dB per doubling rate if the reproduce amplifier noise is less than tape noise. The reproduce amplifier noise typically remains nearly constant regardless of track width of the head. The apparent noise will vary, however, as the gain of the amplifier is adjusted to compensate for changes in the head output due to increased or decreased track width. When tracks are made narrower, the amplifier noise that functions as a coherent source will eventually dominate the tape noise, creating a signal-to-noise loss of 6 dB per halving of tape width.

Fig. 24-13 compares the output voltage and signal-to-noise variation for various track widths, assuming that all noise sources are truly random for a noiseless preamplifier and a typical preamplifier. When the amplifier noise begins to dominate the other noise sources, there is a rapid loss of signal-to-noise ratio with decreasing track width.

24.3.4.2 Thermal Noise

Both the core and winding of the reproduce head contribute random noise to the output signal. For the winding, the noise source is due to the thermal agitation of the atoms in the copper wire. The amount of thermal noise is given by the expression

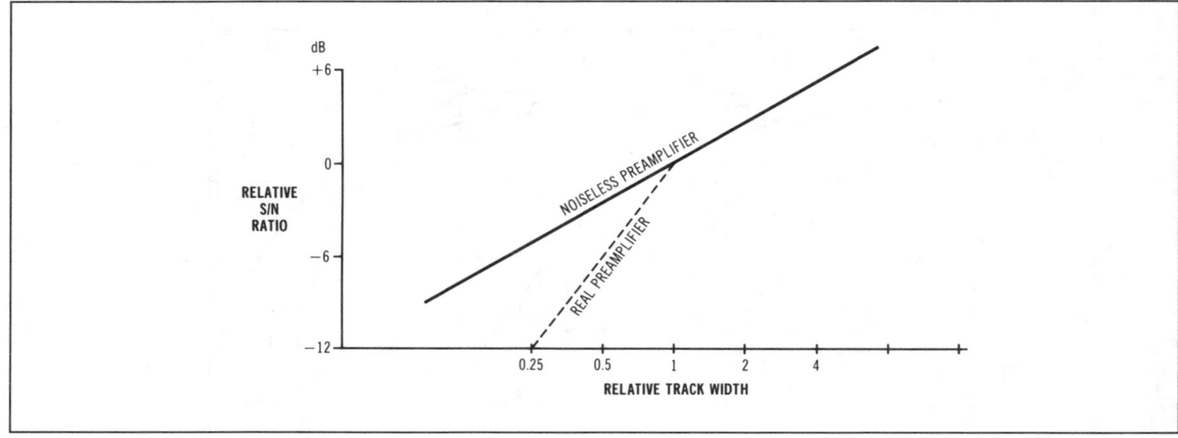

Figure 24-13 Noise changes with track width.

$$\text{thermal noise} = (4KTRB)^{1/2} = 1.82 \times 10^{-8} \times (R)^{1/2} \text{ volts for a 20-kHz bandwidth at room temperature} \quad (24\text{-}8)$$

where,

K is the Boltzmann's constant (1.38×10^{-23} joules/°k)
T is the absolute temperature in degrees Kelvin,
R is the resistance in ohms,
B is the measurement bandwidth in hertz.

A 100-Ω resistor will produce 0.182 μV of noise voltage. Depending upon the core size and number of turns, a playback head may exhibit a resistance from 10 to 1000 Ω, yielding thermal noise contributions of 0.06 to 0.6 μV. The increase in noise due to more turns of finer wire in high inductance heads is offset by a rise in head output voltage, producing little net change in signal-to-noise ratio.

24.3.4.3 Barkhausen Noise

Another major noise source is *Barkhausen noise*, a noise due to jumps in the magnetic boundaries of the core material. The core metal consists of a collection of many microscopic magnetic zones or domains. When a magnetic field is applied to the core, the boundaries or walls of the domains will change as small domains merge to form larger domains. This merging occurs in discrete steps since the small domains act as single units that must each merge completely in one jump. The resulting step change in the magnetic field generates a noise burst in the head winding. Since the core contains millions of constantly switching domains, a statistically independent random noise is generated. Reducing the size of the basic domains will decrease the amplitude of the Barkhausen noise.

24.3.4.4 Magnetostrictive Noise

The magnetic core material also exhibits magnetostriction—a change in magnetic field due to stress. The microscopically rough surface of the magnetic tape will therefore produce a small magnetic field change in the core as the tape slides across the head. This field change generates a magnetostrictive noise component in the winding.

Both the Barkhausen and magnetostrictive noises are absent when no tape is moving over the surface of the head. The residual standby noise, which is measured under these conditions, is the absolute noise floor for the reproduce head and amplifier. The comparison of this standby noise level with the bulk-erased and biased noise levels is covered in the test and maintenance section.

24.3.5 Record Heads

The magnetic core and gap of a reproduce head obey the principle of reciprocity, which states that the roles of an excitation source and sensor can be interchanged. For a head used in the reproduce mode, external flux at the gap produces a voltage across the head winding. If, instead, a voltage is applied to the head winding by an oscillator, a concentrated external flux field, which is generated at the gap, can be used to record a signal on a piece of moving tape.

The shape and strength of the magnetic field at the gap is the basis for the operation of a recording head. The flux generated in the core by the current in the winding must jump across the gap to complete a closed magnetic path. The gap, which is a very poor magnetic path compared to the core, produces an obstruction that forces the flux to spread sideways, as shown in Fig. 24-14.

An analogous situation occurs with a crowd of people

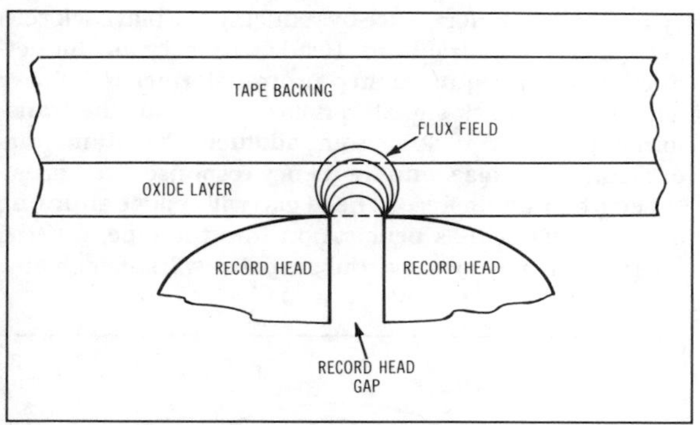

Figure 24-14 Record head fields.

moving down a hallway. If the hallway widens for a crossing corridor or small lobby, the crowd will broaden out into the open area and then neck down again to reenter the continuation of the hallway. The broadening will increase if the pressure within the hallway should increase due to an emergency such as a fire. The stress is greatest at the transitions between the wide and narrow spaces since this is where people are squeezing to try to change the shape of the flow.

A magnetic tape passing over a record head gap experiences a similar buildup and decline in the magnetic recording field as it moves across the gap. To produce a permanent recording on the tape, the flux must first rise to a level sufficient to overcome the magnetic memory force of the tape, which normally keeps the magnetic particles on the tape from changing state spontaneously. In the central zone of complete excitation, the tape particles will follow any change in the input signal driving the head. As the tape particles exit the strong central zone, a well-defined point will be reached at which the driving flux drops below the memory force, leaving a fixed magnetic image impressed upon the tape. This transition region in which the image freezes at the trailing edge of the gap is called the *trapping plane.*

The shape of the trapping plane depends primarily upon the gap size and the thickness and magnetic characteristics of the tape. Since trapping planes that are narrow and vertical will produce short wavelength recordings that are more easily reproduced, several techniques have been developed to sharpen the transition zone, as shown in Fig. 24-15. The focused gap technique in Fig. 24-15B uses a silver gap shim to serve as a barrier to flux jumping straight across the gap. Eddy currents in the shim force the flux away from the shim, squirting the flux deeper into the tape. The steeper edges of the field sharpen the trapping plane.

A second technique, which yields similar results, is the *crossed field or X-field* (Fig. 24-15A). This method typically places heads on opposite sides of the tape to create a shaped flux field jumping from one head to the other.

The magnetization of the tape particles is not easily changed due to the memory force or hysteresis of the particles. In fact, we could think of the particles as lethargic—sleepy little particles that must be aroused before they will do anything and then being quite content to immediately fall asleep as soon as the excitation stops. This lethargy produces a jerky recording characteristic that ignores weak signals and responds only to strong signals. Since the resulting distortion levels are intolerable for audio application, a method of waking up the sleepy particles must be employed.

If a rapidly varying signal of sufficient amplitude to just begin magnetizing the particles is added to the audio flux signal, the magnetic particles will more readily conform to changes in the audio waveform. The high-frequency

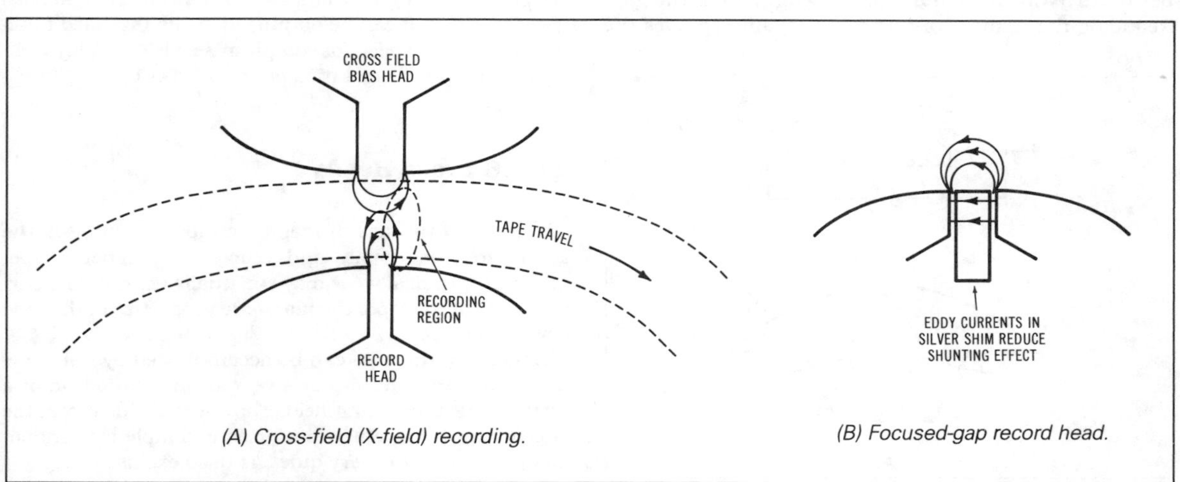

(A) Cross-field (X-field) recording.

(B) Focused-gap record head.

Figure 24-15 Focused gap and cross-field (X-field) head.

biasing signal produces a hysteresis-free or anhysteretic recording.

The audio and bias signals must be added together in a linear manner without generating any of the sidebands that are present in either amplitude or frequency modulation techniques. The short-wavelength bias signal can therefore be easily filtered out during playback by the gap and thickness losses so that only the audio signal remains. (The high level of bias signal transformer crosstalk that is present during sync/overdub operation requires a sharp notch filter in the playback preamplifier to remove the bias signal.)

Typical bias frequencies range from 100 kHz for slow-speed recorders to over 10 MHz for high-speed tape duplicators. Although high bias frequencies are desirable to permit easy filtering and thorough tape excitation, a practical upper limit for mastering recorders is reached at 500 kHz due to a combination of increased eddy current and hysteresis losses in the core and the increase in bias drive voltage required due to the inductance of the head.

Head losses can be reduced by using a very small core to reduce hysteresis losses and by choosing either thin laminations or a ferrite material to reduce eddy current losses. If, however, the record head will also be used for the reproduce function during sync/overdub, a small core will cause serious long-wavelength contour effects. The compromise "hammerhead" design shown in Fig. 24-16 improves the playback performance of the small core by adding extensions to the face of the core. The tips function only to play back low-frequency signals for which core losses are insignificant.

The bias voltage required to drive a record head doubles each time the bias frequency is doubled due to the inductance of the record head. To keep the required bias voltage within the range of common integrated circuits, the inductance can be lowered either by reducing the number of turns in the winding or by lengthening the gap. Reducing the number of turns once again degrades the sync/overdub performance by reducing the playback voltage generated by the head. Heads with very low inductance typically require a step-up transformer to achieve adequate playback signal-to-noise ratios, but the transformer will also contribute some additional small amounts of distortion, noise, and frequency response anomalies.

Lengthening the record head gap will reduce shunting and give better bias penetration into the tape, but the short-wavelength sync/overdub response will suffer greatly.

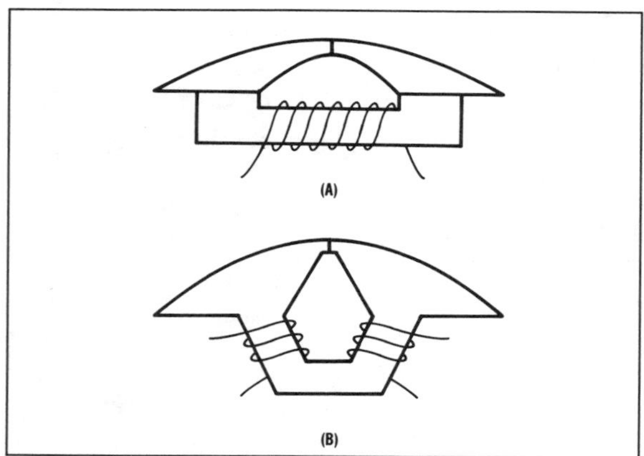

Figure 24-16 "Hammerhead" cores.

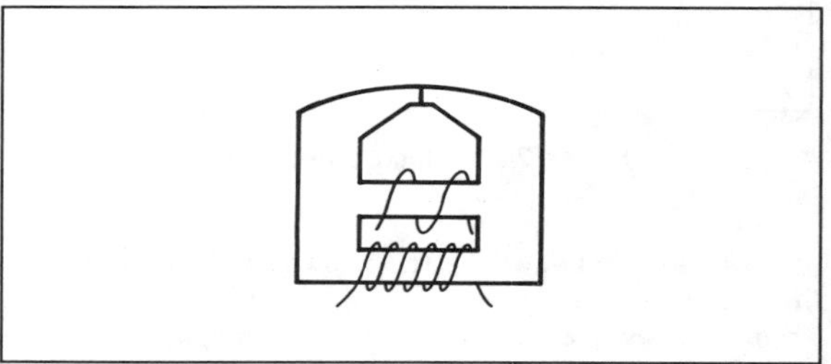

Figure 24-17 Dual winding record head.

A more straightforward approach to optimize the record head for both recording and playback is to use separate flux paths or windings for each of the functions. One simple method of switching windings and flux paths is to use parallel paths that can be selectively blocked. As shown in Fig. 24-17, when the high-inductance playback winding is shorted, flux will be blocked from the playback shunt magnetic leg of the core, effectively eliminating this path and thereby forcing all of the flux from the low-impedance bias winding to the front of the head. During reproduce, when the bias winding is shorted, the flux picked up from the tape will pass only through the reproduce winding. Although the cost of this dual-winding head is significantly higher than for a conventional single-path design, each coil can be optimized for its intended function without the need for compromise, yielding playback-to-record inductance ratios of up to 1000:1.

24.3.6 Erase Heads

A major advantage of magnetic tape recording is the ability to erase easily and reuse the magnetic tape. Although physical wear may eventually degrade the performance of the tape, the magnetic properties of the tape never wear out.

Erasure of the tape can be accomplished by remagnetizing the tape with either a very strong static field or a very strong alternating field. For audio applications the alternating field, which produces a completely random flux pattern that is very quiet, is used exclusively.

A very large electromagnet, known as a *bulk eraser* or *degausser*, is used for rapid erasure of an entire reel of

Figure 24-18 Tape eraser. *(Courtesy Taber Manufacturing & Engineering Co.)*

tape. As shown in Fig. 24-18, the coil and core of the degausser are similar to a large recording head. The very strong flux field created across the eraser gap penetrates the magnetic tape, driving the magnetic particles to complete saturation. Any magnetic patterns on the tape are completely erased when all the tape particles are alternately saturated in one direction and then the other by the changing field.

To leave the tape in a neutral stage, the strength of the erasing field must gradually decrease from hard saturation to zero. A common technique is to move the tape slowly away from the eraser so that the 60-Hz excitation field will drop gradually from one cycle to the next.

A few degausser models include control devices that gradually reduce the current in the eraser coil to zero, thereby eliminating the need for the operator to move the reel. Other models contain motor-driven actuators that slowly remove the tape from the field automatically.

A dc current or permanent magnet can also be used to erase unwanted signals from the tape, but the tape particles will not be left in a neutral state. A dc-erased tape will usually produce a very noisy recording that contains high levels of even-order harmonic distortion components. Digital recorders frequently utilize dc erasure since these noise and distortion products do not degrade the digitally encoded audio program.

Selective erasure of small portions of a reel of tape requires the use of an erase head on the tape recorder. The function of the head is similar to the bulk eraser in that the tape is slowly withdrawn from a saturating ac flux field. For a tape speed of 30 in./s and a typical decay length of the erase head field of 0.005 in., the drop from saturation to zero occurs in 0.17 ms. If the tape is to experience at least 20 complete cycles during the decay, the erase frequency must be

$$\begin{aligned}\text{erase frequency} &= \text{number of cycles/decay time}\\ &= 20/0.0017 \qquad (24\text{-}9)\\ &= 120\,\text{kHz}\end{aligned}$$

The long flux field required for erasure can be produced by a conventional coil-and-core head that has a very wide gap. Although such heads will produce approximately 50 dB of erasure, some of the original signal will still remain. A second pass over the erase head will provide the additional erasure that is required to erase the unwanted signal completely.

The reason for the incomplete erasure is a phenomenon known as *gap jumping*. As the tape leaves the saturation zone of the erase gap, the flux level experienced by the tape particles will pass through a level that creates a recording zone similar to the trapping plane of the record head. Any audio variations in the erase field would be recorded at this point. Such audio variations are created by the unerased program that is starting to enter the erase field at the other side of the gap. This incoming flux adds to the erase head flux, creating an unwanted recording at the trailing edge of the erase field just as if the audio signal had jumped across the gap.

Complete erasure can be achieved without multiple passes if the erase head contains two magnetically isolated gaps. The tape is erased by the first gap, and then immediately reerased by the second gap. A wide center spacer isolates the two gaps so that flux cannot jump both gaps.

Although both bulk erasers and erase heads are capable of completely erasing all recorded material from a tape, the residual noise level left by the erase head will be slightly higher than the virgin-tape level achieved by the bulk eraser due to small changes in the erase field caused by the tape-to-head contact variations, the tape particle-to-particle magnetic variations, and the recording of Barkhausen noise from the erase core. The record head biasing field produces similar increases in the noise level. The excess noise perceived by a listener due to the erase and record heads may rise as high as 6 dB above the virgin-tape noise floor.

24.3.7 Encoding Methods

Up to this point in the discussion, a direct analog recording process has been considered in which the conversion of the amplitude and temporal frequency at the input terminals to the amplitude and wavelength on the tape has been determined solely by the tape speed. Although this approach is simple and reliable, the designer of the recorder has very little freedom to optimize the wavelength and amplitude performance of the recorder. This limitation can be overcome by introducing an encoding device into the input signal path to modify the amplitude and/or frequency characteristics of the signal that is applied to the tape. A complementary decoder in the output signal path is used to restore the signal to the original form.

24.3.7.1 Amplitude Encoding

Dolby and dbx noise reduction systems are examples of an amplitude-only encoder. Both systems modify the amplitude of the signal to squeeze the dynamic range of the input signal into a smaller dynamic range that will avoid the noise and distortion limitations of the recording tape. The fidelity of these systems is limited not only by the tracking of the encode and decode circuits, but also by the nature of the errors that are generated by noise, nonlinearities, and frequency response anomalies introduced by the record/playback cycle of the tape recorder. These parasitic errors can cause dynamic mistracking that will create distortions of dynamic signals that may not be evident during sine-wave testing.

24.3.7.2 Digital Encoding

A more extreme encoding method is *digital quantization*, which transforms both the amplitude and frequency characteristics of the signal. Encoding an audio signal into digital form changes the frequency response and dynamic range requirements of any recording device that must store the digitized signal. Since the analog signal must be sampled with high resolution several times per cycle, the rate at which digital binary digits or bits are generated is from 10 to 50 times greater than the highest frequency in the audio signal. However, since each bit has only two possible values, 1 or 0, very little dynamic range is needed to store the data. The resulting tradeoff of reduced dynamic range for increased bandwidth permits significant modifications to the tape coating thickness, gap length, track width, and recording method, but all these changes fall within the scope of the previous discussions of basic recording theory.

The high data rate dictates maximizing the short-wavelength performance by using short playback gaps and thin magnetic coatings. Proper choice of the digital encoding scheme can also eliminate all low-frequency content in the data stream, thereby avoiding fringing and contour effects.

The reduced dynamic range requirements permit a sloppy recording, which simply slams the magnetic coating into full saturation of one polarity or the other. The lack of intermediate states eliminates the need to linearize the recording characteristics with high-frequency bias. The data also automatically erases any prior signal by over-recording the old flux pattern with a new pattern of saturated signals.

Typical digital recording methods require only 30 dB of dynamic range to recover the digital bits, a 100 to 1 reduction compared to an analog recorder. The track widths can therefore be narrowed to the point at which tape guiding variations and tape dropouts are the limiting factors controlling the reliability of the data recovery.

The major disadvantage of short-wavelength recordings with low dynamic range comes in the form of reduced data reliability. Spacing loss due to dirt and dropouts due to coating defects contribute much greater errors than indirect analog recording. Not only are the errors more frequent, but the effect of these errors on the decoding process is very detrimental. A small error that would be unnoticed in an analog recording can create a very loud pop if only one bit of the digital data is in error. For this reason, digital recorders encode error detection and correction information into the audio data stream so that errors can be removed during decoding. Although this method works well for typical errors, the price is a further increase in the data rate to include the correction data.

A typical error detection technique adds extra parity bits to the data system, which indicate whether small blocks of data are either odd or even. If an error is generated during storage or retrieval, the odd data may be converted to even data or vice versa. A check of parity bits during decoding will flag the erroneous data so that special handling can be invoked to deal with the error.

Parity error detection suffers from two drawbacks. First, large error bursts may change more than one bit, resulting in offsetting errors that do not result in a change of parity. Although small data blocks minimize this problem, the volume of parity data rises as the blocks are reduced in size. The second drawback is the need to detect errors in the parity data. A bad parity bit could cause the decoder to reject correct data.

One way of minimizing the effects of errors is to disperse the data and parity bits so that a single error burst will change no more than one bit of the data block and parity check word. Interleaving the bits of many blocks scatters the data over a larger area of tape, minimizing the probability of simultaneous errors on several data and parity bits in a given data block.

Error detection does not provide enough information to allow the decoder to determine which of the several bits in the check block is the source of the error flag. More powerful error correction schemes are required to repair the data. Error correction coding requires a higher level of redundancy and hence more overhead or extra bits to find which bits are in error. Elaborate error correction techniques such as cross-interleave convolution coding have been created to provide highly reliable audio data, but the cost may be from 30 to 200% more data, which must be stored.

Standards for compatibility of digitally recorded tapes have become much more difficult to achieve because of the wide range of choices open to the digital audio designer. The common problems of mechanical compatibility of tape speed and track format are still present, plus the sampling rate, data format, timing, and error-handling methods must also be compatible. The rapid evolution of digital audio technology in these areas, which has already rendered several generations of digital audio recorders obsolete, has created a mood of apprehension among potential digital audio users. The compact digital audio disk is the first digital audio recording format to overcome these problems and achieve an internationally recognized standard. If present trends continue, the professional audio market will not reach an equivalent level of standardization for several years.

From an operator's standpoint, the major difference between analog and digital recorders is that the previously mentioned error mechanisms make cleanliness much more necessary with the short-wavelength digital tape. By keeping the heads and transport clean and avoiding fingerprints on the magnetic coating of the tape, the "insurance policy" represented by the error correction system can be reserved for truly unavoidable errors.

24.3.7.3 Frequency-Modulation Recording

Frequency-modulation or FM recording encodes the audio signal as frequency changes in a high-frequency carrier tone recorded on the tape. In most respects relating to the recording process, FM encoding is nearly identical to digital recording in that the same increase in encoded bandwidth and decrease in dynamic range prevails. FM data is also more sensitive to flutter in the tape transport, but various flutter suppression methods can be used to achieve adequate audio dynamic range.

The data reliability of FM recording is midway between direct analog and digital systems. Not only are the wavelengths not quite as short as digital tracks, but the flywheel effect of the typical FM decoder renders a small error unlikely to produce a major pop in the decoded audio.

24.3.7.4 Encoder and Decoder Distortions

In addition to the tape-related errors and distortions, encoding systems introduce additional limitations and degradations that are not at all related to the storage and recovery of the encoded form of the data. These distortion characteristics can be analyzed by testing the encoding system with the encoder output connected directly to the decoder input. Common problems include severe phase distortions and transient errors.

24.4 MAGNETIC TAPE

The gradual evolution of magnetic recording technology continues to yield steady improvements in the fidelity of the recording process. In general, most parameters, such as signal-to-noise ratio, flutter, and distortion have improved by roughly 10 dB. These improvements have made possible the development of new tape formats, such as compact cassettes and 24-channel mastering recorders, thereby opening up new markets and applications.

Closer scrutiny reveals that the dominant contributor to these improvements has been the magnetic tape. Over the years, both the magnetic and the physical attributes of the tape have shown tremendous improvements. Better magnetic particles, stronger binders, tougher base films, and greatly improved manufacturing methods have all contributed to achieving remarkable levels of performance and reliability. Furthermore, ongoing research efforts continue to yield new developments that will sustain this rate of improvement for the foreseeable future.

A recent study conducted for this book by 3M Co. (Minnesota Mining & Mfg. Co.), the makers of Scotch® brand magnetic tapes, reveals some very enlightening comparisons, which illustrate the progress made by tape manufacturers. Using 1955 as the benchmark year, the study found that the cost in 1982 dollars per track for a 1-minute length of professional grade tape has dropped from $1.95 for a full-track ¼-in. recording in 1955 to only $0.15 for a 24-track 2-in. recording in 1983. During the same period, improvements in tape characteristics have more than offset the degradation in signal-to-noise ratio associated with the newer narrow-track format. In addition, the improved tear resistance of today's polyester backing combine with newer high-strength binder materials to produce a much more durable product.

(As an interesting side note, the cost per track for the recorder has remained virtually unchanged, with added features and improved performance offsetting any savings due to advances in solid-state technology.)

The professional audio tape market represents an estimated worldwide market of $1 billion per year, which is growing at a 15 to 20% annual rate. An additional estimated $4 billion of audio tape is used for consumer applications.

The following discussion begins with a description of the components and techniques used to manufacture tape. This is followed by an in-depth study of the small-scale magnetic characteristics of the magnetic particles and how the performance of the tape is specified. Methods for testing tape to detect defects are found in section 24.7.

24.4.1 Tape Components

Modern magnetic tape consists of a powder of very small magnetic particles, which has been glued to one surface of a plastic substrate or base film. The back side of the substrate is coated with a very thin layer of carbon particles to improve winding characteristics and to reduce the buildup of static electricity.

24.4.1.1 Base Films

Although several base film materials were used in the past, including paper and acetate film, virtually all tape manufactured today uses polyester film, such as Dupont's Mylar™. Polyester is not only extremely strong and tear-resistant, but it is also relatively stable with respect to changes in temperature and humidity.

Depending upon the intended application, the nominal base film thickness ranges from 1.4 mils for heavy-duty professional tapes down to a scant 0.25 mil for a C-120 cassette. To achieve reliable performance with these very thin films, the film must be not only very thin but also uniform in thickness from end to end and from edge to edge.

To enhance the strength of the thin base films used for cassettes, the polyester is pre-stretched or Tensilized. Although Tensilized tapes are more resistant to stretching than normal tapes, residual stresses that result from the Tensilizing process can produce physical distortion of the tape. For thin, narrow tapes these distortions are satisfactorily flattened out at the record and playback heads. The thicker, wider tapes used for professional formats, which would manifest severe contact problems due to these distortions, are considered to be strong enough without Tensilizing to provide adequate performance.

24.4.1.2 Binders

The glue or binder that holds the magnetic particles to the base film is a necessary evil, which makes no active contribution to the magnetic performance of the tape. The use of new high-strength binders containing urethanes has improved both the durability and the recording characteristics of recent tapes.

The performance criterion used to determine the useful life of a tape on a given tape transport varies from application to applicaton. Primary factors are the inherent strength of the tape binder system and the abusiveness of the transport. To measure the degradation of the tape, a typical test would consist of monitoring the gradual (hopefully) drop in playback level at the shortest wavelength of interest. When these losses exceed a predetermined limit, the tape is worn out.

Some specialized audio transports designed for repetitive playback are capable of making over 10,000 passes on a tape without producing a drop in level exceeding 2 dB at 15 kHz. On the other hand, a poorly maintained studio recorder can destroy a master tape in 10 passes or less! In general, if the abrasive forces exerted by the transport upon the tape are well below the inherent strength of the binder, the tape will last virtually indefinitely. Any increase in the abrasive force due to dirty contact surfaces, excessive tape tension, or poorly designed tape guiding will accelerate the wear.

A very rapid catastrophic failure will occur once the abrasion force becomes sufficient to build up a small clump of debris on a contact surface. The friction between the debris and the tape surface is very high due to both the similarity of materials and the high pressure exerted by the tip of the clump as it pushes upon the tape. The binder is overwhelmed, causing the clump to grow rapidly to the point at which the tape will show an obvious scratch or crease. If this situation should arise, the source of the problem should be corrected, and a copy of the damaged tape should be used for subsequent work.

A typical 24-track master will accumulate thousands of passes during the repeated shuttling that is common with both sync/overdub recording and extended mixdown sessions. Since not all brands and models of tape recorders produce equal amounts of tape wear, the user should include the expected number of passes in the recorder selection criteria.

From the magnetic performance standpoint, the combination of smoother magnetic particles and newer binders has enabled the tape manufacturers to use a smaller quantity of binder material to affix the magnetic particles. The ratio of useful particles to the magnetically inert binder has thus risen from approximately 40% by volume for typical mastering tapes in 1970 to approximately 60% in 1980. This improved magnetic density yields a higher maximum output for a given particle type and coating thickness.

24.4.1.3 Magnetic Particles

The ultimate performance of a tape recorder is determined not by the tape drive, heads, or electronics, but rather by the physical and magnetic characteristics of the magnetic particles of the tape. If basic performance parameters such as maximum output levels, noise, and distortion are truly determined only by the tape, the recorder is said to be tape limited. As a practical rule of thumb, if the noise and distortion products of the recorder are at least 10 dB lower than the products produced by the tape, the overall performance of the machine and tape will be within 0.5 dB of the theoretical levels of the tape alone. Although no known audio recorder achieves this level of perfection, several machines come close in some areas.

Of primary importance in magnetic recording is the ability of each magnetic tape particle to assume and retain a magnetic pattern. These particles are chosen for their ability to maintain a magnetic field along one preferred direction or axis, permitting alignment of the particles for maximum performance. The amount of preferred orientation or anisotropy in the material depends upon the nature and crystalline structure of the particles. Table 24-5 summarizes the characteristics of several of the particles used for magnetic tapes.

The shape of the particles determines the degree of physical alignment that can be achieved during the coating process. Smooth cylindrical or spherical particles that have no jagged edges or branches can be densely packed, yielding maximum output level.

The size of the particles is determined by the crystalline structure of each material. The residual noise of the tape decreases as the particles become smaller. Small particles with high anisotropy are therefore most desirable. Typical magnetic particles for recording tape are acircular, "cigar-shaped" particles with a length-to-width ratio in the range of 4:1 to 8:1.

COERCIVITY

The *coercivity* is a measure of the magnetic force required to cause the tape particles to change magnetic polarity. High coercivity particles are more difficult to record, but they are also better able to resist external influences due to neighboring particles after recording, reducing the smearing of short-wavelength signals during

Table 24-5. Characteristics of Tape Particles

		Size	Coercivity	Retentivity	Square
Fe_2O_3 (Gamma ferric oxide)	Low Noise	0.3 μm	330 Oe	1300 G	0.75–0.8
	Normal	0.7 μm	280 Oe	1100 G	0.75
Co doped Fe_2O_3		0.3 μm	650–700 Oe	1300 G	0.8
CrO_2		0.6 μm	600 Oe	1500 G	0.9
Metal		0.2 μm	1100 Oe	3500 G	0.8

storage. On the other hand, higher coercivity tapes require stronger bias and erase fields.

Retentivity and Remanence

If the coercivity is considered to be the input drive, then the *retentivity* and *remanence* are both the output of magnetism left in the tape. Retentivity measures the maximum output per unit volume of coating cross section; remanence (remanent flux), which is the output per ¼ in. of tape width, varies not only with retentivity, but also with coating thickness. Remanence specifications should be used to compare the maximum long-wavelength outputs of different tape types.

24.4.2 Magnetic Performance Curves

The input-output relationship for typical magnetic materials is very nonlinear. As shown in Fig. 24-19A, the magnetization characteristic curve can be broken into three zones. For low excitation levels, the initial output is very small and nonlinear. As the excitation increases, a fairly linear region is encountered, which produces low distortions. As the level continues to increase, the magnetic particles finally become fully magnetized or saturated. Further increase at the input yield no more magnetization in the material.

The nonlinear initial region must be avoided in audio recording if low distortion is to be achieved. The high-frequency bias signal provides enough excitation to jolt the magnetic particles into an active state. Optimizing the bias level yields the much more linear transfer characteristic of Fig. 24-19B.

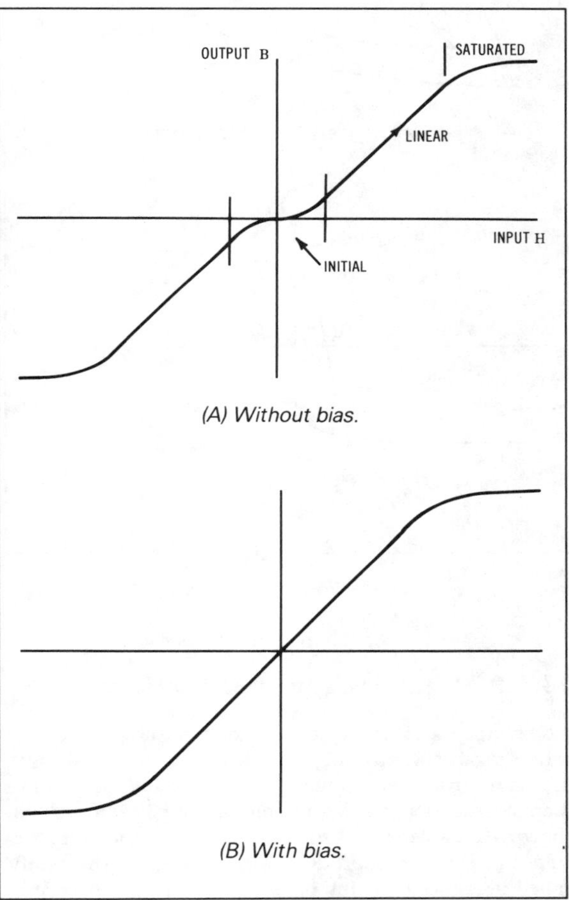

Figure 24-19 Tape transfer characteristics.

Another representation of the magnetic characteristics is given by the B-H curves of the tape, as shown in Fig. 24-20. The curves show the amount of magnetic flux density created within the magnetic material by a cyclically varying intensity of applied magnetic excitation. Since the particles store part of the magnetic field, the path for increasing excitation differs from the decay path for decreasing excitation.

Magnetic recording tapes are typically characterized by the coercivity and retentivity described previously. These points on the B-H curve for full saturation are indicated by H_c and B_r, respectively.

A figure of merit called squareness is commonly used to indicate the uniformity of the magnetic switching characteristics of magnetic coatings. As shown in Fig. 24-21, the squareness is the ratio of the remanent output value where the curve crosses the vertical axis to the saturated output. A perfect squareness of 1.0 would mean that every particle switched at exactly the same excitation level, yielding maximum output level and low distortion at high output levels. Over the past 20 years the squareness has improved from 0.8 to better than 0.9 for the best current audio tapes.

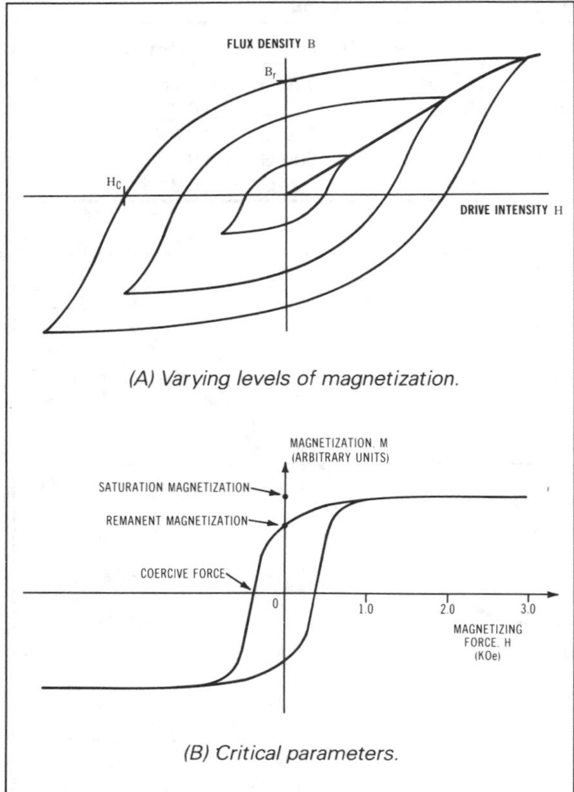

(A) Varying levels of magnetization.

(B) Critical parameters.

Figure 24-20 B-H curves.

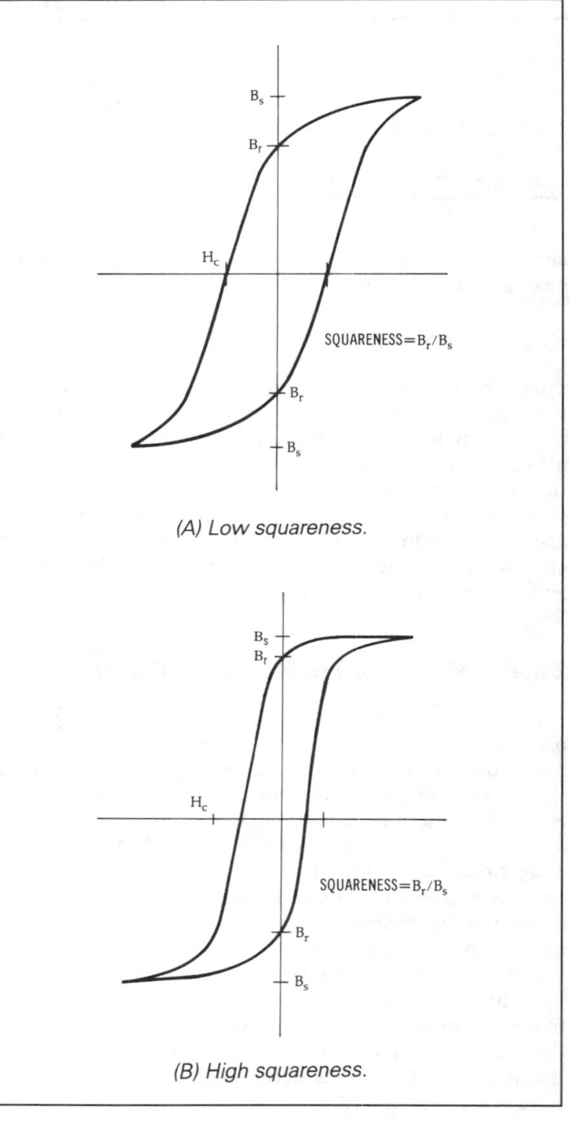

(A) Low squareness.

(B) High squareness.

Figure 24-21 Squareness ratio.

24.4.3 Magnetic Tape Specifications

New tape types are typically intended to replace established products without requiring any major changes in the recording equipment. Tape manufacturers have therefore developed a set of comparative specifications, shown in Table 24-6, which emphasize the improvements of the newer product with respect to the established reference tape. Important parameters in this comparison are bias requirements, frequency response, maximum output level, noise, and print-through, with all values being measured on a common studio recorder adjusted for optimum performance.

A second method, which is gaining in popularity, is the set of absolute performance graphs of Fig. 24-22, which show tape performance over a range of bias levels. Once a bias level has been chosen by the user, some of the parameters can be determined by reading the values at the intersections of each curve with the vertical line at the desired bias level. Other parameters, such as signal-to-noise ratio, can be determined by measuring the distance between two of the curves.

The curves of Fig. 24-22 illustrate several common tape characteristics. Note that the 1- and 10-kHz sensitivity curves do not peak at the same bias level. Only the surface of the tape is read by the playback head at short wavelengths, requiring less bias penetration to achieve optimum bias of these short-wavelength surface layers. Unfortunately, however, full bias penetration is required to minimize long-wavelength distortion. The surface layer is therefore normally overbiased by several decibels, producing a substantial drop in short-wavelength output. Narrowing the record head gap will produce an even greater

Table 24-6. Comparative Tape Specifications

Physical Properties	Test Notes	Units	206	207
Color:				
Oxide Side			Shiny black	Shiny black
Backing Side			Dull black	Dull black
Backing Material			Polyester with special controlled wind treatment	Polyester with special controlled wind treatment
Standard Widths		inches	0.248 0.500 1.000 2.000	0.248 0.500 1.000 2.000
Width Tolerances		inches	+0.000 −0.004	+0.000 −0.004
Thickness:				
Backing	1	mils	1.52	0.95
Oxide Coating	1	mils	0.56	0.56
Total	1	mils	2.08	1.51
Static Tensile:	2			
Yield Strength	3	lb/quar in.	5.9	4.0
Breaking Strength	4	lb/quar in.	9.0	6.0
Backside Resistance	5	mΩ/sq area	0.50	0.50
INTRINSIC MAGNETIC PROPERTIES				
Coercivity (H_{ci})	6	oersteds	320	320
Retentivity (B_{rs})	6	gauss	1050	1050
Remanence (Φ_r)	6	lines/quar in.	0.93	0.93
Erasing Field Required	7	oersteds	1000	1000
ELECTRO-MAGNETIC PROPERTIES (Based on "SCOTCH" Brand No. 202 recording tape as reference)				
Peak Bias	8		100	100
Maximum Undistorted Output (15-mil wavelength)	9	dB	+3.0	+3.0
Weighted Noise Level	10	dB	0.0	0.0
Sensitivity:				
15-mil wavelength	11	dB	+2.0	+2.0
1-mil wavelength	11	dB	+2.0	+2.0
1/2-mil wavelength	11	dB	+2.0	+2.0
Uniformity at 15-mil wavelength:				
within a roll	12	VU	±1/4	±1/4
roll to roll	12	VU	±1.0	±1.0

(Courtesy 3M Co.)

differential, as shown in Fig. 24-23. An equalization boost in the record amplifier must be used to offset this response droop.

An ideal tape would achieve peak long- and short-wavelength sensitivity and minimum distortion and modulation noise at a common bias level. A compromise bias setting is usually required for most applications since the peaks and minima are at different bias values. Minimum harmonic distortion is generally of highest priority, followed by modulation noise. The sensitivities at long and short wavelengths can be corrected as necessary with gain and equalization adjustments.

Although the graphical format provides a more complete set of data, the comparison of graphs for old and new tape types becomes somewhat laborious since values must be read from two graphs and then compared. The user should select the more appropriate set of data for whatever problem is at hand.

Note that the data given by the tape manufacturer is given for a specific test recorder operating at a single speed.

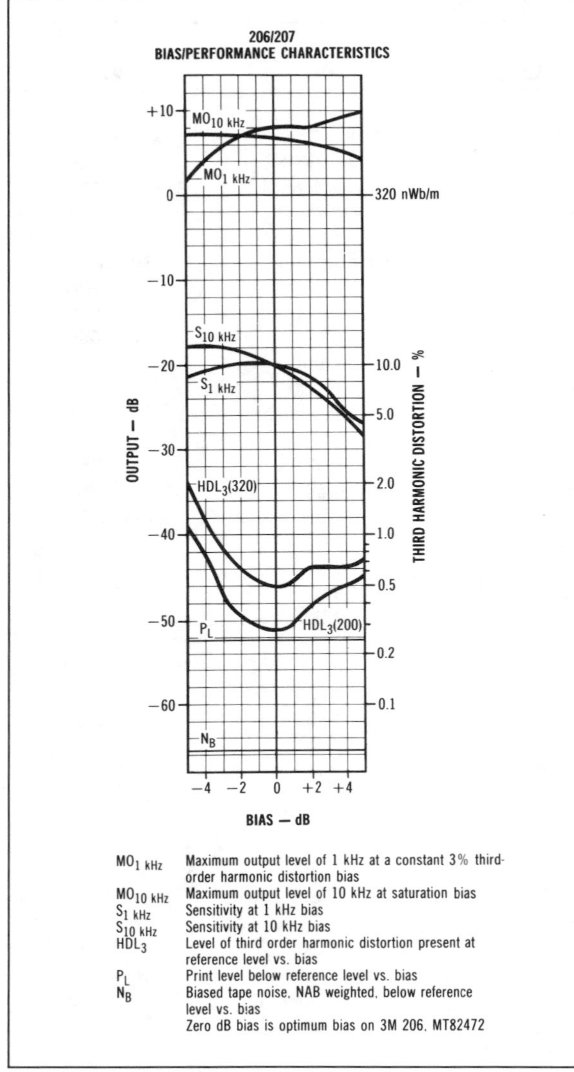

Figure 24-22 Tape performance graphs. *(Courtesy 3M Co., Magnetic Audio/Video Products Div.)*

Other recorders with different heads, bias frequencies, and electronic circuitry may yield substantially different results for noise and short-wavelength performance. Different tape speeds and equalization standards will introduce even larger changes since the performance data is related primarily to wavelength rather than frequency.

24.4.4 Print-Through

The energy required to activate a particle to switch magnetic states depends upon the size of the particle,

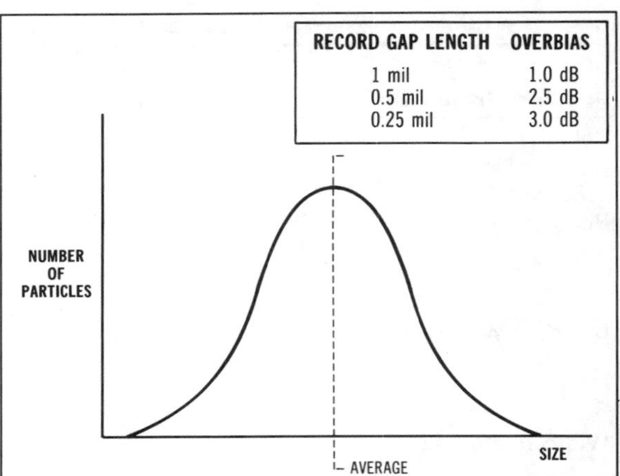

Figure 24-23 Short-wavelength dependence on record gap length.

with the overall characteristics of a magnetic tape being determined by the average size and characteristics of many particles in the coating. A more detailed analysis of the particles would yield a distribution of sizes, as shown in Fig. 24-24. Although the majority of the particles cluster around the average value, a small portion of the particles are either much smaller or much larger than the average. The small particles give rise to spontaneous recording as print-through; the large particles produce noise bursts.

The small particles require so little activation energy to assume a new magnetization state that even the thermal energy of the particles may provide enough bias to cause the particles to be recorded by the stray magnetic fields due to adjacent layers of recorded material. The spontaneous recording of these thermal idiots is most evident as pre- or post-echo at the beginning and end of a recording. The strength of the print-through image depends upon both the percentage of thermal idiots in the coating and the ratio of remanence to coercivity of the tape. The remanence measures the driving force of the signals trying to imprint the thermal idiots. The coercivity, on the other hand, is the stubbornness of the particles to resist this imprinting. The effective coercivity of the small particles is diminished because the domain size is suboptimal, rendering the small particles more susceptible to printing.

The milling process used to provide thorough mixing of the particles, binder, and additives prior to coating is a rather abusive process that can create thermal idiots by fracturing some of the desirable large particles into smaller, low-coercivity particles. Insufficient milling, on the other hand, provides an uneven particle dispersion that creates noise on the tape. The tape manufacturer must strike a compromise that yields both low noise and low print-through.

The user can take several steps that will minimize the amount of print-through. First, the use of thicker base films increases the spacing between layers. Second, avoiding elevated temperatures and stray magnetic fields

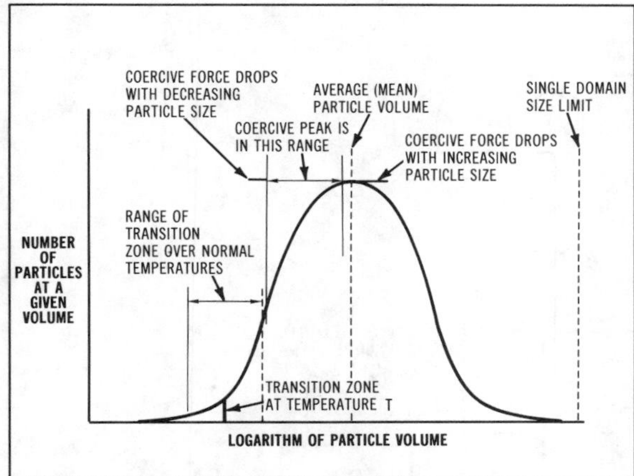

Figure 24-24 Particle size distribution. *(From W. A. Manly, Audio, p. 53, September 1977.)*

during use and storage will decrease the excitation of the thermal idiots. Third, exercising the tape by shuttling the tape from reel to reel several times will partially erase the printed particles. The flexing and rubbing of the tape produces enough activation energy to neutralize some of the printing. For this reason, never copy a stored master tape without exercise. The worst possible print-through level exists on the very first pass of the tape. In some cases print-through can drop as much as 4 to 6 dB with five shuttle cycles.

Due to the vector magnetization components that arise during the recording process, the levels of print on the outer adjacent tape layer are several decibels higher than on the inner adjacent tape layer, as shown in Fig. 24-25. The print-through echoes on musical selections can therefore be minimized by storing the tape "tail out" to bury the louder echo in the decaying signal at the end of the music. The use of nonmagnetic leader tape between selections is also helpful to eliminate pre-echo on selections that begin with a rapid attack.

24.5 TAPE RECORDER ELECTRONICS

The transport mechanism, heads, and tape combine to determine the basic performance limitations of a tape recorder. The electronic circuits of the recorder, on the other hand, do not determine limitations, but rather support the components by providing transparent signal and control networks that give the tape system a specific personality.

The block diagram of the signal electronics of a typical professional audio recorder is shown in Fig. 24-26. In terms of actual hardware, approximately 75% of the audio circuits of a modern professional audio recorder are devoted to operator interfacing and controls; the remaining 25% implement the basic functions of erasing, recording, and playback. Since the variation of features and technology used to implement the interfacing and control functions is too broad to be summarized herein, the following description covers only the latter basic functions.

24.5.1 Playback Amplifiers

The amount of electrical power that can be generated by a magnetic tape passing over the face of a reproduce head is exceedingly small. The output voltage from the head for loud recorded passages will reach no more than

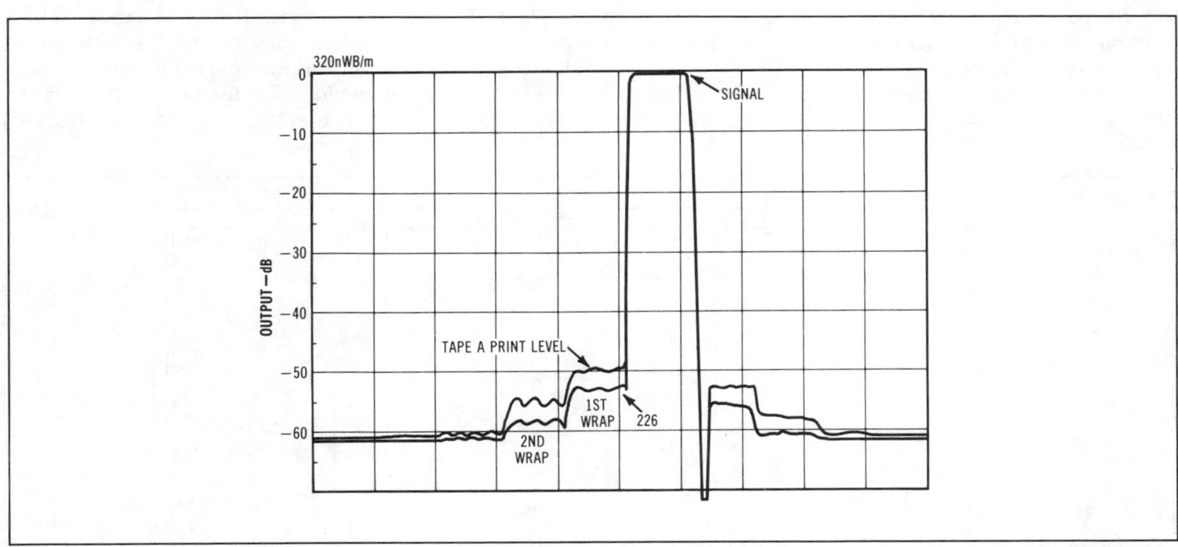

Figure 24-25 Pre- and post-echo print-through. *(Courtesy 3M Co., Magnetic Audio/Video Products Div.)*

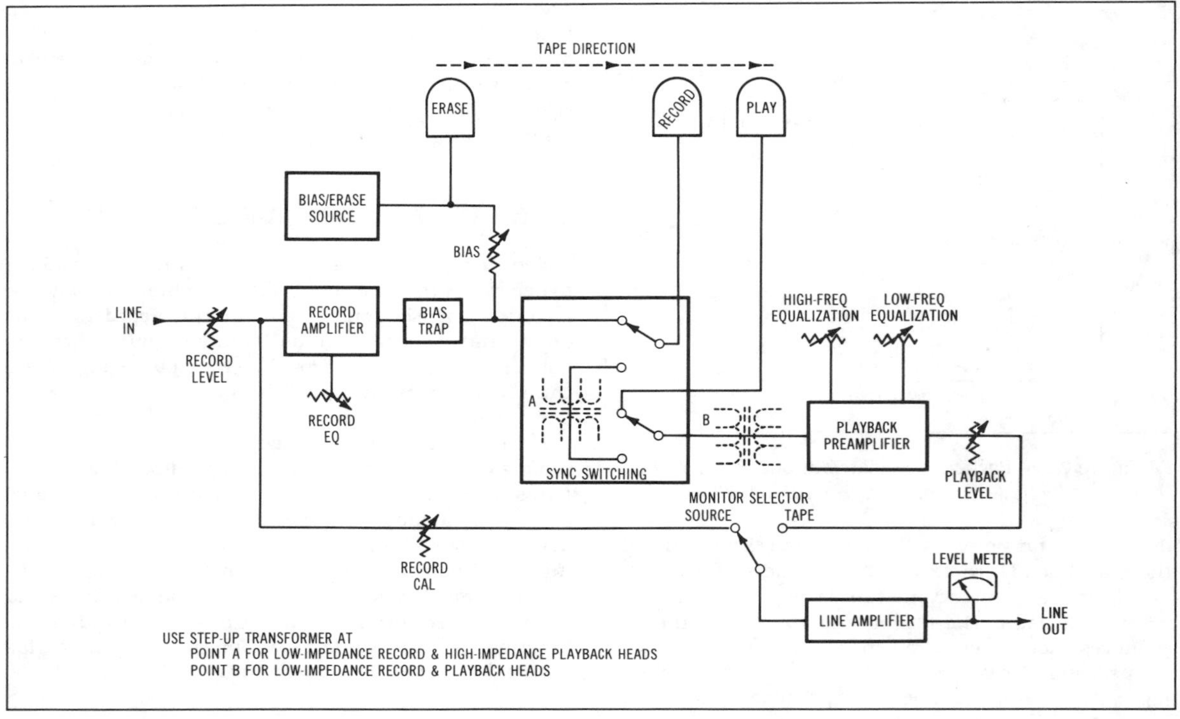

Figure 24-26 Tape recorder signal block diagram.

a few millivolts, with quiet passages dropping into the microvolt region. This weak signal must be carefully boosted without the introduction of additional noise to a higher, more usable level by the first stage of the playback amplifier. Special low-noise amplifier circuits developed for this purpose provide at least 20 dB of voltage gain so that subsequent amplifier stages will not be required to operate near their noise limits.

Since the reproduce head produces an output voltage that is related to the rate of change of the flux on the tape, $d\phi/dt$, the output voltage will rise at a rate of 6-dB/octave. A compensating circuit with a falling 6-dB/octave response, known as an integrator, is used in the playback amplifier to correct for this rise and give a voltage that is proportional to the value of flux sensed by the head.

When the effects of playback head resonance peaking and gap length, spacing, eddy current, and thickness losses are included, the output from the low-noise amplifier and integrator would follow the falling curve in Fig. 24-27 for 15 in./s operation. (See Fig. 24-12 for details.)

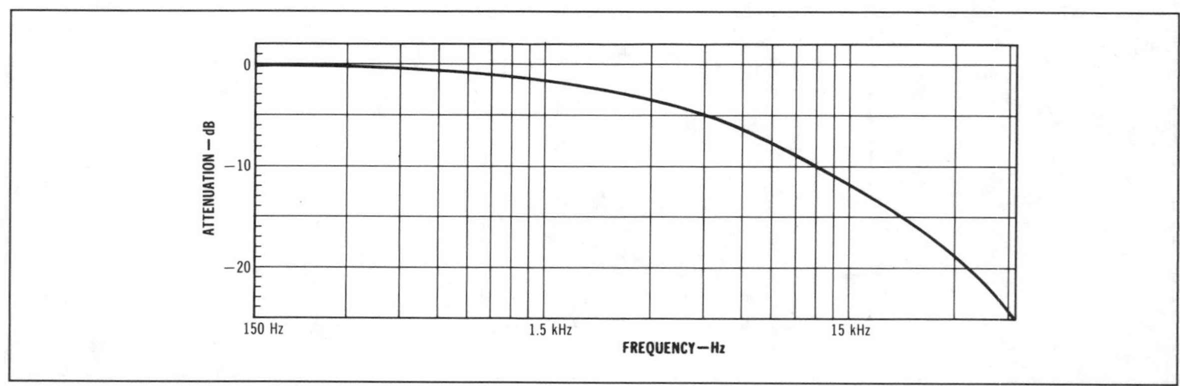

Figure 24-27 Unequalized reproduced head output.

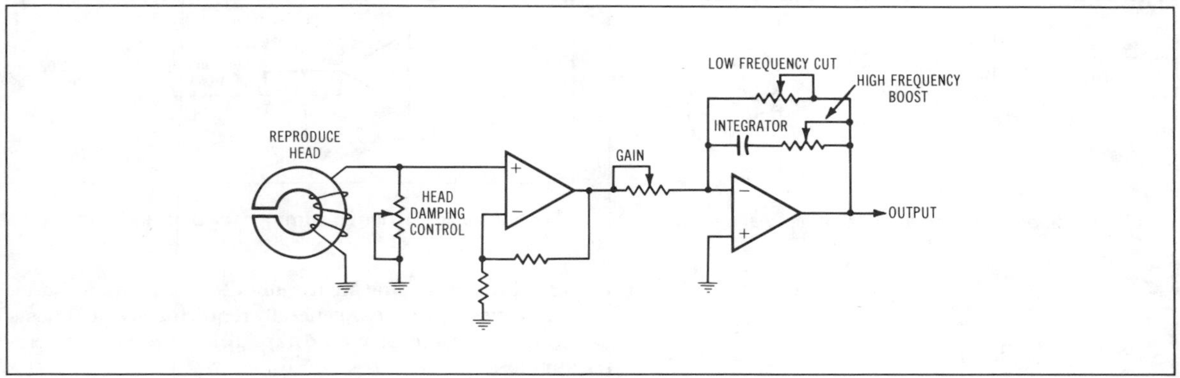

Figure 24-28 Simplified playback amplifier.

This curve must be reshaped by the combined effect of the record and playback equalizers to yield a flat response. The method of partitioning this correction between the record and playback circuits is dictated by the equalization standard chosen by the operator. Since all users of a given equalization standard will be using the same partitioning, the recorded tapes will all be interchangeable.

Fig. 24-28 shows a simplified schematic of a typical operational amplifier type of a playback amplifier capable of the necessary playback corrections. The low-frequency-cut circuit is utilized in some National Association of Broadcasters (NAB) and cassette standards to achieve a decrease in low-frequency playback noise below 100 Hz at the expense of low-frequency headroom. A typical design would include additional ancillary components for amplifier biasing and stabilization.

With one common exception, the same type of circuitry is utilized in the sync/overdub mode to condition and amplify the playback signal from the record head. The exception is in the form of an added voltage-boosting transformer that is commonly necessary to get the signal above the noise floor of the low-noise input section. This problem arises from the low inductance and few turns of wire that are typically found in a record head. The record head must pass the audio plus the high-frequency bias signal; therefore, the inductance must be kept low enough to avoid self-resonance with the head cables at the bias frequency. When fewer turns are used to reduce the inductance, the output voltage goes down proportionately. In essence, these turns are restored in the transformer by a step-up turns ratio ranging from 3:1 to as high as 10:1.

24.5.2 Record Circuits

The primary task of the amplifier that drives the record head is to convert the input audio signal voltage into a proportional amount of current flowing in the windings of the record head. To accomplish this task, the head driver must overcome the rise in head impedance with frequency that is due to the inductance of the head. A common technique to achieve flat current response, as shown in Fig. 24-29A, is to insert a resistor in series with the head so that the combined series impedance of the resistor and the head remain relatively constant throughout the audio band. If the resistance is chosen to be two to three times the reactance of the head at the upper limit of the desired audio band, the desired constant current characteristics can be achieved.

The primary disadvantage of the series resistor is the loss of headroom due to the extra signal drop across the resistor. This problem can be overcome with an active current feedback circuit that senses the current in the head through a small sampling resistor. Fig. 24-29B shows a sampling resistor R_s in series with the return leg of the head. The voltage generated across R_s by the current flowing in the head is fed back to the inverting input for comparison with the incoming audio signal. The high gain of the driver amplifier necessitates only a very small feedback signal, creating a negligible loss in headroom at high frequencies.

The circuits of Fig. 24-29 oversimplify the task of driving the record head since no provisions are included for adding the high-frequency bias signal to the current in the head. A common method of adding the bias and audio signals is shown in Fig. 24-30. The audio driver is isolated from the bias source by a parallel trap tuned to the bias frequency so that the bias signal does not create nonlinearities within the audio driver. The high impedance of the trap at the bias frequency also reduces the loading effect of the audio source on the bias source.

A similar isolation of the bias source is accomplished by the capacitor in series with the bias supply. Since the capacitor looks like a high impedance at audio frequencies, the loading effect of the bias supply on the audio source is minimized. At the higher frequencies of the bias signal, the reactance of the capacitor has dropped to a relatively low value that provides adequate coupling of the bias signal into the record head.

An alternate approach that eliminates some of the previously mentioned isolation requirements is shown in Fig.

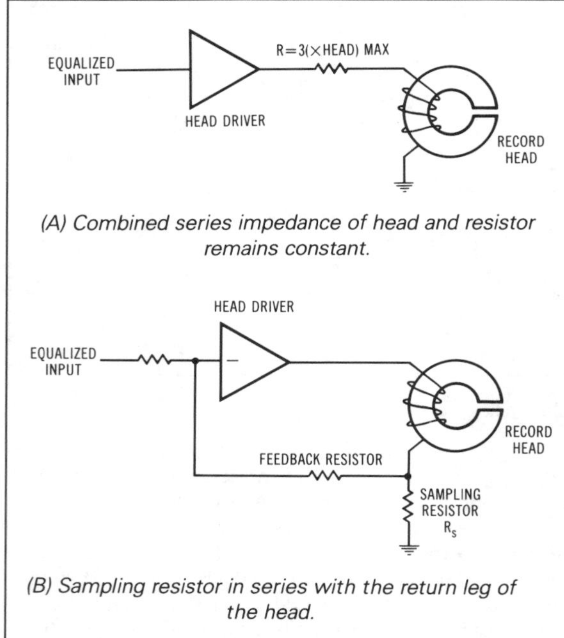

(A) Combined series impedance of head and resistor remains constant.

(B) Sampling resistor in series with the return leg of the head.

Figure 24-29 Constant current record head drivers.

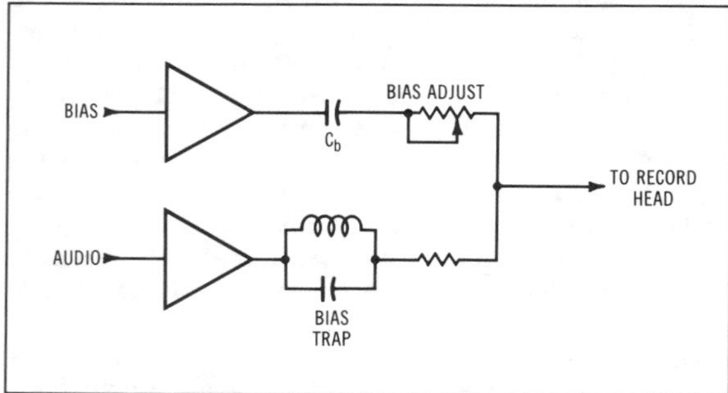

Figure 24-30 Audio and bias coupling to record head.

24-31. In this case, the bias and the audio are added together at the input to a combination bias/audio head driver amplifier. If the amplifier has sufficient headroom and very low distortion, the two signals can be amplified simultaneously by the same amplifier without any interference. The problem of coupling the output to the head for constant current drive must still be overcome, however, by including either a complex coupling network or an active feedback network.

In addition to the head driver circuits, which correct for any response droop due to head inductance, the record amplifier must provide deliberate frequency response tailoring to match the prevailing equalization standards. The standards usually require an adjustable boost at 6

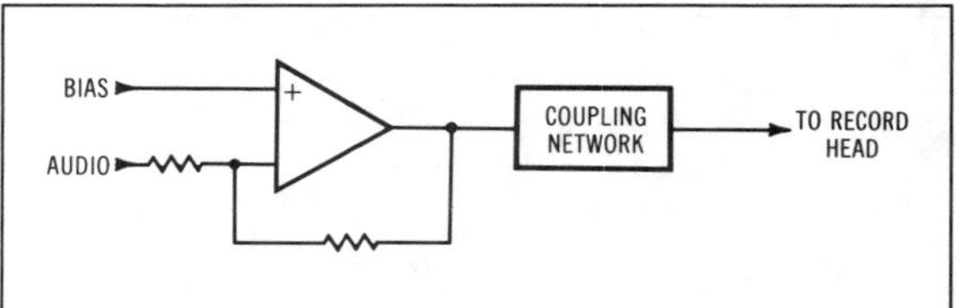

Figure 24-31 Active summer for bias and audio.

dB/octave beginning in the middle of the audio band, with lower tape speeds generally requiring greater boosts to overcome the increased tape thickness and self-erasure losses.

The needed boost is easily implemented by the reactance-capacitance circuit shown in Fig. 24-32A, but the use of a variable capacitor is inconvenient due to the limited range of capacitor adjustment and the awkward size and mounting of the capacitor. Newer designs, therefore, favor operational amplifier configurations that control the amount of boost with a potentiometer. One such circuit, shown in Fig. 24-32B, selectively adds the output of a differentiator circuit, which rises at 6 dB/octave, to the main signal path.

A secondary benefit of the differentiator circuit is the phase change introduced by the inverting characteristics of the differentiator amplifier. Unlike most of the loss-correction circuits of the signal path, which introduce signal delay at high frequencies, the inverted differentia-

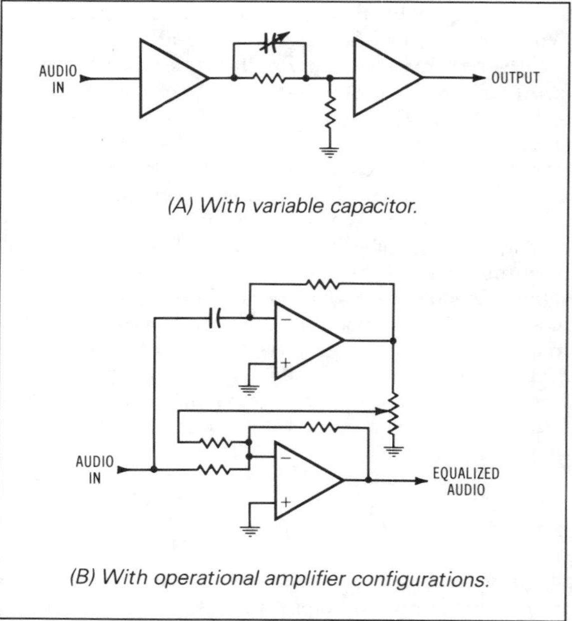

(A) With variable capacitor.

(B) With operational amplifier configurations.

Figure 24-32 High-frequency record boost circuits.

tor advances the high frequencies. The proper combination of advance and delay can provide less phase distortion in the signal, yielding improved transient response with less overshoot. A similar phase-correcting effect has been implemented in other designs by providing an all-pass, phase-shifting network in the reproduce amplifier.

The NAB and compact cassette equalization standards provide an additional record signal boost at low frequencies to overcome the hum and noise limitations of the reproduce amplifiers. Typical circuits for this purpose are shown in Fig. 24-33. In both cases, a 6-dB/octave rise is achieved with a corner frequency of 50 Hz.

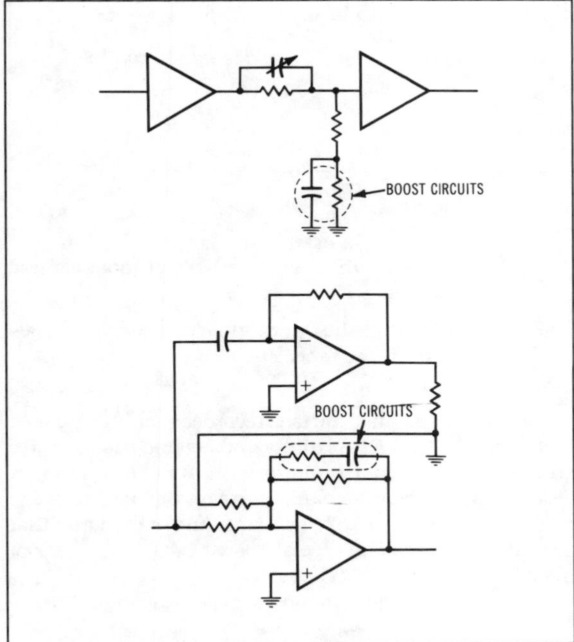

Figure 24-33 Low-frequency record boost circuits.

Abrupt changes in the bias and audio signals on the record head must be avoided whenever the record mode is entered or exited. Ramping circuits are employed for this purpose to control the buildup and decay of these signals. Typical methods include the use of analog switching elements such as bipolar-junction or field-effect transistors. The rate of switching of these elements is limited to a value that does not create abrupt transients but, at the same time, is quick enough to avoid annoying delays, over-recordings, or program holes.

24.5.3 Bias and Erase Circuits

The high-frequency signals required for biasing and erasing all tracks of the tape are derived from a single master oscillator so that no interference or beating of multiple oscillators will occur. Older designs generally employ a tuned push-pull multivibrator oscillator; newer designs favor crystal-stabilized oscillators utilizing digital circuitry. Several designs have used separate bias and erase frequencies, with the erase circuit running at one-third the bias frequency to minimize the power dissipation on the erase head.

In all cases, the primary consideration is purity of the bias and erase current waveform. Any even-order harmonics, including dc, second harmonics, fourth harmonics, and so on, will create a detrimental rise in the background tape noise, reducing the available signal-to-noise ratio for the recorder. Although older designs, such as Fig. 24-34A, relied heavily on push-pull circuits with balancing transformers to minimize these even-order components, newer designs, such as Fig. 24-34B, favor filtering and feedback control to reduce unwanted components.

The erase head is typically coupled to the erase source with an adjustable series resonating capacitor to minimize the voltage required from the driver and to filter out even-order components.

A current sampling resistor is frequently provided in the return leg of the erase head circuit so that the amplitude of the erase current can be conveniently monitored.

24.6 TAPE RECORDER TRANSPORT, MAINTENANCE, AND TESTING

Reliability is no accident! Dependable operation of any complicated electromechanical device, whether it be a tape recorder or a jet airliner, requires nearly constant observation to detect symptoms of problems that could lead to catastrophic failures. Just as the ground crew and pilot always inspect an aircraft prior to flight, the maintenance technician and recording engineer should always inspect and test a tape recorder prior to the beginning of a recording session.

Maintenance begins with inspection and cleaning. Before starting the cleaning procedure, note the location and type of dirt and debris that has accumulated due to prior use. Excessive debris indicates that your recording tape is being slowly destroyed by the tape transport. Just as you would get excited if your automobile suddenly began to belch huge clouds of black smoke, you should heed the maintenance messages that the tape recorder is giving you. Although some of the more common symptoms of problems are covered in the following discussion, don't forget plain old common sense, which is still the most useful tool to achieve reliability. Pay attention!

A deposit of very fine, silky threads indicates that the polyester base film of the tape is being scraped off by a sharp edge on a guide flange. Examine all edge guides for grooves cut into the flanges by the tape. Either reposition the guide to place an unworn surface in contact with the tape or install a new guide if the groove is severe.

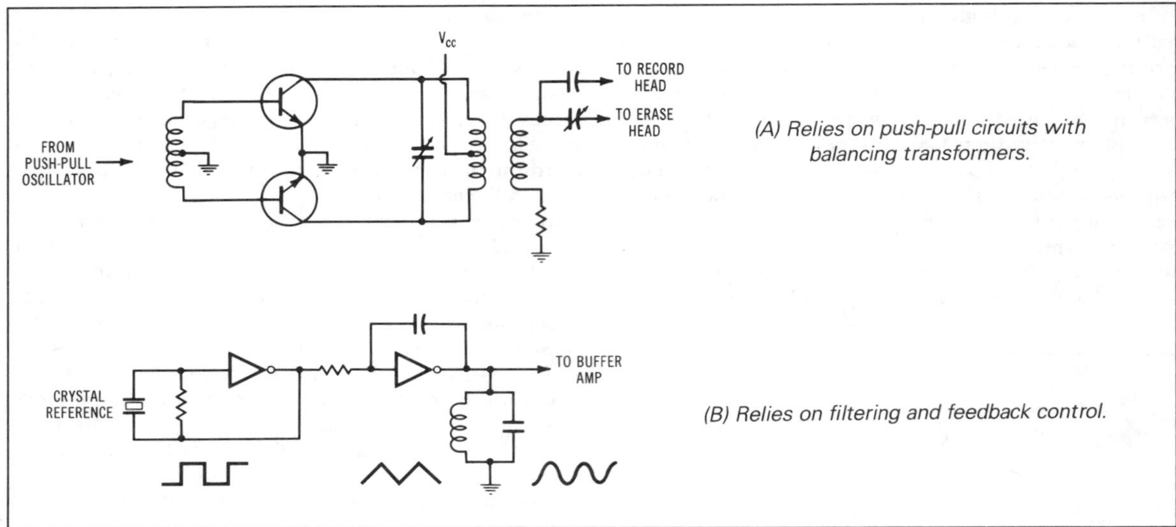

Figure 24-34 Typical bias and erase sources.

Deposits of brown or black dust near the guides indicate that the edges of the tape are being scraped or deformed enough to break small chunks of coating from the edge of the tape. Check the tape tension and the height of the guides and reel hubs.

Any caked-on deposits on the surface of the guides or heads are very serious. Inspect the surface of the tape for scratch marks. If the tape surface is being scratched, continued use will destroy the tape. Correct the cause of the scratches before continuing.

Several types of cleaners are available for cleaning tape machines. Head cleaners, which contain strong solvents to dissolve tape residue, are suitable for cleaning the heads, guides, and metal capstans. Use a soft cotton swab moistened with cleaner to scrub the surfaces. Avoid scraping the face of the head with the stick or core of the swab. Allow adequate time, typically 30 s, for the solvent to evaporate before rethreading the tape.

Head cleaning solvents will attack some plastics and create a hard, glazed surface on some rubber rollers. Use general-purpose cleaners for the plastic components and rubber cleaners or Freon™ for the rubber rollers.

The tape must also be kept completely free of dirt. Keep the surface of the transport clean to avoid dirt being picked up during high-speed spooling. Always return the tape to its storage carton between uses. Avoid touching the edges of the tape pack when handling the reel. (Skin debris from fingers is a source of tape dropouts!)

In addition:

1. Avoid eating french fries, tacos, or other greasy foods while handling tapes.
2. Contamination due to finger oils and debris can be avoided during editing sessions by wearing lint-free editing gloves, which are available at most camera supply stores.
3. Keep cigarette ashes and other powdery materials far away from the tape.

The cooling system of the tape recorder should be cleaned periodically. Clean all air filters and cooling passageways and remove any dust buildup with a vacuum cleaner. Verify that all inlet or exhaust ports on the bottom of the machine are not obstructed by carpeting or dust and that adequate clearance for free air flow exists at the rear of the machine.

Following cleaning, diagnostic servicing should begin

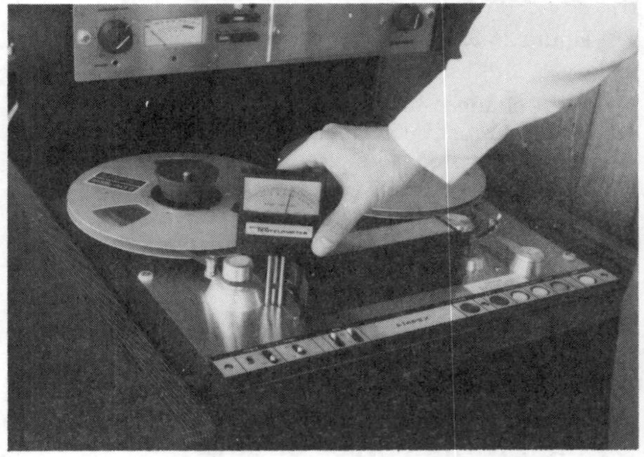

Figure 24-35 Tension measurement. *(Courtesy Ampex Corp.)*

with verification that the tape tension at the heads is adequate to maintain good tape-to-head contact. On many machines a tape tension gauge of the type shown in Fig. 24-35 can be inserted in the tape path near the heads to measure the tension. For other machines that are too crowded in the head area, either the head assembly must be removed or a test location away from the heads must be used. Measure the tension at both the beginning and the end of the reel.

(Note that the stiffness of a piece of tape varies with the width, base film thickness, and type of tape. The tension gauge must be adjusted before use to read correctly for the specific tape sample being used on the transport. A calibration weight is included with the gauge for this purpose.)

Table 24-7. Nominal Tape Tensions

1/4 in.	1/2 in.	1 in.	2 in.
3–4 oz	4–8 oz	6–12 oz	10–24 oz

The tape tension values shown in Table 24-7 indicate the range of tensions commonly encountered on studio recorders. The nominal value for a given model of recorder will be found in the maintenance manual for the machine.

24.6.1 Speed

Absolute tape speed is extremely difficult to measure, even under the controlled conditions of a laboratory. One method available to maintenance personnel is to measure the frequency reproduced from a commercially available speed reference tape. The frequency read on the frequency counter must be corrected for any difference between the tape tension on the playback machine and the tension value used by the manufacturer of the tape during the recording process. A correction table is furnished with the tape for this purpose.

A more common speed test is to check speed consistency from beginning to end of a reel of a tape. The following procedure outlines the general technique:

1. Using an oscillator that has been operating long enough to reach stable conditions, record a reference tone in the range of 1 to 5 kHz at the head end of the tape.
2. Flip the reels so that the head end becomes the tail.
3. Using the console monitoring provisions of the console, mix the reproduced tone with the oscillator tone, listening for any major pitch differences. (If a significant error is detected, flip the reels again to verify that the oscillator has not shifted frequency.)

A more accurate version of this test is to use a frequency counter to measure the frequency at both ends of the reel. The speed error in percent is then calculated as

$$\%\,\text{speed error} = [2\,(\text{head} - \text{tail}) / (\text{head} + \text{tail})] \times 100\% \qquad (24\text{-}10)$$

A speed error of 6% will yield a pitch change of one half-tone step. Typical recorder specifications are in the range of 0.1 to 0.5%.

Possible causes of speed error include excessive tension variations from beginning to end of the reel, tape slippage due to a worn capstan surface or inadequate pinch roller pressure, and unstable capstan speed.

Assuming that tape tension has already been determined to be correct on both sides of the capstan, the next test is to check pinch roller pressure. First, inspect the pinch roller for glazing of the roller surface or excessive wear. Fig. 24-36 shows roller wear patterns that may reduce the traction between the tape and capstan.

Next, a spring scale is coupled to the top (and the bottom, if possible) of the pinch roller yoke or arm, as shown in Fig. 24-37. The scale is pulled at *right angles* to the support arm with just enough force to disengage the roller from the capstan. The force reading at disengagement should be compared with the recorder manufacturer's recommended value.

For some transports the pinch roller force is set as a fixed number of turns of a nut or screw. For this case the roller linkage is first tightened to bring the roller into light contact with the capstan, and then the recom-

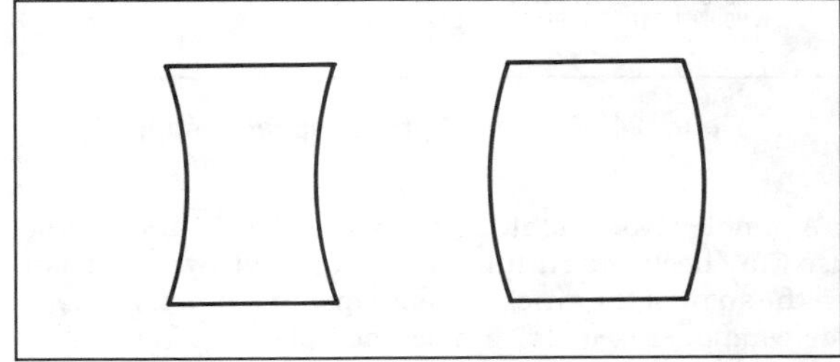

Figure 24-36 Pinch roller wear patterns.

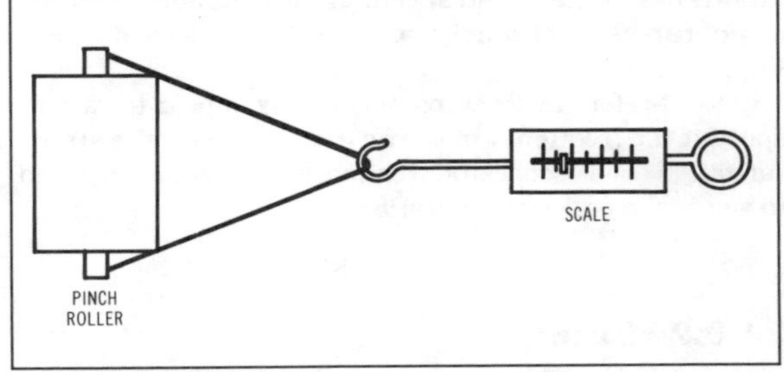

Figure 24-37 Pinch roller force measurement.

mended clamping force is applied by tightening the adjustment by the specified number of additional turns.

The surface of the capstan may become so highly polished by the abrasive action of the tape that slippage will persist for the correct values of tension and pinch roller pressure. In this case the capstan must be resurfaced by plating or sandblasting or both to restore the required traction.

In very rare cases the capstan motor may actually slow down due to excessive loading caused by bad motor bearings or high tension. One noteworthy problem, which can produce excessive loading, are the bushing bearings, which are used on many direct-drive ac synchronous capstan motors and some capstan pinch rollers. Periodic lubrication of these components is essential to maintain low-friction operation. Although these components may appear to spin freely when turned by hand in an unloaded state, the friction can rise dramatically when the engagement solenoid exerts several pounds of side load on the bearings. The resulting drag and wear due to dry bearings may produce substantial speed errors. To avoid problems, follow the manufacturer's recommended lubrication schedule.

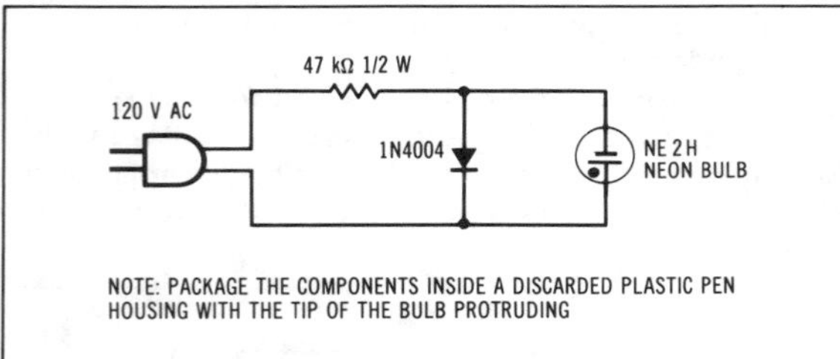
47 kΩ 1/2 W
120 V AC
1N4004
NE 2H
NEON BULB
NOTE: PACKAGE THE COMPONENTS INSIDE A DISCARDED PLASTIC PEN HOUSING WITH THE TIP OF THE BULB PROTRUDING

Figure 24-38 Strobe light for speed testing.

A simple strobe light, as shown in Fig. 24-38, can be used to check the running speed of the flywheel or fan on the shaft of the synchronous capstan motors. Package the components inside a discarded plastic pen housing with the tip of the bulb protruding. Hold the light close enough to the rotating device to observe a reflection. The reflected pattern must remain stationary under all conditions of tape pack and speed. Induction motors, which do not run at synchronous speed, will always yield a moving pattern.

Crystal-referenced servos may falsely appear to vary in speed if the frequency of the ac mains driving the strobe varies. An oscilloscope and frequency counter are required to verify correct servo operation.

24.6.2 Flutter

Speed drift represents only the very lowest-frequency components of the spectrum of speed errors. Measurement of the higher-frequency flutter components requires a specialized frequency demodulating instrument called a *flutter meter.* As seen in Fig. 24-39, the flutter meter resembles the phase-lock servo of Fig. 24-1. The reference signal from the crystal clock must pass through the record/playback process of a tape recorder before being applied to one of the phase comparator inputs. The low-pass filter and voltage-controlled oscillator simulate a large flywheel that stores the average value of the playback frequency. By applying the average value to the second phase comparator input, the phase comparator output will consist of only the short-term variations from the average speed. These variations are divided into various frequency bands for further analysis. The metering circuit provides a convenient quantitative measurement of the speed variations.

The range of flutter components, which can be measured by any frequency demodulator, is determined primarily by the frequency of the test tone. The typical upper frequency is 0.4 times the test frequency. Due to the nature of the sidebands, which are required to operate the demodulator, a typical 18-kHz audio bandwidth can support a 12.5-kHz test tone and a flutter bandwidth of 5 kHz.

Unfortunately, most flutter meters use a low-frequency test tone of 3150 Hz and cut off all flutter components above 250 Hz, ignoring many flutter components due to modern-day servo systems and virtually all scrape components due to the elastic vibration of the tape.

Two methods of specifying flutter performance are commonly encountered. If a flutter-free test tape is available, the flutter reading obtained in the playback mode can be reported. Most professional recorders, however, have flutter levels that are equal to or better than any available test tapes. In this case the test is made by recording and reproducing on the same machine. The method of testing should be noted.

Although test and diagnostic work is commonly conducted with simultaneous record/reproduce, the final testing should always be conducted in the reproduce-only mode. The tape should be started and stopped several times, with the various transport elements reoriented by hand between each run, to achieve a sampling of random combinations of the various record and playback flutter components. The arithmetic average of the maximum values of each sample throughout the reel, excluding any infrequent short-duration bursts, is the reported value.

If the flutter readings are excessive, the next step is to analyze the flutter waveform for information to help pinpoint which tape path component is defective. The following techniques are helpful in isolating the culprit.

1. The human ear and brain form a very versatile spectrum analyzer that frequently can immediately identify the defective component from the characteristics of the flutter signal being reproduced in a monitor loudspeaker. Take advantage of this "free" portable instrument, which is always at your disposal.

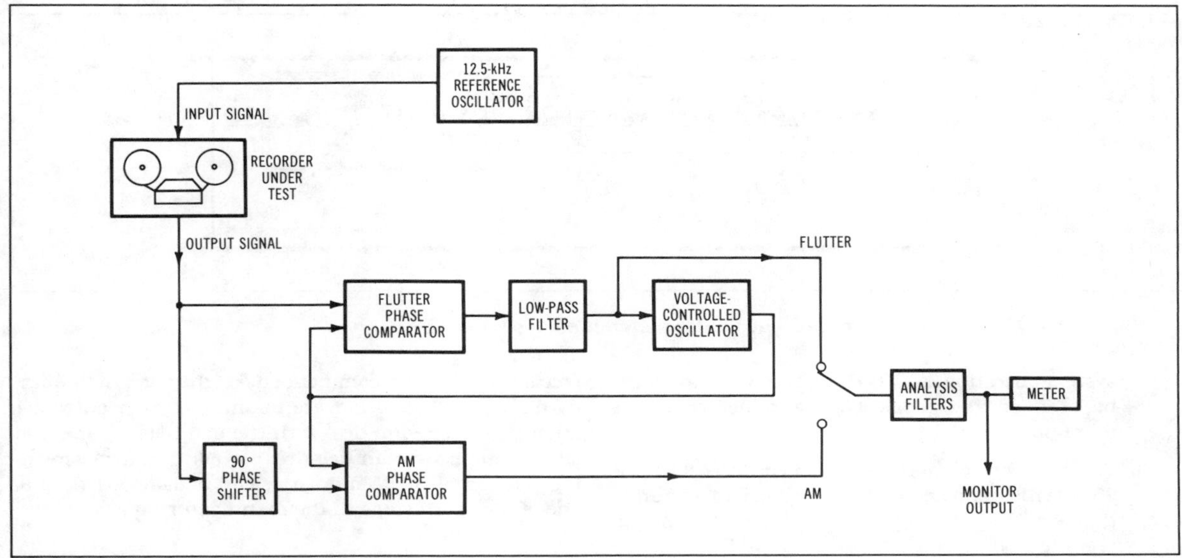

Figure 24-39 Flutter meter block diagram.

2. The various selectable filters of the flutter meter can be used to isolate the general portion of the flutter spectrum in which the offending component is generating flutter.
3. The expected rotational flutter rate from a rotating component can be calculated from the diameter of the component and the tape speed using the expression

$$\text{flutter frequency} = \text{tape speed}/\pi \text{ diameter} \tag{24-11}$$

These frequencies can range from approximately 0.5 Hz for the once-around of full reel of tape to 60 Hz for a small-diameter capstan shaft. Some manufacturers include a table of these flutter frequencies in their maintenance manuals. Additional not-so-obvious flutter components at frequencies higher than the once-around rate are generated by the small balls and retainer clips inside the ball bearings used in many rotating components.

4. If the flutter is very regular, the flutter pattern displayed on the oscilloscope can be utilized to calculate the frequency of the dominant flutter component. Any flutter components caused by ac motors or power supply ripple will remain stationary on the oscilloscope screen if the sweep triggering mode is set to "line."
5. A common search technique is to create flutter deliberately by attaching a small piece of masking tape to the surface of a rotating component. The rate of the flutter "blips" created by the tape can then be compared with the unknown component to determine if the two rates are identical.
6. Note any change in the flutter spectrum when each of the auxiliary rotating components such as guides and flutter idlers are stalled. Stalling the defective component will cause the offending flutter component to cease. A notable exception to this case is the scrape flutter idler. Stalling a scrape flutter idler should usually double or triple the scrape flutter amplitude. If little or no increase is noted, the idler is not functioning properly. Check for dirty or damaged bearings that would keep the idler from spinning freely.

The following procedure describes a flutter test using a wide-bandwidth flutter meter, such as is shown in Fig. 24-40. The general technique also applies to other meters.

1. Connect the reference oscillator output (REF OSC) to the line input of the tape recorder.
2. Connect the demodulator input (INPUT) to the line output of the tape recorder.
3. Connect the demodulated output (MONITOR) to an oscilloscope and an audio monitor.
4. With the tape machine in the record mode, set the recorder's input level control to achieve a playback level of −10 vu. The green Cal light should be illuminated, indicating proper operating level.
5. With the FM/AM and Avg/Peak buttons both out and the 5-kHz and 1.0%-FM buttons in, depress the Cal button. A reading of 0.68% indicates proper

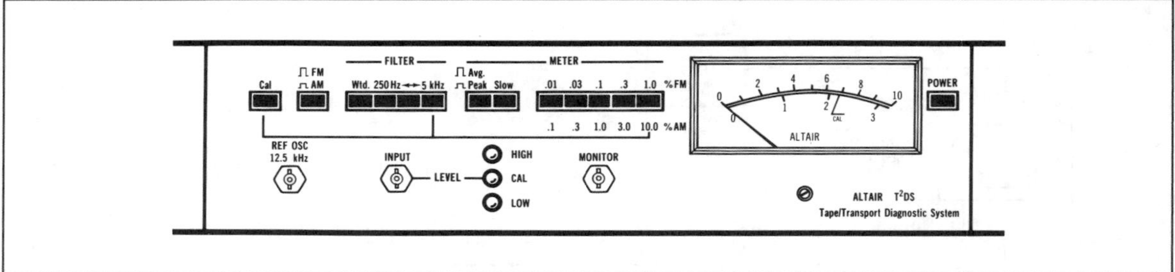

Figure 24-40 Flutter meter. *(Courtesy Altair Electronics)*

system operation. A 150-Hz square-wave tone will be seen on the oscilloscope and heard in the monitor.

6. To begin the actual test of the recorder, select the 250-Hz filter and choose the meter sensitivity range that yields a reading near midscale. The meter reading is the composite value of all flutter components in the frequency band of 0.5 to 250 Hz, including flutter due to not only the rotating capstan, roller, and guides and their associated bearings but also any ac-power-related motor torque pulsations.
7. Select the Wtd. filter. The bandwidth is now reduced to 0.5 to 20 Hz, to emphasize the once-around rates due to eccentricities of the rotating components. Capstans and rollers with diameters of ½ to 2 in. are major contributions in this band.
8. Select the 250-Hz to 5-kHz bandpass filter labeled "⟷". The dominant component in this range is scrape flutter, which typically peaks at 3 to 4 kHz for most recorders. Instabilities or oscillations of the capstan or spooling servos, which tend to occur in the 100 to 500 Hz range, may also be evident.
9. If the machine is equipped with a scrape flutter idler, stall the idler by pressing the point of a pencil against the idler. The scrape flutter component should typically rise to two or three times the normal value. If little or no rise or even a decrease is noted, the scrape flutter idler is not functioning properly. Clean and lubricate the idler bearings according to the manufacturer's instructions. Use the flutter meter to obtain optimum positioning of the idler after cleaning.
10. Select the 5-kHz filter. This overall reading covers the entire range from 0.5 Hz to 5 kHz.

24.7 TAPE TESTING

Contrary to popular belief, not all tape that reaches the customer's hands is fault free. Although the tape manufacturers are to be commended for the very high standards of excellence that are maintained, the customer must be prepared to deal with the bad rolls of tape that slip through the manufacturer's quality control screening. The problems that do arise can usually be traced to one of the seven steps in the manufacturing process:

1. The basic recipe of approximately a dozen ingredients that form the oxide mixture must be correctly formulated. Each ingredient must be pure and must be measured correctly. Errors in mixing and experimental "formula modifications" often lead to nondurable oxides that shed debris onto the guides and heads.
2. The mixing of the ingredients must be thorough but not excessive. Inadequate mixing leads to high modulation noise and high background noise. Excessive mixing reduces noise but increases print-through.
3. The coating process must apply a uniform coating across the width and length of the tape. The coating is applied to jumbo rolls that range from 18 to 36 in. in width. To monitor the entire width of one of these rolls fully would require over 400 channels of conventional record/reproduce circuits!
4. The tape is baked to remove solvents by passing the coated web through a multizone oven. Poor temperature control can lead to either brittle or soft oxides.
5. The jumbo roll is run through heated rollers that make the oxide more dense to increase output and high-frequency response. This calendering step is a major factor in determining the modulation noise content of the finished tape.
6. The tape is slit to the final width by a set of rotary shears. Poor slitting can produce ruffled edges, wavy or crooked tape, and excessive oxide and backing debris on the recording surface.
7. The tape is rewound onto reels or hubs, tested, and then packaged for sale. The tape cartons usually pass through a very large degausser so that no residual signals are left on the tape.

Mistakes during the manufacturing process create four types of problems. The most common of these is signal amplitude variations, which are due to either a nonhomogeneous magnetic dispersion or erratic tape-to-head contact due to physical distortions of the tape. Other common problems include excessive noise or distortion and high print-through.

A common method of testing the signal instability and dropouts is to observe the amplitude variations of a sine-wave signal on either an oscilloscope or a VU meter. While these techniques give some insight into the performance of the tape, they do not yield a quantitative value that can be used for determining acceptable limits of performance.

A more informative method is to amplitude demodulate the test signal to remove the steady tone and magnify the fluctuations. If the output of the demodulator is properly filtered and fed to a metering circuit, quantitative values for the fluctuations in various test bandwidths can be read.

Unlike other flutter test instruments, the flutter meter shown in Fig. 24-40 contains amplitude-demodulating circuitry to be used for testing tape. The AM test configuration is identical to the previous flutter setup, except that the FM/AM selector is set for AM mode testing to connect the phase lock loop as a synchronous amplitude demodulator. The AM meter ranges, which are ten times larger than the flutter ranges, are labeled below the meter ranging pushbuttons.

The AM reading for 15-in./s operation is typically 0.5% rms for a good roll of tape on a professional recorder. The texture of the demodulation products coming from the audio monitor should be a low rumbling with only occasional moderate bursts. The highpass filter "⟷" should produce a uniform hiss.

Typical symptoms of bad rolls of tape include readings that are approximately three times higher than the normal readings or very large frequent bursts that drive the meter pointer hard against the upper stop. Routine studio tests of large quantities of tape stock over a period of two years has shown that these easily spotted characteristics are good indicators of defective tape.

Although amplitude variations are symptomatic of bad tape, the tape transport and heads are also possible sources. If the tape is not being held snugly against the faces of the heads due to inadequate tape tension, the tape may suffer irregular spacing loss. Other contributors are dirt on the heads or heads that have been worn so flat that the gap is no longer pressed firmly against the tape. Mechanical misalignments, such as a twisted head or improperly positioned guides or scrape flutter idlers, can also degrade the contact between the tape and head.

Misadjustments of the bias amplitude or even-order distortions of the bias or erase waveforms can also produce excessive AM levels. Always verify that the bias levels and tuning are correct before condemning the tape.

A simple method of avoiding embarrassment when a defective roll of tape is suspected is to recheck the machine with a reference roll of the same type of tape that is known to be good. If changing from the reference roll to the suspect roll causes a large increase in AM content, then the tape is the source of the problem.

Since none of the tape manufacturers supply information that is useful for specifying the AM performance of a tape, the user must generate data by testing several rolls of tape on machines. Once this process is begun, subsequent additions to the data base will provide even more insight into the expected range of values.

24.8 MAGNETIC HEAD TROUBLESHOOTING AND MAINTENANCE

Troubleshooting any piece of complex equipment requires a methodical search technique to isolate the source of the problem quickly. The most productive technique is to conduct a series of tests that subdivide the faulty portion of the total system into smaller and smaller parts until the fault source is finally isolated. Indeed, if each test could divide the section being tested into a good half and a bad half, only $\log_2(n)$ tests would be required for a system with n components. Although most systems do not break down into neatly nested subsystems within subsystems, the concept of "divide and conquer" can still be applied.

Applying this technique to a magnetic tape recorder would lead to partitioning questions such as:

Is the problem associated with the tape drive, the audio circuitry, or the control logic?

Does the fault occur during recording or during playback?

Is the problem due to the recorder or the roll of tape?

If the problem relates to the audio signal passing through the recorder, a fundamental question that must be answered is whether the problem is wavelength-dependent (spatial) or frequency-dependent (temporal). Spatial problems immediately isolate the problem to the interface between the moving tape and the heads. Temporal problems are usually related to the audio circuits.

The most useful tool for separating spatial problems from temporal problems is a simple device known as a *flux loop*. The flux loop, which consists of nothing more than a few turns of fine magnet wire driven with a constant current from an audio oscillator, creates a magnetic field that simulates a perfect lossless piece of tape. When the flux loop is attached to the gap region of the playback head, the flux from the loop excites the head much like the primary winding on a transformer excites the secondary winding. This direct excitation eliminates all the wavelength effects associated with gap length, azimuth error, and thickness loss. If the reproduce electronics perform correctly when excited by the flux loop but still fail to reproduce a known-good prerecorded test tape correctly, the problem is a wavelength-dependent error at the head-to-tape interface.

The playback response from a simple flux loop is by no means flat. Since the dominant loss due to the coating thickness is not present for flux loop excitation, the high-frequency response will show a pronounced rise that relates to the particular reproduce equalization standard that is being utilized. NAB low-frequency equalization will also produce a rolloff below 50 Hz.

To simplify the measurement process, the oscillator signal feeding the flux loop is usually preequalized to accommodate these effects of the equalization standard. The resulting high-frequency playback response of an equalized flux loop will be flat except for any residual high-frequency discrepancies due to eddy current losses or self-resonance of the playback head and cabling.

The flux loop can also be used in reverse as a pickup device to probe the magnetic fields generated at the gaps of the record and erase heads. If the driving network is disconnected and the loop connected directly to the inputs of an oscilloscope and meter, the relative magnitude of the bias and audio fields can be examined. Care must be exercised to correct for the 6-dB/octave rise in flux loop output voltage due to the inductive nature of the flux loop.

Unfortunately, in spite of the wealth of very precise troubleshooting data that can be gathered with a flux loop, the flux loop remains a rarity in most audio maintenance facilities. Poorly trained technicians seem to prefer to grapple with the intertwined spatial and temporal effects of an alignment tape because of the feeling of security associated with the magic words "Standard Alignment Tape." They forget that many malfunctions are not the result of a mere misalignment, but rather they are due to serious underlying problems that must be located and corrected.

Details regarding the construction and use of a flux loop, along with detailed mechanical alignment procedures for azimuth, height, and tape wrap are available from the various tape recorder manufacturers.

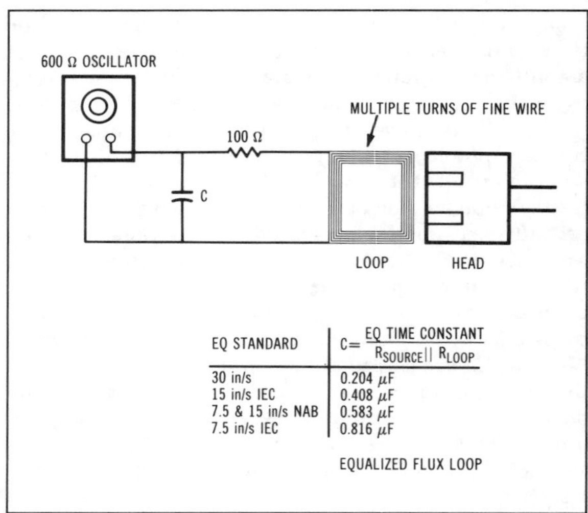

EQ STANDARD	$C = \frac{\text{EQ TIME CONSTANT}}{R_{SOURCE} \| R_{LOOP}}$
30 in/s	0.204 μF
15 in/s IEC	0.408 μF
7.5 & 15 in/s NAB	0.583 μF
7.5 in/s IEC	0.816 μF

Figure 24-41 Flux loop.

24.9 HEAD RELAPPING

The performance characteristics gradually change as the abrasive action of the tape wears away the faces of the heads, as shown in Fig. 24-41. The resulting decreases in gap depth will reduce shunting effects, leading to an increase in efficiency for both the record and playback heads. Bias and audio levels must be gradually reduced to offset the rising efficiency. A critical point is reached, however, when the "useful" face of the head has been completely removed and the length of the gap begins to increase quickly with wear. The playback response will drop abruptly within a matter of only a few hours of use, rendering the recorder unusable. At this point, the head must be replaced to restore normal performance.

The heads on most recorders require attention long before this point of ultimate failure is reached. On most machines, the tape wears away the rounded contour of the face of the head, leading to a drop in contact pressure, which creates erratic short-wavelength performance due to the spacing loss effect.

The common solution is to recontour the face of the head to restore the contact pressure. This process, known as head relapping, can be utilized two or three times during the useful life of a head to restore original performance. The relapping process can be performed by the average trained technician, but the large investment represented by a 2-in. multitrack head assembly suggests that the more exotic relapping tasks should be handled by relapping specialists.

24.10 ROUTINE SIGNAL ALIGNMENT PROCEDURE

A common problem arises with conventional recorders and alignment procedures, namely that the procedures require a change in each adjustment to verify that the optimum point has been reached. This typically leads to not only the premature demise of many trimmer potentiometers (which are typically rated by the manufacturer for a life of 200 adjustment cycles) and head azimuth hardware, but also many operator errors due to the tedious nature of adjusting a multitrack machine that may have as many as 1000 adjustments.

If the operator is willing to adopt a philosophy that most of the adjustments are probably adequately close to optimum and that they need not be readjusted, then the alignment task shifts to looking for the exceptions to the norm rather than arbitrarily resetting everything. This strategy promotes better results since each iteration of the alignment procedure serves to fine-tune the results rather than to erase all past efforts and start afresh for each alignment with a high probability of error.

A few exceptions to the need for tweaking to verify proper performance are worthy of note. For example, head azimuth can be verified with a differential method that uses alternating test segments, which have equal but opposite amounts of deliberate azimuth error. If the drop in level is equal for both directions of tilt, then the head must be correctly aligned to the correct vertical reference. No head adjustments are required if the test results are satisfactory.

A similar noninvasive test procedure for optimizing the bias level can be achieved if the bias system contains a master bias level trimmer, which varies the level of bias for all tracks simultaneously. The bias level can be increased and decreased on all tracks with the single control to verify that the proper level of overbias is achieved without resorting to unnecessary adjustments on each track.

The following sequence of steps represents a comprehensive alignment procedure that would be appropriate whenever the proper performance of a recorder must be verified. Since the details of each step vary with machine type, the operator should consult the operator's manual published by the manufacturer of the recorder.

1. Clean and inspect the tape transport. (Refer to Section 24.6.)

2. Degauss the heads and guides. Before using a degausser, always verify that the tips of the unit are covered with a soft material such as plastic or tape that will not scratch the faces of the magnetic heads.

Degauss the heads and other steel tape-guiding parts with a commercial-grade head degausser. Hold the degausser at least 1 ft from the tape transport when applying power to the degausser. Move the degausser slowly and smoothly from bottom to top along the gap line of each head, moving at a rate of approximately 1/8 in./s. At the top of the head, withdraw the degausser smoothly 6 in. and then move smoothly to the next item to be degaussed.

Multiple degaussing passes on a component do not improve the quality of the results. A single smooth pass is adequate.

Always move the degausser at least 3 ft away from the transport before disconnecting the power from the degausser. The rapid collapse of the magnetic degaussing field at turnoff can easily undo all of the benefits of degaussing if the degausser has not been pulled away sufficiently. (For this reason, avoid degaussers that have momentary power switches that might be accidentally released in the middle of the degaussing routine.)

Although a typical head degausser will not disturb a recorded tape that is more than 1 ft from the degausser, always remove all tapes from the vicinity of the transport prior to energizing the degausser.

3. Calibrate the reproduce section of the recorder with a test tape of known accuracy. Several brands of standard alignment tapes are available for this purpose. Remember that the final results will be no better than the measurement standard that is being used as a reference.

First, verify the perpendicular alignment of the reproduce head with the short-wavelength azimuth test tone on the test tape. The azimuth and/or phase alignment of the head can be measured with an oscilloscope using either a Lissajous pattern or a dual-trace display, with a level meter by summing two tracks and peaking the amplitude of the combined signal, or with a phase meter that reads phase error directly. Since phase alignment at one frequency does not eliminate the possibility of a 360° error, check the phase for several lower frequencies. The voice announcements on the alignment tapes provide a convenient multifrequency sample for this purpose.

Next, establish a convenient reference level for making frequency-response measurements. Check and adjust the high-frequency reproduce equalizer at 10 kHz to match this reference level. Once the equalizer has been set, sweep through the tones on the tape, noting the maximum deviations from the reference value. Readjust the equalizer and the reference level as necessary to obtain the desired degree of flatness.

When the results are satisfactory, write down the results for later comparison. Having a record of correct performance makes troubleshooting much easier.

Two pitfalls exist when making the previously discussed adjustments: one affects the reference level and the other affects the frequency-response and reference level. Some recorders use different track widths for the record and playback heads. For machines that have wider playback heads, the full-track test tapes used for most of the wide-tape formats will produce an enhanced output during testing. The reference level from the tape must be set above the 0 vu reference by the amount of this extra pickup due to the wider head when using the playback head. When setting the reference level for sync/overdub playback, the track width is correct, yielding a true 0-vu level that requires no correction.

If the record head has a wider track, then the error will occur on the sync/overdub level rather than the normal playback level.

The second problem is created by the fringing effect of long wavelengths that produces a rise in playback response at low frequencies whenever additional flux is present beyond the area being scanned by the reproduce head. Such a condition exists for playback of a full-track alignment tape and for test and alignment procedures that apply the same low-frequency signal to all tracks of the recorder simultaneously.

The fringing effect will first create a problem in establishing the correct reference level for the midband level set tone. At 15- and 30-in./s tape speeds, sufficient fringing may exist to create an error of approximately 0.5 to 1 dB, depending upon the track format, tape speed, and geometry of the head cores and shielding. This extra fringing contribution in the reference tone also makes the high-frequency response appear to be deficient, tempting the operator to raise the equalizer adjustment.

Consult the operator's manual for the correct procedure and correction factors for a given model of recorder.

The final step in the reproduce alignment procedure is to set the level and equalization of the sync/overdub circuit. The operator may choose to defer the azimuth alignment of the record head until the following record alignment procedure if the heads have not been disturbed.

4. The record alignment begins with the verification and/or adjustment of the azimuth setting of the record head. Using the playback head as a standard, set the record head alignment while recording a short-wavelength signal such as a 10- or 15-kHz signal to give minimum azimuth or phase error using whatever method was used for the reproduce alignment procedure. This alignment should be rechecked after the bias and record equalization settings are made, since these adjustments can introduce varying amounts of phase delay.

The bias should be set by adjusting for the desired amount of overbias as recommended by the tape and machine manufacturer for the appropriate type of tape, record head gap width, and tape speed. Note that a 10-kHz signal at 30 in./s does not achieve the desired wavelength of 1.5 mils that is typically specified for bias adjustment. The test frequency must be changed to match the tape speed.

The bias should be first decreased to achieve deliberate underbias, then slowly increased to the point at which a peak in the playback level is observed. Continue to increase the bias until the signal drops by the number of decibels desired. Typical overbias settings range from 2 to 5 dB for professional formats.

Once the bias is correctly adjusted, the input signal should be set to the frequency used as a reference during the playback alignment. The record gain control can then be set to produce the reference level when driven with the appropriate 0-vu input level.

Adjust the high-frequency record equalizer to match the record/play response as closely as possible to the alignment tape response noted previously. Smoothness in the midband frequencies is more important than trying to hold small errors at 15 or 20 kHz.

Recheck the record head azimuth to verify that changes in bias and equalization have not created any phase differences. Readjust as necessary until all parameters are optimized.

Set the record gain preset and the input monitor gain calibration to achieve a 0-vu reading in all monitor modes.

5. After the record section has been aligned, a final test and alignment of the low-frequency playback equalizers can be undertaken. To eliminate all the fringing problems previously mentioned, the equalizers should be set in the record/play mode with signal being applied to every other track. Make small adjustments as required to optimize the smoothness of the response.

If any large discrepancies are noticed, rerun the alignment tape. Any failure in the low-frequency record equalizer circuits, such as a faulty switching component, will create an error that should be obvious if a large correction is required. If any doubt still exists, record a full-frequency sweep and then flip the reels over to play the tape backwards. The alignment should be similar within a few tenths of a dB to the values set in the forward direction.

6. The alignment procedure is not completed until the noise level and erasure have been checked. Record a signal at +6 vu, rewind the tape, and then erase the signal. Listen on the monitor speakers to the level of the residual signal and to the subjective nature of the tape noise. The tone should be either completely eliminated or well-buried in the tape noise. The noise should be a smooth hiss without large or frequent bursts or crackling. All tracks should be similar in performance. Also, check for objectional clicks and pops when changing modes.

Although these noise and erasure levels can be read from instruments, the operator should take the time to listen to the machine before issuing his or her "stamp of approval." Many sessions have died aborning because the recorder was never given a final listening test after alignment.

The previous procedure does not include several steps that are more appropriately considered to be maintenance routines. Examples include tuning of the bias or erase sources, or both, tuning of bias traps, checking meter calibration, and testing distortion levels. These tests are not required on a day-to-day basis.

As a final note on alignment, never gloss over large discrepancies. The corrections that should be required for this alignment procedure should be on the order of a small part of a dB, not several dB. Whenever a large change seems required, stop long enough to determine why such a large change is necessary. Look for faulty components and recheck your own procedure. Recheck the maintenance log to establish the proper level of performance that should be expected. Heeding the symptoms may avoid a serious catastrophic failure.

BIBLIOGRAPHY

1. N. H. Bertram, M. K. Stafford, and D. R. Mills, "The Print-Through Phenomenon," *Journal of the AEs*, vol. 28, no. 10, October 1980.
2. K. Clunis and J. T. Mullin, "Advanced Tape Mastering System," *Journal of the AES*, vol. 12, no. 4, 1964.
3. J. F. Dundovic, "Magnetic Head Relapping Techniques." *Journal of the AES*, vol. 24, no. 8, 1976.

4. F. Jorgensen, *The Complete Handbook of Magnetic Recording*, Blue Ridge Summit: Tab Books, 1980.
5. C. D. Manquen, "A Wideband Tape and Transport Diagnostic Method," *Journal of the AES*, preprint 1637. May 1980.
6. C. D. Manguen and J. Martinson, "Maintenance Procedures for Ferrite Heads," *Journal of the AES*, vol. 27, no. 11, November 1979.
7. J. G. McKnight, "Erasure of Magnetic Tape," *Journal of the AES*, vol. 11, no. 3, 1963.
8. J. G. McKnight, "Low-Frequency Response Calibration of Multitrack Magnetic Tape Recording and Reproducing System," *Journal of the AES*, vol. 26, no. 4, 1978.
9. C. D. Mee, *The Physics of Magnetic Recording*, New York: John Wiley & Sons, 1964.
10. R. Morrison, *Standard Tape Manual*, Kensington: R. K. Morrison Illustrative Materials, 1978.
11. C. B. Pears, *Magnetic Recording in Science and Industry*, New York: Reinhold Publishing Corp., 1967

CHAPTER **25**

Digital Recording Systems

by Dale Manquen

25.1 INTRODUCTION

The rapidly expanding field of digital technology has created opportunities for the development of exciting new audio products that offer previously unattainable performance. Starting from relatively simple logic functions for console and tape recorder control, digital audio has grown to engulf every aspect of signal processing, control, and storage. Numerous examples of these applications are found throughout this book.

The recording of audio in digital form offers several advantages when compared to conventional analog recording, including:

1. The theoretical signal-to-noise ratio is solely determined by the encoder parameters and is not degraded by multiple generations of digital rerecording,
2. The audio quality is unaffected by amplitude and frequency anomalies in the recording process, and
3. Print-through, amplitude modulation noise, and flutter are eliminated.

As with any technology, counterbalancing disadvantages also exist, such as:

1. A 60:1 increase in data-packing density is required to accommodate the high digital data rates, leading to more fragile recordings that require cautious handling.
2. The highly complex circuitry used is expensive to purchase and difficult to repair.
3. Critical converter components can change enough due to aging to degrade system performance.
4. Present-day digital recordings will probably not be compatible with future machines.

The following discussion of digital magnetic recording includes part of the history of the 3M Company Digital Mastering System to illustrate the problems to be overcome when transforming the theory of digital recording into a product for the recording studios. Since this history assumes a reasonable familiarity with the concepts of digitizing audio signals and storing information on magnetic tape, the reader may wish to review the fundamentals of digital encoding (Chapter 18) and magnetic recording (Chapter 24) before proceeding. For reference purposes, Fig. 25-1 illustrates the major components of a generalized digital recording system.

25.2 IN THE BEGINNING

During the late 1960s and early 1970s, several prototypes of digital audio recorders had been constructed to demonstrate the practicality of sampling and storing professional-grade audio in digital form. The primary problems of these systems included speed and accuracy limitations of *analog-to-digital (a/d)* converters, the high recording density required to store the encoded data, and the need to correct or conceal data errors introduced by tape defects. Although the demonstration systems produced adequate results under laboratory conditions, the cost and complexity of the units precluded their general use as multitrack workhorses in a typical studio environment. Substantial further development appeared to be necessary to create an acceptable product.

In January of 1974, 3M Company, who was then a leading supplier of multichannel audio recorders, initiated a research program to evaluate digital audio recording technology. Using a derivative of the 3M Isoloop audio transport, Marshal Brookhart immediately began to construct a breadboard system to evaluate various methods and components. In less than six months, Marshal demonstrated a crude system operating at 62,000 samples

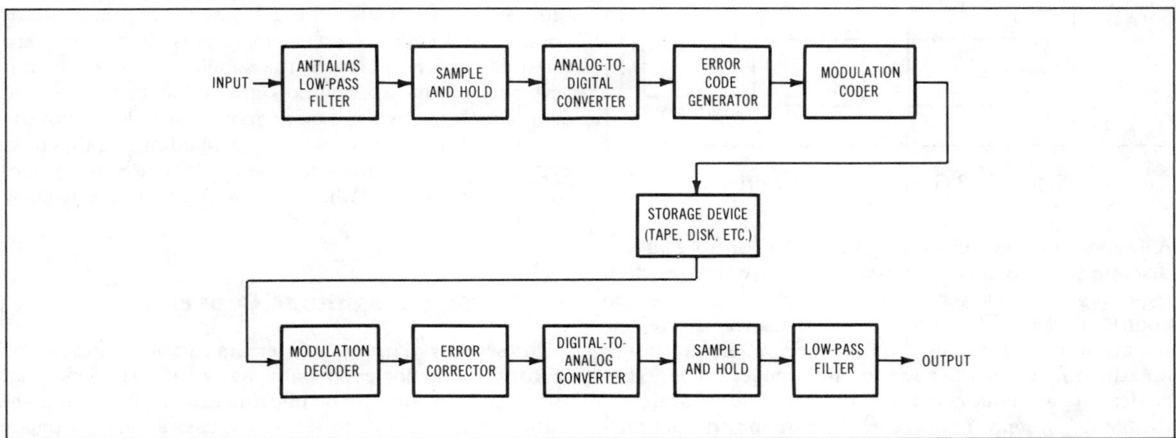

Figure 25-1 Digital recording system.

per second of 13-bit linear-encoded data. The digital tape recorder, running at 60 in./s to achieve a packing density of 20,000 bits/in., stored one channel per recorded track. Although some error detection had been included in the unit, the demonstrations suffered from frequent noise bursts due to uncorrected errors caused by tape dropouts.

Encouraged by the enthusiasm generated among corporate management by these early demonstrations, Marshal began the task of overcoming the shortcomings of the breadboard.

25.3 ANALOG-TO-DIGITAL CONVERTERS

Unlike analog recorders, which are primarily limited by the magnetic characteristics of the tape, the ultimate performance of a digital system is dictated by the choice of quantization levels and sampling rate. Since the 13-bit linear encoding system, which was limited to less than an 80-dB dynamic range, could not provide adequate resolution to achieve professional performance, more bits were needed. Adding more bits to a linear encoder is very expensive, with the encoder cost approximately doubling for each added bit.

25.3.1 Floating-Point Conversion

An alternate method called *gain ranging* or *floating point*, which was used in many early systems, adds a gain control stage at the input to the linear encoder (Fig. 25-2).

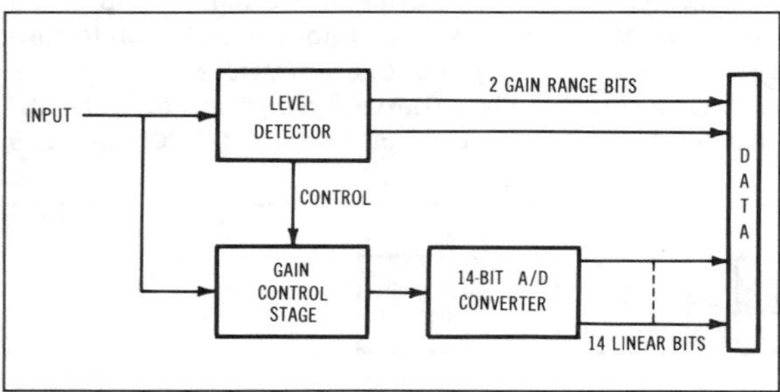

Figure 25-2 Gain-ranging converter.

A level detector switches the gain of the control stage in discrete steps to always keep the signal feeding the analog-to-digital converter at optimum level. Although no additional demands are placed on the linear converter, the accuracy and stability of the detector/gain controller and the tracking of the encoder and decoder become very critical. As with many of the early digital audio systems, the 3M Co. system employed a gain-ranging encoder during the early development period, but later it was modified to use a linear encoder.

25.3.2 Linear Magnitude Converter

Although a straight linear converter overcomes the gain and threshold problems of the gain-ranging converter, another difficult problem arises due to the method of encoding positive and negative polarities of the audio waveform. The linear encoder generates binary values that range from 0 to the full-scale value, and it is made bipolar by offsetting the input signal to one-half the full-scale value. Signals above this offset level are positive, and signals less than this value are negative.

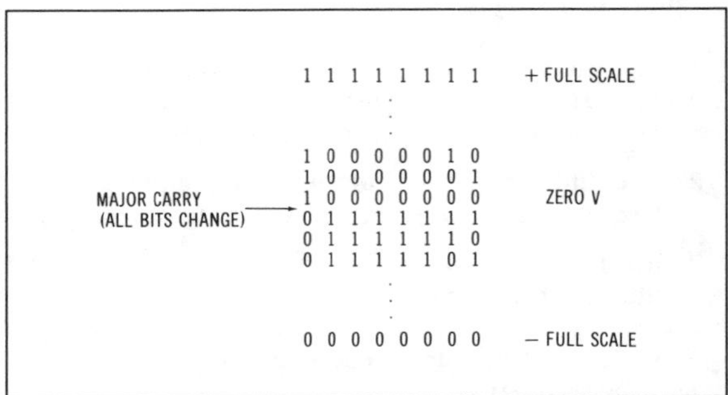

Figure 25-3 Linear magnitude converter output code.

A closer look at the output code generated by a typical eight-bit offset converter illustrates the nature of the error around zero (Fig. 25-3). A properly adjusted converter will yield an output binary word of 10000000 for an input of 0 V. As the input voltage increases in the positive direction, the code counts upward, with the smallest bits changing to 10000001, 10000010, 10000011, . . . , A negative-going signal, on the other hand, first creates a change in every bit of the encoder output, called the *major carry*, jumping from the zero value of 10000000 to 01111111, and then begins changing only the lower-order bits to 01111110, 01111101, ... Since the smallest positive and negative one-step transitions around zero must accurately represent the smallest step of the converter to maintain a low no-signal noise level, the total error generated by the major carry must be less than the size of the least significant bit step. Maintaining this high degree of accuracy over even moderate temperature fluctuations for a useful life of several years is extremely difficult.

25.3.3 Sign/Magnitude Converters

The severity of major carry errors can be minimized by shifting the major carry point away from the no-signal level. This shifting can be implemented with a sign/magnitude converter (Fig. 25-4), which uses a separate polarity detector to determine the value of the most significant or sign bit. Once the polarity is determined, the waveform

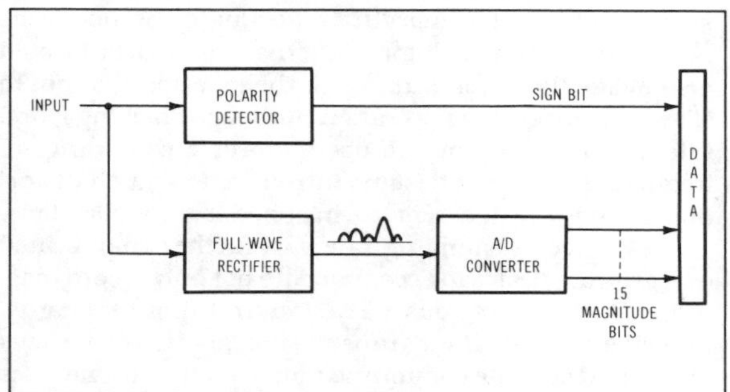

Figure 25-4 Sign-magnitude converter.

is full-wave-rectified to produce a unipolar signal, which is easily encoded by a linear analog-to-digital converter. The 16-bit digital output word from a sign/magnitude converter is assembled by attaching the sign bit from the polarity detector to the output of a 15-bit linear converter.

A major carry problem is still present, but now the major carry point is at + or − half of the full-scale range, a point only 6 dB below peak output. The masking effect of the large signal required to reach this point hides any residual major-carry error. (Most nonaudio uses of digitized waveforms, such as data acquisition systems, do not benefit from the psychoacoustic peculiarities that create the masking effect. Such systems require accurate linear encoding at the major carry to perform correctly.)

As an extra benefit, the auxiliary polarity detector reduces the required number of bits in the converter by one. Thus, a sign-plus-15-bit converter equals a 16-bit magnitude-only converter in resolution. This reduction in bits further reduces the size of the major carry error by a factor of two.

The use of a polarity detector and rectifier introduces a new set of problems to the encoder design. Since these components must operate accurately on the lowest-amplitude signal to be encoded, noise and hysteresis of the detector and rectifier must be minimized. Any small dc offset errors, on the other hand, can be tolerated since direct coupling is usually not required throughout an audio system.

Although the sign/magnitude converter can minimize zero crossing errors, the inherent simplicity of an offset linear converter is attractive to manufacturers. If new offset converters can be designed to provide stabilities of better than one-half the least significant bit step for periods of five years or more, then the offset linear converter could overtake the sign/magnitude converter in the audio marketplace.

25.4 SAMPLING RATE VERSUS FILTER DESIGN

An antialias filter (see section 18.2.2) must be used in a digital audio system to avoid unwanted frequency components that are generated by the sampling process. The typical objective for an audio system is to pass all signals below 20 kHz and exclude all signals above this frequency. To achieve this result, very steep 20-kHz low-pass filters are placed at the input to the sampling device and at the output of the reconstruction device (digital-to-analog converter). As a result, any signal components above 20 kHz are completely blocked. (In comparison, an analog recorder operating at 30 in./s can provide useful response to well beyond 30 kHz.)

25.4.1 Fourier Components of Waveforms

The effect of the antialias filter is most dramatic when a complex waveform such as a square wave is used to test digital and analog systems. All such complex signals can be broken down into pure sine waves by a mathematical process known as *Fourier analysis*. The 10-kHz square wave of 1 V peak-to-peak (V_{p-p}) magnitude shown in Fig. 25-5A can be decomposed into a 10-kHz sine wave of 1.27 V_{p-p}, a 30-kHz sine wave of 0.424 V_{p-p}, a 50-kHz sine wave of 0.254 V_{p-p}, and so on, with diminishing amplitudes at the higher odd harmonics. The phase relationship of the various sine-wave components determines the shape of the final wave. The square-wave components all start from 0° at the leading edge of the square wave. In contrast, the components of the triangle wave in Fig. 25-5B are shifted so that each of the components is at maximum amplitude at the peak of the triangle wave.

If either of the waveforms of Fig. 25-5 were passed through a typical 20-kHz antialias filter, the output waveform would consist of only the sine-wave component. All of the distinguishing characteristics of the waveform will thus be destroyed. If, however, the human hearing combination of ear and brain function as a Fourier analyzer that has absolutely no response above 20 kHz, then a human listener will be unaware that the antialias filter has decimated the original waveform. Although considerable controversy abounds regarding whether or not human hearing actually fits this simplified model, the acceptability of current digital audio recordings tends to support the model.

The sampling rate of 62 k samples/s chosen for the initial 3M Co. breadboard underwent numerous changes as the design progressed. Although the Shannon Sampling theorem dictates a sampling rate that is greater than twice the highest desired audio frequency, the finite cutoff rates of practical filters require the inclusion of a transition region between the passband and stopband of the filter (Fig. 25-6). Narrowing the transition region requires a more complex filter circuit to achieve a sharper cutoff characteristic.

To avoid any possibility of unwanted alias images, the filter must drop to 90 dB of attenuation at half the sampling rate. The original 3M Co. system allowed an 11-kHz transition region [(62 k samples/2) − 20 kHz], which required a mere 213 dB/octave average cutoff slope to

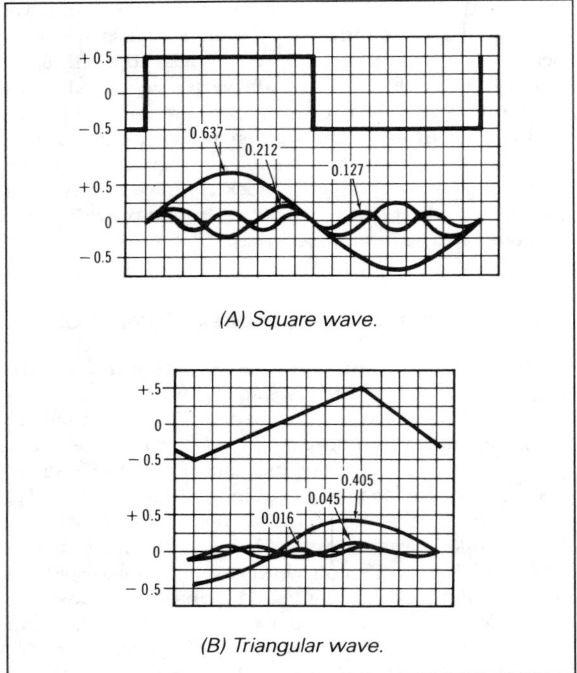

(A) Square wave.

(B) Triangular wave.

Figure 25-5 Partial Fourier decomposition of waveforms.

achieve 90 dB of attenuation at the Nyquist rate. This relatively wide transition region compounded the data storage problem by generating a higher data rate than would be necessary with a more abrupt filter.

Since mastering recorders are frequently run slightly above or below nominal speed to change pitch, the filter cutoff must be set to still provide adequate filtering when the sampling rate drops to the lowest permitted variable speed. A 6% filter margin is adequate for operating underspeed by one half-tone. Alternate approaches would be to make the cutoff filter track the tape speed or not to allow any underspeed operation. Although tracking cutoff filters can be designed to operate over a wide range of frequencies, present designs introduce too much distortion and noise to be acceptable in professional applications.

The choice of sampling rate was further complicated by a growing desire to accommodate not only record mastering, but also various television and film standards. Considerations include transmission standards for telephone and satellite communications; picture frame rates of 25 and 30 frames/s for television versus 24 frames/s for film: and National Television System Committee (NTSC), phase alternation line (PAL), and sequential couleur a'memorie (SECAM) television transmission systems. Various standards committee recommendations kept pushing the sampling rate lower. The original 3M Company sampling rate of 62 k samples/s for the experimental version of the system was later lowered to 50 k samples/s in production models to promote standardization. A competing consortium of manufacturers has proposed a new standard with a revised sampling rate of 48 k samples/s, while the compact audio disk standard has chosen 44 k samples/s. (See the appendix for a summary of proposed tape and compact disk standards.)

The consequences of shrinking the transition region of the low-pass filter by reducing the sampling rate is illustrated in Fig. 25-7 for a seventh-order elliptic filter. The frequency response in Fig. 25-7A has been decomposed in Fig. 25-7B into the individual resonant subsections, which are connected in series to yield the desired filter response. Note that the peaking of the resonant circuit or *pole pair* nearest the cutoff frequency rises rapidly as the transition region is narrowed. This peaking response indicates a high degree of energy storage within the capacitors and inductors of the filter. When a sharp transient excites the filter, this energy is released grad-

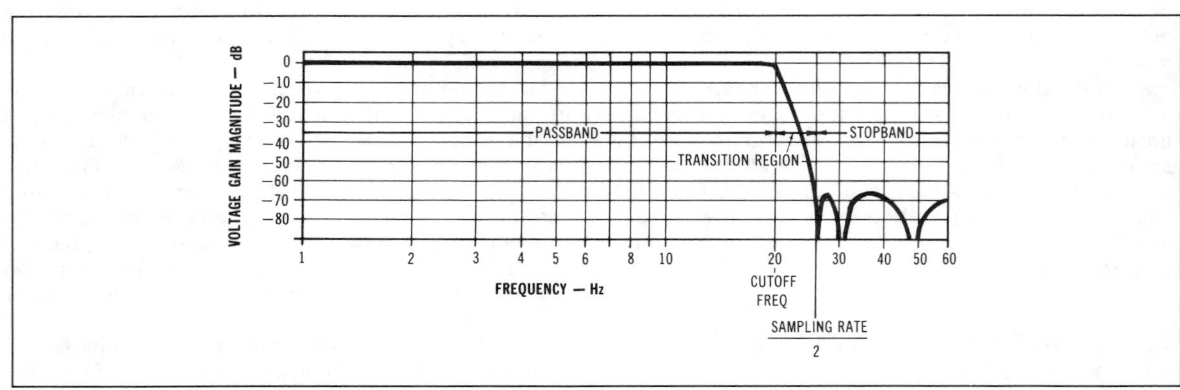

Figure 25-6 Typical low-pass filter response.

ually at the peaking frequency, as shown in Figs. 25-7C and D, much in the same way that a bell rings after being struck. To make the transition region of this filter narrower, the heights of the peaks must be increased, yielding even more ringing.

Any active circuitry in or following the highly peaked filter sections must have adequate headroom to avoid clipping on the peaks. This clipping can be minimized by arranging the sequence of filter sections so that the rolloff and mildly peaked stages attenuate the high frequencies before the signal reaches the highly peaked stages. For this cascade, however, the signal-to-noise ratio for the final stages must then be very high to avoid thrusting circuit noise into the output spectrum at the peaking frequencies.

The same energy storage phenomenon also gives rise to a substantial disturbance of the time alignment of the various frequency components in the audio signal. The higher frequencies are delayed by the filter components, yielding substantial phase shifting at the upper end of the passband. More recent designs minimize this shifting problem by including additional phase correction stages that introduce an offsetting amount of phase advance.

The example of Fig. 25-7, which is taken from a product of only 12-bit resolution, does not fully depict the extreme cutoff characteristics required for a 16-bit professional system. Indeed, the theoretical demands of a 16-bit system are so stringent that the designer may loosen certain system requirements based on the nature of typical audio program material. For example, must the system pass a full-scale signal at 20 kHz without any detectable alias image if no known audio program ever contains 20-kHz levels above 0 vu? (The energy content of most audio material starts dropping beyond 3 kHz at 30 to 40 dB/decade or 9 to 12 dB/octave.) Proper application of these real-world limitations can turn a seemingly impossible nightmare into a manageable task.

25.5 ERROR CORRECTION

Imperfections in the mixing and coating of magnetic tape give rise to unwanted fluctuations in signal amplitude. In an analog recording, these errors create sudden drops in signal level that are not overly objectionable to the listener for moderate error densities. A digital recording, on the other hand, can suffer a reversal of any bit in the digital data or even complete loss of signal for many bits. If only one bit is changed, the severity of the disturbance will be dependent upon the location of the error in the data word and the type of program material. An error in the least significant bit may be unnoticed, but an error in the sign bit may produce a very large disturbance. The very short duration of a single-sample error produces frequency components at the upper edge of the passband, creating a sharp snap or click similar to a scratch on a phonograph record. The error pulse also generates an impulse excitation of the output low-pass filter, which stretches the pulse into decaying sinusoids at the peaked frequencies of the filter poles.

Longer errors produce not only the direct contamination of the data words but may also cause a loss of timing synchronism that is required to sort properly the identical data bits on the tape into meaningful sequences of 16-bit words. To recover from a loss of timing due to a tape dropout, the data clock must be resynchronized. To facilitate resynchronization, the data stream contains special reserved sequences called *sync words*, which are transmitted at regular intervals of from a few data words up to every 256th data word to mark the beginning of each data block. The first sync word after an error will restore correct timing, but a substantial quantity of data may be lost in the interim. An error in the sync word can produce a worst-case situation that destroys the entire data block following the faulty sync word. The loss of a large data block may exceed the capability of the error correction system, causing a large disturbance in the audio output.

The early 3M Co. demonstrations confirmed that errors in the data must be completely corrected to avoid degradation. Error concealment or masking, which attempts to substitute an estimated value or "best guess" whenever an error is detected, could only be used as a last resort.

Error processing can be broken down into three distinct techniques—detection, concealment, and correction. Simple *parity error detection* adds an extra bit to each word to indicate whether the number of ones in the binary word is an odd or even number. The binary word 00110011, for example, has an even number, four 1s; the parity bit for this word could be 0. The binary word 00000001, on the other hand, has an odd number of 1s, yielding a parity bit of 1. (The value of the parity bit can be assigned to be 1 for an odd number of 1s or 1 for an even number of 1s, yielding either an odd parity system or an even parity system.) If an error changes one bit, the parity bit will no longer match the parity count generated by the faulty word. An even number of errors, however, will still yield the correct parity check.

The parity check only indicates that an error is present. Since no information is derived to point out the specific bit is that in error the only available course of action is to throw out the bad word and substitute a new estimated value. Typical substitution or concealment strategies are either to hold the last value or to interpolate by guessing the value midway between the prior and succeeding words. Both of these techniques produce errors in the waveform that, depending upon the actual program material and error location, can degrade the reproduction.

A more effective method of error processing is to find the erroneous bit and correct the value. Isolating a single bit requires more than one parity bit as a pointer. A triangulation scheme similar to a radio navigation system for airplanes shown in Fig. 25-8 can provide the extra reso-

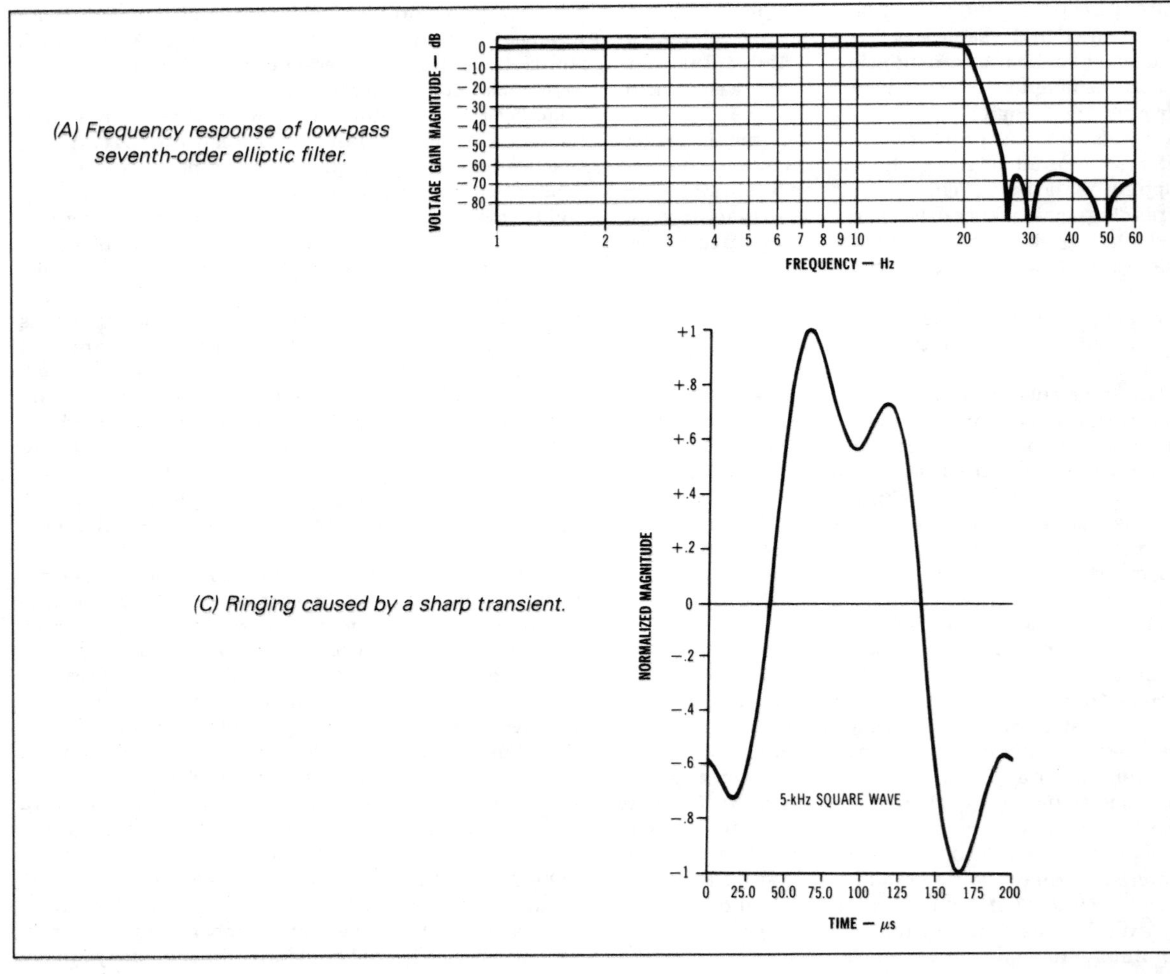

Figure 25-7 Low-pass narrow

lution. A simple example would be to first generate a word parity bit for each 16-bit word as indicated previously. Next, for a block of 16 words, rearrange the bits to form 16 new words of 16 bits each of all the first bits, all the second bits, and so on. Now generate 16 new position pointer parity bits for these new arrays. An isolated, single-bit error will now produce two parity errors, one to indicate the erroneous word and the other to point to the position in the faulty word.

To trap multiple bit errors, this triangulation technique can be extended to more than two dimensions, but the quantity of extra bits increases for each added dimension. Recent developments in multidimension digital audio error correction codes, known as cyclic redundancy codes, have yielded very powerful codes that are capable of full correction of the majority of anticipated error situations. These codes typically require one correction code bit for every pair of data bits, a 50% increase in the total amount of data that must be stored.

The error correction burden of these codes is somewhat lightened by taking maximum advantage of the known characteristics of magnetic recording errors. Typical data errors due to coating imperfections and dirt tend to occur as groups or bursts. The error correction scheme can deal with these errors more easily if the erroneous bits are dispersed among the data words. For example, a strategy for a system that typically has burst errors less than 32 bits in length might be to spread out the data bits and the error correction bits so that at least 32 bits of other data fall between each bit of the word. This interleave shuffle structure for the data bits shown in Fig. 25-9 greatly reduces the vulnerability to burst errors without requir-

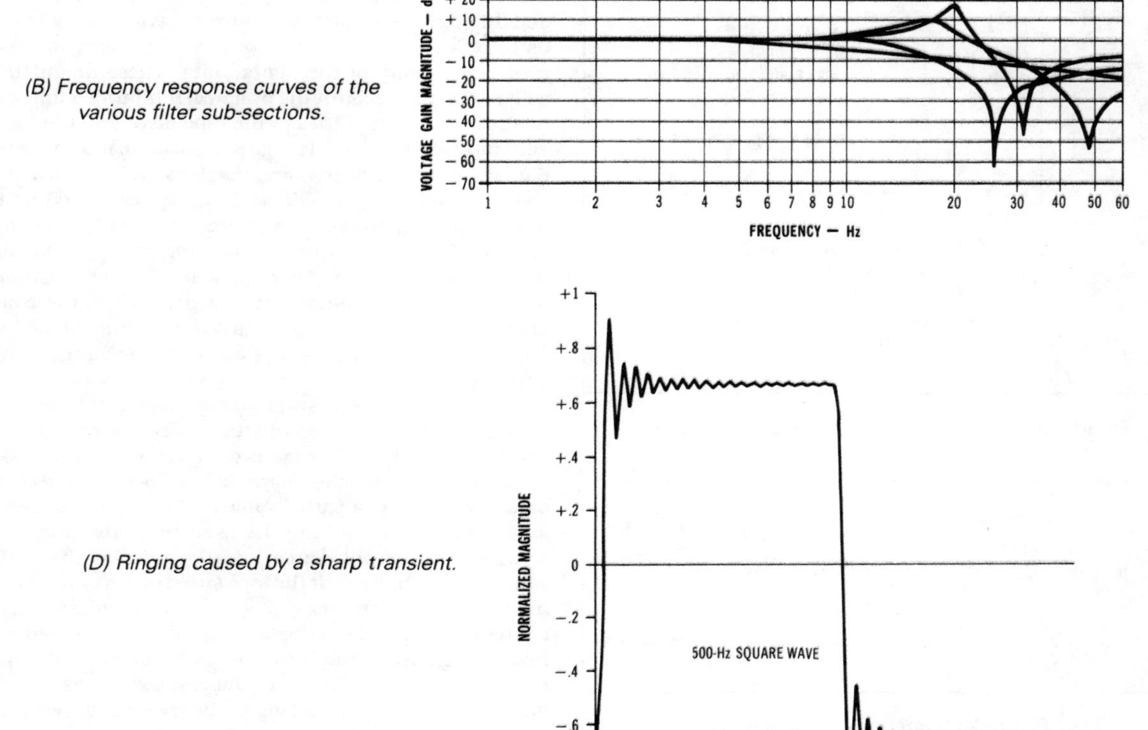

(B) Frequency response curves of the various filter sub-sections.

(D) Ringing caused by a sharp transient.

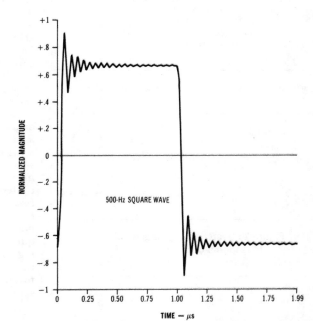

transition region filter.

ing any extra data capacity. An error burst that is 32 bits in length would now change only one bit per data word, well within the correction capability of a simple error code. The data is unshuffled after the errors have been detected and corrected to restore the original data word structure.

25.6 DATA UPDATING FOR SYNC/OVERDUB

The basic timing requirements of the data stream require additional overhead for sync words and block separators between groups of data. Under ideal conditions that have no dropouts or start/stop operations, the data stream could start at the beginning of a recording and continue without interruption to the end. Typical studio operation demands not only the ability to start/stop and recover from errors but also to edit by inserting changes into the data stream. To achieve this flexibility, small independent blocks can be dilineated by unique boundary words that serve as flags for editing operation.

On-the-fly editing of the data stream can be easily implemented if a playback or read head is inserted in the tape path just upstream of the record or write head. The time interval required for a point on the tape to move from the read head to the write head can be utilized to modify or replace the original data stream without losing synchronism, as shown in Fig. 25-10. The data from the read head can be separated into blocks, modified, delayed in a shift register, and then rewritten on the tape at the point of origin.

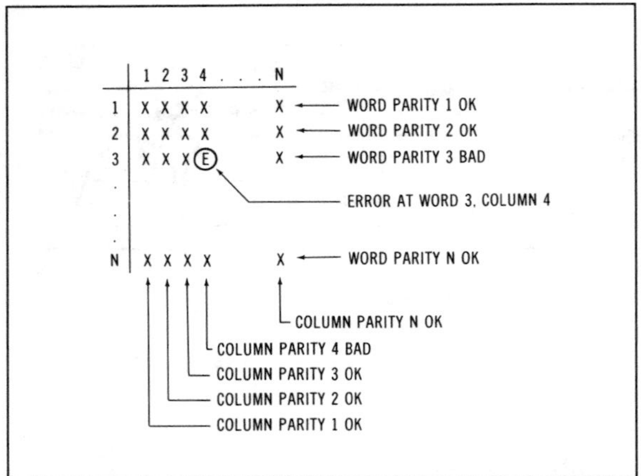

Figure 25-8 Two-dimension error correction scheme.

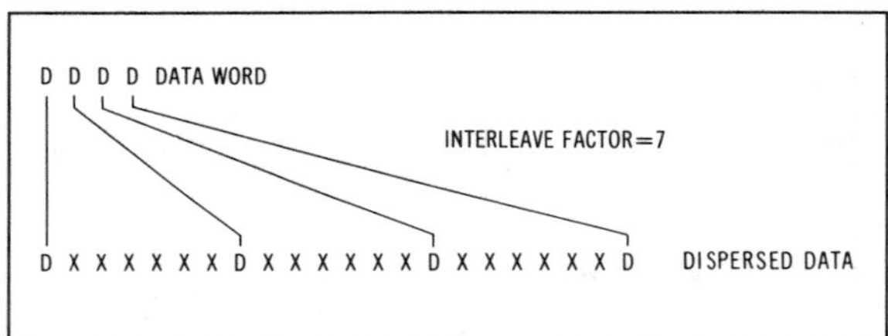

Figure 25-9 Interleaving data bits to disperse burst errors.

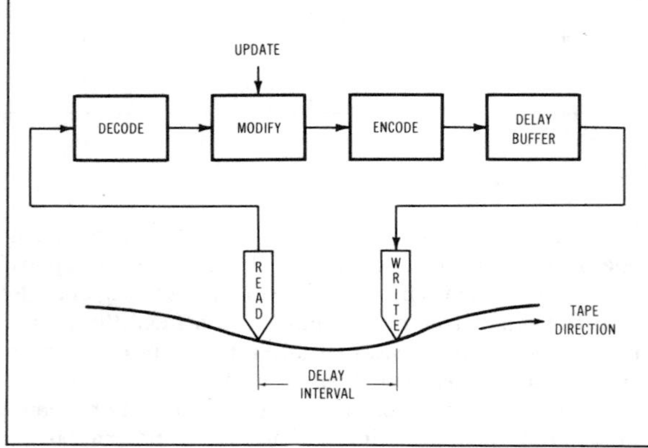

Figure 25-10 Data updating for sync-overdub operation.

25.7 MODULATION CODES

The magnetic pattern recorded on the tape consists of a saturated recording of rapidly alternating magnetic polarity. The digital information is encoded by varying the time interval between adjacent polarity reversals. Several different techniques for converting the binary 1s and 0s to polarity transitions have been developed to maximize the density of the digital data. These modulation codes take into account the practical limitations imposed by the speed instabilities of the tape drive and the interactions of closely spaced magnetic pulses to minimize the data error rate while maximizing density. In general, the codes are made to be self-clocking to ease decoding by forcing polarity transitions to occur during long strings of 1s or 0s. By breaking up the long strings, the data detector never sees long periods without any transitions for timing resynchronization. The detector is, therefore, able to monitor the average data rate continuously so that any small speed disturbances can be quickly sensed and suppressed.

Even though the instantaneous data rate may vary slightly due to these speed disturbances, the output data can be made fully synchronous with a master crystal clock by using a data buffer, as shown in Fig. 25-11. The decoded data is loaded into a partially filled delay buffer that serves as a rubber band linking the asynchronous input to a synchronous output. Under ideal conditions the buffer would be only half full. If the tape speed drops or increases momentarily, the buffer will decrease or increase in data content to maintain a constant output rate. A speed correction signal generated by the under- or over-filled status of the buffer adjusts the tape speed to restore the buffer to half capacity. As long as the speed servo responds quickly enough to keep the buffer from emptying or filling completely, the buffer output will always be free of timing errors. This feature eliminates all degradation due to flutter, thereby increasing the clarity of the reproduced sound.

25.7.1 Data Storage Techniques

Many of the problems of digital audio recording stem from the very high data rates required to transmit high audio fidelity. For 16-bit words at a rate of 50,000 samples/s, the data rate prior to any overhead due to error correction, timing, and formatting reaches 800,000 bits/s. A typical overhead factor of 50% for the "housekeeping bits" raises the overall rate to over 1.2 million bits/s (M bits/s) per channel.

25.7.2 Magnetic Disks

Based upon the above numbers, a 32-channel mastering recorder would generate nearly 40 Mbits/s. At this rate, even the largest available magnetic disk drive for computer use would be filled in only a few minutes. An improvement of at least an order of magnitude will be required before multitrack recording can be transferred to computer disk. (In terms more meaningful to the per-

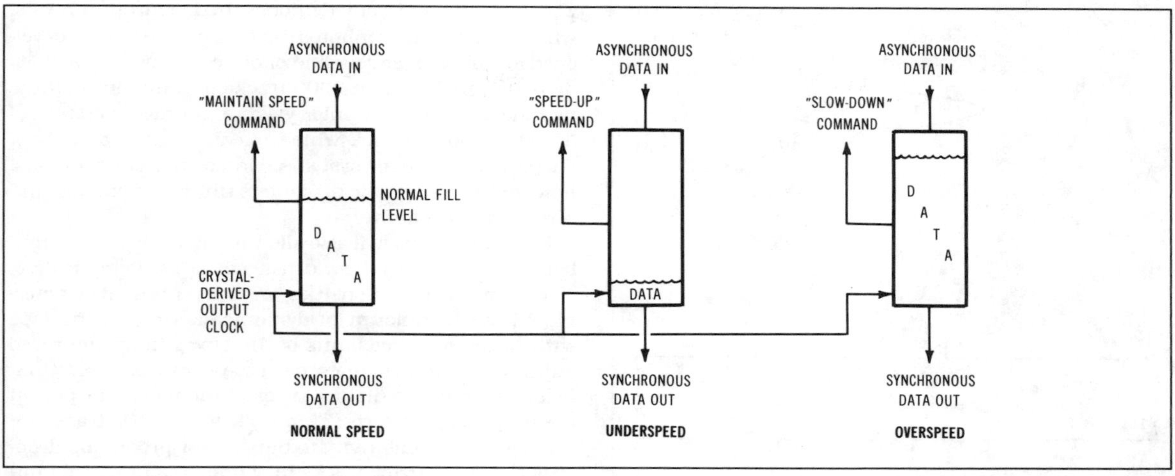

Figure 25-11 Corrections of speed errors with a synchronous buffer.

sonal computer user, 20 floppy disks of 0.25 Mbyte capacity would be required to store just one second of recording!)

The very large computer disk drives store the data on the large stack of rigid disks that cannot be removed from the drive for storage. A secondary dump device must be utilized to store the finished version of the program on tape or some other bulk medium for archival storage.

Stereo recordings, on the other hand, generate data at a rate of only 2.4 Mbits/s, permitting 10 minutes of program to be stored on a computer drive that uses removable disk packs. Extremely versatile editing systems based upon disk pack storage have been in service for several years.

25.7.3 Magnetic Tape

Tape offers two performance advantages over computer disk drives. First, the head is actually touching the tape rather than flying over the surface of a disk on a cushion of air. Although this leads to increased wear for both the head and the recording surface, a greater number of bits per linear inch of recording can be stored on tape. The second advantage is a much larger recording area. A 5000-ft roll of 1-in. wide digital audio tape on a 10½-in. reel provides 60,000 in.^{2} of surface; the largest computer disk drives have only 2000 in.^{2} of useful area.

Tape, on the other hand, is a serial technique that requires spooling through great lengths of tape to find a desired selection. A jump from beginning to end of a tape reel may take in excess of 2 min, compared to only 1/20 s for disk drive.

When comparing the cost and storage space for a reel of tape versus a disk pack, the tape achieves an order-of-magnitude advantage, making tape the overwhelming choice for archival storage.

Since the data rate of a tape drive is determined by the tape speed multiplied by the number of tracks across the width of the tape, certain tradeoffs can be made in running speed versus track density. For example, if 32 simultaneous audio channels are required, a 1-in. tape with 32 magnetic tracks, running at 30 in./s might be chosen. If only 2 channels were required, however, the format could be changed to ¼-in. tape with four tracks per channel, running at 7.5 in./s. Both of these configurations yield the same data density on the tape.

25.7.4 Optical Disks

Primarily in the area of playback-only devices, magnetic recording has recently been challenged as a digital storage medium by laser-based optical disk systems. Digital data is stored on the surface of the optical disk as a series of tiny pits that can be detected with a tightly focused laser beam. Both types of systems utilize similar encode/decode techniques, modulation schemes, and error correction techniques.

The primary advantage of an optical system is the use of a light beam to read the stored data without contacting the actual surface upon which the data is stored, as shown in Fig. 25-12. This remote-sensing capability allows the data disk to be encapsulated in a transparent protective sandwich that can endure rough handling. The steep angle formed by the laser beam also spreads the light over a relatively large area at the outer surface of the protective layer, minimizing the percentage of light that is blocked by a surface scratch or piece of dust. However, large obstructions and imperfections within the protective layer and data surface produce burst errors that are very much like the errors found in magnetic recording, requiring similar error correction methods.

The theoretical limitations of optical disk systems are set by the nature of light. A collimated beam of laser light

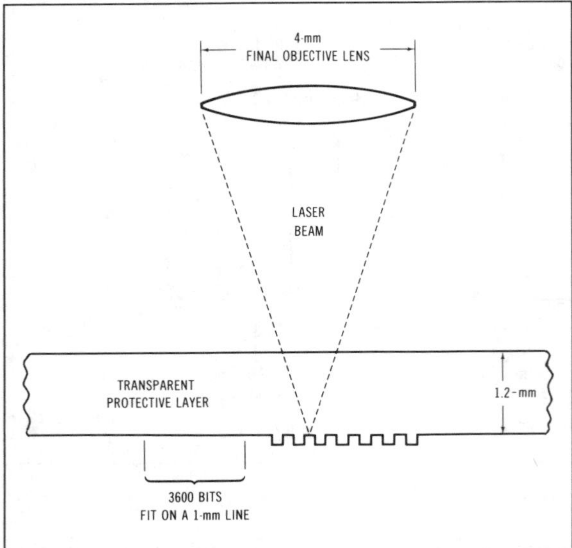

Figure 25-12 Scanning beam for optical disk.

can be focused to a spot that is approximately one wavelength in diameter. The data cells recorded on the disk are also approximately one wavelength in diameter. For present-day infrared lasers with 0.8-μm wavelength, this yields approximately 30,000 bits per linear inch of data, about the same density as digital magnetic tape recorders. The big advantage for optical recordings is that the track-to-track spacing of optical tracks can be approximately 1.6 μm or 65 μin., one tenth the current spacing of magnetic tracks, giving optical disks a 10:1 advantage in track density and data density.

Higher optical densities would be possible with lasers of shorter wavelengths. For example, a violet laser at 0.4 μm could quadruple the storage capacity of a disk. Other possible improvements include multiple color systems, multilayer data surfaces, and enhanced encoding methods that put more than one data bit in each cell.

Optical systems that can record user data, and in some cases even erase and rerecord data, are starting to appear, but these systems are much more exotic than a playback-only device. Primarily intended for archival storage at this time, these recording devices may eventually challenge magnetic devices as general-purpose storage devices.

25.7.5 Magnetic Versus Optical

Magnetic recording is by no means a dead horse in this race for storage density. Unlike the theoretically fixed-wavelength limitations of optical systems, the magnetic wavelengths are continuing to drop dramatically, with magnetic packing densities of greater than 100,000 bits per linear inch already demonstrated. Thin-film heads, which use the microphotolithography techniques developed to fabricate semiconductor devices, may achieve track densities greater than 3000 tracks/in. Combining these two developments would yield a storage density of 300,000,000 bits/in.^{2}, which is equal to the density of current optical disk systems. Unlike the optical disks, however, the magnetic disk offers unlimited erasure and rerecording capability.

Thin-film heads will also allow an increase in the number of tracks across the width of a piece of magnetic tape. The limit on track densities on tape is primarily determined by the amount of dynamic skewing of the tape within the tolerance limits of the tape guides. Improved guiding techniques, or even servo-positioned heads that follow the guiding disturbances of the tape, may permit the track density to rise eventually to over 100 tracks/in. The increased sensitivity to burst-error-producing dropouts for very narrow tracks may impose a practical limit on the track density due to decreased data reliability.

Both storage methods will continue to compete for various applications. The ease with which many optical disks can be quickly manufactured by a stamping process very similar to conventional record pressing should make optical disks ideal for consumer distribution of video or audio recordings and computer software. Magnetic tape and disks should dominate in low-volume applications, such as record mastering, mixing, and editing, and in similar applications where erasing and rerecording are necessary.

A fundamental question that can only be answered in hindsight 20 years from now is, "How important are the enduring standards of analog disks and tapes that allow us to play 35-year-old recordings on today's equipment with better-than-new results?"

If this need for compatibility is crucial, we may be unable to make future improvements in digital technology because an earlier digital standard adopted today is incompatible. Indeed, the incredible versatility of digital audio technology may be, in the long run, its greatest limitation.

25.8 DASH DIGITAL TAPE STANDARDS PROPOSAL

The *DASH (digital audio stationary head)* is a format covering a wide range of application from two-channel recorders (19.05 cm/s, ¼-in. tape) to 48-channel recorders (76.20 cm/s, ½-in tape) suitable for broadcasters, top studios, small studios, or production houses.

25.8.1 Format Structure

The format has three versions depending on tape speed (fast, medium, and slow versions). The necessary num-

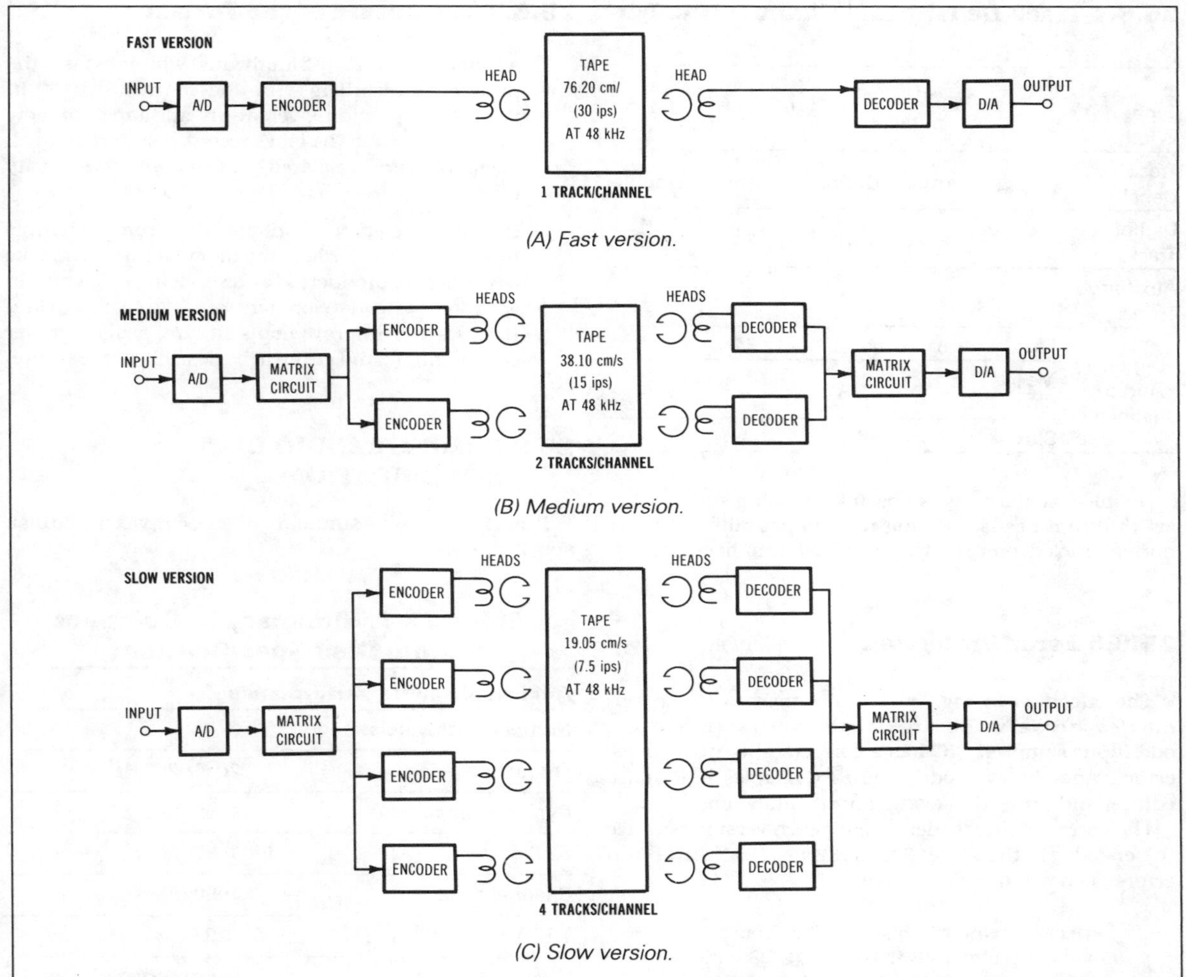

(A) Fast version.

(B) Medium version.

(C) Slow version.

Figure 25-13 Three tape speed versions of the DASH format. (Encoders and decoders of all versions are identical.) *(Courtesy Matsushita Electrical Industrial Co., Ltd.)*

ber of tracks to record one channel is one, two, and four for fast, medium, and slow versions, respectively (Fig. 25-13).

25.8.2 Tape Speed/Sampling Rate

Sampling Rate	Fast	Tape Speed Medium	Slow
48 kHz	76.20 cm/s (30 in./s)	38.10 cm/s (15 in./s)	19.05 cm/s (7.5 in./s)
44.1 kHz	70.01 cm/s (27.56 in./s)	35.00 cm/s (13.78 in./s)	17.50 cm/s (6.89 in./s)

25.8.3 Linear Packing Density (Common to All Versions)

1.51 k bits/mm (38.4 kbits/in.)
1.01 k flux reversals/mm (25.6 k flux reversals/in.)
λ_{min} = 1.99 μm (78.2 mils)
(minimum wavelength to be recorded)
λ_{max} = 5.96 μm (235 mils)
(maximum wavelength to be recorded)

Thanks to the newly developed modulation code HDM-1 by Sony, the minimum wavelength is 50% longer than the conventional code such as modified frequency modulation (MFM).

25.8.4 Track Density and Channel Number

Tape Width		¼ in.		½ in.	
Track Density		Normal	Double	Normal	Double
Digital Tracks		8	16	24	48
Auxiliary Tracks		4	4	4	4
Digital Audio Channels	Fast	8	16	24	48
	Medium	—	8	—	24
	Slow	2	4	—	—

Double-track density is possible by using state-of-the-art thin-film heads, keeping the compatibility with the normal track density for the initial half number of tracks.

25.8.5 Error Protection

The encoders in Fig. 25-13 implement a *CIC (cross interleave code)* with a large interleave between even and odd input samples. CIC has a correctability up to triple errors, and the even-odd interleave enables tape-splice editing and protection against accidental damage.

The correctability is identical for each version because the encoder is the same. The ability to deal with burst errors is shown here:

Perfect correction 8,640 bits (0.57 cm)
Good concealment 33,982 bits (2.23 cm)
Marginal concealment 83,232 bits (5.51 cm)

Error protection is independent on each track in each version. Even if one of the tracks is seriously damaged, the error correction performance on the other tracks is not affected.

This feature will ensure reliability and good performance of the recording even under bad conditions.

25.8.6 Editing

Cross fading can be provided in:

1. Punching in/out,
2. Tape-splice editing,
3. Electronic editing.

25.8.7 The Future of the Format

1. Adaptation of thin-film heads will increase the number of recorders with double-track density in the future, providing versatility and tape economy to the end users. The tapes recorded at normal-track density can even be played back on the double-density recorders.
2. By using a common configuration from 2-channel to 48-channel recorders, the manufacturers can take advantage of production and servicing efficiency. In addition, with development of large-scale integration, further improvements in size, weight, power consumption, and cost will be possible in the future.

25.9 COMPACT AUDIO DISK SPECIFICATIONS

Table 25-1 shows a summary of the compact audio disk specifications.

Table 25-1. Summary of Compact Audio Disk Specifications

Achievable audio performance	
Number of channels	2
Frequency range	20 Hz-20 kHz
Dynamic range	> 90 dB
S/N ratio	> 90 dB
Channel separation	> 90 dB
T.H.D. (incl. noise)	< 0.005%
Wow and flutter	Quartz crystal precision
Signal format	
Sampling frequency	44.1 kHz
Quantization	16 bits linear/channel
Audio bit-rate	1.4112 Mbit/s
Binary number presentation	2's complement
Error correction system	Cross Interleave Reed Solomon Code (CIRC)[1]
Modulation system	Eight to Fourteen Modulation (EFM)[2]
Channel bit-rate	4.3218 Mbit/s
Pre-emphasis	no or 50/15 μs[3]

Table 25-1—cont. Summary of Compact Audio Disk Specifications

Frame Format	
2 × 6 audio samples	24 audio symbols of 8 bits
Error correction information	8 parity symbols of 8 bits
Control and display information	1 C & D symbol of 8 bits
Frame before modulation	33 symbols of 8 bits
Frame after modulation (EFM) (33 symbols of 14 bits)	462 channel bits
For merging and LF suppression (3 bits per symbol of 14 bits)	99 channel bits
Synchronization pattern incl. 3 bits of merging and LF suppression	27 channel bits
Total frame	588 channel bits
Disk	
Diameter	120 mm
Thickness	1.2 mm
Diameter of centerhole	15 mm
Program area start diameter	50 mm
Disk *continued*	
Program area maximum diameter	116 mm
Sense of rotation (seen from reading side)	Anti-clockwise
Scanning velocity	1.2-1.4m/s
Rotation speed	500-200 rpm (approx.)
Maximum recording time	60 min. stereo
Track pitch	1.6 μm
Material	Transparent plastic, with aluminumized reflective coating, sealed with protective lacquer
Optical stylus (laser)	
Wavelength of AlGaAs laser	0.78 μm
Numerical aperture	0.45
Focus depth	Approx. 2 μm
Beam diameter at disk surface	Aprox. 1.0 mm

(Courtesy Philips Industries)

[1]CIRC: new error correction code for protection against scratches with high error correction capability for random errors and low probability of undetectable errors.

[2]EFM: new modulation method for increasing packing density and meeting requirements of optical servo systems.

[3]On choice: player will switch automatically.

BIBLIOGRAPHY

T. T. Doi, "Channel Codings for Digital Audio Recordings," *Journal of the AES*, vol. 31, no. 4, p. 224, April 1983.

T. T. Doi, "General Information on a Compact Digital Audio Disc," *Journal of the AES*, vol. 29, no. 1/2, p. 60, 1981.

H. N. H. Iwamura, A. Miyashita, and T. Anagawa, "Pulse-Code Modulation Recording System," *Journal of the AES*, vol. 21, no. 7, p. 535, 1973.

J. P. Myers and A. Feinberg, "High-Quality Professional Recording Using New Digital Techniques," *Journal of the AES*, vol. 20, no. 8, p. 622, 1972.

N. Stato, "PCM Recorder—A New Type of Audio Magnetic Type Recorder," *Journal of the AES*, vol. 21, no. 7, p. 542, 1973.

PART 6

Design Applications

CHAPTER **26**

Sound System Design

by Chris Foreman

There are many different types of sound systems with purposes as diverse as special effects and voice paging, yet most share common design criteria. This section covers many of these design criteria using sound-reinforcement systems as design examples. Included are discussions of other types of systems such as *foldback* (stage) monitor systems and some types of playback-only systems as well as some of the practical aspects of sound system design, such as equipment choice and installation techniques.

26.1 SOUND SYSTEM BASICS: A SIMPLIFIED SOUND-REINFORCEMENT SYSTEM

Figure 26-1 shows a simplified sound-reinforcement system with a talker, a listener, a microphone, and a loudspeaker. (The somewhat awkward term "talker" is used in place of the term "speaker" to avoid confusion between the person talking and the loudspeaker system.) The talker could be replaced by a musician playing an instrument with no changes in the following discussions (although a very loud, amplified instrument or direct box connection would change things somewhat).

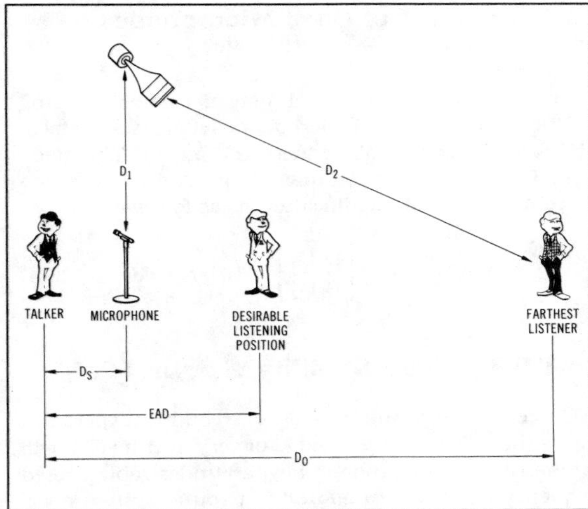

Figure 26-1 A simplified sound reinforcement system. *(Courtesy Altec Lansing Corp.)*

The primary simplification for this simplified system is to ignore echoes and reverberation. It's a good assumption for an outdoor system, away from any large buildings or other sources of echoes. Fortunately, the simplified description can be readily modified to include the effects of indoor echoes and reverberation.

26.1.1 Definitions

It is conventional to use the terms D_s, D_1, D_2, and D_o when referring to the *distances between the elements* of this simple system.

D_s is the distance between the talker and the microphone.

D_1 is the distance between the loudspeaker and the microphone.

D_2 is the distance between the loudspeaker and the listener (if there are many listeners, D_2 is usually considered to be the distance between the loudspeaker and the *farthest* listener).

D_o is the distance between the talker and the listener (again, the *farthest* listener when there are many listeners).

The term D_s can be remembered as ***D**istance **s**ource* (the source being the talker), and the term D_o can be remembered as ***D**istance **o**bserver* (the observer being the listener). Since there are only two terms left, D_1 and D_2, they can be easily remembered as the distance from the loudspeaker to the microphone (the beginning of the system so this distance is D_1) and the distance from the loudspeaker to the listener (the end of the system so this distance is D_2).

26.1.2 Attenuation with Increasing Distance

As the listener moves farther away from the loudspeaker, the level of pressure L_P (or sound pressure level, SPL) at the listener's ears will decrease. Neglecting the effect of echoes (outdoors, away from buildings this is a good approximation), the L_P level will decrease exactly 6.02 dB every time the listeners double their distance from the loudspeaker (Fig. 26-2). This effect is known as the *inverse-square law* and can be stated mathematically as

$$L_P' = L_P - 20\log(D'/D) \quad (26\text{-}1)$$

Example:

Let,

$L_P = 110$ dB
$D = 4$ ft
$D' = 200$ ft

$$L_P' = 110 - 20\log(200/4)$$
$$= 76.0 \text{ dB}$$

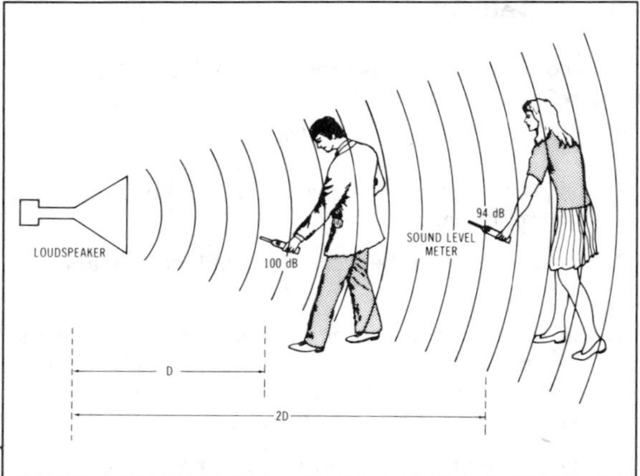

Figure 26-2 Inverse-square law. (L_p drops 6.02 dB when the distance from the source doubles in free field.)

In Eq. 26-1, L_P is the sound pressure level (in dB SPL) the listener hears at distance D from the source (the loudspeaker in the simplified system). L_P is the new sound pressure level the listener would hear at distance D′ from the loudspeaker. If distance D′ is smaller than distance D (the listener has moved closer to the loudspeaker), then the term 20 log (D′/D) will be a negative number, and the new L_P' will be greater than the original L_P'. Note that because the equation uses a distance *ratio*, the distances may be measured in any convenient unit (feet, yards, meters) as long as both distances are measured in the *same* unit.

26.1.3 Acoustic Gain

Of all the reasons for a sound-reinforcement system, the most important is implied by its name, *sound reinforcement*. That is, the sound coming from the talker is reinforced so that the listener hears a louder sound with the system on than with the system off. *Acoustic gain* describes the difference, in decibels, between the sound pressure level (L_P) at the listener's ears with the system on and with the system off. In most cases, the listener is, again, the *farthest listener*, although the acoustic gain may be specified for any number of different listeners in a complex system. Acoustic gain may be described mathematically by a simple equation

$$\text{acoustic gain (dB)} = L_{P\,ON} - L_{P\,OFF} \qquad (26\text{-}2)$$

Adequate acoustic gain is a primary design goal for a sound-reinforcement system. Techniques for reaching this goal are described later. A simple technique for measuring the acoustic gain of a system is to place a *sound level meter (SLM)* at the position of the farthest listener and measure the L_P from the talker with the system off. Then turn the system on and measure the L_P again. The difference between the two readings is the acoustic gain of the system. (Replace the talker with a pink-noise source, through a small loudspeaker, for a more accurate reading.)

26.1.4 Feedback and Potential Acoustic Gain (PAG)

The acoustic gain of this simple sound-reinforcement system can be increased by turning up the volume control, but, at some point, this process will be interrupted by *feedback (howling)*.

Feedback is an undesirable *oscillation* of the entire sound-reinforcement system that occurs when the sound from the loudspeaker feeds back to the microphone at a level high enough that the system begins to reinforce *itself* as well as the talker.

Potential acoustic gain or *PAG* is the maximum acoustic gain that can be obtained from the system before feedback occurs. For this simplified system (neglecting reverberation and echoes), the PAG can be stated mathematically as

$$\text{PAG} = 20\log\left[\frac{D_oD_1}{D_sD_2}\right] \qquad (26\text{-}3)$$

26.1.5 Number of Open Microphones (NOM)

This example system has only one microphone. Adding additional open (in-use) microphones increases the possibility of feedback and reduces the potential acoustic gain. The PAG calculation, including a Number of Open Microphones (NOM) modification, is as follows:

$$\text{PAG} = 20\log\left[\frac{D_oD_1}{D_sD_2}\right] - 10\log\text{NOM} \qquad (26\text{-}4)$$

26.1.6 Feedback Stability Margin (FSM)

This equation is theoretically correct, but experience shows that a system operated at or very near its PAG will exhibit ringing and probably have an undesirably peaked frequency response. In addition, a sound system operated near its PAG will increase the effective room reverberation time. Thus, a 6-dB *feedback stability margin* is normally subtracted from the calculated PAG. Systems operated 6 dB or more below their PAG are usually free of the problems of feedback or ringing. The final PAG calculation for the simplified system, then, should include a feedback stability margin modifier as follows:

$$\text{PAG} = 20\log\left[\frac{D_oD_1}{D_sD_2}\right] - 10\log\text{NOM} - 6\text{ dB} \qquad (26\text{-}5)$$

Example:

Let,

$D_s = 2$ ft,
$D_o = 128$ ft,
$D_1 = 45$ ft,
$D_2 = 90$ ft,
NOM = 3,

$$PAG = 20 \log\left[\frac{128 \times (45)}{2 \times (90)}\right] - 10 \log 3 - 6$$

$$= 19.3 \, dB$$

26.1.7 Noise

Unwanted noise (traffic, wind, audience noises, and so on) can interfere with the listener's ability to hear the talker. Ideally, the sound from the loudspeaker should be at least 25 dB above the noise level; that is, there should be a 25-dB *signal-to-noise ratio (SNR).*

In some high-noise situations, a 25-dB SNR may not be achievable. See section 26.13.5. Nevertheless, 25 dB is a common rule of thumb that will almost always ensure that a listener can hear and understand the talker in an outdoor system.

26.1.8 Headroom and Electrical Power Required (EPR)

If ambient noise is 45-dB L_p (usually measured on the A scale of a sound level meter) and a 25-dB SNR is desired, then the desired L_P at the listener's ears is 70 dB. That 70 dB, however, is the *average* level at the listener's ears, and the *peak* L_P level must be considered as well. The difference between *peak* and *average* level is referred to as the system headroom (Fig. 26-3). For a speech-only sound-reinforcement system about 10 dB of headroom is considered adequate. Thus, the peak level in this example system would be 80-dB L_P for an average level of 70-dB L_P.

In a high-noise system, a 10-dB headroom factor may not be achievable. By using a limiter, the headroom factor can be reduced to as low as 6 dB while maintaining reasonable voice intelligibility. For music-reinforcement systems, on the other hand, as much as 20-dB headroom may be desirable to avoid clipping important musical peaks. For the simplified (outdoor) system, however, a 10-dB headroom factor will be assumed.

How large an amplifier is needed to achieve the desired L_P? And, what information is needed about the loudspeaker? The answers are contained in this next equation:

$$EPR = 10^{\left[\frac{L_P + H - SENS + 20\log\left(\frac{D_2}{4}\right)}{10}\right]} \qquad (26\text{-}6)$$

where,

L_P is the average L_P required at distance D_2,
H is the headroom in decibels,
SENS is the sensitivity of the loudspeaker,
D_2 is the distance to the farthest listener.

Example:

Let,

$L_P = 90$ dB,
H = 10 dB,
SENS = 113 dB/4 ft/1 W,
$D_2 = 128$ ft.

$$EPR = 10^{\left[\frac{90 + 10 - 113 + 20\log\left(\frac{128}{4}\right)}{10}\right]}$$

$$= 10^{1.71}$$

$$= 51.3 \, W$$

Note: For 1-W/m sensitivity, change the constant 4 in the 20 log (D_2/4) term to 1 and give D_2 in meters.

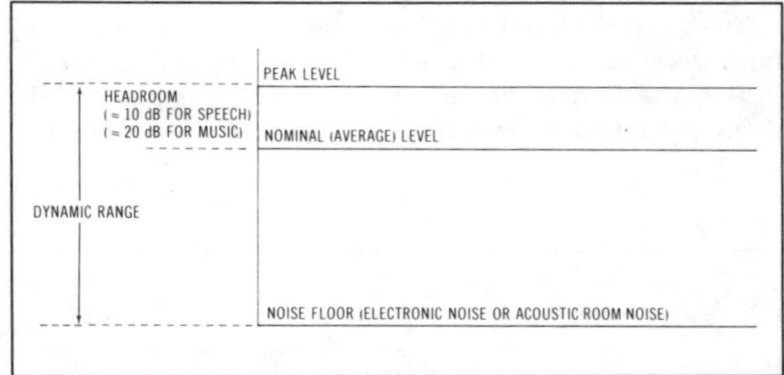

Figure 26-3 Dynamic range and headroom.

The term *SENS* is the *sensitivity* of the loudspeaker. This number represents the sound pressure level that the loudspeaker will produce for a specified input power level and must be obtained from the manufacturer's specifications or from measurements performed in the field. Normally, the manufacturer will rate the loudspeaker's sensitivity as so-many-dB SPL at 1 m from the loudspeaker with 1 W input power. Thus, this sensitivity is usually referred to as the 1-W/1-m sensitivity. Other manufacturers use 4 ft (the 1-W/4-ft sensitivity). Either sensitivity will work in the EPR equation, but consistent units (either feet or meters) must be used throughout the equation. In addition, the value 4, used as a denominator for D_2, assumes a 1-W/4-ft sensitivity. To convert a 1-W/4-ft sensitivity to a 1-W/1-m sensitivity, add a 1.72-dB sound pressure level. To convert from 1-W/1-m to 1-W/4-ft, subtract 1.72 dB.

The value of H (headroom), of course, may be changed for a particular system, and a different D_2 could be used to find the EPR at some other distance.

26.1.9 Equivalent Acoustic Distance (EAD)

If, in the simplified system, the talker were to stand relatively close to the listener, the talker could be heard and understood easily without the need for a sound system. One way of stating the goal of the sound system, then, is to say that it should create the illusion that the talker is actually quite close to the listener. In any given situation, a simple experiment can determine just how close the talker would need to be to the listener for comfortable communication. Simply talk in a normal voice and walk backward away from the listener until communication becomes difficult. Then, walk toward the listener again until communication is comfortable. At this point, the *equivalent acoustic distance (EAD)* has been established. The idea is to use the sound system to create the illusion that the talker is this equivalent acoustic distance away from the listener (Fig. 26-4).

In the simplified system, a 25-dB signal-to-noise ratio is the goal. that means the L_P at the farthest listener's ears should reach 70 dB for an assumed noise level of 45 dB. Looking at the chart for a normal-voice talker and a 70-dB (noise plus 25-dB SNR) level, the normal-voice talker would have to be about 2 ft from the listener to achieve this desired level. A raised-voice talker would only have to be about 4 ft from the talker. *Depending on the talker, one of these distances would be the required EAD.* If the actual voice level from a talker (at some reference distance like 1 m or 4 ft) is known, the EAD (outdoors) is as follows:

$$EAD = D_s 10^{\left[\frac{L_{PT} - L_{pd}}{20}\right]} \tag{26-7}$$

Note: L_{PT} must be given for a distance equal to D_s.

Let,

$D_s = 2$ ft,

$L_{PT} = 71$ dB (at 2 ft),

$L_{Pd} = 65$ dB,

$$EAD = (2) \times 10^{\left[\frac{71-65}{20}\right]}$$
$$= 3.99 \text{ ft}$$

Here, the term D_s is the (reference) distance at which the L_P from the talker was measured. The term D_s (the microphone to talker distance discussed earlier) is used because it is a convenient number (normally about 1 m) and because it will make the next calculation (needed acoustic gain) easier. L_{PT} is the sound pressure level from the talker at that reference distance D_s, and L_{Pd} is the desired sound pressure level at the listener (normally, this will be equal to the ambient noise plus a 25-dB signal-to-noise ratio). EAD, then, is the equivalent acoustic distance number to be used in the next calculation, that of *needed acoustic gain (NAG).*

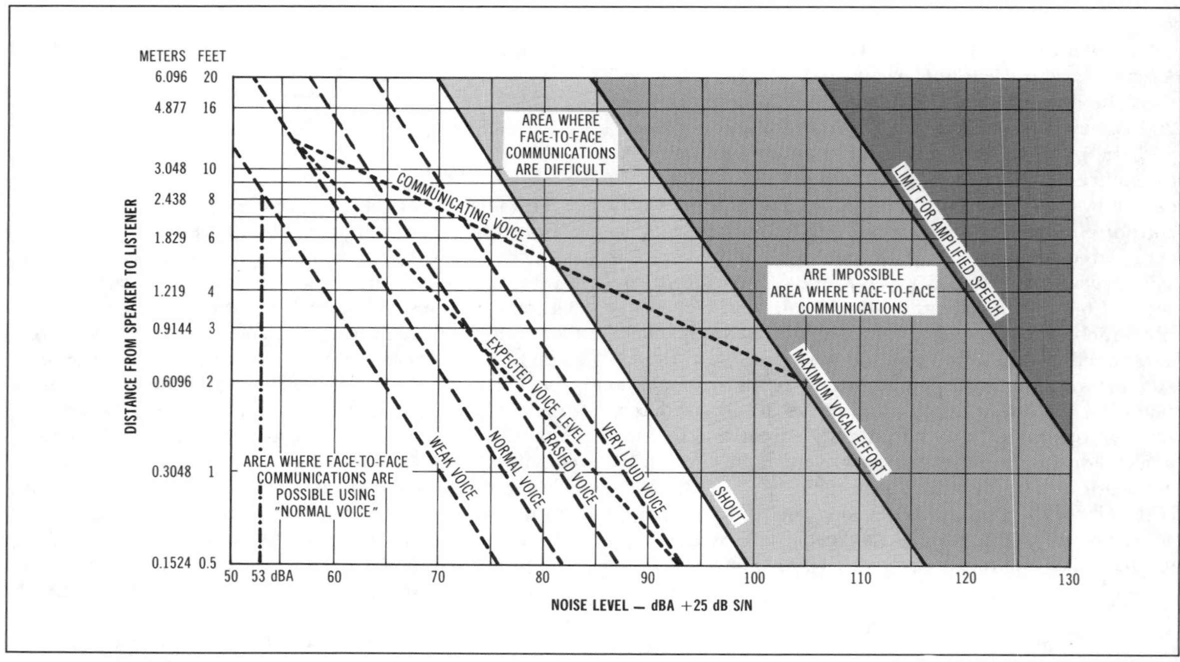

Figure 26-4 Nomograph for finding the EAD. *(Courtesy Synergetic Audio Concepts)*

26.1.10 Needed Acoustic Gain (NAG)

The next question to be answered is, "How much acoustic gain is needed to achieve this desired L_P for a given talker's voice level?" This *needed acoustic gain* or *NAG* is the gain in decibels needed to produce the desired L_P at the listener's ears L_{Pd} given an equivalent acoustic distance (EAD) as calculated before

$$NAG = 20 \log \left[\frac{D_o}{EAD} \right] \qquad (26\text{-}8)$$

where,

D_o is (as before) the distance from the talker to the farthest listener.

Example:

Let

D_o = 128 ft,

EAD = 4 ft,

$$NAG = 20 \log \left[\frac{128}{4} \right]$$
$$= 30.1 \text{ dB}$$

26.1.11 Will the System Feed Back?

If the *potential acoustic gain (PAG)* from Eq. 26-5 is greater than or equal to the needed acoustic gain from Eq. 26-8, there is every reason to believe that the system will be stable and not feed back. If, on the other hand, the potential acoustic gain is less than the needed acoustic gain, chances are good that the system won't work because turning up the volume control enough for the farthest listener to hear properly will always cause the system to be at or near feedback.

26.1.12 The Effect of Directional Microphones and Loudspeakers

The PAG and NAG equations assume an omnidirectional microphone and an omnidirectional loudspeaker. Some improvement in acoustic gain before feedback may be obtained by using a directional microphone (like a cardioid pattern microphone) and/or by using a directional loudspeaker (like a horn-type loudspeaker). This only occurs if the D_1 is less than the critical distance D_c. (D_c is discussed in section 26.2.1.5. It is only important in an indoor environment.)

A cardioid microphone could provide as much as 6 dB of additional gain before feedback if the rear of the microphone were pointed directly at the loudspeaker, as often happens with foldback stage monitor loudspeakers. The more typical case of a microphone at a podium and an overhead loudspeaker is a much less favorable arrangement since the side, not the rear, of the microphone will be pointed at the loudspeaker and D_1 is at or near D_c, providing 1 or 2 dB of additional gain before feedback at best. Because the microphone's cardioid pattern varies with frequency (it is nearly omnidirectional at low frequencies), even this 1 or 2 dB of feedback reduction may be optimistic. Thus, while a directional microphone *may* provide some additional gain before feedback, it's best to plan the system as if an omnidirectional microphone were to be used and take any additional gain provided by a cardioid as a welcome bonus.

A directional loudspeaker may also provide some additional gain before feedback. For a horn-type loudspeaker pointed at the farthest listener, for example, the microphone will be off-axis of the horn, and the sound level at that off-axis angle may be −6 dB or more (down) compared to the on-axis level. This could theoretically provide an additional 6-dB gain before feedback. By using a highly directional horn, this 6 dB might be increased to 10 dB or even more. The fault with this theory is that there will almost always be more than one horn in the system and at least one horn will be aimed at listeners near the microphone. This horn then becomes the limiting factor in the feedback loop. Even when the nearest listeners are far enough away from the microphone that the horn can be aimed well away from the microphone, the system woofer remains a potential feedback problem-causer. A highly directional low-frequency horn is physically very large and, thus, is seldom used in a cluster. A smaller low-frequency horn or vented, box-type, low-frequency component will be almost omnidirectional at low frequencies. Thus, the use of directional horns usually cannot improve gain before feedback because the feedback problems simply shift to below the crossover frequency!

26.1.13 Four Questions

There are many other things to consider for even a simplified system. Outdoors, for example, there are the effects of wind, humidity, and temperature layers, for starters. (See Chapter 1 and section 26.13.8.) However, the answers to the following four questions supply a great deal of information about whether or not a system will actually reinforce sound in a satisfactory manner.

26.1.13.1 Question 1: Is It Loud Enough?

The answer to the question, "Is it loud enough?" can be obtained from Eq. 26-6. This equation doesn't take gain or feedback into account; those are covered in question 4.

26.1.13.2 Question 2: Can Everybody Hear?

This question "Can everybody hear?" involves the coverage patterns of the loudspeakers and the way they are aimed into the audience. This topic is covered in detail later.

26.1.13.3 Question 3: Can Everybody Understand?

For the simplified (outdoor) system, the answer to this question is "yes" if the system is loud enough (question 1) and if it avoids problems like very poor frequency response and excessive distortion. Indoors, this question also involves the effects of reverberation.

26.1.13.4 Question 4: Will It Feed Back?

The answer to the question "Will it feed back?" is "no" (the desired answer) if PAG is equal to or greater than NAG (Eqs. 26-5 and 26-8).

Again, there's a lot more to sound system design than answering four questions, but these particular four questions are important enough that, in the next section, they form the basis for an expansion of the simplified system to cover the effects of reverberation on indoor systems.

26.2 THE INDOOR ENVIRONMENT

So far, the discussion of sound reinforcement has been simplified by neglecting the effects of echoes and reverberation. Now, however, it's time to modify the mathematical model of the sound-reinforcement system to include these effects. Doing this, of course, creates a much more useful model, one that can be used successfully both indoors and out.

The equations presented in this section used to determine *indoor attenuation*, *critical distance*, *potential* and *needed acoustic gain*, and *electrical power required* are derived from concepts presented by Hopkins and Stryker. The equation for AL_{cons} was derived by Peutz and Klein. The acoustic gain (potential, and needed) equations were developed by Don Davis of Synergetic Audio Concepts. The critical distance (D_c) equation was developed by Don Davis and Mel Sprinkle. The equations have been manipulated and modified by a number of writers to make them more useful to sound system designers. The most notable of these writers are Don and Carolyn Davis.

The equations presented here are basically the same as those used in *Sound System Engineering*. They have been manipulated to make them somewhat easier to explain and to make them more adaptable to computer analysis.

26.2.1 Echoes and Reverberation

Echoes and reverberation are both reflections of sound. An *echo* assumes that the time between the original source of the sound and a reflection is long enough that both sounds can be heard distinctly. The reflected sound is then called an echo. If a room has lots of echoes and they are closely spaced in time so that distinct reflections are not audible, this large number of echoes is known as *reverberation*. A much more detailed discussion of echoes, reverberation, and general room acoustics can be found in Chapters 1, 3, 5, and 7.

26.2.1.1 When an Echo Is a Problem

Some rooms have one or more distinct echoes but very little reverberation. A conference room with carpeting, draperies, padded seating, and acoustical ceiling tile, for example, may have little or no reverberation. That same room, however, may have a hard rear wall that produces a single slap-back echo (so called because it slaps back at talkers every time they try to speak from a location in the front of the room). Other, larger, rooms may have multiple distinct echoes. Superdome-sized rooms are an obvious example. In most cases, problem echoes must be dealt with by acoustic treatment. In many cases, in fact, a sound system will only aggravate an echo problem!

26.2.1.2 Can an Echo Be Useful?

When an audible reflection arrives at a listener's ears within about 60 ms or less after the original sound, the listener will probably not hear the reflection as a distinct echo. When the arrival time difference between source and reflection shortens to about 40 ms or less, the reflected sound adds to the original sound in a beneficial way, that is, the reflection can actually aid the ability to hear and understand the source. As the arrival time difference lengthens, the reflected sound becomes less useful until it finally begins to muddy the sound and eventually becomes a distinct echo. In addition, there is evidence that very short delays between the arrival of direct and reflected sound (perhaps delays shorter than about 4 ms or so) may also degrade sound quality because of the comb filtering they cause. Thus, audible reflections can be useful, questionable, or undesirable, depending primarily on the difference in the arrival time at the listener's ears (and somewhat on the difference in level between the direct and reflected sound).

26.2.1.3 When Reverberation Is Useful

Some reverberation is often desirable, especially for a musical performance. The reverberation of a large cathedral; for example, enhances the organ and choir sound. Some musical compositions, like those written for pipe organ, are actually meant for a large, reverberant room.

A small amount of reverberation can enhance a speech-reinforcement system, too. Reverberation can fill out a vocal sound to make it more natural. Those reflections in a reverberant field that reach the listener's ears a short time (but not too short a time) after the source can also, as explained previously, improve the ability to understand speech by effectively making it louder.

26.2.1.4 When Reverberation Is a Problem

If some reverberation is useful, too much reverberation causes muddy or boomy sound quality in a musical performance and makes speech very difficult to understand. In this case, the reverberation is a problem similar to that of too much ambient noise except that the reverberation gets louder as the signal gets louder so that a reverberation problem cannot be solved by simply turning up the volume control!

26.2.1.5 Reverberation and the Sound Reinforcement System

The indoor sound system model can be simplified by assuming two things: (1) the room has no distinct echoes, and (2) it has a well-developed and statistically random reverberant field (Fig. 26-5). The first assumption is good, since a room with distinct echoes should be treated acoustically. The second assumption is acceptable for the purposes of this section, although it should be understood that differences in reflecting and absorbing surfaces in any real room prevent true randomness.

The reason the reverberant field must be considered is that it will help the system maintain a more consistent L_P from seat to seat, even though it will hinder, to some extent, the attempt to provide *intelligible* sound to every seat.

Direct/Reverberant Ratio

Direct/reverberant ratio is a ratio of the direct sound at some point in a room to the reverberant sound, which is assumed to be the same everywhere in the room. A high direct/reverberant ratio means good speech intelligibility (if all other factors are favorable).

Q

Q is a measure of the directional properties of a loudspeaker (also see Chapter 14). An omnidirectional loudspeaker has a Q of 1. A loudspeaker radiating into a hemisphere has a Q of 2. A loudspeaker radiating into half a hemisphere has a Q of 4 and so on, as shown in Fig. 26-6. A related term, *DI (directivity index)*, is simply ten times the log (base 10) of Q. That is,

$$DI = 10 \log Q \tag{26-9}$$

A loudspeaker with a high Q will have a narrow coverage pattern and will, therefore, concentrate its sound energy on fewer seats than a low-Q loudspeaker. Thus, the high-Q loudspeaker can provide higher levels of *direct* sound and, likewise, higher direct/reverberant ratios. This leads to better intelligibility, at least in the single loudspeaker case.

Q compares the on-axis sound *intensity* of a single loudspeaker to what that intensity would be if the loud-

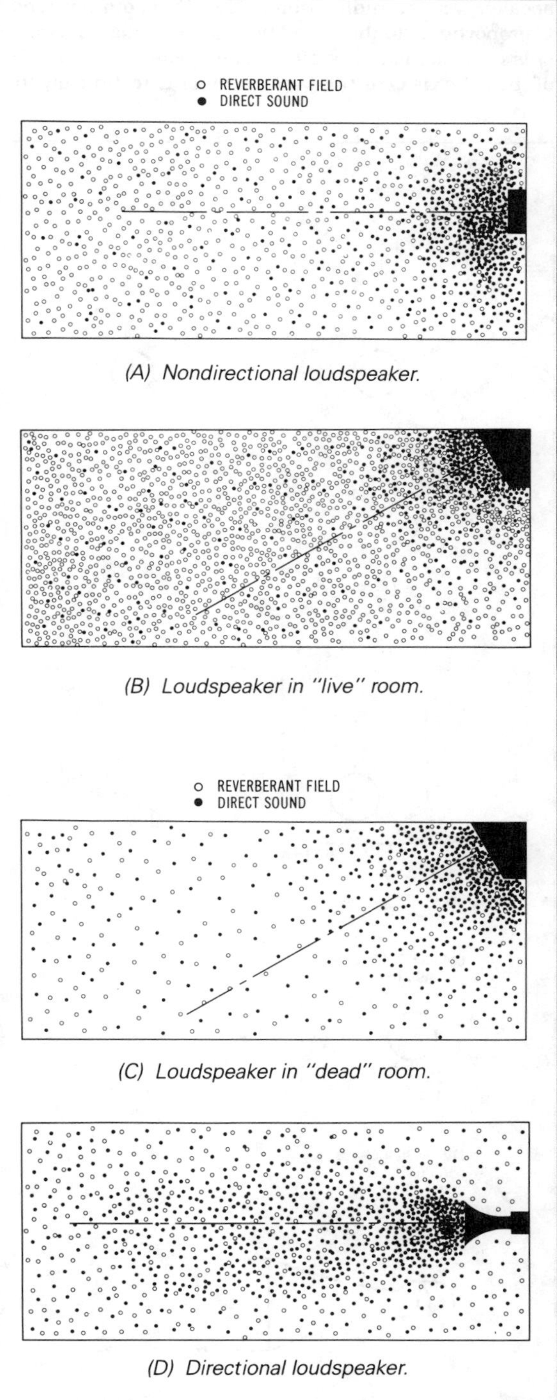

Figure 26-5 Direct and reverberant fields in a room. *(Courtesy JBL Inc./UREI)*

speaker were omnidirectional. Note that sound intensity is proportional to the sound pressure L_P squared. Because Q is only defined for a single loudspeaker, any mention of the *off-axis Q* or the *Q of a cluster* is technically inaccurate. A value for off-axis Q is useful, however, in calculating AL_{cons} for a listener not directly on axis of a loudspeaker. A value for the Q of a cluster could be useful to help determine AL_{cons} for a listener seated on-axis of

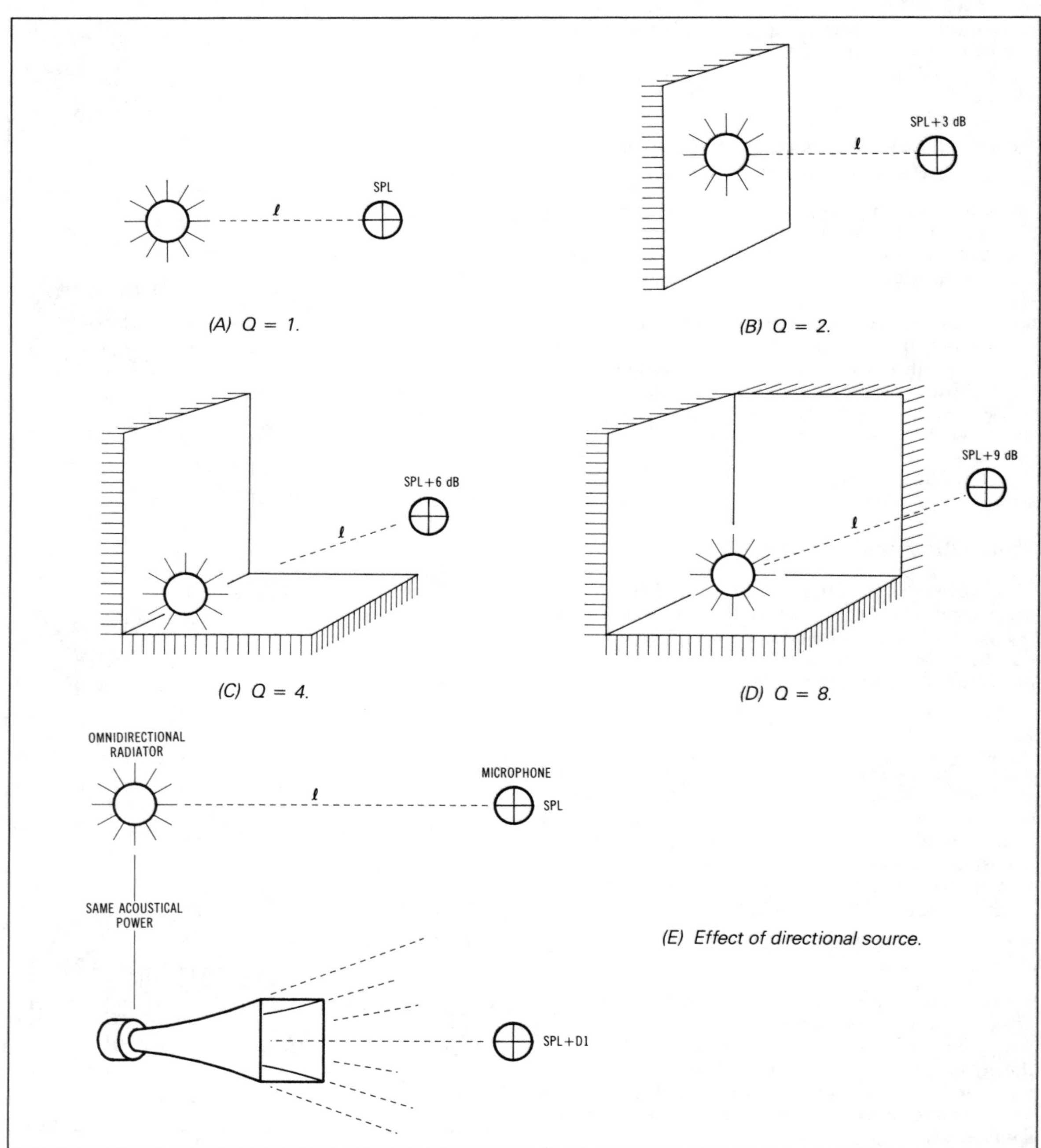

Figure 26-6 Directivity, angular coverage, directivity index (DI) and directivity factor (Q). *(Courtesy JBL Inc./UREI)*

a single horn in a multihorn system. Thus, the concept of Q is often extended to include these and other ideas. (AL_{cons} is discussed in section 26.2.3.2.)

The off-axis Q of a horn, for example, can be determined from an examination of the on-axis DI and the difference in sound pressure level on axis versus off-axis at the angle of interest. Subtract this difference from the on-axis DI and convert back to Q. For example, for a 90° (horizontal) horn, at 45° off-axis horizontally, the SPL is −6 dB from its on-axis value. Thus, if the on-axis DI is 12, the off-axis DI will be 6. If DI is known,

$$Q = 10^{DI/10} \qquad (26\text{-}10)$$

Thus, the off-axis Q in this example is $10^{6/10}$ or approximately 2.

The concept of the Q of a cluster is more difficult. In theory, it would be possible to calculate the Q of a cluster for a listener seated at any point in the room by comparing the direct L_P at that position with the overall acoustic power output of the entire cluster. In practice, this is complex since it requires a detailed knowledge of the efficiency of each loudspeaker and the electrical input to each driver as well as the directional characteristics and efficiency of each horn and any alterations that may be made in the horn's directional characteristics by the baffling effects of the cluster. One way to deal with these problems is discussed in section 26.3.4.6, where the calculation of this D_c modifier is discussed.

Room Constant

R or Sā is a measure of the relative liveness of a room (a live room has a well-developed, very audible reverberant field). A low room constant (R) or Sā means a very live room. A high R or Sā means a dead room. The R or Sā value depends on the size of the room, so a specific value of R or Sā is not enough to judge the reverberation characteristics of a room. Mathematically, a room constant is calculated as follows:

$$R = \frac{S\bar{a}}{1 - \bar{a}} \qquad (26\text{-}11)$$

where,
S is the total surface area of the room,
ā is the average absorption constant.

One version of the equation for critical distance uses the room constant in place of the Sā term. While room constant was commonly used to specify a room (in the D_c equation) in the past, it has fallen into disuse and is usually replaced in most equations by the Sā term.

Critical Distance

D_c (critical distance) is the distance (from a source) at which the direct sound from the source is exactly the same sound pressure level as the reverberant field (Fig. 26-7). Critical distance is important in a number of concepts including intelligibility.

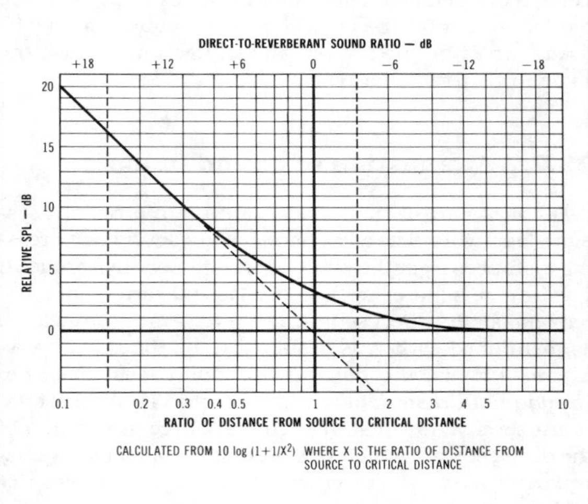

Figure 26-7 Critical distance. *(Courtesy JBL Inc./UREI)*

A good estimate of the critical distance for a given source (usually a loudspeaker) in a given room can be made by playing a pink-noise source through the loudspeaker and walking away from it holding a sound level meter. At some distance, the L_P will cease to change. Now walk back toward the source until the L_P increases exactly 3 dB. That distance will be the critical distance. (Since the direct sound and reverberant sound are equal here, the total is 3 dB above the reverberant sound alone.) Critical distance depends on the Q of the source and the absorption in the room; thus, it can vary with frequency, and this test shows only a broadband approximation of critical distance:

$$D_c = \sqrt{\frac{QS\bar{a}}{16\pi N}} = 0.161\sqrt{QS\bar{a}} \qquad (26\text{-}12)$$

where,
Q is the Q of the source,
S is the total surface area of the room,
ā is the average absorption coefficient for the surfaces in the room,
N is the total number of loudspeakers producing the same acoustic power as the loudspeaker pointed at the farthest listener.

Example:

Let,
Q = 5,
S = 28,000,
ā = 0.35,
N = 1,

$$D_c = \sqrt{\frac{5\,(28{,}000)\,0.35}{16\,\pi\,(1)}} = 31.2\,\text{ft}$$

For a more detailed discussion of the concept of N, see section 26.2.4.6. The critical distance equation may be used with either metric or English (feet) units (use the same units throughout).

26.2.2 Attenuation of Sound Indoors

The first part of the indoor sound-reinforcement system model will tell us what happens to a sound at increasing distances from the source in an indoor environment. The inverse-square law (Eq. 26-1) is still correct indoors, *but only for the direct sound.* The reverberant sound level, as mentioned earlier, is assumed to be the same everywhere—that is, *the reverberant sound level does not change with distance from the source.* Thus, the total sound level, at any distance from a source, is the *sum* of the direct sound, which has been attenuated by inverse-square law, and the reverberant sound, which does not change with distance:

$$L_P' = L_P - 20\log\left(\frac{D'}{D}\right) + 10\log\left[\frac{g(D')}{g(D)}\right] \qquad (26\text{-}13)$$

where,
D is the original distance from the source,
D' is the new distance from the source,
L_P is the original L_P at D,
L_P' is the new L_P at the distance D'.

g(x) is found from the following equation:

$$g(x) = D_c^2 + x^2 \text{ (for any distance x)} \qquad (26\text{-}14)$$

Where x is any variable, note that the equation for indoor attenuation is exactly the same as Eq. 26-1 for outdoor attenuation (inverse-square law) except for the final term: $10 \log [g(D')/g(D)]$, which can be interpreted as a contribution from the indoor reverberant field.

Example:

Let,
$L_P = 90$ dB,
$D = 4$ ft,
$D' = 125$ ft,
$D_c = 31.2$ ft.

$$L_P' = 90 - 20\log\left(\frac{125}{4}\right) + 10\log\left[\frac{g(125)}{g(4)}\right]$$

$$= 72.3\,\text{dB}$$

Notes: Dimensions may be in feet or meters but be consistent. To compare to outdoor attenuation (Eq. 26-1), simply ignore the

$$10\log\left[\frac{gD'}{gD}\right]$$

term.

Indoor attenuation can also be found from another equation as follows:

$$L'_P = L_P - \Delta\text{ dB} \qquad (26\text{-}15)$$

where,

$$\Delta\text{dB} = \Delta D' - \Delta D$$

and

$$\Delta x = -10\log\left[\frac{Q}{4\pi x^2} + \frac{4}{S\bar{a}}\right]$$

Example:

Let,
$L_p = 90$,
$D = 4$ ft,
$D' = 125$ ft,
$Q = 5$,
$S = 28{,}000$,
$\bar{a} = 0.35$,

$$\Delta D = -10\log\left[\frac{5}{4\pi(4)^2} + \frac{4}{(28{,}000)(0.35)}\right]$$
$$= 16.0\,\text{dB}$$

$$\Delta D' = -10\log\left[\frac{5}{4\pi(125)^2} + \frac{4}{(28{,}000)(0.35)}\right]$$
$$= 33.6\,\text{dB}$$

then,

$$\Delta\text{dB} = 33.6\,\text{dB} - 16.0\,\text{dB}$$
$$= 17.6\,\text{dB}$$

and

$$L'_P = 90 - 17.6$$
$$= 72.4\,\text{dB}$$

Note: Except for round-off errors, this answer and the answer to the example for Eq. 26-14 are the same.

Eq. 26-15 is more common in the literature. Eq. 26-14 may be easier to understand and to use in a computer program. The two equations are mathematically the same and will produce the same answers for equal data.

26.2.3 Four Questions Again

Question 2: "Can everybody hear?" is discussed in section 26.3.3.1. Questions 1, 3, and 4, however, can be answered with the information obtained so far.

26.2.3.1 Question 1: Is It Loud Enough?

In the simplified (outdoor) system, the answer to this question depended on the required L_P at the farthest listener (at D_2), the required head room in decibels and the sensitivity of the loudspeaker. In the indoor system, the room affects the analysis. Yet, although the room adds complexity to the answer to question 1, it makes things a little easier in the actual design of an indoor sound-reinforcement system, because, after the critical distance is passed, the sound can only attenuate another 3 dB. Thus, for farther distance, no more power is needed to maintain the same L_P! This cannot be extended forever (unfortunately, there is still no "free lunch"), since intelligibility suffers at distances well into the reverberant field. But that is the topic of question 3. For now, here is the equation for indoor electrical power required:

$$EPR = 10^{\left[\frac{Lp + H - SENS + 20\log\left(\frac{D_2}{4}\right) - 10\log\left(\frac{g(D_2)}{g(4)}\right)}{10}\right]} \qquad (26\text{-}16)$$

where,

$g(x) = D_c^2 + x^2$

Example:

Let,

$L_P = 90$ dB,
H = 10 dB,
SENS = 113 dB /1 W/4 ft,
$D_c = 31.2$ ft.

$$EPR = 10^{\left[\frac{90 + 10 - 113 + 20\log\left(\frac{128}{4}\right) - 10\log\left(\frac{17{,}357}{989.4}\right)}{10}\right]}$$

$$= 2.93\,W$$

Notes: Dimensions may be in feet or meters, but be consistent and give appropriate SENS and D_c. For dimensions in meters, change the constant 4 in both log terms to 1. To compare with outdoor EPR equation (Eq. 26-6), simply ignore the

$$10\log\left[\frac{g(D)_2}{g(4)}\right]$$

term.

As in the simplified EPR equation (Eq. 26-13), SENS is the sensitivity of the loudspeaker at 4 ft, and the distances (such as D_2) are given in feet. To use metric (1 m) sensitivity, change the value 4 in the term 20 log (D_2/4) to 1 and give all distances in meters. (Also give a 1-W/1-m value for loudspeaker sensitivity.) The value L_P in the first line of the equation is the desired L_P at D_2. The value H is a desired value for headroom, usually assumed to be 10 dB. That 10 dB, of course, may be changed for a particular system. D_c is the critical distance given in Eq. 26-12. It is instructive to note that this equation is the same as the simplified EPR equation (Eq. 26-13) except for the term:

$$10\log\left[\frac{g(D_2)}{g(4)}\right]$$

which can be interpreted as a contribution from the reverberant field.

EPR can also be found from an equation that is more common in the literature:

$$EPR = 10^{\left[\frac{L_P + 10 + \Delta D_2 - \Delta 4 - SENS}{10}\right]} \qquad (26\text{-}17)$$

where,

$$\Delta x = -10\log\left[\frac{Q}{4\pi x^2} + \frac{4}{S\bar{a}}\right]$$

Example:

Let,

$L_P = 90$,
$D_2 = 128$,
SENS = 113,
Q = 5,
S = 28,000,
$\bar{a} = 0.35$.

then

$$\Delta D_2 = 33.6$$

and

$$\Delta 4 = 16.0$$

and

$$EPR = 10^{\left[\frac{90 + 10 + 33.6 - 16.0 - 113}{10}\right]}$$

$$= 2.91\,W$$

Note: Except for round-off errors, this answer and the answer to the previous example are the same.

This equation may be more familiar to some readers. However, it and Eq. 26-16 are mathematically equivalent and will produce the same answers from the same data. Eq. 26-16, however, may be easier to understand and to use in a computer program.

26.2.3.2 Question 3: Can Everybody Understand?

In the simplified system, this question was answered by considering the required signal-to-noise ratio and making certain that the sound system output was sufficiently above the ambient noise level to provide intelligible sound (speech). Indoor intelligibility depends also on the direct-to-reverberant ratio, and an unfavorable direct-to-reverberant ratio cannot be made better by merely increasing the sound pressure level from the loudspeakers, since that will also increase the reverberant field level!

If the direct-to-reverberant ratio is unfavorable, one or more of the following may help:

1. Decrease the reverberant field by adding absorption to the room (usually a costly process).
2. Move the listener closer to the loudspeaker (in a reverberant church with the pews half filled, people sitting near the loudspeakers will hear and understand better than those farther away from the loudspeakers).
3. Move the loudspeakers closer to the listeners (adding additional loudspeakers, as described later, is a common way to improve the direct-to-reverberant ratio).
4. Use a loudspeaker with higher Q (this is ideal provided the required Q doesn't mean that you have a very narrow coverage pattern that cannot cover all the listeners).

How is a direct-to-reverberant ratio determined? What is a favorable direct-to-reverberant ratio? It is possible to determine this ratio directly, but it is more common to use the *articulation loss of consonants* concept. If the articulation loss of consonants (AL_{cons}) is 15% or less and the signal-to-noise ratio is favorable (+25 dB or greater), there is every reason to believe the answer to question 3 will be "yes." Note that the AL_{cons} equation is most accurate in rooms with reverberation times of 1.6 s or longer and its use is not necessary in very dead rooms.

$$\%AL_{cons} = \frac{656\,(D_2)^2(RT_{60})^2\,N}{QV} \qquad (26\text{-}18)$$

where,
656 is a constant for distances in feet (use 200 for distances in meters),
D_2 is the distance to the farthest listener,
RT_{60} is the room reverberation time,
N is a number that attempts to compensate for the fact that there are most likely several loudspeakers in the cluster and only one will be pointed at the farthest listener (but all add to the reverberant field),
Q is the Q of the loudspeaker,
V is the volume of the room.

Example:

Let,
$D_2 = 125$ ft,
$RT_{60} = 2.5$ s,
$V = 500{,}000$ ft^3,
$Q = 10$,
$N = 1$,

$$\%Al_{cons} = \frac{656\,(125^2)\,2.5^2\,(1)}{10\,(500{,}000)}$$
$$= 12.8\,\%\ \text{(acceptable)}$$

One way to interpret N is the total number of loudspeakers producing the same acoustic power as the loudspeaker pointed at the farthest listener. For a more detailed discussion of the concept of N, see section 26.3.4.6.

26.2.3.3 Question 4: Will It Feed Back?

The PAG and NAG concepts work indoors, too, but are modified by the room. Here are the new equations:

$$PAG = 20\log\left[\frac{D_oD_1}{D_sD_2}\right] - 10\log NOM - 6\text{ dB} - 10\log\left[\frac{g(D_o)g(D_1)}{g(D_s)g(D_2)}\right] \qquad (26\text{-}19)$$

where,
$g(x) = D_c^2 + x^2$

Example:

Let,
$D_s = 2$ ft,
$D_o = 128$ ft,
$D_1 = 45$ ft,
$D_2 = 90$ ft,
$D_c = 31.2$ ft,
NOM = 3,

$$PAG = 20\log\left[\frac{128(45)}{2(90)}\right] - 10\log 3 - 6 - 10\log\left[\frac{17{,}357(2998.4)}{977.4(9073.4)}\right]$$
$$= 11.6\,\text{dB}$$

Note: Dimensions may be in feet or meters, but be consistent and use appropriate D_c. To compare to outdoor PAG (Eq. 26-5), simply ignore the

$$10\log\left[\frac{g(D_o)g(D_1)}{g(D_s)g(D_2)}\right]$$

term.

$$NAG = 20\log\left[\frac{D_o}{EAD}\right] - 10\log\left[\frac{g(D_o)}{g(EAD)}\right] \qquad (26\text{-}20)$$

where,

$g(x) = D_c^2 + x^2$

Example:

Let,
D_o = 128 ft,
EAD = 4 ft,
D_c = 31.2 ft.

$$\text{NAG} = 20\log\left[\frac{128}{4}\right] - 10\log\left[\frac{g(128)}{g(4)}\right]$$

$$= 17.7\,\text{dB}$$

Notes: Dimensions may be in feet or meters, but be consistent and use appropriate D_c. To compare to Eq. 26-8, simply ignore the term:

$$10\log\left[\frac{g(D_o)}{g(EAD)}\right]$$

Alternate forms of the PAG and NAG equations, which are more common in the literature, follow:

$$\text{PAG} = \Delta D_o + \Delta D_1 - \Delta D_s - \Delta D_2 - 10\log \text{NOM} - 6\text{ dB} \qquad (26\text{-}21)$$

where,

$$\Delta x = -10\log\left[\frac{Q}{4\pi x^2} + \frac{4}{S\bar{a}}\right] \text{(for any distance x)}$$

Example:

Let,
D_o = 128 ft,
D_1 = 45 ft,
D_s = 2 ft,
D_2 = 90 ft,
Q = 5,
S = 28,000 ft^2,
$\bar{a}$ = 0.35,
NOM = 3,

then,
ΔD_o = 33.6,
ΔD_1 = 32.2,
ΔD_s = 10.0,
ΔD_2 = 33.4,

and

$$\text{PAG} = 33.6 + 32.2 - 10 - 33.4 - 10\log 3 - 6 = 11.6\,\text{dB}$$

Note: Except for round-off errors, this answer and the answer to the example for Eq. 26-19 are the same.

$$\text{NAG} = \Delta D_o - \Delta \text{EAD} \qquad (26\text{-}22)$$

where,

$$\Delta x = -10\log\left[\frac{Q}{4\pi x^2} + \frac{4}{S\bar{a}}\right] \text{(for any distance x)}$$

Example:

Let,
D_o = 128 ft,
EAD = 4 ft,
Q = 5,
S = 28,000 ft^2,
$\bar{a}$ = 0.35,

then,
ΔD_o = 33.6,
ΔEAD = 16.0,

and,

NAG = 33.6 − 16.0 = 17.6 dB

Note: Except for round-off errors, this answer and the answer to the example for Eq. 26-20 are the same.

These two equations are mathematically equivalent to Eqs. 26-19 and 26-20 and will produce the same answers given the same data. Eqs. 26-19 and 26-20 may be easier to understand and to insert in a computer program.

In addition, it should be noted that some users prefer to place the NOM (number of open microphones) and 6-dB feedback stability margin (FSM) terms in the NAG equation rather than in the PAG equation. This author believes that they belong in the PAG equation since including them produces a value of PAG more nearly equal to that which will be measured in the installed system. While PAG and NAG values will differ with placement of the two terms, the PAG − NAG value (which is the most important result) will be the same regardless of the placement of the two terms.

Also, as before, if PAG is greater than or equal to NAG, it's reasonable to assume that the system will be stable and not feed back.

In Eq. 26-18, the terms D_s, D_1, D_2, D_o, and NOM are as explained in the simplified system. The term EAD should be estimated as for the simplified system, ignoring the effects of the reverberant field. This puts the estimate "on the safe side" for the NAG calculation. The equations for PAG and NAG are similar to the equations given for the simplified system (Eqs. 26-5 and 26-8) except for the 10 log [ ] terms that can be interpreted as modifications caused by the room reverberant field.

26.2.3.4 The Effect of Directional Microphones and Loudspeakers

In a reverberant room, the effect of directional microphones and loudspeakers is even less than in the outdoor case. The reason is that the amount of reverberant sound energy picked up by the microphone depends very little on the microphone's pickup pattern (a cardioid microphone picks up more reverberant sound from the front, which compensates for its reduced rear pickup). Directional loudspeakers may reduce the amount of direct sound energy reaching the microphone but do not substantially reduce the amount of reverberant sound reaching the microphone, since this is usually dominated by the non-directional low-frequency loudspeakers. Note that the indoor PAG equation (Eq. 26-19) already includes the effect of directional loudspeakers on the reverberant field anyway. Thus, it is probably best to assume that no additional gain before feedback will be provided by directional microphones and loudspeakers.

26.2.4 Validity of the Model in a Geometrically Complex Room

In effect, the equations just presented form a mathematical model of the interactions between a room and a sound system. The question arises, "Just how valid is this model?"

The answer is to remember that the model assumes a well-developed, statistically random reverberant field in a room with simple geometry. Thus the model can be very accurate in a room like a high-school gymnasium or a rectangular church. Add balconies, transepts, or other complexities, and the equations, while still useful, cannot describe the entire room.

One way to deal with more complex rooms is to treat them as two or more acoustically separate spaces. A large stage with hardwood floors and reflecting walls and ceiling, for example, may be coupled to an audience seating area with padded seats, carpeting, and draped walls. A reverberant cathedral may have an under-balcony area that is very different acoustically from the main room. System design and the use of the equations will be improved by treating these different spaces as entirely different rooms that just happen to share a common boundary (an imaginary wall).

An equation for the overall combined reverberation time in such a dual-space room follows:

$$RT_{60T} = \sqrt[3]{(RT_{60A})^3 + (RT_{60B})^3} \qquad (26\text{-}23)$$

Some rooms, of course, do not lend themselves to analysis by the given equations. One example is the superdome-sized room that has no true reverberant field because the individual reflections are spaced far enough apart in time that they are more accurately called echoes, not reverberation. These rooms may have an *apparent* dramatic increase in reverberation when excited by a high sound pressure level sound system (similar to those used for concert sound reinforcement). Another example is the acoustically dry conference room that has no significant reverberant field because of an abundance of carpeting, draperies, padded seating, and acoustical ceiling tile. One approach to design in both these spaces is to use the simplified (outdoor system) equations where needed, since they deal with the direct sound. In the large space, echoes must be considered (they are not included in any of the equations); in the small space, table top and other nearby reflections must be considered.

26.2.5 A Modification for Low RT_{60} Rooms

Recently, a useful equation has been developed to describe the behavior of sound in an acoustically dry room. Qualitatively, what happens in such a room is that the attenuation of sound with increasing distance from the source is greater than would be predicted from Eq. 26-12. According to Eq. 26-12, the L_P from a source should not attenuate more than 3 dB at *any* distance past D_c (critical distance). In these rooms, however, the actual attenuation of sound for distances past D_c is somewhere between the value predicted by Eq. 26-12 and the value that would be predicted by the inverse-square law, Equation 26-1, (Fig. 26-8). V.M.A. Peutz, one of the originators of the AL_{cons} concept, has investigated this phenomenon, and the following equation for attenuation in an acoustically dry room is derived from his work:

$$L_P' = L_P - 0.734\left[\frac{\sqrt{V}}{h(RT_{60})}\right]\left[\log\left(\frac{D'}{D}\right)\right] \qquad (26\text{-}24)$$

where,

H is the room height,
V is the room volume.

Example

Let,

$V = 4275\ ft^3$,
$H = 9.5$ ft,
$L_P = 90$ dB,
$RT_{60} = 0.4$ s,
$D = 10$ ft,
$D' = 20$ ft.

Note: Both D and D′ must be greater than *calculated* D_c for Eq. 26-24 to work. D_c *calculated* for this room = 7.22 ft, so that Eq. 26-24 may be used with D = 10 and D′ = 20.

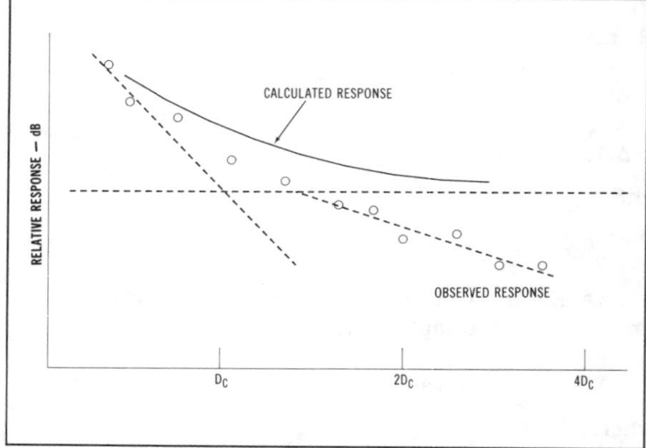

Figure 26-8 Attenuation with distance in a relatively dead room. *(Courtesy JBL Inc./UREI)*

Then,

$$L_P' = 90 - 0.734\left[\frac{\sqrt{4275}}{9.5(0.4)}\right]\left[\log\left(\frac{20}{10}\right)\right]$$
$$= 86.2\text{ dB}$$

Note the similarity between Eq. 26-24 and the inverse-square law (Eq. 26-1). The answer, 86.2 dB, is, as expected, between the 84 dB predicted by Eq. 26-1 and the 88.7 dB predicted by Eq. 26-13. Dimensions are assumed to be in feet. Also, note that Eq. 26-24 should be used only in rooms with very low reverberation times. Eq. 26-24 will accurately predict attenuation for distances D', which are greater than the *calculated* critical distance, D_c, whenever an on-site measurement shows the actual L_P to be 1 to 5 dB below the predicted L_P at a distance equal to twice the calculated D_c from a source.

26.3 DESIGNING THE LOUDSPEAKER SYSTEM

The answer to Question 2: "Can Everybody Hear?" comes from evaluating the success of the loudspeaker system, in particular, how well the loudspeakers have been aimed to cover the entire audience and how well the patterns of individual loudspeakers combine to cover areas with complex shapes.

26.3.1 Types of Loudspeakers

Note: See Chapter 14 for more detailed information on subjects discussed in the following sections.

26.3.1.1 Cone Loudspeakers

Large cone loudspeakers (15- and 18-in. diameters) are normally used as the low-frequency components of two-way, three-way, or multiway systems. Also, 12- and 10-in. cone loudspeakers may be used as the low-frequency component in a low-power, two-way system or as the lower midrange component in a three-way or multiway system.

Smaller cone loudspeakers (8 and 4 in.) may be used as low-frequency or midrange components in a packaged loudspeaker system offered by a manufacturer. Other 8- and 4-in. cone loudspeakers are designed for relatively full-range performance and are used in ceiling-type distributed systems and as the components in column loudspeaker systems.

26.3.1.2 Cone Loudspeaker Enclosures

There are three basic types of loudspeaker enclosures in use in professional systems: *sealed* (often improperly called "infinite baffle"), *vented* (also called "ported" or "bass reflex"), and *horn-loaded*.

A sealed enclosure is relatively simple to design and construct; it has a smooth frequency response curve, good transient response and helps protect the loudspeaker from over-excursion at low frequencies.

A vented enclosure works as a Helmholtz resonator to boost the low-frequency response of a loudspeaker above the response of a similarly sealed enclosure design. Transient response and frequency response smoothness may suffer somewhat, although these problems are small in a good design. An electrical high-pass filter should be used to help protect the loudspeaker against over-excursion at frequencies below the enclosure resonance frequency f_b.

Horn-loaded enclosures place a horn in front of the loudspeaker and a sealed compression chamber behind the loudspeaker. The loudspeaker thus becomes a compression driver. Properly designed, a horn-loaded enclosure boosts the overall efficiency of the loudspeaker-enclosure combination above a sealed or vented enclosure and provides some measure of control over the dispersion pattern. In addition, the sealed chamber behind the loudspeaker helps prevent over-excursion at low frequencies.

One type of horn-loaded enclosure, often called a *vented horn*, adds a vented chamber behind the loudspeaker (instead of the sealed chamber) to boost the low-frequency response below the horn's cutoff frequency.

Another type of horn-loaded enclosure, known as a *folded horn*, is a relatively long horn that has been folded back on itself to reduce the external package size (Fig. 26-9).

Because of their efficiency, horn-loaded enclosures were popular in the early days of sound when power amplifiers were small and expensive. Unfortunately, a horn designed to work well at low frequencies is quite large, and with power amplifiers larger and less expensive per watt, many designers now choose vented enclosures because they fit in the smaller spaces provided in modern buildings. It can be shown mathematically that, for a given amount of space (volume), a loudspeaker system using vented

Figure 26-9 A pair of dual 15-in. driver folded-horn enclosures shown with accessory midrange and high-frequency horns. *(Courtesy Klipsch & Associates, Inc.)*

enclosures can produce more total acoustic power than a horn-loaded loudspeaker system. The vented system simply uses more loudspeakers and amplifiers to achieve this victory. Horn-loaded enclosures, therefore, are used primarily in large, outdoor systems where their large size can be tolerated, and their efficiency can be put to good use. They are traditionally used in theater (cinema) systems.

When making a choice of loudspeakers and enclosures, keep in mind that the manufacturer of the loudspeaker normally designs the loudspeaker for a specific type of enclosure. Using a loudspeaker in any other type of enclosure may degrade its performance.

26.3.1.3 Compression Drivers and Horns

One class of components is designed specifically for use on a horn. These components are called *compression drivers*, and they are used almost exclusively as the midrange and high-frequency components of two-way, three-way, and multiway systems. At these frequencies, horn sizes are more tolerable. Because of the efficiency and dispersion control of the horn, especially in the critical midrange and high-frequencies, horns and compression drivers are the midrange and high-frequency components most often used in loudspeaker clusters (Fig. 26-10).

Figure 26-10 Photo comparing several radial exponential horns, multicell horns, and Mantaray

Exponential horns come in both straight and radial designs. They provide good loading for the driver, which helps prevent over-excursion at low frequencies, and the on-axis frequency response of an exponential horn is usually very smooth. Exponential horns are usually smaller in size than other horn types (for a given driver size and low-frequency cutoff). For these reasons, exponential horns are often used in packaged loudspeaker systems and when space is tight. The dispersion of an exponential horn narrows with increasing frequency (beams), which is a disadvantage in cluster design, since it is more difficult to predict the overall cluster dispersion at various frequencies. A radial, exponential horn has some measure of dispersion control in its horizontal pattern and, thus, may be a better choice than a straight, exponential horn. Most reentrant (folded) paging horns are essentially straight exponential designs and beam at high frequencies. Some newer paging horns, however, are designed for improved dispersion control.

Multicell horns are made of a number of straight or exponential cells. The purpose of this design is to reduce the high-frequency beaming problem. Unfortunately, each cell still beams at high frequencies, and the overall horn will have fingers at high frequencies. For this reason, multicell horns are not often used in newer system designs.

A newer class of horns, known generically as *constant directivity horns*, has very good dispersion control (pattern control) over a wide frequency band. Although somewhat larger than exponential or multicell horns, the dispersion control advantage of constant directivity horns is so overwhelming that they have become the most popular choice for new loudspeaker cluster designs. The rest of this discussion assumes the use of constant directivity horns.

26.3.2 Choosing Loudspeakers

Besides the obvious question of budget, a few other things to consider in making a choice of loudspeakers are discussed.

26.3.2.1 Power Handling

The loudspeaker system should be able to handle the full power output of the chosen power amplifier for an extended period of time over the full-rated frequency range of the loudspeaker. (Also see sections 26.3.4.4 and 26.6.2.)

26.3.2.2 Frequency Range and Response

The loudspeaker's response should be smooth over its intended operating range. If the system will be used primarily for voice, a loudspeaker system whose low-frequency response is limited to 70 or 80 Hz should suffice. For an entire musical group, especially a popular musical group, the system's low-frequency response should extend down to 40 Hz. Frequencies below 40 Hz are limited to a few instruments, such as the pipe organ, synthesizer, and bass drum. When it is necessary to reinforce these very low frequencies, a separate subwoofer system should be used to avoid the added stress these low frequencies would place on the normal system woofers.

26.3.2.3 Sensitivity

This is an indication of the loudspeaker's efficiency. A loudspeaker's sensitivity is the number L_P the loudspeaker will produce at a given distance, on axis, when the input power is a certain number of watts. High sensitivity is an advantage because it increases maximum L_P. Remember that a decrease of only 3 dB in sensitivity means double the amplifier power needed to maintain the same L_P.

26.3.2.4 Coverage Pattern

Pre-packaged systems usually have a short-throw coverage pattern (commonly 90° horizontally by 40° vertically). In a component system, several mid- and/or high-frequency horns with different coverage patterns can be chosen for long-throw, medium-throw, and short-throw applications. Long-throw horns are usually 40° horizontal by 20° vertical and are usually only needed in large concert systems and permanently installed systems. Medium-throw horns are usually 60° horizontal by 40° vertical and are valuable in many portable as well as permanent systems to reach farther back in an audience. Short-throw horns are usually 90° or 120° horizontal by 40° vertical and are used to reach the front of an audience or may be used to cover an entire audience in a small portable system.

26.3.2.5 Sound Quality

Sound quality is an entirely subjective evaluation, which means that personal tastes play an important part. The goal of a sound-reinforcement system is not to alter but to reinforce and, to some extent, to enhance the sound of a performance. Thus, the subjective evaluation of the sound quality of a loudspeaker system should be based on how well that loudspeaker system will accurately reinforce a performance.

The subjective evaluation of a loudspeaker requires a knowledge of the way the performance sounds without reinforcement. Listening tests should be done with live sources if at all possible. Recorded music of any kind, especially if played from a cassette machine or tuner, hides many defects in a loudspeaker system. Live music, or even a simple live microphone test, because of its increased dynamic range and transients, reveals the true nature of a loudspeaker system.

26.3.3 Types of Loudspeaker Systems

There are two primary types of loudspeaker systems as used in sound-reinforcement systems, the *central cluster* and the *distributed* system. In addition, there are variations and combinations of these two types.

26.3.3.1 The Central Cluster

A *central cluster* is a group of horns and woofers placed in a central location and aimed at a listening area. The traditional central cluster is placed above a stage (on the

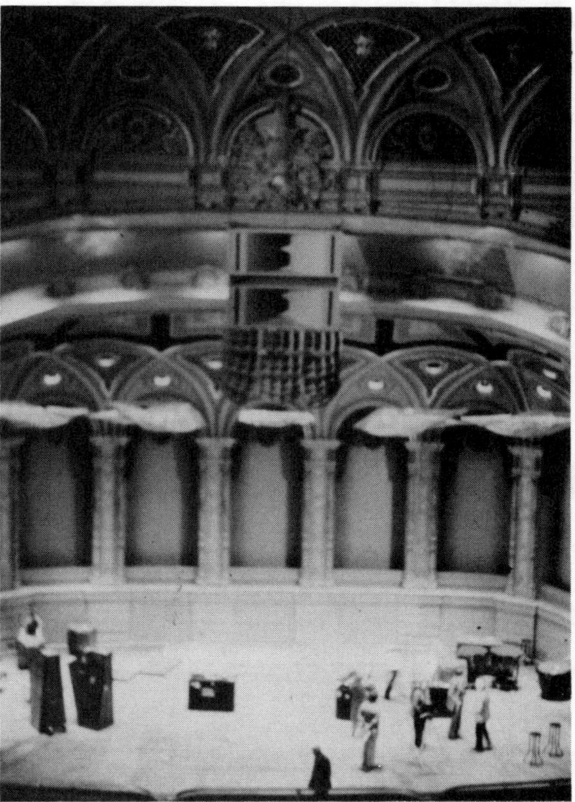

Figure 26-11 Typical central cluster. *(Courtesy Bolt, Beranek, and Neumann, Inc.)*

proscenium) or above the primary microphone location (Fig. 26-11).

A location above the audience makes the difference between the distance from the cluster to the nearest listener and the distance from the cluster to the farthest listener more nearly equal. This, in turn, makes the job of designing the cluster for even audience coverage easier. In most cases, however, the cluster should not be more than about 30 to 45 ft above the heads of the listeners. This is because listeners seated near the talker can often hear both the talker and the cluster. If the cluster is more than about 30 to 45 ft above the heads of the listeners, they will notice a hollow sound or even a distinct echo due to the natural delay between the sound from the talker and the sound from the cluster (often incorrectly called time delay).

The human ear can accurately discriminate the location of sounds from a left-right perspective, but not as well from an up-down perspective. Thus, another advantage of a central cluster, if it is placed near the center of the room or approximately above the primary microphone location (and assuming other factors are favorable), is that the sound will appear to emanate from the talker, and not from the cluster.

A final, significant advantage of a central cluster is that, compared to an equally well-designed distributed loudspeaker system, the central cluster is almost always less costly.

Sometimes, esthetic considerations prevent the installation of a central cluster. The large loudspeakers may block the line of sight to a stained-glass window in a church, for example.

In some rooms, the ceiling is too low compared to the length of the room to allow a central cluster to work well. This problem prevents adequate gain before feedback in the back of the room (PAG is too low). A good rule of thumb is that D_2 should be no more than about four times D_1 for a single central cluster to work properly. If the 45-ft height rule is followed, this seems to limit central clusters to rooms with dimensions of 180 ft or less. However, the 45-ft rule can be ignored if the listeners cannot hear the talker without the aid of the sound system, as is often the case in large indoor sports arenas.

26.3.3.2 Variations on the Central Cluster

Sometimes, in a long room with a relatively low ceiling, a second cluster is installed. The second (and third if more than two are used) cluster is installed some distance out in the room and electronically delayed so that a listener able to hear both clusters will seem to hear only one source (Fig. 26-12). The second cluster effectively divides the room into two rooms, and the first cluster now only has to cover a room that is half as long.

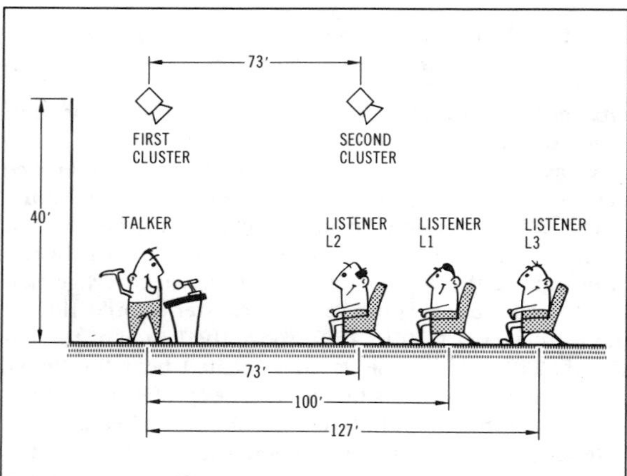

Figure 26-12 Two-cluster (front, back) system. *(Courtesy Altec Lansing Corp.)*

26.3.3.3 The Split Cluster

One way to install a central-cluster-type system and preserve central sight lines is to split the cluster with part on the left and part on the right (Fig. 26-13). Despite the very common use of this design, it has a number of problems.

A listener seated in position A will hear primarily the left cluster and will probably find the system to be satisfactory. A listener at position B will hear primarily the right cluster with similarly good results. A listener at position C, exactly midway between the two clusters will hear the sound from both clusters at equal levels and with no delay from one cluster or the other. Thus, the listener at position C is likely to find the system satisfactory. A listener at position D, however, will hear the two clusters at approximately equal levels but at two different times. That is, the sound from the left cluster will be slightly delayed in reaching the listener compared to the sound coming from the right cluster. The difference in arrival times will seldom be long enough to cause a discernible echo, but it will cause a phenomenon known as comb filtering, an undesirable result of the acoustic phase cancellations caused by the differing arrival times. This phenomenon will be most clearly audible when the listener at position D moves his or her head from side to side.

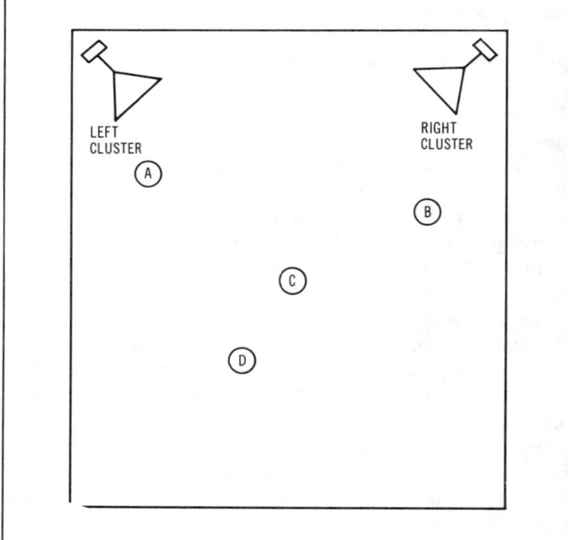

Figure 26-13 The split cluster.

One way to overcome this problem, at least partially, is to lower the sound pressure level of one of the clusters about 3 dB and use that lower-level cluster to cover only those listeners who cannot adequately be covered by the other cluster. Design the louder cluster to cover as much of the listening audience as possible in this situation.

The only other good reason for using a split cluster is when true stereo sound is required. In this case, in order for every listener to hear the stereo effect, *both clusters must cover the entire audience.*

26.3.3.4 The Distributed Loudspeaker System

Distributed systems are usually installed in rooms with ceilings that are too low for a central cluster. Typically, a distributed system will consist of a large number of cone-type loudspeakers installed in the ceiling and arranged in such a way as to cover a listening audience evenly.

Because every listener is more or less the same distance from a loudspeaker, coverage can be very uniform from a distributed system. In addition, if the system is carefully designed, the potential for feedback should be very low, and because reverberation times in this type of room are usually quite low, intelligibility is often very good.

Thus, in the ideal case, a well-designed distributed system can work very well. One problem with even the ideal distributed system, however, is that the listeners will hear the sound coming from over their heads—that is, the natural localization provided by a central cluster is not provided by a distributed system. This minor problem can be helped by using an electronic *time delay* in combination with a localizer loudspeaker, a subject covered in section 26.5.2.

Sometimes, a distributed system will be installed in a very large room with a high reverberation time. A convention hall exhibit room or high-ceiling airport terminal is a good example. Here the system will probably be used for paging and perhaps for background music, and, thus, the localization of a central cluster is not needed. The high reverberation and high noise present in rooms like this, however, present problems to the system designer. These problems can be at least partially overcome by a dense enough layout and careful equalization (also see section 26.5.2). In these areas N also plays an important role. The distributed system has an additional advantage over the central cluster in this case because it effectively reduces the value of D_2 (the distance from the loudspeaker to the farthest listener) and, thus, improves signal-to-noise ratio and direct-to-reverberant ratio.

One other reason for using a distributed system, even in a room that could utilize a central cluster, is that the distributed system allows a more flexible room layout than the central cluster. In some multipurpose rooms, for example, the stage location may be changed from event to event, and some events may not use a stage at all. The distributed system allows almost any location to be used as the stage or primary microphone location without the distraction that would be caused by having a central cluster behind the heads of the audience! In addition, in large, reverberant spaces, like sports arenas, distributed loudspeakers above unused portions of the room can be turned off. This helps intelligibility because it improves the direct/reverberant ratio by lowering the amount of energy uselessly put into the reverberant field.

26.3.3.5 Central Cluster Plus Distributed System

In some rooms with central clusters and rear balconies, listeners seated under the balcony are not adequately covered by the central cluster. In this case, a distributed system, placed under the balcony, on electronic time delay, can solve the problem (Fig. 26-14). A good rule of thumb is that every listener under a balcony should have good line of sight to the loudspeaker covering their area in order to hear the central cluster well. If any part of the central cluster is shadowed by the balcony, consider a distributed, under-balcony signal-delayed system.

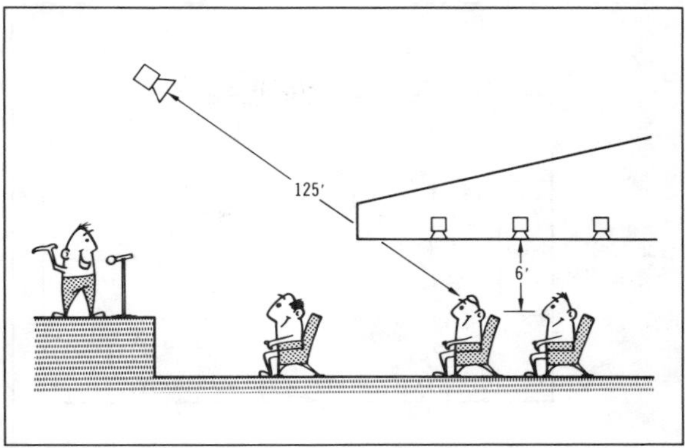

Figure 26-14 Central cluster plus under-balcony distributed loudspeakers on time delay. *(Courtesy Altec Lansing Corp.)*

26.3.3.6 Variations on the Distributed System

A multicluster system could be considered a distributed system. Also, in the large arenas and exhibit halls mentioned previously, horn/woofer components more typical of a central cluster may be used in the distributed system simply to produce a higher L_P capability.

One common variation on the distributed system is called a distributed column system (Fig. 26-15). This type of system is normally installed in a long, narrow church where a central cluster cannot be installed for esthetic reasons. A group of column-type loudspeakers (or some other type of packaged loudspeaker systems with appropriate dispersion) are installed. Electronic time delay and a localizer loudspeaker are included. This system can have the same problems as the split cluster described earlier, however, and should be used only in narrow rooms to minimize these problems.

Another distributed variation for churches is known as the *pew-back system*. In this system, a large number of small loudspeakers (usually one loudspeaker for every two to three listeners) is placed on the backs of the pews facing the listeners. Time delay is required. One problem with a pew-back system is the significant change in D_2 and loudspeaker Q when the listeners stand up (the listeners move both farther away from the loudspeaker and more off axis of the loudspeaker). Another problem is the large value of N caused by the large number of active loudspeakers. To partially overcome the N problem, add a

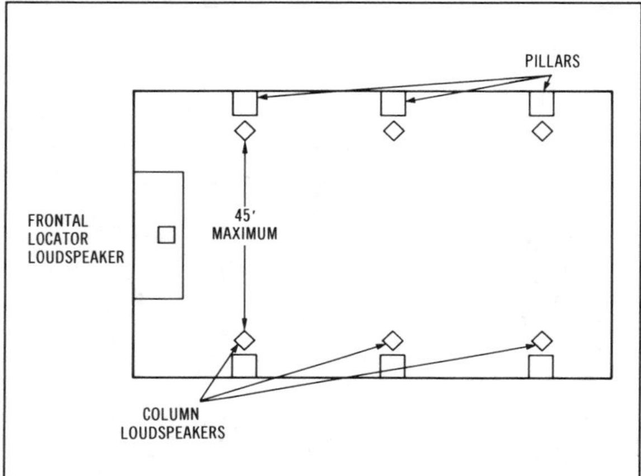

Figure 26-15 A distributed column loudspeaker system with time delay. *(Courtesy Altec Lansing Corp.)*

latching relay in each enclosure and a push-to-listen button. This way, loudspeakers in pews with no listeners will not be turned on, and those loudspeakers will not uselessly add to the reverberant field intensity.

Both the distributed column system and the pew-back system are difficult to design and install properly. As with any difficult design, a qualified consultant may be the best answer to getting a costly job done right the first time.

26.3.4 Designing a Central Cluster in a Simple Rectangular Room

There are any number of approaches to designing a central cluster. The approach presented here in outline form is by no means the only one, nor is it necessarily the best approach for every situation. It is a systematic, workable approach, however, and it includes methods of design that, when tempered by experience, will lead to a central cluster that covers an audience area evenly with intelligible sound.

26.3.4.1 Evaluating the Room

If the room exists, measure its reverberation time and physical dimensions (drawings will help in physical measurements). Calculate the room volume and total surface area. Using the Sabine reverberation time equation, derive the average absorption coefficient, $\bar{a}$, as follows:

$$RT_{60} = \frac{0.049V}{S\bar{a}} \qquad (26\text{-}25)$$

where,

V is the room volume,

S is the room surface,

$\bar{a}$ is the average absorption coefficient.

From this equation, the average absorption coefficient, $\bar{a}$, can be found by using

$$\bar{a} = \frac{0.049V}{(S)RT_{60}} \qquad (26\text{-}26)$$

Note that the constant, 0.049, assumes English units, use 0.161 for metric measurements.

If the room is in the planning stages only, estimate its average absorption coefficient, total surface area, and volume from the architectural data.

26.3.4.2 Choosing the Cluster Location

The ideal cluster location will probably be approximately above the primary microphone location; that is, in a rectangular room, the cluster should be near the top, center of an end wall of the room. Compromise locations should be chosen recalling the criteria discussed in section 26.3.3.

26.3.4.3 Evaluating the Cluster Location

The potential success of a proposed cluster location and cluster design can be evaluated by answering "The Four Questions," starting with Question 4: "Will it feed back?" Using available data and Eq. 26-18, answer this question before moving on to choose loudspeaker types.

26.3.4.4 Choosing the Loudspeakers

Assume the design will center around choices of constant-directivity-type horns for a two-way speech or speech-and music-reinforcement-type system.

Begin the design by choosing a horn for coverage in the rear of the room. Use trigonometry or one of the cluster layout methods discussed in section 26.3.4.5, and determine the horizontal (side-to-side) coverage angle required at the rear of the room. Using more than one horn to cover an area is discussed in the next section. *Remember that the listener's ears are approximately 4 ft above the floor when determining required coverage angles.* (This can be simulated in most design methods by placing an imaginary floor at 4 ft above the actual floor.)

Once a rear coverage horn has been chosen, use its Q value (from the manufacturer's specification sheet) and the known parameters of the room to answer Question 3: "Can everyone understand?" by calculating the articulation loss of consonants (AL_{cons}) from Eq. 26-18. Assume N = 1, then do the calculation over again using N = 2 and N = 3 to simulate the effects of adding horns to the system. If AL_{cons} is less than or equal to 15% for each of these calculations, the system design will work from the criteria of Question 3. If AL_{cons} exceeds 15% for any of theses calculations, a second cluster or a distributed system may be required. It might seem logical, in this case, to simply choose a horn with a higher Q value, since this would reduce the AL_{cons}. That horn will also have a narrower coverage pattern and might not adequately cover the entire audience. Using additional high-Q horns will not solve the problem either since they increase the value of N. Thus, if AL_{cons} is too high, about the only alternative to a second cluster or distributed system is to reduce the room reverberation time with acoustic treatment.

Aiming the Horns

If the AL_{cons} is acceptable, additional horns can be chosen to cover the rest of the room, providing a "yes" answer to Question 2: "Can everybody hear?" In many rectangular rooms, only one or two additional (wider angle) horns will be required. Since the edge of the defined coverage pattern of a horn is its −6-dB point, to overlap the coverage somewhat and to avoid aiming horns at hard rear or side walls (which could result in echoes) or directly down at the microphone (which could increase the possibility of feedback). Again, remember to aim the horns at the listener's ears (about 4 ft above the floor for a seated audience).

Question 4: Will It Feed Back?

Question 4: "Will it feed back?" can be answered by performing the calculations for PAG and NAG discussed in sections 26.1.4 and 26.1.10. The answers to the PAG and NAG equations may be tempered by recalculating D_c for an increased value of N, as discussed in section 26.2.1.5. If feedback seems possible, consider moving the cluster, using an automatic microphone mixer to keep NOM = 1 (see section 26.8.1 and Chapter 15) or, most effective of all, teach the users to talk closer to the microphone (which reduces D_s). Directional loudspeakers and microphones *may* provide some additional gain before feedback, but it's best not to plan for this additional gain.

Powering the Cluster

The remaining question, Question 1: "Is the system loud enough?" can be answered by choosing horn drivers and power amplifiers to satisfy Eq. 26-13 remembering the criteria for headroom and signal-to-noise ratio.

Low-Frequency Loudspeakers

Unless the room is very large and large low-frequency horns are esthetically acceptable, the low-frequency design is usually limited to vented enclosures or a combination of horn and vented enclosures. This limits the capability to aim the low-frequency loudspeakers, and it means that their Q values will be relatively low. Fortunately, the low frequencies are not critical to intelligibility. Thus, it is not necessary to perform an AL_{cons} calculation for the low-frequency loudspeakers. The "Will it feed back?" calculations performed for the high-frequency horns are equally valid for the low-frequency loudspeakers, so it should not be necessary to recalculate PAG or NAG. Experience shows, however, that, in many two-way systems, feedback frequencies are primarily in the frequency range of the low-frequency loudspeakers. This indicates that the low-frequency loudspeakers are the cause of the feedback. Why is this?

The high-frequency horns are higher Q than the low-frequency loudspeakers and thus produce less acoustic power output than the low-frequency loudspeakers for the same direct L_P at the listener's position. Thus, the high-frequency loudspeakers produce a lower reverberant field energy than the low-frequency loudspeakers. If, as assumed in the PAG and NAG equations, the microphone is entirely in the reverberant field of the loudspeaker cluster, the low frequencies will dominate in the reverberant field and will, therefore, dominate in any feedback problems. If the microphone is receiving any significant amount of direct sound from either low- or high-frequency loudspeakers, the PAG and NAG equations will not accurately predict feedback problems. This potential direct sound feedback problem must be considered qualitatively in the design of the cluster by aiming the loudspeakers away from the microphones. Since the low-frequency loudspeakers are normally low Q and cannot be effectively aimed away from the microphone, they are often placed nearest the ceiling to be as far from the microphone as physically possible.

Answering Question 1: "Is the system loud enough?" for the low-frequency loudspeakers involves calculating the EPR for the low-frequency loudspeakers from the manufacturer's data on the chosen low-frequency loudspeaker and the known room conditions.

Often, one or two low-frequency loudspeakers are enough for a one- to three-horn system. The second low-frequency loudspeaker may not be required from the criteria of Question 1, but it allows the midrange frequencies (which, in a two-way system, come partly from the low-frequency section) to be aimed in a similar manner to the way the high-frequency horns are aimed for smoother coverage at all frequencies.

Other Considerations

At this point, the basic cluster design is finished. Consideration should be given, of course, to overall system head room, frequency response, distortion, and other sound-quality factors.

26.3.4.5 Cluster Computer™, Array Perspective™, and CADP™

The cluster design process outlined in the last section includes little help in actually choosing and aiming the horns. Several new techniques help take this process from the guesswork stage and into a scientific analysis stage.

Cluster Computer

The Cluster Computer was developed by John Prohs at Ambassador College in Pasadena, California, and licensed to Community Light and Sound, Inc. The *Cluster Computer* process uses a clear plastic sphere enscribed with latitude and longitude lines like a world globe (Fig. 26-16). If this sphere were to be placed at the actual cluster location (it is not), a line from the center of the sphere to a given point in the room would pass through a single point on the surface of the sphere. Thus, by choosing points around the perimeter of seating areas, the room can be mapped in angular form onto this imaginary sphere. Because the room is in angular form on the sphere, front and rear coverage angles or any other coverage angles can be obtained directly by simply observing. A computer program that comes with the Cluster Computer license helps the user map a room onto the sphere from simple room measurements.

The Cluster Computer user receives maps of loudspeaker coverage patterns on very thin clear plastic overlays that fit over the surface of the sphere. The concept is similar to mapping a room onto the sphere. If an imaginary miniature horn were placed at the center of the sphere and a sound level meter were moved about the surface of the sphere, the sound pressure level from the loudspeaker could be marked onto the surface of the sphere. If a line were drawn through all points at −3 dB from the on-axis level, another line were drawn through the −6-dB points, and a third line were drawn through the −9-dB points, the three lines would form concentric shapes that would be an angular representation of the coverage pattern of the loudspeaker. Various manufacturers have provided data on their loudspeakers so that the Cluster Computer user can receive these overlays for a number of different loudspeakers. In other words, the user must plot the room onto the primary plastic sphere, the loudspeaker overlays are provided and need not be generated by the user.

In actual use, a room is mapped onto the surface of the sphere, and a loudspeaker overlay is placed onto the map. Because both the room and the loudspeaker are in angular form on the sphere, moving the loudspeaker overlay around the room map accurately displays the results of various aiming strategies. Because the loudspeaker overlays are very thin and clear, additional loudspeaker overlays can be added to examine the results of multiple horn aiming strategies. An available computer program allows the user to plot lines of constant sound pressure level onto the room map. These are lines between points that are equidistant from the cluster location so that the direct sound from the cluster will be attenuated by the same amount anywhere along one of these lines. Using these lines along with the loudspeaker overlays, the user can examine the direct sound level at any point in the room (and can add the effects of multiple loudspeakers).

Array Perspective

Developed by Ted Uzzle at Altec Lansing Corp., *Array Perspective* is a simplification of the Cluster Computer concept (although Array Perspective was actually devel-

Figure 26-16 The cluster computer. *(Courtesy Community Light and Sound, Inc.)*

oped prior to the Cluster Computer). Array Perspective takes the sphere surrounding the cluster and unrolls it into a flat map in a similar manner to the way a world globe is mapped onto a flat map of the world.

Instead of receiving a plastic sphere, the Array Perspective user receives a flat paper grid with latitude and longitude lines every 5°. Loudspeaker overlays are flat clear plastic (Fig. 26-17).

The Array Perspective user maps a room onto the paper grid and manipulates the loudspeaker overlays on the resulting angular map of the room. Although Array Perspective is somewhat simpler to use than the Cluster Computer, it does involve some distortion at the edges of the grid. This could be compared to the fact that Greenland appears to be larger than Australia on a flat map when, in fact, Greenland is smaller than Australia. The distortions are small for most rooms, however, and Array Perspective allows users to make their own loudspeaker overlays from clear plastic (flat) sheets and the loudspeaker contour data now being published by most horn manufacturers.

ADVANTAGES

Users of either the Cluster Computer or Array Perspective quickly gain an appreciation of the power of these techniques. Alternate horn-aiming strategies can be evaluated quickly, and accurate designs can be performed in significantly less time than by older trigonometric methods. It's important to remember, however, that simply aiming the horns is not a complete cluster design. Aiming the horns will help answer Question 2. Questions 1, 3, and 4 must be answered as well. The Cluster Computer or Array Perspective can help answer these other questions by providing direct sound pressure level data at various points in the room. They cannot deal with the reverberant field, however, and thus cannot help determine AL_{cons}, for example.

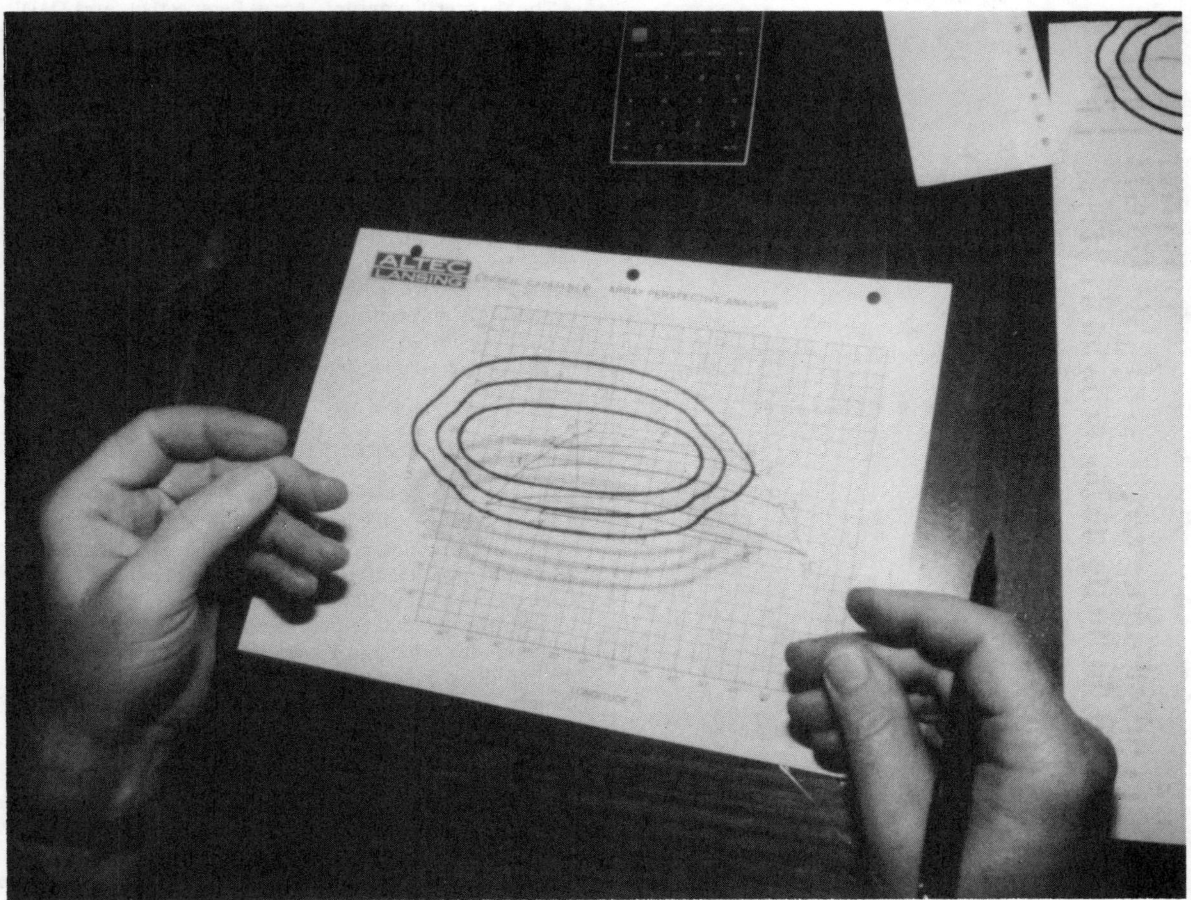

Figure 26-17 Array perspective. *(Courtesy Altec Lansing Corp.)*

Computer Array Design Program

The *Computer Array Design Program (CADP)* from JBL is an entirely different approach. CADP is a computer program, written in compiled BASIC for the IBM Personal Computer. CADP allows the user to plot a room plan onto the computer screen and to see the results of aiming various loudspeakers from the cluster location onto the room plan (Fig. 26-18). The projection of the loudspeaker onto the room plan is displayed as an array of numeric L_P values at up to 200 points in the room. The program calculates the value of direct sound, the direct-to-reverberant ratio, and the AL_{cons} for each of these room points and for a single loudspeaker or for several loudspeakers in a complex cluster. The program also works for a system with more than one cluster location. The screen display can be printed on a graphics-equipped dot-matrix printer.

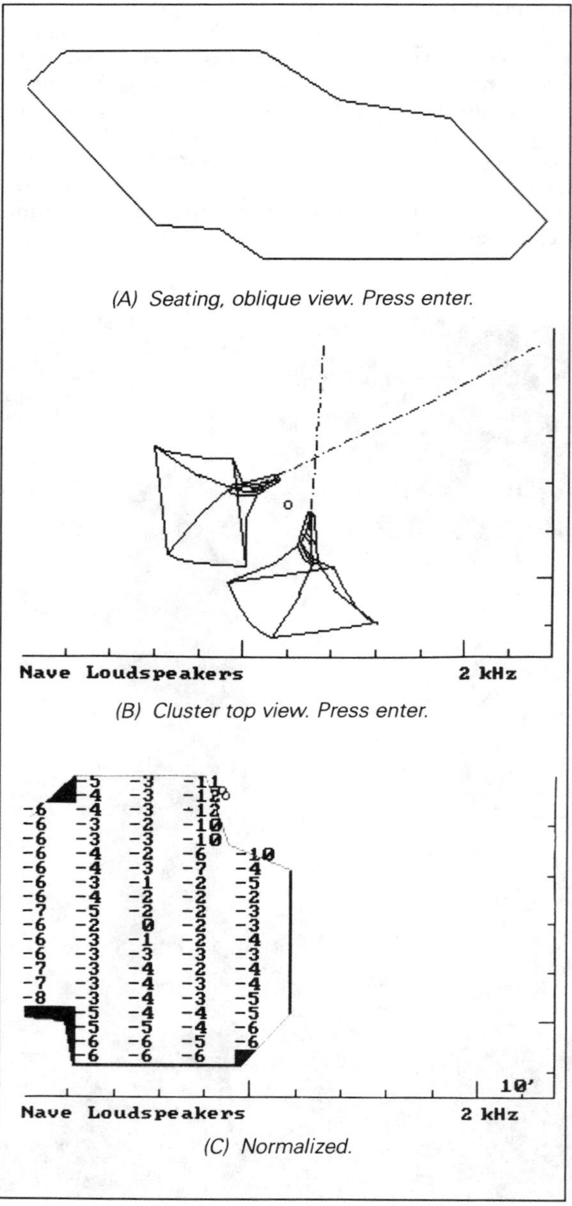

(A) Seating, oblique view. Press enter.

(B) Cluster top view. Press enter.

(C) Normalized.

Figure 26-18 Computer Array Design Program. *(Courtesy JBL Inc./UREI)*

CADP is a powerful program that is different in concept from either the Cluster Computer or Array Perspective. It is somewhat cumbersome, however, to quickly see the results of multiple changes in horn-aiming strategies with CADP due to the computer calculation time. Thus, a CADP user may wish to do a preliminary layout with the Cluster Computer or Array Perspective and use CADP to check the design.

The Future of the Cluster Design Aids

The Cluster Computer, Array Perspective, and CADP represent only the beginning of sophisticated design aids that will be offered in coming years. In particular, if computer prices continue to decrease while memory, speed, and graphics capabilities increase (as seems to be the trend), extremely powerful and sophisticated computer design aids will unquestionably become available.

It may be within the realm of possibility that a computer with an artificial intelligence program could completely replace the human designer. Until that unlikely time, however, techniques like the Cluster Computer, Array Perspective, CADP, and those that will follow are *design aids* and nothing more. The information gained from these design aids can help the human designer but must be tempered by experience and engineering judgment.

26.3.4.6 Designing the Complex Cluster

In concept, the design of a multihorn central cluster in a room with complex geometry is no different from the simple rectangular room design discussed in section 26.3.4. In practice, the complex cluster shown in Fig. 26-19 presents a set of new difficulties.

First, the complex cluster is most often designed for a large public facility. In practically every such situation, the budget will be tight, leaving no room for errors in design. It is simply not economically possible to redesign a large cluster after it has been installed. As an example, an EPR (electrical power required) calculation for a simple three-horn cluster calls for 1 W with a 10-dB headroom for each high-frequency driver or 10 W maximum per driver. (In many small- to medium-sized facilities, these numbers are typical.) A later recalculation, based on a new measurement of ambient noise in the room puts the EPR at 4 W per driver with 10 dB of headroom or 40 W per driver maximum, a +6-dB increase. For this simple system, this +6-dB error in the initial design will prob-

Figure 26-19 A large, complex cluster. *(Courtesy Bolt, Beranek, and Neumann, Inc.)*

ably result in no more than a new setting of the input attenuators on the high-frequency power amplifiers. For a complex system, with each high-frequency driver used to its power capacity limits, a +6-dB error would require four times the original quantity of drivers, horns, and power amplifiers!

Second, many of the approximations used in the simple cluster design method are too gross to be used in the design of a complex cluster. The approximations used for the value of N, for example, in the AL_{cons} equation need to be refined for a complex cluster design.

Here, based on the four questions, is a primarily qualitative explanation of some of the refinements needed for the design of a complex cluster. Some quantitative explanations are given, but a full, quantitative analysis of the complex cluster is beyond the scope of this handbook. In any case, the complexity of the design process and the economic consequences of errors are significant enough that the services of an experienced, qualified consultant are highly recommended.

The Fundamental Complexity

When a cluster involves more than perhaps two or three horns, its operation becomes complex. The calculation of AL_{cons} for a far-throw horn, for example, cannot ignore the reverberant field contributions from the other horns in the cluster. A *qualitative* method of dealing with the problem is straightforward. The direct sound level at each listener can be calculated via the inverse-square law (Eq. 26-1) from a knowledge of which horn or horns are aimed at the listener. The total reverberant field sound pressure level can be calculated by adding the total acoustic power output of all the horns and placing this value into a modified form of the room reverberation equation. Answering the four questions becomes a matter of using either the direct sound, the direct plus reverberant sound, or a direct-to-reverberant ratio.[5,6]

Calculating the reverberant field level in the room requires a detailed knowledge of the room's acoustic parameters, however, and, in many rooms, the acoustic parameters change dramatically from position to position in the room. A church in the shape of a cross (cruciform church), with balconies in each wing, for example, may have several totally acoustically different spaces that can be covered from the same cluster location. While each space has different acoustics, they interact with each other in a complex way further complicating the process of calculating the reverberant field at any listener's location (Fig. 26-20).

Even in rooms that are fairly well behaved acoustically and have a statistically random reverberant field, the calculation of reverberant field level is not simple. This is because this calculation requires a thorough knowledge of the characteristics of the cluster. Each horn adds an amount to the reverberant field that depends on the electrical power applied to the driver and the efficiency of the horn and driver combination. While few manufacturers provide direct data on the efficiency of their loudspeakers, this can be calculated from a knowledge of the on-axis sensitivity and the Q.

All the factors involved in the reverberant field calculation vary with frequency so that a new set of calculations must be performed for each frequency of interest.

Another Approach via the D_c Modifier

The equations used to answer Questions 1 and 4 use the value of critical distance D_c. The equation for D_c (Eq. 26-12) includes a D_c Modifier N in its denominator. Calculating a value of N for a complex cluster is not easy, but it is possible; this value of N allows continued usage of the same equations used for the simple cluster design. In addition, the value of N may be used in answering question 3 (the AL_{cons} equation), extending this equation's usefulness to the complex cluster.

A simple estimate of N is "the total number of loudspeakers producing the same acoustic power as the loudspeaker pointed at any given listener." For example, if there are three loudspeakers in the system, all producing the same acoustic power, and only one loudspeaker is pointed at the listener, then N equals 3. If there are four loudspeakers, two of which are pointed at the listener, the situation is equivalent to two loudspeakers with one pointed at the listener. In this case, N would equal 2. Use

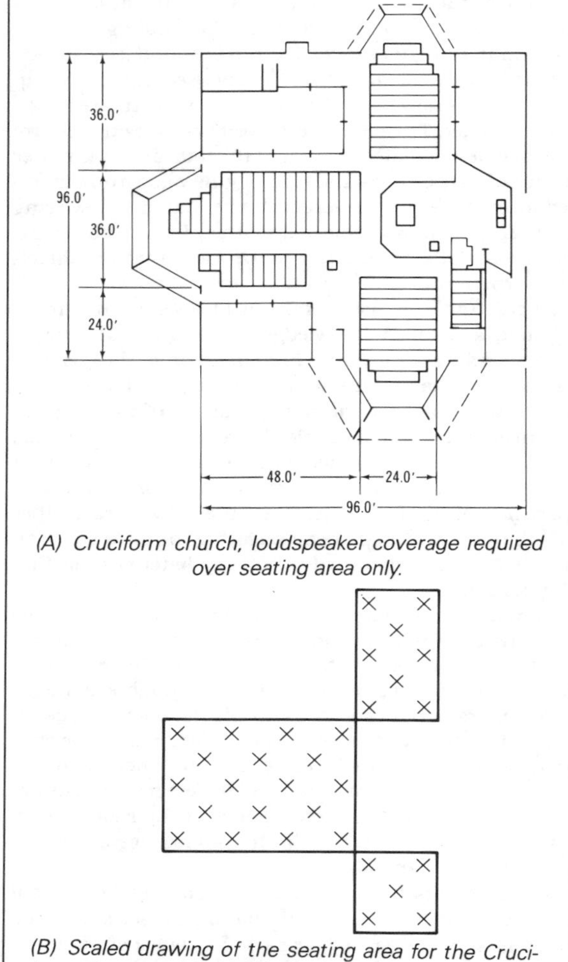

(A) Cruciform church, loudspeaker coverage required over seating area only.

(B) Scaled drawing of the seating area for the Cruciform Church using 4-in. loudspeakers at 4000 Hz (magnified times 1).

Figure 26-20 A cruciform church showing distributed loudspeaker coverage. *(Courtesy Altec Lansing Corp.)*

only those loudspeakers producing voice-range frequencies. That is, in a two-way system, count only the number of high-frequency horns, not the woofers.

If it is necessary to perform a more accurate determination of N, here is a recommended process.

Determine the DI (DI = 10 log Q) for each horn and the electrical input power for each driver. Use the far-throw horn-driver as a reference. For each horn-driver, determine a value of n as follows:

Step 1: Determine $x = SENS - SENS_r$ where SENS is the sensitivity of the horn-driver in question and $SENS_r$ is the sensitivity of the far-thrown horn-driver. This is a driver sensitivity difference and thus must be determined on the same model horn. If the two-horn driver combinations are the same models, the difference, x, will be 0 dB. If the horn-driver in question has a lower sensitivity rating than the reference (far-throw) horn driver, the value of x will be negative.

Step 2: Find $y = 10 \log (P/P_r)$, where P is the actual electrical power fed to the driver in question, and P_r is the actual electrical power fed to the reference (far-throw) driver. These values must be the actual powers that will be fed to the drivers when they are installed in the finished cluster.

Step 3: Find $z = DI_r - DI$, where DI_r is the directivity index of the reference (far-throw) horn, and DI is the directivity index of the horn in question.

Step 4: Find n for the horn and driver combination in question from the following equation:

$$n = 10^{\left[\frac{x+y+z}{10}\right]} \qquad (26\text{-}27)$$

Add the values of n for all horns in the cluster including a value of n = 1 for the reference far-throw horn. This value is the value of N to be used in the AL_{cons} equation (Eq. 26-18) and in the D_c equation (Eq. 26-12).

Example: Given a three-horn cluster let,
F be the far-throw (reference) horn-driver,
M be the mid-throw horn-driver,
N be the near-throw horn-driver, and

Let,
$Q_F = 40$ so that $DI_F = 16$ (Eq. 26-9),
$Q_M = 20$ so that $DI_M = 13$ (Eq. 26-9),
$Q_N = 10$ so that $DI_N = 10$ (Eq. 26-9).

and let,
$SENS_F = 114$ dB/1 W/4 ft,
$SENS_M = 112$ dB/1 W/4 ft,
$SENS_N = 110$ dB/1 W/4 ft.
$P_F = 5$ W (electrical power to F),
$P_M = 3$ W (electrical power to M),
$P_N = 1$ W (electrical power to N).

Note: The values for P_F, P_M, and P_N may be determined from EPR Eq. 26-16, using a value of D_c Eq. 26-12, which assumes N = 1. The values for P_F, P_M, and P_N obtained will be slightly higher than needed. This points out a flaw in the process, namely the EPR values (used for P_F, P_M, and P_N) are needed to calculate a value of N, but a value for N is needed to calculate EPR! This circular problem could be solved by a computer loop but using a value of N = 1 in calculating EPR is not unreasonable for this process.

Step 1:
$x_F = 0$ (reference compared to reference),
$x_M = 112 - 114 = -2$ dB,
$x_N = 110 - 114 = -4$ dB.

Step 2:
$y_F = 0$ (reference compared to reference),
$y_M = 10\log(3/5) = -2.22$ dB,
$y_N = 10\log(1/5) = -6.99$ dB.

Step 3:
$z_F = 0$ (reference compared to reference),
$z_M = 16 - 13 = +3$ dB,
$z_N = 16 - 10 = +6$ dB.

Then,

$$n_F = 10^{\left[\frac{0+0+0}{10}\right]} = 1 \text{ (as it must)},$$

$$n_M = 10^{\left[\frac{-2-2.22+3}{10}\right]} = 0.755,$$

$$n_N = 10^{\left[\frac{-4-6.99+6}{10}\right]} = 0.317,$$

and

$$n = 1 + 0.755 + 0.317 = 2.07$$

which are to be used in D_c (Eq. 26-12) and AL_{cons} (Eq. 26-18).

26.3.4.7 Another D_c Modifier

The modifier M consists of two parts, *Ma (architectural modifier)* and *Me (electroacoustic modifier)*. Ma considers the effect on system operation of a loudspeaker system pointed at an acoustically absorptive audience in an otherwise reverberant room. Me considers factors that affect the direct sound level in the room but that do not affect the reverberant sound level. One example would be a shortening of D_2 by moving the loudspeaker closer to the listener. The M modifiers are seldom used in practice and are included here for completeness.

26.3.4.8 The Four Questions Answered

QUESTION 1: IS THE SYSTEM LOUD ENOUGH?

For the complex cluster, a new approach is indicated. That approach is to find the total direct sound level at the listener's position, to find independently, the total reverberant sound level at the listener's position, and to add them to get the overall total sound level at the listener's position. Comparing and adjusting this overall level with the desired L_P (i.e., Is it at least 25 dB above ambient noise?) will provide the required EPR. It is also possible to use the original indoor EPR equation (Eq. 26-16) by calculating a value for the D_c modifier N and using this value of N in the critical distance portion of the EPR calculations.

One way to avoid some of the complexity in this calculation is to realize that increasing evidence indicates that, although the reverberant energy in a room can aid the perception of useful loudness, it is the direct sound level that is most important. The L_{Pd} can, of course, always be calculated via the inverse-square law (Eq. 26-1). If a listener is in the direct field of more than one horn, the direct sound from all such horns can be added to obtain the total L_{Pd} at the listener (adding levels expressed in decibels is discussed in section 2.1). If the L_{Pd} level at the listener is high enough, the L_{PT} will also be high enough, thus, answering Question 1 satisfactorily. It should be noted, however, that this method will result in a requirement for more horns, drivers, and amplifiers than the method that actually calculates the reverberant field level.

QUESTION 2: CAN EVERYBODY HEAR?

The methods for a complex cluster are straightforward and similar to the methods for a simple cluster. Use of the Array Perspective, the Cluster Computer, and/or the JBL CADP program are highly recommended. In the complex cluster, interactions among horns become more significant simply because of the quantity of horns in the cluster. Thus, more time is involved to calculate, for example, the L_{PTd} at a listener's position resulting from several horns whose edges cover that position. The CADP program, significantly, can make those calculations almost instantly, even showing the effects of comb filtering on the direct sound level.

The actual choice of horns and aiming of them, however, is still primarily a matter of experience and engineering judgment. There are no hard and fast rules like "use a long-throw horn for a balcony." That balcony could end up to require a very wide dispersion horn from the viewpoint of the cluster (watch out for poor direct-to-reverberant ratio in this case). Or, experience might dictate the choice of a pair of narrower angle horns.

QUESTION 3: CAN EVERYBODY UNDERSTAND?

The AL_{cons} equation, like the EPR equation, may be used for a complex cluster by calculating a value of N as discussed in section 26.3.4.6.

Another method is to calculate the direct field and the reverberant field at each listener's position of interest and perform a direct-to-reverberant comparison. Since the AL_{cons} concept is based on the direct-to-reverberant ratio, a knowledge of the actual numeric direct-to-reverberant ratio is equivalent to a knowledge of the numeric value of AL_{cons}. As noted in the discussion of Question 1, calculating the reverberant field at any seat can be complicated, but once the direct and reverberant levels are found, their ratio provides a quick way to judge AL_{cons}.

It is important to remember that the AL_{cons} equation assumes a 25-dB signal-to-noise ratio and that the AL_{cons}

equation does not necessarily provide accurate results for rooms with reverberation times lower than about 1.6 s. Distortion, frequency response, and overall system sound quality also affect intelligibility, as do the human factors of talker experience and listener interest.

Question 4: Will It Feed Back?

This question can be answered by calculating the total sound level (direct plus reverberant) reaching the microphone from the cluster. If this level is equal to or greater than the level expected from the talker at the microphone, then the system will surely feed back. If the total direct plus reverberant level at the microphone is at least −6 dB below the expected level from the talker, the system will probably be stable.

Reference 6 provides a method, if complicated, for calculating the total reverberant level at the microphone from a complex cluster. The PAG and NAG equations may be used with a value of N, calculated as discussed in section 26.3.4.6 for the complex cluster, although the direct plus reverberant approach will probably give a more accurate result.

The actual feedback process also involves reflections from near the microphone, since these reflections can increase the sound level at the microphone by as much as 6 dB (for a reflection from a hard surface that is in phase with the source sound and, therefore, adds coherently with the source sound). Thus, such a reflection could cause a system to feed back even when calculations would show a 6-dB feedback stability margin.

Addition of more than one microphone to the complex cluster system will not automatically lower the gain before feedback by 3 dB. That is because each microphone may receive a different amount of direct sound from the cluster and may be subjected to different nearby reflections. Assuming similar microphone locations, however, simplifies the calculation, and a 3-dB reduction in gain before feedback is a reasonable assumption in most systems. This means that the total sound level from the cluster reaching either microphone must be about −9 dB below the expected talker level at that microphone to achieve the 6-dB feedback stability margin. This also, of course, assumes that the gain (volume control setting) of each microphone is similar.

26.4 EQUALIZATION

26.4.1 The Concept of Equalization

Sound system equalization is a process of adjusting the electronic frequency response of a system to compensate for uneven loudspeaker response and room acoustics. The goals of equalization are to provide a natural-sounding system with good intelligibility and to minimize feedback that might be caused by peaks in the frequency response.

In performing systems, program equalization may also be used to enhance the sound quality of, for example, a nasal-sounding performer's voice. This use of equalization is very different from the other uses and, in general, it is better to avoid using the same equalizer to both equalize the system and provide enhancement of a performer.

26.4.2 What Equalization Can and Cannot Do

Equalization can make a well-designed system sound (subjectively) better. It can improve intelligibility by smoothing the frequency response or by deliberately peaking response in the intelligibility frequencies (approximately 1500 to 5000 Hz). Equalization can help minimize feedback caused by frequency-response irregularities.

Equalization cannot make a poorly designed system sound good. Equalization cannot significantly improve the sound quality of low-cost paging-type drivers (nor can it make any other poor-sounding loudspeaker sound significantly better). Equalization cannot affect the reverberation time in a room in any way. Equalization cannot significantly improve a feedback problem in a room where the PAG (potential acoustic gain) is unacceptable.

26.4.3 System Design Criteria for Equalization

Equalization should be the "icing on the cake" for a well-designed system. A system to be equalized should be designed using high-quality, low-distortion loudspeakers and electronics with adequate headroom. Loudspeaker systems should be full range, and individual component loudspeakers should be chosen to complement each other's response. Do not, for example, choose a low-frequency loudspeaker (for a two-way system) with poor response above 300 Hz (a common problem) and expect to use an equalizer to smooth the system response through the crossover region.

26.4.4 System Equipment

The system to be equalized must have an equalizer permanently installed in its signal chain. The most common type of equalizer will be a one-third-octave graphic although one-octave types can be used to reduce costs with a corresponding loss in precision (Fig. 26-21). So-called parametric equalizers, whose parameters (filter bandwidth and frequency) can be altered by the user, are gaining popularity for the equalization process. In any case, the equalizer must remain in the system after the equalization process has been performed and thus should be a

(A) A high-quality passive equalizer. (Courtesy White Instruments, Inc.)

(B) An active one-third octave "graphic" equalizer. (Courtesy JBL Inc./UREI)

(C) An active "Parametric" equalizer. (Courtesy Orban Associates, Inc.)

Figure 26-21 Three equalizers.

high-quality device with low distortion, low noise, and for most systems, balanced input and output. Filters should combine smoothly between sections; that is, a graph of the electrical frequency response of the equalizer should remain smooth even when several adjacent filters are in use at differing control settings (see section 17.5). For a parametric, this can be accomplished by using as broad a bandwidth as possible during equalization and overlapping the bandwidth of adjacent filters just enough to keep the electrical response smooth.

26.4.5 The Boost-and-Cut Equalizers Versus Cut-Only Equalizers Controversy

Early equalizers were made from passive components and, thus, could not amplify a signal. These were cut-only equalizers. Some passive models had a preset loss, and individual frequency bands could be boosted up to a 0-dB loss. When active models were developed, however, they included electronic amplifiers for the purpose of buffering the impedance of the filters and, in some cases, of allowing the frequency response to be boosted at any given frequency as well as cut. These true boost-and-cut equalizers were primarily developed for enhancement purposes, not for room equalization. Nevertheless, they are commonly used for equalization.

Proponents of the cut-only equalization process note that a boost-type equalizer may not have smoothly combining filters (some don't) and will thus make the system response more ragged, not less. Some boost-and-cut equalizers are also *nonminimum phase,* which means that, for any given frequency response curve, these equalizers cause more phase delay than a minimum-phase equalizer would cause. Proponents of boost-and-cut equalizers correctly note that a boost-and-cut equalizer can be designed to alleviate both of these problems (many high-quality boost-and-cut equalizers are so designed).

Proponents of the cut-only equalization process note that boosting a frequency band only 3 dB during the equalization process demands twice the system power in that frequency band. Thus, boost-and-cut equalizers can significantly reduce the headroom in a system. In addition, a boost-and-cut-type equalizer can be incorrectly used to attempt to boost a frequency band where the loss is caused by an acoustic diaphragmatic absorption. Attempting to boost this type of problem will result in a more ragged frequency response and decreased headroom. Proponents of the boost-and-cut equalizer note that a cut-only equalizer plus a post-equalizer gain restoration amplifier result in the same equalization curve as a boost-and-cut equalizer and, therefore, potentially result in the same headroom problems. (All cut-only equalizers should have this amplifier either as part of the equalizer itself or, in passive sets, as a separate amplifier located after the equalizer or as part of the gain in the power amplifier.)

One final advantage to a passive filter set, which, as mentioned, will be cut only, is that the passive circuitry is, by nature, very low noise and highly unlikely to fail. Both of these advantages are good arguments for using passive filter sets and, thus, become arguments for using cut-only equalization.

There is probably no final answer to the question of what type of equalizer to use for a given system. It becomes as much a subjective choice on the part of the designer as anything else. A cut-only, one-third-octave-type equalizer, however, is almost always a safe choice for any system, since it is the standard around which most systems are designed and because the real-time analyzers currently in use for the equalization process assume this type of equalizer.

26.4.6 Test Equipment

Test equipment should include a calibrated, flat-response microphone, a one-third-octave, real-time audio spectrum analyzer (often just called a real-time), and a pink-noise generator (Fig. 26-22). All equipment should be high quality and properly calibrated. If available, a sound level meter, with a flat response position, is useful. Some meters have a line-level output and can thus be used as the system test microphone (Fig. 26-23).

Often, a *house mic* is substituted for the calibrated microphone in the equalization process. This allows the system response to be adjusted to compensate for the response of the microphone as well as the loudspeakers

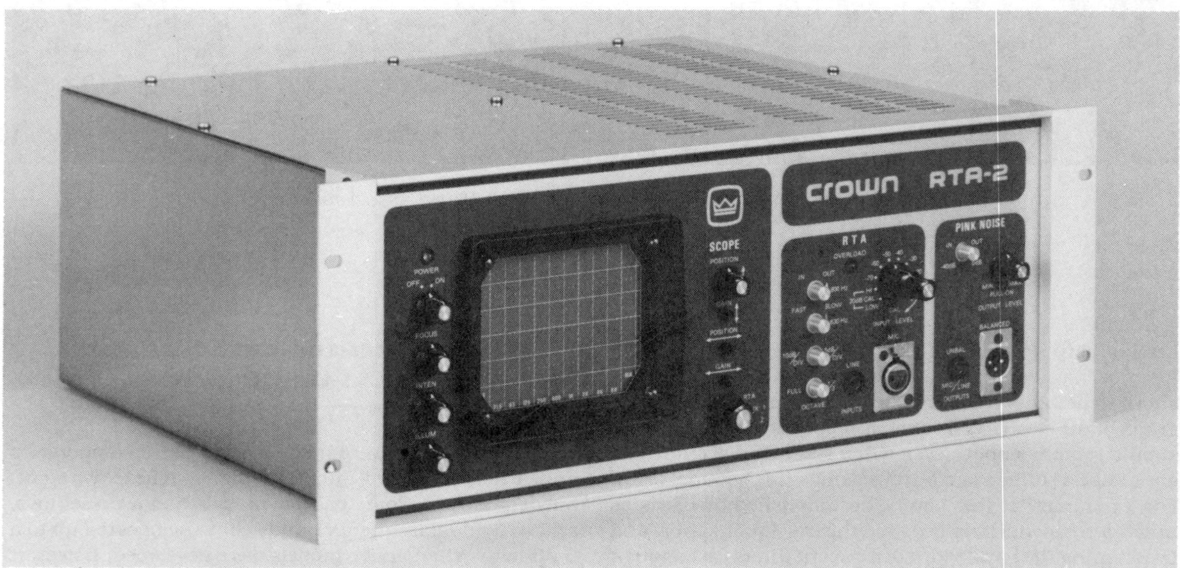

Figure 26-22 A real-time, one-third-octave, audio spectrum analyzer. *(Courtesy Crown International, Inc.)*

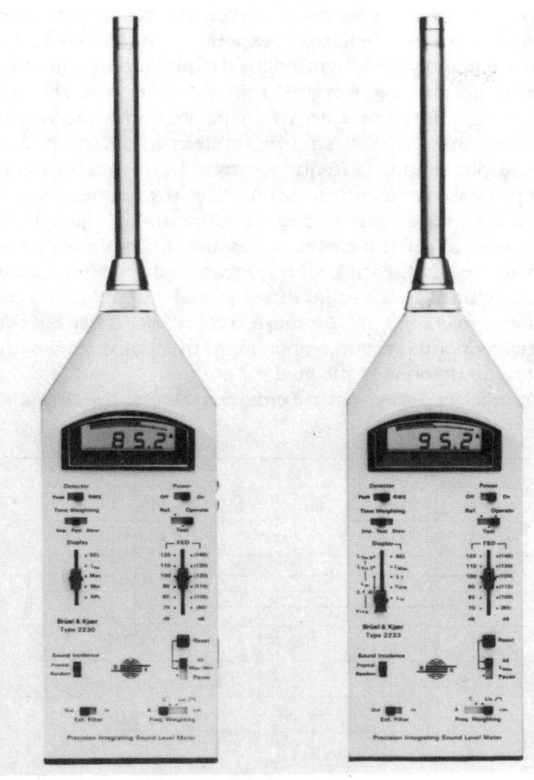

(A) Precision integrating sound-level meters.

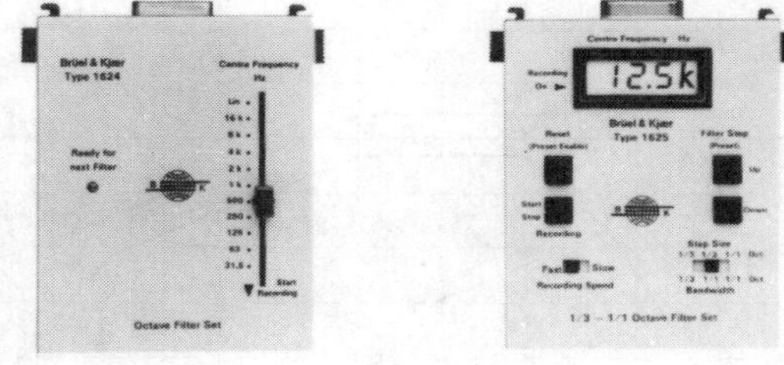

(B) Octave filter set and one-third octave filter set.

Figure 26-23 Precision integrating sound-level meters and accessory filter sets. *(Courtesy of Bruel & Kjaer Instruments, Inc.)*

and the room acoustics. The house microphone, however, should only be used when there is only one type of microphone in the system (and all such microphones have manufacturer's response curves that are very similar to each other). If more than one type of microphone is used in the system, either a separate equalizer must be used for each type of microphone (indicating a separate mixer) or the calibrated microphone should be used for the equalization process and mixer tone controls used to adjust for different microphone types.

A one-octave analyzer may be used when a one-octave equalizer is installed in the system, which results in a loss of precision but may be acceptable in low-budget installations. The hand-held, one-octave analyzers now available are very useful for "walking the room" to gauge the changes in system response from place to place but may not be precise or accurate enough for any more than a rough system equalization.

26.4.6.1 The Test Setup

Connect the pink-noise generator to a typical microphone input (use a pad if necessary to connect a line-level pink-noise generator to a microphone input). Set all system tone controls to their flat positions, and set the equalizer controls to flat. Place the real-time analyzer near the equalizer and place the test microphone in a typical listening position. Avoid placing the microphone directly on axis of the cluster or of any individual horn (Fig. 26-24).

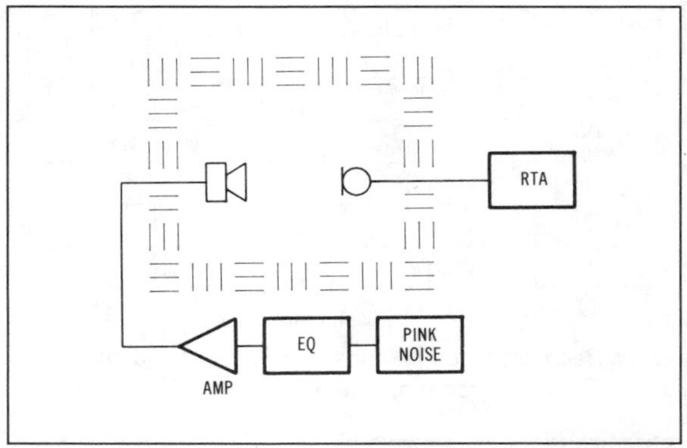

Figure 26-24 Equalization test setup diagram.

Turn on the system and the pink-noise generator, and using the sound-level meter in its flat and slow response positions, set the system gain for the design level. That is, if the system was designed for 90 dB with 10 dB of headroom, increase the system gain until the meter reads 90 dB.

Turn on the real-time analyzer and observe the response. Note any significant peaks or dips. Move the test microphone to several different locations and note the changes. If the analyzer has memories, these can be used in comparing microphone positions. If the system response changes radically from position to position or has significant peaks or dips at any position, attend to these problems before beginning the equalization process.

To equalize the system, first adjust the high-frequency and low-frequency power amplifiers (in a biamplified system) or the system crossover network (in a passively crossed over system) for the flattest response as indicated on the real-time analyzer. Then, begin the process of adjusting the equalizer by observing the real-time analyzer and choosing a frequency area that peaks above the rest of the response curve. Using the system equalizer, reduce the response in this frequency area. In the beginning of the process, avoid cutting or boosting any frequency more than about 3 dB since later adjustments of adjacent filters may affect the earlier adjustment. Do the same at any other significant peaking areas. If the system equalizer includes boost capabilities, boost carefully between system peaks (again, no more than about 3 dB at first) to help smooth system response. At this point, a *smooth*, not *flat*, response is the goal.

In most two-way, central cluster systems, the response

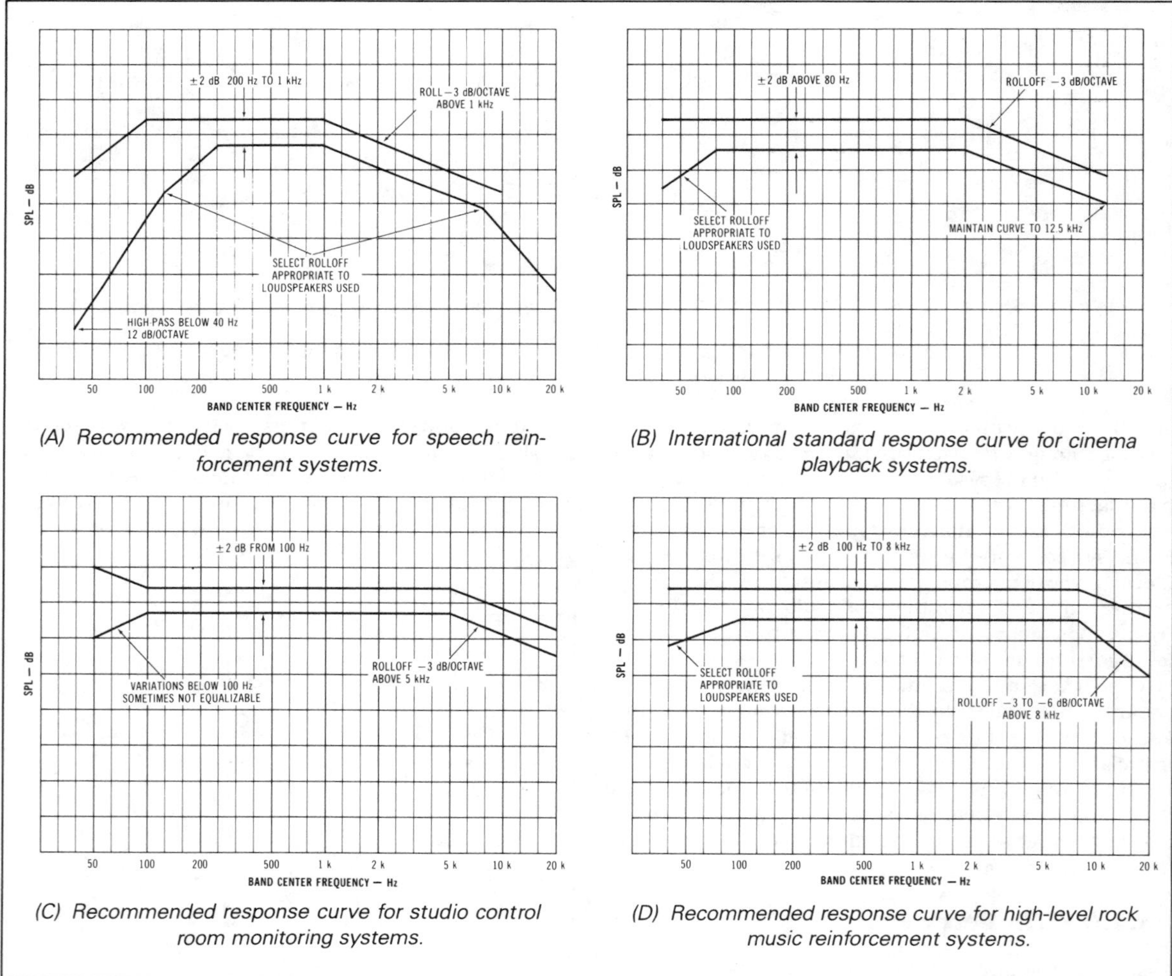

(A) Recommended response curve for speech reinforcement systems.

(B) International standard response curve for cinema playback systems.

(C) Recommended response curve for studio control room monitoring systems.

(D) Recommended response curve for high-level rock music reinforcement systems.

Figure 26-25 Various recommended response curves for equalization. *(Courtesy Altec Lansing Corp.)*

peaks will come in the neighborhood of 200 to 2000 Hz. These frequencies are the efficiency peaks of the low- and high-frequency loudspeakers and reflect the normal mid-range deficiency of most two-way systems. These peaks are, therefore, the first place to make system adjustments, again, working for smooth response at first.

Once the system response is reasonably smooth, begin adjustments toward the desired system response curve, as shown in Fig. 26-25. For a speech-only system, the final curve should be relatively flat from its low-frequency limit (about 50 to 80 Hz) up to about 1000 Hz. At 1000 Hz, the response should begin a rolloff of about 3 dB/octave to about 8 to 10 kHz. Response above this frequency should roll off rapidly (use a system low-pass filter if available). For a music or music and voice system, begin the rolloff at about 2000 Hz and allow the response to follow this rolloff to 12.5 kHz or higher with rapid rolloff above the desired maximum frequency.

This high-frequency rolloff is a guideline and should be modified for each individual system on the basis of *subjective sound quality*. The purpose of the rolloff is to improve the system sound quality, since a perfectly flat system response, as displayed on the real-time analyzer, will sound overly crisp, and vocal sibilants (high-frequency breath sounds) will be overly emphasized.

The final equalization curve will probably not follow these rolloff curves perfectly. A final system curve within ±2 dB of the desired curve is, in most cases, more than adequate. Avoid filter settings more than a 6-dB boost or cut whenever possible, remembering that a 6-dB boost requires four times the amplifier power output and four times the loudspeaker power capacity. For this reason, a final equalization curve that requires only a ±3-dB setting on any individual filter but is within only ±3 dB of the desired curve may sound *better* than a final curve that is within ±1 dB of the desired curve but required ±6 dB of equalization at several filter positions (and, therefore, reduced system headroom and increased system noise).

26.4.6.2 The Regenerative Response Method of Equalization

First promoted by Don Davis, co-author of *Sound System Engineering*,[4] the *regenerative response method* of equalization is useful because it emphasizes frequency response peaks and dips and allows the effects of equalization to be readily seen.

To utilize this method, set up the system as described for a normal equalization but also set up the primary system microphone in its normal position and connect it to the system mixer in the way it will normally be used, as shown in Fig. 26-26. Turn on the pink noise and observe the system response. Now turn up the microphone carefully until the beginnings of feedback can be heard mixed in with the noise. Keep the microphone level just below feedback so that ringing can be heard in the system while performing the equalization. Turn off the system microphone for the final frequency-response curve tailoring.

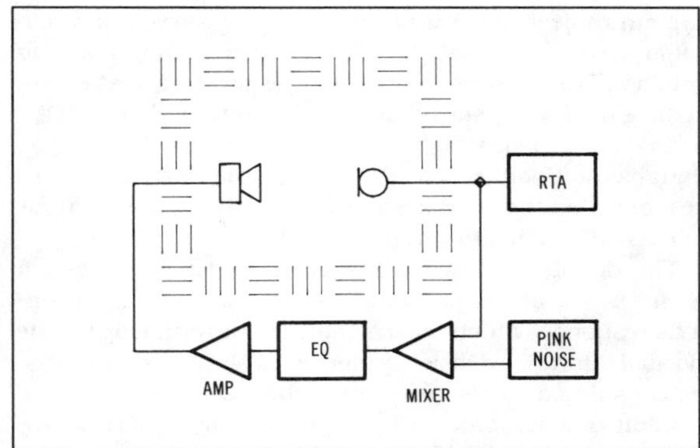

Figure 26-26 Regenerative response equalization test setup diagram.

The regeneration caused by allowing the microphone to pick up the pink noise from the loudspeakers and feed it back into the system causes any frequency-response peaks and dips to be accentuated (so they can be seen more easily) and also helps the equalization process to compensate for the characteristics of the microphone. Many users of this method report a more satisfactory equalization with this process than with the normal method of equalization.

26.4.6.3 Use of High- and Low-Pass Filters

A 12- or 18-dB/octave high-pass filter, at approximately 50 to 160 Hz, will enhance the performance of a voice-only system by filtering out unwanted low-frequency transients like dropped microphones and breath pops. For a music or music-plus-voice system, use a high-pass filter at 20 Hz or above. Most music systems are *improved* by a high-pass filter at 40 to 80 Hz. In addition, a vented-box-type, low-frequency enclosure should be high passed at a frequency slightly below the box resonant frequency f_b to help protect the loudspeaker from over-excursion.

A 12- or 18-dB/octave low-pass filter at 12.5 to 20 kHz will reduce unwanted radio-frequency signals and will help prevent system electronic oscillation. In a music system, a high pass at 16 to 20 kHz will improve the system for the same reasons.

Separate electronic high-pass and low-pass filters are available, and in many cases, such filters are included as part of the system equalizer.

26.4.6.4 Another Point of View on Equalization

A number of sound system designers now believe that the primary purpose of equalization should be to remove frequency-response peaks from the system loudspeakers. A secondary purpose, according to this viewpoint, is to roll off the low- and high-frequency response to make the system subjectively sound better. The high-frequency rolloff is used, *if needed*, to reduce an overly sibilant sound quality. The low-frequency rolloff is used, *if needed*, to reduce the boomy sound quality in rooms with long RT_{60} at low frequencies. In other words, by this philosophy, equalization has very little to do with the room and a flat-response loudspeaker system will eliminate the need for extensive equalization in many cases.

The definition of a flat-response loudspeaker system includes flat acoustic power response as well as flat on-axis response, which means that, by this philosophy, the normal midrange deficiency of most two-way systems must be considered as discussed in section 26.11.8.

Additionally, some users of time-delay spectrometry (TDS) or time-energy-frequency (TEF) test equipment are reporting very good success in equalizing the direct sound from the loudspeaker system, ignoring (at least temporarily) the frequency response of the reverberant sound. This tends to support the idea that the primary usefulness of equalization may be to smooth the response of the loudspeakers, not the room.

26.4.6.5 Alternate Test Equipment Setup

The use of time-delay spectrometry and time-energy-frequency type equipment in equalization is covered in Chapter 30.

26.4.7 Use of Narrow-Band Filters in Equalization

Very narrow-band filters are often added to an equalized system for the purpose of controlling feedback and the ringing that occurs in a system that is near feedback. Used in a well-designed and carefully equalized system, narrow-band filters can be very successful for these purposes. Common filter types include parametric filters tuned to a very narrow bandwidth and active and passive narrow-band or notch filters.

Narrow-band techniques for controlling feedback work best in fixed systems in rooms with constant microphone and loudspeaker positions. Even in a portable system, a skilled operator may be able to readjust a set of narrow-band filters to make them useful for feedback control. As in any attempt at feedback control by filtering or equalization, only two or three feedback (or ringing) frequencies can usually be eliminated before a point of diminishing returns is reached.

26.5 DESIGNING DISTRIBUTED LOUDSPEAKER SYSTEMS

A distributed loudspeaker system, instead of using a single point source, has a large number of sources distributed throughout a listening area. These sources may be 3-in. loudspeakers mounted on the desks of a city council chambers. They may be 8-in. coaxial loudspeakers mounted in the ceiling of a supermarket for background music and paging. They may be 12- or 15-in. coaxial loudspeakers mounted in the ceiling of a large, low-ceiling multipurpose room. They may be full-range clusters with high-frequency horns and low-frequency woofers used in a distributed fashion to cover the seating areas of a large circular stadium.

The goals for distributed system design are the same as those for central cluster design. That is, answering the four questions will provide reasonable assurance of satisfactory system operation.

26.5.1 Distributed Cluster System

A distributed cluster system consists of two or more clusters separated in space. Two clusters, for example, might be used to cover a long, narrow church where a single cluster could not provide acceptable intelligibility in the rear seats. An examination of the AL_{cons} equation (Eq. 26-18) shows that either increasing Q or decreasing D_2 will improve intelligibility. In the case where a horn with high enough Q will not provide wide enough coverage or where a horn with high enough Q is simply not available, moving the cluster closer to the farthest listener (decreasing D_2) may be the answer.

Design the first cluster to cover the seating areas out to (and slightly beyond) the position of the second cluster. All other design criteria for the first cluster remain the same as if it were the only cluster. The value of N (the D_c modifier) for either cluster must include the effects of both clusters, however. Design the second cluster to cover the remaining seating area to the farthest listener. In many systems of this type, the second cluster can have a reduced low-frequency section covering the frequencies below about 200 Hz. This is because the frequencies below 200 Hz do not contribute to intelligibility and because the reverberant field in most rooms requiring a second cluster will carry the low frequencies to the farthest listener with no need for reinforcement from the second cluster.

In calculating AL_{cons} (or EPR or PAG and NAG) for either cluster, the value of N must take into account the loudspeakers in both clusters, although the value of D_2, of course, will be shorter than it would have been for a single cluster in the same room.

26.5.1.1 Signal Delay in a Distributed Cluster System

The second cluster in the previous example must receive a signal that is electronically delayed from the signal sent to the first cluster. The amount of delay may be calculated by choosing a typical listener in the coverage pattern of the second cluster who can still hear the first cluster. Calculate the distance from this listener to the first cluster and subtract the distance from this listener to the second cluster. Perform this calculation for several listeners in the coverage of the second cluster who can also hear the first cluster. Choose an average value, biased toward those listeners who can hear the first cluster best. Multiply this average value times 1.13 for distances in feet or 3.71 for distances in meters, to obtain the starting point for time delay in milliseconds. Add 6 to 20 ms (the exact amount is best determined on site by listening) to take advantage of the localization known as the *Haas effect*. A more detailed description of the use of signal delay can be found in Chapter 18.

26.5.1.2 Distributed Clusters with No Delay

In a circular stadium or on long, narrow bleachers such as at a race track, a system of distributed clusters may provide the best coverage and not require electronic delay because the sound reaching each listener is primarily from one cluster and any nearby cluster is essentially the same distance from the listener (and thus not acoustically delayed). Design of each cluster in such a system is straightforward. Choose a seating area that can be easily covered by a single cluster. Calculate the difference in distance from a typical listener to adjacent clusters. Avoid wide spacing between clusters that could cause a listener hearing two clusters to hear the second cluster as an echo of the first. Provide sufficient overlap between coverage areas to ensure adequate sound pressure level to all listeners but avoid wide overlap areas to prevent the problems inherent in the split cluster discussed in section 26.3.3.3.

26.5.1.3 Equalizing the Distributed Cluster System

If all clusters are the same and are covering areas with similar acoustics, equalization may be performed for a single area. Check the response of the other areas to confirm the equalized curve is similar. If clusters are covering acoustically different areas or if they are designed from different loudspeakers, each type of area or loudspeaker must receive separate equalization (the central cluster plus under-balcony distributed system, for example).

26.5.2 Distributed Ceiling Loudspeaker Systems

Distributed ceiling loudspeaker systems are normally installed in rooms with low ceilings (low compared to the length and width dimensions of the room) where a central cluster or distributed cluster system cannot adequately cover the room. In some situations where a central cluster would work from a design point of view, a distributed system is chosen for its versatility. A distributed system (without delay) does not have the psychoacoustic localization of a central cluster. Thus, microphone locations can be varied without worrying about the effects on localization. Loudspeakers can be turned off above microphone locations making multiple (or varying) microphone locations possible while reducing feedback potential. Loudspeakers can also be turned off in areas not in use to avoid exciting the reverberant field in those areas. Adding variable time delay makes it possible to provide the psychoacoustic localization of a central cluster from any chosen microphone location (Fig. 26-27).

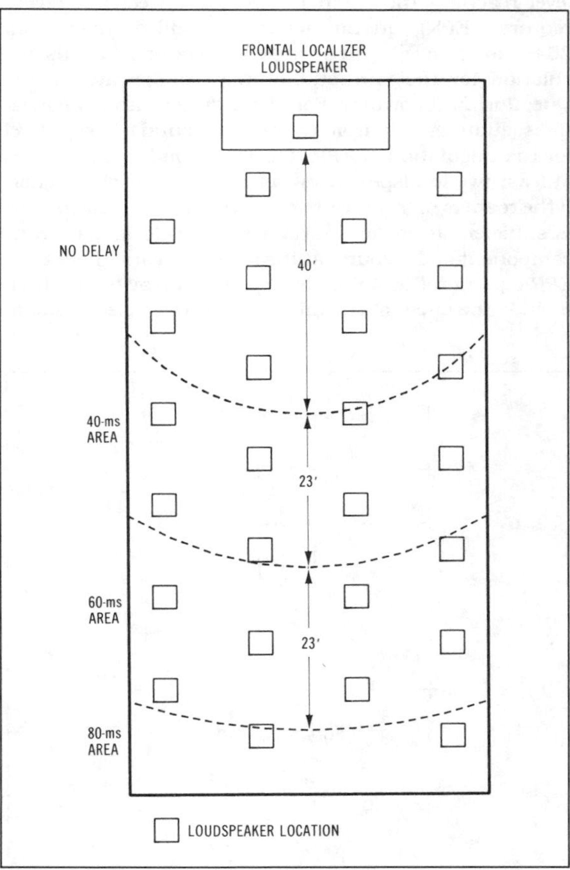

Figure 26-27 Ceiling distributed loudspeaker system with signal delay and "localizer" loudspeaker. *(Courtesy Altec Lansing Corp.)*

The primary disadvantage of a distributed system is its (usual) higher cost compared with a central cluster designed for the same space (assuming that a central cluster could work in the space).

26.5.2.1 Designing the Distributed Ceiling System

Yes, the four questions apply! Skipping Question 2 momentarily, here are discussions of the other three questions for a distributed ceiling system.

Question 1: Is It Loud Enough?

One of the advantages of a distributed system is that a typical listener is about the same distance from the nearest loudspeaker as any other listener. In addition, these distances are usually short compared to the critical distance D_c. Thus, the direct sound, not the reverberant sound, is the primary component of the sound pressure level reaching the listener. Thus, the electrical power required (EPR) equation for the simplified system (Eq. 26-6) can be used. Use a single loudspeaker for this calculation for the minimum-overlap configurations (see Question 2, following). For the 50% overlap configurations, subtract 3 dB from the desired sound pressure level for the calculation of EPR to a single loudspeaker, since at least two loudspeakers will be covering each listener. If the room is highly reverberant and/or the ceiling height is sufficient to make the reverberant field a significant component of the sound at the listener's ears, the indoor EPR equation (Eq. 26-16 or Eq. 26-17) may be used. To include the effect of the multiple sources, use a value of $Q = 3/N$, where N is the total number of distributed loudspeakers in the critical distance D_c calculation. The number 3 is a typical Q for a distributed coaxial loudspeaker (an actual Q should be used if available). The value of N should be divided by two if each listener can hear the direct sound from two nearby loudspeakers and so on. Using the simplified method of Eq. 26-6 will always provide a safe answer to Question 1 since it considers direct sound only.

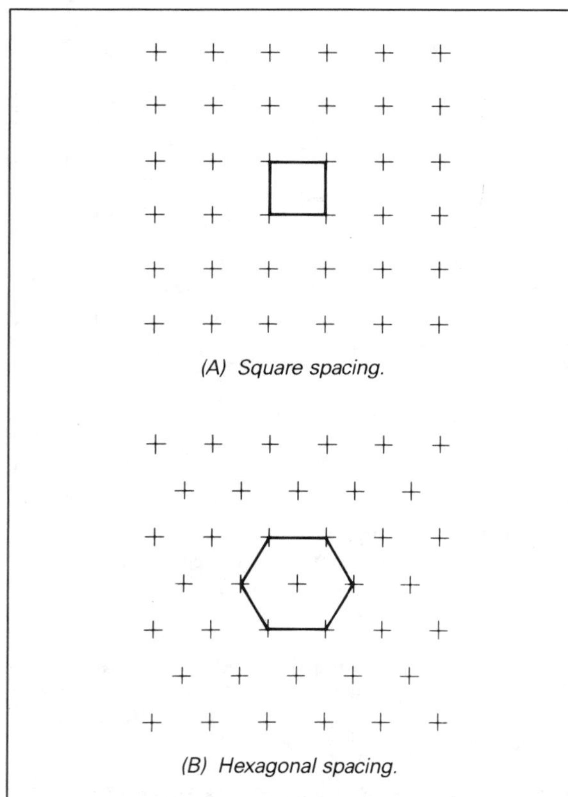

Figure 26-28 Square and hexagonal patterns for distributed loudspeaker systems. *(Courtesy Altec Lansing Corp.)*

Question 3: Can Everybody Understand?

The AL_{cons} equation (Eq. 26-18) works well for a distributed system. For the value of N, divide the total number of distributed loudspeakers in the room by the number of loudspeakers producing direct sound to a listener. Thus, if each listener is in the direct field of two loudspeakers, use a value of N equal to one-half the total number of loudspeakers and so on. Use a value of Q equal to the actual Q of each individual distributed loudspeaker. A good estimate for a coaxial ceiling loudspeaker is $Q = 3$. As with a central cluster system, try to maintain a 25-dB signal-to-noise ratio and keep distortion, hum, and so on at a minimum for best intelligibility. In addition, remember that the AL_{cons} equation works best for rooms with reverberation times of at least 1.6 s.

Question 4: Will It Feed Back?

Avoid placing microphones directly under a working loudspeaker. Provide switches to turn off loudspeakers above microphones when microphone positions will vary. Use the PAG and NAG equations (Eqs. 28-19 and 26-20) with $Q = 3/N$ (see discussion under Question 1 previously) if the room has a significant reverberant component.

Question 2: Can Everybody Hear?

Although there may be an infinite number of ways to position the loudspeakers in a distributed system, there are two basic patterns that have gained wide acceptance. They are the square and hexagonal patterns, as shown in Fig. 26-28. There are at least three variations of each of these two patterns, as shown in Figs. 26-29 and 26-30. The variations are in the spacing between the loudspeakers. An edge-to-edge spacing places the loudspeakers so that their coverage patterns just touch each other. A minimum-overlap spacing overlaps the coverage of the loudspeakers just enough to cover the dead spot in the edge-to-edge pattern. A 50% overlap is just that; each loudspeaker's coverage pattern overlaps the pattern of its neighbor by 50%. The result is that the pattern of each loudspeaker is completely overlapped by a group of the patterns of its neighbors.

Choice of one of these patterns should be made on the basis of the acoustics of the room, the ambient noise, and the type of listeners and talkers. In a poor situation, such as might be encountered in a reverberant space with

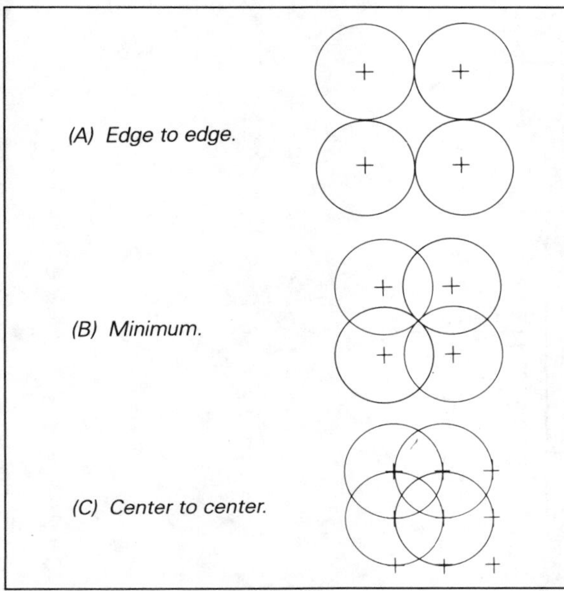

Figure 26-29 Methods of square overlap for distributed loudspeaker systems.

significant ambient noise and some listeners with hearing difficulties, a 50% overlap is indicated. In a dead room, designed for polite (?) press conferences with a trained public speaker, an edge-to-edge pattern may suffice. Budget, of course, may force acceptance of an edge to edge or minimum overlap when a higher density would be desirable. In this case, the designer should make the client aware of the potential deficiency before the system is installed!

In any choice of coverage pattern, room obstacles, microphone locations, and seating area should be considered. There is no reason, for example, to cover wide aisles unless people will frequently be standing there. In addition, remember that coverage pattern choice should be made at about 4 ft above the floor (ear height), not on the floor itself.

26.5.2.2 Distributed Systems in Rooms with Sloped Floors or Ceilings

The traditional approach to this kind of system is to provide fewer loudspeakers per unit area in the higher-ceiling portion of the room. Layout can be made separately for an individual section at a given height and again for the next section at a lower height allowing overlap between the two sections as desired, as shown in

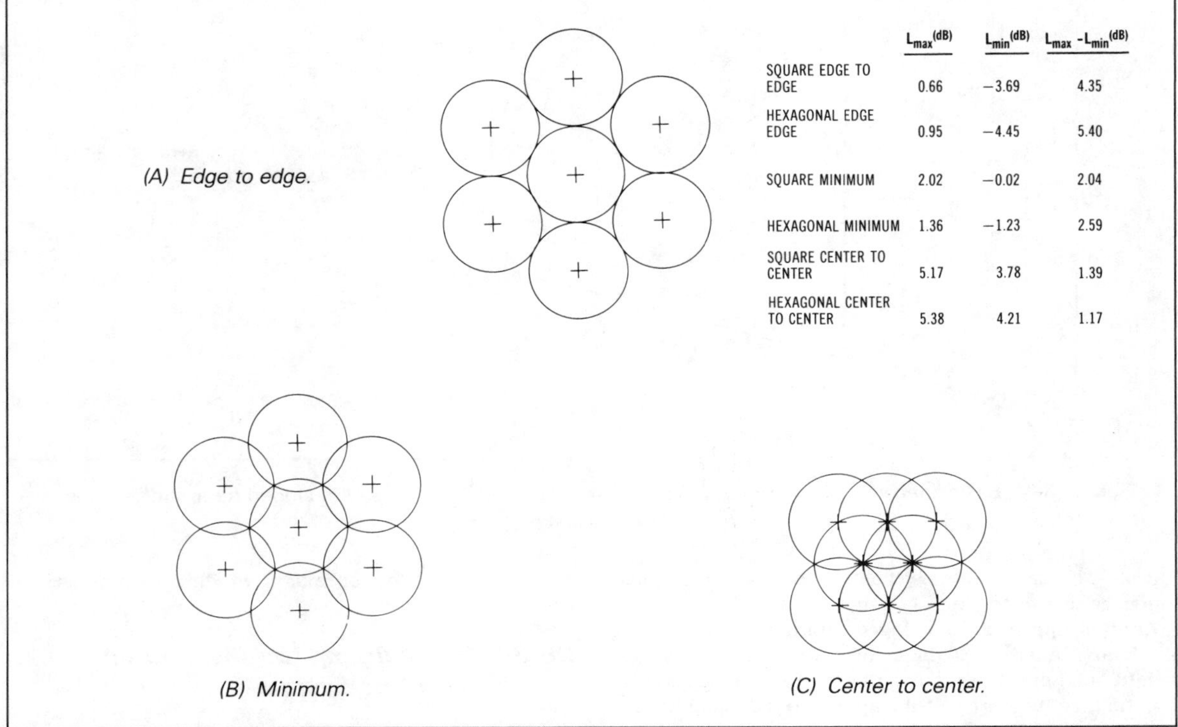

	L_{max}(dB)	L_{min}(dB)	L_{max} - L_{min}(dB)
SQUARE EDGE TO EDGE	0.66	−3.69	4.35
HEXAGONAL EDGE EDGE	0.95	−4.45	5.40
SQUARE MINIMUM	2.02	−0.02	2.04
HEXAGONAL MINIMUM	1.36	−1.23	2.59
SQUARE CENTER TO CENTER	5.17	3.78	1.39
HEXAGONAL CENTER TO CENTER	5.38	4.21	1.17

Figure 26-30 Methods of hexagonal overlap.

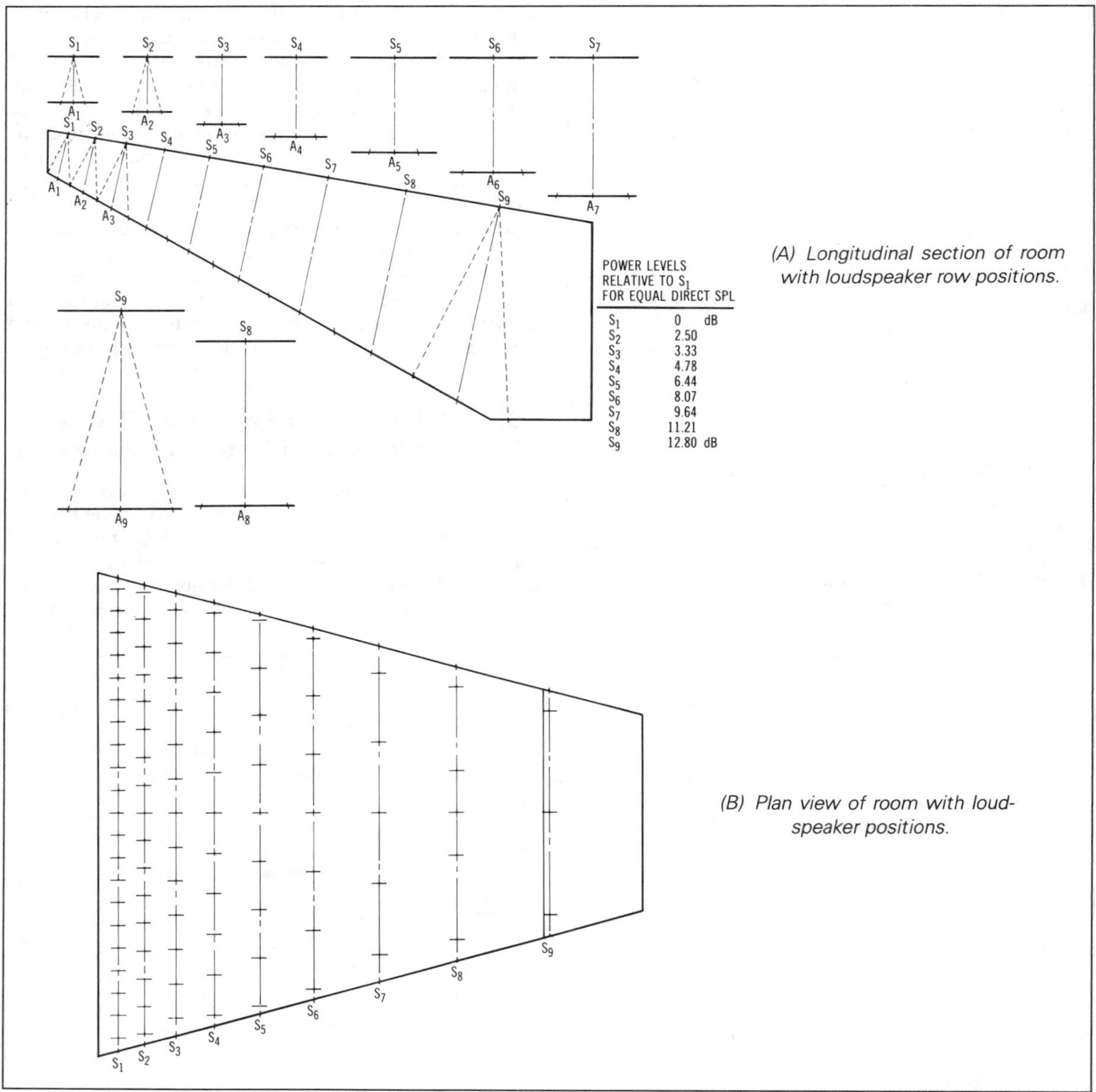

(A) Longitudinal section of room with loudspeaker row positions.

(B) Plan view of room with loudspeaker positions.

Figure 26-31 Basic concepts for distributed loudspeaker placement in rooms with sloped floor and/or ceiling. *(Courtesy Altec Lansing Corp.)*

Fig. 26-31. Additional power must be allocated to those loudspeakers in the high-ceiling portions.

Another approach to a sloped-ceiling room is to place the loudspeakers as if the ceiling was flat at the lowest height and apply the same power to each loudspeaker. In the high-ceiling areas this approach adds additional loudspeakers at the same power instead of fewer loudspeakers at a higher power level. While the design is simplified and the layout more symmetric, this approach results in more loudspeakers, which may increase the cost.

26.5.2.3 Equalizing the Distributed Ceiling System

In general, the equalization process is the same as for a central cluster system. A typical listener may be best chosen as in the overlap area of the loudspeakers for a

50% overlap system, or about 20° off axis of a single loudspeaker for an edge-to-edge or minimum-overlap system. As in the central cluster process, choose several typical positions and equalize for a position that seems to be a good average as far as the before-equalization response. In an acoustically dry room (no significant reverberation field) the equalized response should show more high frequencies than the cluster system guidelines would indicate. This is because there is no low-frequency reverberation to boost the low frequencies artificially and bias the display on the real-time analyzer.

26.6 PROTECTING THE LOUDSPEAKERS

Note: More information on loudspeakers and loudspeaker failure modes can be found in Chapter 14.

26.6.1 Loudspeaker Failure Modes

Discounting manufacturing defects that may cause random failures, loudspeakers normally fail from either *excessive average power* or from *excessive peak power* at low frequencies.

Excessive average power causes voice coil heating and eventually voice coil failure (or failure of other components in the voice coil area). Excessive low-frequency peak power causes mechanical failure of the loudspeaker due to over-excursion. The voice coil may separate from the rest of the loudspeaker or the loudspeaker cone (or driver diaphragm) may tear or shatter.

Protecting a loudspeaker, then, is primarily a matter of preventing these two failure modes.

26.6.2 Choosing Power Amplifiers to Prevent Excessive Average Power

It is possible to destroy a loudspeaker by using a too-large power amplifier (one whose power output exceeds the power capacity of the loudspeaker by some margin). It is also possible, under some conditions, to destroy a loudspeaker by using a too-small amplifier!

The too-small amplifier is one that does not have enough power output to meet the requirements of both the needed L_P at the farthest listener and the system headroom (from the electrical power required equation). Attempting to reach the system requirements will exceed output capabilities of the amplifier, which will cause the amplifier to clip, turning sine waves into semi-square waves and vastly increasing distortion levels. There are two significant problems here. First, the square wave can actually draw *twice* the power output from the power amplifier. That is, if the amplifier is rated at 100 W, a full-voltage square wave can cause the amplifier to deliver as much as 200 W, depending on power-supply limitations and the internal protection circuits of the amplifier. This double power output can be a threat to the loudspeaker all by itself. Second, the square wave causes the loudspeaker cone/diaphragm to move outward (or inward) and stay there for a while, then move in the other direction and stay there for a while. Although the loudspeaker cone/diaphragm is not moving (at the top and bottom of the square wave), the energy supplied to the voice coil is being entirely converted into heat, with obvious consequences. Thus, one way to prevent loudspeaker damage is to use a power amplifier that has enough output to reach the maximum L_P requirement and the system headroom requirement. Fortunately, in most sound-reinforcement systems, actual electrical power required is small, and the problem of a too-small power amplifier shows up primarily in popular music-oriented entertainment systems.

Loudspeaker power capacity is usually rated using some type of noise with a specified headroom factor. For example, a loudspeaker may be rated at "100 W continuous pink noise, with a 10-dB *crest factor* from 50 to 1000 Hz." That crest factor is the difference between the average and peak power in the pink-noise signal. Thus, in theory, this loudspeaker can be fed 100 W of pink noise, band limited from 50 to 1000 Hz and with peaks that reach 1000 W! The 100-W loudspeaker is, theoretically, safe with a 1000-W amplifier if system headroom is kept at 10 dB or above. In practice, of course, it is very risky to power a 100-W loudspeaker from a 1000-W amplifier. The reasons are many but include the operator who will push the system past its design limits, ignoring distortion and the possibility of sustained feedback that can, of course, draw full power from the power amplifier for an extended period.

What then is a safe power amplifier size for a 100-W loudspeaker? In most systems, about twice the rated power capacity of the loudspeaker will be safe provided other potential problems are considered, as discussed in sections 26.6.3 and 26.6.4. In addition, the amplifier should, as previously discussed, be at least capable of supplying enough power to meet the system maximum L_P and headroom needs. Full-power, sustained feedback can still, of course, destroy the loudspeaker, but at only twice the rated power capacity of the loudspeaker, the system will likely sound very distorted before the loudspeaker is in danger. This should prompt the system operator to turn down the level, preventing damage.

26.6.3 Protecting Against Excessive Low-Frequency Peak Power

The cone/diaphragm excursion of a loudspeaker increases at low frequencies. The exact amount of increase depends partly on the enclosure or horn the loudspeaker (or high-frequency driver) is used with. Nevertheless, there is some frequency below which each loudspeaker/enclosure or driver/horn should not be used. This low-frequency limit is normally given in the manufacturer's specifications or, for a vented enclosure design, may be calculated (see Chapter 14). At very low input power, frequencies lower than this limit will not cause damage. At normal to high power inputs, however, low frequencies can cause loudspeaker damage due to over-excursion.

The cure for this over-excursion is simply to prevent these low frequencies from ever reaching the loudspeaker by using some type of high-pass filter. This may be in the form of a system crossover network, which prevents low frequencies from reaching the high-frequency loudspeaker, or in the form of a separate high-pass filter (often part of a graphic equalizer), which prevents very low frequencies from reaching the low-frequency loudspeaker. One valuable protection device is a series capacitor, used on the high-frequency loudspeaker, which can reduce the effects of any low frequencies that may pass through the power amplifier due to such problems as turnon/turnoff transients (see Chapter 15).

Significantly, excessive power input to a loudspeaker at frequencies above its rated frequency range can also be dangerous. Since the loudspeaker cannot produce sound from these frequencies, the input power is completely converted into heat, adding to the potential problem of excessive average power.

26.6.4 Loudspeaker Protection Devices

Careful system design and operation by an experienced operator are the best protection against loudspeaker failure. The following devices can help, however, and may be used in almost any system design.

26.6.4.1 Fuses

Fuses are actually very inadequate protection devices. Standard fuses may be capable of protecting a loudspeaker against excessive average power, but they are too slow to protect a loudspeaker successfully against sudden peaks. Fast-blow instrumentation fuses, with improved time response, may blow on normal program peaks and needlessly disrupt sound system operation. Slow-blowing fuses, on the other hand, may not blow quickly enough to prevent loudspeaker damage due to voice coil overheating. If fuses are used, fuse each loudspeaker separately so that a single fuse failure will not completely interrupt system operation. Choose a starting fuse size from the following equation:

$$F = 0.75\sqrt{\frac{P}{Z}} \tag{26-28}$$

where,
F is the fuse size in amperes,
P is the rated power capacity of the loudspeaker,
Z is the rated impedance of the loudspeaker.

This equation gives a fuse size that will blow when the input power to the loudspeaker reaches 75% of its rated value. Fuse size may be increased if this fuse blows frequently, but avoid fuses larger than about twice this value since they will pass enough current to overpower the loudspeaker.

Early direct-coupled power amplifiers, when they failed, would often pass their full dc supply voltage to the loudspeaker. This voltage can result in loudspeaker/driver voice coils that are quite literally "french fried." A fuse will help protect a loudspeaker against this type of power amplifier failure mode. On high-frequency loudspeakers, however, a capacitor is probably a better protection device against this problem. In addition, most modern power amplifiers have some kind of internal protection that should prevent the problem of dc at the output even when the amplifier itself fails.

26.6.4.2 Capacitors

A series capacitor (connected electrically in series with one of the loudspeaker's input leads) can help prevent excessive low-frequency power and can protect the loudspeaker against dc power from a faulty power amplifier.

Capacitors can be chosen from the following equation:

$$C = 500{,}000/(\pi fZ) \tag{26-29}$$

where,
C is the value of the capacitor in microfarads,
π is equal to 3.14,
Z is the rated impedance of the loudspeaker,
f is a frequency chosen as follows:

If the system is two way (or three way, and so on), choose f equal to one-half the system crossover frequency. If the capacitor is to be used as a high-pass protection device in a voice-only system, choose f equal to the desired high-pass frequency, remembering that a single series capacitor provides about a 6-dB/octave slope rate.

Choosing a low-frequency value for f in the equation results in a very large capacitor. Thus, a capacitor is usually an impractical method of protecting a low-frequency loudspeaker. A high-pass filter prior to the power amplifier is better for a low-frequency loudspeaker.

For a high-frequency driver, using the driver's rated impedance for Z may result in errors since the actual impedance can be much higher at frequencies below crossover. Thus, it may be a good idea to actually measure the driver's impedance at the chosen frequency f and use this in the equation.

Choose a capacitor with a voltage rating at least equal to the maximum peak-to-peak voltage output of the power amplifier. This will be the sum of the absolute values of the positive and negative power supply voltages for a direct-coupled amplifier and can be approximated from the following equation for either direct-coupled or transformer-coupled amplifiers:

$$V = 2.828\sqrt{PZ} \tag{26-30}$$

where,

V is the peak-to-peak voltage output of the power amplifier,

P is the rated output power of the amplifier,

Z is the rated load impedance of the amplifier (on the output transformer tap to be used for a transformer-coupled amplifier).

The value of 2.828 is twice the square root of two. The value of V resulting from this equation may be conservative, since most amplifiers can produce power output in excess of their rated value for short periods. Thus, the actual voltage rating for the capacitor should probably be somewhat higher.

The capacitor must be nonpolarized. Motor run types are considered best for sound system applications. Motor start capacitors may be used. Standard electrolytic capacitors, if nonpolarized, can be used, but these capacitors normally have a very poor tolerance in actual capacitance value and, thus, may not provide the expected protection.

26.6.4.3 Limiters

A limiter is not normally considered a loudspeaker protection device, but it may be one of the best and most practical. The limiter (Fig. 26-32) can be adjusted to prevent the system power amplifier from exceeding its power output capabilities and can help prevent high-power peaks from reaching the loudspeakers. In systems where sound quality is a primary consideration, adjust the limiter so that its threshold is high and its compression ratio is high. This way, the limiter will not be in operation until a potentially dangerous peak is detected. Then, the high compression ratio of the limiter will clamp the peak and help prevent loudspeaker damage.

26.6.4.4 Patronis/Altec Feedback Controller

A device invented by Dr. Eugene Patronis at the Georgia Institute of Technology and marketed by Altec Lansing Corp. (Fig. 26-33) accurately senses actual feedback and reduces system gain until the feedback ceases. The device works on the concept of a *phase-locked loop* and will sense a feedback very quickly in most cases before it has a chance to damage a loudspeaker system. The phase-locked loop circuitry effectively discriminates between a feedback frequency (which is a very pure tone) and program material, even when that program material includes musical tones. This device would be very valuable in an unattended system (one without an operator present) especially if the user is allowed the freedom to move the microphone or if the user has access to a master volume control.

26.6.4.5 Other Protection Devices

Transformers can help protect loudspeakers because they cannot pass dc. Some transformers even include series capacitors to limit the low-frequency energy to a

Figure 26-32 A versatile high-quality compressor/limiter. *(Courtesy dbx, Inc.)*

Figure 26-33 Device that actually senses feedback and reduces system gain. *(Courtesy Altec Lansing Corp.)*

high-frequency driver. Autotransformers, on the other hand, may pass dc to a loudspeaker since they have only a single winding.

Passive crossover networks, because they include one or more series capacitors, provide good protection for high-frequency drivers and some protection for the low-frequency loudspeaker (against excessive high-frequency power levels).

High-pass and low-pass filters, similar to those often found on a graphic equalizer, are valuable in any system. A high-pass filter helps keep out unwanted low frequencies that could cause over-excursion. A general rule is that, except for subwoofer systems, a 40- to 160-Hz high-pass filter should be used in all systems. Even for subwoofers, a 10- to 20-Hz or higher high-pass filter can help prevent dangerous overexcursion. High-pass filters are often available on mixer input channels. Using them here can help reduce problems like dropped microphones. Low-pass filters help prevent heat-producing radio-frequency energy (picked up from outside sources or from faulty system electronics) from reaching the loudspeakers. Low-pass filters also keep out audio frequencies above the loudspeaker's range (which would also cause unwanted heating).

Other types of loudspeaker protection devices are available from several manufacturers (Fig. 26-34). These may be valuable in many systems.

Figure 26-34 Special-purpose loudspeaker protection device. *(Courtesy Electro-Voice, Inc.)*

26.7 CROSSOVER NETWORKS AND BIAMPLIFICATION

Loudspeaker crossover networks are discussed in more detail in Chapters 14 and 17.

26.7.1 Definitions

A *crossover network* is a device that routes high frequencies to a high-frequency loudspeaker and low frequencies to a low-frequency loudspeaker. If the crossover network is part of a biamplified system, it will do its frequency division prior to the power amplifiers. Three-way and four-way crossovers perform the same function but divide the frequencies into more sections.

A *passive device* uses no active components (tubes,

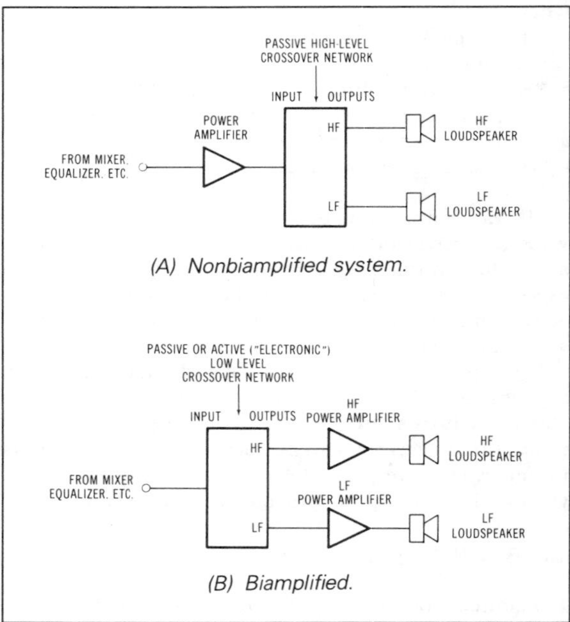

(A) Nonbiamplified system.

(B) Biamplified.

Figure 26-35 Biamplified and nonbiamplified systems.

transistors, ICs) and needs no power supply (ac, dc, battery). The crossover network in a typical packaged loudspeaker system is a passive device.

An *active device* uses one or more active components and requires some type of power supply. An *electronic crossover*, used in a biamplified system, is an active device.

Passive crossovers may be designed, however, to work at line levels (as opposed to loudspeaker levels). These line-level passive crossovers can be used in a biamplified system in approximately the same configuration as an electronic crossover, which is an active device. The primary difference in usage is the requirement for terminating the input and output of the passive crossover, a process discussed in section 26.9.

A *biamplified system* uses an electronic crossover or a line-level passive crossover and separate power amplifiers for the high- and low-frequency loudspeakers (Fig. 26-35). A *triamplified system* is a three-way loudspeaker system with a three-way electronic crossover and separate power amplifiers for the low-, mid-, and high-frequency loudspeakers. Systems can also be *quadamplified* or *multiamplified*.

Headroom is the difference, in decibels, between the peak and rms levels in the program material.

26.7.2 Advantages of a Biamplified (or Triamplified and so on) System

One advantage of a biamplified system is that it can actually provide more headroom per watt of amplifier power than a system with a traditional (loudspeaker level) passive crossover.

The reason this happens is that most music, especially popular music, is bass heavy; that is, there is much more energy at low frequencies than at high frequencies. When both high- and low-frequency materials are present in a program, the high-energy bass frequencies will dominate the power output of the system power amplifier leaving little or no power for the high frequencies. The result can be severe amplifier clipping (distortion) of the high-frequency material. By biamping the system, with an electronic crossover or line-level passive crossover, the high-frequency material can be routed to its own power amplifier avoiding the clipping problem. This results in an effective increase in headroom that is greater than that which would be obtained by simply using a single power amplifier of equal power output.

Another advantage of biamplification is that a loudspeaker-level passive crossover actually absorbs some of the amplifier power. Thus, biamplification, by removing this loudspeaker-level crossover, improves the overall system efficiency.

Improved damping factor is another advantage of biamplification. The *damping factor* of a power amplifier is a number found by dividing its load impedance (the loudspeakers) by the actual output impedance of the amplifier, which will be very low for a modern solid-state power amplifier. An amplifier with a high damping factor can exert a greater control over the motions of a loudspeaker cone than an amplifier with a low damping factor. Thus, a high damping factor may improve the sound quality of a system (this subject is one of continuous debate, however). A loudspeaker-level passive crossover lowers the damping factor by inserting its impedance between the amplifier and the loudspeakers. Removing the loudspeaker-level passive crossover, and biamplifying the system, can thus improve the damping factor.

Biamplification can lower distortion by increasing headroom as explained previously. However, if clipping distortion occurs anyway, it may be less audible in a biamplified system. In a conventional, nonbiamplified system, the high-frequency harmonics generated by clipping of a low-frequency transient are passed through the loud-speaker-level crossover to the high-frequency loudspeaker where they will be quite audible. In a biamplified system, there is no crossover and no high-frequency loudspeaker after the low-frequency power amplifier. Thus, the clipped low-frequency note and its harmonics would be restricted to the low-frequency loudspeaker that, due to its poor high-frequency response, would attenuate the audibility of the harmonics.

26.7.3 When To Use a Loudspeaker-Level Passive Crossover

In small sound systems where high sound levels aren't needed and economy is a major consideration, a loudspeaker system with a traditional passive crossover network may be the best choice. In addition, the crossover in a packaged loudspeaker system from a manufacturer usually includes a certain amount of equalization designed to smooth the frequency response of the loudspeakers. Biamplifying this system would require the addition of a graphic or parametric equalizer in addition to the additional power amplifier and electronic crossover. Thus, it's usually best to use the manufacturer's loudspeaker-level passive crossover in a packaged system unless the manufacturer has made specific provision for biamplification.

26.8 COMPONENTS

26.8.1 Automatic Microphone Mixing

Many of the tasks a human operator performs on a nonautomatic mixer are predictable. For example, the human operator turns up the volume controls for microphones that are in use and turns down the volume controls for microphones that are not in use. In addition, an experienced human operator will turn down the master volume control about 3 dB each time the number of in-use microphones doubles to help avoid feedback from the NOM problem discussed in section 26.1.5. An automatic mixer performs these two functions without the aid of an operator. (See Chapter 15.)

26.8.1.1 Mixers

The first commercially successful automatic mixer was invented and patented by Dan Dugan, a consultant in San Francisco, and marketed by Altec Lansing Corp. The Dugan automatic mixer exclusively used analog circuitry to perform the automatic mixing process according to the following equation:

$$L_N' = L_N - (\text{Sum}(L_n) - L_N) \quad (26\text{-}31)$$

where,

L_N is the level in an individual mixer channel before the automatic circuitry has attenuated that channel,

L_N' is the level in the channel after attenuation,

$\text{Sum}(L_n)$ is the sum of the levels in all channels before they are attenuated.

All values are in decibel notation.

In effect, the equation says that each individual input channel is attenuated by an amount in decibels equal to the difference in decibels between the level of that channel and the sum of all channel levels.

The significance of this equation is that, while it performs the two functions mentioned previously, it does not mention the word "threshold" nor the word "switch." The original Dugan system varies the microphone levels in a continuous manner depending only on the relationship of each individual channel level to the sum of all the channel levels.

A user sets up the Dugan mixer by adjusting each individual volume control to a position suitable for the person talking. That means the volume control for a quiet talker's microphone will have a higher setting than that for a loud talker. These volume control settings assure that the circuitry treats all microphones equally in the equation. After this initial volume control adjustment, the user ceases interacting with the mixer. New talkers, of course, or significant changes in talker input level require human intervention. A dummy microphone modification helps keep the mixer's automatic circuitry from being fooled by ambient noise.

Other automatic mixer designs switch microphones on (to a volume control level preset by the user) when someone talks into the microphone and off when no one talks into the microphone. They also reduce the master volume control by approximately 3 dB when the number of in-use microphones doubles. Several of these mixers incorporate sophisticated digital circuitry to make the decisions about when to turn a microphone on or off and exactly how much to attenuate the master volume control. As a result, a well-designed automatic mixer of either type can be successfully used in a system designed for automatic mixing.

26.8.1.2 Special Features

A number of additional functions/features are either standard or optional on most automatic mixers. Specific features, of course, depend on the make and model chosen.

For example, on the switching-type mixers, users may have the option of adjusting the threshold setting. The threshold is the L_P at which the mixer turns on a microphone channel. In very high noise areas, for example, a user could increase the threshold to reduce the problem of microphones turning on from ambient noise input. Another feature available on some mixers is adjustment of the amount of off attenuation. That is, the off state can be redefined from no attenuation at all to effectively infinite attenuation (true off). By selecting no attenuation, the on-off switching feature is defeated, and the mixer functions only as a number of open microphones (NOM) attenuator.

One valuable feature found on most mixers is a *logic output*. This logic output is a dc voltage output, usually compatible with transistor-transistor logic circuitry levels, and it goes high when the microphone is on and goes low when the microphone is off. This logic output can be used to activate relays for zone paging or to activate complex microphone priority switching in conference systems.

Most automatic mixers also allow the user to defeat the automatic circuitry on an individual input channel. This allows a tape machine or other nonmicrophone input to be added to the mix without affecting (and without being affected by) the automatic mixing of the system microphones.

26.8.1.3 Applications for Automatic Mixing

In systems with undemanding, predictable mixing requirements, the automatic mixer may be able to completely replace the human operator. Examples are conference and courtroom systems and speech-oriented systems in religious facilities. In these systems, the installer sets up the system volume controls and instructs the user simply to turn the entire system on and off since the automatic mixer will take care of everything else.

In actuality, systems like these are somewhat rare. More common are systems where the automatic mixer becomes an operator aid rather than completely replacing the human mixer. Any of the previously mentioned systems where different talkers use the same microphone would require some human intervention. But the automatic mixer can also aid the human operator in more sophisticated systems including entertainment-oriented systems and dramatic (live) theater presentations.

Some automatic mixers are not suitable for mixing musical presentations; however, most can be used effectively for voice mixing of footlight microphones in a theater, and some automatic mixers may find use in submixing of instruments or vocals in an entertainment-oriented system. In all cases, the ability of the mixer to sense in-use microphones and attenuate (or to turn off) other microphones is a valuable aid in reducing unwanted noise pickup. In addition, the ability to help reduce the possibility of feedback (the NOM function) is welcome in any system.

26.8.1.4 Problems in Automatic Mixing

Despite sophisticated circuitry, ambient noise may still turn a microphone channel on at the wrong time. Another problem is coherent input signals, that is, signals that are in-phase and have similar waveshape, which may fool the mixer and allow it to raise its gain to a feedback condition. Nearly coherent signals may arrive at the microphones from a slammed door, for example.

One manufacturer, Shure Brothers, Inc., has introduced a special microphone to work with its automatic mixer. The Shure microphone/automatic mixer does not turn a microphone on unless the source is within a prescribed microphone acceptance angle. This feature helps solve the problems of ambient noise turnon and coherent signal pickup.

An obvious problem with all automatic mixers is that they do not know when a new talker approaches the microphone. Thus, the mixer cannot readjust a microphone level for a loud- versus quiet-voiced talker. A compressor could be added to the mixer to adjust the level to compensate but this would defeat the number of open microphones (NOM) function and could cause the system to go into feedback. Thus, the human operator is (fortunately) at least occasionally essential in most systems.

Despite their problems, automatic mixers are extremely

useful, and a well-designed system with an automatic mixer is more likely than ever before to be audibly transparent to an audience.

6.8.2 Compressors and Limiters

Dynamic range is the difference in dB, between the highest and lowest volume levels in any audio program.

A *compressor* is a device that shrinks that dynamic range. The *compression ratio* is the ratio of output level change to input level change in dB.

A *limiter* is a compressor with a high compression ratio, usually 10:1 or higher. Unlike a true compressor, a limiter begins its operation only above a certain (usually adjustable) input level called the *threshold*. Often a single device (Fig. 26-36) can be used for either compression or limiting, since the distinction depends mainly on the threshold and compression ratio settings.

26.8.2.1 Sound System Applications for a Compressor/Limiter

In a paging system, a compressor can keep the average level of the voices of different announcers more constant so that paging can reach noisy areas of a factory or airport more consistently. In addition, because of reduced dynamic range, peaks are lowered, reducing the chance of clipping distortion.

In a large sound-reinforcement system, such as a concert sound system, a compressor/limiter can reduce the chance of peak clipping and can thus help avoid amplifier or speaker damage from large turnon/turnoff transients or from sudden, loud feedback.

26.8.2.2 Problems with Compressor/Limiters

While useful, compressor/limiters are not cure-all devices. The compressor makes its decision to begin compressing by continuously monitoring the program level. Unfortunately, the highest levels are usually low bass notes. Thus, the compressor/limiter may compress the high frequencies needlessly when it detects a bass note that is too loud. One solution to this problem is to use a compressor on each output of an electronic crossover on a biamplified or triamplified system so that the compressor acts only on the frequencies in each band. Another solution is to use a separate compressor on each mixer input that may receive excessive program levels. Perhaps the best solution, for quality-conscious systems, is to use the compressor/limiter as a *limiter* whose purpose is to limit peaks. Set up the limiter with a high compression ratio and a high threshold so that it begins limiting only on potentially dangerous peaks and then limits them hard. With this setup, the limiter should be inaudible at normal program levels.

26.8.3 Pads

(Also see Chapter 16.) A pad is a resistor circuit that reduces the output level from a source device to make it level compatible with a load device.

Pads can be designed for balanced or for unbalanced circuits. The most common types of pads for unbalanced circuits are L and T pads. (See Figs. 16-1 and 16-9.) The advantage of an L pad is that it is very easy to design and construct. Calculate the required resistor values using voltage division techniques remembering to include the effects of actual source and load impedances. Alternately, use the tables in Chapter 16. The L pad is ideal in the case where the source prefers a high-impedance load and the load prefers a low-impedance source. Since almost all active circuits have those impedance requirements, the L pad is a logical choice.

A T pad has a third resistor that gives it the advantage of being able to provide impedance matching for both source and load. The T pad is thus the right choice for impedance-sensitive devices like a passive graphic equalizer. Calculating the required resistor values for a T pad is somewhat more complex than for an L pad. The tables in Chapter 16, however, will make the job easier. It is significant that these tables assume that *matched impedances* (source matched to pad input and load matched to pad output) are required.

Balanced pads are normally of the U or H design. (See Figs. 16-2 and 16-15.) A balanced U pad can be designed by designing an appropriate L pad and dividing the top leg resistor in two. Perform a similar transformation on a T pad to get an H pad (Fig. 26-37).

26.8.4 Transformers

Transformers are devices that can sometimes be used to connect devices with unlike impedances and levels.

Figure 26-36 Professional compressor/limiter with threshold and compression ratio adjustments. *(Courtesy dbx, Inc.)*

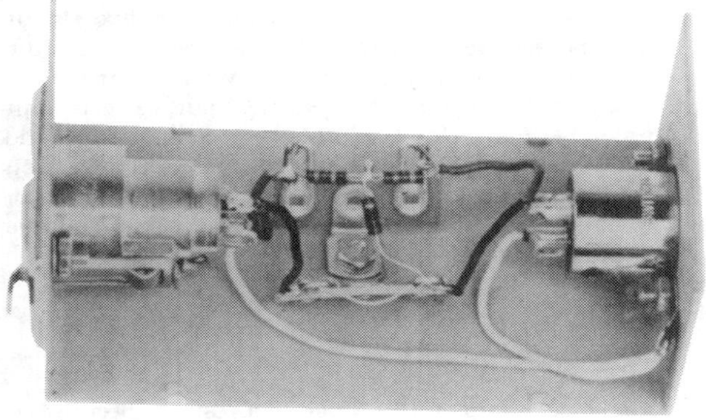

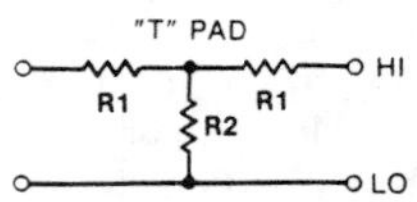

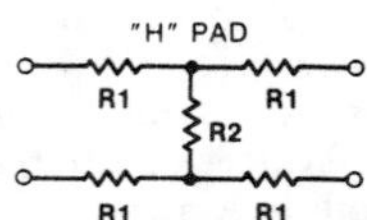

(A) Pads constructed in mini boxes.

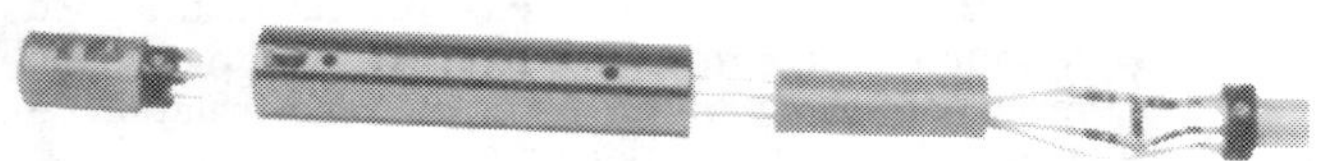

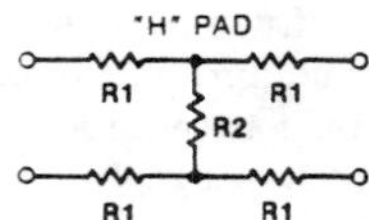

(B) Pad constructed in Switchcraft model S3FM.

Figure 26-37 Suggested pad construction techniques. *(Courtesy Yamaha International Corp.)*

For example, a hi-Z to lo-Z microphone transformer converts the high (voltage) level and high impedance of a high-impedance microphone to the low (voltage) level and low impedance of a low-impedance microphone. Other transformers can convert high-impedance, high-line-level devices to low-impedance, low-line-level devices.

Because a transformer is not an active device, however, it cannot *amplify*. Thus, when a transformer is used to convert from high impedance to low impedance, for example, it also converts from a high-voltage level to a low-voltage level. A transformer cannot convert impedance without also converting level. Transformers are also level-sensitive. That is, a microphone hi-Z to lo-Z transformer cannot be used for line-level impedance conversion. (It would distort.) Neither can a line-level transformer be used for microphone-level conversions. (It would also distort, although in a different manner.) Thus, when selecting transformers, needs must be defined in terms of both the impedance ratio desired and the level of the devices that will be connected to the transformer.

One valuable use of a microphone hi-Z to lo-Z transformer is to convert a high-impedance microphone to low-impedance to allow it to be used with longer cable lengths. A high-impedance to low-impedance line-level transformer could be used to allow a high-impedance, line-level device to be used with longer cable lengths, too.

Also see Chapter 10.

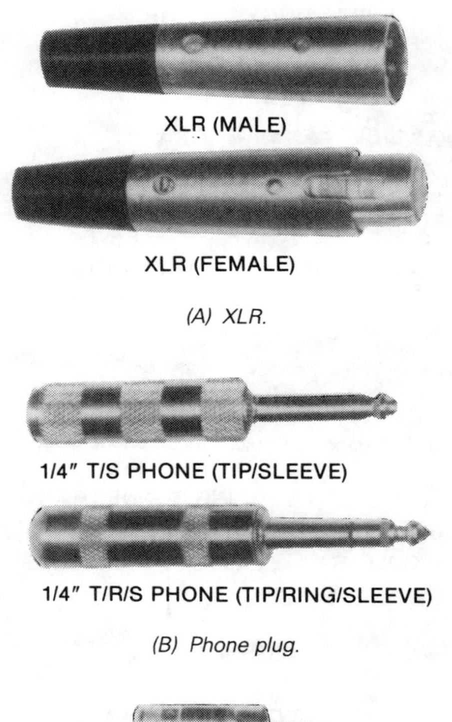

(A) XLR.

(B) Phone plug.

(C) RCA. (phono)

Figure 26-38 Various audio connectors.

26.8.5 Connectors and Cabling

As simple a subject as this may seem, faulty connectors and cabling are the source of a majority of sound system problems. Well-made cabling, of the proper type, with the right connectors for the job, on the other hand, will keep a system operating at maximum efficiency with a minimum of noise pickup.

26.8.5.1 General Notes on Cable

A cable is a group of two or more wires, usually in a single outer (insulating) sheath, and it is designed for a particular function.

Cables for portable audio systems should always be made from stranded, not solid, wire. Solid wire cables will break after the repeated flexing of portable usage. Shields should be braided wire, not foil, for the same reason. Cable for permanently installed systems, on the other hand, can utilize foil shields. In addition, while a tough, rubberized outer sheath is desirable for portable cable (like microphone cable), a smooth vinyl-type sheath will benefit the permanent system installer, since it pulls through conduit more easily.

26.8.5.2 General Notes on Connectors

There are only a few types of connectors in general use in commercial and professional sound systems, as shown in Figs. 26-38 and 26-39. The most common of these are discussed here.

XLR-Type Connectors

The term *XLR* was first used by the Cannon Company but has almost become a generic label for these high-quality audio connectors, now made not only by Cannon but also by Switchcraft, Neutrik, ADC, and others. XLRs are the connector of choice for any balanced low-level or line-level audio signal.

Phone Plugs

The term "phone" comes from the telephone company who used a type of phone plug in their early, nonautomated switchboards. Recording studio and other patch bays are close relatives of these telephone switchboards and often use some type of phone plug. The most common type of phone plug used in pro audio has a ¼-in. diameter shank and comes in two-wire (known as *tip/sleeve* or *T/S*) and three-wire (known as *tip/ring/sleeve* or *T/R/S*) versions. The ¼-in. phone plugs are commonly used for instrument amplifiers and hi-Z microphones. Unlike XLRs, which are almost invariably high quality, the quality of commercially available phone plugs can vary widely.

RCA-Type Phono Plugs

Note the term "phono," not phone, indicating that these plugs got their start on phonographs (assumably those manufactured by the RCA company). Phono plugs, or "RCAs," are used primarily on hi-fi equipment but may be used to adapt a hi-fi tuner or cassette machine, for example, to an input of a professional mixer. Phono plugs, however, are fragile and do not make good general-purpose pro-audio connectors.

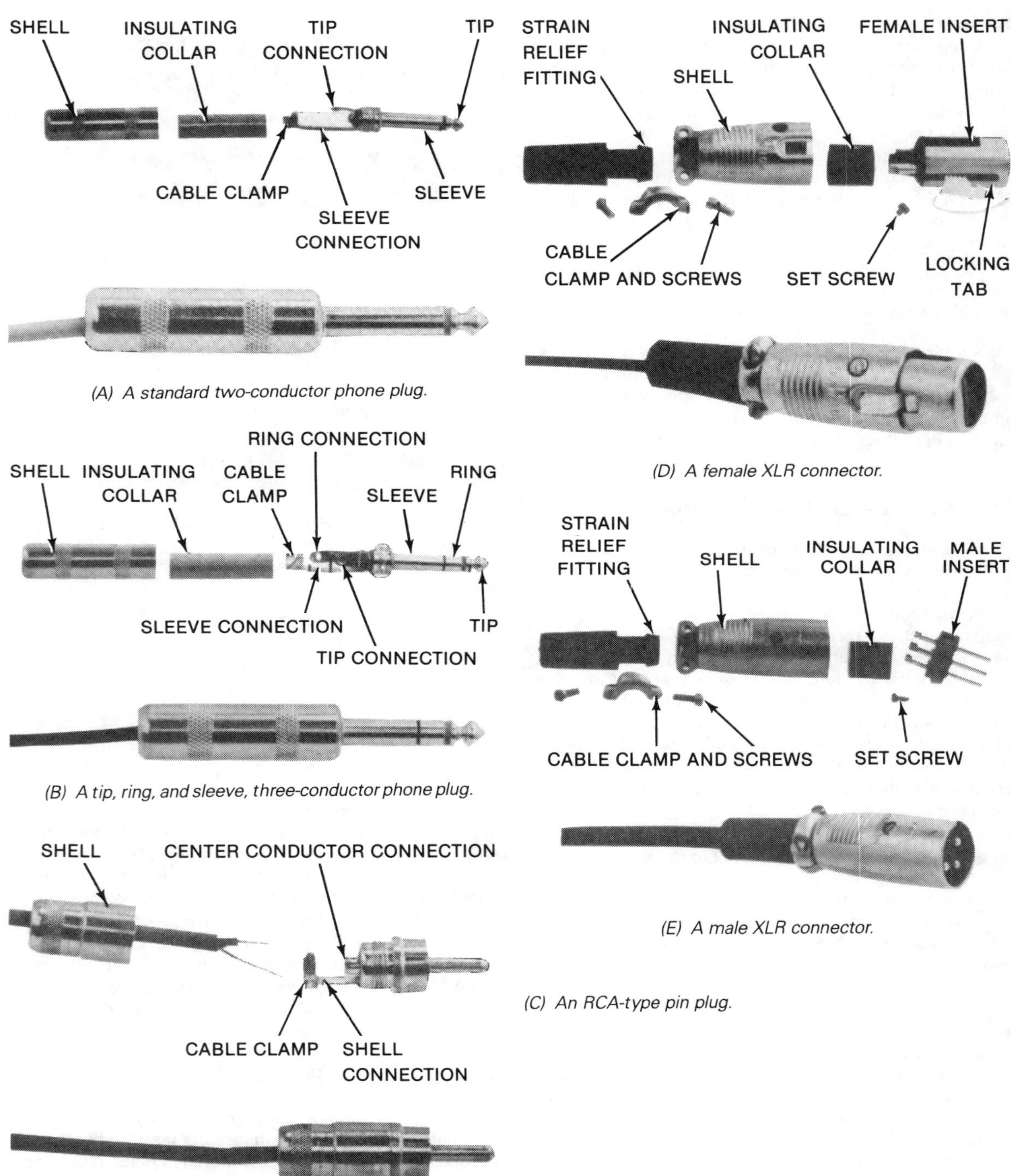

(A) A standard two-conductor phone plug.

(B) A tip, ring, and sleeve, three-conductor phone plug.

(C) An RCA-type pin plug.

(D) A female XLR connector.

(E) A male XLR connector.

Figure 26-39 Various audio connectors with parts identified. *(Courtesy Yamaha International Corp.)*

26.8.5.3 Cable and Connectors for Microphones and Other Low-Level Devices

Lo-Z balanced microphones use shielded, two-wire cable and XLR-type connectors. Hi-Z (unbalanced) microphones usually use a ¼-in. phone plug connector. Exposed (portable) microphone cable should have a flexible, tough outer sheath, a braided shield, and stranded inner wires.

Although the XLR-type connector is an industry standard for lo-Z balanced microphones, unfortunately, the wiring of these connectors is not completely standardized. Although pin 1 on the connector is almost always connected to the cable shield, some manufacturers use pin 2 as high or + and other manufacturers use pin 3 as high or + (with the remaining pin low or −). Use of two microphones with different polarity to mike the same instrument or voice can result in undesirable phase cancellations. The EIA (Electronic Industries Association), a standards organization, has recently established an XLR-type connector standard wiring where pin 2 is + and connected to the black wire. This EIA standard should promote the use of pin 2 as + or high among most manufacturers.

MICROPHONE SNAKE CABLES

A *snake cable* is actually a group of microphone or line-level cables all in one outer sheath. These cables use foil shields to reduce their overall diameter to a reasonable size. Because of the fragility of the foil shields in a snake cable (and because of the high cost per foot), extra care must be taken in their handling.

CABLE AND CONNECTORS FOR LINE-LEVEL DEVICES

Line-level devices normally use the same type of cable and connectors as microphones and other low-level devices. That is, balanced line-level devices normally use XLR-type connectors and unbalanced line-level devices normally use ¼-in. phone plug connectors. Some balanced line-level devices use three-conductor, ¼-in. tip/ring/sleeve (T/R/S) connectors.

Polarity is, again, unfortunately, not standardized on balanced line-level devices using XLR connectors. Either pin 2 or pin 3 may be the + pin (pin 1 will almost always be the shield).

26.8.5.4 Cable and Connectors for Loudspeakers

Loudspeaker cable carries much higher levels of electrical power than either microphone or line-level cable. For this reason, loudspeaker cables use larger gauge wire. Typical loudspeaker cable uses anywhere from number 18 gauge wire to as large as number 10 wire (or even larger). Number 18 gauge wire is suitable only for low-level loudspeakers (like the hi-fi speakers in your den). Number 16 gauge wire is suitable for short runs (less than 25 ft) of low- to medium-level pro audio loudspeakers. Number 14 gauge wire is suitable for most pro audio work unless loudspeaker runs are longer than about 75 ft. In that case, number 12 gauge wire should be used. For very long runs of high-power loudspeaker cable, use number 10 (or even number 8) wire. A better way to handle long loudspeaker cable runs, however, is to move the power amplifier closer to the loudspeakers and run line-level signals over the long distance.

The most common loudspeaker connector in pro audio is the ¼-in. phone plug. Except for very high-quality phone plugs, however, they are actually not very suitable for the high-current use they get in pro audio. Thus, ¼-in. phone plugs are only suitable for low- and medium-level loudspeakers (perhaps up to 200 W or so per loudspeaker). For higher power loudspeakers, a higher current connector, like a "dual banana" connector is a good choice. XLR connectors are sometimes used for loudspeaker connectors, but their current capacity, like the capacity of a phone plug, is limited, and they should not be used for higher power capacity systems. Another problem with XLR connectors for loudspeakers is that their common usage for microphones allows a microphone to be accidentally connected to a loudspeaker line (even an amplifier output line), which could cause microphone damage.

26.9 INTERWIRING

26.9.1 Understanding Balanced and Unbalanced Lines

Every audio signal requires at least two wires. In an unbalanced line, the shield (outer conductor) is also one of the audio signal wires. Thus, an unbalanced line (Fig. 26-40B) needs only the shield and one additional wire (a total of two wires). In a balanced line, the shield does not carry audio signals. Thus, a balanced line (Fig. 26-40A) requires two additional wires to carry the audio signal (for a total of three wires).

In a true balanced line, the audio signal level is balanced between the two audio wires and the shield. Thus, two VU meters, each connected between one of the audio wires and the shield, would display the same reading (½ the total audio signal level). The primary advantage of a balanced line is that it is much less likely to pick up external electronic noises (hum, buzzing, static, radio stations) than an unbalanced line.

Most transformer-coupled, balanced devices are actually *floating*. On a floating line, connecting two VU meters between each of the two wires and ground would show undetermined results—each wire floats at an undetermined voltage from ground. In most cases, floating lines provide the same advantages as balanced lines. In other words, the difference, for practical purposes, is aca-

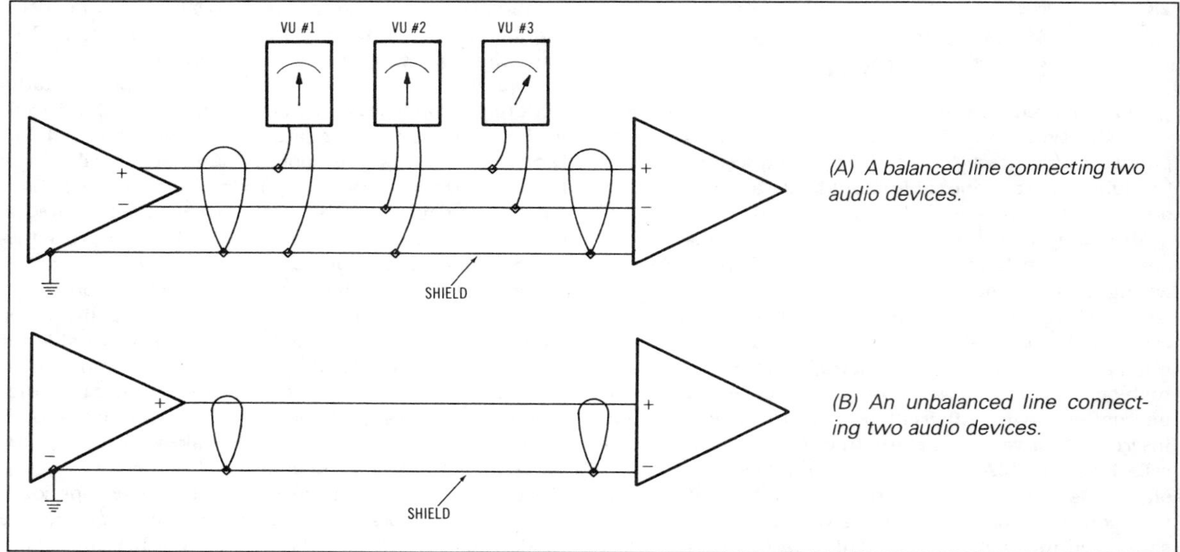

Figure 26-40 Balanced and unbalanced lines. *(Courtesy Fender Musical Instruments)*

demic, and the two terms may be treated as equivalent. Also see Chapters 13 and 15.

26.9.2 Impedance and Level Watching

While some passive devices require *impedance matching*, most active devices do not require matched impedances. What they do require is *impedance compatibility*. In addition, all audio devices require *signal level compatibility*. Thus, *impedance and level watching* mean establishing and maintaining that impedance and level compatibility.

26.9.2.1 Terms: Source, Input, Output, Load

In Fig. 26-41, the microphone is the source, the input is the input to the mixer/amplifier, the output is the output from the mixer/amplifier, and the loudspeaker is the load, but these four terms are relative. For example, the input to the mixer-amplifier can be called a load from the viewpoint of the microphone. And, the mixer-amplifier output can be called a source from the viewpoint of the loudspeaker.

Thus, the input impedance of the mixer/amplifier can be called the load impedance for the microphone, and the output impedance of the mixer/amplifier can be called the source impedance for the loudspeaker.

These four terms—source, input, output, and load—and their relative nature are important to an understanding of impedance and level watching. As an example, consider a microphone whose impedance is 200 Ω. That impedance is actually the internal impedance of the microphone and should be called the source or output impedance of the microphone. (The microphone is a source from the viewpoint of the mixer/amplifier.)

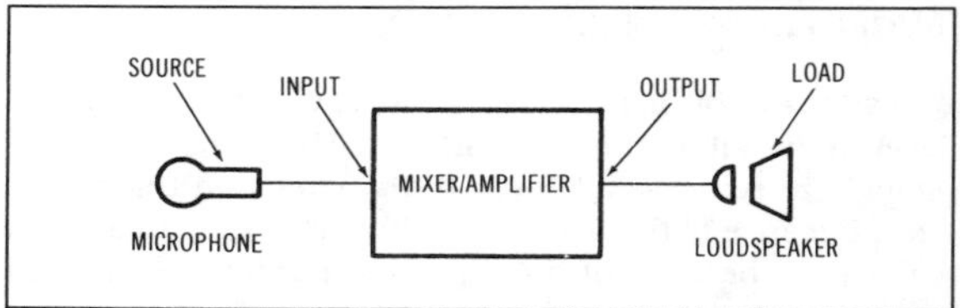

Figure 26-41 Origin of terms. *(Courtesy Fender Musical Instruments)*

That same microphone should probably be loaded with an impedance of 1500 Ω or higher. That load impedance is actually the input impedance of the mixer-amplifier (the input of the mixer/amplifier is a load to the microphone).

26.9.2.2 Impedance Compatibility

Impedance watching just means making sure that when two devices are connected together, they are *compatible* from an impedance viewpoint (Fig. 26-42). Here are some rules to help watch impedances.

PASSIVE DEVICES

In the special case of a passive filter, like a loudspeaker crossover network or a passive graphic equalizer, input and output impedances must be *matched*. These devices are the origin of the familiar term "impedance matching." Impedance matching means that if the device is a loud-

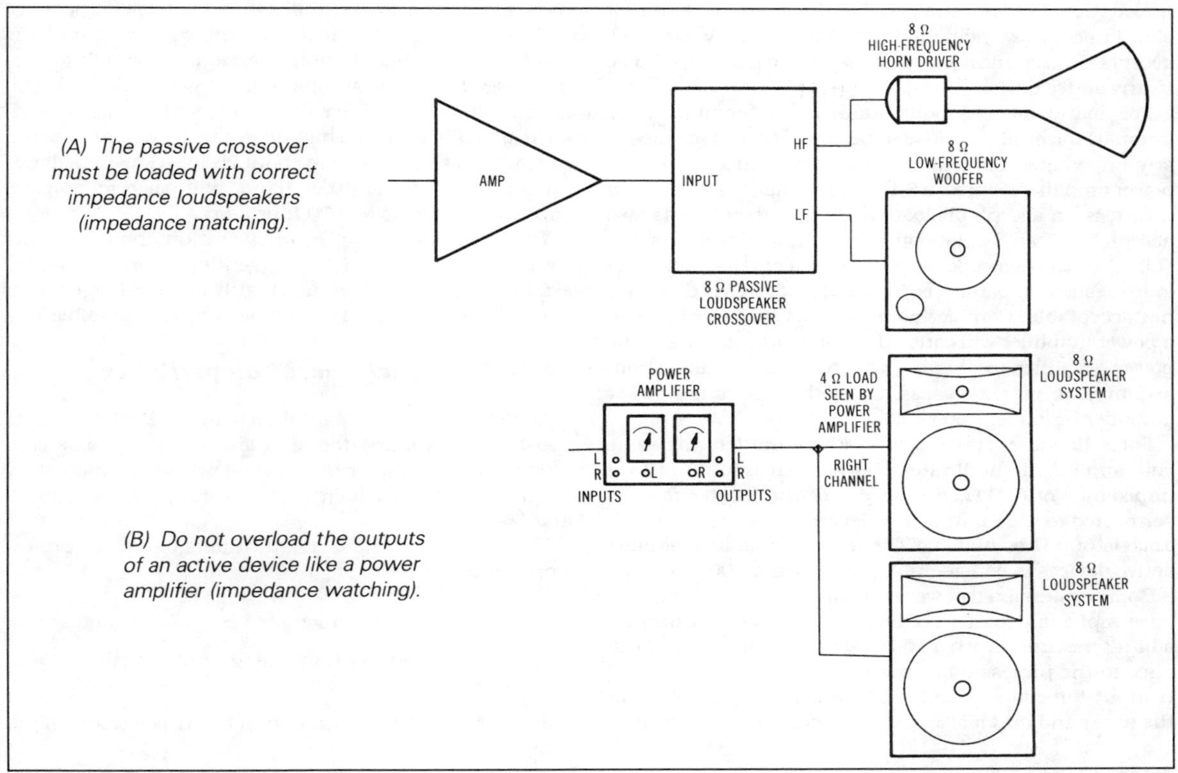

Figure 26-42 Impedance watching. *(Courtesy Fender Musical Instruments)*

speaker crossover network and it has an 8-Ω low-frequency output impedance and an 8-Ω high-frequency output impedance, then it *must* be connected to an 8-Ω low-frequency loudspeaker and an 8-Ω high-frequency loudspeaker. Any other impedance, either higher or lower, will degrade the performance of the crossover network. (The *input* to a modern loudspeaker crossover network is designed for the very low actual output impedance of a modern power amplifier.)

A passive graphic equalizer has similar requirements. If such a device has a 600-Ω *input* impedance, then it must be connected to a *source* impedance of exactly 600 Ω. The same goes for the output. If the passive graphic has a 600-Ω *output* impedance, then it must be connected to a *load* impedance of exactly 600 Ω to ensure proper operation of the graphic equalizer. In many cases, build-out and termination resistors must be added to match these impedances.

Passive Sources

Impedance watching for a passive source, like a dynamic microphone or guitar pickup, simply means supplying a *compatible* load impedance for that device. The device specifications should be a reasonably accurate guide to the proper load impedance. A good rule of thumb for dynamic microphones is that the microphone load impedance (which is probably the *input* impedance of a mixer or preamplifier) should be at least five to ten times the microphone's rated *source* impedance. Thus, for a 150-Ω (source impedance) microphone, the optimum load impedance would be 750 to 1500 Ω or higher. This requirement is satisfied by the input of almost all lo-Z mixer inputs. Note that the load impedance required by a high-impedance microphone is many times higher than the load impedance required by a low-impedance microphone. High-impedance microphones, therefore, can only be used with mixers having special inputs designed for these high impedances.

Active Devices

An active device is one that uses batteries or ac power and has one or more tubes, transistors, or ICs. Impedance watching for an active device means not overloading its output, that is, not connecting too low a load impedance to the output of the active device. A too-low impedance is an overload because the lower the impedance, the closer it is to a short circuit.

It's usually very easy to follow this rule because almost every active device comes with a set of specifications that indicates the value in ohms of the lowest allowable load impedance. This is usually called the *rated* or *minimum* load impedance. Incidentally, in almost every case, it's acceptable to connect a higher than rated load impedance to any active device.

For many modern solid-state power amplifiers, for example, the minimum load impedance is 4 Ω. That means any impedance down to 4 Ω may be connected to this power amplifier. Since an 8-Ω loudspeaker is greater than 4 Ω, it is an acceptable load; a 16-Ω loudspeaker is also acceptable. Two 8-Ω loudspeakers in parallel equals a 4-Ω load so this arrangement is also acceptable. Four 4-Ω loudspeakers in parallel equal a 1-Ω load; this is definitely not acceptable. Connecting a too-low load impedance to a power amplifier will cause the protection circuits of the power amplifier to operate, which increases distortion, and may, in extreme cases, cause damage to the power amplifier or loudspeakers.

For a line-level active device, like a limiter, the same rule applies. If the limiter has a rated minimum load impedance of 600 Ω, the output of the limiter may be connected to the input of any device whose input impedance is 600 Ω or higher. (The input impedance of most active devices is considerably higher than 600 Ω.)

Some professional power amplifiers, on the other hand, have input impedances of 5000 Ω or lower. Connecting a hi-fi-type tuner, with a 10,000-Ω minimum load impedance to the professional power amplifier, with its 5000-Ω input impedance would reduce the output level from the tuner and might also cause an increase in distortion.

Active Sources

Active sources like battery or phantom-powered condenser microphones should receive the same treatment as any other active device.

26.9.2.3 Impedance and Cable Length

One more aspect of impedance watching involves the effect of cable length on the frequency response of high-impedance microphones. From the following information, we can see that a too-long cable on a high-impedance microphone will cause a loss in high-frequency response; that is, the sound from the microphone will be dull, and voices will lack intelligibility. This results from the interaction between the capacitance in the cable and the high impedance of the microphone, which form a low-pass filter. The lower impedance of a low-impedance microphone also interacts with the capacitance of the cable, but the effect is noticeable only at very high frequencies (out of the audio range). A good rule of thumb is to avoid cables longer than 15 ft with a high-impedance microphone (some high-impedance microphones will tolerate cable lengths up to about 25 ft). A low-impedance microphone, on the other hand, will perform properly with cables as long as 200 ft or more.

Cable Losses*

Microphone Impedance (Ω)	Cable Length (ft) Causing 1-dB Loss at 10 kHz
50	920
150	310
250	190

*Courtesy Electro-Voice, Inc.

This same cable length consideration applies to line-level devices. The hi-fi tuner mentioned previously, for example, should not be used with a cable longer than about 15 ft. (The cable should be shorter if possible.)

26.9.2.4 Signal-Level Compatibility

Achieving level compatibility between devices means two things: avoiding too-high levels, which cause clipping distortion, and avoiding too-low levels, which allow electronic noises (usually hiss), as shown in Figs. 26-43 and 26-44.

There are three basic classifications of level in professional audio devices:

1. Low-level devices (microphones, pickups, and so on).
2. Line-level devices (limiters, graphic equalizers, and so on).
3. High-level devices (the output from a power amplifier).

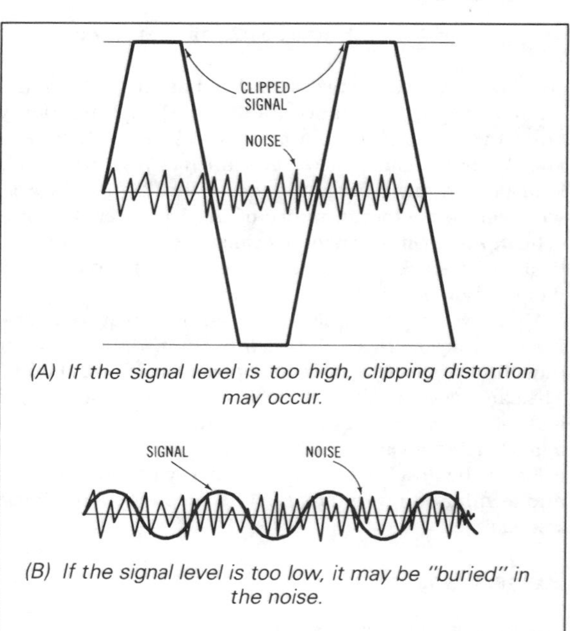

(A) If the signal level is too high, clipping distortion may occur.

(B) If the signal level is too low, it may be "buried" in the noise.

Figure 26-43 Level watching. *(Courtesy Fender Musical Instruments)*

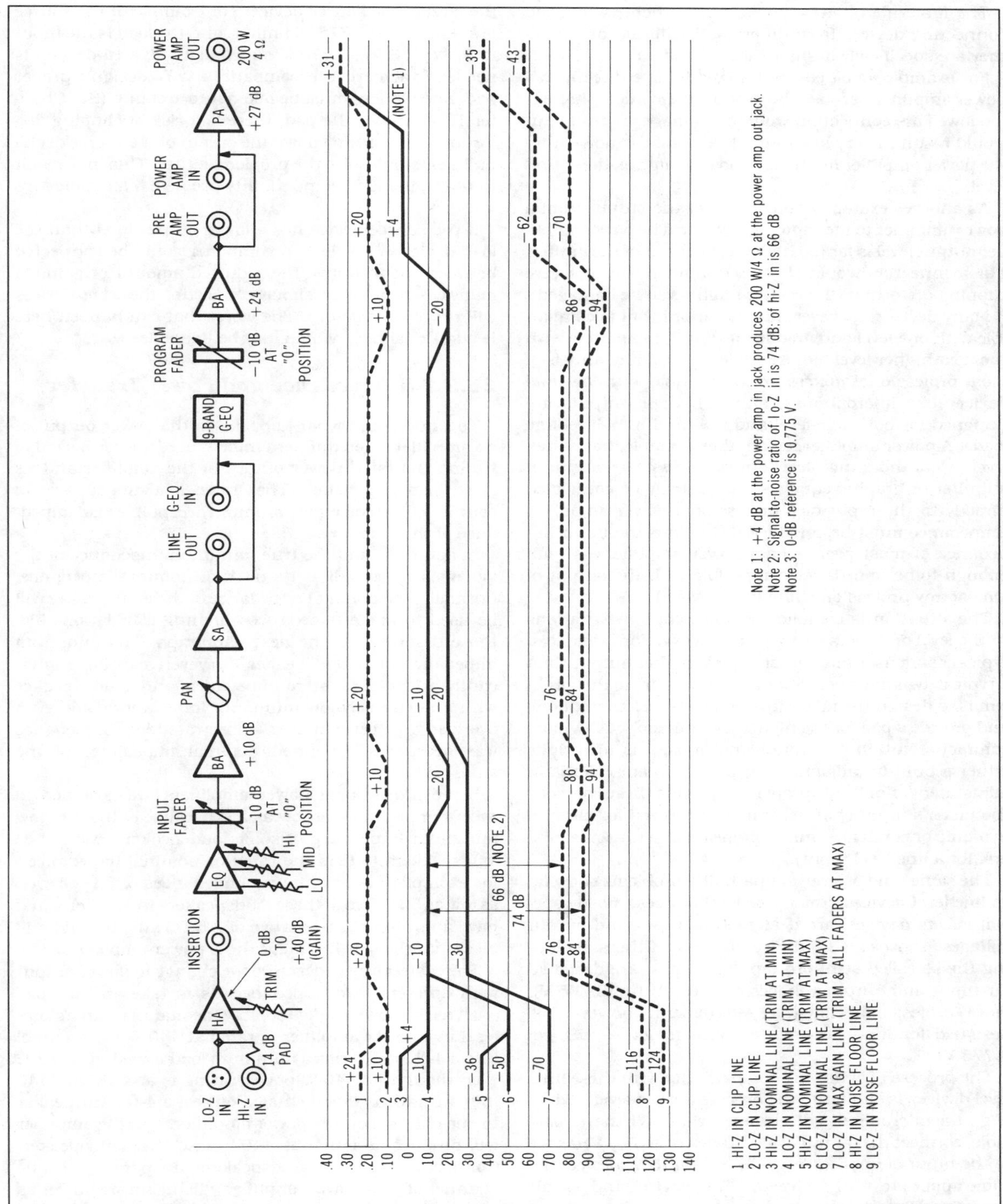

Figure 26-44 Typical sound reinforcement system gain/level chart. *(Courtesy Fender Musical Instruments)*

The first rule of level compatibility, then, is to avoid connecting devices from different classifications unless they are specifically designed for each other.

For example, don't connect a microphone directly to a power amplifier because the output of the microphone is too low. This connection wouldn't damage anything but would result in very low sound level, and the noise from the power amplifier might be almost as high as the sound level.

As another example, don't connect the output from a power amplifier to the input of a limiter. The power amplifier output level is far too high for the input of the limiter. This connection would almost certainly result in severe clipping distortion (the limiter might even be damaged).

Many devices, however, have an input that is compatible with one level and an output that is compatible with the next higher level. For example, the input channels of most professional mixers are compatible with low-level devices like microphones, although their outputs are designed for both mic-level and low- and high-level line loads. A power amplifier, as another example, has a line-level input and a high-level output. Thus, the output of a limiter or graphic equalizer can usually be connected directly to the input of a professional power amplifier. (Impedance must be considered, too, but the input impedance of most professional power amplifiers is high enough to be impedance-compatible with the output of almost any professional line-level device.)

The situation is complicated somewhat by variations in the level of devices in a given category. For example, a typical condenser microphone has a higher output than a typical dynamic microphone. One solution to this problem is to design the mixer for the lower-level microphone and provide a pad for the higher-level microphone. A more common solution on professional mixers is to include either a built-in (adjustable) pad or a preamplifier gain adjustment or both. By properly adjusting these controls, the mixer's input channel can be optimized for either a dynamic or condenser microphone (and, with some mixers, for a line-level input).

The same kind of level-compatibility problems show up in line-level devices. Some line-level devices, mostly special effects devices, are designed for input and output voltages as low as − 20 dB (re: 0.775 V). Others, including the so-called semi-pro tape machines, are designed for input and output voltages of −10 dB (re: 0.775 V). Most professional line-level equipment, however, is designed for input and output voltages of +4 dB (re: 0.775 V).

The process of achieving compatibility with these line-level devices is similar to the process for low-level devices (e.g., the microphones discussed earlier). Whenever possible, connect the output of a −20-dB (re: 0.775 V) device to the input of another −20-dB (re: 0.775 V) device (the same applies to −10-dB (re: 0.775 V) devices and +4-dB (re: 0.775 V) devices).

If this isn't possible and the source device has a higher output level than the load device, use a pad to attenuate the level of the source device. For example, if the source is a +4-dB (re: 0.775 V) limiter, and the load is the input to a −10-dB (re: 0.775 V) tape machine, a 14-dB pad is needed to achieve level compatibility. To design a proper pad, impedances must be taken into account. (See Chapter 16.) Without the pad, there is a risk of clipping distortion. Just turning down the output of the source device probably won't solve the problem, either. This may result in that other level-compatibility problem, *electronic hiss noise*.

If the source device has a lower output level than the load device, a line-level preamplifier could be connected between them to give the required amount of gain. In many cases, however, simply connecting these two devices will prove satisfactory. The worst that can happen here is additional hiss, which may be tolerable.

26.9.2.5 Impedance and Power Transfer

To understand what happens to the power output of an amplifier when different impedances are connected to it, find the rated power output of the amplifier and its rated load impedance. That rated load impedance, of course, will often be the minimum acceptable load impedance of the amplifier.

In addition, find the true minimum impedance of the loudspeaker as well as its rated or nominal impedance. Normally, the nominal impedance of the loudspeaker will be used to make impedance-watching calculations like those described in the next paragraph. The minimum impedance of a loudspeaker, however, can fall significantly below its nominal impedance, and a loudspeaker with an extremely low minimum impedance could even overload a power amplifier whose rated load impedance was acceptable for rated nominal impedance of the loudspeaker.

Some professional power amplifiers are designed to accept impedances as low as 2 Ω because of the very low minimum impedance of some loudspeakers. Many 8-Ω loudspeakers (8 Ω is the rated or nominal impedance), for example, have minimum impedances of 6 Ω or even as low as 5 Ω. Two of these loudspeakers in parallel would have a minimum impedance of 2.5 Ω, which would still be within the safe limits for these power amplifiers.

The easiest way to describe the change in power output with different load impedances is to take an example, such as is shown in Fig. 26-45. One manufacturer's professional power amplifier is rated at 440 W per channel into a 4-Ω load. It has a minimum load impedance of 2 Ω even though its 440-W power rating is at 4 Ω, and 440 into 4 Ω means exactly that. Connect a 4-Ω loudspeaker to one channel of this power amplifier, and the amplifier will produce as much as 440 W into that loudspeaker. Connecting two 8-Ω loudspeakers (in parallel) to one channel of this power amplifier will, again, result in as much as 440 W into the resulting total impedance of 4 Ω. Each 8-Ω loudspeaker in this example will receive exactly one-half of the total power, or a maximum of 220 W.

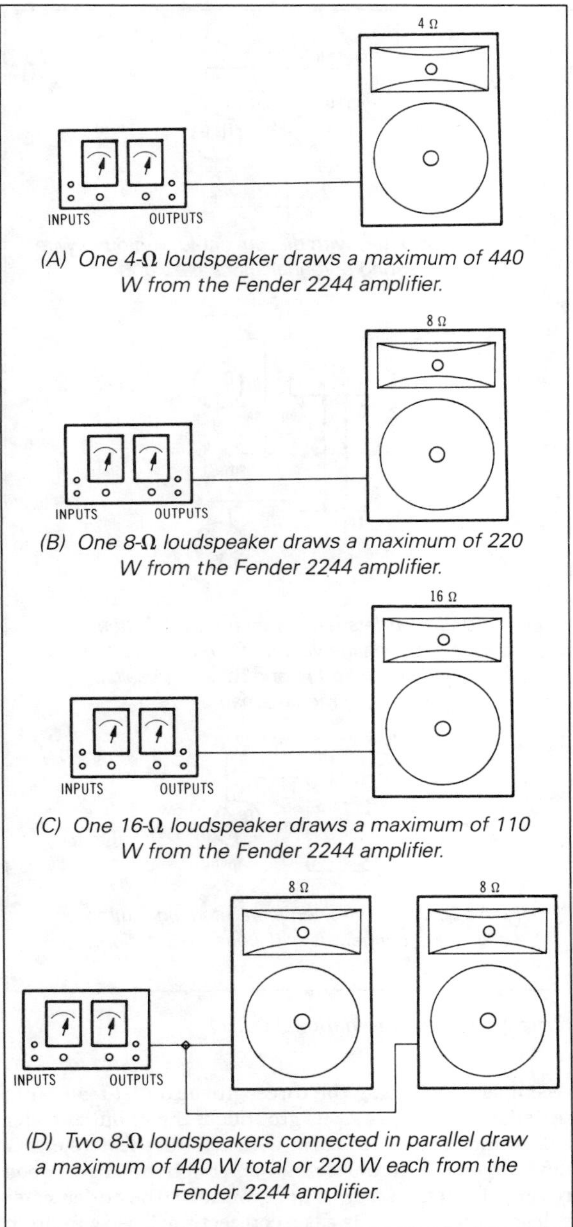

(A) One 4-Ω loudspeaker draws a maximum of 440 W from the Fender 2244 amplifier.

(B) One 8-Ω loudspeaker draws a maximum of 220 W from the Fender 2244 amplifier.

(C) One 16-Ω loudspeaker draws a maximum of 110 W from the Fender 2244 amplifier.

(D) Two 8-Ω loudspeakers connected in parallel draw a maximum of 440 W total or 220 W each from the Fender 2244 amplifier.

Figure 26-45 Impedance and power transfer. *(Courtesy Fender Musical Instruments)*

Connect a single 8-Ω loudspeaker to one channel of this power amplifier, and that loudspeaker will still only receive a maximum of about 220 W. (The actual power will be slightly higher.) Connect a single 16-Ω loud- speaker, and it will receive a maximum of about 110 W. In other words, doubling the load impedance halves the power output of a power amplifier. Conversely, halving the load impedance doubles the power output of the amplifier. Remembering this simple relationship can help ensure that a loudspeaker and power amplifier will be compatible in terms of impedance and power levels.

26.9.3 Grounding and Shielding

Caution: In any audio system installation, governmental and insurance underwriters' electrical codes must be observed. These codes are based on safety and may vary in different localities. In all cases, local codes take precedence over any suggestions contained in this section of this *Handbook*.

Note: The ac power discussions in this section apply to the U.S. only. The general discussions of grounding and shielding, however, should be applicable to audio systems used in any location. Always obey local fire and electrical safety regulations.

There are two primary reasons for careful grounding and shielding in an audio system. The first reason is safety. A poorly grounded system, especially outdoors, may be a shock hazard. The second reason is to reduce pickup of external noise. That external noise expresses itself in the form of hums and buzzes and other noises including radio station pickup.

26.9.3.1 Grounding for Safety

The third (round) prong on the ac cable of any piece of audio equipment is the ac safety ground. When plugged into a properly wired ac receptacle, the third prong of the ac cable connects the chassis of the audio device to the ac ground through the third prong of the ac receptacle.

This is the ideal situation from a safety viewpoint. Under these conditions, there is almost no combination of events that could cause a shock hazard from a single audio device by itself. It is unfortunate (from a safety viewpoint) any audio device is seldom used by itself; there are always other pieces of equipment involved, and most of the time, these are also ac powered. In addition, one or both of the following may be encountered: (1) older audio equipment (in particular, guitar amplifiers) with two-wire ac plugs and ground or hum switches, or (2) older, two-wire ac receptacles or improperly wired three-wire ac receptacles.

26.9.3.2 Improperly Wired AC Receptacles

Two inexpensive items can help locate potential ac problems. One of these is a three-prong outlet tester; the second is a neon lamp ac voltage tester.

The three-prong outlet tester indicates proper or improper outlet wiring. An improperly wired outlet (Fig. 26-46) may have its two ac wires reversed (polarity reversal), or it may have a disconnected ground. Any fault in the wiring of the ac receptacle is potentially hazardous, and, thus, the best, and perhaps only safe, way to deal

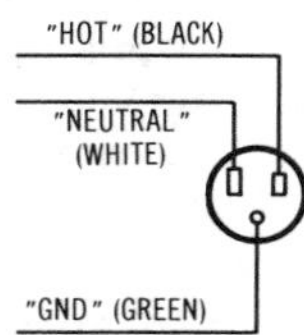

(A) Properly wired 110-V ac outlet.

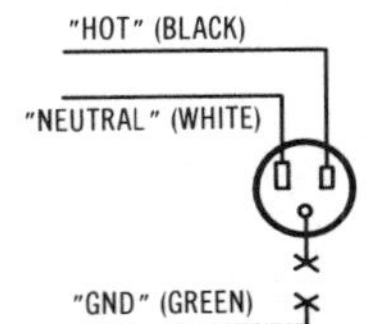

(B) 110-V ac outlet with disconnected ac ground wire creating potential shock hazard.

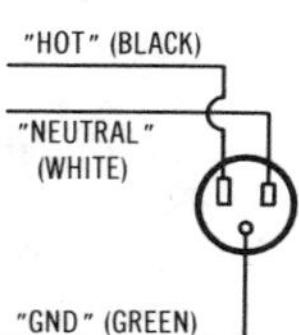

(C) 110-V ac outlet with polarity (hot and neutral), reversed creating shock hazard and causing possible noise.

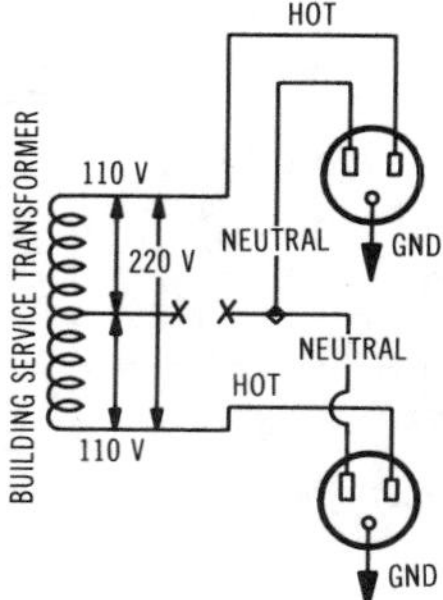

(D) 110-V ac outlets with open neutral. Outlets will operate with voltage varying from 0 to 220 V ac, creating shock hazard and causing possible equipment damage.

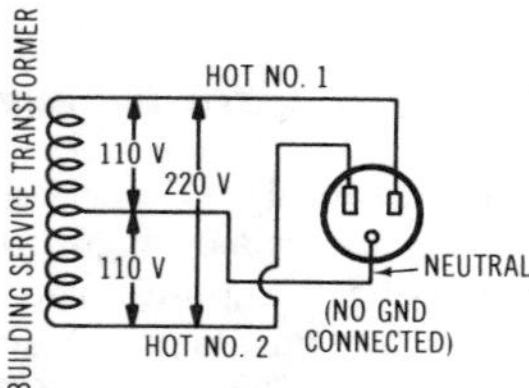

(E) 110-V ac outlet with a 220-V ac circuit connected to it. This is a highly dangerous and illegal connection.

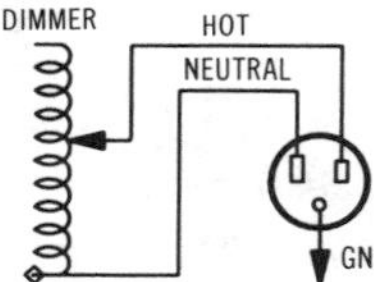

(F) A 110-V ac outlet connected to a light dimmer circuit, a dangerous and illegal connection.

Figure 26-46 Ac receptacle problems. *(Courtesy Yamaha International Corp.)*

with an improperly wired ac receptacle is to simply refuse to use it until it has been repaired.

26.9.3.3 Two-Wire AC Receptacles

The problem with two-wire ac receptacles is that they don't have that important third ground prong. Thus, to use one of these two-wire receptacles, it's necessary to adapt it to the three-wire ac plug on a more modern piece of audio equipment. Properly used, these adapters maintain a safe ground for the three-wire audio equipment.

To make this two-wire adapter work properly, connect the loose wire on the two-wire end to a grounded screw on the two-wire ac receptacle. To check the safety of the two-wire to three-wire connection, first, connect the loose wire on the adapter to the screw on the two-wire receptacle; then plug the two-wire adapter into the two-wire receptacle. Next, plug the three-wire ac outlet tester into the adapter. If the screw is grounded, the ac outlet tester will so indicate. (Most three-wire ac outlet testers either have a "good" light or else they don't light at all on a good receptacle.) If the screw is not grounded, the outlet tester will so indicate. In this case, connect the loose wire from the adapter to some other grounded screw in order to maintain a safe ground.

If the outlet tester shows a good ground but reversed polarity on the two-wire to three-wire adapter, simply reverse the adapter in the receptacle.

26.9.3.4 Older Two-Wire Audio Equipment

Some newer equipment may come with a two-wire ac cable. This newer equipment may be as safe as if it had a three-wire ac cable. A good example of such a piece of (nonaudio) equipment with a two-wire ac cable is one of the so-called double-insulated power tools (drills, saws, and so on). One way to judge the safety of a piece of audio equipment with a two-wire ac cable is to look for a UL (Underwriter's Laboratories) sticker. Other reliable safety agencies are the City of Los Angeles and the CSA (Canadian Safety Organization). Seals from any of these three organizations are reliable indicators of the fire and shock safety of a piece of equipment.

It's the older, two-wire audio equipment, however, that can be potentially hazardous. The details of how a shock hazard can develop are complex, but dealing with this problem is straightforward. The shock hazard, if there is one, will probably develop between the chassis of an older, two-wire device like a guitar amplifier and the chassis of a microphone.

The chassis of the microphone is connected to the chassis of the microphone-preamplifier-mixer through the shield of the connecting cable. Thus, if the mixer is properly grounded, the chassis of the microphone is properly grounded, too, and neither the microphone nor the mixer will present any safety hazard. The guitar amplifier (or other two-wire equipment), however, is, potentially, not properly grounded. That means that a hazardous ac voltage could be present on the chassis of the guitar amp or on the strings of a guitar, which are connected to the chassis of the amplifier through the shield of the guitar cord.

Use the neon lamp ac tester (or, even better, a high-impedance ac voltmeter). Place one lead on the chassis of the guitar amp and the other lead on the chassis of the microphone. (Don't touch both the chassis of the microphone and the chassis of the guitar amp at the same time with your hands.) If the lamp lights or the voltmeter shows even a few volts difference, a potential ac hazard exists. One possible way to solve the problem is by reversing the guitar amplifier's ac plug in the ac receptacle (pull it out, twist it one-half turn, and put it back in). Also, try reversing the position of the hum switch if the guitar amplifier has one. If the problem doesn't go away, try plugging the guitar amp into a different ac receptacle (on the same building ac circuit as the mixer, if possible).

Another worthwhile measurement is the actual ac receptacle voltage, especially in an unfamiliar facility. Voltages that are too high or too low could cause improper operation, or even damage the equipment; too-high voltages could also pose a shock hazard. Most audio equipment will work fine on an ac outlet with voltages as low as about 105 V ac and as high as about 125 V ac. Check the specifications for the equipment if there is any doubt.

26.9.3.5 Grounding for Safety Outdoors

The most common safety problems outdoors are improperly wired portable ac cables and wet ground or stages (and, of course, rain). Check the wiring carefully, using the same techniques as if the system were indoors. Consider canceling a performance if rain begins. If a performance must proceed on wet ground or in the rain, the best way to avoid shock hazards to the performers is to use wireless microphones and wireless instrument transmitters. These same outdoor problems, of course, can develop indoors on a damp floor.

26.9.3.6 Grounding To Reduce External Noise Pickup

One myth about grounding is that a piece of equipment must be earth grounded to avoid noise pickup. Anyone who owns a portable cassette machine knows that this simply isn't true. The primary reason for grounding audio equipment is for safety. An important secondary reason is that, with ac-powered equipment, under some conditions, proper grounding can help reduce external noise pickup.

The third reason to pay attention to grounding is that, although proper grounding won't always reduce external noise pickup, poor grounding can unquestionably increase external noise pickup!

Poor grounding practice usually results in ground loops, and avoiding these ground loops is the second most important part of proper grounding (the first most important part, of course, is maintaining the safety ground).

26.9.3.7 Definitions: Ground, Earth, Common

A *common connection* in an audio system is some point where a group of circuits (usually shields or other zero-signal circuit lines) connect together. Ground in an audio system is the primary zero signal reference for the system. In a typical system, there may be a common connection of all audio signal shields and a separate common connection of all power-supply negative terminals. At some physical point in the system, these commons are connected together. That point becomes the system ground and is called the zero signal reference potential because that is the place where a voltmeter reference lead would be placed. An *earth connection* is a connection directly to the earth usually made via a copper rod driven into moist, salted soil. The system ground is physically connected to the "earth" at this copper rod. These terms are not fixed in meaning, however, and the term "ground," for example, is often used in place of either of the other two terms, or "grounding" may be used as a general term to describe the practice of external noise reduction. In addition, in England, the term "earth" is often used in place of the term "ground" to indicate the system zero signal reference potential.

26.9.3.8 Ground Loops in Unbalanced Systems

A couple of examples will help explain what ground loops are and how to avoid them. In Figs. 26-47, 26-48, and 26-49, the loop is between two audio cables that connect a limiter to a two-channel power amplifier with unbalanced inputs. This is an example of an unavoidable ground

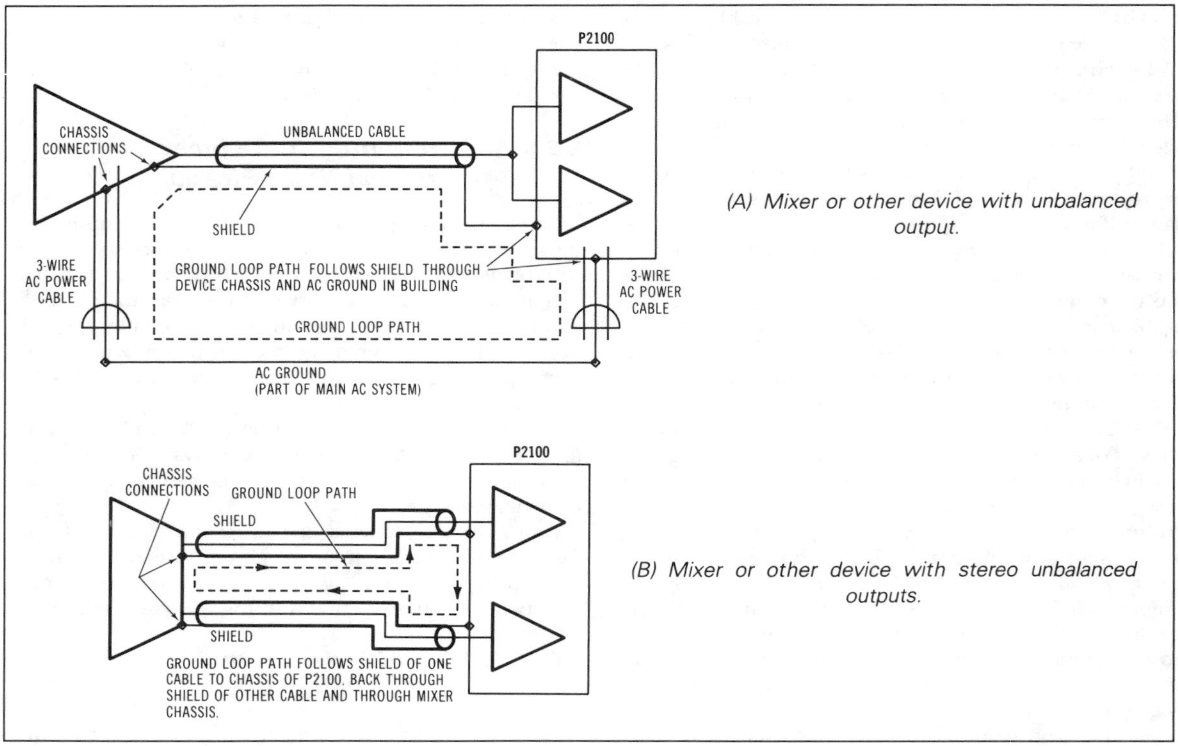

(A) Mixer or other device with unbalanced output.

(B) Mixer or other device with stereo unbalanced outputs.

Figure 26-47 Two possible ground loops in an audio system. *(Courtesy Yamaha International Corp.)*

loop. The best way to deal with this type of ground loop is to place the two audio cables physically as close together as possible (lace or tape them together if the setup will allow it). This reduces the area enclosed by the loop, which will significantly reduce the pickup of external noise.

26.9.3.9 Ground Loops in Balanced Systems and Using the Telescoping Shield Connection

By using balanced connections between two pieces of audio equipment, the shield at the sending end can be lifted (disconnected) to interrupt one type of ground loop. This lifted ground results in what is known as a *telescoping shield.* Since, in a balanced line, the shield does not carry audio signal, it can be disconnected at one end without interrupting the audio signal (and without disrupting the effectiveness of the shield). Unfortunately, this is not a very practical solution to the problem in a portable audio system because it would require special cables that have the shield disconnected on one end.

In Fig. 26-50 the ground loop occurs between a microphone-mixer and an external power amplifier. Even though there is only one audio cable connecting the two devices, a second ground connection, through the ac cables of the devices, makes the return connection and forms a ground loop. Using a telescoping shield breaks the ground loop and thus helps prevent pickup of magnetically coupled noise.

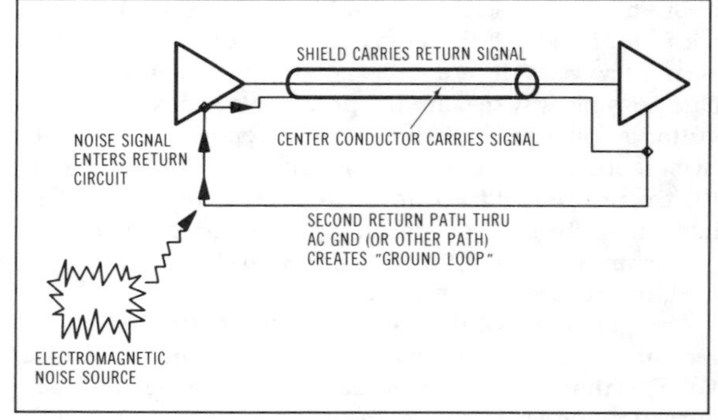

Figure 26-48 Noise entering a system through a ground loop. *(Courtesy Yamaha International Corp.)*

Another way to break the ground loop in Fig. 26-50 is to lift the ac ground on the power amplifier with a two-wire to three-wire ac adapter (leaving the loose wire on

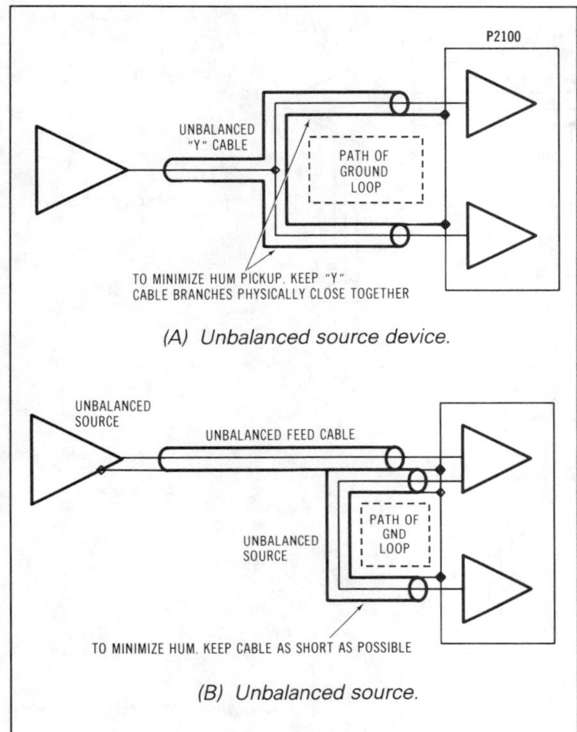

(A) Unbalanced source device.

(B) Unbalanced source.

Figure 26-49 Minimizing hum with unavoidable ground loops. *(Courtesy Yamaha International Corp.)*

the adapter unconnected). This action could interrupt the ground loop even if the signal connection were unbalanced. Because this practice is in conflict with the ac safety ground, here are two rules to minimize the safety conflict: (1) Don't lift the safety ground on any piece of equipment unless it demonstrably reduces noise pickup. (2) Never defeat the ac safety ground on the microphone mixer by using a two-wire to three-wire ac adapter in this manner. The reason for this second rule is that the mixer chassis is connected to the chassis of all the system microphones, and proper grounding of the mixer helps maintain a safe ground at the microphones. Always maintain at least this one ground for safety! A far better way to interrupt a ground loop of this type, of course, is to introduce line transformers to balance the signal connection, which allows the use of the telescoping shield concept.

26.9.3.10 Using Proper Shielding To Reduce Noise Pickup

Proper grounding helps prevent pickup of noise that is transmitted magnetically. Magnetically transmitted noise most often comes from motors or, more commonly in audio, for large ac power transformers (either building transformers or the power transformers in a power amplifier or other piece of audio equipment). Proper *shielding*, on the other hand, helps prevent pickup of noise that is transmitted *capacitively*. Capacitively transmitted noise may be in the form of radio waves from a radio station or citizens band radio, or it may be in the form of static from certain types of motors or from lighting dimmers. (Noise from lighting dimmers may also come through the ac lines, as discussed in section 26.9.3.11.)

Proper shielding, except in severe noise situations, is straightforward. Use high-quality shielded cables on all microphones and on all line-level equipment, and, if at all possible, install the electronics in a metal equipment rack (preferably steel since this also provides some protection against magnetically coupled noise). Some very low-cost audio cables including guitar cables have poor quality shields. Watch for these potential sources of noise pickup (Fig. 26-51).

It is seldom necessary to use shielded cable for loudspeakers, since they operate at a very high level and a very low impedance. The noise picked up by a loudspeaker cable is actually at the same level as the noise picked up by a microphone cable. However, because the loudspeaker operates at a much higher level than the microphone, the signal-to-noise ratio is vastly better, and the noise is seldom a problem.

26.9.3.11 Reducing Noise Pickup from AC Lines

Some types of noise, notably noise from lighting dimmers, enter audio equipment from the ac power lines. There are four ways to reduce this problem. (1) Install filters on the dimmer circuits (filters at the audio equipment won't help as much and probably will cost a lot more). (2) Make sure the dimmer circuits are properly loaded. In other words, if the dimmers are rated for 1500-W loads, make sure they have 1500 W worth of lighting connected to them. (Or add a suitable dummy load to simulate a full-rated load on the dimmer.) The reason for doing this is that the noise filters (if there are any) will only work properly when the dimmer is loaded properly (this is an example of impedance matching). (3) Make sure the lighting circuits are properly grounded (improper grounding can increase noise levels at the source as well as at the audio equipment). (4) Use a different ac circuit.

26.9.3.12 Tips on Reducing Noise Pickup

1. *Rack mount the equipment.* Rack mounting, especially when the rack mount rails are made of metal, connects together the chassis of all the equipment into a unitized shield. Perhaps more important, rack mounting allows the use of shorter connecting cables and keeps them closer together. When rack mounting large power amplifiers, however, do not place sensitive, low-level equipment right next to them in the rack. The power transformer in a large power amplifier can produce a large

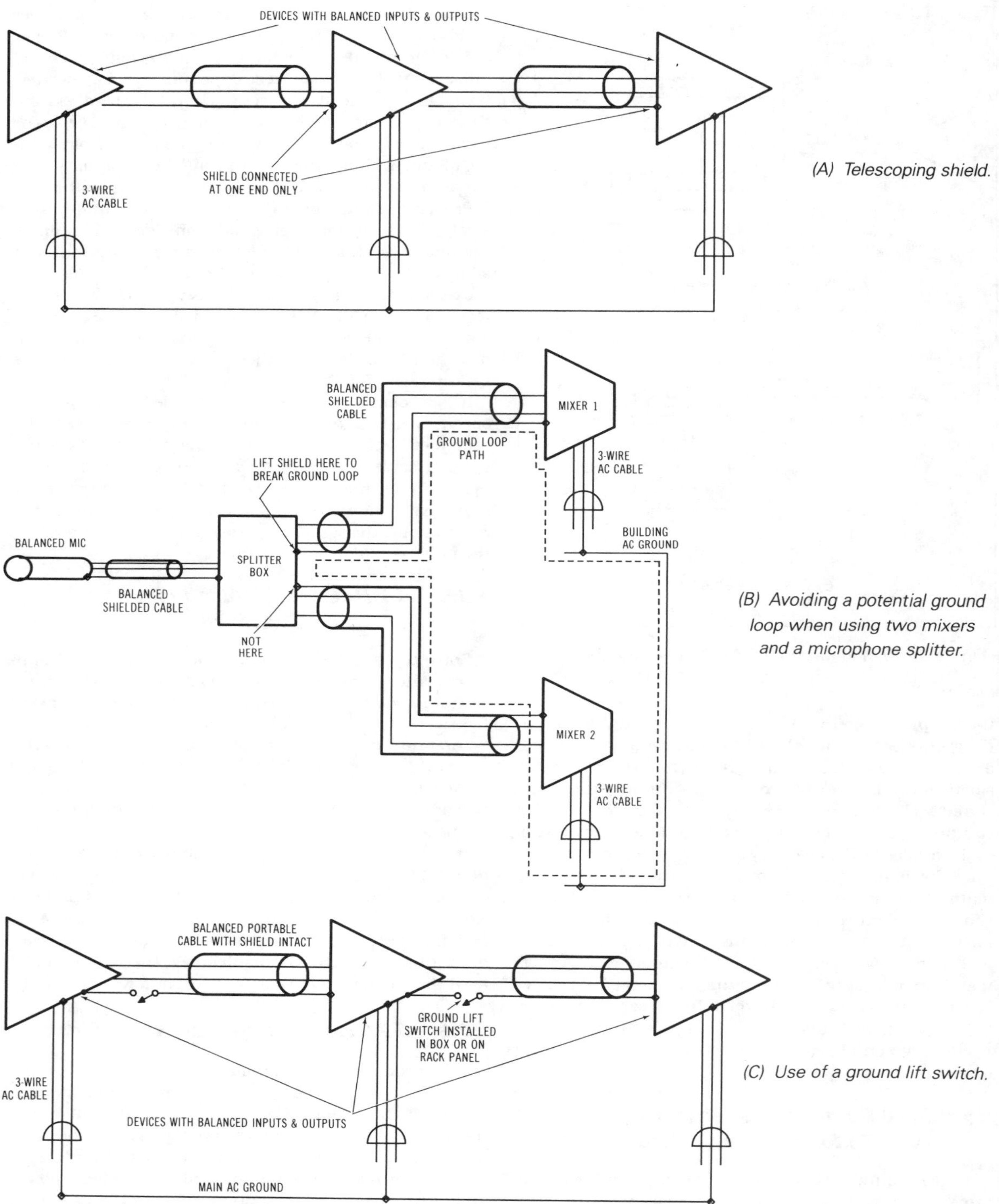

(A) Telescoping shield.

(B) Avoiding a potential ground loop when using two mixers and a microphone splitter.

(C) Use of a ground lift switch.

Figure 26-50 Balanced system ground loops. *(Courtesy Yamaha International Corp.)*

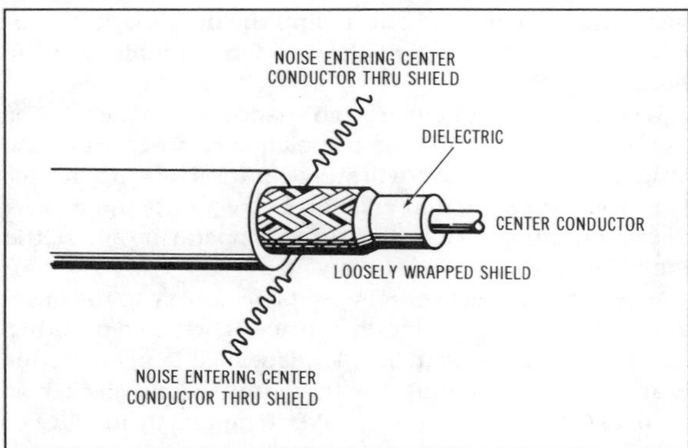

Figure 26-51 Poor-quality shielded cable. *(Courtesy Yamaha International Corp.)*

alternating magnetic field that can induce hum in low-level equipment.

2. *Keep the cables short.* Rack mounting can help here, as can simple neatness.

3. *Keep cables of the same type close together* (that is, group cables that carry the same signal level). Especially when they form an unavoidable ground loop, keeping cables close together will help reduce noise pickup.

4. *Keep cables of different types as far apart as possible.* That means keep the microphone cables away from loudspeaker cables. And keep all audio cables away from the ac power cables. On long cable runs, keep line-level cables and microphone cables separated. It's a common, but risky, procedure to run microphones through a snake (a multimicrophone cable) to a mixer and then run the outputs from the mixer back to the power amplifier through the same snake. This mixing of levels, in a long cable run (greater than about 25 ft could be a problem) can cause a form of electronic feedback that could cause harmful oscillations in the system mixer.

5. *Keep the wiring neat.* Carefully made cables, of the proper length (not too long), that are carefully laid out on a stage or in an installation are probably the best way of all to reduce external noise pickup (Fig. 26-52).

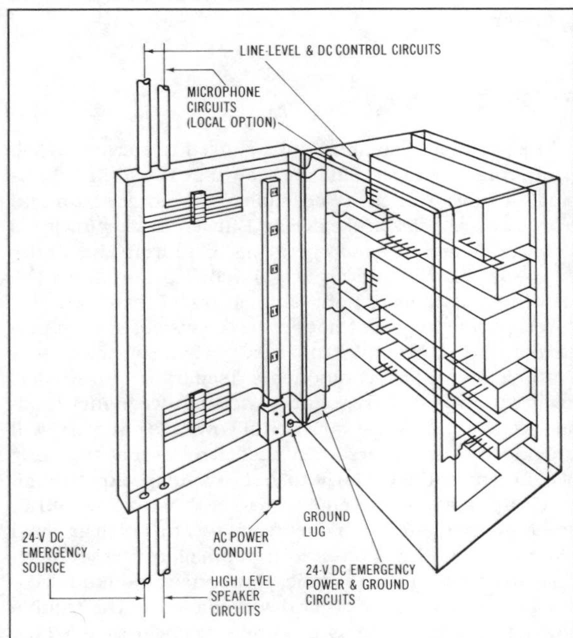

Figure 26-52 Cable routing in equipment rack. *(From Reference 4)*

26.10 TROUBLESHOOTING A SOUND SYSTEM

Repairing a sound system may require the skills of a trained technician. *Troubleshooting,* that is, finding the problem, is something almost anyone can do if they (1) know the block diagram of their system, (2) understand what each component in the system is supposed to do, and (3) know where to look for common trouble spots.

26.10.1 Know the Block Diagram

A sound system *block diagram* explains how the various components in the system are connected to each other and what happens to a signal as it flows through the system. Because the block diagram shows the way the sound system operates, it is extremely useful in the troubleshooting process.

As obvious as it may sound, it's not possible to tell whether a component is working properly or not unless its original function is well understood. Thus, it's a good idea to keep instruction manuals on all components handy. Some repairs are as simple as repositioning a control knob or throwing a switch that someone has inadvertently changed.

Cables and connectors are by far the most common sources of problems in audio systems. This is the best reason to keep lots of spares, especially of cables that are moved around a lot, like microphone cables.

Other common trouble spots are fuses and circuit breakers, as well as switches and controls that are in the wrong positions and problems with house ac power.

26.10.2 Logical Troubleshooting

The process of troubleshooting involves logical thought and methodical tracking down of a problem by elimination.

Logical thought processes come into play when a problem first occurs. If a single microphone goes suddenly dead, logic says that the power amplifier probably isn't at fault. If, on the other hand, an entire system is suddenly quiet, the power amplifier might be at fault, but it's not likely that all the microphones have failed at once.

A methodical elimination process can track down the source of most problems very quickly, as shown in Figs. 26-53 and 26-54. The idea is to find out what component (microphone, cable, mixer, amplifier, loudspeaker) is causing the problem and to replace or repair it. During a live performance, of course, replacing a faulty component is the most likely cure since a repair might take up too much time.

The system mixer is a good place to begin the troubleshooting process because it has the controls for the entire system. A noise in the system, for example, can be traced by looking at the VU meters or other indicators of the mixer. This alone, may indicate that the noise problem is coming from one microphone. Pull down the fader for that input channel. If the noise goes away, check out the microphone, or more likely, the microphone cable.

If the entire system suddenly goes dead, again, check out the VU meters and other indicators of the mixer. If they are still active, then the system is working at least through the mixer. Thus, some component further along in the system must be the culprit. Think through the block diagram at this point to find the next suspect component. (One component that's often a problem is the house ac power!)

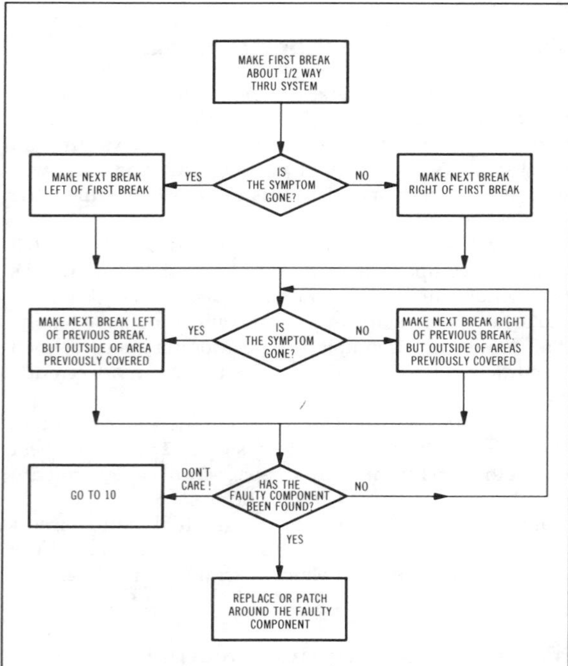

Figure 26-53 Troubleshooting part 1. Assumes that the problem is hum, noise, or oscillation and that block diagram flow is from left to right. Method is to break system (disconnect) at indicated points until faulty component is located.

When possible, patch around suspect components. For example, a limiter can be completely removed from the system, and the system will still operate. Thus, if a limiter is suspect, use a patch cable to bypass it. If the bypass operation causes the system to begin operating again, the limiter is at fault.

When the suspect component is necessary to the operation of the system, try to replace it with some other equivalent component. If a loudspeaker is suspect, for example, try switching it with a similar loudspeaker or even a stage monitor loudspeaker temporarily in place of a main system loudspeaker. If the mixer is suspect, try running a tape machine directly into the system power amplifier to make sure that portion of the system is still working.

26.11 PORTABLE SYSTEMS

Portable systems range from voice-only paging systems, as might be used at a local street fair, up to the giant systems used for outdoor rock music festivals. The design criteria for a portable system build on the criteria discussed for permanently installed systems, adding to and modifying the system to take into account such obvious considerations as travel and less obvious considerations as the potential for abuse by an inexperienced operator.

26.11.1 Packaging

The portable system must be rugged to survive travel. It must be packaged efficiently so that it will fit into as small a travel vehicle as possible and so that setup and teardown are quick and efficient. Efficient packaging leads to lower ownership and operating costs from the ability to use smaller (or fewer large) vehicles and from the requirement of fewer hours for setup and teardown.

Yet, packaging must not get in the way of system performance. For example, in larger portable systems, separate loudspeaker components (separate, subwoofer, low-frequency, mid-frequency, and high-frequency loudspeakers) with several varieties of coverage patterns, will provide the kind of versatility needed to cover a multitude of different audience layouts. Yet, a loudspeaker system made up of same-size enclosures, each with low-, mid-, and high-frequency components, will set up and tear down more easily and will often fit in a smaller travel vehicle. The trouble with the separate component system is lack of travel and setup and teardown efficiency; the trouble with the system made up of same-size enclosures is lack of performance flexibility.

A reasonable compromise may be to package loudspeaker components separately but in same-size or com-

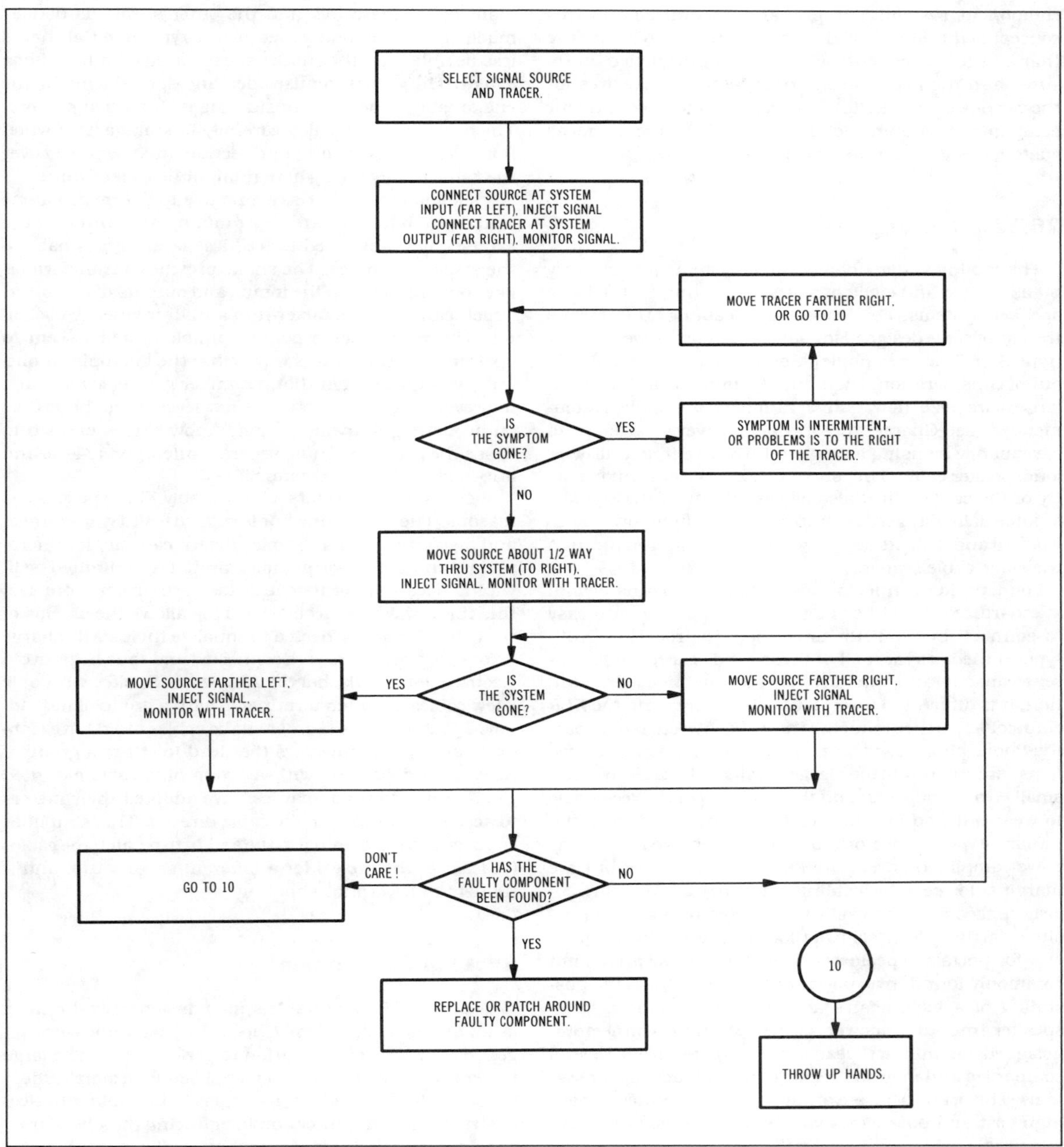

Figure 26-54 Troubleshooting part 2. Assumes that the problem is distortion or interruption of signal and the block diagram flow is from left to right. Method is use of signal generator and tracer (a tape deck and powered loudspeaker may suffice) to locate the faulty component.

patibly sized enclosures. That is, the mid- and high-frequency components may be housed in an enclosure that is exactly one-half the size of the low-frequency enclosure. Wide-angle horns may be housed in an enclosure that is the full width of the low-frequency enclosure. This modular packaging scheme allows most of the travel and setup advantages of the all-in-one systems while maintaining the performance flexibility of a separate component system. The primary disadvantage to this concept is the additional design time needed to make sure that all the components will fit in their assigned enclosures and the need to construct custom enclosures for the various components. Some larger concert sound tour companies have even had mid- and high-frequency horns custom designed for systems like this.

26.11.2 Cabling

The cabling system for a portable system must be every bit as rugged and efficient as the packaging for the loudspeaker systems. For loudspeaker cabling, this means the use of cable designed for outdoor electric power cabling (type S or SR, for example). Solid-core wire is absolutely out of consideration. High-quality, multistrand wire of a large wire size (low gauge number) is highly recommended (see Chapter 12). Do not, however, attempt to save money by using a single return wire in a multiwire loudspeaker cable. This not only taxes the current capacity of the cable, but it also allows mixing of the signals, a potentially dangerous problem when high-power subwoofers and delicate super-tweeters are powered through the same cable system.

Loudspeaker connectors, which are unfortunately not standardized, must be rugged, high capacity, and easy to connect (but difficult to connect improperly!). XLR-type connectors meet all of these needs except high-current capacity and thus are not recommended. In addition, it is difficult to insert large-sized wires into the XLR connector, further reducing their effective current capacity. Phone plugs, used on small portable loudspeaker systems, are unsuitable for larger systems because of their small current capacity and the tendency of the receptacle to wear out and lose its ability to connect to the plug. Banana-type connectors, as used on the rear of many power amplifiers, are quite useful inside a rack but are marginal for portable cabling since they are not particularly rugged and can easily be inserted backward (opposite polarity). Electrical twist-lock connectors work quite well for portable speaker cabling, but choose a type not commonly found in ac power usage to eliminate the possibility of a technician's accidentally plugging a loudspeaker into an ac power source! Multipin connectors, designed for military usage, are available from several companies and may be very suitable for loudspeaker systems. The primary disadvantages of these connectors are high cost and poor local availability (carry spares when traveling).

Microphone and line-level signals require equally rugged cable with the addition of a high-quality shield. Wire must be stranded, and the shield should be a tight braid of stranded wire. Foil shields will crack and break from the continuous flexing of portable use. Microphone cables should have a rubber-type outer sheath for flexibility. One exception to this rule is the snake cable, a group of individually shielded, twisted-pair cables in one outer sheath. The shields in a snake cable are foil to reduce the overall diameter of the cable, and the outer sheath is usually made of vinyl or some other plastic-type material that is less flexible than the rubber sheath used on microphone cables. These compromises demand special care for the snake cable, especially considering its high cost per foot. The cable must be coiled carefully in storage, and when it is in use, a mat or other protection must be placed over the cable in any area where it might be walked on.

It's a common, but risky, practice to run microphone signals from a stage area to a mixing area through the same snake cable used to feed line-level signals back to the stage electronics. The snake provides a transformer-like coupling between the inputs and outputs of the mixer, which can turn the mixer into a high-frequency oscillator. The reason some popular music systems seem to operate successfully this way is that the microphone output levels are so high that the mixer gain is low enough to prevent the oscillation. One low-level microphone (like an acoustic guitar microphone), however, is enough to cause the problem. Thus, separate microphone-level and line-level snakes are recommended.

Microphone connectors are invariably XLR type for good reasons. The XLR connector is rugged yet easy to connect and disconnect. It has ample current capacity for microphone and line-level signals, and it has limited self-wiping (cleaning) of its contacts. Furthermore, pin 1 of the XLR always connects first. This allows the shields of the cables being connected to equalize their static charge before the signal wires are connected and thus helps avoid electrical (static discharge) transients. Snakes with only a few cables are often terminated with a group of individual XLR connectors. Larger snake cables often have elaborate multipin connectors that lead to either a group of XLRs or a metal box with a group of chassis-mounted XLRs. Some tour companies have adapted their mixers to accept a multipin snake cable directly. This simplifies connections but eliminates the ability to repatch the cables (at least at the mixer) for a different stage setup, and it hinders quick troubleshooting.

26.11.3 Electronics

Electronics for a portable system is generally the same as for an installed system. Choose the electronics for ruggedness, however, in addition to performance. The large power transformer on a power amplifier, for example, must be securely fastened to its chassis to avoid physical destruction of the power amplifier during the jolts of traveling over rough roads.

Most portable equipment will be rack mounted. Thus, the equipment must be designed to survive the jolts of travel when mounted in a rack. Experienced tour companies often support the rear of large rack-mounted components to help prevent damage. The racks themselves, of course, must be rugged and travel well, and small racks can mean heat buildup so that extra cooling fans should be considered.

Some manufacturers offer electronic packages specifically designed for traveling. The *powered mixer* is a good example. Some of these include a full-function mixing console, internal effects (usually reverberation), one or more graphic equalizers, compressor/limiters, and one to four power amplifiers. For a small- to medium-sized portable system, these powered mixers are often the only electronics needed.

Mixers and other nonrack-mounted equipment must be carried in padded road cases. Similar cases can be used for microphones, cabling, and system accessories.

26.11.4 Loudspeaker Systems and Setup

Using any of the loudspeaker component types discussed in section 26.3, there are two basic types of portable loudspeaker system: *stacked*, including single, floor-standing systems, and *hung*.

Stacked systems are the most common, consisting of groups of individual components (or multicomponent enclosures) stacked on top of each other and arrayed in a way to cover an audience. In most cases, there will be at least two stacked systems, one on each side of the stage, where the stage can be any area where someone talks or an entertainment group performs. Although a single stack located in the center of a stage area might cover an audience better with fewer phasing problems, the dual stack avoids the obvious problem of sight-line blockage. The dual stack also allows at least some stereo mixing techniques, and it surrounds the performers with sound, which can enhance stage monitoring.

To work well, stacked systems should include short-, medium-, and long-throw type components and some method of arraying them to cover balconies and rear seating areas as well as front areas. A system with only one type of component (short throw, for example) will be severely limited in its capability to cover varying audience seating areas adequately. The result is a pair of tear-drop-shaped areas in front of each loudspeaker stack where the coverage is good. Between the stacks in front seating areas, stage sounds (amplified instruments, and so on) dominate, and reinforced sounds, like the all-important vocals, suffer. Farther away from the system, room reverberation muddies the sound, and vocals and instrumentals lose clarity and intelligibility. Using a component system built in well-designed modules can help prevent these problems while maintaining excellent portability.

Hanging offers the advantages of a better position for covering an audience seating area and fewer blocked seats. A hanging system (also known as a flown system) may be made of similar components as the stacked system, as shown in Fig. 26-55. The difference is in the hardware

Figure 26-55 A large portable hanging loudspeaker system using component loudspeakers. *(Courtesy Stanal Sound)*

needed for hanging. Hardware should allow flexibility in aiming the components while maintaining a maximum safety factor. Grids from which systems are hung must be designed to hold the maximum possible number of components in a flexible configuration. In addition, grids must be able to be hung from any type of ceiling that may be encountered.

26.11.5 Multichannel Loudspeaker Systems

The primary problem with a multichannel portable loudspeaker system is that, ideally, each member of the audience should be able to hear all of the individual channels. That means, ideally, each loudspeaker channel must cover the entire audience. The large system required to make this happen prevents true stereo sound in most portable systems. Stereo-type effects, however, can be achieved with a traditional dual-stack system, and side and rear loudspeaker systems can be successfully used for fill and, again, for special effects.

26.11.6 Safety in Portable Systems

A portable hanging loudspeaker system is especially dangerous because of the requirement of quick setup and teardown. Even when the system has been designed by a qualified, licensed mechanical engineer (a highly recommended procedure), it's all too easy to neglect people factors. What if the rigger (the person who anchors the grids to the building ceiling) mishangs a single cable? What if one worn cable breaks? What if a local building engineer is unaware of a ceiling inadequacy? One answer is to double-check everything carefully. Another answer is redundancy. If two cables will hold the system, use two cables and two or more safety cables. Don't hang an entire grid of loudspeakers from a single building structural member. Check all hardware, cables, and winches, and then ask someone else to check them again.

Stacked systems, of course, can be dangerous, too. Not only is there the possibility of vibrating loudspeakers slipping out of place in a stack and falling, there is also the possibility of eager audience members climbing the stacks for a better view! Secure the stacks carefully and keep the audience away. In addition, confirm that the support structure is more than adequate to handle the load.

Electrical safety in portable systems is complicated by the uncertain condition of the ac power system of each building. One excellent way to bypass this problem simply is to carry a portable ac power distribution system, which should be designed and constructed by a qualified, licensed electrician. Consult with each building superintendent to determine the best way to connect this portable system to the house ac power. Often, the portable ac system can be connected directly to the building ac service entrance (a local qualified licensed electrician should perform this connection). This not only bypasses any potential safety problems in the house ac system but also provides a (relatively) clean ac power system for the noise-sensitive sound system electronics.

High-L_P hazards are often overlooked but are, nonetheless, dangerous. It is a well-established fact that high L_P, over an extended period of time, can cause permanent hearing damage. Hearing protection is a must, especially when performing high-L_P equalization or other testing or when checking out individual loudspeakers before or during a performance. It is possible to wear concealed ear plugs (the expanding foam type are most comfortable and very effective) during a concert performance, even if you are mixing the performance. The human brain adjusts the hearing mechanism to the point where things begin to sound right again after a short period of wearing hearing protection. The situation is similar to wearing sunglasses. After a period, colors begin to look right again. This type of hearing protection is important especially for the extremely high L_P encountered during stage monitor mixing. When in doubt about whether or not you need hearing protection, listen to the ringing in your ears after a performance. This ringing, known as *tinnitus*, is our body's way of telling us that the sound level is too high. Prolonged exposure to these levels, of course, will almost certainly lead to permanent hearing loss.

26.11.7 Performance Criteria

Any system for popular entertainment must be designed to accept and reinforce an L_P of 100 to 120 dB. These levels represent amplifier power output and loudspeaker power handling in the neighborhood of 1000 times that of a loud speech-only system! Microphone input levels are such that electrical output from a high-sensitivity microphone may be as high as 0 dB (0.775 V) on peaks. Thus, mixers must have high-input capabilities and lots of headroom.

Ideally, system headroom should be as high as 20 dB, although, economically, this may be unobtainable. Extensive use of compressor/limiters can make a 10-dB headroom system sound almost as good as one with 20 dB of headroom (and the loudspeaker and power amplifier costs are as much as 90% lower!).

The frequency response of a system designed for popular music must extend as low as 40 Hz and as high as 12 to 16 kHz. One way to approach the design of a system like this is to design a vocal system with response from about 80 Hz to about 8 kHz and add supertweeters and subwoofers for the very low and very high frequencies. The subwoofers and supertweeters can be considered special effects for this type of system.

26.11.8 Midrange in an Entertainment System

The idea of designing a vocal system to perform from about 80 to 8000 Hz and adding supertweeters and subwoofers is a good one, provided the vocal system has adequate midrange capacity. Traditional two-way vocal systems are often very deficient in performance in the region from about 200 to 350 Hz to about 2000 to 3000 Hz. The problem is that the low-frequency loudspeakers used in these systems were designed to perform down to 40 Hz or below while the high-frequency (horn/driver) loudspeakers were designed to perform as high as 16 kHz and above. The effect of these designs for low- and high-frequency performance has been to degrade midrange performance. As an example, most 15-in. woofers begin to drop off in performance above 200 to 300 Hz. Their on-axis frequency response will hold much higher because of beaming effects, but the actual acoustic power output versus frequency will nose dive above 350 Hz or so. In addition, most high-frequency drivers suffer from significantly reduced power capacity when used below an 800-Hz (or possibly 500-Hz) crossover frequency. Thus, there is a gap in the critical midrange frequencies from 300 to at least 800 Hz. In two-way speech systems, this gap results in the double-humped frequency-response curve seen on the real-time analyzer during equalization.

For low-level systems, equalization is a satisfactory cure. For high-level systems, an additional midrange component may be needed. Alternately, a woofer capable of performance to 800 Hz or above may be used. One common solution for entertainment-oriented systems is the use of a 12-in. mid-bass loudspeaker to supplement the 300- to 800-Hz gap. The mid-bass loudspeaker is often used between about 200 and about 1200 Hz. A dedicated midrange driver, such as is offered by Community Light and Sound, Inc., and by Renkus Heinz, may be an even better solution, since these are designed specifically to solve the midrange problem.

26.11.9 Monitor Systems

Stage monitors are as important as the house loudspeakers for a popular entertainment system for the simple reason that they aid the entertainers and thus help encourage a better performance.

Stage monitor loudspeakers must be unobtrusive yet high performance. One way to accomplish this is to keep the low frequencies out of the stage-monitoring system so that enclosure size can be minimized. Another way is to place full-range stage monitors on the sides of the stage and limited-range monitors at the performer locations.

Whenever possible, treat the stage monitor system as a completely separate system. Split microphone lines on stage, and send one signal to the house mixer and another to a separate monitor mixer. Use a splitter transformer if possible so that grounding isolation can be maintained. Mix, equalize, and power the monitors separately, with the monitor mixer somewhere in the vicinity of the performers, perhaps at one side of the stage so that the operator can hear the results of mixing actions.

Multiple outputs are needed and useful on a monitor mixing system, since each performer may want his or her own mix. For this reason, several manufacturers offer mixers specially designed for the task of monitor mixing.

Equalization of a monitor mixing system is primarily for the purpose of avoiding feedback. Thus, multiband parametric and notch-type filters may be superior to the more common graphic equalizers.

26.11.10 The Entertainment System as a Musical Instrument

Consider that many of the individual instruments used in modern music cannot exist apart from their electronics and loudspeakers. Add a sound system with multiple loudspeakers and, most likely, multiple phasing problems. Close mic the vocals to pick up breath noises not heard in normal conversation. Choose a microphone with lots of proximity effect so that performers can change the quality of their voices by the way they hold the mic. Close mic even the acoustic musical instruments so that feedback can be avoided but so that normal acoustic mixing of the complex acoustic sources in a musical instrument is eliminated. Mix the signals in a way that has little in common with the acoustic mixing that comes from the geographic layout of an orchestra. Add artificial equalization, reverberation, recorded segments, purposeful harmonic distortion, and other special effects. The result, when the sound system operator is as good an artist as the stage performers, is popular music! And, again, that popular music could not exist without the electronics, including the sound system. Finally, more and more, the sound system used in popular entertainment systems bears little resemblance to and cannot rightfully be called a "sound-reinforcement system." It certainly reinforces, but it also enhances, and, to a very great extent, it creates. Thus, there is ample justification for considering the popular entertainment system to be a musical instrument in its own right.

The significance of this, for traditional sound system designers, is that many of the rules of good sound system design can, in fact, must, be modified for the design of a popular entertainment system. Perhaps more significant, a very well-designed and operated popular entertainment system can be extremely effective in performing its design goal, that of helping a group of artists to entertain an audience. A nontechnical member of that audience may believe that the particular type of sound system would be the answer to some sound-reinforcement problem at a local facility. Technical and nontechnical people, then, should understand that the popular entertainment system is, in actuality, a musical instrument, designed for modern popular music, and only for that purpose.

Place the same system in another facility and use it for reinforcement of speech or classical music, and it may be entirely unsuitable.

26.12 SOUND SYSTEMS FOR RELIGIOUS FACILITIES

The primary challenges in designing a sound system for a religious facility are the user interface (many users will be totally unfamiliar with sound system operation), the esthetic design (most religious facilities will want the loudspeakers hidden), and the acoustic environment (many religious facilities are, like the typical "cathedral," highly reverberant).

26.12.1 User Interface

Many users in a religious facility are nontechnical and unfamiliar with sound system operation outside of, perhaps, a home hi-fi system. There are two exceptions: the facility lucky enough to have a trained (usually volunteer) operator and those facilities that have services made up of popular religious music, dramatic presentations, and so on, and make full use of the capabilities of an entertainment-type sound system.

These exceptions should receive a system designed with a trained operator in mind.

26.12.2 Systems for Inexperienced Operators

It's a good idea to place all seldomly used controls and adjustments (including the system equalizer behind the locked door of an equipment rack. Minimize the number of controls seen by the user and minimize the complexity of their function. A typical set of controls might consist of a simple mixer with one set of treble and bass controls and a master volume control. An automatic mixer can be extremely useful since it takes over most of the caretaker functions of mixing. A system with an automatic mixer may need only one user adjustment: the on-off switch.

A compressor/limiter and a feedback detector/gain-reduction device (like that now marketed by Altec Lansing Corp.) would be valuable additions to such a system.

In any such system, provide needed and useful user interfaces such as a cassette player-recorder or phonograph and a volume control for each. It may be possible to integrate these into the automatic mixer so that volume controls on the external devices are all that are needed.

Also keep in mind the possibility that an experienced operator may volunteer in which case the facility may wish to upgrade to a more complex user interface, probably in the form of a mixing console.

26.12.3 System Esthetics

Many religious organizations have large, architecturally beautiful facilities. In general, they do not wish to alter the architectural lines (which may have religious significance) by adding large loudspeakers. In particular, the central cluster type of loudspeaker system almost always ends up in an esthetically undesirable location.

Religious organizations and their architects should be encouraged to design new buildings with a sound system in mind and to ask a qualified sound system consultant to join in the process in the early planning stage. Systems for existing facilities, however, must contend with existing architecture and sight lines.

Occasionally, a cluster can be enclosed in a framework covered with grille cloth chosen to match the room decor. In those facilities with an attic space above the auditorium it may be possible to hide the system behind a large (new) opening in the ceiling, again, covered with grille cloth. Enclose the cluster above the ceiling, too, to prevent the loss of valuable heat through the hole in the ceiling.

A split cluster may solve the problem in some rooms. Remember that a smaller second cluster (the right cluster, for example), designed to cover only those areas that cannot be adequately covered by the first (left), can help avoid the classical split-cluster problem of phase cancellations.

A small central cluster may be acceptable in some cases, augmented by a second cluster on time delay, further toward the rear of the room.

Distributed systems, including column loudspeakers on building pillars and the so-called pew-back approach, may also be acceptable solutions, although these systems are normally more costly than a simple central cluster.

One oft-suggested approach, placing the loudspeakers in an organ chamber, far to the rear of the system microphones and behind a wooden grille, is almost always unworkable. The position of the loudspeakers aims them directly at the system microphones, which usually results in feedback problems. In addition, the wood grille work, which may be fine for organ music, can cause severe acoustic problems (both from cancellations and from vibrations) in the sound system loudspeakers.

26.12.4 Reverberant Room Problem

It is said that the types of chanting services employed by some denominations developed in large reverberant cathedrals before sound systems were invented. Chanting helped carry an intelligible message to the congregation.

All too many religious organizations still have the problem of reverberation, yet many have given up the chanting type of service and now want intelligible speech in their facilities.

The problem of intelligible speech in a reverberant religious facility is no different than in any other reverberant room, except, perhaps, for the desire to hide the loudspeakers. One other consideration, however, is that pipe organs and much religious choir music depend on high levels of reverberation, a criteria that conflicts with the desire for lower reverberation times for speech. Because even a good compromise may be expensive, the services of a qualified consultant are invaluable when this situation arises.

26.13 SPORTS STADIUMS AND OTHER OUTDOOR SYSTEMS

The discussion of outdoor system design presented in section 26.1 was limited to very basic, theoretical considerations only. The following discussions include many of the practical aspects of the design of an outdoor system (Fig. 26-56).

26.13.1 Excess Attenuation of High Frequencies in Air

The friction of air molecules rubbing against each other causes attenuation of sound that adds to the loss caused by the inverse-square law. This frictional loss is normally insignificant in indoor systems (except in very large rooms) but can become a problem in large outdoor systems because of the long distances involved. The problem is considerably worse at the high frequencies, which are important for speech intelligibility, because of the simple fact that the molecules of air are moving faster than at low frequencies. The problem also increases at lower relative humidity, as shown in Fig. 26-57.

The problem shows up in outdoor systems with long distances between loudspeakers and listeners. It often cannot be solved with simple equalization or even by adding additional high-frequency horns. The reason is that the attenuation may be 10 to 20 dB or even more, depending on frequency, distance, and relative humidity.

One potential solution is to add additional high-frequency horns at a position nearer to the listeners and, of course, to place these horns on delay. Since the attenuation of low-frequency information is much less, it is normally unnecessary to add additional low-frequency loudspeakers just to overcome the loss caused by friction in the air.

In many speech-only systems, the loss is simply tolerated. Intelligible, if somewhat telephone quality speech, does not require frequencies much above about 3000 Hz. Except in extreme situations, adding a few extra high-frequency horns and performing some additional equalization will result in an acceptable system. Obviously, the additional equalization should be performed on the long-throw horns only since the distance from the short-throw horns to their listeners will be considerably less than for the long-throw horns.

Figure 26-56 A large outdoor loudspeaker cluster used as a single cluster in a sports stadium. *(Courtesy Altec Lansing Corp.)*

26.13.2 Using Distributed Systems Outdoors

Overcoming excess attenuation of high frequencies is not the only reason to consider a distributed type of system outdoors. The most obvious location for a central cluster in a multilevel stadium, for example, may not be able to cover under-balcony areas. Distributed horns,

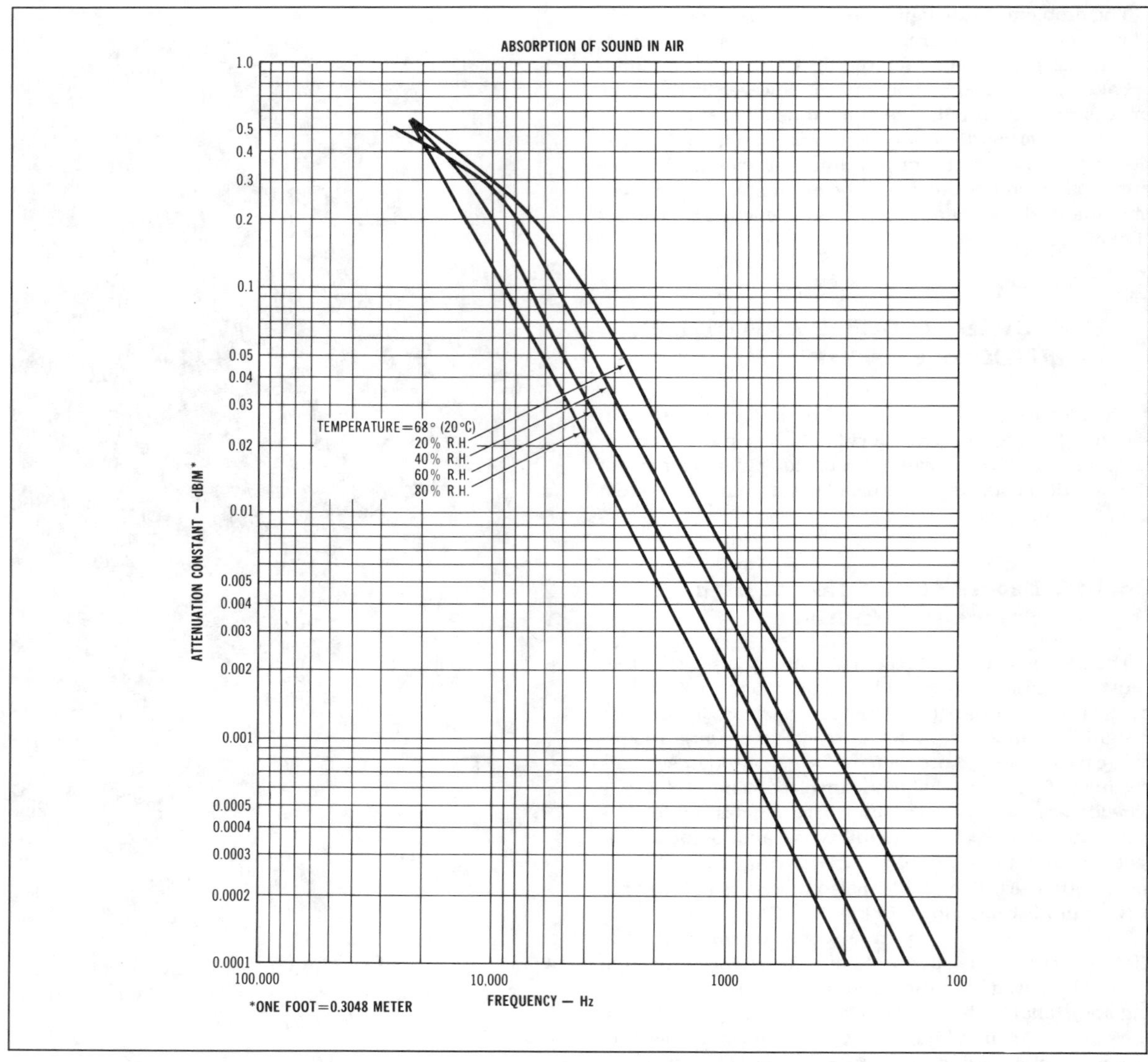

Figure 26-57 Absorption of high frequencies in air. *(Courtesy Altec Lansing Corp.)*

placed on the underside of the balcony, on delay, can solve this problem and still allow the use of the central cluster as a primary sound-reinforcement source.

In some stadiums, there is no desirable location for a central cluster. A round or oval stadium with full round seating is one example. The usual scoreboard location will often be awkward for coverage of nearby seating. Sometimes existing lighting blocks the only workable cluster location. In these or other similar situations, a distributed cluster type of system may be the solution. The clusters can be placed under balconies (under one seating section to cover the one below) or on lighting poles. It is acceptable to place loudspeakers behind the heads of the spectators if this location does not cause signal delay or other problems.

The distributed approach may also work well in small outdoor systems such as a high-school football field system. When the audience sits in one or two relatively small sets of bleachers on either side of the field, it is often easier to place horns on existing lighting poles near the bleachers than to build a large central cluster at one end of the field.

In any distributed system, consider sight lines and watch out for potential artificial echoes.

26.13.3 Echoes Outdoors, Artificial and Otherwise

Normally, echoes are created by sound from a source, such as a loudspeaker cluster, reflecting off a hard surface and reaching a listener at a time that is delayed enough to be perceived as an echo. About the only way to deal with these echoes, outside of treating (or removing) the reflecting surface, is to simply aim the loudspeakers away from the offending surface. Narrow-coverage-angle loudspeakers and constant-directivity horns may help.

Echoes may also be created by the sound system because of poor layout or because of poor use or nonuse of electronic signal delay. See section 26.5.1.1 and Chapter 18 for a discussion of electronic delay. Fig. 26-58 shows one example of an artificial echo caused by poor loudspeaker layout.

One other source of artificial echoes, poorly understood by many designers, is related to feedback. Any sound from the loudspeakers that reaches the system microphone may be delayed by relatively long times in an outdoor system. This sound can be picked up by the microphone, reamplified, and emitted from the loudspeakers as an echo that cannot be distinguished from an echo created by a reflecting surface.

There are several ways to help solve this problem. One is to enclose the talker and microphone in a relatively soundproof room. In large outdoor stadiums, this is often the easiest way to avoid the regeneration type of echo. Another potential solution is to use a noise-canceling microphone located close to the talker's mouth. Close talking any system microphone will help, of course, because it allows reduction of system gain and an equal reduction of the reamplification of an echo. A *noise gate* set to turn off the microphone quickly after the talker stops talking may also help prevent regeneration echoes. This technique, however, will work well only in a situation where the microphone is relatively close to the talker's mouth.

The announcer on the field hears an echo that no one else in the stadium hears! That's because announcers first hear their own voice and then, delayed sometimes by as much as a half second or more, they hear their voice as an echo from the loudspeakers. This can be very confusing to an inexperienced announcer and may be the cause of the failure of many prepared speeches given to graduating classes in a football-field setting!

For the small football field with split bleachers, the distributed system concept may help since the sound is primarily aimed at the bleachers and not at the field. Even if there are some horns aimed at the field, they will normally be closer to the field than the horns on a typical scoreboard cluster. Thus, the signal delay and echo problem will be decreased.

Another partial solution to this problem is to give the announcer a local monitor loudspeaker (or headphones in an announce booth). The sound from this monitor will partially mask the echo from the cluster and may allow even an inexperienced talker to speak comfortably.

26.13.4 Dealing with Long Distances

The throws in an outdoor system may be considerable. High-efficiency, high-power handling and narrow-coverage, constant-directivity horns are the tools to be used

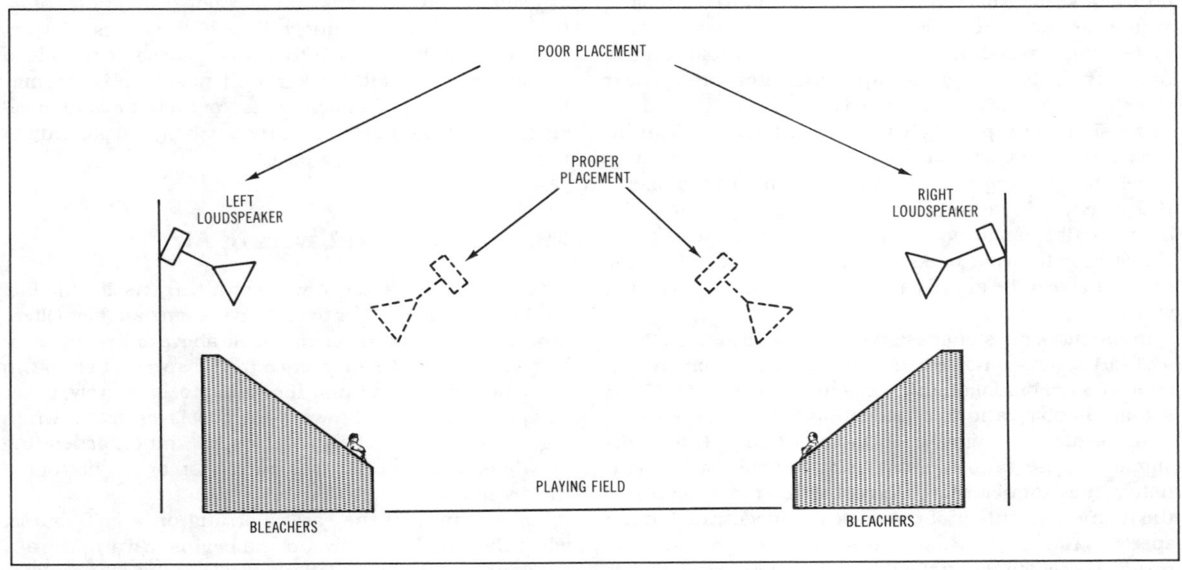

Figure 26-58 An artificial echo caused by poor layout of loudspeakers.

when a single cluster is all that is available. Many times, a long-throw situation can be covered by simply adding more high-frequency horns (and low-frequency loudspeakers if the system requires low-frequency reinforcement). Stacking high-frequency horns vertically may help because this effectively narrows the vertical coverage pattern and thus concentrates the available sound energy more efficiently onto the audience. Stacking low-frequency loudspeakers helps too, for the same reason. In addition, especially with low-frequency loudspeakers, stacking (in both vertical and horizontal directions) creates a larger effective baffle area for the loudspeakers, which can improve their performance at lower frequencies. See Chapter 14 for a more detailed discussion of this phenomenon.

In many situations, giant stacks of high-power devices still cannot provide sufficient L_P at the farthest listener's position. This is especially common when high-frequency reinforcement is required as for an outdoor music-reinforcement system. Another problem with the brute force approach is that listeners seated near the cluster may hear sound that is far too loud, even though the cluster was designed to aim the long-throw energy away from the nearby listeners. In any of these situations, remote loudspeaker clusters, on electronic delay, may be the only workable solution.

26.13.5 High Noise Outdoors (or Indoors)

How much L_P is required at the listener's position? The answer depends almost entirely on the expected ambient noise at the listener's location. Crowd noise in a sports stadium, for example, can easily exceed 90- to 95-dB L_P on the A scale. Noise from aircraft in an airport paging system or noise from race cars in a race-track paging system may exceed this figure by a considerable margin. At a grand prix race, for example, spectators seated near the race track may be subjected to potentially ear-damaging short-term peak L_P levels of as high as 140 dB! In the case of the sports stadium, it may be possible to overcome the crowd noise (budget permitting). In the case of the race track, a software approach is probably the only possible solution. That approach is to ask the announcer to avoid making announcements when the race cars pass the stands and to repeat announcements whenever possible.

In the indoor system design equations in section 26.2, a 25-dB signal-to-noise ratio was assumed. For an outdoor classical-music-reinforcement system, this 25-dB signal-to-noise ratio is still desirable. In many speech-reinforcement systems, both indoors and out, a 25-dB signal-to-noise ratio is simply not possible, and fortunately, it is not necessary. Except in the rare case where the frequency content of the noise is concentrated in the speech band, a 10-dB, signal-to-noise ratio will usually result in acceptably intelligible speech reinforcement. It is possible to achieve intelligible speech reinforcement with a signal-to-noise ratio of lower than 10 dB but it is difficult to predict the success of such a system prior to its installation. When this type of system is contemplated, use a compressor to keep the voice level as consistent as possible. Use a good-quality microphone with a bandpass filter to reduce unneeded low and high frequencies and to avoid the use of a telephone handset as a paging microphone.

Training the announcer in speech articulation will help, as will repeating announcements. In a plant or airport paging system with high noise levels, alerting the listener to an impending announcement by using a pre-page tone can also help improve the effective intelligibility of a paged announcement.

26.13.6 Dealing with Varying Noise Levels

A manufacturing plant may have noise levels that vary widely with time and at different local areas within the building. Dealing with noise that varies in different areas is as simple as varying the quantity, type, and electrical power for the loudspeakers in the different areas. For noise levels that vary with time, there are two primary tools. If the noise varies predictably with time, as for an assembly line that is running or stopped on a predictable schedule, devices are available that vary the audio power fed to a loudspeaker line (usually by varying the input level to a power amplifier) depending on the time of day. Some of these devices will vary several different loudspeaker lines at several different times.

For noise levels that vary unpredictably with time, such as the crowd noise at a sports stadium or the noise of an airplane entering a waiting area at an airport, devices are available to measure the ambient noise level and adjust the paging level accordingly (Fig. 26-59). These devices work quite well, although they may have some trouble in a system that includes background music (the music may be interpreted as ambient noise or may prevent measurement of the noise), and they usually cannot adjust the paging level during a page.

26.13.7 Thermal Layers of Air

Sound travels faster in warmer air. By itself, this fact has little significance for the sound system designer. Often, however, a layer of warm air will lie above or below a layer of cool air, and the difference in the speed of sound in these two layers can cause the sound to, effectively, curve upward or downward toward the cool layer, as shown in Fig. 26-60. This can be a help or a hindrance, depending on whether the cool layer is on the top or the bottom of the warm layer.

For example, in the early morning on a golf course, when the sun first comes up and begins to warm the air, the earth maintains a relatively cool layer near the ground. Thus, a sound wave will curve toward the ground, effec-

(A) Altec 1605 C unit (Courtesy Altec Lansing Corp.)

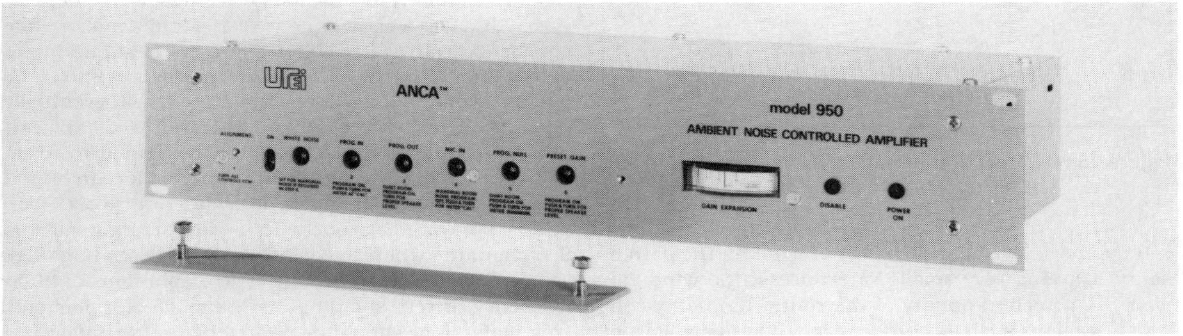

(B) UREI 950 unit (Courtesy JBL Inc./UREI)

Figure 26-59 Devices to increase or decrease sound system level with varying ambient noise.

tively hugging the ground, and can travel a great distance with seemingly little attenuation. Golfers at relatively great distances from each other can speak and be understood almost as if they were just a few feet apart. The same effect occurs over a quiet lake, even in the afternoon sun, since the lake will maintain a cool layer of air all day long. A wind, of course, will mix the layers of air and add noise so that the effect of thermal layers is lost.

In the early evening, when the sun begins to go down, the opposite situation occurs on a hot parking lot. The cool layer is now on top with a warm layer, maintained by the parking lot, on the bottom. The sound effectively curves upward toward the cool air and sound attenuation near the ground is effectively increased.

These phenomena can cause a paging system to work erratically, depending on the time of day! Large-area paging systems, over an airport runway, for example, are sometimes designed to overcome the changes caused by thermal layers. Elaborate systems can be designed to measure the temperature near the ground and above the ground and adjust the electrical input to each component of a vertical array of horns (or even mechanically re-aim the horns) to compensate for the effective curving upward or downward of the sound. In many smaller systems, however, the only necessary action is to test the system for satisfactory operation under worst-case conditions, which will probably be in the late afternoon on a hot day.

26.13.8 The Effect of Wind

A related problem is the effect of wind on sound propagation. This has two components. First, the wind can actually bend the path of the sound travel; second, the wind can cause additional ambient noise, which may vary unpredictably.

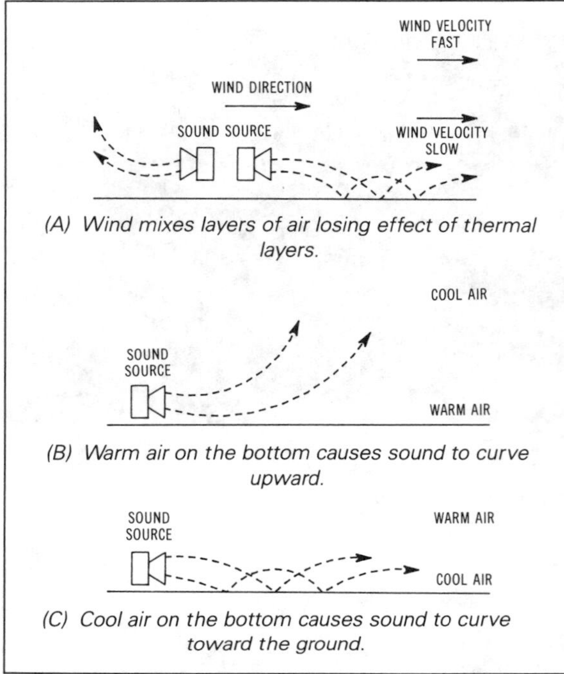

(A) Wind mixes layers of air losing effect of thermal layers.

(B) Warm air on the bottom causes sound to curve upward.

(C) Cool air on the bottom causes sound to curve toward the ground.

Figure 26-60 Effect of thermal air layers on sound travel. *(Courtesy Altec Lansing Corp.)*

It can be shown that the effect of wind on the path of sound travel is very small. Nevertheless, the wind can alter the perceived quality of the sound in quality-conscious systems such as outdoor concert systems. Part of the problem is that these outdoor concert systems usually have two stacks of loudspeakers on either side of the stage, and a cross-wind can cause very perceivable changes in phase-cancellations at a given listener's position. A sudden gust of wind can appear to carry away low-level passages in an outdoor concert system, partly due to the degraded signal-to-noise ratio caused by the wind gust.

While there are no permanent solutions to these problems, outdoor theater designers should be aware of them and should choose a site with as little wind as possible. Sound system designers may want to consider a single central cluster (with side and rear clusters for special effects if needed). Obviously, windscreens on microphones should be used.

26.13.9 Dealing with Weather-Caused Deterioration

The outdoor environment is considerably more hazardous to the life span of a sound system than an artificially lighted, temperature- and humidity-controlled indoor environment. Wind, rain, snow, ice, lightning, direct sun, widely varying temperature, salt air near the ocean, birds, squirrels, vandals, and pollution are just a few of the hazards faced by an outdoor sound system. Most of these hazards, of course, are felt by the loudspeaker system since the remainder of the sound system will usually be installed in a relatively safe indoor environment. Avoid placing system electronics, however, in a small room (equipment shack) that is exposed to direct sun and/or has poor ventilation, and protect or remove microphones, mixers, and so on that may be used in an exposed announcer's booth.

Use an effective lightning arrester above any system that might be exposed to lightning. Earth ground any metal gridwork and the metal chassis of loudspeakers to prevent static charge buildup, which can ultimately lead to arcing from loudspeaker frame to voice coil. Provide some type of static charge bleed to ground on any balanced, transformer-coupled loudspeaker line for the same reason.

Loudspeaker enclosures and metal horns should be coated with some type of weather-resistant finish such as epoxy paint or, for wooden enclosures, a coat of fiberglass. Although a black or gray color is traditional, a white or other reflective color will help prevent heat buildup in hot sunlight. Fiberglass horns and enclosures should be painted white since the fiberglass resin will eventually evaporate in hot, direct sunlight if allowed to absorb heat.

Paper cone loudspeakers should be treated to resist damage from high humidity (this is a good idea in humid indoor environments, such as swimming pools, too). Simply spraying the cone with a waterproofing such as Scotchguard® will help considerably and does not affect the performance significantly. The diaphragms of high-frequency drivers should either be made of a phenolic-type material or should be treated by the manufacturer to resist damage from humidity (most are). These treatments will also help prevent damage from pollution.

To protect against actual rain, install loudspeakers and horns pointing slightly downward if at all possible. If a horn must be pointed upward, use a curved adapter throat (available from the manufacturer) to point the driver downward. The adapter throat should have a weep hole in the bottom of the curve to allow water to drain out.

It's a good idea to install one or two layers of grille cloth over the opening of low-frequency enclosures to prevent driving rain from reaching the loudspeaker cone. Using a horn-loaded enclosure helps by recessing the loudspeaker cone. A layer of hardware cloth in addition to the grille cloth, can help prevent birds and squirrels from nesting in the enclosures and can help prevent damage from vandals throwing rocks, bottles, and so on. The hardware cloth can often be placed over the mouth of a horn, too.

Salt air can be extremely corrosive to metallic portions of loudspeakers, including metallic high-frequency driver diaphragms and metal horns. Use fiberglass or weather-resistant plastic horns, and coat low-frequency enclosures with epoxy paint or fiberglass. Consult with the manufacturer to choose low-frequency loudspeakers and high-frequency drivers that will resist damage from the salt air.

No matter how much care is taken in protecting outdoor loudspeaker systems, they will deteriorate faster than similar indoor systems. Thus, the system design should provide for easy access and repair.

26.14 CONFERENCE AND BOARDROOM SYSTEMS

A conference room sound system has special problems because of the large number of open microphones, their proximity to loudspeakers and the frequent added problems of ambient noise and uncooperative system users.

Some conference rooms are private; that is, they are designed exclusively for the use of the conferees. Other conference rooms include facilities for nonparticipating or infrequently participating observers, such as the stockholders, the press, or the public. Examples of the former are the conference rooms of privately held companies. Examples of the latter are the conference rooms of publicly held companies, unions, and other organizations. The sound systems installed in court rooms are similar to those in conference rooms that include observers.

The primary difference between the two types of systems is in the additional loudspeakers (and roving microphones) needed for the second type of system. Both systems, of course, often include audio recording and playback capabilities and may include video playback and recording, audio or audio and video conferencing capabilities and computer graphics display capabilities and so on.

26.14.1 Local Sound Reinforcement in a Conference Room

Conference room loudspeaker systems are normally laid out in a distributed fashion. One microphone for every participant or one for every two or three participants is the norm. To help avoid feedback from multiple open microphones and to help avoid pickup of paper shuffling and other ambient noises, an automatic mixer is commonly used. Often, the chair position is given an automatic priority switch so that when the person at the chair position speaks, all other microphones are turned off (this may also be accomplished by a manual priority switch).

Another way to help avoid feedback is to use the logic outputs on the back of many automatic mixers to switch off the loudspeaker directly above the head of the person talking. One manufacturer, LVW Electronics of Colorado Springs, Colorado, even offers a device that adjusts the power level to each loudspeaker so that, at a listener's position, the sum of the L_P from the loudspeaker with the L_P direct from the talker is the same at all listener positions regardless of distance from the talker. The device readjusts the level to each loudspeaker (via the logic output on the automatic mixer), depending on which microphone is currently active. This process keeps the level very constant at every listener regardless of who is talking and virtually eliminates feedback problems. It can, however, hinder the kind of back-and-forth conversation where more than one person talks at the same time and there are frequent interruptions. It should be noted that, in a conference room, this kind of conversation is difficult with any system.

Loudspeakers for inactive participants can be on all the time unless a roving microphone is being passed around. In this case, the level to the local loudspeakers may need to be reduced somewhat, and, of course, the feed from the roving microphone to the conference table should be fed to all loudspeakers at equal levels.

26.14.2 Recording a Conference

The multiple-microphone setup of a conference can be a problem for recording. All microphones can simply be mixed and fed to a single channel of a tape recorder, but the multiple microphones may add unwanted ambient noise. Using the output of the automatic mixer helps avoid this problem. A courtroom-style, multichannel, logging recorder may be used to record a number of individual microphones on separate channels. This is especially useful when a transcript of the conference must be made later. In some systems, the chair is given a switch to pause the recording for off-the-record conversations.

26.14.3 Audio Conferencing with a Remote Location

Systems that include remote audio conference capabilities include all the problems of local reinforcement (if needed) plus the problems of the interface with the remote location. Because audio conferencing is a complex subject, only a few details are covered here.

Most audio conferencing takes place over telephone lines or telephone lines in conjunction with microwave relays. More elaborate audio-plus-video conferences usually take place over a satellite linkup. Whichever method is used, the characteristics of the transmission path must be considered. For short-distance telephone lines, the only problems are the audio quality of the transmission and the need to convert the two-wire (transmit/receive) telephone line to a four-wire (separate transmit-from microphones and receive-to loudspeakers) local sound system.

This two- to four-wire conversion can be accomplished with a hybrid transformer (see Chapter 10). It is, however, possible for feedback to occur over a complex path including the telephone transmission line, the (imperfect) hybrid transformer, and the remote microphone and loudspeaker system. Even an automatic mixer may not help here since the remote automatic mixer will think that the sound comes from a person talking and may turn on the microphone. There are two solutions to this problem. One is to use close-microphoning techniques so that microphone channel sensitivity can be reduced and sound from the loudspeakers will not turn on the microphones. This technique is valuable in any conference system but is often impossible because users refuse to allow a microphone in front of their face. The other way to avoid feedback in this type of audio conferencing system is to simply turn off all the local loudspeakers when any local microphone is on, thus interrupting the feedback loop. The type of conference system that shuts off the loudspeaker directly above the talker may suffice in this case especially if the automatic mixer also shuts off all other local microphones.

A related problem occurs in satellite transmission. The path taken by the radio-frequency signal to the satellite and back to a remote earth station is somewhere in the neighborhood of 46,000 miles. The radio-frequency signal takes about ¼ s to traverse this distance and another ¼ s to return. Thus, the sound from a local microphone takes about ¼ s to travel to the remote loudspeaker, where it is picked up by the remote microphone, is retransmitted, and travels back to the local loudspeaker, taking another approximately ¼ s. The result is that a person talking at the local microphone hears his or her own voice about ½ s later as an echo! Elaborate echo-canceling devices are available to help avoid this problem while still allowing full-duplex (simultaneous two-way) transmission. One manufacturer, Shure Brothers, Inc., now offers a system that effectively solves the echo problem by using a sophisticated form of single-duplex (one-way at a time) operation that, because of its fast switching and interruptibility, allows conversations that appear to the user to be normal, two way.

26.15 NOISE-MASKING, SPEECH-PRIVACY SYSTEMS

The purpose of a noise-masking system is to do just that: use an unobtrusive artificial noise to mask other unwanted noises. That unwanted noise could be traffic noise that enters an office building. It could be the noise of typewriters, copiers, or other office equipment. That noise could also be speech if the speech were disruptive to others in an office environment. In addition, by helping mask these noises, including masking the noise of speech, a noise-masking system provides a measure of speech privacy from one office to another. That is, the noise-masking system helps prevent private conversations from being overheard in adjoining offices.

Noise-masking, speech-privacy systems are normally installed in open-plan office buildings but may be installed in any area where unwanted noise is a problem or where speech privacy needs to be insured.

26.15.1 Criteria for the Environment

A limited range of environments is suitable for noise masking. Details are discussed in Chapter 8, but in general the environment must be relatively quiet since the masking noise will need to be louder than the noise to be masked. A general criteria for ambient noise level is about NC-35 (noise criteria curve number 35) or about 45 dB on the A scale. The environment must have a low reverberation time and as few hard, reflecting surfaces as possible. A well-designed open-plan office will usually meet these criteria.

26.15.2 Mechanical Noise Reduction

Noise from typing pool areas, copying machines, and so on should be reduced by mechanical and acoustical means since the noise-masking system cannot be expected to overcome these relatively high-level sources. In addition, mechanical barriers in the form of the so-called acoustical dividers are normally installed between offices to help attenuate noises and speech from point to point. Nonreflective ceilings (preferably dropped acoustical tile) and carpeted floors are almost mandatory. Without these mechanical aids, the noise-masking system cannot perform its function successfully.

26.15.3 Masking Noise

Once higher-level noises have been reduced and an acceptable acoustical environment has been created, low-level noises become more irritating, and speech privacy becomes more important. Masking noise, created by a noise-masking, speech-privacy system, can help solve these problems. One overwhelming criteria for the masking system is that it be completely unnoticeable to the listeners. That is, no one should know there is a noise-masking system in operation unless someone turns it off. The reason for this, of course, is that the purpose of the system is to help reduce distracting noises and to aid speech privacy. If the system itself becomes a distraction, one of its primary purposes has been defeated!

The masking noise is created by an electronic random-noise generator similar to that used for equalization, and it is fed through an equalizer to a set of power amplifiers and loudspeakers. The loudspeakers are normally hidden in the ceiling plenum, above the acoustic tiles.

26.15.4 Criteria for the Loudspeaker System

To meet the primary goals of noise masking and speech privacy and to remain unnoticed by listeners, the loudspeaker system must produce random noise that does not change as a listener moves from place to place within the environment. A traditional downward-facing distributed system (Fig. 26-61B) could achieve this goal, but only with an extremely high density of loudspeakers. Thus, an upward or sideways facing system is more common (see Figs. 26-61A and C). The upward and sideways systems use mechanical structure in the ceiling plenum to reflect and help randomize the noise distribution. In a typical open-plan office with a ceiling height of 8 to 9 ft, the loudspeakers would be spaced in a square or hexagonal pattern (see section 26.5) with approximately 10- to 20-ft spacing between individual loudspeakers. Care must be taken to avoid placing a loudspeaker too near a hard reflecting object, such as an airduct, which might cause a hot spot in the room below. Various ceiling materials and baffles are available to help diffuse the masking noise, and several manufacturers produce special loudspeaker-enclosure combinations designed specifically for noise masking to allow the upward or sideways facing orientation (Fig. 26-62).

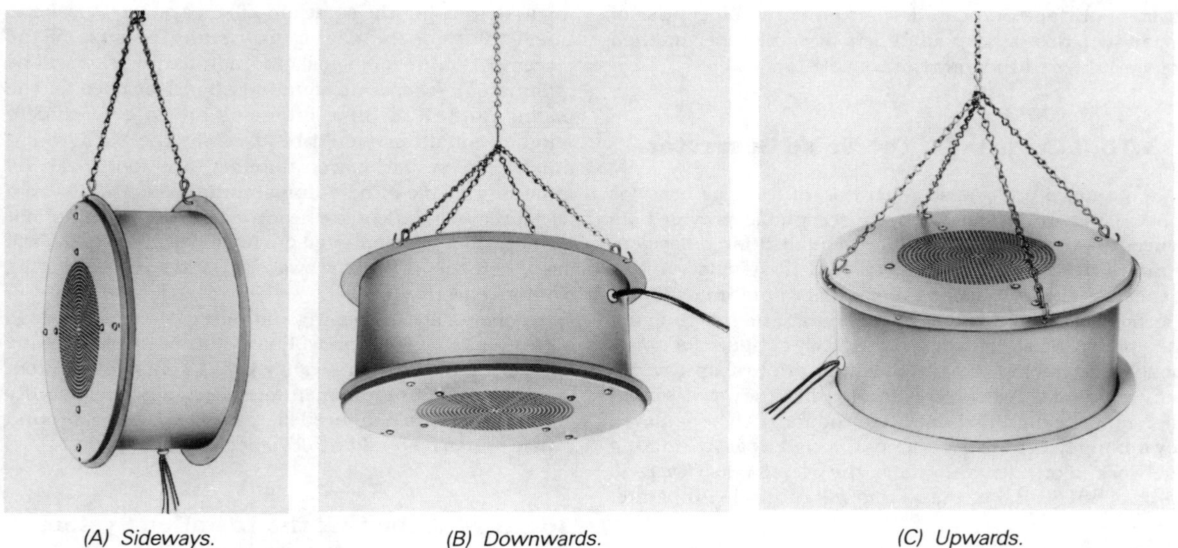

(A) Sideways. *(B) Downwards.* *(C) Upwards.*

Figure 26-61 Noise masking loudspeaker shown in three hanging orientations. *(Courtesy Soundolier Inc.)*

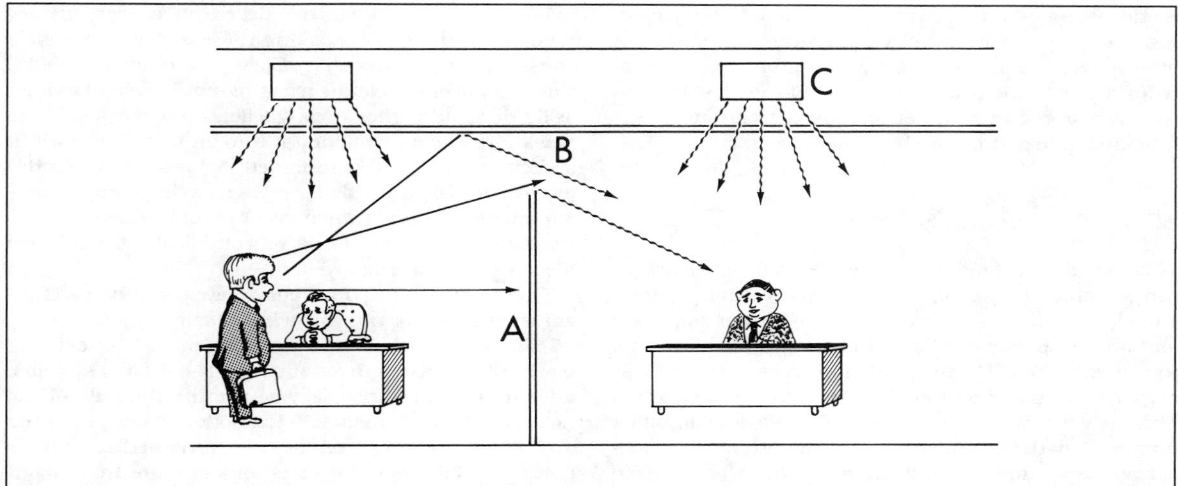

Figure 26-62 Factors affecting speech privacy. *(Courtesy Soundolier Inc.)*

26.15.5 Criteria for the Amplification System

Power amplifiers should be chosen as if the system were to be used for normal speech amplification. That is, the headroom required to avoid clipping the noise source (usually about 10 dB) must be added to the power level required to produce the required nominal masking sound pressure level through the system loudspeakers. An additional requirement is high reliability, since failure of a masking system power amplifier immediately makes the system obvious and can disrupt an entire office. Use of relay-switched backup amplifiers or some other method of amplifier redundancy is advisable.

26.15.6 Criteria for the Noise Generator

A standard pink-noise generator, of the type used for sound system equalization, is acceptable provided its output is random enough. Many equalization noise generators utilize digital circuitry, and their noise output repeats every few seconds. Listeners would immediately become aware of this type of generator, and it is thus not acceptable. Noise generators specifically designed for noise-masking systems are available and are probably worth any extra cost. The noise generator, like the power amplifier, must be highly reliable. Redundancy can be achieved by mixing two noise generators through a passive mixing network. If one generator fails, the overall noise level will drop about 3 dB, but the system will continue to operate.

26.15.7 Criteria for the Equalizer

Because the shape of the final frequency-response curve is critical, a one-third-octave equalizer should be employed. A one-octave equalizer lacks the required precision. A passive-type graphic equalizer will eliminate the need for redundancy in the equalizer section of the masking system. If two, redundant, active equalizers are used, the filter and gain settings on both must be equal.

26.15.8 A Second System

A more random (and thus more effective) system design can be achieved by utilizing three separate noise generators feeding three equalizers and three power amplifiers (or banks of power amplifiers in a large system). Rather than feeding zones of loudspeakers in separate areas, these amplifiers feed adjacent loudspeakers in the same zone. That is, every third loudspeaker will be fed by amplifier number 2, with the loudspeaker on one side fed by amplifier number 1 and the loudspeaker on the other side fed by amplifier number 3. This plan also produces a high level of redundancy since failure of one amplifier or noise generator will produce less than a 3-dB drop in overall masking level. This system can thus be installed with no backup amplifiers if desired. Alternately, a single backup amplifier can be installed in the system rack, ready to replace any single amplifier failure.

26.15.9 Masking Plus Paging or Background Music

Background music or paging may be added to a masking system using the same amplifiers and loudspeakers. Intelligibility of the paging may suffer because of the placement of the loudspeakers (high frequencies will be attenuated). A separate equalizer should be used for the paging, and if all three functions are to be included, another equalizer should be used for the background music. The system power amplifier (and loudspeakers) must be capable of handling simultaneous inputs from all sources with adequate headroom. The noise must not be turned off or attenuated during a page, since this will cause listeners to become aware of the system, detracting from its effectiveness.

In general, adding paging and/or background music to a noise-masking system will have limited success. Many listeners report hearing noisy background music from such a system and, as mentioned, paging intelligibility suffers. Thus, when needed, paging and background music systems should be designed separately.

26.15.10 Adjusting the Installed System

Both the level and frequency response of the masking system must be properly adjusted. Perform the adjustments when office workers are not present. Adjust the masking-noise level for the degree of speech privacy required keeping the masking noise as low as possible consistent with speech privacy requirements. Office workers will often tolerate masking-noise levels of as high as 52 dBa, but higher levels will defeat the purpose of the masking system by making it into an irritation itself. If speech privacy (as determined by on-site subjective experiments by trained observers as well as careful measurements of sound transmission) is not achieved at this masking-noise level, alternate mechanical and acoustical means should be employed.

The frequency-response curve must also be carefully adjusted to conform to the window curve shown in Fig. 26-63. This curve includes the effects of existing mechanical noise sources such as air-handling systems, and these sources normally contribute the bulk of the noise energy below about 250 Hz. Both frequency response and sound pressure level must be measured at multiple points in the room and variations of more than about ±2 dB can spell a degraded system effectiveness.

If other areas of the building, especially on the same

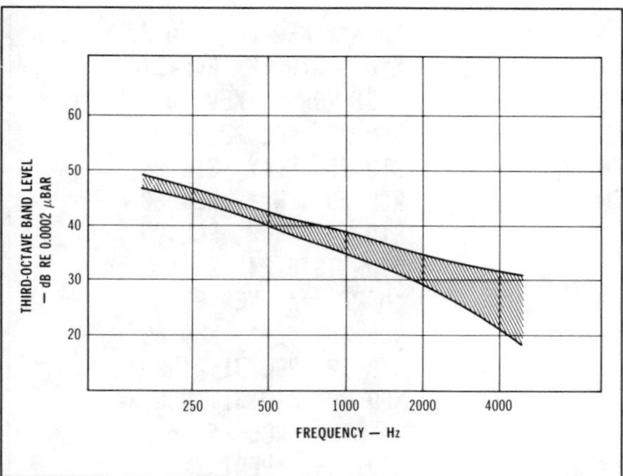

Figure 26-63 Range of typical masking sound spectra. *(Courtesy Soundolier Inc.)*

floor, will not have a noise-masking system, plan the system so that a transition zone can be achieved where the masking noise gradually dies out as a listener moves from one area to another. Adjust this transition zone so that a listener walking from one zone to the other notices only a subjective natural change in noise as might be expected in walking from one area to another.

26.15.11 Subjective and Objective Methods for Measuring System Effectiveness

A subjective evaluation of system effectiveness should be performed by a jury of at least three listeners. Position each listener (one at a time, independently) on the other side of an acoustic barrier from a talker (this simulates the normal usage of the office area). Measure the talker's voices and have them talk louder or quieter until the talker level is about 60 to 65 dBa. Adjust the masking-noise level until the listener agrees that the speech from the talker is audible but not intelligible. Repeat the process for the other two listeners. Final system level should be the highest of the three levels. This "minimal privacy" level should not be exceeded if at all possible.

A single objective criteria for measuring the success of a noise-masking system does not exist. Methods have been developed, however, by several organizations including the Public Buildings Service division of the General Services Administration and the American Society for Testing and Materials. These methods generally involve measurement of signal-to-noise (speech-to-masking-noise) ratios and measurement of overall masking and ambient noise against a set of NC curves and may use a test loudspeaker producing a specified signal in place of the talker.

26.15.12 Conclusion

Noise-masking, speech-privacy systems are related to other sound systems only in the fact that they use many of the same components. Their purposes and design are obviously very different from each other. Masking systems are commonly specified for public buildings. Such specifications are drawn up in great detail and requirements for installation and performance documentation are strict. When a design must be performed from scratch, the help of an experienced consultant will be valuable.

26.16 MICROCOMPUTER SOFTWARE FOR SOUND REINFORCEMENT SYSTEM DESIGNERS

Although a number of commercially available programs exist, the two microcomputer programs presented in the following are in the public domain. Thus, the reader may copy and use these programs freely within the normal limits for public domain software.

Although both programs have been used extensively, the reader is cautioned that the programs are not guaranteed in any way. In addition, programs of this type should be considered to be sound system analysis, not sound system design tools. The engineer performs the design; the microcomputer and its software are merely aids.

The programs perform calculations that answer three of the four questions first discussed in section 26.1.11. That is, they help the designer to determine whether the system will be loud enough, whether the system will feed back, and whether the direct-to-reverberant situation is favorable for intelligibility. Performing these calculations on a computer can remove much of the tedium from sound system design. Computer programs to help the designer with Question 2: "Can Everyone Understand?" were discussed in section 26.2.2.

26.16.1 Sound System Analysis for the HP-41C

The "Sound System Engineering" program is used to design sound systems. The program (Fig. 26-64) is divided into four parts:

A	Room Design
B	Speaker Design
C	Gain and Power
E	Print Sound System Engineering

The program can be used with or without a printer and requires 201 program registers and 40 data memory registers. With the printer connected, you are prompted,

```
                PRP "SSE

 01♦LBL "SSE"
CLRG  "GMB 8-83"

 04♦LBL A
SF 01  CF 21  0  STO 33
"PRINT?"  FS? 55  PROMPT
X≠0?  SF 21

 14♦LBL 16
ADV  "ROOM DESIGN"
AVIEW  ADV  FIX 1
RCL 35  "L="  XEQ 00
CF 22  STO 35  X=0?
GTO 01  RCL 36  "WF="
XEQ 00  STO 36  RCL 37
"WR="  XEQ 00  STO 37
RCL 38  "HF="  XEQ 00
STO 38  RCL 39  "HR="
XEQ 00  STO 39  RCL 38
+  2  /  RCL 36  RCL 37
+  2  /  *  RCL 35  *
STO 01  RCL 38  RCL 39
+  RCL 35  *  RCL 37
RCL 39  *  +  RCL 36
RCL 38  *  +  RCL 36
RCL 37  +  RCL 35  *  +
STO 02

 76♦LBL 01
RCL 01  "V="  XEQ 00
STO 01  RCL 02  "S="
XEQ 00  STO 02  FIX 2
RCL 04  "RT60="  XEQ 00
STO 04  X≠0?  GTO 07
RCL 03  "-a="  XEQ 00
STO 03  X≠0?  GTO 05

 98♦LBL 02
ADV  "X="  XEQ 03  "Y="
XEQ 03  *  "a="  XEQ 03
*  ST+ 33  GTO 02

110♦LBL 03
PROMPT  FC?C 22  GTO 04
ARCL X  FS? 21  PRA  RTN

118♦LBL 00
ARCL X  AVIEW  FS? 01
STOP  FC? 21  RTN
FS?C 22  PRX  RTN

128♦LBL 04
RCL 33  RCL 02  /
STO 03  FIX 2  "-a="
XEQ 00

136♦LBL 05
FIX 1  RCL 17  "≠OBJ="
XEQ 00  STO 17  STO 24
X=0?  GTO 06  RCL 18
"SAB/OBJ="  XEQ 00
STO 18  RCL 17  *
STO 24  RCL 19  "≠OBJ="
XEQ 00  STO 19  RCL 20
"SAB/OBJ="  XEQ 00
STO 20  RCL 19  *
ST+ 24

163♦LBL 06
RCL 03  RCL 02  *
STO 33  RCL 24  +  "Sa="
XEQ 00  STO 06  .049
RCL 01  *  RCL 06  /
FIX 2  "RT60="  XEQ 00
STO 04  GTO B

183♦LBL 07
FIX 1  RCL 01  .049  *
X<>Y  /  "Sa="  XEQ 00
STO 06  RCL 02  /  FIX 2
"-a="  XEQ 00  STO 03
FS?C 07  GTO 09

201♦LBL B
ADV  "SPEAKER DESIGN"
AVIEW  ADV  FIX 1  656
STO 00  RCL 34
"≠ARRAYS="  XEQ 00
STO 34  RCL 07  "D2="
XEQ 00  STO 07  RCL 28
"HF="  XEQ 00  STO 28
X=0?  GTO 08  RCL 27
"1ST ROW="  XEQ 00
STO 27  RCL 28  R-P
STO 25  X<>Y  STO 26
RCL 29  "W="  XEQ 00
STO 29  2  /  RCL 25  /
ATAN  STO 24  2  *
"HORZ ∡="  XEQ 00
RCL 30  "L="  XEQ 00
STO 30  RCL 31  "HR="
XEQ 00  STO 31  RCL 30
/  ATAN  RCL 26  +  90
X<>Y  -  "VERT ∡="
XEQ 00  2  /  SIN
RCL 24  SIN  *  ASIN  PI
R-D  X<>Y  /  STO 08

276♦LBL 08
RCL 08  "REQ Q="  XEQ 00
STO 08  RCL 13
"SPKR Q="  XEQ 00
STO 13  RCL 08  /  1
X<Y?  X<>Y  RCL 34  *
"N="  XEQ 00  STO 12

295♦LBL 09
RCL 06  RCL 13  *
RCL 12  /  SQRT  .141  *
"Dc="  XEQ 00  3.16  *
RCL 07  X>Y?  GTO 19
FIX 1  RCL 00  RCL 07
X↑2  *  RCL 04  X↑2  *
RCL 12  *  RCL 01
RCL 13  *  /

325♦LBL 18
STO 09  "%AL="  XEQ 00
FS?C 06  GTO C  15  X>Y?
XEQ C  RCL 01  *  RCL 13
*  RCL 00  RCL 04  X↑2
*  RCL 12  *  /  SQRT
"MAX D2="  XEQ 00
RCL 00  RCL 07  X↑2  *
RCL 04  X↑2  *  RCL 12
*  RCL 01  /  15  /
```

Figure 26-64 HP-41

Print? If you want to print, press any number and R/S; if not, press R/S. The printer should be in manual mode.

When operated with R/S only, the program sequences A, B, C. At any time, you can go directly to any part. This allows you to rework any section without going through the entire program.

The prompt = includes the previous input to the prompt. This allows you to change only the parameters you prefer. If you do not want to change a particular prompt, key R/S. X =, Y =, a =, in section A does not include the previous prompts.

The program calculates for the parameter that you enter as 0. To make PAG = NAG, one parameter must be calculated in sections A and C.

```
"MIN Q=" XEQ 00 15
RCL 01 * RCL 13 *
RCL 00 RCL 07 X↑2 *
RCL 12 * / SQRT
FIX 2 "MAX RT60="
XEQ 00 CF 22 "NEW D2="
PROMPT FS? 21 XEQ 17
FS?C 22 STO 07
"NEW Q=" PROMPT FS? 21
XEQ 17 FS?C 22 STO 13
"NEW RT60=" PROMPT
FS? 21 XEQ 17 FC?C 22
GTO 09 STO 04 SF 07
GTO 07

401♦LBL 17
FS? 22 RTN ARCL X PRA
RTN

407♦LBL 19
RCL 04 9 * GTO 18

412♦LBL C
ADV "GAIN AND POWER"
AVIEW ADV FIX 1
RCL 07 XEQ 10 STO 05
4 XEQ 10 STO 24
RCL 16 "EAD=" XEQ 00
STO 16 XEQ 10 STO 11
RCL 10 "D1=" XEQ 00
STO 10 XEQ 10 STO 00
RCL 15 "DS=" XEQ 00
STO 15 XEQ 10 STO 09
RCL 21 "NOM=" XEQ 00
STO 21 X=0? XEQ 14
LOG 10 * STO 25
RCL 16 X=0? XEQ 11
RCL 10 X=0? XEQ 12
RCL 15 X=0? XEQ 13
RCL 14 "PROG SPL="
XEQ 00 STO 14 RCL 22
"SPKR SENS=" XEQ 00
STO 22 RCL 14 10 +
X<>Y - RCL 05 RCL 24
- + 10 / 10↑X
"EPR=" XEQ 00 RCL 23
"W AVAIL=" XEQ 00
STO 23 10 / LOG 10
* RCL 22 + RCL 05
RCL 24 - -
"MAX PROG SPL=" XEQ 00
RCL 32 "DO=" XEQ 00
STO 32 XEQ 10 STO 26
RCL 00 + RCL 09 -
RCL 05 - "PAG="
XEQ 00 RCL 26 RCL 11
- 6 + RCL 25 +
"NAG=" XEQ 00 CF 06
BEEP FS? 01 GTO A
STOP
528♦LBL 10
X=0? RTN X↑2 4 * PI
* RCL 13 X<>Y / 4
RCL 12 * RCL 06 / +
LOG 10 * CHS RTN

550♦LBL 11
RCL 05 RCL 25 + 6 +
RCL 09 + RCL 00 -
STO 11 XEQ 15
"MIN EAD=" STO 16
XEQ 00 RTN

566♦LBL 12
RCL 05 RCL 25 + 6 +
RCL 11 - RCL 09 +
STO 00 XEQ 15
"MIN D1=" STO 10
XEQ 00 RTN
582♦LBL 13
RCL 00 RCL 11 +
RCL 05 - RCL 25 - 6
- STO 09 XEQ 15
"MAX DS=" STO 15
XEQ 00 RTN

598♦LBL 14
RCL 00 RCL 11 +
RCL 09 - RCL 05 - 6
- 10 / 10↑X
"MAX NOM=" STO 21
XEQ 00 RTN

615♦LBL 15
CHS 10 / 10↑X 4
RCL 12 * RCL 06 / -
4 * PI * RCL 13
X<>Y / SQRT RTN

635♦LBL E
SF 21 ADV CF 01 SF 12
SF 06 "SOUND SYSTEMENG"
"⊢INEERING" XEQ "PRA"
CF 12 ADV ADV AON
SF 13 "FOR " ACA
CF 13 "CLIENT ?"
PROMPT ACA PRBUF
SF 13 "BY " ACA
CF 13 "BY" PROMPT ACA
PRBUF 4 SKPCHR
"DATE ?" PROMPT ACA
PRBUF AOFF ADV ADV
GTO 16 END
```

program. *(Courtesy Glen Ballou)*

26.16.1.1 Section A

If volume and surface area are known, key 0 after the L= prompt, and the program will go directly to V=.

If you do not know RT_{60} but do know $-a$, key 0 after the RT_{60} prompt and insert the $-a$ value after the $-a$ prompt. R/S then moves you to Sa for two different objects. These values are added to surface area Sa to produce Sa_{total}. If you do not wish to enter objects, press R/S after the first object prompt, and the program will bypass these calculations.

If you do not know RT_{60} or $-a$, press 0 and R/S after each prompt, $-a$ can then be calculated by entering X and Y dimensions and a for each surface area. When all surfaces are calculated, press R/S on prompt X = to continue program.

26.16.1.2 Section B

To find loudspeaker coverage see Fig. 26-65 for the definitions of the prompts.

To determine the horizontal angle at the rear row, use W at the rear row and the first row distance = L.

If you prefer to skip loudspeaker coverage, key 0 after the prompt HF; the program will advance to the prompt Q_{req}=.

The 15% articulation loss of consonants is the go/no-go point in the program that allows continuing the program or returning to change D_2, Q, or RT_{60}. Changing RT_{60} automatically recalculates $-a$. The program tells you minimum or maximum values allowed for 15% AL_{cons}, then allows you to change them.

If you are satisfied with an articulation loss greater than 15%, key C to continue the program otherwise key R/S to return to above calculations. Once $\%AL_{cons}$ becomes 15% or less, R/S will continue the program.

26.16.1.3 Section C

Section C calculates the system gain, program SPL, and power required to complete the sound system design. Last PAG and NAG are calculated to test the design. To make PAG = NAG, one parameter must be put in as 0 so it can be calculated.

26.16.1.4 Section E

Section E prints the program and results for use in specifications. The printer first prints SOUND SYSTEM ENGINEERING and prompts CLIENT. It next prompts BY, which is your company or engineer's name. Last it prompts DATE. Insert the month, day, and year. Upon completion of these prompts, the printer will print the answers to the calculations.

Details of the Sound System Engineering program for the HP-41 (Fig. 26-64) are as follows:

Definition of terms

VOL	Room volume
S	Surface area
#OBJ	Number of objects
SAB/OBJ	Sabines per object
$-a$	Coefficient of absorption
RT_{60}	Reverberation time
Sa	Surface area times average absorption coefficient
# Arrays	Number of loudspeaker arrays
D_2	Distance from loudspeaker to farthest listener
Min Q	Minimum Q required
Req Q	Q required to cover area
Spkr Q	Q available from loudspeaker
N	Ratio of number of loudspeakers covering reverberant to direct sound
D_c	Critical distance
$\%AL_{cons}$	% articulation loss of consonants
MAX RT_{60}	Maximum RT_{60} allowable for 15% AL_{cons}
EAD	Equivalent acoustic distance
D_1	Distance between loudspeaker and microphone

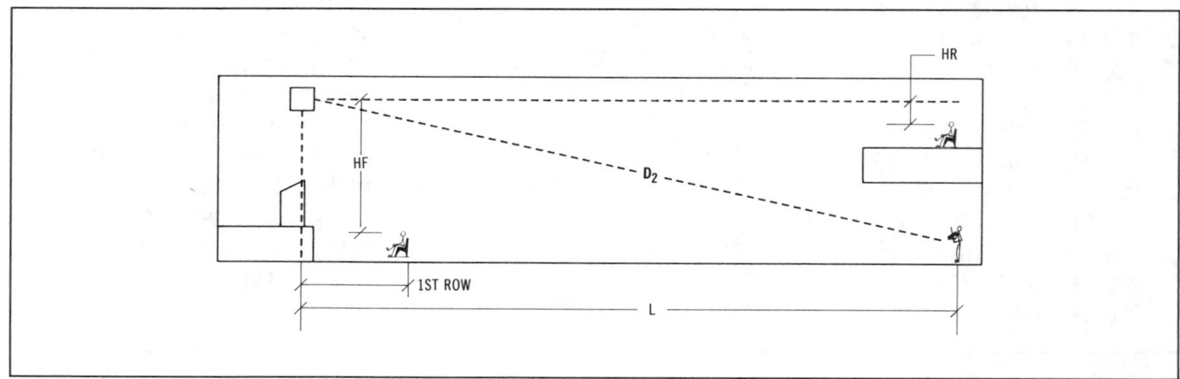

Figure 26-65 Definition of prompts for finding speaker coverage using the HP-41 program.

D_s	Distance between talker and microphone
NOM	Number of open microphones
PROG SPL	Program sound pressure level
SPKR SENS	Speaker sensitivity at 1 W/4 ft
EPR	Electrical power required to the loudspeaker
W AVAIL	Watts available to the loudspeaker
MAX PROG SPL	Maximum program sound pressure level with available power
D_o	Distance between talker and farthest listener
PAG	Potential acoustic gain
NAG	Needed acoustic gain

The formulas used are

$$RT_{60} = \frac{0.049V}{Sa}$$

$$S = \frac{0.049V - RT_{60}(C + D)}{\bar{a}\,RT_{60}}$$

$$\bar{a} = \frac{0.049V - RT_{60}(C + D)}{S(RT_{60})}$$

$$S\bar{a}_{TOTAL} = S\bar{a} + C + D$$

$$C\,\&\,D = \#\,\text{objects (sabines/object)}$$

$$\%AL_{cons} = \frac{656 D_2^2 RT_{60}^2 N}{VQ}$$

$$\%AL_{cons} = 9RT_{60}\ \text{beyond}\ D_L$$

$$Q = \frac{180}{\arc\sin\left(\sin\frac{\theta}{2}\right)\left(\sin\frac{\phi}{2}\right)}$$

$$EPR = 10^{\left[\frac{ProgSpL + 10 + \Delta D_2 - \Delta 4 - Sens}{10}\right]}$$

$$D_c = 0.141\sqrt{\frac{QSa}{N}}$$

$$D_x = -10\log\left[\frac{Q}{4\pi D^2} + \frac{4}{S\bar{a}_{TOTAL}}\right]$$

$$NAG = \Delta D_o - \Delta EAD + 10\log\ NOM + 6$$

$$PAG = \Delta D_o + \Delta D_1 - \Delta D_s - \Delta D_2$$

The storage registers are assigned as follows:

Register	**Storage**	
00	656	D_1
01	VOL	
02	S	
03	−a	
04	RT_{60}	
05	D_X	
06	Sa_{TOTAL}	
07	D_2	
08	Q_{REQ}	
09	$\%AL_{cons}$	
10	D_1	
11	D_c	
12	N	
13	Q_{AVAIL}	
14	PROG SPL	
15	D_s	
16	EAD	
17	#OBJ	
18	SAB/OBJ	
19	#OBJ	
20	SAB/OBJ	
21	NOM	
22	SPKR SENS	
23	W_{AVAIL}	
24	Sa(17 × 18 + 19 × 20) work 4′	
25	NOM	
26	D_o	LBL B (26–31)
27	1st Row	
28	HF	
29	W	
30	L	
31	HR	
32	D_o	
33	Sa working	
34	NO. OF ARRAYS	
35	ROOM LENGTH	
36	ROOM WIDTH (FRONT)	
37	ROOM WIDTH (REAR)	
38	ROOM HEIGHT (FRONT)	
39	ROOM HEIGHT (REAR)	

26.16.1.5 Sample Problem

Design a sound system for ABC. The room is 40 ft high, 80 ft wide, and 130 ft long. The loudspeaker shall be 2 ft from the ceiling, and the audience will be seated. The loudspeaker shall be mounted 10 ft in front of the first row. L = 120, D_2 = 125 ft, D_1 = 30 ft, D_s ?, D_o = 120 ft. The floor is raised 10 ft at the rear. The a for the walls and ceiling is 0.1 and 0.5 for the floor. Use 1000 people @ 4.5 sabines/person and 200 empty seats @ 1 sabine per seat. The program SPL = 90 dB, the loudspeaker sensitivity

```
1 REM*SABINE CONFIGURATION 1-19-83
5 REM* REVISED 2-8-74
6 REM* OSI BASIC 5-5-80
10 REM* TYMESHARE SUPER-BASIC COMPATABLE
20 DIM R(36)
25 LET R(3)=0
30 LET PI=3.1415927
32 A$="POSITIVE (>0)"
33 PRINT:PRINT:PRINT
35 PRINT"AMBASSADOR COLLEGE":PRINT"SYN-AUD-CON"
38 PRINT
40 PRINT"SOUND SYSTEM DESIGN":PRINT"PROGRAM"
50 PRINT"INTERNAL VOLUME":PRINT"IN CUBIC FEET ";
55 INPUT R(1)
58 PRINT
60 IF R(1)>0 THEN 75
65 PRINT A$
70 GOTO  50
75 PRINT"BOUNDARY SURFACE":PRINT"IN SQUARE FEET ";
80 INPUT R(2)
83 PRINT
85 IF R(2)>0 THEN 100
90 PRINT A$
95 GOTO 75
100 PRINT"REVERB TIME (RT60)":PRINT"IN SECONDS ";
105 INPUT R(4)
107 PRINT
110 IF R(4)>0 THEN 155
115 IF R(4)=0 THEN 130
120 PRINT A$
125 GOTO 100
130 PRINT"AVERAGE ABSORPTION COEFFICIENT ";
135 INPUT R(3)
140 IF R(3)<=1 THEN IF R(3)>=0 THEN 155
145 PRINT"ABS. COEF. (RANGE: 0.0 TO 1.0)";
150 GOTO 135
155 IF R(3)<>0 THEN IF R(4)<>0 THEN 215
156 LET R(5)=R(2)*R(3)
160 IF R(3)<>0 THEN 200
165 IF R(4)<>0 THEN 185
170 PRINT"INSUFFICIENT DATA. ENTER EITHER ABSORPTION COEFFICIENT"
175 PRINT"OR  REVERBERATION TIME."
180 GOTO 100
185 LET R(3)=(.049*R(1))/(R(2)*R(4))
190 PRINT"ABSORPTION COEFFICENT IS ";INT(R(3)*1000+.5)/1000
195 GOTO 215
200 LET R(4)=.049*R(1)/R(5)
205 PRINT"REVERBERATION TIME (RT60) IS ";INT(R4)*100+.5)/100;
210 PRINT" SECONDS."
215 LET R(5)=R(2)*R(3)
220 PRINT"SABINS = ";INT(R(5)+.5);" UNITS."
222 PRINT
235 PRINT"DISTANCE FROM FURTHEST ":PRINT"LISTENER TO CLOSEST"
```

Figure 26-66 "Sound System Analysis" program in BASIC.

```
236 PRINT"LOUDSPEAKER"
240 PRINT" (D2) IN FEET ";
245 INPUT R(7)
247 PRINT
250 IF R(7)>0 THEN 265
255 PRINT A$
260 GOTO 235
265 IF R(4)>1.5 THEN 290
270 PRINT"REVERBERATION TIME (RT60) IS LESS THAN OR EQUAL"
275 PRINT"TO 1.5 SECONDS, THEREFORE ARTICULATION LOSS OF CON-"
280 PRINT"SONANTS (AL-CONS) IS LESS THAN OR EQUAL TO 15%."
290 LET R(8)=(656*R(7)*R(7)*R(4))/(15*R(1))
295 PRINT INT(R(8)*10+.5)/10;" IS THE MINIMUM":PRINT"DIRECTIVITY-FACTOR"
300 PRINT"FOR 15% AL-CONS."
302 PRINT
305 PRINT"SELECTED (Q) ";
310 INPUT R(9)
315 IF R(9)>1 THEN 330
320 PRINT A$
325 GOTO 305
330 LET R(12)=SQR((15*R(1)*R(9))/(656*R(7)*R(7)))
335 IF R(8)<=R(9) THEN 450
340 LET R(10)=SQR((15*R(1)*R(9))/(656*R(4)*R(4)))
345 LET R3=(.049*R(1))/(R(12))
350 PRINT"A (D2) OF ";INT(R(7)+.5);" FEET":PRINT"IS REQUIRED. BUT"
351 PRINT INT(R(10)+.5);" FEET IS THE"
355 PRINT"MAXIMUM (D2) ACHIEVABLE":PRINT"WITH THE SELECTED (Q)"
356 PRINT"AND AVAILABLE ABSORPTION COEFFICIENT "
365 PRINT"IF NOT ACCEPTABLE,":PRINT"EITHER:"
370 PRINT"(1) INCREASE THE (Q) FROM "INT(R(9)*10+.5)/10;
371 PRINT" TO "INT(R8)*10+.5)/10; " OR:"
380 PRINT"(2) INCREASE THE":PRINT"ABSORPTION COEFFICIENT":PRINT"FROM ";
385 PRINT INT(R(3)*1000+.5)/1000; " TO ";
390 PRINT INT (R3*1000+.5)/1000; " BY "
395 PRINT"ADDING "; INT(R(2)*R3-R(5)+.5);
400 PRINT" SABINS OF ABSORPTION. THE (RT60) WILL THEN DECREASE"
405 PRINT"FROM ";INT(R(4)*100+.5)/100; " TO ";
410 PRINT INT(R(12)*100+.5)/100; " SECONDS."
415 PRINT"FOR YOUR OPTIONS, STRIKE EITHER '1' OR '2' AND 'RETURN',"
420 PRINT"OR '0' AND 'RETURN' ONLY IF (D2) IS ACCEPTABLE ";
425 INPUT X
430 IF X=0 THEN 450
435 IF X=1 THEN 305
440 IF X=2 THEN 100
445 GOTO 415
450 LET R(11)=(656*R(4)*R(4)*R(7)*R(7))/R(1)*R(9))
455 PRINT"SELECTED (Q) ;YIELDS ";INT(R(11)*10+.5)/10;" %AL-CONS."
460 PRINT"WITH SELECTED (Q) AND (D2), MAXIMUM (RT60) IS ";
465 PRINT INT(R(12)*10+.5)/10; " SEC. FOR 15% AL-CONS."
470 LET R(13)=SQR(2)/10*SQR(R(5)*R(9))
475 PRINT"CRITICAL-DISTANCE (DC) IS ";INT(R(13)+.5);" FEET."
480 LET R(14)=SQR(10)*R(13)
485 PRINT"LIMITING-DISTANCE (DL) IS ";INT(R(14)=.5);" FEET."
```

(Contributed by John Prohs at Ambassador College)

cont. on next page

```
490 PRINT"EQUIVALENT-ACOUSTIC-DISTANCE (EAD), IN FEET ";
495 INPUT R(15)
500 IF R(15)>=0 THEN 515
505 PRINT A$
510 GOTO 490
515 LET R(16)=R(15)
520 IF R(16)<=R(13) THEN 535
525 PRINT"SMALLER (<=(DC)) ";
530 GOTO 490
535 IF R(16)=0 THEN 550
540 GOSUB 970
545 LET R(17)=R(15)
550 PRINT"DISTANCE FROM MICROPHONE TO LOUDSPEAKER (D1), IN FEET ";
555 INPUT R(15)
560 IF R(15)>=0 THEN IF R(16)>0 THEN 580
565 IF R(15)>0 THEN IF R(16)=0 THEN 580
570 PRINT"INSUFFICIENT DATA, ENTER EITHER (EAD), (D1), OR BOTH."
575 GOTO 490
580 LET R(18)=R(15)
585 IF R(18)<>0 THEN GOSUB 970
590 LET R(19)=R(15)
595 PRINT"DISTANCE FROM MICROPHONE TO TALKER (DS), IN FEET ";
600 INPUT R(15)
605 IF R(15)>0 THEN IF R(16>0 THEN IF R(18)>=0 THEN 645
610 IF R(15)>0 THEN IF R(16>=0 THEN IF R(18)>0 THEN 645
615 IF R(15)=0 THEN IF R(16>0 THEN IF R(18)>0 THEN 645
620 IF R(16)=0 THEN 635
625 PRINT"INSUFFICIENT DATA; ENTER EITHER (D1), (DS), OR BOTH."
630 GOTO 550
635 PRINT"INSUFFICIENT DATA; ENTER EITHER (EAD), (DS), OR BOTH."
640 GOTO 490
645 LET R(21)=R(15)
650 IF R(21)<>0 THEN GOSUB 970
655 LET R(22)=R(15)
660 LET R(15)=R(7)
665 GOSUB 970
670 LET R(20)=R(15)
675 PRINT"NUMBER OF OPEN MICROPHONES (NOM) ";
680 INPUT R(23)
685 IF R(23)>0 THEN 700
690 PRINT A$
695 GOTO 675
700 IF R(23)-INT(R(23))=0 THEN 715
705 PRINT"INTEGRAL (!) ";
710 GOTO 675
715 LET R(24)=10*(LOG(R(23))/LOG(10)
720 IF R(16)<>0 THEN 755
725 LET R(25)=R(22)-R(19)+R(20)+R(24)+6
730 LET R(17)=R(25)
735 GOSUB 980
740 LET R(16)=R(25)
745 PRINT"MINIMUM (EAD) IS ";INT(R(16)*10+.5)/10;" FEET."
750 GOTO 820
```

Figure 26-66—cont. "Sound System Analysis" program in BASIC.

```
755 IF R(18)<>0 THEN 790
760 LET R(25)=R(22)+R(20)-R(17)+R(24)+6
765 LET R(19)=R(25)
770 GOSUB 980
775 LET R(18)=R(25)
780 PRINT"MINIMUM (D1) IS ";INT(R(18)*10+.5)/10;" FEET."
785 GOTO 820
790 IF R(21)<>0 THEN 820
795 LET R(25)=R(19)-R(20)+R(17)-R(24)-6
800 LET R(22)=R(25)
805 GOSUB 980
810 LET R(21)=R(25)
815 PRINT"MAXIMUM (DS) IS ";INT(R(21)*10+.5)/10;" FEET."
820 PRINT"MAXIMUM SOUND-PRESSURE-LEVEL (SPL) AT (D2) ";
825 INPUT R(31)
830 IF R(31)>0 THEN 845
835 PRINT A$
840 GOTO 820
845 LET R(15)=4
850 GOSUB 970
855 LET R(32)=R(15)
860 PRINT"LOUDSPEAKER SENSITIVITY IN (X) DB-SPL AT (Y) FEET ";
865 PRINT"WITH (Z) WATTS."
870 PRINT"(INPUT IN THIS FORM, SEPARATING WITH COMMAS: X,Y,Z) ";
875 INPUT X,Y,Z
880 IF X>0 THEN IF Y>0 THEN IF Z>0 THEN 895
885 PRINT A$
890 GOTO 870
895 LET R(33)=X-20*(LOG(4/Y)/LOG(10))-(LOG(Z)/LOG(10))
900 LET R(34)=10^((R(31)+10+R(20)-R(32)-R(33))/10
905 PRINT"ELECTRICAL POWER REQUIRED (EPR) IS ";
910 PRINT INT(R(34)*10+.5)/10; " WATTS."
915 PRINT"WATTS AVAILABLE ";
920 INPUT R(35)
925 IF R(35)>0 THEN 940
930 PRINT A$
935 GOTO 915
940 LET R(36)=10*(LOG(R(35)/10)/LOG(10))-R(R(20)+R(32)+R(33)
945 PRINT"MAXIMUM PROGRAM LEVEL IS ";INT(R(36)+.5);" DB-SPL."
950 FOR X=1 TO 8
955 PRINT
960 NEXT X
965 GOTO 25
970 LET R(15)=-10*(LOG(R(9)/4*PI*R(15)*R(15))+(4/R(5)))/LOG(10))
975 RETURN
980 LET R(25)=SQR((R(9)/(10^(-R(25)/10)-(4/R(5))))/(4*PI))
985 RETURN
990 END
```

(Contributed by John Prohs at Ambassador College)

= 99 dB, and Q = 15. Amplifier power = 100 W, NOM = 2, and EAD = 8. The printer is connected and to be used.

26.16.2 Sound System Analysis in BASIC

The program in Fig. 26-66 was contributed by John Prohs at Ambassador College, Pasadena, California. It is an adaptation of a program that had its origins at Synergetic Audio Concepts and uses the equations developed there. The current program (Fig. 26-66) has been used, in its various versions, at Ambassador College for several years and contains valuable error-trapping features. Although the program is written in a version of Microsoft BASIC, users may need to make some modifications for their own computers. In addition, users may wish to add to the program, for example, to calculate the value of N in a cluster.

REFERENCES

1. H. F. Hopkins and N. R. Stryker, "A Proposed Loudness-Efficiency Rating for Loudspeakers and the Determination of System Power Requirements for Enclosures," *Journal of the Proc. of the IRE*, March 1948.
2. V. M. A. Peutz, "Articulation Loss of Consonants as a Criterion for Speech Transmission in a Room," *Journal of the AES*, vol. 19, no. 11, December 1971.
3. W. Klein, "Articulation Loss of Consonants as a Basis for the Design and Judgment of Sound Reinforcement Systems," *Journal of the AES*, vol. 19, no. 11, December 1971.
4. D. Davis and C. Davis, *Sound System Engineering*, Indianapolis: Howard W. Sams & Co., 1975.
5. E. Lethert, "Calculating 'N' for Mixed Acoustic Sources," *Synergetic-Audio-Concepts Tech Topics*, vol. 5, no. 5, January 1978.
6. E. T. Patronis and C. Donders, "Central Cluster Design Technique for Large Multipurpose Auditoria," *Journal of the AES*, vol. 30, no. 6, June 1982.

BIBLIOGRAPHY FOR SOUND REINFORCEMENT

Journal of the AES. Available to members only. AES Membership Information, 60 East 42nd Street, New York, NY 10017.

D. L. Klepper, Ed., *Sound Reinforcement, An Anthology*, New York: AES.

The PA Bible. A continuing series available from Electro-Voice Inc., 600 Cecil St., Buchanan, MI 49107.

J. R. Prohs and D. E. Harris, "An Accurate and Easily Implemented Method of Modeling Loudspeaker Array Coverage," AES preprint 1941(A-8), October 1982.

H. G. Smith, "Acoustic Design Considerations for Speech Intelligibility," *Journal of the AES*, vol. 29, no. 6, June 1981.

Sound System Design Reference Manual and other publications available from JBL Inc., 8500 Balboa Blvd., P. O. Box 2200, Northridge, CA 91329.

Synergetic-Audio-Concepts Tech Topics, P.O. Box 1239 Bedford, IN 47421. (A continuing series of technical newsletters published by Synergetic Audio Concepts.)

Technical Letters. A continuing series of technical and application notes available from Altec Lansing, Oklahoma City, OK

T. Uzzle, "Loudspeaker Coverage by Architectural Mapping," AES preprint 1786(G-3), May 1981.

ACKNOWLEDGMENTS

The author extends his personal thanks to the following individuals for their help with this chapter of the *Handbook for Sound Engineers*:

Glen Ballou
Editor
Handbook for Sound Engineers
Guilford, CT

Rollins Brook
Consultant
Bolt, Beranek and Neumann
Canoga Park, CA

Don and Carolyn Davis
Synergetic Audio Concepts
Bedford, IN

Douglas Wilkens
Peirce Phelps
Philadelphia, PA

In addition, the author thanks the following companies who generously allowed portions of their published documents to be adapted for this chapter:

Fender/CBS Musical Instruments
Pro Sound Division
Fullerton, CA

Altec Lansing Corp.
Oklahoma City, OK

Yamaha International Corp.
Pro Sound Division
Buena Park, CA

JBL Incorporated
Northridge, CA

Soundolier
St. Louis, MO

Electro-Voice, Inc.
Buchanan, MI

CHAPTER **27**

Systems for the Hearing Impaired

by Rollins Brook and Lawrence Philbrick

27.1 NATURE OF THE PROBLEM

There are millions of people in the world—20 million in America alone—with hearing impairments for whom the acoustical and electronic systems described elsewhere in this book are inadequate. It is surprising that the special hearing needs of so large a group have been largely ignored for so long, especially when each of us faces the very real probability of joining that group through disease, trauma, or just by growing old.

The hearing impaired are not just the people who wear aids. In fact, only about 20% of the hearing impaired wear aids. Many people with hearing losses are able to function in close or face-to-face situations but are lost in noisy or reverberant settings. Even people who wear hearing aids have problems in reverberant rooms or where there is a high background noise level. Our standards for speech intelligibility are based upon listening tests with normal-hearing subjects and are not directly applicable to the hearing impaired. Noise and reverberation degrade intelligibility far more rapidly for the hearing-impaired individuals—whether they are fitted with hearing aids or not. Often the very highly prized acoustical qualities of our theaters and concert halls operate against the needs of the hearing impaired. The acoustical design of classrooms and lecture halls are almost always inadequate for the needs of the hearing-impaired student.

For years the only special assistance offered to the hearing impaired was provided by a few churches in the form of headphones in a couple of pews in the front of the sanctuary. In recent years whole new technologies have been developed or adapted to meet the special needs of the hearing impaired in public assembly spaces. Each of these new systems has one thing in common—they are wireless. No longer is the user restricted to a specially wired seat; now every seat is available; no special ticketing is required. The user is free to sit with family and friends.

There are four basic types of wireless systems: magnetic induction, FM broadcast, AM broadcast, and infrared light. Each type has its own set of advantages, problems, and limitations. There is no single best system for every application; each system is simple to operate and to install.

27.2 SOUND PICKUP

The system, no matter what type, must have a pickup of the program sound. In a fully mic'ed event, this pickup could be a feed from the reinforcement control console. Where the event is not mic'ed, there must be a special microphone to feed the hearing-impaired system. It is very important that the feed to the system be of the highest quality possible with a minimum of reverberation pickup and extraneous noises. A PZM-type microphone on the forestage floor or mounted on an acoustical reflector panel over the forestage would be good for many shows. The usefulness of the system to the hearing-impaired patron depends in large measure on the quality of the sound pickup going into the system.

27.3 MAGNETIC INDUCTION LOOPS

Magnetic induction, sometimes called a *loop system*, is one of the oldest and most popular systems. The principal advantage of this system is that it can operate directly into the user's hearing aid without the need for a portable receiver as required by all other systems. A loop of wire is wrapped around the seating area, usually under the carpet, and connected to an amplifier. The electrical current flowing through the loop will create a magnetic field (as the primary of a transformer) that can be picked up by a hearing aid equipped with a *T-coil* (T as in telephone). About 60% of the hearing aids in the United States have these T-coils for magnetic coupling with the earpiece of a telephone. Portable receivers are available for use by patrons who do not have an aid with a T-coil.

There are several problems with the loop system. Most buildings have other magnetic fields that will be picked up by the T-coil. Ordinary electrical wiring will radiate a large 60-Hz field throughout the room, so the T-coil and the portable receivers are designed to have no response in the low-bass region in order to avoid the 60-Hz hum. There are other power-line-related noises that cannot be filtered out—motors, dimmers, and fluorescent lamps being among the more common. The size and shape of the loop and the amount of nearby steel in the building or in the seats will affect the strength and uniformity of the magnetic field. Simultaneous use of loops in adjoining rooms is often a problem because of crosstalk between the systems. Quality of reception is also dependent upon the quality of construction of the T-coil in the hearing aid. It is a disgraceful truth that the quality control for T-coils of most manufacturers is very poor. All these factors combine to provide reception that sometimes has poor sound quality, is noisy, and varies in volume depending upon the location of the listeners and how they turn their heads.

The limited statistics available indicate that of the people needing hearing assistance, only about 20% are actually wearing aids, and only 60% of those aids are equipped with T-coils, which suggests that only 12% of those needing help are able to make use of a magnetic loop through their hearing aids. It has been argued that the majority of those without T-coils actually are young children and the very old; active adults are most likely to have T-coils. Despite the comparatively limited availability of T-coils and the several substantial limitations of the magnetic loop system, it remains very popular and enjoys the vocal support of many of those 2.5 million people who have T-coils.

The cost of a magnetic induction loop system is largely the cost of the amplifier and the labor of installing the wire loop. The receivers are inexpensive. Until recently, the magnetic loop was the least costly system. However, advances in solid-state electronics have made the AM and FM broadcast systems very competitive in price. Where large areas are to be covered, the magnetic loop is probably not as cost effective as a broadcast system.

27.3.1 Loop Design Criteria

The international standard for the magnetic field strength of a loop system with an input signal of normal speech level is 0.1 A/m. (Magnetic field strength H = 0.1 A/m in SI units or 0.125 Oe in cgs units.) This field strength produces an audio voltage in the T-coil about equal to the output of the hearing aid's microphone at normal speech levels (Fig. 27-1). Thus, the user will not have to make volume control adjustments when switching between microphone and T-coil. Also, this field is strong enough that noise and interference problems are minimized, yet it is not so strong as to overload the hearing-aid amplifier.

The field strength should be as uniform as possible over the coverage area. An achievable criterion for uniformity is a maximum variation of ±3 dB in the audio output signal.

System design is based upon the vertical component of the magnetic field, ignoring the horizontal field components for three reasons:

1. The vertical field strength predominates over most of the loop area as shown in Fig. 27-2.
2. The T-coils in hearing aids are typically positioned to be most sensitive to the vertical field.
3. Rotation of the hearing aid about the vertical axis (as in turning the head) results in no change in the pickup of the vertical component, whereas the pickup of the horizontal component will change from maximum to zero with such rotation.

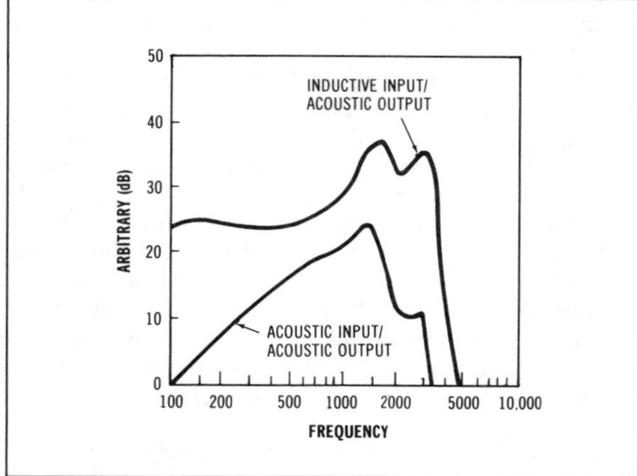

Figure 27-1 Typical hearing aid response. *(From Reference 1)*

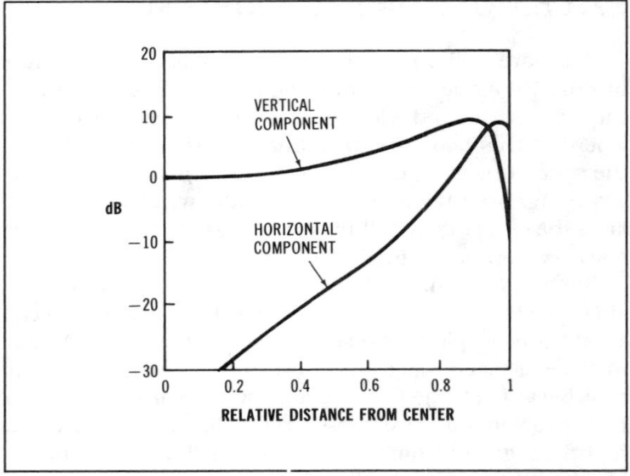

Figure 27-2 Field strength along the diagonal of a square loop. *(From Reference 2)*

27.3.2 Loop Location and Size

The field strength produced by the loop will vary in intensity from the edge of the loop to the center (Fig. 27-3). The range of variation is dependent upon the area (A) and shape of the loop and the listening height (h), which is the vertical distance between the plane of the loop and the receiver. This interrelationship is expressed as the relative listening height (h_r):

$$h_r = \frac{h}{\sqrt{0.5A}} \tag{27-1}$$

Fig. 27-4 shows the normalized field strength along the

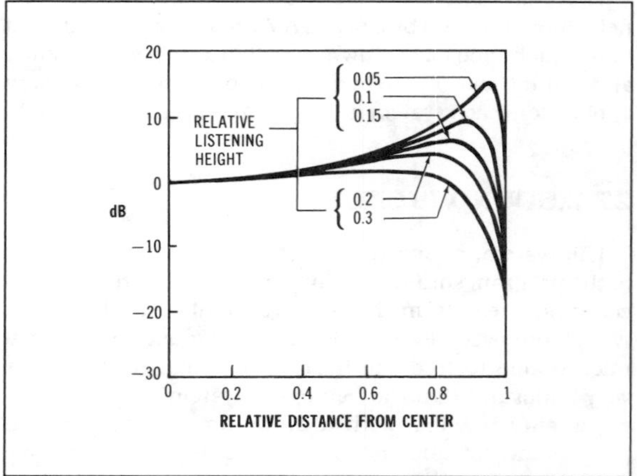

Figure 27-3 Vertical field strength along the diagonal of a square loop. *(From Reference 2)*

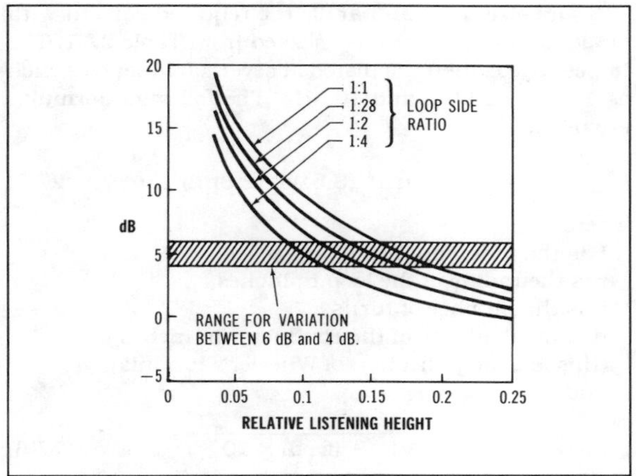

Figure 27-4 Vertical field strength along the diagonal of rectangular loops. *(From Reference 2)*

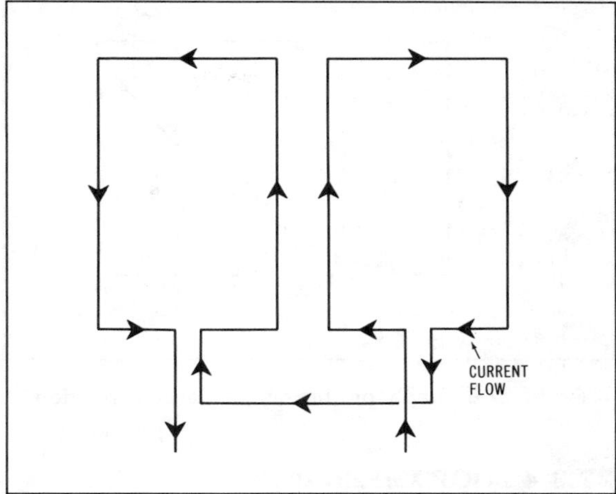

Figure 27-5 Multiple-loop current flow diagram.

diagonal of loops of various shapes and the corresponding range of acceptable values for h_r.

By application of Eq. 27-1 and the h_r values found in Fig. 27-4, it is possible to design a loop of acceptable shape, area, and listening height. The penalty for an inequality in Eq. 27-1 is degraded uniformity of field strength, as can be seen in Fig. 27-4.

If the loop is to be placed at floor level (h = 48 in. for seated listeners), square loops falling within the acceptable h_r range will vary from 28 × 28 ft to 38 × 38 ft. A rectangular 1:4 loop may range in size from 24 × 96 ft to 32 × 126 ft. Smaller loop dimensions will require a smaller h; larger areas need a higher (larger) h.

As h grows larger, the field-distorting effect of steel in the structure of the building and in the audience chairs becomes more pronounced. This field distortion is manifest by dead spots within the loop. At its worst, the entire system may be rendered useless.

The great listening height required of large loops also presents architectural problems. Often the only practical place to locate a loop is at floor level, either below the floor or under the carpet. Where it is not feasible to locate the loop far above (or far below) floor level, the single, large loop can be broken up into a number of smaller loops that can be sized to locate at floor level. Because the vertical field strength rapidly falls to a miminum above the conductors, it is important to locate the loop wires in aisles or other areas that do not require coverage. For multiple loops, the current in parallel conductors of adjacent loops must flow in the same direction as shown in Fig. 27-5.

Unfortunately, multiple loops will almost always have poorer uniformity than a single loop of the same size as one of the multiples. There is a special design technique for achieving a more nearly constant vertical field strength when using multiple loops. It involves the use of two sets of overlapping loops that are driven with electrical signals 90° out of phase. This complex procedure is described by Bosman and Joosten.[3]

27.3.3 LOOP CURRENT

Once the size and location of the loop are fixed, the required current in the loop can be calculated. The strength of the magnetic field is directly dependent upon the current in the loop. The required current I in a single-turn loop is

$$I = \left(\frac{(0.1\ \text{A/m})\pi A}{2D}\right)(1 + 2h_r^2)(\sqrt{1 + h_r^2}) \qquad (27\text{-}2)$$

where,
0.1 A/m is the field strength criterion,
A is the loop area in square meters,
D is the loop diagonal in meters.

The equivalent formula in English units (feet) is

$$I = \left(\frac{(0.0305\ \text{A/ft})\pi A}{2D}\right)(1 + 2h_r^2)(\sqrt{1 + h_r^2}) \qquad (27\text{-}3)$$

The terms containing h_r are a correction for the distance of the listener from the plane of the loop and can be obtained from Fig. 27-6.

If a multiturn loop is used, the required current in the loop is

$$I_1 = I/n \qquad (27\text{-}4)$$

where,
I is the current from Eqs. 27-2 or 27-3,
n is the number of turns.

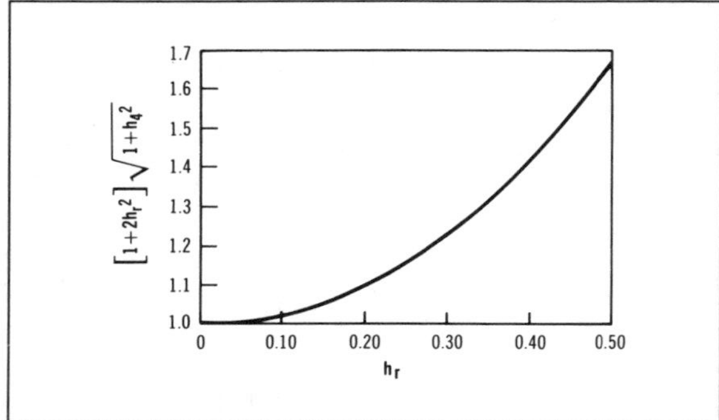

Figure 27-6 Graph for obtaining distance correction.

27.3.4 LOOP IMPEDANCE

A wire size and number of turns in the loop must be selected to handle the required current safely and to control the range of variation of impedance across the audio band. A loop can be designed to provide the required magnetic field strength by using a relatively small wire with one turn or by using a larger wire with several turns. In the first case the loop impedance would be mainly resistive; in the second, it would be heavily inductive.

The impedance will, of course, increase with frequency because of the inductive reactance of the loop. This increase should be limited by adjusting wire size and the number of turns to result in an impedance at 1000 Hz that is no more than three times the impedance at 100 Hz. This moderately rising impedance characteristic (and falling loop current) will complement the rising sensitivity characteristic of the T-coil, as shown in Fig. 27-7. Too high an impedance at high frequencies will result in too low current, hence, poor response and degraded signal-to-noise ratios.

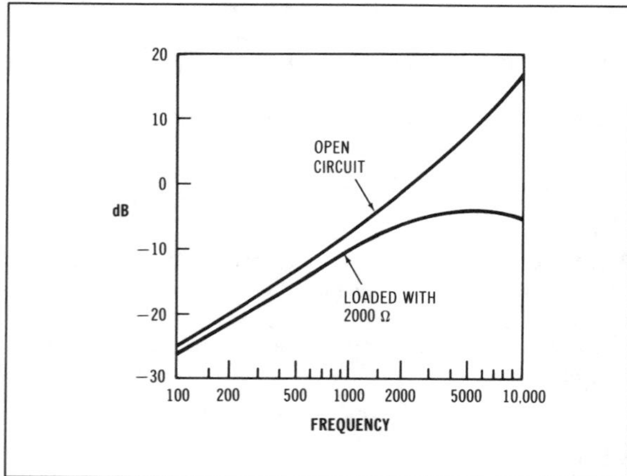

Figure 27-7 Sensitivity of typical inductive coil. *(From Reference 1)*

A wire size that can handle the required current with an acceptable heat rise is selected from Table 27-1. The impedance is then calculated at several frequencies such as 100 Hz, 1 kHz, and 10 kHz. The following formulas are useful:

$$L = (rn^2/13.5)\log(2.8r/d) \qquad (27\text{-}5)$$

where,
L is the inductance in henrys,
r is the radius of the loop in inches,
n is the number of turns,
d is the diameter of the conductor in inches (this is a simplification of Wheeler's formula); and

$$Z = \sqrt{R^2 + (2\pi fL \times 10^{-6})^2} \qquad (27\text{-}6)$$

where,
Z is the loop impedance,
R is the dc resistance,
f is the frequency of interest,
L is the inductance.

Throughout this design procedure there is a certain amount of approximation involved; for instance, Eq. 27-5 applies to round loops; therefore, an error is introduced in calculating the inductance of a square or rectangular loop. However, the error is not great enough to render the computations useless.

27.3.5 ELECTRONIC SYSTEM

A power amplifier is selected that can supply the required current to the loop. The power required is determined with the basic formula

$$P = I^2Z$$

The adjustment of the output current is determined by the formula

$$I = E/Z$$

An autotransformer or other suitable impedance matching is used to match the amplifier to the loop. In the absence of an impedance meter, the loop dc resistance may be used for matching to the amplifier because at the minimum impedance point (low frequencies), the impedance is largely resistive.

A typical loop system diagram is shown in Fig. 27-8. In very large halls, a delay unit may be required in the more distant loops in order to avoid excessive time delays between the loop signal and the acoustic signal. Equalization is desirable to compensate for any frequency response irregularities. The equalizer is adjusted to provide a natural sound quality with a typical receiver and to ensure that power is not transmitted outside the limits of the receiver.

Table 27-1. Copper Wire Data

AWG#	Ohms per 1000 ft	Diameter, in.	Current for Heat Rise* 5°C	10°C	20°C	Melting Current
24	25.67	0.02010	2.3 A	3.2 A	4.5 A	29.2 A
22	16.14	0.02535	3.0 A	4.2 A	5.9 A	41.2 A
20	10.15	0.03196	4.0 A	5.5 A	7.8 A	58.6 A
18	6.375	0.04030	5.5 A	7.8 A	10.0 A	82.4 A
16	4.016	0.05082	7.5 A	10.0 A	15.0 A	117.0 A

*Heat rise based on an insulation thickness of 10 mils. Heavier insulation allows more current for the same heat rise.

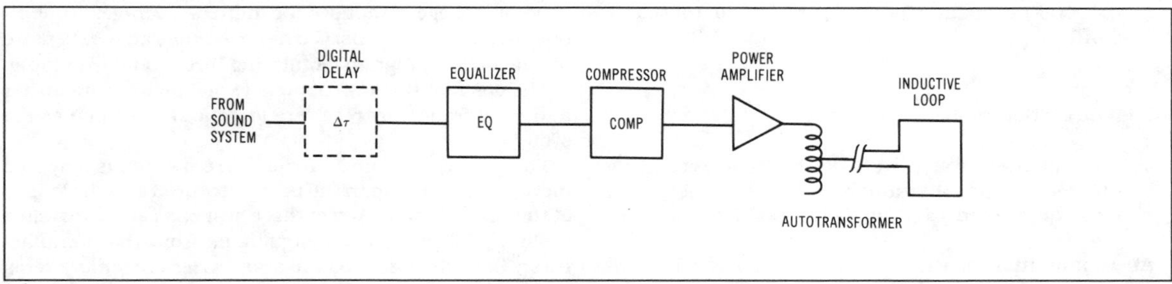

Figure 27-8 Induction loop system block diagram.

A compressor is needed to ensure that the system does not produce excessive distortion at high signal levels, either from clipping the amplifier or from overloading the hearing aid T-coil. The compressor should be adjusted according to the nature of the principal program material. If the system is used mostly for music, a compression ratio of about 4:1 will result in minimal harm to the music. If speech is the principal program, compression ratios up to 20:1 can be used to improve both intelligibility and signal-to-noise ratios.

27.3.6 Installation

If the loop is to be installed in conduit, it must be in pvc or other nonmetallic conduit and should be placed so that there is little (or no) steel between the loop and the listener. Most commonly, the conduit is run in the top of a concrete slab or below a wood-framed floor; but it can also be run in walls or even the ceiling of a room. When installing in an existing room, it is often easiest to run the loop wire under the carpet, using conduit only for the run to the amplifier.

27.4 FM BROADCAST

FM broadcast systems have almost totally replaced magnetic loops in classrooms where hearing-impaired children are taught because the FM signal is normally free from noise and provides a more uniform and reliable signal. Several channels are available; thus, systems can be used in adjacent rooms. The sound quality is excellent. The useful receiving range will vary from 100 to 300 ft depending upon the amount of steel in the building. Transmitters are available for operation from the powerline for permanent installations or by battery for portable applications.

The Federal Communications Commission (FCC) has set aside a band of frequencies (72.025 to 75.975 MHz) for FM broadcasting to the hearing impaired. These frequencies cannot be used for any other purpose, such as language translation systems or communications applications. No license is required, although the manufacturer of the transmitter is required to have FCC approval of the transmitter design. The FCC restricts radiation to a maximum field strength of 8000 μV/m at 30 m. The system requires no special knowledge to install; sufficient instructions are provided by the manufacturers.

The receivers are fixed-frequency devices and cannot be tuned to any other channel, nor can regular commerical FM broadcasting receivers be used. The receivers are small—mostly pocket size. Where more than one channel is in use, as in a school, separate sets of receivers would be required for each operating channel.

27.5 AM BROADCAST

AM broadcast systems are largely unregulated by the Federal Communications Commission (FCC). The basic rules (from FCC Bulletin OEC 12 dated July 1977) follow:

1. The system must not cause any interference to an existing licensed service.

2. The operating frequency must be in the AM broadcast band or below (10 to 490 kHz and 510 to 1600 kHz).
3. In the 510- to 1600-kHz band, an open-wire antenna may be used providing it does not exceed 10 ft in length and providing the transmitter is restricted to an input power of 100 mwatts.

   Or Any type of antenna and transmitter power may be used provided the field strength does not exceed:

   (2400/F) μV/m at 300 m in the 10- to 490-kHz band
   (24000/F) μV/m at 30 m in the 510- to 1600-kHz band

where,
F is the carrier frequency in kilohertz.

4. Carrier current system radiation limits are set slightly differently. The radiation from the electrical system must not exceed 15 μV/m at 157,000/F feet.

An examination of these radiation restrictions indicates that the lowest operating frequency results in the greatest coverage area. AM systems typically operate on carrier frequencies below 700 kHz.

The sound quality and noise level of an AM broadcast signal are better than from a magnetic induction loop but inferior to an FM system. In general, if a pocket AM radio receives a local station well in the space, the low-power broadcasting system will work as well. Systems operating in the commercial broadcasting band (540 to 1600 kHz) may be picked up on any AM receiver. Systems operating below the standard broadcast band are available with fixed-frequency, nontunable receivers.

At first it may seem economically attractive to select a system operating in the regular broadcast band because the patrons could be expected to furnish their own receivers. But upon reflection, there is much to be said in favor of the special nontunable receiver. For example, picture a hearing-impaired patron in the third row trying to find the local broadcast with the earphone unplugged and the loudspeaker blasting away as the receiver is tuned across every rock-and-roll station in town!

The coverage area to be expected from an AM system depends upon the type of antenna employed. The three types of antenna are *open wire*, *lossy coaxial cable*, and *carrier current*. The quality of the broadcast sound is very little dependent upon the antenna type; only the coverage area is affected by the antenna.

Open-wire antenna systems with their restricted power and antenna length usually achieve coverage ranging from 50 to 150 ft depending upon the amount of steel in the building. Fixed-frequency, below-the-broadcast-band systems usually employ an open-wire antenna. These systems are used by many churches.

Lossy coaxial cable systems employ a special type of coaxial cable that has a very loose or open shield, thus, allowing a little radiation to occur all along the cable. The usable reception range is 50 to 75 ft from the cable. The length of the cable may be quite long if necessary. The lossy coaxial technique is found in drive-in cinemas, stadiums, and arenas and can be used for broadcasting flight arrival and departure information along the highway approaches to airports.

The most common type of AM system is carrier current. In this system the output of the transmitter is capacitively coupled into the main power distribution wiring of the building. The radio signal travels throughout the building on the electrical wiring. This system is widely used on college campuses for limited-coverage, student-operated radio stations. Carrier current is an inexpensive way to provide program monitoring throughout a building.

The costs of the low-frequency, open-wire transmitter and fixed-frequency receivers are about the same as FM systems.

The lossy coaxial and carrier-current systems may cost more, depending upon the power required and the length of the coaxial cable. Any of these systems can be installed easily by following the instructions from the manufacturer. Both the lossy coaxial and carrier-current systems should be planned through consultation with the manufacturer of the transmitter.

27.6 INFRARED

Infrared light can be used to broadcast a very high-quality signal. Presently available systems can broadcast up to nine different programs on the same emitter, thus making infrared very useful for large-scale language translation systems. It is the only system that can transmit in stereo. Also unlike the other systems, infrared broadcasts are completely contained within the room because infrared behaves like visible light; it cannot go through a wall; even a heavy cloth is an opaque barrier. This control of the broadcast range is a significant factor where confidentiality is important, as in corporate meeting rooms. For this reason and because of its outstanding sound quality, infrared is the system of choice of almost every professional theater and concert hall in New York and Los Angeles.

There is a unique limitation to the use of infrared: it cannot be used in bright daylight. The infrared light occurring as a natural part of daylight will wipe out the lower power-modulated light from the system. The system can also receive interference from incandescent lamps at very high levels such as on a film or television production stage. Partially dimmed incandescent lamps can be a problem in some situations because the reduced voltage to the lamps causes a shift toward red that greatly increases the infrared output of the lamp. This increase in infrared interference can, on rare occasions, be a problem where audience down lights are left at a dimmed setting if the infrared beam from the system is also weak. Deep under a balcony is a likely trouble spot. When this problem occurs, it is necessary to dim the lights more or add more emitters to the infrared system.

The infrared system hardware consists of a transmitter, power supply, and two or more emitter panels. The useful coverage pattern of the emitter varies with distance and the number of channels being transmitted, as shown in Fig. 27-9. The number of emitters required depends upon the size and shape of the area to be covered and upon the number of channels in use. Emitters are usually employed in pairs, located at each front side of the audience and cross fired across the seating area so that each person receives an infrared beam from each side. This cross firing helps to eliminate shadowing from other people in the audience.

The manufacturer provides detailed instructions for planning and installing the system. A useful tool in aiming the emitters is a low-cost, black-and-white television camera and monitor. Most monochrome television cameras have useful sensitivity in the infrared region. With the room lights off, observe on the television monitor the part of the room illuminated by the infrared beam. The well-illuminated area will be the area of good reception. A corollary to this procedure is that the infrared television viewing system can be used to view a darkened stage—say for coordination of rigging and prop moves in a fast, complicated change in the dark.

27.7 RECEIVERS

Receivers are required with all systems, though fewer are needed with an induction loop because many patrons will have aids equipped with T-coils. Most manufacturers of systems for the hearing impaired offer several types of earphones with their receivers. Typically these include a single earpiece, a stethoscope-type dual earpiece, and an induction loop for use with the patron's T-coil. Most users report a strong preference for the dual earpiece instruments. Most users also report a strong dislike for an over-the-head type headphone because they are uncomfortable for long periods of use and destructive to hair styles. Two types of induction loops are available. One is a small coil that hooks over the ear close by the hearing aid; this type is often hard for elderly people to use properly. The more popular loop is a lanyard type that hangs around the neck and may be used to support the receiver.

Many theaters and churches that have installed a system for the hearing impaired have found normal-hearing

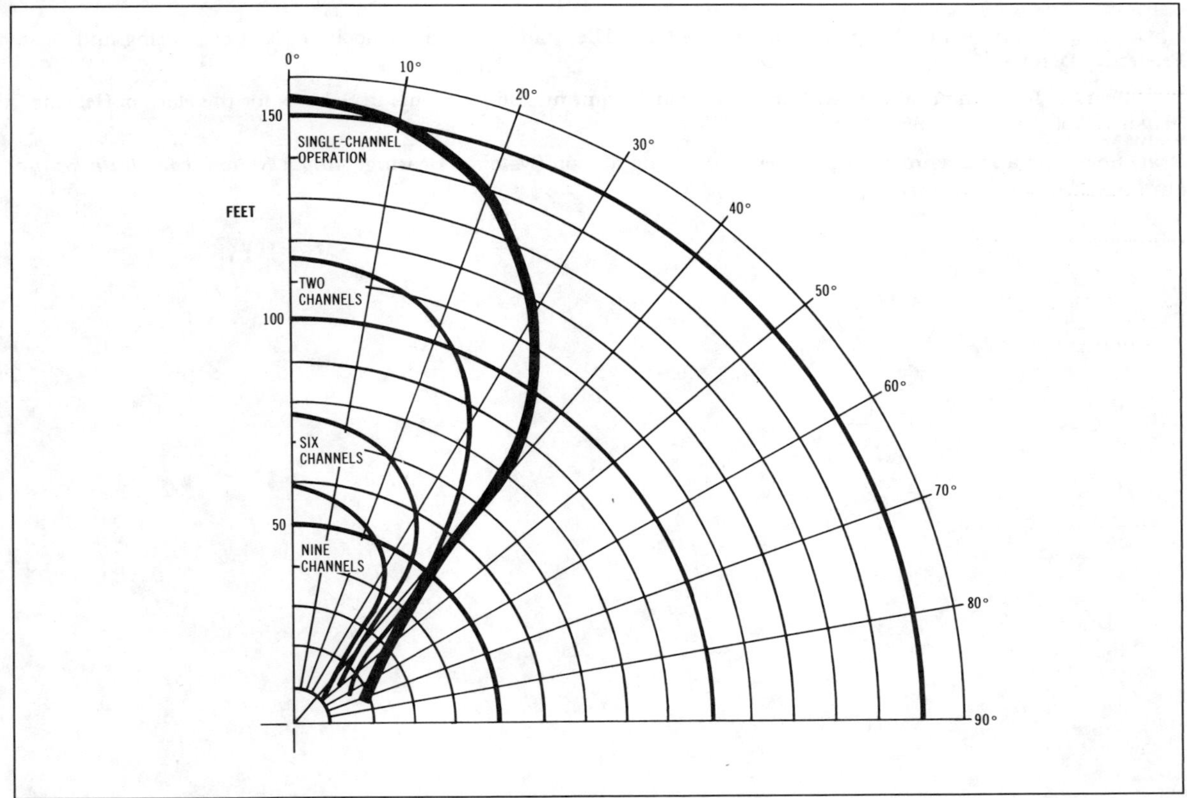

Figure 27-9 Infrared emitter panel coverage patterns.

patrons using the system to enhance their listening comfort, which is especially true in larger houses with seats in areas of poor natural acoustics. These normal-hearing patrons universally prefer the dual earpiece both because it sounds more natural and because a single earpiece leaves one ear open to receive the live sound from the stage with a time-delay annoyance. Depending upon the distance from the stage, this delay can be very distracting to those with less than profound hearing impairments.

Battery replacement and earpiece sanitizing are the principal maintenance problems with the systems. Some users have reported a battery life of one year, although that seems an uncommonly long life if the receivers are being used often. The infrared receivers have rechargeable batteries, which the manufacturer suggests should be recharged after each use. Earpieces are most commonly sanitized by replacing the plastic ear tips or by using replaceable foam balls.

Most theaters and concert halls provide receivers to their patrons for no charge or for a small fee to cover the cost of handling, batteries, and sanitizing. Some organizations have been successful in selling receivers to regular patrons, especially in communities where several theaters and churches use the same technology.

REFERENCES

1. M. C. Martin, "Power Requirements for Inductive Loops," *Royal National Institute for the Deaf*, London, England.
2. S. C. Dalsgaard, "Field Distribution Inside Rectangular Induction Loops," State Hearing Centers, Research Laboratory for Technical Audiology, University Hospital, Odente, Denmark.
3. D. Bosman and L.J.M. Joosten, "A New Approach to a Space-Confined Magnetic Loop Induction System." *IEEE Transactions on Audio*, May/June 1965.

BIBLIOGRAPHY FOR LOOP SYSTEMS

K. Borrild, "The Induction Loop and Its Possibilities," The State Boarding School for Hard of Hearing and Deaf, Frederica, Denmark.

E. deBoer, C. Kruidenier, and K. W. Kortschot, "On Communication Systems in Schools for the Hard-of-Hearing," *Acustica*, vol. 19, no. 3, 1967-1968.

RNID Scientific and Technical Department, Installing a Loop System. "Hearing," *Royal National Institute for the Deaf*, October 1977.

CHAPTER **28**

The Broadcast Chain

by Douglas W. Fearn

An audio source (record, tape, live microphone, and so on) must pass through a multitude of links in the broadcast chain before it is heard by the listener, as shown in Fig. 28-1. There is a wide range of equipment quality, complexity, and vintage found in radio and television stations, but certain links will always be found. This discussion focuses primarily on radio broadcasting; television audio is basically similar.

28.1 TRANSMISSION LINKS

28.1.1 Consoles

The various sources, such as turntables, tape cartridge players, microphones, network lines, reel-to-reel tape machines, and so on, all pass through a mixing console. This mixer (Fig. 28-2) has, at a minimum, faders for level control, routing switches to determine the destination of an input, and meter(s) to monitor the levels. The console may also contain active or passive input on-off switching, voltage-controlled amplifiers (VCAs), equalizers and/or filters, and provision for outboard processing (e.g., limiter, noise gate, external equalization). In a stereo console all circuits (except "cue") would be duplicated. Pan pots might be included for some monaural inputs on a stereo console.

Broadcast consoles tend to be much simpler than recording consoles, but many recording studio features are being added to modern broadcast consoles, especially in consoles designed for production or live-performance

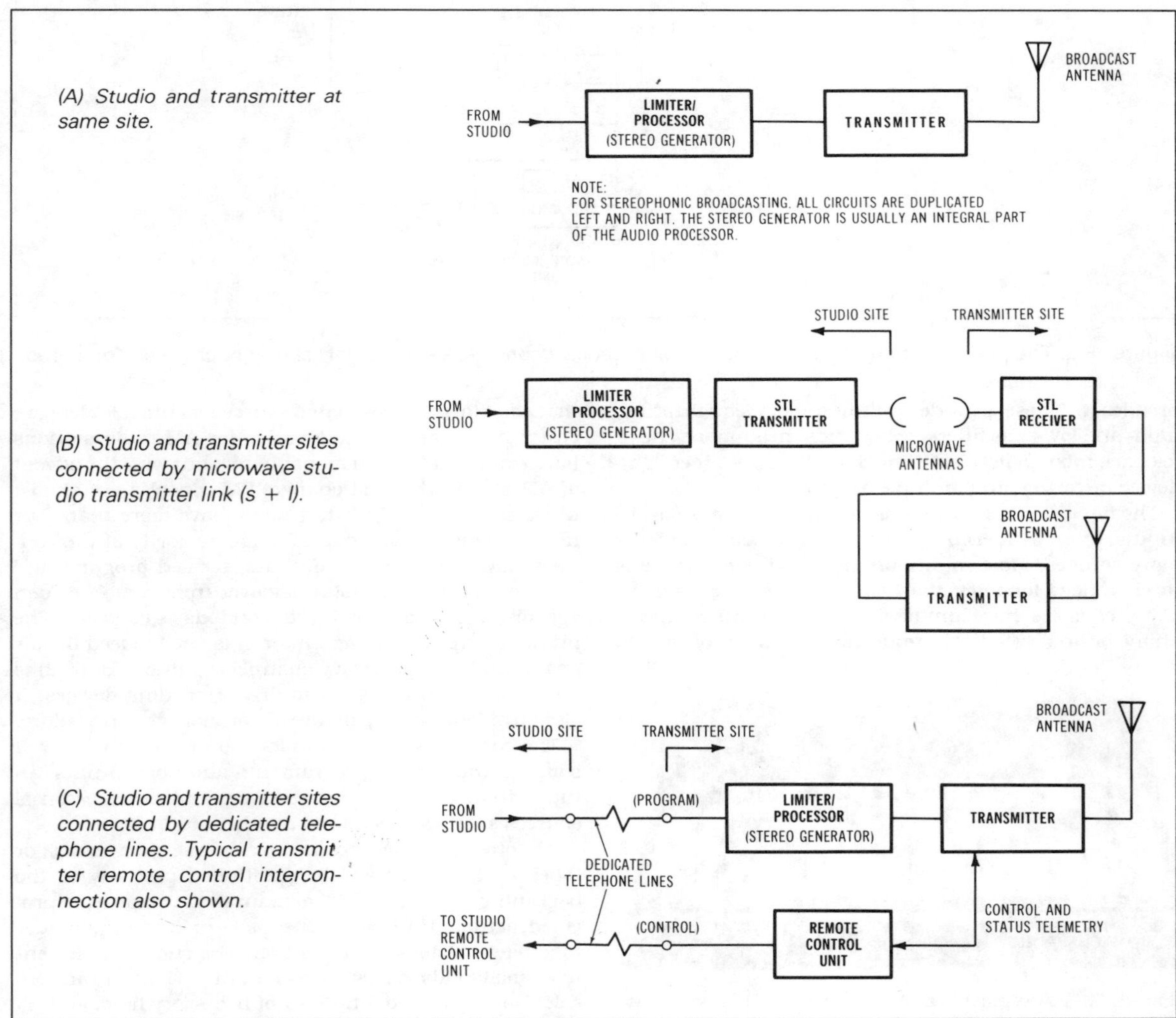

Figure 28-1 The broadcast chain.

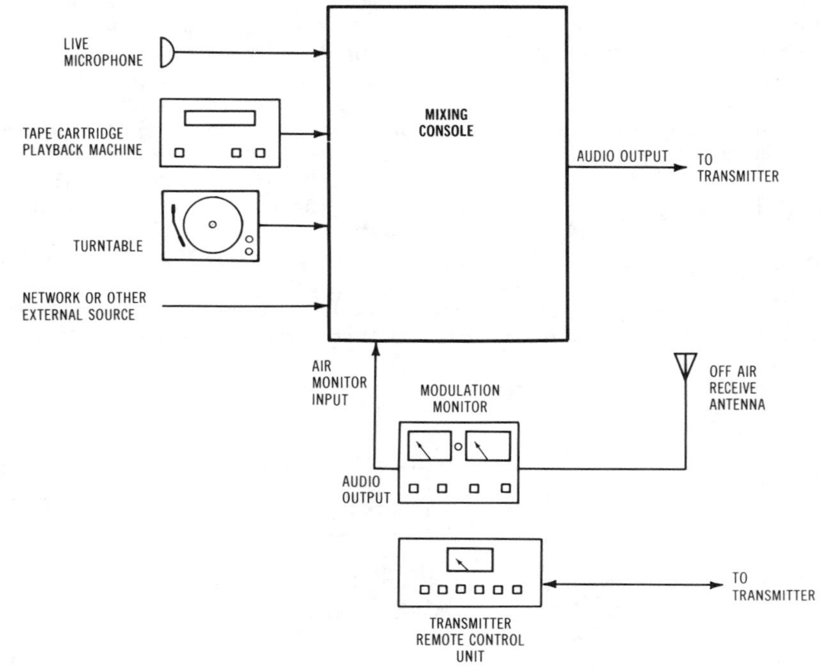

Figure 28-2 The block diagram of a typical monaural broadcast console. Duplicate left and right channels for stereo.

broadcast. These include multifrequency equalization, high- and low-pass filters, echo sends, headphone cue or foldback mixing, light-emitting diode (LED) or other light-device metering, and multiple output buses.

The typical on-air radio console (Fig. 28-3), has 8 to 16 inputs, often with each input switchable between two or more sources. Most inputs are line level, since there is rarely a need for more than two or three microphones. Many consoles have inputs that can be either microphone or line level. Each input includes an on-off switch that can start the associated source machine. Faders are either rotary or linear. Consoles for AM radio stations have traditionally been monophonic, but with the advent of AM stereo, this will change. FM consoles are almost universally stereo, but they rarely have more than four independent output channels. The majority of the consoles have two separate outputs, termed program and audition on older units, a holdover from radio's golden age, or just A and B, or 1 and 2 on today's consoles. The primary output (program, A, or 1) is used to feed the air chain, and the secondary channel (audition, B, or 2) is an auxiliary output used to drive recording devices. It also provides a back up in case of a primary channel failure.

Figure 28-3 A typical broadcast console. This one uses light-emitting diode meters in place of conventional volume-unit meters. *(Courtesy Radio Systems, Inc.)*

The console has provision for monitoring a variety of sources: the various program and audition outputs, an input from an off-the-air receiver, and other external sources such as a feed from another studio.

It is often necessary to cue up a source such as disk or tapes so that they will be positioned precisely at the beginning of the audio. A monaural cue channel is provided, actuated by turning the rotary or linear input fader to a detent at its lowest position. The cue signal is sent to a small loudspeaker, often mounted right in the console. Quality reproduction is not necessary here, and, in fact, quality could be a source of confusion as to what is on the air and what is in cue. (If quality evaluation is required, the audition channel would be used.) Some consoles have *solo* or *prefade listen* switches that allow each input to be monitored either on a separate cue loudspeaker or by utilizing the main monitors, muting the usual monitor source temporarily. Solo is usually a monaural system that can be activated with the input faders either on or off (as opposed to a traditional cue system that requires the fader to be fully off).

If the station has audio sources from other than the main control room (from a news studio, for example), talk-back facilities allow communication between the rooms. The talk-back circuitry is built into most consoles.

All broadcast consoles must have provision for muting (or sometimes dimming) the monitor loudspeakers when the microphone is on. This same circuitry is used to illuminate on-air warning lights and possibly to mute other potential sources of noise such as talkback loudspeakers or telephone bells.

It is not unusual for signal processing, usually a limiter, or an equalizer, reverberation, and/or a noise gate, to be inserted in the main microphone channel. This processing is necessary in some instances to make the live microphone sound compatible with highly processed vocals on records and commercials. Noise gates may be utilized to minimize mechanical noise in the control room or to make a room with poor acoustics less objectionable.

In most modern consoles, the input on button can be wired to simultaneously start the associated source, such as a turntable, a cartridge machine, or a reel-to-reel tape machine, and to reset a digital timer used to keep track of the running time of each source as it is started.

28.1.2 Tape Cartridges

The primary source material for most radio stations today is music derived from phonograph records. Although many stations play directly from records, maintaining disks in top condition while in daily use is next to impossible. Therefore, many stations have chosen to transfer their music to tape cartridges (Fig. 28-4).

The tape cartridge is a continuous-loop device using a lubricated ¼-in. tape. The tape is pulled from the inside of the tape pack, guided past the heads, and returned to the outside of the tape pack. The tape hub revolves, but the tape must also slip within the pack to compensate for the difference in inner and outer diameter. The tape is normally run at 7½ in./s, although some cartridge machines are designed for 3¾ or 15 in./s. The cartridges are made in three package sizes, each with a different maximum playing time; the smallest size is most often employed. These can be loaded with up to about 9 min of tape, although most standard lengths are shorter. Since the tape is pulled from the center of the pack and is returned to the outside of the pack, it would appear that the system would require additional tape to magically be provided after the capstan. The solution is to use a lubricated tape that slips between winding layers as the cartridge runs. This slippage causes several problems: the tape is under a constant stretching force, and the tape tension across the heads is somewhat dependent on the cartridge itself and will change as the tape lubrication wears out.

Figure 28-4 Tape cartridges are continuous-loop devices. *(Courtesy Fidelipac Corp.)*

Pressure pads inside the cartridge are used to force the tape against the heads. The quality and accuracy of these pads have a large effect on the reproduced audio. Some cartridges use metal springs directly opposite the head to press a foam or fabric pad against the tape. Other designs rely on the compression of a foam block to provide the necessary tape-to-head contact.

One of the biggest problems is that much of the tape path guiding is in the cartridge and not in the machine and thus is different for each cartridge inserted. Consistent high-frequency response, accurate phasing between channels, and minimum wow and flutter require a precise tape path. Obtaining and maintaining this precision with plastic parts is quite difficult. Cartridges are often subjected to daily or even hourly use and may be dropped or otherwise abused. Ingenious cartridge and machine designs have been developed to provide a surprisingly high quality of reproduction, comparable to that obtained from reel-to-reel machines in some systems.

Regular maintenance is necessary to obtain this performance, including head cleaning at frequent intervals (several times a day in stations with heavy usage), weekly alignment of all mechanical and electrical systems, and prompt replacement of worn parts. The heads in a cartridge machine are quite vulnerable and can be easily knocked out of alignment by hasty cartridge insertion.

The cartridge transport uses only a capstan and pressure roller to move the tape. When no cartridge is being played, the pressure roller is recessed below the level of the deck plate. In a typical machine (Fig. 28-5), inserting the cartridge iluminates a ready light and may start the capstan motor if the motor does not run continuously.

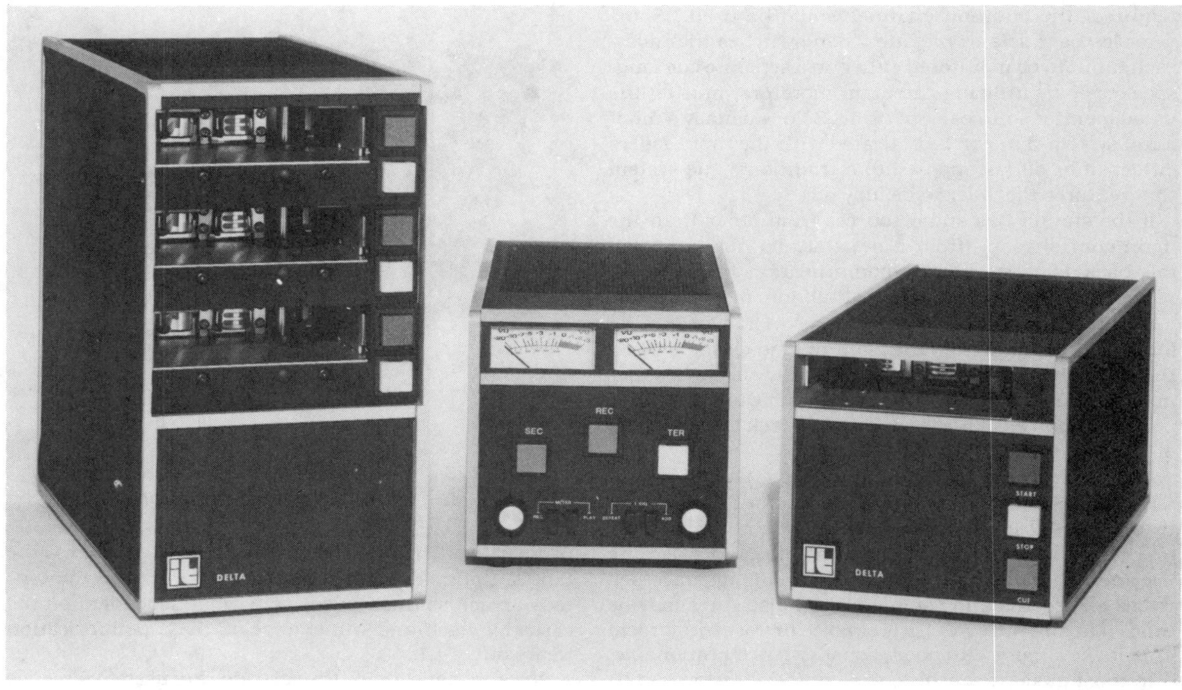

Figure 28-5 The tape cartridge transport is designed for rapid insertion and removal of the cartridge. *(Courtesy International Tapetronics Corp., a division of 3M Co.)*

In some machines, a lever is moved to bring the pressure roller up and into the cartridge, a short distance from contacting the capstan. Starting this type of machine only requires a solenoid to move the pressure roller a small distance. Most machines have a solenoid that brings the pressure roller from rest below the deck plate to capstan contact in one motion when the start button is pressed. Since these machines are usually located in close proximity to live microphones, the mechanism must operate very quietly. Air-damped solenoids are often used.

The pressure roller travels in an arc to meet the capstan, and, therefore, the angle between the capstan and the roller can be inaccurate if the mechanism is not properly aligned. If the capstan and the roller are not precisely parallel, the tape will tend to skew up or down on the capstan and the heads, causing many problems: phase errors between stereo tracks, loss of high-frequency response, lowered output levels, channel balance problems, inability to detect cue tones, and even tape damage.

For mono, two tracks are used: the upper track for the program material and the lower track for cue tones. Cue tones are used to stop the cartridge automatically prior to the beginning of the recorded material. For stereo cartridges, three tracks are used. The top and center tracks are left and right program, respectively, and the bottom track is for cue tones. The primary cue tone is 1 kHz and is used to stop the tape mechanism. Additional cue tones of 150 Hz and 8 kHz may also be recorded on the tape. These secondary and tertiary tones may be used to start the next source, warn the operator that the material is about to run out, automatically mute the cartridge machine output at the end of the audio, or automatically log frequency shift digital data that was previously recorded on the cue track.

Some machines include a high-speed cue mode, which runs the tape at several times normal speed. Often this mode is initiated by the detection of a particular cue tone recorded at the end of the program material.

Because of the limited exposed tape space available and the continuous-loop nature of the system, cartridge machines do not contain erase heads. Tape cartridges must be bulk erased prior to recording. Some cartridge machines contain built-in bulk erasers, but normally hand-held erasers are used. The erasing process must be done carefully, or low-frequency thumps or even some of the previous program may be audible on the finished recording.

Since the tape is a continuous loop, there must be a splice at some point in the cartridge. Recording over this splice will usually cause a dropout. Prior to recording, the tape in the cartridge can be observed while running, and the machine stopped after the splice passes the heads. Also, there are devices that automatically detect the splice and stop the cartridge at the proper point. Splice detection may be done either optically, from the increased reflectivity of the splicing tape, or mechanically, responding to the slight thickening of the tape at the splice. There is at least one cartridge machine that includes a built-in bulk eraser and splice finder.

The cartridge medium has many inherent problems, especially in stereo, and manufacturers of the cartridges and the transports have developed ingenious schemes to obtain high-quality audio. The most serious problem is obtaining an accurate and stable phase relationship between the two stereo channels. Machines have been developed that automatically align the record head for each cartridge before recording in order to obtain minimum high-frequency phase error. Lacking such a machine, stations have installed oscilloscopes in the production studios set up to monitor left and right channels in an XY manner. A high-frequency tone (10 kHz or higher) is made available and recorded (in phase) on both tracks. Head alignment is adjusted for minimum phase error between the channels.

Some cartridges have adjustable tape guides that may be aligned to provide the most accurate and stable phasing between tracks.

Another approach is to record left plus right audio on one track and left minus right on the other. A matrix in the playback machine decodes these tracks to left and right, which allows a much greater tape skewing error or head azimuth misalignment before serious audio distortion occurs.

The relatively slow tape speed and narrow track width can reduce the signal-to-noise ratio as compared to the source material; therefore, some stations are using noise-reduction systems.

Tape saturation, especially from high frequencies, can also be a problem. But with high-quality tape, cartridges, and machines, and with regular and careful maintenance and alignment, the cartridge system can provide high-performance audio.

28.1.3 Turntables, Pickups, and Preamplifiers

Broadcast equipment for playing phonograph records must be rugged and reliable. Most turntables used today are of the direct-drive type, with rapid starting speed. Records are cued to the beginning of the audio, and then rotated backward a third of a revolution. This requires a pickup and stylus capable of being back cued. Preamplifiers must be stable and reliable. Since some stations have their studios and transmitters in the same building, the preamplifier must also be immune to the high rf field present.

28.1.4 Microphones

Since most broadcast stations use the announcer or disk jockey as the equipment operator, the microphone is located in the control room. Although the equipment is usually reasonably quiet, directional microphones are used to minimize the pickup of mechanical noise from cartridge machines and other devices. A wide variety of microphones may be found in radio studios; announcers often have a personal favorite that they feel makes them sound best. Dynamic microphones are most popular, but both ribbon and condenser types are also used.

28.1.5 Telephone Interface and Delay

Many stations feature live call-in telephone shows during which members of the listening audience may participate in the program by making comments or asking questions. This type of program requires a system that will allow the caller audio to be routed to the console for broadcast but at the same time prevent the announcer's voice quality from being degraded by the telephone system. Elaborate schemes have been devised that utilize active or transformer hybrid devices, audio gates, limiters, equalizers, and so on to achieve good isolation between incoming and outgoing telephone audio and to obtain the greatest intelligibility and fidelity from the 300- to 3000-Hz telephone system.

In addition, some form of delay is necessary permitting the broadcast personnel to delete any undesirable remarks made by a caller. Delay can be done with specially designed tape delay systems, usually with a 3- to 10-s delay. Cartridge machines, with an erase head, reversed record and play heads, and short cartridge, can also be used (Fig. 28-6). The program is recorded on the tape, travels through the cartridge, and is played back 3 to 8 seconds later. An erase head (not normally present in tape cartridge machines) erases the tape prior to rerecording. The erase head may be combined with the record head in some designs. The trend now is toward digital delay devices. A timing problem exists in getting into and out of the delayed portion of the program. This problem is particularly troublesome if a specific time event is included in the program (such as a network newscast). The digital delay device may be capable of gradually increasing or decreasing the delay time, using the natural pauses in between words to change the delay time.

28.1.6 Reel-to-Reel Tape Machines

Reel-to-reel machines used in broadcasting are generally similar to those used for recording. Such recording refinements as synchronized recording, over-dubbing capability, variable-speed operation, motion-sensing tape handling, and servo-controlled tape tension are finding their way into the broadcast studio, especially in the more sophisticated production rooms. Multitrack machines, usually four-track but sometimes eight-tracks or even more, are being used by some stations, particularly if they do a lot of commercial production.

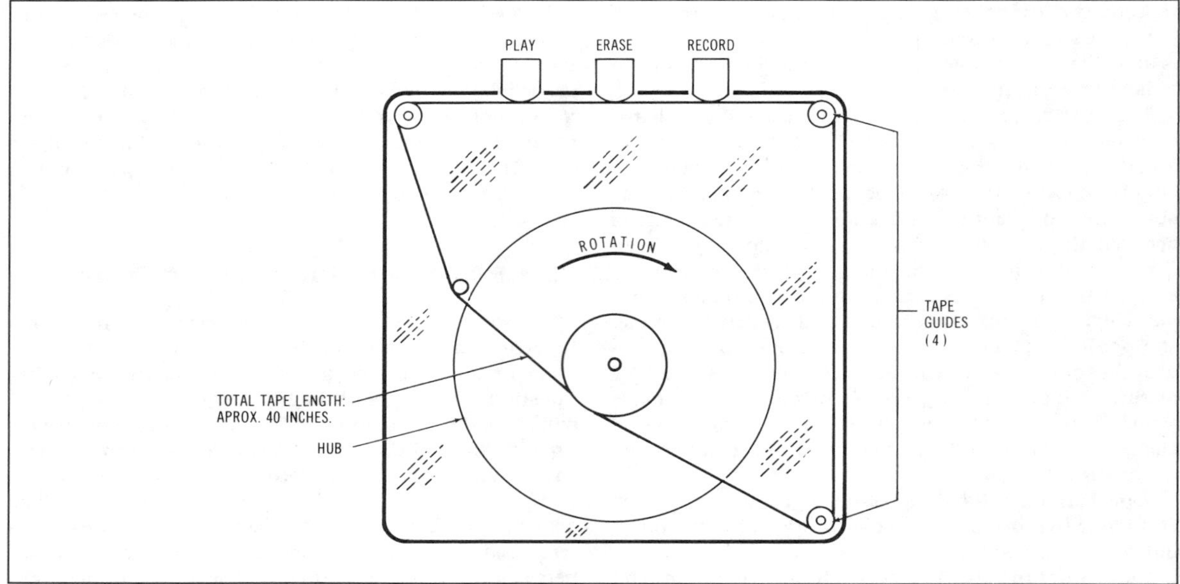

Figure 28-6 Tape-delay cartridge arrangement.

The workhorse tape machine is still a basic model, perhaps even a playback-only version if it is used only for on-air reproduction.

28.1.7 Studio-Transmitter Link

The broadcast studio building is often in a business area of a city, but the transmitter is located in an area chosen to optimize the signal over the coverage area. This separation requires a high-quality audio link between the two. Leased telephone lines were the only available connection for many years, but microwave links, called *stls* (for studio-transmitter link), are replacing phone lines (Fig. 27-7). Telephone lines can be a high-quality transmission medium, but they require equalization and amplification along their route if it is more than a couple of miles long. Lines are available in a variety of bandwidths, ranging from voice grade (300 to 3000 Hz) to high quality (50 Hz to 15 kHz). For stereo it is vital that two matched lines have identical routing and that the equalization and amplification be closely matched to avoid phase errors. The actual length of the line may be considerably longer than the distance between the studio and transmitter because of the various telephone company offices that the line must run through for equalization and amplification.

The microwave link has the advantage of being more direct and completely under the control of the station. The stereo program is sent from the studio to the transmitter as a *composite* signal, which includes the necessary stereo pilot signal and subchannel modulation generation. Transmission as a composite signal eliminates the potential phase-error problems of separate channels; however, it is possible to use two matched transmitters and receivers operating on slightly different frequencies. The transmission uses frequency modulation, is at ultra-high frequencies (typically in the 950-MHz region), and is generally limited to line-of-sight paths. Depending on the terrain, a microwave link can be used over ten miles or more, although most links are shorter. It is also possible to use relay stations to increase the range or to overcome obstacles in the path.

28.1.8 Broadcast Transmitters and Antennas

A typical broadcast transmitter generates the radio-frequency signal and amplifies it to the required level. A 30-kW FM transmitter is shown in Fig. 28-8. The resulting signal generated by the transmitter is connected to the antenna by way of a coaxial transmission line.

The antennas for FM or television stations are generally mounted on the side or at the top of a steel tower. Wavelengths for these services are relatively short, and the basic antennas are not large. The antenna often consists of a number of separate bays, to increase the gain of the system.

AM frequencies are much lower, and the wavelength is correspondingly large. An AM station utilizes the entire steel tower as the radiating element. Many AM stations are licensed as *directional*; that is, they must limit their signals in specified directions, which is accomplished

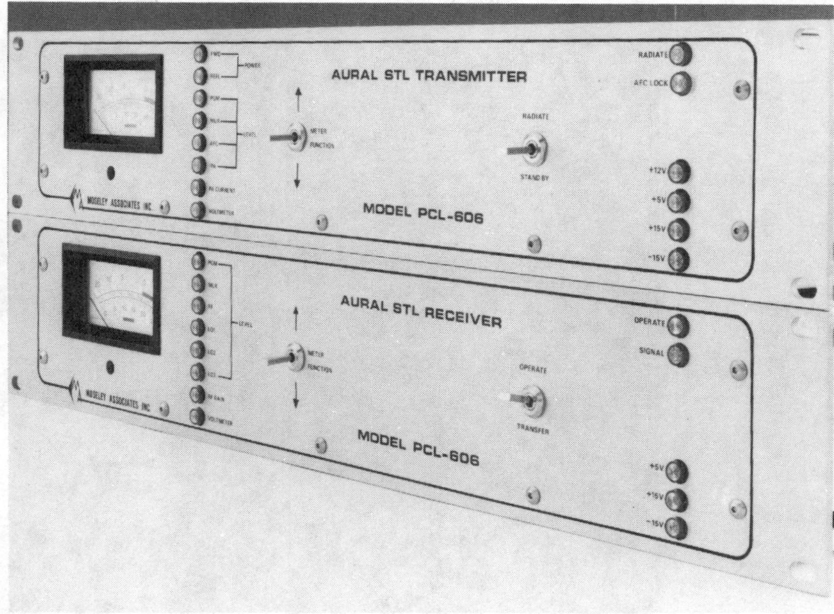

Figure 28-7 Microwave transmitter and receiver used as a studio-to-transmitter link (stl). *(Courtesy Moseley Associates Inc.)*

through the use of two or more towers, each fed with rf power at calculated phase and amplitude.

In any antenna system, insufficient bandwidth in the antenna system can have deleterious effects on the received audio. On AM signals, high-frequency response suffers; on FM signals, stereo separation is reduced.

28.1.9 Monitoring Systems

Although technically not a part of the chain of equipment between the source and the listener, the monitor system used must provide the broadcasting personnel with an accurate representation of the on-air sound. Since a good deal of processing may occur between the source and the transmitter, it is necessary to monitor the signal off the air. Modulation monitors (Fig. 28-9) are required by the FCC regulations to ensure that modulation is within tolerance. (The block diagram in Fig. 28-10 shows a typical FM monitor.) The modulation monitor is a sophisticated receiver with precision metering circuitry for measuring modulation percentage. Since a mechanical meter cannot follow peaks of short duration, a flashing light is provided that will illuminate for a few seconds every time a peak above a selectable percentage of modulation is detected. In addition, facilities are provided for measurement of signal-to-noise ratio, stereo separation, stereo pilot-level injection, stereo subchannel modulation, subcarrier modulation percentage, and crosstalk between the various channels. Although no longer required by law, some monitors also measure the transmitter frequency and, when used, the frequencies of the stereo pilot and subcarrier.

Modulation monitors have outputs for external test equipment, such as a distortion analyzer, a frequency counter, or an oscilloscope. An audio output is provided, from which most stations derive their air monitor, which is routed through the console and then to a power amplifier and monitor loudspeakers.

Although not usually as large in size nor driven by as much power as recording studio monitor systems, broadcast monitors are usually of high quality. A typical broadcast monitor, as shown in Fig. 28-11, is a two- or three-way system of the larger bookshelf variety. Some consoles, usually older designs, have built-in power amplifiers to drive the monitor loudspeaker(s). More often, an external amplifier of 20 to 75 W per channel is used.

28.2 TRANSMISSION CHARACTERISTICS

28.2.1 Modulation

AM and FM broadcasting differ in many ways, some due to the physics of the modulating process and others because of the frequencies used, and still others due to FCC regulations, as shown in Figs. 28-12 and 28-13. AM was the first modulation method used because it is more easily received by simple receivers. Because of the physics involved, the maximum amount of modulation of an AM signal is restricted to 100%, at least in the negative direc-

Figure 28-8 A 30-kW transmitter. *(Courtesy Broadcast Electronics, Inc.)*

tion. There is no theoretical limit to the amount of positive modulation, but the FCC regulations restrict it to 125%. Exceeding the 100% negative maximum modulation causes distortion and possible interference to other stations. Positive modulation in excess of 100% is achieved by introducing, or increasing, asymmetry in the audio waveform so that the positive peaks are a couple of decibels higher than the corresponding negative peaks. This distortion has not been found to be particularly irritating, since most natural sounds are not symmetrical. Asymmetrical modulation increases the loudness of the signal.

It is important not to exceed these limits of 100% negative and 125% positive, and many techniques have been developed to ensure compliance. Various limiting and clipping schemes have been used, many which limit the negative modulation to 100% while permitting up to 125% positive modulation. All these devices reduce the dynamic range of the program material and often introduce at least some distortion or noise. They are considered necessary to provide a high average audio level to the listener, especially to listeners in noisy environments such as automobiles, as well as to comply with the law.

FM has no such physical limit on the modulation, but the greater the modulation the more bandwidth the signal occupies. The modulation of an FM signal is, therefore, restricted by law to a deviation of ±75 kHz. FM broadcasting has a system of preemphasis and deem-

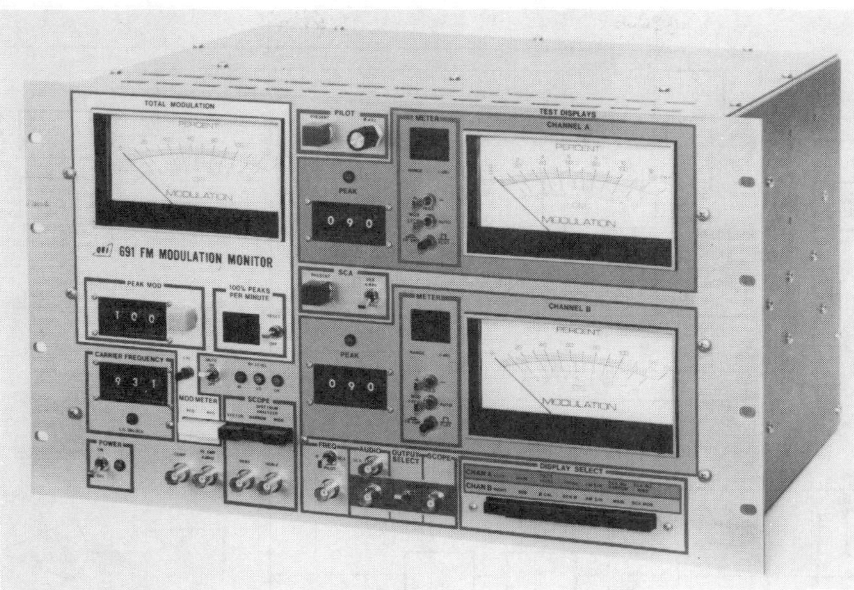

Figure 28-9 An FM modulation monitor. The meters and peak indicators can be switched to measure a variety of parameters of the air signal. *(Courtesy QEI Corp.)*

phasis similar to that used in cutting disks and in tape recording. The high audio frequencies are boosted in transmission and correspondingly attenuated in the receiver, which improves the signal-to-noise ratio. The preemphasis used results in a boost of approximately 17 dB at 15 kHz, as shown in Fig. 28-14. With some program material this presents no special problems since the energy content of most music and voices decreases with frequency. But with much contemporary music, a large amount of high-frequency equalization may have been added during recording, resulting in potential overmodulation of the FM signal. The solution is either to reduce the amount of modulation to accommodate the high frequencies or to use a frequency selective limiter that has increased sensitivity to high frequencies (corresponding to the preemphasis curve). The first approach retains the proper frequency balance but reduces the signal-to-noise ratio at the receiver (and makes the station sound less loud than other stations). The second approach will reduce the brightness of the program material. A number of highly sophisticated devices have been developed to cope with this problem. Fig. 28-15 shows a signal-processing device for FM broadcasting.

The unit accepts left and right inputs, and outputs a composite signal consisting of the main (monaural) modulation, the stereo subchannel (L − R), and the stereo 19-kHz pilot. The modulation level is controlled by sophisticated limiting and clipping circuitry designed to provide high average audio levels while minimizing objectionable byproducts and maintaining the modulation within legal limits.

28.2.2 FM Stereo

The system used for FM stereo transmission must be compatible with monaural receivers. That is, the audio from a monaural receiver must be the sum of the left and right stereo channels, which is accomplished by alternately transmitting the left and right channels as the main modulation on the carrier at a 38-kHz rate (Fig. 28-16). The various byproducts of the chopping process are filtered out. The stereo information, in the form of a *left minus right*, or *difference* signal derived from a phase reversal of one channel, is transmitted as an amplitude-modulated subchannel centered at 38 kHz removed from the main carrier, as shown in Fig. 28-17. This subchannel occupies the space from 23 to 53 kHz, representing a double sideband, amplitude-modulated signal with a 15-kHz bandwidth. The carrier is suppressed at least 40 dB below 100% modulation. The carrier is regenerated in the receiver by doubling the 19-kHz stereo pilot subcarrier. The proper phase relationship must exist between the pilot and the 38-kHz carrier for optimum stereo separation. The subchannel frequency response, noise, and distortion must be comparable to the main channel characteristics. In the receiver, the subchannel is used to regenerate the left and right channels.

By making measurements of the individual left and right channel frequency response, noise, and distortion, the proper operation of the subchannel can be determined. In order to avoid separation and distortion problems, the stereo generator must have very sharp cutoff low-pass filters in the left and right audio channels. The filters

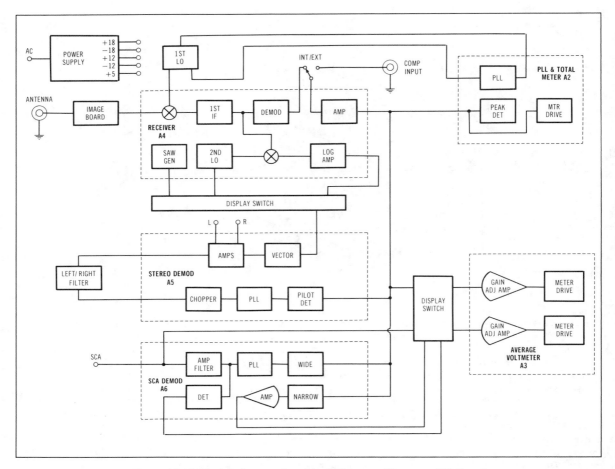

Figure 28-10 Modulation monitor, block diagram. *(Courtesy QEI Corp.)*

Figure 28-11 Typical broadcast monitor loudspeaker. *(Courtesy JBL Inc./UREI)*

must have negligible effect at 15 kHz but have an extremely sharp notch at 19 kHz, with minimal response above 19 kHz.

28.2.3 Loudness

Broadcasters are justifiably concerned with maintaining high audio modulation levels in order to provide listeners with consistent intelligibility. The FCC regulations require that program peaks be at least 85% modulation. Various automatic gain control devices and limiters are used to obtain uniformly high modulation levels despite program source material changes. These devices have the effect of reducing the dynamic range of the original recording, but when done in moderation, this processing adds more than it subtracts, particularly for listeners in cars where the ambient noise level is quite high.

The employment of such signal processing has also been used in order to make a station seem louder than other

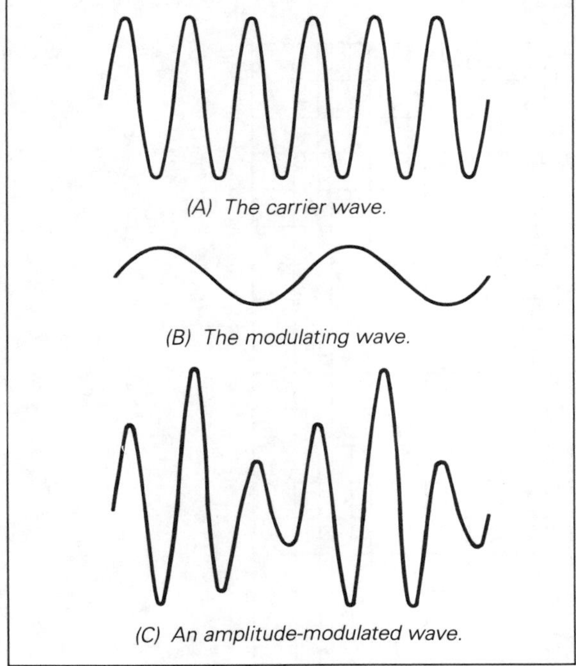

Figure 28-12 AM waves.

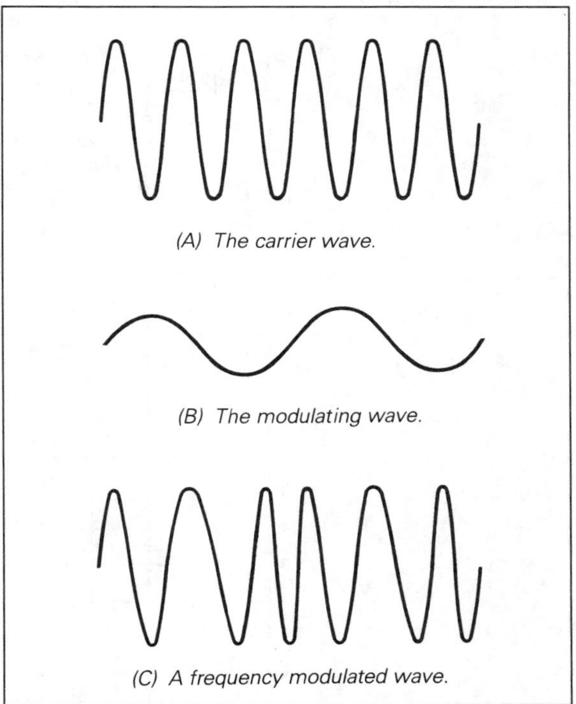

Figure 28-13 FM waves. Note that the carrier wave and the modulating waves are the same as for the AM signal but the waveform of the modulated wave is quite different.

stations in the market. When carried to an extreme, this can become very fatiguing to the listener. Also, heavy processing usually results in increased distortion and may actually degrade the signal-to-noise ratio of the station by boosting the system noise in the absence of audio. Broadcasters are becoming increasingly aware of the psychological effects of listener fatigue, and cleaner audio is the result.

28.2.4 Subcarrier Authorization (SCA)

Many FM stations have received FCC authorization to transmit additional information on their signals in the form of subcarriers. These are frequency-modulated signals not normally detected by the receiver. Most subcarriers are located 67 kHz removed from the main carrier and are modulated to provide a ±4- or 6-kHz frequency swing.

The SCA is most often used to distribute background music to subscriber stores, businesses, restaurants, etc. However, the subcarrier may be used to broadcast specialized information: reading for the blind, teletype, facsimile (still pictures), slow-scan television, or information networks for special interests, such as stock reports or medical news. Recent deregulation permits the subcarriers to be used for other nonbroadcast uses, such as paging or traffic control.

Special receivers, usually crystal controlled and tuned to the main FM station's frequency, are used to decode the subchannel information. The audio quality obtainable from an SCA is not generally full fidelity—50 Hz to 5 kHz is typical. Although full audio bandwidth is possible, the problems inherent in transmitting additional information on one main carrier become increasingly difficult to solve as the subcarrier modulation becomes more sophisticated. Crosstalk from the subcarrier to the main channel or stereo subchannel can be a problem. Good separation (70 dB or better) requires exceptionally low distortion in the generation, amplification, and transmission of the composite signal. (The composite signal is the audio plus stereo pilot and modulated subcarrier(s).)

Poor receiver design, or sometimes multipath reception, can degrade the SCA to main channel separation. This lack of separation is usually not evident as subcarrier audio but rather as increased noise, which often varies with the subcarrier modulation.

Some FM stations utilize their subcarrier to return telemetry data from the transmitter to the studio in the form of audio frequency shift keying.

The SCA carrier modulates the main carrier at a fixed percentage, usually about 8% but always under 10%. For telemetry, lower levels of subcarrier injection are used. This 8% represents a loss in modulation capability for

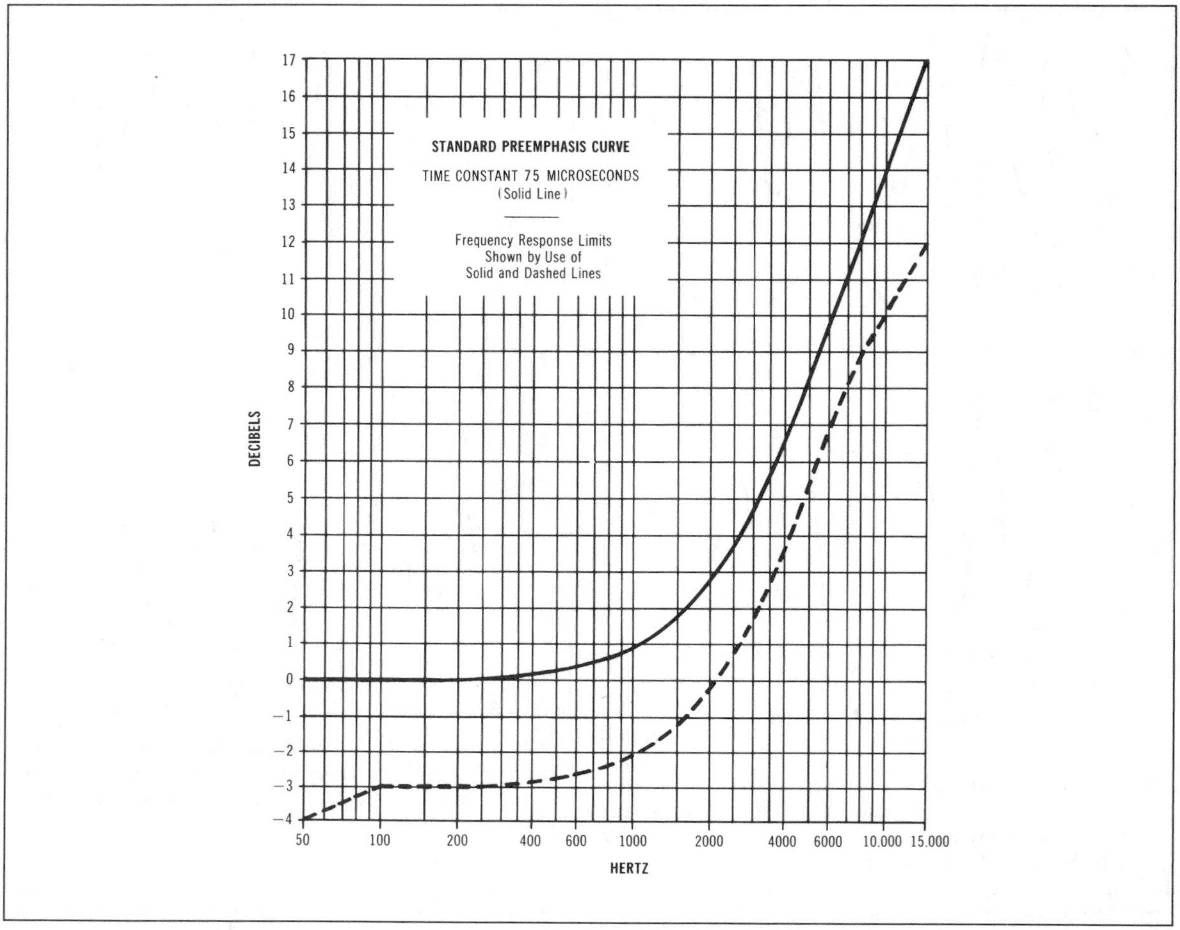

STANDARD PREEMPHASIS CURVE

TIME CONSTANT 75 MICROSECONDS
(Solid Line)

Frequency Response Limits
Shown by Use of
Solid and Dashed Lines

DECIBELS: 17, 16, 15, 14, 13, 12, 11, 10, 9, 8, 7, 6, 5, 4, 3, 2, 1, 0, −1, −2, −3, −4

HERTZ: 50, 100, 200, 400, 600, 1000, 2000, 4000, 6000, 10.000, 15.000

Figure 28-14 The preemphasis curve the Federal Communications Commission requires all FM broadcast stations to use.

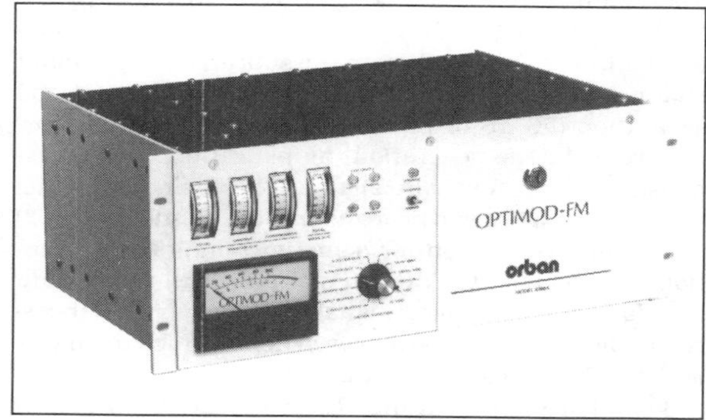

Figure 28-15 A typical FM stereo processor which combines compression, peak limiting, and a stereo generator in one package. *(Courtesy Orban Associates Inc.)*

the main channel, which results in audio that may not be as loud as it might otherwise be. Some stations tolerate this loss, which is less than a couple of decibels at most, feeling that they are compensated by the revenue the SCA can generate when it is leased out. Stations using SCA for telemetry turn the subcarrier on for a few minutes every couple of hours when they must log the transmitter operating parameters.

28.2.5 Comparison of AM and FM Audio Characteristics

If AM and FM broadcasting had been developed at the same time in history, their characteristics might not be as different as they are. AM was developed first, at a time when an audio signal with 100-Hz to 3-kHz bandwidth and 10% distortion was considered good fidelity. By the

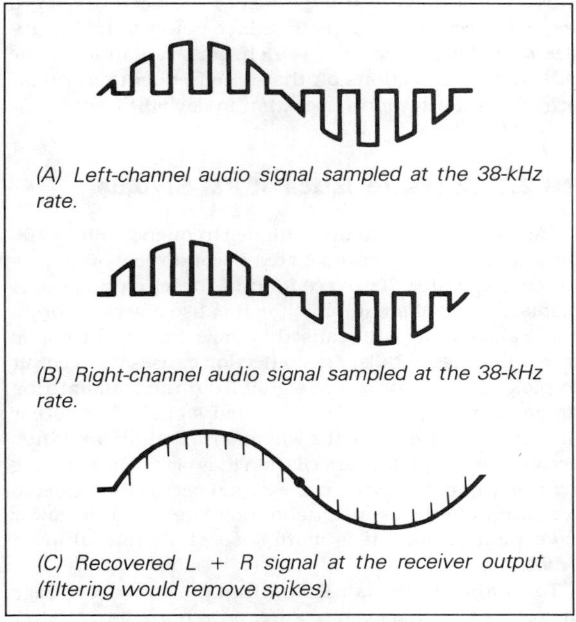
(A) Left-channel audio signal sampled at the 38-kHz rate.

(B) Right-channel audio signal sampled at the 38-kHz rate.

(C) Recovered L + R signal at the receiver output (filtering would remove spikes).

Figure 28-16 FM stereo waveforms.

time FM (and later television) broadcasting standards were being developed, considerable improvements had been made in technical quality.

The Federal Communications Commission (FCC) specifies certain minimum performance criteria that all U.S. broadcasting stations must meet. Although considered quite stringent at their inception, today they are quite easily met. Many consumer receivers exceed the quality of transmission required by law.

Broadcasters realize that just meeting the minimum standards is not always enough, especially in markets with heavy competition for sophisticated listeners.

28.2.5.1 AM Specifications

The standards for AM are quite undemanding. A simplified summary of the requirements: a 100- to 5000-Hz bandwidth (plus or minus 2 dB, referenced to 1 kHz), 5% total harmonic distortion (THD) below 85% modulation, and 7.5% THD from 85 to 95% modulation, and a 45-dB signal-to-noise ratio (measured in a 30-Hz to 20-kHz band, referenced to 100% modulation at 400 Hz). There is no reason why an AM station cannot do far better than this, and many do. However, the typical AM receiver has a built-in rolloff in high-frequency response beginning at about 3000 Hz, which minimizes interference from adjacent channel signals and helps improve the signal-to-noise ratio. The highest frequency transmitted is directly related to the bandwidth occupied by the signal. The bandwidth is twice the highest modulating frequency. The FCC permits AM stations to transmit full fidelity audio, up to 15 kHz, but all emissions above 15 kHz must be attenuated 25 dB or more, which requires stations to rolloff the high end somewhat, but it is possible to transmit a 50-Hz to 10-kHz signal, with less than 1% THD, and a 55-dB signal-to-noise ratio. Many AM stations do achieve this.

AM stereo is now permitted. Unlike FM, where the FCC evaluated various stereo systems and then adopted a standard, the decision as to what AM stereo system to be used has been left to the broadcasters and receiver manufacturers. But like FM stereo, it is required that the signal can be received on mono receivers with no degradation of quality. There are currently several systems in use, all incompatible with one another, although universal receivers capable of decoding any of the existing AM stereo systems are available.

28.2.5.2 FM Specifications

FM was developed at a time of greater awareness of the potential of broadcast audio quality. FM has an intrinsic immunity to atmospheric and high-frequency noise sig-

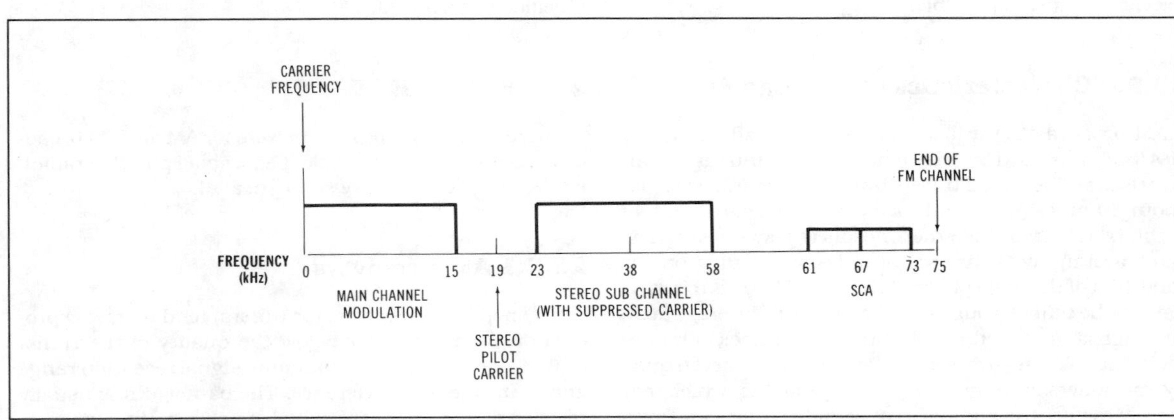

Figure 28-17 FM stereo channel with typical subcarrier.

nals, which are amplitude modulated in character, and the VHF frequencies employed allow greater signal bandwidth (the FM band is about 13 times larger than the AM band; FM signals use about 15 times as much spectrum as AM signals). FM broadcasters are required to have a frequency response of 50 Hz to 15 kHz, within the limits specified in the preemphasis curve shown in Fig. 28-14. This can be defined as a resulting response (after deemphasis) of approximately ± 1.5 dB throughout most of the audio band, with somewhat relaxed requirements at the extreme low and high ends. Total harmonic distortion must be below 2.5% throughout most of the audio range, with 3.5% permitted from 50 to 100 Hz, and 3.0% permitted from 7.5 kHz to 15 kHz. Noise must be 60 dB below 100% modulation. AM noise, resulting from residual amplitude modulation of the transmitter, must be at least 50 dB down from 100% modulation. Many of today's FM stations have flat response from below 50 Hz, but because of the 19-kHz stereo pilot subcarrier, it is necessary to have a sharp cutoff beyond 15 kHz. Distortion figures in the tenths or hundredths of a percent are possible, and signal-to-noise ratios exceeding 75 dB can be achieved.

Keep in mind that this performance must be achieved from the microphone input to the transmitter output, with all normal equipment in the circuit, for both AM and FM stations. Limiters and other processing devices must be included, but their gain control functions and any equalization must be disabled.

28.2.5.3 Television Specifications

Television audio must meet minimum standards very similar to FM. The bandwidth allotted to the audio portion of the television signal is considerably less than that of FM, so meeting these requirements can be quite challenging. Unfortunately, the quality available from film and video tape sound tracks is often inferior to the transmission potential, although with the use of synchronized high-quality audio tape machines, high-fidelity, even stereo television audio is possible.

28.2.6 Characteristics of AM Signals

AM broadcasting utilizes relatively low radio frequencies (535 to 1605 kHz), which have certain intrinsic characteristics. The signal travels by both a ground wave (for about 30 miles or so, with decreasing strength) and, at night, by reflection from the ionosphere (sky wave), which can travel many thousands of miles, depending on the condition of the ionosphere at the time. The ground wave tends to be quite strong and reliable in the coverage area, although large structures like bridges will block or reduce the signal. The sky-wave signal is usually of uneven quality and suffers from frequency-selective fading, which may grossly distort the audio. Because AM signals can travel vast distances at night, stations on the same frequency will interfere with one another at intermediate points. Various solutions to this problem have been developed requiring certain stations to reduce power at night, utilize directional antennas, which limit radiation in the direction(s) of stations on the same frequency at night, or restrict the station's operation to daylight hours.

28.2.7 Characteristics of FM Signals

FM signals are at a much higher frequency (88 to 108 MHz) and are rarely propagated beyond their 30- to 40-mi coverage area. The reception of these frequencies is primarily line of sight, which can cause a serious problem, called multipath, caused by reflection of the signal from buildings or hills. This reflection causes the receiver to pick up both the direct signal from the transmitting antenna and one or more reflected signals from other directions. Since the paths will differ in length (and thus arrival time), a phase cancellation may occur. In a moving vehicle, rapid dropouts in the signal occur. Since stereo reception often has a signal-to-noise ratio 20 dB lower than monophonic, it is more susceptible to multipath problems.

To obtain an adequate level within the normal coverage area of the station usually requires only the built-in receiver antenna, which often is coupled to the ac power cord using the building ac wiring as an antenna. If the receiver is located in an area where there is multipath reception or if the signal strength is too low, an outdoor antenna of the Yagi type with three or more elements will probably help. This antenna should be connected to the receiver with 75-Ω coaxial cable, particularly where multipath is a problem. The shielding of the coaxial cable prevents pickup of the signal from directions other than that toward which the antenna is pointed. This can occur when unshielded line, such as conventional 300-Ω twin lead, is used. Although a balanced line such as twin lead should be immune to common-mode voltages, it is often unbalanced by its proximity to metal objects. The transmission line can actually act like an antenna if it is not properly shielded or balanced.

28.3 RECEIVERS

There are many types of receivers for AM and FM broadcasts. Some are quite simple (i.e., a small portable radio), while others can be very sophisticated.

28.3.1 AM Receivers

In general, AM receivers (or tuners) tend to have reproduction capabilities far below the quality of the transmitted signal to provide maximum signal reception range and to minimize interference. The bandwidth is usually restricted to 6 or 8 kHz, which improves the signal-to-noise ratio at the expense of high-frequency response. The tuned circuits used to control the bandwidth are usually quite simple, so the high-frequency rolloff is gradual, beginning around 3 kHz.

28.3.2 FM Receivers*

In FM receivers bandwidth does not affect frequency response but does to some extent determine sensitivity and selectivity (ability to reject adjacent signals). FM receivers exhibit a characteristic called capture in which the stronger of two signals will be heard and the weaker will be totally undetectable. Normally, this characteristic is an advantage, but when two signals of very similar strength are received, the one heard may shift back and forth unpredictably; this problem is particularly true in car receivers. A common specification for consumer FM receivers or tuners is a 1.5-dB capture ratio, which means that one signal need only be 1.5 dB stronger than another in order for that signal to be the only one heard.

The receiver must process a number of different signals that are located on different portions of the composite FM signal. In addition to the main channel modulation, the receiver must properly decode the stereo subchannel and use its information to recreate the original stereo audio. Keeping all these signals separate requires filters of good design. Poor filters cause a lack of separation. If the station has SCA (a secondary subcarrier for background music or other service), the filters must reject its signal. Sometimes poor receiver design will cause beat notes of 9 or 10 kHz to be produced when harmonics of the 19-kHz pilot mix with the 67-kHz SCA carrier. When the subcarrier is modulated (it is also frequency modulated), the beat note will vary at an audio rate, producing an odd swishing sound.

Selectivity is often considered the most important single specification for an FM receiver. Ideally, the receiver should have perfectly flat amplitude and linear phase response across the entire FM channel to which it is tuned. In addition, there should be a rapid dropoff of response outside the channel. This eliminates adjacent channel interference and is particularly important in weak signal areas or when one desires to listen to a weak signal with a much stronger signal on a nearby frequency. However, if the response begins to roll off within the 200-kHz FM channel, stereo separation will decrease, and increased distortion may result.

Sensitivity is the ability of the FM receiver to detect weak signals, and it is of particular importance in automobile receivers where a short antenna close to the ground is necessitated. Most modern FM receivers are capable of providing a listenable monaural signal with less than 10 μV input from the antenna. However, for stereo reception, 25 μV or more are required before the ultimate signal-to-noise ratio (full quieting) is achieved. In general, monaural reception has about a 20-dB signal-to-noise advantage over the same stereo signal. With adequate signal strengths, stereo signals have comparable signal-to-noise ratios. But as signal strength decreases, stereo reception becomes increasingly noisy. Switching the receiver to mono will allow reception long after the stereo signal becomes unlistenable.

An excessively sensitive receiver may suffer from additional problems. Since the front end of an FM receiver is relatively broad (due to Q restraints), a strong signal in the vicinity, even a television signal (especially channel 6, which is just below the FM band), can cause intermodulation products to be generated within the receiver. The front end (up to the IF filter) must be linear over a wide range of RF voltages presented to it. In high signal strength areas, it may be desirable to decrease the sensitivity of the front end. Some receivers incorporate resistive pads in the antenna input that can be switched in and out. This switch is sometimes labeled "local/distant."

Most FM receivers being built today utilize an integrated-circuit quadrature detector. Such a device is capable of an 80-dB signal-to-noise ratio and less than 0.05% total harmonic distortion, which has made all other types of detectors obsolescent.

Stereo decoders are also commonly a single IC device. These make a high-quality FM receiver quite easy to manufacture at reasonable cost. The audio circuitry following the stereo decoder is conventional.

One other receiver characteristic has become more important with the increased use of subcarriers by FM stations (see section 28.2.4). The ability of the receiver to reject interference from the subcarrier modulation is necessary to achieve ultimate audio quality. Interference from the subcarrier may be heard as whistles or "birdies" or possibly as an increase in noise. Only rarely is the actual modulation of the subcarrier detectable in the main channel output. A receiver should have at least 60 to 65 dB of subcarrier to main channel isolation. Under some conditions, even subcarrier interference more than 70 dB down can be heard. This type of interference can occur in the transmission system but is much more likely to occur in the receiver.

With careful attention to circuit design and construction, an FM receiver can be a very good source of quality audio, with frequency response, distortion, and noise often limited by the source material rather than the transmission medium.

*Special thanks to Charlie Haubrich of QEI Corporation for his assistance in preparing this section on FM Receivers.

BIBLIOGRAPHY

NAB Engineering Handbook, Sixth Edition, Washington, DC: National Association of Broadcasters, 1975.

The Radio Amateur's Handbook, 58th Edition, Newington, CT: American Radio Relay League, 1981.

CHAPTER **29**

Image Projection

by Glen Ballou

29.1 BASICS

Image projection, whether still or with motion, requires a light source, an image to be projected, a means of focusing the image, and a surface to project the image onto. In the normal projection system, these elements are designed to produce the best picture. Light sources, for instance, must have the proper color temperature to produce accurate colors, and reflectors must gather as much of the available light as possible. The quality of film has been improved to give a sharp picture in color or black and white. Lenses are made to transmit maximum light with maximum clarity across the image, and screens are made to produce either even response on or off axis or high gain on axis, depending on the characteristic required.

29.1.1 Light Sources, Condensers, and Heat Shields

The most common light sources are incandescent lamps, halogen lamps, xenon lamps, and arc lamps. The intensity of direct sunlight is approximately 10,000 fc. Fig. 29-1 is a graphical comparison for four sources of light—sunlight, incandescent, conventional arc light, and xenon gas lamps. The xenon lamp best approaches that of the sun in the shorter wavelengths. The selection of a proper light source is an important factor, particularly for color images.

The advantages of incandescent and halogen are cost and the ability to control intensity by varying the voltage; the advantages of xenon and arc are the high intensity and color. An incandescent lamp produces only 27 candle power per square millimeter of heated surface while a high-power arc lamp can produce 700 candle power per square millimeter of heated surface.

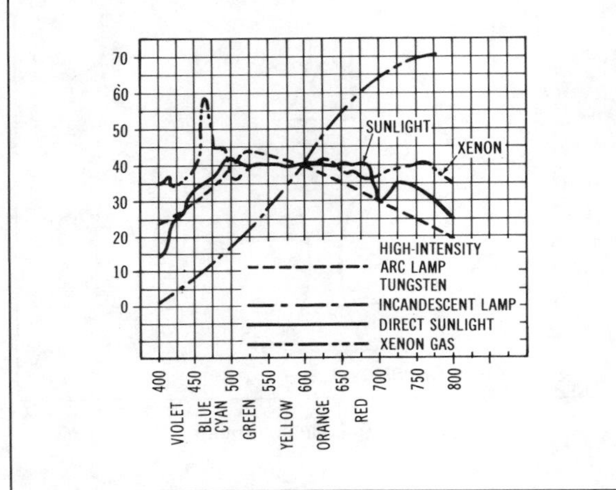

Figure 29-1 Relative intensity of various light sources including direct sunlight.

A major problem with an arc lamp is that it burns the electrodes, requiring ventilation and a motorized system of moving the carbon electrode to maintain the proper spacing between the electrodes.

Xenon lamps are high-pressure, gas-filled lamps designed for dc operation. The outstanding features of these lamps include a color temperature that resembles natural daylight (which is a mixture of direct sunlight and reflected skylight), immediate readiness for operation, extreme brightness, and extremely good stability. The light color of xenon lamps is independent of variations in the supply voltage and will remain unchanged even when the light output is being regulated. Xenon lamps emit a strong medium- and long-wave ultraviolet radiation with a continuous spectrum and have several radiation maxima in the short wavelength infrared range between 8000 and 10,000 Å. A typical installation of such a lamp is shown in Fig. 29-2.

Figure 29-2 Installation of xenon lamp in a motion picture projector. *(Courtesy Carbons, Inc.)*

The envelope of a xenon lamp consists of a quartz case of ellipsoidal shape, with two electrodes placed diametrically opposite. The cathode (negative) must be made small, and the anode (positive) must be relatively large in comparison to dissipate the heat. The overall length of the lamp is determined by the temperature gradient between the electrodes and the bases. Because of the prefocus base, the lamp may be replaced by a similar lamp without making any adjustment. A special property of the xenon arc lamp is that it absorbs only a minimum of its own radiation. Although the concentration of power is high, xenon lamps need no forced-air cooling because of their shape. Because of the glare, the ultraviolet radiation, and the high operating pressure, the lamp must be completely enclosed in the lamphouse with air vents.

The gas filling has an excess pressure of several atmospheres even when the lamp is not in use. Therefore, protective gloves and mask must be worn when handling the lamp. The burning position is always vertical, with the smaller electrode downward, as shown. To ignite the lamp, a special ignition device is used. A 1600-W xenon lamp is shown in Fig. 29-3.

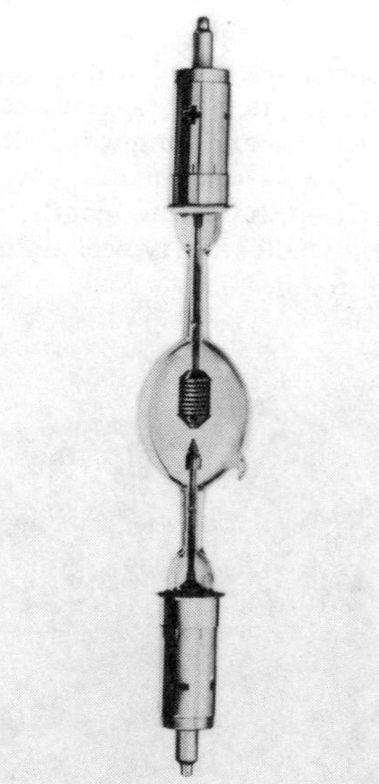

Figure 29-3 A 1600-W xenon high-pressure projection lamp. *(Courtesy Radio Systems, Inc.)*

The life of these lamps is generally terminated by the blackening of the quartz glass. The degree of blackening is influenced by the magnitude of the current pulsations and the number of starts. The average life for a 150-W lamp is 1200 hr; for 450- to 1600-W lamps, the life is 200 hr; for 2500-W lamps, the life is about 100 hr.

Because light sources distribute an equal amount of light in all directions and because it is desirable to direct as much of this light as possible toward the film, a reflector is precisely positioned behind the light source. This reflector increases the use of the light from the source by reflecting most of the light radiation forward toward the condensing lenses, Fig. 29-2.

Two types of condensing lenses are often used particularly in 16-mm motion picture and 35-mm still pictures. The one closest to the light source is an aspheric type (Fig. 29-4F) used to collect the greatest possible share of light emitted by the projection lamp. The other lens is a plano-convex condensing lens (Fig. 29-4A) used to converge and concentrate this light upon the picture frame in the aperture.

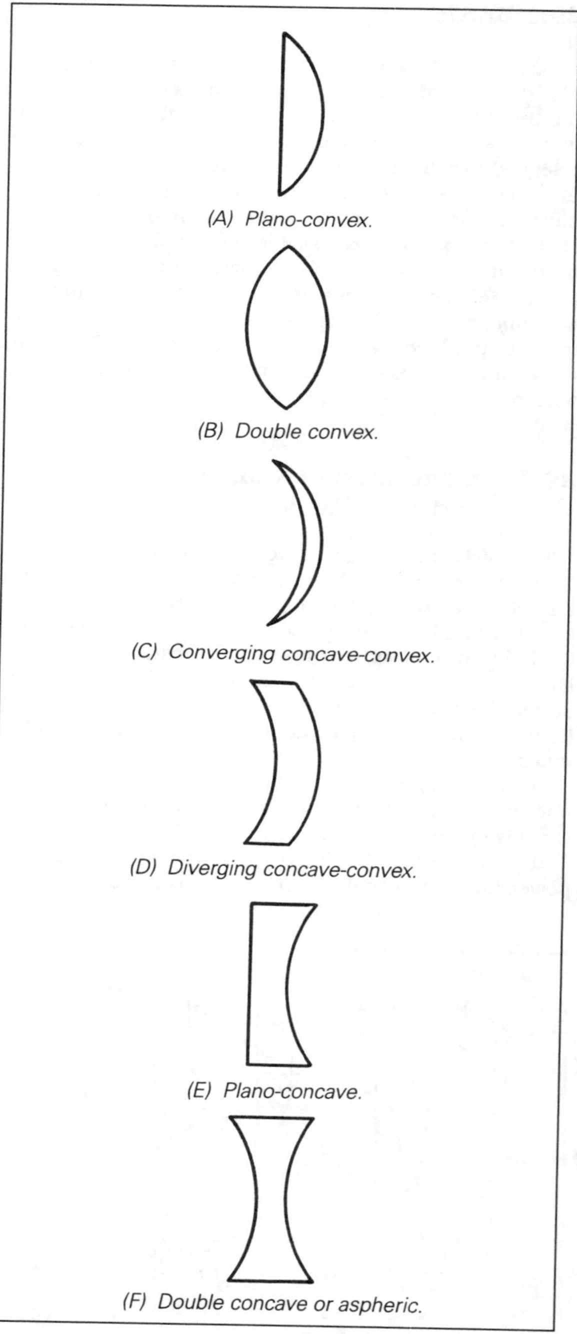

(A) Plano-convex.

(B) Double convex.

(C) Converging concave-convex.

(D) Diverging concave-convex.

(E) Plano-concave.

(F) Double concave or aspheric.

Figure 29-4 Basic lenses.

Not all of the light from the light source reaches the screen. About 5% of the light striking the lens is reflected, with another one-half percent lost because of the density of the lens system. The aperture at the film reduces the light approximately 50%. Thus, it is evident that less than 50% of the light actually reaches the screen. If dirt is permitted to accumulate on the lens and porthole glass, an additional loss is induced. It is not uncommon to find that only 30% of the light leaving the source arrives at the screen.

The heat as well as light is focused by the lens system; therefore, it must be removed before reaching the film. This is often accomplished by forced-air ventilation and/or a heat-shield glass which does not allow the heat to pass through. The heat shield normally has a green tint which produces a green rather than a white light.

29.1.2 Lenses

Lenses are used to focus the picture on the screen. The basic types of lenses are: plano-convex, double-convex, concave-convex (sometimes called a meniscus), plano-concave, and double-concave. Lenses are divided into two groups, positive and negative. A positive lens converges the light rays and must be thicker at the center than at the outer edges. A negative lens diverges the light and must be thicker at the borders than at the center. Basic lenses are shown in Fig. 29-4. Lenses are designated by their focal length and f-stop.

Modern projection lenses must be cleaned very carefully. Although they may be coated and present a fairly hard surface, the coating is microscopically thin and may be scratched very easily. Solvents such as alcohol and petroleum should be used sparingly, since these solvents may attack the optical cement or the lens-mount lacquer. A lens should be cleaned with a lint-free cotton cloth and a camel's hair brush. Heavy dirt may be removed with a cleaning solution of mild pure soap in water. Precaution should be taken that the solution contains no caustic soda. Isopropyl alcohol has been found to be a good cleaner. Several commercial lens cleaners, sold under various tradenames, are also available.

29.1.2.1 Focal Length

The *focal length* is the distance between the film gate and the lens node, as shown in Fig. 29-5.

Due to the extremely high frequencies of optics, that is, the wavelength is much shorter than the lenses that

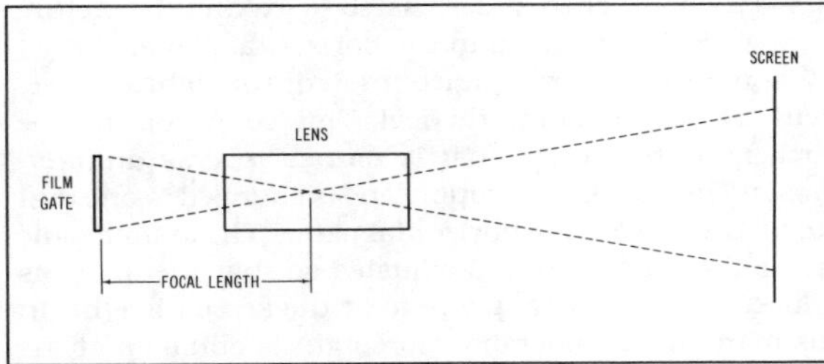

Figure 29-5 Focal length of a simple lens system.

are being used, light travels in a straight line. Therefore, for long screen-to-film gate distances, the following formula can be used to determine image width:

$$\text{image width/screen to film gate distance} = \text{film aperture/lens focal length} \quad (29\text{-}1)$$

where,

$$\text{image width} = \text{image height} \times \text{aperture width/aperture height} \quad (29\text{-}2)$$

For short screen-to-film gate distances, such as are used in rear projection systems, the classical lens formula should be used.

$$\text{Screen-to-film gate distance} = F[2+M+(1/M)] + d \quad (29\text{-}3)$$

where,

M is the image width/aperture width,

d is the internodal distance.

Most lenses are of the compound type, which requires knowing the internodal distance (d) of the lens if the projection distance is to be calculated exactly (Fig. 29-6). Unfortunately, many lenses such as the Buhl ECU-RP series lens, which has one fixed lens and one moving lens, has a constantly changing d; therefore, it is usually better to determine screen-to-film gate distances from manufacturers' prepared charts. Tables 29-1 through 29-6 are projection charts for 35-mm (2 × 2) still projection and 16-mm motion picture projection.

A long focal length lens, will produce a smaller picture than a short focal length lens for the same projection distance.

29.1.2.2 Zoom Lenses

A *zoom lens* is a lens with a variable focal length. In a zoom lens there are five lens elements, as shown in Fig. 29-7[1]: the *focuser lens*, the *variator*, the *erector*, the *compensator*, and the *relay lens*. The focuser is used to focus the picture, while the movable variator varies the focal length of the zoom. The third element, the erector, is stationary and rotates the image 180°. The fourth element, the compensator, is linked mechanically to the variator and compensates for focal plane shift. Finally, the fifth element, the relay, gives the proper frame size. In a real lens, each group is often made up of multiple lenses.

Common problems with zoom lenses are the change in focus while changing zoom size and the general overall softness of the picture. The advantages are the ability to go into a room or an area and adjust the lens to the throw distance and image size rather than to adjust the throw distance and/or image size to the lens.

29.1.2.3 Anamorphic Lenses

Anamorphosis is a term applied to a lens system used in the photographing and reproduction of wide-screen

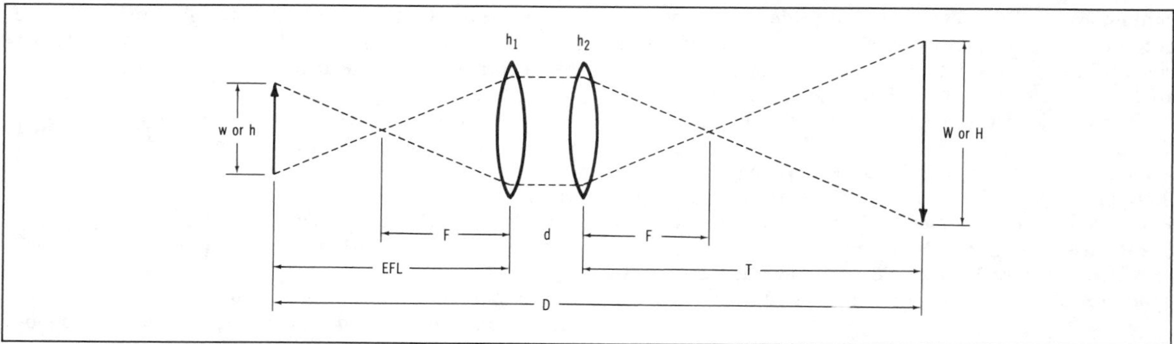

Figure 29-6 The focal length and effective focal length (EFL) of a complex lens system.

Table 29-1. 2 × 2-in. Double Frame—35-mm Slides; Aperture width : 1.34 in.

Lens Focal Length	Screen Width												
	40″	50″	60″	70″	84″	8′	9′	10′	12′	14′	16′	18′	20′
	Projection Distance in Feet												
1″	2.5	3.1	3.7	4.4	5.2	6.0	6.7	7.5	9.0	10.4	11.9	13.4	14.9
1.4″	3.5	4.4	5.2	6.1	7.3	8.4	9.4	10.4	12.5	14.6	16.7	18.8	20.9
2″	5.0	6.2	7.5	3.7	10.4	11.9	13.4	14.9	17.9	20.9	23.9	26.9	29.9
3″	7.5	10.3	11.2	13.1	15.7	17.9	20.1	22.4	26.9	31.3	35.8	40.3	44.8
4″	10.0	12.4	14.9	17.4	20.9	23.9	26.8	29.9	35.8	41.8	47.8	53.8	59.7
5″	12.4	15.5	18.7	21.8	26.1	29.9	33.6	37.3	44.8	52.2	59.7	67.2	74.6
5½″	13.7	17.1	20.5	23.9	28.7	32.8	36.9	41.0	49.2	57.5	65.7	73.9	82.1
6″	14.9	18.7	22.4	26.1	31.3	35.8	40.3	44.8	53.7	62.7	71.6	80.6	89.6
6½″	16.2	20.2	24.3	28.3	34.0	38.8	43.7	48.5	58.2	67.9	77.6	88.8	97.0
7″	17.4	21.8	26.1	30.5	36.6	41.8	47.0	52.3	62.7	73.1	83.6	94.0	104.5
7.5″	18.7	23.3	28.0	32.6	39.2	44.8	50.4	56.0	67.2	78.4	89.6	100.7	111.9
8″	19.9	24.9	29.9	34.8	41.8	47.8	53.7	59.7	71.6	83.6	95.5	107.5	119.4
8½″	21.1	26.4	31.7	37.0	44.4	50.7	57.1	63.4	76.1	88.8	101.5	114.2	126.9
9″	22.4	28.0	33.6	39.2	47.0	53.7	60.4	67.2	80.6	94.0	107.5	120.9	134.3
9½″	23.6	29.5	35.4	41.4	49.6	56.7	63.8	70.9	85.1	99.3	113.4	127.6	141.8
10″	24.9	31.1	37.3	43.5	52.2	59.7	67.2	74.6	89.6	104.5	119.4	134.3	149.3
12½″	31.1	38.9	46.6	54.4	65.3	74.6	84.0	93.3	111.9	130.6	149.3	167.9	186.6
15½″	39.3	48.1	57.8	67.5	81.0	92.5	104.1	115.7	138.8	161.9	185.1	208.2	231.3
20″	49.8	62.2	74.6	87.1	104.5	119.4	134.3	149.3	179.1	209.0	238.8	268.7	298.5

motion pictures. The image is photographed using a predistorted optical image, which compresses the image in the horizontal plane. The image is restored to its normal appearance by the use of the lens system in the projector which has a reverse characteristic of the lens system used to photograph the image.

Anamorphic lenses are specified by their magnification or spreading ratio, which indicates how much the picture can be spread on a horizontal plane. The height of the picture remains the same; thus, for a 2:1 ratio the picture is twice the width of a standard picture.

Anamorphic lenses are adjusted using a picture or test film. With the regular projection lens in place, the image is focused on the screen, and the image size is adjusted to fill the screen in a vertical direction. The anamorphic lens is then attached and adjusted to expand the picture to the proper dimension in the horizontal plane.

When a long throw is encountered, the light requirements may become impractical. This condition may be partially overcome by what is termed *reverse anamorphosis*. The normal projection lens is changed to one that will fill the screen in a horizontal plane. The anamorphic lens is then installed and adjusted so that the image is reduced in the vertical plane to fit the screen height. In this manner, considerably more light is obtained at the screen.

Table 29-2. 2 × 2-in. Super Slides; Aperture Width 1.5 in.

Lens Focal Length		Screen Width 40″	50″	60″	70″	84″
1″	Projection Distance in Feet	2.2	2.8	3.3	3.9	4.7
1.4″		3.1	3.9	4.7	5.4	6.6
2″		4.4	5.6	6.7	7.8	9.3
3″		6.7	8.3	10.0	11.7	14.0
4″		8.9	11.1	13.3	15.6	18.7
5″		11.1	13.9	16.7	19.4	23.3
6″		13.3	16.7	20.0	23.3	28.0
7″		15.6	19.4	23.3	27.2	32.7
8″		17.8	22.2	26.7	31.1	37.3
9″		20.0	25.0	30.0	35.0	42.0
10″		22.2	27.8	33.3	38.9	46.7

Lens Focal Length		Screen Width 8′	9′	10′	12′	14′	16′	18′	20′
1″	Projection Distance in Feet	5.3	6.0	6.7	8.0	9.3	10.7	12.0	13.3
1.4″		7.5	8.4	9.3	11.2	13.1	14.9	16.8	18.7
2″		10.7	12.0	13.3	16.0	18.7	21.3	24.0	26.7
3″		16.0	18.0	20.0	24.0	28.0	32.0	36.0	40.0
4″		21.3	24.0	26.7	32.0	37.3	42.7	48.0	53.3
5″		26.7	30.0	33.3	40.0	46.7	53.3	60.0	66.7
6″		32.0	36.0	40.0	48.0	56.0	64.0	72.0	80.0
7″		37.3	42.0	46.7	56.0	65.3	74.7	84.0	93.3
8″		42.7	48.0	53.3	64.0	74.7	85.3	96.0	106.7
9″		48.0	54.0	60.0	72.0	84.0	96.0	108.0	120.0
10″		53.3	60.0	66.7	80.0	93.3	106.7	120.0	133.3

Table 29-3. Overhead Projection

Lens Focal Length	Aperture Size	Square Screen Size 50"	60"	70"	84"	8'	10'	12'	14'	16'	18'	20'
		Projection Distance in Feet										
6½"	5"	5.4	6.5	7.6	9.1	10.4	13.0	15.6	18.2	20.8	23.4	26.0
12"	7"	7.1	8.6	10.0	12.0	13.7	17.1	20.6	24.0	27.4	30.9	34.3
12½"	7"	7.4	8.9	10.4	12.5	14.3	17.9	21.4	25.0	28.6	32.1	35.7
8.8"	10"	5.7	4.4	5.1	6.2	7.0	8.8	10.6	12.3	14.1	15.8	17.6
12½"	10"	5.3	6.3	7.3	8.8	10.0	12.5	15.0	17.5	20.0	22.5	25.0
14"	10"	5.8	7.0	8.2	9.8	11.2	14.0	16.8	19.6	22.4	25.2	28.0
15½"	10"	6.5	7.8	9.0	10.9	12.4	15.5	18.6	21.7	24.8	27.9	31.0
18"	10"	7.5	9.0	10.5	12.6	14.4	18.0	21.6	25.2	28.8	32.4	36.0
22"	10"	9.2	11.0	12.8	15.4	17.6	22.0	26.4	30.8	35.2	39.6	44.0
24"	10"	10.0	12.0	14.0	16.8	19.2	24.0	28.8	33.6	38.4	43.2	48.0
26"	10"	10.8	13.0	15.2	18.2	20.8	26.0	31.2	36.4	41.6	46.8	52.0
30"	10"	12.5	15.0	17.5	21.0	24.0	30.0	36.0	42.0	48.0	54.0	60.0
36"	10"	15.0	18.0	21.0	25.2	28.8	36.0	43.2	50.4	57.6	64.8	72.0
40"	10"	16.7	20.0	23.3	28.0	32.0	40.0	48.0	56.0	64.0	72.0	80.0

Table 29-4. Regular 8 mm Motion Pictures Aperture Width—0.172 in.

Lens Focal Length	Square Screen Size 40"	50"	60"	70"	84"	8'	9'	10'	12'
	Projection Distance in Feet								
12.7mm–½"	9.7	12.1	14.6	16.9	20.4	23.3	26.2	29.1	34.9
14.28mm–9/16"	10.9	13.6	16.4	19.1	22.9	26.2	29.4	32.1	39.2
17mm–43/64"	13.0	16.2	19.5	22.7	27.3	31.2	35.1	39.0	46.7
18.5mm–45/64"	14.1	17.6	21.2	24.7	29.7	33.9	38.2	42.4	50.9
19mm–¾"	14.5	18.2	21.8	25.5	30.5	34.9	39.2	43.6	52.3
22mm–55/64"	16.8	21.0	25.2	29.4	35.3	40.3	45.4	50.4	60.5
25.4mm–1"	19.3	24.2	29.1	33.9	40.7	46.5	52.3	58.2	69.8
27mm–1 1/16"	20.6	25.7	31.0	36.0	43.3	49.5	55.7	61.8	74.2
28mm–1 3/32"	21.4	26.7	32.1	37.4	44.9	51.3	57.7	64.1	77.0
32mm–1¼"	24.2	30.3	36.3	42.4	50.9	58.2	65.4	72.7	87.3

Table 29-5. Super 8-mm Motion Pictures Aperture Width—0.211 in.

Lens Focal Length	Screen Width 40"	50"	60"	70"	84"	8'	9'	10'	12'
	Projection Distance in Feet								
12.7 mm–½"	7.9	9.9	11.9	13.8	16.6	19.0	21.4	23.7	28.4
14.28 mm–9/16"	8.9	11.1	13.4	15.5	18.7	21.3	24.0	26.7	32.0
17 mm–41/64"	10.6	13.2	15.9	18.5	22.2	25.4	28.6	31.8	38.1
18.5 mm–45/64"	11.5	14.4	17.3	20.1	24.2	27.6	31.1	34.6	41.4
19 mm–¾"	11.8	14.8	17.8	20.7	24.8	28.4	31.9	35.5	42.6
22 mm–55/64"	13.7	17.1	20.6	23.9	28.8	32.9	37.0	41.1	49.3
25.4 mm–1"	15.8	19.7	23.7	27.6	33.2	38.0	42.7	47.4	56.9
27 mm–1 1/16"	16.8	21.0	25.2	29.4	35.3	40.3	45.4	50.4	60.05
28 mm–1 3/32"	17.4	21.8	26.2	30.5	36.6	41.8	47.0	52.3	62.7
32 mm–1¼"	19.9	24.9	29.9	34.8	41.8	47.8	53.8	59.8	71.7

Table 29.6. 16-mm Motion Pictures
Aperture Width—0.380″

Lens Focal Length	Screen Width 40″	50″	60″	70″	84″	8′	9′	10′	12′
	Projection Distance in Feet								
½″	4.4	5.5	6.6	7.7	9.2	10.5	11.8	13.2	15.8
⅝″	5.5	6.9	8.2	9.6	11.5	13.2	14.8	16.4	19.7
¾″	6.6	8.2	9.9	11.5	13.8	15.8	17.8	19.7	23.7
1″	8.8	11.0	13.2	15.4	18.4	21.1	23.7	26.3	31.6
1½″	13.2	16.4	19.7	23.0	27.6	31.6	35.8	39.5	47.4
2″	17.5	21.9	26.3	30.7	36.8	42.1	47.4	52.6	63.2
2½″	21.9	27.4	32.9	38.4	46.1	52.6	59.2	65.8	78.9
2¾″	24.0	30.2	36.2	42.2	50.7	57.9	65.1	72.4	86.8
3″	26.3	32.9	39.5	46.1	55.3	63.2	71.1	78.9	94.7
3½″	30.7	38.4	46.1	53.7	64.5	73.7	82.4	92.1	110.5
4″	35.1	43.9	52.6	61.4	73.7	84.2	94.7	105.3	126.3

Lens Focal Length	Screen Width 14′	16′	18′	20′	22′	24′	26′	28′	30′
	Projection Distance in Feet								
½″	18.4	21.1	23.7	26.3	29.0	31.6	34.2	36.9	39.5
⅝″	23.0	26.3	29.6	32.9	36.2	39.5	42.8	46.1	49.3
¾″	27.6	31.6	35.5	39.5	43.4	47.4	51.3	55.3	59.2
1″	36.8	42.1	47.4	52.6	57.9	63.2	68.4	73.7	78.9
1½″	55.3	63.2	71.1	78.9	86.8	94.7	102.6	110.5	118.4
2″	73.7	84.2	94.7	105.3	115.8	126.3	136.8	147.4	157.9
2½″	92.1	105.3	118.4	131.6	144.7	157.9	171.1	184.2	197.4
2¾″	101.3	115.8	125.0	144.7	159.2	173.7	188.2	202.6	217.1
3″	110.5	126.3	142.1	157.9	173.7	189.5	205.3	221.1	236.8
3½″	128.9	147.4	165.8	184.2	202.6	221.1	239.5	257.9	276.3
4″	147.4	168.4	189.5	210.5	231.6	252.6	273.7	294.7	315.3

29.1.2.4 Lens Speed

The *f number* of the lens is used to indicate the speed of a lens. The f number is equal to the focal length divided by the effective aperture. A lens with an f1 rating means that for every inch of focal length there will be one inch of lens diameter. Therefore, an f1, 6-in. focal length lens will have a diameter of 6 in. An f2, 6-in. lens will have a 3-in. diameter, or 2 in. of focal length for every inch of diameter.

The lens may also be given a T stop number. The T-stop number is an individual calibration of a lens relative to its light-passing capabilities. A T-stop calibration takes into account the light lost by reflection, the number of elements in the optical train, the light lost by absorption as it passes through the lens elements, and the manufacturing tolerances.

In the f system of lens calibration, each f value is computed mathematically from the physical dimensions of the lens systems. Lenses calibrated by the T-stop method use a calibrating light, which is passed through the lens, and the loss of light is measured by means of a photocell. Thus, a T-stop calibration is an individual calibration of the true light-passing capabilities of the lens. As a rule, lenses used in the motion-picture industry are calibrated at regular intervals or after they have been serviced. The term *T* is short for *transmission*.

To keep the T-stop number close to the theoretical f-stop number, the elements of the lenses are coated to reduce reflections from the surface of the glass and to improve the transmission of light. A coated lens will transmit approximately 30% more light than an uncoated one. As an example, uncoated glass reflects about 6.5% of the light falling upon it. When the lens is coated, this

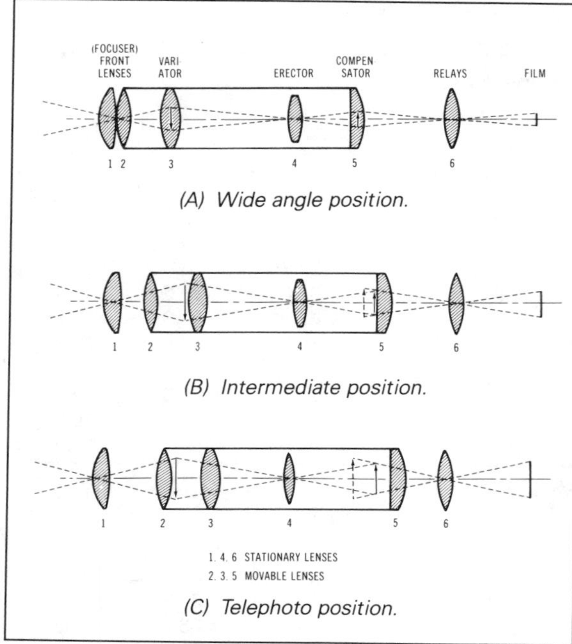

(A) Wide angle position.

(B) Intermediate position.

(C) Telephoto position.

Figure 29-7 The optical principle of the zoomar zoom lens.

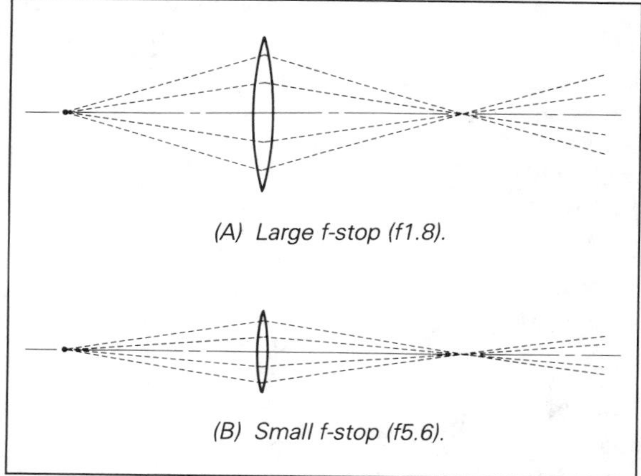

(A) Large f-stop (f1.8).

(B) Small f-stop (f5.6).

Figure 29-8 Large f-stop lenses require the light to bend farther and require a larger surface to be optically good.

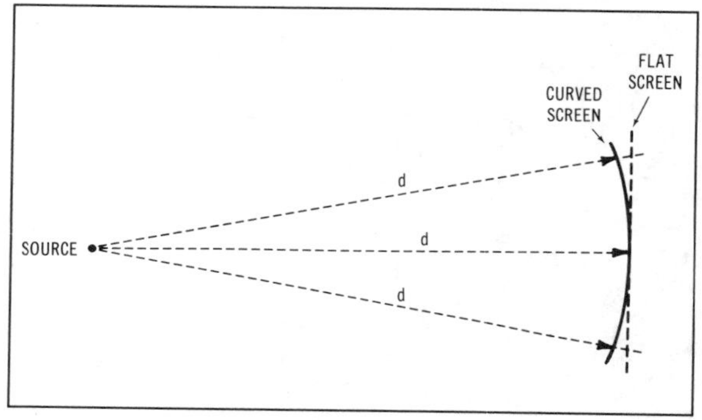

Figure 29-9 A standard lens is designed to focus on a curved screen. To be sharp on a flat surface, a flat field lens should be used.

figure drops to about 0.30%. A six-element uncoated lens may transmit 73% of the light, but when coated, this same lens will transmit 94% of the light. An eight-element uncoated lens may transmit 66% of the light, but when coated, the transmission is increased to 92%.

Coated lenses may be identified by shining a light on their surfaces and noting the color of the reflected light. If the lens is coated, the reflected light will appear light blue or brown in color.

The large f-stops have large diameter elements that translate to a short depth of field and less overall sharpness, particularly on the edges. This is because of the sharp bending angles of the light as shown in Fig. 29-8 and because the larger surfaces must also be optically good. If brightness is not a problem, a slower lens (i.e., f5.6 instead of f1.8) should be used since the overall picture quality should be better.

The standard f numbers are increased by the square root of the area doubled. The number is rounded off for simplicity. The system of f numbers allows you to easily double or halve the light entering or leaving the lens system. The standard f numbers are 1.3, 1.8, 2.8, 4, 5.6, 8, 11, 16, 22, 32.

Lenses can be either standard curved field or flat field. A standard lens has the same throw distance on axis as off axis; therefore, it is only sharp on a curved screen, as shown in Fig. 29-9. A flat-field lens has been corrected to focus on a flat screen by having the throw distance vary between the center and edge of the screen.

29.1.2.5 Aberrations

There are many types of aberrations found in lenses. Some, such as Newton rings, are also found in glass-mounted slides.

The optical axis of a lens is the one path through the optical system that does not change the direction of light rays transmitted by the lens; therefore, it usually produces the most accurate reproduction.

Spherical aberration is an image fault caused by the failure of light passing through the center and edges of the lens to focus on the same plane, resulting in a blurred image.

Chromatic aberration is an image fault caused by the lens focusing different colors of the spectrum at different distances, causing color bands to appear at the borders between light and dark picture areas.

Considering Sir Isaac Newton's many contributions not

only to science in general, but specifically to photography, it's too bad we named a trouble after him. The phenomenon called Newton rings is an interference pattern that appears when rays of light get in each other's way. There are similar phenomena in other branches of science. When radio waves of different frequencies interfere with each other, we get the *heterodyne* or *beat effect*, which makes modern radio receivers possible; a beat effect that results when sound waves conflict with each other is used in tuning pianos.

Generally, Newton rings are a series of irregular, concentric colored rings (kind of a moiré or op-art effect in the round) seen when two transparent surfaces are not quite in overall contact or have the same curvature.

Moisture condenses on lenses when a cold lens is placed in a projector, and light is projected through it. A lens with moisture (haze) on it produces a soft, fuzzy, low-contrast picture. To eliminate this problem, cold lenses should be prewarmed to room temperature.

29.2 STILL PICTURES

Still pictures come in various sizes ranging from the common 35-mm to 10 × 10 in. overhead transparency. Table 29-7 is the aperture dimensions and aspect ratio for common still projection.

The most common today are 35-mm double frame and superslides. Superslides have an advantage of more area in which to place information; however, they are also harder to keep in focus from edge to edge. Lantern slides were popular years ago but are seldom used today.

Overhead projection is used when the presenter wants to talk to the slide. The transparency is about 8 × 10 in. and can be written on. The overhead projector, with its mirror, allows the presenter to face the audience. The primary disadvantage of the overhead projector is its bright light, which produces glare in the room and on the screen. Another disadvantage lies in the fact that they cannot be automated.

Multi-image presentations have become very popular. A multi-image presentation can consist of two projectors on a single screen to 24 or more projectors on one or many screens. The normal presentation is computer controlled and synchronized to sound.

Among the various screen sizes and shapes is the soft-edge panorama. When screens became wider, projectors were put side by side to change the ratio of 2/3 to 2/6 or 1/3, as shown in Fig. 29-10. The panorama had a butt joint down the center where the two images met. Unfortunately, the joint always showed due to projector and slide alignment. To eliminate the problem, the soft-edge panorama was introduced. The same two slides are used with a third slide superimposed on the center, as shown in Fig. 29-11. A special variable-density mask is installed with the slides so the butt edge of the outside slides fade

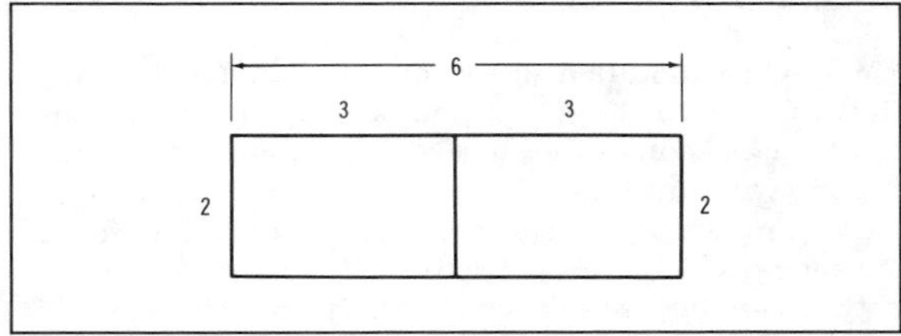

Figure 29-10 Two-projector, 3:1 aspect ratio panorama.

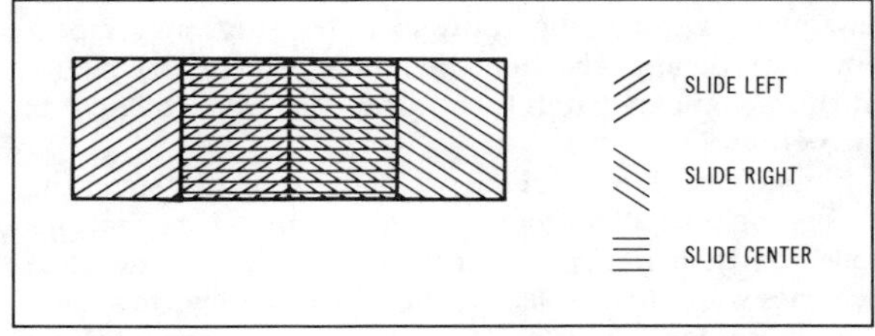

Figure 29-11 Three-projector, 3:1 aspect ratio panorama.

Table 29-7. Aperture Dimensions and Aspect Ratio for Common Still Projections

Medium	mm	Aspect Ratio	Aperture in inches H	W
2 × 2 slides:				
35-mm double frame	(22.9 × 34.2)	1:1.493	0.902	1.346
35-mm half frame	(15.9 × 22.9)	1.440	0.626	0.902
35-mm square	(22.9 × 22.9)	1.000	0.902	0.902
Superslides	(38.0 × 38.0)	1.000	1.496	1.496
Instamatic	(26.5 × 26.5)	1.000	1.043	1.043
35-mm film strip	(17.5 × 23.0)	1.314	0.689	0.906
2¾ × 2¾ slide		1.00	2.187	2.187
3¼ × 4 Lantern slide		1.09	2.75	3.00
3¾ × 4 Polaroid slide		1.36	2.40	3.26
4 × 5 Lantern slide		1.28	3.50	4.50

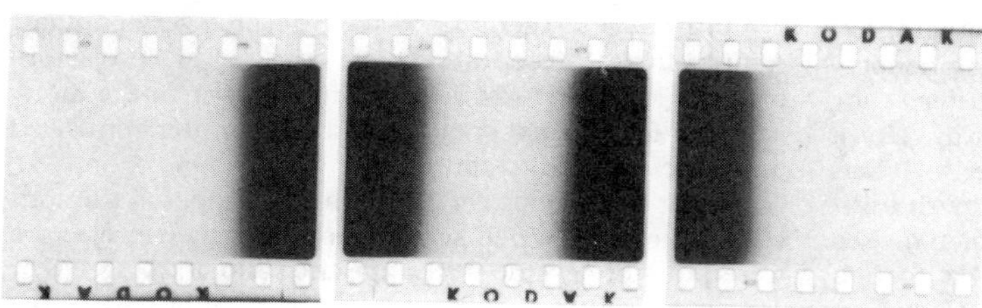

Figure 29-12 Soft-edged panorama slides require varible-density masks that allow aligning three slides on each other without visible overlap.

to black, while the center slide has both edges fading to black, as shown in Fig. 29-12. By proper rolloff of the variable intensity, the picture intensity remains the same across the screen, and alignment is not quite as critical as before.

29.2.1 Aberrations

With glass-mounted slides you often see Newton rings on the screen in all their prismatic glory. The defect may be visible as soon as the slide is glass-mounted, or it may not show up until the fifth, tenth, or twentieth time the slide is projected. The reason is because moisture between the slide-cover glasses will expand from the heat of projection, causing imperfect contact. The moisture may get in long after the slide is mounted.

The most common origin of the moisture is climatic, and in climates with high humidity, great care should be taken to ensure very dry glass and film when the slide is assembled. During long, rainy spells the rings may appear and then disappear when the slides become dry again. At times you can watch them disappear from the heat of projection.

Sometimes this moisture problem can cause steaming or fogging on a slide from an excess of moisture that has collected in a paper or cardboard mask. As the slide becomes warm in a projector, the moisture turns to steam. Kept warm long enough, the steam disappears, and the slide becomes entirely dry and moisture-free.

One way to get rid of Newton rings is by using slides in cardboard ready-mounts without glass covers. Slides will actually run cooler without a glass mount. This is not recommended with valuable slides, however, unless they are used in automatic tray-operated projectors where the slides are never handled. You may still have a focus problem; the slide may pop out of focus as it warms up. One cure is film preheating which pops the film into focus just before it moves into projection position. Unfortunately, they may not all pop into the same plane of focus. If a fast projection lens (faster than f:3.5; i.e., f:2.0, f:2.5, f:2.8) is used, the center of the picture can be focused, but the corners will not be sharp or vice versa. If duplicate slides are mixed with originals, one will often pop in a different direction from the other.

When using glass covers on slides, use anti-Newton ring glass which is ground or etched to interfere with the interference pattern.

Sealed-in film is not desirable. Although it prevents some moisture from getting in the slide, it also seals in any possible moisture present in mask, film, or glass, and it would constantly fog or steam the slides. The mount should allow the film and mask to breath off such moisture. Most glass mounts on the market today accomplish this.

29.3 MOTION PICTURES

The apparently continuous motion that we see when viewing a movie is an optical illusion that is realized by projecting a series of still pictures in rapid succession. These still pictures or frames are recorded by a motion-picture camera on a strip of film as successive and distinct stages of action, but the difference from frame to frame is small and projection speeds are so rapid that an apparent continuity results.

The fact that we do not see the change from frame to frame is possible only because of a characteristic of the human eye known as "persistence of vision," whereas the eye retains an image for a fraction of a second after the image is gone. The projection must move from frame to frame during this fraction of a second or a blurred and streaked effect will result.

Fig. 29-13 is a simple projection system that illustrates the basic components. The light source is located behind the film. This light is concentrated on the film by condensing lenses in order to obtain maximum brilliance of the projected picture. A reflector, which is located either behind the projection lamp or is part of the lamp, collects the light transmitted toward the back and reflects it back through the lamp into the condensing lens. Often the reflector and condenser are eliminated since the newer light sources have built-in reflectors and point sources that, when mounted close to the film, produce intense directional light.

The illuminated picture frame image is focused on the screen by the projection lens. The projection lens is adjustable so a sharp image can be obtained on the screen at any given distances. The screen must always be at right angles to the optical axis to prevent distortion of the projected image. This distortion is called *keystoning*.

The shuttle alternately engages and disengages perforations in the film to advance the film at the rate of 24 frames per second. As each frame is advanced, one blade on the shutter interrupts the light beam so that the film

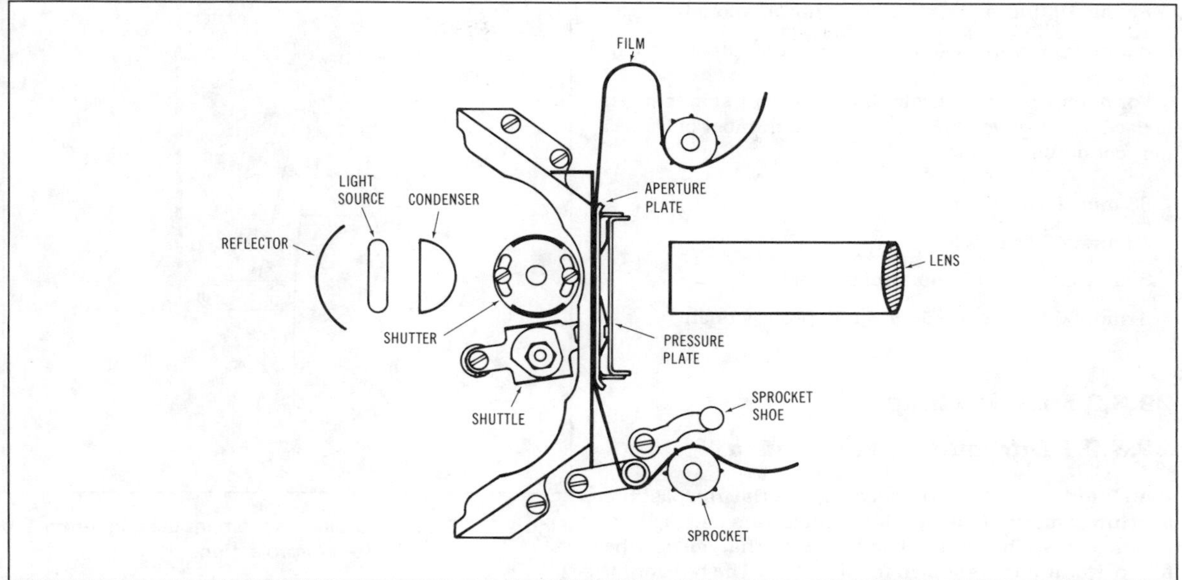

Figure 29-13 Simple motion-picture projection system.

movement is not projected on the screen. As the cam-actuated shuttle disengages the film after each frame advancement, the film is stationary momentarily, and the second shuttle blade interrupts the light beam to eliminate flicker on the screen.

The shuttle and shutter are geared to sprockets and rollers that pull and guide the film through the projector.

29.3.1 Film Specifications

Film is specified as the width in millimeters and by its aspect ratio. Table 29-8 gives the aperture dimensions for the various types of film.

The number of perforations per frame of picture are as follows:

8 mm: one hole above and below the frame, on the frame line, one edge only.

16 mm single perforation: one hole above and below the frame, on the frame line, one edge only.

16 mm double perforation: one hole above and below the frame, on the frame line, both edges.

35 mm: four holes each side of the frame splitting the frame line.

55 mm: 6 perforations.

70 mm: 5 and 6 perforations.

As a rule, double perforated 16-mm film is used only in the amateur photographic field.

Table 29-8. Aperture Dimensions for Various Types of Motion Picture Film

Film Width		Aspect Ratio	Aperture Dimensions
35 mm	(Academy standard)	1.34:1	0.825 × 0.600 in.
33 mm		2:1	0.839 × 0.715 in.
70 mm		2.21:1	1.913 × 0.866 in.
35 mm		2.21:1	0.839 × 0.715 in.
70 mm		2.21:1	1.913 × 0.866 in.
3 × 35 mm	(Ultra-Panavision)	2.27:1	0.985 × 1.088 in.
70 mm		2.27:1	1.913 × 0.866 in.
35 mm		2.34:1	0.839 × 0.715 in.
35 mm		2.35:1	0.839 × 0.715 in.
55.6 mm		2.55:1	1.340 × 1.050 in.
3 × 35 mm	(Cinerama)	2.77:1	0.985 × 1.088 in.
70 mm		2.94:1	1.913 × 0.811 in.
8 mm standard		1.33:1	0.172 × 0.129 in.
8 mm super 8		1.33:1	0.211 × 0.158 in.
16 mm		1.34:1	0.380 × 0.284 in.
16 mm C'scope		2.68:1	0.380 × 0.284 in.
35 mm standard		1.38:1	0.825 × 0.600 in.

Sound motion pictures must be reproduced at exactly the same linear speed at which they were recorded. Standard linear speeds in the industry are as follows:

35 mm: 90 ft/min, or 18 in./s,

16 mm: 36 ft/min, or 7.2 in./s,

8 mm: 18 ft/min, or 3.6 in./s (nonprofessional),

8 mm: 20 ft/min, or 4 in./s (super 8 mm professional).

For home use or nonprofessional use, the slower speed is used to conserve film. The standard number of frames per foot of film is as follows:

35 mm: 16 frames/ft

16 mm: 40 frames/ft

8 mm: 72 frames/ft (nonprofessional)

8 mm: 80 frames/ft (super 8-mm professional)

29.3.2 Film Handling

29.3.2.1 Intermittent Mechanism

An *intermittent mechanism* advances the film past the aperture. One method for 16-mm projectors uses a shuttle and cams. The shuttle has two teeth that engage the film perforations, as shown in Fig. 29-14. The horizontal cam drives the shuttle forward and backward in conjunction with the vertical cam, which drives the shuttle up and down. The horizontal cam is mounted directly behind the vertical cam on the shuttle shaft. The shuttle is geared to the shutter and film sprockets.

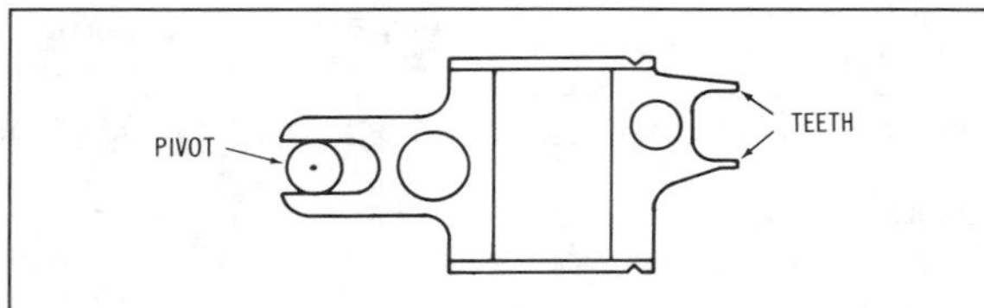

Figure 29-14 A simple two-tooth shuttle.

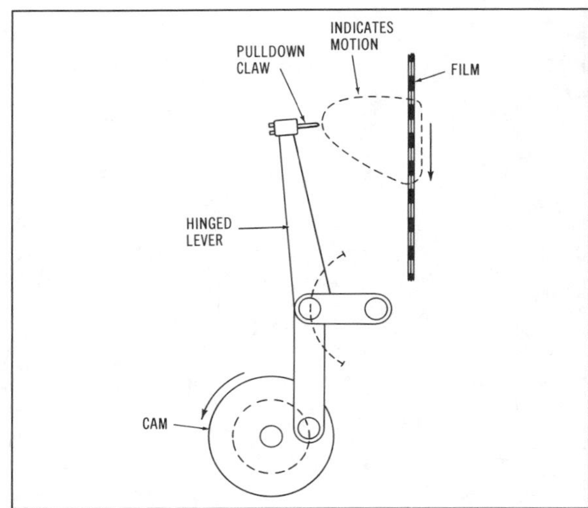

Figure 29-15 Askania Claw movement used in 8-mm and 16-mm projection.

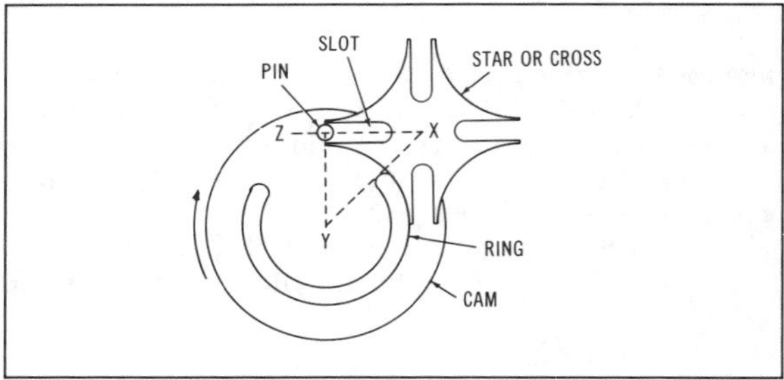

Figure 29-16 A Geneva intermittent movement used in 35-mm and 70-mm projectors.

Another intermittent movement is the Askania Claw movement, as shown in Fig. 29-15. This movement has a ratio of 1:1. As shown in Fig. 29-15, the hinged lever modifies the motion of the cam and imparts to the pulldown claw the motion indicated by the dotted line, which moves the film in the direction shown by the arrow. Because of the film wear induced by this movement, it is used only in 16-mm and 8-mm projectors.

Intermittent, Geneva-type movements used in 35-mm and 70-mm projectors are too expensive for the average 16-mm projector. A Geneva intermittent movement is shown in Fig. 29-16. The movement consists of four parts: a pin, a star or cross, a cam, and a ring.

If point X, the center of the star (connected to the intermittent sprocket), and point Y, the center of the cam, are continued to the center Z of the pin, a right angle is formed. The arrow indicates the direction of travel of the cam. The pin is shown at the exact instant it starts to engage the slot in the star. Until the cam has reached this position there is no movement of the star.

At the instant the pin engages the slot, the pin travels along the line ZX. Therefore, the pin will enter the slot cleanly with no chatter along the side walls of the slot. At the exact instant the pin enters the slot, there is still no movement of the star, inasmuch as the motion of the pin coincides with the slot. After the pin passes completely into the slot, its motion no longer coincides with the slot, and the star begins turning. This movement is slow at first and gradually increases until the star has reached its maximum speed when the pin is completely in the slot and is in line with the centers X and Y. When the pin leaves this position, the star (and consequently the film) begins to slow down. At the end of the movement, the pin leaves the slot and returns to its original position. When the pin leaves the slot, the star has stopped moving.

The purpose of the ring is to hold the star stationary

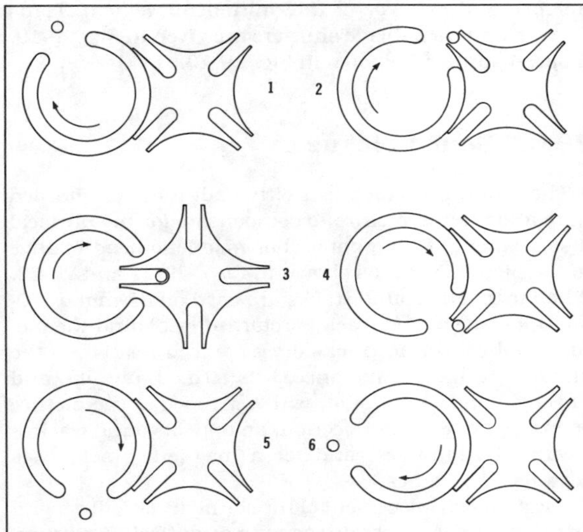

Figure 29-17 Six stages of movement of a Geneva intermittent movement.

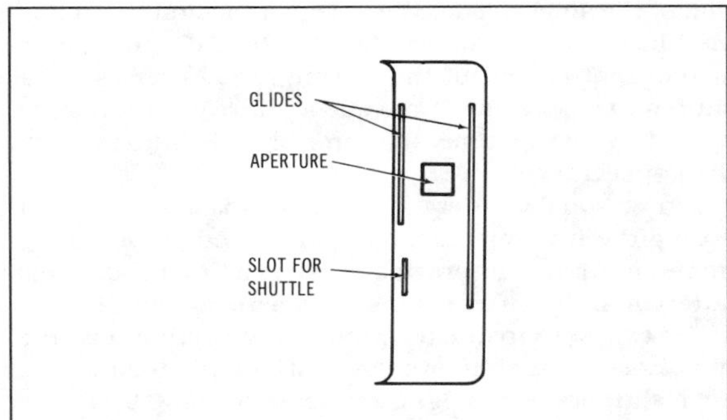

Figure 29-18 Aperture plate. The glides are used to keep the plate from scratching the film.

after the pin leaves the slot. As a result, the film is motionless during the time the cam completes its movement.

A study of the six positions shown in Fig. 29-17 will show that, from the time the pin enters and leaves the slot, the star has made a quarter revolution. For one complete revolution of the cam, one-fourth or 90° of its time is devoted to moving the film. This is called a 4:1 or 90° movement; 35-mm film travels at a speed of 90 ft/min or 24 frames/s. Therefore, each frame has 1/24 s devoted to it. The film is in motion one-fourth of the time or 1/96 s for each frame. To ensure quiet and smooth operation, the complete movement is placed in a sealed casting where it runs in a continuous bath of oil.

29.3.2.2 Film Sprockets

The *film sprockets* are driven at a constant speed to provide synchronized film movement at all points in the projector. Film rolls off the feed reel, passes the sound drum, and winds back on the take-up reel at a constant speed. However, it goes through the film gate in a move/stop/move motion. The upper sprocket is the feed that unwinds the film from the feed reel and maintains a loop of film above the aperture plate. The center sprocket is the sound sprocket that feeds film to the sound head and maintains a proper-length film loop below the aperture plate. A third sprocket is the take-up sprocket that moves the film away from the sound head, therefore, keeping the speed of the film over the sound head constant.

The sprocket shoes lock the film under the sprockets. The shoes maintain the registration between the film perforations and the sprocket teeth by positively guiding the film.

29.3.2.3 Aperture Plate

The purpose of the *aperture plate* in Fig. 29-18 is to achieve accurate framing of the picture on the screen. The opening in the aperture plate is made so that only one frame is projected. If the keystone is excessive, it may be corrected by filing the opening of the aperture plate to obtain a rectangular image on the screen. When the projection angle is greater than 0° downward, an undersized aperture plate is used and filed out to fit the particular projection angle. The bottom of the undersized plate is filed to the correct horizontal dimension to obtain the necessary width at the top of the picture. If the projection angle is −0° (projector shooting upward), the filing procedure is reversed. For curved screens, an undersized aperture will also be required and must be filed in a similar manner in order that the top and bottom will appear horizontal and parallel to each other on the screen. After the inside edges are filed, they are beveled about 30°, with the sharp edge toward the film, to eliminate fringe effects at the edges of the picture. The bevel is then painted dead black or black anodized to prevent reflections.

29.3.2.4 Pressure Plate

The film is maintained at right angles to the optical axis by the pressure plate. This plate holds the film against the aperture plate with proper tension when the projector is being operated. The film gate lever moves the pressure plate in and out from the aperture plate to allow loading the film into the film track.

29.3.2.5 Shutter

The sole purpose of a shutter in a projection machine is to cut the illumination off when the intermittent mechanism pulls the film downward. This occurs at the rate of 24 frames/s. Many different designs of shutters have appeared over the years. One of the original shutters was that of the single-blade type, used on the first projection machines. This was followed by a two-bladed shutter, used at the front or rear of the picture head. Then, similar shutters were placed in front and at the rear of the picture head. During this time, the three-bladed shutters made their appearance.

Conventional shutters are required to cut off the light during the intermittent pull-down period of 1/96 s (90 frames/min) and to provide a balanced cutoff of equal duration in the middle of the dwell period, resulting in a 48-Hz exposure frequency. Under these conditions, the two blades of the shutter must be of equal angular width. Such shutters have a light transmission of 50%.

The most efficient shutter at the present time is the barrel-and-cone type, placed at the rear of the picture head. It is the type used with most 70-mm projectors. The closer a shutter can be placed to the picture aperture, the more efficient it becomes.

In the design of projector shutters, several factors must be considered. Among these are the light level at the screen, the speed of the lens system in the lamphouse (concave mirror), and the type of intermittent movement. Plans for two- and three-blade shutters are given in Fig. 29-19. A barrel shutter is shown in Fig. 29-20.

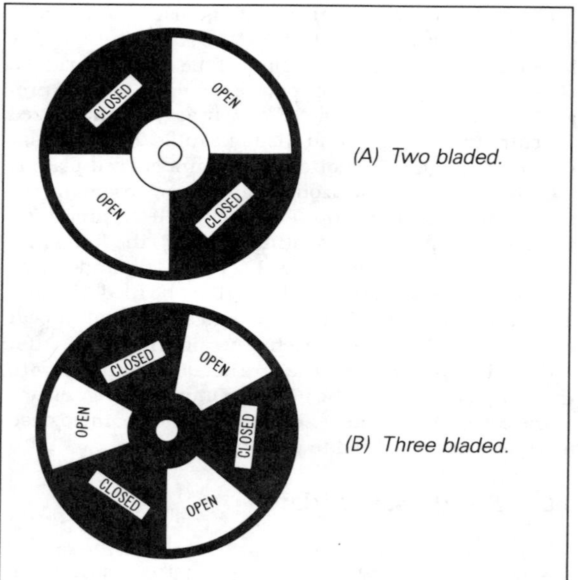

Figure 29-19 Blade shutters.

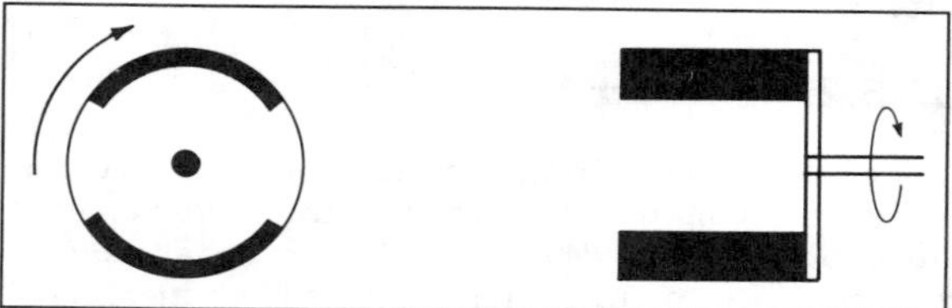

Figure 29-20 Barrel shutter.

29.3.3 Sound Pickup

The sound-track pickup is either advanced or retarded in relation to the picture to compensate for the physical displacement of the photocell or magnetic head relative to the picture head, as shown in Figs. 29-21 and 29-22. When magnetic sound tracks are used on 35-mm or 70-mm film, the sound track is retarded or behind the picture. Optical sound tracks are advanced relative to the picture. In the first instance, it is termed, *pull-up*, and in the second, *pull-down*, with reference to the picture aperture. For 8-mm projection, an optical sound track is advanced 22 frames, and for a magnetic track, it is advanced 18 frames.

The actual displacement of the sound track will depend on whether the track is magnetic or optical. For reproducing a 35-mm optical sound track, the phototube and its associated equipment is placed in a sound head below the picture head, and the magnetic reproducing head is housed in a penthouse above the picture head.

In large theaters where the projection throw is greater than 100 ft, it may be necessary to advance or retard the sound track a few sprocket holes to bring the sound into proper synchronization at audience distances of 100 ft or more from the screen. This may be accomplished for an optical sound track by threading the sound start mark at the 19th, rather than the 20th, frame. In the average theater, it is necessary to emit the sound before the cor-

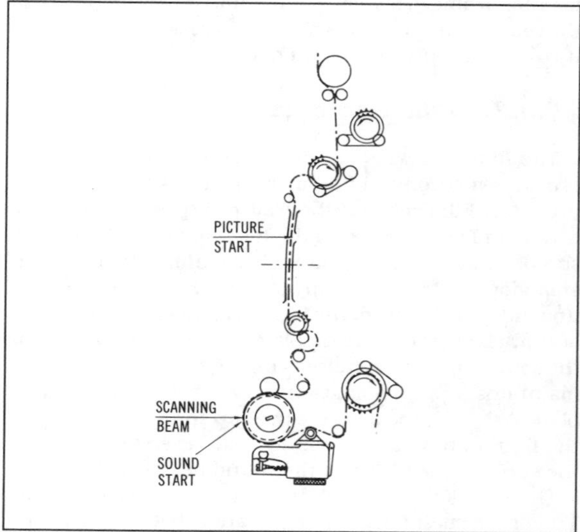

Figure 29-21 Film threading path for 35-mm and 70-mm film using optical sound-track reproduction.

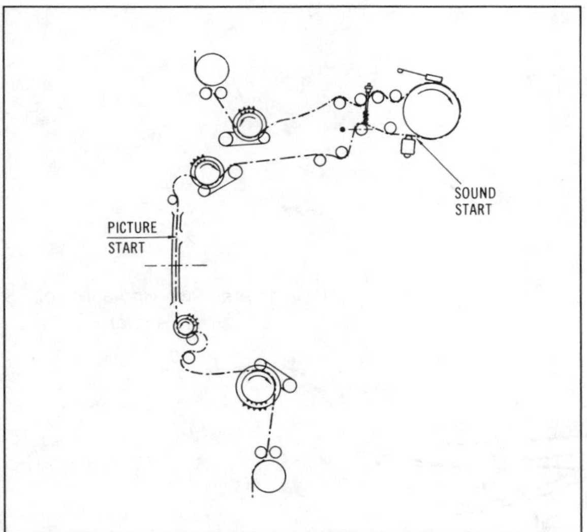

Figure 29-22 Film threading path for 35-mm and 70-mm film using magnetic sound-track reproduction.

responding picture frame is projected, since sound travels at approximately 1100 ft/s or about 50 ft/frame for a normal projection rate of 24 frames/s. The projectionist can place the sound in synchronization in the theater by varying the length of the threading path between the projector and the sound head.

The length of film between the aperture opening and the scanning beam must be 26 frames. The film has a loop in it as it leaves the aperture channel. The size of this loop determines the length of film that will exist between the two points. When the film is badly damaged, worn, or poorly spliced, the lower loop is usually lost. Depressing the loop setter until it hits the stop then releasing it resets the loop. The lower loop will react automatically to the precise size required for synchronization of the picture and sound.

29.4 PROJECTION TECHNIQUES

29.4.1 Front Projection

In front projection the projector and the audience are on the same side of the screen; therefore, seeing the picture relies completely on reflection. The main disadvantages of front projection are that the ambient light must be kept low and that obstacles including smoke and people affect the picture.

29.4.1.1 Illumination

The amount of brightness is determined by the light source and the screen reflectivity and transmission. The light source puts out a light intensity given in candelas (see Chapter 31.) The amount of luminous sensation that the light source produces is given in lumens and can be found by the formula:

$$\text{luminance} = 4\pi\,(\text{candle power})\,(\text{efficiency of the optics}) \quad (29\text{-}4)$$

The illumination on the screen is determined by dividing the illumination available by the image area

$$\text{screen illumination} = \text{projector lumens/image area} \quad (29\text{-}5)$$

As the image size increases, the brightness decreases by a square factor.

The actual luminance or brightness perceived by the viewer is equal to the screen illumination times the screen gain

$$\text{luminance} = \text{illumination (screen gain)} \quad (29\text{-}6)$$

The image brightness is related to the projector illumination, and the nonimage brightness is caused by the luminance due to stray illumination from lights, windows, and stray light from the projector. The contrast ratio is

$$\text{contrast ratio} = \text{image brightness/nonimage brightness} \quad (29\text{-}7)$$

The acceptable contrast ratio varies with the source, black-and-white word slides requiring a ratio of 5:1 and color motion pictures and slides requiring a 100:1 ratio for acceptable projection.

29.4.1.2 Screens

An ideal screen would be one that would diffuse all the light from the projector into the audience spaces with uniform brightness for every viewer and simultaneously reject any stray light falling on the screen, reflecting it away from the audience. Such a screen would provide maximum projection efficiency and maximum contrast ratio.[2]

Calcium carbonate comes very close to being a Lambertian surface, or one that reflects 100% of the light striking it. This type of screen would be considered to have a gain of 1. A matte white screen has a gain of 0.98. For a screen to have increased gain, it must take the same amount of light and reflect it back into a narrower viewing angle. For instance, a matte white screen has an even brightness through 180° while a beaded screen is 3.5 times brighter on axis, equal to a matte white at 20° off axis and less than a matte white screen beyond 20°, as shown in Fig. 29-23.

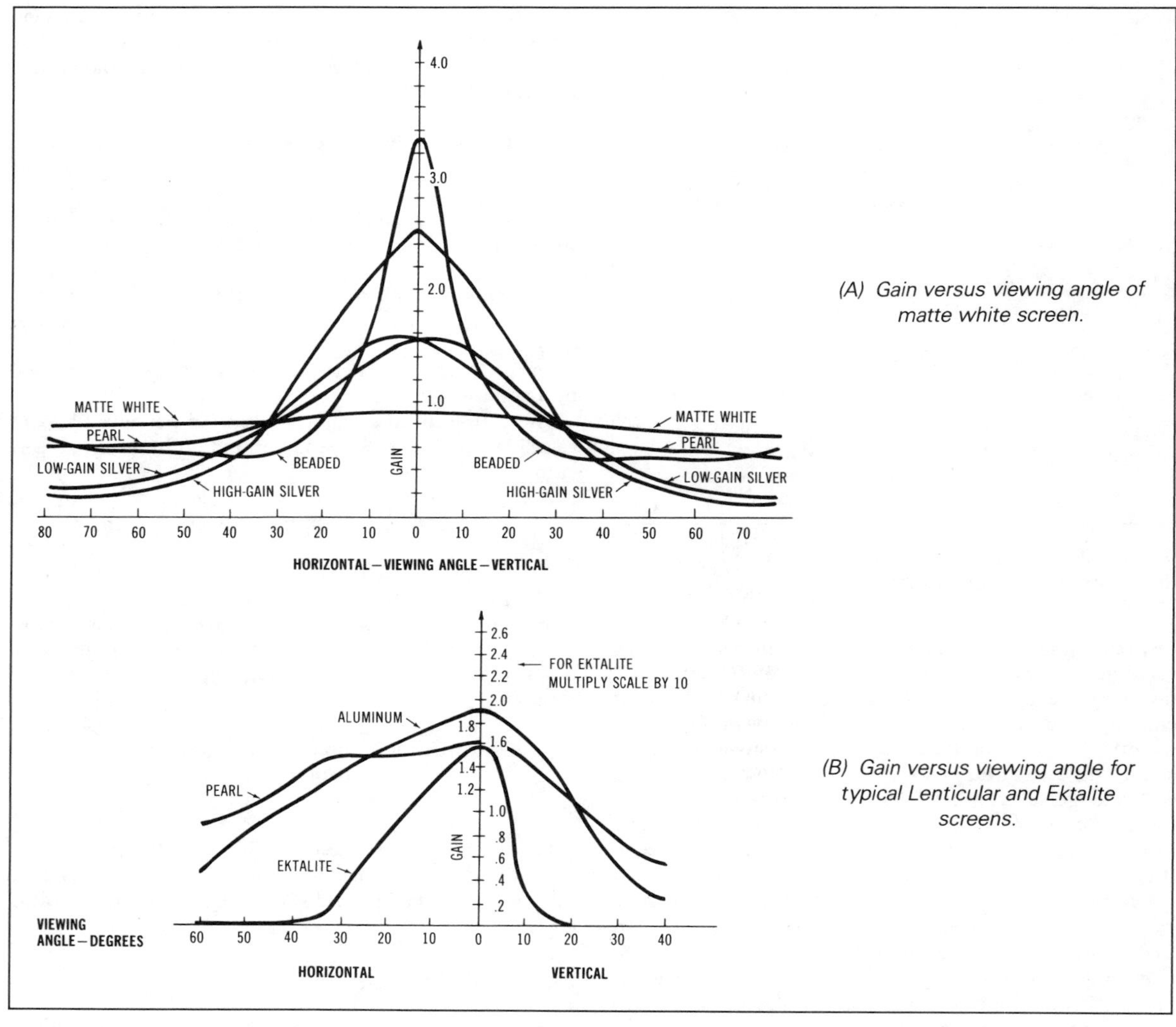

Figure 29-23 Reflectance of various types of screens. Note Kodak Ektalite and aluminum have different gain for vertical and horizontal viewing.

Matte white screens may have a solid or perforated (sound) surface. Images projected on this type of screen diffuse the projected light evenly in all directions. About 15% of the incident light is lost.

Lenticulated screens are constructed of minute horizontal and vertical reflective areas in the form of diamonds or rectangles. The size of the lenticulation affects the viewing angles and brightness. Such screens are capable of providing images several times brighter than those shown on a white matte screen within a narrower viewing angle. Lenticulated screens are not perforated for sound.

Beaded screens are quite popular for 16-mm home projection, halls, and auditoriums. They may be considered to be a type of lenticulation accomplished by surfacing the screen with small glass beads approximately 0.5 to 0.1 mm in diameter. This results in a bright image but a narrow viewing angle. If used in a high ambient light, the brightness of the image is reduced. These screens are not perforated.

Black lenticulated screens, developed by Sasuke Takahashi of Japan, are unique because of the black lenticulated vertical and horizontal surface. It is claimed by the inventor that in comparison with a matte white screen, it is 25 times greater in black-and-white contrast and ideal for color projection. Also, it absorbs scattered stray ambient light and prevents halation on the surface with wide-angle viewing. It may also be used for stereographic projection. With no light on its surface, the screen appears black. This is advantageous for some types of display. Because of the lenticulation, the surface is not perforated for sound.

29.4.1.3 Keystoning

When the projection angle is 0° (i.e., the light beam forms a 90° angle to the screen) minimum distortion will occur. However, if the projector is not in alignment, keystone distortion occurs because the throw distance is not equal on all sides of the image, as shown in Fig. 29-24. Note the picture not only takes on a trapezoidal shape but the side with the longer throw distance is larger than normal. The difference in image size can be calculated by using Eqs. 29-1 or 29-3 for each edge of the screen. The difference in picture size can be determined by using the following equation:

$$L = L_{normal} \pm (L_{normal}/\cos\alpha) \quad (29\text{-}8)$$

The percent distortion caused by keystoning can be found with the following equation:

$$\%\ distortion = 100\sin\theta/\cos(\theta+\phi) = 100\sin\theta/\cos[\sin^{-1}(\sin\theta) + H/2T)] \quad (29\text{-}9)$$

where,
θ is the projection angle,
ϕ is the one-half angle subtended by projected light,
H is the screen height,
T is the projection throw distance.

Keystoning may be offset somewhat by tilting the top of the screen forward or backward in an attempt to equalize the throw between the top and the bottom of the screen.

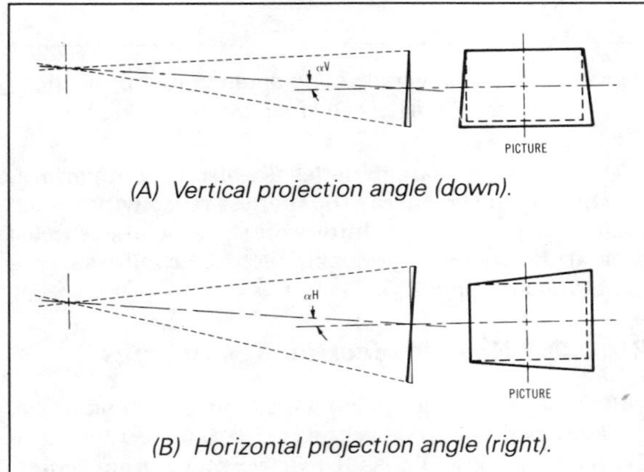

Figure 29-24 Effects of vertical or horizontal keystoning on the image.

The use of curved screens to compensate for these effects is of some help; however, keystoning cannot be entirely eliminated because of the relationship between the projectors and the screen. To obtain a square frame line and eliminate the distortion of the aperture outline on the screen, the aperture can be shaped to obtain a square frame line on the screen. Also, the screen can be masked at the sides, top, and bottom into a small amount of the picture, to help reduce the visual effects of keystoning.

In the design of theaters, keystoning should be kept to a minimum. If possible, the axes of the projector's lens should be at least 8 ft from the floor level to clear persons standing at the rear of the room. The screen should be installed in such a manner that the vertical keystone is not more than 8°. Multiprojectors should be set as close together as possible to reduce the horizontal keystone effect to not more than 6°. If the keystone is excessive, distortion and out-of-focus conditions will prevail at the edges of the picture.

29.4.2 Rear Projection

Rear projection permits the use of projected visuals in normally illuminated rooms, which allows visual contact between the instructor and the audience as well as reference to other material and the taking of notes.

With projectors behind the screen, distraction is minimized. Movement of both the instructor and the audience is permitted without projector beam interference.

29.4.2.1 Illumination

Illumination for rear screen projection is related to the transmission of the screen and varies with the bend angle. The nonimage brightness is related to the reflectance of the screen and varies with the viewing angle. Screen gain is found with the equation

$$gain = \frac{\text{transmission of screen}}{\text{reflectance of } MgCO_3 \text{ screen}} \quad (29\text{-}10)$$

The nonimage brightness is found with the equation

$$brightness = \frac{\text{reflectance of screen}}{\text{reflectance of } MgCO_3 \text{ screen}} \quad (29\text{-}11)$$

The contrast ratio is found with Eq. 29-7.

29.4.2.2 Rear Projection Screens

Rear screens can be a soft, foldable material, a plastic base, or a glass base.

The soft, flexible plastic screens are portable and can be made into very large sizes because they are snapped or tied to a frame. Large screens have a tendency to pump when the pressure between sides changes, such as when opening a door or window, and they have very poor sound isolation.

The glass base provides maximum sound isolation and long service life along with top optical qualities. Its strength and rigidity recommend it for larger sizes. It has good resistance to scratching but weighs approximately twice as much as an acrylic screen. Installation by a glazier is recommended. Glass is available in 1/8, 1/4, 3/8, and 1/2-in. thicknesses.

The acrylic plastic base offers good sound isolation, although it is not as good as glass. Being less rigid than glass, it is more resistant to breakage, thus commending it for some installations. Its lower weight results in lower freight costs and usually lower installation cost. Plastic is available in 1/8, 1/4, 3/8, and 1/2-in. thicknesses. Also 1/16 in. is available in sizes up to 4 square feet[4] for special applications, and 1/4-in. thickness is recommended for sizes to 6 ft × 10 ft, 3/8 in. to 8 ft × 18 ft, and 1/2 in. to 10 ft × 20 ft or 8 ft × 24 ft.

A rigid, rear projection screen consists of a specially formulated optical coating deposited on a transparent sheet of glass or acrylic plastic. The following coatings by Dalite Screen Co. meet a wide variety of rear projection requirements.

- DA-1N—A wide-angle type especially suited for multiple projection. This is a dark coating that provides the most even light distribution but requires a more powerful projector light source. Contrast is excellent with good color reproduction.
- DA-3N—The most popular coating and fits most rear screen applications. Its neutral gray tint provides excellent contrast for black and white as well as high-color fidelity. This is a medium-wide angle-type coating.
- DA-5N—Provides brighter images within narrower viewing angles. Not recommended for wide-angle or short focal length lenses.
- DA-8N—A specialized coating for extra bright images over limited viewing angles as for instrument use. Best for low-powered projectors with long focal length lenses.

Rigid screens have a polished and a matte or coated surface and can be used with either surface toward the audience without affecting the optical characteristics.

Placing the polished side forward, the coated surface is protected from accidental scuffing, scratching, and general abuse. However, glare and reflection from lights, table tops, and other surface reflections can be objectionable and annoying. The glare and reflection can be minimized by using shielded, masked, or recessed lights; removing bright and reflective objects; or tilting the screen forward. The tilt should not be more than 3° to control image keystoning.

The coated side forward is used in most large-sized installations and performs best if required to face general and uncontrolled room lighting. The matte surface eliminates glare and reflection. However, care must be taken to protect this coated or matte surface from public abuse or accidental damage, such as writing on it with chalk. Drapes, curtains, sliding chalkboards, or cover panels are often used for protection when it's not in use. To preserve the long life of the screen, it should be ordered with a protective finish.

Like front projection screens, rear projection screens can also have gain with respect to a flat white screen. As the gain increases, the bend angle must be less as falloff becomes predominant (Fig. 29-25). Note the screen with a gain of 500% has a gain of only 100% at 26° and a gain of 60% at 32°. The screen with a gain of 300% has a gain of 100% at 26°, and a screen with a gain of 150% has a gain of 100% at 20° and a gain of 60% at 34°.

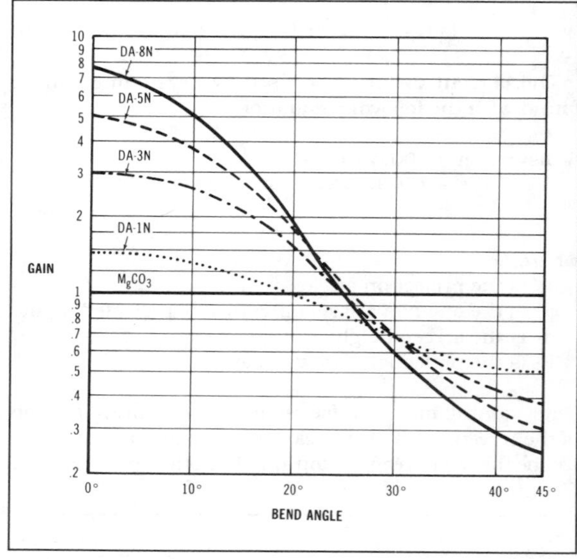

Figure 29-25 Gain versus bend angle of rear projection screens. *(Courtesy Da-lite Screen Co., Inc.)*

The reflection characteristics are also very important. The high-gain screen has the highest reflectivity, which means that ambient light hitting the screen will be reflected back at the audience, reducing picture brightness, contrast, and sharpness.

29.4.2.3 Rear Projection Techniques

Because of the light falloff with increased bend angle, the audience should be kept as close to the centerline of the screen as possible. As the viewer moves from centerline to either side, a hot spot moves with him. This is caused because the minimim bend angle follows the viewer.

Fig. 29-26 shows two rear-projection setups.[3] The projector in system 1 has a throw of five times the screen width. From a viewing point twice the screen width away from the screen along the line DE, light emanating from the right side of the projector along the line HG must be deflected by the screen at point G to points A, B, C, and D. From the left side of the projector along the line HF, deflection must be made to points A, B, C, and D. At point A the projector light is deflected through angles AFB and AGI. At point B the deflection angles are BFB or zero and BGI on the right.

The deflection angles for the various viewing positions are given in the first two columns of Table 29-9. The maximum difference in deflection of 36° of the light from the projector occurs at point B. Point D is an angle of 30°

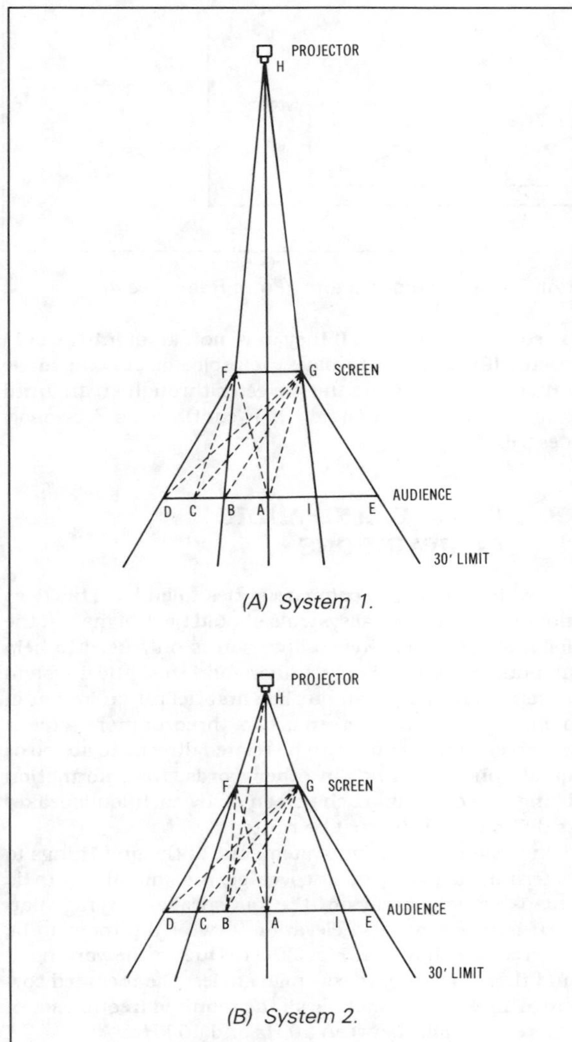

Figure 29-26 Two rear projection setups with the audience located in the same position and the screen the same size. *(From Reference 3)*

Table 29-9. Variations and Intensity Ratios for Various Viewing Positions

Viewing position	Deflection angle range, degrees	% Transmission from curve LS60F	Intensity ratio
	System 1		
A	0 to 20	215 to 112	0.52
B	0 to 36	215 to 57	0.27
C	12 to 44	152 to 40	0.26
D	24 to 52	97 to 28	0.29
	System 2		
A	0 to 32	215 to 68	0.32
B	0 to 49	215 to 32	0.15
C	0 to 68	215 to 13	0.06
D	13 to 77	147 to 8.4	0.06

with the normal, and the deflection is as much as 52° in angle DGI. Consequently, it should not be thought that a 30° position requires only a 30° deflection.

System 2 is identical to system 1 except that a projector lens having a shorter focal length is used, resulting in a projector throw of 1½ times the screen width. The same calculations have been made for system 2 as for system 1. The screen must deflect the light at greater angles for a short focal length lens than for a long focal length lens. The position along the extremes of the projector line again has the greatest difference in deflection angle.

By using the angles given in column two of Table 29-9 and applying them to the distribution curve of Fig. 29-27, the values of the third column in Table 29-9 are obtained. These values represent transmission at the various angles. By dividing the percent of light transmission

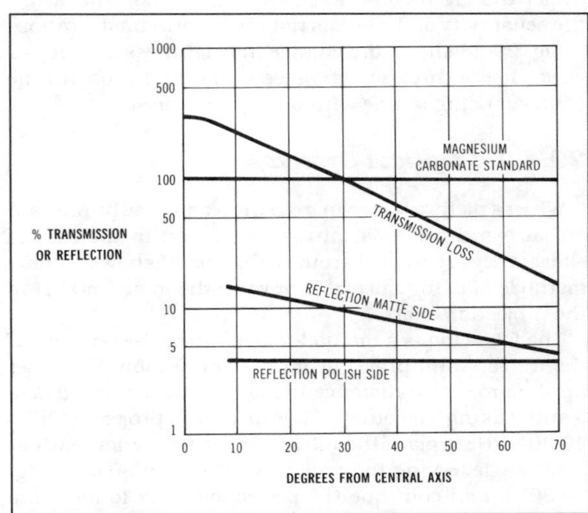

Figure 29-27 Distribution curves of reflection characteristics of a screen (Polocoat LS60F).

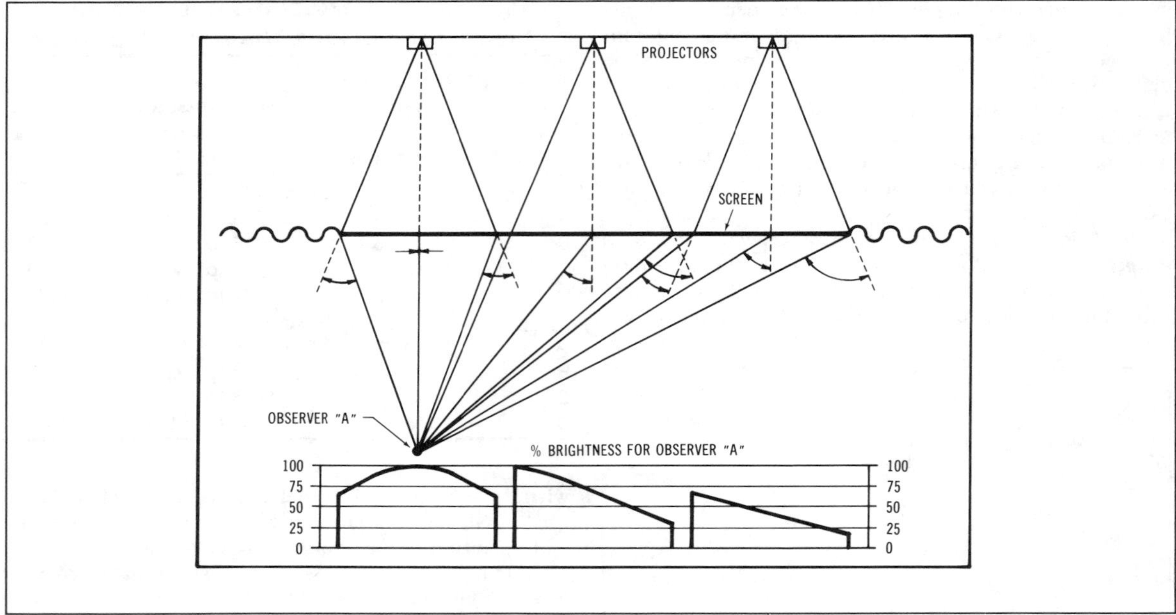

Figure 29-28 Bend angles and brightness distribution for multiple projectors. *(From Reference 4)*

for the minimum deflection angle with that of the maximum deflection angle, a light intensity ratio is obtained, which is shown in the fourth column of this table. This value is a ratio of the intensity range of the transmitted light for a given viewing position. The values given are based on an ideally uniform distribution of light by a projector, which is never the case in practice.

The intensity ratios are arithmetical ratios of the light energy for this particular screen (the Polacoat Inc. LS60F) under the given conditions. One very important factor, the sensitivity of the eye, is not taken into consideration.

Fig. 29-28 shows the change in brightness in percentages when a three-screen presentation is given with the observer being in line with one of the side screens.[4]

29.4.2.4 Optical Systems

When a picture is shown from the rear, it will be reversed or backward unless a mirror is used or, in the case of slides, they are turned around. Fig. 29-29 shows various methods of using mirrors to reverse the image or shrink the projection space.

The following is a method to determine the position of the mirrors and projector for rear projection. First, set up the projection distance using Eqs. 29-1 through 29-3 and making a layout as if it were a front projection (Fig. 29-30A). Next place the mirror in the projection path at a 45° angle. Swing the projector through a 90° arc (Fig. 29-30B), and continue the projection lines to meet the projector. Continue this process for as many mirrors as necessary. Note that edge 1 plus edge 2 is the same length as edge 3 plus edge 4. If they were not, keystoning would occur. If you prefer to have the projector at some angle other than 90°, rotate the projector through an arc until angle α and α' are equal, then continue as previously described.

29.5 OPTICAL AND AUDIO COMPARISONS

It is interesting to compare optics to audio. This does not mean that optical systems should be designed in the following manner; the comparison is only used to help an audio person to better understand the optical system in terms familiar to audio. The first definition is that of a *multiscreen*. Multiscreen is two, three, or more screens or screen areas, and it can be related directly to stereo or quadraphonic sound. In other words, the information being presented on each screen or by each loudspeaker is different, but it must be related.

In designing a sound system, one of the first things to determine is loudspeaker coverage. A common way to do this is actually to lay out the loudspeaker coverage pattern on the plan and elevation view of the room to be covered, as shown in Fig. 29-31. Due to the varying Q and therefore varying coverage angles, the included coverage angles must include all the required frequencies of interest, usually between 50 Hz and 10 kHz.

Due to the extremely high frequencies of optics, that is, the wavelength is much shorter than the lenses that are being used, light travels in a straight line; therefore,

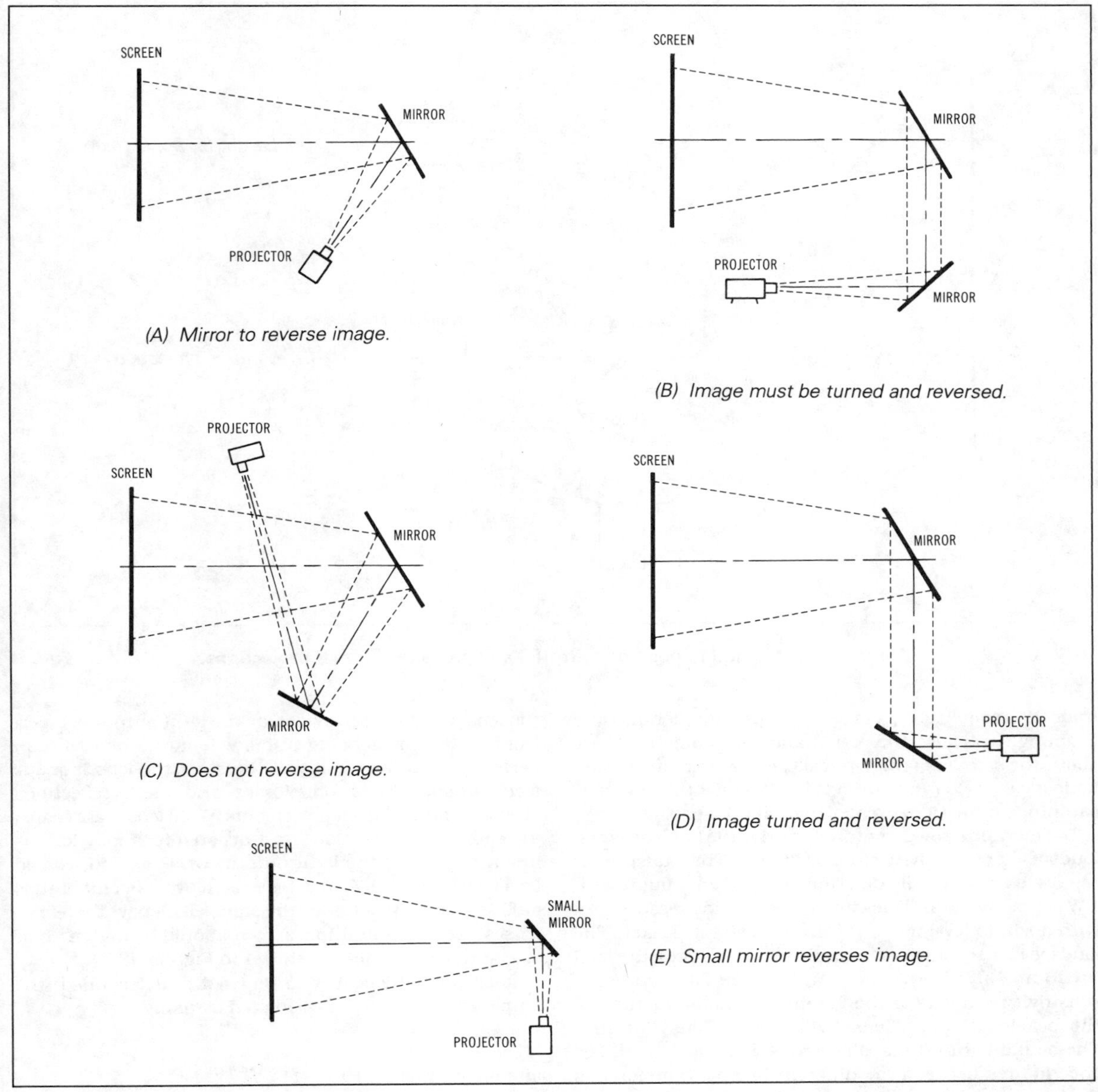

Figure 29-29 Various projection methods.

for long screen-to-film gate distances, Eq. 29-1 is used to determine image width.

For short screen-to-film gate distances, such as are used in rear projection systems in board rooms, the classical lens equation (Eq. 29-3) should be used.

In the case of 35-mm slides, image width to image height or aspect ratio is 1.5:1, and for 16-mm motion pictures, it is 1.33:1. *Note:* It is interesting that aspect ratios are given with respect to height although most projection charts are related to width.

The equation for the geometric Q of the average loudspeaker and lens is

$$Q_{geo} = \frac{180°}{\arcsin}\left(\sin\frac{\theta}{2}\right)\left(\sin\frac{\phi}{2}\right) \quad (29\text{-}12)$$

The real Q of a loudspeaker, however, is something less

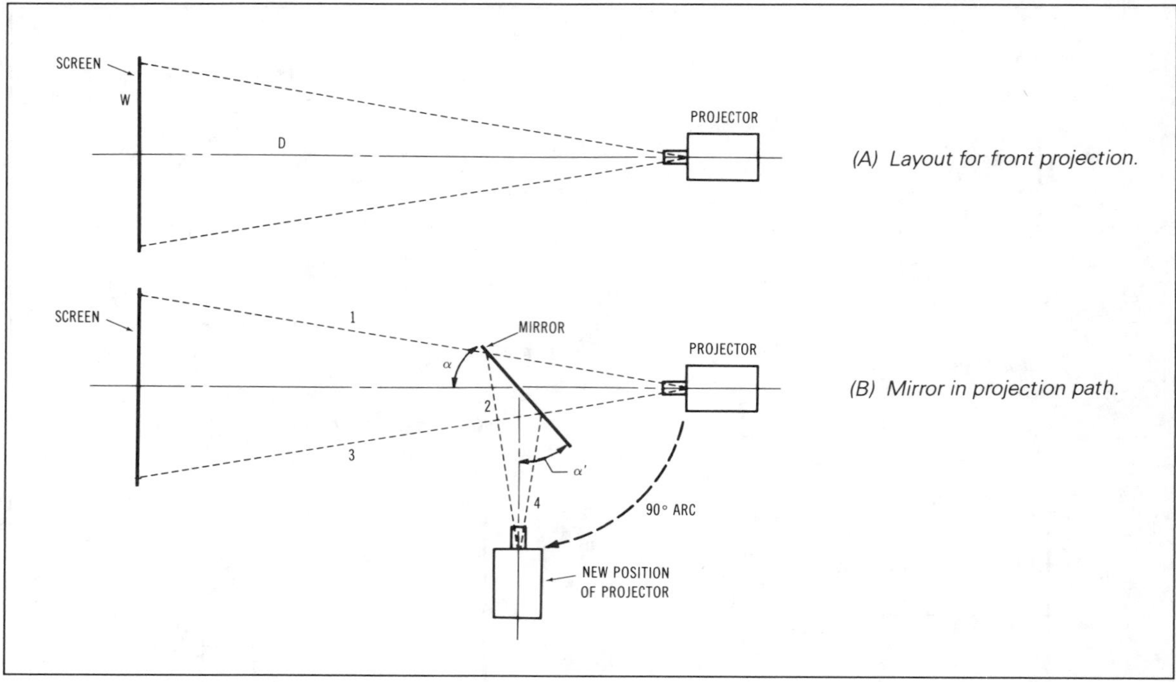

(A) Layout for front projection.

(B) Mirror in projection path.

Figure 29-30 Method to position mirror(s) and projector for rear projections.

than the geometric Q because of diffraction, lobing, and beaming. Optically, the real Q and the geometric Q are about the same, making optical Q measurements easier. Loudspeaker Qs range from 2 to 50, while the optical Q can range from 14 to greater than 4000.

To determine power required to drive the loudspeakers, loudspeaker sensitivity must be known. The loudspeaker sensitivity is normally determined by energizing it with 1 W of pink noise and measuring the sound pressure level with a sound level meter 4 ft from the loudspeaker. The loudspeaker sensitivity is specified in sound pressure level in dB at 4 ft 1 W or 1m 1 W (Fig. 29-32). Optically, sensitivity of a lens or the f-stop of a lens is the ratio of the focal length of the lens divided by the lens diameter. The actual light output differences would be the difference in area between the different f-stops; therefore, as the f-stops are halved or doubled, the sensitivity changes by a ratio of four.

Efficiency is also an important parameter. A loudspeaker with a 4-ft, 1-watt sensitivity of 107.47 dB and a Q of 1 would have an efficiency of 100%. As the sensitivity of the loudspeaker decreases, so does the efficiency. Efficiency also decreases as the Q of the loudspeaker increases, which is the reason why low-frequency loudspeakers with low Qs and low sensitivities are often more efficient than high-frequency horns with high Qs and high sensitivities, as shown in Fig. 29-33.

The efficiency of a lens is equal to the light output of the lens being tested divided by the light output of a perfect lens. The lens being tested will always be less than perfect due to the quality of the glass the lens is made from, which creates some losses, and due to reflections off the surfaces of the lens elements. Good lenses are coated to reduce this reflection. An uncoated lens may lose as much as 40% of the light output, while a good, coated lens may lose only 5%. For this reason two different brands of f2 lenses may not have the same efficiency; therefore, lenses used on a multiple screen should be matched for size and light output, as shown in Fig. 29-33.

Once the loudspeaker to be used is determined, the amplifier power can be calculated by using

$$\text{amplifier power} = 10^{\text{(Program Level + 10 dB crest factor + Acoustic Level Change} - \text{Lsens/10)}} \quad (29\text{-}13)$$

It is important that the amplifier power does not exceed the maximum power the loudspeaker is capable of accepting. If the amplifier power required is greater than the power capabilities of the loudspeaker, then either more loudspeakers or a more efficient loudspeaker must be used to accept the total amplifier power needed to deliver the required sound-pressure level.

In the optical system, the projector output in lumens is equal to the luminance on the screen times the screen area divided by the screen efficiency and lens efficiency:

$$\text{projector lumens required} = \frac{\text{luminance required} \times \text{screen area}}{\%\ \text{screen efficiency} \times \%\ \text{lens efficiency}} \qquad (29\text{-}14)$$

In a front projection system, a matte white screen is considered 100% efficient or has a gain of 1, while a beaded or high-gain screen or lenticular screen can have a gain of 2 to 7. In rear projection, the on-axis screen gain can vary from 0.5 to 10. Unfortunately, high-gain rear projection screens have a very narrow viewing angle and, therefore, are only used where the audience is only one or two people in a fixed position. For board rooms, low-gain, wide-angle screens are used. Efficient lenses, like efficient loudspeakers, mean less power required. Since power is large, heavy, and expensive, there is a decided cost and maintenance advantage in using high efficiency and low power. If, on the other hand, the extra money is in the budget, and there is enough room to install the larger projector, the advantage realized will be a brighter picture. If a lower sensitivity lens is used, a sharper picture will result.

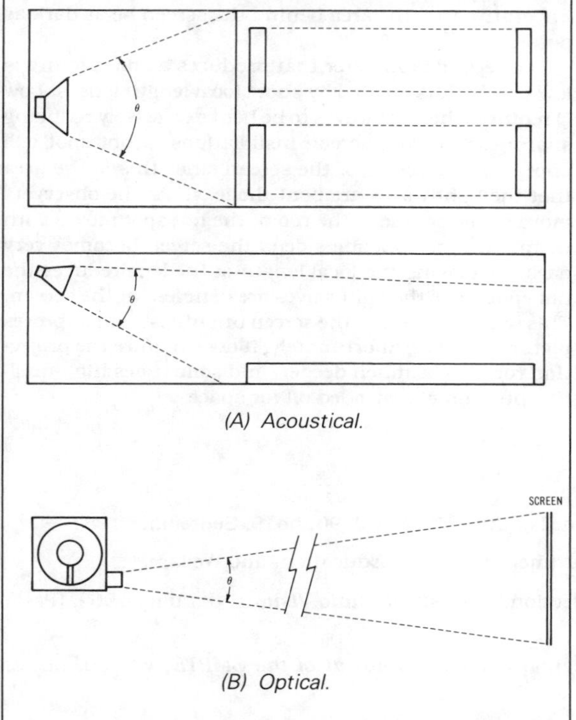

Figure 29-31 Optical and acoustic coverage patterns.

The final important matter to be determined acoustically is the articulation loss of consonants in rooms with reverberant times greater than 1.6 s:

$$\%AL_{cons} = 656(RT_{60})^2 D_2^2 / VQ \qquad (29\text{-}15)$$

where,

RT_{60} is the reverberation time in 2-kHz octave bands,
D_2 is the loudspeaker to farthest listener distance,
V is the volume,
Q is the directivity of loudspeaker.

If the loudspeaker Q is too low, the articulation loss will exceed 15%, and the Q will have to be increased or the D_2 distance will have to be reduced.

If the ambient sound is too loud, the signal-to-noise ratio deteriorates to a point where the ambient noise must be reduced to improve intelligibility to an acceptance level.

The loudspeaker Q can be increased by either changing loudspeakers or by stacking loudspeakers. Reducing noise usually requires the service of an acoustician.

In projection systems, assuming the optics are of good

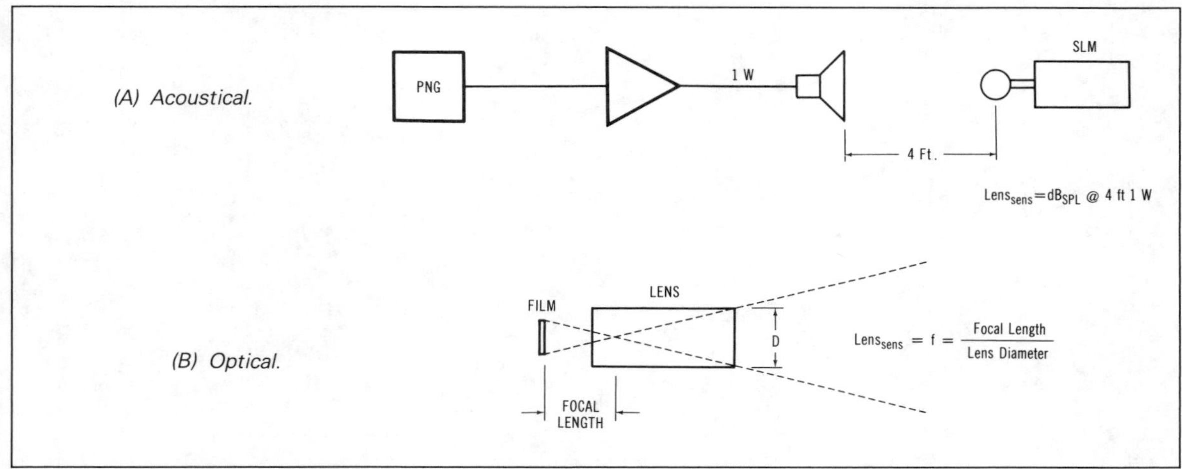

Figure 29-32 Optical and acoustic sensitivity.

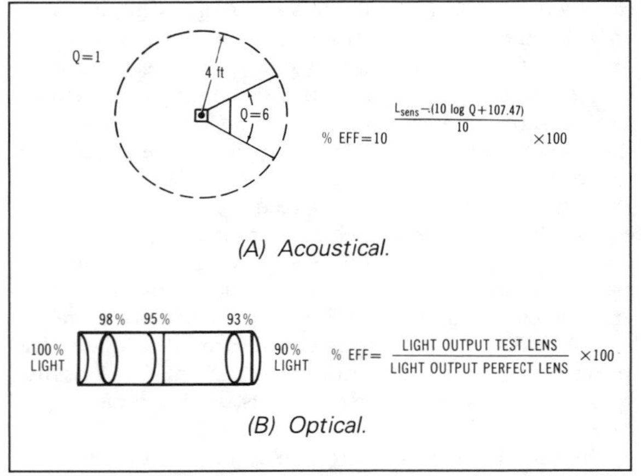

(A) Acoustical.

(B) Optical.

Figure 29-33 Optical and acoustic efficiency.

quality (i.e., low distortion and aberration), then acceptable viewing quality is basically determined by two parameters. Like signal-to-noise ratio, ambient light, which hits the screen and reflects back to the audience, reduces intelligibility by reducing picture contrast. If ambient light hitting the screen is excessive, it must be reduced. One of the main advantages of rear projection is its ability to perform satisfactorily under relatively high ambient light. It is important, however, that the light be kept away from the screen as much as possible and imperative that the area behind the screen be as dark as possible.

The second parameter that produces a poor picture is low Q, which is created by short focal length lenses. Low Q requires the light waves to be bent excessively reducing sharpness. In rear screen installations, a hot spot will appear in the center of the screen since this is the area that the light waves are bent the least. As the observers move to either side of the room, the hot spot moves with them, and the opposite side of the screen becomes very dark. Increasing the focal length of the lens reduces the hot spot since the light waves are bent less at the screen. This usually increases the screen brightness and improves picture quality. Unfortunately, it does require the projection room to be much deeper, and sometimes high-quality optics must be traded off for space.

REFERENCES

1. F. G. Back, "Zoom Lenses—Their Development," *Journal of the SMPTE*, vol. 90, no. 9, September 1981.
2. W. Szabo, "Audiovisual Projection Systems," U.S. Department of Health, Education, and Welfare.
3. J. F. Dreyer, "Operational Characteristics of Rear Projection," *Industrial Audio-Visuals*, January 1969. (Parts copied with permission.)
4. P. Vlahos, "Selection and Specification of Rear-Projection Screens," *Journal of the SMPTE*, vol. 70, no. 2, February 1961.

PART 7

Measurements

CHAPTER **30**

Audio Measurements

by Don Davis

30.1 THE WORD "AUDIO" IN MEASUREMENT

The word "audio" in the *American College Dictionary* is defined as, "for hearing." Thus, it benefits the audio measurer to evaluate the parameter to be measured in terms of its audibility, as well as in terms of any physical parameters under measurement. Many measurements offered up for consideration today, however, have little or no meaning in terms of audio, but have evolved from specification competition among various audio apparatus manufacturers.

Young audio engineers are sometimes unaware of the history behind the various measurements they encounter. Many are vaguely aware that some devices meet specs and others do not and that the way this is determined is by measurement. Often the invocation of a particular measurement is more on grounds of faith than on reasons of objective fact. Many audio engineers erroneously accept that the measurement of the amplitude versus the sequence of primitive periods (frequency) is the total frequency response of a system or component because they have been taught by the audio priesthood that this is so. Often, upon inspection of the historical development of the particular measurement, it is found that, back when the measurement was first used, it was the only parameter engineers had a tool with which to measure it and that the choice had little or no relationship to what should have been measured.

As the understanding of measurements has progressed, a form of measurement philosophy has gradually expanded as well.

"In order to make a sensible choice of measurement parameters, it is necessary to know the system response in advance—in which case there would be no reason to measure it."[1]

To one preparing to make a measurement of a *device under test (DUT)*, the initial parameters can be chosen by one of the three techniques:

1. Experience with similar devices.
2. Mathematical analysis of the device and its most likely performance.
3. Cut-and-try experimentation.

In the final analysis, we are dealing physically with the dynamic motion of molecules disturbed by a phenomenon called *sound energy*. What parameters of that energy are meaningful and relevant to our needs in audio and acoustics and what tools are useful in making these measurements?

Which came first, the measurement or the instrument is a chicken-and-egg type of question. All instruments are based upon the fact that all electrical measurements can be defined in terms of length m, mass kg, and time s. See Table 30-1.

30.2 WAVES

Longitudinal waves occur when individual particles of a medium vibrate back and forth in the direction in which the waves travel. Sound in air consists of longitudinal waves, as shown in Fig. 30-1A.

Transverse waves occur when the individual particles of a medium vibrate from side to side perpendicular to the direction in which the waves travel. The vibrations of stretched string are transverse waves, as shown in Fig. 30-1B.

30.2.1 Choice of a Suitable Measurement Signal

At a first glance a square wave might appear mathematically attractive because its peak, average, and rms amplitudes are all the same value. It is not, however, a signal that occurs in nature, and aural judgments of its purity are difficult. Random noise is a frequently used signal, but it theoretically has an infinitely high peak value, and the extraction of phase information is quite difficult. Because of these and other difficulties, the most frequently encountered test signal for measurement work is the steady-state sine wave.

30.2.2 Simple Sine Wave

An alternating current (ac) sinusoidal signal's amplitude may be measured as:

1. Peak-to-peak amplitude,
2. Peak amplitude (0.5 peak to peak),
3. Rectified average amplitude (0.636 peak),
4. Root-mean-square amplitude (rms) (0.707 peak).

It is this last value (rms) that is the most frequently used, because in linear circuits the dissipated power depends directly on the rms or effective value. From the illustration in Fig. 30-2, you can see that the simple sine wave has three basic parameters:

1. Peak-to-peak amplitude (A_{p-p}),
2. Primitive period (p),
3. Velocity of propagation (c).

A simple sine wave (sin x) has the following basic parameters:

1. Period (p)—The primitive period (p) of sin x is 2π or 360° (i.e., one cycle).

Table 30-1. Metric Base Units—Commonly Used Conversions

Quantity	Name of Base SI Unit	Symbol	Relationship	Name of Base US Unit	Symbol
Length	Meter	m	$\frac{3.281\ \text{ft}}{\text{M}}$	Feet	ft
Mass	Kilogram	kg	$\frac{0.06852\ \text{slg}}{\text{kg}}$	Slug	slug
Time	Seconds	s	$\frac{\text{s}}{\text{s}}$	Seconds	s
Electric Current	Ampere	A	$\frac{\text{A}}{\text{A}}$	Ampere	A
Thermodynamic Temperature	Kelvin	K	$\frac{\left(\frac{°\text{F} + 459.67}{1.8}\right)}{\text{K}}$	Degree Fahrenheit	°F
Amount of Substance	Mole	mol	$\frac{\text{mol}}{\text{mol}}$	Mole	mol
Luminous Intensity	Candela	cd	$\frac{\text{cd}}{\text{cd}}$	Candela	cd
Plane Angle	Radians	rad	$\frac{360°}{2\pi\ \text{rad}}$	Degrees	∠°
Solid Angle	Steradians	sr	$\frac{\text{sphere}}{4\pi\ \text{sr}}$	Sphere	SPH

Common Electrical and Acoustical "Derived" Units

$\text{Pa} = \text{KG} \cdot \text{m}^{-1} \cdot \text{s}^{-2}$	(Pascal)	Pressure
$\text{watt} = \text{m}^2 \cdot \text{kg} \cdot \text{s}^{-3}$	(Watt)	Power
$\text{N} = \text{m} \cdot \text{kg} \cdot \text{s}^{-2}$	(Newton)	Force
$\text{J} = \text{m}^2 \cdot \text{kg} \cdot \text{s}^{-2}$	(Joule)	Work
$\text{V} = \text{m}^2 \cdot \text{kg} \cdot \text{s}^{-3} \cdot \text{A}^{-2}$	(Volt)	Electromotive Force
$\Omega = \text{m}^2 \cdot \text{kg} \cdot \text{s}^{-3} \cdot \text{A}^{-2}$	(Ohm)	Electrical Resistance
$\text{Hz} = \text{s}^{-1}$	(Hertz)	Frequency
$\text{F} = \text{m}^{-4} \cdot \text{kg}^{-1} \cdot \text{s}^4 \cdot \text{A}^2$	(Farad)	Capacitance
$\text{H} = \text{m}^2 \cdot \text{kg} \cdot \text{s}^{-2} \cdot \text{A}^{-2}$	(Henry)	Inductance

2. Amplitude measured peak to peak (A_{p-p})—The amplitude may be in volts (V), current (I), and so on.
3. Time (t)—The time interval is Np in seconds, where N is the number of periods.

From these basic parameters we derive:

1. Phase (P)—P = (t/p) and is a ratio. When t = 1.0 s, the rate of phase revolution is labeled hertz (Hz) and called the frequency.
2. Phase angle (θ)—θ = 360 (t/p) in degrees. θ = 2π(t/p) in radians.
3. Frequency (f)—f = (1.0/p) in hertz.
4. Wavelength (λ)—The wavelength is the distance between points of corresponding phase of two consecutive cycles. λ = phase velocity/f.
5. $0.5A_{p-p}$ is the peak amplitude (A_p), $0.636A_p$ is the average amplitude (A_{av}), $0.707A_p$ is the root-mean-square amplitude (A_{rms}).

30.3 POLARITY MEASUREMENTS

The *absolute polarity* of a sound system has been shown to be of importance especially in speech-reinforcement systems. Polarity is often confused with *phase* by the beginner in audio. *Polarity* is by definition *nonfrequency dependent. Phase* is by definition *frequency dependent.* Fig. 30-3 illustrates the fundamental differences between phase and polarity.

Polarity measurements are easily made on modern time-energy-frequency (TEF) analyzers (Figs. 30-4 and 30-5). Avoid impulse measurements for low-frequency devices

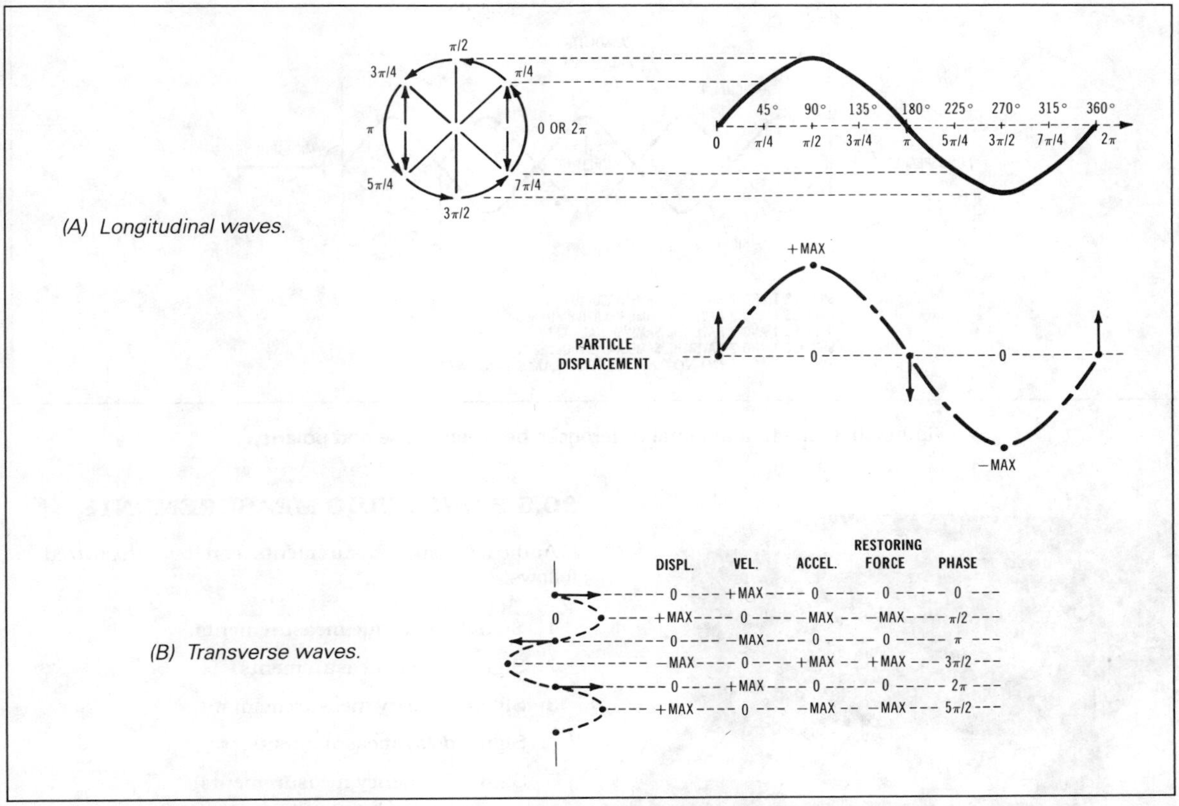

(A) Longitudinal waves.

(B) Transverse waves.

Figure 30-1 Graphing of rotary and oscillatory motion.

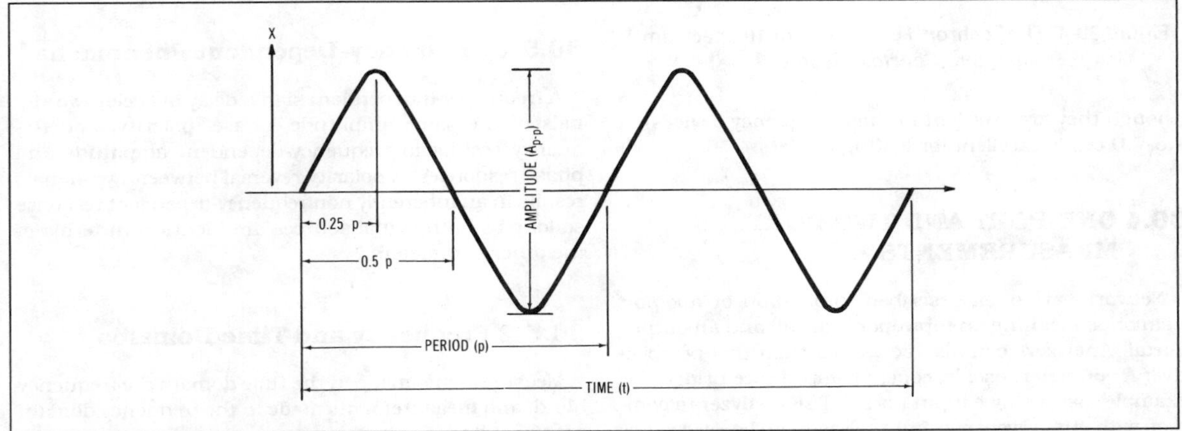

Figure 30-2 The simple sine wave.

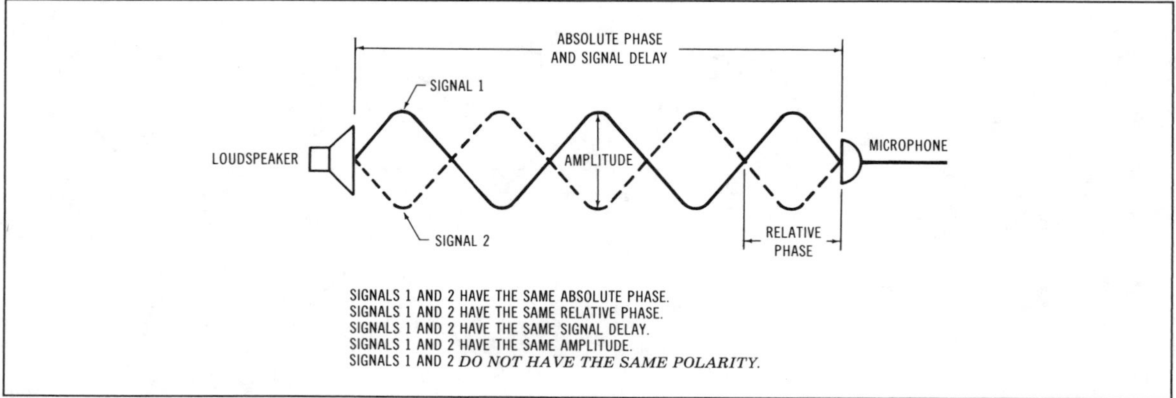

Figure 30-3 The fundamental differences between phase and polarity.

Figure 30-4 The Techron TEF® System 10 spectrum analyzer. *(Courtesy Techron)*

(though they are excellent for high-frequency devices). A 1.5-V D cell is excellent for testing woofers.

30.4 ONE-PORT AND TWO-PORT MEASUREMENTS

Networks are often described as *one-port* or *two-port networks*, meaning an input port (portal) and an output portal. Analyzers can also be viewed from this perspective. A voltmeter, oscilloscope, or impedance bridge, for example, has a single input port. A TEF analyzer in common with other swept spectral analyzers can be used either in a two-port or a one-port configuration (real TEF measurements are always two port). There is an immense advantage in two-port measurements, namely, preknowledge of the source signal, which allows optimization of the analyzer's receive path for the high-resolution analysis of the device under test.

30.5 BASIC AUDIO MEASUREMENTS

Audio system measurements can be categorized as follows:

1. Signal amplitude measurements,
2. Signal phase measurements,
3. Signal polarity measurements,
4. Signal delay measurements,
5. Signal frequency measurements,
6. Signal level measurements,
7. Circuit impedance measurements.

30.5.1 Frequency-Dependent Phenomena

A frequency-independent signal delay between two signals of the same amplitude, phase, polarity, and frequency results in frequency-dependent amplitude and phase responses. A polarity reversal between two signals results in an inherently nonfrequency-dependent response so long as both signal sources are identical in terms of the other parameters.

30.5.2 Frequency and Time Domains

Measurements made in the time domain are frequency blind, and measurements made in the frequency domain are time blind. For instance, an amplitude measurement of a signal made on a wideband voltmeter tells us nothing about the frequency involved. A measurement of the frequency of the signal made on a precision counter tells us nothing of its time of arrival or for that matter of its amplitude. From these basic parameters we are able to derive:

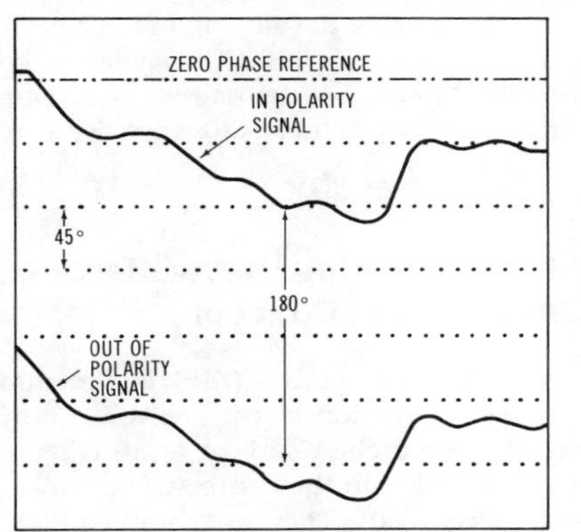

(A) Phase versus hertz (PFC) measurement. The top measurement is in polarity and the bottom is 180° out of polarity.

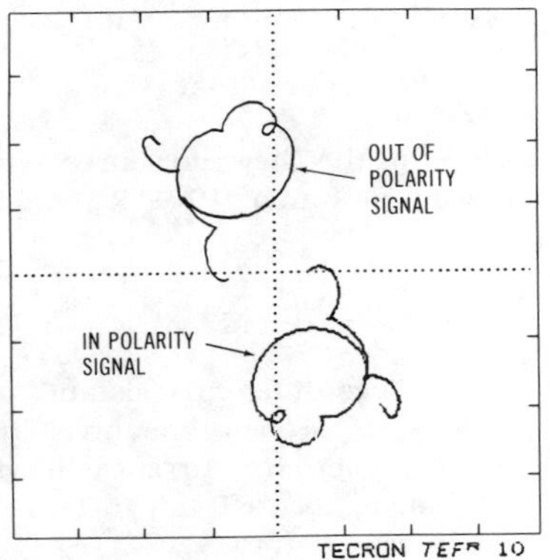

(B) Nyquist measurement of in and out of polarity signals.

Figure 30-5 Phase versus hertz and Nyquist measurements. *(Courtesy Techron)*

1. The absolute phase

$$\phi = d/pc \qquad (30\text{-}1)$$

where,
d is the distance and the same dimension as c,
p is the time of one period or cycle,
c is the speed of sound.

2. The relative phase

$$\theta = FRC\,(D/Pc) \qquad (30\text{-}2)$$

where,
FRC is the "fractional part of."

3. The absolute phase angle

$$\Phi\angle = K\Phi \qquad (30\text{-}3)$$

where,
K is 360 for angles in degrees and 2π for angles in radians.

4. The relative phase angle is $\theta\angle$

$$\theta\angle = K(FRC\,\phi) \qquad (30\text{-}4)$$

5. The frequency in hertz

$$Hz = 1/p \qquad (30\text{-}5)$$

6. The wavelength

$$\lambda = c/f \qquad (30\text{-}6)$$

30.5.3 Amplitude Relationships for Sinusoidal Signals

For pure sine-wave signals, the following amplitude relationships hold:

$$A_p = 0.5A_{p-p} \qquad (30\text{-}7)$$

$$\text{rectified } A_{avg} = (\sin 10° + \sin 20° + \ldots \sin 180°)/18 \qquad (30\text{-}8)$$
$$= 0.636A_p$$

$$A_{rms} = \sqrt{\frac{(\sin 10°)^2 + (\sin 20°)^2 + \ldots (\sin 180°)^2}{18}} \qquad (30\text{-}9)$$
$$= 0.707\,A_p$$

As stated previously, the reason for choosing the root-mean-square amplitude in almost every case in audio is because it is directly related to the power:

$$P_{avg} = (E_{rms})^2/R \qquad (30\text{-}10)$$

Since $(0.707)^2/1 = 0.5$, the average power is exactly one-half the peak power rating when the sine-wave signal is the source employed for the measurement.

30.5.4 Crest Factor and Form Factor

Voltage and current amplitudes can be characterized by their *crest factor* or their *form factor*:

$$\text{crest factor} = \text{peak amplitude/rms amplitude} \qquad (30\text{-}11)$$
$$\text{form factor} = \text{rms amplitude/average amplitude} \qquad (30\text{-}12)$$

For sine waves these become easily calculated values of

$$\text{crest factor} = 1/0.707 = 1.41$$

$$\text{form factor} = 0.707/0.636 = 1.11$$

30.5.5 Signal Level

Signal amplitude is one of the components of signal level. The other component is the resistance across which the signal amplitude appears. "Level" is always a power level and is always expressed in decibel (dB) notation. There exists a reference power of 0.001 W (1.0 mW). Any power when compared to this reference power can be turned into a power level by using

$$\text{power level in dBm} = 10\log(x\,\text{W}/0.001\,\text{W}) \quad (30\text{-}13)$$

Back in 1924, W. H. Martin of the Bell Telephone Laboratories wrote,

> It should be noted particularly that the change in output power of the system is the real measure of the effect of any part of the circuit on the efficiency of the system and that the ratio of the power leaving any part to that entering it is not necessarily the measure of this effect. For example, a pure reactance placed in series between the transmitter and the line may change the power delivered to the line by the transmitter and hence the output of the receiver, the magnitude and direction of change being determined by the impedance relations at the point of insertion. The ratio of the power leaving the reactance to that entering it is, of course, unity, as no power is dissipated in a pure reactance. In other words, the transmission efficiency of any part of a circuit cannot be considered solely from the standpoint of the ratio of output to input power for that part, or the power dissipated in that part, but must be defined in terms of its effect on the ratio of output to input power for the whole system.

This means that in measuring audio levels throughout a system our measurement technique must be such that the addition and subtraction of all these levels from input to output accurately predict the actual output level.

30.5.6 Concepts of Gain and Loss

The concepts of *gain* and *loss* are among the earliest audio measurements. A part of a system is said to have gain if the power at the output of this system increases upon that part being inserted into the system. A part of a system is said to have loss if upon insertion of that part into the system the power at the output of the system decreases.

From all the remarks previously made, it is apparent that the measurement of the gain or loss of a device to be inserted into a system requires a knowledge of the power *available* at the input, not the power *consumed* by the input, and the power produced at a specified load at the output.

30.5.7 Understanding the Available Input Power (AIP) Concept

The *available input power (AIP)* is the maximum available power that a source can deliver to a matched load. If we call the matched load the input resistance R_{in} of the device attached to the source whose AIP is being calculated and we call the Thevenin source voltage E_S the energy source and we have available the internal source resistance R_S, we can then calculate the AIP.

Ohm's law tells us that the power developed across a resistance is

$$P = I^2R \quad (30\text{-}14)$$

Ohm's law further states that $I = E/R$; hence, $I^2 = E^2/R^2$.

If we define our E^2 as the Thevenin source voltage $(E_S)^2$ and the R in E/R as the sum of $(R_S + R_{in})$, then we can write

$$I^2 = (E_S)^2/(R_S + R_{in})^2 \quad (30\text{-}15)$$

Note that we have two different resistances involved here. One is the $(R_S + R_{in})$ seen by the source. The second resistance is the R_{in}, where the current is flowing in to produce the AIP. This R_{in} is the R in I^2R. Therefore, our equation I^2R can be rewritten to be

$$P = \left(\frac{E_S)^2}{(R_S + R_{in})^2}\right)\left(\frac{R_{in}}{1}\right) \quad (30\text{-}16)$$

But, we have defined the AIP as the matched case (i.e., $R_S = R_{in}$ for maximum power transfer), as shown in Fig. 30-6.

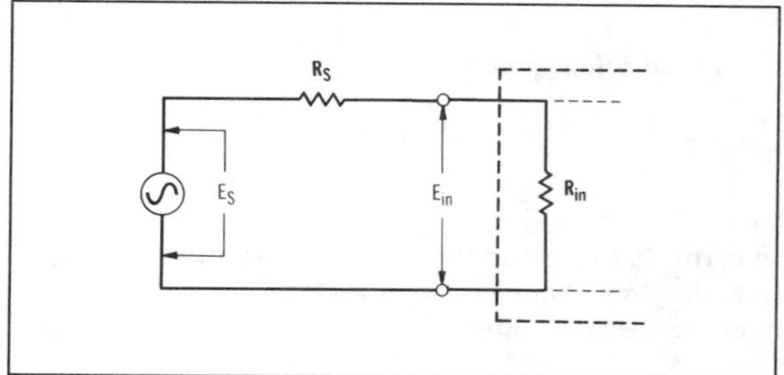

Figure 30-6 Available input power (AIP) level for a matched-case condition.

This means that we can substitute R_S for R_{in} wherever R_{in} appears in the equations. This makes the matched power P_M equal to

$$P_M = \left(\frac{E_S{}^2}{(2R_S)^2}\right)\left(\frac{R_S}{1}\right) \qquad (30\text{-}17)$$
$$= (E_S)^2/4\,R_S$$

This is our AIP in watts. To find the AIP level in dBm we write

$$\text{AIP in dBm} = 10\log[(E_S)^2/0.001\,(4R_S)]$$

or

$$10\log[(E_S)^2/0.001\,R_S] - 6.02\text{ dB} \qquad (30\text{-}18)$$

because

$$10\log(1/4) = -6.02$$

Example: We have an audio oscillator we wish to use as a source for gain and loss measurements, as shown in Fig. 30-7, where all measurements are made at terminals 1 and 2.

1. $R_S + R_b$ is measured.
2. E_S is the open circuit voltage at terminals 1 and 2.
3. AIP in dBm $= 10\log\left(\frac{E_S{}^2}{0.001(R_S + R_b)}\right) - 6.02$ dB.

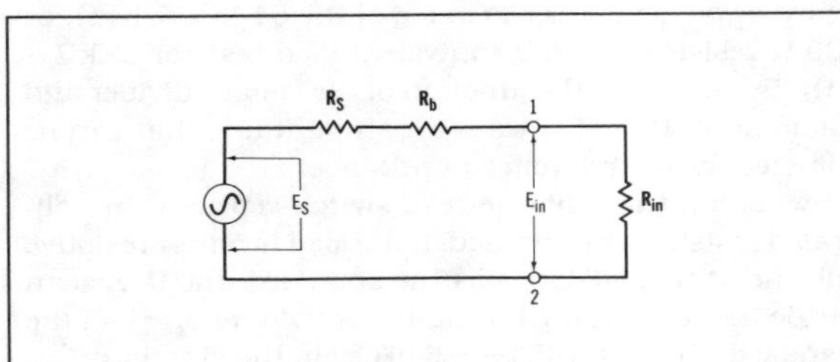

Figure 30-7 Circuit for available input power measurements.

We want to know its AIP when it's used as a 150-Ω source and as a 600-Ω source. The oscillator source resistance (R_S) is 49 Ω, and its open circuit output voltage $E_o = E_S$ is 6.16 V.

We calculate the AIP for both cases:

$$\text{AIP in dBm for } R_S = 150\,\Omega$$
$$= 10\log[(6.16)^2/0.001(150)] - 6.02\text{ dB}$$
$$= 18.01\text{ dBm}$$

and,

$$\text{AIP in dBm for } R_S = 600\,\Omega$$
$$= 10\log[(6.16)^2/0.001\,(600)] - 6.02$$
$$= 11.99\text{ dBm}$$

30.5.8 Measuring the Available Input Power (AIP)

In real-life sound systems the measurement of available input power (AIP) can be reduced to a series of simple, easy-to-implement steps.

1. Measure the input resistance R_{in} of the device being driven by the source. It is for the source device, however, that we want the AIP rating.
2. Measure the internal source resistance (R_S) of the source device. (Include any buildouts that may be present.)
3. Measure the input voltage E_{in} across the R_{in} when the source device is connected to it in the normal manner.

Once these measurements are obtained, we turn to the calculations necessary to find the source's AIP.

Because AIP uses the source voltage (E_S), which may or may not be directly accessible to us, we normally calculate E_S from E_{in} and the R_S and R_{in} resistance values:

$$E_S = E_{in}[(R_S + R_{in})/R_{in}] \qquad (30\text{-}20)$$

Note that when $R_S = R_{in}$, $E_S = 2E_{in}$, and that when R_{in} is much greater than R_S (i.e., more than ten times), $R_S = R_{in}$. Since we want the AIP in dBm (i.e., referenced to 0.001 W), we do the following calculation:

$$\text{AIP in dBm} = 10\log\left(\frac{E_S{}^2}{0.001\,R_S}\right) - 6.02\text{ dB} \qquad (30\text{-}21)$$

30.5.9 Impedance Measurements

I encourage the reader to look up the rigorous definition of impedance in the *IEEE Dictionary*, Second Edition, pages 318–319. A generalized definition suitable to our discussion is the ratio Z is commonly expressed in terms of its orthogonal (rectangular) components, thus,

$$Z = R + jX \qquad (30\text{-}22)$$

where,

Z, R, and X are respectively termed the impedance, resistance, and reactance, all being measured in ohms.

The polar form is

$$Z\angle\theta = R + jX \tag{30-23}$$

or,

$$Ze^{i\theta} = R + jX$$

where,

$\angle\theta$ is the phase angle in degrees,
$e^{i\theta}$ is the phase angle in radians.

See Fig. 30-8 for examples of rectangular and polar forms of impedance.

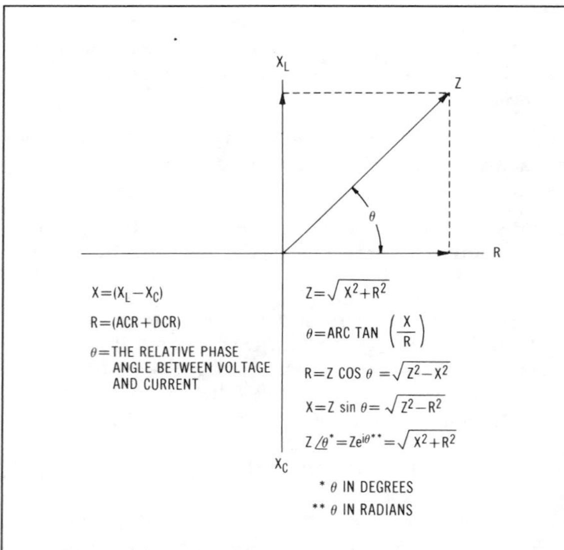

Figure 30-8 Graphic representation of impedance (Z).

Impedance measurements have both a magnitude and a phase response. Impedance is frequency dependent and exhibits, on occasion, signal delay behavior as well as phase shift.

The magnitude of the impedance consists of both resistive and reactive components. It is the resistance component that dissipates power. The reactive component reflects the energy sent to it (Lenz's law). The phase angle in this case is the angle between voltage and current (*ELI* the *ICE* man reminds you that E leads I when L (inductance) is predominant and I leads E when C (capacitance) is predominant.)

The maximum reactive phase angle is of interest because of the possibility of amplifier instability when the angle is large.

30.5.9.1 Measuring Electrical Impedance

A standard demonstration is the measurement of the magnitude of the electrical impedance (Z) at the terminals of the loudspeaker using the garden variety one-third-octave *real-time analyzer (RTA)*.

The basic theory involved utilizes the fact that a constant-current output device (i.e., a power amplifier with a "build-out" resistance in its output) has its voltage output vary directly as the impedance to which it is connected varies (Fig. 30-9).

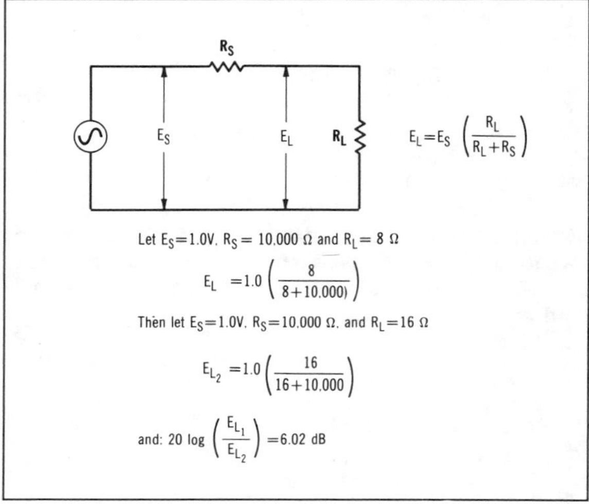

Figure 30-9 A constant-current source.

A practical real-life setup is shown in Fig. 30-10. The theory of operation is as follows. At "Calibrate" in the figure a voltage divider is made of the 51-kΩ, 5.1-kΩ, or 430-Ω resistor and the equivalent load resistor (5 kΩ–4 Ω). By observing the junction of the voltage divider and common on the RTA, we see a straight line that can be adjusted for the reference impedance.

Switching the calibrate-read switch replaces the calibrated resistor with the load. If the load is purely resistive and the same resistance as the standard, the RTA scan will be the same. If the impedance is twice or one-half the standard, the RTA will be ±6 dB from the standard:

$$Z_{unknown} = (10^{dB/20})Z_{standard} \tag{30-24}$$

If the load is not a pure resistance, the scan will vary up and down around the standard, depending on the impedance at each frequency.

Fig. 30-11 shows a woofer measured in its enclosure. (No crossover network or other drivers present.) In Fig. 30-11C the duct is closed by a cover over its opening on the front of the loudspeaker enclosure. In Fig. 30-11D the

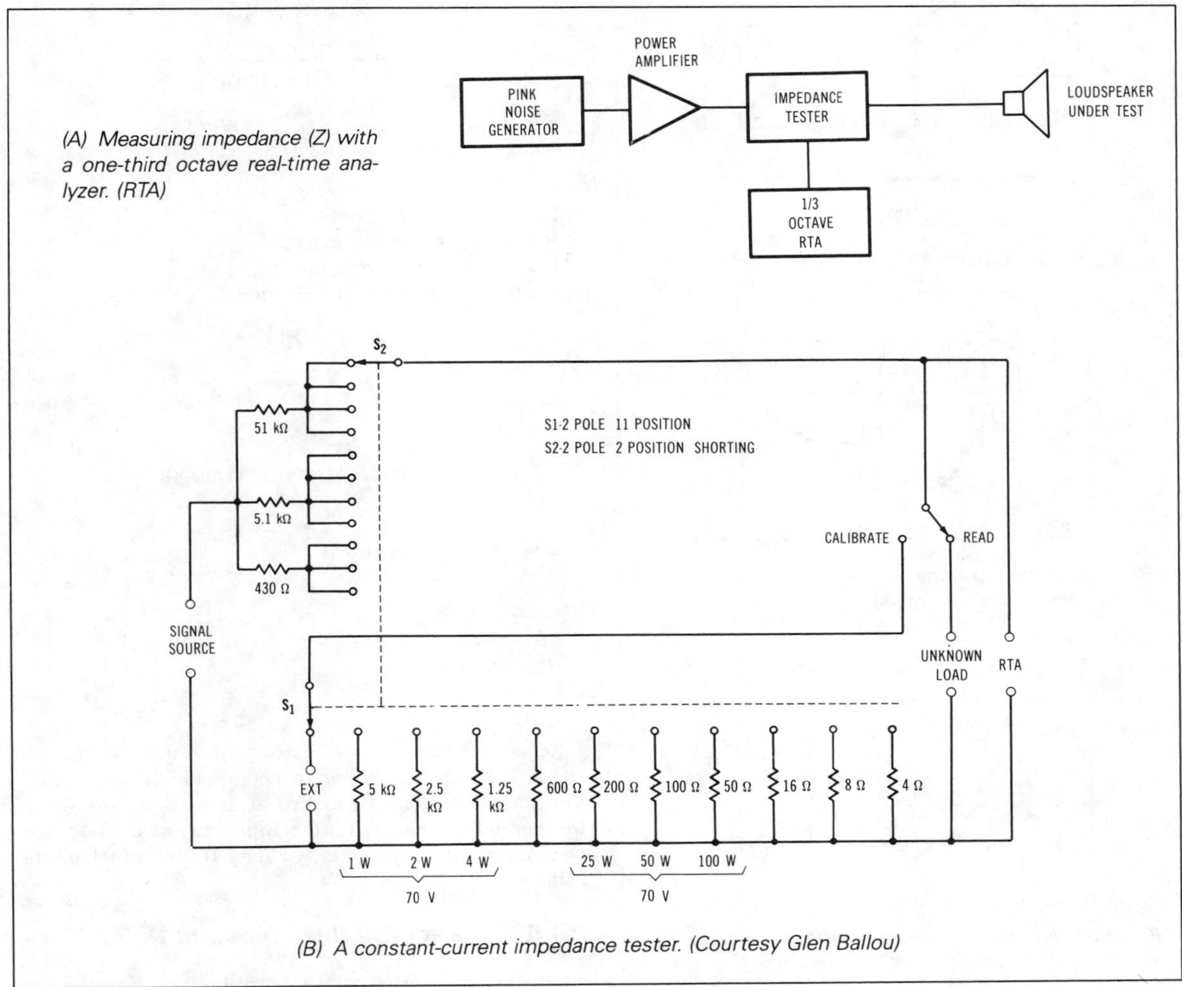

(A) *Measuring impedance (Z) with a one-third octave real-time analyzer. (RTA)*

(B) *A constant-current impedance tester. (Courtesy Glen Ballou)*

Figure 30-10 Measuring impedance.

low-frequency driver cone is being blocked (held by hand so it can't move), revealing that the low-frequency impedance peaks are actually caused by reverse electromotive force (Lenz's law) imitating the reflected energy a capacitance and inductance would have caused at those frequencies had they been present.

30.5.9.2 When a Sound System Installer Should Measure Z

Knowing the actual source, input, output, and load impedances is necessary if systems are to be properly installed. It is of vital importance that the installer be aware of the difference between the values normally specified by manufacturers of equipment and the actual measured values needed by the installer for matching purposes (Fig. 30-12). There is usually a *rated* R_S, R_{in}, R_{out}, and R_L as well as an *actual* value. R_S is the actual *source impedance* (quite often an electroacoustic transducer). R_{in} is the actual input impedance of a system device. (Rated input impedances are of often the desired R_S.) R_{out} is the actual *output impedance* of a system device (as distinguished from its output impedance rating). R_L is the *load impedance* (output impedance ratings are usually the desired R_L).

The term "matching" may be read as appropriate match. Normally, only in the case of passive devices is the appropriate value also the exact value. See Fig. 30-13 for illustrations of *buildout* and *terminating* resistances.

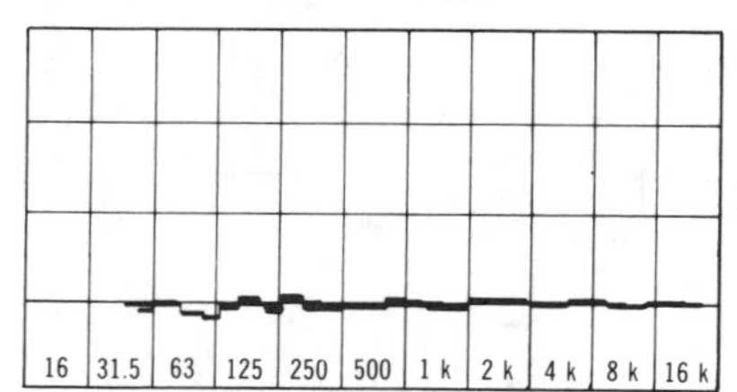

(A) Calibration resistor (8 Ω) on screen of RTA 20 to 20,000 Hz.

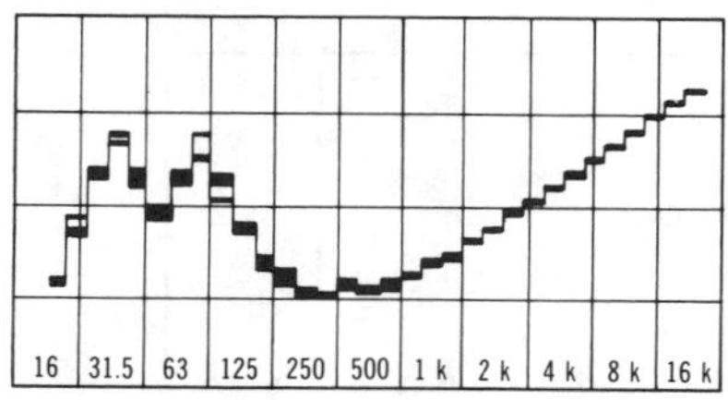

(B) Impedance magnitude versus frequency on screen of RTA. Note twin low-frequency peaks indicating a "tuned duct."

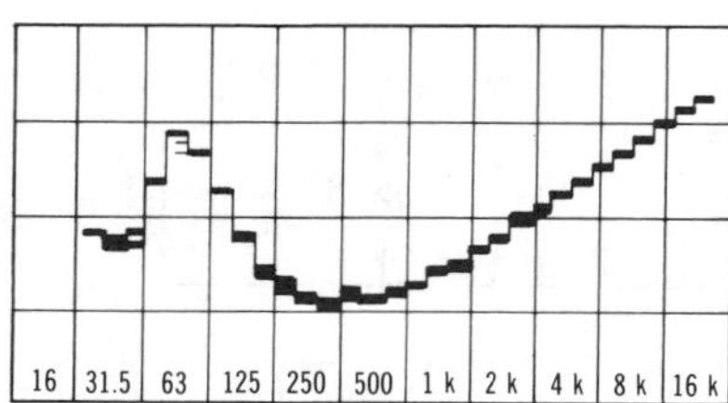

(C) Impedance magnitude versus frequency on screen of RTA when "tuned duct" is closed.

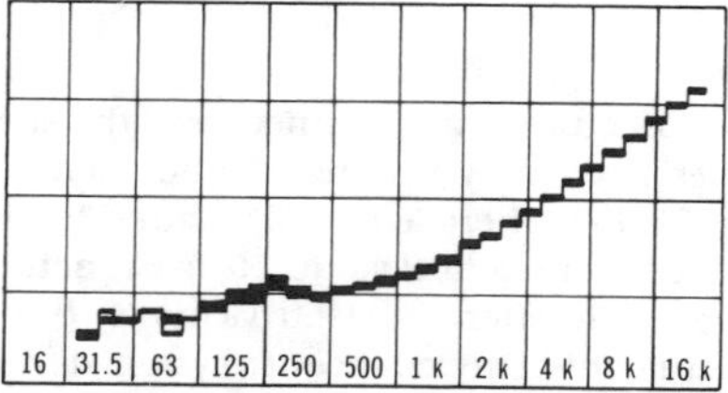

(D) Impedance magnitude versus frequency on screen of RTA when cone movement is "locked."

Figure 30-11 Impedance measurements of a woofer in its enclosure. Vertical division 5 dB/div, 20 to 20,000 Hz.

$$R_b = (R_{in} - R_S)$$

$$R_T = \frac{1}{(1/R_D) - (1/R_M)}$$

or,

$$1/R_T = (1/R_D) - (1/R_S)$$

where,

R_b is a *buildout* resistor,
R_T is a *termination* resistor,
R_D is the *desired* resistance,
R_M is the *measured* impedance.

Example:

$$R_b = (600 - 110)$$
$$= 490$$

$$(1/RT) = (1/600) - (1/3000)$$
$$= 1/1.33 \times 10^{-3}$$

whose reciprocal is 750 Ω.

where,

R_S = 110 Ω,
R_M = 3000 Ω,
R_{in} = 600 Ω,
R_{out} = 600 Ω.

Reactance comes in two flavors—inductive and capacitive. Resistance also has two components—ac and dc. Impedance also can be looked at as being composed of *lumped parameters* (circuit components all in one place) or *distributed parameters*, such as 100 mi of telephone cable.

30.5.9.3 Rectangular Plots and Polar Plots

The phase angle associated with the impedance can be plotted either as the angle in degrees or radians versus the frequency or as a polar plot of reactance versus frequency, as shown in Fig. 30-14.

To find the phase angle (the relative phase between the voltage and the current expressed as an angular rotation) from our RTA curve proceed as follows:

1. Find the lowest Z reading, which more than likely is the ac resistance. (An R_{ac} bridge can be used if available.)

2. Read the Z value from the RTA in dB and convert into ohms:

$$Z = Z_{ref}[\,10^{(+\text{dB from ref}/20)}] \tag{30-25}$$

3. Find the reactance by using

$$X = \sqrt{Z^2 - R_{ac}{}^2} \tag{30-26}$$

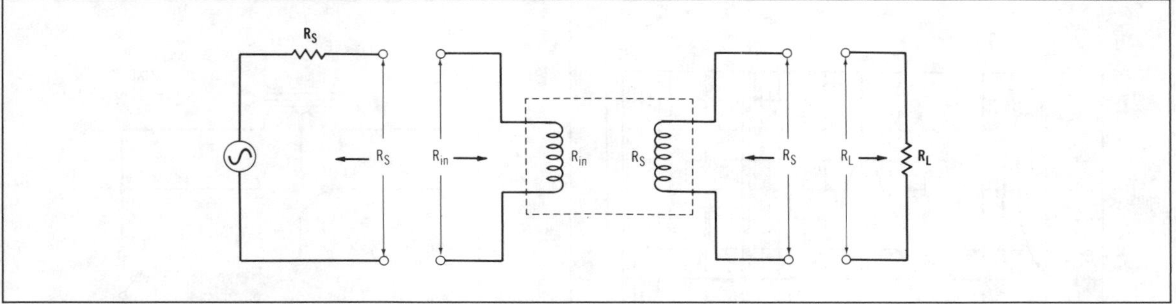

Figure 30-12 Circuit descriptions of input and output terminals.

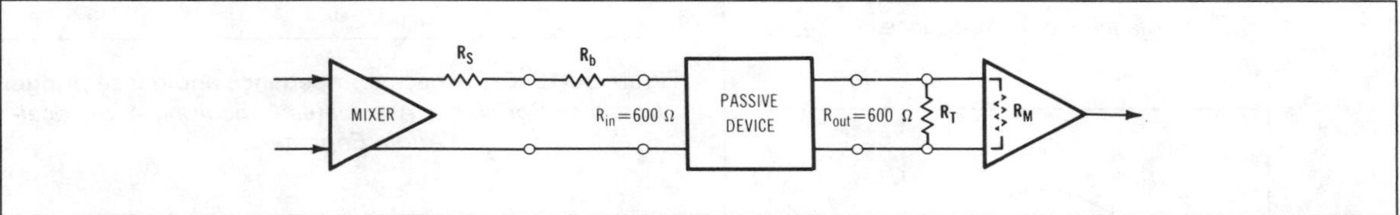

Figure 30-13 "Build out" and "terminating" resistors.

4. Find the phase angle by using

$$\theta = \arctan(X/R_{ac}) \qquad (30\text{-}27)$$

An independent way to obtain θ is to use a Grutzmacher bridge, as shown in Fig. 30-15. An interesting observation can be made in those cases where the phase angle measured by the Grutzmacher bridge and the angle calculated from the RTA display do not agree—the circuit undergoing measurement is not a minimum-phase circuit. The procedure entails the following:

1. Adjust R until voltages V_1 and V_2 are equal.
2. Then the magnitude or numerical value of the impedance Z_x is equal to R.
3. The phase angle (θ) is found by measuring voltage V_3 and calculating

$$\sin(\theta/2) = V_3/V_1$$
$$= V_3/V_2$$

or,

$$\theta = 2 \times \arcsin V_3/V_1$$

30.5.9.4 System Problems Located by Z Measurements

Problems detectable via Z measurements vary from reactive 70-V transformers overloading power amplifiers, woofers in incorrectly ported enclosures, link circuits not matching passive devices to be inserted in them, discovery of intermittent circuits, and so on. See Fig. 30-16 for examples of direct-reading impedance meters.

30.5.10 Phase Measurements

Unlike voltage and current or power, all of which can be measured directly in a single signal, the measurement of phase shift inherently involves a comparison of two signals. It is meaningless to speak of the phase of a signal except with respect to another signal.

A typical phase measurement involves, in its simplest form, the arrangement shown in Fig. 30-17. The input and output signals of the device under test are monitored by bridging amplifiers or other sampling means that do not disturb the signals being measured. These two signals are then compared in a phase detector.

When the signal has undergone significant signal delay (SD) such as in satellite transmission or in an acoustic measurement some distance from a transducer, then the technique shown in Fig. 30-18 is employed. It is important to remember that *phase shift* is the measurement of what we have defined as *relative phase* (i.e., the change in phase since the last zero crossing).

30.5.11 Phase Distortion

Phase distortion has been generalized as "phase shift not proportional to frequency." Whenever the devices under

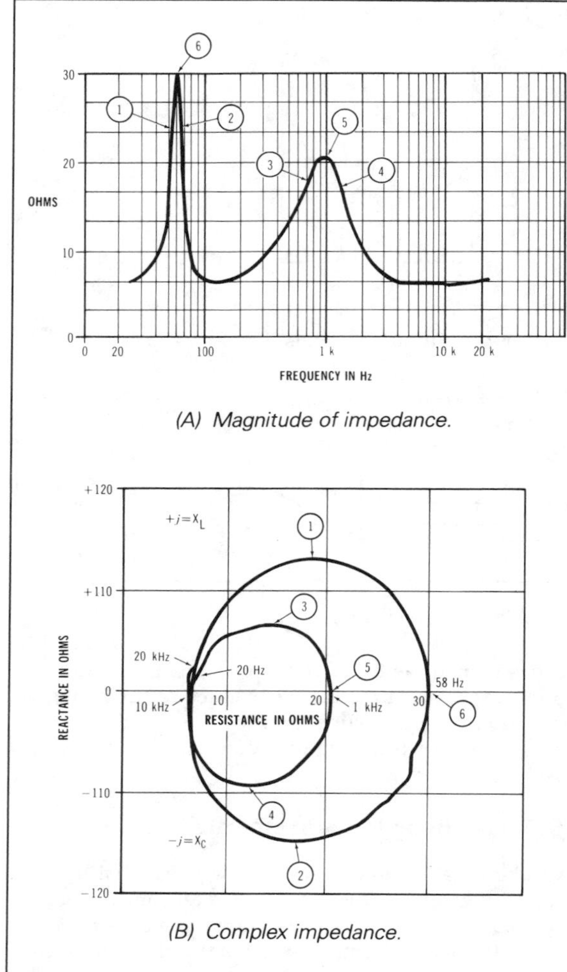

Figure 30-14 Rectangular and polar plots of impedance.

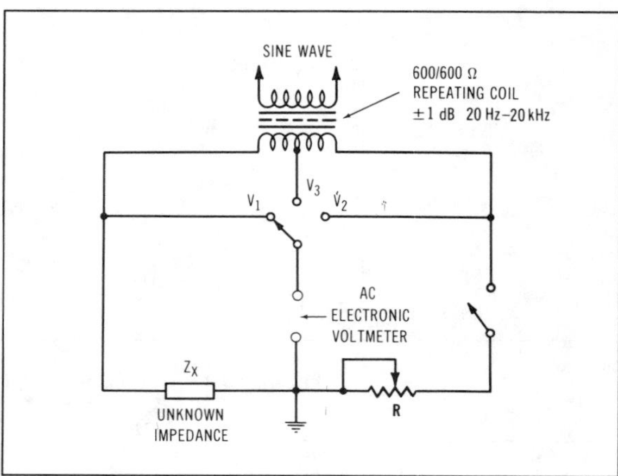

Figure 30-15 Grutzmacher impedance and phase bridge. *(Courtesy Sprinkle & Associates Consulting Acoustical-Audio Engineers)*

test are minimum-phase circuits (i.e., no zeros in the right half of the s plane) or have an added constant delay, a measurement of its amplitude characteristics uniquely defines its phase characteristics as well. In fact, the easiest way to determine the nonminimum phase of a device under test is to observe that its phase response does not match that for a minimum-phase network having the same amplitude characteristics. See Fig. 30-19 for a relatively inexpensive level recorder, which was used to make the measurements in Fig. 30-20.

30.5.12 Precautions To Observe in Sine-Wave Testing

Care must always be taken to ensure that (1) the data obtained is in response to the desired signal only, and (2) the system is being operated in its linear range.

Some quick tests that ensure that the previously discussed conditions are being met is to:

1. Make sure there is no output with no input.
2. Make sure that doubling the input doubles the output.
3. Examine for spurious outputs (i.e., instabilities that are transient in nature).
4. Make sure that proper buildout and termination resistances are employed.

30.6 SOUND SYSTEM MEASUREMENTS

30.6.1 Meaningful and Useful Electrical Measurements of Sound Systems

1. Is it stable under shock excitation (i.e., being driven into +6 dB of clipping)?
2. Does the load impedance attached to the output of the system meet the specified load requirements of the output device?
3. Does the measured electrical gain of the system match the calculated electrical gain of the system?
4. Are all source impedances and input impedances measured and recorded?
5. Are all available input power levels and output power levels measured and recorded on a gain chart?
6. Does the system sound good on a voice test?

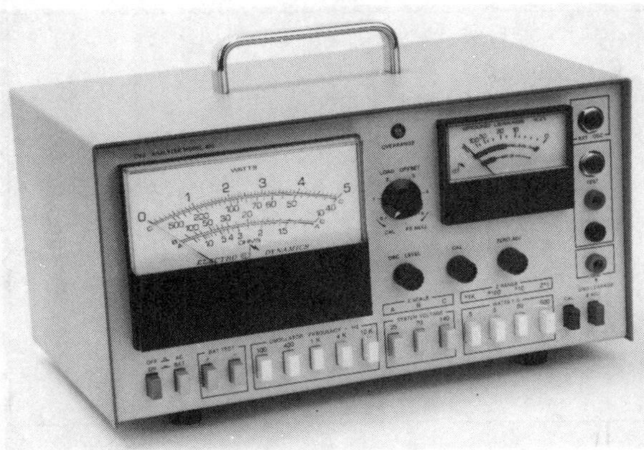

(A) CVS analyzer model 400 direct reading impedance meter. (Courtesy Electro-Dynamics Development Co.)

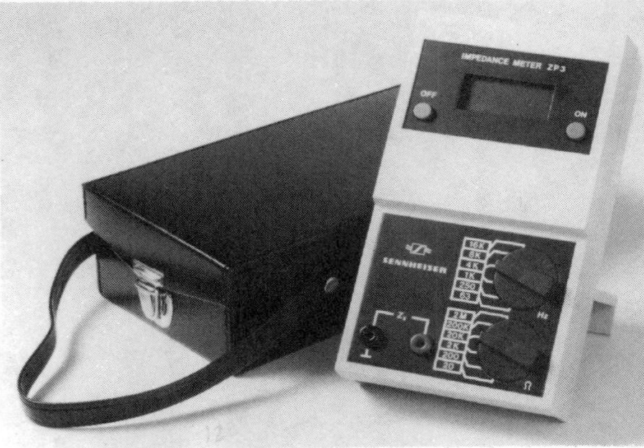

(B) Model ZP3 direct reading impedance meter. (Courtesy Sennheiser Electronics Corp.)

Figure 30-16 Impedance meters.

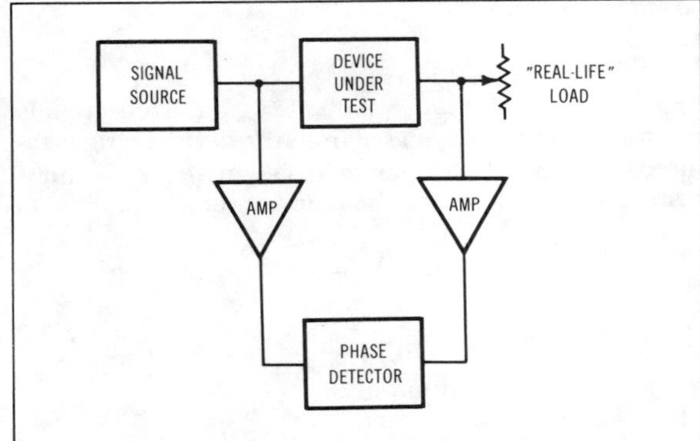

Figure 30-17 Electrical phase measurement.

30.6.2 Meaningful and Useful Acoustical Measurements of Sound Systems

1. Does the measured acoustic gain match the calculated acoustic gain?
2. Is the sound coverage uniform and free of excessive comb filtering?
3. Are there excessive signal delays (i.e., echoes or blurrings)?

30.7 CHOICE AND PLACEMENT OF MEASUREMENT MICROPHONES

There are occasions for both relative acoustic measurements and absolute acoustic measurements. Where absolute levels are to be measured, a true measurement microphone such as those manufactured by Brüel and Kjaer should be chosen. The diaphragm size, free-field or pressure calibration, sensitivity, and directional characteristics are dictated by parameters associated with the desired measurement. For example, examination of very low acoustic levels dictates a larger diaphragm, whereas a desire to examine higher frequencies dictates a smaller diaphragm. Instruction manuals on the selection of measurement microphones are lengthy documents of normal book size. If not already totally familiar with the complex interwoven parameters associated with measurement microphones, we suggest the assistance of a competent factory engineer such as is available from firms who specialize in these activities (e.g., Brüel and Kjaer). (See Figs. 30-21, 30-22, 30-23, and 30-24.)

A discussion of the placement of a measurement microphone would provide enough information to fill its own volume. In general terms, the user must be aware of the type of sound field to measure (i.e., free field, early reflections, reverberant field, ambient noise, and so on). In some cases, several different types of microphones may be required to obtain complete data. The directional orientation of the microphone depends both upon its calibration and the particular sound field being examined. In past decades care had to be taken in the placement of microphones in appropriate sound fields. Today with TEF analyzers, the undesired data is simply windowed out. Again, today because of TEF analyzers we are vitally concerned with a microphone's phase, time, and amplitude response in addition to its sensitivity, noise floor, directional characteristics, and sensitivity to noise and external electrical and magnetic fields. The key ruling factor in microphone placement is the inspection of the c/f distance to the nearest reflecting surface

where,

f is the lowest frequency in hertz that is to be measured,

c is the velocity of the signal in the media.

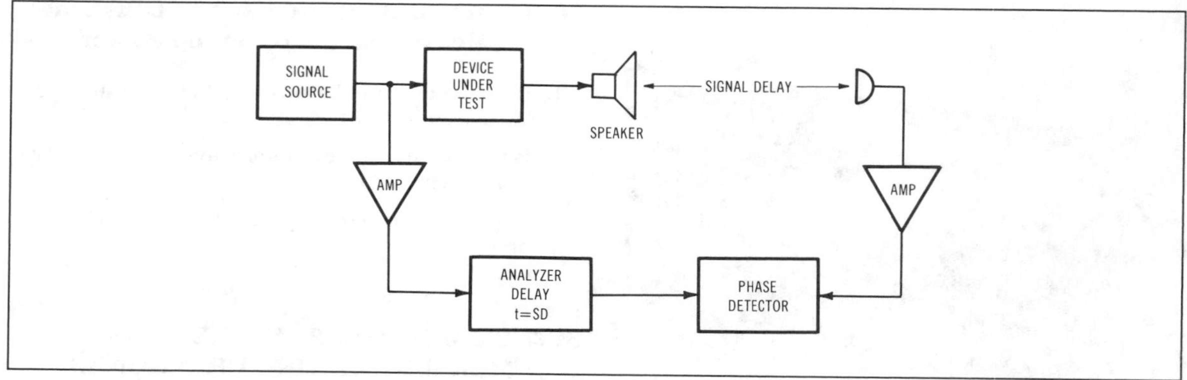

Figure 30-18 Acoustical phase measurement.

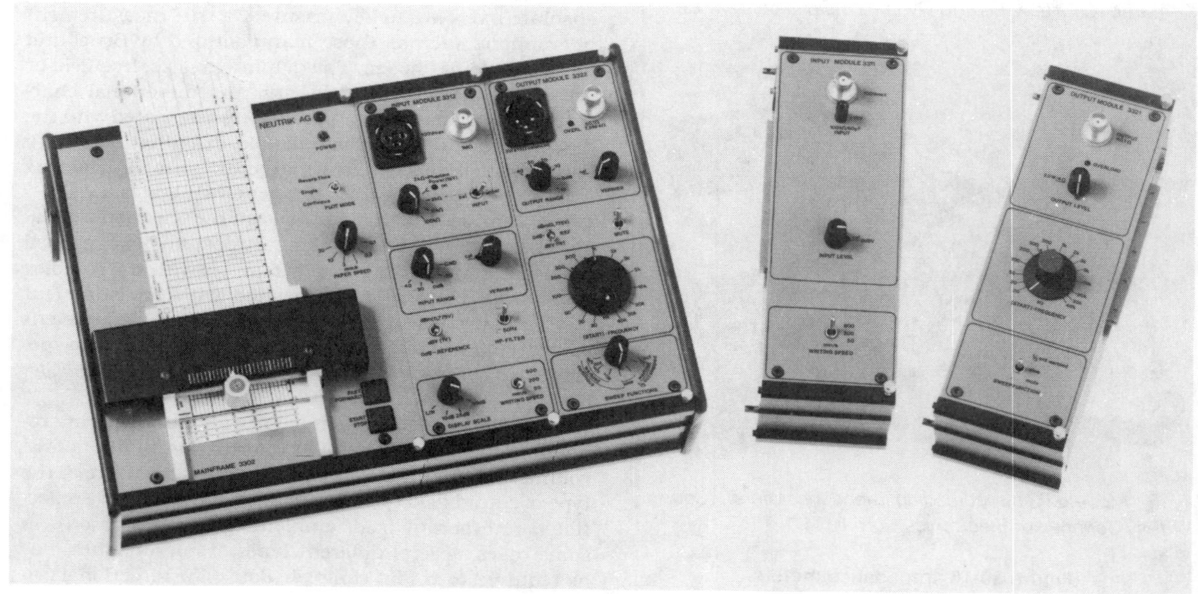

Figure 30-19 The versatile Neutrik level recorder can be updated with plug-in modules. *(Courtesy Neutrik Products)*

Example: If you are in an enclosed space where an *energy-time curve (ETC)* measurement shows the nearest reflection to be 6 ft behind the direct sound, then the lowest frequency that can be measured without including energy from the reflecting surface becomes:

$$f = \frac{c}{\text{distance}} = 1130/6 = 188.33\,\text{Hz} \quad (30\text{-}28)$$

This same 1/f distance when expressed as a time window provides the most likely frequency resolution to be employed (i.e., 1/188.33 = 0.00531 s). If the reflection is lower in level than the signal from the device being measured, higher resolutions can be achieved without destructive interference. The time-bandwidth product is

$$t_R(f_R) = 1.0 \quad (30\text{-}29)$$

where,

t_R is the time resolution in S,
S is the sweep rate in hertz,
f_R is the frequency resolution in hertz.

Thus,

$$1/f_R = t_R$$

and,

$$1/t_R = f_R$$

30.8 RELATIVE MEASUREMENTS

Often in audio systems work, we do not require a knowledge of *absolute levels* but of *relative changes in level*. Checking the coverage of a loudspeaker system is such a case wherein an arbitrary reference level is established in the audience area and variations above or below that level are observed and recorded. Often standard sound system microphones are used for such measurements with perfectly satisfactory results.

Shure Brothers, Inc., manufactures extremely high-quality recording microphones that approach measurement microphone level stability and frequency response. The Shure SM-81, shown in Chapter 13, is an excellent choice when a directional microphone is desired for use in the measurement of acoustic absorption.

30.9 REAL-TIME ANALYZERS FOR AUDIO

One-third-octave (actually one-tenth-decade) analyzers (frequently mislabeled as *third*-octave analyzers) are highly useful everyday work tools for the adjustment of audio systems. These devices are constant percentage bandwidth (CPB) analyzers that utilize bandpass filters with bandwidths that are 23% of their center frequency (f_c).

The filters employed can have skirts that attenuate unwanted signals by 6, 12, 18, 24, 36 dB or even greater rates per octave (i.e., dB/octave). These analyzers are used with random noise generators of the constant-power-per-octave type (i.e., pink noise) that on an energy-per-hertz basis show decreasing energy with increasing frequency. A constant energy-per-octave signal observed on a constant percentage bandwidth analyzer is displayed as a uniform frequency response.

30.10 A COMMON ERROR IN THE SELECTION OF A ONE-THIRD-OCTAVE RTA

If the only input to a one-third-octave RTA were random noise signals, then the highest resolution would be obtained by using the highest-order filters (36 dB/octave or greater). In actual fact, however, oscillators and sound system acoustic feedback signals are often the input signal. When such is the case, 6-dB/octave filters allow the widest range of frequencies to be observed to the greatest resolution above the ambient noise level (usually within 10 Hz in the 1000-Hz region). It is for this reason that we recommend the analyzers with the simplest filters for sound system measurements (Fig. 30-25).

The higher-order filters have their place in noise control measurements but are both less effective and far more costly when applied to sound system work (Fig. 30-26).

Next to those using the decibel scale on voltmeters to read what they think is the level, one-third-octave analyzers are the next most frequently misused measurement tool. An example of only one of the problems in the use of the real-time analyzer is illustrated in Fig. 30-27. Two loudspeakers are offset by a little over a foot (see Fig. 30-27A showing the energy time curve and the Nyquist phase plot measured on a TEF analyzer in Fig. 30-27B). The comb filter shown in Figs. 30-27C and D are approximately 1180 Hz apart.

Note that the bandpass filters on the RTA allow only a portion of the first of a series of comb filters to show on the RTA, around 350 Hz, as shown in Fig. 30-27E. All the rest are obscured by the skirts on the filters on the RTA.

30.11 FAST FOURIER TRANSFORM (FFT) ANALYZERS

Joseph Fourier (1768–1830) in his work with infinite trigonometric series showed that any complex waveform in the time domain can be transformed into a series of individual sine-wave frequencies of various amplitudes. Digital technology has allowed the economical construction of *discrete Fourier transforms (DFT)* and their *inverse (IDFT)*.

The advantage of the FFT (i.e., DFT) analyzer is that a single, short-duration impulse can be passed through a system and be transformed into a full analysis of the system's response in the frequency domain. By using dual-channel FFTs, the phase can be obtained as well.

The basic disadvantages of the FFT analyzer as implemented in today's technology are:

1. The transform is only valid for the analysis of linear response systems.
2. A desirably small time window results in an undesirably small dynamic range.
3. While economically feasible in terms of past techniques for accessing the same data, they are much more expensive than the far more accurate, high-resolution TEF analyzers that will replace them for all two-port measurements. (See Figs. 30-28, 30-29, and 30-30.)

30.12 REVERBERATION

The use of reverberation time measurements as an indicator of how an enclosed space will sound to a listener is akin to measuring temperature with a barometer. When the barometer goes to a lower reading, the weather will eventually cool.

30.12.1 Liveness and Deadness

The subjective judgment by a listener of how live or how dead a room is acoustically is not dependent upon the reverberant sound field but rather on the initial time-delay gap and the ratio of direct sound level (L_D) to the early reflection level (L_{RE}).

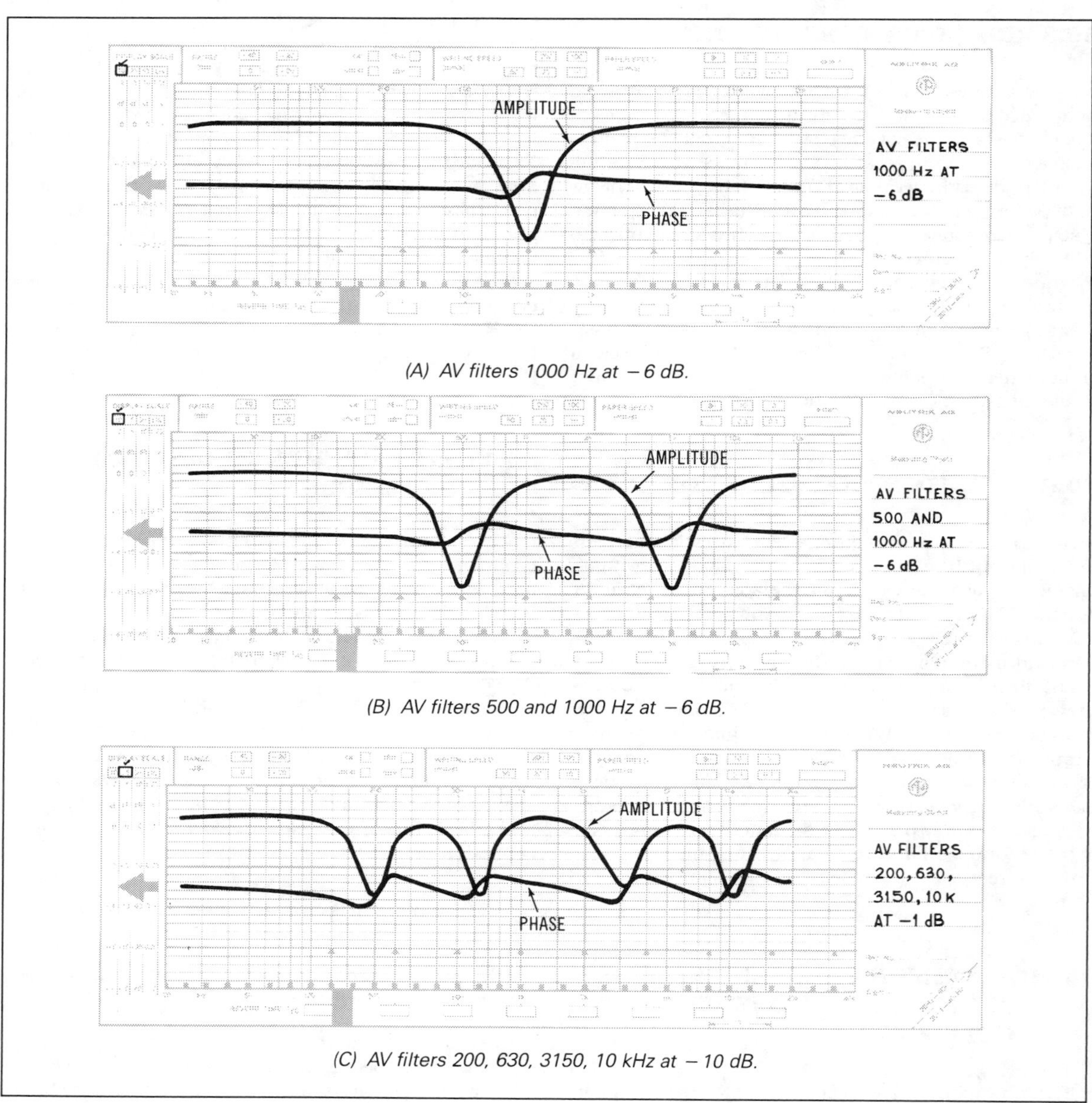

(A) AV filters 1000 Hz at −6 dB.

(B) AV filters 500 and 1000 Hz at −6 dB.

(C) AV filters 200, 630, 3150, 10 kHz at −10 dB.

Figure 30-20 Examples of typical equalizer measurements using the Neutrik level recorder and the phase- and be used with

It is important to note that RT_{60} measurements are not intended to measure the decay rate of early discrete reflections, but rather to measure the decay of an exponentially growing and exponentially decaying homogeneous, mixing sound field of sufficient density to be uniform everywhere. This requirement essentially eliminates any meaningful RT_{60} measurements in extremely small-volume rooms containing moderate to high absorption or extremely large-volume rooms wherein distances of 1000+ ft between surfaces preclude a mixing homogeneous sound field.

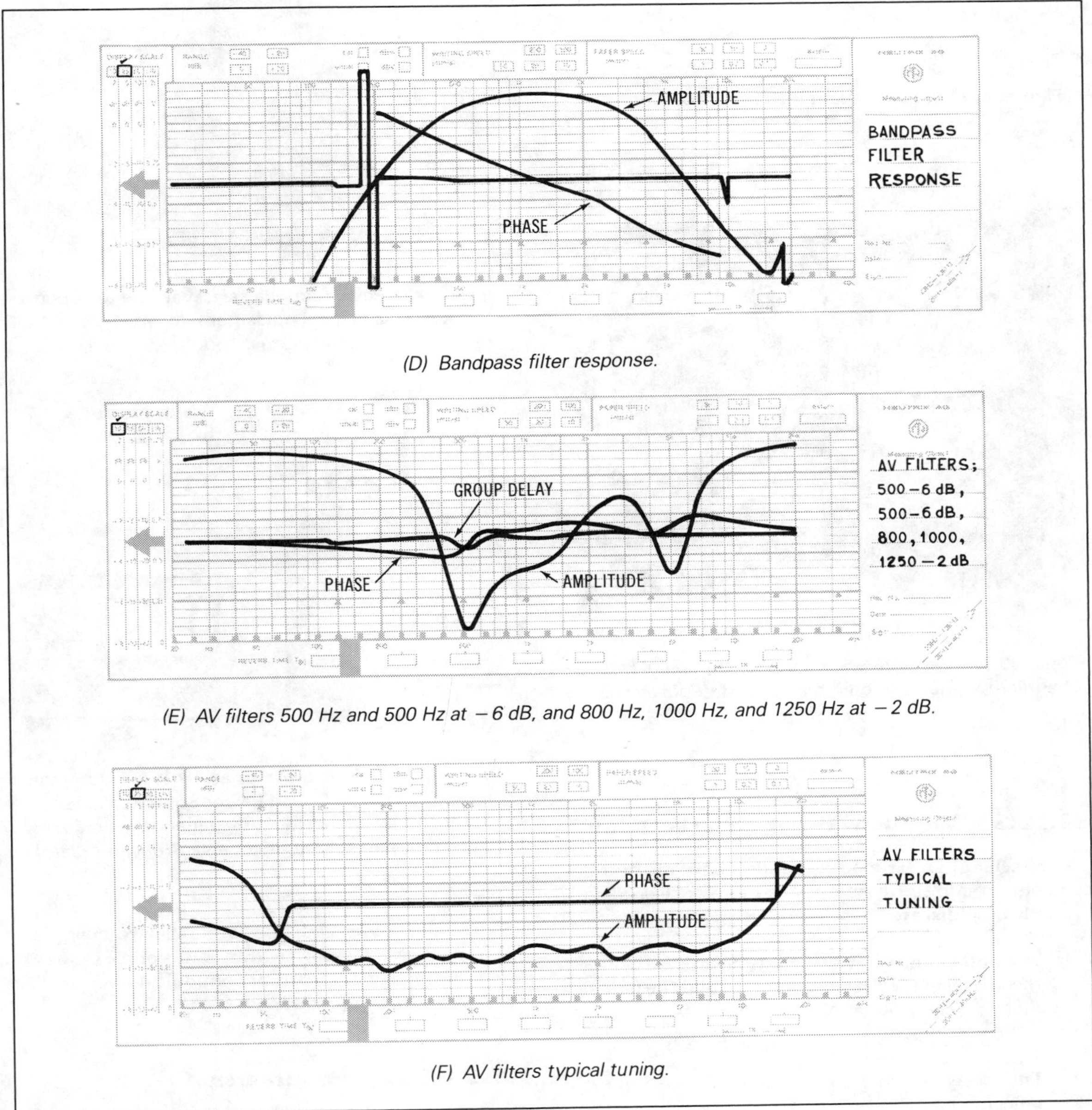

(D) Bandpass filter response.

(E) AV filters 500 Hz and 500 Hz at –6 dB, and 800 Hz, 1000 Hz, and 1250 Hz at –2 dB.

(F) AV filters typical tuning.

group-delay module. The group-delay feature is useful in examining electronics and passive networks. It should not loudspeakers.

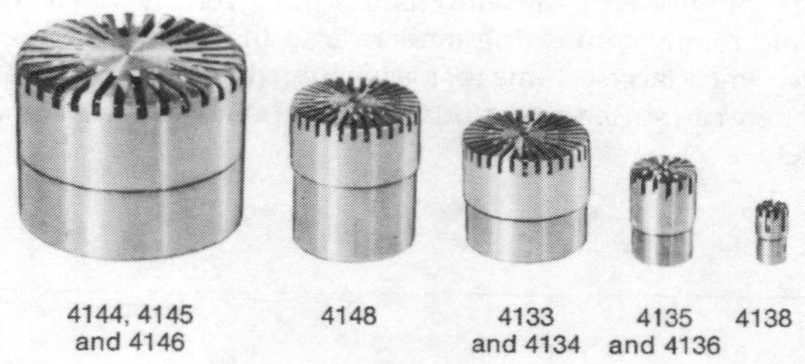

Figure 30-21 Measurement microphones. *(Courtesy Brüel and Kjaer)*

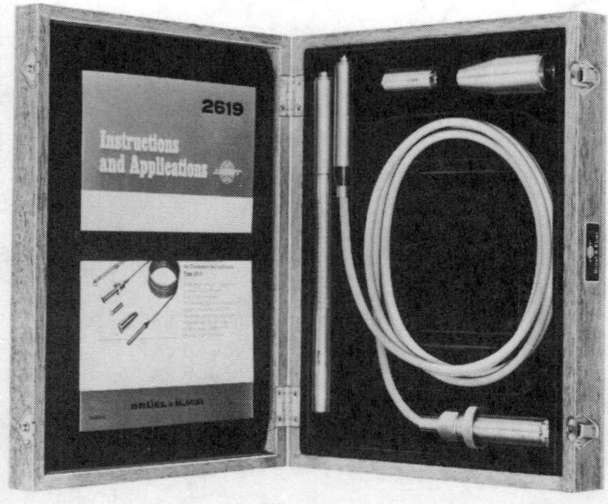

Figure 30-22 Preamplifiers are necessary adjuncts to the the microphones are to be maintained. *(Courtesy Brüel and Kjaer)*

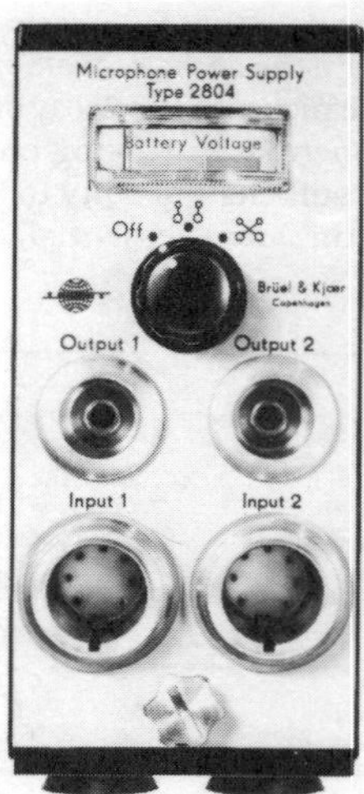

Figure 30-23 Power supplies are available to support every acoustical measurement situation. *(Courtesy Brüel and Kjaer)*

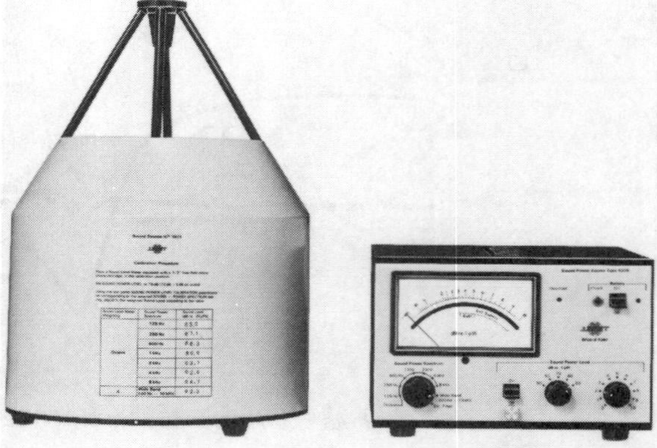

Figure 30-24 Unique tools for acoustic measurement work such as the Sound Power Source originally designed by James Moir, the legendary English acoustical consultant. *(Courtesy Brüel and Kjaer)*

30.12.2 What Then, If Not Reverberation?

Parameters that have been found to have direct influence on our subjective impression of an enclosed space acoustic qualities are:

1. The initial time-delay gap (the time interval between the arrival of the first direct sound and the first significant reflection, as shown in Fig. 30-31).
2. The ratio in dB is $L_D - L_{RE}$ (Fig. 30-32)
3. The delay spacing of the first 50 ms of early reflections.
4. The presence of any reflections delayed longer than 50 ms after the L_D and at a level higher than L_{RE}.
5. The density of both the early reflected energy L_{RE} (i.e., early reflections within 50 ms of the L_D arrival) and the true reverberant sound field level L_R when such is present, as shown in Fig. 30-33.

30.12.3 RT_{60} Measurements

RT_{60} measurements are, at best, only roughly correlated to listener subjective judgment. The simplest form of measurement is recommended (Fig. 30-34). Since almost

Figure 30-25 David Andrews of Andews Audio in New York using a one-third octave Crown real-time analyzer to equalize the sound system at the Waldorf Astoria Hotel. *(Courtesy Andrews Audio Consultants)*

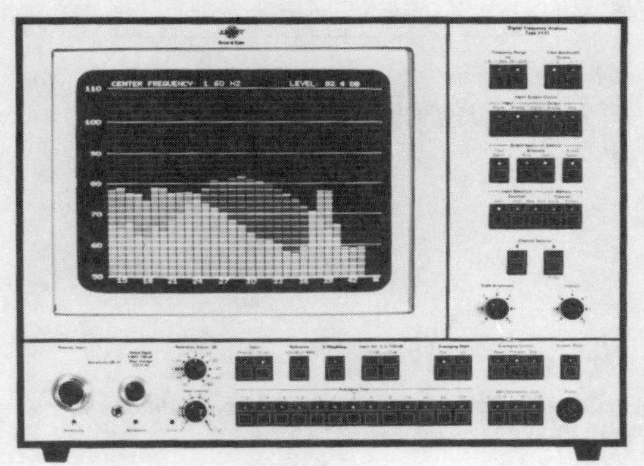

Figure 30-26 Instrument quality full-octave and one-third octave analyzers are made by Bruel and Kjaer as well as GenRad, Nicolet, and others. *(Courtesy Brüel and Kjaer)*

all simple forms are sufficiently accurate for sound system work (perhaps not for concert hall design) once a true reverberant sound field is actually present (i.e., a reasonable volume room with an RT_{60} of 2.0 s or greater).

The use of the term *reverberation time* is nearly ubiquitous today among recording studio designers. It seems almost everyone is familiar with the definition of reverberation time as:

> The reverberation time of a room is the time, in seconds, that would be required for the mean squared sound-pressure level therein, originally in a steady state, to decrease 60 dB after the source is stopped.[2]

A basic requirement of this measurement that is almost universally overlooked in the overwhelming enthusiasm for making measurements is that we are supposed to be measuring the time it takes the *diffuse* far reverberant sound field to decay. By this is meant that there is sufficient reflected energy mixing in the enclosure, wherein the measurements are being made.

Many practical architectural spaces are semireverberant but still have much energy from a diffused field present.

A quick practical test for the presence or absence of such a sound field is as follows:

1. Measure the direct sound output level (L_D) in decibels of the sound source at 4 to 8 ft.
2. Extrapolate by the inverse-square law out to a distant measuring point.
3. At the distant measuring point, measure the total sound level (L_T) in decibels.
4. To find the reverberant sound level (L_R), subtract L_D at the distant point from L_T in the following manner:

$$L_R = 10\log[10(L_T/10) - 10(L_D/10)] \qquad (30\text{-}30)$$

5. See whether the reverberant sound level (L_R) is above the ambient noise level (L_{AMB}) by at least 30 dB (enough to allow a minimum of 20 dB of decay with a signal-to-noise ratio of 10 dB at the low-level end of the decay).

If the previous conditions are met, then an RT_{60} measurement can be considered as valid.

This means that the intention of the measurement is to measure the level change with a time of L_R. This, of course, means that we first move far enough from the sound source so as to minimize the influence of the direct sound level L_D.

30.12.4 Cause and Effect in the Reverberant Sound Field

L_R is dependent upon the total acoustic power (L_W) of the source used and the total acoustic absorption (Sa) of the room boundaries and furnishings. The directivity factor of the loudspeaker (Q) does not enter in, except in the limiting case wherein the restriction of the source's output is such that it falls entirely into an area of infinite absorption. We can write that

$$L_D = L_W + 10\log\frac{Q}{4\pi(D_X)^2} + 10.5 \qquad (30\text{-}31)$$

where,

L_W ref to 10^{-12} W,

D_X is in feet.

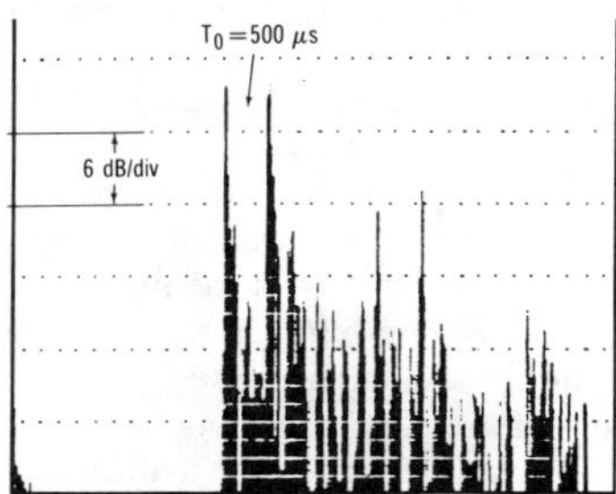

(A) Energy density versus time curve (ETC) of two loudspeakers offset a little over 1 ft.

(B) Nyquist of offset loudspeakers, showing a phase reversal for each comb filter.

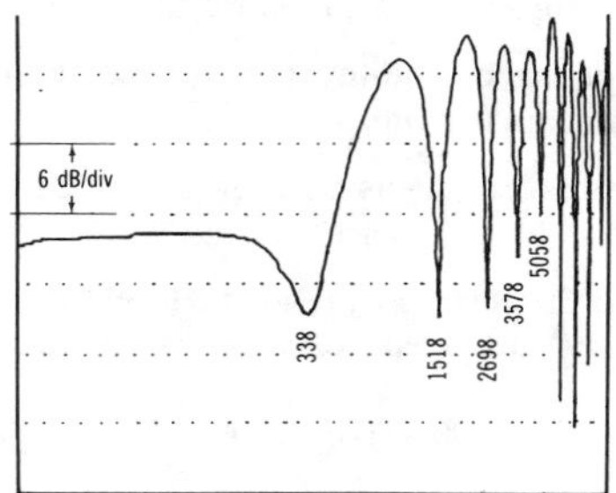

(C) Log display of comb filters produced by offsetting two loudspeakers for a little over 1 ft.

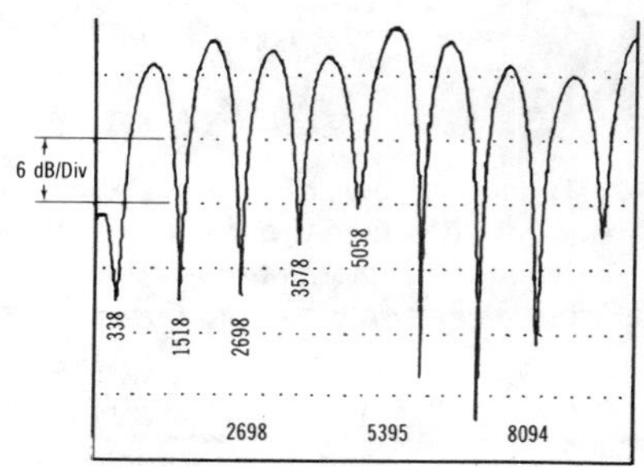

(D) Linear scale: 2698.12 Hz/in. or 1062.25 Hz/cm. Horizontal: 0.00 Hz to 9868.43 Hz.

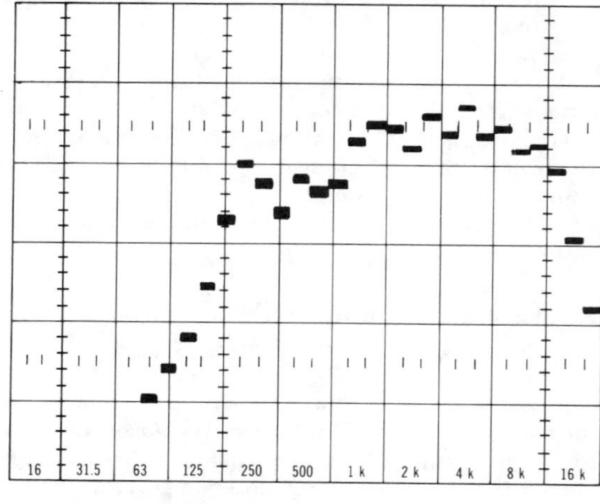

(E) One-third octave RTA plot of same conditions as in Figs. 30-27A through D.

Figure 30-27 Without observing the serious, highly audible problem measured by the TEF analyzer shown, we might conclude from the one-third octave RTA that a little equalization would correct the minor problem between 250 and 500 Hz.

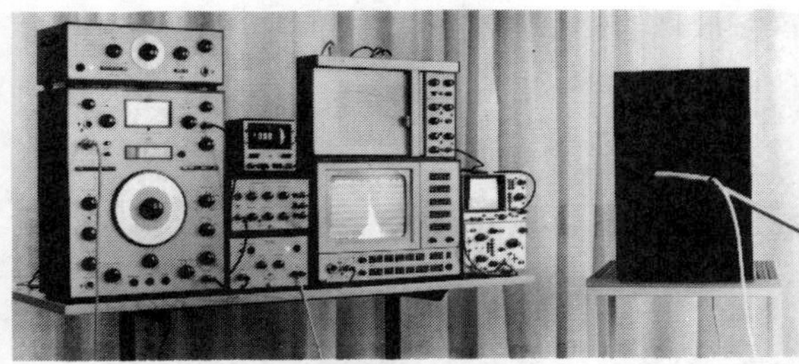

Figure 30-28 The TDS system. *(Courtesy Brüel and Kjaer)*

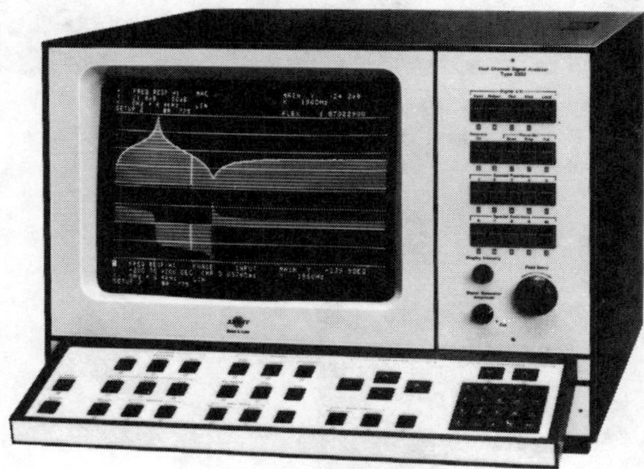

Figure 30-29 This dual-channel fast fourier transform signal analyzer is the best unit of its type for audio and acoustic work. *(Courtesy Brüel and Kjaer, Naerum, Denmark)*

and

$$L_R = L_W + 10 \log 4/Sa + 10.5 \qquad (30\text{-}32)$$

where,
Sa is in square feet.

This combines into the textbook Hopkins-Stryker equation

$$L_T = L_W + 10 \log \frac{Q}{4\pi(D_X)^2} + \frac{4}{Sa} + 10.5 \qquad (30\text{-}33)$$

This equation predicts a reverberant sound field beyond a point known as critical distance (D_c) derived from the previous equation.

$$D_c = 0.141\sqrt{QSa} \qquad (30\text{-}34)$$

Further, as Sa is substantially increased, significant deviations from the expected level beyond D_c occur. V. M. A. Peutz has filled this void with his ΔdB equation

$$\Delta dB = 0.221\sqrt{V/hRT_{60}} \qquad (30\text{-}35)$$

where,
h is the ceiling height in feet.

We have had the theoretical means to sense the difficulty for many years.

30.12.5 Measurements in Rooms Where the ΔdB ≥ 6 dB

It has been a common experience that small studios and control rooms do not depart from inverse-square law level changes when one-third-octave bands of noise are used as source material. This observation was largely ignored by the few that took the trouble to measure it and assigned to it "the room is sure dead" type of comments.

Observe the energy time curve (ETC) measurements made in a standard control room (Fig. 30-35). The only two reflections of any significance whatsoever occur in the early sound field, and there is no late or reverberant sound field present.

If we were to assume for the sake of this example that the L_D = 90 dB, then reflection number 1 is

$$(90 - 18) = 72 \text{ dB}$$

and reflection number 2 is

$$(90 - 19) = 71 \text{ dB}$$

Their effect on L_T becomes

$$L_T = 10 \log[10(L_D/10) + 10(L_{R1}/10) + 10(L_{R2}/10)] \qquad (30\text{-}36)$$

or,

$$L_T = 10 \log[10(90/10) + 10(72/10) + 10(71/10)] = 90.12 \text{ dB}$$

Thus, at the measuring point (the mixing engineer's head position), the only reflections with any significant level whatsoever contribute approximately 0.12 dB to L_T.

Therefore, we are not guessing or making theoretical assumptions when we say that in most of these rooms the measurement of reverberation time is a totally meaningless exercise, when a reverberant sound field in a meaningful, measurable sense does not exist.

30.13 TEST SIGNAL PARAMETERS

Every audio signal has the following parameters to be measured when a sine-wave signal source is used:

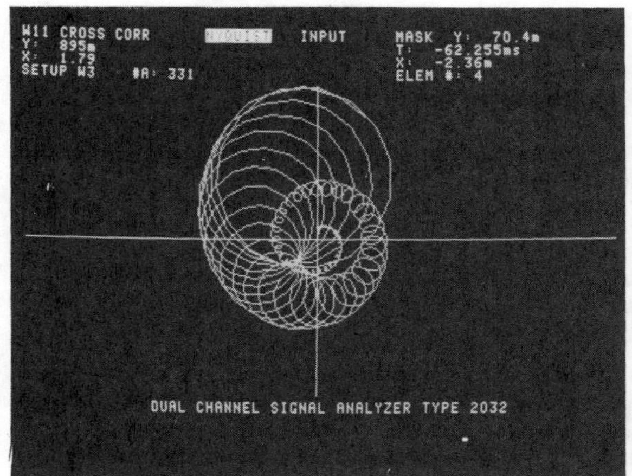

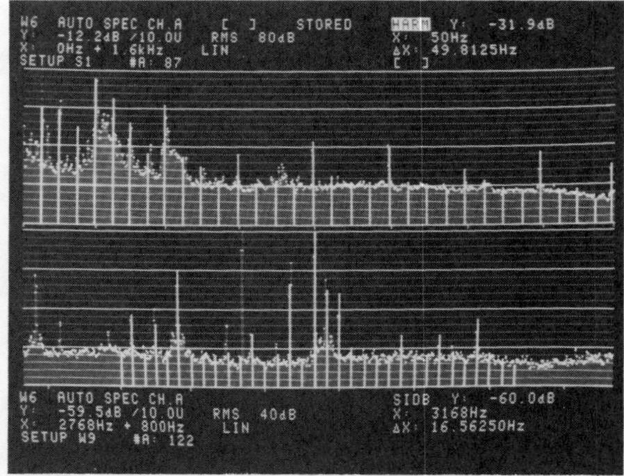

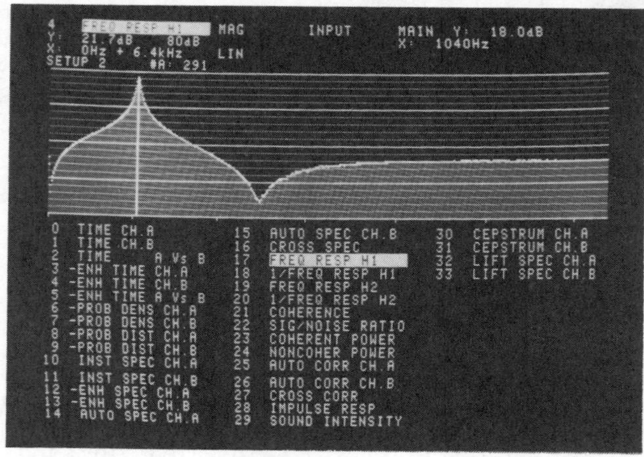

Figure 30-30 Examples of the display annotation available on FFT analyzers. acoustic work. *(Courtesy Brüel and Kjaer)*

1. *Amplitude (A)* can be measured as a total summation of all energy over the total time of the measurement at all frequencies within the bandpass of the instrument. It can also be measured as the amplitude at a given frequency over the entire time of the measurement, or it can be measured as the given amplitude at a given instant of time interval at a given frequency interval.
2. *Period (p)* of sin x is 2π radians or 360°.
3. *Time (t)* interval is arbitrary but in audio and acoustics it is normally the second (s).

From these primary parameters, we derive all the rest:

1. Frequency (f) in hertz

$$f = t/p \tag{30-37}$$

2. Wavelength (λ) is the distance between points of corresponding phase of two consecutive cycles

$$\lambda = \text{phase velocity}/f \tag{30-38}$$

3. Phase (ϕ)

$$\phi = t/p \text{ and is a ratio} \tag{30-39}$$

4. Phase angle (θ)

$$\theta = 360\,(t/p) \text{ in degrees} \tag{30-40}$$

$$= 2\pi\,(t/p) \text{ in radians} \tag{30-41}$$

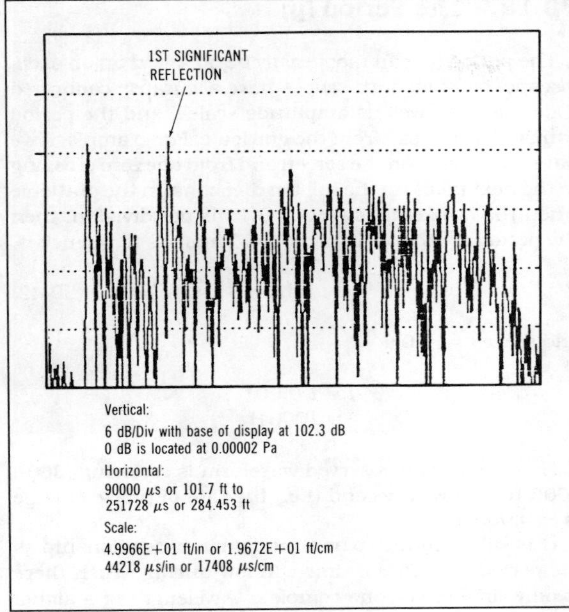

Figure 30-31 Energy density versus time curve (ETC) of a great concert hall in the United States. Initial time-delay gap is 28 ft.

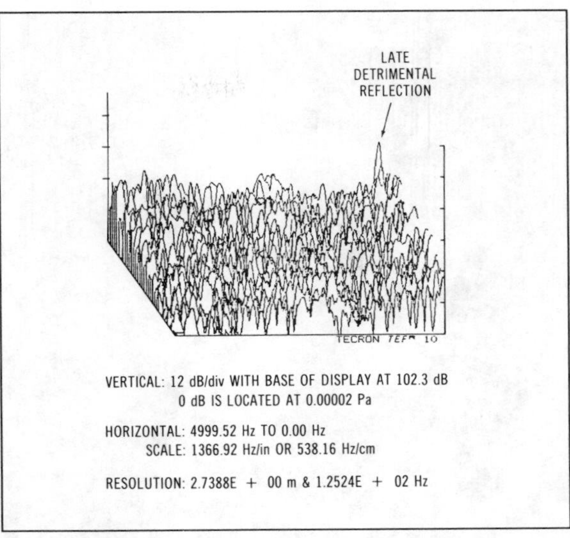

Figure 30-33 Waterfall of an exceptional concert hall in Europe with good diffusion, but of a seat with a very late, detrimental reflection.

5. Sine waves only:

$0.5(p-p)$ = peak amplitude (A_p)

$0.636(A_p)$ = rectified average amplitude (A_{AV})

$0.707(A_p)$ = root-mean-square amplitude (A_{rms})

$A_{rms}{}^2/R$ = average power in watts

30.13.1 Amplitude (A)

The easiest way to find the amplitude characteristics of an electronic device is to place a known signal source at its input and measure its output across a realistic load with a voltmeter, ammeter, wattmeter, oscilloscope, wave analyzer, or other amplitude-measuring instruments as shown in Fig. 30-36.

1. With the switch at position 1, find maximum A_{rms} at R_L (output steps in amplitude with input).

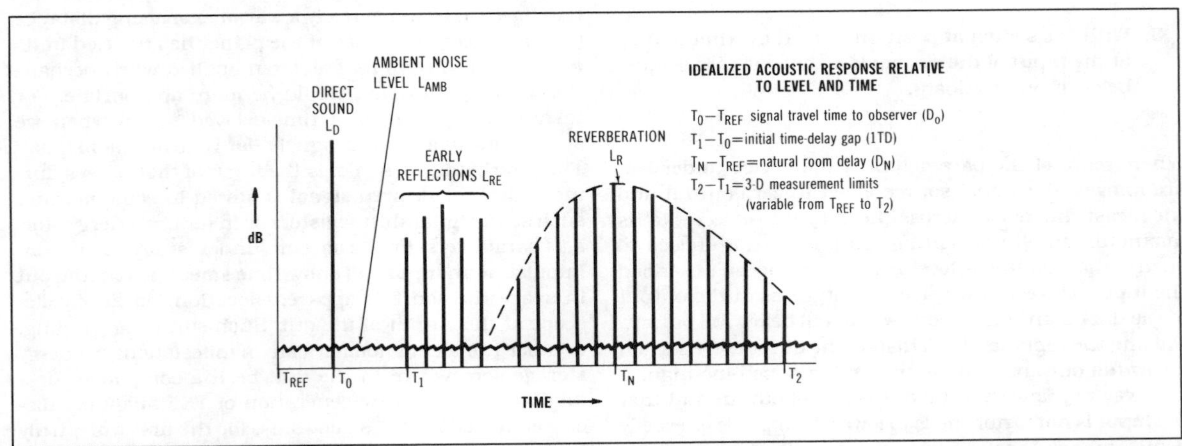

Figure 30-32 Large room acoustic response showing ratio of L_D/L_{RE} and the reverberant field.

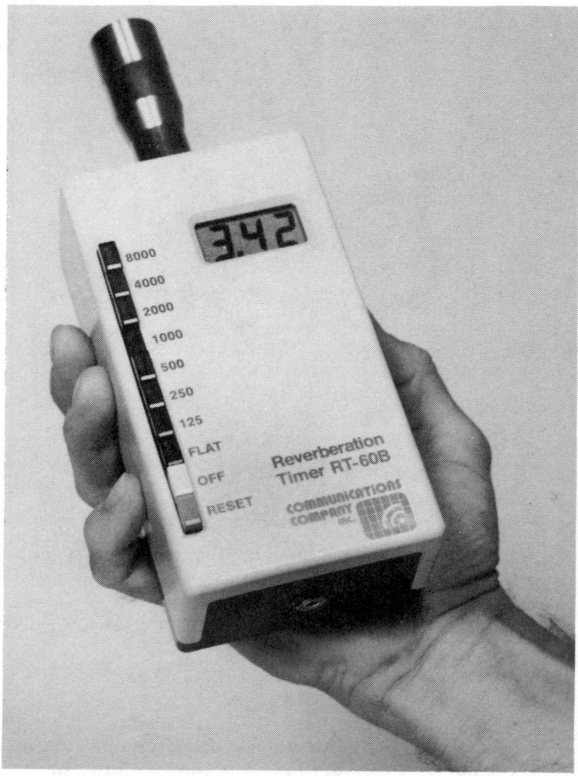

Figure 30-34 A simple reverberation timer. *(Courtesy Communications Company, Inc.)*

2. With the switch at position 1, raise the signal source (ss) output until distortion is observed at R_L when dut is not at full output.

3. With the switch at position 2, read maximum A_{rms} at the input of the system (i.e., output of ss set just below input overload).

Where more of the parameters of the device under test are known, the signal source is set to zero output and the measuring device across the output load is set to its maximum amplitude setting. Care is then exercised to ensure that, as the ss level is raised, it doesn't overload the input. Observe the waveform of the ss at the output of the dut on an oscilloscope when well below full output. Raising the input level will distort the output, even when below full output, if the input level is raised too high. A safe way to know that the dut is at full output and that the input is not distorting is to lower the input level exactly 6 dB and see that the output level also lowers exactly 6 dB.

30.13.2 The Period (p)

The period (p) can most easily be observed on an oscilloscope. Most modern scopes have accurately calibrated time scales as well as amplitude scales, and the period can be directly read from the graticule. For example, if we have a sine wave on the screen and from one zero crossing to the next takes up the full ten divisions on the graticule when the horizontal sweep is 0.1 ms per division, then the period is $10 \times 0.1 = 1.0$ ms. Thus, its frequency is

$$f = t/p \qquad (30\text{-}42)$$

and since $t = 1.0$ s

$$\begin{aligned} f &= 1/0.001 \\ &= 1000\,\text{Hz} \end{aligned}$$

This means the observed waveform is revolving (360°) 1000 times every second (i.e., the rate of phase change is 360,000°/s).

This will be found to be a fundamental relationship as the period describes a time window during which there is only time to see one complete wavelength of a signal with a frequency of 1000 Hz as the lower limit (i.e., there's plenty of time to see one or more wavelengths at higher frequencies). Frequency counters will also give this information on suitable waveforms, yet erratic waveforms often trigger counters erroneously. You will find that the ubiquitous sine wave is one of the best test signals because of our wealth of mathematical knowledge about its behavior.

30.13.3 Time (t)

At first glance, time (t) would seem to simply drop out of the equation by being made unity.

Time is an interesting concept of human civilization. It is inexorable and is really a way of expressing distance (the distance the surface of the planet has traveled in its rotation). The term *time* is often applied when perhaps the term *signal delay* would be more appropriate. For instance, we speak of a time-delayed signal when we actually mean a delayed signal relative to another signal. The time being spoken of is the interval that passes during which the delayed signal is stored in some manner such as in digital shift registers or in natural energy storage parameters in the circuit under study. Thus, an impulse at an input will show time smear (spreading out in space the source's apparent location) on an oscilloscope at the output of the dut. Such smearing, ringing, or other transient anomalies are manifestations of energy storage somewhere in the dut, be it a component or a total system. The new generation of TEF analyzers discussed in section 30.8 allows us, for the first time, truly accurate high-resolution, detailed views of these phenomena.

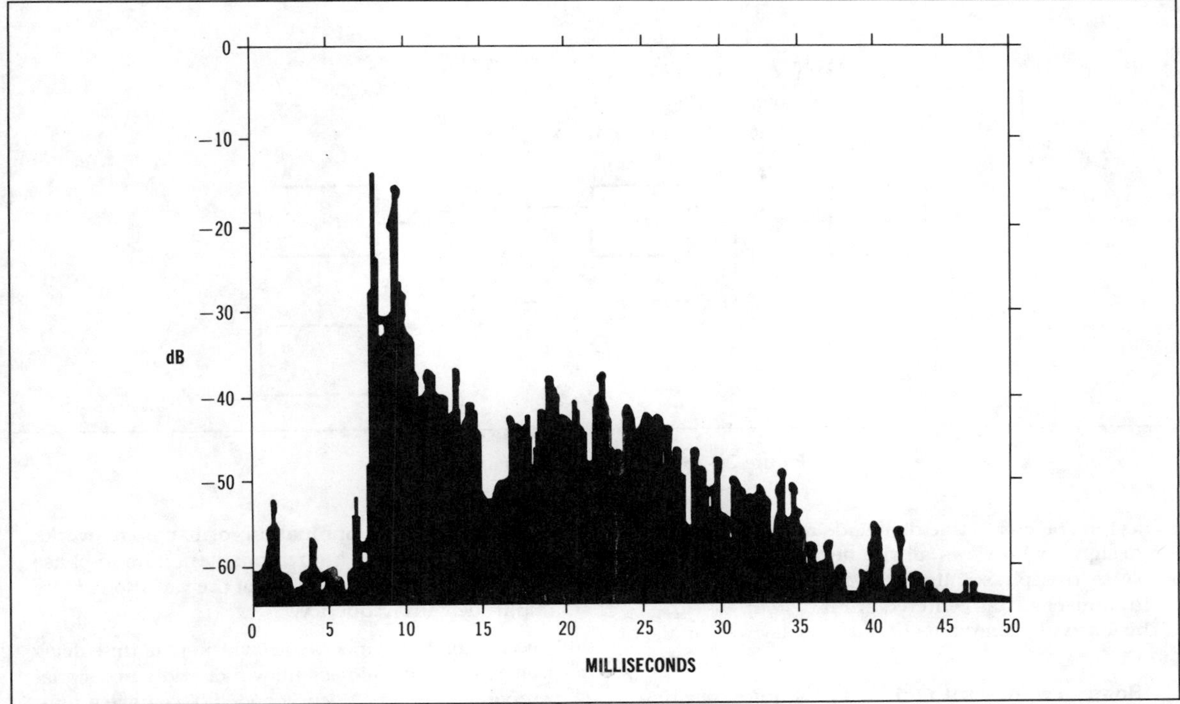

Figure 30-35 Early reflections of a standard "control" room as shown with an energy density versus time curve (ETC) measurement.

30.13.4 Frequency (f)

Frequency can be observed on oscilloscopes, frequency counters, and all types of spectrum analyzers.

The principal types of spectrum analyzers are:

1. Constant percentage bandwidth (cpb)
2. Constant bandwidth (cb)

Constant percentage bandwidth analyzers are found in:

- full-octave units
- one-third-octave units
- one-tenth-octave units
- 1% bandwidth units
- other values built for special purposes but not in widespread usage.

Constant-bandwidth analyzers today fall into three categories:

1. Heterodyne spectrum analyzers (usually low-cost analog devices),
2. Fast Fourier transform (FFT) analyzers (can, on occasion, be quite sophisticated),
3. TEF analyzers (based on the time-delayed spectropectry (TDS) analysis of Richard C. Heyser and, in terms of audio and acoustic measurements, currently have no peers).

30.13.5 Phase (ϕ and θ)

There is absolute phase (ϕ), which is the distance from the sound source expressed as the number of phase revolutions that occur over the distance due to the finite phase velocity of the medium.

Then there is relative phase (θ), which is the fractional portion of the absolute phase ratio (i.e., the value since the last zero crossing, times either 360° or 2π radians). On either dual-channel FFTs or on TEF analyzers, the phase parameter is the one used to the greatest advantage by advanced transducer designers. Neglected because of ways to measure phase economically (both in time and

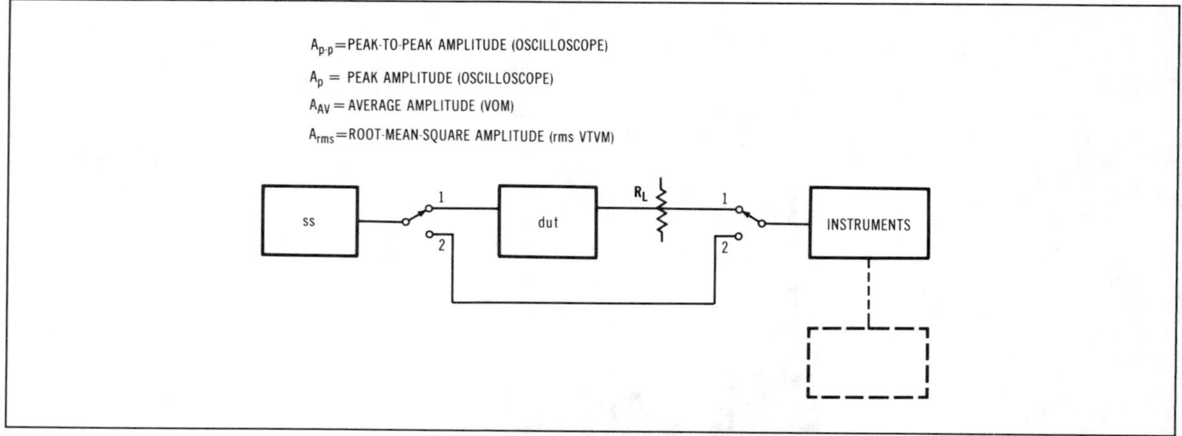

Figure 30-36 Measuring audio amplitudes.

money) in the past, large dividends are now available to the designer who views all the neglected, accumulated problems this phase blindness caused. A great deal of recent nonsense has centered around *group delay*.

The following comments on group delay were made by Heyser.[3]

> How can we deal with this delay? Our first reaction is to turn to the use of group delay but when we do that we immediately encounter logical inconsistencies. A headlong application of group delay to loudspeaker measurement discloses that for many frequencies the pressure wave is calculated to occur before the electrical signal giving rise to it! This violation of causality is absolutely unacceptable. Group delay clearly cannot be used. The reason for this is that group delay, defined as the negative of the rate of change of phase with frequency, cannot be used as a measure of time delay when the amplitude of the response shows a nonzero rate of change with frequency. In fact, it has recently been demonstrated that group delay can never be used as a measure of time delay when applied to any nontrivial minimum-phase network. Exit group delay. Then what is left?
>
> The solution to this problem must be offered by a completely new look at network time delay. Without going into details since it is covered elsewhere, there is one special type of network for which the time delay of each frequency component is always positive and coincides with the definition of group delay corresponding to the negative of the slope of the phase versus frequency. The network is the all-pass transmission function, which is strictly nonminimum-phase.
>
> What has this got to do with loudspeakers and other networks which have a frequency-dependent amplitude response? The surprising answer is that properly mixed parallel combinations of all-pass networks can be used to imitate any reasonable minimum-phase response function, regardless of the variations of its amplitude with frequency.
>
> This means that since we know the true time-delay properties of the all-pass networks and since signal components can be linearly added if we have a noninteracting parallel combination of such all-pass networks, there is a proper analytical tool that can be used to calculate the amount of time delay that can be expected from a loudspeaker or any network element.
>
> If a signal is fed to a loudspeaker, the resultant response can be equated to that of an ensemble of parallel all-pass elements. Each all-pass element has a perfectly uniform amplitude response and a frequency-dependent phase response with a slope that never becomes positive with increasing frequency.
>
> A dip in the loudspeaker frequency response corresponds to a cancellation by destructive interference in the equivalent ensemble response of all-pass elements. A peak is the converse. Since this is a model, we know that the actual loudspeaker, as a network, is not composed of these conceptual elements but the fact remains that if we compute and measure as though it were made of these elements, we will achieve results indistinguishable from the physical case.
>
> What I actually found was that I could learn from the loudspeaker how to improve the holes in my own background of communication theory. A case in point is group delay, a concept which I frankly never understood in college studies but which I had been assured was properly defined "somewhere." Everyone knows that there is some actual time delay for a signal passing through a physical system but when group delay,

which pretended to be that delay, was applied, noncausal solutions frequently resulted. Textbook derivations made a great deal of fuss about explaining that "anticipatory transients" did not really exist and could be explained as resulting from approximations in the presumed frequency response. It was vaguely hinted that group delay could not be used near frequencies of absorption. But how close? And was it valid farther away? If so, then how far away?

As long as such problems lurked only at the fringes of measurement, no one seemed bothered. But suddenly with loudspeakers, I found myself deep in such considerations. The problems could not be ignored, particularly since they seemed to be at the heart of considerations of the importance of phase response to quality of reproduction.

I did finally find a solution to the mystery of time delay in a dispersive absorptive medium but only after I was forced to do so by practical considerations of loudspeaker reproduction. This solution has since been folded back into electromagnetic problems to obtain correct answers. Group delay, it turns out, is never equal to causal time delay in a minimum-phase system. One should not compute the time delay of a loudspeaker by a measurement of group delay.

All audio measurements should be submitted to two important criteria:

1. Is it an audible parameter?
2. Is it a natural or unnatural distortion?

30.14 MEASUREMENT SCALING

Two principal scaling techniques are employed:

1. Logarithmic
   a. decades
   b. octaves
   c. hertz
   d. % bandwidth
   e. decibels
2. Linear
   a. volts, amperes, and so on
   b. time*
   c. Hz

30.14.1 Linear Scales

A linear scale gives equal weight per cycle. To construct a linear scale, we must first decide on the number of measurement points and intervals desired on the scale. For example, suppose we want a scale from 0 Hz to 10 kHz with ten measurement intervals. The number of points then is (N + 1), where N is the number of measurement intervals. The first point is zero; the last point will be 10 kHz, as shown in Fig. 30-37A.

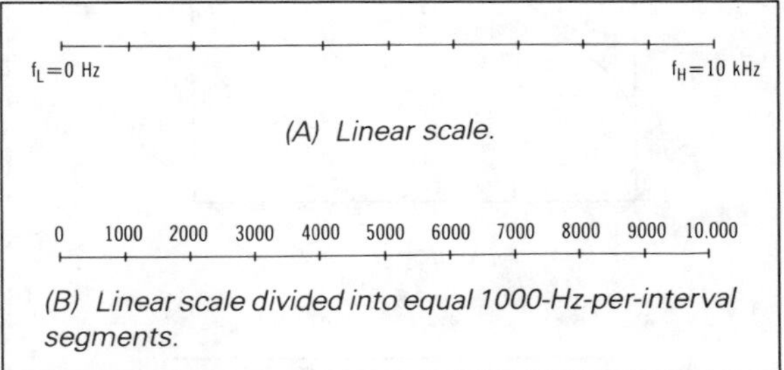

Figure 30-37 Two scales for measuring audio amplitudes.

Dividing the total bandpass ($F_H - F_L$) by the ten intervals

$$10{,}000/10 = 1000 \text{ Hz per interval}$$

as shown in Fig. 30-37B. To find any frequency on the scale, simply count N points and multiply [($f_H - f_L$)/N intervals] times (N − 1) points.

30.14.2 Logarithmic Scales

A logarithmic scale gives equal weight per bandwidth.

30.14.2.1 Decades

The number of decades is found by

$$f_H/f_L = 10^{(x\ \text{decade})}$$

$$\ln f_H - \ln f_L = \ln 10(x\,\text{decades}) \quad (30\text{-}43)$$

$$(\ln f_H - \ln f_L)/\ln 10 = x\,\text{decades}$$

Fig. 30-38 shows a log and linear display. Fig. 30-39 reveals an interesting distortion when the log scale is used to measure a filter. The linear measurement shows the real shape of the filter.

30.14.2.2 Octaves

The number of octaves is found by

$$f_H/f_L = 2^{(x\ \text{octave})} \quad (30\text{-}44)$$

$$\ln f_H - \ln f_L/\ln 2 = x \text{ octaves} \quad (30\text{-}45)$$

*This can be ambivalent as $e^{j\theta}$ represents a time interval and is, of course, logarithmic.

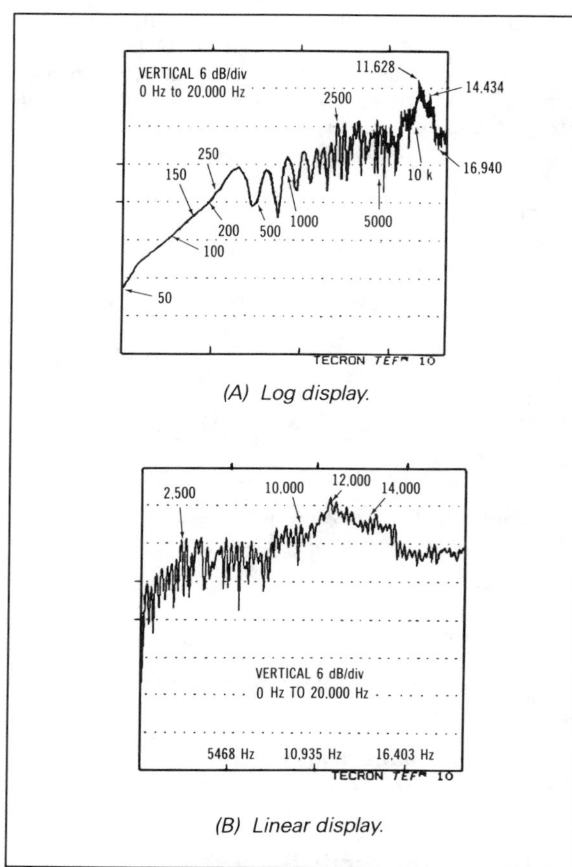

Figure 30-38 Comparison of log and linear displays of the same response curve.

30.14.2.3 % Bandwidth

$$f_c(X\%)/100 = f_{(BP)}$$

where,

f_c is the center frequency of the filter or measuring point,

X% is the % bandpass,

f_{BP} is the bandpass in hertz (i.e., the $[f_H - 3.01 \; - f_L - 3.01\;]$).

30.14.2.4 Renard Numbers

The Renard numbers were developed in France in 1879 by Charles Renard because of a need for a rational basis for grading cotton rope. Based upon a geometric progression, these numbers can represent the most logical method for covering a range of numbers with the minimum number of terms.

In the Renard number system, one octave is specified as the 3⅓ series (i.e., $10^{(1/3.333)}$ is the multiplier "M" used to increment each interval).

To find any other Renard series, multiply 3.333 by the reciprocal of the fractional octave desired:

$$\text{one-sixth octave} = 6 \times 3.333 = 20 \text{ series}$$

$$\text{one-tenth octave} = 10 \times 3.333 = 33⅓ \text{ series}$$

General Case Equation:

$$f \text{ intervals} = (f_L \times M)M \cdots M_N$$

Example: To obtain one-third-octave intervals (actually, one-tenth-decade intervals) from 100 Hz up:

$$f \text{ intervals} = (100(10^{(1/10)})(10^{(1/10)})(10^{(1/10)}) \cdots (N10^{(1/10)}) \quad (30\text{-}46)$$

30.14.2.5 Constructing Logarithmic Scales

To have ten equal logarithmic intervals, we need to first find the multiplier M. If the frequency interval is from 1 Hz to 10 kHz (*Note:* 1 Hz on a logarithmic scale is the same as 0 Hz on a linear scale because $10^0 = 1.0$), we proceed as follows:

$$[f_H/f_L]^{(1/N \text{ intervals})}$$

or,

$$[10{,}000/1]^{(1/10)} = 2.51189\ldots$$

Since the number of points is N + 1 times the number of intervals, we have a scale as shown in Fig. 30-40. Manipulation of these basic equations allows freedom in the evaluation of key measurement parameters surrounding frequency scaling choices. FFT analyzers often have 400-line resolution and, on their logarithmic scaling, provide 2.7 decades. Thus, if we selected an f_H of 20 kHz, our f_L would be

$$f_L = \epsilon^{\,\ln f_H \; - \; 2.7 \text{ decades } \ln 10} = 40\,\text{Hz}$$

Therefore, our bandwidth would be 40 Hz to 20 kHz, and the apparent filter width would be

$$20{,}000\,\text{Hz}/400\,\text{lines} = 50\,\text{Hz/line}$$

because the original data is from a linear measurement with that resolution.

30.14.3 Time-Bandwidth Product

FFT analysis is tied to the time-bandwidth product such that

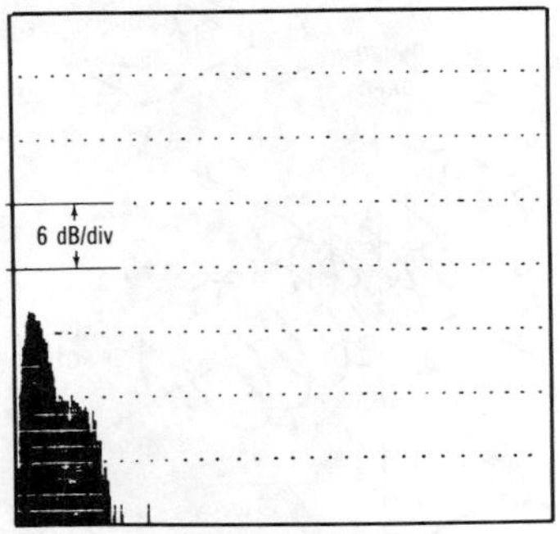

(A) *Energy density versus time curve (ETC) of 500-Hz high-pass filter and 1000-Hz low-pass filter.*

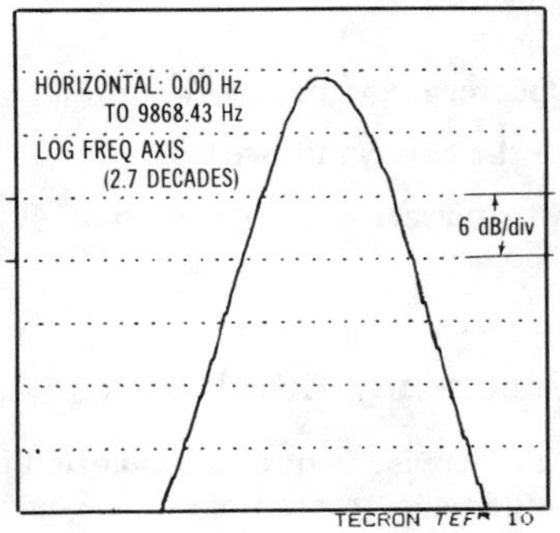

(B) *Same filter, log frequency scale.*

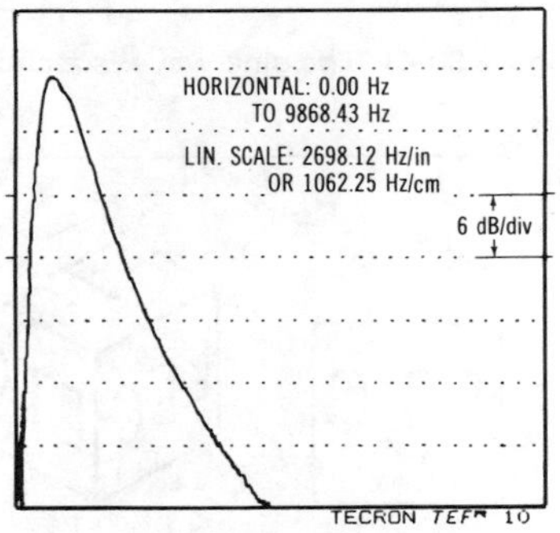

(C) *Same filter, linear frequency scale.*

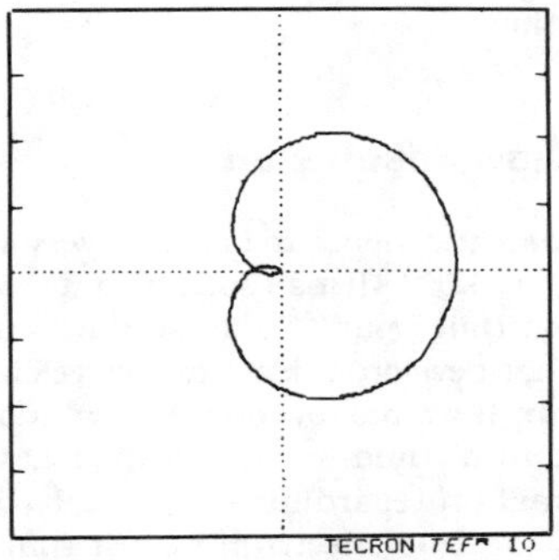

(D) *Same filter, Nyquist phase response. Frequency range: 0.00 Hz to 9868.43 Hz.*

Figure 30-39 The log display reveals an interesting "distortion" when used to measure a filter. The linear measurement shows the real shape of the filter.

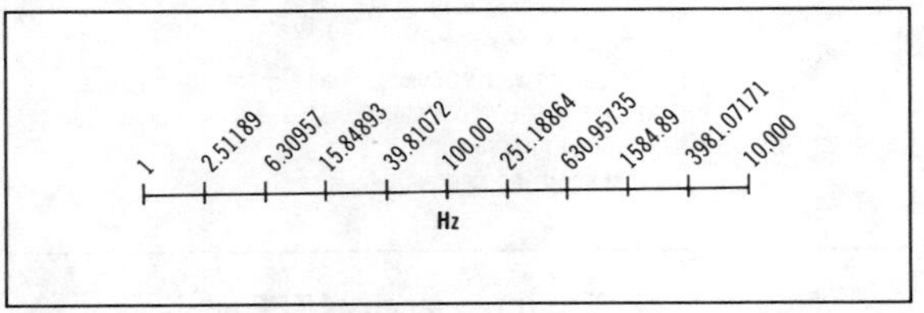

Figure 30-40 A logarithmic scale from 1 Hz to 1kHz.

$$f_R \times t_R = 1.0 \tag{30-47}$$

where,
f_R is the frequency resolution in hertz,
t_R is the time resolution in seconds.

This, of course, means that

$$t_R = 1/f_R \tag{30-48}$$

and

$$f_R = 1/t_R \tag{30-49}$$

So that if, as in the case above, we want a bandwidth of 20 kHz and we have 400 lines of resolution, then the f_R becomes

$$f_R = 20{,}000/400$$
$$= 50\,\text{Hz}$$

and the t_R then is

$$t_R = 1/50\,\text{Hz}$$
$$= 0.020\,\text{s}$$

If we want a smaller (i.e., shorter) time window, we have to:

1. Take a poorer frequency resolution.
2. Increase the bandwidth we look at.
3. Find an analyzer with more than 400 lines of resolution.

30.14.4 Frequency Resolution

If we wish to increase frequency resolution to its maximum, we would use a receiver of infinite bandpass and a transmitter of pure sine-wave signals. The receiver could then, at any time during the measurement, hear any frequency effect while our transmitter produced sequentially one frequency at a time. We would, however, have an infinite time window ($t_R = \infty$) and would have zero time information.

30.14.5 Time Resolution

We could, instead, choose to look at a very small increment of time (i.e., 0.001 s [1 ms]) and find out what occurred in that limited time span. To do so limits us to those frequencies that develop at least one wavelength within that time span. If we narrow our time window down to an exact instant of time, we would then have zero frequency information regarding that signal—we couldn't be sure what the true spectrum was at that instant of time. TEF analysis allows the exploration of that grey area between these two domains wherein both our amplitude and our frequency information gradually smears as our time resolution sharpens. There are many very useful compromise measurements that provide remarkable insight into these basic relationships such as the causality of physical systems.

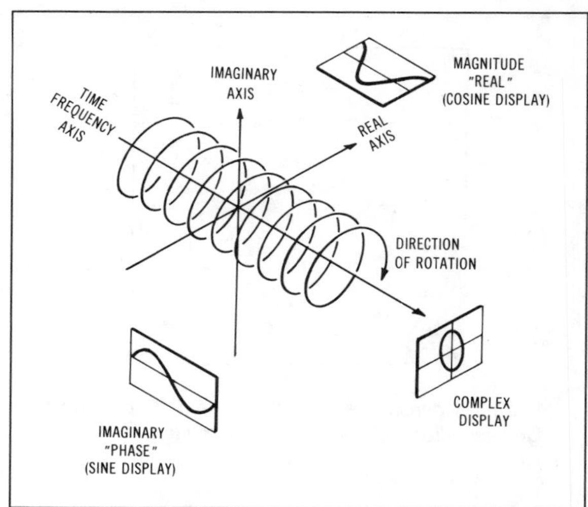

Figure 30-41 The sine wave is a circle.

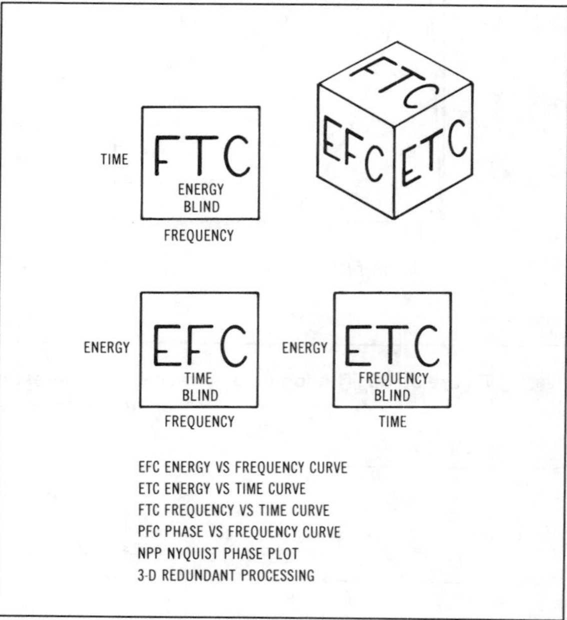

Figure 30-42 The three faces of TEF analysis.

30.15 TEF ANALYSIS

The ultimate audio and acoustic measurement tool available today is the Tecron TEF System 10. This is a dedicated TEF analyzer capable of doing every audio or acoustic measurement required today with higher resolution, greater accuracy, and superior speed than any other available technique. TEF stands for time, energy, and frequency. (See Figs. 30-41, 30-42, and 30-43.)

30.15.1 Elimination of Anechoic Chambers

The original attraction TEF measurements held for most workers in audio and acoustics was its ability to provide anechoic (echo-free) measurements in reverberant spaces. It does so by allowing a tremendously wide range of time windows so that high-resolution frequency measurements, either logarithmic or linear based, can be made anywhere that the nearest reflecting surface is at an acoustic distance greater than

$$d = c/f_L \tag{30-50}$$

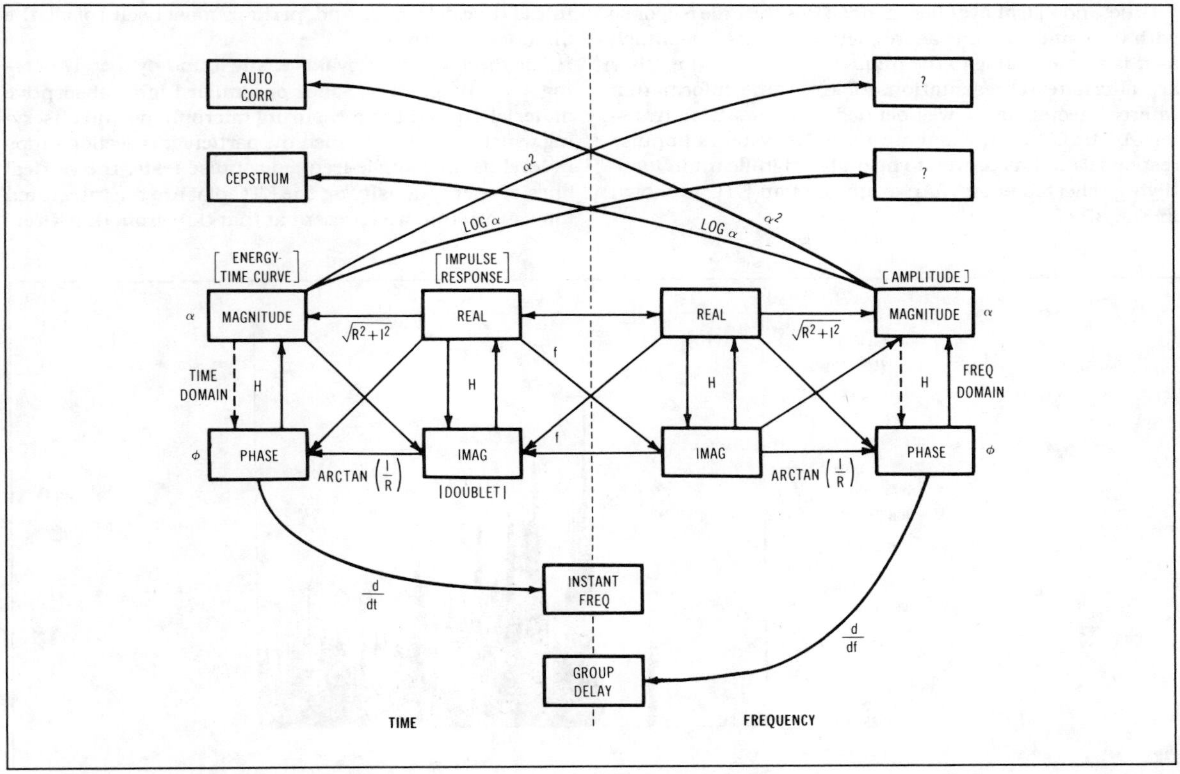

Figure 30-43 Measurement domains. *(Courtesy Brüel & Kjaer Instruments, Inc.)*

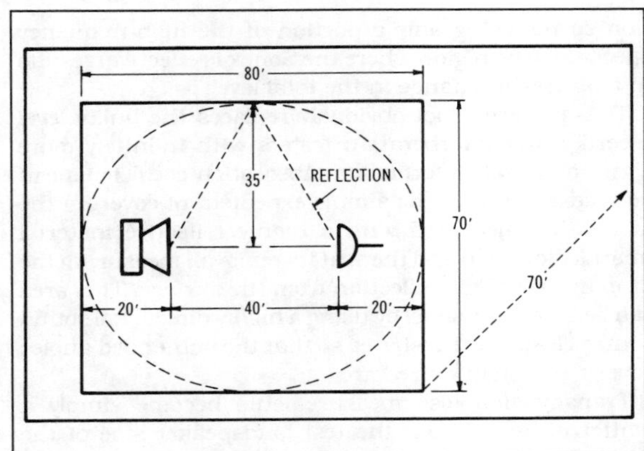

Figure 30-44 Approximate room constraints on 30-Hz measurements.

where,

c is the phase velocity of the medium,

f_L is the lowest frequency of interest.

For example, if we want a 2.7 decade logarithmic frequency scale measurement of a loudspeaker from 40 to 20,000 Hz, then the nearest reflecting surfaces arrival at our measuring microphone must be (0.885 s/ft)(1130 ft/s)/(40 Hz) later than the direct sound. In other words, a loudspeaker mounted 15 ft above a floor and below a ceiling with side walls 30 ft away can be measured interference free down to 40 Hz, as shown in Fig. 30-44.

30.15.2 Establishing T_R

A measurement labeled energy time curve (ETC) by its inventor, Richard C. Heyser, allows an immediate accurate view of the available t_R. See Eqs. 30-28 and 30-29 for any measurement that may be required by displaying the L_D, L_{RE}, and L_R distinctly and separately in time versus energy density, where

L_D = direct sound level

L_{RE} = early reflection levels

L_R = statistical exponentially shaped reverberant sound field

Brüel and Kjaer have chosen to call this the time response with the same meaning as frequency response inasmuch as it is a true analog to the frequency response (i.e., they are alternate representations of the same information interconnected by a well-defined mathematical transform). The ETC is the magnitude of the system's impulse response and has proven to be highly significant in identifying reflected energy. An example of an ETC is shown in Fig. 30-45.

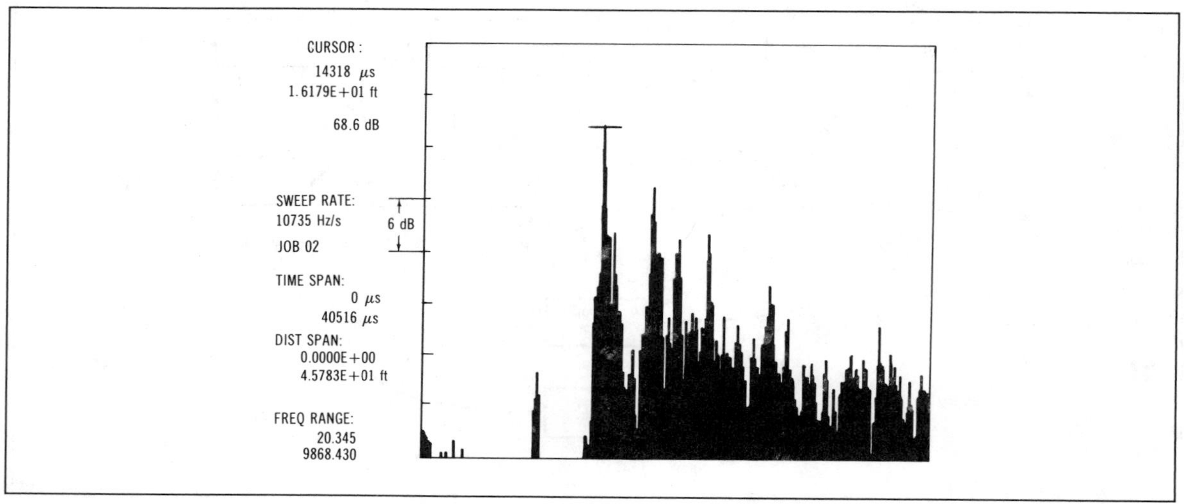

Figure 30-45 Energy-time curves, with keyboard controlled cursor, provide accurate information on reflections.

The TEF analyzer has *special function* keys that allow t_0, t_1, and t_2 to be specified. Let t_0 define the single-sweep energy-density versus frequency (EFC) signal delay. Then t_1 defines the beginning of the three-dimensional (redundant processing) plots, and t_2 defines the end of the same plot. This time interval is divided into 32 equal increments (Fig. 30-46). If only the L_D is desired, then the time window would be set to include all of L_D but nothing beyond; in this case, the t_1 indicated on the ETC. It is also possible to examine only the L_{RE} or the L_R if desired. Fig. 30-46 shows the initiation of a small dead room's modal response. Note that the first reflection is not a bad replica of the direct sound (reflection off of a metal door) but that the phase cancellations of other reflections rapidly determine the key modal frequencies and, interestingly enough, cause them to vary in frequency as they decay. Is this reverberation? Certainly not in any classic meaning of the word, yet we see people trying to measure reverberation time in rooms of this type (i.e., recording studio control rooms), as shown in Fig. 30-47.

ETC measurements quickly reveal not only the amplitude and the time of arrival but also the density of the field, its approach to exponential growth and decay, the initial time delay gap, and, perhaps most useful of all, the direction of arrival.

The direction of arrival is easily found by merely passing a 1.0 ft^2 piece of Sonex or similar highly absorptive material around the measuring microphone and observing which path it is in when the particular reflection drops in level. Unlike single-frequency pulse tests, the vertical lines of energy density on the ETC plot are the integrated total sweep that was present at that time from that direction so removing only a portion of the high-frequency spectrum (the region where the Sonex is effective) results in a noticeable change in the total level.

This powerful tool obviously replaces the bulky level recorder and reverberation testers with infinitely more accurate, usable information. Absorption coefficients can be read directly by the simple expedient of covering the area to be measured with a highly reflective material (marble, formica) and then, at its removal, measuring the drop in level of the reflection from the surface. This area can be kept quite small by using a highly directional sound source close to the test area so that the subtended angles cover a reasonably sized area.

Transmission loss measurements become simply a matter of one plot on the test loudspeaker side of the partition and another plot on the receiver side of the partition. Here a wireless instrumentation microphone system such as the HM Electronics' PAL (precision audio link) is unexcelled for the ease of operation now allowed with this formerly awkward measurement. The test rooms remain sealed, the analyzer remains in a convenient location, and the total accuracy is the same as was formerly available using cables (Figs. 30-48 and 30-49).

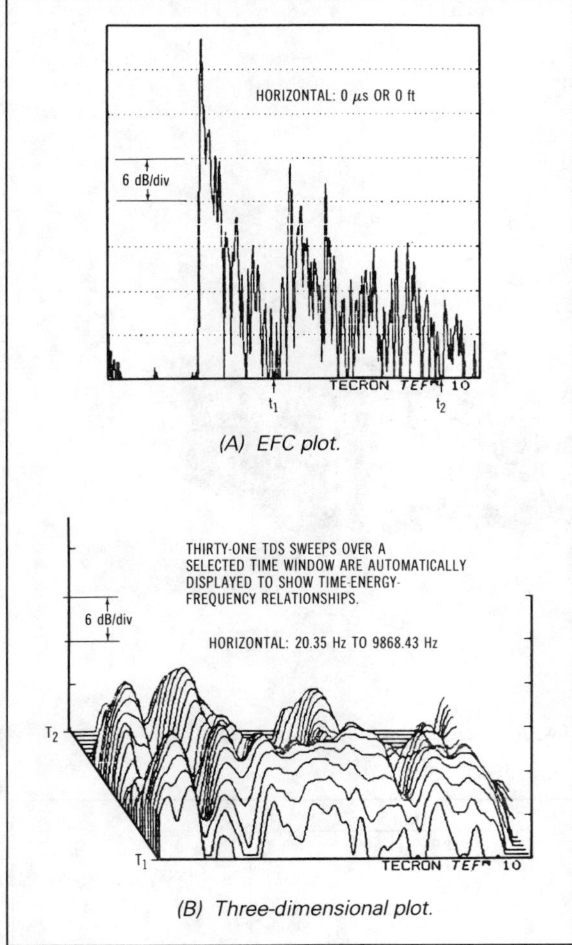

(A) EFC plot.

(B) Three-dimensional plot.

Figure 30-46 TEF analyzer EFC and three-dimensional plots.

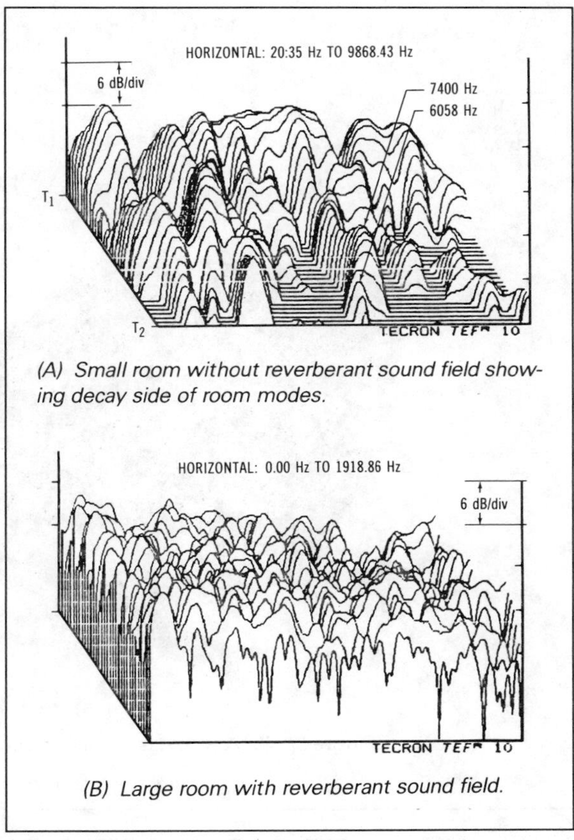

(A) Small room without reverberant sound field showing decay side of room modes.

(B) Large room with reverberant sound field.

Figure 30-47 Room modes. Vivid proof that a fundamental difference between a small reverberant space and a large reverberant space exists.

The one fact to remember about ETC measurements is that they contain no frequency information other than the knowledge of the range being swept. They do give us precise information about the optimum time window we will want to use for our frequency domain measurements.

30.15.3 Frequency Domain Measurements

The common term "frequency response" usually calls for an amplitude versus frequency plot. In acoustic measurements, the amplitude scale is usually the energy density versus the frequency for a selected time window. What is not always realized as the engineer gazes at the two-dimensional plot in hand is that some frequencies on it were emitted from a relative source position and are quite different than other frequencies. If the plot was made in an anechoic chamber using a level recorder with a relatively slow sweep but fast writing rate, some dips resulted from delay or, more correctly, signal storage effects in the system and not from failure to output at that frequency. That next bump just above the dip might be the later arrival of that energy adding to the normal arrival of that frequency, and the dip and bump observed is the result of signal delay, not signal output. The frequency domain measurements made on a TEF analyzer allow such interesting aberrations to not only be observed but corrected as well; once the sin is uncovered, it's 90% destroyed.

30.15.4 Phase Versus Frequency (PFC)

The *phase versus frequency curves (PFC)*, whether made on a linear scale or a logarithmic frequency scale,

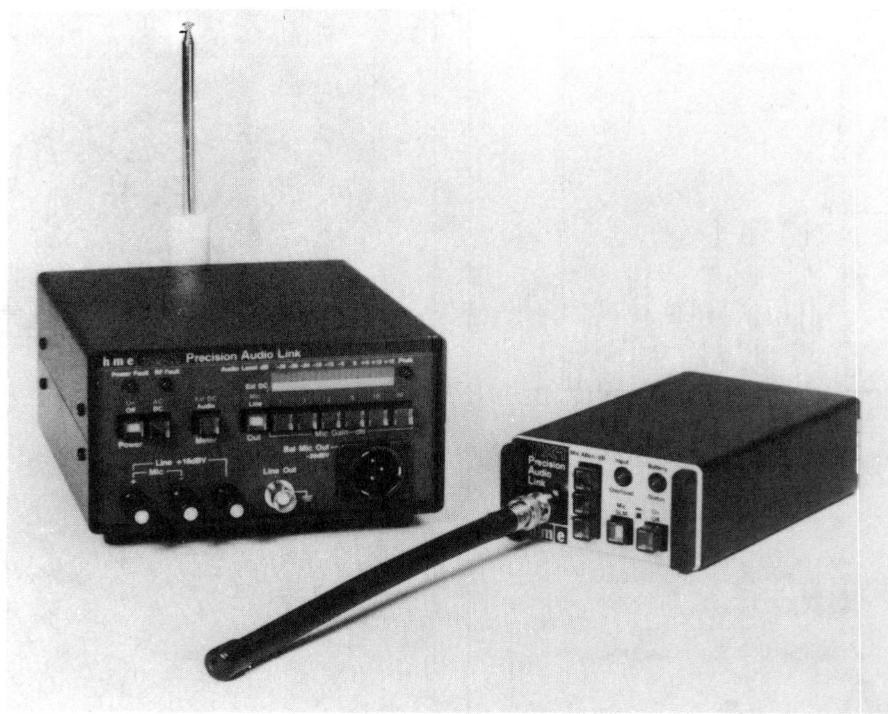

Figure 30-48 A wireless precision audio link. *(Courtesy HM Electronics Inc.)*

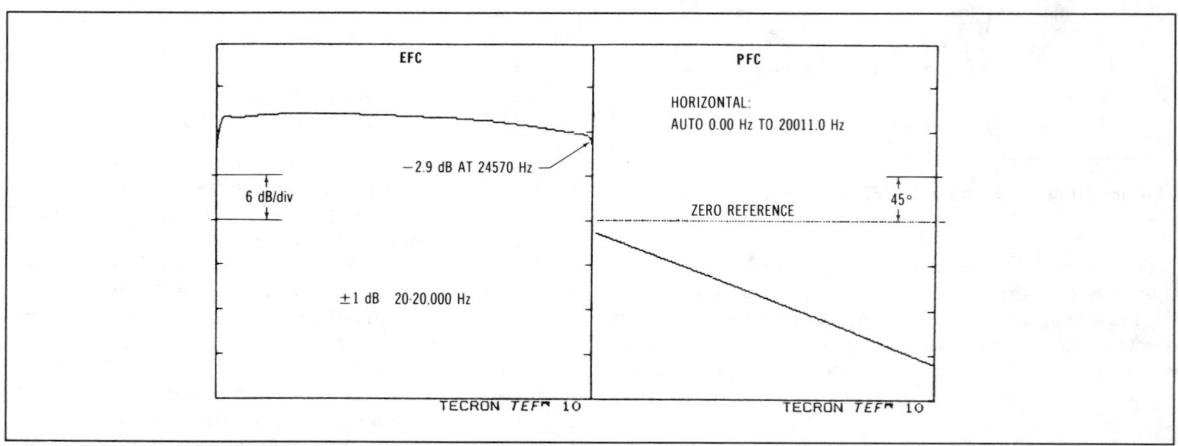

Figure 30-49 A final EFC plot out to 25,000 Hz shows the extended-range capability of the HM Electronics PAL.

provide us with the delay normal to the bandpass of the system and any nonlinearities that may be present. So long as the phase versus frequency is a straight line, harmful nonlinearities can be assumed to not be present. The slope of the straight line denotes the inherent signal delay of the circuit (the greater the slope, the greater the signal delay). It is considered desirable for the signal delay to be the same for all frequencies. This relationship is shown mathematically in Fig. 30-50. Also illustrated in that figure is the concept of envelope delay and delay distortion (i.e., the difference between the signal delay considered unavoidable for the passband and that actually

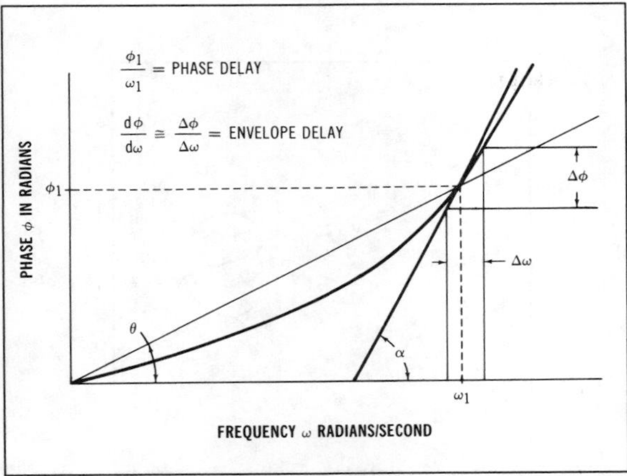

Figure 30-50 Phase delay and envelope delay defined.

measured). Present researchers tend toward the opinion that discontinuities in the signal delay are the audible portions. In our opinion this is the area of experimentation that will be beautifully resolved once TEF analysis is available and understood by the psychoacoustic community. The literature on this subject is fraught with contradictions, and thorough workers who start back at Ohm's law and Helmholtz's law and work their way forward with the tools of today carefully applied to relevant experiments will have the pleasure of collating correctly all the earlier guesses plus their own insights gained from such an effort.

Table 30-2. Analysis of a Minimum-Phase Filter

Let H = transfer function of a single band reject filter that produces a notch at ω_0 of −14 dB.

$$H_1 = \frac{S^2 + \frac{0.2\omega_0 S + \omega_0^2}{Q}}{S^2 + \frac{\omega_0 S}{Q} + \omega_0^2}$$

If this filter is one-third octave wide between the −7-dB points, Q must be 1.93. For convenience let ω_0 = 1 rad/s,

$$H_1 = \frac{S^2 + 0.104S + 1}{S^2 + 0.52S + 1}$$

Consider a second such filter having a center frequency one octave higher than the first.

$$H_2 = \frac{S^2 + 0.208S + 4}{S^2 + 1.04S + 4}$$

Table 30-2—cont. Analysis of a Minimum-Phase Filter

For steady state, $S = j\omega$

$$H_1 = \frac{(1 - \omega^2) + j(0.104\omega)}{(1 - \omega^2) + j(0.52\omega)}$$

and

$$H_2 = \frac{(4 - \omega^2) + j(0.208\omega)}{(4 - \omega^2) + j(1.04\omega)}$$

$$H_1 = \frac{\sqrt{1 - 2\omega^2 + \omega^4 + 0.0108\omega^2}\, e^{j\tan^{-1}[0.104\omega/(1-\omega^2)]}}{\sqrt{1 - 2\omega^2 + \omega^4 + 0.2704\omega^2}\, e^{j\tan^{-1}[(0.52\omega)/(1-\omega^2)]}}$$

$$H_2 = \frac{\sqrt{16 - 8\omega^2 + \omega^4 + 0.043264\omega^2}\, e^{j\tan^{-1}[0.208\omega/(4-\omega^2)]}}{\sqrt{16 - 8\omega^2 + \omega^4 + 1.0816\omega^2}\, e^{j\tan^{-1}[1.04\omega/(4-\omega^2)]}}$$

Overall transfer function,

$$H = H_1 H_2$$

and

$$H = |H|e^{j\phi}$$

ω	|H|	φ
0.1	0.998	−3.6°
0.2	0.993	−7.0°
0.3	0.983	−11.4°
0.4	0.966	−16.0°
0.5	0.938	−21.5°
0.6	0.890	−28.2°
0.7	0.805	−36.7°
0.8	0.652	−47.2°
0.9	0.403	−54.7°
1.0	0.189	−15.2°
1.1	0.364	+23.7°
1.2	0.540	+18.6°
1.3	0.632	+ 9.7°
1.4	0.662	+ 1.2°
1.5	0.648	− 6.8°
1.6	0.595	−14.1°
1.7	0.507	−20.5°
1.8	0.388	−23.8°
1.9	0.258	−17.1°
2.0	0.189	+15.2°
2.1	0.257	+46.7°
2.2	0.376	+54.4°
2.3	0.488	+53.7°
2.4	0.580	+50.7°
2.5	0.652	+47.2°
3.0	0.839	+33.7°
3.5	0.907	+26.1°
4.0	0.938	+21.5°

Courtesy Dr. Eugene Patronis

30.15.5 Phase Delay and Envelope Delay

Phase distortion and envelope delay distortion are often confused. Phase delay is insertion phase shift divided by frequency, ϕ/ω. Envelope delay is the first derivative of phase with respect to frequency, $d\phi/d\omega$, as shown in Table 30-2. Phase delay distortion and envelope delay vary nonlinearly with frequency. It is possible to have phase delay distortion without envelope delay distortion, but envelope delay distortion is always accompanied by phase delay distortion.

Phase delay is

$$t = \theta/\omega \tag{30-51}$$

where,
t is the delay in seconds,
θ is the relative phase in radians,
ω is the $2\pi f$ rate of phase change in radians per second.

Envelope delay is calculated with the equation

$$ED = d\theta/d\omega \tag{30-52}$$

where,
ED is the envelope delay,

$$ED = d\theta/d\omega \cong \Delta\theta/\Delta\omega$$

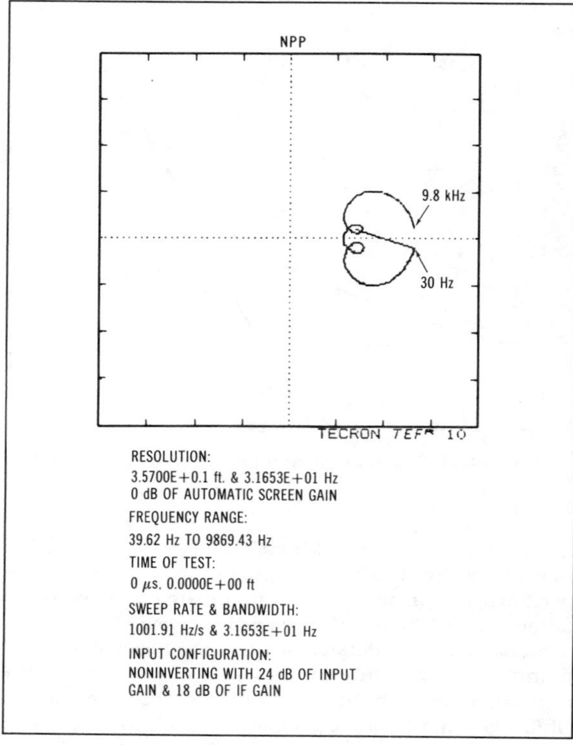

Figure 30-51 Frequencies at which epicycles appear.

30.15.6 The Nyquist Phase Plot (NPP)

The *Nyquist phase plot (NPP)* is a marvelously useful tool whenever excess signal delay is present in a system. An epicycle on a Nyquist phase plot can indicate the presence of a nonminimum phase frequency. The NPP is the tip of the analytic signal traced out on the screen through one sweep of the analyzer. A signal late in time always causes a second complete loop in form. Unfortunately, an epicycle does not always mean that we have a nonminimum phase frequency like the one shown in Table 30-2, but an epicycle always appears when we do.

Frequencies at which epicycles appear as shown in Figs. 30-51, 30-52, and 30-53, can then be examined as energy frequency curve (EFC) data to see if the amplitude requirements necessary to produce an epicycle are present. If not, then the reasonable assumption is that we have a nonminimum-phase frequency to deal with (i.e., a signal delay). If we have both the capability and/or facilities to perform the Laplace transform analysis onto the S plane, then the nonminimum-phase frequency will have a zero in the right half plane. This is important to a practical sound system engineer because it determines the effectiveness of using minimum-phase equalizers with such a transducer.

Phase measurements are the most precise indicators of alignment (i.e., a resolution of 1.0 μs). The availability of an analyzer that allows signal delays up to 400 s (85.61 mi for a medium with a phase velocity of 1130 ft/s) to be compensated for means precise relative acoustic phase measurements can be made.

30.15.7 TEF® Three-Dimensional Plots or Redundant Processing

Here's the tool that even the most expert instrumentation veterans may find sends them to the books for a refresher. At first nothing could seem more obvious than redundant processing and indeed, if the manufacturer of a two-channel FFT has provided us with a preprogrammed locked up set of test parameters, it may be relatively easy to grasp what's left—a severely limited program. That's really what's so different about TEF. A superior set of measurement transforms is provided, but we are provided with the setup latitude to use or misuse as our experience and wisdom dictates. The TEF user is expected to be sufficiently well informed or trainable if he or she has not previously encountered concepts such as Heisenberg's Uncertainty Principle, time bandwidth products, impulse versus swept frequency-modulated chirps, Hilbert transforms versus Fourier transforms, and other similar concepts so that the instrument need not

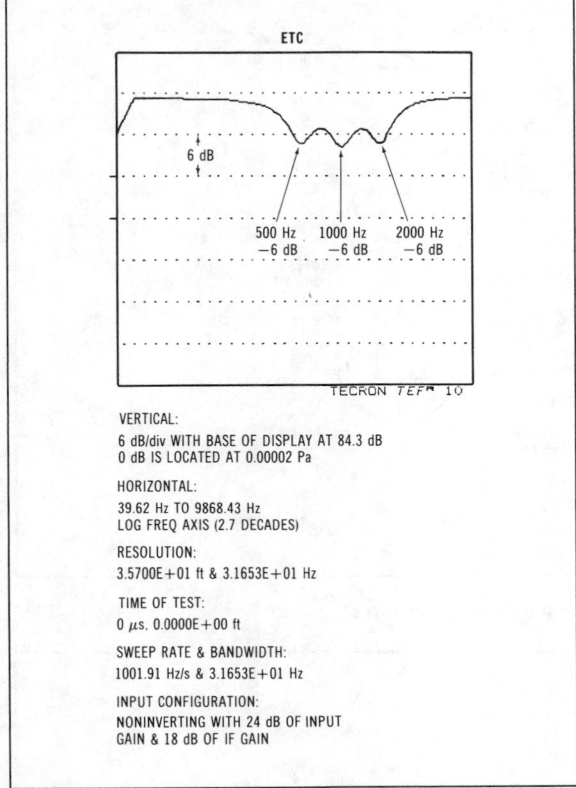

ETC
6 dB
500 Hz
−6 dB
1000 Hz
−6 dB
2000 Hz
−6 dB
TECRON TEF 10
VERTICAL:
6 dB/div WITH BASE OF DISPLAY AT 84.3 dB
0 dB IS LOCATED AT 0.00002 Pa
HORIZONTAL:
39.62 Hz TO 9868.43 Hz
LOG FREQ AXIS (2.7 DECADES)
RESOLUTION:
3.5700E+01 ft & 3.1653E+01 Hz
TIME OF TEST:
0 μs, 0.0000E+00 ft
SWEEP RATE & BANDWIDTH:
1001.91 Hz/s & 3.1653E+01 Hz
INPUT CONFIGURATION:
NONINVERTING WITH 24 dB OF INPUT
GAIN & 18 dB OF IF GAIN

Figure 30-52 The epicycles were caused by these amplitude variations.

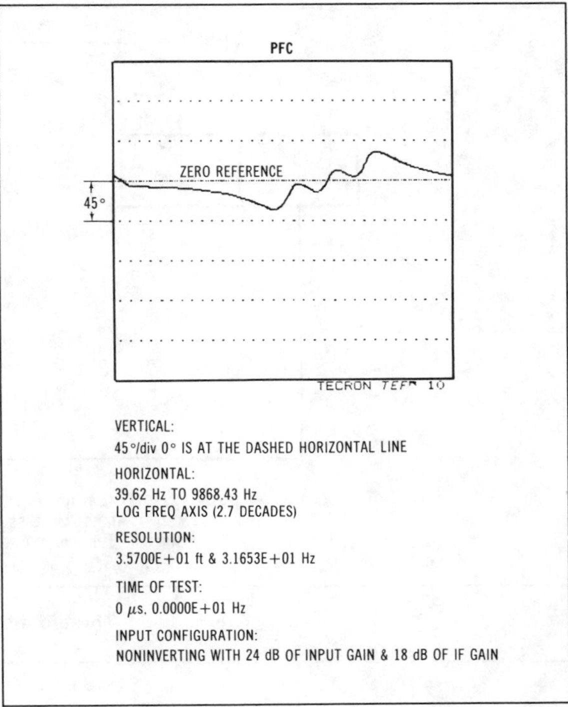

Figure 30-53 Phase response of the epicycles.

be programmed in a restrictive manner to save the operator from himself or herself.

30.15.7.1 Some Not So Obvious Points

If an FFT analyzer is used to evaluate a rapid sinusoidal sweep upward or downward in frequency, it generates in reality two signals. One is the shock impulse at the start and stop of the sweep and the other is the sweep itself. The TEF analyzer avoids this problem by sweeping through zero-to-negative frequency and then back up but at a 90° phase shift in each direction thereby passing through the base band minus the shock excitation.

30.15.7.2 Some Uses of Three-Dimensional Plots

The obvious use the analyzer was intended for is the stepping of each sweep in a signal delay sequence that allows both the steady state and the transient response to be viewed in relative time. What is not immediately apparent to the first-time user is the usefulness of having the effective bandwidth made several times broader than each step taken by the sweeps. This allows a visualization of the flow of the energy from one state to another that, although not rigorously true, is indeed representative of the actual mechanism.

By setting the first of the 31 steps to the same signal delay offset as the last step, we obtain 31 sweeps with no relative time increments. Now, if we place an electroacoustic transducer on a turntable, we can turn it 10° per sweep (step), and the result is a three-dimensional polar plot of that transducer's energy (Figs. 30-54, 30-55, 30-56, 30-57, and 30-58). Fig. 30-58 shows the devastating effect two misaligned loudspeakers have on coverage.

The three-dimensional plot of an impedance can be a fascinating experience, especially if there are distributed parameters (i.e., a long-line telephone circuit). In fact, the three-dimensional plot can be used to monitor any incremental influence measurable by a wave analyzer.

30.16 SUMMARY

The art and science of audio and acoustic measurements is rapidly advancing into a new era of rapid, easy, accurate access to the full transfer function of all the components we use as well as their behavior in systems we build.

MEASURING MICROPHONE
TEF SEND
TEF RECEIVE
MICROPHONE TO LOUDSPEAKER DISTANCE=10 FT
SWEEP #16 "ON AXIS" OR 0°
DIRECTION OF LOUDSPEAKER ROTATION (FRONT VIEW)
J.W. DAVIS TURNTABLE
SWEEP #1 AT 210°
SWEEP #31 AT 150°
SWEEPS ON 3-D PLOTS ARE AT 10° INCREMENTS
"FRONT" VIEW STARTS AT 210° AND ENDS AT 150°
"REAR" VIEW STARTS AT 150° AND COUNTERROTATES TO 210°

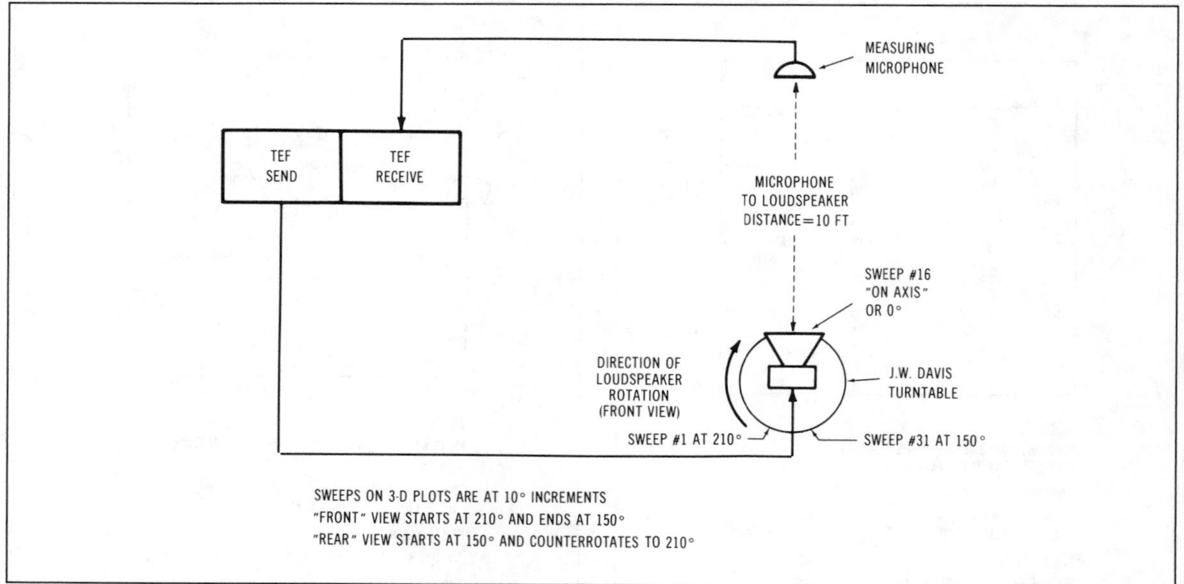

Figure 30-54 Three-dimensional polar response test.

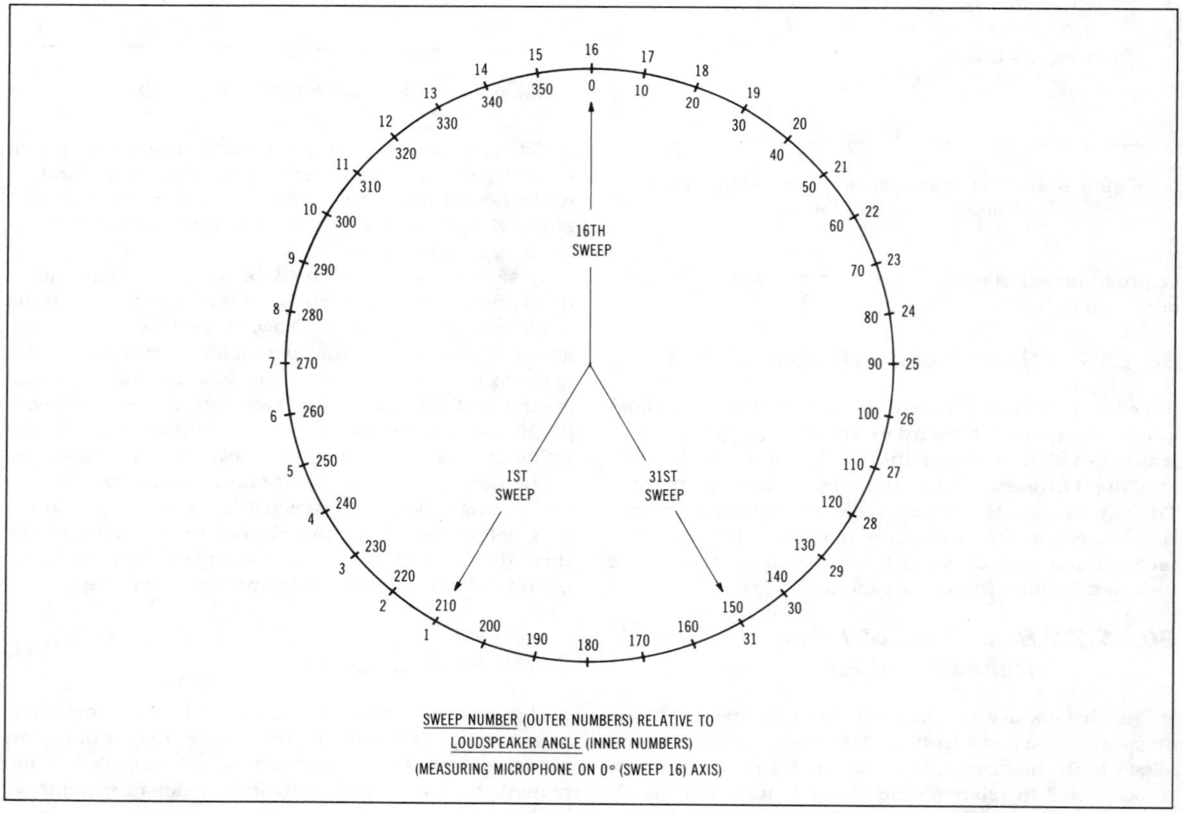

16TH SWEEP
1ST SWEEP
31ST SWEEP
SWEEP NUMBER (OUTER NUMBERS) RELATIVE TO
LOUDSPEAKER ANGLE (INNER NUMBERS)
(MEASURING MICROPHONE ON 0° (SWEEP 16) AXIS)

Figure 30-55 Rotation of transducer to measure polar response.

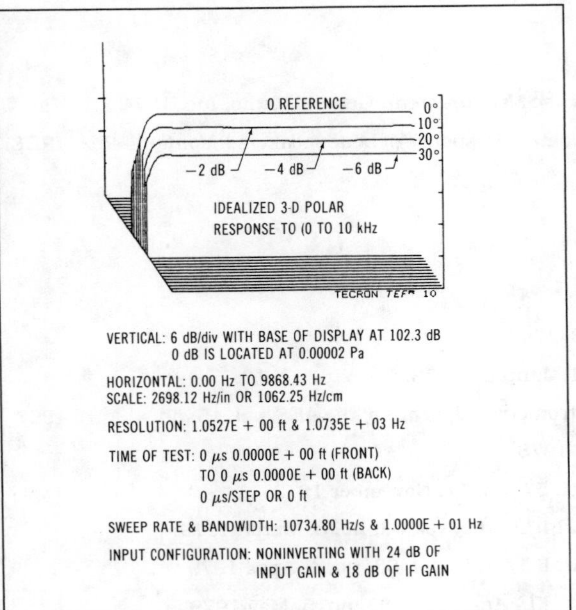

Figure 30-56 Idealized three-dimensional polar response. *(Courtesy Techron)*

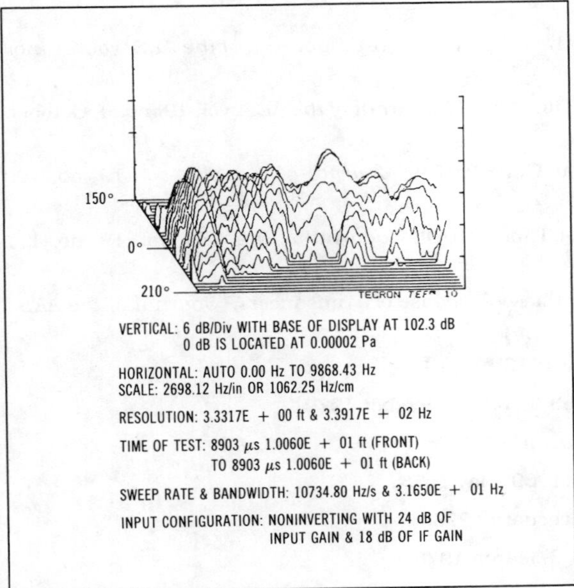

Figure 30-57 Response of two aligned loudspeakers.

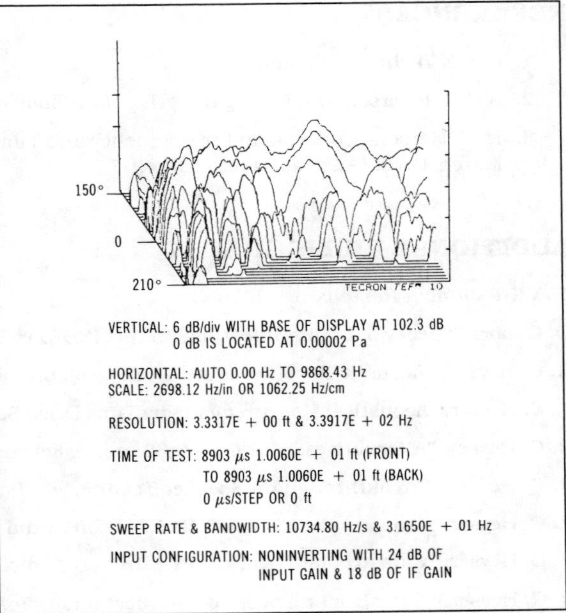

150°
0
210°
TECRON TEF™ 10
VERTICAL: 6 dB/div WITH BASE OF DISPLAY AT 102.3 dB
0 dB IS LOCATED AT 0.00002 Pa
HORIZONTAL: AUTO 0.00 Hz TO 9868.43 Hz
SCALE: 2698.12 Hz/in OR 1062.25 Hz/cm
RESOLUTION: 3.3317E + 00 ft & 3.3917E + 02 Hz
TIME OF TEST: 8903 μs 1.0060E + 01 ft (FRONT)
TO 8903 μs 1.0060E + 01 ft (BACK)
0 μs/STEP OR 0 ft
SWEEP RATE & BANDWIDTH: 10734.80 Hz/s & 3.1650E + 01 Hz
INPUT CONFIGURATION: NONINVERTING WITH 24 dB OF
INPUT GAIN & 18 dB OF IF GAIN

Figure 30-58 Three-dimensional polar response of two misaligned loudspeakers. Note that smooth coverage has been destroyed. *(Courtesy Techron)*

REFERENCES

1. *B & K Technical Review*, no. 1, 1983.
2. A.P.G. Peterson and E. E. Gross, Jr., *Handbook of Noise Measurement*, General Radio, Inc. 1974
3. R. C. Heyser, "Concepts in the Frequency and Time Domain Response of Loudspeakers," *Monitor—Proc. IREE*, March 1976. (Australian publication)

ADDITIONAL BIBLIOGRAPHY

B & K Technical Review, no. 2, 1983.

D. Gabor, "Theory of Communications," *Proc. IEEE*, vol. 93, 1946.

R. C. Heyser, "Acoustic Rosetta Stone," *Audio*, vol. 63, no. 1, January 1979.

R. C. Heyser, "Acoustical Measurements by Time Delay Spectrometry," *Journal of the AES*, vol. 15, no. 4, April 1967.

R. C. Heyser, "Alternatives," *Audio*, vol. 62, no. 2, February 1978.

R. C. Heyser, "Breakthrough on Speaker Testing," *Audio*, vol. 57, no. 11, November 1973.

R. C. Heyser, "Catastrophe Theory & Its Effect on Audio, Part I," *Audio*, vol. 63, no. 3, March 1979.

R. C. Heyser, "Catastrophe Theory & Its Effect on Audio, Part II," *Audio*, vol. 63, no. 4, April 1979.

R. C. Heyser, "Catastrophe Theory & Its Effect on Audio, Part III," *Audio*, vol. 63, no. 5, May 1979.

R. C. Heyser, "The Concept of Distortion," *Synergetic-Audio-Concepts Newsletter*, vol. 7, no. 4, Summer 1980.

R. C. Heyser, "Crescendo Test," *Audio*, vol. 60, no. 5, May 1976.

R. C. Heyser, "The Delay Plane, Objective Analysis of Subjective Properties, Part I," *Journal of the AES*, vol. 21, no. 9, November 1973.

R. C. Heyser, "The Delay Plane, Objective Analysis of Subjective Properties, Part II," *Journal of the AES*, vol. 21, no. 10, December 1973.

R. C. Heyser, "Determination of Loudspeaker Signal Arrival Time, Part I," *Journal of the AES*, vol. 19, no. 9, October 1971.

R. C. Heyser, "Determination of Loudspeaker Signal Arrival Time, Part II," *Journal of the AES*, vol. 19, no. 10, November 1971.

R. C. Heyser, "Determination of Loudspeaker Signal Arrival Time, Part III," *Journal of the AES*, vol. 19, no. 11, December 1971.

R. C. Heyser, "Determining the Acoustic Position for Proper Phase Response of Transducers," *Journal of the AES*, vol. 32, no. 1/2, January/February 1984.

R. C. Heyser, "Energy-Time Test," *Audio*, vol. 60, no. 4, June 1976.

R. C. Heyser, "The Forum-Polarity Convention," *Audio*, vol. 63, no. 9, September 1979.

R. C. Heyser, "Fuzzy Alternatives," *Journal of the AES*, vol. 26, no. 3, March 1978.

R. C. Heyser, "Geometry of Sound Perception," AES preprint 1009, May 1975.

R. C. Heyser, "Harmonic Distortion," *Audio*, vol. 60, no. 2, February 1976.

R. C. Heyser, "Hearing vs. Measurement," *Audio*, vol. 62, no. 3, March 1978.

R. C. Heyser, "Holomorph Recording," AES preprint 1115, March 1976.

R. C. Heyser, "Imprecise Descriptions," AES preprint, May 1978.

R. C. Heyser, "Loudspeaker Phase & Time Delay Distortion, Part I," *Journal of the AES*, vol. 17, no. 1, January 1969.

R. C. Heyser, "Loudspeaker Phase & Time Delay Distortion, Part II," *Journal of the AES*, vol. 17, no. 2, April 1969.

R. C. Heyser, "IM Distortion in Speaker Systems," *Audio*, vol. 60, no. 3, March 1976.

R. C. Heyser, "A Rosetta Stone for Audio?" *Journal of the AES*, vol. 22, no. 4, May 1974.

R. C. Heyser, "Some New Audio Measurements," AES preprint 1008, May 1975.

R. C. Heyser, "Some Useful Graphic Relationships," *Journal of the AES*, vol. 23, no. 7, September 1976.

R. C. Heyser, "Speaker Tests—Impedance," *Audio*, vol. 58, no. 10, October 1974.

R. C. Heyser, "Speaker Tests—Phase Response," *Audio*, vol. 58, no. 12, December 1974.

R. C. Heyser, "Speaker Tests—Polar Response," *Audio*, vol. 59, no. 5, May 1975.

R. C. Heyser, "Speaker Tests—Room Test," *Audio*, vol. 59, no. 1, January 1975.

R. C. Heyser, "Square Wave Testing," *Synergetic-Audio-Concepts Newsletter*, 1976.

R. C. Heyser, "Time & Frequency in Loudspeaker Measurements," *Audio*, vol. 61, no. 7, July 1977.

R. C. Heyser, "A View Through Different Windows," *Audio*, vol. 63, no. 2, February 1979.

G. R. Stanley, "The Microprocessor Based TEF Analyzer," AES preprint 1946, October 1982.

G. R. Stanley, "TDS Computing," *Audio*, vol. 67, no. 11, November 1983.

CHAPTER **31**

Fundamentals and Units of Measurement

by Glen Ballou

31.1 UNITS OF MEASUREMENT[1, 2, 3]

Measurement is the method used to define many things in life. A *dimension* is any measurable extent such as length, thickness or weight. A *measurement system* is any group of related unit names that state the quantity of properties for the items we see, taste, hear, smell, or touch.

A *unit of measurement* is the size of a quantity in the terms that the quantity is measured or expressed, for instance, inches, miles, centimeters, and meters.

The *laws of physics*, which include sound, are defined through dimensional formulas that are defined as an asymbolic representation of the definition of a physical quantity obtained from its units of measurements of mass, length, and time. For instance, area = L × W, and velocity = L/T. A physical quantity is specified by a number and a unit, for instance: 12 in. or 5 m.

31.1.1 SI System[3]

The *SI system (Systeme International d'Unites)* is the accepted international system of units. It is used worldwide with the exception of the U.S. and Great Britain, which are slowly converting to it.

The SI system has the following advantages:

- It is internationally accepted.
- All values, except time, are decimal multiples or submultiples of the basic unit.
- It is easy to use.
- It is easy to teach.
- It improves international trade and understanding.

When using the U.S. or SI system, exponents or symbol prefixes are commonly used. Table 31-1 is a chart of the accepted name of the number, its exponential form, symbol, and prefix name.

31.1.2 Fundamental Quantities

There are seven fundamental quantities in physics: *length, mass, time, intensity of electric current, temperature, luminous intensity*, and *molecular substance*. Two supplementary quantities are *plane angle* and *solid angle*.

31.1.3 Derived Quantities

Derived quantities are those defined in terms of the seven fundamental quantities, for instance, speed = length/time. Here are 16 derived quantities with names of their own: *energy* (work, quantity of heat), *force, pressure, power, electric charge, electric potential difference* (voltage), *electric resistance, electric conductance, electric capacitance, electric inductance, frequency, magnetic flux, magnetic flux density, luminous flux, illuminance*, and *customary temperature*. Here are 13 additional derived quantities that carry the units of the original units that are combined. They are *area, volume, density, velocity, acceleration, angular velocity, angular acceleration, kinematic viscosity, dynamic viscosity, electric field strength, magnetomotive force, magnetic field strength*, and *luminance*.

31.1.4 Definitions of the Quantities

The quantities will be defined in SI units, and their U.S. customary unit equivalent values will also be given.

31.1.4.1 Length (l)

Length is the measure of how long something is from end to end.

The *meter* (abbreviated m) is the SI unit of length. The meter is the 1 650 763.73 wavelengths, in vacuum, of the radiation corresponding to the unperturbed transition between energy level 2P10 and $5d_5$ of the krypton 86 atom. The result is an orange-red line with a wavelength of $6\ 057.802 \times 10^{-10}$ m. The meter is equivalent to 39.370 079 in.

31.1.4.2 Mass (M)

Mass is a measure of the inertia of a particle. The mass of a body is defined by the equation

$$M = (A_s/a)M_s$$

where,

A_s is the acceleration of the standard mass M_s,
a is the acceleration of the unknown mass M when the two bodies interact.

The *kilogram (kg)* is the unit of mass. Small masses may be described in *grams (g)* or *milligrams (mg)* and large masses in *tonnes (t)*,

where,

$$1 \text{ tonne} = 10^3 \text{ kg}$$

The present international definition of the kilogram is the mass of a special cylinder of platinum iridium alloy maintained at the International Bureau of Weights & Measures, Sevrs, France. One kilogram is equal to 2.204 622 6 avoirdupois pounds (lb). A liter of pure water at standard temperature and pressure has a mass of 1 kg ± one part in 10^4.

Mass of a body is often revealed by its weight, which the gravitational attraction of the earth gives to that body.

Table 31-1. Multiple and Submultiple Prefixes

Name of Number	Exponential Form
Googol	1.0×10^{100}
Vigintillion	1.0×10^{63}
Novemdecillion	1.0×10^{60}
Octodecillion	1.0×10^{57}
Septendecillion	1.0×10^{54}
Sexdecillion	1.0×10^{51}
Quindecillion	1.0×10^{48}
Quattuordecillion	1.0×10^{45}
Tredecillion	1.0×10^{42}
Duodecillion	1.0×10^{39}
Undecillion	1.0×10^{36}
Decillion	1.0×10^{33}
Nonillion	1.0×10^{30}
Octillion	1.0×10^{27}
Septillion	1.0×10^{24}
Sextillion	1.0×10^{21}

Name of Number	Number	Exponential Form	Symbol	Prefix
Quintillion	1,000,000,000,000,000,000.	1.0×10^{18}	E	Exa-
Quadrillion	1,000,000,000,000,000.	1.0×10^{15}	P	Peta-
Trillion	1,000,000,000,000.	1.0×10^{12}	T	Tera-
Billion	1,000,000,000.	1.0×10^{9}	G	Giga-
Million	1,000,000.	1.0×10^{6}	M	Mega-
Thousand	1,000.	1.0×10^{3}	k	Kilo-
Hundred	100.	1.0×10^{2}	h	Hecto-
Ten	10.	1.0×10^{1}	da	Deka-
Unit	1.	1.0×10^{0}	—	——
Tenth	0.1	1.0×10^{-1}	d	deci-
Hundredth	0.01	1.0×10^{-2}	c	centi-
Thousandth	0.001	1.0×10^{-3}	m	milli-
Millionth	0.000 001	1.0×10^{-6}	μ	micro-
Billionth	0.000 000 001	1.0×10^{-9}	n	nano-
Trillionth	0.000 000 000 001	1.0×10^{-12}	p	pico-
Quadrillionth	0.000 000 000 000 001	1.0×10^{-15}	f	femto-
Quintillionth	0.000 000 000 000 000 001	1.0×10^{-18}	a	atto-

If a mass is weighed on the moon, its mass would be the same as on earth, but its weight would be less due to the small amount of gravity

$$M = W/g$$

where,

W is the weight,
g is the acceleration due to gravity.

31.1.4.3 Time (t)

Time is the period between two events or that time during which something exists, happens, etc.

The *second (s)* is the unit of time. Time is the one dimension that does not have powers of ten multipliers in the SI system. Short periods of time can be described in milliseconds (ms) and microseconds (μs). Long periods of time are expressed in minutes (1 min = 60 s) and hours (1 hr = 3600 s). Longer periods of time are still the day, week, month, and year. The present international definition of the second is the time duration of 9 192 631 770 periods of the radiation of the transition between the two hyperfine levels of the ground state of the atom of Cs 133. It is also defined as 1/86 400 of the mean solar day.

31.1.4.4 Current (I)

Current is the rate of flow of electrons.

The *ampere (A)* is the unit of current. Small currents are measured in milliamperes (mA) and microamperes

(μA), and large currents are in kiloamperes (kA). The international definition of the ampere is the constant current that, if maintained in two straight parallel conductors of infinite length and negligible cross-sectional area and placed exactly 1 m apart in a vacuum, will produce between them a force of 2×10^{-7} N/m^2 length of wire.

A simple definition of one ampere of current is the intensity of electron flow through a 1-Ω resistance under a pressure of 1 V of potential difference.

31.1.4.5 Temperature (T)

Temperature is the degree of hotness or coldness of anything.

The *kelvin (K)* is the unit of temperature. The kelvin is 1/273.16 of the thermodynamic temperature of the triple point of pure water.

Ordinary temperature measurements are made with the Celsius scale on which water freezes at 0°C and boils at 100°C. A change of 1° Celsius is equal to a change of 1 kelvin, therefore, 0°C = 273.15 K; 0°C = 32°F.

31.1.4.6 Luminous Intensity (I_L)

The *luminous flux* emitted per unit solid angle by a point source in a given direction.

The *candela (cd)* is the unit of *luminous intensity*. One candela will produce a luminous flux of 1 lumen within a solid angle of 1 steradian.

The international definition of the candela is the luminous intensity, perpendicular to the surface, of 1/600 000 m^2 of a blackbody at the temperature of freezing platinum under a pressure of 101 325 N/m^2 (pascals).

31.1.4.7 Molecular Substance (n)

Molecular substance is the amount of substance of a system that contains as many elementary entities as there are atoms in 0.012 kg of carbon 12.

The *mole* is the unit of molecular substance. One mole of any substance is the gram molecular weight of the material. For example, 1 mole of water (H_2O) weighs 18.016 g

$$H_2 = 2\,\text{atoms} \times 1.008\,\text{atomic weight}$$

$$O = 1\,\text{atom} \times 16\,\text{atomic weight}$$

$$H_2O = 18.016\,\text{g}$$

31.1.4.8 Plane Angle (α)

The *plane angle* is formed between two straight lines or surfaces that meet.

The *radian* (*rad* or *r*) is the unit of plane angles. One radian is the angle formed between two radii of a circle and subtended by an arc whose length is equal to the radius. There are 2π radians in 360°.

Ordinary measurements are still made in degrees. The degree can be divided into minutes and seconds or into tenths and hundredths of a degree. For small angles, the latter is most useful.

31.1.4.9 Solid Angle (ω)

A *solid angle* subtends three dimensions. The solid angle is measured by the area, subtended (by projection) on a sphere of unit radius by the ratio of the area A, intercepted on a sphere of radius r to the square of the radius (A/r^2).

The *steradian (sr)* is the unit of solid angle. The steradian is the solid angle at the center of a sphere that subtends an area on the spherical surface, which is equal to that of a square whose sides are equal to the radius of the sphere.

31.1.4.10 Energy (E)

Energy is the property of a system that is a measure of its ability to do work. There are two main forms of energy, potential energy and kinetic energy.

1. *Potential Energy* (U) is the energy possessed by a body or system by virtue of position and is equal to the work done in changing the system from some standard configuration to its present state. For example, a mass M placed at a height h above a datum level in a gravitational field with an acceleration of free fall (g), has a potential energy given by U = Mgh. This potential energy is converted into kinetic energy when the body falls between the levels.
2. *Kinetic Energy* (T) is the energy possessed by virtue of motion and is equal to the work that would be required to bring the body to rest. A body undergoing translational motion with velocity, v, has a kinetic energy given by

$$T = 0.5\,Mv^2$$

where,
M is the mass of the body.

For a body undergoing rotational motion

$$T = 0.5I\omega^2$$

where,
I is the moment of inertia of the body about its axis of rotation,
ω is the angular velocity.

The *joule (J)* is the unit of energy. The mechanical definition is the work done when the force of 1 newton is applied for a distance of 1 meter in the direction of its application or 1 N·m. The electrical unit of energy is the *kilowatthour (kWh)*, which is equal to 3.6×10^6 J.

In physics, the unit of energy is the *electronvolt (eV)*, which is equal to $(1.602\ 10 \pm 0.000\ 07) \times 10^{-19}$ J. A joule is also equal to 0.737 562 ft·lb.

31.1.4.11 Force (F)

Force is any action that changes, or tends to change, a body's state of rest or uniform motion in a straight line.

The *newton (N)* is the unit of force and is that force which, when applied to a body having a mass of 1 kg, gives it an acceleration of 1 m/s^2. One newton equals 1 J/m, 1 kg(m)/s^2, 10^5 dynes, and 0.224 809 lb force.

31.1.4.12 Pressure (p)

Pressure is the force (in a fluid) exerted per unit area on an infinitesimal plane situated at the point. In a fluid at rest, the pressure at any point is the same in all directions. A *fluid* is any material substance that in static equilibrium cannot exert tangential force across a surface but can exert only pressure. Liquids and gases are fluids.

The *pascal (Pa)* is the unit of pressure. The pascal is equal to the newton per square meter (N/m^2).

$$\begin{aligned} 1\ \text{Pa} &= 10^{-5}\ \text{bars} \\ &= 1.450\ 38 \times 10^{-4}\ \text{lb/in.}^2 \end{aligned}$$

31.1.4.13 Power (W)

Power is the rate at which energy is expended or work is done.

The *watt (W)* is the unit of power and is the power that generates energy at the rate of 1 J/s.

$$\begin{aligned} 1\ \text{W} &= 1\ \text{J/s} \\ &= 3.414\ 42\ \text{Btu/h} \\ &= 44.253\ 7\ \text{ft·lb/min} \\ &= 0.001\ 341\ 02\ \text{hp} \end{aligned}$$

31.1.4.14 Electric Charge (Q)

Electric charge is the quantity of electricity or electrons that flow past a point in a period of time.

The *coulomb (C)* is the unit of electric charge and is the quantity of electricity moved in 1 second by a current of 1 ampere. The coulomb is also defined as $6.241\ 96 \times 10^{18}$ electronic charges.

31.1.4.15 Electric Potential Difference (V)

Often called electromotive force (emf) and voltage (V), *electric potential difference* is the line integral of the electric field strength between two points.

The *volt (V)* is the unit of electric potential. The volt is the potential difference that will cause a current flow of 1 A between two points in a circuit when the power dissipated between those two points is 1 W.

A simpler definition would be to say a potential difference of 1 V will drive a current of 1 A through a resistance of 1 Ω.

$$\begin{aligned} \text{Volt} &= \text{W/A} \\ &= \text{J/A(s)} \\ &= \text{kg(m}^2\text{)/s}^3\text{A} \\ &= \text{A}(\Omega) \end{aligned}$$

31.1.4.16 Electric Resistance (R)

Electric resistance is the property of conductors that, depending on their dimensions, material, and temperature, determines the current produced by a given difference of potential. It is also that property of a substance that impedes current and results in the dissipation of power in the form of heat.

The *ohm (Ω)* is the unit of resistance and is the resistance that will limit the current flow to 1 A when a potential difference of 1 V is applied to it.

$$\begin{aligned} \text{R} &= \text{V/A} \\ &= \text{kg(m}^2\text{)/s}^3\text{A}^2 \end{aligned}$$

31.1.4.17 Electric Conductance (G)

Electric conductance is the reciprocal of resistance.

The *siemens (S)* is the unit of electric conductance. A passive device that has a conductance of 1 S will allow a current flow of 1 A when 1 V potential is applied to it:

$$\begin{aligned} \text{S} &= 1/\Omega \\ &= \text{A/V} \end{aligned}$$

31.1.4.18 Electric Capacitance (C)

Electric capacitance is the property of an isolated conductor or set of conductors and insulators to store electric charge.

The *farad (F)* is the unit of electric capacitance and is defined as the capacitance that exhibits a potential difference of 1 V when it holds a charge of 1 C:

$$\begin{aligned} \text{F} &= \text{C/V} \\ &= \text{A(S)/V} \end{aligned}$$

31.1.4.19 Electric Inductance (L)

Electric inductance is the property that opposes any change in the existing current. Inductance is only present when the current is changing.

The *henry (H)* is the unit of inductance and is the inductance of a circuit in which an electromotive force of 1 V is developed by a current change of 1 A/s:

$$\text{H} = \text{V(s)/A}$$

31.1.4.20 Frequency (f)

Frequency is the number of recurrences of a periodic phenomenon in a unit of time.

The *hertz (Hz)* is the unit of frequency and is equal to one cycle per second, 1 Hz = 1 cps. Frequency is often measured in hertz (Hz), kilohertz (kHz), and megahertz (MHz).

31.1.4.21 Sound Intensity (W/m^2)

The rate of flow of sound energy through a unit area normal to the direction of flow. For a sinusoidally varying sound wave the *intensity I* is related to the sound pressure p and the density β of the medium by

$$I = p^2/\beta c$$

where,

c is the velocity of sound.

The *watt per square meter (W/m^2)* is the unit of sound intensity.

31.1.4.22 Magnetic Flux (Φ)

Magnetic flux is a measure of the total size of a magnetic field. The *weber (Wb)* is the unit of magnetic flux, and is the amount of flux that produces an electromotive force of 1 V in a one-turn conductor as it reduces uniformly to zero in 1 s:

$$\begin{aligned} Wb &= V(s) \\ &= 10^8 \text{ lines of flux} \\ &= kg(m^2)/s^2A \end{aligned}$$

31.1.4.23 Magnetic Flux Density (B)

The *magnetic flux density* is the flux passing through the unit area of a magnetic field in the direction at right angles to the magnetic force. The vector product of the magnetic flux density and the current in a conductor gives the force per unit length of the conductor.

The *tesla (T)* is the unit of magnetic flux density and is defined as a density of 1 Wb/m^2:

$$\begin{aligned} T &= Wb/m^2 \\ &= V(s)/m^2 \\ &= kg/s^2(A) \end{aligned}$$

31.1.4.24 Luminous Flux (Φ_v)

The rate of flow of radiant energy is evaluated by the luminous sensation that it produces.

The *lumen (lm)* is the unit of luminous flux, which is the amount of luminous flux emitted by a uniform point source whose intensity is one candela into a solid angle of 1 steradian.

$$\begin{aligned} lm &= cd(sr/m^2) \\ &= 0.079\,577\,4 \text{ candlepower} \end{aligned}$$

31.1.4.25 Luminous Flux Density (E_v)

The *luminous flux density* is the luminous flux incident on a given surface per unit area. It is sometimes called illumination or intensity of illumination. At any point on a surface, the illumination is given by

$$E_v = d\Phi_v/dA$$

The *lux (lx)* is the unit of luminous flux density, which is the density of radiant flux of $1m/m^2$,

$$\begin{aligned} lx &= lm/m^2 \\ &= cd(sr/m^2) \\ &= 0.092\,903\,0 \text{ fc} \end{aligned}$$

31.1.4.26 Displacement

Displacement is a change in position or the distance moved by a given particle of a system from its position of rest, when acted upon by a disturbing force.

31.1.4.27 Speed/Velocity

Speed is the rate of increase of distance traveled by a body. Average speed is found by the equation

$$S = l/t$$

where,

S is the speed,
l is the length or distance,
t is the time to travel.

Speed is a scalar quantity because it is not referenced to direction. Instantaneous speed = dl/dt. *Velocity* is the rate of increase of distance transversed by a body in a particular direction. Velocity is a vector quantity as both speed and direction are indicated. The l/t can often be the same for the velocity and speed of an object; however, when speed is given, the direction of movement is not known. If a body describes a circular path and each successive equal distances along the path are described in equal times, the speed would be constant, but the velocity would constantly change due to the change in direction.

31.1.4.28 Weight

Weight is the force exerted on a mass by the gravitation pull of the planet, star, moon, etc., that the mass is near. The weight experienced on earth is due to the earth's gravitational pull, which is 9.806 65 m/s^2, and causes an object to accelerate toward earth at a rate of 9.806 65 m/s^2 or 32 ft/s.

The weight of a mass M is M(g). If M is in kg and g in

m/s^2, the weight would be in newtons (N). Weight in the English system is in pounds (lb).

31.1.4.29 Acceleration

Acceleration is the rate of change in velocity or the rate of increase or decrease in velocity with time. Acceleration is expressed in meters per second squared (m/s^2).

31.1.4.30 Amplitude

Amplitude is the magnitude of variation in a changing quantity from its zero value. Amplitude should always be modified with adjectives such as peak, rms, maximum, instantaneous, etc.

31.1.4.31 Wavelength (λ)

In a periodic wave, the distance between two points of the corresponding phase of two consecutive cycles is the *wavelength*. Wavelength is related to the velocity of propagation (c) and frequency (f) by the equation $\lambda = c/f$. The wavelength of a wave traveling in air at sea level and standard temperature and pressure (STP) is

$$\lambda = (331.4 \text{ m/s})/f$$

or

$$\lambda = (1087.42 \text{ ft/s})/f$$

For instance, the length of a 1000-Hz wave would be 0.33 m or 1.09 ft.

31.1.4.32 Phase

Phase is the fraction of the whole period that has elapsed, measured from a fixed datum. A sinusoidal quantity may be expressed as a rotating vector 0A. When rotated a full 360°, it represents a sine wave. At any position around the circle, 0X is equal in length but said to be X° out of phase with 0A.

It may also be stated that the phase difference between 0A and 0X is α. When particles in periodic motion due to the passage of a wave are moving in the same direction with the same relative displacement, they are said to be in phase. Particles in a wavefront are in the same phase of vibration when the distance between consecutive wavefronts is equal to the wavelength. The phase difference of two particles at distances X_1 and X_2 is

$$\alpha = 2\pi (X_2 - X_1)/\lambda$$

Periodic waves, having the same frequency and waveform, are said to be in phase if they reach corresponding amplitudes simultaneously.

31.1.4.33 Phase Angle

The angle between two vectors representing two periodic functions that have the same frequency is the *phase angle*. Phase angle can also be considered the difference, in degrees, between corresponding stages of the progress of two cycle operations.

31.1.4.34 Phase Difference (ϕ)

Phase difference is the difference in electrical degrees or time, between two waves that have the same frequency and are referenced to the same point in time.

31.1.4.35 Phase Shift

Any change that occurs in the phase of one quantity or in the phase difference between two or more quantities is the *phase shift*.

31.1.4.36 Phase Velocity

The *phase velocity* is when a point of constant phase is propagated in a progressive sinusoidal wave.

31.2 TEMPERATURE

Temperature is the measure of the amount of coldness or hotness. Temperature can be referenced to °C, degrees Celsius; °F, degrees Fahrenheit; K, kelvin; or °R, Rankine. In defining the common temperature scales, two conveniently reproducible temperatures called fixed points are used:

The lower fixed point (the ice point) is the temperature of a mixture of pure ice and water exposed to the air at standard atmospheric pressure.

The upper fixed point (the steam point) is the temperature of steam from pure water boiling at standard atmospheric pressure.

In the Celsius scale, named after Anders Celsius (1701–1744) and originally called centigrade, the fixed points are 0°C and 100°C. This scale is used in the SI system.

The English or Fahrenheit scale, named after Gabriel Daniel Fahrenheit in 1714, has the fixed points at 32°F and 212°F.

To interchange between °C and °F, use the following equations:

$$°C = 5/9 \times °F - 32$$
$$°F = 9/5 \times °C + 32$$

The absolute temperature scale operates from absolute zero of temperature. Absolute zero is the point that a body cannot be further cooled because all the available thermal energy is extracted.

Absolute zero is 0 kelvin (0 K) or 0 degrees Rankine (0°R). The kelvin scale, named after Lord Kelvin (1850), is used in the SI System and is related to °C

$$0°C = 273.15\,K$$

The Rankine scale is related to the Fahrenheit system

$$32°F = 459.67°R$$

The velocity of sound is affected by temperature. The approximate formula is

$$C = 331.4 + 0.607(t)\,m/s \qquad \textit{SI units}$$

where,
t is the temperature in °C

$$C = 1052 + 1.106(t)\,ft/s \qquad \textit{English units}$$

where,
t is the temperature in °F.

31.3 THEVENIN'S THEOREM

Thévenin's theorem is a method used for reducing complicated networks to a simple circuit consisting of a voltage source and a series impedance. The theorem is applicable to both ac and dc circuits under steady-state conditions.

The theorem states, the current in a terminating impedance connected to any network is the same as if the network were replaced by a generator with a voltage equal to the open-circuit voltage of the network, and whose impedance is the impedance seen by the termination looking back into the network. All generators in the network are replaced with impedance equal to the internal impedances of the generators.

31.4 KIRCHHOFF'S LAWS

The laws of Kirchhoff can be used for both dc and ac circuits. When used in ac analysis, phase must also be taken into consideration.

31.4.1 Kirchhoff's Voltage Law (KVL)

Kirchhoff's voltage law states that the sum of the branch voltages for any closed loop is zero at any time. Stated another way, for any closed loop, the sum of the voltage drops equals the sum of the voltage rises at any time.

In the laws of Kirchhoff, we are working with individual electric circuit elements connected according to some wiring plan or schematic. In any closed loop, the voltage drops must be equal to the voltage rises. For instance, in the dc circuit of Fig. 31-1, V_1 is the voltage source or rise such as a battery and V_2, V_3, V_4, and V_5 are voltage drops (possibly across resistors) so

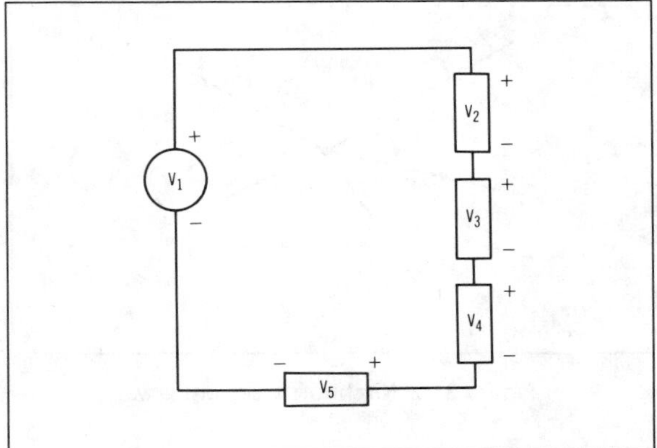

Figure 31-1 Kirchhoff's voltage law.

$$V_1 = V_2 + V_3 + V_4 + V_5$$

or,

$$V_1 - V_2 - V_3 - V_4 - V_5 = 0$$

In an ac circuit, phase must be taken into consideration, therefore, the voltage would be

$$V_1e^{j\omega t} - V_2e^{j\omega t} - V_3e^{j\omega t} - V_4e^{j\omega t} - V_5e^{j\omega t} = 0$$

where,
$e^{j\omega t}$ is cos ω t + *j*sin ωt or Euler's identity.

31.4.2 Kirchhoff's Current Law (KCL)

Kirchhoff's current law states that the sum of the branch currents leaving any node must equal the sum of the branch currents entering that node at any time.

Stated another way, the sum of all branch currents incident at any node is zero at any time.

In Fig. 31-2 the connection on node current in a dc circuit is equal to 0 and is equal to the sum of currents I_1, I_2, I_3, I_4, and I_5 or

$$I_1 = I_2 + I_3 + I_4 + I_5$$

or

$$I_1 - I_2 - I_3 - I_4 - I_5 = 0$$

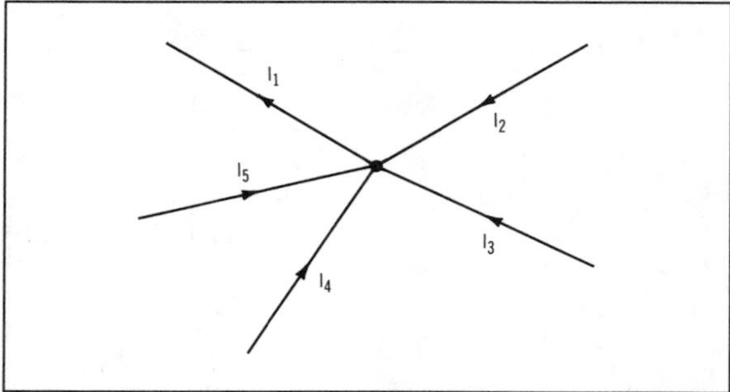

Figure 31-2 Kirchhoff's current law.

The current throughout the circuit is also a function of the current from the power source (V_1) and the current through all the branch circuits.

In an ac circuit, phase must be taken into consideration, therefore, the current would be

$$I_1e^{j\omega t} - I_2e^{j\omega t} - I_3e^{j\omega t} - I_4e^{j\omega t} - I_5e^{j\omega t} = 0$$

where,

$e^{j\omega t}$ is cos ωt + $j$sin ωt or Euler's identity.

31.5 OHM'S LAW

Ohm's law states that the ratio of applied voltage to the resultant current is a constant at every instant and that this ratio is defined to be the resistance.

If the voltage is expressed in volts and the current in amperes, the resistance is expressed in ohms. In equation form it is

$$R = V/I$$

or

$$R = e/i$$

where,

e and i are instantaneous voltage and current.
V and I are constant voltage and current.
R is the resistance.

Through the use of Ohm's law, the relationship between voltage, current, resistance or impedance, and power can be calculated.

Power is the rate of doing work and can be expressed in terms of potential difference between two points (voltage) and the rate of flow required to transform the potential energy from one point to the other (current). If the voltage is in volts or J/C and the current is in amperes or C/s, the product is joules per second or watts:

$$P = VI$$

or

$$J/C \times (C/s) = J/s$$

Fig. 31-3 is a wheel chart that relates current, voltage, resistance or impedance, and power. The power factor (PF) is cos θ, where θ is the phase angle between e and i. A power factor is required in ac circuits.

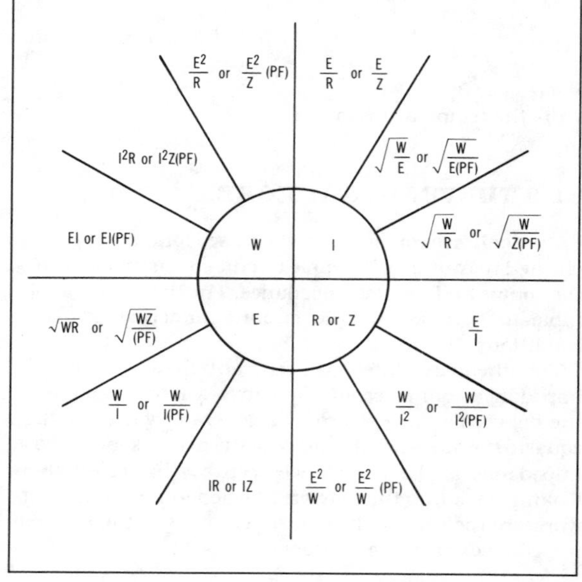

Figure 31-3 Power, voltage, current wheel.

31.6 RESONANT FREQUENCY

When an inductor and capacitor are connected in series or parallel, they form a resonant circuit. The resonant frequency can be determined from the equation:

$$f = 1/2\pi\sqrt{LC}$$
$$= 1/2\pi CX_C$$
$$= X_L/2\pi L$$

The resonant frequency can also be determined through the use of a reactance chart developed by the Bell Tele-

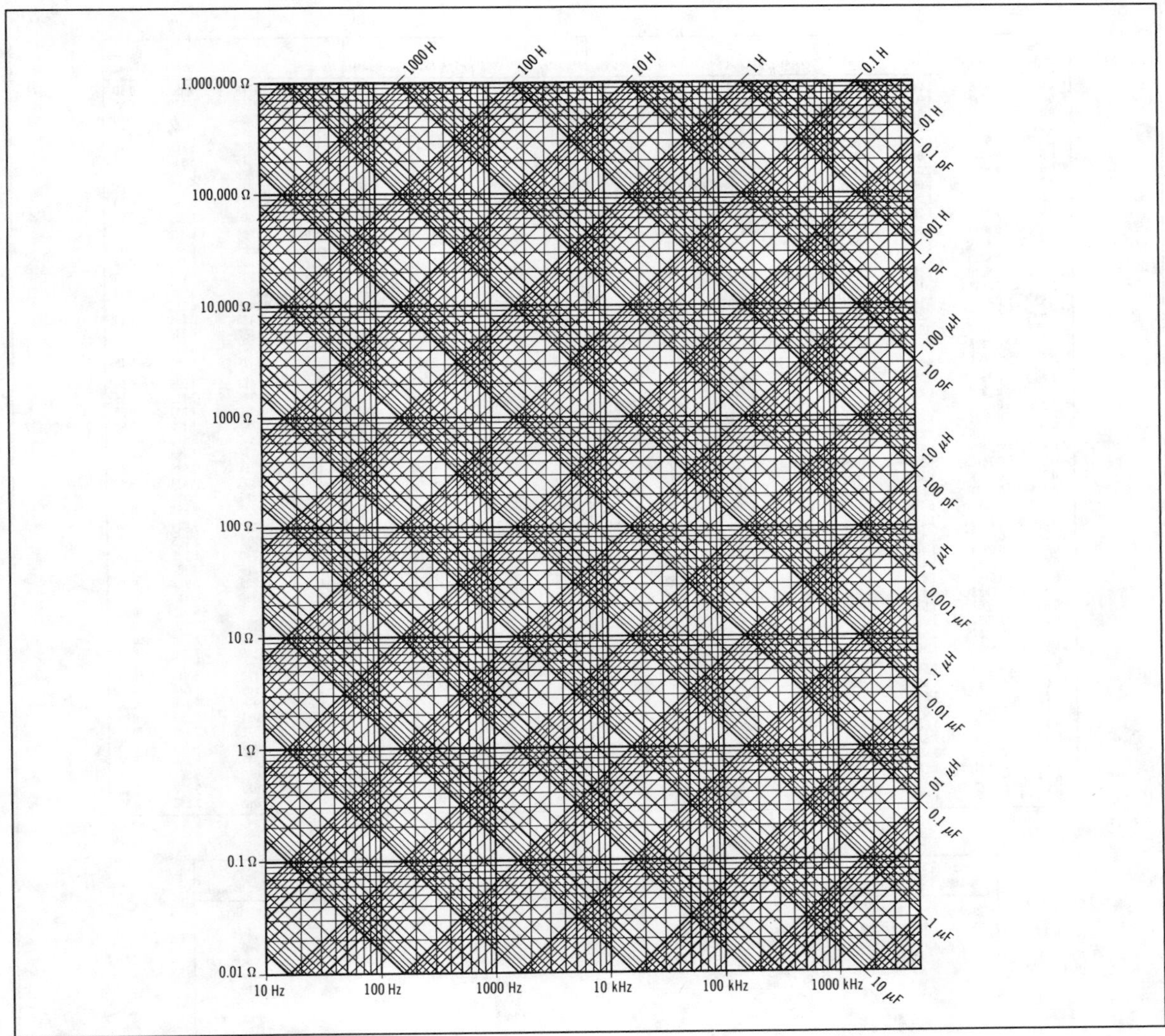

Figure 31-4 Reactance chart. *(Courtesy AT & T Bell Laboratories)*

phone Laboratories (Fig. 31-4). This chart can be used for solving problems of inductance, capacitance, frequency, and impedance. If two of the values are known, the third and fourth values may be found with its use. As an example, what is the value of capacitance and inductance required to resonate at a frequency of 1000 Hz in a circuit having an impedance of 500 Ω? Entering the chart on the 1000-Hz vertical line and following it to the 500-Ω line (impedance is shown along the left-hand margin) the value of inductance is indicated by the diagonal line running upward as 0.08 H (80 mH), and the capacitance indicated by the diagonal line running downward at the right-hand margin is 0.3 μF.

31.7 DECIBELS

Decibels (dB) are a logarithmic ratio of two numbers. The decibel is derived from two power levels and is also used to show voltage ratios indirectly (by relating voltage to power). The formulas for decibels are

$$\textit{Power}\ \ \text{dB} = 10 \log (P_1/P_2)$$

$$\textit{Voltage}\ \text{dB}_v = 20 \log (E_1/E_2)$$

Fig. 31-5 shows the relationship between decibel, current, voltage, and power ratios.

Decibel (Voltage)	Loss	Gain	Decibel (Power)	Decibel (Voltage)	Loss	Gain	Decibel (Power)	Decibel (Voltage)	Loss	Gain	Decibel (Power)	Decibel (Voltage)	Loss	Gain	Decibel (Power)
0.0	**1.0000**	**1.000**	**0.0**	**5.0**	**0.5623**	**1.778**	**0.50**	**10.0**	**0.3162**	**3.162**	**5.00**	**15.0**	**0.1778**	**5.623**	**0.50**
0.1	0.9886	1.012	0.05	0.1	0.5559	1.799	0.55	0.1	0.3126	3.199	0.05	0.1	0.1758	5.689	0.55
0.2	0.9772	1.023	0.10	0.2	0.5495	1.820	0.60	0.2	0.3090	3.236	0.10	0.2	0.1738	5.754	0.60
0.3	0.9661	1.035	0.15	0.3	0.5433	1.841	0.65	0.3	0.3055	3.273	0.15	0.3	0.1718	5.821	0.65
0.4	0.9550	1.047	0.20	0.4	0.5370	1.862	0.70	0.4	0.3020	3.311	0.20	0.4	0.1698	5.888	0.70
0.5	0.9441	1.059	0.25	0.5	0.5309	1.884	0.75	0.5	0.2985	3.350	0.25	0.5	0.1679	5.957	0.75
0.6	0.9333	1.072	0.30	0.6	0.5248	1.905	0.80	0.6	0.2951	3.388	0.30	0.6	0.1660	6.026	0.80
0.7	0.9226	1.084	0.35	0.7	0.5188	1.928	0.85	0.7	0.2917	3.428	0.35	0.7	0.1641	6.095	0.85
0.8	0.9120	1.096	0.40	0.8	0.5129	1.950	0.90	0.8	0.2884	3.467	0.40	0.8	0.1622	6.166	0.90
0.9	0.9016	1.109	0.45	0.9	0.5070	1.972	0.95	0.9	0.2851	3.508	0.45	0.9	0.1603	6.237	0.95
1.0	**0.8913**	**1.122**	**0.50**	**6.0**	**0.5012**	**1.995**	**3.00**	**11.0**	**0.2818**	**3.548**	**0.50**	**16.0**	**0.1585**	**6.310**	**8.00**
0.1	0.8810	1.135	0.55	0.1	0.4955	2.018	0.05	0.1	0.2786	3.589	0.55	0.1	0.1567	6.383	0.05
0.2	0.8710	1.148	0.60	0.2	0.4898	2.042	0.10	0.2	0.2754	3.631	0.60	0.2	0.1549	6.457	0.10
0.3	0.8610	1.161	0.65	0.3	0.4842	2.065	0.15	0.3	0.2723	3.673	0.65	0.3	0.1531	6.531	0.15
0.4	0.8511	1.175	0.70	0.4	0.4786	2.089	0.20	0.4	0.2692	3.715	0.70	0.4	0.1514	6.607	0.20
0.5	0.8414	1.189	0.75	0.5	0.4732	2.113	0.25	0.5	0.2661	3.758	0.75	0.5	0.1496	6.683	0.25
0.6	0.8318	1.202	0.80	0.6	0.4677	2.138	0.30	0.6	0.2630	3.802	0.80	0.6	0.1479	6.761	0.30
0.7	0.8222	1.216	0.85	0.7	0.4624	2.163	0.35	0.7	0.2600	3.846	0.85	0.7	0.1462	6.839	0.35
0.8	0.8128	1.230	0.90	0.8	0.4571	2.188	0.40	0.8	0.2570	3.890	0.90	0.8	0.1445	6.918	0.40
0.9	0.8035	1.245	0.95	0.9	0.4519	2.213	0.45	0.9	0.2541	3.936	0.95	0.9	0.1429	6.998	0.45
2.0	**0.7943**	**1.259**	**1.00**	**7.0**	**0.4467**	**2.239**	**0.50**	**12.0**	**0.2512**	**3.981**	**6.00**	**17.0**	**0.1413**	**7.079**	**0.50**
0.1	0.7852	1.274	0.05	0.1	0.4416	2.265	0.55	0.1	0.2483	4.027	0.05	0.1	0.1396	7.161	0.55
0.2	0.7762	1.288	0.10	0.2	0.4365	2.291	0.60	0.2	0.2455	4.074	0.10	0.2	0.1380	7.244	0.60
0.3	0.7674	1.303	0.15	0.3	0.4315	2.317	0.65	0.3	0.2427	4.121	0.15	0.3	0.1365	7.328	0.65
0.4	0.7586	1.318	0.20	0.4	0.4266	2.344	0.70	0.4	0.2399	4.169	0.20	0.4	0.1349	7.413	0.70
0.5	0.7499	1.334	0.25	0.5	0.4217	2.371	0.75	0.5	0.2371	4.217	0.25	0.5	0.1334	7.499	0.75
0.6	0.7413	1.349	0.30	0.6	0.4169	2.399	0.80	0.6	0.2344	4.266	0.30	0.6	0.1318	7.586	0.80
0.7	0.7328	1.365	0.35	0.7	0.4121	2.427	0.85	0.7	0.2317	4.315	0.35	0.7	0.1303	7.674	0.85
0.8	0.7244	1.380	0.40	0.8	0.4074	2.455	0.90	0.8	0.2291	4.365	0.40	0.8	0.1288	7.762	0.90
0.9	0.7161	1.396	0.45	0.9	0.4027	2.483	0.95	0.9	0.2265	4.416	0.45	0.9	0.1274	7.852	0.95
3.0	**0.7079**	**1.413**	**0.50**	**8.0**	**0.3981**	**2.512**	**4.00**	**13.0**	**0.2239**	**4.467**	**0.50**	**18.0**	**0.1259**	**7.943**	**9.00**
0.1	0.6998	1.429	0.55	0.1	0.3936	2.541	0.05	0.1	0.2213	4.519	0.55	0.1	0.1245	8.035	0.05
0.2	0.6918	1.445	0.60	0.2	0.3890	2.570	0.10	0.2	0.2188	4.571	0.60	0.2	0.1230	8.128	0.10
0.3	0.6839	1.462	0.65	0.3	0.3846	2.600	0.15	0.3	0.2163	4.624	0.65	0.3	0.1216	8.222	0.15
0.4	0.6761	1.479	0.70	0.4	0.3802	2.630	0.20	0.4	0.2138	4.677	0.70	0.4	0.1202	8.318	0.20
0.5	0.6683	1.496	0.75	0.5	0.3758	2.661	0.25	0.5	0.2113	4.732	0.75	0.5	0.1189	8.414	0.25
0.6	0.6607	1.514	0.80	0.6	0.3715	2.692	0.30	0.6	0.2089	4.786	0.80	0.6	0.1175	8.511	0.30
0.7	0.6531	1.531	0.85	0.7	0.3673	2.723	0.35	0.7	0.2065	4.842	0.85	0.7	0.1161	8.610	0.35
0.8	0.6457	1.549	0.90	0.8	0.3631	2.754	0.40	0.8	0.2042	4.898	0.90	0.8	0.1148	8.710	0.40
0.9	0.6383	1.567	0.95	0.9	0.3589	2.786	0.45	0.9	0.2018	4.955	0.95	0.9	0.1135	8.810	0.45
4.0	**0.6310**	**1.585**	**2.00**	**9.0**	**0.3548**	**2.818**	**0.50**	**14.0**	**0.1995**	**5.012**	**7.00**	**19.0**	**0.1122**	**8.913**	**0.50**
0.1	0.6237	1.603	0.05	0.1	0.3508	2.851	0.55	0.1	0.1972	5.070	0.05	0.1	0.1109	9.016	0.55
0.2	0.6166	1.622	0.10	0.2	0.3467	2.884	0.60	0.2	0.1950	5.129	0.10	0.2	0.1096	9.120	0.60
0.3	0.6095	1.641	0.15	0.3	0.3428	2.917	0.65	0.3	0.1928	5.188	0.15	0.3	0.1084	9.226	0.65
0.4	0.6026	1.660	0.20	0.4	0.3388	2.951	0.70	0.4	0.1905	5.248	0.20	0.4	0.1072	9.333	0.70
0.5	0.5957	1.679	0.25	0.5	0.3350	2.985	0.75	0.5	0.1884	5.309	0.25	0.5	0.1059	9.441	0.75
0.6	0.5888	1.698	0.30	0.6	0.3311	3.020	0.80	0.6	0.1862	5.370	0.30	0.6	0.1047	9.550	0.80
0.7	0.5821	1.718	0.35	0.7	0.3273	3.055	0.85	0.7	0.1841	5.433	0.35	0.7	0.1035	9.661	0.85
0.8	0.5754	1.738	0.40	0.8	0.3236	3.090	0.90	0.8	0.1820	5.495	0.40	0.8	0.1023	9.772	0.90
0.9	0.5689	1.758	0.45	0.9	0.3199	3.126	0.95	0.9	0.1799	5.559	0.45	0.9	0.1012	9.886	0.95

Decibel (Voltage)	Loss	Gain	Decibel (Power)	Decibel (Voltage)	Loss	Gain	Decibel (Power)
20.0	0.1000 Use the same number as 0-20 dB, but shift point one step to the left. Thus since 10 dB = 0.3162 30 dB = 0.03162	10.00 Use the same number as 0-20 dB, but shift point one step to the right Thus since 10 dB = 3.162 30 dB = 31.62	10.00 This column repeats every 10 dB instead of every 20 dB	**60.0**	0.001 Use the same numbers as 0-20 dB, but shift point three steps to the left. Thus since 10 dB = 0.3162 70 dB = 0.0003162	1,000 Use the same number as 0-20 dB, but shift point three steps to the right. Thus since 10 dB = 3.162 70 dB = 3162.	30.00 This column repeats every 10 dB instead of every 20 dB.
40.0	0.01 Use the same number as 0-20 dB, but shift point two steps to the left. Thus since 10 dB = 0.3162 50 dB = 0.003162	100 Use the same number as 0-20 dB, but shift point two steps to the right. Thus since 10 dB = 3.162 50 dB = 316.2	20.00 This column repeats every 10 dB instead of every 20 dB.	**80.0**	0.0001 Use the same numbers as 0-20 dB, but shift point four steps to the left. Thus since 10 dB = 0.3162 90 dB = 0.00003162	10,000 Use the same number as 0-20 dB, but shift point four steps to the right. Thus since 10 dB = 3.162 90 dB = 31620.	40.00 This column repeats every 10 dB instead of every 20 dB.
				100.0	0.00001	100,000	50.00

Figure 31-5 Relationships between decibel, current, voltage, and power ratios.

Fig. 31-6 shows the relationship between the power, decibels, and voltage. In the figure, "dBm" is the decibels referenced to 1 mW.

Volume unit (VU) meters measure decibels that are related to a 600-Ω impedance, 0 VU is actually +4 dBm.

When measuring decibels referenced to 1 mW at any other impedance than 600 Ω, the following equation is used:

$$\text{dBm at new impedance} = \text{dBm}_{600\Omega} + 10\log(600/Z_{new})$$

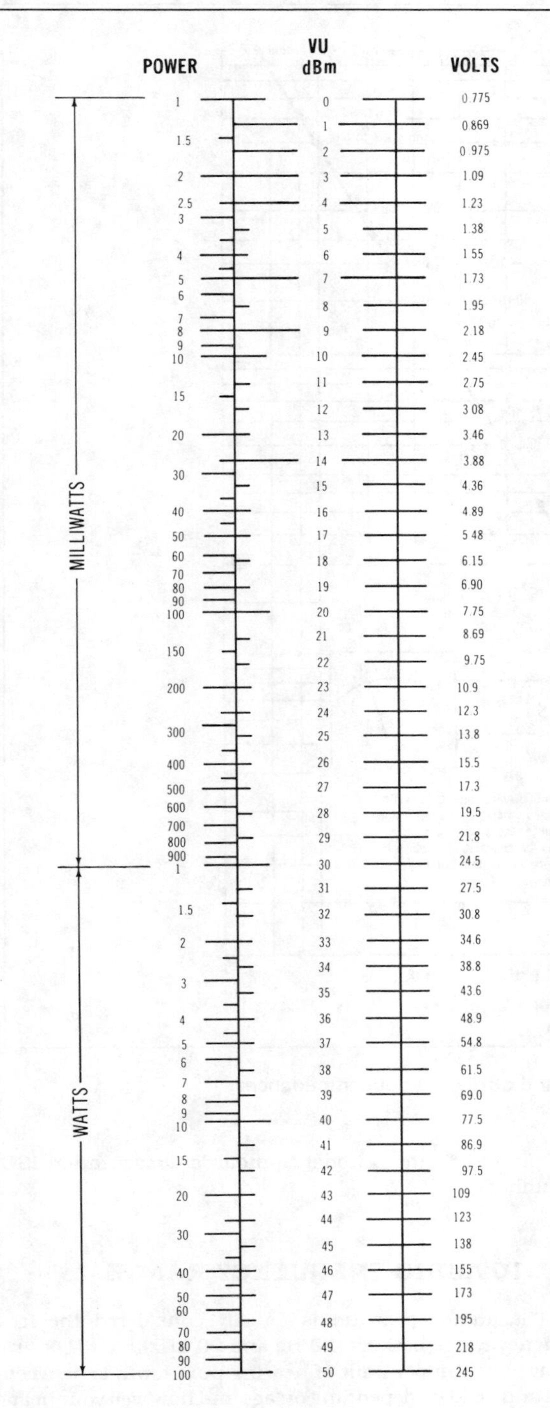

Figure 31-6 Relationship between power, dBm, and voltage.

Example: The dBm for a 32-Ω load is

$$\begin{aligned} dBm_{32} &= 4 + 10 \log(600/32) \\ &= 16.75 \text{ dBm} \end{aligned}$$

This can also be determined by using the graph in Fig. 31-7.

To find the logarithm of a number to some other base than the base 10 and 2.718 . . ., use the following:

$$n = b^L$$

A number is equal to a base raised to its logarithm, then

$$\ln n = \ln b(L)$$

therefore,

$$\ln n / \ln b = L$$

The natural log of a number divided by the natural log of the base equals the logarithm.

Example: Find the logarithm of the number 2 to the base 10:

$$\begin{aligned} \ln 2 / \ln 10 &= 0.693147/2.302585 \\ &= 0.301030 \end{aligned}$$

In information theory work, logarithms to the base 2 are quite commonly employed. To find the $\log_2$ of 26

$$\ln 26 / \ln 2 = 4.70$$

To prove this, raise 2 to the 4.70 power

$$2^{4.70} = 26$$

31.8 SOUND PRESSURE LEVEL[4]

The *sound pressure level (SPL)* is related to acoustic pressure as seen in Fig. 31-8.

31.9 ISO NUMBERS[3]

"Preferred Numbers were developed in France by Charles Renard in 1879 because of a need for a rational basis for grading cotton rope. The sizing system that resulted from his work was based upon a geometric series of mass per unit length such that every fifth step of the series increased the size of rope by a factor of ten."* This same system of preferred numbers is used today in acoustics.

The one-twelfth, one-sixth, one-third, one-half, two-thirds, and one octave preferred center frequency num-

*From the American National Standard for Preferred Numbers.

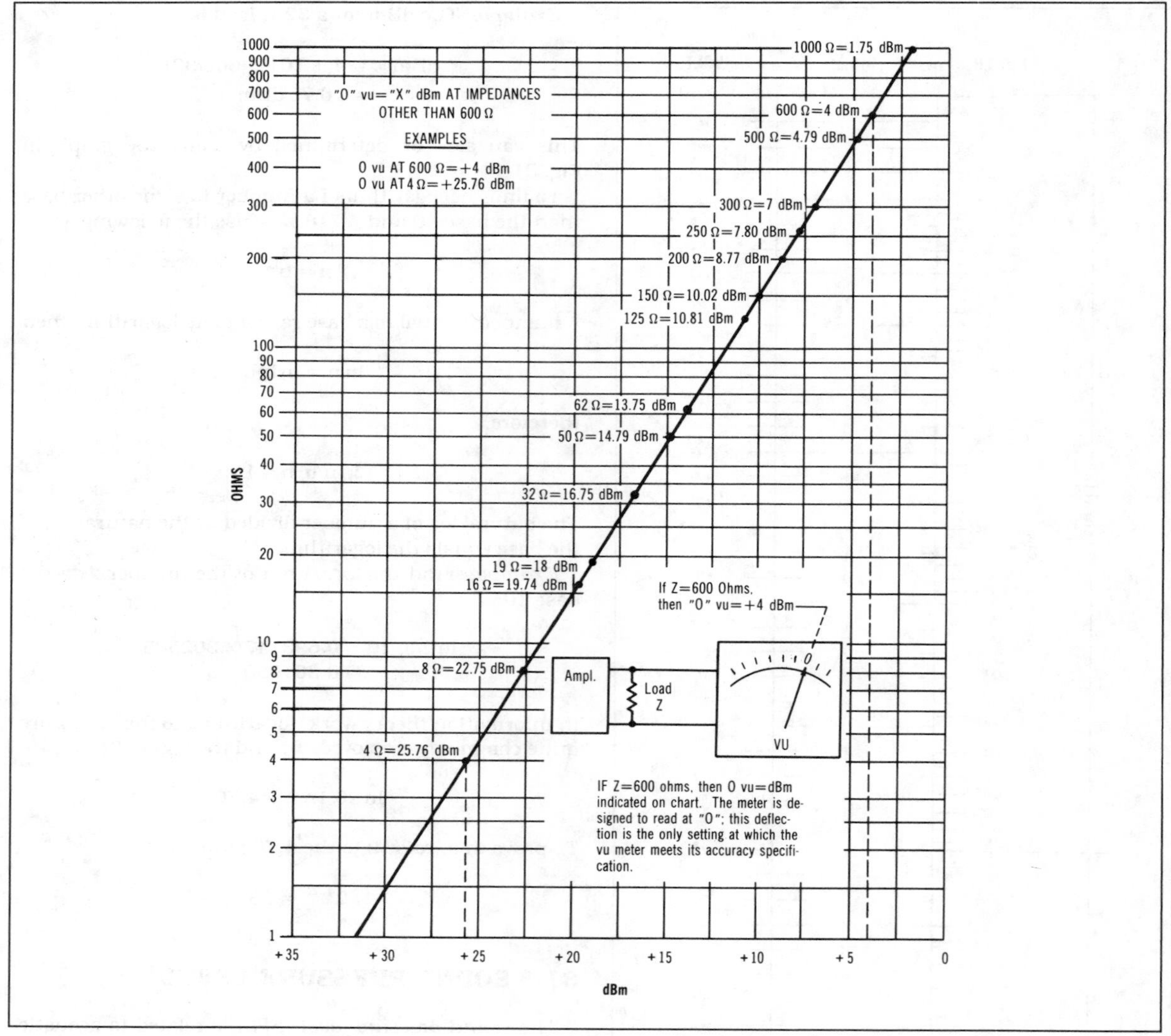

Figure 31-7 Relationship between VU and dBm at various impedances.

bers are not the exact N series number. The exact N series number is found by the formula

$$\text{N series number} = 10^{1/N}(10^{1/N})(10^{1/N}) \ldots$$

where,
N is the ordinal numbers in series.

For instance, the third N number for a 40 series would be

$$10^{1/40}(10^{1/40})(10^{1/40}) = 1.188502227$$

The preferred ISO number is 1.18. Table 31-2 is a table of preferred International Standards Organization ISO numbers.

31.10 AUDIO FREQUENCY RANGE

The audio spectrum is usually considered the frequency range between 20 Hz and 20 kHz (Fig. 31-9). In reality, the upper limit of hearing pure tones is between 12 and 18 kHz, depending on age and how well your hearing has been protected. Frequencies above 20 kHz cannot be heard as a sound, but the effect created by such frequencies (i.e., rapid rise time) can be heard.

The lower end of the spectrum is more often felt than

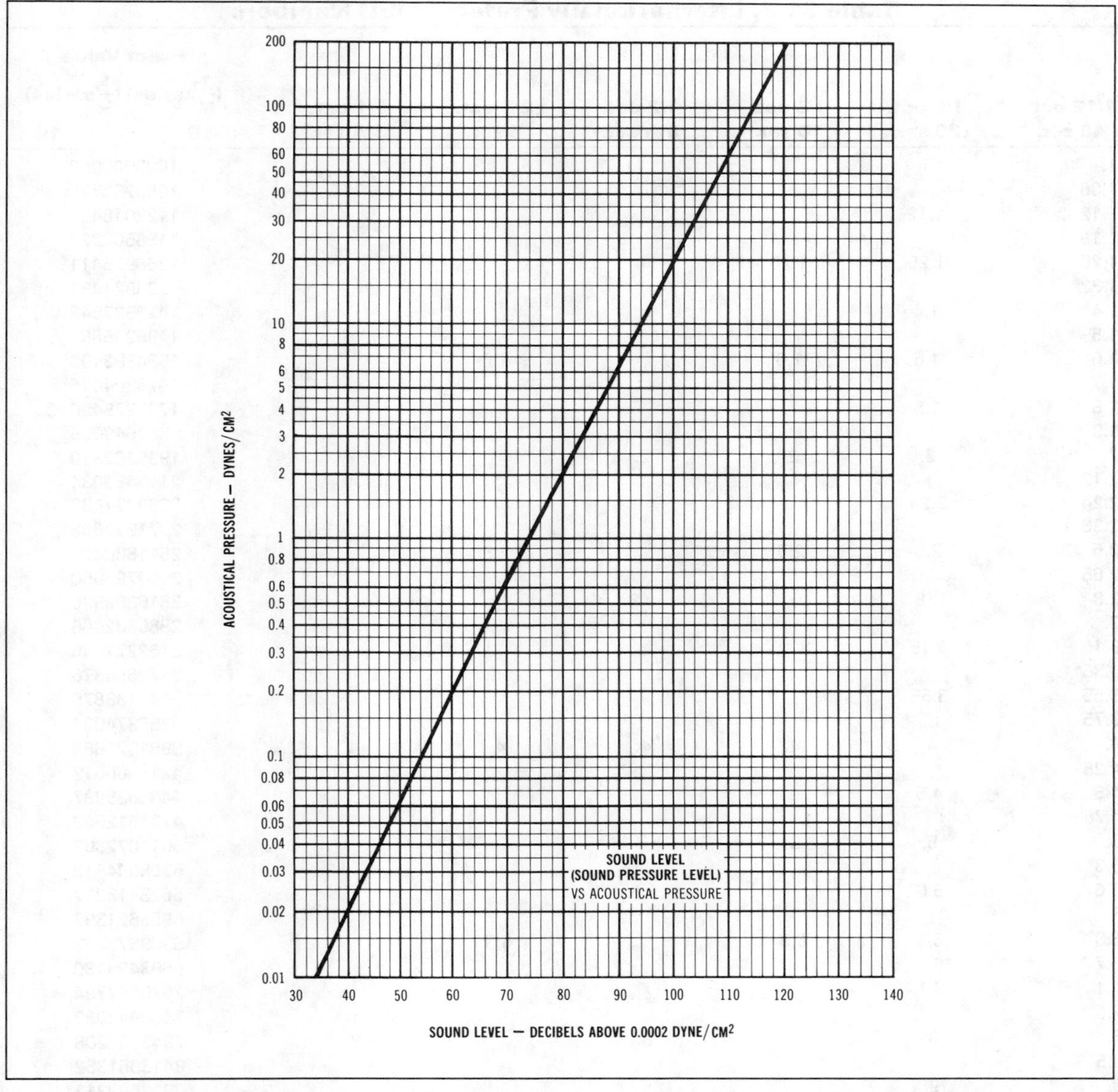

Figure 31-8 Sound pressure level versus acoustic pressure.

heard as a pure tone. Low frequencies below 20 Hz are difficult to reproduce. Often the reproducer actually reproduces the second harmonic of the frequency, and the brain translates it back to the fundamental.

31.11 SOUND SYSTEM QUANTITIES AND DESIGN FORMULAS

Various quantities are used for sound system design that should be defined. They follow.

31.11.1 D_1

D_1 is the distance between the microphone and the loudspeaker (see Fig. 31-10).

31.11.2 D_2

D_2 is the distance between the loudspeaker and the farthest listener (see Fig. 31-10).

Table 31-2. Internationally Preferred ISO Numbers

1/12 oct. 40 ser.	1/6 oct. 20 ser.	1/3 oct. 10 ser.	1/2 oct. 6⅔ ser.	2/3 oct. 5 ser.	1/1 oct. 3⅓ ser.	Exact Value $\left(\frac{1}{N}\text{series}\right)$ $\left(\frac{1}{N}\text{series}\right)$ 10 × 10
1.	1	1	1	1	1	1000000000
1.06						1059253725
1.12	1.12					1122018454
1.18						1188502227
1.25	1.25	1.25				1258925411
1.32						1333521431
1.4	1.4					1412537543
1.5						1496235654
1.6	1.6	1.6		1.6		1584893190
1.7						1678804015
1.8	1.8					1778279406
1.9						1883649085
2.	2.	2.	2.		2.	1995262310
2.12						2113489034
2.24	2.24					2238721132
2.36						2371373698
2.5	2.5	2.5		2.5		2511886423
2.65						2660725050
2.8	2.8		2.8			2818382920
3.						2985382606
3.15	3.15	3.15				3162277646
3.35						3349654376
3.55	3.55					3548133875
3.75						3758374024
4.	4.	4.	4.	4.	4.	3981071685
4.25						4216965012
4.5	4.5					4466835897
4.75						4731512563
5.	5.	5.				5011872307
5.3						5308844410
5.6	5.6		5.6			5623413217
6.						5956621397
6.3	6.3	6.3		6.3		6309573403
6.7						6683439130
7.1	7.1					7079457794
7.5						7498942039
8.	8.	8.	8.		8.	7943282288
8.5						8413951352
9.	9.					8912509312
9.5						9440608688

31.11.3 D_o

D_o is the distance between the talker (sound source) and the farthest listener (see Fig. 31-10).

31.11.4 D_s

D_s is the distance between the talker (sound source) and the microphone (see Fig. 31-10).

31.11.5 D_L

D_L is the limiting distance, equal to $3.16D_c$ for 15% AL_{cons} in a room with a reverberation time of 1.6 s, which means that D_2 cannot be any longer than D_L. As the RT_{60} increases or the required $\%AL_{cons}$ decreases, D_2 becomes less than D_L.

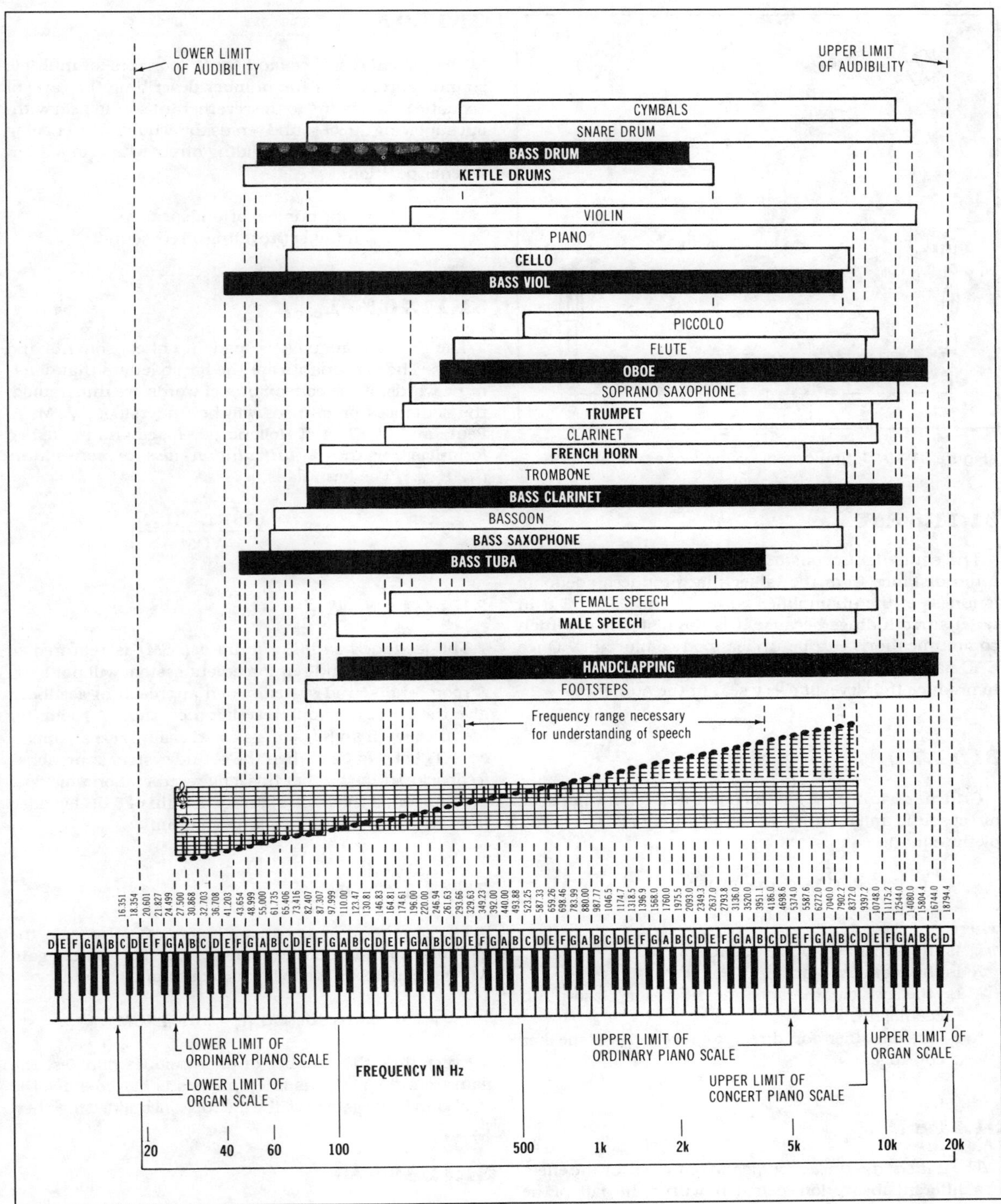

Figure 31-9 Audible frequency range.

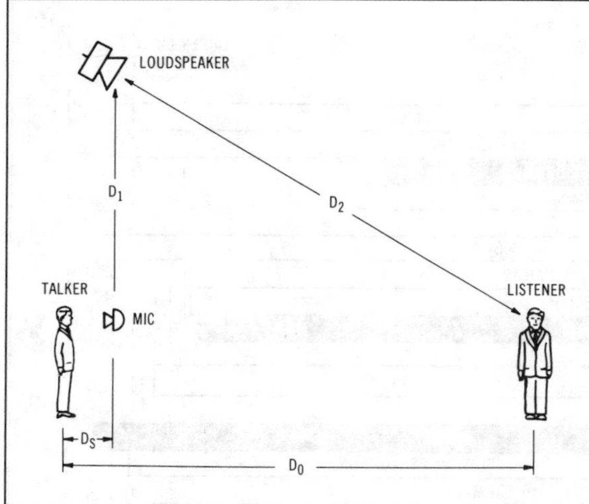

Figure 31-10 Definitions of sound system dimensions.

31.11.6 EAD

The *equivalent acoustic distance (EAD)* is the maximum distance from the talker that produces adequate loudness of the unamplified voice. Often EAD = 8 ft in quiet surroundings because it is the distance at which communications can be understood comfortably. Once EAD has been determined, the sound system is designed to produce that level at every seat in the audience.

31.11.7 D_c

Critical distance (D_c) is the point in a room where the direct sound and reverberant sound are equal. D_c is found by the equation

$$D_c = 0.141\ QRM/N$$

where,

Q is the directivity of the sound source,

R is the room constant,

M is the critical distance modifier for absorption coefficient,

N is the modifier for direct to reverberant speaker coverage.

31.11.8 M

The *critical distance modifier (M)* corrects for the effect of a different absorption coefficient within the path of the loudspeaker's coverage pattern:

$$M = (1 - a_{\text{total room}})/(1 - a_{\text{loudspeaker coverage area}})$$

31.11.9 N

The *critical distance modifier (N)* corrects for multiple sound sources. N is the number describing the ratio of acoustic power going to the reverberant sound field without supplying direct sound versus the acoustic power going from the loudspeakers providing direct sound to a given listener position:

$$N = \text{total number of loudspeakers/ number providing direct sound}$$

31.11.10 %AL_{cons}

The English language is made up of consonants and vowels. The consonants are the harsh letters that determine words. If the consonants of words are understood, the sentences or phrases will be understood. V. M. A. Peutz and W. Klein of Holland developed and published formulas for the % *articulation loss of consonants* (%AL_{cons}). The formula is

$$\%AL_{cons} = \frac{656\ RT_{60}{}^2 D_2{}^2 N}{VQM}$$

31.11.11 FSM

The *feedback stability margin (FSM)* is required to ensure that a sound-reinforcement system will not ring. A room and sound system when approaching feedback give the effect of a long reverberation time. A room, for instance, with an RT_{60} of 3 s could easily have an apparent RT_{60} of 6 to 12 s when the sound system approaches feedback. To ensure that this long reverberation time does not happen, a feedback stability margin of 6 dB is added into the needed acoustic gain equation.

31.11.12 NOM

The *number of open microphones (NOM)* affects the gain of a sound-reinforcement system. The system gain will be reduced by the following equation:

$$\text{gain reduction}_{dB} = 10 \log NOM$$

Every time the number of microphones doubles, the gain from the previous microphones is halved since the total gain is the gain of all the microphones added together.

31.11.13 NAG

The *needed acoustic gain (NAG)* is that required to produce the same level at the farthest listener as at the EAD. NAG in its simplest form is

$$NAG = 20 \log D_0 - 20 \log EAD$$

NAG, however, is also affected by the number of open microphones (NOM) in the system. Each time the NOM doubles, the NAG increases 3 dB. Finally, a 6-dB feedback stability margin (FSM) is added into the NAG equation to ensure that the system never approaches feedback. The final equation for NAG is

$$NAG = \Delta D_0 - \Delta EAD + 10 \log NOM + 6\,dB\,FSM$$

where,

D_0 and EAD are the level change per the Hopkins-Stryker equation.

31.11.14 PAG

The *potential acoustic gain (PAG)* of a sound system is

$$PAG = \Delta D_0 + \Delta D_1 - \Delta D_s - \Delta D_2$$

where,

D_0, D_1, D_s and D_2 are found as in NAG.

31.11.15 Q

The *directivity factor (Q)* of a transducer used for sound emission is the ratio of sound pressure squared, at some fixed distance and specified direction, to the mean sound pressure squared at the same distance averaged over all directions from the transducer. The distance must be great enough so that the sound appears to diverge spherically from the effective acoustic center of the source. Unless otherwise specified, the reference direction is understood to be that of maximum response.

Geometric Q is found by the equations:

For rectangular coverage between 0° and 180°,

$$Q_{Geom} = \frac{180}{\arcsin\left(\frac{\sin\theta}{2}\right)\left(\frac{\sin\phi}{2}\right)}$$

For angles between 180° and 360° when one angle is 180°, and the other angle is some value between 180° and 360°

$$Q_{Geom} = 360°/\text{angle}$$

For conical coverage,

$$Q_{Geom} = 2/[1 - \cos(\theta/2)]$$

31.11.16 $C_\angle$

$C_\angle$ is the included angle of the coverage pattern. Normally, $C_\angle$ is expressed as an angle between the −6-dB points in the coverage pattern.

31.11.17 EPR

EPR is the *electrical power required* to produce the desired SPL at a specific point in the coverage area. It is found by the equation

$$EPR_{watts} = 10^{[(\text{Desired SPL} + \text{10-dB crest}) + (\Delta D_2 - \Delta 4') - L_{sens}]/10}$$

31.11.18 a

The *absorption coefficient (a)* of a material or surface is the ratio of absorbed sound to reflected sound or incident sound ($a = I_A/I_R$). If all sound were reflected, a would be 0. If all sound were absorbed, a would be 1.

31.11.19 $\bar{a}$

The average absorption coefficient ($\bar{a}$) for all the surfaces together is found by

$$\bar{a} = (S_1 a_1 + S_2 a_2 + S_n a_n)/S$$

where,

$S_{1,\,2,\ldots,\,n}$ are individual surface areas in square feet,

$a_{1,\,2,\ldots,\,n}$ are the individual absorption coefficients of the areas,

S is the total surface area in square feet.

31.11.20 Mean-Free Path

The *mean-free path (MFP)* is the average distance between reflections in a space. MFP is found by

$$MFP = 4V/S$$

where,

V is the space volume,

S is the space surface area.

31.11.21 D_x

D_x is an arbitrary level change associated with the specific distance from the Hopkins-Stryker equation so that

$$\Delta D_x = -10 \log\left[\frac{Q}{4\pi D_x^2} + \frac{4N}{Sa}\right]$$

In semireverberant rooms, Peutz describes ΔD_x as

$$-10\log\left[\left(\frac{Q}{4\pi D_x^2}\right)+\left(\frac{4N}{Sa}\right)\right] + \left[\left(\frac{0.221\sqrt{V}}{h\,RT_{60}}\right)\log\left(\frac{D_x > D_c}{D_c}\right)\right]$$

where,

h is the ceiling height.

31.11.22 S/N

S/N is the signal-to-noise ratio. The signal-to-noise ratio is

$$S/N = \frac{35(2-\log \%AL_{cons})}{(2-\log 9RT_{60})} - 10$$

31.11.23 SPL

SPL is the sound-pressure level in dB-SPL re 0.000 02 N/m². SPL is also called L_p.

31.11.24 Max Program Level

Max prog level is the maximum sound pressure level attainable at a specific point from the available input power. Max program level is found by the equation:

$$\text{max prog level} = 10\log\left(\frac{\text{watts}_{avail}}{10}\right) - (\Delta D2 - \Delta 4') + L_{sens}$$

31.11.25 Loudspeaker Sensitivity

Loudspeaker sensitivity (L_{sens}) is the on-axis SPL output of the loudspeaker with a specified power input and at a specified distance. The most common L_{sens} is SPL at 4 ft, 1 W. Another L_{sens} gaining acceptance is SPL at 1 m, 1 W.

31.11.26 Sa

Sa is the total absorption in sabines of all the surface areas times their absorption.

31.11.27 dB-SPL$_T$

The dB-SPL$_T$ is the talker's or sound source's sound pressure level.

31.11.28 dB-SPL$_D$

The dB-SPL$_D$ is the desired sound pressure level.

31.11.29 dB-SPL

The dB-SPL is the sound pressure level in decibels.

31.11.30 EIN

Equivalent input noise (EIN) equals −198 dB + 10 log BW + 10 log Z − 6 dB − 20 log 0.775.

31.11.31 Thermal Noise

Thermal noise is the noise produced in any resistance, including standard resistors. Any resistance that is at a temperature above absolute zero generates noise due to the thermal agitation of free electrons in the material. The magnitude of the noise can be calculated from the resistance, absolute temperature, and equivalent noise bandwidth of the measuring system. A completely noise-free amplifier whose input is connected to its equivalent source resistance will have noise in its output equal to the product of amplification and source resistor noise. This noise is said to be the "theoretical minimum."

Fig. 31-11 provides a quick means for determining the rms value of thermal noise voltage in terms of resistance and circuit bandwidth.

For practical calculations, especially those in which the resistive component is constant across the band of interest, the following expression is used:

$$E_{rms} = \sqrt{4(1.38\times 10^{-23})(T)(f_1 - f_2)(R)}$$

where,

$f_1 - f_2$ is a 3-dB bandwidth in hertz,

R is the resistive component of the impedance, across which the noise is developed,

T is the absolute temperature in kelvins.

$$TN_{dB\ re\ 1\ V} = -198\,dB + 10\log BW + 10\log Z$$

where,

BW is the bandwidth (−3 dB points) in hertz.

31.11.32 RT$_{60}$

RT_{60} is the time required for an interrupted steady-state signal in a space to decay 60 dB.

$$\text{Sabine } RT_{60} = 0.049V/Sa$$

$$\text{Norris Eyring } RT_{60} = 0.049V/-S\ln(1-a)$$

$$\text{Fitzroy } RT_{60} = \frac{0.049V}{S^2}\left[\frac{2XY}{-\ln(1-a_{XY})}+\frac{2XZ}{-\ln(1-a_{XZ})}+\frac{2YZ}{-\ln(1-a_{YZ})}\right]$$

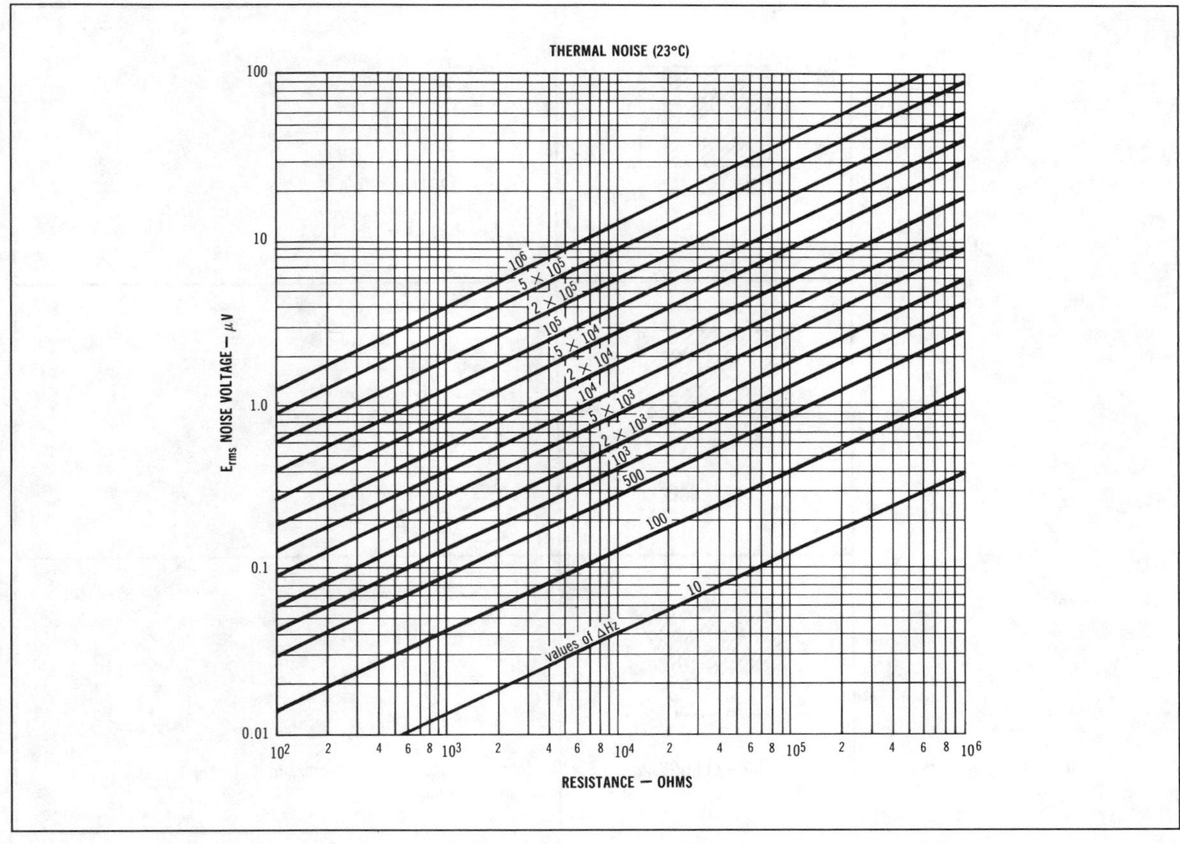

Figure 31-11 Thermal noise graph.

where,
V is the room volume,
S is the surface area,
a is the absorption coefficient,
X is the space length in feet,
Y is the space width in feet,
Z is the space height in feet.

31.11.33 Signal Delay

Time delay is the time required for a signal, traveling at the speed of sound, to travel from the source to a specified point in space:

$$SD_{MS} = Distance_{ft}/c$$

where,
s is the speed of sound.

31.12 SURFACE AREA AND VOLUME FORMULAS

To find the surface area and volume of complex areas, the area can often be divided into a series of simpler areas and handled one at a time. Fig. 31-12 gives the equation for various and unusual volumes.

31.13 GREEK ALPHABET

The Greek alphabet plays a major role in the language of engineering and sound. Table 31-3 shows the Greek alphabet and the terms that are commonly symbolized by it.

31.14 TECHNICAL ABBREVIATIONS

Many units or terms in engineering have abbreviations accepted either by the US Government or by the acous-

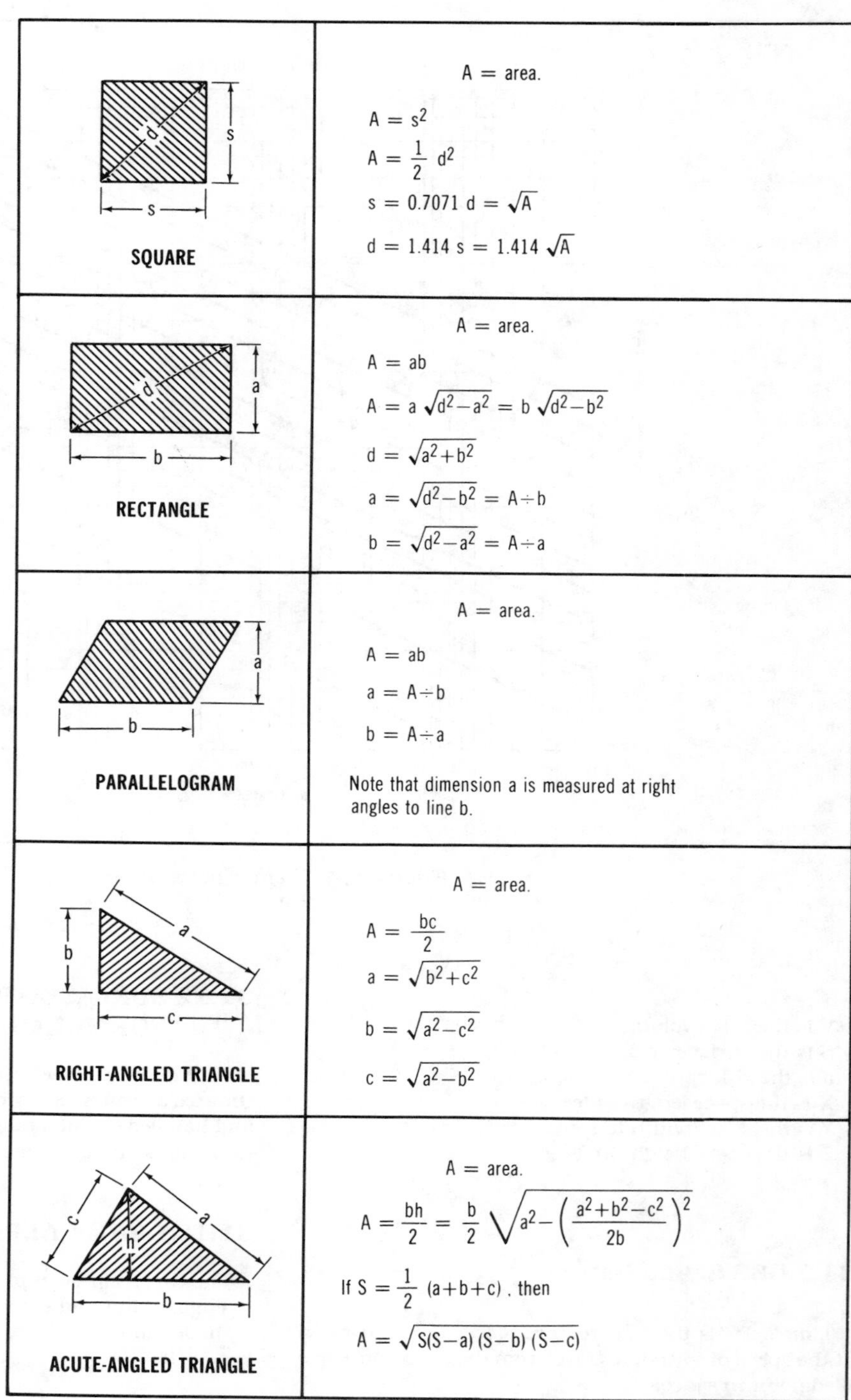

SQUARE	A = area. $A = s^2$ $A = \frac{1}{2} d^2$ $s = 0.7071\ d = \sqrt{A}$ $d = 1.414\ s = 1.414 \sqrt{A}$
RECTANGLE	A = area. $A = ab$ $A = a\sqrt{d^2 - a^2} = b\sqrt{d^2 - b^2}$ $d = \sqrt{a^2 + b^2}$ $a = \sqrt{d^2 - b^2} = A \div b$ $b = \sqrt{d^2 - a^2} = A \div a$
PARALLELOGRAM	A = area. $A = ab$ $a = A \div b$ $b = A \div a$ Note that dimension a is measured at right angles to line b.
RIGHT-ANGLED TRIANGLE	A = area. $A = \frac{bc}{2}$ $a = \sqrt{b^2 + c^2}$ $b = \sqrt{a^2 - c^2}$ $c = \sqrt{a^2 - b^2}$
ACUTE-ANGLED TRIANGLE	A = area. $A = \frac{bh}{2} = \frac{b}{2}\sqrt{a^2 - \left(\frac{a^2 + b^2 - c^2}{2b}\right)^2}$ If $S = \frac{1}{2}(a + b + c)$, then $A = \sqrt{S(S-a)(S-b)(S-c)}$

Figure 31-12 Equations for finding

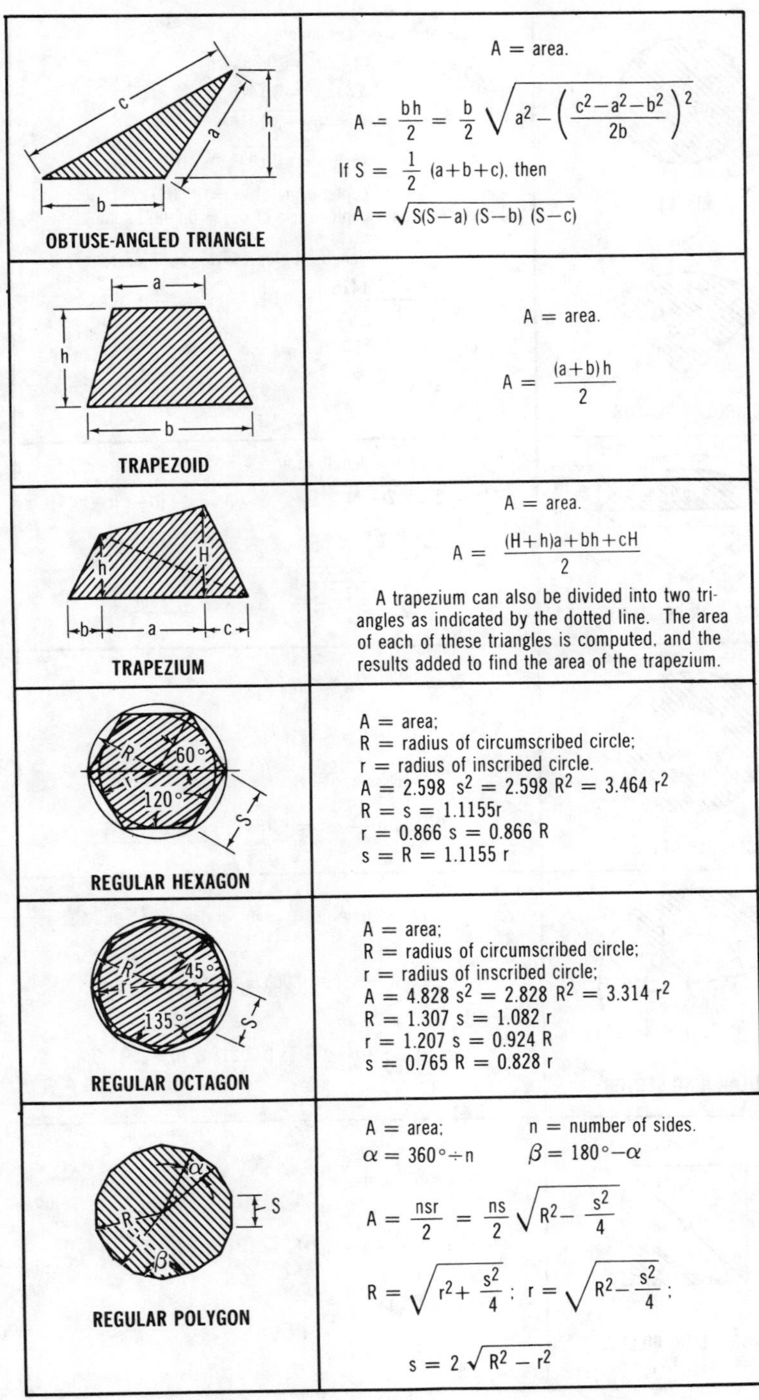

OBTUSE-ANGLED TRIANGLE	A = area. $A = \frac{bh}{2} = \frac{b}{2}\sqrt{a^2 - \left(\frac{c^2-a^2-b^2}{2b}\right)^2}$ If $S = \frac{1}{2}(a+b+c)$, then $A = \sqrt{S(S-a)(S-b)(S-c)}$
TRAPEZOID	A = area. $A = \frac{(a+b)h}{2}$
TRAPEZIUM	A = area. $A = \frac{(H+h)a+bh+cH}{2}$ A trapezium can also be divided into two triangles as indicated by the dotted line. The area of each of these triangles is computed, and the results added to find the area of the trapezium.
REGULAR HEXAGON	A = area; R = radius of circumscribed circle; r = radius of inscribed circle. $A = 2.598\ s^2 = 2.598\ R^2 = 3.464\ r^2$ $R = s = 1.1155r$ $r = 0.866\ s = 0.866\ R$ $s = R = 1.1155\ r$
REGULAR OCTAGON	A = area; R = radius of circumscribed circle; r = radius of inscribed circle; $A = 4.828\ s^2 = 2.828\ R^2 = 3.314\ r^2$ $R = 1.307\ s = 1.082\ r$ $r = 1.207\ s = 0.924\ R$ $s = 0.765\ R = 0.828\ r$
REGULAR POLYGON	A = area; n = number of sides. $\alpha = 360° \div n$ $\beta = 180° - \alpha$ $A = \frac{nsr}{2} = \frac{ns}{2}\sqrt{R^2 - \frac{s^2}{4}}$ $R = \sqrt{r^2 + \frac{s^2}{4}}$; $r = \sqrt{R^2 - \frac{s^2}{4}}$; $s = 2\sqrt{R^2 - r^2}$

cont. on next page

surface areas for complex shapes.

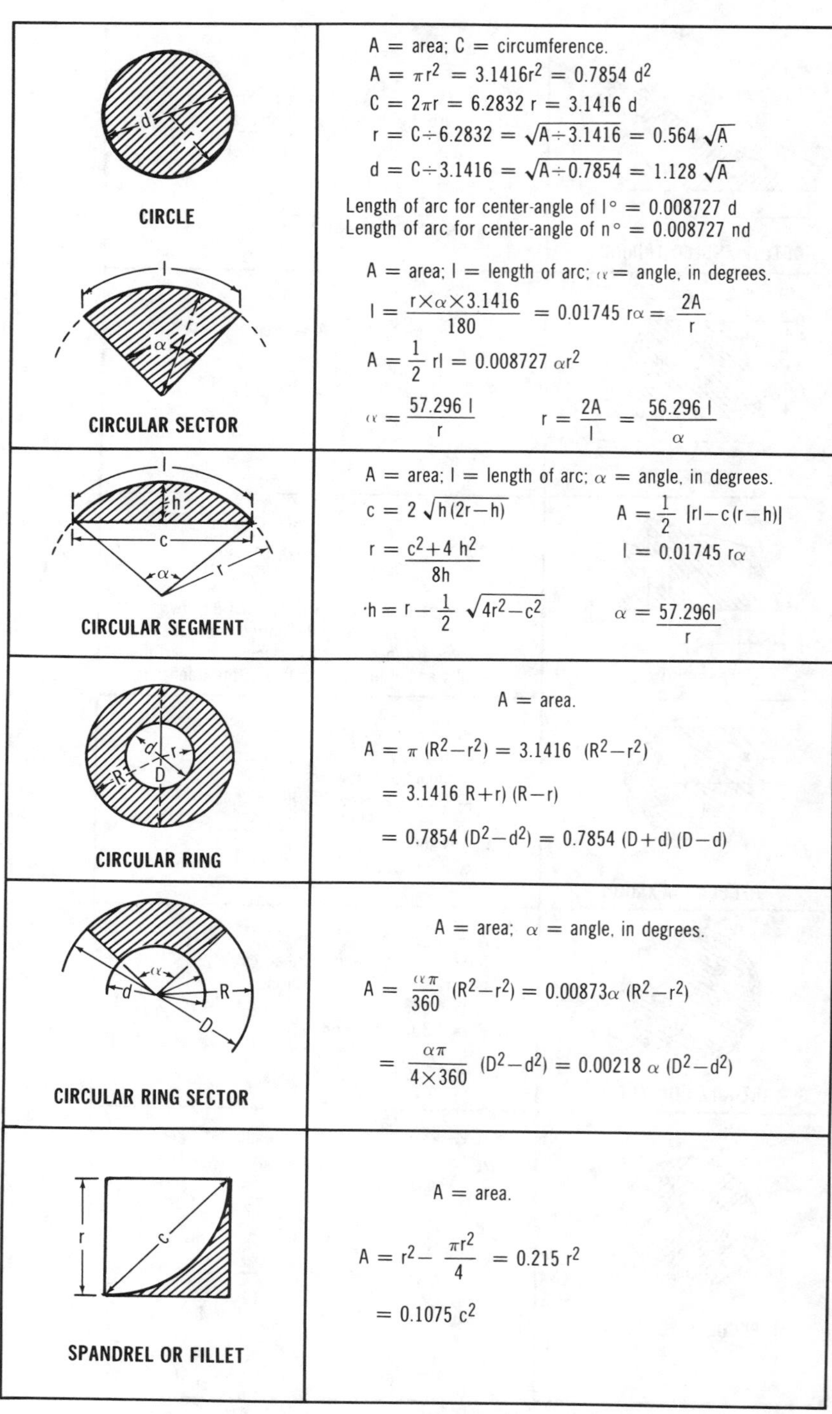

CIRCLE	A = area; C = circumference. $A = \pi r^2 = 3.1416 r^2 = 0.7854\ d^2$ $C = 2\pi r = 6.2832\ r = 3.1416\ d$ $r = C \div 6.2832 = \sqrt{A \div 3.1416} = 0.564 \sqrt{A}$ $d = C \div 3.1416 = \sqrt{A \div 0.7854} = 1.128 \sqrt{A}$ Length of arc for center-angle of 1° = 0.008727 d Length of arc for center-angle of n° = 0.008727 nd
CIRCULAR SECTOR	A = area; l = length of arc; α = angle, in degrees. $l = \frac{r \times \alpha \times 3.1416}{180} = 0.01745\ r\alpha = \frac{2A}{r}$ $A = \frac{1}{2} rl = 0.008727\ \alpha r^2$ $\alpha = \frac{57.296\ l}{r}$ $r = \frac{2A}{l} = \frac{56.296\ l}{\alpha}$
CIRCULAR SEGMENT	A = area; l = length of arc; α = angle, in degrees. $c = 2\sqrt{h(2r-h)}$ $A = \frac{1}{2}[rl - c(r-h)]$ $r = \frac{c^2 + 4h^2}{8h}$ $l = 0.01745\ r\alpha$ $h = r - \frac{1}{2}\sqrt{4r^2 - c^2}$ $\alpha = \frac{57.2961}{r}$
CIRCULAR RING	A = area. $A = \pi (R^2 - r^2) = 3.1416\ (R^2 - r^2)$ $= 3.1416\ R + r)(R - r)$ $= 0.7854\ (D^2 - d^2) = 0.7854\ (D + d)(D - d)$
CIRCULAR RING SECTOR	A = area; α = angle, in degrees. $A = \frac{\alpha\pi}{360}(R^2 - r^2) = 0.00873\alpha\ (R^2 - r^2)$ $= \frac{\alpha\pi}{4 \times 360}(D^2 - d^2) = 0.00218\ \alpha\ (D^2 - d^2)$
SPANDREL OR FILLET	A = area. $A = r^2 - \frac{\pi r^2}{4} = 0.215\ r^2$ $= 0.1075\ c^2$

Figure 31-12—cont. Equations for finding

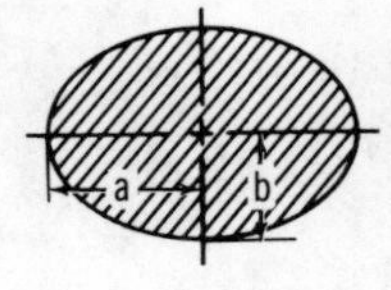

ELLIPSE	A = area; P = perimeter or circumference. $A = \pi ab = 3.1416\ ab.$ An approximate formula for the perimeter is: $P = 3.1416\sqrt{2(a^2+b^2)}$ A closer approximation is: $P = 3.1416\sqrt{2(a^2+b^2)-\frac{(a-b)^2}{2.2}}$
HYPERBOLA	A = area BCD $A = \frac{xy}{2} - \frac{ab}{2}\ \text{hyp. log}\left(\frac{x}{a}+\frac{y}{b}\right)$
PARABOLA	l = length of arc. $l = \frac{p}{2}\left[\sqrt{\frac{2x}{p}\left(I+\frac{2x}{p}\right)} + \text{hyp. log}\sqrt{\frac{2x}{p}+I+\frac{2x}{p}}\right]$ When x is small in proportion to y, the following is a close approximation: $l = y\left[I \div \frac{2}{3}\left(\frac{x}{y}\right)^2 - \frac{2}{5}\left(\frac{x}{y}\right)^4\right]$, or $l = \sqrt{y^2+\frac{4}{3}x^2}$
PARABOLA	A = area. $A = \frac{2}{3}xy$ (The area is equal to two-thirds of the rectangle which has x for its base and y for its height.)
SEGMENT OF PARABOLA	A = area. Area BFC = A = ⅔ area of parallelogram BCDE. If FG is the height of the segment, measured at right angles to BC, then: Area of segment BFC = ⅔ BC×FG
CYCLOID	A = area; l = length of cycloid. $A = 3\pi r^2 = 9.4248\ r^2 = 2.3562\ d^2$ = 3 × area of generating circle $l = 8\ r = 4\ d$

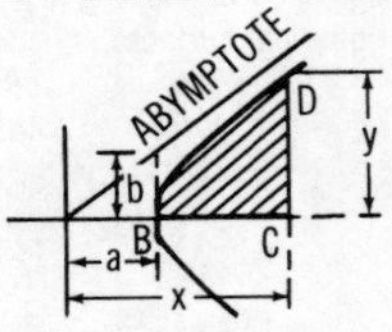

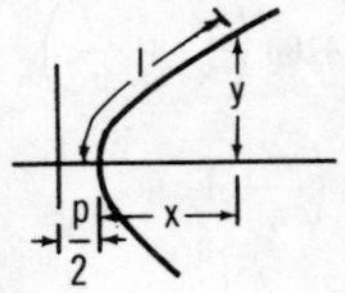

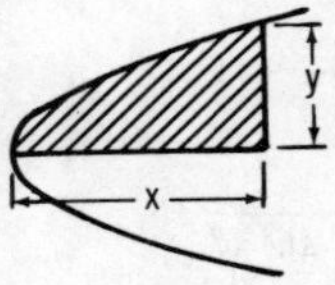

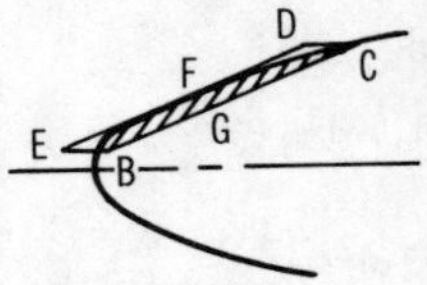

cont. on next page

surface areas for complex shapes.

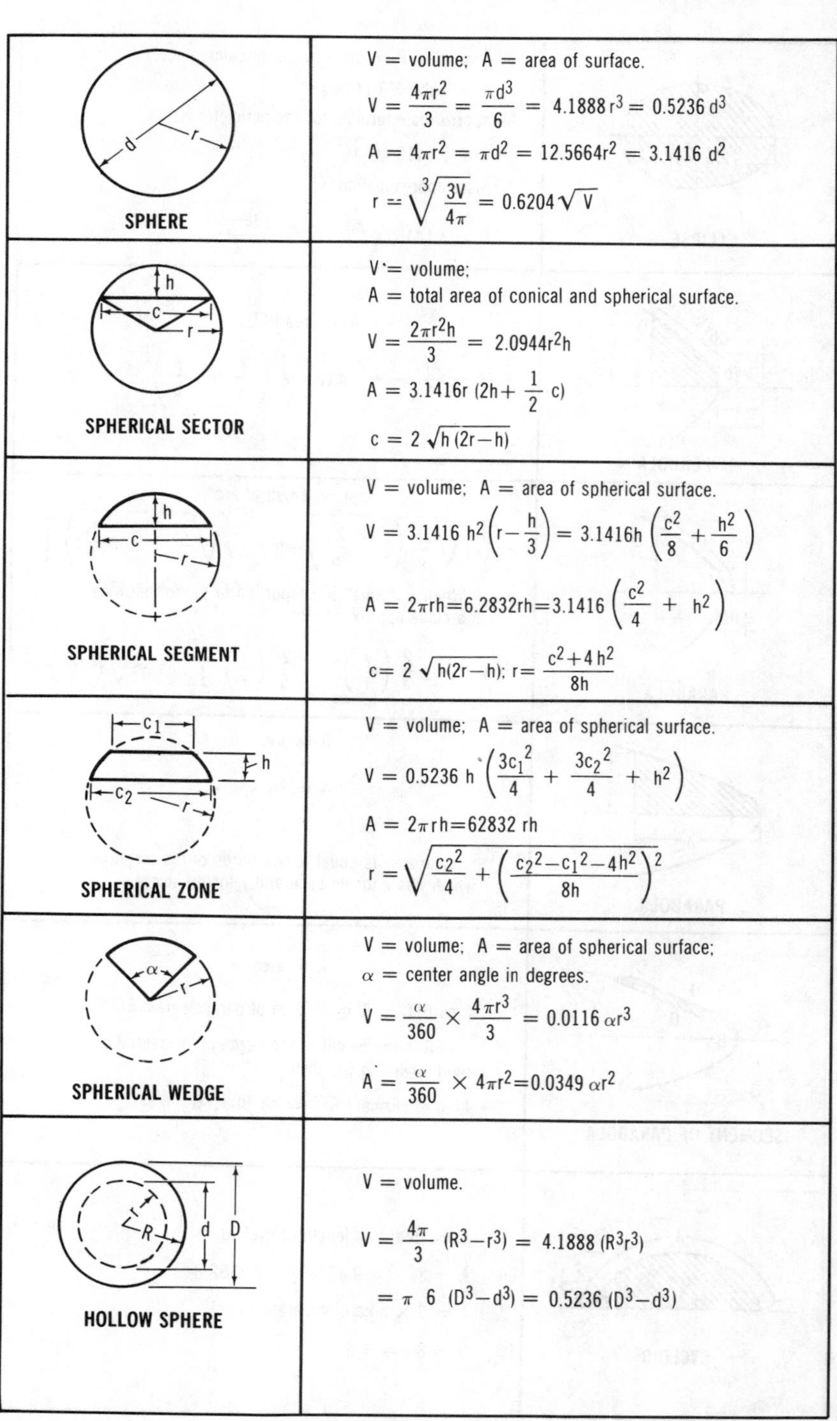

SPHERE	V = volume; A = area of surface. $V = \frac{4\pi r^2}{3} = \frac{\pi d^3}{6} = 4.1888\, r^3 = 0.5236\, d^3$ $A = 4\pi r^2 = \pi d^2 = 12.5664 r^2 = 3.1416\, d^2$ $r = \sqrt[3]{\frac{3V}{4\pi}} = 0.6204 \sqrt{V}$
SPHERICAL SECTOR	V = volume; A = total area of conical and spherical surface. $V = \frac{2\pi r^2 h}{3} = 2.0944 r^2 h$ $A = 3.1416 r\,(2h + \frac{1}{2}\,c)$ $c = 2\sqrt{h\,(2r-h)}$
SPHERICAL SEGMENT	V = volume; A = area of spherical surface. $V = 3.1416\, h^2 \left(r - \frac{h}{3}\right) = 3.1416 h \left(\frac{c^2}{8} + \frac{h^2}{6}\right)$ $A = 2\pi rh = 6.2832 rh = 3.1416 \left(\frac{c^2}{4} + h^2\right)$ $c = 2\sqrt{h(2r-h)};\ r = \frac{c^2 + 4h^2}{8h}$
SPHERICAL ZONE	V = volume; A = area of spherical surface. $V = 0.5236\, h \left(\frac{3{c_1}^2}{4} + \frac{3{c_2}^2}{4} + h^2\right)$ $A = 2\pi rh = 62832\, rh$ $r = \sqrt{\frac{{c_2}^2}{4} + \left(\frac{{c_2}^2 - {c_1}^2 - 4h^2}{8h}\right)^2}$
SPHERICAL WEDGE	V = volume; A = area of spherical surface; α = center angle in degrees. $V = \frac{\alpha}{360} \times \frac{4\pi r^3}{3} = 0.0116\, \alpha r^3$ $A = \frac{\alpha}{360} \times 4\pi r^2 = 0.0349\, \alpha r^2$
HOLLOW SPHERE	V = volume. $V = \frac{4\pi}{3}\,(R^3 - r^3) = 4.1888\,(R^3 r^3)$ $= \pi\ 6\ (D^3 - d^3) = 0.5236\,(D^3 - d^3)$

Figure 31-12—cont. Equations for finding

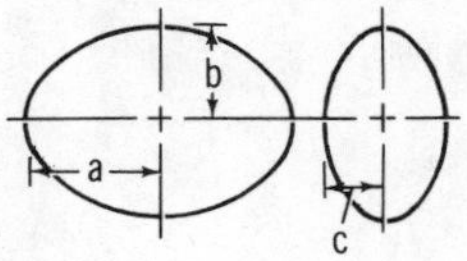

a, b, c **ELLIPSOID**	V = volume; A = area of surface. $V = \frac{4\pi}{3}\ abc = 4.1888\ abc$ In an ellipsoid of revolution, or spheroid, where b = c: $V = 4.1888\ ab^2$, and $A = \frac{4\pi}{\sqrt{2}}\ b\ \sqrt{a^2+b^2}$
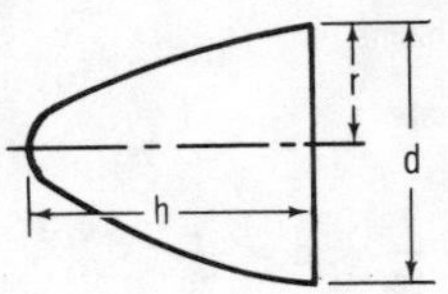 r, d, h **PARABOLOID**	V = volume; $V = \frac{1}{2}\ \pi r^2 h = 0.3927\ d^2 h$ A = area; $A = \frac{2\pi}{3p}\left[\sqrt{\left(\frac{d^2}{4} + p^2\right)^3} - p^3\right]$ in which $p = \frac{d^2}{8h}$
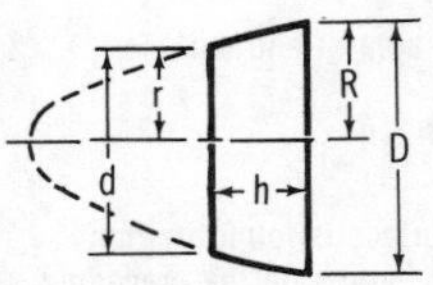 r, R, d, D, h **PARABOLOIDAL SEGMENT**	V = volume. $V = \frac{\pi}{2}\ h\ (R^2+r^2) = 1.5708\ h\ (R^2+r^2)$ $= \frac{\pi}{8}\ h\ (D^2+d^2) = 0.3927\ h\ (D^2+d^2)$
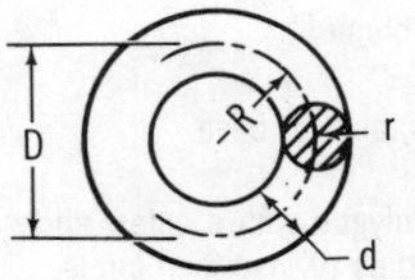 D, R, r, d **TORUS**	V = volume; A = area of surface. $V = 2\pi^2\ Rr^2 = 19.739\ Rr^2$ $= \frac{\pi^2}{4}\ Dd^2 = 2.4674\ Dd^2$ $A = 4\pi^2\ Rr = 39.478\ Rr$ $= \pi^2 Dd = 9.8696\ Dd$
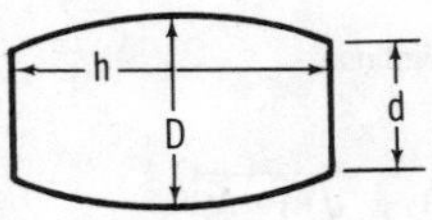 h, D, d **BARREL**	V = approximate volume. If the sides are bent to the arc of a circle: $V = \frac{1}{12}\ \pi h\ (2\ D^2+d^2) = 0.262\ h\ (2\ D^2+d^2)$ If the sides are bent to the arc of a parabola: $V = 0.209\ h\ (2\ D^2+Dd+\frac{3}{4}\ d^2)$
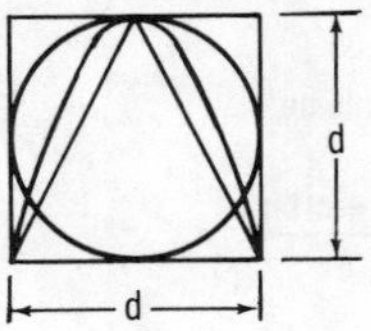 d, d	If d = base diameter and height of a cone, a paraboloid and a cylinder, and the diameter of a sphere, then the volumes of these bodies are to each other as below: Cone: paraboloid: sphere: cylinder $= \frac{1}{3} : \frac{1}{2} : \frac{2}{3} : 1$

cont. on next page

surface areas for complex shapes.

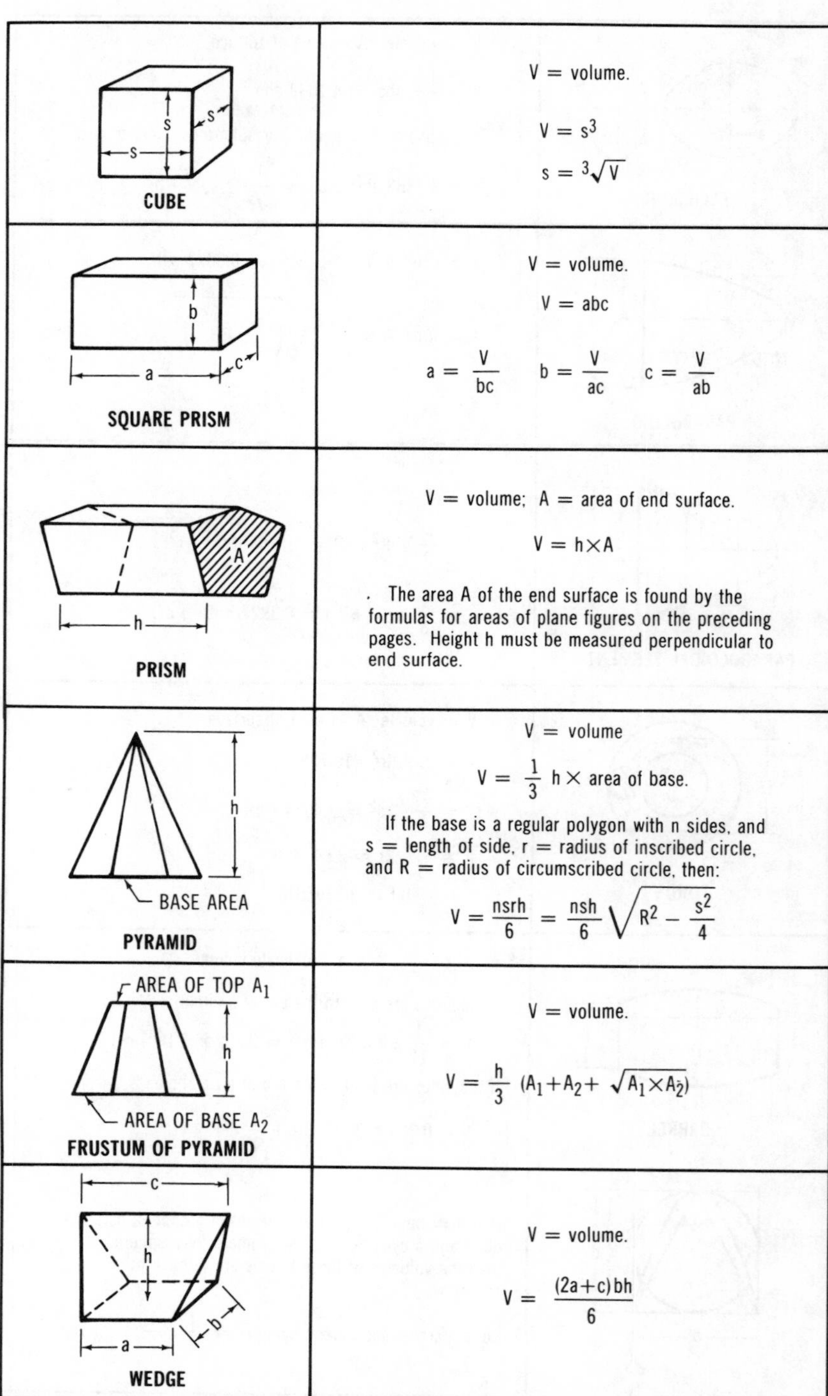

CUBE	V = volume. $V = s^3$ $s = \sqrt[3]{V}$
SQUARE PRISM	V = volume. $V = abc$ $a = \frac{V}{bc}$ $b = \frac{V}{ac}$ $c = \frac{V}{ab}$
PRISM	V = volume; A = area of end surface. $V = h \times A$ The area A of the end surface is found by the formulas for areas of plane figures on the preceding pages. Height h must be measured perpendicular to end surface.
PYRAMID (BASE AREA)	V = volume $V = \frac{1}{3} h \times \text{area of base.}$ If the base is a regular polygon with n sides, and s = length of side, r = radius of inscribed circle, and R = radius of circumscribed circle, then: $V = \frac{nsrh}{6} = \frac{nsh}{6}\sqrt{R^2 - \frac{s^2}{4}}$
FRUSTUM OF PYRAMID (AREA OF TOP A_1; AREA OF BASE A_2)	V = volume. $V = \frac{h}{3}(A_1 + A_2 + \sqrt{A_1 \times A_2})$
WEDGE	V = volume. $V = \frac{(2a+c)bh}{6}$

Figure 3-12—cont. Equations for finding

CYLINDER	V = volume; S = area of cylindrical surface. $V = 3.1416\ r^2h = 0.7854\ d^2h$ $S = 6.2832\ rh = 3.1416\ dh$ Total area A of cylindrical surface and end surfaces: $A = 6.2832\ r(r+h) = 3.1416\ d\left(\frac{1}{2}\ d+h\right)$
PORTION OF CYLINDER	V = volume; S = area of cylindrical surface. $V = 1.5708\ r^2(h_1+h_2) = 0.3927\ d^2\ (h_1+h_2)$ $S = 3.1416\ r\ (h_1+h_2) = 1.5708\ d(h_1+h_2)$
PORTION OF CYLINDER	V = volume; S = area of cylindrical surface. $V = \left(\frac{2}{3}\ a^3\ \pm b \times \text{area ABC}\right) \frac{h}{r \pm b}$ $S = (ad\ \pm b \times \text{length of arc ABC})\ \frac{h}{r \pm b}$ Use + when base area is larger, and − when base area is less than one-half the base circle.
HOLLOW CYLINDER	V = volume. $V = 3.1416\ h(R^2-r^2) = 0.7854\ h(D^2-d^2)$ $= 3.1416\ ht\ (2R-t) = 3.1416\ ht(D-t)$ $= 3.1416\ ht\ (2r+t) = 3.1416\ ht(d+t)$ $= 3.1416\ ht\ (R+r) = 1.5708\ ht(D+d)$
CONE	V = volume; A = area of conical surface $V = \frac{3.1416\ r^2h}{3} = 1.0472\ r^2h = 0.2618\ d^2h$ $A = 3.1416\ r\ \sqrt{r^2+h^2} = 3.1416rs = 1.5708\ ds$ $s = \sqrt{r^2+h^2} = \sqrt{\frac{d^2}{4} + h^2}$
FRUSTUM OF CONE	V = volume; A = area of conical surface. $V = 1.0472\ h(R^2+Rr+r^2) = 0.2618\ h(D^2+Dd+d^2)$ $A = 3.1416\ s(R+r) = 1.5708\ s(D+d)$ $a = R-r \quad s = \sqrt{a^2+h^2} = \sqrt{(R-r)^2+h^2}$

surface areas for complex shapes.

Table 31-3. Greek Alphabet

Name	Capital		Lower Case	
alpha	Α		α	absorption factor, angles, angular acceleration, attenuation constant, common-base current amplification factor, deviation of state parameter, temperature coefficient of linear expansion, temperature coefficient of resistance, thermal expansion coefficient, thermal diffusivity
beta	Β		β	angles, common-emitter current amplification factor, flux density, phase constant, wavelength constant
gamma	Γ		γ	electrical conductivity, Grueneisen parameter
delta	Δ	decrement, increment	δ	angles, damping coefficient (decay constant), decrement, increment, secondary-emission ratio
epsilon	Ε	electric field intensity	ϵ	capacitivity, dielectric coefficient, electron energy, emissivity, permittivity, base of natural logarithms (2.71828)
zeta	Ζ		ζ	
eta	Η		η	chemical potential, dielectric susceptibility (intrinsic capacitance), efficiency, hysteresis, intrinsic impedance of a medium, intrinsic standoff ratio
theta	Θ	angles, thermal resistance	θ	angle of rotation, angles, angular phase displacement, reluctance, transit angle
iota	Ι		ι	
kappa	Κ	coupling coefficient	κ	susceptibility
lambda	Λ		λ	line density of charge, permeance, photosensitivity, wavelength
mu	Μ		μ	amplification factor, magnetic permeability, micron, mobility, permeability, prefix micro
nu	Ν		ν	reluctivity
xi	Ξ		ξ	
omicron	Ο		ο	
pi	Π		π	Peltier coefficient, ratio of circumference to diameter (3.1416)
rho	Ρ		ρ	reflection coefficient, reflection factor, resistivity, volume density of electric charge
sigma	Σ	summation	σ	conductivity, Stefan-Boltzmann constant, surface density of charge
tau	Τ	period	τ	propagation constant, Thomson coefficient, time constant, time-phase displacement, transmission factor
upsilon	Υ	admittance	υ	
phi	Φ	magnetic flux, radiant flux	ϕ	angles, coefficient of performance, contact potential, magnetic flux, phase angle, phase displacement
chi	Χ		χ	angles
psi	Ψ	angles	ψ	dielectric flux, displacement flux, phase difference
omega	Ω	resistance	ω	angular frequency, angular velocity, solid angle

ticians and audio consultants and engineers. Table 31-4 is a list of many of these abbreviations.

Symbols for multiple and submultiple prefixes are shown in Table 31-1.

31.15 PERIODIC TABLE OF THE ELEMENTS

Fig. 31-13 is the periodic table of the elements.

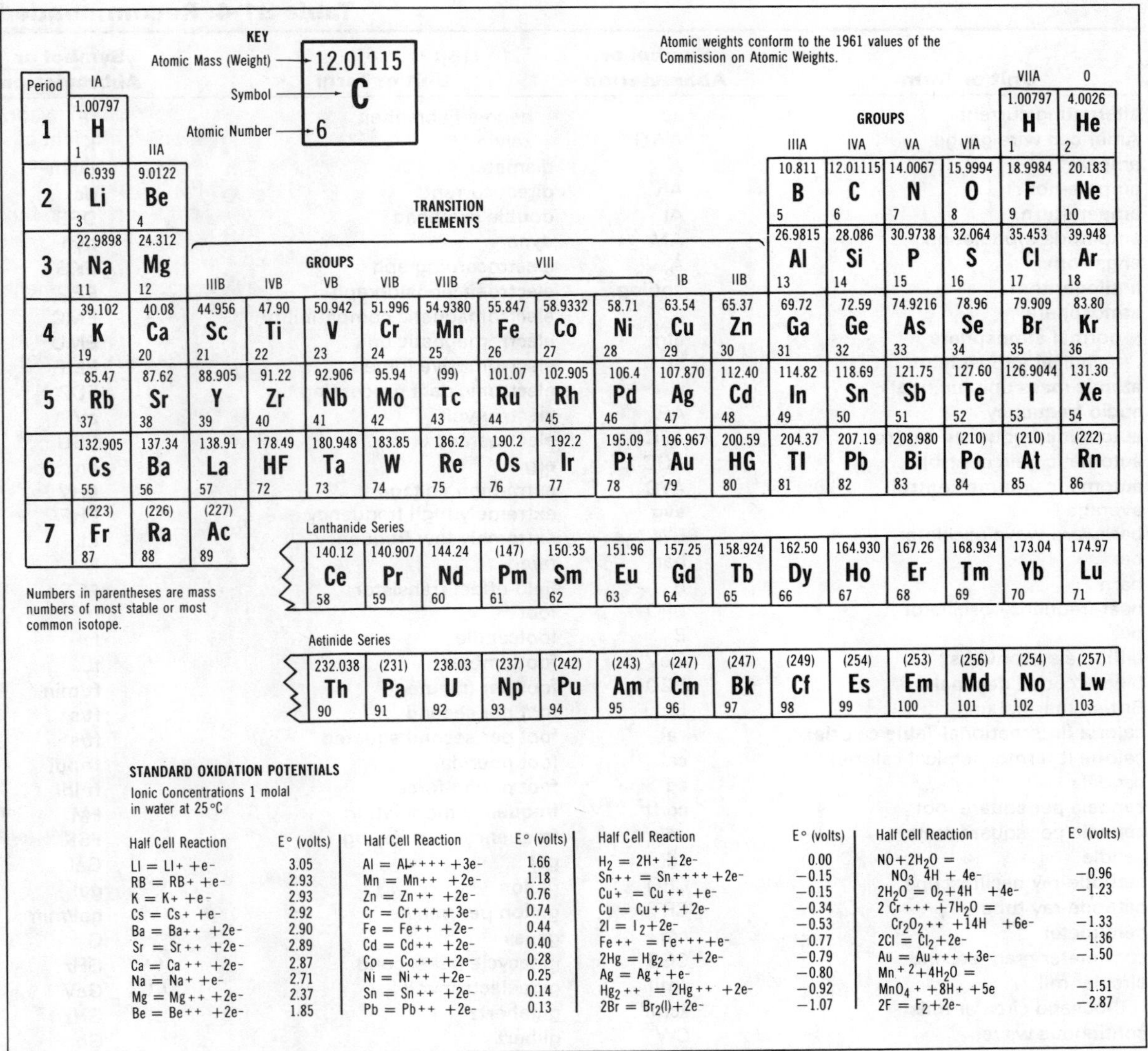

KEY

Atomic Mass (Weight) → 12.01115
Symbol → C
Atomic Number → 6

Atomic weights conform to the 1961 values of the Commission on Atomic Weights.

Period	IA	IIA	IIIB	IVB	VB	VIB	VIIB	VIII	VIII	VIII	IB	IIB	IIIA	IVA	VA	VIA	VIIA	0
1	1.00797 H 1																1.00797 H 1	4.0026 He 2
2	6.939 Li 3	9.0122 Be 4											10.811 B 5	12.01115 C 6	14.0067 N 7	15.9994 O 8	18.9984 F 9	20.183 Ne 10
3	22.9898 Na 11	24.312 Mg 12											26.9815 Al 13	28.086 Si 14	30.9738 P 15	32.064 S 16	35.453 Cl 17	39.948 Ar 18
4	39.102 K 19	40.08 Ca 20	44.956 Sc 21	47.90 Ti 22	50.942 V 23	51.996 Cr 24	54.9380 Mn 25	55.847 Fe 26	58.9332 Co 27	58.71 Ni 28	63.54 Cu 29	65.37 Zn 30	69.72 Ga 31	72.59 Ge 32	74.9216 As 33	78.96 Se 34	79.909 Br 35	83.80 Kr 36
5	85.47 Rb 37	87.62 Sr 38	88.905 Y 39	91.22 Zr 40	92.906 Nb 41	95.94 Mo 42	(99) Tc 43	101.07 Ru 44	102.905 Rh 45	106.4 Pd 46	107.870 Ag 47	112.40 Cd 48	114.82 In 49	118.69 Sn 50	121.75 Sb 51	127.60 Te 52	126.9044 I 53	131.30 Xe 54
6	132.905 Cs 55	137.34 Ba 56	138.91 La 57	178.49 HF 72	180.948 Ta 73	183.85 W 74	186.2 Re 75	190.2 Os 76	192.2 Ir 77	195.09 Pt 78	196.967 Au 79	200.59 HG 80	204.37 Tl 81	207.19 Pb 82	208.980 Bi 83	(210) Po 84	(210) At 85	(222) Rn 86
7	(223) Fr 87	(226) Ra 88	(227) Ac 89															

TRANSITION ELEMENTS

Lanthanide Series

140.12 Ce 58	140.907 Pr 59	144.24 Nd 60	(147) Pm 61	150.35 Sm 62	151.96 Eu 63	157.25 Gd 64	158.924 Tb 65	162.50 Dy 66	164.930 Ho 67	167.26 Er 68	168.934 Tm 69	173.04 Yb 70	174.97 Lu 71

Actinide Series

232.038 Th 90	(231) Pa 91	238.03 U 92	(237) Np 93	(242) Pu 94	(243) Am 95	(247) Cm 96	(247) Bk 97	(249) Cf 98	(254) Es 99	(253) Em 100	(256) Md 101	(254) No 102	(257) Lw 103

Numbers in parentheses are mass numbers of most stable or most common isotope.

STANDARD OXIDATION POTENTIALS

Ionic Concentrations 1 molal in water at 25 °C

Half Cell Reaction	E° (volts)	Half Cell Reaction	E° (volts)	Half Cell Reaction	E° (volts)	Half Cell Reaction	E° (volts)
LI = LI+ +e-	3.05	Al = Al+++ +3e-	1.66	H_2 = 2H+ +2e-	0.00	NO+$2H_2O$ = NO_3 4H + 4e-	−0.96
RB = RB+ +e-	2.93	Mn = Mn++ +2e-	1.18	Sn++ = Sn++++ +2e-	−0.15	$2H_2O$ = O_2+4H +4e-	−1.23
K = K+ +e-	2.93	Zn = Zn++ +2e-	0.76	Cu+ = Cu++ +e-	−0.15	2 Cr+++ +$7H_2O$ = Cr_2O_2++ +14H +6e-	−1.33
Cs = Cs+ +e-	2.92	Cr = Cr+++ +3e-	0.74	Cu = Cu++ +2e-	−0.34	2Cl = Cl_2+2e-	−1.36
Ba = Ba++ +2e-	2.90	Fe = Fe++ +2e-	0.44	2I = I_2+2e-	−0.53	Au = Au+++ +3e-	−1.50
Sr = Sr++ +2e-	2.89	Cd = Cd++ +2e-	0.40	Fe++ = Fe++++e-	−0.77	Mn^{+2}+$4H_2O$ = MnO_4+ +8H+ +5e	−1.51
Ca = Ca++ +2e-	2.87	Co = Co++ +2e-	0.28	2Hg = Hg_2++ +2e-	−0.79	2F = F_2+2e-	−2.87
Na = Na+ +e-	2.71	Ni = Ni++ +2e-	0.25	Ag = Ag+ +e-	−0.80		
Mg = Mg++ +2e-	2.37	Sn = Sn++ +2e-	0.14	Hg_2++ = 2Hg++ +2e-	−0.92		
Be = Be++ +2e-	1.85	Pb = Pb++ +2e-	0.13	2Br = Br_2(l)+2e-	−1.07		

Figure 31-13 Periodic table of the elements.

Table 31-4. Recommended

Unit or Term	Symbol or Abbreviation
alternating current	ac
American wire gauge	AWG
ampere	A
ampere-hour	Ah
ampere-turn	At
amplitude modulation	AM
angstrom	Å
antilogarithm	antilog
atmosphere	
— normal atmosphere	atm
— technical atmosphere	at
atomic mass unit (unified)	u
audio frequency	AF
automatic frequency control	AFC
automatic gain control	AGC
automatic volume control	AVC
average	avg
backward-wave oscillator	BWO
bar	bar
barn	b
beat-frequency oscillator	BFO
bel	B
billion electronvolts*	GeV
binary coded decimal	BCD
British thermal unit	Btu
calorie (International Table calorie)	cal$_{IT}$
calorie (thermochemical calorie)	cal$_{th}$
candela	cd
candela per square foot	cd/ft^2
candela per square meter	cd/m^2
candle	cd
cathode-ray oscilloscope	CRO
cathode-ray tube	CRT
centimeter	cm
centimeter-gram-second	CGS
circular mil	cmil
— thousand circular mils	kcmil
continuous wave	CW
coulomb	C
cubic centimeter	cm^3
cubic foot	ft^3
cubic foot per minute	ft^3/min
cubic foot per second	ft^3/s
cubic inch	in.^{3}
cubic meter	m^3
cubic meter per second	m^3/s
cubic yard	yd^3
curie	Ci
cycle per second	Hz
decibel	dB
decibel referred to one milliwatt	dBm
degree (plane angle)	. . .°
degree (temperature)	
— degree Celsius	°C
— degree Fahrenheit	°F
— kelvin	K
diameter	diam
direct current	dc
double sideband	DSB
dyne	dyn
electrocardiograph	EKG
electroencephalograph	EEG
electromagnetic compatibility	EMC
electromagnetic unit	EMU
electromotive force	EMF
electronic data processing	EDP
electronvolt	eV
electrostatic unit	ESU
erg	erg
extra-high voltage	EHV
extremely high frequency	EHF
extremely low frequency	ELF
farad	F
field-effect transistor	FET
foot	ft
footcandle	fc
footlambert	fL
foot per minute	ft/min
foot per second	ft/s
foot per second squared	ft/s^2
foot poundal	ft·pdl
foot pound-force	ft·lbf
frequency modulation	FM
frequency-shift keying	FSK
gal	Gal
gallon	gal
gallon per minute	gal/min
gauss	G
gigacycle per second	GHz
gigaelectronvolt	GeV
gigahertz	GHz
gilbert	Gb
gram	g
henry	H
hertz	Hz
high frequency	HF
high voltage	HV
horsepower	hp
hour	h
inch	in.
inch per second	in./s
inductance-capacitance	LC
infrared	IR
inside diameter	ID
intermediate frequency	IF
joule	J
joule per kelvin	J/K
kelvin	K

Abbreviations

Unit or Term	Symbol or Abbreviation	Unit or Term	Symbol or Abbreviation
kilocycle per second	kHz	mile per hour	mi/h
kiloelectronvolt	keV	mile (statute)	mi
kilogauss	kG	milliampere	mA
kilogram	kg	millibar	mbar
kilogram-force	kgf	millibarn	mb
kilohertz	kHz	milligal	mGal
kilohm	kΩ	milligram	mg
kilojoule	kJ	millihenry	mH
kilometer	km	milliliter	ml
kilometer per hour	km/h	millimeter	mm
kilovar	kvar	millimeter of mercury, conventional	mmHg
kilovolt	kV	millimicron‡	nm
kilovoltampere	kVA	millisecond	ms
kilowatt	kW	millisiemens—	mS
kilowatthour	kWh	millivolt	mV
knot	knot	milliwatt	mW
lambert	L	minute (plane angle)	. . .′
liter	l	minute (time)	min
liter per second	l/s	nanoampere	nA
logarithm	log	nanofarad	nF
logarithm, natural	ln	nanometer	nm
low frequency	LF	nanosecond	ns
lumen	lm	nanowatt	nW
lumen per square foot	lm/ft^2	nautical mile	nmi
lumen per square meter	lm/m^2	neper	Np
lumen per watt	lm/W	newton	N
lumen second	lm·s	newton meter	N·m
lux	lx	newton per square meter	N/m^2
magnetohydrodynamics	MHD	oersted	Oe
magnetomotive force	MMF	ohm	Ω
maxwell	Mx	ounce (avoirdupois)	oz
medium frequency	MF	outside diameter	OD
megacycle per second	MHz	phase modulation	PM
megaelectronvolt	MeV	picoampere	pA
megahertz	MHz	picofarad	pF
megavolt	MV	picosecond	ps
megawatt	MW	picowatt	pW
megohm	MΩ	pint	pt
metal-oxide semiconductor	MOS	pound	lb
meter	m	poundal	pdl
meter-kilogram-second	MKS	pound-force	lbf
mho	mho	pound-force foot	lbf·ft
microampere	μA	pound-force per square inch	$lbf/in.^2$
microbar	μbar	pound (force) per square inch§	psi
microfarad	μF	power factor	PF
microgram	μg	private branch exchange	PBX
microhenry	μH	pulse-amplitude modulation	PAM
micrometer	μm	pulse-code modulation	PCM
micromho	μmho	pulse-count modulation	PCM
micron†	μm	pulse-duration modulation	PDM
microsecond	μs	pulse-position modulation	PPM
microsiemens	μS	pulse-repetition frequency	PRF
microwatt	μW	pulse-repetition rate	PRR
mil	mil	pulse-time modulation	PTM

Table 31-4. Recommended Abbreviations

Unit or Term	Symbol or Abbreviation	Unit or Term	Symbol or Abbreviation
pulse-width modulation	PWM	tesla	T
quart	qt	thin-film transistor	TFT
rad	rd	ton	ton
radian	rad	tonne	t
radio-frequency	RF	transverse electric	TE
radio-frequency interference	RFI	transverse electromagnetic	TEM
rem	rem	transverse magnetic	TM
resistance-capacitance	RC	traveling-wave tube	TWT
resistance-inductance-capacitance	RLC	ultrahigh frequency	UHF
revolution per minute	r/min	ultraviolet	UV
revolution per second	r/s	(unified) atomic mass unit	u
roentgen	R	vacuum-tube voltmeter	VTVM
root-mean-square	rms	var	var
second (plane angle)	. . ."	variable-frequency oscillator	VFO
second (time)	s	very high frequency	VHF
short wave	SW	very low frequency	VLF
siemens	S	vestigial sideband	VSB
signal-to-noise ratio	SNR	volt	V
silicon controlled rectifier	SCR	voltage-controlled oscillator	VCO
single sideband	SSB	voltage standing-wave ratio	VSWR
square foot	ft^2	voltampere	VA
square inch	$in.^2$	volume unit	VU
square meter	m^2	watt	W
square yard	yd^2	watthour	Wh
standing-wave ratio	SWR	watt per steradian	W/sr
steradian	sr	watt per steradian square meter	$W/(sr{\cdot}m^2)$
superhigh frequency	SHF	weber	Wb
television	TV	yard	yd
television interference	TVI		

*Deprecated; use gigaelectronvolt (GeV).

†The name micrometer (μm) is preferred.

‡The name nanometer is preferred.

§Although the use of the abbreviation psi is common, it is not recommended. See pound-force per square inch.

REFERENCES

1. *Metric Units of Measure and Style Guide*, US Metric Association, Inc., Sugarloaf Star Route, Boulder, CO 80302.
2. V. Antoine, *Guidance for Using the Metric System* (SI Version), Society for Technical Communication, 1010 Vermont Avenue, NW, Washington, DC 20005.
3. H. R. R. Adams, *SI Metric Units, An Introduction*, Revised Edition.
4. D. Davis, *Synergetic Audio Concepts*, vol. 5, no. 2, October 1977.

INDEX

B

E

G

M

T

U